SMOLEY'S

PARALLEL TABLES OF

SLOPES AND RISES

SMOLEY'S
PARALLEL TABLES OF
SLOPES AND RISES

FOR BRIDGE AND STRUCTURAL ENGINEERS, DRAFTSMEN, CHECKERS, TEMPLET MAKERS, BUILDERS AND VOCATIONAL SCHOOLS

by C. K. SMOLEY

Extended by E. R. SMOLEY and N. G. SMOLEY

1974

Published by

C.K. SMOLEY & SONS
Division of Lewis Publishers
P.O. 519, Chelsea, MI 48118

SMOLEY'S SLOPES AND RISES

Books published by

C. K. SMOLEY & SONS, INC.

Chautauqua, N. Y.

Smoley's Four Combined Tables

Smoley's Three Combined Tables

Smoley's Logarithms and Squares

Smoley's Slopes and Rises

Smoley's Segmental Functions

Smoley's Log. Trig. Tables

How to Use Smoley's Tables

Smoley's Metric Four Combined Tables

Printed in the United States of America

CONTENTS

PART 1

Tables of Slopes and Rises

Special Tables

PREFACE TO SECOND EDITION, October 1956

This edition extends the work from bases of 12″ to 22″ by ⅟₁₆″s, and from 40′ to 80′ by 1′ intervals, which doubles the number of pages. The extensions were made by popular request from bridge and structural designers and draftsmen, and on their recommendation the diagrams have been omitted since these extensions replace them and afford more accuracy.

For the calculations of Slopes and Rises extensions, a special set of natural trigonometric functions was calculated. These trigonometric functions were obtained for each exact bevel to 10 decimals with an error less than 3 in the 10th place. The tan. and sec. were then used to calculate the rise and slope respectively and the full 10 decimal accuracy was retained in order to assure that the results were properly rounded in all cases. For the users' convenience to provide more accurate computations, four of the natural trig. functions to 10 decimals are given at the bottom of each new page for each of the 192 bevels.

In the calculations of the Slopes and Rises extensions, computational errors were eliminated by the use of summary checks. In the few cases where rounding was in doubt, re-computation was used to determine proper rounding. Proof was checked against manuscript independently at four different locations. The author will be grateful to anyone who will call his attention to remaining errors, and any suggestions for future editions.

The great amount of time and labor involved in making the extentions to this edition has been gladly contributed by us as a tribute to our father's memory, and has been done with full appreciation of the energy, originality, patience and perseverence he gave to the composition of these books.

E. R. SMOLEY

N. G. SMOLEY

PREFACE TO FIRST EDITION, November 1916

This work is essentially an extension of the author's Smoley's Tables, the first edition of which was published in 1901. The chief aim of that book was to meet the difficulties in the calculations required in bridge and structural work, although in the later editions the scope of Smoley's Tables was enlarged to cover other fields of technical work. Two peculiar features distinguish the computations of bridge and structural work from those of other technical work.

The first is that the linear measures used are expressed in feet, inches, and fractions of an inch, instead of in feet and decimals, as, for instance, in surveying. To meet the difficulties arising from this feature, the Parallel Tables of Logarithms and Squares were devised. These tables have more than fulfilled the expectations of the author. They are well known and need no comment.

The second feature causing tedious computations in structural work is due to the peculiar method of measuring angles formed by the members and parts constituting a framed structure. The arc measure of the angle is here replaced by the so-called bevel, which is the value of the natural tangent of the angle expressed in inches, 1 foot, or 12 inches, being the unit. To obviate in part the inconvenience resulting from this feature, the Tables of Angles and Functions Corresponding to Given Bevels was originated by the author and published for the first time in 1906 in the third edition of Smoley's Tables. This table offers a comparatively simple method of solving a right triangle when one of its sides and the bevel of the hypotenuse are given; but this method still requires considerable work before final results are obtained. The present volume aims to eliminate entirely the work involved in solving such triangles, and offers ready answers for the bevels and distances in common use.

The new volume, therefore, unlike the older book, which is in the nature of a general calculator, covers only a special ground, namely, that of solving right triangles when the bevel is known. Nevertheless, it may be said without exaggeration that, in calculations of structural work, the new tables cover a wider field than the older book, for the following reasons:

The calculations required in the preparation of structural drawings may be divided into two distinctive parts. In the first place the dimensions and bevels of the members of the frame must be determined. For this part of the work, the Parallel Tables of Logarithms and Squares are used. But these computations form only a comparatively small part of the entire work. When they are completed, there remain the layout of the joints and the determination of the dimensions of the material. For this work, as is exemplified in the introduction of this book, the Tables of Slopes and Rises will be found perfectly adapted, because in all the joints the bevels are known. Moreover, the new tables may often be used with advantage, even for the computation of the main dimensions of the frame. This will be the case when the frame is given with the bevels, as, for instance, a roof truss with its pitch or a bent with the batter of the posts.

The author received material aid from his son, N. G. Smoley, a graduate in Civil Engineering, who assisted in the computation of the greater part of the tables. Indeed it is, in a great measure, to his faithfulness, accuracy, and untiring efforts that this volume owes its appearance at the present time.

C. K. SMOLEY

TEXT, EXPLANATION

AND APPLICATION OF THE TABLES

WITH PRACTICAL EXAMPLES

AND FORMULAS

TABLES OF SLOPES AND RISES

EXPLANATION OF THE TABLES

1. The Elementary, or Bevel, Triangle.—The Tables of Slopes and Rises offer a ready solution of a right triangle when any one of its three sides and the bevel of the hypotenuse are given. The bevel is the natural tangent, referred to 1 foot or 12 inches as a unit, of the angle that the hypotenuse makes with the base of the triangle. The bevel is expressed in inches and fractions of an inch, and on structural drawings it is usually given by an *elementary*, or *bevel*, *triangle*, as $M'O'N'$, Fig. 1. The altitude of this triangle, $O'N'$, called the *bevel*, serves as a measure of the angle that the hypotenuse MN makes with the base MO of the right triangle MON. Accordingly, the bevel triangle is drawn so that its base $M'O'$ is parallel to MO and equals 12″. The bevel $N'O'$ is parallel to NO and shows

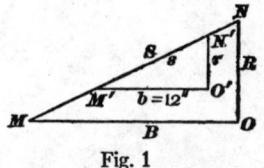

Fig. 1

the rise of the line MN for every 12″ run. The hypotenuse $M'N'$ either is parallel to MN or coincides with it, as is the case in Fig. 1.

2. In the elementary triangle, the bevel will be designated here by r, the base, which always equals 12″, by b, and the hypotenuse by s. The bevel triangle will

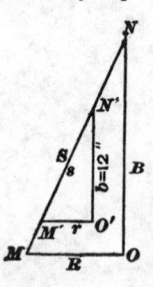

Fig. 2

always be so constructed that r is less than 12″. This is possible only when the angle M, Fig. 1, is less than 45°. When this angle is greater than 45°, as in the triangle MNO, Fig. 2, the elementary triangle is so drawn that the bevel r is parallel to the side MO and is, therefore, less than 12″. It is evident that since the triangle MNO is similar to the elementary triangle, the leg parallel to r is always smaller than the other leg. Thus, in Fig. 1, NO is smaller than MO, and, in Fig. 2, MO is smaller than NO.

3. In any right triangle to be solved, the hypotenuse will be called the **slope** and will be designated by S; the greater leg, which is homologous to b, will be called the **base** and will be designated by B; and the other leg, which is homologous to r, will be called the **rise** and will be designated by R. Thus, in Fig. 1, MO is the base, and NO is the rise, and, in Fig. 2, NO is the base and MO is the rise. MN is, of course, the slope in each case. When a triangle is to be solved, the bevel and one side will be known, and either one or both of the other sides will be required. They may be taken directly from the tables.

4. Construction of the Tables.—At the top of each page of the tables is indicated the bevel for which solutions of triangles are given. The given numbers are the bases B, which vary by $\frac{1}{16}''$ from $0''$ to $12''$ and by $1'$ from $1'$ to $40'$. For each base, the corresponding rise and slope are placed side by side. For example, on page 107, for the bevel $r = 6\frac{5}{8}''$, and for the base $B = 7\frac{13}{16}''$, the rise R is given in the table as $4\frac{5}{16}''$ and the slope S as $8\frac{15}{16}''$. For the same bevel and $B = 35'$, $R = 19'$ $3\frac{7}{8}''$ and $S = 39'$ $11\frac{3}{4}''$.

5. It will be noticed that the answers for the rises and slopes are given exact to the nearest $\frac{1}{32}''$, but since, in practice, such refinement is seldom required, the nearest sixteenth is indicated by a minus or a plus sign, which means *subtract or add $\frac{1}{32}''$ from the answer to obtain the nearest sixteenth*. The minus sign is placed at the right of the fraction, but, for convenience, the plus sign is omitted, it being implied whenever there is no sign after a fraction expressed in thirty-seconds. For example, on page 75, for the bevel $4\frac{5}{8}''$, the rise for the base $10\frac{1}{8}''$ is given in the table as $3\frac{29}{32}''-$. Since there is a minus at the right, the answer to the nearest sixteenth is $\frac{1}{32}''$ less, or $3\frac{7}{8}''$. But, for the same bevel and the same base, the slope is given in the table as $10\frac{27}{32}''$, and as there is no sign at the right of the fraction, a plus is implied; therefore, to obtain the nearest sixteenth, $\frac{1}{32}''$ must be added, giving $10\frac{7}{8}''$.

6. Solving a Triangle When the Rise or Slope is Given.—Although, in the tables the given side is always the base, the parallel arrangement of the tables makes it possible to find any two sides of a triangle when the third is known. For example, to find the base of a triangle when the rise is $8''$ and the bevel $r = 9\frac{1}{2}''$, look for the number $8''$ in the columns of rises for the bevel $9\frac{1}{2}''$ (page 153) and find the corresponding base, which is $10\frac{1}{8}''$. If the exact rise cannot be found in the table, the nearest value should be used. If great accuracy is required, interpolation may then be resorted to. Such refinement, however, will rarely be needed.

7. Simple and Composite Numbers.—As will be noticed, the table for each bevel consists of two parts—the upper part for inches and the lower part for feet. When the base is a number consisting of feet and inches, the corresponding rise, or slope, may be found by adding the tabular value for the inches to that for the feet. To find, for instance, the slope S when the base $B = 23'$ $6\frac{1}{8}''$ and the bevel $r = 8\frac{5}{16}''$, take from the table (page 134) the slope for $B = 23'$, which is $27'$ $11\frac{3}{4}''$; then take the slope for $B = 6\frac{1}{8}''$, which is $8\frac{3}{8}''$. These two slopes added together give $28'$ $8\frac{1}{8}''$, which is the required slope for $B = 23'$ $6\frac{1}{8}''$.

8. When the given composite number is a rise, or slope, the solution may be found by dividing the given side into any two convenient parts and then solving for each part separately and adding the results. For example, let the bevel be $11\frac{3}{8}''$ and the slope $1'$ $9\frac{5}{8}''$; required, the base. On looking in the columns of slopes for this bevel it is found that the nearest slope not containing a fraction is $1'$ $3''$. It will, therefore, be convenient to divide the given slope 1' 9⅝" into 1' 3" and 6⅝", since 1' 3"+6⅝"=1' 9⅝". The corresponding bases are, respectively, 10⅞" and 4¹³⁄₁₆". The required total base is therefore 10⅞"+4¹³⁄₁₆"=1' 3¹¹⁄₁₆".

As another example, let it be required to find the rise when the slope is 17' 8⅝" and the bevel $r=6⅝"$. On looking in the columns of slopes for this bevel, it will be seen that the nearest slope is 17' 1⅝". It will, therefore, be convenient to divide the given slope into 17' 1⅝" and 7". The corresponding rises are, respectively, 8' 3⅜" and 3⅜". Therefore, the required rise is 8' 3⅜"+3⅜"=8' 6¾".

As a third example, let it be required to find S when $R=14' 4⅝"$ and the bevel is 11⁷⁄₁₆". Reference to the table for feet for this bevel will show that the nearest value of R in the column of rises is 14' 3⁹⁄₁₆". By subtracting 14' 3⁹⁄₁₆" from 14' 4⅝", the remainder is found to be 1¹⁄₁₆". The given rise may therefore be divided into 14' 3⁹⁄₁₆" and 1¹⁄₁₆". The corresponding partial slopes are 20' 8¹¹⁄₁₆" and 1⁹⁄₁₆". The required total slope is therefore 20' 8¹¹⁄₁₆"+1⁹⁄₁₆"=20' 10¼".

9. A similar method may be applied when the given side of a triangle is greater than 80'. For example, if, for the bevel 9³⁄₁₆", it is required to find the slope when the base is 88', divide 88' into 58' and 30'. Then, from the table for the bevel 9³⁄₁₆", for the base 58' the slope is 73' 0⁹⁄₁₆", and for the base 30' the slope is 37' 9⅜". The total slope is therefore 73' 0⁹⁄₁₆"+37' 9⅜"=110' 9¹⁵⁄₁₆".

10. To obviate, as far as possible, the necessity of double reference when dealing with composite numbers, the tables of slopes and rises for the bevels most frequently used in practice (particularly in roof work) were extended— the part for the inches, to 32", and the part for the feet, to 80'. These extensions will be found on pages 194 to 219. Six of these special pitches were added in the 1971 editions. (18 pages)

11. In the 1956 edition all tables of Slopes and Rises, were extended to 22" and to 80', pages 2a to 193a.

TABLE OF BEVELS

12. Another method of dealing with composite numbers consists in applying the Table of Bevels. This Table is reprinted from Smoley's Tables. It contains the natural numbers, as well as the logarithms, of the six trigonometric functions corresponding to given bevels; it may therefore be used for solving a right triangle when the bevel and one of its sides are known. In order to use the logarithmic table of bevels, logarithms of numbers are required. These are also reprinted in part from Smoley's Tables.

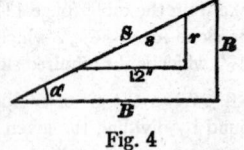

Fig. 4

13. If, in Fig. 4, the angle corresponding to the given bevel be denoted by a, the following formulas may be employed in connection with the Table of Bevels:

x

$$R = B \tan \alpha = S \sin \alpha \dots\dots\dots\dots\dots\dots (1)$$
$$B = R \cot \alpha = S \cos \alpha \dots\dots\dots\dots\dots\dots (2)$$
$$S = B \sec \alpha = R \csc \alpha \dots\dots\dots\dots\dots\dots (3)$$

Hence,

$$\log R = \log B + \log \tan \alpha = \log S + \log \sin \alpha \dots\dots (4)$$
$$\log B = \log R + \log \cot \alpha = \log S + \log \cos \alpha \dots\dots (5)$$
$$\log S = \log B + \log \sec \alpha = \log R + \log \csc \alpha \dots\dots (6)$$

14. EXAMPLE.—By way of comparison, let it be required to find R and B when $r = 10\frac{7}{16}''$ and $S = 5'\ 9\frac{3}{4}''$.

SOLUTION BY THE TABLE OF BEVELS.—Applying formulas **4** and **5**,

$\log\ S = 0.76436$	$\log\ S = 0.76436$
$\log \sin \alpha = 9.81709$	$\log \cos \alpha = 9.87767$
$\log R = 0.58145$	$\log B = 0.64203$

Hence, $R = 3'\ 9\frac{3}{4}''$ and $B = 4'\ 4\frac{5}{8}''$.

SOLUTION BY THE TABLE OF SLOPES AND RISES.—Reference to the table for $r = 10\frac{7}{16}''$ will show that, in this case, it is convenient to divide the given S into $5'\ 3\frac{5}{8}''$ and $6\frac{1}{8}''$. Then, from the table, for $S_1 = 5'\ 3\frac{5}{8}''$,

$$R_1 = 3'\ 5\frac{3}{4}'' \text{ and } B_1 = 4'\ 0''$$

and for $S_2 = 6\frac{1}{8}''$,

$$R_2 = 0'\ 4'' \text{ and } B_2 = 0'\ 4\frac{5}{8}''$$

Hence, for $S = 5'\ 9\frac{3}{4}''$, $\quad R = 3'\ 9\frac{3}{4}''$ and $B = 4'\ 4\frac{5}{8}''$.

It can be seen that, even in this case, the method by the Table of Slopes and Rises is much the simpler. However, the method by the Table of Bevels may be used for the purpose of checking; it may also be preferably applied when the bevel is expressed in thirty-seconds.

APPLICATION OF TABLES

15. Notation.—For convenience, certain symbols have been adopted in this work to indicate solutions, by means of the Tables of Slopes and Rises, of right triangles when one side and the bevel are known. Thus, the relation, that the required quantity is the hypotenuse of a right triangle whose base is $7\frac{3}{4}''$, is expressed in the following manner:

$$x = (S \text{ for } B = 7\frac{3}{4}'')$$

This equation means that the unknown side x is the slope of a right triangle whose base is $7\frac{3}{4}''$. Similarly, the expression

$$y = (R \text{ for } S = 5'')$$

means that the unknown side y is equal to the rise of a right triangle whose slope is $5''$. Of course, it is always implied in such cases that the bevel is known.

Sometimes the quantity sought is composed of sides of two different triangles. Thus, the expression

$$z = (S \text{ for } B = 1\frac{1}{2}'') + (R \text{ for } B = 2'')$$

means that the unknown quantity z is the sum of two parts. One is the slope of a right triangle whose base is $1\frac{1}{2}''$, and the other is the rise of another triangle whose base is $2''$. Of course, it is assumed that the bevel is the same for both triangles.

EXAMPLE 1.—In the preceding expressions for x, y, and z, let the bevel be known to be $6\frac{9}{16}''$. Find the values of x, y, and z.

SOLUTION.—According to the table for this bevel, $x = 8\frac{13}{16}''$, $y = 2\frac{3}{8}''$, and $z = 1\frac{23}{32}'' + 1\frac{1}{32}'' = 2\frac{13}{16}''$.

EXAMPLE 2.—Let it be required to find the values of x and y from the expressions $x = (B \text{ for } S = d)$ and $y = (R \text{ for } S = d)$, when $d = 1' \ 9\frac{3}{4}''$ and the bevel is $11\frac{7}{16}''$.

SOLUTION.—In the table for the given bevel it is found that for $S_1 = 1' \ 0''$, the corresponding $B_1 = 8\frac{11}{16}''$ and $R_1 = 8\frac{9}{32}''$, and for $S_2 = 9\frac{3}{4}''$, $B_2 = 7\frac{1}{16}''$ and $R_2 = 6\frac{23}{32}''$. Therefore, $B = 8\frac{11}{16}'' + 7\frac{1}{16}'' = 1' \ 3\frac{3}{4}''$ and $R = 8\frac{9}{32}'' + 6\frac{23}{32}'' = 1' \ 3''$.

APPLICATION TO STRUCTURAL JOINTS

16. When the dimensions for a structural joint are to be determined, the bevel will be given by a bevel triangle, and there will be one or several triangles similar to the bevel triangle to solve. In each of the triangles to be solved, one side will be known from the sizes of the material used in the joint, and one or both of the other sides, which are to be obtained from the tables, will be required. In performing this work, care must be exercised not to interchange the legs of the triangle to be solved; that is, not to take a rise for a base or vice versa. In the triangle to be solved, it is to be remembered that the base is the longer leg and is homologous to the side of the elementary triangle marked $b = 12''$, while the rise is the shorter leg and is homologous to the side r indicating the bevel. Ordinarily, this identification may be made at a glance.* In some cases, however, a little reflection will be needed. Therefore, to assist the user of these tables, some of the important principles of similar triangles, in so far as they relate to the subject of this book, are here reviewed.

FUNDAMENTAL PRINCIPLES OF SIMILAR TRIANGLES

17. (1) Similar triangles have equal angles, and, conversely, triangles having equal angles are similar.

(2) Since, in right triangles, one angle is always 90° and the sum of the other two angles is also always equal to 90°, it follows that the equality of one acute angle is sufficient to establish the similarity of right triangles, because the other two angles are then equal also.

---

* When the bevel is small, the distinction between the two legs may be easily made, provided the joint is drawn to scale, by their relative lengths. When the bevel approaches $12''$, this distinction can often be made by making a freehand sketch to an exaggerated scale, so as to show the same conditions as they appear when the bevel is small.

(3) In similar right triangles, the hypotenuses are always homologous, and homologous legs lie opposite equal acute angles.

18. Triangles Similar to the Bevel Triangle.—In laying out structural joints, each triangle to be solved is similar to the elementary, or bevel, triangle, and from the relative position of the two triangles, it is always possible to identify in both triangles at least one equal acute angle. Then, in the triangle to be solved the leg opposite this acute angle is a base or a rise, according to whether the corresponding side in the elementary triangle is a base or a rise. In the following illustrations, an angle lying opposite a rise will be indicated by a single arc and one lying opposite a base by a double arc.

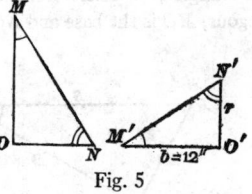

Fig. 5

As an example, let it be known in the triangle *MNO*, Fig. 5, that the angle *M* is equal to the angle *M'* of the elementary triangle *M'N'O'*. Then the side *ON* that is opposite this angle is a rise, and the side *OM* is, of course, a base.

19. Distinguishing Between a Base and a Rise.—From the foregoing, it can be seen that in dealing with a triangle that is similar to the bevel triangle, it is very easy to recognize which leg is a rise and which is a base when the equality of one acute angle has been established. To aid in establishing such equality, the following principles must be kept in mind:

(1) When the hypotenuse and one leg of a right triangle are parallel, respectively, to two sides of the elementary triangle, the angles included between these sides are equal.

(2) When the hypotenuse and one leg of a right triangle are perpendicular, respectively, to any two sides of the elementary triangle, the angles included between the respective sides are equal.

(3) When, in the right triangle to be solved, one side is parallel and another is perpendicular to respective sides of the elementary triangle, one of the sides in each triangle being a hypotenuse, the included angles are not equal, but complementary; that is, their sum equals 90°. This case must be particularly noted, as it is likely to cause confusion owing to the fact that this condition is sufficient to insure the similarity of the triangles, even though the angles included by the sides under consideration are not equal. However, it is evident that equality exists between one of the angles under consideration in one triangle and the other acute angle of the other triangle. A closer examination will show that the third side

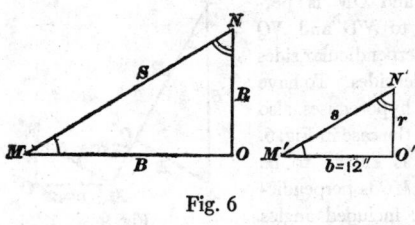

Fig. 6

of either of the triangles must also be either parallel or perpendicular to a side of the other triangle. Therefore, one of the conditions stated under (1) and (2) exists also in this case.

20. Figs. 6 to 10 show the cases frequently occurring in practice. Fig. 6 shows the simplest case. The right triangle MNO has all its sides parallel, respectively, to those of the bevel triangle $M'N'O'$. Hence, angle M =angle M' and angle N =angle N'. Therefore, since the sides that are opposite equal angles are homologous, MO is the base and NO is the rise.

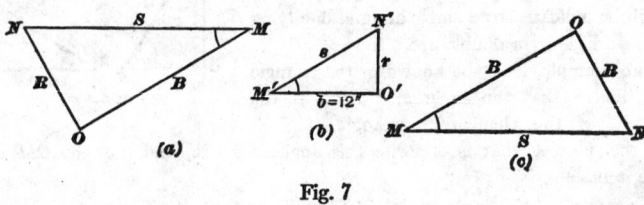

Fig. 7

In Fig. 7 (a) and (c), the hypotenuses MN are parallel to the base $M'O'$ of the bevel triangle shown in (b), and the legs MO are parallel to the slope s. In both cases, angle M =angle M'; consequently, the opposite leg NO is, in each case, homologous to $N'O'$ and is a rise, while the side MO is homologous to $M'O'$ and is a base.

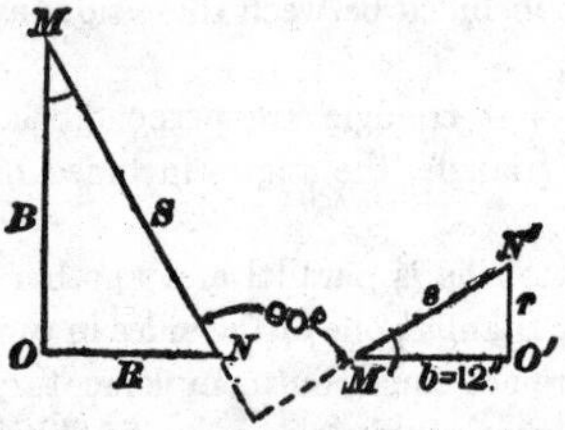

In Fig. 8, the sides of the triangle MNO are perpendicular, respectively, to the sides of the bevel triangle $M'N'O'$. Since the angles included by perpendicular sides are equal, angle M =angle M' and angle N =angle N'. Hence, the opposite sides are homologous. Therefore, OM is a base and ON is a rise. It is to be observed that since OM is perpendicular to $O'M'$ and ON is perpendicular to $O'N'$, MO is parallel to $N'O'$ and NO to $M'O'$; but, in this case, it is the perpendicular sides that are homologous—not the parallel sides. To have the parallel sides homologous, the hypotenuses also should be parallel to each other, as is the case in Fig. 6.

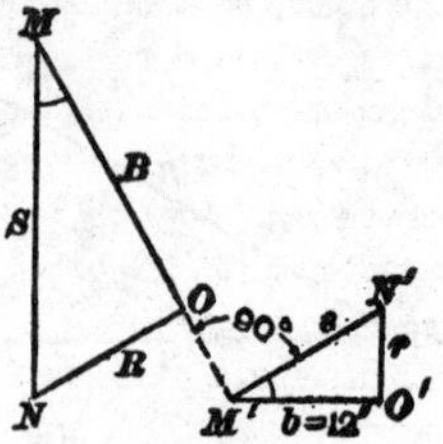

Fig. 8

In Fig. 9, the hypotenuse MN is known to be perpendicular to $M'O'$, and the leg MO is perpendicular to the hypotenuse $M'N'$. The included angles M and M' are therefore equal, and the opposite sides are homologous. Hence, NO is a rise and MO must be a base.

Fig. 9

Finally, let it be known that MO, Fig. 10, is perpendicular to $M'N'$, and that MN is parallel to $N'O'$. Then, according to principle 3, of Art. 19, the angles M and N' included between the sides considered, are not equal, but complementary. The opposite sides are not homologous; but, since M and N' are complementary, angle M=angle M' and angle N=angle N'. Therefore, NO is the rise and OM is the base. This conclusion can also be reached by reasoning as follows: Since it is known that MN is parallel to $N'O'$, MN must be perpendicular to $M'O'$. Thus, the same conditions as those in the previous example obtain.

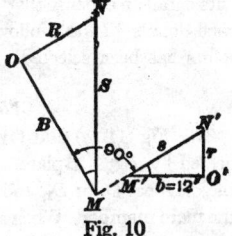

Fig. 10

PRACTICAL EXAMPLES AND FORMULAS

APPLICATION TO STRUCTURAL DETAILS

21. In the following pages is taken up the application of the tables and diagrams to structural details. The method of attacking the problems involved and the procedure in solving them are very simple. To expedite the work of solving, simple formulas* are derived, and it is expected that the draftsman will not experience any difficulty in applying the tables and diagrams to advantage. In order, however, that he may gain confidence and acquire rapidity, it is important for him to study carefully the principles evolved, and to work out a large number of examples similar to those given in the text. It is advisable, also, to commit to memory the more important of the formulas here derived. These formulas cover only the most typical cases, but after a study of this text the intelligent draftsman should be able to prepare such additional formulas as will cover the particular class of details that he uses with frequency. Repeated use will fix many of the formulas in his mind permanently and make reference unnecessary.

22. As far as their application to structural joints is concerned, it is the object of the tables and diagrams to eliminate, as far as possible, special layouts to scales larger than the one to which the shop drawing itself is prepared. Shop drawings are usually laid out to the scale of $\frac{3}{4}''$ or $1''$ to the foot. If accurately executed, a layout to one of these scales is sufficient to show the general features of the construction. The tables may then be used to determine or to check the distances to first rivets of diagonals, in order to assure the proper end distances and clearances, as well as to determine the sizes of gusset plates and the lengths of diagonals. The layout to a larger scale may be used in cases where, for some reason, the use of the tables is impracticable. This may occur when a joint has an irregular outline, that is, when a considerable number of beveled cuts are used in the angles and gusset

---

* The term *formula* is here used not in the ordinary mathematical sense of the word, but to symbolize references to the Tables and Diagrams of Slopes and Rises. Except for the plus and minus signs, which are employed to combine the results of two such references, no arithmetical operations are involved in the formulas here derived.

plates. In this connection, it may be stated that, generally speaking, good practice demands that the construction of such joints be avoided. The time and labor spent in the drafting room, as well as in the shop, in working out details containing beveled cuts entail an expense that is far greater than the cost of the material saved by using such details. In the following examples, for the sake of completeness, a variety of joints has been selected.

CLASSIFICATION OF CONNECTIONS

23. Fig. 11 (a) and (b) shows two joints, each consisting of two members connected by a gusset plate. The member M, or M_1, which extends on both sides of the diagonal D, or D_1, and is therefore to be cleared by the diagonal, will be called the **main member.** When a diagonal makes an angle greater than 45° with the main member, the bevel will be parallel to the main member and will be designated simply as a **parallel bevel**, while when this angle is less than 45°, the bevel will be perpen-

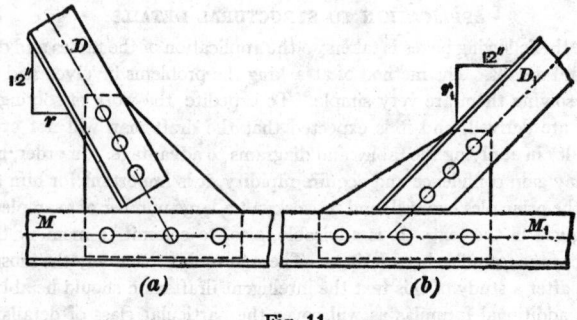

Fig. 11

dicular to the main member and will be called a **perpendicular bevel.** In Fig. 11, r is a parallel bevel, and r_1 is a perpendicular bevel. Another classification of connections is based on the manner in which the ends of the diagonals are cut off. A connection in which the end is cut at right angles to the center, or gauge, line of the diagonal will here be called a **square-end connection;** otherwise, it will be referred to as a **bevel-end connection.** In Fig. 11, (a) represents a square-end connection and (b) a bevel-end connection.

FORMULAS FOR SQUARE-END CONNECTIONS

24. For the sake of simplicity, a uniform notation has been adopted in the following discussion for certain values involved in the calculations. This notation will be observed in the illustrations and formulas. For the same reason, in the numerical examples, unless otherwise stated, the rivet gauges in angle bars are assumed to be standard and the rivet pitch is always taken as 3″, the end distances e as 1½″, and the clearance c as ¼″.

Fig. 12 (a) shows a square-end connection with a parallel bevel. In this joint, it is desired to know the values of z, x, and y. The value of z, which will be called **the clearance distance,** must be such that the diagonal will clear the main member

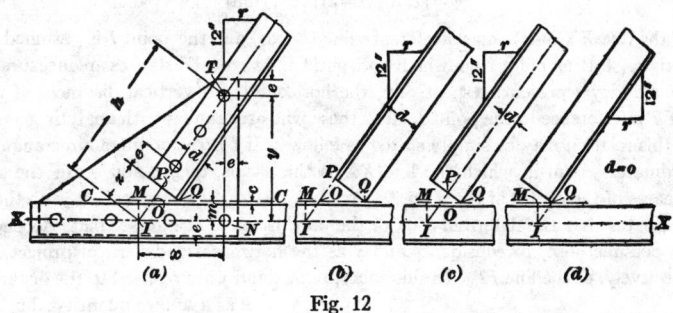

(a)   *(b)*   *(c)*   *(d)*

Fig. 12

by the amount c. The values of x and y are required in order to determine the size of the gusset plate.

From the illustration, it can be seen that $z = IO + OP$; also, that both triangles IMO and OPQ, which are shown shaded and to a larger scale in Fig. 12 (e), are, according to principles 1 and 2 of Art. 19, similar to the bevel triangle. In the triangle IMO, the base MI is known; therefore, $IO = (S \text{ for } B = MI)$. In the triangle OPQ, the base PQ is known; therefore, $OP = (R \text{ for } B = PQ)$. Hence, putting $MI = m$ and $PQ = d$,

$$z = (S \text{ for } B = m) + (R \text{ for } B = d) \ldots \ldots (1a)$$

In this formula, m is the distance of the point Q, which is the point of the diagonal to be cleared from the center line of the main member, and d is the distance of the same point from the center line of the diagonal. For the position of the diagonal shown in Fig. 12 (a), d is equal to the rivet gauge of the diagonal; for that shown in (b), d is the width of the diagonal; for that shown in (c), d is the difference between the width of the angle bar and the gauge; and, finally, in the position of the angle bar shown in (d), this distance is zero. In this case, the second term in the expression for z disappears altogether, and the formula becomes

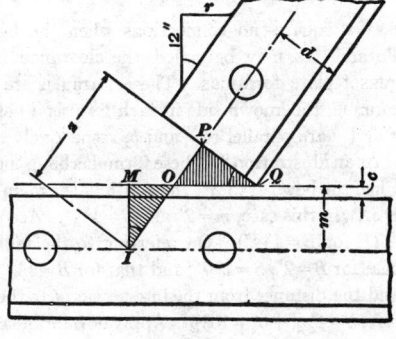

Fig. 12 (e)

$$z = (S \text{ for } B = m)$$

xvii

25. When z has been determined, the value of h will be known; hence, from the triangle ITN, which also is similar to the bevel triangle,

$$x = (R \text{ for } S = h) \dots \dots \text{(2a)}$$
$$y = (B \text{ for } S = h) \dots \dots \text{(3a)}$$

If the line XX is taken as a reference line (x-axis) and the point I is assumed as an origin (starting point from which horizontal and vertical distances are measured), then x and y represent, respectively, the horizontal and vertical distances of the rivet T in reference to the point I. For those who are familiar with analytic geometry, this relation may be simply stated as follows: If I is the origin of a rectangular coordinate system in which the line XX is the x-axis, then x and y are the coordinates of the center of the rivet T. As must be clearly understood, it is on these coordinates that the determination of the dimensions of the gusset plate depends. It is possible, also, to consider x and y as the horizontal and vertical projection, respectively, of the line IT. In this conception, x and y are referred to the distance h as a known quantity; but, as will be seen later, these projections do not always give sufficient information in regard to the size of the gusset plate, whereas the former conception gives the relative position of the extreme rivet T in reference to I and, as indicated before, it is these quantities that must be determined in order to compute the size of the gusset plate.

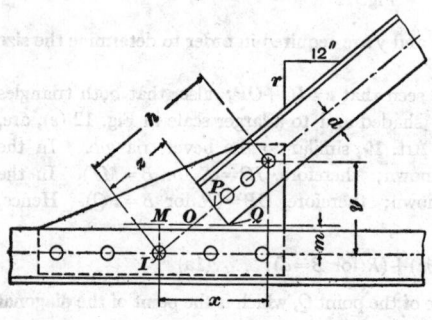

Fig. 13

26. Formulas **1a, 2a,** and **3a** are the fundamental formulas for square-end connections when the bevel is parallel to the main member. Formula **1a** may be called the **clearance formula** and formulas **2a** and **3a** the **gusset plate formulas.** These formulas are easily remembered. In the clearance formula, the known side in each term is a base; and in both gusset-plate formulas, x and y are parallel to r and b, respectively; x is therefore a rise, and y is a base.

As an illustration, let these formulas be applied to the connection shown in Fig. 12(a), when the bevel $r = 5\frac{3}{4}''$, the width of the main member is $4''$, and that of the diagonal is $3''$. In this case, $m = 2''$ and $d = 1\frac{3}{4}''$. According to formula **1a**, $z = (S \text{ for } B = 2'')$ $+ (R \text{ for } B = 1\frac{3}{4}'')$. On referring to the table for the bevel $5\frac{3}{4}''$, it will be found that for $B = 2''$, $S = 2\frac{3}{16}''$, and that for $B = 1\frac{3}{4}''$, $R = \frac{13}{16}''$. Hence, $z = 2\frac{3}{16}'' + \frac{13}{16}'' = 3''$, and the distance from the intersection I to the first rivet is $3'' + 1\frac{1}{2}'' = 4\frac{1}{2}''$. Therefore, $h = 4\frac{1}{2}'' + 6'' = 10\frac{1}{2}''$. Apply now formulas **2a** and **3a**. Then $x = (R \text{ for } S = 10\frac{1}{2}'')$ and $y = (B \text{ for } S = 10\frac{1}{2}'')$. On referring again to the same table it will be found that for $S = 10\frac{1}{2}''$, $R = 4\frac{9}{16}'' = x$, and $B = 9\frac{1}{2}'' = y$. Assuming that the point I is midway between the two adjacent rivets, the horizontal dimension of the gusset plate will be $x+7\frac{1}{2}''=12\frac{1}{16}''$, or say $12''$, and the vertical dimension will be $9\frac{1}{2}''+3''=1'0\frac{1}{2}''$.

27. When the connection has a perpendicular bevel, as in Fig. 13, the general relations remain the same as in Fig. 12, except that in the clearance formula the known values m and d are rises and that x is parallel to b and y is parallel to r. Hence,

$$z=(S \text{ for } R=m)+(B \text{ for } R=d)\ldots\ldots(1e)$$
$$x=(B \text{ for } S=h)\ldots\ldots\ldots\ldots\ldots(2e)$$
$$y=(R \text{ for } S=h)\ldots\ldots\ldots\ldots\ldots(3e)^*$$

It must be particularly noticed that these formulas can be derived from those for the parallel bevel by interchanging the letters B and R and leaving the letter S unchanged. Thus, formula 1e can be obtained from formula 1a by substituting in the first term R for B, and by writing in the second term "B for R" instead of "R for B"; similarly, formula 2e can be obtained from formula 2a by substituting B for R, and formula 3e from 3a by substituting R for B. This principle can be formulated thus:

Rule.—*Any formula or set of formulas giving solutions of triangles for a connection having a parallel bevel can be applied to a connection having a perpendicular bevel, or vice versa, by interchanging the letters B and R and leaving the letter S unchanged.*

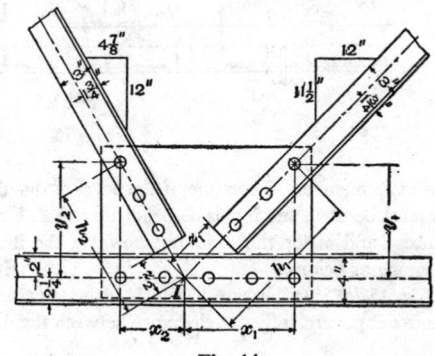

Fig. 14

To show the application of the formulas for a perpendicular bevel, let, in Fig. 13, $r=9\frac{7}{8}''$, $m=1\frac{3}{4}''$, and $d=1\frac{1}{4}''$. Applying formula 1e and referring to the table for the bevel $9\frac{7}{8}''$, it is found that $z=(S \text{ for } R=1\frac{3}{4}'')+(B \text{ for } R=1\frac{1}{4}'')=2\frac{3}{4}''+1\frac{1}{2}''=4\frac{1}{4}''$.

The distance h is therefore $4\frac{1}{4}''+1\frac{1}{2}''+6''=11\frac{3}{4}''$. Hence, applying formulas 2e and 3e, $x=(B \text{ for } S=11\frac{3}{4}'')=9\frac{1}{16}''$ and $y=(R \text{ for } S=11\frac{3}{4}'')=7\frac{7}{16}''$.

Assuming the rivet spacing of the main member to be $4\frac{1}{2}''$, the dimensions of the gusset plate may now be taken as $9\frac{1}{16}''+12''$, say $1'9''$, by $7\frac{7}{16}''+3''$, say $10\frac{1}{2}''$.

28. Fig. 14 shows a joint in which one diagonal has a parallel bevel and the other a perpendicular bevel. Applying the preceding formulas, we have for the perpendicular bevel, $z_1=(S \text{ for } R=2'')+(B \text{ for } R=1\frac{3}{4}'')=2\frac{7}{8}''+1\frac{13}{16}''=4\frac{11}{16}''$.

The distance to the first rivet is $6\frac{3}{16}''$, and $h_1=12\frac{3}{16}''$. Hence, $x_1=(B \text{ for } S=12\frac{3}{16}'')=8\frac{13}{16}''$ and $y_1=(R \text{ for } S=12\frac{3}{16}'')=8\frac{7}{16}''$.

---

*The ideas "parallel" and "perpendicular" are symbolized by the letters a and e, which are the second letters of these respective words.

Similarly, for the parallel bevel, $z_2 = (S$ for $B=2'') + (R$ for $B=1\frac{1}{4}'') = 2\frac{3}{16}'' + \frac{1}{2}'' = 2\frac{11}{16}''$. The distance to the first rivet is $4\frac{5}{16}''$, and $h_2 = 10\frac{3}{16}''$. Hence, $x_2 = (R$ for $S = 10\frac{3}{16}'') = 3\frac{13}{16}''$ and $y_2 = (B$ for $S = 10\frac{3}{16}'') = 9\frac{7}{16}''$. The horizontal dimension of the plate is therefore $x_1 + x_2 + 3'' = 8\frac{13}{16}'' + 3\frac{13}{16}'' + 3'' = 15\frac{5}{8}''$, and the vertical dimension is equal to $y_2 + 3'' = 9\frac{7}{16}'' + 3'' = 12\frac{7}{16}''$, say $1'\text{-}0\frac{1}{2}''$.

29. Clearing a Vertical Angle.—Fig. 15 (a) shows a joint in which the diagonal has to clear the vertical angle A. In this case, the angle A must be considered as

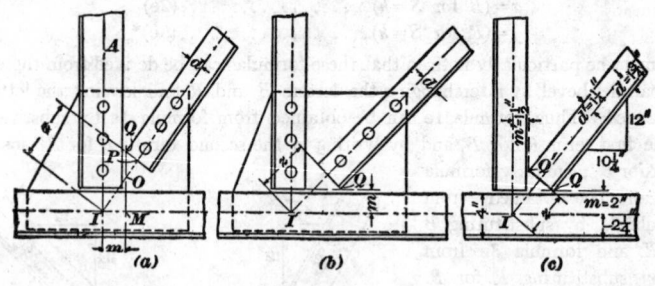

Fig. 15

the main member. Therefore, if the bevel of the diagonal is parallel to A, formula **1a** must be used, and if it is perpendicular to A, formula **1e** is applicable. The distances d and m for this case are shown in the illustration. They have the same meaning as before.

Fig. 15 (b) shows a case in which, although there is a vertical member, the distance z is governed by the clearance between the diagonal and the horizontal member.

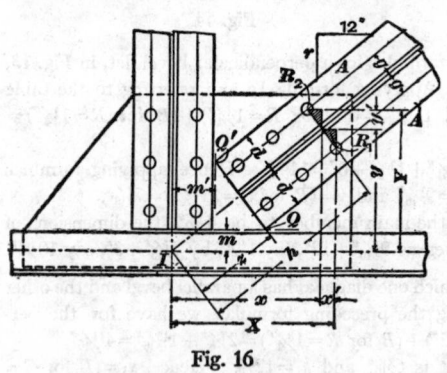

Fig. 16

It is obvious that in this case the values of r, d, and m must be referred to the horizontal member.

Fig. 15 (c) shows a joint in which it is impossible to tell at a glance which angle, the horizontal or the vertical, governs the distance z. In this case z may be determined in reference to both of these angles and the greater value used. Let, for example, in Fig. 15 (c), the bevel be $10\frac{1}{4}''$ and the other dimensions be as shown. For clearing the point Q, the bevel is a parallel one; therefore, applying formula **1a**, $z = (S$ for $B=2'') + (R$ for $B = 1\frac{3}{4}'') = 2\frac{5}{8}'' + 1\frac{1}{2}'' = 4\frac{1}{8}''$. For clearing the point Q', the bevel is a perpendicular one; therefore, applying formula 1e, $z = (S$ for $R = 1\frac{1}{2}'') + (B$ for $R = 1\frac{1}{4}'') = 2\frac{5}{16}'' + 1\frac{7}{16}'' = 3\frac{3}{4}''$. As the first value is the greater, it must be used.

30. The x- and the y-Correction.—Fig. 16 shows a joint in which the center line of the diagonal coincides with the backs of the angles A. The clearance dimension may be determined by formulas 1a and 1e, as previously explained, the value of d being, in this case, equal to the width of the angle bars. But, as can be seen from the illustration, the size of the gusset plate depends in this case on the distance X, which is the x-coordinate of the rivet R_1, and the distance Y, which is the y-coordinate of the rivet R_2, whereas formulas 2e and 3e applied to this case merely express that x and y are the projections of the distance h, as is explained in Art. 25. To obtain the required coordinates X and Y, the values of x and y must be corrected, respectively, by the amounts x' and y'. The values of x' and y' will here be called, respectively, the **x- and the y-correction**.

For the bevel shown in the illustration, $x = (B$ for $S = h)$ and $y = (R$ for $S = h)$. In finding the corrections, it will be noticed that x' and y' are the legs of the two shaded triangles, which are, of course, equal to each other. In these triangles, which will be called **correction triangles**, all the sides are perpendicular, respectively, to those of the bevel triangle. Hence, y' is a base and x' a rise for the same bevel. Therefore, $x' = (R$ for $S = g)$ and $y' = (B$ for $S = g)$. Hence,

$$X = x + x' = (B \text{ for } S = h) + (R \text{ for } S = g)$$
and
$$Y = y + y' = (R \text{ for } S = h) + (B \text{ for } S = g)$$

It is evident that when the bevel is parallel to the horizontal member,

$$X = (R \text{ for } S = h) + (B \text{ for } S = g)$$
and
$$Y = (B \text{ for } S = h) + (R \text{ for } S = g)$$

Each of these formulas can easily be written by a mere inspection of the figure to which it refers. It is to be noticed that in each term the known side is a hypotenuse (h or g). Now, the first terms are easily written, because x or y is a base or a rise according as it is parallel to b or r. When the first terms have been put down, the second terms may be written from the first terms by interchanging the letters B and R and substituting g for h.

To apply these formulas to a numerical example, let, in Fig. 16, $m' = 3\frac{3}{4}''$, $d = 3\frac{1}{2}''$, $m = 2\frac{3}{4}''$, $g = 2''$, and $r = 10\frac{1}{8}''$. Then, to clear Q', $z = (S$ for $B = 3\frac{3}{4}'') + (R$ for $B = 3\frac{1}{2}'') = 5\frac{1}{16}'' + 3\frac{3}{16}'' = 8\frac{1}{4}''$. To clear Q, $z = (S$ for $R = 2\frac{3}{4}'') + (B$ for $R = 3\frac{1}{2}'') = 4\frac{1}{8}'' + 3\frac{7}{8}'' = 8''$.

The value of $8\frac{1}{4}''$ must therefore be used. Hence, $h = 8\frac{1}{4}'' + 1\frac{1}{2}'' + 6'' = 15\frac{3}{4}''$. Then by applying the formulas just given,

$$X = (B \text{ for } S = 15\frac{3}{4}'') + (R \text{ for } S = 2'') = 11\frac{11}{16}'' + 1\frac{3}{8}'' = 13\frac{1}{16}''$$
and
$$Y = (R \text{ for } S = 15\frac{3}{4}'') + (B \text{ for } S = 2'') = 10\frac{9}{16}'' + 1\frac{1}{2}'' = 12\frac{1}{16}''$$

NOTE.—In applying these formulas, the values of the first terms, as well as those of the second, in both formulas may be taken from the table at the same time. Thus, for $S = 15\frac{3}{4}''$, the values of $B = 11\frac{11}{16}''$ and $R = 10\frac{9}{16}''$ can be taken out at the same time. Similarly one reference only is needed for the values of B and R for $S = 2''$.

31. Negative Values of x' and y'.—In making corrections for x and y, it sometimes happens that either one of the values x' or y' must be subtracted from x or y instead of added. An example of this kind is illustrated in Fig. 17. It is obvious

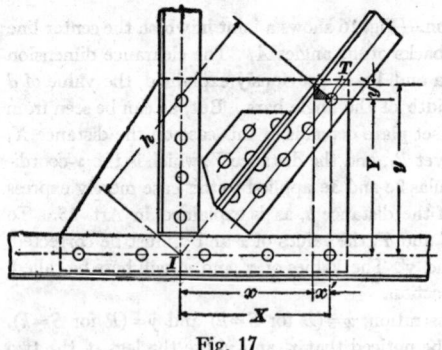

that in order to obtain the coordinates X and Y, of the rivet T, which controls the dimensions of the gusset plate, x' must be added to x, but y' must be subtracted from y. Therefore, in this case, the minus sign must be used before the second term in the formula for Y.

32. As a result of the foregoing discussion the following general gusset-plate formulas may be written:

Fig. 17

When the bevel is a parallel one,

$$X = x \pm x' = (R \text{ for } S=h) \pm (B \text{ for } S=g) \ldots\ldots\ldots \textbf{(4a)}$$
$$Y = y \pm y' = (B \text{ for } S=h) \pm (R \text{ for } S=g) \ldots\ldots\ldots \textbf{(5a)}$$

When the bevel is a perpendicular one,

$$X = x \pm x' = (B \text{ for } S=h) \pm (R \text{ for } S=g) \ldots\ldots\ldots \textbf{(4e)}$$
$$Y = y \pm y' = (R \text{ for } S=h) \pm (B \text{ for } S=g) \ldots\ldots\ldots \textbf{(5e)}$$

To determine whether the plus or minus sign is to be used in a given case, draw the correction triangle for the rivet under consideration; then, according as the coordinates of the rivet, or rivets, under consideration are greater or smaller than x or y the values of x' or y' will be additive or subtractive.

It is evident that in the cases shown in Figs. 12, 13, and 14, $g=0$; therefore, $x'=0$ and $y'=0$, and formulas 2a and 3a, and 2e and 3e are obtained.

33. Special Problem.—In Fig. 18 the value of z_2 may be determined in the usual manner by formula 1a; but the value of z_1 is governed by the condition that the diagonal A_1 must clear the diagonal A_2. This condition is not expressed by any of the

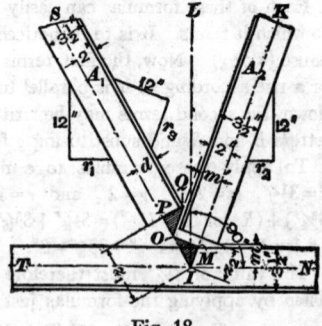

Fig. 18

formulas previously given. If, however, A_2 is considered as a main member in reference to A_1, then, for the bevel r_3, the fundamental formula 1a (or 1e if the bevel is a perpendicular one) is directly applicable here. The correctness of this conclusion may be verified by considering the shaded triangles OIM and OPQ, in which $OI = (S$ for $B = m')$ and $OP = (R$ for $B = d)$. Hence, $z_1 = (S$ for $B = m') + (R$ for $B = d)$. The problem, therefore, resolves itself into finding the bevel r_3. This may easily be done by means of the Table of Bevels, in which may be found the angles SIL and LIK, corresponding to the bevels r_1 and r_2, respectively. The angle SIK will then be equal to the sum of these angles. With angle SIK known, the bevel corresponding to it may be read from the same table. It should be observed that if the angle SIK proves to be greater than 45°, its complement must be used.

As an example, let, in Fig. 18, $r_1 = 7\frac{1}{2}''$ and $r_2 = 4\frac{1}{2}''$. On referring to the Table of Bevels, it is found that the angles corresponding to the bevels $7\frac{1}{2}''$ and $4\frac{1}{2}''$ are, respectively, 32° 00′ 19″ and 20° 33′ 22″. Whence, angle $SIK = 52°$ 33′ 41″. Since this angle is greater than 45°, its complement 90° − 52° 33′ 41″ = 37° 26′ 19″ must be used. The bevel corresponding to this angle is $9\frac{3}{16}''$. This bevel is parallel to A_2; hence, formula 1a must be applied to clear Q. Therefore, $z_1 = (S$ for $B = 2\frac{1}{4}'') + (R$ for $B = 2'') = 2\frac{13}{16}'' + 1\frac{9}{16}'' = 4\frac{3}{8}''$.

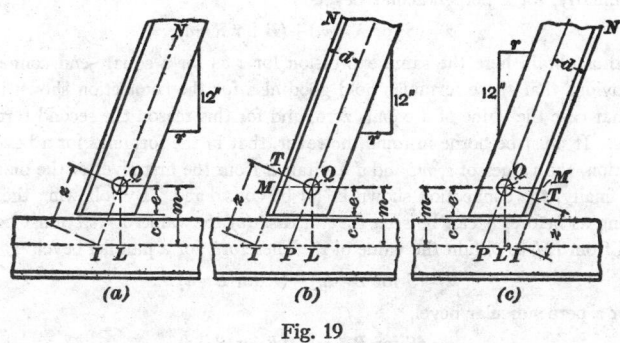

Fig. 19

FORMULAS FOR BEVEL-END CONNECTIONS

34. In the case of a bevel-end connection, the formulas for x and y are the same as for square-end connections. The clearance formula, however, requires special treatment and will be taken up in the following discussion. This discussion will be carried through mainly for connections having parallel bevels, but the deductions and conclusions reached apply also to connections with perpendicular bevels, except that the formulas must be modified in accordance with the rule given in Art. 27.

35. The simple connection shown in Fig. 19 (a), in which the center line of the diagonal NI coincides with the rivet line, will be first considered. It will be convenient to denote here by z the distance from the first rivet Q to the point of intersection I. This rivet must be so located that the end distance e should not be less than the required minimum, and that there should be a clearance c left between the two members. Let, now, m denote the distance of Q from the center line of the main member. Draw QL perpendicular to the main member, thus making $QL=m$. Then, in the triangle QLI, which is similar to the bevel triangle, QL is a base. Therefore,

$$z = (S \text{ for } B=m)$$

and, similarly, for a perpendicular bevel,

$$z = (S \text{ for } R=m)$$

It must be noticed here that these formulas have the same expression as the first terms of the formulas 1a and 1e, respectively.

Let, now, the connection shown in (b) be considered. In this joint, the center line of the diagonal, NI, coincides with the back of the angle. As z is measured on this line, it is equal to IT. Draw QM parallel to IP. Then, $z=IM+MT$. Since $IM=QP$, $z=QP+MT$. But, as previously found, $QP=(S \text{ for } B=m)$ and MT is the altitude of the right triangle QTM whose base $TQ=d$ is the distance of Q from NI. This triangle also is similar to the bevel triangle; therefore,

$$z = (S \text{ for } B=m)+(R \text{ for } B=d)$$

and, similarly, for a perpendicular bevel,

$$z = (S \text{ for } R=m)+(B \text{ for } R=d)$$

We thus obtain here the same expression for z as for a square-end connection. It is obvious that these formulas hold good also for the connection shown in (a), as in that case the value of d equals zero, and for this reason the second term disappears. It must be borne in mind, however, that in the formulas for a bevel-end connection, the values of z, m, and d are taken from the first rivet of the diagonal.

Let, finally, the connection shown in (c) be considered. By following the same reasoning as before, it can be seen that in case (c) the value of TM must be subtracted from IM to obtain the value of z. Therefore, for a parallel bevel,

$$z = (S \text{ for } B=m)-(R \text{ for } B=d)$$

and, for a perpendicular bevel,

$$z = (S \text{ for } R=m)-(B \text{ for } R=d)$$

36. From the foregoing can be drawn the following conclusion: If the values of z, m, and d are taken from the first rivet of the diagonal, formulas 1a and 1e may be applied also to a bevel-end connection, except that in case (c) the minus sign instead of the plus sign must be put before the second term.

The result of the preceding discussion may now be combined into two formulas, which are the same as formulas 1a and 1e, except that the minus sign is inserted, to be used in the connection shown in (c):

$$z = (S \text{ for } B=m) \pm (R \text{ for } B=d) \ldots \ldots \textbf{(6a)}$$

and

$$z = (S \text{ for } R=m) \pm (B \text{ for } R=d) \ldots \ldots \textbf{(6e)}$$

To determine which of the signs, $+$ or $-$, is to be used in any particular case, imagine a line QM parallel to the main member; then, if the point M falls inside IT, the plus sign must be employed and if it falls outside IT, the minus sign should be used.

37. Dimensions at End of Diagonal.—Fig. 20 shows an incomplete outline of a bevel-end connection. To determine the length of the diagonal, the end distance u will be required in addition to the value of s. Of course, the diagonal may be cut off on any line as C-C, so that the end distance should not exceed the minimum required value of e. But, for the beveled cut shown in the figure, it will be necessary to find an expression for the distance u. This distance is equal to $NO+OP=QM+OP$. From the triangle QML, $QM=(S$ for $B=e)$, and from the triangle OPQ, $OP=(R$ for $B=g)$. Therefore, for a parallel bevel,

$$u=(S \text{ for } B=e)+(R \text{ for } B=g)$$

and, for a perpendicular bevel,

$$u=(S \text{ for } R=e)+(B \text{ for } R=g)$$

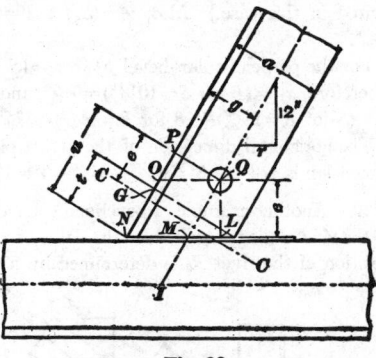

Fig. 20

These formulas are easily remembered. They may be written from formulas 1a and 1e by replacing, respectively, the letters m and d by e and g.

It should be observed that e and g are the respective distances of the extreme point N of the diagonal from the line QO prolonged, and from the center line of the diagonal. With this interpretation of the meaning of e and g, the formulas for u become identical with formulas 1a and 1e, except that here the line through the end rivet parallel to the main member takes the place of the center line of the main member itself.

The distance $t=NG$ also may be needed in order to lay out the beveled cut. It is evident from the figure that, for a parallel bevel,

$$t=(R \text{ for } B=a)$$

and, for a perpendicular bevel,

$$t=(B \text{ for } R=a)$$

It will be noticed that these expressions are the same as the second terms of the formulas for u, a here taking the place of g.

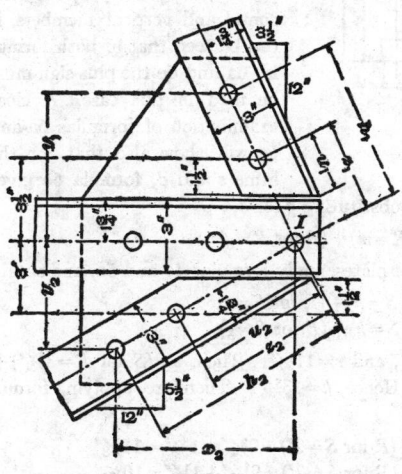

Fig. 21

38. To show the application of the formulas for bevel-end connections, reference is made to Fig. 21, in which case one bevel is parallel to the main member and the other is perpendicular to it. To apply formulas **6a** and **6e**, since $d=0$, the second terms disappear; therefore, for the parallel bevel $3\frac{1}{2}''$, $z_1=(S$ for $B=3\frac{1}{2}'')=3\frac{5}{8}''$. Hence, $h_1=6\frac{5}{8}''$, and $y_1=(B$ for $S=6\frac{5}{8}'')=6\frac{3}{8}''$. ($x_1$ is not required in this case.) Also, $u_1=(S$ for $B=1\frac{1}{2}'')+(R$ for $B=1\frac{3}{4}'')=1\frac{9}{16}''+\frac{1}{2}''=2\frac{1}{16}''$.

For the perpendicular bevel $5\frac{1}{2}''$, $z_2=(S$ for $R=3'')=7\frac{1}{4}''$. Hence, $h_2=10\frac{1}{4}''$. Therefore, $x_2=(B$ for $S=10\frac{1}{4}'')=9\frac{5}{16}''$, and $y_2=(R$ for $S=10\frac{1}{4}'')=4\frac{1}{4}''$. Finally, $u_2=(S$ for $R=1\frac{1}{2}'')+(B$ for $R=1\frac{3}{4}'')=3\frac{3}{16}''+3\frac{13}{16}''=7\frac{3}{8}''$.

The horizontal dimension of the gusset plate is $x_2+3''=12\frac{5}{16}''$, and the vertical dimension is $y_1+y_2+3''=6\frac{3}{8}''+4\frac{1}{4}''+3''=1'\ 1\frac{5}{8}''$.

39. Another example of bevel-end connections is given in Fig. 22. The position of the rivet R_1 is controlled by the value of z, as determined by formula **6a**, and the position of the rivet R_2 is determined by formula **6e**. The greater value must, of

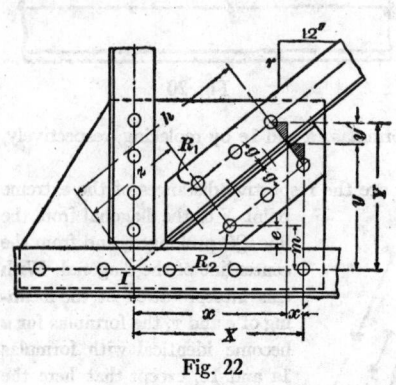

Fig. 22

course, be used, and the rivets located opposite each other; that is, so that the line R_1R_2 is perpendicular to the center line of the diagonal. By proceeding as explained in Art. **36** and imagining lines drawn from R_1 and R_2 parallel, respectively, to the horizontal and vertical members, it can be seen that in both formulas **6a** and **6e** the plus sign must be used in this case. A close examination of formulas **6a** and **6e** will show also that for the same e and d, formula **6e** gives a greater value for z. Therefore, substituting g for d,

$$z=(S\text{ for }R=m)+(B\text{ for }R=g)$$

To determine the size of the gusset plates, apply formulas **4e** and **5e**, and obtain

$$X=(B\text{ for }S=h)+(R\text{ for }S=g)$$
and
$$Y=(R\text{ for }S=h)+(B\text{ for }S=g)$$

Let, for example, $m=3\frac{1}{2}''$, $g=2''$, and $r=11\frac{1}{8}''$. Then, $z=(S$ for $R=3\frac{1}{2}'')+(B$ for $R=2'')=5\frac{1}{8}''+2\frac{3}{16}''=7\frac{5}{16}''$. Hence, $h=13\frac{5}{16}''$. Therefore, applying formulas **4e** and **5e**,

$$X=(B\text{ for }S=1'\ 1\frac{5}{16}'')+(R\text{ for }S=2'')=9\frac{3}{4}''+1\frac{3}{8}''=11\frac{1}{8}''$$
and
$$Y=(R\text{ for }S=1'\ 1\frac{5}{16}'')+(B\text{ for }S=2'')=9\frac{1}{16}''+1\frac{1}{2}''=10\frac{9}{16}''$$

MISCELLANEOUS EXAMPLES

40. Fig. 23 shows a joint in which one angle bar has a square end and the other a beveled end. The position of the rivet R_1 is controlled by the value of z, which may be determined by formula **1a**. The rivet R_4 is opposite rivet R_2. These two rivets must be so located that e_1 will not exceed a certain minimum and that the distance R_1R_2 will have the proper length. The distance R_1R_2 may be assumed, and the first

requirement may be tested by formula **6a**. The size of the gusset plate will usually be determined by the rivet R_6, and, in applying the gusset-plate formulas, the plus sign will have to be taken with formula **4a** and the minus sign with formula **5a**. If it is suspected that the rivet R_3 controls the vertical dimension of the gusset plate, the value of $Y_1 = y_1 + y'_1$ must be determined from formula **5a**, using for S the dimension h_1.

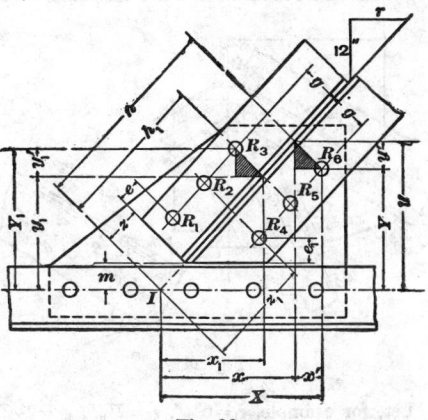

Fig. 23

Assume, for example, that $r = 11\frac{3}{8}''$, $m = 1\frac{3}{4}''$, and $g = 2\frac{1}{2}''$. Then, by formula **1a**, since $d = 0$, and the second term disappears, $z = (S$ for $B = 1\frac{3}{4}'') = 2\frac{7}{16}''$.

Assume that $e = 1\frac{1}{2}''$ and that the rivet pitch is $3''$. Then, $z_1 = 2\frac{7}{16}'' + 1\frac{1}{2}'' + 3'' = 6\frac{15}{16}''$.

To test the location of the rivet R_4, assume that $e_1 = 1\frac{1}{2}''$, then $m_1 = 3\frac{1}{4}''$, and the minimum of z_1 will be, by formula **6a**,

$$z_1 = (S \text{ for } B = 3\frac{1}{4}'') + (R \text{ for } B = 2\frac{1}{2}'') = 4\frac{1}{2}'' + 2\frac{3}{8}'' = 6\frac{7}{8}''$$

This is less than the value previously obtained; the arrangement is therefore satisfactory.

To apply, now, formulas **4a** and **5a**, $h = z + 10\frac{1}{2}'' = 1'\ 0\frac{15}{16}''$. Therefore,

$$X = x + x' = (R \text{ for } S = 1'\ 0\frac{15}{16}'') + (B \text{ for } S = 2\frac{1}{2}'') = 8\frac{7}{8}'' + 1\frac{13}{16}'' = 10\frac{11}{16}''$$

and $$Y = (B \text{ for } S = 1'\ 0\frac{15}{16}'') - (R \text{ for } S = 2\frac{1}{2}'') = 9\frac{3}{8}'' - 1\frac{11}{16}'' = 7\frac{11}{16}''$$

For the rivet R_3,

$$Y_1 = y_1 + y_1' = (B \text{ for } S = 9\frac{15}{16}'') + (R \text{ for } S = 2\frac{1}{2}'') = 7\frac{1}{4}'' + 1\frac{11}{16}'' = 8\frac{15}{16}''$$

The vertical dimension of the gusset plate is therefore governed by the rivet R_3.

41. Fig. 24 shows a connection at a roof-truss peak. Only one-half of the joint is shown fully, because the joint is symmetrical about its center line. The bevel r_1 of the rafter is referred to a horizontal line and is, of course, a perpendicular one; but the beveled cut of the rafter is referred to the center line. Therefore, the bevel for the values of z_1 and t is to be taken as parallel. Hence,

$$t = (R \text{ for } B = g_1)$$

and $$z_1 = (S \text{ for } B = e)$$

When z_1 has been computed, h_1 will be known; therefore,

$$x_1 = (B \text{ for } S = h_1)$$

For the angle bar A_2, in so far as it has to clear the rafter, the bevel r_3 will be required. In a Fink truss in which the panels are equal, $r_3 = r_1$; but, in general, r_3 may

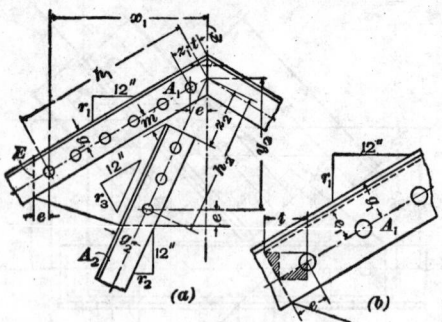

be determined, as is explained in Art. **33**. Then, considering the rafter A_1 as a main member, the bevel r_3 is perpendicular to it; therefore, by formula **1e**,

$$z_2 = (S \text{ for } R = m) + (B \text{ for } R = g_2).$$

When z_2 has been determined, h_2 will be known; therefore, for the bevel r_2,

$$y_2 = (B \text{ for } S = h_2)$$

Fig. 24

The values of y_1 and x_2 will not be needed in this case.

Let, for example, $r_1 = 6\frac{3}{8}''$, $r_2 = 7\frac{7}{16}''$, $g_1 = 2\frac{1}{2}''$, $g_2 = 1\frac{3}{4}''$, and $m = 1\frac{3}{4}''$. Then, for the bevel $6\frac{3}{8}''$, $t = (R \text{ for } B = 2\frac{1}{2}'') = 1\frac{5}{16}''$ and $z_1 = (S \text{ for } B = 1\frac{1}{2}'') = 1\frac{11}{16}''$. Hence, $h_1 = 1' \ 3'' + 1\frac{11}{16}'' = 1' \ 4\frac{11}{16}''$ and $x_1 = (B \text{ for } S = 1' \ 4\frac{11}{16}'') = 1' \ 2\frac{3}{4}''$.

For z_2, the bevel r_3 must be determined. This may be computed by the method given in Art. **33** as $7''$. Hence, applying formula **1e**, $z_2 = (S \text{ for } R = 1\frac{3}{4}'') + (B \text{ for } R = 1\frac{3}{4}'') = 3\frac{1}{2}'' + 3'' = 6\frac{1}{2}''$. Therefore, $h_2 = 6\frac{1}{2}'' + 7\frac{1}{2}'' = 1' \ 2''$. Finally, for the bevel $7\frac{7}{16}''$, $y_2 = (B \text{ for } S = 1' \ 2'') = 11\frac{1}{8}''$.

42. As will be noticed in Fig. 24 (a), the edge E is cut parallel to the center line of the truss. This construction is simple and economical. Sometimes, however, the plate is cut perpendicular to the direction of the rafter, as shown to a larger scale in (b). In this method of construction, the distance i will be needed in order to determine the length of the gusset plate. If e and e_1 denote the end distances of the plate, then, as can be seen from the shaded triangles,

$$i = (R \text{ for } S = e_1) + (B \text{ for } S = e)$$

It is evident that when the bevel of the rafter is a parallel one, the letters B and R must be interchanged.

When $e = e_1$, the value of i is independent of the direction of the bevel and is equal to the sum of the base and rise, for $S = e$. If, for instance, in the numerical example just given $e = e_1 = 1\frac{1}{2}''$, then, for the bevel $6\frac{3}{8}''$, $i = (R \text{ for } S = 1\frac{1}{2}'') + (B \text{ for } S = 1\frac{1}{2}'') = 11\frac{1}{16}'' + 1\frac{5}{16}'' = 2''$.

43. To illustrate further the use of the preceding formulas, reference is made to Fig. 25 (a), which shows a diagonal intersection frequently occurring in practice. The bevels r_1 and r_2, which are usually known, may or may not be equal. Considering the continuous diagonal D_1 as the main member, the bevel r_3 is first determined as explained in Art. 33. Then applying formulas 6a and 1a, respectively, since r_3 is a parallel bevel,

$$z_1 = (S \text{ for } B = m_1)$$

and

$$z_2 = (S \text{ for } B = m_2) + (R \text{ for } B = g)$$

Since the dimensions of the gusset plate are here made parallel and perpendicular to the direction of the diagonal D_2, the values of z_1 and z_2 suffice in this case to determine the length of the gusset plate. The width of this plate will be known when $w = (B \text{ for } S = p)$ is determined. For the end distance of the beveled angle bar, the formula of Art. 37 gives

$$u = (S \text{ for } B = e) + (R \text{ for } B = g)$$

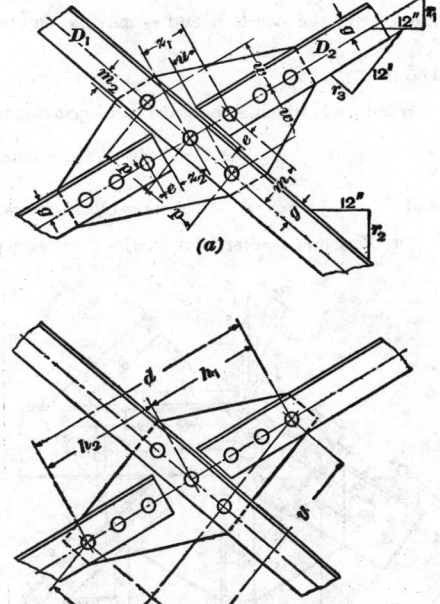

In Fig. 25 (b), the dimensions of the gusset plate are parallel and perpendicular to the direction of the continuous diagonal. The dimensions of the gusset plate are therefore governed in that case by the values of $x = (R \text{ for } S = d)$ and $y = (B \text{ for } S = d)$.

Let, in Fig. 25 (a), $r_1 = r_2 = 7\frac{1}{4}''$, $m_1 = 3\frac{3}{4}''$, $m_2 = 1\frac{3}{4}''$, and $g = 2''$. The angle corresponding to the bevel $7\frac{1}{4}''$ is $31°\ 08'\ 20''$. The angle formed by the diago-

Fig. 25

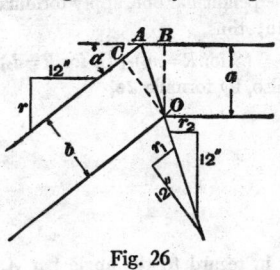

Fig. 26

nals is therefore $31°\ 08'\ 20'' \times 2 = 62°\ 16'\ 40''$. The complement of this angle is $90° - 62°\ 16'\ 40'' = 27°\ 43'\ 20''$, and the corresponding bevel r_3 is $6\frac{5}{16}''$. For this bevel, applying formula 6a, $z_1 = (S \text{ for } B = 3\frac{3}{4}'') = 4\frac{1}{4}''$, and, applying formula 1a, $z_2 = (S$ for $B = 1\frac{3}{4}'') + (R \text{ for } B = 2'') = 2'' + 1\frac{1}{16}'' = 3\frac{1}{16}''$. Finally, $u = (S \text{ for } B = 1\frac{1}{2}'') + (R \text{ for } B = 2'') = 1\frac{11}{16}'' + 1\frac{1}{16}'' = 2\frac{3}{4}''$.

The length of the gusset plate will be $9'' + z_2 + z_1 + 7\frac{1}{2}'' = 9'' + 3\frac{1}{16}'' + 4\frac{1}{4}'' + 7\frac{1}{2}'' = 1'\ 11\frac{13}{16}''$, say $1'\ 11\frac{3}{4}''$. Since $w = (B \text{ for } S = 3'') = 2\frac{11}{16}''$, the width of the plate is $1\frac{1}{2}'' + 2 \times 2\frac{11}{16}'' + 1\frac{1}{2}'' = 8\frac{3}{8}''$, say $8\frac{1}{2}''$.

44. Joint Containing a Miter Cut.— In Smoley's Tables, the following formulas are given for the values of AC and AB, Fig. 26.

$$AC = (a \sec a - b) \cot a$$
$$AB = (b \sec a - a) \cot a$$

These values may be computed by means of the Table of Bevels, as explained and exemplified on page xx of Smoley's Tables. When the values of AC and AB are known, the bevels r_1 and r_2 may be determined from the relations $r_1 = \dfrac{AC}{b}$ and $r_2 = \dfrac{AB}{a}$.

When $a = b$, which is the usual case occurring in practice, then

$$A C = A B = a(\csc a - \cot a) = a \tan \frac{a}{2}$$

and

$$r_1 = r_2 = \csc a - \cot a = \tan \frac{a}{2}$$

Fig. 27 shows a miter joint in which the values of a and b referred to in Fig. 26

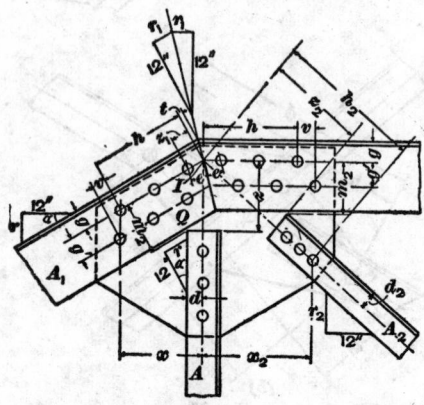

Fig. 27

are equal. The bevel r_1 is obtained by finding the angle a corresponding to the bevel r, and dividing that angle by 2, thus obtaining $\dfrac{a}{2}$; r_1 is then found as the bevel corresponding to $\dfrac{a}{2}$.

When r_1 has been determined, then, for this bevel,

$$z_1 = (S \text{ for } B = e)$$
and $$t = (R \text{ for } B = g)$$

For the bevel r_2, which is a perpendicular one, apply formula **1e**; thus,

$$z_2 = (S \text{ for } R = m_2) + (B \text{ for } R = d_2)$$

also, by formula **2e**,

$$x_2 = (B \text{ for } S = h_2)$$

For the bevel r,

$$v = (R \text{ for } B = g')$$

and, by formula **2e**,

$$x = (B \text{ for } S = h)$$

Considering angle bar A_1 as the main member in regard to the angle bar A, the bevel equals r and is a parallel one; therefore, by formula **1a**,

$$z = (S \text{ for } B = m_2) + (R \text{ for } B = d)$$

Let $r = 11\frac{1}{16}''$, $r_2 = 11\frac{3}{16}''$, $g = 2''$, $g' = 2\frac{1}{2}''$, $m_2 = 4\frac{1}{4}''$, $d = 1\frac{1}{2}''$, and $d_2 = 2''$. Accord ing to the Table of Bevels $a = 42° \ 40' \ 20''$. Hence, $\dfrac{a}{2} = 21° \ 20' \ 10''$ and $r_1 = 4\tfrac{11}{16}''$.

Therefore, $z_1 = (S \text{ for } B = 1\tfrac{1}{2}'') = 1\tfrac{5}{8}''$ and $t = (R \text{ for } B = 2'') = 1\tfrac{3}{16}''$.

For the bevel r, $v = (R \text{ for } B = 2\tfrac{1}{2}'') = 2\tfrac{5}{16}''$, and by formula 1a, $z = (S \text{ for } B = 4\tfrac{1}{4}'') + (R \text{ for } B = 1\tfrac{1}{2}'') = 5\tfrac{3}{4}'' + 1\tfrac{3}{8}'' = 7\tfrac{1}{8}''$. Assume the rivet spacing of the rafter to be $3\tfrac{1}{2}''$; Then, $h = 8\tfrac{5}{8}''$ and $x = (B \text{ for } S = 8\tfrac{5}{8}'') = 6\tfrac{3}{8}''$.

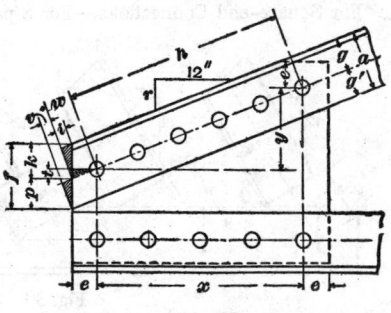

Fig. 28

For the bevel r_2, by formula 1e, $z_2 = (S \text{ for } R = 4\tfrac{1}{4}'') + (B \text{ for } R = 2'') = 6\tfrac{1}{8}'' + 2\tfrac{1}{8}'' = 8\tfrac{1}{4}''$. Hence, $h_2 = 8\tfrac{1}{4}'' + 7\tfrac{1}{2}'' = 1' \ 3\tfrac{3}{4}''$, and $x_2 = (B \text{ for } S = 1' \ 3\tfrac{3}{4}'') = 11\tfrac{1}{16}''$.

Since $h + v = 8\tfrac{5}{8}'' + 2\tfrac{5}{16}'' = 10\tfrac{15}{16}''$, the value of x_2 will control the length of the gusset plate to the right of I. The horizontal dimension of the plate will therefore be $x + x_2 + 3'' = 6\tfrac{3}{8}'' + 11\tfrac{1}{16}'' + 3'' = 1' \ 8\tfrac{13}{16}''$, say $1' \ 8\tfrac{3}{4}''$, and the vertical dimension, $z + 10\tfrac{1}{2}'' = 7\tfrac{1}{8}'' + 10\tfrac{1}{2}'' = 17\tfrac{5}{8}''$, say $17\tfrac{3}{4}''$.

45. Fig. 28 shows a joint that frequently occurs in practice. All the information desired in reference to the beveled cut can be determined from the shaded triangles, in which the bases g, g', and e are known. Thus,

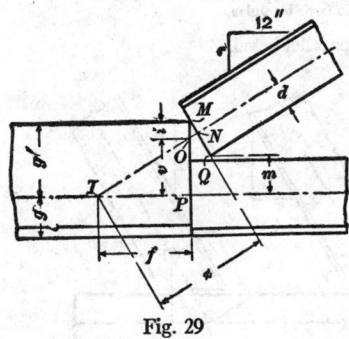

Fig. 29

$$i = (R \text{ for } B = g)$$
$$k = (S \text{ for } B = g)$$
$$v = (R \text{ for } B = g')$$
$$p = (S \text{ for } B = g')$$
$$t = (R \text{ for } B = e)$$
$$w = (S \text{ for } B = e)$$

Also, by formulas 2e and 3e,

$$x = (B \text{ for } S = h)$$
$$y = (R \text{ for } S = h)$$

46. Fig. 29 shows a joint in which the main member consists of two different angles spliced, and the diagonal is to clear both angles. To clear point Q, formula 1e may be applied. To clear point M, the value of z may be determined from the triangles $I \ O \ P$ and $M \ O \ N$. From triangle $I \ O \ P$, $IO = (S \text{ for } B = f)$, and from triangle $M \ O \ N$, $NO = (R \text{ for } S = i)$. Hence,

$$z = IO + NO = (S \text{ for } B = f) + (R \text{ for } S = i),$$
where $\qquad = g' - v$ and $v = (R \text{ for } B = f).$

SUMMARY OF FORMULAS

47. To facilitate reference, the main formulas derived in the foregoing discussion are here subjoined.

FORMULAS FOR THE CLEARANCE DISTANCE

A. For Square-end Connections.—For a parallel bevel,

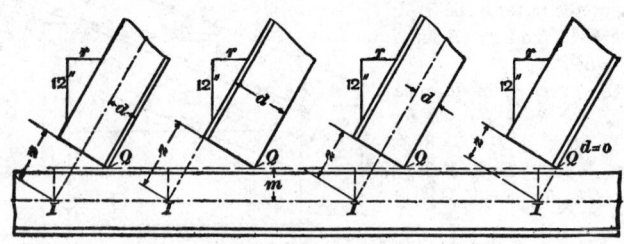

Fig. 30

$$z = (S \text{ for } B=m) + (R \text{ for } B=d)$$

For a perpendicular bevel,

$$z = (S \text{ for } R=m) + (B \text{ for } R=d)$$

In these formulas, m denotes the distance of the point Q from the center line of the main member and d is the distance of the same point from the center line of the diagonal.

NOTE 1.—The figure shows connections with parallel bevels.
NOTE 2.—When $d=0$, the second term disappears in both formulas.

B. For Bevel-end Connections.—For a parallel bevel,

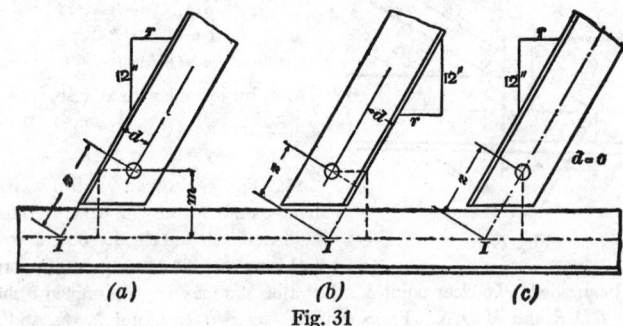

(a)   *(b)*   *(c)*

Fig. 31

$$z = (S \text{ for } B=m) \pm (R \text{ for } B=d)$$

For a perpendicular bevel,

$$z = (S \text{ for } R=m) \pm (B \text{ for } R=d)$$

In these formulas, m denotes the distance of the first rivet of the diagonal from the center line of the main member and d is the distance of this rivet from the center line of the diagonal.

NOTE 1.—The figure shows connections with parallel bevels.

NOTE 2.—In the formulas, the plus sign should be used for the case shown in (a), and the minus sign for the case shown in (b). In the case shown in (c), the second term disappears altogether.

FORMULAS FOR GUSSET PLATES

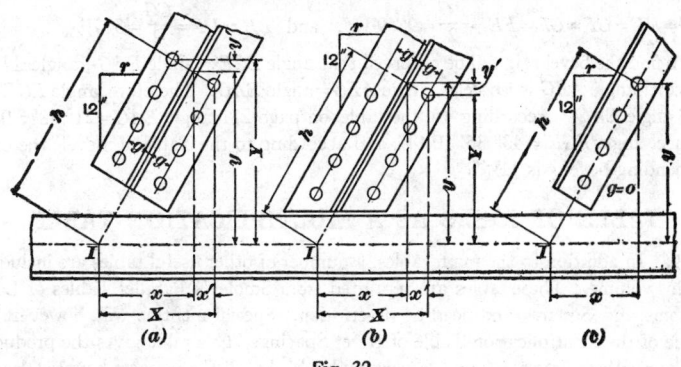

Fig. 32

For a parallel bevel,

$$X = x \pm x' = (R \text{ for } S = h) \pm (B \text{ for } S = g)$$
$$Y = y \pm y' = (B \text{ for } S = h) \pm (R \text{ for } S = g)$$

For a perpendicular bevel,

$$X = x \pm x' = (B \text{ for } S = h) \pm (R \text{ for } S = g)$$
$$Y = y \pm y' = (R \text{ for } S = h) \pm (B \text{ for } S = g)$$

NOTE 1.—The illustration shows connections with parallel bevels.

NOTE 2.—In the case shown in (a), the plus sign must be used in both formulas. For the connection shown in (b), the plus sign must be used in the expression for X and the minus sign in that for Y. For the connection shown in (c), $g = 0$, and the second term disappears altogether.

COMPUTING THE DIMENSIONS OF A FINK TRUSS

48. When a framed structure is given with a bevel, as, for instance, a roof truss with its pitch or a bent with its batter, the Tables of Slopes and Rises may be used with advantage for calculating or checking the dimensions of some, or all, of its members.

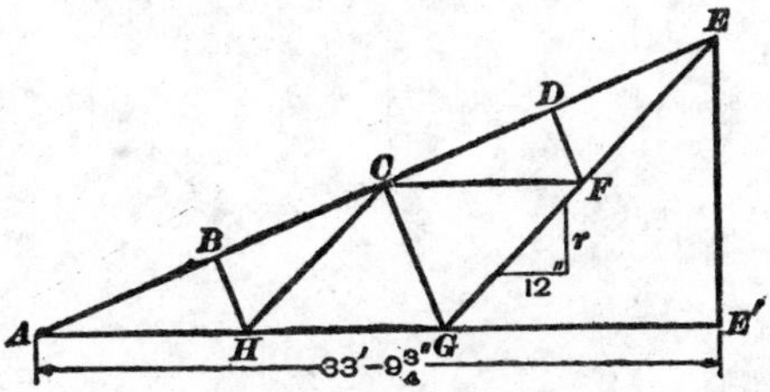

As an illustration, the dimensions of the members of the Fink truss shown in Fig. 33 will be determined. Let

Fig. 33

the span be 67' 7½" and the pitch ⅛. Then, $AE' = 33'\ 9\frac{3}{4}''$. Reference to the table on page 209 shows that $EE' = (R$ for $B = 33'\ 9\frac{3}{4}'') = 13'\ 2^{13}\!\!/_{32}'' + 3^{29}\!\!/_{32}'' = 13'\ 6\frac{5}{16}''$, $AE = (S$ for $B = 33'\ 9\frac{3}{4}'') = 35'\ 6\frac{1}{2}'' + 10\frac{1}{2}'' = 36'\ 5''$, and $AC = CE = \dfrac{AE}{2} = 18'\ 2\frac{1}{2}''$. From the triangle ACG, $CG = (R$ for $B = 18'\ 2\frac{1}{2}'') = 7'\ 2\frac{3}{8}'' + 1'' = 7'\ 3\frac{3}{8}''$, and $AG = (S$ for $B = 18'\ 2\frac{1}{2}'') = 19'\ 4\frac{5}{8}'' + 2^{11}\!\!/_{16}'' = 19'\ 7\frac{5}{16}''$. Hence, $GE' = AE' - AG = 14'\ 2^{7}\!\!/_{16}''$. Finally, $AB = BC = CD = DE = \dfrac{AC}{2} = 9'\ 1\frac{1}{4}''$. $AH = HG = HC = CF = GF = FE = \dfrac{AG}{2} = 9'\ 9^{21}\!\!/_{32}''$, and $BH = DF = \dfrac{CG}{2} = 3'\ 7^{11}\!\!/_{16}''$.

To find the bevel r, it will be observed that angle $EGE' =$ angle $EAG +$ angle AEG. Since triangle AEG is isosceles, angle $AEG =$ angle EAG. Therefore, angle $EGE' = 2 \times$ angle EAG. According to the table on page 211, angle $EAG = 21°\ 48'\ 5.07''$. Hence, angle $EGE' = 43°\ 36'\ 10.14''$, and according to the Table of Bevels the corresponding bevel r is $11^{7}\!\!/_{16}''$.

TABLE OF RISES AS A MULTIPLICATION TABLE

49. In addition to the main tables, a number of other useful tables are included in this volume. These tables are reprinted from Smoley's Parallel Tables of Logarithms and Squares and need no description. Special mention will, however, be made of the Multiplication Table of Rivet Spacing. This table gives the products of the numbers between 0 and 6, varying by ⅛, by all the integers between 1 and 30. It is to be observed in this connection that the rises for the feet, in the Tables of Slopes and Rises, are the products of the numbers indicating the bevel at the top of each page, by all the integers from 1 to 80. For example, the product $7\frac{9}{16}'' \times 35$ may be found by taking the rise for the base 35' and the bevel $7\frac{9}{16}''$, which is $22'\ 0^{11}\!\!/_{16}''$.

As a multiplication table, the Table of Rises is more complete than the Multiplication Table of Rivet Spacing, because the former runs by $\frac{1}{16}''$ to 22". The latter table has, however, the advantage of being more compact than the former.

PARALLEL TABLES OF
SLOPES AND RISES

with bevels varying by 1/16th of an inch
from 0 to 12 inches (192 bevels)
and bases from 0″ to 22″ by ⅟₁₆″
and from 0′ to 80′ by 1′

Inches	0" Rise	0" Slope	1" Rise	1" Slope	2" Rise	2" Slope	3" Rise	3" Slope	4" Rise	4" Slope	5" Rise	5" Slope
0	0	0	0	1	0	2	0	3	1/32	4	1/32	5
1/16	0	1/16	0	1 1/16	0	2 1/16	1/32	3 1/16	1/32	4 1/16	1/32	5 1/16
1/8	0	1/8	0	1 1/8	0	2 1/8	1/32	3 1/8	1/32	4 1/8	1/32	5 1/8
3/16	0	3/16	0	1 3/16	0	2 3/16	1/32	3 3/16	1/32	4 3/16	1/32	5 3/16
1/4	0	1/4	0	1 1/4	0	2 1/4	1/32	3 1/4	1/32	4 1/4	1/32	5 1/4
5/16	0	5/16	0	1 5/16	0	2 5/16	1/32	3 5/16	1/32	4 5/16	1/32	5 5/16
3/8	0	3/8	0	1 3/8	0	2 3/8	1/32	3 3/8	1/32	4 3/8	1/32	5 3/8
7/16	0	7/16	0	1 7/16	0	2 7/16	1/32	3 7/16	1/32	4 7/16	1/32	5 7/16
1/2	0	1/2	0	1 1/2	0	2 1/2	1/32	3 1/2	1/32	4 1/2	1/32	5 1/2
9/16	0	9/16	0	1 9/16	0	2 9/16	1/32	3 9/16	1/32	4 9/16	1/32	5 9/16
5/8	0	5/8	0	1 5/8	0	2 5/8	1/32	3 5/8	1/32	4 5/8	1/32	5 5/8
11/16	0	11/16	0	1 11/16	0	2 11/16	1/32	3 11/16	1/32	4 11/16	1/32	5 11/16
3/4	0	3/4	0	1 3/4	0	2 3/4	1/32	3 3/4	1/32	4 3/4	1/32	5 3/4
13/16	0	13/16	0	1 13/16	0	2 13/16	1/32	3 13/16	1/32	4 13/16	1/32	5 13/16
7/8	0	7/8	0	1 7/8	0	2 7/8	1/32	3 7/8	1/32	4 7/8	1/32	5 7/8
15/16	0	15/16	0	1 15/16	0	2 15/16	1/32	3 15/16	1/32	4 15/16	1/32	5 15/16

Inches	6" Rise	6" Slope	7" Rise	7" Slope	8" Rise	8" Slope	9" Rise	9" Slope	10" Rise	10" Slope	11" Rise	11" Slope
0	1/32	6	1/32	7	1/32	8	1/16	9	1/16	10	1/16	11
1/16	1/32	6 1/16	1/32	7 1/16	1/32	8 1/16	1/16	9 1/16	1/16	10 1/16	1/16	11 1/16
1/8	1/32	6 1/8	1/32	7 1/8	1/32	8 1/8	1/16	9 1/8	1/16	10 1/8	1/16	11 1/8
3/16	1/32	6 3/16	1/32	7 3/16	1/32	8 3/16	1/16	9 3/16	1/16	10 3/16	1/16	11 3/16
1/4	1/32	6 1/4	1/32	7 1/4	1/32	8 1/4	1/16	9 1/4	1/16	10 1/4	1/16	11 1/4
5/16	1/32	6 5/16	1/32	7 5/16	1/32	8 5/16	1/16	9 5/16	1/16	10 5/16	1/16	11 5/16
3/8	1/32	6 3/8	1/32	7 3/8	1/32	8 3/8	1/16	9 3/8	1/16	10 3/8	1/16	11 3/8
7/16	1/32	6 7/16	1/32	7 7/16	1/32	8 7/16	1/16	9 7/16	1/16	10 7/16	1/16	11 7/16
1/2	1/32	6 1/2	1/32	7 1/2	1/32	8 1/2	1/16	9 1/2	1/16	10 1/2	1/16	11 1/2
9/16	1/32	6 9/16	1/32	7 9/16	1/32	8 9/16	1/16	9 9/16	1/16	10 9/16	1/16	11 9/16
5/8	1/32	6 5/8	1/32	7 5/8	1/32	8 5/8	1/16	9 5/8	1/16	10 5/8	1/16	11 5/8
11/16	1/32	6 11/16	1/32	7 11/16	1/32	8 11/16	1/16	9 11/16	1/16	10 11/16	1/16	11 11/16
3/4	1/32	6 3/4	1/32	7 3/4	1/32	8 3/4	1/16	9 3/4	1/16	10 3/4	1/16	11 3/4
13/16	1/32	6 13/16	1/32	7 13/16	1/32	8 13/16	1/16	9 13/16	1/16	10 13/16	1/16	11 13/16
7/8	1/32	6 7/8	1/32	7 7/8	1/32	8 7/8	1/16	9 7/8	1/16	10 7/8	1/16	11 7/8
15/16	1/32	6 15/16	1/32	7 15/16	1/32	8 15/16	1/16	9 15/16	1/16	10 15/16	1/16	11 15/16

Feet	0' Rise	0' Slope	10' Rise	10' Slope	20' Rise	20' Slope	30' Rise	30' Slope
0	0	0	5/8	10-0	1 1/4	20-0	1 7/8	30-0
1	1/16	1-0	11/16	11-0	1 5/16	21-0	1 15/16	31-0
2	1/8	2-0	3/4	12-0	1 3/8	22-0	2	32-0
3	3/16	3-0	13/16	13-0	1 7/16	23-0	2 1/16	33-0
4	1/4	4-0	7/8	14-0	1 1/2	24-0	2 1/8	34-0
5	5/16	5-0	15/16	15-0	1 9/16	25-0	2 3/16	35-0
6	3/8	6-0	1	16-0	1 5/8	26-0	2 1/4	36-0
7	7/16	7-0	1 1/16	17-0	1 11/16	27-0	2 5/16	37-0
8	1/2	8-0	1 1/8	18-0	1 3/4	28-0	2 3/8	38-0
9	9/16	9-0	1 3/16	19-0	1 13/16	29-0	2 7/16	39-0

A=0° 17' 54''; logsin A=7.71669; logcos A=9.99999; logtan A=7.71670; logcot A=2.28330

In.	12" Rise	12" Slope	13" Rise	13" Slope	14" Rise	14" Slope	15" Rise	15" Slope	16" Rise	16" Slope
0	1/16	1-0	1/16	1-1	1/16	1-2	3/32	1-3	3/32	1-4
1/16	1/16	1-0 1/16	1/16	1-1 1/16	1/16	1-2 1/16	3/32	1-3 1/16	3/32	1-4 1/16
1/8	1/16	1-0 1/8	1/16	1-1 1/8	1/16	1-2 1/8	3/32	1-3 1/8	3/32	1-4 1/8
3/16	1/16	1-0 3/16	1/16	1-1 3/16	1/16	1-2 3/16	3/32	1-3 3/16	3/32	1-4 3/16
1/4	1/16	1-0 1/4	1/16	1-1 1/4	1/16	1-2 1/4	3/32	1-3 1/4	3/32	1-4 1/4
5/16	1/16	1-0 5/16	1/16	1-1 5/16	1/16	1-2 5/16	3/32	1-3 5/16	3/32	1-4 5/16
3/8	1/16	1-0 3/8	1/16	1-1 3/8	1/16	1-2 3/8	3/32	1-3 3/8	3/32	1-4 3/8
7/16	1/16	1-0 7/16	1/16	1-1 7/16	1/16	1-2 7/16	3/32	1-3 7/16	3/32	1-4 7/16
1/2	1/16	1-0 1/2	1/16	1-1 1/2	1/16	1-2 1/2	3/32	1-3 1/2	3/32	1-4 1/2
9/16	1/16	1-0 9/16	1/16	1-1 9/16	1/16	1-2 9/16	3/32	1-3 9/16	3/32	1-4 9/16
5/8	1/16	1-0 5/8	1/16	1-1 5/8	1/16	1-2 5/8	3/32	1-3 5/8	3/32	1-4 5/8
11/16	1/16	1-0 11/16	1/16	1-1 11/16	1/16	1-2 11/16	3/32	1-3 11/16	3/32	1-4 11/16
3/4	1/16	1-0 3/4	1/16	1-1 3/4	1/16	1-2 3/4	3/32	1-3 3/4	3/32	1-4 3/4
13/16	1/16	1-0 13/16	1/16	1-1 13/16	1/16	1-2 13/16	3/32	1-3 13/16	3/32	1-4 13/16
7/8	1/16	1-0 7/8	1/16	1-1 7/8	1/16	1-2 7/8	3/32	1-3 7/8	3/32	1-4 7/8
15/16	1/16	1-0 15/16	1/16	1-1 15/16	1/16	1-2 15/16	3/32	1-3 15/16	3/32	1-4 15/16

In.	17" Rise	17" Slope	18" Rise	18" Slope	19" Rise	19" Slope	20" Rise	20" Slope	21" Rise	21" Slope
0	3/32	1-5	3/32	1-6	3/32	1-7	3/32	1-8	1/8	1-9
1/16	3/32	1-5 1/16	3/32	1-6 1/16	3/32	1-7 1/16	3/32	1-8 1/16	1/8	1-9 1/16
1/8	3/32	1-5 1/8	3/32	1-6 1/8	3/32	1-7 1/8	3/32	1-8 1/8	1/8	1-9 1/8
3/16	3/32	1-5 3/16	3/32	1-6 3/16	3/32	1-7 3/16	3/32	1-8 3/16	1/8	1-9 3/16
1/4	3/32	1-5 1/4	3/32	1-6 1/4	3/32	1-7 1/4	3/32	1-8 1/4	1/8	1-9 1/4
5/16	3/32	1-5 5/16	3/32	1-6 5/16	3/32	1-7 5/16	3/32	1-8 5/16	1/8	1-9 5/16
3/8	3/32	1-5 3/8	3/32	1-6 3/8	3/32	1-7 3/8	3/32	1-8 3/8	1/8	1-9 3/8
7/16	3/32	1-5 7/16	3/32	1-6 7/16	3/32	1-7 7/16	3/32	1-8 7/16	1/8	1-9 7/16
1/2	3/32	1-5 1/2	3/32	1-6 1/2	3/32	1-7 1/2	3/32	1-8 1/2	1/8	1-9 1/2
9/16	3/32	1-5 9/16	3/32	1-6 9/16	3/32	1-7 9/16	3/32	1-8 9/16	1/8	1-9 9/16
5/8	3/32	1-5 5/8	3/32	1-6 5/8	3/32	1-7 5/8	3/32	1-8 5/8	1/8	1-9 5/8
11/16	3/32	1-5 11/16	3/32	1-6 11/16	3/32	1-7 11/16	3/32	1-8 11/16	1/8	1-9 11/16
3/4	3/32	1-5 3/4	3/32	1-6 3/4	3/32	1-7 3/4	3/32	1-8 3/4	1/8	1-9 3/4
13/16	3/32	1-5 13/16	3/32	1-6 13/16	3/32	1-7 13/16	3/32	1-8 13/16	1/8	1-9 13/16
7/8	3/32	1-5 7/8	3/32	1-6 7/8	3/32	1-7 7/8	3/32	1-8 7/8	1/8	1-9 7/8
15/16	3/32	1-5 15/16	3/32	1-6 15/16	3/32	1-7 15/16	3/32	1-8 15/16	1/8	1-9 15/16

Feet	40' Rise	40' Slope	50' Rise	50' Slope	60' Rise	60' Slope	70' Rise	70' Slope
0	2 1/2	40-0	3 1/8	50-0	3 3/4	60-0	4 3/8	70-0
1	2 9/16	41-0	3 3/16	51-0	3 13/16	61-0	4 7/16	71-0
2	2 5/8	42-0	3 1/4	52-0	3 7/8	62-0	4 1/2	72-0
3	2 11/16	43-0	3 5/16	53-0	3 15/16	63-0	4 9/16	73-0
4	2 3/4	44-0	3 3/8	54-0	4	64-0	4 5/8	74-0
5	2 13/16	45-0	3 7/16	55-0	4 1/16	65-0	4 11/16	75-0
6	2 7/8	46-0	3 1/2	56-0	4 1/8	66-0	4 3/4	76-0
7	2 15/16	47-0	3 9/16	57-0	4 3/16	67-0	4 13/16	77-0
8	3	48-0	3 5/8	58-0	4 1/4	68-0	4 7/8	78-0
9	3 1/16	49-0	3 11/16	59-0	4 5/16	69-0	4 15/16	79-0

natsin A=0.0052082626; natcos A=0.9999864369; nattan A=0.0052083333; natcot A=192.0000000000

BEVEL 1/8" TO 12"

Inches	0" Rise	0" Slope	1" Rise	1" Slope	2" Rise	2" Slope	3" Rise	3" Slope	4" Rise	4" Slope	5" Rise	5" Slope
0	0	0	0	1	1/32	2	1/32	3	1/32	4	1/16	5
1/16	0	1/16	0	1 1/16	1/32	2 1/16	1/32	3 1/16	1/32	4 1/16	1/16	5 1/16
1/8	0	1/8	0	1 1/8	1/32	2 1/8	1/32	3 1/8	1/32	4 1/8	1/16	5 1/8
3/16	0	3/16	0	1 3/16	1/32	2 3/16	1/32	3 3/16	1/32	4 3/16	1/16	5 3/16
1/4	0	1/4	0	1 1/4	1/32	2 1/4	1/32	3 1/4	1/32	4 1/4	1/16	5 1/4
5/16	0	5/16	0	1 5/16	1/32	2 5/16	1/32	3 5/16	1/32	4 5/16	1/16	5 5/16
3/8	0	3/8	0	1 3/8	1/32	2 3/8	1/32	3 3/8	1/32	4 3/8	1/16	5 3/8
7/16	0	7/16	0	1 7/16	1/32	2 7/16	1/32	3 7/16	1/32	4 7/16	1/16	5 7/16
1/2	0	1/2	0	1 1/2	1/32	2 1/2	1/32	3 1/2	1/16	4 1/2	1/16	5 1/2
9/16	0	9/16	1/32	1 9/16	1/32	2 9/16	1/32	3 9/16	1/16	4 9/16	1/16	5 9/16
5/8	0	5/8	1/32	1 5/8	1/32	2 5/8	1/32	3 5/8	1/16	4 5/8	1/16	5 5/8
11/16	0	11/16	1/32	1 11/16	1/32	2 11/16	1/32	3 11/16	1/16	4 11/16	1/16	5 11/16
3/4	0	3/4	1/32	1 3/4	1/32	2 3/4	1/32	3 3/4	1/16	4 3/4	1/16	5 3/4
13/16	0	13/16	1/32	1 13/16	1/32	2 13/16	1/32	3 13/16	1/16	4 13/16	1/16	5 13/16
7/8	0	7/8	1/32	1 7/8	1/32	2 7/8	1/32	3 7/8	1/16	4 7/8	1/16	5 7/8
15/16	0	15/16	1/32	1 15/16	1/32	2 15/16	1/32	3 15/16	1/16	4 15/16	1/16	5 15/16

Inches	6" Rise	6" Slope	7" Rise	7" Slope	8" Rise	8" Slope	9" Rise	9" Slope	10" Rise	10" Slope	11" Rise	11" Slope
0	1/16	6	1/16	7	3/32	8	3/32	9	3/32	10	1/8	11
1/16	1/16	6 1/16	1/16	7 1/16	3/32	8 1/16	3/32	9 1/16	3/32	10 1/16	1/8	11 1/16
1/8	1/16	6 1/8	1/16	7 1/8	3/32	8 1/8	3/32	9 1/8	3/32	10 1/8	1/8	11 1/8
3/16	1/16	6 3/16	1/16	7 3/16	3/32	8 3/16	3/32	9 3/16	3/32	10 3/16	1/8	11 3/16
1/4	1/16	6 1/4	1/16	7 1/4	3/32	8 1/4	3/32	9 1/4	3/32	10 1/4	1/8	11 1/4
5/16	1/16	6 5/16	1/16	7 5/16	3/32	8 5/16	3/32	9 5/16	3/32	10 5/16	1/8	11 5/16
3/8	1/16	6 3/8	1/16	7 3/8	3/32	8 3/8	3/32	9 3/8	3/32	10 3/8	1/8	11 3/8
7/16	1/16	6 7/16	1/16	7 7/16	3/32	8 7/16	3/32	9 7/16	3/32	10 7/16	1/8	11 7/16
1/2	1/16	6 1/2	1/16	7 1/2	3/32	8 1/2	3/32	9 1/2	1/8	10 1/2	1/8	11 1/2
9/16	1/16	6 9/16	3/32	7 9/16	3/32	8 9/16	3/32	9 9/16	1/8	10 9/16	1/8	11 9/16
5/8	1/16	6 5/8	3/32	7 5/8	3/32	8 5/8	3/32	9 5/8	1/8	10 5/8	1/8	11 5/8
11/16	1/16	6 11/16	3/32	7 11/16	3/32	8 11/16	3/32	9 11/16	1/8	10 11/16	1/8	11 11/16
3/4	1/16	6 3/4	3/32	7 3/4	3/32	8 3/4	3/32	9 3/4	1/8	10 3/4	1/8	11 3/4
13/16	1/16	6 13/16	3/32	7 13/16	3/32	8 13/16	3/32	9 13/16	1/8	10 13/16	1/8	11 13/16
7/8	1/16	6 7/8	3/32	7 7/8	3/32	8 7/8	3/32	9 7/8	1/8	10 7/8	1/8	11 7/8
15/16	1/16	6 15/16	3/32	7 15/16	3/32	8 15/16	3/32	9 15/16	1/8	10 15/16	1/8	11 15/16

Feet	0' Rise	0' Slope	10' Rise	10' Slope	20' Rise	20' Slope	30' Rise	30' Slope
0	0	0	1 1/4	10-0	2 1/2	20-0	3 3/4	30-0 1/32 -
1	1/8	1-0	1 3/8	11-0	2 5/8	21-0	3 7/8	31-0 1/32
2	1/4	2-0	1 1/2	12-0	2 3/4	22-0	4	32-0 1/32
3	3/8	3-0	1 5/8	13-0	2 7/8	23-0	4 1/8	33-0 1/32
4	1/2	4-0	1 3/4	14-0	3	24-0	4 1/4	34-0 1/32
5	5/8	5-0	1 7/8	15-0	3 1/8	25-0 1/32	4 3/8	35-0 1/32
6	3/4	6-0	2	16-0	3 1/4	26-0 1/32	4 1/2	36-0 1/32
7	7/8	7-0	2 1/8	17-0	3 3/8	27-0 1/32	4 5/8	37-0 1/32
8	1	8-0	2 1/4	18-0	3 1/2	28-0 1/32	4 3/4	38-0 1/32
9	1 1/8	9-0	2 3/8	19-0	3 5/8	29-0 1/32	4 7/8	39-0 1/32

A = 0° 35′ 49″; logsin A = 8.01771; logcos A = 9.99998; logtan A = 8.01773; logcot A = 1.98227

Ins.	12" Rise	12" Slope	13" Rise	13" Slope	14" Rise	14" Slope	15" Rise	15" Slope	16" Rise	16" Slope
0	1/8	1-0	1/8	1-1	5/32—	1-2	5/32	1-3	5/32	1-4
1/16	1/8	1-0 1/16	1/8	1-1 1/16	5/32—	1-2 1/16	5/32	1-3 1/16	5/32	1-4 1/16
1/8	1/8	1-0 1/8	1/8	1-1 1/8	5/32—	1-2 1/8	5/32	1-3 1/8	5/32	1-4 1/8
3/16	1/8	1-0 3/16	1/8	1-1 3/16	5/32—	1-2 3/16	5/32	1-3 3/16	5/32	1-4 3/16
1/4	1/8	1-0 1/4	1/8	1-1 1/4	5/32—	1-2 1/4	5/32	1-3 1/4	5/32	1-4 1/4
5/16	1/8	1-0 5/16	1/8	1-1 5/16	5/32—	1-2 5/16	5/32	1-3 5/16	5/32	1-4 5/16
3/8	1/8	1-0 3/8	1/8	1-1 3/8	5/32—	1-2 3/8	5/32	1-3 3/8	5/32	1-4 3/8
7/16	1/8	1-0 7/16	1/8	1-1 7/16	5/32—	1-2 7/16	5/32	1-3 7/16	5/32	1-4 7/16
1/2	1/8	1-0 1/2	1/8	1-1 1/2	5/32—	1-2 1/2	5/32	1-3 1/2	3/16	1-4 1/2
9/16	1/8	1-0 9/16	5/32—	1-1 9/16	5/32—	1-2 9/16	5/32	1-3 9/16	3/16	1-4 9/16
5/8	1/8	1-0 5/8	5/32—	1-1 5/8	5/32—	1-2 5/8	5/32	1-3 5/8	3/16	1-4 5/8
11/16	1/8	1-0 11/16	5/32—	1-1 11/16	5/32—	1-2 11/16	5/32	1-3 11/16	3/16	1-4 11/16
3/4	1/8	1-0 3/4	5/32—	1-1 3/4	5/32—	1-2 3/4	5/32	1-3 3/4	3/16	1-4 3/4
13/16	1/8	1-0 13/16	5/32—	1-1 13/16	5/32—	1-2 13/16	5/32	1-3 13/16	3/16	1-4 13/16
7/8	1/8	1-0 7/8	5/32—	1-1 7/8	5/32—	1-2 7/8	5/32	1-3 7/8	3/16	1-4 7/8
15/16	1/8	1-0 15/16	5/32—	1-1 15/16	5/32—	1-2 15/16	5/32	1-3 15/16	3/16	1-4 15/16

Ins.	17" Rise	17" Slope	18" Rise	18" Slope	19" Rise	19" Slope	20" Rise	20" Slope	21" Rise	21" Slope
0	3/16	1-5	3/16	1-6	3/16	1-7	7/32—	1-8	7/32	1-9
1/16	3/16	1-5 1/16	3/16	1-6 1/16	3/16	1-7 1/16	7/32—	1-8 1/16	7/32	1-9 1/16
1/8	3/16	1-5 1/8	3/16	1-6 1/8	3/16	1-7 1/8	7/32—	1-8 1/8	7/32	1-9 1/8
3/16	3/16	1-5 3/16	3/16	1-6 3/16	3/16	1-7 3/16	7/32—	1-8 3/16	7/32	1-9 3/16
1/4	3/16	1-5 1/4	3/16	1-6 1/4	3/16	1-7 1/4	7/32—	1-8 1/4	7/32	1-9 1/4
5/16	3/16	1-5 5/16	3/16	1-6 5/16	3/16	1-7 5/16	7/32—	1-8 5/16	7/32	1-9 5/16
3/8	3/16	1-5 3/8	3/16	1-6 3/8	3/16	1-7 3/8	7/32—	1-8 3/8	7/32	1-9 3/8
7/16	3/16	1-5 7/16	3/16	1-6 7/16	3/16	1-7 7/16	7/32—	1-8 7/16	7/32	1-9 7/16
1/2	3/16	1-5 1/2	3/16	1-6 1/2	3/16	1-7 1/2	7/32—	1-8 1/2	7/32	1-9 1/2
9/16	3/16	1-5 9/16	3/16	1-6 9/16	7/32—	1-7 9/16	7/32—	1-8 9/16	7/32	1-9 9/16
5/8	3/16	1-5 5/8	3/16	1-6 5/8	7/32—	1-7 5/8	7/32—	1-8 5/8	7/32	1-9 5/8
11/16	3/16	1-5 11/16	3/16	1-6 11/16	7/32—	1-7 11/16	7/32—	1-8 11/16	7/32	1-9 11/16
3/4	3/16	1-5 3/4	3/16	1-6 3/4	7/32—	1-7 3/4	7/32—	1-8 3/4	7/32	1-9 3/4
13/16	3/16	1-5 13/16	3/16	1-6 13/16	7/32—	1-7 13/16	7/32—	1-8 13/16	7/32	1-9 13/16
7/8	3/16	1-5 7/8	3/16	1-6 7/8	7/32—	1-7 7/8	7/32—	1-8 7/8	7/32	1-9 7/8
15/16	3/16	1-5 15/16	3/16	1-6 15/16	7/32—	1-7 15/16	7/32—	1-8 15/16	7/32	1-9 15/16

Feet	40' Rise	40' Slope	50' Rise	50' Slope	60' Rise	60' Slope	70' Rise	70' Slope
0	5	40-0 1/32—	6 1/4	50-0 1/32	7 1/2	60-0 1/32	8 3/4	70-0 1/32
1	5 1/8	41-0 1/32—	6 3/8	51-0 1/32	7 5/8	61-0 1/32	8 7/8	71-0 1/32
2	5 1/4	42-0 1/32—	6 1/2	52-0 1/32	7 3/4	62-0 1/32	9	72-0 1/32
3	5 3/8	43-0 1/32—	6 5/8	53-0 1/32	7 7/8	63-0 1/32	9 1/8	73-0 1/16
4	5 1/2	44-0 1/32—	6 3/4	54-0 1/32	8	64-0 1/32	9 1/4	74-0 1/16
5	5 5/8	45-0 1/32—	6 7/8	55-0 1/32	8 1/8	65-0 1/32	9 3/8	75-0 1/16
6	5 3/4	46-0 1/32—	7	56-0 1/32	8 1/4	66-0 1/32	9 1/2	76-0 1/16
7	5 7/8	47-0 1/32—	7 1/8	57-0 1/32	8 3/8	67-0 1/32	9 5/8	77-0 1/16
8	6	48-0 1/32—	7 1/4	58-0 1/32	8 1/2	68-0 1/32	9 3/4	78-0 1/16
9	6 1/8	49-0 1/32	7 3/8	59-0 1/32	8 5/8	69-0 1/32	9 7/8	79-0 1/16

natsin A=0.0104161015; natcos A=0.9999457510; nattan A=0.0104166666; natcot A=96.0000000000

Inches	0″ Rise	0″ Slope	1″ Rise	1″ Slope	2″ Rise	2″ Slope	3″ Rise	3″ Slope	4″ Rise	4″ Slope	5″ Rise	5″ Slope
0	0	0	0	1	1/32	2	1/16	3	1/16	4	1/16	5
1/16	0	1/16	1/32–	1 1/16	1/32	2 1/16	1/16	3 1/16	1/16	4 1/16	3/32	5 1/16
1/8	0	1/8	1/32–	1 1/8	1/32	2 1/8	1/16	3 1/8	1/16	4 1/8	3/32	5 1/8
3/16	0	3/16	1/32–	1 3/16	1/32	2 3/16	1/16	3 3/16	1/16	4 3/16	3/32	5 3/16
1/4	0	1/4	1/32–	1 1/4	1/32	2 1/4	1/16	3 1/4	1/16	4 1/4	3/32	5 1/4
5/16	0	5/16	1/32–	1 5/16	1/32	2 5/16	1/16	3 5/16	1/16	4 5/16	3/32	5 5/16
3/8	0	3/8	1/32–	1 3/8	1/32	2 3/8	1/16	3 3/8	1/16	4 3/8	3/32	5 3/8
7/16	0	7/16	1/32–	1 7/16	1/32	2 7/16	1/16	3 7/16	1/16	4 7/16	3/32	5 7/16
1/2	0	1/2	1/32–	1 1/2	1/32	2 1/2	1/16	3 1/2	1/16	4 1/2	3/32	5 1/2
9/16	0	9/16	1/32–	1 9/16	1/32	2 9/16	1/16	3 9/16	1/16	4 9/16	3/32	5 9/16
5/8	0	5/8	1/32–	1 5/8	1/32	2 5/8	1/16	3 5/8	1/16	4 5/8	3/32	5 5/8
11/16	0	11/16	1/32–	1 11/16	1/32	2 11/16	1/16	3 11/16	1/16	4 11/16	3/32	5 11/16
3/4	0	3/4	1/32–	1 3/4	1/32	2 3/4	1/16	3 3/4	1/16	4 3/4	3/32	5 3/4
13/16	0	13/16	1/32–	1 13/16	1/32	2 13/16	1/16	3 13/16	1/16	4 13/16	3/32	5 13/16
7/8	0	7/8	1/32–	1 7/8	1/32	2 7/8	1/16	3 7/8	1/16	4 7/8	3/32	5 7/8
15/16	0	15/16	1/32–	1 15/16	1/32	2 15/16	1/16	3 15/16	1/16	4 15/16	3/32	5 15/16

Inches	6″ Rise	6″ Slope	7″ Rise	7″ Slope	8″ Rise	8″ Slope	9″ Rise	9″ Slope	10″ Rise	10″ Slope	11″ Rise	11″ Slope
0	3/32	6	1/8	7	1/8	8	1/8	9	5/32	10	3/16	11
1/16	3/32	6 1/16	1/8	7 1/16	1/8	8 1/16	5/32	9 1/16	5/32	10 1/16	3/16	11 1/16
1/8	3/32	6 1/8	1/8	7 1/8	1/8	8 1/8	5/32	9 1/8	5/32	10 1/8	3/16	11 1/8
3/16	3/32	6 3/16	1/8	7 3/16	1/8	8 3/16	5/32	9 3/16	5/32	10 3/16	3/16	11 3/16
1/4	3/32	6 1/4	1/8	7 1/4	1/8	8 1/4	5/32	9 1/4	5/32	10 1/4	3/16	11 1/4
5/16	3/32	6 5/16	1/8	7 5/16	1/8	8 5/16	5/32	9 5/16	5/32	10 5/16	3/16	11 5/16
3/8	3/32	6 3/8	1/8	7 3/8	1/8	8 3/8	5/32	9 3/8	5/32	10 3/8	3/16	11 3/8
7/16	3/32	6 7/16	1/8	7 7/16	1/8	8 7/16	5/32	9 7/16	5/32	10 7/16	3/16	11 7/16
1/2	3/32	6 1/2	1/8	7 1/2	1/8	8 1/2	5/32	9 1/2	5/32	10 1/2	3/16	11 1/2
9/16	3/32	6 9/16	1/8	7 9/16	1/8	8 9/16	5/32	9 9/16	5/32	10 9/16	3/16	11 9/16
5/8	3/32	6 5/8	1/8	7 5/8	1/8	8 5/8	5/32	9 5/8	5/32	10 5/8	3/16	11 5/8
11/16	3/32	6 11/16	1/8	7 11/16	1/8	8 11/16	5/32	9 11/16	5/32	10 11/16	3/16	11 11/16
3/4	3/32	6 3/4	1/8	7 3/4	1/8	8 3/4	5/32	9 3/4	5/32	10 3/4	3/16	11 3/4
13/16	3/32	6 13/16	1/8	7 13/16	1/8	8 13/16	5/32	9 13/16	5/32	10 13/16	3/16	11 13/16
7/8	3/32	6 7/8	1/8	7 7/8	1/8	8 7/8	5/32	9 7/8	5/32	10 7/8	3/16	11 7/8
15/16	3/32	6 15/16	1/8	7 15/16	1/8	8 15/16	5/32	9 15/16	5/32	10 15/16	3/16	11 15/16

Feet	0′ Rise	0′ Slope	10′ Rise	10′ Slope	20′ Rise	20′ Slope	30′ Rise	30′ Slope
0	0	0	1 1/8	10-0	3 3/4	20-0 1/32	5 5/8	30-0 1/32
1	3/16	1-0	2 1/16	11-0 1/32	3 15/16	21-0 1/32	5 13/16	31-0 1/32
2	3/8	2-0	2 1/4	12-0 1/32	4 1/8	22-0 1/32	6	32-0 1/32
3	9/16	3-0	2 7/16	13-0 1/32	4 5/16	23-0 1/32	6 3/16	33-0 1/16
4	3/4	4-0	2 5/8	14-0 1/32	4 1/2	24-0 1/32	6 3/8	34-0 1/16
5	15/16	5-0	2 13/16	15-0 1/16	4 11/16	25-0 1/32	6 9/16	35-0 1/16
6	1 1/8	6-0	3	16-0 1/16	4 7/8	26-0 1/32	6 3/4	36-0 1/16
7	1 5/16	7-0	3 3/16	17-0 1/16	5 1/16	27-0 1/32	6 15/16	37-0 1/16
8	1 1/2	8-0	3 3/8	18-0 1/32	5 1/4	28-0 1/32	7 1/8	38-0 1/16
9	1 11/16	9-0	3 9/16	19-0 1/32	5 7/16	29-0 1/16	7 5/16	39-0 1/16

A = 0° 53′ 43″; logsin A = 8.19377; logcos A = 9.99995; logtan A = 8.19382; logcot A = 1.80618

Ins.	12" Rise	Slope	13" Rise	Slope	14" Rise	Slope	15" Rise	Slope	16" Rise	Slope
0	3/16	1-0	3/16	1-1	7/32	1-2	1/4	1-3	1/4	1-4
1/16	3/16	1-0 1/16	7/32	1-1 1/16	7/32	1-2 1/16	1/4	1-3 1/16	1/4	1-4 1/16
1/8	3/16	1-0 1/8	7/32	1-1 1/8	7/32	1-2 1/8	1/4	1-3 1/8	1/4	1-4 1/8
3/16	3/16	1-0 3/16	7/32	1-1 3/16	7/32	1-2 3/16	1/4	1-3 3/16	1/4	1-4 3/16
1/4	3/16	1-0 1/4	7/32	1-1 1/4	7/32	1-2 1/4	1/4	1-3 1/4	1/4	1-4 1/4
5/16	3/16	1-0 5/16	7/32	1-1 5/16	7/32	1-2 5/16	1/4	1-3 5/16	1/4	1-4 5/16
3/8	3/16	1-0 3/8	7/32	1-1 3/8	7/32	1-2 3/8	1/4	1-3 3/8	1/4	1-4 3/8
7/16	3/16	1-0 7/16	7/32	1-1 7/16	7/32	1-2 7/16	1/4	1-3 7/16	1/4	1-4 7/16
1/2	3/16	1-0 1/2	7/32	1-1 1/2	7/32	1-2 1/2	1/4	1-3 1/2	1/4	1-4 1/2
9/16	3/16	1-0 9/16	7/32	1-1 9/16	7/32	1-2 9/16	1/4	1-3 9/16	1/4	1-4 9/16
5/8	3/16	1-0 5/8	7/32	1-1 5/8	7/32	1-2 5/8	1/4	1-3 5/8	1/4	1-4 5/8
11/16	3/16	1-0 11/16	7/32	1-1 11/16	7/32	1-2 11/16	1/4	1-3 11/16	1/4	1-4 11/16
3/4	3/16	1-0 3/4	7/32	1-1 3/4	7/32	1-2 3/4	1/4	1-3 3/4	1/4	1-4 3/4
13/16	3/16	1-0 13/16	7/32	1-1 13/16	7/32	1-2 13/16	1/4	1-3 13/16	1/4	1-4 13/16
7/8	3/16	1-0 7/8	7/32	1-1 7/8	7/32	1-2 7/8	1/4	1-3 7/8	1/4	1-4 7/8
15/16	3/16	1-0 15/16	7/32	1-1 15/16	7/32	1-2 15/16	1/4	1-3 15/16	1/4	1-4 15/16

Ins.	17" Rise	Slope	18" Rise	Slope	19" Rise	Slope	20" Rise	Slope	21" Rise	Slope
0	1/4	1-5	9/32	1-6	5/16	1-7	5/16	1-8	5/16	1-9
1/16	9/32	1-5 1/16	9/32	1-6 1/16	5/16	1-7 1/16	5/16	1-8 1/16	11/32	1-9 1/16
1/8	9/32	1-5 1/8	9/32	1-6 1/8	5/16	1-7 1/8	5/16	1-8 1/8	11/32	1-9 1/8
3/16	9/32	1-5 3/16	9/32	1-6 3/16	5/16	1-7 3/16	5/16	1-8 3/16	11/32	1-9 3/16
1/4	9/32	1-5 1/4	9/32	1-6 1/4	5/16	1-7 1/4	5/16	1-8 1/4	11/32	1-9 1/4
5/16	9/32	1-5 5/16	9/32	1-6 5/16	5/16	1-7 5/16	5/16	1-8 5/16	11/32	1-9 5/16
3/8	9/32	1-5 3/8	9/32	1-6 3/8	5/16	1-7 3/8	5/16	1-8 3/8	11/32	1-9 3/8
7/16	9/32	1-5 7/16	9/32	1-6 7/16	5/16	1-7 7/16	5/16	1-8 7/16	11/32	1-9 7/16
1/2	9/32	1-5 1/2	9/32	1-6 1/2	5/16	1-7 1/2	5/16	1-8 1/2	11/32	1-9 1/2
9/16	9/32	1-5 9/16	9/32	1-6 9/16	5/16	1-7 9/16	5/16	1-8 9/16	11/32	1-9 9/16
5/8	9/32	1-5 5/8	9/32	1-6 5/8	5/16	1-7 5/8	5/16	1-8 5/8	11/32	1-9 5/8
11/16	9/32	1-5 11/16	9/32	1-6 11/16	5/16	1-7 11/16	5/16	1-8 11/16	11/32	1-9 11/16
3/4	9/32	1-5 3/4	9/32	1-6 3/4	5/16	1-7 3/4	5/16	1-8 3/4	11/32	1-9 3/4
13/16	9/32	1-5 13/16	9/32	1-6 13/16	5/16	1-7 13/16	5/16	1-8 13/16	11/32	1-9 13/16
7/8	9/32	1-5 7/8	9/32	1-6 7/8	5/16	1-7 7/8	5/16	1-8 7/8	11/32	1-9 7/8
15/16	9/32	1-5 15/16	9/32	1-6 15/16	5/16	1-7 15/16	5/16	1-8 15/16	11/32	1-9 15/16

Feet	40' Rise	Slope	50' Rise	Slope	60' Rise	Slope	70' Rise	Slope
0	7 1/2	40-0 1/16	9 3/8	50-0 1/16	11 1/4	60-0 3/32	1-1 1/8	70-0 3/32
1	7 11/16	41-0 1/16	9 9/16	51-0 1/16	11 7/16	61-0 3/32	1-1 5/16	71-0 3/32
2	7 7/8	42-0 1/16	9 3/4	52-0 1/16	11 5/8	62-0 3/32	1-1 1/2	72-0 3/32
3	8 1/16	43-0 1/16	9 15/16	53-0 1/16	11 13/16	63-0 3/32	1-1 11/16	73-0 3/32
4	8 1/4	44-0 1/16	10 1/8	54-0 3/32	1-0	64-0 3/32	1-1 7/8	74-0 3/32
5	8 7/16	45-0 1/16	10 5/16	55-0 3/32	1-0 3/16	65-0 3/32	1-2 1/16	75-0 1/8
6	8 5/8	46-0 1/16	10 1/2	56-0 3/32	1-0 3/8	66-0 3/32	1-2 1/4	76-0 1/8
7	8 13/16	47-0 1/16	10 11/16	57-0 3/32	1-0 9/16	67-0 3/32	1-2 7/16	77-0 1/8
8	9	48-0 1/16	10 7/8	58-0 3/32	1-0 3/4	68-0 3/32	1-2 5/8	78-0 1/8
9	9 3/16	49-0 1/16	11 1/16	59-0 3/32	1-0 15/16	69-0 3/32	1-2 13/16	79-0 1/8

natsin A=0.0156230930; natcos A=0.9998779521; nattan A=0.0156250000; natcot A=64.0000000000

Inches	0" Rise	0" Slope	1" Rise	1" Slope	2" Rise	2" Slope	3" Rise	3" Slope	4" Rise	4" Slope	5" Rise	5" Slope
0	0	0	1/32	1	1/32	2	1/16	3	3/32	4	3/32	5
1/16	0	1/16	1/32	1 1/16	1/32	2 1/16	1/16	3 1/16	3/32	4 1/16	3/32	5 1/16
1/8	0	1/8	1/32	1 1/8	1/32	2 1/8	1/16	3 1/8	3/32	4 1/8	3/32	5 1/8
3/16	0	3/16	1/32	1 3/16	1/32	2 3/16	1/16	3 3/16	3/32	4 3/16	3/32	5 3/16
1/4	0	1/4	1/32	1 1/4	1/16	2 1/4	1/16	3 1/4	3/32	4 1/4	1/8	5 1/4
5/16	0	5/16	1/32	1 5/16	1/16	2 5/16	1/16	3 5/16	3/32	4 5/16	1/8	5 5/16
3/8	0	3/8	1/32	1 3/8	1/16	2 3/8	1/16	3 3/8	3/32	4 3/8	1/8	5 3/8
7/16	0	7/16	1/32	1 7/16	1/16	2 7/16	1/16	3 7/16	3/32	4 7/16	1/8	5 7/16
1/2	0	1/2	1/32	1 1/2	1/16	2 1/2	1/16	3 1/2	3/32	4 1/2	1/8	5 1/2
9/16	0	9/16	1/32	1 9/16	1/16	2 9/16	1/16	3 9/16	3/32	4 9/16	1/8	5 9/16
5/8	0	5/8	1/32	1 5/8	1/16	2 5/8	1/16	3 5/8	3/32	4 5/8	1/8	5 5/8
11/16	0	11/16	1/32	1 11/16	1/16	2 11/16	1/16	3 11/16	3/32	4 11/16	1/8	5 11/16
3/4	1/32	3/4	1/32	1 3/4	1/16	2 3/4	1/16	3 3/4	3/32	4 3/4	1/8	5 3/4
13/16	1/32	13/16	1/32	1 13/16	1/16	2 13/16	3/32	3 13/16	3/32	4 13/16	1/8	5 13/16
7/8	1/32	7/8	1/32	1 7/8	1/16	2 7/8	3/32	3 7/8	3/32	4 7/8	1/8	5 7/8
15/16	1/32	15/16	1/32	1 15/16	1/16	2 15/16	3/32	3 15/16	3/32	4 15/16	1/8	5 15/16

Inches	6" Rise	6" Slope	7" Rise	7" Slope	8" Rise	8" Slope	9" Rise	9" Slope	10" Rise	10" Slope	11" Rise	11" Slope
0	1/8	6	5/32	7	5/32	8	3/16	9	7/32	10	7/32	11
1/16	1/8	6 1/16	5/32	7 1/16	5/32	8 1/16	3/16	9 1/16	7/32	10 1/16	7/32	11 1/16
1/8	1/8	6 1/8	5/32	7 1/8	5/32	8 1/8	3/16	9 1/8	7/32	10 1/8	7/32	11 1/8
3/16	1/8	6 3/16	5/32	7 3/16	5/32	8 3/16	3/16	9 3/16	7/32	10 3/16	7/32	11 3/16
1/4	1/8	6 1/4	5/32	7 1/4	3/16	8 1/4	3/16	9 1/4	7/32	10 1/4	1/4	11 1/4
5/16	1/8	6 5/16	5/32	7 5/16	3/16	8 5/16	3/16	9 5/16	7/32	10 5/16	1/4	11 5/16
3/8	1/8	6 3/8	5/32	7 3/8	3/16	8 3/8	3/16	9 3/8	7/32	10 3/8	1/4	11 3/8
7/16	1/8	6 7/16	5/32	7 7/16	3/16	8 7/16	3/16	9 7/16	7/32	10 7/16	1/4	11 7/16
1/2	1/8	6 1/2	5/32	7 1/2	3/16	8 1/2	3/16	9 1/2	7/32	10 1/2	1/4	11 1/2
9/16	1/8	6 9/16	5/32	7 9/16	3/16	8 9/16	3/16	9 9/16	7/32	10 9/16	1/4	11 9/16
5/8	1/8	6 5/8	5/32	7 5/8	3/16	8 5/8	3/16	9 5/8	7/32	10 5/8	1/4	11 5/8
11/16	1/8	6 11/16	5/32	7 11/16	3/16	8 11/16	3/16	9 11/16	7/32	10 11/16	1/4	11 11/16
3/4	1/8	6 3/4	5/32	7 3/4	3/16	8 3/4	3/16	9 3/4	7/32	10 3/4	1/4	11 3/4
13/16	5/32	6 13/16	5/32	7 13/16	3/16	8 13/16	3/16	9 13/16	7/32	10 13/16	1/4	11 13/16
7/8	5/32	6 7/8	5/32	7 7/8	3/16	8 7/8	7/32	9 7/8	7/32	10 7/8	1/4	11 7/8
15/16	5/32	6 15/16	5/32	7 15/16	3/16	8 15/16	7/32	9 15/16	7/32	10 15/16	1/4	11 15/16

Feet	0' Rise	0' Slope	10' Rise	10' Slope	20' Rise	20' Slope	30' Rise	30' Slope
0	0	0	2 1/2	10-0 1/32	5	20-0 1/16	7 1/2	30-0 1/16
1	1/4	1-0	2 3/4	11-0 1/32	5 1/4	21-0 1/16	7 3/4	31-0 3/32
2	1/2	2-0	3	12-0 1/32	5 1/2	22-0 1/16	8	32-0 3/32
3	3/4	3-0	3 1/4	13-0 1/32	5 3/4	23-0 1/16	8 1/4	33-0 3/32
4	1	4-0	3 1/2	14-0 1/32	6	24-0 1/16	8 1/2	34-0 3/32
5	1 1/4	5-0	3 3/4	15-0 1/16	6 1/4	25-0 1/16	8 3/4	35-0 3/32
6	1 1/2	6-0	4	16-0 1/16	6 1/2	26-0 1/16	9	36-0 3/32
7	1 3/4	7-0 1/32	4 1/4	17-0 1/16	6 3/4	27-0 1/16	9 1/4	37-0 3/32
8	2	8-0 1/32	4 1/2	18-0 1/16	7	28-0 1/16	9 1/2	38-0 3/32
9	2 1/4	9-0 1/32	4 3/4	19-0 1/16	7 1/4	29-0 1/16	9 3/4	39-0 3/32

A = 1° 11' 37"; logsin A = 8.31866; logcos A = 9.99991; logtan A = 8.31876; logcot A = 1.68124

Ins.	12″ Rise	Slope	13″ Rise	Slope	14″ Rise	Slope	15″ Rise	Slope	16″ Rise	Slope
0	¼	1-0	9/32	1-1	9/32	1-2	5/16	1-3	11/32	1-4
1/16	¼	1-0 1/16	9/32	1-1 1/16	9/32	1-2 1/16	5/16	1-3 1/16	11/32	1-4 1/16
1/8	¼	1-0 1/8	9/32	1-1 1/8	9/32	1-2 1/8	5/16	1-3 1/8	11/32	1-4 1/8
3/16	¼	1-0 3/16	9/32	1-1 3/16	9/32	1-2 3/16	5/16	1-3 3/16	11/32	1-4 3/16
¼	¼	1-0 ¼	9/32	1-1 ¼	5/16	1-2 ¼	5/16	1-3 ¼	11/32	1-4 ¼
5/16	¼	1-0 5/16	9/32	1-1 5/16	5/16	1-2 5/16	5/16	1-3 5/16	11/32	1-4 5/16
3/8	¼	1-0 3/8	9/32	1-1 3/8	5/16	1-2 3/8	5/16	1-3 3/8	11/32	1-4 3/8
7/16	¼	1-0 7/16	9/32	1-1 7/16	5/16	1-2 7/16	5/16	1-3 7/16	11/32	1-4 7/16
½	¼	1-0 ½	9/32	1-1 ½	5/16	1-2 ½	5/16	1-3 ½	11/32	1-4 ½
9/16	¼	1-0 9/16	9/32	1-1 9/16	5/16	1-2 9/16	5/16	1-3 9/16	11/32	1-4 9/16
5/8	¼	1-0 5/8	9/32	1-1 5/8	5/16	1-2 5/8	5/16	1-3 5/8	11/32	1-4 5/8
11/16	¼	1-0 11/16	9/32	1-1 11/16	5/16	1-2 11/16	5/16	1-3 11/16	11/32	1-4 11/16
¾	¼	1-0 ¾	9/32	1-1 ¾	5/16	1-2 ¾	5/16	1-3 ¾	11/32	1-4 ¾
13/16	9/32	1-0 13/16	9/32	1-1 13/16	5/16	1-2 13/16	11/32	1-3 13/16	11/32	1-4 13/16
7/8	9/32	1-0 7/8	9/32	1-1 7/8	5/16	1-2 7/8	11/32	1-3 7/8	11/32	1-4 7/8
15/16	9/32	1-0 15/16	9/32	1-1 15/16	5/16	1-2 15/16	11/32	1-3 15/16	11/32	1-4 15/16

Ins.	17″ Rise	Slope	18″ Rise	Slope	19″ Rise	Slope	20″ Rise	Slope	21″ Rise	Slope
0	11/32	1-5	3/8	1-6	13/32	1-7	13/32	1-8	7/16	1-9
1/16	11/32	1-5 1/16	3/8	1-6 1/16	13/32	1-7 1/16	13/32	1-8 1/16	7/16	1-9 1/16
1/8	11/32	1-5 1/8	3/8	1-6 1/8	13/32	1-7 1/8	13/32	1-8 1/8	7/16	1-9 1/8
3/16	11/32	1-5 3/16	3/8	1-6 3/16	13/32	1-7 3/16	13/32	1-8 3/16	7/16	1-9 3/16
¼	3/8	1-5 ¼	3/8	1-6 ¼	13/32	1-7 ¼	7/16	1-8 ¼	7/16	1-9 ¼
5/16	3/8	1-5 5/16	3/8	1-6 5/16	13/32	1-7 5/16	7/16	1-8 5/16	7/16	1-9 5/16
3/8	3/8	1-5 3/8	3/8	1-6 3/8	13/32	1-7 3/8	7/16	1-8 3/8	7/16	1-9 3/8
7/16	3/8	1-5 7/16	3/8	1-6 7/16	13/32	1-7 7/16	7/16	1-8 7/16	7/16	1-9 7/16
½	3/8	1-5 ½	3/8	1-6 ½	13/32	1-7 ½	7/16	1-8 ½	7/16	1-9 ½
9/16	3/8	1-5 9/16	3/8	1-6 9/16	13/32	1-7 9/16	7/16	1-8 9/16	7/16	1-9 9/16
5/8	3/8	1-5 5/8	3/8	1-6 5/8	13/32	1-7 5/8	7/16	1-8 5/8	7/16	1-9 5/8
11/16	3/8	1-5 11/16	3/8	1-6 11/16	13/32	1-7 11/16	7/16	1-8 11/16	7/16	1-9 11/16
¾	3/8	1-5 ¾	3/8	1-6 ¾	13/32	1-7 ¾	7/16	1-8 ¾	7/16	1-9 ¾
13/16	3/8	1-5 13/16	13/32	1-6 13/16	13/32	1-7 13/16	7/16	1-8 13/16	15/32	1-9 13/16
7/8	3/8	1-5 7/8	13/32	1-6 7/8	13/32	1-7 7/8	7/16	1-8 7/8	15/32	1-9 7/8
15/16	3/8	1-5 15/16	13/32	1-6 15/16	13/32	1-7 15/16	7/16	1-8 15/16	15/32	1-9 15/16

Feet	40′ Rise	Slope	50′ Rise	Slope	60′ Rise	Slope	70′ Rise	Slope
0	10	40-0 3/32	1-0 ½	50-0 1/8	1-3	60-0 5/32	1-5 ½	70-0 3/16
1	10 ¼	41-0 3/32	1-0 ¾	51-0 1/8	1-3 ¼	61-0 5/32	1-5 ¾	71-0 3/16
2	10 ½	42-0 3/32	1-1	52-0 1/8	1-3 ½	62-0 5/32	1-6	72-0 3/16
3	10 ¾	43-0 1/8	1-1 ¼	53-0 1/8	1-3 ¾	63-0 5/32	1-6 ¼	73-0 3/16
4	11	44-0 1/8	1-1 ½	54-0 1/8	1-4	64-0 5/32	1-6 ½	74-0 3/16
5	11 ¼	45-0 1/8	1-1 ¾	55-0 5/32	1-4 ¼	65-0 5/32	1-6 ¾	75-0 3/16
6	11 ½	46-0 1/8	1-2	56-0 5/32	1-4 ½	66-0 5/32	1-7	76-0 3/16
7	11 ¾	47-0 1/8	1-2 ¼	57-0 5/32	1-4 ¾	67-0 3/16	1-7 ¼	77-0 3/16
8	1-0	48-0 1/8	1-2 ½	58-0 5/32	1-5	68-0 3/16	1-7 ½	78-0 3/16
9	1-0 ¼	49-0 1/8	1-2 ¾	59-0 5/32	1-5 ¼	69-0 3/16	1-7 ¾	79-0 7/32

natsin A=0.020 8288136; natcos A=0.9997830566; nattan A=0.0208333333; natcot A=48.0000000000

Inches	0" Rise	0" Slope	1" Rise	1" Slope	2" Rise	2" Slope	3" Rise	3" Slope	4" Rise	4" Slope	5" Rise	5" Slope
0	0	0	1/32	1	1/16	2	1/16	3	3/32	4	1/8	5
1/16	0	1/16	1/32	1 1/16	1/16	2 1/16	3/32	3 1/16	3/32	4 1/16	1/8	5 1/16
1/8	0	1/8	1/32	1 1/8	1/16	2 1/8	3/32	3 1/8	3/32	4 1/8	1/8	5 1/8
3/16	0	3/16	1/32	1 3/16	1/16	2 3/16	3/32	3 3/16	3/32	4 3/16	1/8	5 3/16
1/4	0	1/4	1/32	1 1/4	1/16	2 1/4	3/32	3 1/4	1/8	4 1/4	1/8	5 1/4
5/16	0	5/16	1/32	1 5/16	1/16	2 5/16	3/32	3 5/16	1/8	4 5/16	1/8	5 5/16
3/8	0	3/8	1/32	1 3/8	1/16	2 3/8	3/32	3 3/8	1/8	4 3/8	1/8	5 3/8
7/16	0	7/16	1/32	1 7/16	1/16	2 7/16	3/32	3 7/16	1/8	4 7/16	5/32	5 7/16
1/2	0	1/2	1/32	1 1/2	1/16	2 1/2	3/32	3 1/2	1/8	4 1/2	5/32	5 1/2
9/16	0	9/16	1/32	1 9/16	1/16	2 9/16	3/32	3 9/16	1/8	4 9/16	5/32	5 9/16
5/8	1/32	5/8	1/32	1 5/8	1/16	2 5/8	3/32	3 5/8	1/8	4 5/8	5/32	5 5/8
11/16	1/32	11/16	1/32	1 11/16	1/16	2 11/16	3/32	3 11/16	1/8	4 11/16	5/32	5 11/16
3/4	1/32	3/4	1/32	1 3/4	1/16	2 3/4	3/32	3 3/4	1/8	4 3/4	5/32	5 3/4
13/16	1/32	13/16	1/16	1 13/16	1/16	2 13/16	3/32	3 13/16	1/8	4 13/16	5/32	5 13/16
7/8	1/32	7/8	1/16	1 7/8	1/16	2 7/8	3/32	3 7/8	1/8	4 7/8	5/32	5 7/8
15/16	1/32	15/16	1/16	1 15/16	1/16	2 15/16	3/32	3 15/16	1/8	4 15/16	5/32	5 15/16

Inches	6" Rise	6" Slope	7" Rise	7" Slope	8" Rise	8" Slope	9" Rise	9" Slope	10" Rise	10" Slope	11" Rise	11" Slope
0	5/32	6	3/16	7	7/32	8	1/4	9	1/4	10	9/32	11
1/16	5/32	6 1/16	3/16	7 1/16	7/32	8 1/16	1/4	9 1/16	1/4	10 1/16	9/32	11 1/16
1/8	5/32	6 1/8	3/16	7 1/8	7/32	8 1/8	1/4	9 1/8	1/4	10 1/8	9/32	11 1/8
3/16	5/32	6 3/16	3/16	7 3/16	7/32	8 3/16	1/4	9 3/16	1/4	10 3/16	9/32	11 3/16
1/4	5/32	6 1/4	3/16	7 1/4	7/32	8 1/4	1/4	9 1/4	9/32	10 1/4	9/32	11 1/4
5/16	5/32	6 5/16	3/16	7 5/16	7/32	8 5/16	1/4	9 5/16	9/32	10 5/16	9/32	11 5/16
3/8	5/32	6 3/8	3/16	7 3/8	7/32	8 3/8	1/4	9 3/8	9/32	10 3/8	9/32	11 3/8
7/16	5/32	6 7/16	3/16	7 7/16	7/32	8 7/16	1/4	9 7/16	9/32	10 7/16	5/16	11 7/16
1/2	5/32	6 1/2	3/16	7 1/2	7/32	8 1/2	1/4	9 1/2	9/32	10 1/2	5/16	11 1/2
9/16	5/32	6 9/16	3/16	7 9/16	7/32	8 9/16	1/4	9 9/16	9/32	10 9/16	5/16	11 9/16
5/8	3/16	6 5/8	3/16	7 5/8	7/32	8 5/8	1/4	9 5/8	9/32	10 5/8	5/16	11 5/8
11/16	3/16	6 11/16	3/16	7 11/16	7/32	8 11/16	1/4	9 11/16	9/32	10 11/16	5/16	11 11/16
3/4	3/16	6 3/4	3/16	7 3/4	7/32	8 3/4	1/4	9 3/4	9/32	10 3/4	5/16	11 3/4
13/16	3/16	6 13/16	7/32	7 13/16	7/32	8 13/16	1/4	9 13/16	9/32	10 13/16	5/16	11 13/16
7/8	3/16	6 7/8	7/32	7 7/8	7/32	8 7/8	1/4	9 7/8	9/32	10 7/8	5/16	11 7/8
15/16	3/16	6 15/16	7/32	7 15/16	7/32	8 15/16	1/4	9 15/16	9/32	10 15/16	5/16	11 15/16

Feet	0' Rise	0' Slope	10' Rise	10' Slope	20' Rise	20' Slope	30' Rise	30' Slope
0	0	0	3 1/8	10-0 1/32	6 1/4	20-0 3/32	9 3/8	30-0 1/8
1	5/16	1-0	3 7/16	11-0 1/32	6 9/16	21-0 3/32	9 11/16	31-0 1/8
2	5/8	2-0	3 3/4	12-0 1/16	6 7/8	22-0 3/32	10	32-0 1/8
3	15/16	3-0	4 1/16	13-0 1/16	7 3/16	23-0 3/32	10 5/16	33-0 1/8
4	1 1/4	4-0 1/32	4 3/8	14-0 1/16	7 1/2	24-0 3/32	10 5/8	34-0 1/8
5	1 9/16	5-0 1/32	4 11/16	15-0 1/16	7 13/16	25-0 3/32	10 15/16	35-0 5/32
6	1 7/8	6-0 1/32	5	16-0 1/16	8 1/8	26-0 3/32	11 1/4	36-0 5/32
7	2 3/16	7-0 1/32	5 5/16	17-0 1/16	8 7/16	27-0 1/8	11 9/16	37-0 5/32
8	2 1/2	8-0 1/32	5 5/8	18-0 1/16	8 3/4	28-0 1/8	11 7/8	38-0 5/32
9	2 13/16	9-0 1/32	5 15/16	19-0 1/16	9 1/16	29-0 1/8	1-0 3/16	39-0 5/32

A = 1° 29′ 30″; logsin A = 8.41552; logcos A = 9.99985; logtan A = 8.41567; logcot A = 1.58433

Ins.	12" Rise	Slope	13" Rise	Slope	14" Rise	Slope	15" Rise	Slope	16" Rise	Slope
0	5/16	1-0	11/32	1-1	3/8	1-2	3/8	1-3	13/32	1-4
1/16	5/16	1-0 1/16	11/32	1-1 1/16	3/8	1-2 1/16	13/32	1-3 1/16	13/32	1-4 1/16
1/8	5/16	1-0 1/8	11/32	1-1 1/8	3/8	1-2 1/8	13/32	1-3 1/8	13/32	1-4 1/8
3/16	5/16	1-0 3/16	11/32	1-1 3/16	3/8	1-2 3/16	13/32	1-3 3/16	13/32	1-4 3/16
1/4	5/16	1-0 1/4	11/32	1-1 1/4	3/8	1-2 1/4	13/32	1-3 1/4	7/16	1-4 1/4
5/16	5/16	1-0 5/16	11/32	1-1 5/16	3/8	1-2 5/16	13/32	1-3 5/16	7/16	1-4 5/16
3/8	5/16	1-0 3/8	11/32	1-1 3/8	3/8	1-2 3/8	13/32	1-3 3/8	7/16	1-4 3/8
7/16	5/16	1-0 7/16	11/32	1-1 7/16	3/8	1-2 7/16	13/32	1-3 7/16	7/16	1-4 7/16
1/2	5/16	1-0 1/2	11/32	1-1 1/2	3/8	1-2 1/2	13/32	1-3 1/2	7/16	1-4 1/2
9/16	5/16	1-0 9/16	11/32	1-1 9/16	3/8	1-2 9/16	13/32	1-3 9/16	7/16	1-4 9/16
5/8	11/32	1-0 5/8	11/32	1-1 5/8	3/8	1-2 5/8	13/32	1-3 5/8	7/16	1-4 5/8
11/16	11/32	1-0 11/16	11/32	1-1 11/16	3/8	1-2 11/16	13/32	1-3 11/16	7/16	1-4 11/16
3/4	11/32	1-0 3/4	11/32	1-1 3/4	3/8	1-2 3/4	13/32	1-3 3/4	7/16	1-4 3/4
13/16	11/32	1-0 13/16	3/8	1-1 13/16	3/8	1-2 13/16	13/32	1-3 13/16	7/16	1-4 13/16
7/8	11/32	1-0 7/8	3/8	1-1 7/8	3/8	1-2 7/8	13/32	1-3 7/8	7/16	1-4 7/8
15/16	11/32	1-0 15/16	3/8	1-1 15/16	3/8	1-2 15/16	13/32	1-3 15/16	7/16	1-4 15/16

Ins.	17" Rise	Slope	18" Rise	Slope	19" Rise	Slope	20" Rise	Slope	21" Rise	Slope
0	7/16	1-5	15/32	1-6	1/2	1-7	17/32	1-8	9/16	1-9
1/16	7/16	1-5 1/16	15/32	1-6 1/16	1/2	1-7 1/16	17/32	1-8 1/16	9/16	1-9 1/16
1/8	7/16	1-5 1/8	15/32	1-6 1/8	1/2	1-7 1/8	17/32	1-8 1/8	9/16	1-9 1/8
3/16	7/16	1-5 3/16	15/32	1-6 3/16	1/2	1-7 3/16	17/32	1-8 3/16	9/16	1-9 3/16
1/4	7/16	1-5 1/4	15/32	1-6 1/4	1/2	1-7 1/4	17/32	1-8 1/4	9/16	1-9 1/4
5/16	7/16	1-5 5/16	15/32	1-6 5/16	1/2	1-7 5/16	17/32	1-8 5/16	9/16	1-9 5/16
3/8	7/16	1-5 3/8	15/32	1-6 3/8	1/2	1-7 3/8	17/32	1-8 3/8	9/16	1-9 3/8
7/16	15/32	1-5 7/16	15/32	1-6 7/16	1/2	1-7 7/16	17/32	1-8 7/16	9/16	1-9 7/16
1/2	15/32	1-5 1/2	15/32	1-6 1/2	1/2	1-7 1/2	17/32	1-8 1/2	9/16	1-9 1/2
9/16	15/32	1-5 9/16	15/32	1-6 9/16	1/2	1-7 9/16	17/32	1-8 9/16	9/16	1-9 9/16
5/8	15/32	1-5 5/8	1/2	1-6 5/8	1/2	1-7 5/8	17/32	1-8 5/8	9/16	1-9 5/8
11/16	15/32	1-5 11/16	1/2	1-6 11/16	1/2	1-7 11/16	17/32	1-8 11/16	9/16	1-9 11/16
3/4	15/32	1-5 3/4	1/2	1-6 3/4	1/2	1-7 3/4	17/32	1-8 3/4	9/16	1-9 3/4
13/16	15/32	1-5 13/16	1/2	1-6 13/16	17/32	1-7 13/16	17/32	1-8 13/16	9/16	1-9 13/16
7/8	15/32	1-5 7/8	1/2	1-6 7/8	17/32	1-7 7/8	17/32	1-8 7/8	9/16	1-9 7/8
15/16	15/32	1-5 15/16	1/2	1-6 15/16	17/32	1-7 15/16	17/32	1-8 15/16	9/16	1-9 15/16

Feet	40' Rise	Slope	50' Rise	Slope	60' Rise	Slope	70' Rise	Slope
0	1-0 1/2	40-0 5/32	1-3 5/8	50-0 7/32	1-6 3/4	60-0 1/4	1-9 7/8	70-0 9/32
1	1-0 13/16	41-0 5/32	1-3 15/16	51-0 7/32	1-7 1/16	61-0 1/4	1-10 3/16	71-0 9/32
2	1-1 1/8	42-0 5/32	1-4 1/4	52-0 7/32	1-7 3/8	62-0 1/4	1-10 1/2	72-0 9/32
3	1-1 7/16	43-0 3/16	1-4 9/16	53-0 7/32	1-7 11/16	63-0 1/4	1-10 13/16	73-0 5/16
4	1-1 3/4	44-0 3/16	1-4 7/8	54-0 7/32	1-8	64-0 1/4	1-11 1/8	74-0 5/16
5	1-2 1/16	45-0 3/16	1-5 3/16	55-0 7/32	1-8 5/16	65-0 1/4	1-11 7/16	75-0 5/16
6	1-2 3/8	46-0 3/16	1-5 1/2	56-0 7/32	1-8 5/8	66-0 9/32	1-11 3/4	76-0 5/16
7	1-2 11/16	47-0 3/16	1-5 13/16	57-0 7/32	1-8 15/16	67-0 9/32	2-0 1/16	77-0 5/16
8	1-3	48-0 3/16	1-6 1/8	58-0 1/4	1-9 1/4	68-0 9/32	2-0 3/8	78-0 5/16
9	1-3 5/16	49-0 3/16	1-6 7/16	59-0 1/4	1-9 9/16	69-0 9/32	2-0 11/16	79-0 5/16

natsin A=0.0260328407; natcos A=0.9996610882; nattan A=0.0260416666; natcot A=38.4000000000

Inches	0" Rise	0" Slope	1" Rise	1" Slope	2" Rise	2" Slope	3" Rise	3" Slope	4" Rise	4" Slope	5" Rise	5" Slope
0	0	0	1/32	1	1/16	2	3/32	3	1/8	4	5/32	5
1/16	0	1/16	1/32	1 1/16	1/16	2 1/16	3/32	3 1/16	1/8	4 1/16	5/32	5 1/16
1/8	0	1/8	1/32	1 1/8	1/16	2 1/8	3/32	3 1/8	1/8	4 1/8	5/32	5 1/8
3/16	0	3/16	1/32	1 3/16	1/16	2 3/16	3/32	3 3/16	1/8	4 3/16	5/32	5 3/16
1/4	0	1/4	1/32	1 1/4	1/16	2 1/4	3/32	3 1/4	1/8	4 1/4	5/32	5 1/4
5/16	0	5/16	1/32	1 5/16	1/16	2 5/16	3/32	3 5/16	1/8	4 5/16	5/32	5 5/16
3/8	0	3/8	1/32	1 3/8	1/16	2 3/8	3/32	3 3/8	1/8	4 3/8	5/32	5 3/8
7/16	0	7/16	1/32	1 7/16	1/16	2 7/16	3/32	3 7/16	1/8	4 7/16	5/32	5 7/16
1/2	0	1/2	1/16	1 1/2	1/16	2 1/2	1/8	3 1/2	1/8	4 1/2	3/16	5 1/2
9/16	1/32	9/16	1/16	1 9/16	3/32	2 9/16	1/8	3 9/16	5/32	4 9/16	3/16	5 9/16
5/8	1/32	5/8	1/16	1 5/8	3/32	2 5/8	1/8	3 5/8	5/32	4 5/8	3/16	5 5/8
11/16	1/32	11/16	1/16	1 11/16	3/32	2 11/16	1/8	3 11/16	5/32	4 11/16	3/16	5 11/16
3/4	1/32	3/4	1/16	1 3/4	3/32	2 3/4	1/8	3 3/4	5/32	4 3/4	3/16	5 3/4
13/16	1/32	13/16	1/16	1 13/16	3/32	2 13/16	1/8	3 13/16	5/32	4 13/16	3/16	5 13/16
7/8	1/32	7/8	1/16	1 7/8	3/32	2 7/8	1/8	3 7/8	5/32	4 7/8	3/16	5 7/8
15/16	1/32	15/16	1/16	1 15/16	3/32	2 15/16	1/8	3 15/16	5/32	4 15/16	3/16	5 15/16

Inches	6" Rise	6" Slope	7" Rise	7" Slope	8" Rise	8" Slope	9" Rise	9" Slope	10" Rise	10" Slope	11" Rise	11" Slope
0	3/16	6	7/32	7	1/4	8	9/32	9	5/16	10	11/32	11
1/16	3/16	6 1/16	7/32	7 1/16	1/4	8 1/16	9/32	9 1/16	5/16	10 1/16	11/32	11 1/16
1/8	3/16	6 1/8	7/32	7 1/8	1/4	8 1/8	9/32	9 1/8	5/16	10 1/8	11/32	11 1/8
3/16	3/16	6 3/16	7/32	7 3/16	1/4	8 3/16	9/32	9 3/16	5/16	10 3/16	11/32	11 3/16
1/4	3/16	6 1/4	7/32	7 1/4	1/4	8 1/4	9/32	9 1/4	5/16	10 1/4	11/32	11 1/4
5/16	3/16	6 5/16	7/32	7 5/16	1/4	8 5/16	9/32	9 5/16	5/16	10 5/16	11/32	11 5/16
3/8	3/16	6 3/8	7/32	7 3/8	1/4	8 3/8	9/32	9 3/8	5/16	10 3/8	11/32	11 3/8
7/16	3/16	6 7/16	7/32	7 7/16	1/4	8 7/16	9/32	9 7/16	5/16	10 7/16	11/32	11 7/16
1/2	3/16	6 1/2	1/4	7 1/2	1/4	8 1/2	5/16	9 1/2	5/16	10 1/2	3/8	11 1/2
9/16	7/32	6 9/16	1/4	7 9/16	9/32	8 9/16	5/16	9 9/16	11/32	10 9/16	3/8	11 9/16
5/8	7/32	6 5/8	1/4	7 5/8	9/32	8 5/8	5/16	9 5/8	11/32	10 5/8	3/8	11 5/8
11/16	7/32	6 11/16	1/4	7 11/16	9/32	8 11/16	5/16	9 11/16	11/32	10 11/16	3/8	11 11/16
3/4	7/32	6 3/4	1/4	7 3/4	9/32	8 3/4	5/16	9 3/4	11/32	10 3/4	3/8	11 3/4
13/16	7/32	6 13/16	1/4	7 13/16	9/32	8 13/16	5/16	9 13/16	11/32	10 13/16	3/8	11 13/16
7/8	7/32	6 7/8	1/4	7 7/8	9/32	8 7/8	5/16	9 7/8	11/32	10 7/8	3/8	11 7/8
15/16	7/32	6 15/16	1/4	7 15/16	9/32	8 15/16	5/16	9 15/16	11/32	10 15/16	3/8	11 15/16

Feet	0' Rise	0' Slope	10' Rise	10' Slope	20' Rise	20' Slope	30' Rise	30' Slope
0	0	0	3 3/4	10-0 1/16	7 1/2	20-0 1/8	11 1/4	30-0 3/16
1	3/8	1-0	4 1/8	11-0 1/16	7 7/8	21-0 1/8	11 5/8	31-0 3/16
2	3/4	2-0	4 1/2	12-0 1/16	8 1/4	22-0 1/8	1-0	32-0 3/16
3	1 1/8	3-0 1/32	4 7/8	13-0 1/16	8 5/8	23-0 1/8	1-0 3/8	33-0 3/16
4	1 1/2	4-0 1/32	5 1/4	14-0 3/32	9	24-0 1/8	1-0 3/4	34-0 3/16
5	1 7/8	5-0 1/32	5 5/8	15-0 3/32	9 3/8	25-0 5/32	1-1 1/8	35-0 7/32
6	2 1/4	6-0 1/32	6	16-0 3/32	9 3/4	26-0 5/32	1-1 1/2	36-0 7/32
7	2 5/8	7-0 1/32	6 3/8	17-0 3/32	10 1/8	27-0 5/32	1-1 7/8	37-0 7/32
8	3	8-0 1/32	6 3/4	18-0 3/32	10 1/2	28-0 5/32	1-2 1/4	38-0 7/32
9	3 3/8	9-0 1/16	7 1/8	19-0 1/8	10 7/8	29-0 5/32	1-2 5/8	39-0 7/32

A = 1° 47′ 24″; logsin A = 8.49464; logcos A = 9.99979; logtan A = 8.49485; logcot A = 1.50515

in.	12″ Rise	12″ Slope	13″ Rise	13″ Slope	14″ Rise	14″ Slope	15″ Rise	15″ Slope	16″ Rise	16″ Slope
0	3/8	1-0	13/32	1-1	7/16	1-2	15/32	1-3	1/2	1-4
1/16	3/8	1-0 1/16	13/32	1-1 1/16	7/16	1-2 1/16	15/32	1-3 1/16	1/2	1-4 1/16
1/8	3/8	1-0 1/8	13/32	1-1 1/8	7/16	1-2 1/8	15/32	1-3 1/8	1/2	1-4 1/8
3/16	3/8	1-0 3/16	13/32	1-1 3/16	7/16	1-2 3/16	15/32	1-3 3/16	1/2	1-4 3/16
1/4	3/8	1-0 1/4	13/32	1-1 1/4	7/16	1-2 1/4	15/32	1-3 1/4	1/2	1-4 1/4
5/16	3/8	1-0 5/16	13/32	1-1 5/16	7/16	1-2 5/16	15/32	1-3 5/16	1/2	1-4 5/16
3/8	3/8	1-0 3/8	13/32	1-1 3/8	7/16	1-2 3/8	15/32	1-3 3/8	1/2	1-4 3/8
7/16	3/8	1-0 7/16	13/32	1-1 7/16	7/16	1-2 7/16	15/32	1-3 7/16	1/2	1-4 7/16
1/2	3/8	1-0 1/2	7/16	1-1 1/2	7/16	1-2 1/2	1/2	1-3 1/2	1/2	1-4 1/2
9/16	13/32	1-0 9/16	7/16	1-1 9/16	15/32	1-2 9/16	1/2	1-3 9/16	17/32	1-4 9/16
5/8	13/32	1-0 5/8	7/16	1-1 5/8	15/32	1-2 5/8	1/2	1-3 5/8	17/32	1-4 5/8
11/16	13/32	1-0 11/16	7/16	1-1 11/16	15/32	1-2 11/16	1/2	1-3 11/16	17/32	1-4 11/16
3/4	13/32	1-0 3/4	7/16	1-1 3/4	15/32	1-2 3/4	1/2	1-3 3/4	17/32	1-4 3/4
13/16	13/32	1-0 13/16	7/16	1-1 13/16	15/32	1-2 13/16	1/2	1-3 13/16	17/32	1-4 13/16
7/8	13/32	1-0 7/8	7/16	1-1 7/8	15/32	1-2 7/8	1/2	1-3 7/8	17/32	1-4 7/8
15/16	13/32	1-0 15/16	7/16	1-1 15/16	15/32	1-2 15/16	1/2	1-3 15/16	17/32	1-4 15/16

in.	17″ Rise	17″ Slope	18″ Rise	18″ Slope	19″ Rise	19″ Slope	20″ Rise	20″ Slope	21″ Rise	21″ Slope
0	17/32	1-5	9/16	1-6	19/32	1-7	5/8	1-8	21/32	1-9
1/16	17/32	1-5 1/16	9/16	1-6 1/16	19/32	1-7 1/16	5/8	1-8 1/16	21/32	1-9 1/16
1/8	17/32	1-5 1/8	9/16	1-6 1/8	19/32	1-7 1/8	5/8	1-8 1/8	21/32	1-9 1/8
3/16	17/32	1-5 3/16	9/16	1-6 3/16	19/32	1-7 3/16	5/8	1-8 3/16	21/32	1-9 3/16
1/4	17/32	1-5 1/4	9/16	1-6 1/4	19/32	1-7 1/4	5/8	1-8 1/4	21/32	1-9 1/4
5/16	17/32	1-5 5/16	9/16	1-6 5/16	19/32	1-7 5/16	5/8	1-8 5/16	21/32	1-9 5/16
3/8	17/32	1-5 3/8	9/16	1-6 3/8	19/32	1-7 3/8	5/8	1-8 3/8	21/32	1-9 3/8
7/16	17/32	1-5 7/16	9/16	1-6 7/16	19/32	1-7 7/16	5/8	1-8 7/16	21/32	1-9 7/16
1/2	9/16	1-5 1/2	9/16	1-6 1/2	5/8	1-7 1/2	5/8	1-8 1/2	11/16	1-9 1/2
9/16	9/16	1-5 9/16	19/32	1-6 9/16	5/8	1-7 9/16	21/32	1-8 9/16	11/16	1-9 9/16
5/8	9/16	1-5 5/8	19/32	1-6 5/8	5/8	1-7 5/8	21/32	1-8 5/8	11/16	1-9 5/8
11/16	9/16	1-5 11/16	19/32	1-6 11/16	5/8	1-7 11/16	21/32	1-8 11/16	11/16	1-9 11/16
3/4	9/16	1-5 3/4	19/32	1-6 3/4	5/8	1-7 3/4	21/32	1-8 3/4	11/16	1-9 3/4
13/16	9/16	1-5 13/16	19/32	1-6 13/16	5/8	1-7 13/16	21/32	1-8 13/16	11/16	1-9 13/16
7/8	9/16	1-5 7/8	19/32	1-6 7/8	5/8	1-7 7/8	21/32	1-8 7/8	11/16	1-9 7/8
15/16	9/16	1-5 15/16	19/32	1-6 15/16	5/8	1-7 15/16	21/32	1-8 15/16	11/16	1-9 15/16

Feet	40′ Rise	40′ Slope	50′ Rise	50′ Slope	60′ Rise	60′ Slope	70′ Rise	70′ Slope
0	1-3	40-0 1/2	1-6 3/4	50-0 9/32	1-10 1/2	60-0 11/32	2-2 1/8	70-0 13/32
1	1-3 3/8	41-0 1/4	1-7 1/8	51-0 5/16	1-10 7/8	61-0 11/32	2-2 5/8	71-0 13/32
2	1-3 3/4	42-0 1/4	1-7 1/2	52-0 5/16	1-11 1/4	62-0 3/8	2-3	72-0 13/32
3	1-4 1/8	43-0 1/4	1-7 7/8	53-0 5/16	1-11 5/8	63-0 3/8	2-3 3/8	73-0 7/16
4	1-4 1/2	44-0 1/4	1-8 1/4	54-0 5/16	2-0	64-0 3/8	2-3 3/4	74-0 7/16
5	1-4 7/8	45-0 1/4	1-8 5/8	55-0 5/16	2-0 3/8	65-0 3/8	2-4 1/8	75-0 7/16
6	1-5 1/4	46-0 9/32	1-9	56-0 5/16	2-0 3/4	66-0 3/8	2-4 1/2	76-0 7/16
7	1-5 5/8	47-0 9/32	1-9 3/8	57-0 11/32	2-1 1/8	67-0 13/32	2-4 7/8	77-0 7/16
8	1-6	48-0 9/32	1-9 3/4	58-0 11/32	2-1 1/2	68-0 13/32	2-5 1/4	78-0 15/32
9	1-6 3/8	49-0 9/32	1-10 1/8	59-0 11/32	2-1 7/8	69-0 13/32	2-5 5/8	79-0 15/32

natsin A=0.0312347523; natcos A=0.9995120759; nattan A=0.0312500000; natcot A=32.0000000000

Inches	0" Rise	Slope	1" Rise	Slope	2" Rise	Slope	3" Rise	Slope	4" Rise	Slope	5" Rise	Slope
0	0	0	1/32	1	1/16	2	1/8	3	5/32	4	3/16	5
1/16	0	1/16	1/32	1 1/16	1/16	2 1/16	1/8	3 1/16	5/32	4 1/16	3/16	5 1/16
1/8	0	1/8	1/32	1 1/8	1/16	2 1/8	1/8	3 1/8	5/32	4 1/8	3/16	5 1/8
3/16	0	3/16	1/32	1 3/16	3/32	2 3/16	1/8	3 3/16	5/32	4 3/16	3/16	5 3/16
1/4	0	1/4	1/16	1 1/4	3/32	2 1/4	1/8	3 1/4	5/32	4 1/4	3/16	5 1/4
5/16	0	5/16	1/16	1 5/16	3/32	2 5/16	1/8	3 5/16	5/32	4 5/16	3/16	5 5/16
3/8	0	3/8	1/16	1 3/8	3/32	2 3/8	1/8	3 3/8	5/32	4 3/8	3/16	5 3/8
7/16	1/32	7/16	1/16	1 7/16	3/32	2 7/16	1/8	3 7/16	5/32	4 7/16	3/16	5 7/16
1/2	1/32	1/2	1/16	1 1/2	3/32	2 1/2	1/8	3 1/2	5/32	4 1/2	3/16	5 1/2
9/16	1/32	9/16	1/16	1 9/16	3/32	2 9/16	1/8	3 9/16	5/32	4 9/16	3/16	5 9/16
5/8	1/32	5/8	1/16	1 5/8	3/32	2 5/8	1/8	3 5/8	5/32	4 5/8	7/32	5 5/8
11/16	1/32	11/16	1/16	1 11/16	3/32	2 11/16	1/8	3 11/16	5/32	4 11/16	7/32	5 11/16
3/4	1/32	3/4	1/16	1 3/4	3/32	2 3/4	1/8	3 3/4	3/16	4 3/4	7/32	5 3/4
13/16	1/32	13/16	1/16	1 13/16	3/32	2 13/16	1/8	3 13/16	3/16	4 13/16	7/32	5 13/16
7/8	1/32	7/8	1/16	1 7/8	3/32	2 7/8	5/32	3 7/8	3/16	4 7/8	7/32	5 7/8
15/16	1/32	15/16	1/16	1 15/16	3/32	2 15/16	5/32	3 15/16	3/16	4 15/16	7/32	5 15/16

Inches	6" Rise	Slope	7" Rise	Slope	8" Rise	Slope	9" Rise	Slope	10" Rise	Slope	11" Rise	Slope
0	7/32	6	1/4	7	9/32	8	5/16	9	3/8	10	13/32	11
1/16	7/32	6 1/16	1/4	7 1/16	9/32	8 1/16	11/32	9 1/16	3/8	10 1/16	13/32	11 1/16
1/8	7/32	6 1/8	1/4	7 1/8	9/32	8 1/8	11/32	9 1/8	3/8	10 1/8	13/32	11 1/8
3/16	7/32	6 3/16	1/4	7 3/16	5/16	8 3/16	11/32	9 3/16	3/8	10 3/16	13/32	11 3/16
1/4	7/32	6 1/4	1/4	7 1/4	5/16	8 1/4	11/32	9 1/4	3/8	10 1/4	13/32	11 1/4
5/16	7/32	6 5/16	9/32	7 5/16	5/16	8 5/16	11/32	9 5/16	3/8	10 5/16	13/32	11 5/16
3/8	7/32	6 3/8	9/32	7 3/8	5/16	8 3/8	11/32	9 3/8	3/8	10 3/8	13/32	11 3/8
7/16	1/4	6 7/16	9/32	7 7/16	5/16	8 7/16	11/32	9 7/16	3/8	10 7/16	13/32	11 7/16
1/2	1/4	6 1/2	9/32	7 1/2	5/16	8 1/2	11/32	9 1/2	3/8	10 1/2	13/32	11 1/2
9/16	1/4	6 9/16	9/32	7 9/16	5/16	8 9/16	11/32	9 9/16	3/8	10 9/16	13/32	11 9/16
5/8	1/4	6 5/8	9/32	7 5/8	5/16	8 5/8	11/32	9 5/8	3/8	10 5/8	7/16	11 5/8
11/16	1/4	6 11/16	9/32	7 11/16	5/16	8 11/16	11/32	9 11/16	3/8	10 11/16	7/16	11 11/16
3/4	1/4	6 3/4	9/32	7 3/4	5/16	8 3/4	11/32	9 3/4	13/32	10 3/4	7/16	11 3/4
13/16	1/4	6 13/16	9/32	7 13/16	5/16	8 13/16	11/32	9 13/16	13/32	10 13/16	7/16	11 13/16
7/8	1/4	6 7/8	9/32	7 7/8	5/16	8 7/8	3/8	9 7/8	13/32	10 7/8	7/16	11 7/8
15/16	1/4	6 15/16	9/32	7 15/16	5/16	8 15/16	3/8	9 15/16	13/32	10 15/16	7/16	11 15/16

Feet	0' Rise	Slope	10' Rise	Slope	20' Rise	Slope	30' Rise	Slope
0	0	0	4 3/8	10-0 3/32	8 3/4	20-0 5/32	1-1 1/8	30-0 1/4
1	7/16	1-0	4 13/16	11-0 3/32	9 3/16	21-0 5/32	1-1 9/16	31-0 1/4
2	7/8	2-0 1/32	5 1/4	12-0 3/32	9 5/8	22-0 3/16	1-2	32-0 1/4
3	1 5/16	3-0 1/32	5 11/16	13-0 3/32	10 1/16	23-0 3/16	1-2 7/16	33-0 1/4
4	1 3/4	4-0 1/32	6 1/8	14-0 1/8	10 1/2	24-0 3/16	1-2 7/8	34-0 9/32
5	2 3/16	5-0 1/16	6 9/16	15-0 1/8	10 15/16	25-0 3/16	1-3 5/16	35-0 9/32
6	2 5/8	6-0 1/16	7	16-0 1/8	11 3/8	26-0 7/32	1-3 3/4	36-0 9/32
7	3 1/16	7-0 1/16	7 7/16	17-0 1/8	11 13/16	27-0 7/32	1-4 3/16	37-0 9/32
8	3 1/2	8-0 1/16	7 7/8	18-0 5/32	1-0 1/4	28-0 7/32	1-4 5/8	38-0 5/16
9	3 15/16	9-0 1/16	8 5/16	19-0 5/32	1-0 11/16	29-0 7/32	1-5 1/16	39-0 5/16

A = 2° 05′ 17″; logsin A = 8.56151; logcos A = 9.99971; logtan A = 8.56180; logcot A = 1.43820

Ins.	12″ Rise	12″ Slope	13″ Rise	13″ Slope	14″ Rise	14″ Slope	15″ Rise	15″ Slope	16″ Rise	16″ Slope
0	7/16	1-0	15/32	1-1	1/2	1-2	9/16	1-3	19/32	1-4
1/16	7/16	1-0 1/16	15/32	1-1 1/16	1/2	1-2 1/16	9/16	1-3 1/16	19/32	1-4 1/16
1/8	7/16	1-0 1/8	15/32	1-1 1/8	1/2	1-2 1/8	9/16	1-3 1/8	19/32	1-4 1/8
3/16	7/16	1-0 3/16	15/32	1-1 3/16	17/32	1-2 3/16	9/16	1-3 3/16	19/32	1-4 3/16
1/4	7/16	1-0 1/4	15/32	1-1 1/4	17/32	1-2 1/4	9/16	1-3 1/4	19/32	1-4 1/4
5/16	7/16	1-0 5/16	1/2	1-1 5/16	17/32	1-2 5/16	9/16	1-3 5/16	19/32	1-4 5/16
3/8	7/16	1-0 3/8	1/2	1-1 3/8	17/32	1-2 3/8	9/16	1-3 3/8	19/32	1-4 3/8
7/16	15/32	1-0 7/16	1/2	1-1 7/16	17/32	1-2 7/16	9/16	1-3 7/16	19/32	1-4 7/16
1/2	15/32	1-0 1/2	1/2	1-1 1/2	17/32	1-2 1/2	9/16	1-3 1/2	19/32	1-4 1/2
9/16	15/32	1-0 9/16	1/2	1-1 9/16	17/32	1-2 9/16	9/16	1-3 9/16	19/32	1-4 9/16
5/8	15/32	1-0 5/8	1/2	1-1 5/8	17/32	1-2 5/8	9/16	1-3 5/8	19/32	1-4 5/8
11/16	15/32	1-0 11/16	1/2	1-1 11/16	17/32	1-2 11/16	9/16	1-3 11/16	19/32	1-4 11/16
3/4	15/32	1-0 3/4	1/2	1-1 3/4	17/32	1-2 3/4	9/16	1-3 3/4	5/8	1-4 3/4
13/16	15/32	1-0 13/16	1/2	1-1 13/16	17/32	1-2 13/16	9/16	1-3 13/16	5/8	1-4 13/16
7/8	15/32	1-0 7/8	1/2	1-1 7/8	17/32	1-2 7/8	19/32	1-3 7/8	5/8	1-4 7/8
15/16	15/32	1-0 15/16	1/2	1-1 15/16	17/32	1-2 15/16	19/32	1-3 15/16	5/8	1-4 15/16

Ins.	17″ Rise	17″ Slope	18″ Rise	18″ Slope	19″ Rise	19″ Slope	20″ Rise	20″ Slope	21″ Rise	21″ Slope
0	5/8	1-5	21/32	1-6	11/16	1-7	23/32	1-8	3/4	1-9
1/16	5/8	1-5 1/16	21/32	1-6 1/16	11/16	1-7 1/16	23/32	1-8 1/16	25/32	1-9 1/16
1/8	5/8	1-5 1/8	21/32	1-6 1/8	11/16	1-7 1/8	23/32	1-8 1/8	25/32	1-9 1/8
3/16	5/8	1-5 3/16	21/32	1-6 3/16	11/16	1-7 3/16	3/4	1-8 3/16	25/32	1-9 3/16
1/4	5/8	1-5 1/4	21/32	1-6 1/4	11/16	1-7 1/4	3/4	1-8 1/4	25/32	1-9 1/4
5/16	5/8	1-5 5/16	21/32	1-6 5/16	23/32	1-7 5/16	3/4	1-8 5/16	25/32	1-9 5/16
3/8	5/8	1-5 3/8	21/32	1-6 3/8	23/32	1-7 3/8	3/4	1-8 3/8	25/32	1-9 3/8
7/16	5/8	1-5 7/16	11/16	1-6 7/16	23/32	1-7 7/16	3/4	1-8 7/16	25/32	1-9 7/16
1/2	5/8	1-5 1/2	11/16	1-6 1/2	23/32	1-7 1/2	3/4	1-8 1/2	25/32	1-9 1/2
9/16	5/8	1-5 9/16	11/16	1-6 9/16	23/32	1-7 9/16	3/4	1-8 9/16	25/32	1-9 9/16
5/8	21/32	1-5 5/8	11/16	1-6 5/8	23/32	1-7 5/8	3/4	1-8 5/8	25/32	1-9 5/8
11/16	21/32	1-5 11/16	11/16	1-6 11/16	23/32	1-7 11/16	3/4	1-8 11/16	25/32	1-9 11/16
3/4	21/32	1-5 3/4	11/16	1-6 3/4	23/32	1-7 3/4	3/4	1-8 3/4	25/32	1-9 3/4
13/16	21/32	1-5 13/16	11/16	1-6 13/16	23/32	1-7 13/16	3/4	1-8 13/16	25/32	1-9 13/16
7/8	21/32	1-5 7/8	11/16	1-6 7/8	23/32	1-7 7/8	3/4	1-8 7/8	13/16	1-9 7/8
15/16	21/32	1-5 15/16	11/16	1-6 15/16	23/32	1-7 15/16	3/4	1-8 15/16	13/16	1-9 15/16

Feet	40′ Rise	40′ Slope	50′ Rise	50′ Slope	60′ Rise	60′ Slope	70′ Rise	70′ Slope
0	1-5 1/2	40-0 5/16	1-9 7/8	50-0 13/32	2-2 1/4	60-0 15/32	2-6 5/8	70-0 9/16
1	1-5 15/16	41-0 5/16	1-10 5/16	51-0 13/32	2-2 11/16	61-0 1/2	2-7 1/16	71-0 9/16
2	1-6 3/8	42-0 11/32	1-10 3/4	52-0 13/32	2-3 1/8	62-0 1/2	2-7 1/2	72-0 9/16
3	1-6 13/16	43-0 11/32	1-11 3/16	53-0 7/16	2-3 9/16	63-0 1/2	2-7 15/16	73-0 19/32
4	1-7 1/4	44-0 11/32	1-11 5/8	54-0 7/16	2-4	64-0 1/2	2-8 3/8	74-0 19/32
5	1-7 11/16	45-0 11/32	2-0 1/16	55-0 7/16	2-4 7/16	65-0 17/32	2-8 13/16	75-0 19/32
6	1-8 1/8	46-0 3/8	2-0 1/2	56-0 7/16	2-4 7/8	66-0 17/32	2-9 1/4	76-0 19/32
7	1-8 9/16	47-0 3/8	2-0 15/16	57-0 15/32	2-5 5/16	67-0 17/32	2-9 11/16	77-0 5/8
8	1-9	48-0 3/8	2-1 3/8	58-0 15/32	2-5 3/4	68-0 17/32	2-10 1/8	78-0 5/8
9	1-9 7/16	49-0 13/32	2-1 13/16	59-0 15/32	2-6 3/16	69-0 9/16	2-10 9/16	79-0 5/8

natsin A=0.0364341270; natcos A=0.9993360568; nattan A=0.0364583333; natcot A=27.4285714285

Inches	0" Rise	0" Slope	1" Rise	1" Slope	2" Rise	2" Slope	3" Rise	3" Slope	4" Rise	4" Slope	5" Rise	5" Slope
0	0	0	1/32	1	3/32-	2	1/8	3	5/32	4	7/32-	5
1/16	0	1/16	1/32	1 1/16	3/32-	2 1/16	1/8	3 1/16	5/32	4 1/16	7/32-	5 1/16
1/8	0	1/8	1/16	1 1/8	3/32-	2 1/8	1/8	3 1/8	3/16	4 1/8	7/32-	5 1/8
3/16	0	3/16	1/16	1 3/16	3/32-	2 3/16	1/8	3 3/16	3/16	4 3/16	7/32-	5 3/16
1/4	0	1/4	1/16	1 1/4	3/32	2 1/4	1/8	3 1/4	3/16	4 1/4	7/32	5 1/4
5/16	0	5/16	1/16	1 5/16	3/32	2 5/16	1/8	3 5/16	3/16	4 5/16	7/32	5 5/16
3/8	0	3/8	1/16	1 3/8	3/32	2 3/8	1/8	3 3/8	3/16	4 3/8	7/32	5 3/8
7/16	1/32-	7/16	1/16	1 7/16	3/32	2 7/16	5/32-	3 7/16	3/16	4 7/16	7/32	5 7/16
1/2	1/32-	1/2	1/16	1 1/2	3/32	2 1/2	5/32-	3 1/2	3/16	4 1/2	7/32	5 1/2
9/16	1/32-	9/16	1/16	1 9/16	3/32	2 9/16	5/32-	3 9/16	3/16	4 9/16	7/32	5 9/16
5/8	1/32-	5/8	1/16	1 5/8	1/8	2 5/8	5/32-	3 5/8	3/16	4 5/8	1/4	5 5/8
11/16	1/32-	11/16	1/16	1 11/16	1/8	2 11/16	5/32-	3 11/16	3/16	4 11/16	1/4	5 11/16
3/4	1/32-	3/4	1/16	1 3/4	1/8	2 3/4	5/32-	3 3/4	3/16	4 3/4	1/4	5 3/4
13/16	1/32-	13/16	1/16	1 13/16	1/8	2 13/16	5/32-	3 13/16	3/16	4 13/16	1/4	5 13/16
7/8	1/32-	7/8	1/16	1 7/8	1/8	2 7/8	5/32-	3 7/8	3/16	4 7/8	1/4	5 7/8
15/16	1/32-	15/16	3/32-	1 15/16	1/8	2 15/16	5/32-	3 15/16	7/32-	4 15/16	1/4	5 15/16

Inches	6" Rise	6" Slope	7" Rise	7" Slope	8" Rise	8" Slope	9" Rise	9" Slope	10" Rise	10" Slope	11" Rise	11" Slope
0	1/4	6	9/32	7	11/32-	8	3/8	9	13/32	10	15/32-	11
1/16	1/4	6 1/16	9/32	7 1/16	11/32-	8 1/16	3/8	9 1/16	13/32	10 1/16	15/32-	11 1/16
1/8	1/4	6 1/8	5/16	7 1/8	11/32-	8 1/8	3/8	9 1/8	7/16	10 1/8	15/32-	11 1/8
3/16	1/4	6 3/16	5/16	7 3/16	11/32-	8 3/16	3/8	9 3/16	7/16	10 3/16	15/32-	11 3/16
1/4	1/4	6 1/4	5/16	7 1/4	11/32	8 1/4	3/8	9 1/4	7/16	10 1/4	15/32	11 1/4
5/16	1/4	6 5/16	5/16	7 5/16	11/32	8 5/16	3/8	9 5/16	7/16	10 5/16	15/32	11 5/16
3/8	1/4	6 3/8	5/16	7 3/8	11/32	8 3/8	3/8	9 3/8	7/16	10 3/8	15/32	11 3/8
7/16	9/32-	6 7/16	5/16	7 7/16	11/32	8 7/16	13/32-	9 7/16	7/16	10 7/16	15/32	11 7/16
1/2	9/32-	6 1/2	5/16	7 1/2	11/32	8 1/2	13/32-	9 1/2	7/16	10 1/2	15/32	11 1/2
9/16	9/32-	6 9/16	5/16	7 9/16	11/32	8 9/16	13/32-	9 9/16	7/16	10 9/16	15/32	11 9/16
5/8	9/32-	6 5/8	5/16	7 5/8	3/8	8 5/8	13/32-	9 5/8	7/16	10 5/8	1/2	11 5/8
11/16	9/32-	6 11/16	5/16	7 11/16	3/8	8 11/16	13/32-	9 11/16	7/16	10 11/16	1/2	11 11/16
3/4	9/32-	6 3/4	5/16	7 3/4	3/8	8 3/4	13/32-	9 3/4	7/16	10 3/4	1/2	11 3/4
13/16	9/32-	6 13/16	5/16	7 13/16	3/8	8 13/16	13/32-	9 13/16	7/16	10 13/16	1/2	11 13/16
7/8	9/32-	6 7/8	5/16	7 7/8	3/8	8 7/8	13/32-	9 7/8	7/16	10 7/8	1/2	11 7/8
15/16	9/32-	6 15/16	11/32-	7 15/16	3/8	8 15/16	13/32-	9 15/16	15/32-	10 15/16	1/2	11 15/16

Feet	0' Rise	0' Slope	10' Rise	10' Slope	20' Rise	20' Slope	30' Rise	30' Slope
0	0	0	5	10-0 3/32	10	20-0 7/32-	1-3	30-0 5/16
1	1/2	1-0	5 1/2	11-0 1/8	10 1/2	21-0 7/32-	1-3 1/2	31-0 5/16
2	1	2-0 1/32-	6	12-0 1/8	11	22-0 7/32-	1-4	32-0 11/32-
3	1 1/2	3-0 1/32-	6 1/2	13-0 1/8	11 1/2	23-0 1/4	1-4 1/2	33-0 11/32
4	2	4-0 1/32-	7	14-0 5/32-	1-0	24-0 1/4	1-5	34-0 11/32
5	2 1/2	5-0 1/16	7 1/2	15-0 5/32-	1-0 1/2	25-0 1/4	1-5 1/2	35-0 3/8
6	3	6-0 1/16	8	16-0 5/32	1-1	26-0 9/32-	1-6	36-0 3/8
7	3 1/2	7-0 1/16	8 1/2	17-0 3/16	1-1 1/2	27-0 9/32-	1-6 1/2	37-0 3/8
8	4	8-0 3/32-	9	18-0 3/16	1-2	28-0 9/32	1-7	38-0 13/32
9	4 1/2	9-0 3/32-	9 1/2	19-0 3/16	1-2 1/2	29-0 5/16	1-7 1/2	39-0 13/32

A = 2° 23′ 09″; logsin A = 8.61941; logcos A = 9.99962; logtan A = 8.61979; logcot A = 1.38021

Ins.	12″ Rise	12″ Slope	13″ Rise	13″ Slope	14″ Rise	14″ Slope	15″ Rise	15″ Slope	16″ Rise	16″ Slope
0	1/2	1-0	17/32	1-1	19/32−	1-2	5/8	1-3	21/32	1-4
1/16	1/2	1-0 1/16	17/32	1-1 1/16	19/32−	1-2 1/16	5/8	1-3 1/16	21/32	1-4 1/16
1/8	1/2	1-0 1/8	9/16	1-1 1/8	19/32−	1-2 1/8	5/8	1-3 1/8	11/16	1-4 1/8
3/16	1/2	1-0 3/16	9/16	1-1 3/16	19/32−	1-2 3/16	5/8	1-3 3/16	11/16	1-4 3/16
1/4	1/2	1-0 1/4	9/16	1-1 1/4	19/32	1-2 1/4	5/8	1-3 1/4	11/16	1-4 1/4
5/16	1/2	1-0 5/16	9/16	1-1 5/16	19/32	1-2 5/16	5/8	1-3 5/16	11/16	1-4 5/16
3/8	1/2	1-0 3/8	9/16	1-1 3/8	19/32	1-2 3/8	5/8	1-3 3/8	11/16	1-4 3/8
7/16	17/32−	1-0 7/16	9/16	1-1 7/16	19/32	1-2 7/16	21/32−	1-3 7/16	11/16	1-4 7/16
1/2	17/32−	1-0 1/2	9/16	1-1 1/2	19/32	1-2 1/2	21/32−	1-3 1/2	11/16	1-4 1/2
9/16	17/32−	1-0 9/16	9/16	1-1 9/16	19/32	1-2 9/16	21/32−	1-3 9/16	11/16	1-4 9/16
5/8	17/32−	1-0 5/8	9/16	1-1 5/8	5/8	1-2 5/8	21/32−	1-3 5/8	11/16	1-4 5/8
11/16	17/32−	1-0 11/16	9/16	1-1 11/16	5/8	1-2 11/16	21/32−	1-3 11/16	11/16	1-4 11/16
3/4	17/32	1-0 3/4	9/16	1-1 3/4	5/8	1-2 3/4	21/32	1-3 3/4	11/16	1-4 3/4
13/16	17/32	1-0 13/16	9/16	1-1 13/16	5/8	1-2 13/16	21/32	1-3 13/16	11/16	1-4 13/16
7/8	17/32	1-0 7/8	9/16	1-1 7/8	5/8	1-2 7/8	21/32	1-3 7/8	11/16	1-4 7/8
15/16	17/32	1-0 15/16	19/32−	1-1 15/16	5/8	1-2 15/16	21/32	1-3 15/16	23/32−	1-4 15/16

Ins.	17″ Rise	17″ Slope	18″ Rise	18″ Slope	19″ Rise	19″ Slope	20″ Rise	20″ Slope	21″ Rise	21″ Slope
0	23/32−	1-5	3/4	1-6	25/32	1-7 1/32−	27/32−	1-8 1/32−	7/8	1-9 1/32−
1/16	23/32−	1-5 1/16	3/4	1-6 3/32−	25/32	1-7 3/32−	27/32−	1-8 3/32−	7/8	1-9 3/32−
1/8	23/32−	1-5 1/8	3/4	1-6 5/32−	13/16	1-7 5/32−	27/32−	1-8 5/32−	7/8	1-9 5/32−
3/16	23/32−	1-5 3/16	3/4	1-6 7/32−	13/16	1-7 7/32−	27/32−	1-8 7/32−	7/8	1-9 7/32−
1/4	23/32	1-5 1/4	3/4	1-6 9/32−	13/16	1-7 9/32−	27/32	1-8 9/32−	7/8	1-9 9/32−
5/16	23/32	1-5 5/16	3/4	1-6 11/32−	13/16	1-7 11/32−	27/32	1-8 11/32−	7/8	1-9 11/32−
3/8	23/32	1-5 3/8	3/4	1-6 13/32−	13/16	1-7 13/32−	27/32	1-8 13/32−	7/8	1-9 13/32−
7/16	23/32	1-5 7/16	25/32−	1-6 15/32−	13/16	1-7 15/32−	27/32	1-8 15/32−	29/32−	1-9 15/32−
1/2	23/32	1-5 1/2	25/32−	1-6 17/32−	13/16	1-7 17/32−	27/32	1-8 17/32−	29/32−	1-9 17/32−
9/16	23/32	1-5 9/16	25/32−	1-6 19/32−	13/16	1-7 19/32−	27/32	1-8 19/32−	29/32−	1-9 19/32−
5/8	3/4	1-5 5/8	25/32−	1-6 21/32−	13/16	1-7 21/32−	7/8	1-8 21/32−	29/32−	1-9 21/32−
11/16	3/4	1-5 11/16	25/32−	1-6 23/32−	13/16	1-7 23/32−	7/8	1-8 23/32−	29/32−	1-9 23/32−
3/4	3/4	1-5 3/4	25/32	1-6 25/32−	13/16	1-7 25/32−	7/8	1-8 25/32−	29/32	1-9 25/32−
13/16	3/4	1-5 13/16	25/32	1-6 27/32−	13/16	1-7 27/32−	7/8	1-8 27/32−	29/32	1-9 27/32−
7/8	3/4	1-5 7/8	25/32	1-6 29/32−	13/16	1-7 29/32−	7/8	1-8 29/32−	29/32	1-9 29/32−
15/16	3/4	1-5 15/16	25/32	1-6 31/32−	27/32−	1-7 31/32−	7/8	1-8 31/32−	29/32	1-9 31/32−

Feet	40′ Rise	40′ Slope	50′ Rise	50′ Slope	60′ Rise	60′ Slope	70′ Rise	70′ Slope
0	1-8	40-0 13/32	2-1	50-0 17/32−	2-6	60-0 5/8	2-11	70-0 23/32
1	1-8 1/2	41-0 7/16	2-1 1/2	51-0 17/32−	2-6 1/2	61-0 5/8	2-11 1/2	71-0 3/4
2	1-9	42-0 7/16	2-2	52-0 17/32	2-7	62-0 21/32−	3-0	72-0 3/4
3	1-9 1/2	43-0 7/16	2-2 1/2	53-0 9/16	2-7 1/2	63-0 21/32−	3-0 1/2	73-0 3/4
4	1-10	44-0 15/32−	2-3	54-0 9/16	2-8	64-0 21/32	3-1	74-0 25/32−
5	1-10 1/2	45-0 15/32−	2-3 1/2	55-0 9/16	2-8 1/2	65-0 11/16	3-1 1/2	75-0 25/32−
6	1-11	46-0 15/32	2-4	56-0 19/32−	2-9	66-0 11/16	3-2	76-0 25/32
7	1-11 1/2	47-0 1/2	2-4 1/2	57-0 19/32−	2-9 1/2	67-0 11/16	3-2 1/2	77-0 13/16
8	2-0	48-0 1/2	2-5	58-0 19/32	2-10	68-0 23/32−	3-3	78-0 13/16
9	2-0 1/2	49-0 1/2	2-5 1/2	59-0 5/8	2-10 1/2	69-0 23/32−	3-3 1/2	79-0 13/16

natsin A=0.0416305446; natcos A=0.9991330730; nattan A=0.0416666666; natcot A=24.0000000000

Inches	0" Rise	0" Slope	1" Rise	1" Slope	2" Rise	2" Slope	3" Rise	3" Slope	4" Rise	4" Slope	5" Rise	5" Slope
0	0	0	1⁄16	1	3⁄32	2	1⁄8	3	3⁄16	4	1⁄4	5
1⁄16	0	1⁄16	1⁄16	1 1⁄16	3⁄32	2 1⁄16	5⁄32—	3 1⁄16	3⁄16	4 1⁄16	1⁄4	5 1⁄16
1⁄8	0	1⁄8	1⁄16	1 1⁄8	3⁄32	2 1⁄8	5⁄32—	3 1⁄8	3⁄16	4 1⁄8	1⁄4	5 1⁄8
3⁄16	0	3⁄16	1⁄16	1 3⁄16	3⁄32	2 3⁄16	5⁄32—	3 3⁄16	3⁄16	4 3⁄16	1⁄4	5 3⁄16
1⁄4	0	1⁄4	1⁄16	1 1⁄4	3⁄32	2 1⁄4	5⁄32—	3 1⁄4	3⁄16	4 1⁄4	1⁄4	5 1⁄4
5⁄16	0	5⁄16	1⁄16	1 5⁄16	3⁄32	2 5⁄16	5⁄32—	3 5⁄16	3⁄16	4 5⁄16	1⁄4	5 5⁄16
3⁄8	1⁄32—	3⁄8	1⁄16	1 3⁄8	1⁄8	2 3⁄8	5⁄32—	3 3⁄8	7⁄32	4 3⁄8	1⁄4	5 3⁄8
7⁄16	1⁄32—	7⁄16	1⁄16	1 7⁄16	1⁄8	2 7⁄16	5⁄32—	3 7⁄16	7⁄32	4 7⁄16	1⁄4	5 7⁄16
1⁄2	1⁄32—	1⁄2	1⁄16	1 1⁄2	1⁄8	2 1⁄2	5⁄32—	3 1⁄2	7⁄32	4 1⁄2	1⁄4	5 1⁄2
9⁄16	1⁄32—	9⁄16	1⁄16	1 9⁄16	1⁄8	2 9⁄16	5⁄32—	3 9⁄16	7⁄32	4 9⁄16	1⁄4	5 9⁄16
5⁄8	1⁄32—	5⁄8	1⁄16	1 5⁄8	1⁄8	2 5⁄8	5⁄32—	3 5⁄8	7⁄32	4 5⁄8	1⁄4	5 5⁄8
11⁄16	1⁄32	11⁄16	3⁄32—	1 11⁄16	1⁄8	2 11⁄16	3⁄16	3 11⁄16	7⁄32	4 11⁄16	9⁄32—	5 11⁄16
3⁄4	1⁄32	3⁄4	3⁄32—	1 3⁄4	1⁄8	2 3⁄4	3⁄16	3 3⁄4	7⁄32	4 3⁄4	9⁄32—	5 3⁄4
13⁄16	1⁄32	13⁄16	3⁄32—	1 13⁄16	1⁄8	2 13⁄16	3⁄16	3 13⁄16	7⁄32	4 13⁄16	9⁄32—	5 13⁄16
7⁄8	1⁄32	7⁄8	3⁄32—	1 7⁄8	1⁄8	2 7⁄8	3⁄16	3 7⁄8	7⁄32	4 7⁄8	9⁄32—	5 7⁄8
15⁄16	1⁄32	15⁄16	3⁄32—	1 15⁄16	1⁄8	2 15⁄16	3⁄16	3 15⁄16	7⁄32	4 15⁄16	9⁄32—	5 15⁄16

Inches	6" Rise	6" Slope	7" Rise	7" Slope	8" Rise	8" Slope	9" Rise	9" Slope	10" Rise	10" Slope	11" Rise	11" Slope
0	9⁄32	6	5⁄16	7	3⁄8	8	7⁄16	9	15⁄32	10	1⁄2	11
1⁄16	9⁄32	6 1⁄16	11⁄32	7 1⁄16	3⁄8	8 1⁄16	7⁄16	9 1⁄16	15⁄32	10 1⁄16	17⁄32—	11 1⁄16
1⁄8	9⁄32	6 1⁄8	11⁄32	7 1⁄8	3⁄8	8 1⁄8	7⁄16	9 1⁄8	15⁄32	10 1⁄8	17⁄32—	11 1⁄8
3⁄16	9⁄32	6 3⁄16	11⁄32	7 3⁄16	3⁄8	8 3⁄16	7⁄16	9 3⁄16	15⁄32	10 3⁄16	17⁄32—	11 3⁄16
1⁄4	9⁄32	6 1⁄4	11⁄32	7 1⁄4	3⁄8	8 1⁄4	7⁄16	9 1⁄4	15⁄32	10 1⁄4	17⁄32—	11 1⁄4
5⁄16	9⁄32	6 5⁄16	11⁄32	7 5⁄16	3⁄8	8 5⁄16	7⁄16	9 5⁄16	15⁄32	10 5⁄16	17⁄32—	11 5⁄16
3⁄8	5⁄16	6 3⁄8	11⁄32	7 3⁄8	13⁄32	8 3⁄8	7⁄16	9 3⁄8	1⁄2	10 3⁄8	17⁄32—	11 3⁄8
7⁄16	5⁄16	6 7⁄16	11⁄32	7 7⁄16	13⁄32	8 7⁄16	7⁄16	9 7⁄16	1⁄2	10 7⁄16	17⁄32—	11 7⁄16
1⁄2	5⁄16	6 1⁄2	11⁄32	7 1⁄2	13⁄32—	8 1⁄2	7⁄16	9 1⁄2	1⁄2	10 1⁄2	17⁄32—	11 1⁄2
9⁄16	5⁄16	6 9⁄16	11⁄32	7 9⁄16	13⁄32—	8 9⁄16	7⁄16	9 9⁄16	1⁄2	10 9⁄16	17⁄32—	11 9⁄16
5⁄8	5⁄16	6 5⁄8	11⁄32	7 5⁄8	13⁄32—	8 5⁄8	7⁄16	9 5⁄8	1⁄2	10 5⁄8	9⁄16	11 5⁄8
11⁄16	5⁄16	6 11⁄16	3⁄8	7 11⁄16	13⁄32—	8 11⁄16	15⁄32—	9 11⁄16	1⁄2	10 11⁄16	9⁄16	11 11⁄16
3⁄4	5⁄16	6 3⁄4	3⁄8	7 3⁄4	13⁄32—	8 3⁄4	15⁄32—	9 3⁄4	1⁄2	10 3⁄4	9⁄16	11 3⁄4
13⁄16	5⁄16	6 13⁄16	3⁄8	7 13⁄16	13⁄32—	8 13⁄16	15⁄32—	9 13⁄16	1⁄2	10 13⁄16	9⁄16	11 13⁄16
7⁄8	5⁄16	6 7⁄8	3⁄8	7 7⁄8	13⁄32—	8 7⁄8	15⁄32—	9 7⁄8	1⁄2	10 7⁄8	9⁄16	11 7⁄8
15⁄16	5⁄16	6 15⁄16	3⁄8	7 15⁄16	13⁄32—	8 15⁄16	15⁄32—	9 15⁄16	1⁄2	10 15⁄16	9⁄16	11 15⁄16

Feet	0' Rise	0' Slope	10' Rise	10' Slope	20' Rise	20' Slope	30' Rise	30' Slope
0	0	0	5 5⁄8	10-0 1⁄8	11 1⁄4	20-0 1⁄4	1-4 7⁄8	30-0 13⁄32
1	9⁄16	1-0	6 3⁄16	11-0 5⁄32—	11 13⁄16	21-0 9⁄32—	1-5 7⁄16	31-0 13⁄32
2	1 1⁄8	2-0 1⁄32—	6 3⁄4	12-0 5⁄32	1-0 3⁄8	22-0 9⁄32	1-6	32-0 13⁄32
3	1 11⁄16	3-0 1⁄32—	7 5⁄16	13-0 5⁄32—	1-0 15⁄16	23-0 5⁄16	1-6 9⁄16	33-0 7⁄16
4	2 1⁄4	4-0 1⁄16	7 7⁄8	14-0 3⁄16	1-1 1⁄2	24-0 5⁄16	1-7 1⁄8	34-0 7⁄16
5	2 13⁄16	5-0 1⁄16	8 7⁄16	15-0 3⁄16	1-2 1⁄16	25-0 11⁄32—	1-7 11⁄16	35-0 15⁄32—
6	3 3⁄8	6-0 3⁄32—	9	16-0 7⁄32—	1-2 5⁄8	26-0 11⁄32—	1-8 1⁄4	36-0 15⁄32
7	3 15⁄16	7-0 3⁄32—	9 9⁄16	17-0 7⁄32—	1-3 3⁄16	27-0 11⁄32—	1-8 13⁄16	37-0 1⁄2
8	4 1⁄2	8-0 3⁄32—	10 1⁄8	18-0 1⁄4	1-3 3⁄4	28-0 3⁄8	1-9 3⁄8	38-0 1⁄2
9	5 1⁄16	9-0 1⁄8	10 11⁄16	19-0 1⁄4	1-4 5⁄16	29-0 3⁄8	1-9 15⁄16	39-0 1⁄2

A = 2° 41′ 02″; logsin A = 8.67046; logcos A = 9.99952; logtan A = 8.67094; logcot A = 1.32906

Ins.	12″ Rise	Slope	13″ Rise	Slope	14″ Rise	Slope	15″ Rise	Slope	16″ Rise	Slope
0	9/16	1-0	5/8	1-1	21/32	1-2	11/16	1-3 1/32	3/4	1-4 1/32
1/16	9/16	1-0 1/16	5/8	1-1 1/16	21/32	1-2 1/16	23/32	1-3 3/32	3/4	1-4 3/32
1/8	9/16	1-0 1/8	5/8	1-1 1/8	21/32	1-2 1/8	23/32	1-3 5/32	3/4	1-4 5/32
3/16	9/16	1-0 3/16	5/8	1-1 3/16	21/32	1-2 3/16	23/32	1-3 7/32	3/4	1-4 7/32
1/4	9/16	1-0 1/4	5/8	1-1 1/4	21/32	1-2 9/32	23/32	1-3 9/32	3/4	1-4 9/32
5/16	9/16	1-0 5/16	5/8	1-1 5/16	21/32	1-2 11/32	23/32	1-3 11/32	3/4	1-4 11/32
3/8	19/32	1-0 3/8	5/8	1-1 3/8	11/16	1-2 13/32	23/32	1-3 13/32	25/32	1-4 13/32
7/16	19/32	1-0 7/16	5/8	1-1 7/16	11/16	1-2 15/32	23/32	1-3 15/32	25/32	1-4 15/32
1/2	19/32	1-0 1/2	5/8	1-1 1/2	11/16	1-2 17/32	23/32	1-3 17/32	25/32	1-4 17/32
9/16	19/32	1-0 9/16	5/8	1-1 9/16	11/16	1-2 19/32	23/32	1-3 19/32	25/32	1-4 19/32
5/8	19/32	1-0 5/8	5/8	1-1 5/8	11/16	1-2 21/32	23/32	1-3 21/32	25/32	1-4 21/32
11/16	19/32	1-0 11/16	21/32	1-1 11/16	11/16	1-2 23/32	3/4	1-3 23/32	25/32	1-4 23/32
3/4	19/32	1-0 3/4	21/32	1-1 3/4	11/16	1-2 25/32	3/4	1-3 25/32	25/32	1-4 25/32
13/16	19/32	1-0 13/16	21/32	1-1 13/16	11/16	1-2 27/32	3/4	1-3 27/32	25/32	1-4 27/32
7/8	19/32	1-0 7/8	21/32	1-1 7/8	11/16	1-2 29/32	3/4	1-3 29/32	25/32	1-4 29/32
15/16	19/32	1-0 15/16	21/32	1-1 15/16	11/16	1-2 31/32	3/4	1-3 31/32	25/32	1-4 31/32

Ins.	17″ Rise	Slope	18″ Rise	Slope	19″ Rise	Slope	20″ Rise	Slope	21″ Rise	Slope
0	13/16	1-5 1/32	27/32	1-6 1/32	7/8	1-7 1/32	15/16	1-8 1/32	1	1-9 1/32
1/16	13/16	1-5 3/32	27/32	1-6 3/32	29/32	1-7 3/32	15/16	1-8 3/32	1	1-9 3/32
1/8	13/16	1-5 5/32	27/32	1-6 5/32	29/32	1-7 5/32	15/16	1-8 5/32	1	1-9 5/32
3/16	13/16	1-5 7/32	27/32	1-6 7/32	29/32	1-7 7/32	15/16	1-8 7/32	1	1-9 7/32
1/4	13/16	1-5 9/32	27/32	1-6 9/32	29/32	1-7 9/32	15/16	1-8 9/32	1	1-9 9/32
5/16	13/16	1-5 11/32	27/32	1-6 11/32	29/32	1-7 11/32	15/16	1-8 11/32	1	1-9 11/32
3/8	13/16	1-5 13/32	7/8	1-6 13/32	29/32	1-7 13/32	31/32	1-8 13/32	1	1-9 13/32
7/16	13/16	1-5 15/32	7/8	1-6 15/32	7/8	1-7 15/32	31/32	1-8 15/32	1	1-9 15/32
1/2	13/16	1-5 17/32	7/8	1-6 17/32	29/32	1-7 17/32	31/32	1-8 17/32	1	1-9 17/32
9/16	13/16	1-5 19/32	7/8	1-6 19/32	29/32	1-7 19/32	31/32	1-8 19/32	1	1-9 19/32
5/8	13/16	1-5 21/32	7/8	1-6 21/32	29/32	1-7 21/32	31/32	1-8 21/32	1	1-9 21/32
11/16	27/32	1-5 23/32	7/8	1-6 23/32	15/16	1-7 23/32	31/32	1-8 23/32	1 1/32	1-9 23/32
3/4	27/32	1-5 25/32	7/8	1-6 25/32	15/16	1-7 25/32	31/32	1-8 25/32	1 1/32	1-9 25/32
13/16	27/32	1-5 27/32	7/8	1-6 27/32	15/16	1-7 27/32	31/32	1-8 27/32	1 1/32	1-9 27/32
7/8	27/32	1-5 29/32	7/8	1-6 29/32	15/16	1-7 29/32	31/32	1-8 29/32	1 1/32	1-9 29/32
15/16	27/32	1-5 31/32	7/8	1-6 31/32	15/16	1-7 31/32	31/32	1-8 31/32	1 1/32	1-9 31/32

Feet	40′ Rise	Slope	50′ Rise	Slope	60′ Rise	Slope	70′ Rise	Slope
0	1-10 1/2	40-0 17/32	2-4 1/8	50-0 21/32	2-9 3/4	60-0 25/32	3-3 3/8	70-0 15/16
1	1-11 1/16	41-0 17/32	2-4 11/16	51-0 11/16	2-10 5/16	61-0 13/16	3-3 15/16	71-0 15/16
2	1-11 5/8	42-0 9/16	2-5 1/4	52-0 11/16	2-10 7/8	62-0 13/16	3-4 1/2	72-0 15/16
3	2-0 3/16	43-0 9/16	2-5 13/16	53-0 11/16	2-11 7/16	63-0 27/32	3-5 1/16	73-0 31/32
4	2-0 3/4	44-0 19/32	2-6 3/8	54-0 23/32	3-0	64-0 27/32	3-5 5/8	74-0 31/32
5	2-1 5/16	45-0 19/32	2-6 15/16	55-0 23/32	3-0 9/16	65-0 27/32	3-6 3/16	75-1
6	2-1 7/8	46-0 19/32	2-7 1/2	56-0 3/4	3-1 1/8	66-0 7/8	3-6 3/4	76-1
7	2-2 7/16	47-0 5/8	2-8 1/16	57-0 3/4	3-1 11/16	67-0 7/8	3-7 5/16	77-1
8	2-3	48-0 5/8	2-8 5/8	58-0 3/4	3-2 1/4	68-0 29/32	3-7 7/8	78-1 1/32
9	2-3 9/16	49-0 21/32	2-9 3/16	59-0 25/32	3-2 13/16	69-0 29/32	3-8 7/16	79-1 1/32

natsin A=0.0468235862; natcos A=0.9989031743; nattan A=0.0468750000; natcot A=21.3333333333

Inches	0" Rise	0" Slope	1" Rise	1" Slope	2" Rise	2" Slope	3" Rise	3" Slope	4" Rise	4" Slope	5" Rise	5" Slope
0	0	0	1/16	1	3/32	2	5/32	3	7/32	4	1/4	5
1/16	0	1/16	1/16	1 1/16	3/32	2 1/16	5/32	3 1/16	7/32	4 1/16	1/4	5 1/16
1/8	0	1/8	1/16	1 1/8	1/8	2 1/8	5/32	3 1/8	7/32	4 1/8	9/32	5 1/8
3/16	0	3/16	1/16	1 3/16	1/8	2 3/16	5/32	3 3/16	7/32	4 3/16	9/32	5 3/16
1/4	0	1/4	1/16	1 1/4	1/8	2 1/4	5/32	3 1/4	7/32	4 1/4	9/32	5 1/4
5/16	1/32	5/16	1/16	1 5/16	1/8	2 5/16	3/16	3 5/16	7/32	4 5/16	9/32	5 5/16
3/8	1/32	3/8	1/16	1 3/8	1/8	2 3/8	3/16	3 3/8	7/32	4 3/8	9/32	5 3/8
7/16	1/32	7/16	1/16	1 7/16	1/8	2 7/16	3/16	3 7/16	7/32	4 7/16	9/32	5 7/16
1/2	1/32	1/2	1/16	1 1/2	1/8	2 1/2	3/16	3 1/2	1/4	4 1/2	9/32	5 1/2
9/16	1/32	9/16	3/32	1 9/16	1/8	2 9/16	3/16	3 9/16	1/4	4 9/16	9/32	5 9/16
5/8	1/32	5/8	3/32	1 5/8	1/8	2 5/8	3/16	3 5/8	1/4	4 5/8	9/32	5 5/8
11/16	1/32	11/16	3/32	1 11/16	1/8	2 11/16	3/16	3 11/16	1/4	4 11/16	9/32	5 11/16
3/4	1/32	3/4	3/32	1 3/4	5/32	2 3/4	3/16	3 3/4	1/4	4 3/4	5/16	5 3/4
13/16	1/32	13/16	3/32	1 13/16	5/32	2 13/16	3/16	3 13/16	1/4	4 13/16	5/16	5 13/16
7/8	1/32	7/8	3/32	1 7/8	5/32	2 7/8	3/16	3 7/8	1/4	4 7/8	5/16	5 7/8
15/16	1/16	15/16	3/32	1 15/16	5/32	2 15/16	7/32	3 15/16	1/4	4 15/16	5/16	5 15/16

Inches	6" Rise	6" Slope	7" Rise	7" Slope	8" Rise	8" Slope	9" Rise	9" Slope	10" Rise	10" Slope	11" Rise	11" Slope
0	5/16	6	3/8	7	13/32	8	15/32	9	17/32	10	9/16	11
1/16	5/16	6 1/16	3/8	7 1/16	13/32	8 1/16	15/32	9 1/16	17/32	10 1/16	9/16	11 1/16
1/8	5/16	6 1/8	3/8	7 1/8	7/16	8 1/8	15/32	9 1/8	17/32	10 1/8	19/32	11 1/8
3/16	5/16	6 3/16	3/8	7 3/16	7/16	8 3/16	15/32	9 3/16	17/32	10 3/16	19/32	11 3/16
1/4	5/16	6 1/4	3/8	7 1/4	7/16	8 1/4	15/32	9 1/4	17/32	10 1/4	19/32	11 1/4
5/16	11/32	6 5/16	3/8	7 5/16	7/16	8 5/16	1/2	9 5/16	17/32	10 5/16	19/32	11 5/16
3/8	11/32	6 3/8	3/8	7 3/8	7/16	8 3/8	1/2	9 3/8	17/32	10 3/8	19/32	11 3/8
7/16	11/32	6 7/16	3/8	7 7/16	7/16	8 7/16	1/2	9 7/16	17/32	10 7/16	19/32	11 7/16
1/2	11/32	6 1/2	3/8	7 1/2	7/16	8 1/2	1/2	9 1/2	9/16	10 1/2	19/32	11 1/2
9/16	11/32	6 9/16	13/32	7 9/16	7/16	8 9/16	1/2	9 9/16	9/16	10 9/16	19/32	11 19/32
5/8	11/32	6 5/8	13/32	7 5/8	7/16	8 5/8	1/2	9 5/8	9/16	10 5/8	19/32	11 21/32
11/16	11/32	6 11/16	13/32	7 11/16	7/16	8 11/16	1/2	9 11/16	9/16	10 11/16	19/32	11 23/32
3/4	11/32	6 3/4	13/32	7 3/4	15/32	8 3/4	1/2	9 3/4	9/16	10 3/4	5/8	11 25/32
13/16	11/32	6 13/16	13/32	7 13/16	15/32	8 13/16	1/2	9 13/16	9/16	10 13/16	5/8	11 27/32
7/8	11/32	6 7/8	13/32	7 7/8	15/32	8 7/8	1/2	9 7/8	9/16	10 7/8	5/8	11 29/32
15/16	3/8	6 15/16	13/32	7 15/16	15/32	8 15/16	17/32	9 15/16	9/16	10 15/16	5/8	11 31/32

Feet	0' Rise	0' Slope	10' Rise	10' Slope	20' Rise	20' Slope	30' Rise	30' Slope
0	0	0	6 1/4	10-0 5/32	1-0 1/2	20-0 5/16	1-6 3/4	30-0 1/2
1	5/8	1-0 1/32	6 7/8	11-0 3/16	1-1 1/8	21-0 11/32	1-7 3/8	31-0 1/2
2	1 1/4	2-0 1/32	7 1/2	12-0 3/16	1-1 3/4	22-0 11/32	1-8	32-0 17/32
3	1 7/8	3-0 1/16	8 1/8	13-0 7/32	1-2 3/8	23-0 3/8	1-8 5/8	33-0 17/32
4	2 1/2	4-0 1/16	8 3/4	14-0 7/32	1-3	24-0 3/8	1-9 1/4	34-0 9/16
5	3 1/8	5-0 3/32	9 3/8	15-0 1/4	1-3 5/8	25-0 13/32	1-9 7/8	35-0 9/16
6	3 3/4	6-0 3/32	10	16-0 1/4	1-4 1/4	26-0 7/16	1-10 1/2	36-0 19/32
7	4 3/8	7-0 1/8	10 5/8	17-0 9/32	1-4 7/8	27-0 7/16	1-11 1/8	37-0 19/32
8	5	8-0 1/8	11 1/4	18-0 9/32	1-5 1/2	28-0 15/32	1-11 3/4	38-0 5/8
9	5 5/8	9-0 5/32	11 7/8	19-0 5/16	1-6 1/4	29-0 15/32	2-0 5/8	39-0 5/8

A = 2° 58′ 53″; logsin A = 8.71611; logcos A = 9.99941; logtan A = 8.71670; logcot A = 1.28330

Ins.	12″ Rise	12″ Slope	13″ Rise	13″ Slope	14″ Rise	14″ Slope	15″ Rise	15″ Slope	16″ Rise	16″ Slope
0	$\frac{5}{8}$	$1\text{-}0\frac{1}{32}$	$\frac{11}{16}$	$1\text{-}1\frac{1}{32}$	$\frac{23}{32}$	$1\text{-}2\frac{1}{32}$	$\frac{25}{32}$	$1\text{-}3\frac{1}{32}$	$\frac{27}{32}$	$1\text{-}4\frac{1}{32}$
$\frac{1}{16}$	$\frac{5}{8}$	$1\text{-}0\frac{3}{32}$	$\frac{11}{16}$	$1\text{-}1\frac{3}{32}$	$\frac{23}{32}$	$1\text{-}2\frac{3}{32}$	$\frac{25}{32}$	$1\text{-}3\frac{3}{32}$	$\frac{27}{32}$	$1\text{-}4\frac{3}{32}$
$\frac{1}{8}$	$\frac{5}{8}$	$1\text{-}0\frac{5}{32}$	$\frac{11}{16}$	$1\text{-}1\frac{5}{32}$	$\frac{3}{4}$	$1\text{-}2\frac{5}{32}$	$\frac{25}{32}$	$1\text{-}3\frac{5}{32}$	$\frac{27}{32}$	$1\text{-}4\frac{5}{32}$
$\frac{3}{16}$	$\frac{5}{8}$	$1\text{-}0\frac{7}{32}$	$\frac{11}{16}$	$1\text{-}1\frac{7}{32}$	$\frac{3}{4}$	$1\text{-}2\frac{7}{32}$	$\frac{25}{32}$	$1\text{-}3\frac{7}{32}$	$\frac{27}{32}$	$1\text{-}4\frac{7}{32}$
$\frac{1}{4}$	$\frac{5}{8}$	$1\text{-}0\frac{9}{32}$	$\frac{11}{16}$	$1\text{-}1\frac{9}{32}$	$\frac{3}{4}$	$1\text{-}2\frac{9}{32}$	$\frac{25}{32}$	$1\text{-}3\frac{9}{32}$	$\frac{27}{32}$	$1\text{-}4\frac{9}{32}$
$\frac{5}{16}$	$\frac{21}{32}$	$1\text{-}0\frac{11}{32}$	$\frac{11}{16}$	$1\text{-}1\frac{11}{32}$	$\frac{3}{4}$	$1\text{-}2\frac{11}{32}$	$\frac{13}{16}$	$1\text{-}3\frac{11}{32}$	$\frac{27}{32}$	$1\text{-}4\frac{11}{32}$
$\frac{3}{8}$	$\frac{21}{32}$	$1\text{-}0\frac{13}{32}$	$\frac{11}{16}$	$1\text{-}1\frac{13}{32}$	$\frac{3}{4}$	$1\text{-}2\frac{13}{32}$	$\frac{13}{16}$	$1\text{-}3\frac{13}{32}$	$\frac{27}{32}$	$1\text{-}4\frac{13}{32}$
$\frac{7}{16}$	$\frac{21}{32}$	$1\text{-}0\frac{15}{32}$	$\frac{11}{16}$	$1\text{-}1\frac{15}{32}$	$\frac{3}{4}$	$1\text{-}2\frac{15}{32}$	$\frac{13}{16}$	$1\text{-}3\frac{15}{32}$	$\frac{27}{32}$	$1\text{-}4\frac{15}{32}$
$\frac{1}{2}$	$\frac{21}{32}$	$1\text{-}0\frac{17}{32}$	$\frac{11}{16}$	$1\text{-}1\frac{17}{32}$	$\frac{3}{4}$	$1\text{-}2\frac{17}{32}$	$\frac{13}{16}$	$1\text{-}3\frac{17}{32}$	$\frac{7}{8}$	$1\text{-}4\frac{17}{32}$
$\frac{9}{16}$	$\frac{21}{32}$	$1\text{-}0\frac{19}{32}$	$\frac{23}{32}$	$1\text{-}1\frac{19}{32}$	$\frac{3}{4}$	$1\text{-}2\frac{19}{32}$	$\frac{13}{16}$	$1\text{-}3\frac{19}{32}$	$\frac{7}{8}$	$1\text{-}4\frac{19}{32}$
$\frac{5}{8}$	$\frac{21}{32}$	$1\text{-}0\frac{21}{32}$	$\frac{23}{32}$	$1\text{-}1\frac{21}{32}$	$\frac{3}{4}$	$1\text{-}2\frac{21}{32}$	$\frac{13}{16}$	$1\text{-}3\frac{21}{32}$	$\frac{7}{8}$	$1\text{-}4\frac{21}{32}$
$\frac{11}{16}$	$\frac{21}{32}$	$1\text{-}0\frac{23}{32}$	$\frac{23}{32}$	$1\text{-}1\frac{23}{32}$	$\frac{3}{4}$	$1\text{-}2\frac{23}{32}$	$\frac{13}{16}$	$1\text{-}3\frac{23}{32}$	$\frac{7}{8}$	$1\text{-}4\frac{23}{32}$
$\frac{3}{4}$	$\frac{21}{32}$	$1\text{-}0\frac{25}{32}$	$\frac{23}{32}$	$1\text{-}1\frac{25}{32}$	$\frac{25}{32}$	$1\text{-}2\frac{25}{32}$	$\frac{13}{16}$	$1\text{-}3\frac{25}{32}$	$\frac{7}{8}$	$1\text{-}4\frac{25}{32}$
$\frac{13}{16}$	$\frac{21}{32}$	$1\text{-}0\frac{27}{32}$	$\frac{23}{32}$	$1\text{-}1\frac{27}{32}$	$\frac{25}{32}$	$1\text{-}2\frac{27}{32}$	$\frac{13}{16}$	$1\text{-}3\frac{27}{32}$	$\frac{7}{8}$	$1\text{-}4\frac{27}{32}$
$\frac{7}{8}$	$\frac{21}{32}$	$1\text{-}0\frac{29}{32}$	$\frac{23}{32}$	$1\text{-}1\frac{29}{32}$	$\frac{25}{32}$	$1\text{-}2\frac{29}{32}$	$\frac{13}{16}$	$1\text{-}3\frac{29}{32}$	$\frac{7}{8}$	$1\text{-}4\frac{29}{32}$
$\frac{15}{16}$	$\frac{11}{16}$	$1\text{-}0\frac{31}{32}$	$\frac{23}{32}$	$1\text{-}1\frac{31}{32}$	$\frac{25}{32}$	$1\text{-}2\frac{31}{32}$	$\frac{27}{32}$	$1\text{-}3\frac{31}{32}$	$\frac{7}{8}$	$1\text{-}4\frac{31}{32}$

Ins.	17″ Rise	17″ Slope	18″ Rise	18″ Slope	19″ Rise	19″ Slope	20″ Rise	20″ Slope	21″ Rise	21″ Slope
0	$\frac{7}{8}$	$1\text{-}5\frac{1}{32}$	$\frac{15}{16}$	$1\text{-}6\frac{1}{32}$	1	$1\text{-}7\frac{1}{32}$	$1\frac{1}{32}$	$1\text{-}8\frac{1}{32}$	$1\frac{3}{32}$	$1\text{-}9\frac{1}{32}$
$\frac{1}{16}$	$\frac{7}{8}$	$1\text{-}5\frac{3}{32}$	$\frac{15}{16}$	$1\text{-}6\frac{3}{32}$	1	$1\text{-}7\frac{3}{32}$	$1\frac{1}{32}$	$1\text{-}8\frac{3}{32}$	$1\frac{3}{32}$	$1\text{-}9\frac{3}{32}$
$\frac{1}{8}$	$\frac{29}{32}$	$1\text{-}5\frac{5}{32}$	$\frac{15}{16}$	$1\text{-}6\frac{5}{32}$	1	$1\text{-}7\frac{5}{32}$	$1\frac{1}{16}$	$1\text{-}8\frac{5}{32}$	$1\frac{3}{32}$	$1\text{-}9\frac{5}{32}$
$\frac{3}{16}$	$\frac{29}{32}$	$1\text{-}5\frac{7}{32}$	$\frac{15}{16}$	$1\text{-}6\frac{7}{32}$	1	$1\text{-}7\frac{7}{32}$	$1\frac{1}{16}$	$1\text{-}8\frac{7}{32}$	$1\frac{3}{32}$	$1\text{-}9\frac{7}{32}$
$\frac{1}{4}$	$\frac{29}{32}$	$1\text{-}5\frac{9}{32}$	$\frac{15}{16}$	$1\text{-}6\frac{9}{32}$	1	$1\text{-}7\frac{9}{32}$	$1\frac{1}{16}$	$1\text{-}8\frac{9}{32}$	$1\frac{3}{32}$	$1\text{-}9\frac{9}{32}$
$\frac{5}{16}$	$\frac{29}{32}$	$1\text{-}5\frac{11}{32}$	$\frac{31}{32}$	$1\text{-}6\frac{11}{32}$	1	$1\text{-}7\frac{11}{32}$	$1\frac{1}{16}$	$1\text{-}8\frac{11}{32}$	$1\frac{1}{8}$	$1\text{-}9\frac{11}{32}$
$\frac{3}{8}$	$\frac{29}{32}$	$1\text{-}5\frac{13}{32}$	$\frac{31}{32}$	$1\text{-}6\frac{13}{32}$	1	$1\text{-}7\frac{13}{32}$	$1\frac{1}{16}$	$1\text{-}8\frac{13}{32}$	$1\frac{1}{8}$	$1\text{-}9\frac{13}{32}$
$\frac{7}{16}$	$\frac{29}{32}$	$1\text{-}5\frac{15}{32}$	$\frac{31}{32}$	$1\text{-}6\frac{15}{32}$	1	$1\text{-}7\frac{15}{32}$	$1\frac{1}{16}$	$1\text{-}8\frac{15}{32}$	$1\frac{1}{8}$	$1\text{-}9\frac{15}{32}$
$\frac{1}{2}$	$\frac{29}{32}$	$1\text{-}5\frac{17}{32}$	$\frac{31}{32}$	$1\text{-}6\frac{17}{32}$	1	$1\text{-}7\frac{17}{32}$	$1\frac{1}{16}$	$1\text{-}8\frac{17}{32}$	$1\frac{1}{8}$	$1\text{-}9\frac{17}{32}$
$\frac{9}{16}$	$\frac{29}{32}$	$1\text{-}5\frac{19}{32}$	$\frac{31}{32}$	$1\text{-}6\frac{19}{32}$	$1\frac{1}{32}$	$1\text{-}7\frac{19}{32}$	$1\frac{1}{16}$	$1\text{-}8\frac{19}{32}$	$1\frac{1}{8}$	$1\text{-}9\frac{19}{32}$
$\frac{5}{8}$	$\frac{29}{32}$	$1\text{-}5\frac{21}{32}$	$\frac{31}{32}$	$1\text{-}6\frac{21}{32}$	$1\frac{1}{32}$	$1\text{-}7\frac{21}{32}$	$1\frac{1}{16}$	$1\text{-}8\frac{21}{32}$	$1\frac{1}{8}$	$1\text{-}9\frac{21}{32}$
$\frac{11}{16}$	$\frac{29}{32}$	$1\text{-}5\frac{23}{32}$	$\frac{31}{32}$	$1\text{-}6\frac{23}{32}$	$1\frac{1}{32}$	$1\text{-}7\frac{23}{32}$	$1\frac{1}{16}$	$1\text{-}8\frac{23}{32}$	$1\frac{1}{8}$	$1\text{-}9\frac{23}{32}$
$\frac{3}{4}$	$\frac{15}{16}$	$1\text{-}5\frac{25}{32}$	$\frac{31}{32}$	$1\text{-}6\frac{25}{32}$	$1\frac{1}{32}$	$1\text{-}7\frac{25}{32}$	$1\frac{3}{32}$	$1\text{-}8\frac{25}{32}$	$1\frac{1}{8}$	$1\text{-}9\frac{25}{32}$
$\frac{13}{16}$	$\frac{15}{16}$	$1\text{-}5\frac{27}{32}$	$\frac{31}{32}$	$1\text{-}6\frac{27}{32}$	$1\frac{1}{32}$	$1\text{-}7\frac{27}{32}$	$1\frac{3}{32}$	$1\text{-}8\frac{27}{32}$	$1\frac{1}{8}$	$1\text{-}9\frac{27}{32}$
$\frac{7}{8}$	$\frac{15}{16}$	$1\text{-}5\frac{29}{32}$	$\frac{31}{32}$	$1\text{-}6\frac{29}{32}$	$1\frac{1}{32}$	$1\text{-}7\frac{29}{32}$	$1\frac{3}{32}$	$1\text{-}8\frac{29}{32}$	$1\frac{1}{8}$	$1\text{-}9\frac{29}{32}$
$\frac{15}{16}$	$\frac{15}{16}$	$1\text{-}5\frac{31}{32}$	1	$1\text{-}6\frac{31}{32}$	$1\frac{1}{32}$	$1\text{-}7\frac{31}{32}$	$1\frac{3}{32}$	$1\text{-}8\frac{31}{32}$	$1\frac{5}{32}$	$1\text{-}9\frac{31}{32}$

Feet	40′ Rise	40′ Slope	50′ Rise	50′ Slope	60′ Rise	60′ Slope	70′ Rise	70′ Slope
0	$2\text{-}1$	$40\text{-}0\frac{21}{32}$	$2\text{-}7\frac{1}{4}$	$50\text{-}0\frac{13}{16}$	$3\text{-}1\frac{1}{2}$	$60\text{-}0\frac{31}{32}$	$3\text{-}7\frac{3}{4}$	$70\text{-}1\frac{1}{8}$
1	$2\text{-}1\frac{5}{8}$	$41\text{-}0\frac{21}{32}$	$2\text{-}7\frac{7}{8}$	$51\text{-}0\frac{27}{32}$	$3\text{-}2\frac{1}{8}$	$61\text{-}1$	$3\text{-}8\frac{3}{8}$	$71\text{-}1\frac{5}{32}$
2	$2\text{-}2\frac{1}{4}$	$42\text{-}0\frac{11}{16}$	$2\text{-}8\frac{1}{2}$	$52\text{-}0\frac{27}{32}$	$3\text{-}2\frac{3}{4}$	$62\text{-}1$	$3\text{-}9$	$72\text{-}1\frac{5}{32}$
3	$2\text{-}2\frac{7}{8}$	$43\text{-}0\frac{11}{16}$	$2\text{-}9\frac{1}{8}$	$53\text{-}0\frac{7}{8}$	$3\text{-}3\frac{3}{8}$	$63\text{-}1\frac{1}{32}$	$3\text{-}9\frac{5}{8}$	$73\text{-}1\frac{3}{16}$
4	$2\text{-}3\frac{1}{2}$	$44\text{-}0\frac{23}{32}$	$2\text{-}9\frac{3}{4}$	$54\text{-}0\frac{7}{8}$	$3\text{-}4$	$64\text{-}1\frac{1}{32}$	$3\text{-}10\frac{1}{4}$	$74\text{-}1\frac{7}{32}$
5	$2\text{-}4\frac{1}{8}$	$45\text{-}0\frac{23}{32}$	$2\text{-}10\frac{3}{8}$	$55\text{-}0\frac{29}{32}$	$3\text{-}4\frac{5}{8}$	$65\text{-}1\frac{1}{16}$	$3\text{-}10\frac{7}{8}$	$75\text{-}1\frac{7}{32}$
6	$2\text{-}4\frac{3}{4}$	$46\text{-}0\frac{3}{4}$	$2\text{-}11$	$56\text{-}0\frac{29}{32}$	$3\text{-}5\frac{1}{4}$	$66\text{-}1\frac{1}{16}$	$3\text{-}11\frac{1}{2}$	$76\text{-}1\frac{1}{4}$
7	$2\text{-}5\frac{3}{8}$	$47\text{-}0\frac{3}{4}$	$2\text{-}11\frac{5}{8}$	$57\text{-}0\frac{15}{16}$	$3\text{-}5\frac{7}{8}$	$67\text{-}1\frac{3}{32}$	$4\text{-}0\frac{1}{8}$	$77\text{-}1\frac{1}{4}$
8	$2\text{-}6$	$48\text{-}0\frac{25}{32}$	$3\text{-}0\frac{1}{4}$	$58\text{-}0\frac{15}{16}$	$3\text{-}6\frac{1}{2}$	$68\text{-}1\frac{3}{32}$	$4\text{-}0\frac{3}{4}$	$78\text{-}1\frac{9}{32}$
9	$2\text{-}6\frac{5}{8}$	$49\text{-}0\frac{13}{16}$	$3\text{-}0\frac{7}{8}$	$59\text{-}0\frac{31}{32}$	$3\text{-}7\frac{1}{8}$	$69\text{-}1\frac{1}{8}$	$4\text{-}1\frac{3}{8}$	$79\text{-}1\frac{9}{32}$

natsin A=0.0520128341; **natcos** A=0.9986464163; **nattan** A=0.0520833333; **natcot** A=19.2000000000

Inches	0" Rise	0" Slope	1" Rise	1" Slope	2" Rise	2" Slope	3" Rise	3" Slope	4" Rise	4" Slope	5" Rise	5" Slope
0	0	0	1/16	1	1/8	2	3/16	3	7/32	4	9/32	5
1/16	0	1/16	1/16	1 1/16	1/8	2 1/16	3/16	3 1/16	7/32	4 1/16	9/32	5 1/16
1/8	0	1/8	1/16	1 1/8	1/8	2 1/8	3/16	3 1/8	1/4	4 1/8	9/32	5 1/8
3/16	0	3/16	1/16	1 3/16	1/8	2 3/16	3/16	3 3/16	1/4	4 3/16	5/16	5 3/16
1/4	0	1/4	1/16	1 1/4	1/8	2 1/4	3/16	3 1/4	1/4	4 1/4	5/16	5 1/4
5/16	1/32	5/16	1/16	1 5/16	1/8	2 5/16	3/16	3 5/16	1/4	4 5/16	5/16	5 5/16
3/8	1/32	3/8	3/32	1 3/8	1/8	2 3/8	3/16	3 3/8	1/4	4 3/8	5/16	5 3/8
7/16	1/32	7/16	3/32	1 7/16	1/8	2 7/16	3/16	3 7/16	1/4	4 7/16	5/16	5 7/16
1/2	1/32	1/2	3/32	1 1/2	5/32	2 1/2	3/16	3 1/2	1/4	4 1/2	5/16	5 1/2
9/16	1/32	9/16	3/32	1 9/16	5/32	2 9/16	7/32	3 9/16	1/4	4 9/16	5/16	5 9/16
5/8	1/32	5/8	3/32	1 5/8	5/32	2 5/8	7/32	3 5/8	1/4	4 5/8	5/16	5 5/8
11/16	1/32	11/16	3/32	1 11/16	5/32	2 11/16	7/32	3 11/16	9/32	4 11/16	5/16	5 11/16
3/4	1/32	3/4	3/32	1 3/4	5/32	2 3/4	7/32	3 3/4	9/32	4 3/4	11/32	5 3/4
13/16	1/32	13/16	3/32	1 13/16	5/32	2 13/16	7/32	3 13/16	9/32	4 13/16	11/32	5 13/16
7/8	1/16	7/8	3/32	1 7/8	5/32	2 7/8	7/32	3 7/8	9/32	4 7/8	11/32	5 7/8
15/16	1/16	15/16	1/8	1 15/16	5/32	2 15/16	7/32	3 15/16	9/32	4 15/16	11/32	5 15/16

Inches	6" Rise	6" Slope	7" Rise	7" Slope	8" Rise	8" Slope	9" Rise	9" Slope	10" Rise	10" Slope	11" Rise	11" Slope
0	11/32	6	13/32	7	15/32	8	1/2	9	9/16	10 1/32	5/8	11 1/32
1/16	11/32	6 1/16	13/32	7 1/16	15/32	8 1/16	17/32	9 1/16	9/16	10 3/32	5/8	11 3/32
1/8	11/32	6 1/8	13/32	7 1/8	15/32	8 1/8	17/32	9 1/8	19/32	10 5/32	5/8	11 5/32
3/16	11/32	6 3/16	13/32	7 3/16	15/32	8 3/16	17/32	9 3/16	19/32	10 7/32	21/32	11 7/32
1/4	11/32	6 1/4	13/32	7 1/4	15/32	8 1/4	17/32	9 1/4	19/32	10 9/32	21/32	11 9/32
5/16	3/8	6 5/16	13/32	7 5/16	15/32	8 5/16	17/32	9 5/16	19/32	10 11/32	21/32	11 11/32
3/8	3/8	6 3/8	7/16	7 3/8	15/32	8 3/8	9/16	9 3/8	19/32	10 13/32	21/32	11 13/32
7/16	3/8	6 7/16	7/16	7 7/16	7/16	8 7/16	17/32	9 7/16	19/32	10 15/32	21/32	11 15/32
1/2	3/8	6 1/2	7/16	7 1/2	1/2	8 1/2	17/32	9 1/2	19/32	10 17/32	21/32	11 17/32
9/16	3/8	6 9/16	7/16	7 9/16	1/2	8 9/16	9/16	9 19/32	19/32	10 19/32	21/32	11 19/32
5/8	3/8	6 5/8	7/16	7 5/8	1/2	8 5/8	9/16	9 21/32	19/32	10 21/32	21/32	11 21/32
11/16	3/8	6 11/16	7/16	7 11/16	1/2	8 11/16	9/16	9 23/32	5/8	10 23/32	21/32	11 23/32
3/4	3/8	6 3/4	7/16	7 3/4	1/2	8 3/4	9/16	9 25/32	5/8	10 25/32	11/16	11 25/32
13/16	3/8	6 13/16	7/16	7 13/16	1/2	8 13/16	9/16	9 27/32	5/8	10 27/32	11/16	11 27/32
7/8	13/32	6 7/8	7/16	7 7/8	1/2	8 7/8	9/16	9 29/32	5/8	10 29/32	11/16	11 29/32
15/16	13/32	6 15/16	15/32	7 15/16	1/2	8 15/16	9/16	9 31/32	5/8	10 31/32	11/16	11 31/32

Feet	0' Rise	0' Slope	10' Rise	10' Slope	20' Rise	20' Slope	30' Rise	30' Slope
0	0	0	6 7/8	10-0 3/16	1-3 3/4	20-0 13/32	1-8 5/8	30-0 19/32
1	11/16	1-0 1/32	7 9/16	11-0 7/32	1-2 7/16	21-0 13/32	1-9 5/16	31-0 5/8
2	1 3/8	2-0 1/32	8 1/4	12-0 1/4	1-3 1/8	22-0 7/16	1-10	32-0 5/8
3	2 1/16	3-0 1/16	8 15/16	13-0 1/4	1-3 13/16	23-0 7/16	1-10 11/16	33-0 21/32
4	2 3/4	4-0 3/32	9 5/8	14-0 9/32	1-4 1/2	24-0 15/32	1-11 3/8	34-0 21/32
5	3 7/16	5-0 3/32	10 5/16	15-0 9/32	1-5 3/16	25-0 1/2	2-0 1/16	35-0 11/16
6	4 1/8	6-0 1/8	11	16-0 5/16	1-5 7/8	26-0 1/2	2-0 3/4	36-0 23/32
7	4 13/16	7-0 1/8	11 11/16	17-0 11/32	1-6 9/16	27-0 17/32	2-1 7/16	37-0 23/32
8	5 1/2	8-0 5/32	1-0 3/8	18-0 11/32	1-7 1/4	28-0 9/16	2-2 1/8	38-0 3/4
9	6 3/16	9-0 3/16	1-1 1/16	19-0 3/8	1-7 15/16	29-0 9/16	2-2 13/16	39-0 25/32

A = 3° 16' 44''; logsin A = 8.75738; logcos A = 9.99929; logtan A = 8.75809; logcot A = 1.24191

Ins.	12″ Rise	12″ Slope	13″ Rise	13″ Slope	14″ Rise	14″ Slope	15″ Rise	15″ Slope	16″ Rise	16″ Slope
0	11/16	1-0 1/32	3/4	1-1 1/32	13/16	1-2 1/32	7/8	1-3 1/32	29/32	1-4 1/32
1/16	11/16	1-0 3/32	3/4	1-1 3/32	13/16	1-2 3/32	7/8	1-3 3/32	29/32	1-4 3/32
1/8	11/16	1-0 5/32	3/4	1-1 5/32	13/16	1-2 5/32	7/8	1-3 5/32	15/16	1-4 5/32
3/16	11/16	1-0 7/32	3/4	1-1 7/32	13/16	1-2 7/32	7/8	1-3 7/32	15/16	1-4 7/32
1/4	11/16	1-0 9/32	3/4	1-1 9/32	13/16	1-2 9/32	7/8	1-3 9/32	15/16	1-4 9/32
5/16	23/32	1-0 11/32	3/4	1-1 11/32	13/16	1-2 11/32	7/8	1-3 11/32	15/16	1-4 11/32
3/8	23/32	1-0 13/32	25/32	1-1 13/32	13/16	1-2 13/32	7/8	1-3 13/32	15/16	1-4 13/32
7/16	23/32	1-0 15/32	25/32	1-1 15/32	13/16	1-2 15/32	7/8	1-3 15/32	15/16	1-4 15/32
1/2	23/32	1-0 17/32	25/32	1-1 17/32	27/32	1-2 17/32	7/8	1-3 17/32	15/16	1-4 17/32
9/16	23/32	1-0 19/32	25/32	1-1 19/32	27/32	1-2 19/32	29/32	1-3 19/32	15/16	1-4 19/32
5/8	23/32	1-0 21/32	25/32	1-1 21/32	27/32	1-2 21/32	29/32	1-3 21/32	15/16	1-4 21/32
11/16	23/32	1-0 23/32	25/32	1-1 23/32	27/32	1-2 23/32	29/32	1-3 23/32	31/32	1-4 23/32
3/4	23/32	1-0 25/32	25/32	1-1 25/32	27/32	1-2 25/32	29/32	1-3 25/32	31/32	1-4 25/32
13/16	23/32	1-0 27/32	25/32	1-1 27/32	27/32	1-2 27/32	29/32	1-3 27/32	31/32	1-4 27/32
7/8	3/4	1-0 29/32	25/32	1-1 29/32	27/32	1-2 29/32	29/32	1-3 29/32	31/32	1-4 29/32
15/16	3/4	1-0 31/32	13/16	1-1 31/32	27/32	1-2 31/32	29/32	1-3 31/32	31/32	1-4 31/32

Ins.	17″ Rise	17″ Slope	18″ Rise	18″ Slope	19″ Rise	19″ Slope	20″ Rise	20″ Slope	21″ Rise	21″ Slope
0	31/32	1-5 1/32	1 1/32	1-6 1/32	1 3/32	1-7 1/32	1 5/32	1-8 1/32	1 3/16	1-9 1/32
1/16	31/32	1-5 3/32	1 1/32	1-6 3/32	1 3/32	1-7 3/32	1 5/32	1-8 3/32	1 7/32	1-9 3/32
1/8	31/32	1-5 5/32	1 1/32	1-6 5/32	1 3/32	1-7 5/32	1 5/32	1-8 5/32	1 7/32	1-9 5/32
3/16	1	1-5 7/32	1 1/32	1-6 7/32	1 3/32	1-7 7/32	1 5/32	1-8 7/32	1 7/32	1-9 7/32
1/4	1	1-5 9/32	1 1/16	1-6 9/32	1 3/32	1-7 9/32	1 5/32	1-8 9/32	1 7/32	1-9 9/32
5/16	1	1-5 11/32	1 1/16	1-6 11/32	1 3/32	1-7 11/32	1 5/32	1-8 11/32	1 7/32	1-9 11/32
3/8	1	1-5 13/32	1 1/16	1-6 13/32	1 1/8	1-7 13/32	1 5/32	1-8 13/32	1 7/32	1-9 13/32
7/16	1	1-5 15/32	1 1/16	1-6 15/32	1 1/8	1-7 15/32	1 5/32	1-8 15/32	1 7/32	1-9 15/32
1/2	1	1-5 17/32	1 1/16	1-6 17/32	1 1/8	1-7 17/32	1 3/16	1-8 17/32	1 7/32	1-9 17/32
9/16	1	1-5 19/32	1 1/16	1-6 19/32	1 1/8	1-7 19/32	1 3/16	1-8 19/32	1 1/4	1-9 19/32
5/8	1	1-5 21/32	1 1/16	1-6 21/32	1 1/8	1-7 21/32	1 3/16	1-8 21/32	1 1/4	1-9 21/32
11/16	1	1-5 23/32	1 1/16	1-6 23/32	1 1/8	1-7 23/32	1 3/16	1-8 23/32	1 1/4	1-9 23/32
3/4	1 1/32	1-5 25/32	1 1/16	1-6 25/32	1 1/8	1-7 25/32	1 3/16	1-8 25/32	1 1/4	1-9 25/32
13/16	1 1/32	1-5 27/32	1 1/16	1-6 27/32	1 1/8	1-7 27/32	1 3/16	1-8 27/32	1 1/4	1-9 27/32
7/8	1 1/32	1-5 29/32	1 3/32	1-6 29/32	1 1/8	1-7 29/32	1 3/16	1-8 29/32	1 1/4	1-9 29/32
15/16	1 1/32	1-5 31/32	1 3/32	1-6 31/32	1 5/32	1-7 31/32	1 3/16	1-8 31/32	1 1/4	1-9 31/32

Feet	40′ Rise	40′ Slope	50′ Rise	50′ Slope	60′ Rise	60′ Slope	70′ Rise	70′ Slope
0	2-3 1/2	40-0 25/32	2-10 3/8	50-0 31/32	3-5 1/4	60-1 3/16	4-0 1/8	70-1 3/8
1	2-4 3/16	41-0 13/16	2-11 1/16	51-1	3-5 15/16	61-1 3/16	4-0 13/16	71-1 13/32
2	2-4 7/8	42-0 13/16	2-11 3/4	52-1 1/32	3-6 5/8	62-1 7/32	4-1 1/2	72-1 13/32
3	2-5 9/16	43-0 27/32	3-0 7/16	53-1 1/32	3-7 5/16	63-1 1/4	4-2 3/16	73-1 7/16
4	2-6 1/4	44-0 7/8	3-1 1/8	54-1 1/16	3-8	64-1 1/4	4-2 7/8	74-1 15/32
5	2-6 15/16	45-0 7/8	3-1 13/16	55-1 3/32	3-8 11/16	65-1 9/32	4-3 9/16	75-1 15/32
6	2-7 5/8	46-0 29/32	3-2 1/2	56-1 3/32	3-9 3/8	66-1 5/16	4-4 1/4	76-1 1/2
7	2-8 5/16	47-0 15/16	3-3 3/16	57-1 1/8	3-10 1/16	67-1 5/16	4-4 15/16	77-1 1/2
8	2-9	48-0 15/16	3-3 7/8	58-1 5/32	3-10 3/4	68-1 11/32	4-5 5/8	78-1 17/32
9	2-9 11/16	49-0 31/32	3-4 9/16	59-1 5/32	3-11 7/16	69-1 11/32	4-6 5/16	79-1 9/16

natsin A=0.0571978722; natcos A=0.9983628616; nattan A=0.0572916666; natcot A=17.4545454545

BEVEL $\frac{3}{4}$" TO 12"

Inches	0" Rise	0" Slope	1" Rise	1" Slope	2" Rise	2" Slope	3" Rise	3" Slope	4" Rise	4" Slope	5" Rise	5" Slope
0	0	0	1/16	1	1/8	2	3/16	3	1/4	4	5/16	5
1/16	0	1/16	1/16	1 1/16	1/8	2 1/16	3/16	3 1/16	1/4	4 1/16	5/16	5 1/16
1/8	0	1/8	1/16	1 1/8	1/8	2 1/8	3/16	3 1/8	1/4	4 1/8	5/16	5 1/8
3/16	0	3/16	1/16	1 3/16	1/8	2 3/16	3/16	3 3/16	1/4	4 3/16	5/16	5 3/16
1/4	0	1/4	1/16	1 1/4	1/8	2 1/4	3/16	3 1/4	1/4	4 1/4	5/16	5 1/4
5/16	1/32	5/16	1/16	1 5/16	1/8	2 5/16	7/32	3 5/16	9/32	4 5/16	11/32	5 5/16
3/8	1/32	3/8	3/32	1 3/8	5/32	2 3/8	7/32	3 3/8	9/32	4 3/8	11/32	5 3/8
7/16	1/32	7/16	3/32	1 7/16	5/32	2 7/16	7/32	3 7/16	9/32	4 7/16	11/32	5 7/16
1/2	1/32	1/2	3/32	1 1/2	5/32	2 1/2	7/32	3 1/2	9/32	4 1/2	11/32	5 1/2
9/16	1/32	9/16	3/32	1 9/16	5/32	2 9/16	7/32	3 9/16	9/32	4 9/16	11/32	5 9/16
5/8	1/32	5/8	3/32	1 5/8	5/32	2 5/8	7/32	3 5/8	9/32	4 5/8	11/32	5 5/8
11/16	1/32	11/16	3/32	1 11/16	5/32	2 11/16	7/32	3 11/16	9/32	4 11/16	11/32	5 11/16
3/4	1/16	3/4	1/8	1 3/4	3/16	2 3/4	1/4	3 3/4	5/16	4 3/4	3/8	5 3/4
13/16	1/16	13/16	1/8	1 13/16	3/16	2 13/16	1/4	3 13/16	5/16	4 13/16	3/8	5 13/16
7/8	1/16	7/8	1/8	1 7/8	3/16	2 7/8	1/4	3 7/8	5/16	4 7/8	3/8	5 7/8
15/16	1/16	15/16	1/8	1 15/16	3/16	2 15/16	1/4	3 15/16	5/16	4 15/16	3/8	5 15/16

Inches	6" Rise	6" Slope	7" Rise	7" Slope	8" Rise	8" Slope	9" Rise	9" Slope	10" Rise	10" Slope	11" Rise	11" Slope
0	3/8	6	7/16	7	1/2	8	9/16	9 1/32−	5/8	10 1/32−	11/16	11 1/32−
1/16	3/8	6 1/16	7/16	7 1/16	1/2	8 3/32−	9/16	9 3/32−	5/8	10 3/32−	11/16	11 3/32−
1/8	3/8	6 1/8	7/16	7 1/8	1/2	8 5/32−	9/16	9 5/32−	5/8	10 5/32−	11/16	11 5/32−
3/16	3/8	6 3/16	7/16	7 3/16	1/2	8 7/32−	9/16	9 7/32−	5/8	10 7/32−	11/16	11 7/32−
1/4	3/8	6 1/4	7/16	7 1/4	1/2	8 9/32−	9/16	9 9/32−	5/8	10 9/32−	11/16	11 9/32−
5/16	13/32	6 5/16	15/32	7 5/16	17/32	8 11/32−	19/32	9 11/32−	21/32	10 11/32−	23/32	11 11/32−
3/8	13/32	6 3/8	15/32	7 3/8	17/32	8 13/32−	19/32	9 13/32−	21/32	10 13/32−	23/32	11 13/32−
7/16	13/32	6 7/16	15/32	7 7/16	17/32	8 15/32−	19/32	9 15/32−	21/32	10 15/32−	23/32	11 15/32−
1/2	13/32	6 1/2	15/32	7 1/2	17/32	8 17/32−	19/32	9 17/32−	21/32	10 17/32−	23/32	11 17/32−
9/16	13/32	6 9/16	15/32	7 9/16	17/32	8 19/32−	19/32	9 19/32−	21/32	10 19/32−	23/32	11 19/32−
5/8	13/32	6 5/8	15/32	7 5/8	17/32	8 21/32−	19/32	9 21/32−	21/32	10 21/32−	23/32	11 21/32−
11/16	13/32	6 11/16	15/32	7 11/16	17/32	8 23/32−	19/32	9 23/32−	21/32	10 23/32−	23/32	11 23/32−
3/4	7/16	6 3/4	1/2	7 3/4	9/16	8 25/32−	5/8	9 25/32−	11/16	10 25/32−	3/4	11 25/32−
13/16	7/16	6 13/16	1/2	7 13/16	9/16	8 27/32−	5/8	9 27/32−	11/16	10 27/32−	3/4	11 27/32−
7/8	7/16	6 7/8	1/2	7 7/8	9/16	8 29/32−	5/8	9 29/32−	11/16	10 29/32−	3/4	11 29/32−
15/16	7/16	6 15/16	1/2	7 15/16	9/16	8 31/32−	5/8	9 31/32−	11/16	10 31/32−	3/4	11 31/32−

Feet	0' Rise	0' Slope	10' Rise	10' Slope	20' Rise	20' Slope	30' Rise	30' Slope
0	0	0	7 1/2	10-0 1/32−	1-3	20-0 15/32−	1-10 1/2	30-0 11/16
1	3/4	1-0 1/32−	8 1/4	11-0 1/4	1-3 3/4	21-0 1/2	1-11 1/4	31-0 23/32−
2	1 1/2	2-0 1/32−	9	12-0 9/32−	1-4 1/2	22-0 1/2	2-0	32-0 3/4
3	2 1/4	3-0 1/16	9 3/4	13-0 5/16	1-5 1/4	23-0 17/32−	2-0 3/4	33-0 25/32−
4	3	4-0 3/32−	10 1/2	14-0 5/16	1-6	24-0 9/16	2-1 1/2	34-0 25/32−
5	3 3/4	5-0 1/8	11 1/4	15-0 11/32−	1-6 3/4	25-0 19/32−	2-2 1/4	35-0 13/16
6	4 1/2	6-0 1/8	1-0	16-0 3/8	1-7 1/2	26-0 19/32−	2-3	36-0 27/32−
7	5 1/4	7-0 5/32−	1-0 3/4	17-0 13/32−	1-8 1/4	27-0 5/8	2-3 3/4	37-0 7/8
8	6	8-0 3/16	1-1 1/2	18-0 13/32−	1-9	28-0 21/32−	2-4 1/2	38-0 7/8
9	6 3/4	9-0 7/32−	1-2 1/4	19-0 7/16	1-9 3/4	29-0 11/16	2-5 1/4	39-0 29/32−

A=3° 34' 35''; logsin A=8.79503; logcos A=9.99915; logtan A=8.79588; logcot A=1.20412

Ins.	12" Rise	Slope	13" Rise	Slope	14" Rise	Slope	15" Rise	Slope	16" Rise	Slope
0	3/4	1-0 1/32	13/16	1-1 1/32	7/8	1-2 1/32	15/16	1-3 1/32	1	1-4 1/32
1/16	3/4	1-0 3/32	13/16	1-1 3/32	7/8	1-2 3/32	15/16	1-3 3/32	1	1-4 3/32
1/8	3/4	1-0 5/32	13/16	1-1 5/32	7/8	1-2 5/32	15/16	1-3 5/32	1	1-4 5/32
3/16	3/4	1-0 7/32	13/16	1-1 7/32	7/8	1-2 7/32	15/16	1-3 7/32	1	1-4 7/32
1/4	3/4	1-0 9/32	13/16	1-1 9/32	7/8	1-2 9/32	15/16	1-3 9/32	1	1-4 9/32
5/16	25/32	1-0 11/32	27/32	1-1 11/32	29/32	1-2 11/32	31/32	1-3 11/32	1 1/32	1-4 11/32
3/8	25/32	1-0 13/32	27/32	1-1 13/32	29/32	1-2 13/32	31/32	1-3 13/32	1 1/32	1-4 13/32
7/16	25/32	1-0 15/32	27/32	1-1 15/32	29/32	1-2 15/32	31/32	1-3 15/32	1 1/32	1-4 15/32
1/2	25/32	1-0 17/32	27/32	1-1 17/32	29/32	1-2 17/32	31/32	1-3 17/32	1 1/32	1-4 17/32
9/16	25/32	1-0 19/32	27/32	1-1 19/32	29/32	1-2 19/32	31/32	1-3 19/32	1 1/32	1-4 19/32
5/8	25/32	1-0 21/32	27/32	1-1 21/32	29/32	1-2 21/32	31/32	1-3 21/32	1 1/32	1-4 21/32
11/16	25/32	1-0 23/32	27/32	1-1 23/32	29/32	1-2 23/32	31/32	1-3 23/32	1 1/32	1-4 23/32
3/4	13/16	1-0 25/32	7/8	1-1 25/32	15/16	1-2 25/32	1	1-3 25/32	1 1/16	1-4 25/32
13/16	13/16	1-0 27/32	7/8	1-1 27/32	15/16	1-2 27/32	1	1-3 27/32	1 1/16	1-4 27/32
7/8	13/16	1-0 29/32	7/8	1-1 29/32	15/16	1-2 29/32	1	1-3 29/32	1 1/16	1-4 29/32
15/16	13/16	1-0 31/32	7/8	1-1 31/32	15/16	1-2 31/32	1	1-3 31/32	1 1/16	1-4 31/32

Ins.	17" Rise	Slope	18" Rise	Slope	19" Rise	Slope	20" Rise	Slope	21" Rise	Slope
0	1 1/16	1-5 1/32	1 1/8	1-6 1/32	1 3/16	1-7 1/32	1 1/4	1-8 1/32	1 5/16	1-9 1/32
1/16	1 1/16	1-5 3/32	1 1/8	1-6 3/32	1 3/16	1-7 3/32	1 1/4	1-8 3/32	1 5/16	1-9 3/32
1/8	1 1/16	1-5 5/32	1 1/8	1-6 5/32	1 3/16	1-7 5/32	1 1/4	1-8 5/32	1 5/16	1-9 5/32
3/16	1 1/16	1-5 7/32	1 1/8	1-6 7/32	1 3/16	1-7 7/32	1 1/4	1-8 7/32	1 5/16	1-9 7/32
1/4	1 1/16	1-5 9/32	1 1/8	1-6 9/32	1 3/16	1-7 9/32	1 1/4	1-8 9/32	1 5/16	1-9 9/32
5/16	1 3/32	1-5 11/32	1 5/32	1-6 11/32	1 7/32	1-7 11/32	1 9/32	1-8 11/32	1 11/32	1-9 11/32
3/8	1 3/32	1-5 13/32	1 5/32	1-6 13/32	1 7/32	1-7 13/32	1 9/32	1-8 13/32	1 11/32	1-9 13/32
7/16	1 3/32	1-5 15/32	1 5/32	1-6 15/32	1 7/32	1-7 15/32	1 9/32	1-8 15/32	1 11/32	1-9 15/32
1/2	1 3/32	1-5 17/32	1 5/32	1-6 17/32	1 7/32	1-7 17/32	1 9/32	1-8 17/32	1 11/32	1-9 17/32
9/16	1 3/32	1-5 19/32	1 5/32	1-6 19/32	1 7/32	1-7 19/32	1 9/32	1-8 19/32	1 11/32	1-9 19/32
5/8	1 3/32	1-5 21/32	1 5/32	1-6 21/32	1 7/32	1-7 21/32	1 9/32	1-8 21/32	1 11/32	1-9 21/32
11/16	1 3/32	1-5 23/32	1 5/32	1-6 23/32	1 7/32	1-7 23/32	1 9/32	1-8 23/32	1 11/32	1-9 23/32
3/4	1 1/8	1-5 25/32	1 3/16	1-6 25/32	1 1/4	1-7 25/32	1 5/16	1-8 25/32	1 3/8	1-9 25/32
13/16	1 1/8	1-5 27/32	1 3/16	1-6 27/32	1 1/4	1-7 27/32	1 5/16	1-8 27/32	1 3/8	1-9 27/32
7/8	1 1/8	1-5 29/32	1 3/16	1-6 29/32	1 1/4	1-7 29/32	1 5/16	1-8 29/32	1 3/8	1-9 29/32
15/16	1 1/8	1-5 31/32	1 3/16	1-6 31/32	1 1/4	1-7 31/32	1 5/16	1-8 31/32	1 3/8	1-9 31/32

Feet	40' Rise	Slope	50' Rise	Slope	60' Rise	Slope	70' Rise	Slope
0	2-6	40-0 15/16	3-1 1/2	50-1 15/32	3-9	60-1 13/32	4-4 1/2	70-1 5/8
1	2-6 3/4	41-0 31/32	3-2 1/4	51-1 3/16	3-9 3/4	61-1 7/16	4-5 1/4	71-1 21/32
2	2-7 1/2	42-0 31/32	3-3	52-1 7/32	3-10 1/2	62-1 7/16	4-6	72-1 11/16
3	2-8 1/4	43-1	3-3 3/4	53-1 1/4	3-11 1/4	63-1 15/32	4-6 3/4	73-1 23/32
4	2-9	44-1 1/32	3-4 1/2	54-1 1/4	4-0	64-1 1/2	4-7 1/2	74-1 23/32
5	2-9 3/4	45-1 1/16	3-5 1/4	55-1 9/32	4-0 3/4	65-1 17/32	4-8 1/4	75-1 3/4
6	2-10 1/2	46-1 1/16	3-6	56-1 5/16	4-1 1/2	66-1 17/32	4-9	76-1 25/32
7	2-11 1/4	47-1 3/32	3-6 3/4	57-1 11/32	4-2 1/4	67-1 9/16	4-9 3/4	77-1 13/16
8	3-0	48-1 1/8	3-7 1/2	58-1 11/32	4-3	68-1 19/32	4-10 1/2	78-1 13/16
9	3-0 3/4	49-1 5/32	3-8 1/4	59-1 3/8	4-3 3/4	69-1 5/8	4-11 1/4	79-1 27/32

natsin A=0.0623782861; natcos A=0.9980525785; nattan A=0.0625000000; natcot A=16.0000000000

Inches	0" Rise	Slope	1" Rise	Slope	2" Rise	Slope	3" Rise	Slope	4" Rise	Slope	5" Rise	Slope
0	0	0	1/16	1	1/8	2	3/16	3	9/32-	4	11/32-	5
1/16	0	1/16	1/16	1 1/16	1/8	2 1/16	7/32-	3 1/16	9/32-	4 1/16	11/32-	5 1/16
1/8	0	1/8	1/16	1 1/8	5/32	2 1/8	7/32-	3 1/8	9/32-	4 1/8	11/32-	5 1/8
3/16	0	3/16	3/32-	1 3/16	5/32	2 3/16	7/32-	3 3/16	9/32-	4 3/16	11/32-	5 3/16
1/4	1/32-	1/4	3/32-	1 1/4	5/32	2 1/4	7/32	3 1/4	9/32	4 1/4	11/32	5 1/4
5/16	1/32-	5/16	3/32-	1 5/16	5/32	2 5/16	7/32	3 5/16	9/32	4 5/16	3/8	5 5/16
3/8	1/32-	3/8	3/32-	1 3/8	5/32	2 3/8	7/32	3 3/8	9/32	4 3/8	3/8	5 3/8
7/16	1/32-	7/16	3/32-	1 7/16	5/32	2 7/16	7/32	3 7/16	5/16	4 7/16	3/8	5 7/16
1/2	1/32-	1/2	3/32-	1 1/2	5/32	2 1/2	1/4	3 1/2	5/16	4 1/2	3/8	5 1/2
9/16	1/32-	9/16	3/32-	1 9/16	3/16	2 9/16	1/4	3 9/16	5/16	4 9/16	3/8	5 9/16
5/8	1/32-	5/8	1/8	1 5/8	3/16	2 5/8	1/4	3 5/8	5/16	4 5/8	3/8	5 5/8
11/16	1/32-	11/16	1/8	1 11/16	3/16	2 11/16	1/4	3 11/16	5/16	4 11/16	3/8	5 11/16
3/4	1/16-	3/4	1/8	1 3/4	3/16	2 3/4	1/4	3 3/4	5/16	4 3/4	3/8	5 3/4
13/16	1/16-	13/16	1/8	1 13/16	3/16	2 13/16	1/4	3 13/16	5/16	4 13/16	13/32-	5 13/16
7/8	1/16-	7/8	1/8	1 7/8	3/16	2 7/8	1/4	3 7/8	11/32-	4 7/8	13/32-	5 7/8
15/16	1/16-	15/16	1/8	1 15/16	3/16	2 15/16	9/32-	3 15/16	11/32-	4 15/16	13/32-	5 15/16

Inches	6" Rise	Slope	7" Rise	Slope	8" Rise	Slope	9" Rise	Slope	10" Rise	Slope	11" Rise	Slope
0	13/32-	6	15/32-	7 1/32-	17/32-	8 1/32-	5/8	9 1/32-	11/16	10 1/32-	3/4	11 1/32-
1/16	13/32-	6 1/16	15/32-	7 3/32-	17/32-	8 3/32-	5/8	9 3/32-	11/16	10 3/32-	3/4	11 3/32-
1/8	13/32-	6 1/8	15/32-	7 5/32-	9/16	8 5/32-	5/8	9 5/32-	11/16	10 5/32-	3/4	11 5/32-
3/16	13/32-	6 3/16	1/2	7 7/32-	9/16	8 7/32-	5/8	9 7/32-	11/16	10 7/32-	3/4	11 7/32-
1/4	7/16	6 1/4	1/2	7 9/32-	9/16	8 9/32-	5/8	9 9/32-	11/16	10 9/32-	3/4	11 9/32-
5/16	7/16	6 5/16	1/2	7 11/32-	9/16	8 11/32-	5/8	9 11/32-	11/16	10 11/32-	25/32-	11 11/32-
3/8	7/16	6 3/8	1/2	7 13/32-	9/16	8 13/32-	5/8	9 13/32-	11/16	10 13/32-	25/32-	11 13/32-
7/16	7/16	6 7/16	1/2	7 15/32-	9/16	8 15/32-	5/8	9 15/32-	23/32-	10 15/32-	25/32-	11 15/32-
1/2	7/16	6 1/2	1/2	7 17/32-	9/16	8 17/32-	21/32-	9 17/32-	23/32-	10 17/32-	25/32-	11 17/32-
9/16	7/16	6 9/16	1/2	7 19/32-	19/32-	8 19/32-	21/32-	9 19/32-	23/32-	10 19/32-	25/32-	11 19/32-
5/8	7/16	6 5/8	17/32-	7 21/32-	19/32-	8 21/32-	21/32-	9 21/32-	23/32-	10 21/32-	25/32-	11 21/32-
11/16	7/16	6 11/16	17/32-	7 23/32-	19/32-	8 23/32-	21/32-	9 23/32-	25/32-	10 23/32-	25/32-	11 23/32-
3/4	15/32-	6 3/4	17/32-	7 25/32-	19/32-	8 25/32-	21/32-	9 25/32-	23/32-	10 25/32-	25/32-	11 25/32-
13/16	15/32-	6 13/16	17/32-	7 27/32-	19/32-	8 27/32-	21/32-	9 27/32-	23/32-	10 27/32-	13/16	11 27/32-
7/8	15/32-	6 29/32-	17/32-	7 29/32-	19/32-	8 29/32-	21/32-	9 29/32-	3/4	10 29/32-	13/16	11 29/32-
15/16	15/32-	6 31/32-	17/32-	7 31/32-	19/32-	8 31/32-	11/16	9 31/32-	3/4	10 31/32-	13/16	11 31/32-

Feet	0' Rise	Slope	10' Rise	Slope	20' Rise	Slope	30' Rise	Slope
0	0	0	8 1/8	10-0 9/32-	1-4 1/4	20-0 9/16	2-0 3/8	30-0 13/16
1	13/16	1-0 1/32-	8 15/16	11-0 5/16	1-5 1/4	21-0 9/16	2-1 3/16	31-0 27/32-
2	1 5/8	2-0 1/16	9 3/4	12-0 1/32-	1-5 7/8	22-0 19/32-	2-2	32-0 7/8
3	2 7/16	3-0 3/32-	10 9/16	13-0 11/32-	1-6 11/16	23-0 5/8	2-2 13/16	33-0 29/32-
4	3 1/4	4-0 1/8	11 3/8	14-0 3/8	1-7 1/2	24-0 21/32-	2-3 5/8	34-0 15/16
5	4 1/16	5-0 1/8	1-0 3/16	15-0 13/32-	1-8 5/16	25-0 11/16	2-4 7/16	35-0 31/32-
6	4 7/8	6-0 5/32-	1-1	16-0 7/16	1-9 1/8	26-0 23/32-	2-5 1/4	36-1
7	5 11/16	7-0 3/16	1-1 13/16	17-0 15/32-	1-9 15/16	27-0 3/4	2-6 1/16	37-1 1/32-
8	6 1/2	8-0 7/32-	1-2 5/8	18-0 1/2	1-10 3/4	28-0 25/32-	2-6 7/8	38-1 1/32-
9	7 5/16	9-0 1/4	1-3 7/16	19-0 17/32-	1-11 9/16	29-0 25/32-	2-7 11/16	39-1 1/16

A $= 3° 52' 25''$; logsin A $= 8.82965$; logcos A $= 9.99901$; logtan A $= 8.83064$; logcot A $= 1.16936$

Ins.	12″ Rise	Slope	13″ Rise	Slope	14″ Rise	Slope	15″ Rise	Slope	16″ Rise	Slope
0	13/16	1-0 1/32	7/8	1-1 1/32	15/16	1-2 1/32	1	1-3 1/32	1 3/32	1-4 1/32
1/16	13/16	1-0 3/32	7/8	1-1 3/32	15/16	1-2 3/32	1 1/32	1-3 3/32	1 3/32	1-4 3/32
1/8	13/16	1-0 5/32	7/8	1-1 5/32	31/32	1-2 5/32	1 1/32	1-3 5/32	1 3/32	1-4 5/32
3/16	13/16	1-0 7/32	29/32	1-1 7/32	31/32	1-2 7/32	1 1/32	1-3 7/32	1 3/32	1-4 7/32
1/4	27/32	1-0 9/32	29/32	1-1 9/32	31/32	1-2 9/32	1 1/32	1-3 9/32	1 3/32	1-4 9/32
5/16	27/32	1-0 11/32	29/32	1-1 11/32	31/32	1-2 11/32	1 1/32	1-3 11/32	1 3/32	1-4 11/32
3/8	27/32	1-0 13/32	29/32	1-1 13/32	31/32	1-2 13/32	1 1/32	1-3 13/32	1 3/32	1-4 13/32
7/16	27/32	1-0 15/32	29/32	1-1 15/32	31/32	1-2 15/32	1 1/32	1-3 15/32	1 1/8	1-4 15/32
1/2	27/32	1-0 17/32	29/32	1-1 17/32	31/32	1-2 17/32	1 1/16	1-3 17/32	1 1/8	1-4 17/32
9/16	27/32	1-0 19/32	29/32	1-1 19/32	1	1-2 19/32	1 1/16	1-3 19/32	1 1/8	1-4 19/32
5/8	27/32	1-0 21/32	15/16	1-1 21/32	1	1-2 21/32	1 1/16	1-3 21/32	1 1/8	1-4 21/32
11/16	27/32	1-0 23/32	15/16	1-1 23/32	1	1-2 23/32	1 1/16	1-3 23/32	1 1/8	1-4 23/32
3/4	7/8	1-0 25/32	15/16	1-1 25/32	1	1-2 25/32	1 1/16	1-3 25/32	1 1/8	1-4 25/32
13/16	7/8	1-0 27/32	15/16	1-1 27/32	1	1-2 27/32	1 1/16	1-3 27/32	1 1/8	1-4 27/32
7/8	7/8	1-0 29/32	15/16	1-1 29/32	1	1-2 29/32	1 1/16	1-3 29/32	1 5/32	1-4 29/32
15/16	7/8	1-0 31/32	15/16	1-1 31/32	1	1-2 31/32	1 3/32	1-3 31/32	1 5/32	1-4 31/32

Ins.	17″ Rise	Slope	18″ Rise	Slope	19″ Rise	Slope	20″ Rise	Slope	21″ Rise	Slope
0	1 5/32	1-5 1/32	1 7/32	1-6 1/32	1 9/32	1-7 1/32	1 11/32	1-8 1/32	1 7/16	1-9 1/16
1/16	1 5/32	1-5 3/32	1 7/32	1-6 3/32	1 9/32	1-7 3/32	1 11/32	1-8 3/32	1 7/16	1-9 1/8
1/8	1 5/32	1-5 5/32	1 7/32	1-6 5/32	1 9/32	1-7 5/32	1 3/8	1-8 5/32	1 7/16	1-9 3/16
3/16	1 5/32	1-5 7/32	1 7/32	1-6 7/32	1 5/16	1-7 7/32	1 3/8	1-8 7/32	1 7/16	1-9 1/4
1/4	1 5/32	1-5 9/32	1 1/4	1-6 9/32	1 5/16	1-7 9/32	1 3/8	1-8 9/32	1 7/16	1-9 5/16
5/16	1 3/16	1-5 11/32	1 1/4	1-6 11/32	1 5/16	1-7 11/32	1 3/8	1-8 11/32	1 7/16	1-9 3/8
3/8	1 3/16	1-5 13/32	1 1/4	1-6 13/32	1 5/16	1-7 13/32	1 3/8	1-8 13/32	1 7/16	1-9 7/16
7/16	1 3/16	1-5 15/32	1 1/4	1-6 15/32	1 5/16	1-7 15/32	1 3/8	1-8 15/32	1 7/16	1-9 1/2
1/2	1 3/16	1-5 17/32	1 1/4	1-6 17/32	1 5/16	1-7 17/32	1 3/8	1-8 9/16	1 15/32	1-9 9/16
9/16	1 3/16	1-5 19/32	1 1/4	1-6 19/32	1 5/16	1-7 19/32	1 13/32	1-8 5/8	1 15/32	1-9 5/8
5/8	1 3/16	1-5 21/32	1 1/4	1-6 21/32	1 11/32	1-7 21/32	1 13/32	1-8 11/16	1 15/32	1-9 11/16
11/16	1 3/16	1-5 23/32	1 1/4	1-6 23/32	1 11/32	1-7 23/32	1 13/32	1-8 3/4	1 15/32	1-9 3/4
3/4	1 3/16	1-5 25/32	1 9/32	1-6 25/32	1 11/32	1-7 25/32	1 13/32	1-8 13/16	1 15/32	1-9 13/16
13/16	1 7/32	1-5 27/32	1 9/32	1-6 27/32	1 11/32	1-7 27/32	1 13/32	1-8 7/8	1 15/32	1-9 7/8
7/8	1 7/32	1-5 29/32	1 9/32	1-6 29/32	1 11/32	1-7 29/32	1 13/32	1-8 15/16	1 15/32	1-9 15/16
15/16	1 7/32	1-5 31/32	1 9/32	1-6 31/32	1 11/32	1-7 31/32	1 13/32	1-9	1 1/2	1-10

Feet	40′ Rise	Slope	50′ Rise	Slope	60′ Rise	Slope	70′ Rise	Slope
0	2-8 1/2	40-1 3/8	3-4 5/8	50-1 3/8	4-0 3/4	60-1 21/32	4-8 7/8	70-1 15/16
1	2-9 5/16	41-1 1/8	3-5 7/16	51-1 13/32	4-1 9/16	61-1 11/16	4-9 11/16	71-1 15/16
2	2-10 1/8	42-1 5/32	3-6 1/4	52-1 7/16	4-2 3/8	62-1 23/32	4-10 1/2	72-1 31/32
3	2-10 15/16	43-1 3/16	3-7 1/16	53-1 15/32	4-3 3/16	63-1 23/32	4-11 5/16	73-2
4	2-11 3/4	44-1 7/32	3-7 7/8	54-1 15/32	4-4	64-1 3/4	5-0 1/8	74-2 1/32
5	3-0 9/16	45-1 1/4	3-8 11/16	55-1 1/2	4-4 13/16	65-1 25/32	5-0 15/16	75-2 1/16
6	3-1 3/8	46-1 1/4	3-9 1/2	56-1 17/32	4-5 5/8	66-1 13/16	5-1 3/4	76-2 3/32
7	3-2 3/16	47-1 9/32	3-10 5/16	57-1 9/16	4-6 7/16	67-1 27/32	5-2 9/16	77-2 1/8
8	3-3	48-1 5/16	3-11 1/8	58-1 19/32	4-7 1/4	68-1 7/8	5-3 3/8	78-2 5/32
9	3-3 13/16	49-1 11/32	3-11 15/16	59-1 5/8	4-8 1/16	69-1 29/32	5-4 3/16	79-2 5/32

natsin A=0.0675536632; natcos A=0.9977156421; nattan A=0.0677083333; natcot A=14.7692307692

BEVEL ⅞" TO 12"

Inches	0" Rise	0" Slope	1" Rise	1" Slope	2" Rise	2" Slope	3" Rise	3" Slope	4" Rise	4" Slope	5" Rise	5" Slope
0	0	0	1/16	1	5/32	2	7/32	3	9/32	4	3/8	5
1/16	0	1/16	1/16	1 1/16	5/32	2 1/16	7/32	3 1/16	9/32	4 1/16	3/8	5 1/16
1/8	0	1/8	3/32	1 1/8	5/32	2 1/8	7/32	3 1/8	5/16	4 1/8	3/8	5 1/8
3/16	0	3/16	3/32	1 3/16	5/32	2 3/16	7/32	3 3/16	5/16	4 3/16	3/8	5 3/16
1/4	1/32	1/4	3/32	1 1/4	5/32	2 1/4	1/4	3 1/4	5/16	4 1/4	3/8	5 1/4
5/16	1/32	5/16	3/32	1 5/16	5/32	2 5/16	1/4	3 5/16	5/16	4 5/16	3/8	5 5/16
3/8	1/32	3/8	3/32	1 3/8	3/16	2 3/8	1/4	3 3/8	5/16	4 3/8	13/32	5 3/8
7/16	1/32	7/16	3/32	1 7/16	3/16	2 7/16	1/4	3 7/16	5/16	4 7/16	13/32	5 7/16
1/2	1/32	1/2	1/8	1 1/2	3/16	2 1/2	1/4	3 1/2	5/16	4 1/2	13/32	5 1/2
9/16	1/32	9/16	1/8	1 9/16	3/16	2 9/16	1/4	3 9/16	11/32	4 9/16	13/32	5 9/16
5/8	1/32	5/8	1/8	1 5/8	3/16	2 5/8	1/4	3 5/8	11/32	4 5/8	13/32	5 5/8
11/16	1/16	11/16	1/8	1 11/16	3/16	2 11/16	9/32	3 11/16	11/32	4 11/16	13/32	5 11/16
3/4	1/16	3/4	1/8	1 3/4	3/16	2 3/4	9/32	3 3/4	11/32	4 3/4	13/32	5 3/4
13/16	1/16	13/16	1/8	1 13/16	7/32	2 13/16	9/32	3 13/16	11/32	4 13/16	7/16	5 13/16
7/8	1/16	7/8	1/8	1 7/8	7/32	2 7/8	9/32	3 7/8	11/32	4 7/8	7/16	5 7/8
15/16	1/16	15/16	5/32	1 15/16	7/32	2 15/16	9/32	3 15/16	3/8	4 15/16	7/16	5 31/32

Inches	6" Rise	6" Slope	7" Rise	7" Slope	8" Rise	8" Slope	9" Rise	9" Slope	10" Rise	10" Slope	11" Rise	11" Slope
0	7/16	6 1/32	1/2	7 1/32	19/32	8 1/32	21/32	9 1/32	23/32	10 1/32	13/16	11 1/32
1/16	7/16	6 3/32	1/2	7 3/32	19/32	8 3/32	21/32	9 3/32	23/32	10 3/32	13/16	11 3/32
1/8	7/16	6 5/32	17/32	7 5/32	19/32	8 5/32	21/32	9 5/32	3/4	10 5/32	13/16	11 5/32
3/16	7/16	6 7/32	17/32	7 7/32	19/32	8 7/32	21/32	9 7/32	3/4	10 7/32	13/16	11 7/32
1/4	15/32	6 9/32	17/32	7 9/32	19/32	8 9/32	11/16	9 9/32	3/4	10 9/32	13/16	11 9/32
5/16	15/32	6 11/32	17/32	7 11/32	19/32	8 11/32	11/16	9 11/32	3/4	10 11/32	13/16	11 11/32
3/8	15/32	6 13/32	17/32	7 13/32	5/8	8 13/32	11/16	9 13/32	3/4	10 13/32	27/32	11 13/32
7/16	15/32	6 15/32	17/32	7 15/32	5/8	8 15/32	11/16	9 15/32	3/4	10 15/32	27/32	11 15/32
1/2	15/32	6 17/32	9/16	7 17/32	5/8	8 17/32	11/16	9 17/32	3/4	10 17/32	27/32	11 17/32
9/16	15/32	6 19/32	9/16	7 19/32	5/8	8 19/32	11/16	9 19/32	25/32	10 19/32	27/32	11 19/32
5/8	15/32	6 21/32	9/16	7 21/32	5/8	8 21/32	11/16	9 21/32	25/32	10 21/32	27/32	11 21/32
11/16	1/2	6 23/32	9/16	7 23/32	5/8	8 23/32	23/32	9 23/32	25/32	10 23/32	27/32	11 23/32
3/4	1/2	6 25/32	9/16	7 25/32	5/8	8 25/32	23/32	9 25/32	25/32	10 25/32	27/32	11 25/32
13/16	1/2	6 27/32	9/16	7 27/32	21/32	8 27/32	23/32	9 27/32	25/32	10 27/32	7/8	11 27/32
7/8	1/2	6 29/32	9/16	7 29/32	21/32	8 29/32	23/32	9 29/32	25/32	10 29/32	7/8	11 29/32
15/16	1/2	6 31/32	19/32	7 31/32	21/32	8 31/32	23/32	9 31/32	13/16	10 31/32	7/8	11 31/32

Feet	0' Rise	0' Slope	10' Rise	10' Slope	20' Rise	20' Slope	30' Rise	30' Slope
0	0	0	8 3/4	10-0 5/16	1-5 1/2	20-0 5/8	2-2 1/4	30-0 31/32
1	7/8	1-0 1/32	9 5/8	11-0 11/32	1-6 3/8	21-0 21/32	2-3 1/8	31-1
2	1 3/4	2-0 1/16	10 1/2	12-0 3/8	1-7 1/4	22-0 11/16	2-4	32-1 1/32
3	2 5/8	3-0 3/32	11 3/8	13-0 13/32	1-8 1/8	23-0 23/32	2-4 7/8	33-1 1/16
4	3 1/2	4-0 1/8	1-0 1/4	14-0 7/16	1-9	24-0 3/4	2-5 3/4	34-1 3/32
5	4 3/8	5-0 5/32	1-1 1/8	15-0 15/32	1-9 7/8	25-0 25/32	2-6 5/8	35-1 1/8
6	5 1/4	6-0 3/16	1-2	16-0 1/2	1-10 3/4	26-0 27/32	2-7 1/2	36-1 5/32
7	6 1/8	7-0 7/32	1-2 7/8	17-0 17/32	1-11 5/8	27-0 7/8	2-8 3/8	37-1 3/16
8	7	8-0 1/4	1-3 3/4	18-0 9/16	2-0 1/2	28-0 29/32	2-9 1/4	38-1 7/32
9	7 7/8	9-0 9/32	1-4 5/8	19-0 19/32	2-1 3/8	29-0 15/16	2-10 1/8	39-1 1/4

A = 4° 10′ 14″; logsin A = 8.86168; logcos A = 9.99885; logtan A = 8.86283; logcot A = 1.13717

Ins.	12″ Rise	12″ Slope	13″ Rise	13″ Slope	14″ Rise	14″ Slope	15″ Rise	15″ Slope	16″ Rise	16″ Slope
0	$\frac{7}{8}$	$1\text{-}0\frac{1}{32}$	$\frac{15}{16}$	$1\text{-}1\frac{1}{32}$	$1\frac{1}{32}$	$1\text{-}2\frac{1}{32}$	$1\frac{3}{32}$	$1\text{-}3\frac{1}{32}$	$1\frac{5}{32}$	$1\text{-}4\frac{1}{32}$
$\frac{1}{16}$	$\frac{7}{8}$	$1\text{-}0\frac{3}{32}$	$\frac{15}{16}$	$1\text{-}1\frac{3}{32}$	$1\frac{1}{32}$	$1\text{-}2\frac{3}{32}$	$1\frac{3}{32}$	$1\text{-}3\frac{3}{32}$	$1\frac{5}{32}$	$1\text{-}4\frac{3}{32}$
$\frac{1}{8}$	$\frac{7}{8}$	$1\text{-}0\frac{5}{32}$	$\frac{31}{32}$	$1\text{-}1\frac{5}{32}$	$1\frac{1}{32}$	$1\text{-}2\frac{5}{32}$	$1\frac{3}{32}$	$1\text{-}3\frac{5}{32}$	$1\frac{3}{16}$	$1\text{-}4\frac{5}{32}$
$\frac{3}{16}$	$\frac{7}{8}$	$1\text{-}0\frac{7}{32}$	$\frac{31}{32}$	$1\text{-}1\frac{7}{32}$	$1\frac{1}{32}$	$1\text{-}2\frac{7}{32}$	$1\frac{3}{32}$	$1\text{-}3\frac{7}{32}$	$1\frac{3}{16}$	$1\text{-}4\frac{7}{32}$
$\frac{1}{4}$	$\frac{29}{32}$	$1\text{-}0\frac{9}{32}$	$\frac{31}{32}$	$1\text{-}1\frac{9}{32}$	$1\frac{1}{16}$	$1\text{-}2\frac{9}{32}$	$1\frac{1}{8}$	$1\text{-}3\frac{9}{32}$	$1\frac{3}{16}$	$1\text{-}4\frac{9}{32}$
$\frac{5}{16}$	$\frac{29}{32}$	$1\text{-}0\frac{11}{32}$	$\frac{31}{32}$	$1\text{-}1\frac{11}{32}$	$1\frac{1}{16}$	$1\text{-}2\frac{11}{32}$	$1\frac{1}{8}$	$1\text{-}3\frac{11}{32}$	$1\frac{3}{16}$	$1\text{-}4\frac{11}{32}$
$\frac{3}{8}$	$\frac{29}{32}$	$1\text{-}0\frac{13}{32}$	$\frac{31}{32}$	$1\text{-}1\frac{13}{32}$	$1\frac{1}{16}$	$1\text{-}2\frac{13}{32}$	$1\frac{1}{8}$	$1\text{-}3\frac{13}{32}$	$1\frac{3}{16}$	$1\text{-}4\frac{13}{32}$
$\frac{7}{16}$	$\frac{29}{32}$	$1\text{-}0\frac{15}{32}$	$\frac{31}{32}$	$1\text{-}1\frac{15}{32}$	$1\frac{1}{16}$	$1\text{-}2\frac{15}{32}$	$1\frac{1}{8}$	$1\text{-}3\frac{15}{32}$	$1\frac{3}{16}$	$1\text{-}4\frac{15}{32}$
$\frac{1}{2}$	$\frac{29}{32}$	$1\text{-}0\frac{17}{32}$	1	$1\text{-}1\frac{17}{32}$	$1\frac{1}{16}$	$1\text{-}2\frac{17}{32}$	$1\frac{1}{8}$	$1\text{-}3\frac{17}{32}$	$1\frac{3}{16}$	$1\text{-}4\frac{17}{32}$
$\frac{9}{16}$	$\frac{29}{32}$	$1\text{-}0\frac{19}{32}$	1	$1\text{-}1\frac{19}{32}$	$1\frac{1}{16}$	$1\text{-}2\frac{19}{32}$	$1\frac{1}{8}$	$1\text{-}3\frac{19}{32}$	$1\frac{7}{32}$	$1\text{-}4\frac{19}{32}$
$\frac{5}{8}$	$\frac{29}{32}$	$1\text{-}0\frac{21}{32}$	1	$1\text{-}1\frac{21}{32}$	$1\frac{1}{16}$	$1\text{-}2\frac{21}{32}$	$1\frac{1}{8}$	$1\text{-}3\frac{21}{32}$	$1\frac{7}{32}$	$1\text{-}4\frac{21}{32}$
$\frac{11}{16}$	$\frac{15}{16}$	$1\text{-}0\frac{23}{32}$	1	$1\text{-}1\frac{23}{32}$	$1\frac{1}{16}$	$1\text{-}2\frac{23}{32}$	$1\frac{5}{32}$	$1\text{-}3\frac{23}{32}$	$1\frac{7}{32}$	$1\text{-}4\frac{23}{32}$
$\frac{3}{4}$	$\frac{15}{16}$	$1\text{-}0\frac{25}{32}$	1	$1\text{-}1\frac{25}{32}$	$1\frac{1}{16}$	$1\text{-}2\frac{25}{32}$	$1\frac{5}{32}$	$1\text{-}3\frac{25}{32}$	$1\frac{7}{32}$	$1\text{-}4\frac{25}{32}$
$\frac{13}{16}$	$\frac{15}{16}$	$1\text{-}0\frac{27}{32}$	1	$1\text{-}1\frac{27}{32}$	$1\frac{3}{32}$	$1\text{-}2\frac{27}{32}$	$1\frac{5}{32}$	$1\text{-}3\frac{27}{32}$	$1\frac{7}{32}$	$1\text{-}4\frac{27}{32}$
$\frac{7}{8}$	$\frac{15}{16}$	$1\text{-}0\frac{29}{32}$	1	$1\text{-}1\frac{29}{32}$	$1\frac{3}{32}$	$1\text{-}2\frac{29}{32}$	$1\frac{5}{32}$	$1\text{-}3\frac{29}{32}$	$1\frac{7}{32}$	$1\text{-}4\frac{29}{32}$
$\frac{15}{16}$	$\frac{15}{16}$	$1\text{-}0\frac{31}{32}$	$1\frac{1}{32}$	$1\text{-}1\frac{31}{32}$	$1\frac{3}{32}$	$1\text{-}2\frac{31}{32}$	$1\frac{5}{32}$	$1\text{-}3\frac{31}{32}$	$1\frac{1}{4}$	$1\text{-}4\frac{31}{32}$

Ins.	17″ Rise	17″ Slope	18″ Rise	18″ Slope	19″ Rise	19″ Slope	20″ Rise	20″ Slope	21″ Rise	21″ Slope
0	$1\frac{1}{4}$	$1\text{-}5\frac{1}{32}$	$1\frac{5}{16}$	$1\text{-}6\frac{1}{16}$	$1\frac{3}{8}$	$1\text{-}7\frac{1}{16}$	$1\frac{15}{32}$	$1\text{-}8\frac{1}{16}$	$1\frac{17}{32}$	$1\text{-}9\frac{1}{16}$
$\frac{1}{16}$	$1\frac{1}{4}$	$1\text{-}5\frac{3}{32}$	$1\frac{5}{16}$	$1\text{-}6\frac{1}{8}$	$1\frac{3}{8}$	$1\text{-}7\frac{1}{8}$	$1\frac{15}{32}$	$1\text{-}8\frac{1}{8}$	$1\frac{17}{32}$	$1\text{-}9\frac{1}{8}$
$\frac{1}{8}$	$1\frac{1}{4}$	$1\text{-}5\frac{5}{32}$	$1\frac{5}{16}$	$1\text{-}6\frac{3}{16}$	$1\frac{13}{32}$	$1\text{-}7\frac{3}{16}$	$1\frac{15}{32}$	$1\text{-}8\frac{3}{16}$	$1\frac{17}{32}$	$1\text{-}9\frac{3}{16}$
$\frac{3}{16}$	$1\frac{1}{4}$	$1\text{-}5\frac{7}{32}$	$1\frac{5}{16}$	$1\text{-}6\frac{1}{4}$	$1\frac{13}{32}$	$1\text{-}7\frac{1}{4}$	$1\frac{15}{32}$	$1\text{-}8\frac{1}{4}$	$1\frac{17}{32}$	$1\text{-}9\frac{1}{4}$
$\frac{1}{4}$	$1\frac{1}{4}$	$1\text{-}5\frac{9}{32}$	$1\frac{11}{32}$	$1\text{-}6\frac{5}{16}$	$1\frac{13}{32}$	$1\text{-}7\frac{5}{16}$	$1\frac{15}{32}$	$1\text{-}8\frac{5}{16}$	$1\frac{9}{16}$	$1\text{-}9\frac{5}{16}$
$\frac{5}{16}$	$1\frac{1}{4}$	$1\text{-}5\frac{11}{32}$	$1\frac{11}{32}$	$1\text{-}6\frac{3}{8}$	$1\frac{13}{32}$	$1\text{-}7\frac{3}{8}$	$1\frac{15}{32}$	$1\text{-}8\frac{3}{8}$	$1\frac{9}{16}$	$1\text{-}9\frac{3}{8}$
$\frac{3}{8}$	$1\frac{9}{32}$	$1\text{-}5\frac{13}{32}$	$1\frac{11}{32}$	$1\text{-}6\frac{7}{16}$	$1\frac{13}{32}$	$1\text{-}7\frac{7}{16}$	$1\frac{1}{2}$	$1\text{-}8\frac{7}{16}$	$1\frac{9}{16}$	$1\text{-}9\frac{7}{16}$
$\frac{7}{16}$	$1\frac{9}{32}$	$1\text{-}5\frac{15}{32}$	$1\frac{11}{32}$	$1\text{-}6\frac{1}{2}$	$1\frac{13}{32}$	$1\text{-}7\frac{1}{2}$	$1\frac{1}{2}$	$1\text{-}8\frac{1}{2}$	$1\frac{9}{16}$	$1\text{-}9\frac{1}{2}$
$\frac{1}{2}$	$1\frac{9}{32}$	$1\text{-}5\frac{17}{32}$	$1\frac{11}{32}$	$1\text{-}6\frac{9}{16}$	$1\frac{7}{16}$	$1\text{-}7\frac{9}{16}$	$1\frac{1}{2}$	$1\text{-}8\frac{9}{16}$	$1\frac{9}{16}$	$1\text{-}9\frac{9}{16}$
$\frac{9}{16}$	$1\frac{9}{32}$	$1\text{-}5\frac{19}{32}$	$1\frac{11}{32}$	$1\text{-}6\frac{5}{8}$	$1\frac{7}{16}$	$1\text{-}7\frac{5}{8}$	$1\frac{1}{2}$	$1\text{-}8\frac{5}{8}$	$1\frac{9}{16}$	$1\text{-}9\frac{5}{8}$
$\frac{5}{8}$	$1\frac{9}{32}$	$1\text{-}5\frac{21}{32}$	$1\frac{11}{32}$	$1\text{-}6\frac{11}{16}$	$1\frac{7}{16}$	$1\text{-}7\frac{11}{16}$	$1\frac{1}{2}$	$1\text{-}8\frac{11}{16}$	$1\frac{9}{16}$	$1\text{-}9\frac{11}{16}$
$\frac{11}{16}$	$1\frac{9}{32}$	$1\text{-}5\frac{3}{4}$	$1\frac{11}{32}$	$1\text{-}6\frac{11}{16}$	$1\frac{7}{16}$	$1\text{-}7\frac{3}{4}$	$1\frac{1}{2}$	$1\text{-}8\frac{3}{4}$	$1\frac{19}{32}$	$1\text{-}9\frac{3}{4}$
$\frac{3}{4}$	$1\frac{9}{32}$	$1\text{-}5\frac{13}{16}$	$1\frac{3}{8}$	$1\text{-}6\frac{13}{16}$	$1\frac{7}{16}$	$1\text{-}7\frac{13}{16}$	$1\frac{1}{2}$	$1\text{-}8\frac{13}{16}$	$1\frac{19}{32}$	$1\text{-}9\frac{13}{16}$
$\frac{13}{16}$	$1\frac{5}{16}$	$1\text{-}5\frac{7}{8}$	$1\frac{3}{8}$	$1\text{-}6\frac{7}{8}$	$1\frac{7}{16}$	$1\text{-}7\frac{7}{8}$	$1\frac{17}{32}$	$1\text{-}8\frac{7}{8}$	$1\frac{19}{32}$	$1\text{-}9\frac{7}{8}$
$\frac{7}{8}$	$1\frac{5}{16}$	$1\text{-}5\frac{15}{16}$	$1\frac{3}{8}$	$1\text{-}6\frac{15}{16}$	$1\frac{7}{16}$	$1\text{-}7\frac{15}{16}$	$1\frac{17}{32}$	$1\text{-}8\frac{15}{16}$	$1\frac{19}{32}$	$1\text{-}9\frac{15}{16}$
$\frac{15}{16}$	$1\frac{5}{16}$	$1\text{-}6$	$1\frac{3}{8}$	$1\text{-}7$	$1\frac{15}{32}$	$1\text{-}8$	$1\frac{17}{32}$	$1\text{-}9$	$1\frac{19}{32}$	$1\text{-}10$

Feet	40′ Rise	40′ Slope	50′ Rise	50′ Slope	60′ Rise	60′ Slope	70′ Rise	70′ Slope
0	$2\text{-}11$	$40\text{-}1\frac{9}{32}$	$3\text{-}7\frac{3}{4}$	$50\text{-}1\frac{19}{32}$	$4\text{-}4\frac{1}{2}$	$60\text{-}1\frac{29}{32}$	$5\text{-}1\frac{1}{4}$	$70\text{-}2\frac{7}{32}$
1	$2\text{-}11\frac{7}{8}$	$41\text{-}1\frac{5}{16}$	$3\text{-}8\frac{5}{8}$	$51\text{-}1\frac{5}{8}$	$4\text{-}5\frac{3}{8}$	$61\text{-}1\frac{15}{16}$	$5\text{-}2\frac{1}{8}$	$71\text{-}2\frac{1}{4}$
2	$3\text{-}0\frac{3}{4}$	$42\text{-}1\frac{11}{32}$	$3\text{-}9\frac{1}{2}$	$52\text{-}1\frac{21}{32}$	$4\text{-}6\frac{1}{4}$	$62\text{-}1\frac{31}{32}$	$5\text{-}3$	$72\text{-}2\frac{9}{32}$
3	$3\text{-}1\frac{5}{8}$	$43\text{-}1\frac{3}{8}$	$3\text{-}10\frac{3}{8}$	$53\text{-}1\frac{11}{16}$	$4\text{-}7\frac{1}{8}$	$63\text{-}2$	$5\text{-}3\frac{7}{8}$	$73\text{-}2\frac{5}{16}$
4	$3\text{-}2\frac{1}{2}$	$44\text{-}1\frac{13}{32}$	$3\text{-}11\frac{1}{4}$	$54\text{-}1\frac{23}{32}$	$4\text{-}8$	$64\text{-}2\frac{1}{32}$	$5\text{-}4\frac{3}{4}$	$74\text{-}2\frac{11}{32}$
5	$3\text{-}3\frac{3}{8}$	$45\text{-}1\frac{7}{16}$	$4\text{-}0\frac{1}{8}$	$55\text{-}1\frac{3}{4}$	$4\text{-}8\frac{7}{8}$	$65\text{-}2\frac{1}{16}$	$5\text{-}5\frac{5}{8}$	$75\text{-}2\frac{3}{8}$
6	$3\text{-}4\frac{1}{4}$	$46\text{-}1\frac{15}{32}$	$4\text{-}1$	$56\text{-}1\frac{25}{32}$	$4\text{-}9\frac{3}{4}$	$66\text{-}2\frac{3}{32}$	$5\text{-}6\frac{1}{2}$	$76\text{-}2\frac{13}{32}$
7	$3\text{-}5\frac{1}{8}$	$47\text{-}1\frac{1}{2}$	$4\text{-}1\frac{7}{8}$	$57\text{-}1\frac{13}{16}$	$4\text{-}10\frac{5}{8}$	$67\text{-}2\frac{1}{8}$	$5\text{-}7\frac{3}{8}$	$77\text{-}2\frac{7}{16}$
8	$3\text{-}6$	$48\text{-}1\frac{17}{32}$	$4\text{-}2\frac{3}{4}$	$58\text{-}1\frac{27}{32}$	$4\text{-}11\frac{1}{2}$	$68\text{-}2\frac{5}{32}$	$5\text{-}8\frac{1}{4}$	$78\text{-}2\frac{1}{2}$
9	$3\text{-}6\frac{7}{8}$	$49\text{-}1\frac{9}{16}$	$4\text{-}3\frac{5}{8}$	$59\text{-}1\frac{7}{8}$	$5\text{-}0\frac{3}{8}$	$69\text{-}2\frac{3}{16}$	$5\text{-}9\frac{1}{8}$	$79\text{-}2\frac{17}{32}$

natsin A$=0.0727235930$; natcos A$=0.9973521339$; nattan A$=0.0729166666$; natcot A$=13.7142857142$

Inches	0" Rise	0" Slope	1" Rise	1" Slope	2" Rise	2" Slope	3" Rise	3" Slope	4" Rise	4" Slope	5" Rise	5" Slope
0	0	0	1/16	1	5/32	2	1/4	3	5/16	4	3/8	5
1/16	0	1/16	3/32-	1 1/16	5/32	2 1/16	1/4	3 1/16	5/16	4 1/16	13/32-	5 1/16
1/8	0	1/8	3/32-	1 1/8	5/32	2 1/8	1/4	3 1/8	5/16	4 1/8	13/32-	5 1/8
3/16	0	3/16	3/32-	1 3/16	5/32	2 3/16	1/4	3 3/16	5/16	4 3/16	13/32-	5 7/32-
1/4	1/32-	1/4	3/32	1 1/4	3/16	2 1/4	1/4	3 1/4	11/32-	4 1/4	13/32	5 9/32-
5/16	1/32-	5/16	3/32	1 5/16	3/16	2 5/16	1/4	3 5/16	11/32-	4 5/16	13/32	5 11/32-
3/8	1/32-	3/8	3/32	1 3/8	3/16	2 3/8	1/4	3 3/8	11/32-	4 3/8	13/32	5 13/32-
7/16	1/32	7/16	1/8	1 7/16	3/16	2 7/16	9/32-	3 7/16	11/32	4 7/16	7/16	5 15/32-
1/2	1/32	1/2	1/8	1 1/2	3/16	2 1/2	9/32-	3 1/2	11/32	4 1/2	7/16	5 17/32-
9/16	1/32	9/16	1/8	1 9/16	3/16	2 9/16	9/32-	3 9/16	11/32	4 9/16	7/16	5 19/32-
5/8	1/16	5/8	1/8	1 5/8	7/32-	2 5/8	9/32-	3 5/8	3/8	4 5/8	7/16	5 21/32-
11/16	1/16	11/16	1/8	1 11/16	7/32-	2 11/16	9/32	3 11/16	3/8	4 11/16	7/16	5 23/32-
3/4	1/16	3/4	1/8	1 3/4	7/32-	2 3/4	9/32	3 3/4	3/8	4 3/4	7/16	5 25/32-
13/16	1/16	13/16	5/32-	1 13/16	7/32-	2 13/16	5/16	3 13/16	3/8	4 13/16	15/32-	5 27/32-
7/8	1/16	7/8	5/32-	1 7/8	7/32-	2 7/8	5/16	3 7/8	3/8	4 7/8	15/32-	5 29/32-
15/16	1/16	15/16	5/32-	1 15/16	7/32-	2 15/16	5/16	3 15/16	3/8	4 15/16	15/32-	5 31/32-

Inches	6" Rise	6" Slope	7" Rise	7" Slope	8" Rise	8" Slope	9" Rise	9" Slope	10" Rise	10" Slope	11" Rise	11" Slope
0	15/32	6 1/32-	9/16	7 1/32-	5/8	8 1/32-	11/16	9 1/32-	25/32	10 1/32-	7/8	11 1/32-
1/16	15/32	6 3/32-	9/16	7 3/32-	5/8	8 3/32-	23/32	9 3/32-	25/32	10 3/32-	7/8	11 3/32-
1/8	15/32	6 5/32-	9/16	7 5/32-	5/8	8 5/32-	23/32	9 5/32-	25/32	10 5/32-	7/8	11 5/32-
3/16	15/32	6 7/32-	9/16	7 7/32-	5/8	8 7/32-	23/32	9 7/32-	25/32	10 7/32-	7/8	11 7/32-
1/4	1/2	6 9/32-	9/16	7 9/32-	21/32	8 9/32-	23/32	9 9/32-	13/16	10 9/32-	7/8	11 9/32-
5/16	1/2	6 11/32-	9/16	7 11/32-	21/32	8 11/32-	23/32	9 11/32-	13/16	10 11/32-	7/8	11 11/32-
3/8	1/2	6 13/32-	19/32-	7 13/32-	21/32	8 13/32-	23/32	9 13/32-	13/16	10 13/32-	7/8	11 13/32-
7/16	1/2	6 15/32-	19/32-	7 15/32-	21/32	8 15/32-	3/4	9 15/32-	13/16	10 15/32-	29/32-	11 15/32-
1/2	1/2	6 17/32-	19/32-	7 17/32-	21/32	8 17/32-	3/4	9 17/32-	13/16	10 17/32-	29/32-	11 17/32-
9/16	1/2	6 19/32-	19/32-	7 19/32-	21/32	8 19/32-	3/4	9 19/32-	13/16	10 19/32-	29/32-	11 19/32-
5/8	17/32-	6 21/32-	19/32-	7 21/32-	11/16	8 21/32-	3/4	9 21/32-	27/32-	10 21/32-	29/32-	11 21/32-
11/16	17/32-	6 23/32-	19/32-	7 23/32-	11/16	8 23/32-	3/4	9 23/32-	27/32-	10 23/32-	29/32-	11 23/32-
3/4	17/32-	6 25/32-	19/32-	7 25/32-	11/16	8 25/32-	3/4	9 25/32-	27/32-	10 25/32-	29/32-	11 25/32-
13/16	17/32-	6 27/32-	5/8	7 27/32-	11/16	8 27/32-	25/32-	9 27/32-	27/32-	10 27/32-	15/16	11 27/32-
7/8	17/32-	6 29/32-	5/8	7 29/32-	11/16	8 29/32-	25/32-	9 29/32-	27/32-	10 29/32-	15/16	11 29/32-
15/16	17/32-	6 31/32-	5/8	7 31/32-	11/16	8 31/32-	25/32-	9 31/32-	27/32-	10 31/32-	15/16	11 31/32-

Feet	0' Rise	0' Slope	10' Rise	10' Slope	20' Rise	20' Slope	30' Rise	30' Slope
0	0	0	9 3/8	10-0 3/8	1-6 3/4	20-0 23/32-	2-4 1/8	30-1 3/32-
1	15/16	1-0 1/32-	10 5/16	11-0 13/32-	1-7 11/16	21-0 25/32-	2-5 1/16	31-1 3/8
2	1 7/8	2-0 1/8	11 1/4	12-0 7/16	1-8 5/8	22-0 13/16	2-6	32-1 15/32-
3	2 13/16	3-0 1/8	1-0 3/16	13-0 15/32-	1-9 9/16	23-0 27/32-	2-6 15/16	33-1 17/32-
4	3 3/4	4-0 5/32-	1-1 1/8	14-0 1/2	1-10 1/2	24-0 7/8	2-7 7/8	34-1 1/4
5	4 11/16	5-0 3/8	1-2 1/16	15-0 9/16	1-11 7/16	25-0 29/32-	2-8 13/16	35-1 9/32-
6	5 5/8	6-0 7/32-	1-3	16-0 19/32-	2-0 3/8	26-0 15/16	2-9 3/4	36-1 5/16
7	6 9/16	7-0 1/4	1-3 15/16	17-0 5/8	2-1 5/16	27-1	2-10 11/16	37-1 11/32-
8	7 1/2	8-0 9/32-	1-4 7/8	18-0 21/32-	2-2 1/4	28-1 1/16	2-11 5/8	38-1 3/8
9	8 7/16	9-0 11/32-	1-5 13/16	19-0 11/16	2-3 3/16	29-1 1/16	3-0 9/16	39-1 7/16

A = 4° 28' 02": logsin A = 8.89147; logcos A = 9.99868; logtan A = 8.89279; logcot A = 1.10721

Ins.	12″ Rise	Slope	13″ Rise	Slope	14″ Rise	Slope	15″ Rise	Slope	16″ Rise	Slope
0	15/16	1-0 1/32	1	1-1 1/32	1 3/32	1-2 1/32	1 3/16	1-3 1/32	1 1/4	1-4 1/16
1/16	15/16	1-0 3/32	1 1/32	1-1 3/32	1 3/32	1-2 3/32	1 3/16	1-3 3/32	1 1/4	1-4 1/8
1/8	15/16	1-0 5/32	1 1/32	1-1 5/32	1 3/32	1-2 5/32	1 3/16	1-3 5/32	1 1/4	1-4 3/16
3/16	15/16	1-0 7/32	1 1/32	1-1 7/32	1 3/32	1-2 7/32	1 3/16	1-3 7/32	1 1/4	1-4 1/4
1/4	31/32	1-0 9/32	1 1/32	1-1 9/32	1 1/8	1-2 9/32	1 3/16	1-3 9/32	1 9/32	1-4 5/16
5/16	31/32	1-0 11/32	1 1/32	1-1 11/32	1 1/8	1-2 11/32	1 3/16	1-3 11/32	1 9/32	1-4 3/8
3/8	31/32	1-0 13/32	1 1/32	1-1 13/32	1 1/8	1-2 13/32	1 3/16	1-3 13/32	1 9/32	1-4 7/16
7/16	31/32	1-0 15/32	1 1/16	1-1 15/32	1 1/8	1-2 15/32	1 7/32	1-3 1/2	1 9/32	1-4 1/2
1/2	31/32	1-0 17/32	1 1/16	1-1 17/32	1 1/8	1-2 17/32	1 7/32	1-3 9/16	1 9/32	1-4 9/16
9/16	31/32	1-0 19/32	1 1/16	1-1 19/32	1 1/8	1-2 19/32	1 7/32	1-3 5/8	1 9/32	1-4 5/8
5/8	1	1-0 21/32	1 1/16	1-1 21/32	1 5/32	1-2 21/32	1 7/32	1-3 11/16	1 5/16	1-4 11/16
11/16	1	1-0 23/32	1 1/16	1-1 23/32	1 5/32	1-2 23/32	1 7/32	1-3 3/4	1 5/16	1-4 3/4
3/4	1	1-0 25/32	1 1/16	1-1 25/32	1 5/32	1-2 25/32	1 7/32	1-3 13/16	1 5/16	1-4 13/16
13/16	1	1-0 27/32	1 3/32	1-1 27/32	1 5/32	1-2 27/32	1 1/4	1-3 7/8	1 5/16	1-4 7/8
7/8	1	1-0 29/32	1 3/32	1-1 29/32	1 5/32	1-2 29/32	1 1/4	1-3 15/16	1 5/16	1-4 15/16
15/16	1	1-0 31/32	1 3/32	1-1 31/32	1 5/32	1-2 31/32	1 1/4	1-4	1 5/16	1-5

Ins.	17″ Rise	Slope	18″ Rise	Slope	19″ Rise	Slope	20″ Rise	Slope	21″ Rise	Slope
0	1 5/16	1-5 1/16	1 13/32	1-6 1/16	1 1/2	1-7 1/16	1 9/16	1-8 1/16	1 5/8	1-9 1/16
1/16	1 11/32	1-5 1/8	1 13/32	1-6 1/8	1 1/2	1-7 1/8	1 9/16	1-8 1/8	1 21/32	1-9 1/8
1/8	1 11/32	1-5 3/16	1 13/32	1-6 3/16	1 1/2	1-7 3/16	1 9/16	1-8 3/16	1 21/32	1-9 3/16
3/16	1 11/32	1-5 1/4	1 13/32	1-6 1/4	1 1/2	1-7 1/4	1 9/16	1-8 1/4	1 21/32	1-9 1/4
1/4	1 11/32	1-5 5/16	1 7/16	1-6 5/16	1 1/2	1-7 5/16	1 19/32	1-8 5/16	1 21/32	1-9 5/16
5/16	1 11/32	1-5 3/8	1 7/16	1-6 3/8	1 1/2	1-7 3/8	1 19/32	1-8 3/8	1 21/32	1-9 3/8
3/8	1 11/32	1-5 7/16	1 7/16	1-6 7/16	1 1/2	1-7 7/16	1 19/32	1-8 7/16	1 21/32	1-9 7/16
7/16	1 3/8	1-5 1/2	1 7/16	1-6 1/2	1 17/32	1-7 1/2	1 19/32	1-8 1/2	1 11/16	1-9 1/2
1/2	1 3/8	1-5 9/16	1 7/16	1-6 9/16	1 17/32	1-7 9/16	1 19/32	1-8 9/16	1 11/16	1-9 9/16
9/16	1 3/8	1-5 5/8	1 7/16	1-6 5/8	1 17/32	1-7 5/8	1 19/32	1-8 5/8	1 11/16	1-9 5/8
5/8	1 3/8	1-5 11/16	1 15/32	1-6 11/16	1 17/32	1-7 11/16	1 5/8	1-8 11/16	1 11/16	1-9 11/16
11/16	1 3/8	1-5 3/4	1 15/32	1-6 3/4	1 17/32	1-7 3/4	1 5/8	1-8 3/4	1 11/16	1-9 3/4
3/4	1 3/8	1-5 13/16	1 15/32	1-6 13/16	1 17/32	1-7 13/16	1 5/8	1-8 13/16	1 11/16	1-9 13/16
13/16	1 13/32	1-5 7/8	1 15/32	1-6 7/8	1 9/16	1-7 7/8	1 5/8	1-8 7/8	1 23/32	1-9 7/8
7/8	1 13/32	1-5 15/16	1 15/32	1-6 15/16	1 9/16	1-7 15/16	1 5/8	1-8 15/16	1 23/32	1-9 15/16
15/16	1 13/32	1-6	1 15/32	1-7	1 9/16	1-8	1 5/8	1-9	1 23/32	1-10

Feet	40′ Rise	Slope	50′ Rise	Slope	60′ Rise	Slope	70′ Rise	Slope
0	3-1 1/2	40-1 15/32	3-10 7/8	50-1 27/32	4-8 1/4	60-2 3/16	5-5 5/8	70-2 9/16
1	3-2 7/16	41-1 1/2	3-11 13/16	51-1 7/8	4-9 3/16	61-2 7/32	5-6 9/16	71-2 19/32
2	3-3 3/8	42-1 17/32	4-0 3/4	52-1 29/32	4-10 1/8	62-2 9/32	5-7 1/2	72-2 5/8
3	3-4 5/16	43-1 9/16	4-1 11/16	53-1 15/16	4-11 1/16	63-2 5/16	5-8 7/16	73-2 21/32
4	3-5 1/4	44-1 19/32	4-2 5/8	54-1 31/32	5-0	64-2 11/32	5-9 3/8	74-2 23/32
5	3-6 3/16	45-1 21/32	4-3 9/16	55-2	5-0 15/16	65-2 3/8	5-10 5/16	75-2 3/4
6	3-7 1/8	46-1 11/16	4-4 1/2	56-2 1/16	5-1 7/8	66-2 13/32	5-11 1/4	76-2 25/32
7	3-8 1/16	47-1 23/32	4-5 7/16	57-2 3/32	5-2 13/16	67-2 7/16	6-0 3/16	77-2 13/16
8	3-9	48-1 3/4	4-6 3/8	58-2 1/8	5-3 3/4	68-2 1/2	6-1 1/8	78-2 27/32
9	3-9 15/16	49-1 25/32	4-7 5/16	59-2 5/32	5-4 11/16	69-2 17/32	6-2 1/16	79-2 7/8

natsin A=0.0778876672; natcos A=0.9969621413; nattan A=0.0781250000; natcot A=12.8000000000

Inches	0" Rise	0" Slope	1" Rise	1" Slope	2" Rise	2" Slope	3" Rise	3" Slope	4" Rise	4" Slope	5" Rise	5" Slope
0	0	0	3/32-	1	5/32	2	1/4	3	11/32-	4	13/32	5 1/32-
1/16	0	1/16	3/32-	1 1/16	3/16	2 1/16	1/4	3 1/16	11/32-	4 1/16	7/16	5 3/32-
1/8	0	1/8	3/32	1 1/8	3/16	2 1/8	1/4	3 1/8	11/32	4 1/8	7/16	5 5/32-
3/16	0	3/16	3/32	1 3/16	3/16	2 3/16	1/4	3 3/16	11/32	4 3/16	7/16	5 7/32-
1/4	1/32-	1/4	3/32	1 1/4	3/16	2 1/4	9/32-	3 1/4	11/32	4 1/4	7/16	5 9/32-
5/16	1/32-	5/16	1/8	1 5/16	3/16	2 5/16	9/32-	3 5/16	3/8	4 5/16	7/16	5 11/32-
3/8	1/32	3/8	1/8	1 3/8	3/16	2 3/8	9/32	3 3/8	3/8	4 3/8	7/16	5 13/32-
7/16	1/32	7/16	1/8	1 7/16	3/16	2 7/16	9/32	3 7/16	3/8	4 7/16	7/16	5 15/32-
1/2	1/32	1/2	1/8	1 1/2	7/32	2 1/2	9/32	3 1/2	3/8	4 1/2	15/32	5 17/32-
9/16	1/16	9/16	1/8	1 9/16	7/32	2 9/16	5/16	3 9/16	3/8	4 19/32-	15/32	5 19/32-
5/8	1/16	5/8	1/8	1 5/8	7/32	2 5/8	5/16	3 5/8	3/8	4 21/32-	15/32	5 21/32-
11/16	1/16	11/16	1/8	1 11/16	7/32	2 11/16	5/16	3 11/16	3/8	4 23/32-	15/32	5 23/32-
3/4	1/16	3/4	5/32	1 3/4	7/32	2 3/4	5/16	3 3/4	13/32	4 25/32-	15/32	5 25/32-
13/16	1/16	13/16	5/32	1 13/16	1/4	2 13/16	5/16	3 13/16	13/32	4 27/32-	1/2	5 27/32-
7/8	1/16	7/8	5/32	1 7/8	1/4	2 7/8	5/16	3 7/8	13/32	4 29/32-	1/2	5 29/32-
15/16	1/16	15/16	5/32	1 15/16	1/4	2 15/16	5/16	3 15/16	13/32	4 31/32-	1/2	5 31/32-

Inches	6" Rise	6" Slope	7" Rise	7" Slope	8" Rise	8" Slope	9" Rise	9" Slope	10" Rise	10" Slope	11" Rise	11" Slope
0	1/2	6 1/32-	19/32	7 1/32-	21/32	8 1/32-	3/4	9 1/32-	27/32	10 1/32-	29/32	11 1/32-
1/16	1/2	6 3/32-	19/32	7 3/32-	11/16	8 3/32-	3/4	9 3/32-	27/32	10 3/32-	15/16	11 3/32-
1/8	1/2	6 5/32-	19/32	7 5/32-	11/16	8 5/32-	3/4	9 5/32-	27/32	10 5/32-	15/16	11 5/32-
3/16	1/2	6 7/32-	19/32	7 7/32-	11/16	8 7/32-	3/4	9 7/32-	27/32	10 7/32-	15/16	11 7/32-
1/4	17/32	6 9/32-	19/32	7 9/32-	11/16	8 9/32-	25/32	9 9/32-	27/32	10 9/32-	15/16	11 9/32-
5/16	17/32	6 11/32-	5/8	7 11/32-	11/16	8 11/32-	25/32	9 11/32-	7/8	10 11/32-	15/16	11 11/32-
3/8	17/32	6 13/32-	5/8	7 13/32-	11/16	8 13/32-	25/32	9 13/32-	7/8	10 13/32-	15/16	11 13/32-
7/16	17/32	6 15/32-	5/8	7 15/32-	11/16	8 15/32-	25/32	9 15/32-	7/8	10 15/32-	15/16	11 15/32-
1/2	17/32	6 17/32-	5/8	7 17/32-	23/32	8 17/32-	25/32	9 17/32-	7/8	10 17/32-	31/32-	11 17/32-
9/16	9/16	6 19/32-	5/8	7 19/32-	23/32	8 19/32-	13/16	9 19/32-	7/8	10 19/32-	31/32-	11 19/32-
5/8	9/16	6 21/32-	5/8	7 21/32-	23/32	8 21/32-	13/16	9 21/32-	7/8	10 21/32-	31/32-	11 21/32-
11/16	9/16	6 23/32-	5/8	7 23/32-	23/32	8 23/32-	13/16	9 23/32-	7/8	10 23/32-	31/32-	11 23/32-
3/4	9/16	6 25/32-	21/32	7 25/32-	23/32	8 25/32-	13/16	9 25/32-	29/32	10 25/32-	31/32-	11 25/32-
13/16	9/16	6 27/32-	21/32	7 27/32-	3/4	8 27/32-	13/16	9 27/32-	29/32	10 27/32-	1	11 27/32-
7/8	9/16	6 29/32-	21/32	7 29/32-	3/4	8 29/32-	13/16	9 29/32-	29/32	10 29/32-	1	11 29/32-
15/16	9/16	6 31/32-	21/32	7 31/32-	3/4	8 31/32-	13/16	9 31/32-	29/32	10 31/32-	1	11 31/32-

Feet	0' Rise	0' Slope	10' Rise	10' Slope	20' Rise	20' Slope	30' Rise	30' Slope
0	0	0	10	10-0 13/32-	1-8	20-0 27/32-	2-6	30-1 1/4
1	1	1-0 1/16	11	11-0 15/32-	1-9	21-0 7/8	2-7	31-1 9/32-
2	2	2-0 3/32-	1-0	12-0 1/2	1-10	22-0 29/32-	2-8	32-1 11/32-
3	3	3-0 1/8	1-1	13-0 17/32-	1-11	23-0 31/32-	2-9	33-1 3/8
4	4	4-0 5/32	1-2	14-0 19/32-	2-0	24-1	2-10	34-1 13/32-
5	5	5-0 7/32-	1-3	15-0 5/8	2-1	25-1 1/16	2-11	35-1 15/32-
6	6	6-0 1/4	1-4	16-0 21/32-	2-2	26-1 3/32-	3-0	36-1 1/2
7	7	7-0 9/32-	1-5	17-0 23/32-	2-3	27-1 1/8	3-1	37-1 17/32-
8	8	8-0 11/32-	1-6	18-0 3/4	2-4	28-1 5/32	3-2	38-1 19/32-
9	9	9-0 3/8	1-7	19-0 25/32-	2-5	29-1 7/32-	3-3	39-1 5/8

A = 4° 45′ 49″; logsin A = 8.91932; logcos A = 9.99850; logtan A = 8.92082; logcot A = 1.07918

Ins.	12″ Rise	Slope	13″ Rise	Slope	14″ Rise	Slope	15″ Rise	Slope	16″ Rise	Slope
0	1	1-0 1/32	1 3/32−	1-1 1/32	1 5/32	1-2 1/32	1 1/4	1-3 1/16	1 11/32	1-4 1/16
1/16	1	1-0 3/32	1 3/32	1-1 3/32	1 3/16	1-2 1/8	1 1/4	1-3 1/8	1 11/32	1-4 1/8
1/8	1	1-0 5/32	1 3/32	1-1 5/32	1 3/16	1-2 3/16	1 1/4	1-3 3/16	1 11/32	1-4 3/16
3/16	1	1-0 7/32	1 3/32	1-1 7/32	1 3/16	1-2 1/4	1 1/4	1-3 1/4	1 11/32	1-4 1/4
1/4	1 1/32	1-0 9/32	1 3/32	1-1 9/32	1 3/16	1-2 5/16	1 9/32−	1-3 5/16	1 11/32	1-4 5/16
5/16	1 1/32	1-0 11/32	1 1/8	1-1 11/32	1 3/16	1-2 3/8	1 9/32−	1-3 3/8	1 3/8	1-4 3/8
3/8	1 1/32	1-0 13/32	1 1/8	1-1 13/32	1 3/16	1-2 7/16	1 9/32	1-3 7/16	1 3/8	1-4 7/16
7/16	1 1/32	1-0 15/32	1 1/8	1-1 15/32	1 3/16	1-2 1/2	1 9/32	1-3 1/2	1 3/8	1-4 1/2
1/2	1 1/16	1-0 17/32	1 1/8	1-1 17/32	1 7/32−	1-2 9/16	1 9/32	1-3 9/16	1 3/8	1-4 9/16
9/16	1 1/16	1-0 19/32	1 1/8	1-1 5/8	1 7/32−	1-2 5/8	1 5/16	1-3 5/8	1 3/8	1-4 5/8
5/8	1 1/16	1-0 21/32	1 1/8	1-1 11/16	1 7/32	1-2 11/16	1 5/16	1-3 11/16	1 3/8	1-4 11/16
11/16	1 1/16	1-0 23/32	1 1/8	1-1 3/4	1 7/32	1-2 3/4	1 5/16	1-3 3/4	1 3/8	1-4 3/4
3/4	1 1/16	1-0 25/32	1 5/32	1-1 13/16	1 7/32	1-2 13/16	1 5/16	1-3 13/16	1 13/32−	1-4 13/16
13/16	1 1/16	1-0 27/32	1 5/32	1-1 7/8	1 1/4	1-2 7/8	1 5/16	1-3 7/8	1 13/32−	1-4 7/8
7/8	1 1/16	1-0 29/32	1 5/32	1-1 15/16	1 1/4	1-2 15/16	1 5/16	1-3 15/16	1 13/32	1-4 15/16
15/16	1 1/16	1-0 31/32	1 5/32	1-2	1 1/4	1-3	1 5/16	1-4	1 13/32	1-5

Ins.	17″ Rise	Slope	18″ Rise	Slope	19″ Rise	Slope	20″ Rise	Slope	21″ Rise	Slope
0	1 13/32	1-5 1/16	1 1/2	1-6 1/16	1 19/32	1-7 1/16	1 21/32	1-8 1/16	1 3/4	1-9 1/16
1/16	1 7/16	1-5 1/8	1 1/2	1-6 1/8	1 19/32	1-7 1/8	1 11/16	1-8 1/8	1 3/4	1-9 1/8
1/8	1 7/16	1-5 3/16	1 1/2	1-6 3/16	1 19/32	1-7 3/16	1 11/16	1-8 3/16	1 3/4	1-9 3/16
3/16	1 7/16	1-5 1/4	1 1/2	1-6 1/4	1 19/32	1-7 1/4	1 11/16	1-8 1/4	1 3/4	1-9 1/4
1/4	1 7/16	1-5 5/16	1 17/32	1-6 5/16	1 19/32	1-7 5/16	1 11/16	1-8 5/16	1 25/32	1-9 5/16
5/16	1 7/16	1-5 3/8	1 17/32	1-6 3/8	1 5/8	1-7 3/8	1 11/16	1-8 3/8	1 25/32	1-9 3/8
3/8	1 7/16	1-5 7/16	1 17/32	1-6 7/16	1 5/8	1-7 7/16	1 11/16	1-8 7/16	1 25/32	1-9 7/16
7/16	1 7/16	1-5 1/2	1 17/32	1-6 1/2	1 5/8	1-7 1/2	1 11/16	1-8 1/2	1 25/32	1-9 1/2
1/2	1 15/32	1-5 9/16	1 17/32	1-6 9/16	1 5/8	1-7 9/16	1 23/32	1-8 9/16	1 25/32	1-9 9/16
9/16	1 15/32	1-5 5/8	1 9/16	1-6 5/8	1 5/8	1-7 5/8	1 23/32	1-8 5/8	1 13/16	1-9 5/8
5/8	1 15/32	1-5 11/16	1 9/16	1-6 11/16	1 5/8	1-7 11/16	1 23/32	1-8 11/16	1 13/16	1-9 11/16
11/16	1 15/32	1-5 3/4	1 9/16	1-6 3/4	1 5/8	1-7 3/4	1 23/32	1-8 3/4	1 13/16	1-9 3/4
3/4	1 15/32	1-5 13/16	1 9/16	1-6 13/16	1 21/32	1-7 13/16	1 23/32	1-8 13/16	1 13/16	1-9 13/16
13/16	1 1/2	1-5 7/8	1 9/16	1-6 7/8	1 21/32	1-7 7/8	1 3/4	1-8 7/8	1 13/16	1-9 7/8
7/8	1 1/2	1-5 15/16	1 9/16	1-6 15/16	1 21/32	1-7 15/16	1 3/4	1-8 15/16	1 13/16	1-9 15/16
15/16	1 1/2	1-6	1 9/16	1-7	1 21/32	1-8	1 3/4	1-9	1 13/16	1-10

Feet	40′ Rise	Slope	50′ Rise	Slope	60′ Rise	Slope	70′ Rise	Slope
0	3-4	40-1 21/32	4-2	50-2 3/32	5-0	60-2 1/2	5-10	70-2 29/32
1	3-5	41-1 23/32	4-3	51-2 1/8	5-1	61-2 17/32	5-11	71-2 31/32
2	3-6	42-1 3/4	4-4	52-2 5/32	5-2	62-2 19/32	6-0	72-3
3	3-7	43-1 25/32	4-5	53-2 7/32	5-3	63-2 5/8	6-1	73-3 1/32
4	3-8	44-1 27/32	4-6	54-2 1/4	5-4	64-2 21/32	6-2	74-3 1/16
5	3-9	45-1 7/8	4-7	55-2 9/32	5-5	65-2 23/32	6-3	75-3 1/8
6	3-10	46-1 29/32	4-8	56-2 11/32	5-6	66-2 3/4	6-4	76-3 5/32
7	3-11	47-1 31/32	4-9	57-2 3/8	5-7	67-2 25/32	6-5	77-3 3/16
8	4-0	48-2	4-10	58-2 13/32	5-8	68-2 27/32	6-6	78-3 1/4
9	4-1	49-2 1/32	4-11	59-2 15/32	5-9	69-2 7/8	6-7	79-3 9/32

natsin A=0.0830454798; natcos A=0.9965457582; nattan A=0.0833333333; natcot A=12.0000000000

Inches	0" Rise	0" Slope	1" Rise	1" Slope	2" Rise	2" Slope	3" Rise	3" Slope	4" Rise	4" Slope	5" Rise	5" Slope
0	0	0	3/32	1	3/16	2	1/4	3	11/32	4 1/32	7/16	5 1/32
1/16	0	1/16	3/32	1 1/16	3/16	2 1/16	9/32	3 1/16	3/8	4 3/32	7/16	5 3/32
1/8	0	1/8	3/32	1 1/8	3/16	2 1/8	9/32	3 1/8	3/8	4 5/32	15/32	5 5/32
3/16	1/32	3/16	3/32	1 3/16	3/16	2 3/16	9/32	3 3/16	3/8	4 7/32	15/32	5 7/32
1/4	1/32	1/4	1/8	1 1/4	3/16	2 1/4	9/32	3 1/4	3/8	4 9/32	15/32	5 9/32
5/16	1/32	5/16	1/8	1 5/16	7/32	2 5/16	9/32	3 5/16	3/8	4 11/32	15/32	5 11/32
3/8	1/32	3/8	1/8	1 3/8	7/32	2 3/8	5/16	3 3/8	3/8	4 13/32	15/32	5 13/32
7/16	1/32	7/16	1/8	1 7/16	7/32	2 7/16	5/16	3 7/16	13/32	4 15/32	15/32	5 15/32
1/2	1/32	1/2	1/8	1 1/2	7/32	2 1/2	5/16	3 1/2	13/32	4 17/32	1/2	5 17/32
9/16	1/16	9/16	1/8	1 9/16	7/32	2 9/16	5/16	3 9/16	13/32	4 19/32	1/2	5 19/32
5/8	1/16	5/8	5/32	1 5/8	7/32	2 5/8	5/16	3 5/8	13/32	4 21/32	1/2	5 21/32
11/16	1/16	11/16	5/32	1 11/16	1/4	2 11/16	5/16	3 11/16	13/32	4 23/32	1/2	5 23/32
3/4	1/16	3/4	5/32	1 3/4	1/4	2 3/4	11/32	3 3/4	13/32	4 25/32	1/2	5 25/32
13/16	1/16	13/16	5/32	1 13/16	1/4	2 13/16	11/32	3 13/16	7/16	4 27/32	1/2	5 27/32
7/8	1/16	7/8	5/32	1 7/8	1/4	2 7/8	11/32	3 7/8	7/16	4 29/32	17/32	5 29/32
15/16	3/32	15/16	5/32	1 15/16	1/4	2 15/16	11/32	3 15/16	7/16	4 31/32	17/32	5 31/32

Inches	6" Rise	6" Slope	7" Rise	7" Slope	8" Rise	8" Slope	9" Rise	9" Slope	10" Rise	10" Slope	11" Rise	11" Slope
0	17/32	6 1/32	5/8	7 1/32	23/32	8 1/32	13/16	9 1/32	7/8	10 1/32	31/32	11 1/32
1/16	17/32	6 3/32	5/8	7 3/32	23/32	8 3/32	13/16	9 3/32	29/32	10 3/32	31/32	11 3/32
1/8	17/32	6 5/32	5/8	7 5/32	23/32	8 5/32	13/16	9 5/32	29/32	10 5/32	1	11 5/32
3/16	9/16	6 7/32	5/8	7 7/32	23/32	8 7/32	13/16	9 7/32	29/32	10 7/32	1	11 7/32
1/4	9/16	6 9/32	21/32	7 9/32	23/32	8 9/32	13/16	9 9/32	29/32	10 9/32	1	11 9/32
5/16	9/16	6 11/32	21/32	7 11/32	3/4	8 11/32	13/16	9 11/32	29/32	10 11/32	1	11 11/32
3/8	9/16	6 13/32	21/32	7 13/32	3/4	8 13/32	27/32	9 13/32	29/32	10 13/32	1	11 13/32
7/16	9/16	6 15/32	21/32	7 15/32	3/4	8 15/32	27/32	9 15/32	15/16	10 15/32	1	11 15/32
1/2	9/16	6 17/32	21/32	7 17/32	3/4	8 17/32	27/32	9 17/32	15/16	10 17/32	1 1/32	11 17/32
9/16	19/32	6 19/32	21/32	7 19/32	3/4	8 19/32	27/32	9 19/32	15/16	10 19/32	1 1/32	11 19/32
5/8	19/32	6 21/32	11/16	7 21/32	3/4	8 21/32	27/32	9 21/32	15/16	10 21/32	1 1/32	11 21/32
11/16	19/32	6 23/32	11/16	7 23/32	25/32	8 23/32	27/32	9 23/32	15/16	10 23/32	1 1/32	11 23/32
3/4	19/32	6 25/32	11/16	7 25/32	25/32	8 25/32	7/8	9 25/32	15/16	10 25/32	1 1/32	11 25/32
13/16	19/32	6 27/32	11/16	7 27/32	25/32	8 27/32	7/8	9 27/32	31/32	10 27/32	1 1/32	11 27/32
7/8	19/32	6 29/32	11/16	7 29/32	25/32	8 29/32	7/8	9 29/32	31/32	10 29/32	1 1/16	11 29/32
15/16	5/8	6 31/32	11/16	7 31/32	25/32	8 31/32	7/8	9 31/32	31/32	10 31/32	1 1/16	11 31/32

Feet	0' Rise	0' Slope	10' Rise	10' Slope	20' Rise	20' Slope	30' Rise	30' Slope
0	0	0	10 5/8	10-0 15/32	1-9 1/4	20-0 15/16	2-7 7/8	30-1 13/32
1	1 1/16	1-0 1/16	11 11/16	11-0 17/32	1-10 5/16	21-1	2-8 15/16	31-1 15/32
2	2 1/8	2-0 3/32	1-0 3/4	12-0 9/16	1-11 3/8	22-1 1/2	2-10	32-1 1/2
3	3 3/16	3-0 5/32	1-1 13/16	13-0 5/8	2-0 1/2	23-1 3/32	2-11 1/4	33-1 9/16
4	4 1/4	4-0 3/16	1-2 7/8	14-0 21/32	2-1 1/2	24-1 1/8	3-0 1/8	34-1 19/32
5	5 5/16	5-0 1/4	1-3 15/16	15-0 23/32	2-2 9/16	25-1 3/16	3-1 3/16	35-1 21/32
6	6 3/8	6-0 9/32	1-5	16-0 3/4	2-3 5/8	26-1 17/32	3-2 1/4	36-1 11/16
7	7 7/16	7-0 11/32	1-6 1/16	17-0 13/16	2-4 11/16	27-1 9/32	3-3 5/16	37-1 3/4
8	8 1/2	8-0 3/8	1-7 1/8	18-0 27/32	2-5 3/4	28-1 5/16	3-4 3/8	38-1 25/32
9	9 9/16	9-0 7/16	1-8 3/16	19-0 29/32	2-6 13/16	29-1 3/8	3-5 7/16	39-1 27/32

A = 5° 03' 36"; logsin A = 8.94545; logcos A = 9.99830; logtan A = 8.94715; logcot A = 1.05285

Ins.	12″ Rise	12″ Slope	13″ Rise	13″ Slope	14″ Rise	14″ Slope	15″ Rise	15″ Slope	16″ Rise	16″ Slope
0	1 1/16	1-0 1/16	1 5/32	1-1 1/16	1 1/4	1-2 1/16	1 5/16	1-3 1/16	1 13/32	1-4 1/16
1/16	1 1/16	1-0 1/8	1 5/32	1-1 1/8	1 1/4	1-2 1/8	1 11/32	1-3 1/8	1 7/16	1-4 1/8
1/8	1 1/16	1-0 3/16	1 5/32	1-1 3/16	1 1/4	1-2 3/16	1 11/32	1-3 3/16	1 7/16	1-4 3/16
3/16	1 3/32	1-0 1/4	1 5/32	1-1 1/4	1 1/4	1-2 1/4	1 11/32	1-3 1/4	1 7/16	1-4 1/4
1/4	1 3/32	1-0 5/16	1 3/16	1-1 5/16	1 1/4	1-2 5/16	1 11/32	1-3 5/16	1 7/16	1-4 5/16
5/16	1 3/32	1-0 3/8	1 3/16	1-1 3/8	1 9/32	1-2 3/8	1 11/32	1-3 3/8	1 7/16	1-4 3/8
3/8	1 3/32	1-0 7/16	1 3/16	1-1 7/16	1 9/32	1-2 7/16	1 3/8	1-3 7/16	1 7/16	1-4 7/16
7/16	1 3/32	1-0 1/2	1 3/16	1-1 1/2	1 9/32	1-2 1/2	1 3/8	1-3 1/2	1 15/32	1-4 1/2
1/2	1 3/32	1-0 9/16	1 3/16	1-1 9/16	1 9/32	1-2 9/16	1 3/8	1-3 9/16	1 15/32	1-4 9/16
9/16	1 1/8	1-0 5/8	1 3/16	1-1 5/8	1 9/32	1-2 5/8	1 3/8	1-3 5/8	1 15/32	1-4 5/8
5/8	1 1/8	1-0 11/16	1 7/32	1-1 11/16	1 9/32	1-2 11/16	1 3/8	1-3 11/16	1 15/32	1-4 11/16
11/16	1 1/8	1-0 3/4	1 7/32	1-1 3/4	1 5/16	1-2 3/4	1 3/8	1-3 3/4	1 15/32	1-4 3/4
3/4	1 1/8	1-0 13/16	1 7/32	1-1 13/16	1 5/16	1-2 13/16	1 13/32	1-3 13/16	1 15/32	1-4 13/16
13/16	1 1/8	1-0 7/8	1 7/32	1-1 7/8	1 5/16	1-2 7/8	1 13/32	1-3 7/8	1 1/2	1-4 7/8
7/8	1 1/8	1-0 15/16	1 7/32	1-1 15/16	1 5/16	1-2 15/16	1 13/32	1-3 15/16	1 1/2	1-4 15/16
15/16	1 5/32	1-1	1 7/32	1-2	1 5/16	1-3	1 13/32	1-4	1 1/2	1-5

Ins.	17″ Rise	17″ Slope	18″ Rise	18″ Slope	19″ Rise	19″ Slope	20″ Rise	20″ Slope	21″ Rise	21″ Slope
0	1 1/2	1-5 1/16	1 19/32	1-6 1/16	1 11/16	1-7 1/16	1 25/32	1-8 3/32	1 7/8	1-9 3/32
1/16	1 1/2	1-5 1/8	1 19/32	1-6 1/8	1 11/16	1-7 1/8	1 25/32	1-8 5/32	1 7/8	1-9 5/32
1/8	1 17/32	1-5 3/16	1 19/32	1-6 3/16	1 11/16	1-7 3/16	1 25/32	1-8 7/32	1 7/8	1-9 7/32
3/16	1 17/32	1-5 1/4	1 5/8	1-6 1/4	1 11/16	1-7 1/4	1 25/32	1-8 9/32	1 7/8	1-9 9/32
1/4	1 17/32	1-5 5/16	1 5/8	1-6 5/16	1 23/32	1-7 5/16	1 25/32	1-8 11/32	1 7/8	1-9 11/32
5/16	1 17/32	1-5 3/8	1 5/8	1-6 3/8	1 23/32	1-7 3/8	1 13/16	1-8 13/32	1 7/8	1-9 13/32
3/8	1 17/32	1-5 7/16	1 5/8	1-6 7/16	1 23/32	1-7 7/16	1 13/16	1-8 15/32	1 29/32	1-9 15/32
7/16	1 17/32	1-5 1/2	1 5/8	1-6 1/2	1 23/32	1-7 1/2	1 13/16	1-8 17/32	1 29/32	1-9 17/32
1/2	1 9/16	1-5 9/16	1 5/8	1-6 9/16	1 23/32	1-7 9/16	1 13/16	1-8 19/32	1 29/32	1-9 19/32
9/16	1 9/16	1-5 5/8	1 21/32	1-6 5/8	1 23/32	1-7 5/8	1 13/16	1-8 21/32	1 29/32	1-9 21/32
5/8	1 9/16	1-5 11/16	1 21/32	1-6 11/16	1 3/4	1-7 11/16	1 13/16	1-8 23/32	1 29/32	1-9 23/32
11/16	1 9/16	1-5 3/4	1 21/32	1-6 3/4	1 3/4	1-7 3/4	1 27/32	1-8 25/32	1 29/32	1-9 25/32
3/4	1 9/16	1-5 13/16	1 21/32	1-6 13/16	1 3/4	1-7 13/16	1 27/32	1-8 27/32	1 15/16	1-9 27/32
13/16	1 9/16	1-5 7/8	1 21/32	1-6 7/8	1 3/4	1-7 7/8	1 27/32	1-8 29/32	1 15/16	1-9 29/32
7/8	1 19/32	1-5 15/16	1 21/32	1-6 15/16	1 3/4	1-7 15/16	1 27/32	1-8 31/32	1 15/16	1-9 31/32
15/16	1 19/32	1-6	1 11/16	1-7	1 3/4	1-8	1 27/32	1-9 1/32	1 15/16	1-10 1/32

Feet	40′ Rise	40′ Slope	50′ Rise	50′ Slope	60′ Rise	60′ Slope	70′ Rise	70′ Slope
0	3-6 1/2	40-1 7/8	4-5 1/8	50-2 11/32	5-3 3/4	60-2 13/16	6-2 3/8	70-3 9/32
1	3-7 9/16	41-1 15/16	4-6 3/16	51-2 13/32	5-4 13/16	61-2 7/8	6-3 7/16	71-3 11/32
2	3-8 5/8	42-1 31/32	4-7 1/4	52-2 7/16	5-5 7/8	62-2 29/32	6-4 1/2	72-3 3/8
3	3-9 11/16	43-2 1/32	4-8 5/16	53-2 1/2	5-6 15/16	63-2 31/32	6-5 9/16	73-3 7/16
4	3-10 3/4	44-2 1/16	4-9 3/8	54-2 17/32	5-8	64-3	6-6 5/8	74-3 15/32
5	3-11 13/16	45-2 1/8	4-10 7/16	55-2 19/32	5-9 1/16	65-3 1/16	6-7 11/16	75-3 17/32
6	4-0 7/8	46-2 5/32	4-11 1/2	56-2 5/8	5-10 1/8	66-3 3/32	6-8 3/4	76-3 9/16
7	4-1 15/16	47-2 7/32	5-0 9/16	57-2 11/16	5-11 3/16	67-3 5/32	6-9 13/16	77-3 5/8
8	4-3	48-2 1/4	5-1 5/8	58-2 23/32	6-0 1/4	68-3 3/16	6-10 7/8	78-3 21/32
9	4-4 1/16	49-2 5/16	5-2 11/16	59-2 25/32	6-1 5/16	69-3 1/4	6-11 15/16	79-3 23/32

natsin A=0.0881966272; natcos A=0.9961030845; nattan A=0.0885416666; natcot A=11.2941176470

Inches	0" Rise	0" Slope	1" Rise	1" Slope	2" Rise	2" Slope	3" Rise	3" Slope	4" Rise	4" Slope	5" Rise	5" Slope
0	0	0	3/32	1	3/16	2	9/32	3	3/8	4 1/32	15/32	5 1/32
1/16	0	1/16	3/32	1 1/16	3/16	2 1/16	9/32	3 1/16	3/8	4 3/32	15/32	5 3/32
1/8	0	1/8	3/32	1 1/8	3/16	2 1/8	9/32	3 1/8	3/8	4 5/32	15/32	5 5/32
3/16	1/32	3/16	1/8	1 3/16	7/32	2 3/16	5/16	3 3/16	13/32	4 7/32	1/2	5 7/32
1/4	1/32	1/4	1/8	1 1/4	7/32	2 1/4	5/16	3 1/4	13/32	4 9/32	1/2	5 9/32
5/16	1/32	5/16	1/8	1 5/16	7/32	2 5/16	5/16	3 5/16	13/32	4 11/32	1/2	5 11/32
3/8	1/32	3/8	1/8	1 3/8	7/32	2 3/8	5/16	3 3/8	13/32	4 13/32	1/2	5 13/32
7/16	1/32	7/16	1/8	1 7/16	7/32	2 7/16	5/16	3 7/16	13/32	4 15/32	1/2	5 15/32
1/2	1/16	1/2	1/8	1 1/2	1/4	2 1/2	5/16	3 1/2	7/16	4 17/32	17/32	5 17/32
9/16	1/16	9/16	5/32	1 9/16	1/4	2 9/16	11/32	3 19/32	7/16	4 19/32	17/32	5 19/32
5/8	1/16	5/8	5/32	1 5/8	1/4	2 5/8	11/32	3 21/32	7/16	4 21/32	17/32	5 21/32
11/16	1/16	11/16	5/32	1 11/16	1/4	2 11/16	11/32	3 23/32	7/16	4 23/32	17/32	5 23/32
3/4	1/16	3/4	5/32	1 3/4	1/4	2 3/4	11/32	3 25/32	7/16	4 25/32	17/32	5 25/32
13/16	1/16	13/16	5/32	1 13/16	1/4	2 13/16	11/32	3 27/32	7/16	4 27/32	17/32	5 27/32
7/8	3/32	7/8	3/16	1 7/8	9/32	2 7/8	3/8	3 29/32	15/32	4 29/32	9/16	5 29/32
15/16	3/32	15/16	3/16	1 15/16	9/32	2 15/16	3/8	3 31/32	15/32	4 31/32	9/16	5 31/32

Inches	6" Rise	6" Slope	7" Rise	7" Slope	8" Rise	8" Slope	9" Rise	9" Slope	10" Rise	10" Slope	11" Rise	11" Slope
0	9/16	6 1/32	21/32	7 1/32	3/4	8 1/32	27/32	9 1/32	15/16	10 1/32	1 1/32	11 1/16
1/16	9/16	6 3/32	21/32	7 3/32	3/4	8 3/32	27/32	9 3/32	15/16	10 3/32	1 1/32	11 1/8
1/8	9/16	6 5/32	21/32	7 5/32	3/4	8 5/32	27/32	9 5/32	15/16	10 5/32	1 1/32	11 3/16
3/16	19/32	6 7/32	11/16	7 7/32	25/32	8 7/32	7/8	9 7/32	31/32	10 7/32	1 1/16	11 1/4
1/4	19/32	6 9/32	11/16	7 9/32	25/32	8 9/32	7/8	9 9/32	31/32	10 9/32	1 1/16	11 5/16
5/16	19/32	6 11/32	11/16	7 11/32	25/32	8 11/32	7/8	9 11/32	31/32	10 11/32	1 1/16	11 3/8
3/8	19/32	6 13/32	11/16	7 13/32	25/32	8 13/32	7/8	9 13/32	31/32	10 13/32	1 1/16	11 7/16
7/16	19/32	6 15/32	11/16	7 15/32	25/32	8 15/32	7/8	9 15/32	31/32	10 15/32	1 1/16	11 1/2
1/2	5/8	6 17/32	11/16	7 17/32	13/16	8 17/32	7/8	9 17/32	1	10 17/32	1 1/16	11 9/16
9/16	5/8	6 19/32	23/32	7 19/32	13/16	8 19/32	29/32	9 19/32	1	10 19/32	1 3/32	11 5/8
5/8	5/8	6 21/32	23/32	7 21/32	13/16	8 21/32	29/32	9 21/32	1	10 11/16	1 3/32	11 11/16
11/16	5/8	6 23/32	23/32	7 23/32	13/16	8 23/32	29/32	9 23/32	1	10 3/4	1 3/32	11 3/4
3/4	5/8	6 25/32	23/32	7 25/32	13/16	8 25/32	29/32	9 25/32	1	10 13/16	1 3/32	11 13/16
13/16	5/8	6 27/32	23/32	7 27/32	13/16	8 27/32	29/32	9 27/32	1	10 7/8	1 3/32	11 7/8
7/8	21/32	6 29/32	3/4	7 29/32	27/32	8 29/32	15/16	9 29/32	1 1/32	10 15/16	1 1/8	11 15/16
15/16	21/32	6 31/32	3/4	7 31/32	27/32	8 31/32	15/16	9 31/32	1 1/32	11	1 1/8	1-0

Feet	0' Rise	0' Slope	10' Rise	10' Slope	20' Rise	20' Slope	30' Rise	30' Slope
0	0	0	11 1/4	10-0 11/32	1-10 1/2	20-1 1/16	2-9 3/4	30-1 19/32
1	1 1/8	1-0 1/16	1-0 3/8	11-0 19/32	1-11 5/8	21-1 3/8	2-10 7/8	31-1 5/8
2	2 1/4	2-0 3/32	1-1 1/2	12-0 5/8	2-0 3/4	22-1 5/32	3-0	32-1 11/16
3	3 3/8	3-0 5/32	1-2 5/8	13-0 11/16	2-1 7/8	23-1 7/32	3-1 1/8	33-1 3/4
4	4 1/2	4-0 7/32	1-3 3/4	14-0 3/4	2-3	24-1 1/4	3-2 1/4	34-1 25/32
5	5 5/8	5-0 1/4	1-4 7/8	15-0 25/32	2-4 1/8	25-1 5/16	3-3 3/8	35-1 27/32
6	6 3/4	6-0 5/16	1-6	16-0 27/32	2-5 1/4	26-1 3/8	3-4 1/2	36-1 29/32
7	7 7/8	7-0 3/8	1-7 1/8	17-0 29/32	2-6 3/8	27-1 13/32	3-5 5/8	37-1 15/16
8	9	8-0 13/32	1-8 1/4	18-0 15/16	2-7 1/2	28-1 15/32	3-6 3/4	38-2
9	10 1/8	9-0 15/32	1-9 3/8	19-1	2-8 5/8	29-1 17/32	3-7 7/8	39-2 1/16

A = 5° 21' 21"; logsin A = 8.97007; logcos A = 9.99810; logtan A = 8.97197; logcot A = 1.02803

Ins.	12″ Rise	12″ Slope	13″ Rise	13″ Slope	14″ Rise	14″ Slope	15″ Rise	15″ Slope	16″ Rise	16″ Slope
0	1⅛	1-0 1/16	1 7/32	1-1 1/16	1 5/16	1-2 1/16	1 13/32	1-3 1/16	1½	1-4 1/16
1/16	1⅛	1-0⅛	1 7/32	1-1⅛	1 5/16	1-2⅛	1 13/32	1-3⅛	1½	1-4⅛
1/8	1⅛	1-0 3/16	1 7/32	1-1 3/16	1 5/16	1-2 3/16	1 13/32	1-3 3/16	1½	1-4 3/16
3/16	1 5/32	1-0¼	1¼	1-1¼	1 11/32	1-2¼	1 7/16	1-3¼	1 17/32	1-4¼
1/4	1 5/32	1-0 5/16	1¼	1-1 5/16	1 11/32	1-2 5/16	1 7/16	1-3 5/16	1 17/32	1-4 5/16
5/16	1 5/32	1-0⅜	1¼	1-1⅜	1 11/32	1-2⅜	1 7/16	1-3⅜	1 17/32	1-4⅜
3/8	1 5/32	1-0 7/16	1¼	1-1 7/16	1 11/32	1-2 7/16	1 7/16	1-3 7/16	1 17/32	1-4 7/16
7/16	1 5/32	1-0½	1¼	1-1½	1 11/32	1-2½	1 7/16	1-3½	1 17/32	1-4½
1/2	1 3/16	1-0 9/16	1¼	1-1 9/16	1⅜	1-2 9/16	1 7/16	1-3 9/16	1 9/16	1-4 9/16
9/16	1 3/16	1-0⅝	1 9/32	1-1⅝	1⅜	1-2⅝	1 15/32	1-3⅝	1 9/16	1-4⅝
5/8	1 3/16	1-0 11/16	1 9/32	1-1 11/16	1⅜	1-2 11/16	1 15/32	1-3 11/16	1 9/16	1-4 11/16
11/16	1 3/16	1-0¾	1 9/32	1-1¾	1⅜	1-2¾	1 15/32	1-3¾	1 9/16	1-4¾
3/4	1 3/16	1-0 13/16	1 9/32	1-1 13/16	1⅜	1-2 13/16	1 15/32	1-3 13/16	1 9/16	1-4 13/16
13/16	1 3/16	1-0⅞	1 9/32	1-1⅞	1⅜	1-2⅞	1 15/32	1-3⅞	1 9/16	1-4⅞
7/8	1 7/32	1-0 15/16	1 5/16	1-1 15/16	1 13/32	1-2 15/16	1½	1-3 15/16	1 19/32	1-4 15/16
15/16	1 7/32	1-1	1 5/16	1-2	1 13/32	1-3	1½	1-4	1 19/32	1-5

Ins.	17″ Rise	17″ Slope	18″ Rise	18″ Slope	19″ Rise	19″ Slope	20″ Rise	20″ Slope	21″ Rise	21″ Slope
0	1 19/32	1-5 1/16	1 11/16	1-6 3/32	1 25/32	1-7 3/32	1⅞	1-8 3/32	1 31/32	1-9 3/32
1/16	1 19/32	1-5⅛	1 11/16	1-6 5/32	1 25/32	1-7 5/32	1⅞	1-8 5/32	1 31/32	1-9 5/32
1/8	1 19/32	1-5 3/16	1 11/16	1-6 7/32	1 25/32	1-7 7/32	1⅞	1-8 7/32	1 31/32	1-9 7/32
3/16	1⅝	1-5¼	1 23/32	1-6 9/32	1 13/16	1-7 9/32	1 29/32	1-8 9/32	2	1-9 9/32
1/4	1⅝	1-5 5/16	1 23/32	1-6 11/32	1 13/16	1-7 11/32	1 29/32	1-8 11/32	2	1-9 11/32
5/16	1⅝	1-5⅜	1 23/32	1-6 13/32	1 13/16	1-7 13/32	1 29/32	1-8 13/32	2	1-9 13/32
3/8	1⅝	1-5 7/16	1 23/32	1-6 15/32	1 13/16	1-7 15/32	1 29/32	1-8 15/32	2	1-9 15/32
7/16	1⅝	1-5½	1 23/32	1-6 17/32	1 13/16	1-7 17/32	1 29/32	1-8 17/32	2	1-9 17/32
1/2	1⅝	1-5 9/16	1¾	1-6 19/32	1 13/16	1-7 19/32	1 15/16	1-8 19/32	2	1-9 19/32
9/16	1 21/32	1-5⅝	1¾	1-6 21/32	1 27/32	1-7 21/32	1 15/16	1-8 21/32	2 1/32	1-9 21/32
5/8	1 21/32	1-5 11/16	1¾	1-6 23/32	1 27/32	1-7 23/32	1 15/16	1-8 23/32	2 1/32	1-9 23/32
11/16	1 21/32	1-5¾	1¾	1-6 25/32	1 27/32	1-7 25/32	1 15/16	1-8 25/32	2 1/32	1-9 25/32
3/4	1 21/32	1-5 13/16	1¾	1-6 27/32	1 27/32	1-7 27/32	1 15/16	1-8 27/32	2 1/32	1-9 27/32
13/16	1 21/32	1-5⅞	1¾	1-6 29/32	1 27/32	1-7 29/32	1 15/16	1-8 29/32	2 1/32	1-9 29/32
7/8	1 11/16	1-5 31/32	1 25/32	1-6 31/32	1⅞	1-7 31/32	1 31/32	1-8 31/32	2 1/16	1-9 31/32
15/16	1 11/16	1-6 1/32	1 25/32	1-7 1/32	1⅞	1-8 1/32	1 31/32	1-9 1/32	2 1/16	1-10 1/32

Feet	40′ Rise	40′ Slope	50′ Rise	50′ Slope	60′ Rise	60′ Slope	70′ Rise	70′ Slope
0	3-9	40-2 3/32	4-8¼	50-2⅝	5-7½	60-3 5/32	6-6¾	70-3 11/16
1	3-10⅛	41-2 5/32	4-9⅜	51-2 11/16	5-8⅝	61-3 7/32	6-7⅞	71-3¾
2	3-11¼	42-2 7/32	4-10½	52-2¾	5-9¾	62-3¼	6-9	72-3 25/32
3	4-0⅜	43-2¼	4-11⅝	53-2 25/32	5-10⅞	63-3 5/16	6-10⅛	73-3 27/32
4	4-1½	44-2 5/16	5-0¾	54-2 27/32	6-0	64-3⅜	6-11¼	74-3 29/32
5	4-2⅝	45-2⅜	5-1⅞	55-2 29/32	6-1⅛	65-3 13/32	7-0⅜	75-3 15/16
6	4-3¾	46-2 13/32	5-3	56-2 15/16	6-2¼	66-3 15/32	7-1½	76-4
7	4-4⅞	47-2 15/32	5-4⅛	57-3	6-3⅜	67-3 17/32	7-2⅝	77-4 1/16
8	4-6	48-2 17/32	5-5¼	58-3 1/16	6-4½	68-3 9/16	7-3¾	78-4 3/32
9	4-7⅛	49-2 19/32	5-6⅜	59-3 3/32	6-5⅝	69-3⅝	7-4⅞	79-4 5/32

natsin A=0.0933407086; natcos A=0.9956342260; nattan A=0.0937500000; natcot A=10.6666666666

Inches	0" Rise	0" Slope	1" Rise	1" Slope	2" Rise	2" Slope	3" Rise	3" Slope	4" Rise	4" Slope	5" Rise	5" Slope
0	0	0	3/32	1	3/16	2	5/16	3	13/32	4 1/32	1/2	5 1/32
1/16	0	1/16	3/32	1 1/16	7/32	2 1/16	5/16	3 1/16	13/32	4 3/32	1/2	5 3/32
1/8	0	1/8	1/8	1 1/8	7/32	2 1/8	5/16	3 1/8	13/32	4 5/32	1/2	5 5/32
3/16	1/32	3/16	1/8	1 3/16	7/32	2 3/16	5/16	3 3/16	13/32	4 7/32	1/2	5 7/32
1/4	1/32	1/4	1/8	1 1/4	7/32	2 1/4	5/16	3 9/32	13/32	4 9/32	17/32	5 9/32
5/16	1/32	5/16	1/8	1 5/16	7/32	2 5/16	5/16	3 11/32	7/16	4 11/32	17/32	5 11/32
3/8	1/32	3/8	1/8	1 3/8	1/4	2 3/8	11/32	3 13/32	7/16	4 13/32	17/32	5 13/32
7/16	1/32	7/16	5/32	1 7/16	1/4	2 7/16	11/32	3 15/32	7/16	4 15/32	17/32	5 15/32
1/2	1/16	1/2	5/32	1 1/2	1/4	2 1/2	11/32	3 17/32	7/16	4 17/32	17/32	5 17/32
9/16	1/16	9/16	5/32	1 9/16	1/4	2 9/16	11/32	3 19/32	7/16	4 19/32	9/16	5 19/32
5/8	1/16	5/8	5/32	1 5/8	1/4	2 5/8	11/32	3 21/32	15/32	4 21/32	9/16	5 21/32
11/16	1/16	11/16	5/32	1 11/16	9/32	2 11/16	3/8	3 23/32	15/32	4 23/32	9/16	5 23/32
3/4	1/16	3/4	3/16	1 3/4	9/32	2 3/4	3/8	3 25/32	15/32	4 25/32	9/16	5 25/32
13/16	3/32	13/16	3/16	1 13/16	9/32	2 13/16	3/8	3 27/32	15/32	4 27/32	9/16	5 27/32
7/8	3/32	7/8	3/16	1 7/8	9/32	2 7/8	3/8	3 29/32	15/32	4 29/32	19/32	5 29/32
15/16	3/32	15/16	3/16	1 15/16	9/32	2 15/16	3/8	3 31/32	1/2	4 31/32	19/32	5 31/32

Inches	6" Rise	6" Slope	7" Rise	7" Slope	8" Rise	8" Slope	9" Rise	9" Slope	10" Rise	10" Slope	11" Rise	11" Slope
0	19/32	6 1/32	11/16	7 1/32	25/32	8 1/32	7/8	9 1/32	1	10 1/16	1 3/32	11 1/16
1/16	19/32	6 3/32	11/16	7 3/32	13/16	8 3/32	29/32	9 3/32	1	10 1/8	1 3/32	11 1/8
1/8	19/32	6 5/32	23/32	7 5/32	13/16	8 5/32	29/32	9 5/32	1	10 3/16	1 3/32	11 3/16
3/16	5/8	6 7/32	23/32	7 7/32	13/16	8 7/32	29/32	9 7/32	1	10 1/4	1 3/32	11 1/4
1/4	5/8	6 9/32	23/32	7 9/32	13/16	8 9/32	29/32	9 9/32	1	10 5/16	1 1/8	11 5/16
5/16	5/8	6 11/32	23/32	7 11/32	13/16	8 11/32	29/32	9 11/32	1 1/32	10 3/8	1 1/8	11 3/8
3/8	5/8	6 13/32	23/32	7 13/32	27/32	8 13/32	15/16	9 13/32	1 1/32	10 7/16	1 1/8	11 7/16
7/16	5/8	6 15/32	3/4	7 15/32	27/32	8 15/32	15/16	9 15/32	1 1/32	10 1/2	1 1/8	11 1/2
1/2	21/32	6 17/32	3/4	7 17/32	27/32	8 17/32	15/16	9 17/32	1 1/32	10 9/16	1 1/8	11 9/16
9/16	21/32	6 19/32	3/4	7 19/32	27/32	8 19/32	15/16	9 19/32	1 1/32	10 5/8	1 5/32	11 5/8
5/8	21/32	6 21/32	3/4	7 21/32	27/32	8 21/32	15/16	9 11/16	1 1/16	10 11/16	1 5/32	11 11/16
11/16	21/32	6 23/32	3/4	7 23/32	7/8	8 23/32	31/32	9 3/4	1 1/16	10 3/4	1 5/32	11 3/4
3/4	21/32	6 25/32	25/32	7 25/32	7/8	8 25/32	31/32	9 13/16	1 1/16	10 13/16	1 5/32	11 13/16
13/16	11/16	6 27/32	25/32	7 27/32	7/8	8 27/32	31/32	9 7/8	1 1/16	10 7/8	1 5/32	11 7/8
7/8	11/16	6 29/32	25/32	7 29/32	7/8	8 29/32	31/32	9 15/16	1 1/16	10 15/16	1 3/16	11 15/16
15/16	11/16	6 31/32	25/32	7 31/32	7/8	8 31/32	31/32	10	1 3/32	11	1 3/16	1-0

Feet	0' Rise	0' Slope	10' Rise	10' Slope	20' Rise	20' Slope	30' Rise	30' Slope
0	0	0	11 7/8	10-0 19/32	1-11 3/4	20-1 3/16	2-11 5/8	30-1 3/4
1	1 3/16	1-0 1/16	1-1 1/16	11-0 21/32	2-0 15/16	21-1 7/32	3-0 13/16	31-1 13/16
2	2 3/8	2-0 1/8	1-2 1/4	12-0 23/32	2-2 1/8	22-1 9/32	3-2	32-1 7/8
3	3 9/16	3-0 3/16	1-3 7/16	13-0 3/4	2-3 5/16	23-1 11/32	3-3 3/8	33-1 15/16
4	4 3/4	4-0 1/4	1-4 5/8	14-0 13/16	2-4 1/2	24-1 13/32	3-4 3/8	34-2
5	5 15/16	5-0 9/32	1-5 13/16	15-0 7/8	2-5 11/16	25-1 15/32	3-5 9/16	35-2 1/4
6	7 1/8	6-0 11/32	1-7	16-0 15/16	2-6 7/8	26-1 17/32	3-6 3/4	36-2 1/8
7	8 5/16	7-0 13/32	1-8 3/16	17-1	2-8 1/16	27-1 19/32	3-7 15/16	37-2 5/32
8	9 1/2	8-0 15/32	1-9 3/8	18-1 1/16	2-9 1/4	28-1 21/32	3-9 1/8	38-2 7/32
9	10 11/16	9-0 17/32	1-10 9/16	19-1 1/8	2-10 7/16	29-1 11/16	3-10 5/16	39-2 9/32

A = 5° 39' 05"; logsin A = 8.99334; logcos A = 9.99788; logtan A = 8.99545; logcot A = 1.00455

Ins.	12″ Rise	Slope	13″ Rise	Slope	14″ Rise	Slope	15″ Rise	Slope	16″ Rise	Slope
0	$1\frac{3}{16}$	$1\text{-}0\frac{1}{16}$	$1\frac{9}{32}$	$1\text{-}1\frac{1}{16}$	$1\frac{3}{8}$	$1\text{-}2\frac{1}{16}$	$1\frac{1}{2}$	$1\text{-}3\frac{1}{16}$	$1\frac{19}{32}$	$1\text{-}4\frac{3}{32}$
$\frac{1}{16}$	$1\frac{3}{16}$	$1\text{-}0\frac{1}{8}$	$1\frac{9}{32}$	$1\text{-}1\frac{1}{8}$	$1\frac{13}{32}$	$1\text{-}2\frac{1}{8}$	$1\frac{1}{2}$	$1\text{-}3\frac{1}{8}$	$1\frac{19}{32}$	$1\text{-}4\frac{5}{32}$
$\frac{1}{8}$	$1\frac{3}{16}$	$1\text{-}0\frac{3}{16}$	$1\frac{5}{16}$	$1\text{-}1\frac{3}{16}$	$1\frac{13}{32}$	$1\text{-}2\frac{3}{16}$	$1\frac{1}{2}$	$1\text{-}3\frac{3}{16}$	$1\frac{19}{32}$	$1\text{-}4\frac{7}{32}$
$\frac{3}{16}$	$1\frac{7}{32}$	$1\text{-}0\frac{1}{4}$	$1\frac{5}{16}$	$1\text{-}1\frac{1}{4}$	$1\frac{13}{32}$	$1\text{-}2\frac{1}{4}$	$1\frac{1}{2}$	$1\text{-}3\frac{1}{4}$	$1\frac{19}{32}$	$1\text{-}4\frac{9}{32}$
$\frac{1}{4}$	$1\frac{7}{32}$	$1\text{-}0\frac{5}{16}$	$1\frac{5}{16}$	$1\text{-}1\frac{5}{16}$	$1\frac{13}{32}$	$1\text{-}2\frac{5}{16}$	$1\frac{1}{2}$	$1\text{-}3\frac{5}{16}$	$1\frac{19}{32}$	$1\text{-}4\frac{11}{32}$
$\frac{5}{16}$	$1\frac{7}{32}$	$1\text{-}0\frac{3}{8}$	$1\frac{5}{16}$	$1\text{-}1\frac{3}{8}$	$1\frac{13}{32}$	$1\text{-}2\frac{3}{8}$	$1\frac{1}{2}$	$1\text{-}3\frac{3}{8}$	$1\frac{5}{8}$	$1\text{-}4\frac{13}{32}$
$\frac{3}{8}$	$1\frac{7}{32}$	$1\text{-}0\frac{7}{16}$	$1\frac{5}{16}$	$1\text{-}1\frac{7}{16}$	$1\frac{7}{16}$	$1\text{-}2\frac{7}{16}$	$1\frac{17}{32}$	$1\text{-}3\frac{7}{16}$	$1\frac{5}{8}$	$1\text{-}4\frac{15}{32}$
$\frac{7}{16}$	$1\frac{7}{32}$	$1\text{-}0\frac{1}{2}$	$1\frac{11}{32}$	$1\text{-}1\frac{1}{2}$	$1\frac{7}{16}$	$1\text{-}2\frac{1}{2}$	$1\frac{17}{32}$	$1\text{-}3\frac{1}{2}$	$1\frac{5}{8}$	$1\text{-}4\frac{17}{32}$
$\frac{1}{2}$	$1\frac{1}{4}$	$1\text{-}0\frac{9}{16}$	$1\frac{11}{32}$	$1\text{-}1\frac{9}{16}$	$1\frac{7}{16}$	$1\text{-}2\frac{9}{16}$	$1\frac{17}{32}$	$1\text{-}3\frac{9}{16}$	$1\frac{5}{8}$	$1\text{-}4\frac{19}{32}$
$\frac{9}{16}$	$1\frac{1}{4}$	$1\text{-}0\frac{5}{8}$	$1\frac{11}{32}$	$1\text{-}1\frac{5}{8}$	$1\frac{7}{16}$	$1\text{-}2\frac{5}{8}$	$1\frac{17}{32}$	$1\text{-}3\frac{5}{8}$	$1\frac{5}{8}$	$1\text{-}4\frac{21}{32}$
$\frac{5}{8}$	$1\frac{1}{4}$	$1\text{-}0\frac{11}{16}$	$1\frac{11}{32}$	$1\text{-}1\frac{11}{16}$	$1\frac{7}{16}$	$1\text{-}2\frac{11}{16}$	$1\frac{17}{32}$	$1\text{-}3\frac{11}{16}$	$1\frac{21}{32}$	$1\text{-}4\frac{23}{32}$
$\frac{11}{16}$	$1\frac{1}{4}$	$1\text{-}0\frac{3}{4}$	$1\frac{11}{32}$	$1\text{-}1\frac{3}{4}$	$1\frac{15}{32}$	$1\text{-}2\frac{3}{4}$	$1\frac{9}{16}$	$1\text{-}3\frac{3}{4}$	$1\frac{21}{32}$	$1\text{-}4\frac{25}{32}$
$\frac{3}{4}$	$1\frac{1}{4}$	$1\text{-}0\frac{13}{16}$	$1\frac{3}{8}$	$1\text{-}1\frac{13}{16}$	$1\frac{15}{32}$	$1\text{-}2\frac{13}{16}$	$1\frac{9}{16}$	$1\text{-}3\frac{13}{16}$	$1\frac{21}{32}$	$1\text{-}4\frac{27}{32}$
$\frac{13}{16}$	$1\frac{9}{32}$	$1\text{-}0\frac{7}{8}$	$1\frac{3}{8}$	$1\text{-}1\frac{7}{8}$	$1\frac{15}{32}$	$1\text{-}2\frac{7}{8}$	$1\frac{9}{16}$	$1\text{-}3\frac{7}{8}$	$1\frac{21}{32}$	$1\text{-}4\frac{29}{32}$
$\frac{7}{8}$	$1\frac{9}{32}$	$1\text{-}0\frac{15}{16}$	$1\frac{3}{8}$	$1\text{-}1\frac{15}{16}$	$1\frac{15}{32}$	$1\text{-}2\frac{15}{16}$	$1\frac{9}{16}$	$1\text{-}3\frac{15}{16}$	$1\frac{21}{32}$	$1\text{-}4\frac{31}{32}$
$\frac{15}{16}$	$1\frac{9}{32}$	$1\text{-}1$	$1\frac{3}{8}$	$1\text{-}2$	$1\frac{15}{32}$	$1\text{-}3$	$1\frac{9}{16}$	$1\text{-}4$	$1\frac{11}{16}$	$1\text{-}5\frac{1}{32}$

Ins.	17″ Rise	Slope	18″ Rise	Slope	19″ Rise	Slope	20″ Rise	Slope	21″ Rise	Slope
0	$1\frac{11}{16}$	$1\text{-}5\frac{3}{32}$	$1\frac{25}{32}$	$1\text{-}6\frac{3}{32}$	$1\frac{7}{8}$	$1\text{-}7\frac{3}{32}$	$1\frac{31}{32}$	$1\text{-}8\frac{3}{32}$	$2\frac{1}{16}$	$1\text{-}9\frac{3}{32}$
$\frac{1}{16}$	$1\frac{11}{16}$	$1\text{-}5\frac{5}{32}$	$1\frac{25}{32}$	$1\text{-}6\frac{5}{32}$	$1\frac{7}{8}$	$1\text{-}7\frac{5}{32}$	2	$1\text{-}8\frac{5}{32}$	$2\frac{3}{32}$	$1\text{-}9\frac{5}{32}$
$\frac{1}{8}$	$1\frac{11}{16}$	$1\text{-}5\frac{7}{32}$	$1\frac{25}{32}$	$1\text{-}6\frac{7}{32}$	$1\frac{29}{32}$	$1\text{-}7\frac{7}{32}$	2	$1\text{-}8\frac{7}{32}$	$2\frac{3}{32}$	$1\text{-}9\frac{7}{32}$
$\frac{3}{16}$	$1\frac{11}{16}$	$1\text{-}5\frac{9}{32}$	$1\frac{13}{16}$	$1\text{-}6\frac{9}{32}$	$1\frac{29}{32}$	$1\text{-}7\frac{9}{32}$	2	$1\text{-}8\frac{9}{32}$	$2\frac{3}{32}$	$1\text{-}9\frac{9}{32}$
$\frac{1}{4}$	$1\frac{23}{32}$	$1\text{-}5\frac{11}{32}$	$1\frac{13}{16}$	$1\text{-}6\frac{11}{32}$	$1\frac{29}{32}$	$1\text{-}7\frac{11}{32}$	2	$1\text{-}8\frac{11}{32}$	$2\frac{3}{8}$	$1\text{-}9\frac{11}{32}$
$\frac{5}{16}$	$1\frac{23}{32}$	$1\text{-}5\frac{13}{32}$	$1\frac{13}{16}$	$1\text{-}6\frac{13}{32}$	$1\frac{29}{32}$	$1\text{-}7\frac{13}{32}$	2	$1\text{-}8\frac{13}{32}$	$2\frac{3}{8}$	$1\text{-}9\frac{13}{32}$
$\frac{3}{8}$	$1\frac{23}{32}$	$1\text{-}5\frac{15}{32}$	$1\frac{13}{16}$	$1\text{-}6\frac{15}{32}$	$1\frac{29}{32}$	$1\text{-}7\frac{15}{32}$	$2\frac{1}{32}$	$1\text{-}8\frac{15}{32}$	$2\frac{1}{8}$	$1\text{-}9\frac{15}{32}$
$\frac{7}{16}$	$1\frac{23}{32}$	$1\text{-}5\frac{17}{32}$	$1\frac{13}{16}$	$1\text{-}6\frac{17}{32}$	$1\frac{15}{16}$	$1\text{-}7\frac{17}{32}$	$2\frac{1}{32}$	$1\text{-}8\frac{17}{32}$	$2\frac{1}{8}$	$1\text{-}9\frac{17}{32}$
$\frac{1}{2}$	$1\frac{23}{32}$	$1\text{-}5\frac{19}{32}$	$1\frac{27}{32}$	$1\text{-}6\frac{19}{32}$	$1\frac{15}{16}$	$1\text{-}7\frac{19}{32}$	$2\frac{1}{32}$	$1\text{-}8\frac{19}{32}$	$2\frac{1}{8}$	$1\text{-}9\frac{19}{32}$
$\frac{9}{16}$	$1\frac{3}{4}$	$1\text{-}5\frac{21}{32}$	$1\frac{27}{32}$	$1\text{-}6\frac{21}{32}$	$1\frac{15}{16}$	$1\text{-}7\frac{21}{32}$	$2\frac{1}{32}$	$1\text{-}8\frac{21}{32}$	$2\frac{1}{8}$	$1\text{-}9\frac{21}{32}$
$\frac{5}{8}$	$1\frac{3}{4}$	$1\text{-}5\frac{23}{32}$	$1\frac{27}{32}$	$1\text{-}6\frac{23}{32}$	$1\frac{15}{16}$	$1\text{-}7\frac{23}{32}$	$2\frac{1}{32}$	$1\text{-}8\frac{23}{32}$	$2\frac{1}{8}$	$1\text{-}9\frac{23}{32}$
$\frac{11}{16}$	$1\frac{3}{4}$	$1\text{-}5\frac{25}{32}$	$1\frac{27}{32}$	$1\text{-}6\frac{25}{32}$	$1\frac{15}{16}$	$1\text{-}7\frac{25}{32}$	$2\frac{1}{32}$	$1\text{-}8\frac{25}{32}$	$2\frac{5}{32}$	$1\text{-}9\frac{25}{32}$
$\frac{3}{4}$	$1\frac{3}{4}$	$1\text{-}5\frac{27}{32}$	$1\frac{27}{32}$	$1\text{-}6\frac{27}{32}$	$1\frac{31}{32}$	$1\text{-}7\frac{27}{32}$	$2\frac{1}{16}$	$1\text{-}8\frac{27}{32}$	$2\frac{5}{32}$	$1\text{-}9\frac{27}{32}$
$\frac{13}{16}$	$1\frac{3}{4}$	$1\text{-}5\frac{29}{32}$	$1\frac{7}{8}$	$1\text{-}6\frac{29}{32}$	$1\frac{31}{32}$	$1\text{-}7\frac{29}{32}$	$2\frac{1}{16}$	$1\text{-}8\frac{29}{32}$	$2\frac{5}{32}$	$1\text{-}9\frac{29}{32}$
$\frac{7}{8}$	$1\frac{25}{32}$	$1\text{-}5\frac{31}{32}$	$1\frac{7}{8}$	$1\text{-}6\frac{31}{32}$	$1\frac{31}{32}$	$1\text{-}7\frac{31}{32}$	$2\frac{1}{16}$	$1\text{-}8\frac{31}{32}$	$2\frac{5}{32}$	$1\text{-}9\frac{31}{32}$
$\frac{15}{16}$	$1\frac{25}{32}$	$1\text{-}6\frac{1}{32}$	$1\frac{7}{8}$	$1\text{-}7\frac{1}{32}$	$1\frac{31}{32}$	$1\text{-}8\frac{1}{32}$	$2\frac{1}{16}$	$1\text{-}9\frac{1}{32}$	$2\frac{5}{32}$	$1\text{-}10\frac{1}{32}$

Feet	40′ Rise	Slope	50′ Rise	Slope	60′ Rise	Slope	70′ Rise	Slope
0	$3\text{-}11\frac{1}{2}$	$40\text{-}2\frac{11}{32}$	$4\text{-}11\frac{3}{8}$	$50\text{-}2\frac{15}{16}$	$5\text{-}11\frac{1}{4}$	$60\text{-}3\frac{17}{32}$	$6\text{-}11\frac{1}{8}$	$70\text{-}4\frac{3}{32}$
1	$4\text{-}0\frac{11}{16}$	$41\text{-}2\frac{13}{32}$	$5\text{-}0\frac{9}{16}$	$51\text{-}3$	$6\text{-}0\frac{7}{16}$	$61\text{-}3\frac{9}{32}$	$7\text{-}0\frac{5}{16}$	$71\text{-}4\frac{5}{32}$
2	$4\text{-}1\frac{7}{8}$	$42\text{-}2\frac{15}{32}$	$5\text{-}1\frac{3}{4}$	$52\text{-}3\frac{1}{16}$	$6\text{-}1\frac{5}{8}$	$62\text{-}3\frac{5}{8}$	$7\text{-}1\frac{1}{2}$	$72\text{-}4\frac{7}{32}$
3	$4\text{-}3\frac{1}{16}$	$43\text{-}2\frac{17}{32}$	$5\text{-}2\frac{15}{16}$	$53\text{-}3\frac{3}{32}$	$6\text{-}2\frac{13}{16}$	$63\text{-}3\frac{11}{16}$	$7\text{-}2\frac{11}{16}$	$73\text{-}4\frac{9}{32}$
4	$4\text{-}4\frac{1}{4}$	$44\text{-}2\frac{19}{32}$	$5\text{-}4\frac{1}{8}$	$54\text{-}3\frac{5}{32}$	$6\text{-}4$	$64\text{-}3\frac{3}{4}$	$7\text{-}3\frac{7}{8}$	$74\text{-}4\frac{11}{32}$
5	$4\text{-}5\frac{7}{16}$	$45\text{-}2\frac{5}{8}$	$5\text{-}5\frac{5}{16}$	$55\text{-}3\frac{7}{32}$	$6\text{-}5\frac{3}{16}$	$65\text{-}3\frac{13}{16}$	$7\text{-}5\frac{1}{16}$	$75\text{-}4\frac{13}{32}$
6	$4\text{-}6\frac{5}{8}$	$46\text{-}2\frac{11}{16}$	$5\text{-}6\frac{1}{2}$	$56\text{-}3\frac{9}{32}$	$6\text{-}6\frac{3}{8}$	$66\text{-}3\frac{7}{8}$	$7\text{-}6\frac{1}{4}$	$76\text{-}4\frac{15}{32}$
7	$4\text{-}7\frac{13}{16}$	$47\text{-}2\frac{3}{4}$	$5\text{-}7\frac{11}{16}$	$57\text{-}3\frac{11}{32}$	$6\text{-}7\frac{9}{16}$	$67\text{-}3\frac{15}{16}$	$7\text{-}7\frac{7}{16}$	$77\text{-}4\frac{1}{2}$
8	$4\text{-}9$	$48\text{-}2\frac{13}{16}$	$5\text{-}8\frac{7}{8}$	$58\text{-}3\frac{13}{32}$	$6\text{-}8\frac{3}{4}$	$68\text{-}4$	$7\text{-}8\frac{5}{8}$	$78\text{-}4\frac{9}{16}$
9	$4\text{-}10\frac{3}{16}$	$49\text{-}2\frac{7}{8}$	$5\text{-}10\frac{1}{16}$	$59\text{-}3\frac{15}{32}$	$6\text{-}9\frac{15}{16}$	$69\text{-}4\frac{1}{32}$	$7\text{-}9\frac{13}{16}$	$79\text{-}4\frac{5}{8}$

natsin A=0.0984773260; natcos A=0.9951392949; nattan A=0.0989583333; natcot A=10.1052631578

Inches	0" Rise	0" Slope	1" Rise	1" Slope	2" Rise	2" Slope	3" Rise	3" Slope	4" Rise	4" Slope	5" Rise	5" Slope
0	0	0	3/32	1	7/32	2	5/16	3 1/32	13/32	4 1/32	17/32	5 1/32
1/16	0	1/16	1/8	1 1/16	7/32	2 1/16	5/16	3 3/32	7/16	4 3/32	17/32	5 3/32
1/8	0	1/8	1/8	1 1/8	7/32	2 1/8	5/16	3 5/32	7/16	4 5/32	17/32	5 5/32
3/16	1/32	3/16	1/8	1 3/16	7/32	2 3/16	11/32	3 7/32	7/16	4 7/32	17/32	5 7/32
1/4	1/16	1/4	1/8	1 1/4	1/4	2 1/4	11/32	3 9/32	7/16	4 9/32	9/16	5 9/32
5/16	1/32	5/16	1/8	1 5/16	1/4	2 5/16	11/32	3 11/32	7/16	4 11/32	9/16	5 11/32
3/8	1/32	3/8	5/32	1 3/8	1/4	2 3/8	11/32	3 13/32	15/32	4 13/32	9/16	5 13/32
7/16	1/32	7/16	7/32	1 7/16	1/4	2 7/16	11/32	3 15/32	15/32	4 15/32	9/16	5 15/32
1/2	1/16	1/2	5/32	1 1/2	1/4	2 1/2	3/8	3 17/32	15/32	4 17/32	9/16	5 17/32
9/16	1/16	9/16	5/32	1 9/16	9/32	2 9/16	3/8	3 19/32	15/32	4 19/32	19/32	5 19/32
5/8	1/16	5/8	5/32	1 5/8	9/32	2 5/8	3/8	3 21/32	15/32	4 21/32	19/32	5 21/32
11/16	1/16	11/16	3/16	1 11/16	9/32	2 11/16	3/8	3 23/32	1/2	4 23/32	19/32	5 23/32
3/4	1/16	3/4	3/16	1 3/4	9/32	2 3/4	3/8	3 25/32	1/2	4 25/32	19/32	5 25/32
13/16	3/32	13/16	3/16	1 13/16	9/32	2 13/16	13/32	3 27/32	1/2	4 27/32	19/32	5 27/32
7/8	3/32	7/8	3/16	1 7/8	5/16	2 7/8	13/32	3 29/32	1/2	4 29/32	5/8	5 29/32
15/16	3/32	15/16	3/16	1 15/16	5/16	2 31/32	13/32	3 31/32	1/2	4 31/32	5/8	5 31/32

Inches	6" Rise	6" Slope	7" Rise	7" Slope	8" Rise	8" Slope	9" Rise	9" Slope	10" Rise	10" Slope	11" Rise	11" Slope
0	5/8	6 1/32	23/32	7 1/32	27/32	8 1/32	15/16	9 1/16	1 1/32	10 1/16	1 5/32	11 1/16
1/16	5/8	6 3/32	3/4	7 3/32	27/32	8 3/32	15/16	9 1/8	1 1/16	10 1/8	1 5/32	11 1/8
1/8	5/8	6 5/32	3/4	7 5/32	27/32	8 5/32	15/16	9 3/16	1 1/16	10 3/16	1 5/32	11 3/16
3/16	21/32	6 7/32	3/4	7 7/32	27/32	8 7/32	31/32	9 1/4	1 1/16	10 1/4	1 5/32	11 1/4
1/4	21/32	6 9/32	3/4	7 9/32	7/8	8 9/32	31/32	9 5/16	1 1/16	10 5/16	1 3/16	11 5/16
5/16	21/32	6 11/32	3/4	7 11/32	7/8	8 11/32	31/32	9 3/8	1 1/16	10 3/8	1 3/16	11 3/8
3/8	21/32	6 13/32	25/32	7 13/32	7/8	8 13/32	31/32	9 7/16	1 3/32	10 7/16	1 3/16	11 7/16
7/16	21/32	6 15/32	25/32	7 15/32	7/8	8 15/32	31/32	9 1/2	1 3/32	10 1/2	1 3/16	11 1/2
1/2	11/16	6 17/32	25/32	7 17/32	7/8	8 17/32	1	9 9/16	1 3/32	10 9/16	1 3/16	11 9/16
9/16	11/16	6 19/32	25/32	7 19/32	29/32	8 19/32	1	9 5/8	1 3/32	10 5/8	1 7/32	11 5/8
5/8	11/16	6 21/32	25/32	7 21/32	29/32	8 21/32	1	9 11/16	1 3/32	10 11/16	1 7/32	11 11/16
11/16	11/16	6 23/32	13/16	7 23/32	29/32	8 3/4	1	9 3/4	1 1/8	10 3/4	1 7/32	11 3/4
3/4	11/16	6 25/32	13/16	7 25/32	29/32	8 13/16	1	9 13/16	1 1/8	10 13/16	1 7/32	11 13/16
13/16	23/32	6 27/32	13/16	7 27/32	29/32	8 7/8	1 1/32	9 7/8	1 1/8	10 7/8	1 7/32	11 7/8
7/8	23/32	6 29/32	13/16	7 29/32	15/16	8 15/16	1 1/32	9 15/16	1 1/8	10 15/16	1 1/4	11 15/16
15/16	23/32	6 31/32	13/16	7 31/32	15/16	9	1 1/32	10	1 1/8	11	1 1/4	1-0

Feet	0' Rise	0' Slope	10' Rise	10' Slope	20' Rise	20' Slope	30' Rise	30' Slope
0	0	0	1-0 1/2	10-0 21/32	2-1	20-1 5/16	3-1 1/2	30-1 15/16
1	1 1/4	1-0 1/16	1-1 3/4	11-0 23/32	2-2 1/4	21-1 3/8	3-2 3/4	31-2
2	2 1/2	2-0 1/8	1-3	12-0 25/32	2-3 1/2	22-1 7/16	3-4	32-2 1/16
3	3 3/4	3-0 3/16	1-4 1/4	13-0 27/32	2-4 3/4	23-1 1/2	3-5 1/4	33-2 5/32
4	5	4-0 1/4	1-5 1/2	14-0 29/32	2-6	24-1 9/16	3-6 1/2	34-2 7/32
5	6 1/4	5-0 5/16	1-6 3/4	15-0 31/32	2-7 1/4	25-1 5/8	3-7 3/4	35-2 9/32
6	7 1/2	6-0 3/8	1-8	16-1 1/32	2-8 1/2	26-1 11/16	3-9	36-2 11/32
7	8 3/4	7-0 15/32	1-9 1/4	17-1 3/32	2-9 3/4	27-1 3/4	3-10 1/4	37-2 13/32
8	10	8-0 17/32	1-10 1/2	18-1 5/32	2-11	28-1 13/16	3-11 1/2	38-2 15/32
9	11 1/4	9-0 19/32	1-11 3/4	19-1 7/32	3-0 1/2	29-1 7/8	4-0 3/4	39-2 17/32

A = 5° 56' 49"; logsin A = 9.01539; logcos A = 9.99766; logtan A = 9.01773; logcot A = 0.98227

Ins.	12″ Rise	12″ Slope	13″ Rise	13″ Slope	14″ Rise	14″ Slope	15″ Rise	15″ Slope	16″ Rise	16″ Slope
0	1 1/4	1-0 1/16	1 11/32	1-1 1/16	1 15/32	1-2 1/16	1 9/16	1-3 3/32	1 21/32	1-4 3/32
1/16	1 1/4	1-0 1/8	1 3/8	1-1 1/8	1 15/32	1-2 1/8	1 9/16	1-3 5/32	1 11/16	1-4 5/32
1/8	1 1/4	1-0 3/16	1 3/8	1-1 3/16	1 15/32	1-2 3/16	1 9/16	1-3 7/32	1 11/16	1-4 7/32
3/16	1 9/32	1-0 1/4	1 3/8	1-1 1/4	1 15/32	1-2 1/4	1 19/32	1-3 9/32	1 11/16	1-4 9/32
1/4	1 9/32	1-0 5/16	1 3/8	1-1 5/16	1 1/2	1-2 5/16	1 19/32	1-3 11/32	1 11/16	1-4 11/32
5/16	1 9/32	1-0 3/8	1 3/8	1-1 3/8	1 1/2	1-2 3/8	1 19/32	1-3 13/32	1 11/16	1-4 13/32
3/8	1 9/32	1-0 7/16	1 13/32	1-1 7/16	1 1/2	1-2 7/16	1 19/32	1-3 15/32	1 23/32	1-4 15/32
7/16	1 9/32	1-0 1/2	1 13/32	1-1 1/2	1 1/2	1-2 1/2	1 19/32	1-3 17/32	1 23/32	1-4 17/32
1/2	1 5/16	1-0 9/16	1 13/32	1-1 9/16	1 1/2	1-2 19/32	1 5/8	1-3 19/32	1 23/32	1-4 19/32
9/16	1 5/16	1-0 5/8	1 13/32	1-1 5/8	1 17/32	1-2 21/32	1 5/8	1-3 21/32	1 23/32	1-4 21/32
5/8	1 5/16	1-0 11/16	1 13/32	1-1 11/16	1 17/32	1-2 23/32	1 5/8	1-3 23/32	1 23/32	1-4 23/32
11/16	1 5/16	1-0 3/4	1 7/16	1-1 3/4	1 17/32	1-2 25/32	1 5/8	1-3 25/32	1 3/4	1-4 25/32
3/4	1 5/16	1-0 13/16	1 7/16	1-1 13/16	1 17/32	1-2 27/32	1 5/8	1-3 27/32	1 3/4	1-4 27/32
13/16	1 11/32	1-0 7/8	1 7/16	1-1 7/8	1 17/32	1-2 29/32	1 21/32	1-3 29/32	1 3/4	1-4 29/32
7/8	1 11/32	1-0 15/16	1 7/16	1-1 15/16	1 9/16	1-3 1/32	1 21/32	1-3 31/32	1 3/4	1-4 31/32
15/16	1 11/32	1-1	1 7/16	1-2	1 9/16	1-3 3/32	1 21/32	1-4 1/32	1 3/4	1-5 1/32

Ins.	17″ Rise	17″ Slope	18″ Rise	18″ Slope	19″ Rise	19″ Slope	20″ Rise	20″ Slope	21″ Rise	21″ Slope
0	1 25/32	1-5 3/32	1 7/8	1-6 3/32	1 31/32	1-7 3/32	2 3/32	1-8 3/32	2 3/16	1-9 1/8
1/16	1 25/32	1-5 5/32	1 7/8	1-6 5/32	2	1-7 5/32	2 3/32	1-8 5/32	2 3/16	1-9 3/16
1/8	1 25/32	1-5 7/32	1 7/8	1-6 7/32	2	1-7 7/32	2 3/32	1-8 7/32	2 3/16	1-9 1/4
3/16	1 25/32	1-5 9/32	1 29/32	1-6 9/32	2	1-7 9/32	2 3/32	1-8 9/32	2 7/32	1-9 5/16
1/4	1 13/16	1-5 11/32	1 29/32	1-6 11/32	2	1-7 11/32	2 1/8	1-8 3/8	2 7/32	1-9 3/8
5/16	1 13/16	1-5 13/32	1 29/32	1-6 13/32	2	1-7 13/32	2 1/8	1-8 7/16	2 7/32	1-9 7/16
3/8	1 13/16	1-5 15/32	1 29/32	1-6 15/32	2 1/32	1-7 15/32	2 1/8	1-8 1/2	2 7/32	1-9 1/2
7/16	1 13/16	1-5 17/32	1 29/32	1-6 17/32	2 1/32	1-7 17/32	2 1/8	1-8 9/16	2 7/32	1-9 9/16
1/2	1 13/16	1-5 19/32	1 15/16	1-6 19/32	2 1/32	1-7 19/32	2 1/8	1-8 5/8	2 1/4	1-9 5/8
9/16	1 27/32	1-5 21/32	1 15/16	1-6 21/32	2 1/32	1-7 21/32	2 5/32	1-8 11/16	2 1/4	1-9 11/16
5/8	1 27/32	1-5 23/32	1 15/16	1-6 23/32	2 1/32	1-7 23/32	2 5/32	1-8 3/4	2 1/4	1-9 3/4
11/16	1 27/32	1-5 25/32	1 15/16	1-6 25/32	2 1/16	1-7 25/32	2 5/32	1-8 13/16	2 1/4	1-9 13/16
3/4	1 27/32	1-5 27/32	1 15/16	1-6 27/32	2 1/16	1-7 27/32	2 5/32	1-8 7/8	2 1/4	1-9 7/8
13/16	1 27/32	1-5 29/32	1 31/32	1-6 29/32	2 1/16	1-7 29/32	2 5/32	1-8 15/16	2 9/32	1-9 15/16
7/8	1 7/8	1-5 31/32	1 31/32	1-6 31/32	2 1/16	1-7 31/32	2 3/16	1-9	2 9/32	1-10
15/16	1 7/8	1-6 1/32	1 31/32	1-7 1/32	2 1/16	1-8 1/32	2 3/16	1-9 1/16	2 9/32	1-10 1/16

Feet	40′ Rise	40′ Slope	50′ Rise	50′ Slope	60′ Rise	60′ Slope	70′ Rise	70′ Slope
0	4-2	40-2 19/32	5-2 1/2	50-3 1/4	6-3	60-3 29/32	7-3 1/2	70-4 17/32
1	4-3 1/4	41-2 21/32	5-3 3/4	51-3 5/16	6-4 1/4	61-3 31/32	7-4 3/4	71-4 5/8
2	4-4 1/2	42-2 23/32	5-5	52-3 3/8	6-5 1/2	62-4 1/32	7-6	72-4 11/16
3	4-5 3/4	43-2 25/32	5-6 1/4	53-3 7/16	6-6 3/4	63-4 3/32	7-7 1/4	73-4 3/4
4	4-7	44-2 27/32	5-7 1/2	54-3 1/2	6-8	64-4 5/32	7-8 1/2	74-4 13/16
5	4-8 1/4	45-2 29/32	5-8 3/4	55-3 9/16	6-9 1/4	65-4 7/32	7-9 3/4	75-4 7/8
6	4-9 1/2	46-3	5-10	56-3 5/8	6-10 1/2	66-4 9/32	7-11	76-4 15/16
7	4-10 3/4	47-3 1/8	5-11 1/4	57-3 11/16	6-11 3/4	67-4 11/32	8-0 1/4	77-5
8	5-0	48-3 1/8	6-0 1/2	58-3 25/32	7-1	68-4 13/32	8-1 1/2	78-5 1/16
9	5-1 1/4	49-3 3/16	6-1 3/4	59-3 27/32	7-2 1/4	69-4 15/32	8-2 3/4	79-5 1/8

natsin A=0.1036060841; natcos A=0.9946184089; nattan A=0.1041666666; natcot A=9.6000000000

Inches	0″ Rise	0″ Slope	1″ Rise	1″ Slope	2″ Rise	2″ Slope	3″ Rise	3″ Slope	4″ Rise	4″ Slope	5″ Rise	5″ Slope
0	0	0	1/8	1	7/32	2	5/16	3½	7/16	4 1/32	9/16	5 1/32
1/16	0	1/16	1/8	1 1/16	7/32	2 1/16	11/32	3 3/32	7/16	4 3/32	9/16	5 3/32
1/8	0	1/8	1/8	1 1/8	7/32	2 1/8	11/32	3 5/32	7/16	4 5/32	9/16	5 5/32
3/16	1/32	3/16	1/8	1 3/16	1/4	2 3/16	11/32	3 7/32	15/32	4 7/32	9/16	5 7/32
1/4	1/32	1/4	1/8	1 1/4	1/4	2 1/4	11/32	3 9/32	15/32	4 9/32	9/16	5 9/32
5/16	1/32	5/16	5/32	1 5/16	1/4	2 5/16	3/8	3 11/32	15/32	4 11/32	19/32	5 11/32
3/8	1/32	3/8	5/32	1 3/8	1/4	2 3/8	3/8	3 13/32	15/32	4 13/32	19/32	5 13/32
7/16	1/16	7/16	5/32	1 7/16	9/32	2 7/16	3/8	3 15/32	1/2	4 15/32	19/32	5 15/32
1/2	1/16	1/2	5/32	1 1/2	9/32	2 1/2	3/8	3 17/32	1/2	4 17/32	19/32	5 17/32
9/16	1/16	9/16	5/32	1 9/16	9/32	2 9/16	3/8	3 19/32	1/2	4 19/32	19/32	5 19/32
5/8	1/16	5/8	3/16	1 5/8	9/32	2 21/32	13/32	3 21/32	1/2	4 21/32	5/8	5 21/32
11/16	1/16	11/16	3/16	1 11/16	9/32	2 23/32	13/32	3 23/32	1/2	4 23/32	5/8	5 23/32
3/4	3/32	3/4	3/16	1 3/4	5/16	2 25/32	13/32	3 25/32	17/32	4 25/32	5/8	5 25/32
13/16	3/32	13/16	3/16	1 13/16	5/16	2 27/32	13/32	3 27/32	17/32	4 27/32	5/8	5 27/32
7/8	3/32	7/8	7/32	1 7/8	5/16	2 29/32	7/16	3 29/32	17/32	4 29/32	21/32	5 29/32
15/16	3/32	15/16	7/32	1 15/16	5/16	2 31/32	7/16	3 31/32	17/32	4 31/32	21/32	5 31/32

Inches	6″ Rise	6″ Slope	7″ Rise	7″ Slope	8″ Rise	8″ Slope	9″ Rise	9″ Slope	10″ Rise	10″ Slope	11″ Rise	11″ Slope
0	21/32	6 1/32	3/4	7 1/32	7/8	8 1/32	1	9 1/16	1 3/32	10 1/16	1 3/16	11 1/16
1/16	21/32	6 3/32	25/32	7 3/32	7/8	8 1/8	1	9 1/8	1 3/32	10 1/8	1 7/32	11 1/8
1/8	21/32	6 5/32	25/32	7 5/32	7/8	8 3/16	1	9 3/16	1 3/32	10 3/16	1 7/32	11 3/16
3/16	11/16	6 7/32	25/32	7 7/32	29/32	8 1/4	1	9 1/4	1 1/8	10 1/4	1 7/32	11 1/4
1/4	11/16	6 9/32	25/32	7 9/32	29/32	8 5/16	1	9 5/16	1 1/8	10 5/16	1 7/32	11 5/16
5/16	11/16	6 11/32	13/16	7 11/32	29/32	8 3/8	1 1/32	9 3/8	1 1/8	10 3/8	1 1/4	11 3/8
3/8	11/16	6 13/32	13/16	7 13/32	29/32	8 7/16	1 1/32	9 7/16	1 1/8	10 7/16	1 1/4	11 7/16
7/16	23/32	6 15/32	13/16	7 15/32	15/16	8 1/2	1 1/32	9 1/2	1 5/32	10 1/2	1 1/4	11 1/2
1/2	23/32	6 17/32	13/16	7 17/32	15/16	8 9/16	1 1/32	9 9/16	1 5/32	10 9/16	1 1/4	11 9/16
9/16	23/32	6 19/32	13/16	7 19/32	15/16	8 5/8	1 1/32	9 5/8	1 5/32	10 5/8	1 1/4	11 5/8
5/8	23/32	6 21/32	27/32	7 21/32	15/16	8 11/16	1 1/16	9 11/16	1 5/32	10 11/16	1 9/32	11 11/16
11/16	23/32	6 23/32	27/32	7 23/32	15/16	8 3/4	1 1/16	9 3/4	1 5/32	10 3/4	1 9/32	11 3/4
3/4	3/4	6 25/32	27/32	7 25/32	31/32	8 13/16	1 1/16	9 13/16	1 3/16	10 13/16	1 9/32	11 13/16
13/16	3/4	6 27/32	27/32	7 27/32	31/32	8 7/8	1 1/16	9 7/8	1 3/16	10 7/8	1 9/32	11 7/8
7/8	3/4	6 29/32	7/8	7 15/16	31/32	8 15/16	1 3/32	9 15/16	1 3/16	10 15/16	1 5/16	11 15/16
15/16	3/4	6 31/32	7/8	8	31/32	9	1 3/32	10	1 3/16	11	1 5/16	1-0

Feet	0′ Rise	0′ Slope	10′ Rise	10′ Slope	20′ Rise	20′ Slope	30′ Rise	30′ Slope
0	0	0	1-1 1/8	10-0 23/32	2-2 1/4	20-1 7/16	3-3 3/8	30-2 5/32
1	15/16	1-0 1/16	1-2 1/16	11-0 25/32	2-3 9/16	21-1 1/2	3-4 11/16	31-2 7/32
2	2 5/8	2-0 5/32	1-3 3/4	12-0 27/32	2-4 7/8	22-1 9/16	3-6	32-2 9/32
3	3 15/16	3-0 7/32	1-5 1/16	13-0 15/16	2-6 3/16	23-1 21/32	3-7 5/16	33-2 3/8
4	5 1/4	4-0 9/32	1-6 3/8	14-1	2-7 1/2	24-1 23/32	3-8 5/8	34-2 7/16
5	6 9/16	5-0 11/32	1-7 11/16	15-1 1/16	2-8 13/16	25-1 25/32	3-9 15/16	35-2 1/2
6	7 7/8	6-0 7/16	1-9	16-1 5/32	2-10 1/8	26-1 7/8	3-11 1/4	36-2 9/16
7	9 3/16	7-0 1/2	1-10 5/16	17-1 7/32	2-11 7/16	27-1 15/16	4-0 9/16	37-2 21/32
8	10 1/2	8-0 9/16	1-11 5/8	18-1 9/32	3-0 3/4	28-2	4-1 7/8	38-2 23/32
9	11 13/16	9-0 21/32	2-0 15/16	19-1 3/8	3-2 1/16	29-2 1/16	4-3 3/16	39-2 25/32

A = 6° 14′ 31″; logsin A = 9.03634; logcos A = 9.99742; logtan A = 9.03892; logcot A = 0.96108

ins.	12″ Rise	12″ Slope	13″ Rise	13″ Slope	14″ Rise	14″ Slope	15″ Rise	15″ Slope	16″ Rise	16″ Slope
0	1 5/16	1-0 1/16	1 7/16	1-1 1/16	1 17/32	1-2 3/32	1 5/8	1-3 3/32	1 3/4	1-4 3/32
1/16	1 5/16	1-0 1/8	1 7/16	1-1 1/8	1 17/32	1-2 5/32	1 21/32	1-3 5/32	1 3/4	1-4 5/32
1/8	1 5/16	1-0 3/16	1 7/16	1-1 7/32	1 17/32	1-2 7/32	1 21/32	1-3 7/32	1 3/4	1-4 7/32
3/16	1 11/32	1-0 1/4	1 7/16	1-1 9/32	1 9/16	1-2 9/32	1 21/32	1-3 9/32	1 25/32	1-4 9/32
1/4	1 11/32	1-0 5/16	1 7/16	1-1 11/32	1 9/16	1-2 11/32	1 21/32	1-3 11/32	1 25/32	1-4 11/32
5/16	1 11/32	1-0 3/8	1 15/32	1-1 13/32	1 9/16	1-2 13/32	1 11/16	1-3 13/32	1 25/32	1-4 13/32
3/8	1 11/32	1-0 7/16	1 15/32	1-1 15/32	1 9/16	1-2 15/32	1 11/16	1-3 15/32	1 25/32	1-4 15/32
7/16	1 3/8	1-0 1/2	1 15/32	1-1 17/32	1 19/32	1-2 17/32	1 11/16	1-3 17/32	1 13/16	1-4 17/32
1/2	1 3/8	1-0 9/16	1 15/32	1-1 19/32	1 19/32	1-2 19/32	1 11/16	1-3 19/32	1 13/16	1-4 19/32
9/16	1 3/8	1-0 5/8	1 15/32	1-1 21/32	1 19/32	1-2 21/32	1 11/16	1-3 21/32	1 13/16	1-4 21/32
5/8	1 3/8	1-0 11/16	1 1/2	1-1 23/32	1 19/32	1-2 23/32	1 23/32	1-3 23/32	1 13/16	1-4 23/32
11/16	1 3/8	1-0 3/4	1 1/2	1-1 25/32	1 19/32	1-2 25/32	1 23/32	1-3 25/32	1 13/16	1-4 25/32
3/4	1 13/32	1-0 13/16	1 1/2	1-1 27/32	1 5/8	1-2 27/32	1 23/32	1-3 27/32	1 27/32	1-4 27/32
13/16	1 13/32	1-0 7/8	1 1/2	1-1 29/32	1 5/8	1-2 29/32	1 23/32	1-3 29/32	1 27/32	1-4 29/32
7/8	1 13/32	1-0 15/16	1 17/32	1-1 31/32	1 5/8	1-2 31/32	1 3/4	1-3 31/32	1 27/32	1-4 31/32
15/16	1 13/32	1-1	1 17/32	1-2 1/32	1 5/8	1-3 1/32	1 3/4	1-4 1/32	1 27/32	1-5 1/32

ins.	17″ Rise	17″ Slope	18″ Rise	18″ Slope	19″ Rise	19″ Slope	20″ Rise	20″ Slope	21″ Rise	21″ Slope
0	1 7/8	1-5 3/32	1 31/32	1-6 3/32	2 1/16	1-7 1/8	2 3/16	1-8 1/8	2 5/16	1-9 1/8
1/16	1 7/8	1-5 5/32	1 31/32	1-6 5/32	2 3/32	1-7 3/16	2 3/16	1-8 3/16	2 5/16	1-9 3/16
1/8	1 7/8	1-5 7/32	1 31/32	1-6 7/32	2 3/32	1-7 1/4	2 3/16	1-8 1/4	2 5/16	1-9 1/4
3/16	1 7/8	1-5 9/32	2	1-6 9/32	2 3/32	1-7 5/16	2 7/32	1-8 5/16	2 5/16	1-9 5/16
1/4	1 7/8	1-5 11/32	2	1-6 11/32	2 3/32	1-7 3/8	2 7/32	1-8 3/8	2 5/16	1-9 3/8
5/16	1 29/32	1-5 13/32	2	1-6 13/32	2 1/8	1-7 7/16	2 7/32	1-8 7/16	2 11/32	1-9 7/16
3/8	1 29/32	1-5 15/32	2	1-6 1/2	2 1/8	1-7 1/2	2 7/32	1-8 1/2	2 11/32	1-9 1/2
7/16	1 29/32	1-5 17/32	2 1/32	1-6 9/16	2 1/8	1-7 9/16	2 1/4	1-8 9/16	2 11/32	1-9 9/16
1/2	1 29/32	1-5 19/32	2 1/32	1-6 5/8	2 1/8	1-7 5/8	2 1/4	1-8 5/8	2 11/32	1-9 5/8
9/16	1 29/32	1-5 21/32	2 1/32	1-6 11/16	2 1/8	1-7 11/16	2 1/4	1-8 11/16	2 11/32	1-9 11/16
5/8	1 15/16	1-5 23/32	2 1/32	1-6 3/4	2 5/32	1-7 3/4	2 1/4	1-8 3/4	2 3/8	1-9 3/4
11/16	1 15/16	1-5 25/32	2 1/32	1-6 13/16	2 5/32	1-7 13/16	2 1/4	1-8 13/16	2 3/8	1-9 13/16
3/4	1 15/16	1-5 27/32	2 1/16	1-6 7/8	2 5/32	1-7 7/8	2 9/32	1-8 7/8	2 3/8	1-9 7/8
13/16	1 15/16	1-5 29/32	2 1/16	1-6 15/16	2 5/32	1-7 15/16	2 9/32	1-8 15/16	2 3/8	1-9 15/16
7/8	1 31/32	1-5 31/32	2 1/16	1-7	2 3/16	1-8	2 9/32	1-9	2 13/32	1-10
15/16	1 31/32	1-6 1/32	2 1/16	1-7 1/16	2 3/16	1-8 1/16	2 9/32	1-9 1/16	2 13/32	1-10 1/16

Feet	40′ Rise	40′ Slope	50′ Rise	50′ Slope	60′ Rise	60′ Slope	70′ Rise	70′ Slope
0	4-4 1/2	40-2 7/8	5-5 5/8	50-3 19/32	6-6 3/4	60-4 9/32	7-7 7/8	70-5
1	4-5 13/16	41-2 15/16	5-6 15/16	51-3 21/32	6-8 1/16	61-4 3/8	7-9 3/16	71-5 3/32
2	4-7 1/8	42-3	5-8 1/4	52-3 23/32	6-9 3/8	62-4 7/16	7-10 1/2	72-5 5/32
3	4-8 7/16	43-3 1/16	5-9 9/16	53-3 25/32	6-10 11/16	63-4 1/2	7-11 13/16	73-5 7/32
4	4-9 3/4	44-3 5/32	5-10 7/8	54-3 7/8	7-0	64-4 19/32	8-1 1/8	74-5 9/32
5	4-11 1/16	45-3 7/32	6-0 3/16	55-3 15/16	7-1 5/16	65-4 21/32	8-2 7/16	75-5 3/8
6	5-0 3/8	46-3 9/32	6-1 1/2	56-4	7-2 5/8	66-4 23/32	8-3 3/4	76-5 7/16
7	5-1 11/16	47-3 3/8	6-2 13/16	57-4 3/32	7-3 15/16	67-4 25/32	8-5 1/16	77-5 1/2
8	5-3	48-3 7/16	6-4 1/8	58-4 5/32	7-5 1/4	68-4 7/8	8-6 3/8	78-5 19/32
9	5-4 5/16	49-3 1/2	6-5 7/16	59-4 7/32	7-6 9/16	69-4 15/16	8-7 11/16	79-5 21/32

natsin A=0.1087265912; natcos A=0.9940716918; nattan A=0.1093750000; natcot A=9.1428571428

Inches	0" Rise	0" Slope	1" Rise	1" Slope	2" Rise	2" Slope	3" Rise	3" Slope	4" Rise	4" Slope	5" Rise	5" Slope
0	0	0	1/8	1	7/32	2	11/32	3 1/32	15/32	4 1/32	9/16	5 1/32
1/16	0	1/16	1/8	1 1/16	1/4	2 1/16	11/32	3 3/32	15/32	4 3/32	19/32	5 3/32
1/8	0	1/8	1/8	1 1/8	1/4	2 1/8	11/32	3 5/32	15/32	4 5/32	19/32	5 5/32
3/16	1/32	3/16	1/8	1 3/16	1/4	2 3/16	3/8	3 7/32	15/32	4 7/32	19/32	5 7/32
1/4	1/32	1/4	5/32	1 1/4	1/4	2 1/4	3/8	3 9/32	1/2	4 9/32	19/32	5 9/32
5/16	1/32	5/16	5/32	1 5/16	1/4	2 5/16	3/8	3 11/32	1/2	4 11/32	19/32	5 11/32
3/8	1/32	3/8	5/32	1 3/8	9/32	2 3/8	3/8	3 13/32	1/2	4 13/32	5/8	5 13/32
7/16	1/16	7/16	5/32	1 7/16	9/32	2 15/32	13/32	3 15/32	1/2	4 15/32	5/8	5 15/32
1/2	1/16	1/2	3/16	1 1/2	9/32	2 17/32	13/32	3 17/32	1/2	4 17/32	5/8	5 17/32
9/16	1/16	9/16	3/16	1 9/16	9/32	2 19/32	13/32	3 19/32	17/32	4 19/32	5/8	5 19/32
5/8	1/16	5/8	3/16	1 5/8	5/16	2 21/32	13/32	3 21/32	17/32	4 21/32	21/32	5 21/32
11/16	3/32	11/16	3/16	1 11/16	5/16	2 23/32	7/16	3 23/32	17/32	4 23/32	21/32	5 23/32
3/4	3/32	3/4	3/16	1 3/4	5/16	2 25/32	7/16	3 25/32	17/32	4 25/32	21/32	5 25/32
13/16	3/32	13/16	7/32	1 13/16	5/16	2 27/32	7/16	3 27/32	9/16	4 27/32	21/32	5 27/32
7/8	3/32	7/8	7/32	1 7/8	11/32	2 29/32	7/16	3 29/32	9/16	4 29/32	11/16	5 29/32
15/16	3/32	15/16	7/32	1 15/16	11/32	2 31/32	7/16	3 31/32	9/16	4 31/32	11/16	5 31/32

Inches	6" Rise	6" Slope	7" Rise	7" Slope	8" Rise	8" Slope	9" Rise	9" Slope	10" Rise	10" Slope	11" Rise	11" Slope
0	11/16	6 1/32	13/16	7 1/32	29/32	8 1/32	1 1/32	9 1/32	1 5/32	10 1/16	1 1/4	11 1/16
1/16	11/16	6 3/32	13/16	7 3/32	15/16	8 1/8	1 1/32	9 1/8	1 5/32	10 1/8	1 9/32	11 1/8
1/8	11/16	6 5/32	13/16	7 5/32	15/16	8 3/16	1 1/32	9 3/16	1 5/32	10 3/16	1 9/32	11 3/16
3/16	23/32	6 7/32	13/16	7 1/4	15/16	8 1/4	1 1/16	9 1/4	1 5/32	10 1/4	1 9/32	11 1/4
1/4	23/32	6 9/32	27/32	7 5/16	15/16	8 5/16	1 1/16	9 5/16	1 3/16	10 5/16	1 9/32	11 5/16
5/16	23/32	6 11/32	27/32	7 3/8	15/16	8 3/8	1 1/16	9 3/8	1 3/16	10 3/8	1 9/32	11 3/8
3/8	23/32	6 13/32	27/32	7 7/16	31/32	8 7/16	1 1/16	9 7/16	1 3/16	10 7/16	1 5/16	11 7/16
7/16	3/4	6 15/32	27/32	7 1/2	31/32	8 1/2	1 3/32	9 1/2	1 3/16	10 1/2	1 5/16	11 1/2
1/2	3/4	6 17/32	7/8	7 9/16	31/32	8 9/16	1 3/32	9 9/16	1 3/16	10 9/16	1 5/16	11 9/16
9/16	3/4	6 19/32	7/8	7 5/8	31/32	8 5/8	1 3/32	9 5/8	1 7/32	10 5/8	1 5/16	11 5/8
5/8	3/4	6 21/32	7/8	7 11/16	1	8 11/16	1 3/32	9 11/16	1 7/32	10 11/16	1 11/32	11 11/16
11/16	25/32	6 23/32	7/8	7 3/4	1	8 3/4	1 1/8	9 3/4	1 7/32	10 3/4	1 11/32	11 3/4
3/4	25/32	6 25/32	7/8	7 13/16	1	8 13/16	1 1/8	9 13/16	1 7/32	10 13/16	1 11/32	11 13/16
13/16	25/32	6 27/32	29/32	7 7/8	1	8 7/8	1 1/8	9 7/8	1 1/4	10 7/8	1 11/32	11 7/8
7/8	25/32	6 29/32	29/32	7 15/16	1 1/32	8 15/16	1 1/8	9 15/16	1 1/4	10 15/16	1 3/8	11 15/16
15/16	25/32	6 31/32	29/32	8	1 1/32	9	1 1/8	10	1 1/4	11	1 3/8	1-0

Feet	0' Rise	0' Slope	10' Rise	10' Slope	20' Rise	20' Slope	30' Rise	30' Slope
0	0	0	1-1 3/4	10-0 25/32	2-3 1/2	20-1 9/16	3-5 1/4	30-2 11/32
1	1 3/8	1-0 3/32	1-3 1/8	11-0 7/8	2-4 7/8	21-1 21/32	3-6 5/8	31-2 7/16
2	2 3/4	2-0 5/32	1-4 1/2	12-0 15/16	2-6 1/4	22-1 23/32	3-8	32-2 1/2
3	4 1/8	3-0 1/4	1-5 7/8	13-1 1/32	2-7 5/8	23-1 13/16	3-9 3/8	33-2 19/32
4	5 1/2	4-0 5/16	1-7 1/4	14-1 3/32	2-9	24-1 7/8	3-10 3/4	34-2 21/32
5	6 7/8	5-0 13/32	1-8 5/8	15-1 3/16	2-10 3/8	25-1 31/32	4-0 1/8	35-2 3/4
6	8 1/4	6-0 15/32	1-10	16-1 1/4	2-11 3/4	26-2 1/32	4-1 1/2	36-2 13/16
7	9 5/8	7-0 9/16	1-11 3/8	17-1 11/32	3-1 1/8	27-2 1/8	4-2 7/8	37-2 29/32
8	11	8-0 5/8	2-0 3/4	18-1 13/32	3-2 1/2	28-2 3/16	4-4 1/4	38-2 31/32
9	1-0 3/8	9-0 23/32	2-2 1/8	19-1 1/2	3-3 7/8	29-2 9/32	4-5 5/8	39-3 1/16

A = 6° 32′ 12″; logsin A = 9.05629; logcos A = 9.99717; logtan A = 9.05912; logcot A = 0.94088

In.	12″ Rise	12″ Slope	13″ Rise	13″ Slope	14″ Rise	14″ Slope	15″ Rise	15″ Slope	16″ Rise	16″ Slope
0	$1\frac{3}{8}$	$1\text{-}0\frac{3}{32}$	$1\frac{1}{2}$	$1\text{-}1\frac{3}{32}$	$1\frac{19}{32}$	$1\text{-}2\frac{3}{32}$	$1\frac{23}{32}$	$1\text{-}3\frac{3}{32}$	$1\frac{27}{32}$	$1\text{-}4\frac{3}{32}$
$\frac{1}{16}$	$1\frac{3}{8}$	$1\text{-}0\frac{5}{32}$	$1\frac{1}{2}$	$1\text{-}1\frac{5}{32}$	$1\frac{5}{8}$	$1\text{-}2\frac{5}{32}$	$1\frac{23}{32}$	$1\text{-}3\frac{5}{32}$	$1\frac{27}{32}$	$1\text{-}4\frac{5}{32}$
$\frac{1}{8}$	$1\frac{3}{8}$	$1\text{-}0\frac{7}{32}$	$1\frac{1}{2}$	$1\text{-}1\frac{7}{32}$	$1\frac{5}{8}$	$1\text{-}2\frac{7}{32}$	$1\frac{23}{32}$	$1\text{-}3\frac{7}{32}$	$1\frac{27}{32}$	$1\text{-}4\frac{7}{32}$
$\frac{3}{16}$	$1\frac{13}{32}$	$1\text{-}0\frac{9}{32}$	$1\frac{1}{2}$	$1\text{-}1\frac{9}{32}$	$1\frac{5}{8}$	$1\text{-}2\frac{9}{32}$	$1\frac{3}{4}$	$1\text{-}3\frac{9}{32}$	$1\frac{27}{32}$	$1\text{-}4\frac{9}{32}$
$\frac{1}{4}$	$1\frac{13}{32}$	$1\text{-}0\frac{11}{32}$	$1\frac{17}{32}$	$1\text{-}1\frac{11}{32}$	$1\frac{5}{8}$	$1\text{-}2\frac{11}{32}$	$1\frac{3}{4}$	$1\text{-}3\frac{11}{32}$	$1\frac{7}{8}$	$1\text{-}4\frac{11}{32}$
$\frac{5}{16}$	$1\frac{13}{32}$	$1\text{-}0\frac{13}{32}$	$1\frac{17}{32}$	$1\text{-}1\frac{13}{32}$	$1\frac{5}{8}$	$1\text{-}2\frac{13}{32}$	$1\frac{3}{4}$	$1\text{-}3\frac{13}{32}$	$1\frac{7}{8}$	$1\text{-}4\frac{13}{32}$
$\frac{3}{8}$	$1\frac{13}{32}$	$1\text{-}0\frac{15}{32}$	$1\frac{17}{32}$	$1\text{-}1\frac{15}{32}$	$1\frac{21}{32}$	$1\text{-}2\frac{15}{32}$	$1\frac{3}{4}$	$1\text{-}3\frac{15}{32}$	$1\frac{7}{8}$	$1\text{-}4\frac{15}{32}$
$\frac{7}{16}$	$1\frac{7}{16}$	$1\text{-}0\frac{17}{32}$	$1\frac{17}{32}$	$1\text{-}1\frac{17}{32}$	$1\frac{21}{32}$	$1\text{-}2\frac{17}{32}$	$1\frac{25}{32}$	$1\text{-}3\frac{17}{32}$	$1\frac{7}{8}$	$1\text{-}4\frac{17}{32}$
$\frac{1}{2}$	$1\frac{7}{16}$	$1\text{-}0\frac{19}{32}$	$1\frac{9}{16}$	$1\text{-}1\frac{19}{32}$	$1\frac{21}{32}$	$1\text{-}2\frac{19}{32}$	$1\frac{25}{32}$	$1\text{-}3\frac{19}{32}$	$1\frac{7}{8}$	$1\text{-}4\frac{19}{32}$
$\frac{9}{16}$	$1\frac{7}{16}$	$1\text{-}0\frac{21}{32}$	$1\frac{9}{16}$	$1\text{-}1\frac{21}{32}$	$1\frac{21}{32}$	$1\text{-}2\frac{21}{32}$	$1\frac{25}{32}$	$1\text{-}3\frac{21}{32}$	$1\frac{29}{32}$	$1\text{-}4\frac{21}{32}$
$\frac{5}{8}$	$1\frac{7}{16}$	$1\text{-}0\frac{23}{32}$	$1\frac{9}{16}$	$1\text{-}1\frac{23}{32}$	$1\frac{11}{16}$	$1\text{-}2\frac{23}{32}$	$1\frac{25}{32}$	$1\text{-}3\frac{23}{32}$	$1\frac{29}{32}$	$1\text{-}4\frac{23}{32}$
$\frac{11}{16}$	$1\frac{15}{32}$	$1\text{-}0\frac{25}{32}$	$1\frac{9}{16}$	$1\text{-}1\frac{25}{32}$	$1\frac{11}{16}$	$1\text{-}2\frac{25}{32}$	$1\frac{13}{16}$	$1\text{-}3\frac{25}{32}$	$1\frac{29}{32}$	$1\text{-}4\frac{25}{32}$
$\frac{3}{4}$	$1\frac{15}{32}$	$1\text{-}0\frac{27}{32}$	$1\frac{9}{16}$	$1\text{-}1\frac{27}{32}$	$1\frac{11}{16}$	$1\text{-}2\frac{27}{32}$	$1\frac{13}{16}$	$1\text{-}3\frac{27}{32}$	$1\frac{29}{32}$	$1\text{-}4\frac{7}{8}$
$\frac{13}{16}$	$1\frac{15}{32}$	$1\text{-}0\frac{29}{32}$	$1\frac{19}{32}$	$1\text{-}1\frac{29}{32}$	$1\frac{11}{16}$	$1\text{-}2\frac{29}{32}$	$1\frac{13}{16}$	$1\text{-}3\frac{29}{32}$	$1\frac{15}{16}$	$1\text{-}4\frac{15}{16}$
$\frac{7}{8}$	$1\frac{15}{32}$	$1\text{-}0\frac{31}{32}$	$1\frac{19}{32}$	$1\text{-}1\frac{31}{32}$	$1\frac{23}{32}$	$1\text{-}2\frac{31}{32}$	$1\frac{13}{16}$	$1\text{-}3\frac{31}{32}$	$1\frac{15}{16}$	$1\text{-}5$
$\frac{15}{16}$	$1\frac{15}{32}$	$1\text{-}1\frac{1}{32}$	$1\frac{19}{32}$	$1\text{-}2\frac{1}{32}$	$1\frac{23}{32}$	$1\text{-}3\frac{1}{32}$	$1\frac{13}{16}$	$1\text{-}4\frac{1}{32}$	$1\frac{15}{16}$	$1\text{-}5\frac{1}{16}$

In.	17″ Rise	17″ Slope	18″ Rise	18″ Slope	19″ Rise	19″ Slope	20″ Rise	20″ Slope	21″ Rise	21″ Slope
0	$1\frac{15}{16}$	$1\text{-}5\frac{1}{8}$	$2\frac{1}{16}$	$1\text{-}6\frac{1}{8}$	$2\frac{3}{16}$	$1\text{-}7\frac{1}{8}$	$2\frac{9}{32}$	$1\text{-}8\frac{1}{8}$	$2\frac{13}{32}$	$1\text{-}9\frac{1}{8}$
$\frac{1}{16}$	$1\frac{31}{32}$	$1\text{-}5\frac{3}{16}$	$2\frac{1}{16}$	$1\text{-}6\frac{3}{16}$	$2\frac{3}{16}$	$1\text{-}7\frac{3}{16}$	$2\frac{5}{16}$	$1\text{-}8\frac{3}{16}$	$2\frac{13}{32}$	$1\text{-}9\frac{3}{16}$
$\frac{1}{8}$	$1\frac{31}{32}$	$1\text{-}5\frac{1}{4}$	$2\frac{1}{16}$	$1\text{-}6\frac{1}{4}$	$2\frac{3}{16}$	$1\text{-}7\frac{1}{4}$	$2\frac{5}{16}$	$1\text{-}8\frac{1}{4}$	$2\frac{13}{32}$	$1\text{-}9\frac{1}{4}$
$\frac{3}{16}$	$1\frac{31}{32}$	$1\text{-}5\frac{5}{16}$	$2\frac{3}{32}$	$1\text{-}6\frac{5}{16}$	$2\frac{3}{16}$	$1\text{-}7\frac{5}{16}$	$2\frac{5}{16}$	$1\text{-}8\frac{5}{16}$	$2\frac{7}{16}$	$1\text{-}9\frac{5}{16}$
$\frac{1}{4}$	$1\frac{31}{32}$	$1\text{-}5\frac{3}{8}$	$2\frac{3}{32}$	$1\text{-}6\frac{3}{8}$	$2\frac{7}{32}$	$1\text{-}7\frac{3}{8}$	$2\frac{5}{16}$	$1\text{-}8\frac{3}{8}$	$2\frac{7}{16}$	$1\text{-}9\frac{3}{8}$
$\frac{5}{16}$	$1\frac{31}{32}$	$1\text{-}5\frac{7}{16}$	$2\frac{3}{32}$	$1\text{-}6\frac{7}{16}$	$2\frac{7}{32}$	$1\text{-}7\frac{7}{16}$	$2\frac{5}{16}$	$1\text{-}8\frac{7}{16}$	$2\frac{7}{16}$	$1\text{-}9\frac{7}{16}$
$\frac{3}{8}$	2	$1\text{-}5\frac{1}{2}$	$2\frac{3}{32}$	$1\text{-}6\frac{1}{2}$	$2\frac{7}{32}$	$1\text{-}7\frac{1}{2}$	$2\frac{11}{32}$	$1\text{-}8\frac{1}{2}$	$2\frac{7}{16}$	$1\text{-}9\frac{1}{2}$
$\frac{7}{16}$	2	$1\text{-}5\frac{9}{16}$	$2\frac{1}{8}$	$1\text{-}6\frac{9}{16}$	$2\frac{7}{32}$	$1\text{-}7\frac{9}{16}$	$2\frac{11}{32}$	$1\text{-}8\frac{9}{16}$	$2\frac{15}{32}$	$1\text{-}9\frac{9}{16}$
$\frac{1}{2}$	2	$1\text{-}5\frac{5}{8}$	$2\frac{1}{8}$	$1\text{-}6\frac{5}{8}$	$2\frac{1}{4}$	$1\text{-}7\frac{5}{8}$	$2\frac{11}{32}$	$1\text{-}8\frac{5}{8}$	$2\frac{15}{32}$	$1\text{-}9\frac{21}{32}$
$\frac{9}{16}$	2	$1\text{-}5\frac{11}{16}$	$2\frac{1}{8}$	$1\text{-}6\frac{11}{16}$	$2\frac{1}{4}$	$1\text{-}7\frac{11}{16}$	$2\frac{11}{32}$	$1\text{-}8\frac{11}{16}$	$2\frac{15}{32}$	$1\text{-}9\frac{23}{32}$
$\frac{5}{8}$	$2\frac{1}{32}$	$1\text{-}5\frac{3}{4}$	$2\frac{1}{8}$	$1\text{-}6\frac{3}{4}$	$2\frac{1}{4}$	$1\text{-}7\frac{3}{4}$	$2\frac{3}{8}$	$1\text{-}8\frac{3}{4}$	$2\frac{15}{32}$	$1\text{-}9\frac{25}{32}$
$\frac{11}{16}$	$2\frac{1}{32}$	$1\text{-}5\frac{13}{16}$	$2\frac{5}{32}$	$1\text{-}6\frac{13}{16}$	$2\frac{1}{4}$	$1\text{-}7\frac{13}{16}$	$2\frac{3}{8}$	$1\text{-}8\frac{13}{16}$	$2\frac{1}{2}$	$1\text{-}9\frac{27}{32}$
$\frac{3}{4}$	$2\frac{1}{32}$	$1\text{-}5\frac{7}{8}$	$2\frac{5}{32}$	$1\text{-}6\frac{7}{8}$	$2\frac{1}{4}$	$1\text{-}7\frac{7}{8}$	$2\frac{3}{8}$	$1\text{-}8\frac{7}{8}$	$2\frac{1}{2}$	$1\text{-}9\frac{29}{32}$
$\frac{13}{16}$	$2\frac{1}{32}$	$1\text{-}5\frac{15}{16}$	$2\frac{5}{32}$	$1\text{-}6\frac{15}{16}$	$2\frac{9}{32}$	$1\text{-}7\frac{15}{16}$	$2\frac{3}{8}$	$1\text{-}8\frac{15}{16}$	$2\frac{1}{2}$	$1\text{-}9\frac{31}{32}$
$\frac{7}{8}$	$2\frac{1}{16}$	$1\text{-}6$	$2\frac{5}{32}$	$1\text{-}7$	$2\frac{9}{32}$	$1\text{-}8$	$2\frac{13}{32}$	$1\text{-}9$	$2\frac{1}{2}$	$1\text{-}10\frac{1}{32}$
$\frac{15}{16}$	$2\frac{1}{16}$	$1\text{-}6\frac{1}{16}$	$2\frac{5}{32}$	$1\text{-}7\frac{1}{16}$	$2\frac{9}{32}$	$1\text{-}8\frac{1}{16}$	$2\frac{13}{32}$	$1\text{-}9\frac{1}{16}$	$2\frac{1}{2}$	$1\text{-}10\frac{3}{32}$

Feet	40′ Rise	40′ Slope	50′ Rise	50′ Slope	60′ Rise	60′ Slope	70′ Rise	70′ Slope
0	$4\text{-}7$	$40\text{-}3\frac{5}{32}$	$5\text{-}8\frac{3}{4}$	$50\text{-}3\frac{15}{16}$	$6\text{-}10\frac{1}{2}$	$60\text{-}4\frac{23}{32}$	$8\text{-}0\frac{1}{4}$	$70\text{-}5\frac{1}{2}$
1	$4\text{-}8\frac{3}{8}$	$41\text{-}3\frac{7}{32}$	$5\text{-}10\frac{1}{8}$	$51\text{-}4$	$6\text{-}11\frac{7}{8}$	$61\text{-}4\frac{25}{32}$	$8\text{-}1\frac{5}{8}$	$71\text{-}5\frac{9}{16}$
2	$4\text{-}9\frac{3}{4}$	$42\text{-}3\frac{5}{16}$	$5\text{-}11\frac{1}{2}$	$52\text{-}4\frac{3}{32}$	$7\text{-}1\frac{1}{4}$	$62\text{-}4\frac{7}{8}$	$8\text{-}3$	$72\text{-}5\frac{21}{32}$
3	$4\text{-}11\frac{1}{8}$	$43\text{-}3\frac{3}{8}$	$6\text{-}0\frac{7}{8}$	$53\text{-}4\frac{5}{32}$	$7\text{-}2\frac{5}{8}$	$63\text{-}4\frac{15}{16}$	$8\text{-}4\frac{3}{8}$	$73\text{-}5\frac{23}{32}$
4	$5\text{-}0\frac{1}{2}$	$44\text{-}3\frac{15}{32}$	$6\text{-}2\frac{1}{4}$	$54\text{-}4\frac{1}{4}$	$7\text{-}4$	$64\text{-}5\frac{1}{32}$	$8\text{-}5\frac{3}{4}$	$74\text{-}5\frac{13}{16}$
5	$5\text{-}1\frac{7}{8}$	$45\text{-}3\frac{17}{32}$	$6\text{-}3\frac{5}{8}$	$55\text{-}4\frac{5}{16}$	$7\text{-}5\frac{3}{8}$	$65\text{-}5\frac{3}{32}$	$8\text{-}7\frac{1}{8}$	$75\text{-}5\frac{7}{8}$
6	$5\text{-}3\frac{1}{4}$	$46\text{-}3\frac{5}{8}$	$6\text{-}5$	$56\text{-}4\frac{13}{32}$	$7\text{-}6\frac{3}{4}$	$66\text{-}5\frac{3}{16}$	$8\text{-}8\frac{1}{2}$	$76\text{-}5\frac{31}{32}$
7	$5\text{-}4\frac{5}{8}$	$47\text{-}3\frac{11}{16}$	$6\text{-}6\frac{3}{8}$	$57\text{-}4\frac{15}{32}$	$7\text{-}8\frac{1}{8}$	$67\text{-}5\frac{1}{4}$	$8\text{-}9\frac{7}{8}$	$77\text{-}6\frac{1}{32}$
8	$5\text{-}6$	$48\text{-}3\frac{25}{32}$	$6\text{-}7\frac{3}{4}$	$58\text{-}4\frac{9}{16}$	$7\text{-}9\frac{1}{2}$	$68\text{-}5\frac{11}{32}$	$8\text{-}11\frac{1}{4}$	$78\text{-}6\frac{1}{8}$
9	$5\text{-}7\frac{3}{8}$	$49\text{-}3\frac{27}{32}$	$6\text{-}9\frac{1}{8}$	$59\text{-}4\frac{5}{8}$	$7\text{-}10\frac{7}{8}$	$69\text{-}5\frac{13}{32}$	$9\text{-}0\frac{5}{8}$	$79\text{-}6\frac{3}{16}$

natsin A=0.1138384583; natcos A=0.9934992730; nattan A=0.1145833333; natcot A=8.7272727272

Inches	0" Rise	0" Slope	1" Rise	1" Slope	2" Rise	2" Slope	3" Rise	3" Slope	4" Rise	4" Slope	5" Rise	5" Slope
0	0	0	1/8	1	1/4	2	3/8	3 1/32	15/32	4 1/32	19/32	5 1/32
1/16	0	1/16	1/8	1 1/16	1/4	2 1/16	3/8	3 3/32	1/2	4 3/32	19/32	5 3/32
1/8	0	1/8	1/8	1 1/8	1/4	2 1/8	3/8	3 5/32	1/2	4 5/32	5/8	5 5/32
3/16	1/32	3/16	5/32	1 3/16	1/4	2 7/32	3/8	3 7/32	1/2	4 7/32	5/8	5 7/32
1/4	1/32	1/4	5/32	1 1/4	9/32	2 9/32	3/8	3 9/32	1/2	4 9/32	5/8	5 9/32
5/16	1/32	5/16	5/32	1 5/16	9/32	2 11/32	13/32	3 11/32	17/32	4 11/32	5/8	5 11/32
3/8	1/32	3/8	5/32	1 3/8	9/32	2 13/32	13/32	3 13/32	17/32	4 13/32	21/32	5 13/32
7/16	1/16	7/16	3/16	1 7/16	9/32	2 15/32	13/32	3 15/32	17/32	4 15/32	21/32	5 15/32
1/2	1/16	1/2	3/16	1 1/2	5/16	2 17/32	13/32	3 17/32	17/32	4 17/32	21/32	5 17/32
9/16	1/16	9/16	3/16	1 9/16	5/16	2 19/32	7/16	3 19/32	17/32	4 19/32	21/32	5 19/32
5/8	1/16	5/8	3/16	1 5/8	5/16	2 21/32	7/16	3 21/32	9/16	4 21/32	11/16	5 21/32
11/16	3/32	11/16	3/16	1 11/16	5/16	2 23/32	7/16	3 23/32	9/16	4 23/32	11/16	5 23/32
3/4	3/32	3/4	7/32	1 3/4	11/32	2 25/32	7/16	3 25/32	9/16	4 25/32	11/16	5 25/32
13/16	3/32	13/16	7/32	1 13/16	11/32	2 27/32	15/32	3 27/32	9/16	4 27/32	11/16	5 27/32
7/8	3/32	7/8	7/32	1 7/8	11/32	2 29/32	15/32	3 29/32	19/32	4 29/32	23/32	5 29/32
15/16	1/8	15/16	7/32	1 15/16	11/32	2 31/32	15/32	3 31/32	19/32	4 31/32	23/32	5 31/32

Inches	6" Rise	6" Slope	7" Rise	7" Slope	8" Rise	8" Slope	9" Rise	9" Slope	10" Rise	10" Slope	11" Rise	11" Slope
0	23/32	6 1/32	27/32	7 1/16	31/32	8 1/16	1 1/16	9 1/16	1 3/16	10 1/16	1 5/16	11 3/32
1/16	23/32	6 3/32	27/32	7 1/8	31/32	8 1/8	1 3/32	9 1/8	1 7/32	10 1/8	1 5/16	11 5/32
1/8	23/32	6 5/32	27/32	7 3/16	31/32	8 3/16	1 3/32	9 3/16	1 7/32	10 3/16	1 11/32	11 7/32
3/16	3/4	6 7/32	7/8	7 1/4	31/32	8 1/4	1 3/32	9 1/4	1 7/32	10 1/4	1 11/32	11 9/32
1/4	3/4	6 9/32	7/8	7 5/16	1	8 5/16	1 3/32	9 5/16	1 7/32	10 5/16	1 11/32	11 11/32
5/16	3/4	6 11/32	7/8	7 3/8	1	8 3/8	1 1/8	9 3/8	1 1/4	10 3/8	1 11/32	11 13/32
3/8	3/4	6 13/32	7/8	7 7/16	1	8 7/16	1 1/8	9 7/16	1 1/4	10 7/16	1 3/8	11 15/32
7/16	25/32	6 15/32	29/32	7 1/2	1	8 1/2	1 1/8	9 1/2	1 1/4	10 1/2	1 3/8	11 17/32
1/2	25/32	6 17/32	29/32	7 9/16	1 1/32	8 9/16	1 1/8	9 9/16	1 1/4	10 9/16	1 3/8	11 19/32
9/16	25/32	6 5/8	29/32	7 5/8	1 1/32	8 5/8	1 5/32	9 5/8	1 1/4	10 5/8	1 3/8	11 21/32
5/8	25/32	6 11/16	29/32	7 11/16	1 1/32	8 11/16	1 5/32	9 11/16	1 9/32	10 11/16	1 13/32	11 23/32
11/16	13/16	6 3/4	29/32	7 3/4	1 1/32	8 3/4	1 5/32	9 3/4	1 9/32	10 3/4	1 13/32	11 25/32
3/4	13/16	6 13/16	15/16	7 13/16	1 1/16	8 13/16	1 5/32	9 13/16	1 9/32	10 13/16	1 13/32	11 27/32
13/16	13/16	6 7/8	15/16	7 7/8	1 1/16	8 7/8	1 3/16	9 7/8	1 9/32	10 7/8	1 13/32	11 29/32
7/8	13/16	6 15/16	15/16	7 15/16	1 1/16	8 15/16	1 3/16	9 15/16	1 5/16	10 15/16	1 7/16	11 31/32
15/16	27/32	7	15/16	8	1 1/16	9	1 3/16	10	1 5/16	11 1/32	1 7/16	1-0 1/32

Feet	0' Rise	0' Slope	10' Rise	10' Slope	20' Rise	20' Slope	30' Rise	30' Slope
0	0	0	1-2 3/8	10-0 27/32	2-4 3/4	20-1 23/32	3-7 1/8	30-2 9/16
1	1 7/16	1-0 3/32	1-3 13/16	11-0 15/16	2-6 3/4	21-1 13/16	3-8 9/16	31-2 21/32
2	2 7/8	2-0 5/32	1-5 1/4	12-1 1/32	2-7 5/8	22-1 7/8	3-10	32-2 3/4
3	4 5/16	3-0 1/4	1-6 11/16	13-1 1/8	2-9 1/16	23-1 31/32	3-11 7/16	33-2 27/32
4	5 3/4	4-0 11/32	1-8 1/8	14-1 3/16	2-10 1/2	24-2 1/16	4-0 7/8	34-2 29/32
5	7 3/16	5-0 7/16	1-9 9/16	15-1 9/32	2-11 15/16	25-2 5/32	4-2 5/16	35-3
6	8 5/8	6-0 1/2	1-11	16-1 3/8	3-1 3/8	26-2 7/32	4-3 3/4	36-3 3/32
7	10 1/16	7-0 19/32	2-0 7/16	17-1 15/32	3-2 13/16	27-2 5/16	4-5 3/16	37-3 3/16
8	11 1/2	8-0 11/16	2-1 7/8	18-1 17/32	3-4 1/4	28-2 13/16	4-6 5/8	38-3 1/4
9	1-0 15/16	9-0 25/32	2-3 5/16	19-1 5/8	3-5 11/16	29-2 1/2	4-8 1/16	39-3 11/32

A = 6° 49′ 52″; logsin A = 9.07533; logcos A = 9.99691; logtan A = 9.07843; logcot A = 0.92157

Ins.	12″ Rise	12″ Slope	13″ Rise	13″ Slope	14″ Rise	14″ Slope	15″ Rise	15″ Slope	16″ Rise	16″ Slope
0	1⁷⁄₁₆	1-0³⁄₃₂	1⁹⁄₁₆	1-1³⁄₃₂	1¹¹⁄₁₆	1-2³⁄₃₂	1¹³⁄₁₆	1-3³⁄₃₂	1²⁹⁄₃₂	1-4¹⁄₈
¹⁄₁₆	1⁷⁄₁₆	1-0⁵⁄₃₂	1⁹⁄₁₆	1-1⁵⁄₃₂	1¹¹⁄₁₆	1-2⁵⁄₃₂	1¹³⁄₁₆	1-3⁵⁄₃₂	1¹⁵⁄₁₆	1-4³⁄₁₆
¹⁄₈	1⁷⁄₁₆	1-0⁷⁄₃₂	1⁹⁄₁₆	1-1⁷⁄₃₂	1¹¹⁄₁₆	1-2⁷⁄₃₂	1¹³⁄₁₆	1-3⁷⁄₃₂	1¹⁵⁄₁₆	1-4¹⁄₄
³⁄₁₆	1¹⁵⁄₃₂	1-0⁹⁄₃₂	1¹⁹⁄₃₂	1-1⁹⁄₃₂	1¹¹⁄₁₆	1-2⁹⁄₃₂	1¹³⁄₁₆	1-3⁹⁄₃₂	1¹⁵⁄₁₆	1-4⁵⁄₁₆
¹⁄₄	1¹⁵⁄₃₂	1-0¹¹⁄₃₂	1¹⁹⁄₃₂	1-1¹¹⁄₃₂	1²³⁄₃₂	1-2¹¹⁄₃₂	1¹³⁄₁₆	1-3¹¹⁄₃₂	1¹⁵⁄₁₆	1-4³⁄₈
⁵⁄₁₆	1¹⁵⁄₃₂	1-0¹³⁄₃₂	1¹⁹⁄₃₂	1-1¹³⁄₃₂	1²³⁄₃₂	1-2¹³⁄₃₂	1²⁷⁄₃₂	1-3⁷⁄₁₆	1³¹⁄₃₂	1-4⁷⁄₁₆
³⁄₈	1¹⁵⁄₃₂	1-0¹⁵⁄₃₂	1¹⁹⁄₃₂	1-1¹⁵⁄₃₂	1²³⁄₃₂	1-2¹⁵⁄₃₂	1²⁷⁄₃₂	1-3¹⁄₂	1³¹⁄₃₂	1-4¹⁄₂
⁷⁄₁₆	1¹⁄₂	1-0¹⁷⁄₃₂	1⁵⁄₈	1-1¹⁷⁄₃₂	1²³⁄₃₂	1-2¹⁷⁄₃₂	1²⁷⁄₃₂	1-3⁹⁄₁₆	1³¹⁄₃₂	1-4⁹⁄₁₆
¹⁄₂	1¹⁄₂	1-0¹⁹⁄₃₂	1⁵⁄₈	1-1¹⁹⁄₃₂	1³⁄₄	1-2¹⁹⁄₃₂	1²⁷⁄₃₂	1-3⁵⁄₈	1³¹⁄₃₂	1-4⁵⁄₈
⁹⁄₁₆	1¹⁄₂	1-0²¹⁄₃₂	1⁵⁄₈	1-1²¹⁄₃₂	1³⁄₄	1-2²¹⁄₃₂	1⁷⁄₈	1-3¹¹⁄₁₆	1³¹⁄₃₂	1-4¹¹⁄₁₆
⁵⁄₈	1¹⁄₂	1-0²³⁄₃₂	1⁵⁄₈	1-1²³⁄₃₂	1³⁄₄	1-2²³⁄₃₂	1⁷⁄₈	1-3³⁄₄	2	1-4³⁄₄
¹¹⁄₁₆	1¹⁷⁄₃₂	1-0²⁵⁄₃₂	1⁵⁄₈	1-1²⁵⁄₃₂	1³⁄₄	1-2²⁵⁄₃₂	1⁷⁄₈	1-3¹³⁄₁₆	2	1-4¹³⁄₁₆
³⁄₄	1¹⁷⁄₃₂	1-0²⁷⁄₃₂	1²¹⁄₃₂	1-1²⁷⁄₃₂	1²⁵⁄₃₂	1-2²⁷⁄₃₂	1⁷⁄₈	1-3⁷⁄₈	2	1-4⁷⁄₈
¹³⁄₁₆	1¹⁷⁄₃₂	1-0²⁹⁄₃₂	1²¹⁄₃₂	1-1²⁹⁄₃₂	1²⁵⁄₃₂	1-2²⁹⁄₃₂	1²⁹⁄₃₂	1-3¹⁵⁄₁₆	2	1-4¹⁵⁄₁₆
⁷⁄₈	1¹⁷⁄₃₂	1-0³¹⁄₃₂	1²¹⁄₃₂	1-1³¹⁄₃₂	1²⁵⁄₃₂	1-2³¹⁄₃₂	1²⁹⁄₃₂	1-4	2¹⁄₃₂	1-5
¹⁵⁄₁₆	1⁹⁄₁₆	1-1¹⁄₃₂	1²¹⁄₃₂	1-2¹⁄₃₂	1²⁵⁄₃₂	1-3¹⁄₃₂	1²⁹⁄₃₂	1-4¹⁄₁₆	2¹⁄₃₂	1-5¹⁄₁₆

Ins.	17″ Rise	17″ Slope	18″ Rise	18″ Slope	19″ Rise	19″ Slope	20″ Rise	20″ Slope	21″ Rise	21″ Slope
0	2¹⁄₃₂	1-5¹⁄₈	2⁵⁄₃₂	1-6¹⁄₈	2⁹⁄₃₂	1-7¹⁄₈	2¹³⁄₃₂	1-8⁵⁄₃₂	2¹⁄₂	1-9⁵⁄₃₂
¹⁄₁₆	2¹⁄₃₂	1-5³⁄₁₆	2⁵⁄₃₂	1-6³⁄₁₆	2⁹⁄₃₂	1-7³⁄₁₆	2¹³⁄₃₂	1-8⁷⁄₃₂	2¹⁷⁄₃₂	1-9⁷⁄₃₂
¹⁄₈	2¹⁄₁₆	1-5¹⁄₄	2⁵⁄₃₂	1-6¹⁄₄	2⁹⁄₃₂	1-7¹⁄₄	2¹³⁄₃₂	1-8⁹⁄₃₂	2¹⁷⁄₃₂	1-9⁹⁄₃₂
³⁄₁₆	2¹⁄₁₆	1-5⁵⁄₁₆	2³⁄₁₆	1-6⁵⁄₁₆	2⁵⁄₁₆	1-7⁵⁄₁₆	2¹³⁄₃₂	1-8¹¹⁄₃₂	2¹⁷⁄₃₂	1-9¹¹⁄₃₂
¹⁄₄	2¹⁄₁₆	1-5³⁄₈	2³⁄₁₆	1-6³⁄₈	2⁵⁄₁₆	1-7³⁄₈	2⁷⁄₁₆	1-8¹³⁄₃₂	2¹⁷⁄₃₂	1-9¹³⁄₃₂
⁵⁄₁₆	2¹⁄₁₆	1-5⁷⁄₁₆	2³⁄₁₆	1-6⁷⁄₁₆	2⁵⁄₁₆	1-7⁷⁄₁₆	2⁷⁄₁₆	1-8¹⁵⁄₃₂	2⁹⁄₁₆	1-9¹⁵⁄₃₂
³⁄₈	2³⁄₃₂	1-5¹⁄₂	2³⁄₁₆	1-6¹⁄₂	2⁵⁄₁₆	1-7¹⁄₂	2⁷⁄₁₆	1-8¹⁷⁄₃₂	2⁹⁄₁₆	1-9¹⁷⁄₃₂
⁷⁄₁₆	2³⁄₃₂	1-5⁹⁄₁₆	2⁷⁄₃₂	1-6⁹⁄₁₆	2¹¹⁄₃₂	1-7⁹⁄₁₆	2⁷⁄₁₆	1-8¹⁹⁄₃₂	2⁹⁄₁₆	1-9¹⁹⁄₃₂
¹⁄₂	2³⁄₃₂	1-5⁵⁄₈	2⁷⁄₃₂	1-6⁵⁄₈	2¹¹⁄₃₂	1-7⁵⁄₈	2¹⁵⁄₃₂	1-8²¹⁄₃₂	2⁹⁄₁₆	1-9²¹⁄₃₂
⁹⁄₁₆	2³⁄₃₂	1-5¹¹⁄₁₆	2⁷⁄₃₂	1-6¹¹⁄₁₆	2¹¹⁄₃₂	1-7¹¹⁄₁₆	2¹⁵⁄₃₂	1-8²³⁄₃₂	2¹⁹⁄₃₂	1-9²³⁄₃₂
⁵⁄₈	2¹⁄₈	1-5³⁄₄	2⁷⁄₃₂	1-6³⁄₄	2¹¹⁄₃₂	1-7³⁄₄	2¹⁵⁄₃₂	1-8²⁵⁄₃₂	2¹⁹⁄₃₂	1-9²⁵⁄₃₂
¹¹⁄₁₆	2¹⁄₈	1-5¹³⁄₁₆	2¹⁄₄	1-6¹³⁄₁₆	2¹¹⁄₃₂	1-7²⁷⁄₃₂	2¹⁵⁄₃₂	1-8²⁷⁄₃₂	2¹⁹⁄₃₂	1-9²⁷⁄₃₂
³⁄₄	2¹⁄₈	1-5⁷⁄₈	2¹⁄₄	1-6⁷⁄₈	2³⁄₈	1-7²⁹⁄₃₂	2¹⁄₂	1-8²⁹⁄₃₂	2¹⁹⁄₃₂	1-9²⁹⁄₃₂
¹³⁄₁₆	2¹⁄₈	1-5¹⁵⁄₁₆	2¹⁄₄	1-6¹⁵⁄₁₆	2³⁄₈	1-7³¹⁄₃₂	2¹⁄₂	1-8³¹⁄₃₂	2⁵⁄₈	1-9³¹⁄₃₂
⁷⁄₈	2⁵⁄₃₂	1-6	2¹⁄₄	1-7	2³⁄₈	1-8¹⁄₃₂	2¹⁄₂	1-9¹⁄₃₂	2⁵⁄₈	1-10¹⁄₃₂
¹⁵⁄₁₆	2⁵⁄₃₂	1-6¹⁄₁₆	2⁹⁄₃₂	1-7¹⁄₁₆	2³⁄₈	1-8³⁄₃₂	2¹⁄₂	1-9³⁄₃₂	2⁵⁄₈	1-10³⁄₃₂

Feet	40′ Rise	40′ Slope	50′ Rise	50′ Slope	60′ Rise	60′ Slope	70′ Rise	70′ Slope
0	4-9¹⁄₂	40-3⁷⁄₁₆	5-11⁷⁄₈	50-4⁹⁄₃₂	7-2¹⁄₄	60-5⁵⁄₃₂	8-4⁵⁄₈	70-6
1	4-10¹⁵⁄₁₆	41-3¹⁷⁄₃₂	6-1⁵⁄₁₆	51-4³⁄₈	7-3¹¹⁄₁₆	61-5⁷⁄₃₂	8-6¹⁄₁₆	71-6³⁄₃₂
2	5-0³⁄₈	42-3¹⁹⁄₃₂	6-2³⁄₄	52-4¹⁵⁄₃₂	7-5¹⁄₈	62-5⁵⁄₁₆	8-7¹⁄₂	72-6³⁄₁₆
3	5-1¹³⁄₁₆	43-3¹¹⁄₁₆	6-4³⁄₁₆	53-4⁹⁄₁₆	7-6⁹⁄₁₆	63-5¹³⁄₃₂	8-8¹⁵⁄₁₆	73-6¹⁄₄
4	5-3¹⁄₄	44-3²⁵⁄₃₂	6-5⁵⁄₈	54-4⁵⁄₈	7-8	64-5¹⁄₂	8-10³⁄₈	74-6¹¹⁄₃₂
5	5-4¹¹⁄₁₆	45-3⁷⁄₈	6-7¹⁄₁₆	55-4²³⁄₃₂	7-9⁷⁄₁₆	65-5⁹⁄₁₆	8-11¹³⁄₁₆	75-6⁷⁄₁₆
6	5-6¹⁄₈	46-3¹⁵⁄₁₆	6-8¹⁄₂	56-4¹³⁄₁₆	7-10⁷⁄₈	66-5²¹⁄₃₂	9-1¹⁄₄	76-6¹⁷⁄₃₂
7	5-7⁹⁄₁₆	47-4¹⁄₃₂	6-9¹⁵⁄₁₆	57-4⁷⁄₈	8-0⁵⁄₁₆	67-5³⁄₄	9-2¹¹⁄₁₆	77-6¹⁹⁄₃₂
8	5-9	48-4¹⁄₈	6-11³⁄₈	58-4³¹⁄₃₂	8-1³⁄₄	68-5²⁷⁄₃₂	9-4¹⁄₈	78-6¹¹⁄₁₆
9	5-10⁷⁄₁₆	49-4⁷⁄₃₂	7-0¹³⁄₁₆	59-5¹⁄₁₆	8-3³⁄₁₆	69-5²⁹⁄₃₂	9-5⁹⁄₁₆	79-6²⁵⁄₃₂

natsin A=0.1189413000; natcos A=0.9929012876; nattan A=0.1197916666; natcot A=8.3478260869

Inches	0" Rise	0" Slope	1" Rise	1" Slope	2" Rise	2" Slope	3" Rise	3" Slope	4" Rise	4" Slope	5" Rise	5" Slope
0	0	0	1/8	1	1/4	2	3/8	3 1/32	1/2	4 1/32	5/8	5 1/32
1/16	0	1/16	1/8	1 1/16	1/4	2 3/32	3/8	3 3/32	1/2	4 3/32	5/8	5 3/32
1/8	0	1/8	1/8	1 1/8	1/4	2 5/32	3/8	3 5/32	1/2	4 5/32	5/8	5 5/32
3/16	1/32	3/16	5/32	1 3/16	9/32	2 7/32	13/32	3 7/32	17/32	4 7/32	21/32	5 7/32
1/4	1/32	1/4	5/32	1 1/4	9/32	2 9/32	13/32	3 9/32	17/32	4 9/32	21/32	5 9/32
5/16	1/32	5/16	5/32	1 5/16	9/32	2 11/32	13/32	3 11/32	17/32	4 11/32	21/32	5 11/32
3/8	1/16	3/8	3/16	1 3/8	5/16	2 13/32	7/16	3 13/32	9/16	4 13/32	11/16	5 13/32
7/16	1/16	7/16	3/16	1 7/16	5/16	2 15/32	7/16	3 15/32	9/16	4 15/32	11/16	5 15/32
1/2	1/16	1/2	3/16	1 1/2	5/16	2 17/32	7/16	3 17/32	9/16	4 17/32	11/16	5 17/32
9/16	1/16	9/16	3/16	1 9/16	5/16	2 19/32	7/16	3 19/32	9/16	4 19/32	11/16	5 19/32
5/8	1/16	5/8	3/16	1 5/8	5/16	2 21/32	7/16	3 21/32	9/16	4 21/32	11/16	5 21/32
11/16	3/32	11/16	7/32	1 11/16	11/32	2 23/32	15/32	3 23/32	19/32	4 23/32	23/32	5 23/32
3/4	3/32	3/4	7/32	1 3/4	11/32	2 25/32	15/32	3 25/32	19/32	4 25/32	23/32	5 25/32
13/16	3/32	13/16	7/32	1 13/16	11/32	2 27/32	15/32	3 27/32	19/32	4 27/32	23/32	5 27/32
7/8	1/8	7/8	1/4	1 7/8	3/8	2 29/32	1/2	3 29/32	5/8	4 29/32	3/4	5 29/32
15/16	1/8	15/16	1/4	1 15/16	3/8	2 31/32	1/2	3 31/32	5/8	4 31/32	3/4	5 31/32

Inches	6" Rise	6" Slope	7" Rise	7" Slope	8" Rise	8" Slope	9" Rise	9" Slope	10" Rise	10" Slope	11" Rise	11" Slope
0	3/4	6 1/32	7/8	7 1/16	1	8 1/16	1 1/8	9 1/16	1 1/4	10 1/16	1 3/8	11 3/32
1/16	3/4	6 1/8	7/8	7 1/8	1	8 1/8	1 1/8	9 1/8	1 1/4	10 5/32	1 3/8	11 5/32
1/8	3/4	6 3/16	7/8	7 3/16	1	8 3/16	1 1/8	9 3/16	1 1/4	10 7/32	1 3/8	11 7/32
3/16	25/32	6 1/4	29/32	7 1/4	1 1/32	8 1/4	1 5/32	9 1/4	1 9/32	10 9/32	1 13/32	11 9/32
1/4	25/32	6 5/16	29/32	7 5/16	1 1/32	8 5/16	1 5/32	9 5/16	1 9/32	10 11/32	1 13/32	11 11/32
5/16	25/32	6 3/8	29/32	7 3/8	1 1/32	8 3/8	1 5/32	9 3/8	1 9/32	10 13/32	1 13/32	11 13/32
3/8	13/16	6 7/16	15/16	7 7/16	1 1/16	8 7/16	1 3/16	9 7/16	1 5/16	10 15/32	1 7/16	11 15/32
7/16	13/16	6 1/2	15/16	7 1/2	1 1/16	8 1/2	1 3/16	9 1/2	1 5/16	10 17/32	1 7/16	11 17/32
1/2	13/16	6 9/16	15/16	7 9/16	1 1/16	8 9/16	1 3/16	9 9/16	1 5/16	10 19/32	1 7/16	11 19/32
9/16	13/16	6 5/8	15/16	7 5/8	1 1/16	8 5/8	1 3/16	9 5/8	1 5/16	10 21/32	1 7/16	11 21/32
5/8	13/16	6 11/16	15/16	7 11/16	1 1/16	8 11/16	1 3/16	9 11/16	1 5/16	10 23/32	1 7/16	11 23/32
11/16	27/32	6 3/4	31/32	7 3/4	1 3/32	8 3/4	1 7/32	9 3/4	1 11/32	10 25/32	1 15/32	11 25/32
3/4	27/32	6 13/16	31/32	7 13/16	1 3/32	8 13/16	1 7/32	9 13/16	1 11/32	10 27/32	1 15/32	11 27/32
13/16	27/32	6 7/8	31/32	7 7/8	1 3/32	8 7/8	1 7/32	9 7/8	1 11/32	10 29/32	1 15/32	11 29/32
7/8	7/8	6 15/16	1	7 15/16	1 1/8	8 15/16	1 1/4	9 15/16	1 3/8	10 31/32	1 1/2	11 31/32
15/16	7/8	7	1	8	1 1/8	9	1 1/4	10	1 3/8	11 1/32	1 1/2	1-0 1/32

Feet	0' Rise	0' Slope	10' Rise	10' Slope	20' Rise	20' Slope	30' Rise	30' Slope
0	0	0	1-3	10-0 15/16	2-6	20-1 7/8	3-9	30-2 13/16
1	1 1/2	1-0 3/32	1-4 1/2	11-1 1/32	2-7 1/2	21-1 31/32	3-10 1/2	31-2 29/32
2	3	2-0 3/16	1-6	12-1 1/8	2-9	22-2 1/16	4-0	32-3
3	4 1/2	3-0 9/32	1-7 1/2	13-1 7/32	2-10 1/2	23-2 5/32	4-1 1/2	33-3 3/32
4	6	4-0 3/8	1-9	14-1 5/16	3-0	24-2 1/4	4-3	34-3 3/16
5	7 1/2	5-0 15/32	1-10 1/2	15-1 13/32	3-1 1/2	25-2 11/32	4-4 1/2	35-3 9/32
6	9	6-0 9/16	2-0	16-1 1/2	3-3	26-2 7/16	4-6	36-3 3/8
7	10 1/2	7-0 21/32	2-1 1/2	17-1 19/32	3-4 1/2	27-2 17/32	4-7 1/2	37-3 15/32
8	1-0	8-0 3/4	2-3	18-1 11/16	3-6	28-2 5/8	4-9	38-3 9/16
9	1-1 1/2	9-0 27/32	2-4 1/2	19-1 25/32	3-7 1/2	29-2 23/32	4-10 1/2	39-3 21/32

A = 7° 07' 30"; logsin A = 9.09354; logcos A = 9.99663; logtan A = 9.09691; logcot A = 0.90309

ins.	12″ Rise	Slope	13″ Rise	Slope	14″ Rise	Slope	15″ Rise	Slope	16″ Rise	Slope
0	$1\frac{1}{2}$	$1\text{-}0\frac{3}{32}$	$1\frac{5}{8}$	$1\text{-}1\frac{3}{32}$	$1\frac{3}{4}$	$1\text{-}2\frac{3}{32}$	$1\frac{7}{8}$	$1\text{-}3\frac{1}{8}$	2	$1\text{-}4\frac{1}{8}$
$\frac{1}{16}$	$1\frac{1}{2}$	$1\text{-}0\frac{5}{32}$	$1\frac{5}{8}$	$1\text{-}1\frac{5}{32}$	$1\frac{3}{4}$	$1\text{-}2\frac{5}{32}$	$1\frac{7}{8}$	$1\text{-}3\frac{3}{16}$	2	$1\text{-}4\frac{3}{32}$
$\frac{1}{8}$	$1\frac{1}{2}$	$1\text{-}0\frac{7}{32}$	$1\frac{5}{8}$	$1\text{-}1\frac{7}{32}$	$1\frac{3}{4}$	$1\text{-}2\frac{1}{4}$	$1\frac{7}{8}$	$1\text{-}3\frac{1}{4}$	2	$1\text{-}4\frac{1}{4}$
$\frac{3}{16}$	$1\frac{17}{32}$	$1\text{-}0\frac{9}{32}$	$1\frac{21}{32}$	$1\text{-}1\frac{9}{32}$	$1\frac{25}{32}$	$1\text{-}2\frac{5}{16}$	$1\frac{29}{32}$	$1\text{-}3\frac{5}{16}$	$2\frac{1}{32}$	$1\text{-}4\frac{5}{16}$
$\frac{1}{4}$	$1\frac{17}{32}$	$1\text{-}0\frac{11}{32}$	$1\frac{21}{32}$	$1\text{-}1\frac{11}{32}$	$1\frac{25}{32}$	$1\text{-}2\frac{3}{8}$	$1\frac{29}{32}$	$1\text{-}3\frac{3}{8}$	$2\frac{1}{32}$	$1\text{-}4\frac{3}{8}$
$\frac{5}{16}$	$1\frac{17}{32}$	$1\text{-}0\frac{13}{32}$	$1\frac{21}{32}$	$1\text{-}1\frac{13}{32}$	$1\frac{25}{32}$	$1\text{-}2\frac{7}{16}$	$1\frac{29}{32}$	$1\text{-}3\frac{7}{16}$	$2\frac{1}{32}$	$1\text{-}4\frac{7}{16}$
$\frac{3}{8}$	$1\frac{9}{16}$	$1\text{-}0\frac{15}{32}$	$1\frac{11}{16}$	$1\text{-}1\frac{15}{32}$	$1\frac{13}{16}$	$1\text{-}2\frac{1}{2}$	$1\frac{15}{16}$	$1\text{-}3\frac{1}{2}$	$2\frac{1}{16}$	$1\text{-}4\frac{1}{2}$
$\frac{7}{16}$	$1\frac{9}{16}$	$1\text{-}0\frac{17}{32}$	$1\frac{11}{16}$	$1\text{-}1\frac{17}{32}$	$1\frac{13}{16}$	$1\text{-}2\frac{9}{16}$	$1\frac{15}{16}$	$1\text{-}3\frac{9}{16}$	$2\frac{1}{16}$	$1\text{-}4\frac{9}{16}$
$\frac{1}{2}$	$1\frac{9}{16}$	$1\text{-}0\frac{19}{32}$	$1\frac{11}{16}$	$1\text{-}1\frac{19}{32}$	$1\frac{13}{16}$	$1\text{-}2\frac{5}{8}$	$1\frac{15}{16}$	$1\text{-}3\frac{5}{8}$	$2\frac{1}{16}$	$1\text{-}4\frac{5}{8}$
$\frac{9}{16}$	$1\frac{9}{16}$	$1\text{-}0\frac{21}{32}$	$1\frac{11}{16}$	$1\text{-}1\frac{21}{32}$	$1\frac{13}{16}$	$1\text{-}2\frac{11}{16}$	$1\frac{15}{16}$	$1\text{-}3\frac{11}{16}$	$2\frac{1}{16}$	$1\text{-}4\frac{11}{16}$
$\frac{5}{8}$	$1\frac{9}{16}$	$1\text{-}0\frac{23}{32}$	$1\frac{11}{16}$	$1\text{-}1\frac{23}{32}$	$1\frac{13}{16}$	$1\text{-}2\frac{3}{4}$	$1\frac{15}{16}$	$1\text{-}3\frac{3}{4}$	$2\frac{1}{16}$	$1\text{-}4\frac{3}{4}$
$\frac{11}{16}$	$1\frac{19}{32}$	$1\text{-}0\frac{25}{32}$	$1\frac{23}{32}$	$1\text{-}1\frac{25}{32}$	$1\frac{27}{32}$	$1\text{-}2\frac{13}{16}$	$1\frac{31}{32}$	$1\text{-}3\frac{13}{16}$	$2\frac{3}{32}$	$1\text{-}4\frac{13}{16}$
$\frac{3}{4}$	$1\frac{19}{32}$	$1\text{-}0\frac{27}{32}$	$1\frac{23}{32}$	$1\text{-}1\frac{27}{32}$	$1\frac{27}{32}$	$1\text{-}2\frac{7}{8}$	$1\frac{31}{32}$	$1\text{-}3\frac{7}{8}$	$2\frac{3}{32}$	$1\text{-}4\frac{7}{8}$
$\frac{13}{16}$	$1\frac{19}{32}$	$1\text{-}0\frac{29}{32}$	$1\frac{23}{32}$	$1\text{-}1\frac{29}{32}$	$1\frac{27}{32}$	$1\text{-}2\frac{15}{16}$	$1\frac{31}{32}$	$1\text{-}3\frac{15}{16}$	$2\frac{3}{32}$	$1\text{-}4\frac{15}{16}$
$\frac{7}{8}$	$1\frac{5}{8}$	$1\text{-}0\frac{31}{32}$	$1\frac{3}{4}$	$1\text{-}1\frac{31}{32}$	$1\frac{7}{8}$	$1\text{-}3$	2	$1\text{-}4$	$2\frac{1}{8}$	$1\text{-}5$
$\frac{15}{16}$	$1\frac{5}{8}$	$1\text{-}1\frac{1}{32}$	$1\frac{3}{4}$	$1\text{-}2\frac{1}{32}$	$1\frac{7}{8}$	$1\text{-}3\frac{1}{32}$	2	$1\text{-}4\frac{1}{16}$	$2\frac{1}{8}$	$1\text{-}5\frac{1}{16}$

ins.	17″ Rise	Slope	18″ Rise	Slope	19″ Rise	Slope	20″ Rise	Slope	21″ Rise	Slope
0	$2\frac{1}{8}$	$1\text{-}5\frac{1}{8}$	$2\frac{1}{4}$	$1\text{-}6\frac{1}{8}$	$2\frac{3}{8}$	$1\text{-}7\frac{5}{32}$	$2\frac{1}{2}$	$1\text{-}8\frac{5}{32}$	$2\frac{5}{8}$	$1\text{-}9\frac{5}{32}$
$\frac{1}{16}$	$2\frac{1}{8}$	$1\text{-}5\frac{3}{16}$	$2\frac{1}{4}$	$1\text{-}6\frac{3}{16}$	$2\frac{3}{8}$	$1\text{-}7\frac{7}{32}$	$2\frac{1}{2}$	$1\text{-}8\frac{7}{32}$	$2\frac{5}{8}$	$1\text{-}9\frac{7}{32}$
$\frac{1}{8}$	$2\frac{1}{8}$	$1\text{-}5\frac{1}{4}$	$2\frac{1}{4}$	$1\text{-}6\frac{9}{32}$	$2\frac{3}{8}$	$1\text{-}7\frac{9}{32}$	$2\frac{1}{2}$	$1\text{-}8\frac{9}{32}$	$2\frac{5}{8}$	$1\text{-}9\frac{9}{32}$
$\frac{3}{16}$	$2\frac{5}{32}$	$1\text{-}5\frac{5}{16}$	$2\frac{9}{32}$	$1\text{-}6\frac{11}{32}$	$2\frac{13}{32}$	$1\text{-}7\frac{11}{32}$	$2\frac{17}{32}$	$1\text{-}8\frac{11}{32}$	$2\frac{21}{32}$	$1\text{-}9\frac{11}{32}$
$\frac{1}{4}$	$2\frac{5}{32}$	$1\text{-}5\frac{3}{8}$	$2\frac{9}{32}$	$1\text{-}6\frac{13}{32}$	$2\frac{13}{32}$	$1\text{-}7\frac{13}{32}$	$2\frac{17}{32}$	$1\text{-}8\frac{13}{32}$	$2\frac{21}{32}$	$1\text{-}9\frac{13}{32}$
$\frac{5}{16}$	$2\frac{5}{32}$	$1\text{-}5\frac{7}{16}$	$2\frac{9}{32}$	$1\text{-}6\frac{15}{32}$	$2\frac{13}{32}$	$1\text{-}7\frac{15}{32}$	$2\frac{17}{32}$	$1\text{-}8\frac{15}{32}$	$2\frac{21}{32}$	$1\text{-}9\frac{15}{32}$
$\frac{3}{8}$	$2\frac{3}{16}$	$1\text{-}5\frac{1}{2}$	$2\frac{5}{16}$	$1\text{-}6\frac{17}{32}$	$2\frac{7}{16}$	$1\text{-}7\frac{17}{32}$	$2\frac{9}{16}$	$1\text{-}8\frac{17}{32}$	$2\frac{11}{16}$	$1\text{-}9\frac{17}{32}$
$\frac{7}{16}$	$2\frac{3}{16}$	$1\text{-}5\frac{9}{16}$	$2\frac{5}{16}$	$1\text{-}6\frac{19}{32}$	$2\frac{7}{16}$	$1\text{-}7\frac{19}{32}$	$2\frac{9}{16}$	$1\text{-}8\frac{19}{32}$	$2\frac{11}{16}$	$1\text{-}9\frac{19}{32}$
$\frac{1}{2}$	$2\frac{3}{16}$	$1\text{-}5\frac{5}{8}$	$2\frac{5}{16}$	$1\text{-}6\frac{21}{32}$	$2\frac{7}{16}$	$1\text{-}7\frac{21}{32}$	$2\frac{9}{16}$	$1\text{-}8\frac{21}{32}$	$2\frac{11}{16}$	$1\text{-}9\frac{21}{32}$
$\frac{9}{16}$	$2\frac{3}{16}$	$1\text{-}5\frac{11}{16}$	$2\frac{5}{16}$	$1\text{-}6\frac{23}{32}$	$2\frac{7}{16}$	$1\text{-}7\frac{23}{32}$	$2\frac{9}{16}$	$1\text{-}8\frac{23}{32}$	$2\frac{11}{16}$	$1\text{-}9\frac{23}{32}$
$\frac{5}{8}$	$2\frac{3}{16}$	$1\text{-}5\frac{3}{4}$	$2\frac{5}{16}$	$1\text{-}6\frac{25}{32}$	$2\frac{7}{16}$	$1\text{-}7\frac{25}{32}$	$2\frac{9}{16}$	$1\text{-}8\frac{25}{32}$	$2\frac{11}{16}$	$1\text{-}9\frac{25}{32}$
$\frac{11}{16}$	$2\frac{7}{32}$	$1\text{-}5\frac{13}{16}$	$2\frac{11}{32}$	$1\text{-}6\frac{27}{32}$	$2\frac{15}{32}$	$1\text{-}7\frac{27}{32}$	$2\frac{19}{32}$	$1\text{-}8\frac{27}{32}$	$2\frac{23}{32}$	$1\text{-}9\frac{27}{32}$
$\frac{3}{4}$	$2\frac{7}{32}$	$1\text{-}5\frac{7}{8}$	$2\frac{11}{32}$	$1\text{-}6\frac{29}{32}$	$2\frac{15}{32}$	$1\text{-}7\frac{29}{32}$	$2\frac{19}{32}$	$1\text{-}8\frac{29}{32}$	$2\frac{23}{32}$	$1\text{-}9\frac{29}{32}$
$\frac{13}{16}$	$2\frac{7}{32}$	$1\text{-}5\frac{15}{16}$	$2\frac{11}{32}$	$1\text{-}6\frac{31}{32}$	$2\frac{15}{32}$	$1\text{-}7\frac{31}{32}$	$2\frac{19}{32}$	$1\text{-}8\frac{31}{32}$	$2\frac{23}{32}$	$1\text{-}9\frac{31}{32}$
$\frac{7}{8}$	$2\frac{1}{4}$	$1\text{-}6$	$2\frac{3}{8}$	$1\text{-}7\frac{1}{32}$	$2\frac{1}{2}$	$1\text{-}8\frac{1}{32}$	$2\frac{5}{8}$	$1\text{-}9\frac{1}{32}$	$2\frac{3}{4}$	$1\text{-}10\frac{1}{32}$
$\frac{15}{16}$	$2\frac{1}{4}$	$1\text{-}6\frac{1}{16}$	$2\frac{3}{8}$	$1\text{-}7\frac{3}{32}$	$2\frac{1}{2}$	$1\text{-}8\frac{3}{32}$	$2\frac{5}{8}$	$1\text{-}9\frac{3}{32}$	$2\frac{3}{4}$	$1\text{-}10\frac{3}{32}$

Feet	40′ Rise	Slope	50′ Rise	Slope	60′ Rise	Slope	70′ Rise	Slope
0	$5\text{-}0$	$40\text{-}3\frac{3}{4}$	$6\text{-}3$	$50\text{-}4\frac{21}{32}$	$7\text{-}6$	$60\text{-}5\frac{19}{32}$	$8\text{-}9$	$70\text{-}6\frac{17}{32}$
1	$5\text{-}1\frac{1}{2}$	$41\text{-}3\frac{27}{32}$	$6\text{-}4\frac{1}{2}$	$51\text{-}4\frac{3}{4}$	$7\text{-}7\frac{1}{2}$	$61\text{-}5\frac{11}{16}$	$8\text{-}10\frac{1}{2}$	$71\text{-}6\frac{5}{8}$
2	$5\text{-}3$	$42\text{-}3\frac{15}{16}$	$6\text{-}6$	$52\text{-}4\frac{27}{32}$	$7\text{-}9$	$62\text{-}5\frac{25}{32}$	$9\text{-}0$	$72\text{-}6\frac{23}{32}$
3	$5\text{-}4\frac{1}{2}$	$43\text{-}4$	$6\text{-}7\frac{1}{2}$	$53\text{-}4\frac{15}{32}$	$7\text{-}10\frac{1}{2}$	$63\text{-}5\frac{7}{8}$	$9\text{-}1\frac{1}{2}$	$73\text{-}6\frac{13}{16}$
4	$5\text{-}6$	$44\text{-}4\frac{3}{4}$	$6\text{-}9$	$54\text{-}5\frac{1}{2}$	$8\text{-}0$	$64\text{-}5\frac{31}{32}$	$9\text{-}3$	$74\text{-}6\frac{29}{32}$
5	$5\text{-}7\frac{1}{2}$	$45\text{-}4\frac{3}{16}$	$6\text{-}10\frac{1}{2}$	$55\text{-}5\frac{1}{8}$	$8\text{-}1\frac{1}{2}$	$65\text{-}6\frac{1}{16}$	$9\text{-}4\frac{1}{2}$	$75\text{-}7$
6	$5\text{-}9$	$46\text{-}4\frac{9}{32}$	$7\text{-}0$	$56\text{-}5\frac{7}{32}$	$8\text{-}3$	$66\text{-}6\frac{5}{32}$	$9\text{-}6$	$76\text{-}7\frac{3}{32}$
7	$5\text{-}10\frac{1}{2}$	$47\text{-}4\frac{3}{8}$	$7\text{-}1\frac{1}{2}$	$57\text{-}5\frac{5}{16}$	$8\text{-}4\frac{1}{2}$	$67\text{-}6\frac{1}{4}$	$9\text{-}7\frac{1}{2}$	$77\text{-}7\frac{5}{16}$
8	$6\text{-}0$	$48\text{-}4\frac{15}{32}$	$7\text{-}3$	$58\text{-}5\frac{13}{32}$	$8\text{-}6$	$68\text{-}6\frac{11}{32}$	$9\text{-}9$	$78\text{-}7\frac{9}{32}$
9	$6\text{-}1\frac{1}{2}$	$49\text{-}4\frac{9}{16}$	$7\text{-}4\frac{1}{2}$	$59\text{-}5\frac{1}{2}$	$8\text{-}7\frac{1}{2}$	$69\text{-}6\frac{7}{16}$	$9\text{-}10\frac{1}{2}$	$79\text{-}7\frac{3}{8}$

natsin A=0.1240347345; natcos A=0.9922778767; nattan A=0.1250000000; natcot A=8.0000000000

Inches	0" Rise	Slope	1" Rise	Slope	2" Rise	Slope	3" Rise	Slope	4" Rise	Slope	5" Rise	Slope
0	0	0	1/8	1	1/4	2 1/32	3/8	3 1/32	17/32	4 1/32	21/32	5 1/32
1/16	0	1/16	1/8	1 1/16	9/32	2 3/32	13/32	3 3/32	17/32	4 3/32	21/32	5 3/32
1/8	1/32	1/8	5/32	1 1/8	9/32	2 5/32	13/32	3 5/32	17/32	4 5/32	21/32	5 5/32
3/16	1/32	3/16	5/32	1 3/16	9/32	2 7/32	13/32	3 7/32	17/32	4 7/32	11/16	5 7/32
1/4	1/32	1/4	5/32	1 1/4	9/32	2 9/32	7/16	3 9/32	9/16	4 9/32	11/16	5 9/32
5/16	1/32	5/16	5/32	1 5/16	5/16	2 11/32	7/16	3 11/32	9/16	4 11/32	11/16	5 11/32
3/8	1/16	3/8	3/16	1 3/8	5/16	2 13/32	7/16	3 13/32	9/16	4 13/32	11/16	5 13/32
7/16	1/16	7/16	3/16	1 7/16	5/16	2 15/32	7/16	3 15/32	9/16	4 15/32	23/32	5 15/32
1/2	1/16	1/2	3/16	1 1/2	5/16	2 17/32	15/32	3 17/32	19/32	4 17/32	23/32	5 17/32
9/16	1/16	9/16	7/32	1 9/16	11/32	2 19/32	15/32	3 19/32	19/32	4 19/32	23/32	5 5/8
5/8	3/32	5/8	7/32	1 5/8	11/32	2 21/32	15/32	3 21/32	19/32	4 21/32	23/32	5 11/16
11/16	3/32	11/16	7/32	1 11/16	11/32	2 23/32	15/32	3 23/32	5/8	4 23/32	3/4	5 3/4
3/4	3/32	3/4	7/32	1 3/4	11/32	2 25/32	1/2	3 25/32	5/8	4 25/32	3/4	5 13/16
13/16	3/32	13/16	1/4	1 13/16	3/8	2 27/32	1/2	3 27/32	5/8	4 27/32	3/4	5 7/8
7/8	1/8	7/8	1/4	1 29/32	3/8	2 29/32	1/2	3 29/32	5/8	4 29/32	3/4	5 15/16
15/16	1/8	15/16	1/4	1 31/32	3/8	2 31/32	1/2	3 31/32	21/32	4 31/32	25/32	6

Inches	6" Rise	Slope	7" Rise	Slope	8" Rise	Slope	9" Rise	Slope	10" Rise	Slope	11" Rise	Slope
0	25/32	6 1/16	29/32	7 1/16	1 1/32	8 1/16	1 3/16	9 1/16	1 5/16	10 3/32	1 7/16	11 3/32
1/16	25/32	6 1/8	29/32	7 1/8	1 1/16	8 1/8	1 3/16	9 1/8	1 5/16	10 5/32	1 7/16	11 5/32
1/8	13/16	6 3/16	15/16	7 3/16	1 1/16	8 3/16	1 3/16	9 3/16	1 5/16	10 7/32	1 7/16	11 7/32
3/16	13/16	6 1/4	15/16	7 1/4	1 1/16	8 1/4	1 3/16	9 1/4	1 5/16	10 9/32	1 15/32	11 9/32
1/4	13/16	6 5/16	15/16	7 5/16	1 1/16	8 5/16	1 7/32	9 5/16	1 11/32	10 11/32	1 15/32	11 11/32
5/16	13/16	6 3/8	15/16	7 3/8	1 3/32	8 3/8	1 7/32	9 13/32	1 11/32	10 13/32	1 15/32	11 13/32
3/8	27/32	6 7/16	31/32	7 7/16	1 3/32	8 7/16	1 7/32	9 15/32	1 11/32	10 15/32	1 15/32	11 15/32
7/16	27/32	6 1/2	31/32	7 1/2	1 3/32	8 1/2	1 7/32	9 17/32	1 11/32	10 17/32	1 1/2	11 17/32
1/2	27/32	6 9/16	31/32	7 9/16	1 3/32	8 9/16	1 1/4	9 19/32	1 3/8	10 19/32	1 1/2	11 19/32
9/16	27/32	6 5/8	1	7 5/8	1 1/8	8 11/16	1 1/4	9 21/32	1 3/8	10 21/32	1 1/2	11 21/32
5/8	7/8	6 11/16	1	7 11/16	1 1/8	8 11/16	1 1/4	9 23/32	1 3/8	10 23/32	1 1/2	11 23/32
11/16	7/8	6 3/4	1	7 3/4	1 1/8	8 3/4	1 1/4	9 25/32	1 13/32	10 25/32	1 17/32	11 25/32
3/4	7/8	6 13/16	1	7 13/16	1 1/8	8 13/16	1 9/32	9 27/32	1 13/32	10 27/32	1 17/32	11 27/32
13/16	7/8	6 7/8	1 1/32	7 7/8	1 5/32	8 7/8	1 9/32	9 29/32	1 13/32	10 29/32	1 17/32	11 29/32
7/8	29/32	6 15/16	1 1/32	7 15/16	1 5/32	8 15/16	1 9/32	9 31/32	1 13/32	10 31/32	1 17/32	11 31/32
15/16	29/32	7	1 1/32	8	1 5/32	9	1 9/32	10 1/32	1 7/16	11 1/32	1 9/16	1-0 1/32

Feet	0' Rise	Slope	10' Rise	Slope	20' Rise	Slope	30' Rise	Slope
0	0	0	1-3 5/8	10-1	2-7 1/4	20-2 1/2	3-10 7/8	30-3 1/32
1	1 9/16	1-0 3/8	1-5 3/16	11-1 1/8	2-8 13/16	21-2 1/8	4-0 7/16	31-3 1/8
2	3 1/8	2-0 3/16	1-6 3/4	12-1 7/32	2-10 3/8	22-2 7/32	4-2	32-3 1/4
3	4 11/16	3-0 5/16	1-8 5/16	13-1 5/16	2-11 15/16	23-2 11/32	4-3 9/16	33-3 11/32
4	6 1/4	4-0 13/32	1-9 7/8	14-1 13/32	3-1 1/2	24-2 7/16	4-5 1/8	34-3 7/16
5	7 13/16	5-0 1/2	1-11 7/16	15-1 17/32	3-3 1/16	25-2 17/32	4-6 11/16	35-3 17/32
6	9 3/8	6-0 19/32	2-1	16-1 5/8	3-4 5/8	26-2 5/8	4-8 1/4	36-3 21/32
7	10 15/16	7-0 23/32	2-2 9/16	17-1 23/32	3-6 3/16	27-2 3/4	4-9 13/16	37-3 3/4
8	1-0 1/2	8-0 13/16	2-4 1/8	18-1 13/16	3-7 3/4	28-2 27/32	4-11 3/8	38-3 27/32
9	1-2 1/16	9-0 29/32	2-5 11/16	19-1 15/16	3-9 5/16	29-2 15/16	5-0 15/16	39-3 15/16

A = 7° 25′ 07″; logsin A = 9.11099; logcos A = 9.99635; logtan A = 9.11464; logcot A = 0.88536

Ins.	12″ Rise	12″ Slope	13″ Rise	13″ Slope	14″ Rise	14″ Slope	15″ Rise	15″ Slope	16″ Rise	16″ Slope
0	1 9/16	1-0 3/32	1 11/16	1-1 1/8	1 13/16	1-2 1/8	1 15/16	1-3 1/8	2 3/32	1-4 1/8
1/16	1 9/16	1-0 5/32	1 11/16	1-1 3/16	1 27/32	1-2 3/16	1 31/32	1-3 3/16	2 3/32	1-4 3/16
1/8	1 19/32	1-0 7/32	1 23/32	1-1 1/4	1 27/32	1-2 1/4	1 31/32	1-3 1/4	2 3/32	1-4 1/4
3/16	1 19/32	1-0 9/32	1 23/32	1-1 5/16	1 27/32	1-2 5/16	1 31/32	1-3 5/16	2 3/32	1-4 5/16
1/4	1 19/32	1-0 11/32	1 23/32	1-1 3/8	1 27/32	1-2 3/8	2	1-3 3/8	2 1/8	1-4 3/8
5/16	1 19/32	1-0 13/32	1 23/32	1-1 7/16	1 7/8	1-2 7/16	2	1-3 7/16	2 1/8	1-4 7/16
3/8	1 5/8	1-0 15/32	1 3/4	1-1 1/2	1 7/8	1-2 1/2	2	1-3 1/2	2 1/8	1-4 1/2
7/16	1 5/8	1-0 17/32	1 3/4	1-1 9/16	1 7/8	1-2 9/16	2	1-3 9/16	2 1/8	1-4 9/16
1/2	1 5/8	1-0 19/32	1 3/4	1-1 5/8	1 7/8	1-2 5/8	2 1/32	1-3 5/8	2 5/32	1-4 5/8
9/16	1 5/8	1-0 21/32	1 25/32	1-1 11/16	1 29/32	1-2 11/16	2 1/32	1-3 11/16	2 5/32	1-4 11/16
5/8	1 21/32	1-0 23/32	1 25/32	1-1 3/4	1 29/32	1-2 3/4	2 1/32	1-3 3/4	2 5/32	1-4 3/4
11/16	1 21/32	1-0 25/32	1 25/32	1-1 13/16	1 29/32	1-2 13/16	2 1/32	1-3 13/16	2 3/16	1-4 27/32
3/4	1 21/32	1-0 27/32	1 25/32	1-1 7/8	1 29/32	1-2 7/8	2 1/16	1-3 7/8	2 3/16	1-4 29/32
13/16	1 21/32	1-0 29/32	1 13/16	1-1 15/16	1 15/16	1-2 15/16	2 1/16	1-3 15/16	2 3/16	1-4 31/32
7/8	1 11/16	1-0 31/32	1 13/16	1-2	1 15/16	1-3	2 1/16	1-4	2 3/16	1-5 1/32
15/16	1 11/16	1-1 1/32	1 13/16	1-2 1/16	1 15/16	1-3 1/16	2 1/16	1-4 1/16	2 1/32	1-5 3/32

Ins.	17″ Rise	17″ Slope	18″ Rise	18″ Slope	19″ Rise	19″ Slope	20″ Rise	20″ Slope	21″ Rise	21″ Slope
0	2 7/32	1-5 5/32	2 11/32	1-6 5/32	2 15/32	1-7 5/32	2 19/32	1-8 5/32	2 3/4	1-9 3/8
1/16	2 7/32	1-5 7/32	2 11/32	1-6 7/32	2 15/32	1-7 7/32	2 5/8	1-8 7/32	2 3/4	1-9 1/4
1/8	2 7/32	1-5 9/32	2 3/8	1-6 9/32	2 1/2	1-7 9/32	2 5/8	1-8 9/32	2 3/4	1-9 5/16
3/16	2 1/4	1-5 11/32	2 3/8	1-6 11/32	2 1/2	1-7 11/32	2 5/8	1-8 11/32	2 3/4	1-9 3/8
1/4	2 1/4	1-5 13/32	2 3/8	1-6 13/32	2 1/2	1-7 13/32	2 5/8	1-8 13/32	2 25/32	1-9 7/16
5/16	2 1/4	1-5 15/32	2 3/8	1-6 15/32	2 1/2	1-7 15/32	2 21/32	1-8 15/32	2 25/32	1-9 1/2
3/8	2 1/4	1-5 17/32	2 13/32	1-6 17/32	2 17/32	1-7 17/32	2 21/32	1-8 9/16	2 25/32	1-9 9/16
7/16	2 9/32	1-5 19/32	2 13/32	1-6 19/32	2 17/32	1-7 19/32	2 21/32	1-8 5/8	2 25/32	1-9 5/8
1/2	2 9/32	1-5 21/32	2 13/32	1-6 21/32	2 17/32	1-7 21/32	2 21/32	1-8 11/32	2 13/16	1-9 11/16
9/16	2 9/32	1-5 23/32	2 13/32	1-6 23/32	2 9/16	1-7 23/32	2 11/16	1-8 3/4	2 13/16	1-9 3/4
5/8	2 9/32	1-5 25/32	2 7/16	1-6 25/32	2 9/16	1-7 25/32	2 11/16	1-8 13/16	2 13/16	1-9 13/16
11/16	2 5/16	1-5 27/32	2 7/16	1-6 27/32	2 9/16	1-7 27/32	2 11/16	1-8 7/8	2 13/16	1-9 7/8
3/4	2 5/16	1-5 29/32	2 7/16	1-6 29/32	2 9/16	1-7 29/32	2 11/16	1-8 15/16	2 27/32	1-9 15/16
13/16	2 5/16	1-5 31/32	2 7/16	1-6 31/32	2 19/32	1-7 31/32	2 23/32	1-9	2 27/32	1-10
7/8	2 5/16	1-6 1/32	2 15/32	1-7 1/32	2 19/32	1-8 1/32	2 23/32	1-9 1/8	2 27/32	1-10 1/16
15/16	2 11/16	1-6 3/32	2 15/32	1-7 3/32	2 19/32	1-8 3/32	2 23/32	1-9 1/8	2 27/32	1-10 1/8

Feet	40′ Rise	40′ Slope	50′ Rise	50′ Slope	60′ Rise	60′ Slope	70′ Rise	70′ Slope
0	5-2 1/2	40-4 1/16	6-6 1/8	50-5 1/16	7-9 3/4	60-6 1/16	9-1 3/8	70-7 3/32
1	5-4 1/16	41-4 5/32	6-7 11/16	51-5 5/32	7-11 5/16	61-6 3/16	9-2 15/16	71-7 3/16
2	5-5 5/8	42-4 1/4	6-9 1/4	52-5 5/32	8-0 7/8	62-6 3/8	9-4 1/2	72-7 9/32
3	5-7 3/8	43-4 11/32	6-10 13/16	53-5 3/8	8-2 7/16	63-6 5/8	9-6 1/16	73-7 13/32
4	5-8 3/4	44-4 15/32	7-0 3/8	54-5 15/32	8-4	64-6 15/32	9-7 5/8	74-7 1/2
5	5-10 5/16	45-4 9/16	7-1 15/16	55-5 5/8	8-5 9/16	65-6 19/32	9-9 3/8	75-7 19/32
6	5-11 7/8	46-4 21/32	7-3 1/2	56-5 11/16	8-7 1/8	66-6 11/16	9-10 3/4	76-7 11/16
7	6-1 7/16	47-4 3/4	7-5 1/16	57-5 25/32	8-8 11/16	67-6 25/32	10-0 5/16	77-7 13/16
8	6-3	48-4 7/8	7-6 5/8	58-5 7/8	8-10 1/4	68-6 7/8	10-1 7/8	78-7 29/32
9	6-4 9/16	49-4 31/32	7-8 3/16	59-5 31/32	8-11 13/16	69-7	10-3 7/16	79-8

natsin A=0.1291183836; natcos A=0.9916291863; nattan A=0.1302083333; natcot A=7.6800000000

BEVEL 1⁵⁄₈" TO 12"

Inches	0" Rise	0" Slope	1" Rise	1" Slope	2" Rise	2" Slope	3" Rise	3" Slope	4" Rise	4" Slope	5" Rise	5" Slope
0	0	0	1/8	1	9/32	2 1/32	13/32	3 1/32	17/32	4 1/32	11/16	5 1/32
1/16	0	1/16	5/32	1 1/16	9/32	2 3/32	13/32	3 3/32	9/16	4 3/32	11/16	5 3/32
1/8	1/32	1/8	5/32	1 1/8	9/32	2 5/32	7/16	3 5/32	9/16	4 5/32	11/16	5 5/32
3/16	1/32	3/16	5/32	1 3/16	9/32	2 7/32	7/16	3 7/32	9/16	4 7/32	11/16	5 1/4
1/4	1/32	1/4	5/32	1 1/4	5/16	2 9/32	7/16	3 9/32	9/16	4 9/32	23/32	5 5/16
5/16	1/16	5/16	3/16	1 5/16	5/16	2 11/32	7/16	3 11/32	19/32	4 11/32	23/32	5 3/8
3/8	1/16	3/8	3/16	1 3/8	5/16	2 13/32	15/32	3 13/32	19/32	4 13/32	23/32	5 7/16
7/16	1/16	7/16	3/16	1 7/16	11/32	2 15/32	15/32	3 15/32	19/32	4 15/32	3/4	5 1/2
1/2	1/16	1/2	3/16	1 1/2	11/32	2 17/32	15/32	3 17/32	5/8	4 17/32	3/4	5 9/16
9/16	1/16	9/16	7/32	1 9/16	11/32	2 19/32	15/32	3 19/32	5/8	4 19/32	3/4	5 5/8
5/8	3/32	5/8	7/32	1 5/8	11/32	2 21/32	1/2	3 21/32	5/8	4 21/32	3/4	5 11/16
11/16	3/32	11/16	7/32	1 11/16	3/8	2 23/32	1/2	3 23/32	5/8	4 23/32	25/32	5 3/4
3/4	3/32	3/4	1/4	1 25/32	3/8	2 25/32	1/2	3 25/32	21/32	4 25/32	25/32	5 13/16
13/16	1/8	13/16	1/4	1 27/32	3/8	2 27/32	17/32	3 27/32	21/32	4 27/32	25/32	5 7/8
7/8	1/8	7/8	1/4	1 29/32	3/8	2 29/32	17/32	3 29/32	21/32	4 29/32	25/32	5 15/16
15/16	1/8	15/16	1/4	1 31/32	13/32	2 31/32	17/32	3 31/32	21/32	4 31/32	13/16	6

Inches	6" Rise	6" Slope	7" Rise	7" Slope	8" Rise	8" Slope	9" Rise	9" Slope	10" Rise	10" Slope	11" Rise	11" Slope
0	13/16	6 1/16	15/16	7 1/16	1 3/32	8 1/16	1 7/32	9 3/32	1 11/32	10 3/32	1 1/2	11 3/32
1/16	13/16	6 1/8	31/32	7 1/8	1 3/32	8 1/8	1 7/32	9 5/32	1 3/8	10 5/32	1 1/2	11 5/32
1/8	27/32	6 3/16	31/32	7 3/16	1 3/32	8 3/16	1 1/4	9 7/32	1 3/8	10 7/32	1 1/2	11 7/32
3/16	27/32	6 1/4	31/32	7 1/4	1 3/32	8 1/4	1 1/4	9 9/32	1 3/8	10 9/32	1 1/2	11 9/32
1/4	27/32	6 5/16	31/32	7 5/16	1 1/8	8 5/16	1 1/4	9 11/32	1 3/8	10 11/32	1 17/32	11 11/32
5/16	27/32	6 3/8	1	7 3/8	1 1/8	8 3/8	1 1/4	9 13/32	1 13/32	10 13/32	1 17/32	11 13/32
3/8	7/8	6 7/16	1	7 7/16	1 1/8	8 7/16	1 9/32	9 15/32	1 13/32	10 15/32	1 17/32	11 15/32
7/16	7/8	6 1/2	1	7 1/2	1 5/32	8 1/2	1 9/32	9 17/32	1 13/32	10 17/32	1 9/16	11 17/32
1/2	7/8	6 9/16	1	7 9/16	1 5/32	8 9/16	1 9/32	9 19/32	1 7/16	10 19/32	1 9/16	11 19/32
9/16	7/8	6 5/8	1 1/32	7 5/8	1 5/32	8 21/32	1 9/32	9 21/32	1 7/16	10 21/32	1 9/16	11 21/32
5/8	29/32	6 11/16	1 1/32	7 11/16	1 5/32	8 23/32	1 5/16	9 23/32	1 7/16	10 23/32	1 9/16	11 23/32
11/16	29/32	6 3/4	1 1/32	7 3/4	1 3/16	8 25/32	1 5/16	9 25/32	1 7/16	10 25/32	1 19/32	11 25/32
3/4	29/32	6 13/16	1 1/16	7 13/16	1 3/16	8 27/32	1 5/16	9 27/32	1 15/32	10 27/32	1 19/32	11 27/32
13/16	15/16	6 7/8	1 1/16	7 7/8	1 3/16	8 29/32	1 11/32	9 29/32	1 15/32	10 29/32	1 19/32	11 29/32
7/8	15/16	6 15/16	1 1/16	7 15/16	1 3/16	8 31/32	1 11/32	9 31/32	1 15/32	10 31/32	1 19/32	11 31/32
15/16	15/16	7	1 1/16	8	1 7/32	9 1/32	1 11/32	10 1/32	1 15/32	11 1/32	1 5/8	1-0 1/32

Feet	0' Rise	0' Slope	10' Rise	10' Slope	20' Rise	20' Slope	30' Rise	30' Slope
0	0	0	1-4 1/4	10-1 3/32	2-8 1/2	20-2 3/16	4-0 3/4	30-3 9/32
1	1 5/8	1-0 1/8	1-5 7/8	11-1 7/32	2-10 1/8	21-2 5/16	4-2 3/8	31-3 13/32
2	3 1/4	2-0 7/32	1-7 1/2	12-1 5/16	2-11 3/4	22-2 13/32	4-4	32-3 1/2
3	4 7/8	3-0 11/32	1-9 1/8	13-1 7/16	3-1 3/8	23-2 17/32	4-5 5/8	33-3 5/8
4	6 1/2	4-0 7/16	1-10 3/4	14-1 17/32	3-3	24-2 5/8	4-7 1/4	34-3 23/32
5	8 1/8	5-0 9/16	2-0 3/8	15-1 21/32	3-4 5/8	25-2 3/4	4-8 7/8	35-3 27/32
6	9 3/4	6-0 21/32	2-2	16-1 3/4	3-6 1/4	26-2 27/32	4-10 1/2	36-3 15/16
7	11 3/8	7-0 25/32	2-3 5/8	17-1 7/8	3-7 7/8	27-2 31/32	5-0 1/8	37-4 1/16
8	1-1	8-0 7/8	2-5 1/4	18-1 31/32	3-9 1/2	28-3 1/16	5-1 3/4	38-4 5/32
9	1-2 5/8	9-1	2-6 7/8	19-2 3/32	3-11 1/8	29-3 3/16	5-3 3/8	39-4 9/32

A = 7° 42' 43"; logsin A = 9.12773; logcos A = 9.99605; logtan A = 9.13167; logcot A = 0.86833

In.	12″ Rise	12″ Slope	13″ Rise	13″ Slope	14″ Rise	14″ Slope	15″ Rise	15″ Slope	16″ Rise	16″ Slope
0	1$\frac{5}{8}$	1-0$\frac{1}{8}$	1$\frac{3}{4}$	1-1$\frac{1}{8}$	1$\frac{29}{32}$	1-2$\frac{1}{8}$	2$\frac{1}{32}$	1-3$\frac{1}{8}$	2$\frac{5}{32}$	1-4$\frac{5}{32}$
$\frac{1}{16}$	1$\frac{5}{8}$	1-0$\frac{3}{16}$	1$\frac{25}{32}$	1-1$\frac{3}{16}$	1$\frac{29}{32}$	1-2$\frac{3}{16}$	2$\frac{1}{32}$	1-3$\frac{3}{16}$	2$\frac{3}{16}$	1-4$\frac{7}{32}$
$\frac{1}{8}$	1$\frac{21}{32}$	1-0$\frac{1}{4}$	1$\frac{25}{32}$	1-1$\frac{1}{4}$	1$\frac{29}{32}$	1-2$\frac{1}{4}$	2$\frac{1}{16}$	1-3$\frac{1}{4}$	2$\frac{3}{16}$	1-4$\frac{9}{32}$
$\frac{3}{16}$	1$\frac{21}{32}$	1-0$\frac{5}{16}$	1$\frac{25}{32}$	1-1$\frac{5}{16}$	1$\frac{29}{32}$	1-2$\frac{5}{16}$	2$\frac{1}{16}$	1-3$\frac{5}{16}$	2$\frac{3}{16}$	1-4$\frac{11}{32}$
$\frac{1}{4}$	1$\frac{21}{32}$	1-0$\frac{3}{8}$	1$\frac{25}{32}$	1-1$\frac{3}{8}$	1$\frac{15}{16}$	1-2$\frac{3}{8}$	2$\frac{1}{16}$	1-3$\frac{3}{8}$	2$\frac{3}{16}$	1-4$\frac{13}{32}$
$\frac{5}{16}$	1$\frac{21}{32}$	1-0$\frac{7}{16}$	1$\frac{13}{16}$	1-1$\frac{7}{16}$	1$\frac{15}{16}$	1-2$\frac{7}{16}$	2$\frac{1}{16}$	1-3$\frac{7}{16}$	2$\frac{7}{32}$	1-4$\frac{15}{32}$
$\frac{3}{8}$	1$\frac{11}{16}$	1-0$\frac{1}{2}$	1$\frac{13}{16}$	1-1$\frac{1}{2}$	1$\frac{15}{16}$	1-2$\frac{1}{2}$	2$\frac{3}{32}$	1-3$\frac{1}{2}$	2$\frac{7}{32}$	1-4$\frac{17}{32}$
$\frac{7}{16}$	1$\frac{11}{16}$	1-0$\frac{9}{16}$	1$\frac{13}{16}$	1-1$\frac{9}{16}$	1$\frac{31}{32}$	1-2$\frac{9}{16}$	2$\frac{3}{32}$	1-3$\frac{19}{32}$	2$\frac{7}{32}$	1-4$\frac{19}{32}$
$\frac{1}{2}$	1$\frac{11}{16}$	1-0$\frac{5}{8}$	1$\frac{13}{16}$	1-1$\frac{5}{8}$	1$\frac{31}{32}$	1-2$\frac{5}{8}$	2$\frac{3}{32}$	1-3$\frac{21}{32}$	2$\frac{1}{4}$	1-4$\frac{21}{32}$
$\frac{9}{16}$	1$\frac{11}{16}$	1-0$\frac{11}{16}$	1$\frac{27}{32}$	1-1$\frac{11}{16}$	1$\frac{31}{32}$	1-2$\frac{11}{16}$	2$\frac{3}{32}$	1-3$\frac{23}{32}$	2$\frac{1}{4}$	1-4$\frac{23}{32}$
$\frac{5}{8}$	1$\frac{23}{32}$	1-0$\frac{3}{4}$	1$\frac{27}{32}$	1-1$\frac{3}{4}$	1$\frac{31}{32}$	1-2$\frac{3}{4}$	2$\frac{1}{8}$	1-3$\frac{25}{32}$	2$\frac{1}{4}$	1-4$\frac{25}{32}$
$\frac{11}{16}$	1$\frac{23}{32}$	1-0$\frac{13}{16}$	1$\frac{27}{32}$	1-1$\frac{13}{16}$	2	1-2$\frac{13}{16}$	2$\frac{1}{8}$	1-3$\frac{27}{32}$	2$\frac{1}{4}$	1-4$\frac{27}{32}$
$\frac{3}{4}$	1$\frac{23}{32}$	1-0$\frac{7}{8}$	1$\frac{7}{8}$	1-1$\frac{7}{8}$	2	1-2$\frac{7}{8}$	2$\frac{1}{8}$	1-3$\frac{29}{32}$	2$\frac{9}{32}$	1-4$\frac{29}{32}$
$\frac{13}{16}$	1$\frac{3}{4}$	1-0$\frac{15}{16}$	1$\frac{7}{8}$	1-1$\frac{15}{16}$	2	1-2$\frac{15}{16}$	2$\frac{5}{32}$	1-3$\frac{31}{32}$	2$\frac{9}{32}$	1-4$\frac{31}{32}$
$\frac{7}{8}$	1$\frac{3}{4}$	1-1	1$\frac{7}{8}$	1-2	2	1-3	2$\frac{5}{32}$	1-4$\frac{1}{32}$	2$\frac{9}{32}$	1-5$\frac{1}{32}$
$\frac{15}{16}$	1$\frac{3}{4}$	1-1$\frac{1}{16}$	1$\frac{7}{8}$	1-2$\frac{1}{16}$	2$\frac{1}{32}$	1-3$\frac{1}{16}$	2$\frac{5}{32}$	1-4$\frac{3}{32}$	2$\frac{9}{32}$	1-5$\frac{3}{32}$

In.	17″ Rise	17″ Slope	18″ Rise	18″ Slope	19″ Rise	19″ Slope	20″ Rise	20″ Slope	21″ Rise	21″ Slope
0	2$\frac{5}{16}$	1-5$\frac{5}{32}$	2$\frac{7}{16}$	1-6$\frac{5}{32}$	2$\frac{9}{16}$	1-7$\frac{3}{16}$	2$\frac{23}{32}$	1-8$\frac{3}{16}$	2$\frac{27}{32}$	1-9$\frac{3}{16}$
$\frac{1}{16}$	2$\frac{5}{16}$	1-5$\frac{7}{32}$	2$\frac{7}{16}$	1-6$\frac{7}{32}$	2$\frac{19}{32}$	1-7$\frac{1}{4}$	2$\frac{23}{32}$	1-8$\frac{1}{4}$	2$\frac{27}{32}$	1-9$\frac{1}{4}$
$\frac{1}{8}$	2$\frac{5}{16}$	1-5$\frac{9}{32}$	2$\frac{15}{32}$	1-6$\frac{9}{32}$	2$\frac{19}{32}$	1-7$\frac{5}{16}$	2$\frac{23}{32}$	1-8$\frac{5}{16}$	2$\frac{7}{8}$	1-9$\frac{5}{16}$
$\frac{3}{16}$	2$\frac{5}{16}$	1-5$\frac{11}{32}$	2$\frac{15}{32}$	1-6$\frac{11}{32}$	2$\frac{19}{32}$	1-7$\frac{3}{8}$	2$\frac{23}{32}$	1-8$\frac{3}{8}$	2$\frac{7}{8}$	1-9$\frac{3}{8}$
$\frac{1}{4}$	2$\frac{11}{32}$	1-5$\frac{13}{32}$	2$\frac{15}{32}$	1-6$\frac{13}{32}$	2$\frac{19}{32}$	1-7$\frac{7}{16}$	2$\frac{3}{4}$	1-8$\frac{7}{16}$	2$\frac{7}{8}$	1-9$\frac{7}{16}$
$\frac{5}{16}$	2$\frac{11}{32}$	1-5$\frac{15}{32}$	2$\frac{15}{32}$	1-6$\frac{15}{32}$	2$\frac{5}{8}$	1-7$\frac{1}{2}$	2$\frac{3}{4}$	1-8$\frac{1}{2}$	2$\frac{7}{8}$	1-9$\frac{1}{2}$
$\frac{3}{8}$	2$\frac{11}{32}$	1-5$\frac{17}{32}$	2$\frac{1}{2}$	1-6$\frac{17}{32}$	2$\frac{5}{8}$	1-7$\frac{9}{16}$	2$\frac{3}{4}$	1-8$\frac{9}{16}$	2$\frac{29}{32}$	1-9$\frac{9}{16}$
$\frac{7}{16}$	2$\frac{3}{8}$	1-5$\frac{19}{32}$	2$\frac{1}{2}$	1-6$\frac{19}{32}$	2$\frac{5}{8}$	1-7$\frac{5}{8}$	2$\frac{25}{32}$	1-8$\frac{5}{8}$	2$\frac{29}{32}$	1-9$\frac{5}{8}$
$\frac{1}{2}$	2$\frac{3}{8}$	1-5$\frac{21}{32}$	2$\frac{1}{2}$	1-6$\frac{21}{32}$	2$\frac{5}{8}$	1-7$\frac{11}{16}$	2$\frac{25}{32}$	1-8$\frac{11}{16}$	2$\frac{29}{32}$	1-9$\frac{11}{16}$
$\frac{9}{16}$	2$\frac{3}{8}$	1-5$\frac{23}{32}$	2$\frac{1}{2}$	1-6$\frac{23}{32}$	2$\frac{21}{32}$	1-7$\frac{3}{4}$	2$\frac{25}{32}$	1-8$\frac{3}{4}$	2$\frac{29}{32}$	1-9$\frac{3}{4}$
$\frac{5}{8}$	2$\frac{3}{8}$	1-5$\frac{25}{32}$	2$\frac{17}{32}$	1-6$\frac{25}{32}$	2$\frac{21}{32}$	1-7$\frac{13}{16}$	2$\frac{25}{32}$	1-8$\frac{13}{16}$	2$\frac{15}{16}$	1-9$\frac{13}{16}$
$\frac{11}{16}$	2$\frac{13}{32}$	1-5$\frac{27}{32}$	2$\frac{17}{32}$	1-6$\frac{27}{32}$	2$\frac{21}{32}$	1-7$\frac{7}{8}$	2$\frac{13}{16}$	1-8$\frac{7}{8}$	2$\frac{15}{16}$	1-9$\frac{7}{8}$
$\frac{3}{4}$	2$\frac{13}{32}$	1-5$\frac{29}{32}$	2$\frac{17}{32}$	1-6$\frac{29}{32}$	2$\frac{11}{16}$	1-7$\frac{15}{16}$	2$\frac{13}{16}$	1-8$\frac{15}{16}$	2$\frac{15}{16}$	1-9$\frac{15}{16}$
$\frac{13}{16}$	2$\frac{13}{32}$	1-5$\frac{31}{32}$	2$\frac{9}{16}$	1-6$\frac{31}{32}$	2$\frac{11}{16}$	1-8	2$\frac{13}{16}$	1-9	2$\frac{31}{32}$	1-10
$\frac{7}{8}$	2$\frac{13}{32}$	1-6$\frac{1}{32}$	2$\frac{9}{16}$	1-7$\frac{1}{16}$	2$\frac{11}{16}$	1-8$\frac{1}{16}$	2$\frac{13}{16}$	1-9$\frac{1}{16}$	2$\frac{31}{32}$	1-10$\frac{1}{16}$
$\frac{15}{16}$	2$\frac{7}{16}$	1-6$\frac{3}{32}$	2$\frac{9}{16}$	1-7$\frac{1}{2}$	2$\frac{11}{16}$	1-8$\frac{1}{8}$	2$\frac{27}{32}$	1-9$\frac{3}{16}$	2$\frac{31}{32}$	1-10$\frac{1}{8}$

Feet	40′ Rise	40′ Slope	50′ Rise	50′ Slope	60′ Rise	60′ Slope	70′ Rise	70′ Slope
0	5-5	40-4$\frac{3}{8}$	6-9$\frac{1}{4}$	50-5$\frac{15}{32}$	8-1$\frac{1}{2}$	60-6$\frac{9}{16}$	9-5$\frac{3}{4}$	70-7$\frac{21}{32}$
1	5-6$\frac{5}{8}$	41-4$\frac{1}{2}$	6-10$\frac{7}{8}$	51-5$\frac{19}{32}$	8-3$\frac{1}{8}$	61-6$\frac{11}{16}$	9-7$\frac{3}{8}$	71-7$\frac{25}{32}$
2	5-8$\frac{1}{4}$	42-4$\frac{19}{32}$	7-0$\frac{1}{2}$	52-5$\frac{11}{16}$	8-4$\frac{3}{4}$	62-6$\frac{25}{32}$	9-9	72-7$\frac{7}{8}$
3	5-9$\frac{7}{8}$	43-4$\frac{23}{32}$	7-2$\frac{1}{8}$	53-5$\frac{13}{16}$	8-6$\frac{3}{8}$	63-6$\frac{29}{32}$	9-10$\frac{5}{8}$	73-8
4	5-11$\frac{1}{2}$	44-4$\frac{13}{16}$	7-3$\frac{3}{4}$	54-5$\frac{29}{32}$	8-8	64-7	10-0$\frac{1}{4}$	74-8$\frac{3}{32}$
5	6-1$\frac{1}{8}$	45-4$\frac{15}{16}$	7-5$\frac{3}{8}$	55-6$\frac{1}{32}$	8-9$\frac{5}{8}$	65-7$\frac{1}{8}$	10-1$\frac{7}{8}$	75-8$\frac{7}{32}$
6	6-2$\frac{3}{4}$	46-5$\frac{1}{32}$	7-7	56-6$\frac{1}{8}$	8-11$\frac{1}{4}$	66-7$\frac{7}{32}$	10-3$\frac{1}{2}$	76-8$\frac{5}{16}$
7	6-4$\frac{3}{8}$	47-5$\frac{5}{32}$	7-8$\frac{5}{8}$	57-6$\frac{1}{4}$	9-0$\frac{7}{8}$	67-7$\frac{11}{32}$	10-5$\frac{1}{4}$	77-8$\frac{7}{16}$
8	6-6	48-5$\frac{1}{4}$	7-10$\frac{1}{4}$	58-6$\frac{11}{32}$	9-2$\frac{1}{2}$	68-7$\frac{7}{16}$	10-6$\frac{3}{4}$	78-8$\frac{17}{32}$
9	6-7$\frac{5}{8}$	49-5$\frac{3}{8}$	7-11$\frac{7}{8}$	59-6$\frac{15}{32}$	9-4$\frac{1}{8}$	69-7$\frac{9}{16}$	10-8$\frac{3}{8}$	79-8$\frac{21}{32}$

natsin A=0.1341918726; natcos A=0.9909553679; nattan A=0.1354166666; natcot A=7.3846153846

Inches	0" Rise	0" Slope	1" Rise	1" Slope	2" Rise	2" Slope	3" Rise	3" Slope	4" Rise	4" Slope	5" Rise	5" Slope
0	0	0	1/8	1	9/32	2 1/32	7/16	3 1/32	9/16	4 1/32	11/16	5 1/16
1/16	0	1/16	5/32	1 1/16	9/32	2 3/32	7/16	3 3/32	9/16	4 3/32	23/32	5 1/8
1/8	1/32	1/8	5/32	1 1/8	5/16	2 5/32	7/16	3 5/32	19/32	4 5/32	23/32	5 3/16
3/16	1/32	3/16	5/32	1 3/16	5/16	2 7/32	7/16	3 7/32	19/32	4 7/32	23/32	5 1/4
1/4	1/32	1/4	3/16	1 1/4	5/16	2 9/32	15/32	3 9/32	19/32	4 9/32	3/4	5 5/16
5/16	1/32	5/16	3/16	1 5/16	5/16	2 11/32	15/32	3 11/32	19/32	4 11/32	3/4	5 3/8
3/8	1/16	3/8	3/16	1 3/8	11/32	2 13/32	15/32	3 13/32	5/8	4 13/32	3/4	5 7/16
7/16	1/16	7/16	3/16	1 7/16	11/32	2 15/32	15/32	3 15/32	5/8	4 15/32	3/4	5 1/2
1/2	1/16	1/2	7/32	1 1/2	11/32	2 17/32	1/2	3 17/32	5/8	4 17/32	25/32	5 9/16
9/16	3/32	9/16	7/32	1 9/16	3/8	2 19/32	1/2	3 19/32	21/32	4 19/32	25/32	5 5/8
5/8	3/32	5/8	7/32	1 21/32	3/8	2 21/32	1/2	3 21/32	21/32	4 21/32	25/32	5 11/16
11/16	3/32	11/16	1/4	1 23/32	3/8	2 23/32	17/32	3 23/32	21/32	4 23/32	13/16	5 3/4
3/4	3/32	3/4	1/4	1 25/32	3/8	2 25/32	17/32	3 25/32	21/32	4 25/32	13/16	5 13/16
13/16	1/8	13/16	1/4	1 27/32	13/32	2 27/32	17/32	3 27/32	11/16	4 7/8	13/16	5 7/8
7/8	1/8	7/8	1/4	1 29/32	13/32	2 29/32	17/32	3 29/32	11/16	4 15/16	13/16	5 15/16
15/16	1/8	15/16	9/32	1 31/32	13/32	2 31/32	9/16	3 31/32	11/16	5	27/32	6

Inches	6" Rise	6" Slope	7" Rise	7" Slope	8" Rise	8" Slope	9" Rise	9" Slope	10" Rise	10" Slope	11" Rise	11" Slope
0	27/32	6 1/16	1	7 1/16	1 1/8	8 3/32	1 1/4	9 3/32	1 13/32	10 3/32	1 9/16	11 3/32
1/16	27/32	6 1/8	1	7 1/8	1 1/8	8 5/32	1 9/32	9 5/32	1 13/32	10 5/32	1 9/16	11 5/32
1/8	7/8	6 3/16	1	7 3/16	1 5/32	8 7/32	1 9/32	9 7/32	1 7/16	10 7/32	1 9/16	11 1/4
3/16	7/8	6 1/4	1	7 1/4	1 5/32	8 9/32	1 9/32	9 9/32	1 7/16	10 9/32	1 9/16	11 5/16
1/4	7/8	6 5/16	1 1/32	7 5/16	1 5/32	8 11/32	1 5/16	9 11/32	1 7/16	10 11/32	1 19/32	11 3/8
5/16	7/8	6 3/8	1 1/32	7 3/8	1 5/32	8 13/32	1 5/16	9 13/32	1 7/16	10 13/32	1 19/32	11 7/16
3/8	29/32	6 7/16	1 1/32	7 7/16	1 3/16	8 15/32	1 5/16	9 15/32	1 15/32	10 15/32	1 19/32	11 1/2
7/16	29/32	6 1/2	1 1/32	7 1/2	1 3/16	8 17/32	1 5/16	9 17/32	1 15/32	10 17/32	1 19/32	11 9/16
1/2	29/32	6 9/16	1 1/16	7 9/16	1 3/16	8 19/32	1 11/32	9 19/32	1 15/32	10 19/32	1 5/8	11 5/8
9/16	15/16	6 5/8	1 1/16	7 5/8	1 3/16	8 21/32	1 11/32	9 21/32	1 1/2	10 21/32	1 5/8	11 11/16
5/8	15/16	6 11/16	1 1/16	7 11/16	1 7/32	8 23/32	1 11/32	9 23/32	1 1/2	10 23/32	1 5/8	11 3/4
11/16	15/16	6 3/4	1 3/32	7 3/4	1 7/32	8 25/32	1 3/8	9 25/32	1 1/2	10 25/32	1 21/32	11 13/16
3/4	15/16	6 13/16	1 3/32	7 13/16	1 7/32	8 27/32	1 3/8	9 27/32	1 1/2	10 27/32	1 21/32	11 7/8
13/16	31/32	6 7/8	1 3/32	7 7/8	1 1/4	8 29/32	1 3/8	9 29/32	1 17/32	10 29/32	1 21/32	11 15/16
7/8	31/32	6 15/16	1 3/32	7 15/16	1 1/4	8 31/32	1 3/8	9 31/32	1 17/32	10 31/32	1 21/32	1-0
15/16	31/32	7	1 1/8	8	1 1/4	9 1/32	1 13/32	10 1/32	1 17/32	11 1/32	1 11/16	1-0 1/16

Feet	0' Rise	0' Slope	10' Rise	10' Slope	20' Rise	20' Slope	30' Rise	30' Slope
0	0		1-4 7/8	10-1 3/16	2-9 3/4	20-2 3/8	4-2 5/8	30-3 17/32
1	1 11/16	1-0 1/8	1-6 9/16	11-1 5/16	2-11 7/16	21-2 15/32	4-4 5/16	31-3 21/32
2	3 3/8	2-0 1/4	1-8 1/4	12-1 13/32	3-1 1/8	22-2 19/32	4-6	32-3 25/32
3	5 1/16	3-0 11/32	1-9 15/16	13-1 17/32	3-2 13/16	23-2 23/32	4-7 11/16	33-3 29/32
4	6 3/4	4-0 15/32	1-11 5/8	14-1 21/32	3-4 1/2	24-2 27/32	4-9 3/8	34-4
5	8 7/16	5-0 19/32	2-1 5/16	15-1 25/32	3-6 3/16	25-2 15/16	4-11 1/16	35-4 1/8
6	10 1/8	6-0 23/32	2-3	16-1 7/8	3-7 7/8	26-3 1/16	5-0 3/4	36-4 1/4
7	11 13/16	7-0 13/16	2-4 11/16	17-2	3-9 9/16	27-3 3/16	5-2 7/16	37-4 3/8
8	1-1 1/2	8-0 15/16	2-6 3/8	18-2 1/8	3-11 1/4	28-3 5/16	5-4 1/8	38-4 1/2
9	1-3 3/16	9-1 1/16	2-8 1/16	19-2 1/4	4-0 15/16	29-3 7/16	5-5 13/16	39-4 19/32

A=8° 00′ 17″; logsin A=9.14381; logcos A=9.99575; logtan A=9.14806; logcot A=0.85194

Ins.	12″ Rise	Slope	13″ Rise	Slope	14″ Rise	Slope	15″ Rise	Slope	16″ Rise	Slope
0	1 11/16	1-0 1/8	1 13/16	1-1 1/8	1 31/32	1-2 1/8	2 1/8	1-3 5/32	2 1/4	1-4 5/32
1/16	1 11/16	1-0 3/16	1 27/32	1-1 3/16	1 31/32	1-2 3/16	2 1/8	1-3 7/32	2 1/4	1-4 7/32
1/8	1 23/32	1-0 1/4	1 27/32	1-1 1/4	2	1-2 1/4	2 1/8	1-3 9/32	2 9/32	1-4 9/32
3/16	1 23/32	1-0 5/32	1 27/32	1-1 5/16	2	1-2 5/16	2 1/8	1-3 11/32	2 9/32	1-4 11/32
1/4	1 23/32	1-0 3/8	1 7/8	1-1 3/8	2	1-2 3/8	2 5/32	1-3 13/32	2 9/32	1-4 13/32
5/16	1 23/32	1-0 7/16	1 7/8	1-1 7/16	2	1-2 15/32	2 5/32	1-3 15/32	2 9/32	1-4 15/32
3/8	1 3/4	1-0 1/2	1 7/8	1-1 1/2	2 1/32	1-2 17/32	2 5/32	1-3 17/32	2 5/16	1-4 17/32
7/16	1 3/4	1-0 9/16	1 7/8	1-1 9/16	2 1/32	1-2 19/32	2 5/32	1-3 19/32	2 5/16	1-4 19/32
1/2	1 3/4	1-0 5/8	1 29/32	1-1 5/8	2 1/32	1-2 21/32	2 3/16	1-3 21/32	2 5/16	1-4 21/32
9/16	1 25/32	1-0 11/16	1 29/32	1-1 11/16	2 1/16	1-2 23/32	2 3/16	1-3 23/32	2 11/32	1-4 23/32
5/8	1 25/32	1-0 3/4	1 29/32	1-1 3/4	2 1/16	1-2 25/32	2 3/16	1-3 25/32	2 11/32	1-4 25/32
11/16	1 25/32	1-0 13/16	1 15/16	1-1 13/16	2 1/16	1-2 27/32	2 7/32	1-3 27/32	2 11/32	1-4 27/32
3/4	1 25/32	1-0 7/8	1 15/16	1-1 7/8	2 1/16	1-2 29/32	2 7/32	1-3 29/32	2 11/32	1-4 29/32
13/16	1 13/16	1-0 15/16	1 15/16	1-1 15/16	2 3/32	1-2 31/32	2 7/32	1-3 31/32	2 3/8	1-4 31/32
7/8	1 13/16	1-1	1 15/16	1-2	2 3/32	1-3 1/32	2 7/32	1-4 1/32	2 3/8	1-5 1/32
15/16	1 13/16	1-1 1/16	1 31/32	1-2 1/16	2 3/32	1-3 3/32	2 1/4	1-4 3/32	2 3/8	1-5 3/32

Ins.	17″ Rise	Slope	18″ Rise	Slope	19″ Rise	Slope	20″ Rise	Slope	21″ Rise	Slope
0	2 3/8	1-5 5/32	2 17/32	1-6 3/16	2 11/16	1-7 3/16	2 13/16	1-8 3/16	2 15/16	1-9 7/32
1/16	2 13/32	1-5 7/32	2 17/32	1-6 1/4	2 11/16	1-7 1/4	2 13/16	1-8 1/4	2 31/32	1-9 9/32
1/8	2 13/32	1-5 9/32	2 9/16	1-6 5/16	2 11/16	1-7 5/16	2 27/32	1-8 5/16	2 31/32	1-9 11/32
3/16	2 13/32	1-5 11/32	2 9/16	1-6 3/8	2 11/16	1-7 3/8	2 27/32	1-8 3/8	2 31/32	1-9 13/32
1/4	2 7/16	1-5 13/32	2 9/16	1-6 7/16	2 23/32	1-7 7/16	2 27/32	1-8 7/16	3	1-9 15/32
5/16	2 7/16	1-5 15/32	2 9/16	1-6 1/2	2 23/32	1-7 1/2	2 27/32	1-8 1/2	3	1-9 17/32
3/8	2 7/16	1-5 17/32	2 19/32	1-6 9/16	2 23/32	1-7 9/16	2 7/8	1-8 9/16	3	1-9 19/32
7/16	2 7/16	1-5 19/32	2 19/32	1-6 5/8	2 23/32	1-7 5/8	2 7/8	1-8 5/8	3	1-9 21/32
1/2	2 15/32	1-5 11/16	2 19/32	1-6 11/16	2 3/4	1-7 11/16	2 7/8	1-8 11/16	3 1/32	1-9 23/32
9/16	2 15/32	1-5 3/4	2 5/8	1-6 3/4	2 3/4	1-7 3/4	2 29/32	1-8 3/4	3 1/32	1-9 25/32
5/8	2 15/32	1-5 13/16	2 5/8	1-6 13/16	2 3/4	1-7 13/16	2 29/32	1-8 13/16	3 1/32	1-9 27/32
11/16	2 1/2	1-5 7/8	2 5/8	1-6 7/8	2 25/32	1-7 7/8	2 29/32	1-8 29/32	3 1/16	1-9 29/32
3/4	2 1/2	1-5 15/16	2 5/8	1-6 15/16	2 25/32	1-7 15/16	2 29/32	1-8 31/32	3 1/16	1-9 31/32
13/16	2 1/2	1-6	2 21/32	1-7	2 25/32	1-8	2 15/16	1-9 1/32	3 1/16	1-10 1/32
7/8	2 1/2	1-6 1/16	2 21/32	1-7 1/16	2 25/32	1-8 1/16	2 15/16	1-9 3/32	3 1/16	1-10 3/32
15/16	2 17/32	1-6 1/8	2 21/32	1-7 1/8	2 13/16	1-8 1/8	2 15/16	1-9 5/32	3 3/32	1-10 5/32

Feet	40′ Rise	Slope	50′ Rise	Slope	60′ Rise	Slope	70′ Rise	Slope
0	5-7 1/2	40-4 23/32	7-0 3/8	50-5 29/32	8-5 1/4	60-7 3/32	9-10 1/8	70-8 1/4
1	5-9 3/16	41-4 27/32	7-2 1/16	51-6 1/32	8-6 15/16	61-7 3/16	9-11 13/16	71-8 3/8
2	5-10 7/8	42-4 31/32	7-3 3/4	52-6 1/8	8-8 5/8	62-7 5/16	10-1 1/2	72-8 1/2
3	6-0 9/16	43-5 1/16	7-5 7/16	53-6 1/4	8-10 5/16	63-7 7/16	10-3 3/16	73-8 5/8
4	6-2 1/4	44-5 3/16	7-7 1/8	54-6 3/8	9-0	64-7 9/16	10-4 7/8	74-8 3/4
5	6-3 15/16	45-5 5/16	7-8 13/16	55-6 1/2	9-1 11/16	65-7 11/16	10-6 9/16	75-8 27/32
6	6-5 5/8	46-5 7/16	7-10 1/2	56-6 5/8	9-3 3/8	66-7 25/32	10-8 1/4	76-8 31/32
7	6-7 5/16	47-5 9/16	8-0 3/16	57-6 23/32	9-5 1/16	67-7 29/32	10-9 15/16	77-9 3/32
8	6-9	48-5 21/32	8-1 7/8	58-6 27/32	9-6 3/4	68-8 1/32	10-11 5/8	78-9 7/32
9	6-10 11/16	49-5 25/32	8-3 9/16	59-6 31/32	9-8 7/16	69-8 5/32	11-1 5/16	79-9 5/16

natsin A=0.1392548313; natcos A=0.9902565788; nattan A=0.1406250000; natcot A=7.1111111111

Inches	0" Rise	0" Slope	1" Rise	1" Slope	2" Rise	2" Slope	3" Rise	3" Slope	4" Rise	4" Slope	5" Rise	5" Slope
0	0	0	5/32	1	9/32	2 1/32	7/16	3 1/32	19/32	4 1/32	23/32	5 1/16
1/16	0	1/16	5/32	1 1/16	5/16	2 3/32	7/16	3 3/32	19/32	4 3/32	3/4	5 1/8
1/8	1/32	1/8	5/32	1 1/8	5/16	2 5/32	15/32	3 5/32	19/32	4 5/32	3/4	5 5/32
3/16	1/32	3/16	3/16	1 3/16	5/16	2 7/32	15/32	3 7/32	5/8	4 7/32	3/4	5 1/4
1/4	1/32	1/4	3/16	1 1/4	5/16	2 9/32	15/32	3 9/32	5/8	4 9/32	25/32	5 5/16
5/16	1/32	5/16	3/16	1 5/16	11/32	2 11/32	15/32	3 11/32	5/8	4 11/32	25/32	5 3/8
3/8	1/16	3/8	3/16	1 3/8	11/32	2 13/32	1/2	3 13/32	5/8	4 13/32	25/32	5 7/16
7/16	7/16	7/16	7/32	1 7/16	11/32	2 15/32	1/2	3 15/32	21/32	4 1/2	25/32	5 1/2
1/2	1/16	1/2	7/32	1 17/32	3/8	2 17/32	1/2	3 17/32	21/32	4 9/16	13/16	5 9/16
9/16	3/32	9/16	7/32	1 19/32	3/8	2 19/32	17/32	3 19/32	21/32	4 5/8	13/16	5 5/8
5/8	3/32	5/8	1/4	1 21/32	3/8	2 21/32	17/32	3 21/32	11/16	4 11/16	13/16	5 11/16
11/16	3/32	11/16	1/4	1 23/32	13/32	2 23/32	17/32	3 23/32	11/16	4 3/4	27/32	5 3/4
3/4	1/8	3/4	1/4	1 25/32	13/32	2 25/32	9/16	3 25/32	11/16	4 13/16	27/32	5 13/16
13/16	1/8	13/16	1/4	1 27/32	13/32	2 27/32	9/16	3 27/32	11/16	4 7/8	27/32	5 7/8
7/8	1/8	7/8	9/32	1 29/32	13/32	2 29/32	9/16	3 29/32	23/32	4 15/16	27/32	5 15/16
15/16	1/8	15/16	9/32	1 31/32	7/16	2 31/32	9/16	3 31/32	23/32	5	7/8	6

Inches	6" Rise	6" Slope	7" Rise	7" Slope	8" Rise	8" Slope	9" Rise	9" Slope	10" Rise	10" Slope	11" Rise	11" Slope
0	7/8	6 1/16	1 1/32	7 1/16	1 5/32	8 3/32	1 5/16	9 3/32	1 15/32	10 3/32	1 19/32	11 1/8
1/16	7/8	6 1/8	1 1/32	7 1/8	1 3/16	8 5/32	1 5/16	9 5/32	1 15/32	10 5/32	1 5/8	11 3/16
1/8	29/32	6 3/16	1 1/32	7 3/16	1 3/16	8 7/32	1 11/32	9 7/32	1 15/32	10 7/32	1 5/8	11 1/4
3/16	29/32	6 1/4	1 1/16	7 1/4	1 3/16	8 9/32	1 11/32	9 9/32	1 1/2	10 9/32	1 5/8	11 5/16
1/4	29/32	6 5/16	1 1/16	7 5/16	1 3/16	8 11/32	1 11/32	9 11/32	1 1/2	10 11/32	1 5/8	11 3/8
5/16	29/32	6 3/8	1 1/16	7 3/8	1 7/32	8 13/32	1 11/32	9 13/32	1 1/2	10 13/32	1 21/32	11 7/16
3/8	15/16	6 7/16	1 1/16	7 7/16	1 7/32	8 15/32	1 3/8	9 15/32	1 1/2	10 1/2	1 21/32	11 1/2
7/16	15/16	6 1/2	1 3/32	7 17/32	1 7/32	8 17/32	1 3/8	9 17/32	1 17/32	10 9/16	1 21/32	11 9/16
1/2	15/16	6 9/16	1 3/32	7 19/32	1 1/4	8 19/32	1 3/8	9 19/32	1 17/32	10 5/8	1 11/16	11 5/8
9/16	31/32	6 5/8	1 3/32	7 21/32	1 1/4	8 21/32	1 13/32	9 21/32	1 17/32	10 11/16	1 11/16	11 11/16
5/8	31/32	6 11/16	1 1/8	7 23/32	1 1/4	8 23/32	1 13/32	9 23/32	1 9/16	10 3/4	1 11/16	11 3/4
11/16	31/32	6 3/4	1 1/8	7 25/32	1 9/32	8 25/32	1 13/32	9 25/32	1 9/16	10 13/16	1 23/32	11 13/16
3/4	1	6 13/16	1 1/8	7 27/32	1 9/32	8 27/32	1 7/16	9 27/32	1 9/16	10 7/8	1 23/32	11 7/8
13/16	1	6 7/8	1 1/8	7 29/32	1 9/32	8 29/32	1 7/16	9 29/32	1 9/16	10 15/16	1 23/32	11 15/16
7/8	1	6 15/16	1 5/32	7 31/32	1 9/32	8 31/32	1 7/16	9 31/32	1 19/32	11	1 23/32	1-0
15/16	1	7	1 5/32	8 1/32	1 5/16	9 1/32	1 7/16	10 1/32	1 19/32	11 1/16	1 3/4	1-0 1/16

Feet	0' Rise	0' Slope	10' Rise	10' Slope	20' Rise	20' Slope	30' Rise	30' Slope
0	0	0	1-5 1/2	10-1 9/32	2-11	20-2 1/32	4-4 1/2	30-3 13/16
1	1 3/4	1-0 1/8	1-7 1/4	11-1 13/32	3-0 3/4	21-2 21/32	4-6 1/4	31-3 15/16
2	3 1/2	2-0 1/4	1-9	12-1 17/32	3-2 1/2	22-2 25/32	4-8	32-4 1/16
3	5 1/4	3-0 3/8	1-10 3/4	13-1 21/32	3-4 1/4	23-2 29/32	4-9 3/4	33-4 3/16
4	7	4-0 1/2	2-0 1/2	14-1 25/32	3-6	24-3 1/32	4-11 1/2	34-4 5/16
5	8 3/4	5-0 5/8	2-2 1/4	15-1 29/32	3-7 3/4	25-3 3/16	5-1 1/4	35-4 7/16
6	10 1/2	6-0 3/4	2-4	16-2 1/32	3-9 1/2	26-3 5/16	5-3	36-4 9/16
7	1-0 1/4	7-0 7/8	2-5 3/4	17-2 5/32	3-11 1/4	27-3 7/16	5-4 3/4	37-4 11/16
8	1-2	8-1	2-7 1/2	18-2 9/32	4-1	28-3 9/16	5-6 1/2	38-4 13/16
9	1-3 3/4	9-1 5/32	2-9 1/4	19-2 13/32	4-2 3/4	29-3 11/16	5-8 1/4	39-4 15/16

A = 8° 17' 50''; logsin A = 9.15929; logcos A = 9.99543; logtan A = 9.16386; logcot A = 0.83614

ins.	12″ Rise	Slope	13″ Rise	Slope	14″ Rise	Slope	15″ Rise	Slope	16″ Rise	Slope
0	1 3/4	1-0 1/8	1 29/32	1-1 1/8	2 1/32	1-2 5/32	2 3/16	1-3 5/32	2 11/32	1-4 5/32
1/16	1 3/4	1-0 3/16	2 1/16	1-1 3/16	2 1/16	1-2 7/32	2 3/16	1-3 7/32	2 11/32	1-4 7/32
1/8	1 25/32	1-0 1/4	1 29/32	1-1 1/4	2 1/16	1-2 9/32	2 7/32	1-3 9/32	2 11/32	1-4 9/32
3/16	1 25/32	1-0 5/16	1 15/16	1-1 5/16	2 1/16	1-2 11/32	2 7/32	1-3 11/32	2 3/8	1-4 11/32
1/4	1 25/32	1-0 3/8	1 15/16	1-1 3/8	2 1/16	1-2 13/32	2 7/32	1-3 13/32	2 3/8	1-4 7/32
5/16	1 25/32	1-0 7/16	1 15/16	1-1 15/32	2 3/32	1-2 15/32	2 7/32	1-3 15/32	2 3/8	1-4 1/2
3/8	1 13/16	1-0 1/2	1 15/16	1-1 17/32	2 3/32	1-2 17/32	2 1/4	1-3 17/32	2 3/8	1-4 9/16
7/16	1 13/16	1-0 9/16	1 31/32	1-1 19/32	2 3/32	1-2 19/32	2 1/4	1-3 19/32	2 13/32	1-4 5/8
1/2	1 13/16	1-0 5/8	1 31/32	1-1 21/32	2 1/8	1-2 21/32	2 1/4	1-3 21/32	2 13/32	1-4 11/16
9/16	1 27/32	1-0 11/16	1 31/32	1-1 23/32	2 1/8	1-2 23/32	2 9/32	1-3 23/32	2 13/32	1-4 3/4
5/8	1 27/32	1-0 3/4	2	1-1 25/32	2 1/8	1-2 25/32	2 9/32	1-3 25/32	2 7/16	1-4 13/16
11/16	1 27/32	1-0 13/16	2	1-1 27/32	2 5/32	1-2 27/32	2 9/32	1-3 27/32	2 7/16	1-4 7/8
3/4	1 7/8	1-0 7/8	2	1-1 29/32	2 5/32	1-2 29/32	2 5/16	1-3 29/32	2 7/16	1-4 15/16
13/16	1 7/8	1-0 15/16	2	1-1 31/32	2 5/32	1-2 31/32	2 5/16	1-3 31/32	2 7/16	1-5
7/8	1 7/8	1-1	2 1/32	1-2 1/32	2 5/32	1-3 1/32	2 5/16	1-4 1/32	2 15/32	1-5 1/16
15/16	1 7/8	1-1 1/16	2 1/32	1-2 3/32	2 3/16	1-3 3/32	2 5/16	1-4 3/32	2 15/32	1-5 1/8

ins.	17″ Rise	Slope	18″ Rise	Slope	19″ Rise	Slope	20″ Rise	Slope	21″ Rise	Slope
0	2 15/32	1-5 3/16	2 5/8	1-6 3/16	2 25/32	1-7 3/32	2 29/32	1-8 7/32	3 1/16	1-9 7/32
1/16	2 1/2	1-5 1/4	2 5/8	1-6 1/4	2 25/32	1-7 1/4	2 15/16	1-8 9/32	3 1/16	1-9 9/32
1/8	2 1/2	1-5 5/16	2 21/32	1-6 5/16	2 25/32	1-7 5/16	2 15/16	1-8 11/32	3 3/32	1-9 11/32
3/16	2 1/2	1-5 3/8	2 21/32	1-6 3/8	2 13/16	1-7 3/8	2 15/16	1-8 13/32	3 3/32	1-9 13/32
1/4	2 1/2	1-5 7/16	2 21/32	1-6 7/16	2 13/16	1-7 15/32	2 15/16	1-8 15/32	3 3/32	1-9 15/32
5/16	2 17/32	1-5 1/2	2 21/32	1-6 1/2	2 13/16	1-7 17/32	2 31/32	1-8 17/32	3 3/32	1-9 17/32
3/8	2 17/32	1-5 9/16	2 11/16	1-6 9/16	2 13/16	1-7 19/32	2 31/32	1-8 19/32	3 1/8	1-9 19/32
7/16	2 17/32	1-5 5/8	2 11/16	1-6 5/8	2 27/32	1-7 21/32	2 31/32	1-8 21/32	3 1/8	1-9 21/32
1/2	2 9/16	1-5 11/16	2 11/16	1-6 11/16	2 27/32	1-7 23/32	3	1-8 23/32	3 1/8	1-9 23/32
9/16	2 9/16	1-5 3/4	2 23/32	1-6 3/4	2 27/32	1-7 25/32	3	1-8 25/32	3 5/32	1-9 25/32
5/8	2 9/16	1-5 13/16	2 23/32	1-6 13/16	2 7/8	1-7 27/32	3	1-8 27/32	3 5/32	1-9 27/32
11/16	2 19/32	1-5 7/8	2 23/32	1-6 7/8	2 7/8	1-7 29/32	3 1/32	1-8 29/32	3 5/32	1-9 29/32
3/4	2 19/32	1-5 15/16	2 3/4	1-6 15/16	2 7/8	1-7 31/32	3 1/32	1-8 31/32	3 3/16	1-9 31/32
13/16	2 19/32	1-6	2 3/4	1-7	2 7/8	1-8 1/32	3 1/32	1-9 1/32	3 3/16	1-10 1/32
7/8	2 19/32	1-6 1/16	2 3/4	1-7 1/16	2 29/32	1-8 3/32	3 1/32	1-9 3/32	3 3/16	1-10 3/32
15/16	2 5/8	1-6 1/8	2 3/4	1-7 1/8	2 29/32	1-8 5/32	3 1/16	1-9 5/32	3 3/16	1-10 5/32

Feet	40′ Rise	Slope	50′ Rise	Slope	60′ Rise	Slope	70′ Rise	Slope
0	5-10	40-5 1/16	7-3 1/2	50-6 11/32	8-9	60-7 5/8	10-2 1/2	70-8 7/8
1	5-11 3/4	41-5 7/32	7-5 1/4	51-6 15/32	8-10 3/4	61-7 3/4	10-4 1/4	71-9
2	6-1 1/2	42-5 11/32	7-7	52-6 19/32	9-0 1/2	62-7 7/8	10-6	72-9 1/8
3	6-3 1/4	43-5 15/32	7-8 3/4	53-6 23/32	9-2 1/4	63-8	10-7 3/4	73-9 9/32
4	6-5	44-5 19/32	7-10 1/2	54-6 27/32	9-4	64-8 1/8	10-9 1/2	74-9 13/32
5	6-6 3/4	45-5 23/32	8-0 1/4	55-6 31/32	9-5 3/4	65-8 1/4	10-11 1/4	75-9 17/32
6	6-8 1/2	46-5 27/32	8-2	56-7 3/32	9-7 1/2	66-8 3/8	11-1	76-9 21/32
7	6-10 1/4	47-5 31/32	8-3 3/4	57-7 1/4	9-9 1/4	67-8 1/2	11-2 3/4	77-9 25/32
8	7-0	48-6 3/32	8-5 1/2	58-7 3/8	9-11	68-8 5/8	11-4 1/2	78-9 29/32
9	7-1 3/4	49-6 7/32	8-7 1/4	59-7 1/2	10-0 3/4	69-8 3/4	11-6 1/4	79-10 1/32

natsin A=0.1443068930; natcos A=0.9895329811; nattan A=0.1458333333; natcot A=6.8571428571

Inches	0" Rise	0" Slope	1" Rise	1" Slope	2" Rise	2" Slope	3" Rise	3" Slope	4" Rise	4" Slope	5" Rise	5" Slope
0	0	0	5/32	1	5/16	2 1/32	7/16	3 1/32	19/32	4 1/32	3/4	5 1/16
1/16	0	1/16	5/32	1 1/16	5/16	2 3/32	15/32	3 3/32	5/8	4 3/32	3/4	5 1/8
1/8	1/32	1/8	5/32	1 1/8	5/16	2 5/32	15/32	3 5/32	5/8	4 5/32	25/32	5 3/16
3/16	1/32	3/16	3/16	1 13/16	11/32	2 7/32	15/32	3 7/32	5/8	4 1/4	25/32	5 1/4
1/4	1/32	1/4	3/16	1 1/4	11/32	2 9/32	1/2	3 9/32	21/32	4 5/16	25/32	5 5/16
5/16	1/16	5/16	3/16	1 5/16	11/32	2 11/32	1/2	3 11/32	21/32	4 3/8	13/16	5 3/8
3/8	1/16	3/8	7/32	1 3/8	11/32	2 13/32	1/2	3 13/32	21/32	4 7/16	13/16	5 7/16
7/16	1/16	7/16	7/32	1 15/32	3/8	2 15/32	17/32	3 15/32	21/32	4 1/2	13/16	5 1/2
1/2	1/16	1/2	7/32	1 17/32	3/8	2 17/32	17/32	3 17/32	11/16	4 9/16	27/32	5 9/16
9/16	3/32	9/16	1/4	1 19/32	3/8	2 19/32	17/32	3 19/32	11/16	4 5/8	27/32	5 5/8
5/8	3/32	5/8	1/4	1 21/32	13/32	2 21/32	9/16	3 21/32	11/16	4 11/16	27/32	5 11/16
11/16	3/32	11/16	1/4	1 23/32	13/32	2 23/32	9/16	3 23/32	23/32	4 3/4	27/32	5 3/4
3/4	1/8	3/4	1/4	1 25/32	13/32	2 25/32	9/16	3 25/32	23/32	4 13/16	7/8	5 13/16
13/16	1/8	13/16	9/32	1 27/32	7/16	2 27/32	9/16	3 27/32	23/32	4 7/8	7/8	5 7/8
7/8	1/8	7/8	9/32	1 29/32	7/16	2 29/32	19/32	3 29/32	3/4	4 15/16	7/8	5 15/16
15/16	5/32	15/16	9/32	1 31/32	7/16	2 31/32	19/32	3 31/32	3/4	5	29/32	6

Inches	6" Rise	6" Slope	7" Rise	7" Slope	8" Rise	8" Slope	9" Rise	9" Slope	10" Rise	10" Slope	11" Rise	11" Slope
0	29/32	6 1/16	1 1/16	7 3/32	1 7/32	8 3/32	1 3/8	9 3/32	1 1/2	10 1/8	1 21/32	11 1/8
1/16	29/32	6 1/8	1 1/16	7 5/32	1 7/32	8 5/32	1 3/8	9 5/32	1 17/32	10 3/16	1 21/32	11 3/16
1/8	15/16	6 3/16	1 1/16	7 7/32	1 7/32	8 7/32	1 3/8	9 7/32	1 17/32	10 1/4	1 11/16	11 1/4
3/16	15/16	6 1/4	1 3/32	7 9/32	1 1/4	8 9/32	1 3/8	9 9/32	1 17/32	10 5/16	1 11/16	11 5/16
1/4	15/16	6 5/16	1 3/32	7 11/32	1 1/4	8 11/32	1 13/32	9 11/32	1 9/16	10 3/8	1 11/16	11 3/8
5/16	31/32	6 3/8	1 3/32	7 13/32	1 1/4	8 13/32	1 13/32	9 13/32	1 9/16	10 7/16	1 23/32	11 7/16
3/8	31/32	6 7/16	1 1/8	7 15/32	1 1/4	8 15/32	1 13/32	9 15/32	1 9/16	10 1/2	1 23/32	11 1/2
7/16	31/32	6 1/2	1 1/8	7 17/32	1 9/32	8 17/32	1 7/16	9 17/32	1 9/16	10 9/16	1 23/32	11 9/16
1/2	31/32	6 9/16	1 1/8	7 19/32	1 9/32	8 19/32	1 7/16	9 19/32	1 19/32	10 5/8	1 3/4	11 5/8
9/16	1	6 5/8	1 5/32	7 21/32	1 9/32	8 21/32	1 7/16	9 21/32	1 19/32	10 11/16	1 3/4	11 11/16
5/8	1	6 11/16	1 5/32	7 23/32	1 5/16	8 23/32	1 15/32	9 23/32	1 19/32	10 3/4	1 3/4	11 3/4
11/16	1	6 3/4	1 5/32	7 25/32	1 5/16	8 25/32	1 15/32	9 13/16	1 5/8	10 13/16	1 3/4	11 13/16
3/4	1 1/32	6 13/16	1 5/32	7 27/32	1 5/16	8 27/32	1 15/32	9 7/8	1 5/8	10 7/8	1 25/32	11 7/8
13/16	1 1/32	6 7/8	1 3/16	7 29/32	1 11/32	8 29/32	1 15/32	9 15/16	1 5/8	10 15/16	1 25/32	11 15/16
7/8	1 1/32	6 15/16	1 3/16	7 31/32	1 11/32	8 31/32	1 1/2	10	1 21/32	11	1 25/32	1-0
15/16	1 1/16	7 1/32	1 3/16	8 1/32	1 11/32	9 1/32	1 1/2	10 1/16	1 21/32	11 1/16	1 13/16	1-0 1/16

Feet	0' Rise	0' Slope	10' Rise	10' Slope	20' Rise	20' Slope	30' Rise	30' Slope
0	0	0	1-6 1/8	10-1 3/8	3-0 1/4	20-2 23/32	4-6 3/8	30-4 3/32
1	1 13/16	1-0 1/8	1-7 15/16	11-1 1/2	3-2 1/16	21-2 27/32	4-8 3/16	31-4 7/32
2	3 5/8	2-0 9/32	1-9 3/4	12-1 5/8	3-3 7/8	22-3	4-10	32-4 11/32
3	5 7/16	3-0 13/32	1-11 9/16	13-1 25/32	3-5 11/16	23-3 1/8	4-11 13/16	33-4 1/2
4	7 1/4	4-0 17/32	2-1 3/8	14-1 29/32	3-7 1/2	24-3 9/32	5-1 5/8	34-4 5/8
5	9 1/16	5-0 11/16	2-3 3/16	15-2 1/32	3-9 5/16	25-3 13/32	5-3 7/16	35-4 3/4
6	10 7/8	6-0 13/16	2-5	16-2 3/16	3-11 1/8	26-3 17/32	5-5 1/4	36-4 29/32
7	1-0 11/16	7-0 15/16	2-6 13/16	17-2 5/16	4-0 15/16	27-3 11/16	5-7 1/16	37-5 1/32
8	1-2 1/2	8-1 3/32	2-8 5/8	18-2 7/16	4-2 3/4	28-3 13/16	5-8 7/8	38-5 3/16
9	1-4 5/16	9-1 7/32	2-10 7/16	19-2 19/32	4-4 9/16	29-3 15/16	5-10 11/16	39-5 5/16

A = 8° 35' 21"; logsin A = 9.17420; logcos A = 9.99510; logtan A = 9.17910; logcot A = 0.82090

In.	12″ Rise	Slope	13″ Rise	Slope	14″ Rise	Slope	15″ Rise	Slope	16″ Rise	Slope
0	1 13/16	1-0 1/8	1 31/32	1-1 5/32	2 1/8	1-2 5/32	2 1/4	1-3 5/32	2 13/32	1-4 3/16
1/16	1 13/16	1-0 3/16	1 31/32	1-1 7/32	2 1/8	1-2 7/32	2 9/32	1-3 7/32	2 7/16	1-4 1/4
1/8	1 27/32	1-0 1/4	1 31/32	1-1 9/32	2 1/8	1-2 9/32	2 9/32	1-3 9/32	2 7/16	1-4 5/16
3/16	1 27/32	1-0 5/16	2	1-1 11/32	2 5/32	1-2 11/32	2 9/32	1-3 3/8	2 7/16	1-4 3/8
1/4	1 27/32	1-0 3/8	2	1-1 13/32	2 5/32	1-2 13/32	2 5/16	1-3 7/16	2 15/32	1-4 7/16
5/16	1 7/8	1-0 7/16	2	1-1 15/32	2 5/32	1-2 15/32	2 5/16	1-3 1/2	2 15/32	1-4 1/2
3/8	1 7/8	1-0 1/2	2 1/32	1-1 17/32	2 5/32	1-2 17/32	2 5/16	1-3 9/16	2 15/32	1-4 9/16
7/16	1 7/8	1-0 19/32	2 1/32	1-1 19/32	2 3/16	1-2 19/32	2 11/32	1-3 5/8	2 15/32	1-4 5/8
1/2	1 7/8	1-0 21/32	2 1/32	1-1 21/32	2 3/16	1-2 21/32	2 11/32	1-3 11/16	2 1/2	1-4 11/16
9/16	1 29/32	1-0 23/32	2 1/16	1-1 23/32	2 3/16	1-2 23/32	2 11/32	1-3 3/4	2 1/2	1-4 3/4
5/8	1 29/32	1-0 25/32	2 1/16	1-1 25/32	2 7/32	1-2 25/32	2 3/8	1-3 13/16	2 1/2	1-4 13/16
11/16	1 29/32	1-0 27/32	2 1/16	1-1 27/32	2 7/32	1-2 27/32	2 3/8	1-3 7/8	2 17/32	1-4 7/8
3/4	1 15/16	1-0 29/32	2 1/16	1-1 29/32	2 7/32	1-2 29/32	2 3/8	1-3 15/16	2 17/32	1-4 15/16
13/16	1 15/16	1-0 31/32	2 3/32	1-1 31/32	2 1/4	1-2 31/32	2 3/8	1-4	2 17/32	1-5
7/8	1 15/16	1-1 1/32	2 3/32	1-2 1/32	2 1/4	1-3 1/32	2 13/32	1-4 1/16	2 9/16	1-5 1/16
15/16	1 31/32	1-1 3/32	2 3/32	1-2 3/32	2 1/4	1-3 3/32	2 13/32	1-4 1/8	2 9/16	1-5 1/8

In.	17″ Rise	Slope	18″ Rise	Slope	19″ Rise	Slope	20″ Rise	Slope	21″ Rise	Slope
0	2 9/16	1-5 3/16	2 23/32	1-6 1/32	2 7/8	1-7 7/32	3 1/32	1-8 7/32	3 3/16	1-9 1/4
1/16	2 9/16	1-5 1/4	2 23/32	1-6 9/32	2 7/8	1-7 9/32	3 1/32	1-8 9/32	3 3/16	1-9 5/16
1/8	2 19/32	1-5 5/16	2 3/4	1-6 11/32	2 7/8	1-7 11/32	3 1/32	1-8 11/32	3 3/16	1-9 3/8
3/16	2 19/32	1-5 3/8	2 3/4	1-6 13/32	2 29/32	1-7 13/32	3 1/16	1-8 13/32	3 3/16	1-9 7/16
1/4	2 19/32	1-5 7/16	2 3/4	1-6 15/32	2 29/32	1-7 15/32	3 1/16	1-8 15/32	3 7/32	1-9 1/2
5/16	2 5/8	1-5 1/2	2 25/32	1-6 17/32	2 29/32	1-7 17/32	3 1/16	1-8 17/32	3 7/32	1-9 9/16
3/8	2 5/8	1-5 9/16	2 25/32	1-6 19/32	2 15/16	1-7 19/32	3 1/16	1-8 19/32	3 7/32	1-9 5/8
7/16	2 5/8	1-5 5/8	2 25/32	1-6 21/32	2 15/16	1-7 21/32	3 3/32	1-8 21/32	3 1/4	1-9 11/16
1/2	2 21/32	1-5 11/16	2 25/32	1-6 23/32	2 15/16	1-7 23/32	3 3/32	1-8 23/32	3 1/4	1-9 3/4
9/16	2 21/32	1-5 3/4	2 13/16	1-6 25/32	2 31/32	1-7 25/32	3 3/32	1-8 25/32	3 1/4	1-9 13/16
5/8	2 21/32	1-5 13/16	2 13/16	1-6 27/32	2 31/32	1-7 27/32	3 1/8	1-8 27/32	3 9/32	1-9 7/8
11/16	2 21/32	1-5 7/8	2 13/16	1-6 29/32	2 31/32	1-7 29/32	3 1/8	1-8 15/16	3 9/32	1-9 15/16
3/4	2 11/16	1-5 15/16	2 27/32	1-6 31/32	2 31/32	1-7 31/32	3 1/8	1-9	3 9/32	1-10
13/16	2 11/16	1-6	2 27/32	1-7 1/32	3	1-8 1/32	3 5/32	1-9 1/16	3 9/32	1-10 1/16
7/8	2 11/16	1-6 1/16	2 27/32	1-7 3/32	3	1-8 3/32	3 5/32	1-9 1/8	3 5/16	1-10 1/8
15/16	2 23/32	1-6 1/8	2 7/8	1-7 5/32	3	1-8 5/32	3 5/32	1-9 3/16	3 5/16	1-10 3/16

Feet	40′ Rise	Slope	50′ Rise	Slope	60′ Rise	Slope	70′ Rise	Slope
0	6-0 1/2	40-5 7/16	7-6 5/8	50-6 13/16	9-0 3/4	60-8 5/32	10-6 7/8	70-9 17/32
1	6-2 5/16	41-5 19/32	7-8 7/16	51-6 15/16	9-2 9/16	61-8 5/16	10-8 11/16	71-9 21/32
2	6-4 1/8	42-5 23/32	7-10 1/4	52-7 1/16	9-4 3/8	62-8 7/16	10-10 1/2	72-9 13/16
3	6-5 15/16	43-5 27/32	8-0 1/16	53-7 3/16	9-6 3/16	63-8 5/8	11-0 5/16	73-9 15/16
4	6-7 3/4	44-6	8-1 7/8	54-7 11/32	9-8	64-8 23/32	11-2 1/8	74-10 1/16
5	6-9 9/16	45-6 1/8	8-3 11/16	55-7 1/2	9-9 13/16	65-8 27/32	11-3 15/16	75-10 7/32
6	6-11 3/8	46-6 1/4	8-5 1/2	56-7 5/8	9-11 5/8	66-8 31/32	11-5 3/4	76-10 11/32
7	7-1 3/16	47-6 13/32	8-7 5/16	57-7 3/4	10-1 7/16	67-9 1/8	11-7 9/16	77-10 15/32
8	7-3	48-6 17/32	8-9 1/8	58-7 29/32	10-3 1/4	68-9 1/4	11-9 3/8	78-10 5/8
9	7-4 13/16	49-6 21/32	8-10 15/16	59-8 1/32	10-5 1/16	69-9 13/32	11-11 3/16	79-10 3/4

natsin A=0.1493476953; natcos A=0.9887847419; nattan A=0.1510416666; natcot A=6.6206896551

Inches	0" Rise	0" Slope	1" Rise	1" Slope	2" Rise	2" Slope	3" Rise	3" Slope	4" Rise	4" Slope	5" Rise	5" Slope
0	0	0	5/32	1	5/16	2 1/32	15/32	3 1/32	5/8	4 1/16	25/32	5 1/16
1/16	0	1/16	5/32	1 1/16	5/16	2 3/32	15/32	3 3/32	5/8	4 1/8	25/32	5 1/8
1/8	1/32	1/8	3/16	1 1/8	11/32	2 5/32	1/2	3 5/32	21/32	4 3/16	13/16	5 3/16
3/16	1/32	3/16	3/16	1 3/16	11/32	2 7/32	1/2	3 7/32	21/32	4 1/4	13/16	5 1/4
1/4	1/32	1/4	3/16	1 1/4	11/32	2 9/32	1/2	3 9/32	21/32	4 5/16	13/16	5 5/16
5/16	1/16	5/16	7/32	1 11/32	3/8	2 11/32	17/32	3 11/32	11/16	4 3/8	27/32	5 3/8
3/8	1/16	3/8	7/32	1 13/32	3/8	2 13/32	17/32	3 13/32	11/16	4 7/16	27/32	5 7/16
7/16	1/16	7/16	7/32	1 15/32	3/8	2 15/32	17/32	3 15/32	11/16	4 1/2	27/32	5 1/2
1/2	1/16	1/2	1/4	1 17/32	3/8	2 17/32	9/16	3 17/32	11/16	4 9/16	7/8	5 9/16
9/16	3/32	9/16	1/4	1 19/32	13/32	2 19/32	9/16	3 19/32	23/32	4 5/8	7/8	5 5/8
5/8	3/32	5/8	1/4	1 21/32	13/32	2 21/32	9/16	3 21/32	23/32	4 11/16	7/8	5 11/16
11/16	3/32	11/16	1/4	1 23/32	13/32	2 23/32	9/16	3 23/32	23/32	4 3/4	7/8	5 3/4
3/4	1/8	3/4	9/32	1 25/32	7/16	2 25/32	19/32	3 25/32	3/4	4 13/16	29/32	5 13/16
13/16	1/8	13/16	9/32	1 27/32	7/16	2 27/32	19/32	3 27/32	3/4	4 7/8	29/32	5 7/8
7/8	1/8	7/8	9/32	1 29/32	7/16	2 29/32	19/32	3 15/16	3/4	4 15/16	29/32	5 15/16
15/16	5/32	15/16	5/16	1 31/32	15/32	2 31/32	5/8	4	25/32	5	15/16	6

Inches	6" Rise	6" Slope	7" Rise	7" Slope	8" Rise	8" Slope	9" Rise	9" Slope	10" Rise	10" Slope	11" Rise	11" Slope
0	15/16	6 1/8	1 3/32	7 3/32	1 1/4	8 3/32	1 13/32	9 3/32	1 9/16	10 1/8	1 23/32	11 1/8
1/16	15/16	6 1/8	1 3/32	7 5/32	1 1/4	8 5/32	1 13/32	9 3/16	1 9/16	10 3/16	1 23/32	11 3/16
1/8	31/32	6 3/16	1 1/8	7 7/32	1 9/32	8 7/32	1 7/16	9 1/4	1 19/32	10 1/4	1 3/4	11 1/4
3/16	31/32	6 1/4	1 1/8	7 9/32	1 9/32	8 9/32	1 7/16	9 5/16	1 19/32	10 5/16	1 3/4	11 5/16
1/4	31/32	6 5/16	1 1/8	7 11/32	1 9/32	8 11/32	1 7/16	9 3/8	1 19/32	10 3/8	1 3/4	11 3/8
5/16	1	6 3/8	1 5/32	7 13/32	1 5/16	8 13/32	1 15/32	9 7/16	1 5/8	10 7/16	1 25/32	11 7/16
3/8	1	6 7/16	1 5/32	7 15/32	1 5/16	8 15/32	1 15/32	9 1/2	1 5/8	10 1/2	1 25/32	11 1/2
7/16	1	6 1/2	1 5/32	7 17/32	1 5/16	8 17/32	1 15/32	9 9/16	1 5/8	10 9/16	1 25/32	11 9/16
1/2	1	6 19/32	1 3/16	7 19/32	1 11/32	8 19/32	1 1/2	9 5/8	1 5/8	10 5/8	1 13/16	11 5/8
9/16	1 1/32	6 21/32	1 3/16	7 21/32	1 11/32	8 21/32	1 1/2	9 11/16	1 21/32	10 11/16	1 13/16	11 11/16
5/8	1 1/32	6 23/32	1 3/16	7 23/32	1 11/32	8 23/32	1 1/2	9 3/4	1 21/32	10 3/4	1 13/16	11 25/32
11/16	1 1/32	6 25/32	1 3/16	7 25/32	1 11/32	8 25/32	1 1/2	9 13/16	1 21/32	10 13/16	1 13/16	11 27/32
3/4	1 1/16	6 27/32	1 7/32	7 27/32	1 3/8	8 27/32	1 17/32	9 7/8	1 11/16	10 7/8	1 27/32	11 29/32
13/16	1 1/16	6 29/32	1 7/32	7 29/32	1 3/8	8 29/32	1 17/32	9 15/16	1 11/16	10 15/16	1 27/32	11 31/32
7/8	1 1/16	6 31/32	1 7/32	7 31/32	1 3/8	8 31/32	1 17/32	10	1 11/16	11	1 27/32	1-0 1/32
15/16	1 3/32	7 1/32	1 1/4	8 1/32	1 13/32	9 1/32	1 9/16	10 1/16	1 23/32	11 1/16	1 7/8	1-0 3/32

Feet	0' Rise	0' Slope	10' Rise	10' Slope	20' Rise	20' Slope	30' Rise	30' Slope
0	0	0	1-6 3/4	10-1 15/32	3-1 1/2	20-2 29/32	4-8 1/4	30-4 3/8
1	1 7/8	1-0 5/32	1-8 5/8	11-1 19/32	3-3 3/8	21-3 1/16	4-10 1/8	31-4 1/2
2	3 3/4	2-0 9/32	1-10 1/2	12-1 3/4	3-5 1/4	22-3 7/32	5-0	32-4 21/32
3	5 5/8	3-0 7/16	2-0 3/8	13-1 29/32	3-7 1/8	23-3 11/16	5-1 7/8	33-4 13/16
4	7 1/2	4-0 19/32	2-2 1/4	14-2 1/16	3-9	24-3 1/2	5-3 3/4	34-4 15/16
5	9 3/8	5-0 23/32	2-4 1/8	15-2 3/16	3-10 7/8	25-3 5/8	5-5 5/8	35-5 3/32
6	11 1/4	6-0 7/8	2-6	16-2 11/32	4-0 3/4	26-3 3/4	5-7 1/2	36-5 1/4
7	1-1 1/8	7-1 1/32	2-7 7/8	17-2 15/32	4-2 5/8	27-3 15/16	5-9 3/8	37-5 3/8
8	1-3	8-1 5/32	2-9 3/4	18-2 5/8	4-4 1/2	28-4 1/16	5-11 1/4	38-5 17/32
9	1-4 7/8	9-1 5/16	2-11 5/8	19-2 25/32	4-6 3/8	29-4 3/32	6-1 1/8	39-5 11/16

A = 8° 52' 50"; logsin A = 9.18858; logcos A = 9.99476; logtan A = 9.19382; logcot A = 0.80618

Ins.	12″		13″		14″		15″		16″	
	Rise	Slope	Rise	Slope	Rise	Slope	Rise	Slope	Rise	Slope
0	1 7/8	1-0 5/32−	2 1/32	1-1 5/32	2 3/16	1-2 5/32	2 11/32	1-3 3/16	2 1/2	1-4 3/16
1/16	1 7/8	1-0 7/32−	2 1/32	1-1 7/32	2 3/16	1-2 7/32	2 11/32	1-3 1/4	2 1/2	1-4 1/4
1/8	1 29/32−	1-0 9/32−	2 1/16	1-1 9/32	2 7/32−	1-2 9/32	2 3/8	1-3 5/16	2 17/32−	1-4 5/16
3/16	1 29/32−	1-0 11/32−	2 1/16	1-1 11/32	2 7/32−	1-2 3/8	2 3/8	1-3 3/8	2 17/32−	1-4 3/8
1/4	1 29/32	1-0 13/32−	2 1/16	1-1 13/32	2 7/32	1-2 7/16	2 3/8	1-3 7/16	2 17/32	1-4 7/16
5/16	1 15/16	1-0 15/32−	2 3/32−	1-1 15/32	2 1/4	1-2 1/2	2 13/32−	1-3 1/2	2 9/16	1-4 1/2
3/8	1 15/16	1-0 17/32−	2 3/32−	1-1 17/32	2 1/4	1-2 9/16	2 13/32−	1-3 9/16	2 9/16	1-4 9/16
7/16	1 15/16	1-0 19/32−	2 3/32	1-1 19/32	2 1/4	1-2 5/8	2 13/32	1-3 5/8	2 9/16	1-4 5/8
1/2	1 15/16	1-0 21/32−	2 1/8	1-1 21/32	2 1/4	1-2 11/16	2 7/16	1-3 11/16	2 9/16	1-4 11/16
9/16	1 31/32−	1-0 23/32−	2 1/8	1-1 23/32	2 9/32−	1-2 3/4	2 7/16	1-3 3/4	2 19/32−	1-4 3/4
5/8	1 31/32	1-0 25/32−	2 1/8	1-1 25/32	2 9/32	1-2 13/16	2 7/16	1-3 13/16	2 19/32	1-4 13/16
11/16	1 31/32	1-0 27/32−	2 1/8	1-1 27/32	2 9/32	1-2 7/8	2 7/16	1-3 7/8	2 19/32	1-4 7/8
3/4	2	1-0 29/32−	2 5/32−	1-1 29/32	2 5/16	1-2 15/16	2 15/32−	1-3 15/16	2 5/8	1-4 31/32−
13/16	2	1-0 31/32−	2 5/32	1-1 31/32	2 5/16	1-3	2 15/32	1-4	2 5/8	1-5 1/32−
7/8	2	1-1 1/32−	2 5/32	1-2 1/32	2 5/16	1-3 1/16	2 15/32	1-4 1/16	2 5/8	1-5 3/32−
15/16	2 1/32−	1-1 3/32	2 3/16	1-2 3/32	2 11/32−	1-3 1/8	2 1/2	1-4 1/8	2 21/32−	1-5 5/32−

Ins.	17″		18″		19″		20″		21″	
	Rise	Slope	Rise	Slope	Rise	Slope	Rise	Slope	Rise	Slope
0	2 21/32	1-5 7/32−	2 13/16	1-6 7/32−	2 31/32	1-7 7/32	3 1/8	1-8 1/4	3 9/32	1-9 1/4
1/16	2 21/32	1-5 9/32−	2 13/16	1-6 9/32	2 31/32	1-7 9/32	3 1/8	1-8 5/16	3 9/32	1-9 5/16
1/8	2 11/16	1-5 11/32−	2 27/32−	1-6 11/32	3	1-7 11/32	3 5/32−	1-8 3/8	3 5/16	1-9 3/8
3/16	2 11/16	1-5 13/32−	2 27/32−	1-6 13/32	3	1-7 13/32	3 5/32−	1-8 7/16	3 5/16	1-9 7/16
1/4	2 11/16	1-5 15/32−	2 27/32	1-6 15/32	3	1-7 15/32	3 5/32	1-8 1/2	3 5/16	1-9 1/2
5/16	2 23/32−	1-5 17/32−	2 7/8	1-6 17/32	3 1/32−	1-7 17/32	3 3/16	1-8 9/16	3 11/32−	1-9 9/16
3/8	2 23/32−	1-5 19/32−	2 7/8	1-6 19/32	3 1/32−	1-7 5/8	3 3/16	1-8 5/8	3 11/32−	1-9 5/8
7/16	2 23/32	1-5 21/32−	2 7/8	1-6 21/32	3 1/32	1-7 11/16	3 3/16	1-8 11/16	3 11/32	1-9 11/16
1/2	2 3/4	1-5 23/32−	2 7/8	1-6 23/32	3 1/16	1-7 3/4	3 3/16	1-8 3/4	3 3/8	1-9 3/4
9/16	2 3/4	1-5 25/32−	2 29/32−	1-6 25/32	3 1/16	1-7 13/16	3 7/32−	1-8 13/16	3 3/8	1-9 13/16
5/8	2 3/4	1-5 27/32−	2 29/32	1-6 27/32	3 1/16	1-7 7/8	3 7/32	1-8 7/8	3 3/8	1-9 7/8
11/16	2 3/4	1-5 29/32−	2 29/32	1-6 29/32	3 1/16	1-7 15/16	3 7/32	1-8 15/16	3 3/8	1-9 15/16
3/4	2 25/32−	1-5 31/32−	2 15/16	1-6 31/32	3 3/32−	1-8	3 1/4	1-9	3 13/32−	1-10
13/16	2 25/32	1-6 1/32−	2 15/16	1-7 1/32	3 3/32	1-8 1/16	3 1/4	1-9 1/16	3 13/32	1-10 1/16
7/8	2 25/32	1-6 3/32−	2 15/16	1-7 3/32	3 3/32	1-8 1/8	3 1/4	1-9 1/8	3 13/32	1-10 1/8
15/16	2 13/16	1-6 5/32−	2 31/32−	1-7 5/32	3 1/8	1-8 3/16	3 9/32−	1-9 3/16	3 7/16	1-10 7/32−

Feet	40′		50′		60′		70′	
	Rise	Slope	Rise	Slope	Rise	Slope	Rise	Slope
0	6-3	40-5 13/16	7-9 3/4	50-7 9/32−	9-4 1/2	60-8 3/4	10-11 1/4	70-10 3/16
1	6-4 7/8	41-5 31/32	7-11 5/8	51-7 7/16	9-6 3/8	61-8 7/8	11-1 1/8	71-10 11/32−
2	6-6 3/4	42-6 1/8	8-1 1/2	52-7 9/16	9-8 1/4	62-9 1/32−	11-3	72-10 15/32
3	6-8 5/8	43-6 1/4	8-3 3/8	53-7 23/32−	9-10 1/8	63-9 3/16	11-4 7/8	73-10 5/8
4	6-10 1/2	44-6 13/32	8-5 1/4	54-7 7/8	10-0	64-9 5/16	11-6 3/4	74-10 25/32−
5	7-0 3/8	45-6 9/16	8-7 1/8	55-8	10-1 7/8	65-9 15/32−	11-8 5/8	75-10 29/32
6	7-2 1/4	46-6 11/16	8-9	56-8 5/32−	10-3 3/4	66-9 5/8	11-10 1/2	76-11 1/16
7	7-4 1/8	47-6 27/32−	8-10 7/8	57-8 5/16	10-5 5/8	67-9 3/4	12-0 3/8	77-11 7/32−
8	7-6	48-7	9-0 3/4	58-8 7/16	10-7 1/2	68-9 29/32−	12-2 1/4	78-11 11/32
9	7-7 7/8	49-7 1/8	9-2 5/8	59-8 19/32−	10-9 3/8	69-10 1/32	12-4 1/8	79-11 1/2

natsin A=0.1543768802; natcos A=0.9880120338; nattan A=0.1562500000; natcot A=6.4000000000

Inches	0" Rise	0" Slope	1" Rise	1" Slope	2" Rise	2" Slope	3" Rise	3" Slope	4" Rise	4" Slope	5" Rise	5" Slope
0	0	0	5/32	1	5/16	2 1/32	1/2	3 1/32	21/32	4 1/16	13/16	5 1/16
1/16	0	1/16	5/32	1 1/16	11/32	2 3/32	1/2	3 3/32	21/32	4 1/8	13/16	5 1/8
1/8	1/32	1/8	3/16	1 1/8	11/32	2 5/32	1/2	3 5/32	21/32	4 3/16	13/16	5 3/16
3/16	1/32	3/16	3/16	1 3/16	11/32	2 7/32	1/2	3 7/32	11/16	4 1/4	27/32	5 1/4
1/4	1/8	1/4	3/16	1 9/32	3/8	2 9/32	17/32	3 9/32	11/16	4 5/16	27/32	5 5/16
5/16	1/16	5/16	7/32	1 11/32	3/8	2 11/32	17/32	3 11/32	11/16	4 3/8	27/32	5 3/8
3/8	1/16	3/8	7/32	1 13/32	3/8	2 13/32	17/32	3 13/32	23/32	4 7/16	7/8	5 7/16
7/16	1/16	7/16	7/32	1 15/32	13/32	2 15/32	9/16	3 15/32	23/32	4 1/2	7/8	5 1/2
1/2	3/32	1/2	1/4	1 17/32	13/32	2 17/32	9/16	3 17/32	23/32	4 9/16	7/8	5 9/16
9/16	3/32	9/16	1/4	1 19/32	13/32	2 19/32	9/16	3 19/32	3/4	4 5/8	29/32	5 5/8
5/8	3/32	5/8	1/4	1 21/32	7/16	2 21/32	19/32	3 11/16	3/4	4 11/16	29/32	5 11/16
11/16	1/8	11/16	9/32	1 23/32	7/16	2 23/32	19/32	3 3/4	3/4	4 3/4	29/32	5 3/4
3/4	1/8	3/4	9/32	1 25/32	7/16	2 25/32	19/32	3 13/16	25/32	4 13/16	15/16	5 13/16
13/16	1/8	13/16	9/32	1 27/32	15/32	2 27/32	5/8	3 7/8	25/32	4 7/8	15/16	5 7/8
7/8	5/32	7/8	5/16	1 29/32	15/32	2 29/32	5/8	3 15/16	25/32	4 15/16	15/16	5 15/16
15/16	5/32	15/16	5/16	1 31/32	15/32	2 31/32	5/8	4	13/16	5	31/32	6

Inches	6" Rise	6" Slope	7" Rise	7" Slope	8" Rise	8" Slope	9" Rise	9" Slope	10" Rise	10" Slope	11" Rise	11" Slope
0	31/32	6 1/16	1 1/8	7 3/32	1 9/32	8 3/32	1 7/16	9 1/8	1 5/8	10 1/8	1 25/32	11 1/32
1/16	31/32	6 5/32	1 1/8	7 5/32	1 5/16	8 5/32	1 15/32	9 3/32	1 5/8	10 3/16	1 25/32	11 7/32
1/8	1	6 7/32	1 5/32	7 7/32	1 5/16	8 7/32	1 15/32	9 1/4	1 5/8	10 1/4	1 25/32	11 9/32
3/16	1	6 9/32	1 5/32	7 9/32	1 5/16	8 9/32	1 15/32	9 5/16	1 21/32	10 5/16	1 13/16	11 11/32
1/4	1	6 11/32	1 5/32	7 11/32	1 11/32	8 11/32	1 1/2	9 3/8	1 21/32	10 3/8	1 13/16	11 13/32
5/16	1 1/32	6 13/32	1 3/16	7 13/32	1 11/32	8 13/32	1 1/2	9 7/16	1 21/32	10 7/16	1 13/16	11 15/32
3/8	1 1/32	6 15/32	1 3/16	7 15/32	1 11/32	8 15/32	1 1/2	9 1/2	1 11/16	10 1/2	1 27/32	11 17/32
7/16	1 1/32	6 17/32	1 3/16	7 17/32	1 3/8	8 17/32	1 17/32	9 9/16	1 11/16	10 9/16	1 27/32	11 19/32
1/2	1 1/8	6 19/32	1 7/32	7 19/32	1 3/8	8 5/8	1 17/32	9 5/8	1 11/16	10 5/8	1 27/32	11 21/32
9/16	1 1/16	6 21/32	1 7/32	7 21/32	1 3/8	8 11/16	1 17/32	9 11/16	1 23/32	10 11/16	1 7/8	11 23/32
5/8	1 1/16	6 23/32	1 7/32	7 23/32	1 13/32	8 3/4	1 9/16	9 3/4	1 23/32	10 3/4	1 7/8	11 25/32
11/16	1 3/32	6 25/32	1 1/4	7 25/32	1 13/32	8 13/16	1 9/16	9 13/16	1 23/32	10 13/16	1 7/8	11 27/32
3/4	1 3/32	6 27/32	1 1/4	7 27/32	1 13/32	8 7/8	1 9/16	9 7/8	1 3/4	10 7/8	1 29/32	11 29/32
13/16	1 3/32	6 29/32	1 1/4	7 29/32	1 7/16	8 15/16	1 19/32	9 15/16	1 3/4	10 15/16	1 29/32	11 31/32
7/8	1 1/8	6 31/32	1 9/32	7 31/32	1 7/16	9	1 19/32	10	1 3/4	11 1/2	1 29/32	1-0 1/8
15/16	1 1/8	7 1/32	1 9/32	8 1/32	1 7/16	9 1/16	1 19/32	10 1/32	1 25/32	11 3/4	1 15/16	1-0 5/8

Feet	0' Rise	0' Slope	10' Rise	10' Slope	20' Rise	20' Slope	30' Rise	30' Slope
0	0	0	1-7 3/8	10-1 9/16	3-2 3/4	20-3 3/4	4-10 1/8	30-4 21/32
1	1 15/16	1-0 5/32	1-9 5/16	11-1 23/32	3-4 11/16	21-3 1/4	5-0 1/16	31-4 13/32
2	3 7/8	2-0 5/16	1-11 1/4	12-1 7/8	3-6 5/8	22-3 13/32	5-2	32-4 31/32
3	5 13/16	3-0 15/32	2-1 3/16	13-2 1/32	3-8 9/16	23-3 9/16	5-3 15/16	33-5 1/8
4	7 3/4	4-0 5/8	2-3 1/8	14-2 3/16	3-10 1/2	24-3 23/32	5-5 7/8	34-5 9/32
5	9 11/16	5-0 25/32	2-5 1/16	15-2 11/32	4-0 7/16	25-3 7/8	5-7 13/16	35-5 7/16
6	11 5/8	6-0 15/16	2-7	16-2 1/2	4-2 3/8	26-4 1/32	5-9 3/4	36-5 19/32
7	1-1 9/16	7-1 3/32	2-8 15/16	17-2 21/32	4-4 5/16	27-4 3/32	5-11 11/16	37-5 3/4
8	1-3 1/2	8-1 1/4	2-10 7/8	18-2 13/16	4-6 1/4	28-4 11/32	6-1 5/8	38-5 29/32
9	1-5 7/16	9-1 13/32	3-0 13/16	19-2 15/16	4-8 3/8	29-4 1/2	6-3 9/16	39-6 1/16

A = 9° 10′ 18″; logsin A = 9.20247; logcos A = 9.99441; logtan A = 9.20806; logcot A = 0.79194

Ins.	12″ Rise	12″ Slope	13″ Rise	13″ Slope	14″ Rise	14″ Slope	15″ Rise	15″ Slope	16″ Rise	16″ Slope
0	1 15/16	1-0 5/32	2 3/32	1-1 5/32	2 1/4	1-2 3/16	2 7/16	1-3 3/8	2 19/32	1-4 7/32
1/16	1 15/16	1-0 7/32	2 3/32	1-1 7/32	2 9/32	1-2 1/4	2 7/16	1-3 1/4	2 19/32	1-4 9/32
1/8	1 31/32	1-0 9/32	2 1/8	1-1 9/32	2 9/32	1-2 5/16	2 7/16	1-3 5/16	2 19/32	1-4 11/32
3/16	1 31/32	1-0 11/32	2 1/8	1-1 11/32	2 9/32	1-2 3/8	2 7/16	1-3 3/8	2 5/8	1-4 13/32
1/4	1 31/32	1-0 13/32	2 1/8	1-1 13/32	2 5/16	1-2 7/16	2 15/32	1-3 7/16	2 5/8	1-4 15/32
5/16	2	1-0 15/32	2 5/32	1-1 1/2	2 5/16	1-2 1/2	2 15/32	1-3 1/2	2 5/8	1-4 17/32
3/8	2	1-0 17/32	2 5/32	1-1 9/16	2 5/16	1-2 9/16	2 15/32	1-3 9/16	2 21/32	1-4 19/32
7/16	2	1-0 19/32	2 5/32	1-1 5/8	2 11/32	1-2 5/8	2 1/2	1-3 5/8	2 21/32	1-4 21/32
1/2	2 1/32	1-0 21/32	2 3/16	1-1 11/16	2 11/32	1-2 11/16	2 1/2	1-3 11/16	2 21/32	1-4 23/32
9/16	2 1/32	1-0 23/32	2 3/16	1-1 3/4	2 11/32	1-2 3/4	2 1/2	1-3 3/4	2 11/16	1-4 25/32
5/8	2 1/32	1-0 25/32	2 3/16	1-1 13/16	2 3/8	1-2 13/16	2 17/32	1-3 13/16	2 11/16	1-4 27/32
11/16	2 1/16	1-0 27/32	2 7/32	1-1 7/8	2 3/8	1-2 7/8	2 17/32	1-3 29/32	2 11/16	1-4 29/32
3/4	2 1/16	1-0 29/32	2 7/32	1-1 15/16	2 3/8	1-2 15/16	2 17/32	1-3 31/32	2 23/32	1-4 31/32
13/16	2 1/16	1-0 31/32	2 7/32	1-2	2 13/32	1-3	2 9/16	1-4 1/32	2 23/32	1-5 1/32
7/8	2 3/32	1-1 1/32	2 1/4	1-2 1/16	2 13/32	1-3 1/16	2 9/16	1-4 3/32	2 23/32	1-5 3/32
15/16	2 3/32	1-1 3/32	2 1/4	1-2 1/8	2 13/32	1-3 1/8	2 9/16	1-4 5/32	2 3/4	1-5 5/32

Ins.	17″ Rise	17″ Slope	18″ Rise	18″ Slope	19″ Rise	19″ Slope	20″ Rise	20″ Slope	21″ Rise	21″ Slope
0	2 3/4	1-5 7/32	2 29/32	1-6 7/32	3 1/16	1-7 1/4	3 7/32	1-8 1/4	3 3/8	1-9 9/32
1/16	2 3/4	1-5 9/32	2 29/32	1-6 9/32	3 1/16	1-7 5/16	3 1/4	1-8 5/16	3 13/32	1-9 11/32
1/8	2 3/4	1-5 11/32	2 15/16	1-6 3/8	3 3/32	1-7 3/8	3 1/4	1-8 3/8	3 13/32	1-9 13/32
3/16	2 25/32	1-5 13/32	2 15/16	1-6 7/16	3 3/32	1-7 7/16	3 1/4	1-8 7/16	3 13/32	1-9 15/32
1/4	2 25/32	1-5 15/32	2 15/16	1-6 1/2	3 3/32	1-7 1/2	3 9/32	1-8 1/2	3 7/16	1-9 17/32
5/16	2 25/32	1-5 17/32	2 31/32	1-6 9/16	3 1/8	1-7 9/16	3 9/32	1-8 9/16	3 7/16	1-9 19/32
3/8	2 13/16	1-5 19/32	2 31/32	1-6 5/8	3 1/8	1-7 5/8	3 9/32	1-8 5/8	3 7/16	1-9 21/32
7/16	2 13/16	1-5 21/32	2 31/32	1-6 11/16	3 1/8	1-7 11/16	3 5/16	1-8 11/16	3 15/32	1-9 23/32
1/2	2 13/16	1-5 23/32	3	1-6 3/4	3 5/32	1-7 3/4	3 5/16	1-8 3/4	3 15/32	1-9 25/32
9/16	2 27/32	1-5 25/32	3	1-6 13/16	3 5/32	1-7 13/16	3 5/16	1-8 27/32	3 15/32	1-9 27/32
5/8	2 27/32	1-5 27/32	3	1-6 7/8	3 5/32	1-7 7/8	3 11/32	1-8 29/32	3 1/2	1-9 29/32
11/16	2 27/32	1-5 29/32	3 1/32	1-6 15/16	3 3/16	1-7 15/16	3 11/32	1-8 31/32	3 1/2	1-9 31/32
3/4	2 7/8	1-5 31/32	3 1/32	1-7	3 3/16	1-8	3 11/32	1-9 1/32	3 1/2	1-10 1/32
13/16	2 7/8	1-6 1/32	3 1/32	1-7 1/16	3 3/16	1-8 1/16	3 3/8	1-9 3/32	3 17/32	1-10 3/32
7/8	2 7/8	1-6 3/32	3 1/16	1-7 1/8	3 7/32	1-8 1/8	3 3/8	1-9 5/32	3 17/32	1-10 5/32
15/16	2 29/32	1-6 5/32	3 1/16	1-7 3/16	3 7/32	1-8 3/16	3 3/8	1-9 7/32	3 17/32	1-10 7/32

Feet	40′ Rise	40′ Slope	50′ Rise	50′ Slope	60′ Rise	60′ Slope	70′ Rise	70′ Slope
0	6-5 1/2	40-6 7/32	8-0 7/8	50-7 25/32	9-8 1/4	60-9 5/16	11-3 5/8	70-10 7/8
1	6-7 1/16	41-6 3/8	8-2 13/16	51-7 15/16	9-10 3/16	61-9 15/32	11-5 9/16	71-11 1/32
2	6-9 3/8	42-6 17/32	8-4 3/4	52-8 3/32	10-0 1/8	62-9 5/8	11-7 1/2	72-11 3/16
3	6-11 15/16	43-6 11/16	8-6 11/16	53-8 1/4	10-2 1/16	63-9 25/32	11-9 7/16	73-11 11/32
4	7-1 1/4	44-6 27/32	8-8 5/8	54-8 13/32	10-4	64-9 15/16	11-11 3/8	74-11 1/2
5	7-3 3/16	45-7	8-10 9/16	55-8 9/16	10-5 15/16	65-10 3/32	12-1 5/16	75-11 21/32
6	7-5 1/8	46-7 5/32	9-0 1/2	56-8 11/16	10-7 7/8	66-10 1/4	12-3 1/4	76-11 13/16
7	7-7 1/16	47-7 5/16	9-2 7/16	57-8 27/32	10-9 13/16	67-10 13/32	12-5 3/16	77-11 31/32
8	7-9	48-7 15/32	9-4 3/8	58-9	10-11 3/4	68-10 9/16	12-7 1/8	79-0 1/8
9	7-10 15/16	49-7 5/8	9-6 5/16	59-9 5/32	11-1 11/16	69-10 23/32	12-9 1/16	80-0 9/32

natsin A=0.1593940939; natcos A=0.9872150337; nattan A=0.1614583333; natcot A=6.1935483870

Inches	0" Rise	0" Slope	1" Rise	1" Slope	2" Rise	2" Slope	3" Rise	3" Slope	4" Rise	4" Slope	5" Rise	5" Slope
0	0	0	5/32	1	11/32	2 1/32	1/2	3 1/32	21/32	4 1/16	27/32	5 1/16
1/16	0	1/16	3/16	1 1/16	11/32	2 3/32	1/2	3 3/32	11/16	4 1/8	27/32	5 1/8
1/8	1/32	1/8	3/16	1 1/8	11/32	2 5/32	17/32	3 5/32	11/16	4 3/16	27/32	5 3/16
3/16	1/32	3/16	3/16	1 7/32	3/8	2 7/32	17/32	3 7/32	11/16	4 1/4	7/8	5 1/4
1/4	1/32	1/4	7/32	1 9/32	3/8	2 9/32	17/32	3 9/32	23/32	4 5/16	7/8	5 5/16
5/16	1/16	5/16	7/32	1 11/32	3/8	2 11/32	9/16	3 11/32	23/32	4 3/8	7/8	5 3/8
3/8	1/16	3/8	7/32	1 13/32	13/32	2 13/32	9/16	3 13/32	23/32	4 7/16	29/32	5 7/16
7/16	1/16	7/16	1/4	1 15/32	13/32	2 15/32	9/16	3 1/2	3/4	4 1/2	29/32	5 1/2
1/2	3/32	1/2	1/4	1 17/32	13/32	2 17/32	19/32	3 9/16	3/4	4 9/16	29/32	5 9/16
9/16	3/32	9/16	1/4	1 19/32	7/16	2 19/32	19/32	3 5/8	3/4	4 5/8	15/16	5 5/8
5/8	3/32	5/8	9/32	1 21/32	7/16	2 21/32	19/32	3 11/16	25/32	4 11/16	15/16	5 11/16
11/16	3/32	11/16	9/32	1 23/32	7/16	2 23/32	5/8	3 3/4	25/32	4 3/4	15/16	5 25/32
3/4	1/8	3/4	9/32	1 25/32	15/32	2 25/32	5/8	3 13/16	25/32	4 13/16	31/32	5 27/32
13/16	1/8	13/16	5/16	1 27/32	15/32	2 27/32	5/8	3 7/8	13/16	4 7/8	31/32	5 29/32
7/8	3/32	7/8	5/16	1 29/32	15/32	2 29/32	21/32	3 15/16	13/16	4 15/16	31/32	5 31/32
15/16	5/32	15/16	5/16	1 31/32	1/2	2 31/32	21/32	4	13/16	5	1	6 1/32

Inches	6" Rise	6" Slope	7" Rise	7" Slope	8" Rise	8" Slope	9" Rise	9" Slope	10" Rise	10" Slope	11" Rise	11" Slope
0	1	6 3/32	1 5/32	7 3/32	1 11/32	8 1/8	1 1/2	9 1/8	1 21/32	10 1/8	1 27/32	11 5/32
1/16	1	6 5/32	1 3/16	7 5/32	1 11/32	8 3/16	1 1/2	9 3/16	1 11/16	10 3/16	1 27/32	11 7/32
1/8	1 1/32	6 7/32	1 3/16	7 7/32	1 11/32	8 1/4	1 17/32	9 1/4	1 11/16	10 1/4	1 27/32	11 9/32
3/16	1 1/32	6 9/32	1 3/16	7 9/32	1 3/8	8 5/16	1 17/32	9 5/16	1 11/16	10 5/16	1 7/8	11 11/32
1/4	1 1/16	6 11/32	1 7/32	7 11/32	1 3/8	8 3/8	1 17/32	9 3/8	1 23/32	10 13/32	1 7/8	11 13/32
5/16	1 1/16	6 13/32	1 7/32	7 13/32	1 3/8	8 7/16	1 9/16	9 7/16	1 23/32	10 15/32	1 7/8	11 15/32
3/8	1 1/16	6 15/32	1 7/32	7 15/32	1 13/32	8 1/2	1 9/16	9 1/2	1 23/32	10 17/32	1 29/32	11 17/32
7/16	1 1/16	6 17/32	1 1/4	7 17/32	1 13/32	8 9/16	1 9/16	9 9/16	1 3/4	10 19/32	1 29/32	11 19/32
1/2	1 3/32	6 19/32	1 1/4	7 19/32	1 13/32	8 5/8	1 19/32	9 5/8	1 3/4	10 21/32	1 29/32	11 21/32
9/16	1 3/32	6 21/32	1 1/4	7 21/32	1 7/16	8 11/16	1 19/32	9 11/16	1 3/4	10 23/32	1 15/16	11 23/32
5/8	1 3/32	6 23/32	1 9/32	7 23/32	1 7/16	8 3/4	1 19/32	9 3/4	1 25/32	10 25/32	1 15/16	11 25/32
11/16	1 1/8	6 25/32	1 9/32	7 25/32	1 7/16	8 13/16	1 5/8	9 13/16	1 25/32	10 27/32	1 15/16	11 27/32
3/4	1 1/8	6 27/32	1 9/32	7 27/32	1 15/32	8 7/8	1 5/8	9 7/8	1 25/32	10 29/32	1 31/32	11 29/32
13/16	1 1/8	6 29/32	1 5/16	7 29/32	1 15/32	8 15/16	1 5/8	9 15/16	1 13/16	10 31/32	1 31/32	11 31/32
7/8	1 5/32	6 31/32	1 5/16	7 31/32	1 15/32	9	1 21/32	10	1 13/16	11 1/32	1 31/32	1-0 1/32
15/16	1 5/32	7 1/32	1 5/16	8 1/16	1 1/2	9 1/16	1 21/32	10 1/16	1 13/16	11 3/32	2	1-0 3/32

Feet	0' Rise	0' Slope	10' Rise	10' Slope	20' Rise	20' Slope	30' Rise	30' Slope
0	0	0	1-8	10-1 21/32	3-4	20-3 5/16	5-0	30-4 31/32
1	2	1-0 5/32	1-10	11-1 13/16	3-6	21-3 5/16	5-2	31-5 1/8
2	4	2-0 11/32	2-0	12-2	3-8	22-3 21/32	5-4	32-5 9/32
3	6	3-0 1/2	2-2	13-2 5/32	3-10	23-3 13/16	5-6	33-5 15/32
4	8	4-0 21/32	2-4	14-2 5/16	4-0	24-3 31/32	5-8	34-5 5/8
5	10	5-0 13/16	2-6	15-2 15/32	4-2	25-4 1/8	5-10	35-5 25/32
6	1-0	6-1	2-8	16-2 5/8	4-4	26-4 5/16	6-0	36-5 31/32
7	1-2	7-1 5/32	2-10	17-2 13/16	4-6	27-4 15/32	6-2	37-6 1/8
8	1-4	8-1 5/16	3-0	18-2 31/32	4-8	28-4 5/8	6-4	38-6 9/32
9	1-6	9-1 1/2	3-2	19-3 5/32	4-10	29-4 13/16	6-6	39-6 15/32

A = 9° 27' 44"; logsin A = 9.21590; logcos A = 9.99405; logtan A = 9.22185; logcot A = 0.77815

Ins.	12″ Rise	12″ Slope	13″ Rise	13″ Slope	14″ Rise	14″ Slope	15″ Rise	15″ Slope	16″ Rise	16″ Slope
0	2	1-0 5/32	2 5/32	1-1 3/16	2 11/32	1-2 3/16	2 1/2	1-3 7/32	2 21/32	1-4 7/32
1/16	2	1-0 7/32	2 3/16	1-1 1/4	2 11/32	1-2 1/4	2 1/2	1-3 9/32	2 11/16	1-4 9/32
1/8	2 1/32	1-0 9/32	2 3/16	1-1 5/16	2 11/32	1-2 5/16	2 17/32	1-3 11/32	2 11/16	1-4 11/32
3/16	2 1/32	1-0 11/32	2 3/16	1-1 3/8	2 3/8	1-2 3/8	2 17/32	1-3 13/32	2 11/16	1-4 13/32
1/4	2 1/32	1-0 13/32	2 7/32	1-1 7/16	2 3/8	1-2 7/16	2 17/32	1-3 15/32	2 23/32	1-4 15/32
5/16	2 1/16	1-0 15/32	2 7/32	1-1 1/2	2 3/8	1-2 1/2	2 9/16	1-3 17/32	2 23/32	1-4 17/32
3/8	2 1/16	1-0 17/32	2 7/32	1-1 9/16	2 13/32	1-2 9/16	2 9/16	1-3 19/32	2 23/32	1-4 19/32
7/16	2 1/16	1-0 19/32	2 1/4	1-1 5/8	2 13/32	1-2 5/8	2 9/16	1-3 21/32	2 3/4	1-4 21/32
1/2	2 3/32	1-0 11/16	2 1/4	1-1 11/16	2 13/32	1-2 11/16	2 19/32	1-3 23/32	2 3/4	1-4 23/32
9/16	2 3/32	1-0 3/4	2 1/4	1-1 3/4	2 7/16	1-2 3/4	2 19/32	1-3 25/32	2 3/4	1-4 25/32
5/8	2 3/32	1-0 13/32	2 9/32	1-1 13/16	2 7/16	1-2 13/16	2 19/32	1-3 27/32	2 25/32	1-4 27/32
11/16	2 1/8	1-0 7/8	2 9/32	1-1 7/8	2 7/16	1-2 7/8	2 5/8	1-3 29/32	2 25/32	1-4 29/32
3/4	2 1/8	1-0 15/16	2 9/32	1-1 15/16	2 15/32	1-2 31/32	2 5/8	1-3 31/32	2 25/32	1-4 31/32
13/16	2 1/8	1-1	2 5/16	1-2	2 15/32	1-3 1/32	2 5/8	1-4 1/32	2 13/16	1-5 1/32
7/8	2 5/32	1-1 1/16	2 5/16	1-2 1/16	2 15/32	1-3 3/32	2 21/32	1-4 3/32	2 13/16	1-5 3/32
15/16	2 5/32	1-1 1/8	2 5/16	1-2 1/8	2 1/2	1-3 5/32	2 21/32	1-4 5/32	2 13/16	1-5 5/32

Ins.	17″ Rise	17″ Slope	18″ Rise	18″ Slope	19″ Rise	19″ Slope	20″ Rise	20″ Slope	21″ Rise	21″ Slope
0	2 27/32	1-5 1/4	3	1-6 1/4	3 5/32	1-7 1/4	3 11/32	1-8 9/32	3 1/2	1-9 9/32
1/16	2 27/32	1-5 5/16	3	1-6 5/16	3 3/16	1-7 5/16	3 11/32	1-8 11/32	3 1/2	1-9 11/32
1/8	2 27/32	1-5 3/8	3 1/32	1-6 3/8	3 3/16	1-7 3/8	3 11/32	1-8 13/32	3 17/32	1-9 13/32
3/16	2 7/8	1-5 7/16	3 1/32	1-6 7/16	3 3/16	1-7 7/16	3 3/8	1-8 15/32	3 17/32	1-9 15/32
1/4	2 7/8	1-5 1/2	3 1/32	1-6 1/2	3 7/32	1-7 1/2	3 3/8	1-8 17/32	3 17/32	1-9 17/32
5/16	2 7/8	1-5 9/16	3 1/16	1-6 9/16	3 7/32	1-7 19/32	3 3/8	1-8 19/32	3 9/16	1-9 19/32
3/8	2 29/32	1-5 5/8	3 1/16	1-6 5/8	3 7/32	1-7 21/32	3 13/32	1-8 21/32	3 9/16	1-9 21/32
7/16	2 29/32	1-5 11/16	3 1/16	1-6 11/16	3 1/4	1-7 23/32	3 13/32	1-8 23/32	3 9/16	1-9 23/32
1/2	2 29/32	1-5 3/4	3 3/32	1-6 3/4	3 1/4	1-7 25/32	3 13/32	1-8 25/32	3 19/32	1-9 25/32
9/16	2 15/16	1-5 13/16	3 3/32	1-6 13/16	3 1/4	1-7 27/32	3 7/16	1-8 27/32	3 19/32	1-9 7/8
5/8	2 15/16	1-5 7/8	3 3/32	1-6 7/8	3 9/32	1-7 29/32	3 7/16	1-8 29/32	3 19/32	1-9 15/16
11/16	2 15/16	1-5 15/16	3 1/8	1-6 15/16	3 9/32	1-7 31/32	3 7/16	1-8 31/32	3 5/8	1-10
3/4	2 31/32	1-6	3 1/8	1-7	3 9/32	1-8 1/32	3 15/32	1-9 1/32	3 5/8	1-10 1/16
13/16	2 31/32	1-6 1/16	3 1/8	1-7 1/16	3 5/16	1-8 3/32	3 15/32	1-9 3/32	3 5/8	1-10 1/8
7/8	2 31/32	1-6 1/8	3 5/32	1-7 1/8	3 5/16	1-8 5/32	3 15/32	1-9 5/32	3 21/32	1-10 3/16
15/16	3	1-6 3/16	3 5/32	1-7 3/16	3 5/16	1-8 7/32	3 1/2	1-9 7/32	3 21/32	1-10 1/4

Feet	40′ Rise	40′ Slope	50′ Rise	50′ Slope	60′ Rise	60′ Slope	70′ Rise	70′ Slope
0	6-8	40-6 5/8	8-4	50-8 9/32	10-0	60-9 15/16	11-8	70-11 19/32
1	6-10	41-6 25/32	8-6	51-8 7/16	10-2	61-10 3/32	11-10	71-11 3/4
2	7-0	42-6 15/16	8-8	52-8 19/32	10-4	62-10 1/4	12-0	72-11 29/32
3	7-2	43-7 1/8	8-10	53-8 25/32	10-6	63-10 7/16	12-2	74-0 3/32
4	7-4	44-7 9/32	9-0	54-8 15/16	10-8	64-10 19/32	12-4	75-0 1/4
5	7-6	45-7 7/16	9-2	55-9 3/32	10-10	65-10 3/4	12-6	76-0 13/32
6	7-8	46-7 5/8	9-4	56-9 9/32	11-0	66-10 15/16	12-8	77-0 19/32
7	7-10	47-7 25/32	9-6	57-9 7/16	11-2	67-11 3/32	12-10	78-0 3/4
8	8-0	48-7 15/16	9-8	58-9 19/32	11-4	68-11 1/4	13-0	79-0 29/32
9	8-2	49-8 1/8	9-10	59-9 25/32	11-6	69-11 13/32	13-2	80-1 1/16

natsin A=0.1643989872; natcos A=0.9863939238; nattan A=0.1666666666; natcot A=6.0000000000

inches	0" Rise	0" Slope	1" Rise	1" Slope	2" Rise	2" Slope	3" Rise	3" Slope	4" Rise	4" Slope	5" Rise	5" Slope
0	0	0	3/16	1	11/32	2 1/32	1/2	3 1/32	11/16	4 1/16	7/8	5 1/16
1/16	0	1/16	3/16	1 1/16	11/32	2 3/32	17/32	3 3/32	11/16	4 1/8	7/8	5 1/8
1/8	1/32	1/8	3/16	1 5/32	3/8	2 5/32	17/32	3 5/32	23/32	4 3/16	7/8	5 3/16
3/16	1/32	3/16	7/32	1 7/32	3/8	2 7/32	9/16	3 7/32	23/32	4 1/4	29/32	5 1/4
1/4	1/16	1/4	7/32	1 9/32	3/8	2 9/32	9/16	3 5/16	23/32	4 5/16	29/32	5 5/16
5/16	1/16	5/16	7/32	1 11/32	13/32	2 11/32	9/16	3 3/8	3/4	4 3/8	29/32	5 3/8
3/8	1/16	3/8	1/4	1 13/32	13/32	2 13/32	19/32	3 7/16	3/4	4 7/16	15/16	5 15/32
7/16	1/16	7/16	1/4	1 15/32	13/32	2 15/32	19/32	3 1/2	3/4	4 1/2	15/16	5 17/32
1/2	3/32	1/2	1/4	1 17/32	7/16	2 17/32	19/32	3 9/16	25/32	4 9/16	15/16	5 19/32
9/16	3/32	9/16	9/32	1 19/32	7/16	2 19/32	5/8	3 5/8	25/32	4 5/8	31/32	5 21/32
5/8	3/32	5/8	9/32	1 21/32	7/16	2 21/32	5/8	3 11/16	25/32	4 11/16	31/32	5 23/32
11/16	1/8	11/16	9/32	1 23/32	15/32	2 23/32	5/8	3 3/4	13/16	4 3/4	31/32	5 25/32
3/4	1/8	3/4	5/16	1 25/32	15/32	2 25/32	21/32	3 13/16	13/16	4 13/16	1	5 27/32
13/16	1/8	13/16	5/16	1 27/32	15/32	2 27/32	21/32	3 7/8	13/16	4 7/8	1	5 29/32
7/8	5/32	7/8	5/16	1 29/32	1/2	2 29/32	21/32	3 15/16	27/32	4 15/16	1	5 31/32
15/16	5/32	15/16	11/32	1 31/32	1/2	2 31/32	11/16	4	27/32	5	1 1/32	6 1/32

inches	6" Rise	6" Slope	7" Rise	7" Slope	8" Rise	8" Slope	9" Rise	9" Slope	10" Rise	10" Slope	11" Rise	11" Slope
0	1 1/32	6 3/32	1 3/16	7 3/32	1 3/8	8 1/8	1 9/16	9 1/8	1 23/32	10 5/32	1 7/8	11 5/32
1/16	1 1/32	6 5/32	1 7/32	7 5/32	1 3/8	8 3/16	1 9/16	9 3/16	1 23/32	10 7/32	1 29/32	11 7/32
1/8	1 1/16	6 7/32	1 7/32	7 7/32	1 13/32	8 1/4	1 9/16	9 1/4	1 3/4	10 9/32	1 29/32	11 9/32
3/16	1 1/16	6 9/32	1 1/4	7 9/32	1 13/32	8 5/16	1 19/32	9 5/16	1 3/4	10 11/32	1 15/16	11 11/32
1/4	1 1/16	6 11/32	1 1/4	7 11/32	1 13/32	8 3/8	1 19/32	9 3/8	1 3/4	10 13/32	1 15/16	11 13/32
5/16	1 3/32	6 13/32	1 1/4	7 13/32	1 7/16	8 7/16	1 19/32	9 7/16	1 25/32	10 15/32	1 15/16	11 15/32
3/8	1 3/32	6 15/32	1 9/32	7 15/32	1 7/16	8 1/2	1 5/8	9 1/2	1 25/32	10 17/32	1 31/32	11 17/32
7/16	1 3/32	6 17/32	1 9/32	7 17/32	1 7/16	8 9/16	1 5/8	9 9/16	1 25/32	10 19/32	1 31/32	11 19/32
1/2	1 1/8	6 19/32	1 9/32	7 5/8	1 15/32	8 5/8	1 5/8	9 5/8	1 13/16	10 21/32	1 31/32	11 21/32
9/16	1 1/8	6 21/32	1 5/16	7 11/16	1 15/32	8 11/16	1 21/32	9 11/16	1 13/16	10 23/32	2	11 23/32
5/8	1 1/8	6 23/32	1 5/16	7 3/4	1 15/32	8 3/4	1 21/32	9 25/32	1 13/16	10 25/32	2	11 25/32
11/16	1 5/32	6 25/32	1 5/16	7 13/16	1 1/2	8 13/16	1 21/32	9 27/32	1 27/32	10 27/32	2	11 27/32
3/4	1 5/32	6 27/32	1 11/32	7 7/8	1 1/2	8 7/8	1 11/16	9 29/32	1 27/32	10 29/32	2 1/32	11 15/16
13/16	1 5/32	6 29/32	1 11/32	7 15/16	1 1/2	8 15/16	1 11/16	9 31/32	1 27/32	10 31/32	2 1/32	1-0
7/8	1 3/16	6 31/32	1 11/32	8	1 17/32	9	1 11/16	10 1/32	1 7/8	11 1/32	2 1/32	1-0 1/16
15/16	1 3/16	7 1/32	1 3/8	8 1/16	1 17/32	9 1/16	1 23/32	10 3/32	1 7/8	11 3/32	2 1/16	1-0 1/8

Feet	0' Rise	0' Slope	10' Rise	10' Slope	20' Rise	20' Slope	30' Rise	30' Slope
0	0	0	1-8 5/8	10-1 3/4	3-5 1/4	20-3 17/32	5-1 7/8	30-5 9/32
1	2 1/16	1-0 3/16	1-10 11/16	11-1 15/16	3-7 5/16	21-3 11/16	5-3 15/16	31-5 15/32
2	4 1/8	2-0 11/32	2-0 3/4	12-2 1/8	3-9 3/8	22-3 7/8	5-6	32-5 5/8
3	6 3/16	3-0 17/32	2-2 13/16	13-2 9/32	3-11 7/16	23-4 1/16	5-8 1/16	33-5 13/16
4	8 1/4	4-0 23/32	2-4 7/8	14-2 15/32	4-1 1/2	24-4 7/32	5-10 1/8	34-5 31/32
5	10 5/16	5-0 7/8	2-6 15/16	15-2 5/8	4-3 9/16	25-4 13/32	6-0 3/16	35-6 5/32
6	1-0 3/8	6-1 1/16	2-9	16-2 13/16	4-5 5/8	26-4 9/16	6-2 1/4	36-6 11/32
7	1-2 7/16	7-1 1/4	2-11 1/16	17-3	4-7 11/16	27-4 3/4	6-4 5/16	37-6 1/2
8	1-4 1/2	8-1 13/32	3-1 1/8	18-3 5/32	4-9 3/4	28-4 15/16	6-6 3/8	38-6 11/32
9	1-6 9/16	9-1 19/32	3-3 3/16	19-3 11/32	4-11 13/16	29-5 3/32	6-8 7/16	39-6 7/8

A = 9° 45′ 09″; logsin A = 9.22889; logcos A = 9.99368; logtan A = 9.23521; logcot A = 0.76479

Ins.	12″ Rise	12″ Slope	13″ Rise	13″ Slope	14″ Rise	14″ Slope	15″ Rise	15″ Slope	16″ Rise	16″ Slope
0	2 1/16	1-0 3/16	2 1/4	1-1 3/16	2 13/32	1-2 7/32	2 9/16	1-3 1/32	2 3/4	1-4 1/4
1/16	2 1/16	1-0 1/4	2 1/4	1-1 1/4	2 13/32	1-2 9/32	2 19/32	1-3 9/32	2 3/4	1-4 5/16
1/8	2 3/32	1-0 5/16	2 1/4	1-1 5/16	2 7/16	1-2 11/32	2 19/32	1-3 11/32	2 25/32	1-4 3/8
3/16	2 3/32	1-0 3/8	2 9/32	1-1 3/8	2 7/16	1-2 13/32	2 5/8	1-3 13/32	2 25/32	1-4 7/16
1/4	2 3/32	1-0 7/16	2 9/32	1-1 7/16	2 7/16	1-2 15/32	2 5/8	1-3 15/32	2 25/32	1-4 1/2
5/16	2 1/8	1-0 1/2	2 9/32	1-1 1/2	2 15/32	1-2 17/32	2 5/8	1-3 17/32	2 13/16	1-4 9/16
3/8	2 1/8	1-0 9/16	2 5/16	1-1 9/16	2 15/32	1-2 19/32	2 21/32	1-3 19/32	2 13/16	1-4 5/8
7/16	2 1/8	1-0 5/8	2 5/16	1-1 5/8	2 15/32	1-2 21/32	2 21/32	1-3 21/32	2 13/16	1-4 11/16
1/2	2 5/32	1-0 11/16	2 5/16	1-1 11/16	2 1/2	1-2 23/32	2 21/32	1-3 23/32	2 27/32	1-4 3/4
9/16	2 5/32	1-0 3/4	2 11/32	1-1 3/4	2 1/2	1-2 25/32	2 11/16	1-3 25/32	2 27/32	1-4 13/16
5/8	2 5/32	1-0 13/16	2 11/32	1-1 13/16	2 1/2	1-2 27/32	2 11/16	1-3 27/32	2 7/8	1-4 7/8
11/16	2 3/16	1-0 7/8	2 11/32	1-1 7/8	2 17/32	1-2 29/32	2 11/16	1-3 29/32	2 7/8	1-4 15/16
3/4	2 3/16	1-0 15/16	2 3/8	1-1 15/16	2 17/32	1-2 31/32	2 23/32	1-3 31/32	2 7/8	1-5
13/16	2 3/16	1-1	2 3/8	1-2	2 17/32	1-3 1/32	2 23/32	1-4 1/32	2 7/8	1-5 1/16
7/8	2 7/32	1-1 1/16	2 3/8	1-2 3/32	2 9/16	1-3 3/32	2 23/32	1-4 3/32	2 29/32	1-5 1/8
15/16	2 7/32	1-1 1/8	2 13/32	1-2 5/32	2 9/16	1-3 5/32	2 3/4	1-4 5/32	2 29/32	1-5 3/16

Ins.	17″ Rise	17″ Slope	18″ Rise	18″ Slope	19″ Rise	19″ Slope	20″ Rise	20″ Slope	21″ Rise	21″ Slope
0	2 15/16	1-5 1/4	3 3/32	1-6 1/4	3 1/4	1-7 9/32	3 7/16	1-8 9/32	3 5/8	1-9 5/16
1/16	2 15/16	1-5 5/16	3 3/32	1-6 5/16	3 9/32	1-7 11/32	3 7/16	1-8 11/32	3 5/8	1-9 3/8
1/8	2 15/16	1-5 3/8	3 1/8	1-6 13/32	3 9/32	1-7 13/32	3 15/32	1-8 13/32	3 5/8	1-9 7/16
3/16	2 31/32	1-5 7/16	3 1/8	1-6 15/32	3 5/16	1-7 15/32	3 15/32	1-8 15/32	3 21/32	1-9 1/2
1/4	2 31/32	1-5 1/2	3 1/8	1-6 17/32	3 5/16	1-7 17/32	3 15/32	1-8 9/16	3 21/32	1-9 9/16
5/16	2 31/32	1-5 9/16	3 5/32	1-6 19/32	3 5/16	1-7 19/32	3 1/2	1-8 5/8	3 21/32	1-9 5/8
3/8	3	1-5 5/8	3 5/32	1-6 21/32	3 11/32	1-7 21/32	3 1/2	1-8 11/16	3 11/16	1-9 11/16
7/16	3	1-5 11/16	3 5/32	1-6 23/32	3 11/32	1-7 23/32	3 1/2	1-8 3/4	3 11/16	1-9 3/4
1/2	3	1-5 3/4	3 3/16	1-6 25/32	3 11/32	1-7 25/32	3 17/32	1-8 13/16	3 11/16	1-9 13/16
9/16	3 1/32	1-5 13/16	3 3/16	1-6 27/32	3 3/8	1-7 27/32	3 17/32	1-8 7/8	3 23/32	1-9 7/8
5/8	3 1/32	1-5 7/8	3 3/16	1-6 29/32	3 3/8	1-7 29/32	3 17/32	1-8 15/16	3 23/32	1-9 15/16
11/16	3 1/32	1-5 15/16	3 7/32	1-6 31/32	3 3/8	1-7 31/32	3 9/16	1-9	3 23/32	1-10
3/4	3 1/16	1-6	3 7/32	1-7 1/32	3 13/32	1-8 1/32	3 9/16	1-9 1/16	3 3/4	1-10 1/16
13/16	3 1/16	1-6 1/16	3 7/32	1-7 3/32	3 13/32	1-8 3/32	3 9/16	1-9 1/8	3 3/4	1-10 1/8
7/8	3 1/16	1-6 1/8	3 1/4	1-7 5/32	3 13/32	1-8 5/32	3 19/32	1-9 3/16	3 3/4	1-10 3/16
15/16	3 3/32	1-6 3/16	3 1/4	1-7 7/32	3 7/16	1-8 7/32	3 19/32	1-9 1/4	3 25/32	1-10 1/4

Feet	40′ Rise	40′ Slope	50′ Rise	50′ Slope	60′ Rise	60′ Slope	70′ Rise	70′ Slope
0	6-10 1/2	40-7 1/32	8-7 1/8	50-8 13/16	10-3 3/4	60-10 9/16	12-0 3/8	71-0 5/16
1	7-0 9/16	41-7 7/32	8-9 3/16	51-8 31/32	10-5 13/16	61-10 23/32	12-2 7/16	72-0 1/2
2	7-2 5/8	42-7 3/8	8-11 1/4	52-9 5/32	10-7 7/8	62-10 29/32	12-4 1/2	73-0 21/32
3	7-4 11/16	43-7 9/16	9-1 5/16	53-9 5/16	10-9 15/16	63-11 3/32	12-6 9/16	74-0 27/32
4	7-6 3/4	44-7 3/4	9-3 3/8	54-9 1/2	11-0	64-11 1/4	12-8 5/8	75-1 1/32
5	7-8 13/16	45-7 29/32	9-5 7/16	55-9 11/16	11-2 1/16	65-11 7/16	12-10 11/16	76-1 3/16
6	7-10 7/8	46-8 3/32	9-7 1/2	56-9 27/32	11-4 1/8	66-11 5/8	13-0 3/4	77-1 3/8
7	8-0 15/16	47-8 9/32	9-9 9/16	57-10 1/32	11-6 3/16	67-11 25/32	13-2 13/16	78-1 9/16
8	8-3	48-8 7/16	9-11 5/8	58-10 7/32	11-8 1/4	68-11 31/32	13-4 7/8	79-1 23/32
9	8-5 1/16	49-8 5/8	10-1 11/16	59-10 3/8	11-10 5/16	70-0 5/32	13-6 15/16	80-1 29/32

natsin A=0.1693912156; natcos A=0.9855488907; nattan A=0.1718750000; natcot A=5.8181818181

Inches	0" Rise	0" Slope	1" Rise	1" Slope	2" Rise	2" Slope	3" Rise	3" Slope	4" Rise	4" Slope	5" Rise	5" Slope
0	0	0	3/16	1	11/32	2 1/32	17/32	3 1/32	23/32	4 1/16	7/8	5 1/16
1/16	0	1/16	3/16	1 3/16	3/8	2 3/32	17/32	3 1/8	23/32	4 1/8	29/32	5 5/32
1/8	1/32	1/8	3/16	1 5/32	3/8	2 5/32	9/16	3 3/16	23/32	4 3/16	29/32	5 7/32
3/16	1/32	3/16	7/32	1 7/32	3/8	2 7/32	9/16	3 1/4	3/4	4 1/4	29/32	5 9/32
1/4	1/16	1/4	7/32	1 9/32	13/32	2 9/32	9/16	3 5/16	3/4	4 5/16	15/16	5 11/32
5/16	1/16	5/16	7/32	1 11/32	13/32	2 11/32	19/32	3 3/8	3/4	4 3/8	15/16	5 13/32
3/8	3/32	3/8	1/4	1 13/32	13/32	2 13/32	19/32	3 7/16	25/32	4 7/16	15/16	5 15/32
7/16	1/16	7/16	1/4	1 15/32	7/16	2 15/32	19/32	3 1/2	25/32	4 1/2	31/32	5 17/32
1/2	3/32	1/2	1/4	1 17/32	7/16	2 17/32	5/8	3 9/16	13/16	4 9/16	31/32	5 19/32
9/16	3/32	9/16	9/32	1 19/32	15/32	2 19/32	5/8	3 5/8	13/16	4 5/8	1	5 21/32
5/8	1/8	5/8	9/32	1 21/32	15/32	2 21/32	21/32	3 11/16	13/16	4 11/16	1	5 23/32
11/16	1/8	11/16	5/16	1 23/32	15/32	2 23/32	21/32	3 3/4	27/32	4 3/4	1	5 25/32
3/4	1/8	3/4	5/16	1 25/32	1/2	2 25/32	21/32	3 13/16	27/32	4 13/16	1 1/4	5 27/32
13/16	5/32	13/16	5/16	1 27/32	1/2	2 27/32	11/16	3 7/8	27/32	4 7/8	1 1/32	5 29/32
7/8	5/32	7/8	11/32	1 29/32	1/2	2 29/32	11/16	3 15/16	7/8	4 15/16	1 1/32	5 31/32
15/16	5/32	15/16	11/32	1 31/32	17/32	2 31/32	11/16	4	7/8	5	1 1/16	6 1/32

Inches	6" Rise	6" Slope	7" Rise	7" Slope	8" Rise	8" Slope	9" Rise	9" Slope	10" Rise	10" Slope	11" Rise	11" Slope
0	1 1/16	6 3/32	1 1/4	7 3/32	1 13/16	8 1/8	1 19/32	9 1/8	1 25/32	10 5/32	1 15/16	11 5/32
1/16	1 1/16	6 5/32	1 1/4	7 3/16	1 7/16	8 3/16	1 19/32	9 7/32	1 25/32	10 7/32	1 31/32	11 1/4
1/8	1 3/32	6 7/32	1 1/4	7 1/4	1 7/16	8 1/4	1 5/8	9 9/32	1 25/32	10 9/32	1 31/32	11 5/16
3/16	1 3/32	6 9/32	1 9/32	7 5/16	1 7/16	8 5/16	1 5/8	9 11/32	1 13/16	10 11/32	1 31/32	11 3/8
1/4	1 3/32	6 11/32	1 9/32	7 3/8	1 15/32	8 3/8	1 5/8	9 13/32	1 13/16	10 13/32	2	11 7/16
5/16	1 1/8	6 13/32	1 9/32	7 7/16	1 15/32	8 7/16	1 21/32	9 15/32	1 13/16	10 15/32	2	11 1/2
3/8	1 1/8	6 15/32	1 5/16	7 1/2	1 15/32	8 1/2	1 21/32	9 17/32	1 27/32	10 17/32	2	11 9/16
7/16	1 1/8	6 17/32	1 5/16	7 9/16	1 1/2	8 9/16	1 21/32	9 19/32	1 27/32	10 19/32	2 1/32	11 5/8
1/2	1 5/32	6 19/32	1 5/16	7 5/8	1 1/2	8 5/8	1 11/16	9 21/32	1 7/8	10 21/32	2 1/32	11 11/16
9/16	1 5/32	6 21/32	1 11/32	7 11/16	1 17/32	8 11/16	1 11/16	9 23/32	1 7/8	10 23/32	2 1/16	11 3/4
5/8	1 3/16	6 23/32	1 11/32	7 3/4	1 17/32	8 3/4	1 23/32	9 25/32	1 7/8	10 25/32	2 1/16	11 13/16
11/16	1 3/16	6 25/32	1 3/8	7 13/16	1 17/32	8 13/16	1 23/32	9 27/32	1 29/32	10 27/32	2 1/16	11 7/8
3/4	1 3/16	6 27/32	1 3/8	7 7/8	1 9/16	8 7/8	1 23/32	9 29/32	1 29/32	10 29/32	2 3/32	11 15/16
13/16	1 7/32	6 29/32	1 3/8	7 15/16	1 9/16	8 15/16	1 3/4	9 31/32	1 29/32	10 31/32	2 3/32	1-0
7/8	1 7/32	6 31/32	1 13/32	8	1 9/16	9	1 3/4	10 1/32	1 15/16	11 1/32	2 3/32	1-0 1/16
15/16	1 7/32	7 1/32	1 13/32	8 1/16	1 19/32	9 1/16	1 3/4	10 3/32	1 15/16	11 3/32	2 1/8	1-0 1/8

Feet	0' Rise	0' Slope	10' Rise	10' Slope	20' Rise	20' Slope	30' Rise	30' Slope
0	0	0	1-9 1/4	10-1 7/8	3-6 1/2	20-3 23/32	5-3 3/4	30-5 19/32
1	2 1/8	1-0 3/16	1-11 3/8	11-2 1/16	3-8 5/8	21-3 29/32	5-5 7/8	31-5 25/32
2	4 1/4	2-0 3/8	2-1 1/2	12-2 1/4	3-10 3/4	22-4 3/32	5-8	32-5 31/32
3	6 3/8	3-0 9/16	2-3 5/8	13-2 7/16	4-0 7/8	23-4 9/32	5-10 1/8	33-6 5/32
4	8 1/2	4-0 3/4	2-5 3/4	14-2 5/8	4-3	24-4 15/32	6-0 1/4	34-6 11/32
5	10 5/8	5-0 15/16	2-7 7/8	15-2 13/16	4-5 1/8	25-4 21/32	6-2 3/8	35-6 17/32
6	1-0 3/4	6-1 1/8	2-10	16-3	4-7 1/4	26-4 27/32	6-4 1/2	36-6 23/32
7	1-2 7/8	7-1 5/16	3-0 1/8	17-3 3/16	4-9 3/8	27-5 1/32	6-6 5/8	37-6 29/32
8	1-5	8-1 1/2	3-2 1/4	18-3 3/8	4-11 1/2	28-5 7/32	6-8 3/4	38-7 3/32
9	1-7 1/8	9-1 11/16	3-4 3/8	19-3 9/16	5-1 5/8	29-5 13/32	6-10 7/8	39-7 9/32

A = 10° 02′ 31″; logsin A = 9.24147; logcos A = 9.99330; logtan A = 9.24818; logcot A = 0.75182

Ins.	12″ Rise	12″ Slope	13″ Rise	13″ Slope	14″ Rise	14″ Slope	15″ Rise	15″ Slope	16″ Rise	16″ Slope
0	2 1/8	1-0 3/16	2 5/16	1-1 3/16	2 15/32	1-2 7/32–	2 21/32	1-3 7/32	2 27/32–	1-4 1/4
1/16	2 1/8	1-0 1/4	2 5/16	1-1 9/32–	2 1/2	1-2 9/32	2 21/32	1-3 9/32	2 27/32	1-4 5/16
1/8	2 5/32–	1-0 5/16	2 5/16	1-1 11/32–	2 1/2	1-2 11/32	2 11/16	1-3 3/8	2 27/32	1-4 3/8
3/16	2 5/32	1-0 3/8	2 11/32–	1-1 13/32–	2 1/2	1-2 13/32	2 11/16	1-3 7/16	2 7/8	1-4 7/16
1/4	2 5/32	1-0 7/16	2 11/32	1-1 15/32–	2 17/32–	1-2 15/32	2 11/16	1-3 1/2	2 7/8	1-4 1/2
5/16	2 3/16	1-0 1/2	2 11/32	1-1 17/32–	2 17/32	1-2 17/32	2 23/32–	1-3 9/16	2 7/8	1-4 9/16
3/8	2 3/16	1-0 9/16	2 3/8	1-1 19/32–	2 17/32	1-2 19/32	2 23/32	1-3 5/8	2 29/32–	1-4 5/8
7/16	2 3/16	1-0 5/8	2 3/8	1-1 21/32–	2 9/16	1-2 21/32	2 23/32	1-3 11/16	2 29/32	1-4 11/16
1/2	2 7/32–	1-0 11/16	2 3/8	1-1 23/32–	2 9/16	1-2 23/32	2 3/4	1-3 3/4	2 15/16	1-4 3/4
9/16	2 7/32	1-0 3/4	2 13/32–	1-1 25/32–	2 19/32–	1-2 25/32	2 3/4	1-3 13/16	2 15/16	1-4 13/16
5/8	2 1/4	1-0 13/16	2 13/32	1-1 27/32–	2 19/32–	1-2 27/32	2 25/32–	1-3 7/8	2 15/16	1-4 7/8
11/16	2 1/4	1-0 7/8	2 7/16	1-1 29/32–	2 19/32	1-2 29/32	2 25/32–	1-3 15/16	2 31/32–	1-4 15/16
3/4	2 1/4	1-0 15/16	2 7/16	1-1 31/32–	2 5/8	1-2 31/32	2 25/32	1-4	2 31/32–	1-5
13/16	2 9/32–	1-1	2 7/16	1-2 1/32–	2 5/8	1-3 1/32	2 13/16	1-4 1/16	2 31/32	1-5 1/16
7/8	2 9/32–	1-1 1/16	2 15/32–	1-2 3/32–	2 5/8	1-3 3/32	2 13/16	1-4 1/8	3	1-5 1/8
15/16	2 9/32	1-1 1/8	2 15/32–	1-2 5/32–	2 21/32–	1-3 5/32	2 13/16	1-4 3/16	3	1-5 3/16

Ins.	17″ Rise	17″ Slope	18″ Rise	18″ Slope	19″ Rise	19″ Slope	20″ Rise	20″ Slope	21″ Rise	21″ Slope
0	3	1-5 1/4	3 3/16	1-6 9/32–	3 3/8	1-7 9/32	3 17/32	1-8 5/16	3 23/32	1-9 5/16
1/16	3 1/32–	1-5 5/16	3 3/16	1-6 11/32–	3 3/8	1-7 11/32	3 9/16	1-8 3/8	3 23/32	1-9 3/8
1/8	3 1/32	1-5 13/32–	3 7/32–	1-6 13/32	3 3/8	1-7 7/16	3 9/16	1-8 7/16	3 3/4	1-9 15/32–
3/16	3 1/32	1-5 15/32–	3 7/32	1-6 15/32	3 13/32–	1-7 1/2	3 9/16	1-8 1/2	3 3/4	1-9 17/32–
1/4	3 1/16	1-5 17/32–	3 7/32	1-6 17/32	3 13/32	1-7 9/16	3 19/32–	1-8 9/16	3 3/4	1-9 19/32–
5/16	3 1/16	1-5 19/32–	3 1/4	1-6 19/32	3 13/32	1-7 5/8	3 19/32	1-8 5/8	3 25/32–	1-9 21/32–
3/8	3 1/16	1-5 21/32–	3 1/4	1-6 21/32	3 7/16	1-7 11/16	3 19/32	1-8 11/16	3 25/32	1-9 23/32–
7/16	3 3/32–	1-5 23/32–	3 1/4	1-6 23/32	3 7/16	1-7 3/4	3 5/8	1-8 3/4	3 25/32	1-9 25/32–
1/2	3 3/32	1-5 25/32–	3 9/32–	1-6 25/32	3 7/16	1-7 13/16	3 5/8	1-8 13/16	3 13/16	1-9 27/32–
9/16	3 1/8	1-5 27/32–	3 9/32	1-6 27/32	3 15/32–	1-7 7/8	3 21/32–	1-8 7/8	3 13/16	1-9 29/32–
5/8	3 1/8	1-5 29/32–	3 5/16	1-6 29/32	3 15/32	1-7 15/16	3 21/32–	1-8 15/16	3 27/32–	1-9 31/32–
11/16	3 1/8	1-5 31/32–	3 5/16	1-6 31/32	3 1/2	1-8	3 21/32	1-9	3 27/32–	1-10 1/32–
3/4	3 5/32–	1-6 1/32–	3 5/16	1-7 1/32	3 1/2	1-8 1/16	3 11/16	1-9 1/16	3 27/32	1-10 3/32–
13/16	3 5/32–	1-6 3/32–	3 11/32–	1-7 3/32	3 1/2	1-8 1/8	3 11/16	1-9 1/8	3 7/8	1-10 5/32–
7/8	3 5/32	1-6 5/32–	3 11/32–	1-7 5/32	3 17/32–	1-8 3/16	3 11/16	1-9 3/16	3 7/8	1-10 7/32–
15/16	3 3/16	1-6 7/32–	3 11/32	1-7 7/32	3 17/32–	1-8 1/4	3 23/32–	1-9 1/4	3 7/8	1-10 9/32–

Feet	40′ Rise	40′ Slope	50′ Rise	50′ Slope	60′ Rise	60′ Slope	70′ Rise	70′ Slope
0	7-1	40-7 15/32–	8-10 1/4	50-9 11/32–	10-7 1/2	60-11 3/16	12-4 3/4	71-1 1/16
1	7-3 1/8	41-7 21/32–	9-0 3/8	51-9 17/32–	10-9 5/8	61-11 3/8	12-6 7/8	72-1 1/4
2	7-5 1/4	42-7 27/32–	9-2 1/2	52-9 23/32–	10-11 3/4	62-11 9/16	12-9	73-1 7/16
3	7-7 3/8	43-8 1/32–	9-4 5/8	53-9 29/32–	11-1 7/8	63-11 3/4	12-11 1/8	74-1 5/8
4	7-9 1/2	44-8 7/32–	9-6 3/4	54-10 3/32–	11-4	64-11 15/16	13-1 1/4	75-1 13/16
5	7-11 5/8	45-8 13/32–	9-8 7/8	55-10 9/32–	11-6 1/8	66-0 1/8	13-3 3/8	76-2
6	8-1 3/4	46-8 19/32–	9-11	56-10 15/32–	11-8 1/4	67-0 5/16	13-5 1/2	77-2 3/16
7	8-3 7/8	47-8 25/32–	10-1 1/8	57-10 21/32–	11-10 3/8	68-0 1/2	13-7 5/8	78-2 3/8
8	8-6	48-8 31/32–	10-3 1/4	58-10 27/32–	12-0 1/2	69-0 11/16	13-9 3/4	79-2 9/16
9	8-8 1/8	49-9 5/32–	10-5 3/8	59-11	12-2 5/8	70-0 7/8	13-11 7/8	80-2 3/4

natsin A=0.1743704389; natcos A=0.9846801257; nattan A=0.1770833333; natcot A=5.6470588235.

Inches	0″ Rise	0″ Slope	1″ Rise	1″ Slope	2″ Rise	2″ Slope	3″ Rise	3″ Slope	4″ Rise	4″ Slope	5″ Rise	5″ Slope
0	0	0	3/16	1 1/32	3/8	2 1/32	9/16	3 1/16	23/32	4 1/16	29/32	5 3/32
1/16	0	1/16	3/16	1 3/32	3/8	2 3/32	9/16	3 1/8	3/4	4 1/8	15/16	5 5/32
1/8	1/32	1/8	7/32	1 5/32	3/8	2 5/32	9/16	3 3/16	3/4	4 3/16	15/16	5 7/32
3/16	1/32	3/16	7/32	1 7/32	13/32	2 7/32	19/32	3 1/4	3/4	4 1/4	15/16	5 9/32
1/4	1/32	1/4	7/32	1 9/32	13/32	2 9/32	19/32	3 5/16	25/32	4 5/16	31/32	5 11/32
5/16	1/16	5/16	1/4	1 11/32	13/32	2 11/32	19/32	3 3/8	25/32	4 3/8	31/32	5 13/32
3/8	1/16	3/8	1/4	1 13/32	7/16	2 13/32	5/8	3 7/16	13/16	4 7/16	31/32	5 15/32
7/16	9/32	7/16	1/4	1 15/32	7/16	2 15/32	5/8	3 1/2	13/16	4 1/2	1	5 17/32
1/2	3/32	1/2	9/32	1 17/32	15/32	2 17/32	5/8	3 9/16	13/16	4 9/16	1	5 19/32
9/16	3/32	9/16	9/32	1 19/32	15/32	2 19/32	21/32	3 5/8	27/32	4 5/8	1	5 21/32
5/8	1/8	5/8	9/32	1 21/32	15/32	2 21/32	21/32	3 11/16	27/32	4 11/16	1 1/32	5 23/32
11/16	1/8	11/16	5/16	1 23/32	1/2	2 23/32	11/16	3 3/4	27/32	4 3/4	1 1/32	5 25/32
3/4	1/8	3/4	5/16	1 25/32	1/2	2 25/32	11/16	3 13/16	7/8	4 27/32	1 1/16	5 27/32
13/16	5/32	13/16	11/32	1 27/32	1/2	2 27/32	11/16	3 7/8	7/8	4 29/32	1 1/16	5 29/32
7/8	5/32	7/8	11/32	1 29/32	17/32	2 15/16	23/32	3 15/16	7/8	4 31/32	1 1/16	5 31/32
15/16	5/32	15/16	11/32	1 31/32	17/32	3	23/32	4	29/32	5 1/32	1 3/32	6 1/32

Inches	6″ Rise	6″ Slope	7″ Rise	7″ Slope	8″ Rise	8″ Slope	9″ Rise	9″ Slope	10″ Rise	10″ Slope	11″ Rise	11″ Slope
0	1 3/32	6 3/32	1 9/32	7 1/8	1 15/32	8 1/8	1 5/8	9 5/32	1 13/16	10 5/32	2	11 3/16
1/16	1 3/32	6 5/32	1 9/32	7 3/16	1 15/32	8 3/16	1 21/32	9 7/32	1 27/32	10 7/32	2 1/32	11 1/4
1/8	1 1/8	6 7/32	1 5/16	7 1/4	1 15/32	8 1/4	1 21/32	9 9/32	1 27/32	10 9/32	2 1/32	11 5/16
3/16	1 1/8	6 9/32	1 5/16	7 5/16	1 1/2	8 5/16	1 11/16	9 11/32	1 27/32	10 11/32	2 1/32	11 3/8
1/4	1 1/8	6 11/32	1 5/16	7 3/8	1 1/2	8 3/8	1 11/16	9 13/32	1 7/8	10 13/32	2 1/16	11 7/16
5/16	1 5/32	6 13/32	1 11/32	7 7/16	1 1/2	8 7/16	1 11/16	9 15/32	1 7/8	10 15/32	2 1/16	11 1/2
3/8	1 5/32	6 15/32	1 11/32	7 1/2	1 17/32	8 1/2	1 23/32	9 17/32	1 29/32	10 17/32	2 1/16	11 9/16
7/16	1 3/16	6 17/32	1 11/32	7 9/16	1 17/32	8 9/16	1 23/32	9 19/32	1 29/32	10 5/8	2 3/32	11 5/8
1/2	1 3/16	6 19/32	1 3/8	7 5/8	1 9/16	8 5/8	1 23/32	9 21/32	1 29/32	10 11/16	2 3/32	11 11/16
9/16	1 3/16	6 21/32	1 3/8	7 11/16	1 9/16	8 23/32	1 3/4	9 23/32	1 15/16	10 3/4	2 3/32	11 3/4
5/8	1 7/32	6 23/32	1 3/8	7 3/4	1 9/16	8 25/32	1 3/4	9 25/32	1 15/16	10 13/16	2 1/8	11 13/16
11/16	1 7/32	6 13/16	1 13/32	7 13/16	1 19/32	8 27/32	1 25/32	9 27/32	1 15/16	10 7/8	2 1/8	11 7/8
3/4	1 7/32	6 7/8	1 13/32	7 7/8	1 19/32	8 29/32	1 25/32	9 29/32	1 31/32	10 15/16	2 5/32	11 15/16
13/16	1 1/4	6 15/16	1 7/16	7 15/16	1 19/32	8 31/32	1 25/32	9 31/32	1 31/32	11	2 5/32	1-0
7/8	1 1/4	7	1 7/16	8	1 5/8	9 1/32	1 13/16	10 1/32	1 31/32	11 1/16	2 5/32	1-0 1/8
15/16	1 1/4	7 1/16	1 7/16	8 1/16	1 5/8	9 3/32	1 13/16	10 3/32	2	11 1/8	2 3/16	1-0 1/8

Feet	0' Rise	0' Slope	10' Rise	10' Slope	20' Rise	20' Slope	30' Rise	30' Slope
0	0	0	1-9 7/8	10-1 31/32	3-7 3/4	20-3 31/32	5-5 5/8	30-5 15/16
1	2 3/16	1-0 3/16	2-0 1/16	11-2 3/16	3-9 15/16	21-4 3/32	5-7 13/16	31-6 1/8
2	4 3/8	2-0 13/32	2-2 1/4	12-2 3/8	4-0 1/8	22-4 11/32	5-10	32-6 5/16
3	6 9/16	3-0 19/32	2-4 7/16	13-2 9/16	4-2 5/16	23-4 9/16	6-0 3/16	33-6 17/32
4	8 3/4	4-0 25/32	2-6 5/8	14-2 25/32	4-4 1/2	24-4 3/4	6-2 3/8	34-6 23/32
5	10 15/16	5-1	2-8 13/16	15-2 31/32	4-6 11/16	25-4 15/16	6-4 9/16	35-6 29/32
6	1-1 1/8	6-1 3/16	2-11	16-3 5/32	4-8 7/8	26-5 5/32	6-6 3/4	36-7 1/8
7	1-3 5/16	7-1 3/8	3-1 3/16	17-3 3/8	4-11 1/16	27-5 11/32	6-8 15/16	37-7 5/16
8	1-5 1/2	8-1 9/32	3-3 3/8	18-3 9/16	5-1 1/4	28-5 17/32	6-11 1/8	38-7 1/2
9	1-7 11/16	9-1 25/32	3-5 9/16	19-3 3/4	5-3 7/16	29-5 3/4	7-1 5/16	39-7 23/32

A = 10° 19′ 52″; logsin A = 9.25367; logcos A = 9.99290; logtan A = 9.26077; logcot A = 0.73923

Ins.	12″ Rise	12″ Slope	13″ Rise	13″ Slope	14″ Rise	14″ Slope	15″ Rise	15″ Slope	16″ Rise	16″ Slope
0	2 3/16	1-0 3/16	2 3/8	1-1 1/32	2 9/16	1-2 7/32	2 3/4	1-3 1/4	2 29/32	1-4 1/4
1/16	2 3/16	1-0 1/4	2 3/8	1-1 9/32	2 9/16	1-2 9/32	2 3/4	1-3 5/16	2 15/16	1-4 5/16
1/8	2 7/32	1-0 5/16	2 13/32	1-1 11/32	2 9/16	1-2 11/32	2 3/4	1-3 3/8	2 15/16	1-4 13/32
3/16	2 7/32	1-0 3/8	2 13/32	1-1 13/32	2 19/32	1-2 13/32	2 25/32	1-3 7/16	2 15/16	1-4 15/32
1/4	2 7/32	1-0 7/16	2 13/32	1-1 15/32	2 19/32	1-2 1/2	2 25/32	1-3 1/2	2 31/32	1-4 17/32
5/16	2 1/4	1-0 1/2	2 7/16	1-1 17/32	2 19/32	1-2 9/16	2 25/32	1-3 9/16	2 31/32	1-4 19/32
3/8	2 1/4	1-0 19/32	2 7/16	1-1 19/32	2 5/8	1-2 5/8	2 13/16	1-3 5/8	3	1-4 21/32
7/16	2 9/32	1-0 21/32	2 7/16	1-1 21/32	2 5/8	1-2 11/16	2 13/16	1-3 11/16	3	1-4 23/32
1/2	2 9/32	1-0 23/32	2 15/32	1-1 23/32	2 21/32	1-2 3/4	2 13/16	1-3 3/4	3	1-4 25/32
9/16	2 9/32	1-0 25/32	2 15/32	1-1 25/32	2 21/32	1-2 13/16	2 27/32	1-3 13/16	3 1/32	1-4 27/32
5/8	2 5/16	1-0 27/32	2 15/32	1-1 27/32	2 21/32	1-2 7/8	2 27/32	1-3 7/8	3 1/32	1-4 29/32
11/16	2 5/16	1-0 29/32	2 1/2	1-1 29/32	2 11/16	1-2 15/16	2 7/8	1-3 15/16	3 1/32	1-4 31/32
3/4	2 5/16	1-0 31/32	2 1/2	1-1 31/32	2 11/16	1-3	2 7/8	1-4	3 1/16	1-5 1/32
13/16	2 11/32	1-1 1/16	2 17/32	1-2 1/32	2 11/16	1-3 1/16	2 7/8	1-4 1/16	3 1/16	1-5 3/32
7/8	2 11/32	1-1 3/32	2 17/32	1-2 3/32	2 23/32	1-3 3/16	2 29/32	1-4 1/8	3 1/16	1-5 5/32
15/16	2 11/32	1-1 5/32	2 17/32	1-2 5/32	2 23/32	1-3 3/32	2 29/32	1-4 3/16	3 3/32	1-5 7/32

Ins.	17″ Rise	17″ Slope	18″ Rise	18″ Slope	19″ Rise	19″ Slope	20″ Rise	20″ Slope	21″ Rise	21″ Slope
0	3 3/32	1-5 9/32	3 9/32	1-6 9/32	3 15/32	1-7 5/16	3 21/32	1-8 11/32	3 13/16	1-9 11/32
1/16	3 1/8	1-5 11/32	3 9/32	1-6 3/8	3 15/32	1-7 3/8	3 21/32	1-8 13/32	3 27/32	1-9 13/32
1/8	3 1/8	1-5 13/32	3 5/16	1-6 7/16	3 1/2	1-7 7/16	3 21/32	1-8 15/32	3 27/32	1-9 15/32
3/16	3 1/8	1-5 15/32	3 5/16	1-6 1/2	3 1/2	1-7 1/2	3 11/16	1-8 17/32	3 7/8	1-9 17/32
1/4	3 5/32	1-5 17/32	3 5/16	1-6 9/16	3 1/2	1-7 9/16	3 11/16	1-8 19/32	3 7/8	1-9 19/32
5/16	3 5/32	1-5 19/32	3 11/32	1-6 5/8	3 17/32	1-7 5/8	3 11/16	1-8 21/32	3 7/8	1-9 21/32
3/8	3 5/32	1-5 21/32	3 11/32	1-6 11/16	3 17/32	1-7 11/16	3 23/32	1-8 23/32	3 29/32	1-9 23/32
7/16	3 3/16	1-5 23/32	3 3/8	1-6 3/4	3 17/32	1-7 3/4	3 23/32	1-8 25/32	3 29/32	1-9 25/32
1/2	3 3/16	1-5 25/32	3 3/8	1-6 13/16	3 9/16	1-7 13/16	3 3/4	1-8 27/32	3 29/32	1-9 27/32
9/16	3 3/16	1-5 27/32	3 3/8	1-6 7/8	3 9/16	1-7 7/8	3 3/4	1-8 29/32	3 15/16	1-9 29/32
5/8	3 7/32	1-5 29/32	3 13/32	1-6 15/16	3 9/16	1-7 15/16	3 3/4	1-8 31/32	3 15/16	1-9 31/32
11/16	3 7/32	1-5 31/32	3 13/32	1-7	3 19/32	1-8	3 25/32	1-9 1/32	3 31/32	1-10 1/32
3/4	3 1/4	1-6 1/32	3 13/32	1-7 1/16	3 19/32	1-8 1/16	3 25/32	1-9 3/32	3 31/32	1-10 3/16
13/16	3 1/4	1-6 3/32	3 7/16	1-7 1/8	3 5/8	1-8 1/8	3 25/32	1-9 5/32	3 31/32	1-10 3/16
7/8	3 1/4	1-6 5/32	3 7/16	1-7 3/16	3 5/8	1-8 3/16	3 13/16	1-9 7/32	4	1-10 1/4
15/16	3 9/32	1-6 7/32	3 7/16	1-7 1/4	3 5/8	1-8 9/32	3 13/16	1-9 9/32	4	1-10 5/16

Feet	40′ Rise	40′ Slope	50′ Rise	50′ Slope	60′ Rise	60′ Slope	70′ Rise	70′ Slope
0	7-3 1/2	40-7 29/32	9-1 3/8	50-9 7/8	10-11 1/4	60-11 7/8	12-9 1/8	71-1 27/32
1	7-5 11/16	41-8 3/32	9-3 9/16	51-10 3/32	11-1 1/16	62-0 1/16	12-11 5/16	72-2 1/32
2	7-7 7/8	42-8 5/16	9-5 3/4	52-10 9/32	11-3 5/8	63-0 1/4	13-1 1/2	73-2 1/4
3	7-10 1/16	43-8 1/2	9-7 15/16	53-10 15/32	11-5 13/16	64-0 15/32	13-3 11/16	74-2 7/16
4	8-0 1/4	44-8 11/16	9-10 1/8	54-10 11/16	11-8	65-0 21/32	13-5 7/8	75-2 5/8
5	8-2 7/16	45-8 29/32	10-0 5/16	55-10 7/8	11-10 3/8	66-0 27/32	13-8 1/16	76-2 27/32
6	8-4 5/8	46-9 3/32	10-2 1/2	56-11 1/16	12-0 3/8	67-1 1/16	13-10 1/4	77-3 1/32
7	8-6 13/16	47-9 9/32	10-4 11/16	57-11 9/32	12-2 9/16	68-1 1/4	14-0 1/16	78-3 7/32
8	8-9	48-9 1/2	10-6 7/8	58-11 15/32	12-4 3/4	69-1 7/16	14-2 5/8	79-3 7/16
9	8-11 3/16	49-9 11/16	10-9 1/16	59-11 21/32	12-6 15/16	70-1 21/32	14-4 13/16	80-3 5/8

natsin A=0.1793363220; natcos A=0.9837878243; nattan A=0.1822916666; natcot A=5.4857142857

Inches	0" Rise	0" Slope	1" Rise	1" Slope	2" Rise	2" Slope	3" Rise	3" Slope	4" Rise	4" Slope	5" Rise	5" Slope
0	0	0	3/16	1 1/32	3/8	2 1/32	9/16	3 1/16	3/4	4 1/16	15/16	5 3/32
1/16	0		1/16	3/16	1 3/32	3/8	2 3/32	9/16	3 1/8	3/4	4 1/8	15/16	5 5/32
1/8	1/32		1/8	7/32	1 5/32	13/32	2 5/32	19/32	3 3/16	25/32	4 3/16	31/32	5 7/32
3/16	1/32		3/16	7/32	1 7/32	13/32	2 7/32	19/32	3 1/4	25/32	4 1/4	31/32	5 9/32
1/4	1/16		1/4	1/4	1 9/32	7/16	2 9/32	5/8	3 5/16	13/16	4 5/16	1	5 11/32
5/16	1/16		5/16	1/4	1 11/32	7/16	2 11/32	5/8	3 3/8	13/16	4 3/8	1	5 13/32
3/8	1/16		3/8	1/4	1 13/32	7/16	2 13/32	5/8	3 7/16	13/16	4 7/16	1	5 15/32
7/16	3/32		7/16	9/32	1 15/32	15/32	2 15/32	21/32	3 1/2	27/32	4 1/2	1 1/32	5 17/32
1/2	3/32		1/2	9/32	1 17/32	15/32	2 17/32	21/32	3 9/16	27/32	4 19/32	1 1/32	5 19/32
9/16	3/32		9/16	9/32	1 19/32	15/32	2 19/32	21/32	3 5/8	27/32	4 21/32	1 1/32	5 21/32
5/8	1/8		5/8	5/16	1 21/32	1/2	2 21/32	11/16	3 11/16	7/8	4 23/32	1 1/16	5 23/32
11/16	1/8		11/16	5/16	1 23/32	1/2	2 23/32	11/16	3 3/4	7/8	4 25/32	1 1/16	5 25/32
3/4	1/8		3/4	5/16	1 25/32	1/2	2 13/16	11/16	3 13/16	7/8	4 27/32	1 1/16	5 27/32
13/16	5/32		13/16	11/32	1 27/32	17/32	2 7/8	23/32	3 7/8	29/32	4 29/32	1 3/32	5 29/32
7/8	5/32		7/8	11/32	1 29/32	17/32	2 15/16	23/32	3 15/16	29/32	4 31/32	1 3/32	5 31/32
15/16	3/16		31/32	3/8	1 31/32	9/16	3	3/4	4	15/16	5 1/32	1 1/8	6 1/32

Inches	6" Rise	6" Slope	7" Rise	7" Slope	8" Rise	8" Slope	9" Rise	9" Slope	10" Rise	10" Slope	11" Rise	11" Slope
0	1 1/8	6 3/32	1 5/16	7 1/8	1 1/2	8 1/8	1 11/16	9 5/32	1 7/8	10 3/16	2 1/16	11 3/16
1/16	1 1/8	6 5/32	1 5/16	7 3/16	1 1/2	8 3/16	1 11/16	9 7/32	1 7/8	10 1/4	2 1/16	11 1/4
1/8	1 5/32	6 7/32	1 11/32	7 1/4	1 17/32	8 9/32	1 23/32	9 9/32	1 29/32	10 5/16	2 3/32	11 5/16
3/16	1 5/32	6 9/32	1 11/32	7 5/16	1 17/32	8 11/32	1 23/32	9 11/32	1 29/32	10 3/8	2 3/32	11 3/8
1/4	1 3/16	6 11/32	1 3/8	7 3/8	1 9/16	8 13/32	1 3/4	9 13/32	1 15/16	10 7/16	2 1/8	11 7/16
5/16	1 3/16	6 7/16	1 3/8	7 7/16	1 9/16	8 15/32	1 3/4	9 15/32	1 15/16	10 1/2	2 1/8	11 1/2
3/8	1 3/16	6 1/2	1 3/8	7 1/2	1 9/16	8 17/32	1 3/4	9 17/32	1 15/16	10 9/16	2 1/8	11 9/16
7/16	1 7/32	6 9/16	1 13/32	7 9/16	1 19/32	8 19/32	1 25/32	9 19/32	1 31/32	10 5/8	2 5/32	11 5/8
1/2	1 7/32	6 5/8	1 13/32	7 5/8	1 19/32	8 21/32	1 25/32	9 21/32	1 31/32	10 11/16	2 5/32	11 11/16
9/16	1 7/32	6 11/16	1 13/32	7 11/16	1 19/32	8 23/32	1 25/32	9 23/32	1 31/32	10 3/4	2 5/32	11 3/4
5/8	1 1/4	6 3/4	1 7/16	7 3/4	1 5/8	8 25/32	1 13/16	9 25/32	2	10 13/16	2 3/16	11 13/16
11/16	1 1/4	6 13/16	1 7/16	7 13/16	1 5/8	8 27/32	1 13/16	9 27/32	2	10 7/8	2 3/16	11 29/32
3/4	1 1/4	6 7/8	1 7/16	7 7/8	1 5/8	8 29/32	1 13/16	9 29/32	2	10 15/16	2 3/16	11 31/32
13/16	1 9/32	6 15/16	1 15/32	7 15/16	1 21/32	8 31/32	1 27/32	9 31/32	2 1/4	11	2 7/32	1-0 1/32
7/8	1 9/32	7	1 15/32	8	1 21/32	9 1/32	1 27/32	10 1/16	2 1/32	11 1/16	2 7/32	1-0 3/32
15/16	1 5/16		1 1/2	8 1/16	1 11/16	9 3/32	1 7/8	10 1/8	2 1/16	11 1/8	2 1/4	1-0 5/32

Feet	0' Rise	0' Slope	10' Rise	10' Slope	20' Rise	20' Slope	30' Rise	30' Slope
0	0	0	1-10 1/2	10-2 3/32	3-9	20-4 3/16	5-7 1/2	30-6 9/32
1	2 1/4	1-0 7/32	2-0 3/4	11-2 5/16	3-11 1/4	21-4 13/32	5-9 3/4	31-6 15/32
2	4 1/2	2-0 13/32	2-3	12-2 1/2	4-1 1/2	22-4 19/32	6-0	32-6 11/16
3	6 3/4	3-0 5/8	2-5 1/4	13-2 23/32	4-3 3/4	23-4 13/16	6-2 1/4	33-6 29/32
4	9	4-0 27/32	2-7 1/2	14-2 15/16	4-6	24-5 1/32	6-4 1/2	34-7 1/8
5	11 1/4	5-1 1/32	2-9 3/4	15-3 1/8	4-8 1/4	25-5 7/32	6-6 3/4	35-7 5/16
6	1-1 1/2	6-1 1/4	3-0	16-3 11/32	4-10 1/2	26-5 7/16	6-9	36-7 17/32
7	1-3 3/4	7-1 15/32	3-2 1/4	17-3 9/16	5-0 3/4	27-5 21/32	6-11 1/4	37-7 3/4
8	1-6	8-1 11/16	3-4 1/2	18-3 3/4	5-3	28-5 27/32	7-1 1/2	38-7 15/16
9	1-8 1/4	9-1 7/8	3-6 3/4	19-3 31/32	5-5 1/4	29-6 1/16	7-3 3/4	39-8 5/32

A = 10° 37′ 11″; logsin A = 9.26350; logcos A = 9.99250; logtan A = 9.27300; logcot A = 0.72700

Ins.	12″ Rise	12″ Slope	13″ Rise	13″ Slope	14″ Rise	14″ Slope	15″ Rise	15″ Slope	16″ Rise	16″ Slope
0	$2\tfrac14$	$1\text{-}0\tfrac{7}{32}$	$2\tfrac{7}{16}$	$1\text{-}1\tfrac{7}{32}$	$2\tfrac58$	$1\text{-}2\tfrac14$	$2\tfrac{13}{16}$	$1\text{-}3\tfrac14$	3	$1\text{-}4\tfrac{9}{32}$
$\tfrac1{16}$	$2\tfrac14$	$1\text{-}0\tfrac{9}{32}$	$2\tfrac{7}{16}$	$1\text{-}1\tfrac{9}{32}$	$2\tfrac58$	$1\text{-}2\tfrac{5}{16}$	$2\tfrac{13}{16}$	$1\text{-}3\tfrac{5}{16}$	3	$1\text{-}4\tfrac{11}{32}$
$\tfrac18$	$2\tfrac{9}{32}$	$1\text{-}0\tfrac{11}{32}$	$2\tfrac{15}{32}$	$1\text{-}1\tfrac{11}{32}$	$2\tfrac{21}{32}$	$1\text{-}2\tfrac38$	$2\tfrac{27}{32}$	$1\text{-}3\tfrac38$	$3\tfrac{1}{32}$	$1\text{-}4\tfrac{13}{32}$
$\tfrac3{16}$	$2\tfrac{9}{32}$	$1\text{-}0\tfrac{13}{32}$	$2\tfrac{15}{32}$	$1\text{-}1\tfrac{13}{32}$	$2\tfrac{21}{32}$	$1\text{-}2\tfrac{7}{16}$	$2\tfrac{27}{32}$	$1\text{-}3\tfrac{7}{16}$	$3\tfrac{1}{32}$	$1\text{-}4\tfrac{15}{32}$
$\tfrac14$	$2\tfrac{5}{16}$	$1\text{-}0\tfrac{15}{32}$	$2\tfrac12$	$1\text{-}1\tfrac{15}{32}$	$2\tfrac{11}{16}$	$1\text{-}2\tfrac12$	$2\tfrac78$	$1\text{-}3\tfrac{17}{32}$	$3\tfrac{1}{16}$	$1\text{-}4\tfrac{17}{32}$
$\tfrac5{16}$	$2\tfrac{5}{16}$	$1\text{-}0\tfrac{17}{32}$	$2\tfrac12$	$1\text{-}1\tfrac{17}{32}$	$2\tfrac{11}{16}$	$1\text{-}2\tfrac{9}{16}$	$2\tfrac78$	$1\text{-}3\tfrac{19}{32}$	$3\tfrac{1}{16}$	$1\text{-}4\tfrac{19}{32}$
$\tfrac38$	$2\tfrac{5}{16}$	$1\text{-}0\tfrac{19}{32}$	$2\tfrac12$	$1\text{-}1\tfrac{19}{32}$	$2\tfrac{11}{16}$	$1\text{-}2\tfrac58$	$2\tfrac78$	$1\text{-}3\tfrac{21}{32}$	$3\tfrac{1}{16}$	$1\text{-}4\tfrac{21}{32}$
$\tfrac7{16}$	$2\tfrac{11}{32}$	$1\text{-}0\tfrac{21}{32}$	$2\tfrac{17}{32}$	$1\text{-}1\tfrac{21}{32}$	$2\tfrac{23}{32}$	$1\text{-}2\tfrac{11}{16}$	$2\tfrac{29}{32}$	$1\text{-}3\tfrac{23}{32}$	$3\tfrac{3}{32}$	$1\text{-}4\tfrac{23}{32}$
$\tfrac12$	$2\tfrac{11}{32}$	$1\text{-}0\tfrac{23}{32}$	$2\tfrac{17}{32}$	$1\text{-}1\tfrac34$	$2\tfrac{23}{32}$	$1\text{-}2\tfrac34$	$2\tfrac{29}{32}$	$1\text{-}3\tfrac{25}{32}$	$3\tfrac{3}{32}$	$1\text{-}4\tfrac{25}{32}$
$\tfrac9{16}$	$2\tfrac{11}{32}$	$1\text{-}0\tfrac{25}{32}$	$2\tfrac{17}{32}$	$1\text{-}1\tfrac{13}{16}$	$2\tfrac{23}{32}$	$1\text{-}2\tfrac{13}{16}$	$2\tfrac{29}{32}$	$1\text{-}3\tfrac{27}{32}$	$3\tfrac{3}{32}$	$1\text{-}4\tfrac{27}{32}$
$\tfrac58$	$2\tfrac38$	$1\text{-}0\tfrac{27}{32}$	$2\tfrac{9}{16}$	$1\text{-}1\tfrac78$	$2\tfrac34$	$1\text{-}2\tfrac78$	$2\tfrac{15}{16}$	$1\text{-}3\tfrac{29}{32}$	$3\tfrac18$	$1\text{-}4\tfrac{29}{32}$
$\tfrac{11}{16}$	$2\tfrac38$	$1\text{-}0\tfrac{29}{32}$	$2\tfrac{9}{16}$	$1\text{-}1\tfrac{15}{16}$	$2\tfrac34$	$1\text{-}2\tfrac{15}{16}$	$2\tfrac{15}{16}$	$1\text{-}3\tfrac{31}{32}$	$3\tfrac18$	$1\text{-}4\tfrac{31}{32}$
$\tfrac34$	$2\tfrac38$	$1\text{-}0\tfrac{31}{32}$	$2\tfrac{9}{16}$	$1\text{-}2$	$2\tfrac34$	$1\text{-}3$	$2\tfrac{15}{16}$	$1\text{-}4\tfrac{1}{32}$	$3\tfrac{5}{32}$	$1\text{-}5\tfrac{1}{32}$
$\tfrac{13}{16}$	$2\tfrac{13}{32}$	$1\text{-}1\tfrac{1}{32}$	$2\tfrac{19}{32}$	$1\text{-}2\tfrac{1}{16}$	$2\tfrac{25}{32}$	$1\text{-}3\tfrac{1}{16}$	$2\tfrac{31}{32}$	$1\text{-}4\tfrac{3}{32}$	$3\tfrac{5}{32}$	$1\text{-}5\tfrac{3}{32}$
$\tfrac78$	$2\tfrac{13}{32}$	$1\text{-}1\tfrac{3}{32}$	$2\tfrac{19}{32}$	$1\text{-}2\tfrac18$	$2\tfrac{25}{32}$	$1\text{-}3\tfrac18$	$2\tfrac{31}{32}$	$1\text{-}4\tfrac{5}{32}$	$3\tfrac{5}{32}$	$1\text{-}5\tfrac{5}{32}$
$\tfrac{15}{16}$	$2\tfrac{7}{16}$	$1\text{-}1\tfrac{5}{32}$	$2\tfrac58$	$1\text{-}2\tfrac{3}{16}$	$2\tfrac{13}{16}$	$1\text{-}3\tfrac{3}{16}$	3	$1\text{-}4\tfrac{7}{32}$	$3\tfrac{3}{16}$	$1\text{-}5\tfrac{7}{32}$

Ins.	17″ Rise	17″ Slope	18″ Rise	18″ Slope	19″ Rise	19″ Slope	20″ Rise	20″ Slope	21″ Rise	21″ Slope
0	$3\tfrac{3}{16}$	$1\text{-}5\tfrac{9}{32}$	$3\tfrac38$	$1\text{-}6\tfrac{5}{16}$	$3\tfrac{9}{16}$	$1\text{-}7\tfrac{11}{32}$	$3\tfrac34$	$1\text{-}8\tfrac{11}{32}$	$3\tfrac{15}{16}$	$1\text{-}9\tfrac38$
$\tfrac1{16}$	$3\tfrac{3}{16}$	$1\text{-}5\tfrac38$	$3\tfrac38$	$1\text{-}6\tfrac38$	$3\tfrac{9}{16}$	$1\text{-}7\tfrac{13}{32}$	$3\tfrac34$	$1\text{-}8\tfrac{13}{32}$	$3\tfrac{15}{16}$	$1\text{-}9\tfrac{7}{16}$
$\tfrac18$	$3\tfrac{7}{32}$	$1\text{-}5\tfrac{7}{16}$	$3\tfrac{13}{32}$	$1\text{-}6\tfrac{7}{16}$	$3\tfrac{19}{32}$	$1\text{-}7\tfrac{15}{32}$	$3\tfrac{25}{32}$	$1\text{-}8\tfrac{15}{32}$	$3\tfrac{31}{32}$	$1\text{-}9\tfrac12$
$\tfrac3{16}$	$3\tfrac{7}{32}$	$1\text{-}5\tfrac12$	$3\tfrac{13}{32}$	$1\text{-}6\tfrac12$	$3\tfrac{19}{32}$	$1\text{-}7\tfrac{17}{32}$	$3\tfrac{25}{32}$	$1\text{-}8\tfrac{17}{32}$	$3\tfrac{31}{32}$	$1\text{-}9\tfrac{9}{16}$
$\tfrac14$	$3\tfrac14$	$1\text{-}5\tfrac{9}{16}$	$3\tfrac{7}{16}$	$1\text{-}6\tfrac{9}{16}$	$3\tfrac58$	$1\text{-}7\tfrac{19}{32}$	$3\tfrac{13}{16}$	$1\text{-}8\tfrac{19}{32}$	4	$1\text{-}9\tfrac58$
$\tfrac5{16}$	$3\tfrac14$	$1\text{-}5\tfrac58$	$3\tfrac{7}{16}$	$1\text{-}6\tfrac58$	$3\tfrac58$	$1\text{-}7\tfrac{21}{32}$	$3\tfrac{13}{16}$	$1\text{-}8\tfrac{21}{32}$	4	$1\text{-}9\tfrac{11}{16}$
$\tfrac38$	$3\tfrac14$	$1\text{-}5\tfrac{11}{16}$	$3\tfrac{7}{16}$	$1\text{-}6\tfrac{11}{16}$	$3\tfrac58$	$1\text{-}7\tfrac{23}{32}$	$3\tfrac{13}{16}$	$1\text{-}8\tfrac{23}{32}$	4	$1\text{-}9\tfrac34$
$\tfrac7{16}$	$3\tfrac{9}{32}$	$1\text{-}5\tfrac34$	$3\tfrac{15}{32}$	$1\text{-}6\tfrac34$	$3\tfrac{21}{32}$	$1\text{-}7\tfrac{25}{32}$	$3\tfrac{27}{32}$	$1\text{-}8\tfrac{25}{32}$	$4\tfrac{1}{32}$	$1\text{-}9\tfrac{13}{16}$
$\tfrac12$	$3\tfrac{9}{32}$	$1\text{-}5\tfrac{13}{16}$	$3\tfrac{15}{32}$	$1\text{-}6\tfrac{13}{16}$	$3\tfrac{21}{32}$	$1\text{-}7\tfrac{27}{32}$	$3\tfrac{27}{32}$	$1\text{-}8\tfrac{27}{32}$	$4\tfrac{1}{32}$	$1\text{-}9\tfrac78$
$\tfrac9{16}$	$3\tfrac{9}{32}$	$1\text{-}5\tfrac78$	$3\tfrac{15}{32}$	$1\text{-}6\tfrac78$	$3\tfrac{21}{32}$	$1\text{-}7\tfrac{29}{32}$	$3\tfrac{27}{32}$	$1\text{-}8\tfrac{29}{32}$	$4\tfrac{1}{32}$	$1\text{-}9\tfrac{15}{16}$
$\tfrac58$	$3\tfrac{5}{16}$	$1\text{-}5\tfrac{15}{16}$	$3\tfrac12$	$1\text{-}6\tfrac{15}{16}$	$3\tfrac{11}{16}$	$1\text{-}7\tfrac{31}{32}$	$3\tfrac78$	$1\text{-}9$	$4\tfrac{1}{16}$	$1\text{-}10$
$\tfrac{11}{16}$	$3\tfrac{5}{16}$	$1\text{-}6$	$3\tfrac12$	$1\text{-}7$	$3\tfrac{11}{16}$	$1\text{-}8\tfrac{1}{32}$	$3\tfrac78$	$1\text{-}9\tfrac{1}{16}$	$4\tfrac{1}{16}$	$1\text{-}10\tfrac{1}{16}$
$\tfrac34$	$3\tfrac{5}{16}$	$1\text{-}6\tfrac{1}{16}$	$3\tfrac12$	$1\text{-}7\tfrac{1}{16}$	$3\tfrac{11}{16}$	$1\text{-}8\tfrac{3}{32}$	$3\tfrac78$	$1\text{-}9\tfrac18$	$4\tfrac{1}{16}$	$1\text{-}10\tfrac18$
$\tfrac{13}{16}$	$3\tfrac{11}{32}$	$1\text{-}6\tfrac18$	$3\tfrac{17}{32}$	$1\text{-}7\tfrac18$	$3\tfrac{23}{32}$	$1\text{-}8\tfrac{5}{32}$	$3\tfrac{29}{32}$	$1\text{-}9\tfrac{3}{16}$	$4\tfrac{3}{32}$	$1\text{-}10\tfrac{3}{16}$
$\tfrac78$	$3\tfrac{11}{32}$	$1\text{-}6\tfrac{3}{16}$	$3\tfrac{17}{32}$	$1\text{-}7\tfrac{3}{32}$	$3\tfrac{23}{32}$	$1\text{-}8\tfrac{7}{32}$	$3\tfrac{29}{32}$	$1\text{-}9\tfrac14$	$4\tfrac{3}{32}$	$1\text{-}10\tfrac14$
$\tfrac{15}{16}$	$3\tfrac38$	$1\text{-}6\tfrac14$	$3\tfrac{9}{16}$	$1\text{-}7\tfrac{9}{32}$	$3\tfrac34$	$1\text{-}8\tfrac{9}{32}$	$3\tfrac{15}{16}$	$1\text{-}9\tfrac{5}{16}$	$4\tfrac18$	$1\text{-}10\tfrac{5}{16}$

Feet	40′ Rise	40′ Slope	50′ Rise	50′ Slope	60′ Rise	60′ Slope	70′ Rise	70′ Slope
0	$7\text{-}6$	$40\text{-}8\tfrac38$	$9\text{-}4\tfrac12$	$50\text{-}10\tfrac{15}{32}$	$11\text{-}3$	$61\text{-}0\tfrac{9}{16}$	$13\text{-}1\tfrac12$	$71\text{-}2\tfrac58$
1	$7\text{-}8\tfrac14$	$41\text{-}8\tfrac{9}{16}$	$9\text{-}6\tfrac34$	$51\text{-}10\tfrac{21}{32}$	$11\text{-}5\tfrac14$	$62\text{-}0\tfrac34$	$13\text{-}3\tfrac34$	$72\text{-}2\tfrac{27}{32}$
2	$7\text{-}10\tfrac12$	$42\text{-}8\tfrac{25}{32}$	$9\text{-}9$	$52\text{-}10\tfrac78$	$11\text{-}7\tfrac12$	$63\text{-}0\tfrac{31}{32}$	$13\text{-}6$	$73\text{-}3\tfrac{1}{16}$
3	$8\text{-}0\tfrac34$	$43\text{-}9$	$9\text{-}11\tfrac14$	$53\text{-}11\tfrac{3}{32}$	$11\text{-}9\tfrac34$	$64\text{-}1\tfrac{3}{16}$	$13\text{-}8\tfrac14$	$74\text{-}3\tfrac14$
4	$8\text{-}3$	$44\text{-}9\tfrac{3}{16}$	$10\text{-}1\tfrac12$	$54\text{-}11\tfrac{9}{32}$	$12\text{-}0$	$65\text{-}1\tfrac38$	$13\text{-}10\tfrac12$	$75\text{-}3\tfrac{15}{32}$
5	$8\text{-}5\tfrac14$	$45\text{-}9\tfrac{13}{32}$	$10\text{-}3\tfrac34$	$55\text{-}11\tfrac12$	$12\text{-}2\tfrac14$	$66\text{-}1\tfrac{19}{32}$	$14\text{-}0\tfrac34$	$76\text{-}3\tfrac{11}{16}$
6	$8\text{-}7\tfrac12$	$46\text{-}9\tfrac58$	$10\text{-}6$	$56\text{-}11\tfrac{23}{32}$	$12\text{-}4\tfrac12$	$67\text{-}1\tfrac{13}{16}$	$14\text{-}3$	$77\text{-}3\tfrac{29}{32}$
7	$8\text{-}9\tfrac34$	$47\text{-}9\tfrac{27}{32}$	$10\text{-}8\tfrac14$	$57\text{-}11\tfrac{29}{32}$	$12\text{-}6\tfrac34$	$68\text{-}2$	$14\text{-}5\tfrac14$	$78\text{-}4\tfrac{3}{32}$
8	$9\text{-}0$	$48\text{-}10\tfrac{1}{32}$	$10\text{-}10\tfrac12$	$59\text{-}0\tfrac18$	$12\text{-}9$	$69\text{-}2\tfrac{7}{32}$	$14\text{-}7\tfrac12$	$79\text{-}4\tfrac{5}{16}$
9	$9\text{-}2\tfrac14$	$49\text{-}10\tfrac14$	$11\text{-}0\tfrac34$	$60\text{-}0\tfrac{11}{32}$	$12\text{-}11\tfrac14$	$70\text{-}2\tfrac{7}{16}$	$14\text{-}9\tfrac34$	$80\text{-}4\tfrac{17}{32}$

natsin A=0.1842885350; natcos A=0.9828721868; nattan A=0.1875000000; natcot A=5.3333333333

Inches	0" Rise	0" Slope	1" Rise	1" Slope	2" Rise	2" Slope	3" Rise	3" Slope	4" Rise	4" Slope	5" Rise	5" Slope
0	0	0	3/16	1 1/32	3/8	2 1/32	9/16	3 1/16	25/32	4 1/16	31/32	5 3/32
1/16	0	1/16	7/32	1 3/32	13/32	2 3/32	19/32	3 1/8	25/32	4 1/8	31/32	5 5/32
1/8	1/32	1/8	7/32	1 5/32	13/32	2 5/32	19/32	3 3/16	25/32	4 3/16	1	5 7/32
3/16	1/32	3/16	7/32	1 7/32	13/32	2 7/32	5/8	3 1/4	13/16	4 1/4	1	5 9/32
1/4	1/16	1/4	1/4	1 9/32	7/16	2 9/32	5/8	3 5/16	13/16	4 11/32	1	5 11/32
5/16	1/16	5/16	1/4	1 11/32	7/16	2 11/32	5/8	3 3/8	27/32	4 13/32	1 1/32	5 13/32
3/8	1/16	3/8	1/4	1 13/32	15/32	2 13/32	21/32	3 7/16	27/32	4 15/32	1 1/32	5 15/32
7/16	3/32	7/16	9/32	1 15/32	15/32	2 15/32	21/32	3 1/2	27/32	4 17/32	1 1/16	5 17/32
1/2	3/32	1/2	9/32	1 17/32	15/32	2 17/32	11/16	3 9/16	7/8	4 19/32	1 1/16	5 19/32
9/16	3/32	9/16	5/16	1 19/32	1/2	2 5/8	11/16	3 5/8	7/8	4 21/32	1 1/16	5 21/32
5/8	1/8	5/8	5/16	1 21/32	1/2	2 11/16	11/16	3 11/16	29/32	4 23/32	1 3/32	5 23/32
11/16	1/8	11/16	5/16	1 23/32	17/32	2 3/4	23/32	3 3/4	29/32	4 25/32	1 3/32	5 25/32
3/4	5/32	3/4	11/32	1 25/32	17/32	2 13/16	23/32	3 13/16	29/32	4 27/32	1 3/32	5 27/32
13/16	5/32	13/16	11/32	1 27/32	17/32	2 7/8	3/4	3 7/8	15/16	4 29/32	1 1/8	5 29/32
7/8	5/32	29/32	3/8	1 29/32	9/16	2 15/16	3/4	3 15/16	15/16	4 31/32	1 1/8	5 31/32
15/16	3/16	31/32	3/8	1 31/32	9/16	3	3/4	4	15/16	5 1/32	1 5/32	6 1/2

Inches	6" Rise	6" Slope	7" Rise	7" Slope	8" Rise	8" Slope	9" Rise	9" Slope	10" Rise	10" Slope	11" Rise	11" Slope
0	1 5/32	6 1/8	1 11/32	7 1/8	1 17/32	8 5/32	1 3/4	9 5/32	1 15/16	10 3/16	2 1/8	11 3/16
1/16	1 5/32	6 3/16	1 3/8	7 3/16	1 9/16	8 7/32	1 3/4	9 7/32	1 15/16	10 1/4	2 1/8	11 9/32
1/8	1 3/16	6 1/4	1 3/8	7 1/4	1 9/16	8 9/32	1 3/4	9 9/32	1 15/16	10 5/16	2 5/32	11 11/32
3/16	1 3/16	6 5/16	1 3/8	7 5/16	1 9/16	8 11/32	1 25/32	9 11/32	1 31/32	10 3/8	2 5/32	11 13/32
1/4	1 7/32	6 3/8	1 13/32	7 3/8	1 19/32	8 13/32	1 25/32	9 13/32	1 31/32	10 7/16	2 5/32	11 15/32
5/16	1 7/32	6 7/16	1 13/32	7 7/16	1 19/32	8 15/32	1 25/32	9 15/32	2	10 1/2	2 3/16	11 17/32
3/8	1 7/32	6 1/2	1 13/32	7 1/2	1 5/8	8 17/32	1 13/16	9 9/16	2	10 9/16	2 3/16	11 19/32
7/16	1 1/4	6 9/16	1 7/16	7 9/16	1 5/8	8 19/32	1 13/16	9 5/8	2	10 5/8	2 7/32	11 21/32
1/2	1 1/4	6 5/8	1 7/16	7 5/8	1 5/8	8 21/32	1 27/32	9 11/16	2 1/32	10 11/16	2 7/32	11 23/32
9/16	1 1/4	6 11/16	1 15/32	7 11/16	1 21/32	8 23/32	1 27/32	9 3/4	2 1/32	10 3/4	2 7/32	11 25/32
5/8	1 9/32	6 3/4	1 15/32	7 3/4	1 21/32	8 25/32	1 27/32	9 13/16	2 1/16	10 13/16	2 1/4	11 27/32
11/16	1 9/32	6 13/16	1 15/32	7 27/32	1 11/16	8 27/32	1 7/8	9 7/8	2 1/16	10 7/8	2 1/4	11 29/32
3/4	1 5/16	6 7/8	1 1/2	7 29/32	1 11/16	8 29/32	1 7/8	9 15/16	2 1/16	10 15/16	2 1/4	11 31/32
13/16	1 5/16	6 15/16	1 1/2	7 31/32	1 11/16	8 31/32	1 29/32	10	2 3/32	11	2 9/32	1-0 1/32
7/8	1 5/16	7	1 17/32	8 1/32	1 23/32	9 1/32	1 29/32	10 1/16	2 3/32	11 1/16	2 9/32	1-0 3/32
15/16	1 11/32	7 1/16	1 17/32	8 3/32	1 23/32	9 3/32	1 29/32	10 1/8	2 3/32	11 1/8	2 5/16	1-0 5/32

Feet	0' Rise	0' Slope	10' Rise	10' Slope	20' Rise	20' Slope	30' Rise	30' Slope
0	0	0	1-11 1/8	10-2 5/32	3-10 1/4	20-4 13/32	5-9 3/8	30-6 5/8
1	2 5/16	1-0 7/32	2-1 7/16	11-2 7/16	4-0 9/16	21-4 5/8	5-11 11/16	31-6 27/32
2	4 5/8	2-0 7/16	2-3 3/4	12-2 21/32	4-2 7/8	22-4 27/32	6-2	32-7 1/16
3	6 15/16	3-0 21/32	2-6 1/16	13-2 7/8	4-5 3/16	23-5 1/16	6-4 5/16	33-7 9/32
4	9 1/4	4-0 7/8	2-8 3/8	14-3 3/32	4-7 1/2	24-5 5/16	6-6 5/8	34-7 1/2
5	11 9/16	5-1 3/32	2-10 11/16	15-3 5/16	4-9 13/16	25-5 17/32	6-8 15/16	35-7 23/32
6	1-1 7/8	6-1 5/16	3-1	16-3 17/32	5-0 1/8	26-5 3/4	6-11 1/4	36-7 15/16
7	1-4 3/16	7-1 17/32	3-3 5/16	17-3 3/4	5-2 7/16	27-5 31/32	7-1 9/16	37-8 5/32
8	1-6 1/2	8-1 25/32	3-5 5/8	18-3 31/32	5-4 3/4	28-6 3/16	7-3 7/8	38-8 3/8
9	1-8 13/16	9-2	3-7 15/16	19-4 3/16	5-7 1/16	29-6 13/32	7-6 3/16	39-8 5/8

A = 10° 54′ 28″; logsin A = 9.27698; logcos A = 9.99208; logtan A = 9.28490; logcot A = 0.71510

Ins.	12″ Rise	12″ Slope	13″ Rise	13″ Slope	14″ Rise	14″ Slope	15″ Rise	15″ Slope	16″ Rise	16″ Slope
0	2 5/16	1-0 7/32	2 1/2	1-1 1/4	2 11/16	1-2 1/4	2 7/8	1-3 9/32−	3 3/32−	1-4 9/32
1/16	2 5/16	1-0 9/32	2 17/32−	1-1 5/16	2 23/32−	1-2 5/16	2 29/32−	1-3 11/32−	3 3/32	1-4 11/32
1/8	2 11/32−	1-0 11/32	2 17/32−	1-1 3/8	2 23/32	1-2 3/8	2 29/32	1-3 13/32−	3 3/32	1-4 13/32
3/16	2 11/32	1-0 13/32	2 17/32	1-1 7/16	2 23/32	1-2 7/16	2 15/16	1-3 15/32−	3 1/8	1-4 1/2
1/4	2 3/8	1-0 15/32	2 9/16	1-1 1/2	2 3/4	1-2 1/2	2 15/16	1-3 17/32−	3 1/8	1-4 9/16
5/16	2 3/8	1-0 17/32	2 9/16	1-1 9/16	2 3/4	1-2 9/16	2 15/16	1-3 19/32	3 5/32−	1-4 5/8
3/8	2 3/8	1-0 19/32	2 9/16	1-1 5/8	2 25/32−	1-2 5/8	2 31/32−	1-3 21/32	3 5/32−	1-4 11/16
7/16	2 13/32−	1-0 21/32	2 19/32−	1-1 11/16	2 25/32	1-2 23/32−	2 31/32	1-3 23/32	3 5/32	1-4 3/4
1/2	2 13/32	1-0 23/32	2 19/32	1-1 3/4	2 25/32	1-2 25/32−	3	1-3 25/32	3 3/16	1-4 13/16
9/16	2 13/32	1-0 25/32	2 5/8	1-1 13/16	2 13/16	1-2 27/32−	3	1-3 27/32	3 3/16	1-4 7/8
5/8	2 7/16	1-0 27/32	2 5/8	1-1 7/8	2 13/16	1-2 29/32−	3	1-3 29/32	3 7/32−	1-4 15/16
11/16	2 7/16	1-0 29/32	2 5/8	1-1 15/16	2 27/32−	1-2 31/32−	3 1/32−	1-3 31/32	3 7/32−	1-5
3/4	2 15/32−	1-1	2 21/32−	1-2	2 27/32−	1-3 1/32−	3 1/32	1-4 1/32	3 7/32	1-5 1/16
13/16	2 15/32	1-1 1/16	2 21/32	1-2 1/16	2 27/32	1-3 3/32−	3 1/16	1-4 3/32	3 1/4	1-5 1/8
7/8	2 15/32	1-1 1/8	2 11/16	1-2 1/8	2 7/8	1-3 5/32−	3 1/16	1-4 5/32	3 1/4	1-5 3/16
15/16	2 1/2	1-1 3/16	2 11/16	1-2 3/16	2 7/8	1-3 7/32−	3 1/16	1-4 7/32	3 1/4	1-5 1/4

Ins.	17″ Rise	17″ Slope	18″ Rise	18″ Slope	19″ Rise	19″ Slope	20″ Rise	20″ Slope	21″ Rise	21″ Slope
0	3 9/32−	1-5 5/16	3 15/32	1-6 11/32−	3 21/32	1-7 11/32	3 27/32	1-8 3/8	4 1/16	1-9 3/8
1/16	3 9/32	1-5 3/8	3 15/32	1-6 13/32−	3 11/16	1-7 13/32	3 7/8	1-8 7/16	4 1/16	1-9 7/16
1/8	3 5/16	1-5 7/16	3 1/2	1-6 15/32−	3 11/16	1-7 15/32	3 7/8	1-8 1/2	4 1/16	1-9 1/2
3/16	3 5/16	1-5 1/2	3 1/2	1-6 17/32−	3 11/16	1-7 17/32	3 7/8	1-8 9/16	4 3/32−	1-9 9/16
1/4	3 5/16	1-5 9/16	3 17/32−	1-6 19/32−	3 23/32−	1-7 19/32	3 29/32−	1-8 5/8	4 3/32	1-9 21/32−
5/16	3 11/32−	1-5 5/8	3 17/32−	1-6 21/32−	3 23/32	1-7 21/32	3 29/32	1-8 11/16	4 3/32	1-9 23/32−
3/8	3 11/32	1-5 11/16	3 17/32	1-6 23/32−	3 23/32	1-7 23/32	3 15/16	1-8 3/4	4 1/8	1-9 25/32−
7/16	3 3/8	1-5 3/4	3 9/16	1-6 25/32−	3 3/4	1-7 25/32	3 15/16	1-8 13/16	4 1/8	1-9 27/32−
1/2	3 3/8	1-5 13/16	3 9/16	1-6 27/32−	3 3/4	1-7 27/32	3 15/16	1-8 7/8	4 5/32−	1-9 29/32−
9/16	3 3/8	1-5 7/8	3 9/16	1-6 29/32−	3 25/32−	1-7 15/16	3 31/32−	1-8 15/16	4 5/32−	1-9 31/32−
5/8	3 13/32−	1-5 15/16	3 19/32−	1-6 31/32−	3 25/32	1-8	3 31/32	1-9	4 5/32	1-10 1/32−
11/16	3 13/32	1-6	3 19/32	1-7 1/32	3 25/32	1-8 1/16	4	1-9 1/16	4 3/16	1-10 3/32−
3/4	3 13/32	1-6 1/16	3 5/8	1-7 3/32	3 13/16	1-8 1/8	4	1-9 1/8	4 3/16	1-10 5/32−
13/16	3 7/16	1-6 1/8	3 5/8	1-7 5/32	3 13/16	1-8 3/16	4	1-9 3/16	4 7/32−	1-10 7/32−
7/8	3 7/16	1-6 7/32−	3 5/8	1-7 7/32	3 27/32−	1-8 1/4	4 1/32−	1-9 1/4	4 7/32−	1-10 9/32−
15/16	3 15/32−	1-6 9/32−	3 21/32−	1-7 9/32	3 27/32−	1-8 5/16	4 1/32	1-9 5/16	4 7/32	1-10 11/32−

Feet	40′ Rise	40′ Slope	50′ Rise	50′ Slope	60′ Rise	60′ Slope	70′ Rise	70′ Slope
0	7-8 1/2	40-8 27/32−	9-7 5/8	50-11 1/32	11-6 3/4	61-1 1/4	13-5 7/8	71-3 15/32−
1	7-10 13/16	41-9 1/16	9-9 15/16	51-11 1/4	11-9 1/16	62-1 15/32−	13-8 3/16	72-3 11/16
2	8-1 1/8	42-9 9/32−	10-0 1/4	52-11 15/32	11-11 3/8	63-1 11/16	13-10 1/2	73-3 29/32−
3	8-3 7/16	43-9 1/2	10-2 9/16	53-11 11/16	12-1 11/16	64-1 29/32	14-0 13/16	74-4 1/8
4	8-5 3/4	44-9 23/32−	10-4 7/8	54-11 15/16	12-4	65-2 1/8	14-3 1/8	75-4 11/32−
5	8-8 1/16	45-9 15/16	10-7 3/16	56-0 5/32−	12-6 5/16	66-2 11/32	14-5 7/16	76-4 9/16
6	8-10 3/8	46-10 5/32−	10-9 1/2	57-0 3/8	12-8 5/8	67-2 9/16	14-7 3/4	77-4 25/32−
7	9-0 11/16	47-10 3/8	10-11 13/16	58-0 19/32−	12-10 15/16	68-2 25/32	14-10 1/16	78-5
8	9-3	48-10 19/32	11-2 1/8	59-0 13/16	13-1 1/4	69-3	15-0 3/8	79-5 7/32
9	9-5 5/16	49-10 13/16	11-4 7/16	60-1 1/32−	13-3 9/16	70-3 7/32	15-2 11/16	80-5 7/16

natsin A=0.1892267522; natcos A=0.9819334173; nattan A=0.1927083333; natcot A=5.1891891891

Inches	0" Rise	0" Slope	1" Rise	1" Slope	2" Rise	2" Slope	3" Rise	3" Slope	4" Rise	4" Slope	5" Rise	5" Slope
0	0	0	3/16	1 1/32	13/32	2 1/8	19/32	3 1/16	25/32	4 1/16	1	5 3/32
1/16	0	1/16	7/32	1 3/32	13/32	2 3/32	19/32	3 1/8	13/16	4 5/32	1	5 5/32
1/8	1/32	1/8	7/32	1 5/32	13/32	2 5/32	5/8	3 3/16	13/16	4 7/32	1	5 7/32
3/16	1/32	3/16	1/4	1 7/32	7/16	2 7/32	5/8	3 1/4	27/32	4 9/32	1 1/32	5 9/32
1/4	1/16	1/4	1/4	1 9/32	7/16	2 9/32	21/32	3 5/16	27/32	4 11/32	1 1/32	5 11/32
5/16	1/16	5/16	1/4	1 11/32	15/32	2 11/32	21/32	3 3/8	27/32	4 13/32	1 1/16	5 13/32
3/8	1/16	3/8	9/32	1 13/32	15/32	2 13/32	21/32	3 7/16	7/8	4 15/32	1 1/16	5 15/32
7/16	3/32	7/16	9/32	1 15/32	1/2	2 1/2	11/16	3 1/2	7/8	4 17/32	1 1/16	5 17/32
1/2	3/32	1/2	5/16	1 17/32	1/2	2 9/16	11/16	3 9/16	7/8	4 19/32	1 3/32	5 19/32
9/16	3/32	9/16	5/16	1 19/32	1/2	2 5/8	23/32	3 5/8	29/32	4 21/32	1 3/32	5 21/32
5/8	1/8	5/8	5/16	1 21/32	17/32	2 11/16	23/32	3 11/16	29/32	4 23/32	1 1/8	5 23/32
11/16	1/8	11/16	11/32	1 23/32	17/32	2 3/4	23/32	3 3/4	15/16	4 25/32	1 1/8	5 13/16
3/4	5/32	3/4	11/32	1 25/32	17/32	2 13/16	3/4	3 13/16	15/16	4 27/32	1 1/8	5 7/8
13/16	5/32	27/32	11/32	1 27/32	9/16	2 7/8	3/4	3 7/8	15/16	4 29/32	1 5/32	5 15/16
7/8	3/16	29/32	3/8	1 29/32	9/16	2 15/16	25/32	3 15/16	31/32	4 31/32	1 5/32	6
15/16	3/16	31/32	3/8	1 31/32	19/32	3	25/32	4	31/32	5 1/32	1 3/16	6 1/16

Inches	6" Rise	6" Slope	7" Rise	7" Slope	8" Rise	8" Slope	9" Rise	9" Slope	10" Rise	10" Slope	11" Rise	11" Slope
0	13/16	6 1/8	1 3/8	7 1/8	1 19/32	8 5/32	1 25/32	9 3/16	1 31/32	10 3/16	2 3/16	11 7/32
1/16	13/16	6 3/16	1 13/32	7 3/32	1 19/32	8 7/32	1 25/32	9 1/4	2	10 1/4	2 3/16	11 9/32
1/8	17/32	6 1/4	1 13/32	7 1/4	1 19/32	8 9/32	1 13/16	9 5/16	2	10 5/16	2 3/16	11 11/32
3/16	17/32	6 5/16	1 7/16	7 5/16	1 5/8	8 11/32	1 13/16	9 3/8	2 1/32	10 3/8	2 7/32	11 13/32
1/4	1 1/4	6 3/8	1 7/16	7 13/32	1 5/8	8 13/32	1 27/32	9 7/16	2 1/32	10 7/16	2 7/32	11 15/32
5/16	1 1/4	6 7/16	1 7/16	7 15/32	1 21/32	8 15/32	1 27/32	9 1/2	2 1/16	10 1/2	2 1/4	11 17/32
3/8	1 1/4	6 1/2	1 15/32	7 17/32	1 21/32	8 17/32	1 27/32	9 9/16	2 1/16	10 9/16	2 1/4	11 19/32
7/16	1 9/32	6 9/16	1 15/32	7 19/32	1 21/32	8 19/32	1 7/8	9 5/8	2 1/16	10 5/8	2 1/4	11 21/32
1/2	1 9/32	6 5/8	1 1/2	7 21/32	1 11/16	8 21/32	1 7/8	9 11/16	2 3/32	10 23/32	2 9/32	11 23/32
9/16	1 5/16	6 11/16	1 1/2	7 23/32	1 11/16	8 23/32	1 29/32	9 3/4	2 3/32	10 25/32	2 9/32	11 25/32
5/8	1 5/16	6 3/4	1 1/2	7 25/32	1 23/32	8 25/32	1 29/32	9 13/16	2 3/32	10 27/32	2 5/16	11 27/32
11/16	1 5/16	6 13/16	1 17/32	7 27/32	1 23/32	8 27/32	1 29/32	9 7/8	2 1/8	10 29/32	2 5/16	11 29/32
3/4	1 11/32	6 7/8	1 17/32	7 29/32	1 23/32	8 29/32	1 15/16	9 15/16	2 1/8	10 31/32	2 5/16	11 31/32
13/16	1 11/32	6 15/16	1 17/32	7 31/32	1 3/4	8 31/32	1 15/16	10	2 1/8	11 1/32	2 11/32	1-0 1/32
7/8	1 3/8	7	1 9/16	8 1/32	1 3/4	9 1/16	1 31/32	10 1/16	2 5/32	11 3/32	2 11/32	1-0 3/32
15/16	1 3/8	7 1/16	1 9/16	8 3/32	1 25/32	9 1/8	1 31/32	10 1/8	2 5/32	11 5/32	2 3/8	1-0 5/32

Feet	0' Rise	0' Slope	10' Rise	10' Slope	20' Rise	20' Slope	30' Rise	30' Slope
0	0	0	1-11 3/4	10-2 5/16	3-11 1/2	20-4 21/32	5-11 1/4	30-6 31/32
1	2 3/8	1-0 7/32	2-2 1/8	11-2 9/16	4-1 7/8	21-4 7/8	6-1 5/8	31-7 7/32
2	4 3/4	2-0 15/32	2-4 1/2	12-2 25/32	4-4 1/4	22-5 1/8	6-4	32-7 1/2
3	7 1/8	3-0 11/16	2-6 7/8	13-3 1/32	4-6 5/8	23-5 11/32	6-6 3/8	33-7 11/16
4	9 1/2	4-0 15/16	2-9 1/4	14-3 1/4	4-9	24-5 19/32	6-8 3/4	34-7 29/32
5	11 7/8	5-1 5/32	2-11 5/8	15-3 1/2	4-11 3/8	25-5 13/16	6-11 1/8	35-8 5/32
6	1-2 1/4	6-1 13/32	3-2	16-3 23/32	5-1 3/4	26-6 1/16	7-1 1/2	36-8 3/8
7	1-4 5/8	7-1 5/8	3-4 3/8	17-3 31/32	5-4 1/8	27-6 9/32	7-3 7/8	37-8 5/8
8	1-7	8-1 7/8	3-6 3/4	18-4 3/16	5-6 1/2	28-6 17/32	7-6 1/4	38-8 27/32
9	1-9 3/8	9-2 3/32	3-9 1/8	19-4 7/16	5-8 7/8	29-6 3/4	7-8 5/8	39-9 1/16

A = 11° 11′ 42″; logsin A = 9.28814; logcos A = 9.99166; logtan A = 9.29648; logcot A = 0.70352

In.	12″ Rise	12″ Slope	13″ Rise	13″ Slope	14″ Rise	14″ Slope	15″ Rise	15″ Slope	16″ Rise	16″ Slope
0	$2\frac{3}{8}$	$1\text{-}0\frac{7}{32}$	$2\frac{9}{16}$	$1\text{-}1\frac{1}{4}$	$2\frac{25}{32}$	$1\text{-}2\frac{9}{32}$	$2\frac{31}{32}$	$1\text{-}3\frac{9}{32}$	$3\frac{5}{32}$	$1\text{-}4\frac{5}{16}$
$\frac{1}{16}$	$2\frac{5}{8}$	$1\text{-}0\frac{9}{32}$	$2\frac{19}{32}$	$1\text{-}1\frac{5}{16}$	$2\frac{25}{32}$	$1\text{-}2\frac{11}{32}$	$2\frac{31}{32}$	$1\text{-}3\frac{11}{32}$	$3\frac{3}{16}$	$1\text{-}4\frac{3}{8}$
$\frac{1}{8}$	$2\frac{13}{32}$	$1\text{-}0\frac{3}{8}$	$2\frac{19}{32}$	$1\text{-}1\frac{3}{8}$	$2\frac{25}{32}$	$1\text{-}2\frac{13}{32}$	3	$1\text{-}3\frac{13}{32}$	$3\frac{3}{16}$	$1\text{-}4\frac{7}{16}$
$\frac{3}{16}$	$2\frac{13}{32}$	$1\text{-}0\frac{7}{16}$	$2\frac{5}{8}$	$1\text{-}1\frac{7}{16}$	$2\frac{13}{16}$	$1\text{-}2\frac{15}{32}$	3	$1\text{-}3\frac{15}{32}$	$3\frac{7}{32}$	$1\text{-}4\frac{1}{2}$
$\frac{1}{4}$	$2\frac{7}{16}$	$1\text{-}0\frac{1}{2}$	$2\frac{5}{8}$	$1\text{-}1\frac{1}{2}$	$2\frac{13}{16}$	$1\text{-}2\frac{17}{32}$	$3\frac{1}{32}$	$1\text{-}3\frac{17}{32}$	$3\frac{7}{32}$	$1\text{-}4\frac{9}{16}$
$\frac{5}{16}$	$2\frac{7}{16}$	$1\text{-}0\frac{9}{16}$	$2\frac{5}{8}$	$1\text{-}1\frac{9}{16}$	$2\frac{27}{32}$	$1\text{-}2\frac{19}{32}$	$3\frac{1}{32}$	$1\text{-}3\frac{5}{8}$	$3\frac{7}{32}$	$1\text{-}4\frac{5}{8}$
$\frac{3}{8}$	$2\frac{7}{16}$	$1\text{-}0\frac{5}{8}$	$2\frac{21}{32}$	$1\text{-}1\frac{5}{8}$	$2\frac{27}{32}$	$1\text{-}2\frac{21}{32}$	$3\frac{1}{32}$	$1\text{-}3\frac{11}{16}$	$3\frac{1}{4}$	$1\text{-}4\frac{11}{16}$
$\frac{7}{16}$	$2\frac{15}{32}$	$1\text{-}0\frac{11}{16}$	$2\frac{21}{32}$	$1\text{-}1\frac{11}{16}$	$2\frac{27}{32}$	$1\text{-}2\frac{23}{32}$	$3\frac{1}{16}$	$1\text{-}3\frac{3}{4}$	$3\frac{1}{4}$	$1\text{-}4\frac{3}{4}$
$\frac{1}{2}$	$2\frac{15}{32}$	$1\text{-}0\frac{3}{4}$	$2\frac{11}{16}$	$1\text{-}1\frac{3}{4}$	$2\frac{7}{8}$	$1\text{-}2\frac{25}{32}$	$3\frac{1}{16}$	$1\text{-}3\frac{13}{16}$	$3\frac{1}{4}$	$1\text{-}4\frac{13}{16}$
$\frac{9}{16}$	$2\frac{1}{2}$	$1\text{-}0\frac{13}{16}$	$2\frac{11}{16}$	$1\text{-}1\frac{13}{16}$	$2\frac{7}{8}$	$1\text{-}2\frac{27}{32}$	$3\frac{3}{32}$	$1\text{-}3\frac{7}{8}$	$3\frac{9}{32}$	$1\text{-}4\frac{7}{8}$
$\frac{5}{8}$	$2\frac{1}{2}$	$1\text{-}0\frac{7}{8}$	$2\frac{11}{16}$	$1\text{-}1\frac{7}{8}$	$2\frac{29}{32}$	$1\text{-}2\frac{29}{32}$	$3\frac{3}{32}$	$1\text{-}3\frac{15}{16}$	$3\frac{9}{32}$	$1\text{-}4\frac{15}{16}$
$\frac{11}{16}$	$2\frac{1}{2}$	$1\text{-}0\frac{15}{16}$	$2\frac{23}{32}$	$1\text{-}1\frac{15}{16}$	$2\frac{29}{32}$	$1\text{-}2\frac{31}{32}$	$3\frac{3}{32}$	$1\text{-}4$	$3\frac{5}{16}$	$1\text{-}5$
$\frac{3}{4}$	$2\frac{17}{32}$	$1\text{-}1$	$2\frac{23}{32}$	$1\text{-}2\frac{1}{32}$	$2\frac{29}{32}$	$1\text{-}3\frac{1}{32}$	$3\frac{1}{8}$	$1\text{-}4\frac{1}{16}$	$3\frac{5}{16}$	$1\text{-}5\frac{1}{16}$
$\frac{13}{16}$	$2\frac{17}{32}$	$1\text{-}1\frac{1}{16}$	$2\frac{23}{32}$	$1\text{-}2\frac{3}{32}$	$2\frac{15}{16}$	$1\text{-}3\frac{3}{32}$	$3\frac{1}{8}$	$1\text{-}4\frac{1}{8}$	$3\frac{5}{16}$	$1\text{-}5\frac{1}{8}$
$\frac{7}{8}$	$2\frac{9}{16}$	$1\text{-}1\frac{1}{8}$	$2\frac{3}{4}$	$1\text{-}2\frac{5}{32}$	$2\frac{15}{16}$	$1\text{-}3\frac{5}{32}$	$3\frac{5}{32}$	$1\text{-}4\frac{3}{16}$	$3\frac{11}{32}$	$1\text{-}5\frac{3}{16}$
$\frac{15}{16}$	$2\frac{9}{16}$	$1\text{-}1\frac{3}{16}$	$2\frac{3}{4}$	$1\text{-}2\frac{7}{32}$	$2\frac{31}{32}$	$1\text{-}3\frac{7}{32}$	$3\frac{5}{32}$	$1\text{-}4\frac{1}{4}$	$3\frac{11}{32}$	$1\text{-}5\frac{9}{32}$

In.	17″ Rise	17″ Slope	18″ Rise	18″ Slope	19″ Rise	19″ Slope	20″ Rise	20″ Slope	21″ Rise	21″ Slope
0	$3\frac{3}{8}$	$1\text{-}5\frac{11}{32}$	$3\frac{9}{16}$	$1\text{-}6\frac{11}{32}$	$3\frac{3}{4}$	$1\text{-}7\frac{3}{8}$	$3\frac{31}{32}$	$1\text{-}8\frac{3}{8}$	$4\frac{5}{32}$	$1\text{-}9\frac{13}{32}$
$\frac{1}{16}$	$3\frac{3}{8}$	$1\text{-}5\frac{13}{32}$	$3\frac{9}{16}$	$1\text{-}6\frac{13}{32}$	$3\frac{25}{32}$	$1\text{-}7\frac{7}{16}$	$3\frac{31}{32}$	$1\text{-}8\frac{7}{16}$	$4\frac{5}{32}$	$1\text{-}9\frac{15}{32}$
$\frac{1}{8}$	$3\frac{3}{8}$	$1\text{-}5\frac{15}{32}$	$3\frac{19}{32}$	$1\text{-}6\frac{15}{32}$	$3\frac{25}{32}$	$1\text{-}7\frac{1}{2}$	$3\frac{31}{32}$	$1\text{-}8\frac{1}{2}$	$4\frac{3}{16}$	$1\text{-}9\frac{17}{32}$
$\frac{3}{16}$	$3\frac{13}{32}$	$1\text{-}5\frac{17}{32}$	$3\frac{19}{32}$	$1\text{-}6\frac{17}{32}$	$3\frac{13}{16}$	$1\text{-}7\frac{9}{16}$	4	$1\text{-}8\frac{19}{32}$	$4\frac{3}{16}$	$1\text{-}9\frac{19}{32}$
$\frac{1}{4}$	$3\frac{13}{32}$	$1\text{-}5\frac{19}{32}$	$3\frac{5}{8}$	$1\text{-}6\frac{19}{32}$	$3\frac{13}{16}$	$1\text{-}7\frac{5}{8}$	4	$1\text{-}8\frac{21}{32}$	$4\frac{7}{32}$	$1\text{-}9\frac{21}{32}$
$\frac{5}{16}$	$3\frac{7}{16}$	$1\text{-}5\frac{21}{32}$	$3\frac{5}{8}$	$1\text{-}6\frac{21}{32}$	$3\frac{13}{16}$	$1\text{-}7\frac{11}{16}$	$4\frac{1}{32}$	$1\text{-}8\frac{23}{32}$	$4\frac{7}{32}$	$1\text{-}9\frac{23}{32}$
$\frac{3}{8}$	$3\frac{7}{16}$	$1\text{-}5\frac{23}{32}$	$3\frac{5}{8}$	$1\text{-}6\frac{23}{32}$	$3\frac{27}{32}$	$1\text{-}7\frac{3}{4}$	$4\frac{1}{32}$	$1\text{-}8\frac{25}{32}$	$4\frac{7}{32}$	$1\text{-}9\frac{25}{32}$
$\frac{7}{16}$	$3\frac{7}{16}$	$1\text{-}5\frac{25}{32}$	$3\frac{21}{32}$	$1\text{-}6\frac{25}{32}$	$3\frac{27}{32}$	$1\text{-}7\frac{13}{16}$	$4\frac{1}{32}$	$1\text{-}8\frac{27}{32}$	$4\frac{1}{4}$	$1\text{-}9\frac{27}{32}$
$\frac{1}{2}$	$3\frac{15}{32}$	$1\text{-}5\frac{27}{32}$	$3\frac{21}{32}$	$1\text{-}6\frac{27}{32}$	$3\frac{7}{8}$	$1\text{-}7\frac{7}{8}$	$4\frac{1}{16}$	$1\text{-}8\frac{29}{32}$	$4\frac{1}{4}$	$1\text{-}9\frac{29}{32}$
$\frac{9}{16}$	$3\frac{15}{32}$	$1\text{-}5\frac{29}{32}$	$3\frac{11}{16}$	$1\text{-}6\frac{15}{16}$	$3\frac{7}{8}$	$1\text{-}7\frac{15}{16}$	$4\frac{1}{16}$	$1\text{-}8\frac{31}{32}$	$4\frac{9}{32}$	$1\text{-}9\frac{31}{32}$
$\frac{5}{8}$	$3\frac{1}{2}$	$1\text{-}5\frac{31}{32}$	$3\frac{11}{16}$	$1\text{-}7$	$3\frac{7}{8}$	$1\text{-}8$	$4\frac{3}{32}$	$1\text{-}9\frac{1}{32}$	$4\frac{9}{32}$	$1\text{-}10\frac{1}{32}$
$\frac{11}{16}$	$3\frac{1}{2}$	$1\text{-}6\frac{1}{32}$	$3\frac{11}{16}$	$1\text{-}7\frac{1}{32}$	$3\frac{29}{32}$	$1\text{-}8\frac{1}{16}$	$4\frac{3}{32}$	$1\text{-}9\frac{3}{32}$	$4\frac{9}{32}$	$1\text{-}10\frac{3}{32}$
$\frac{3}{4}$	$3\frac{1}{2}$	$1\text{-}6\frac{3}{32}$	$3\frac{23}{32}$	$1\text{-}7\frac{1}{8}$	$3\frac{29}{32}$	$1\text{-}8\frac{1}{8}$	$4\frac{3}{32}$	$1\text{-}9\frac{5}{32}$	$4\frac{5}{16}$	$1\text{-}10\frac{3}{32}$
$\frac{13}{16}$	$3\frac{17}{32}$	$1\text{-}6\frac{5}{32}$	$3\frac{23}{32}$	$1\text{-}7\frac{3}{16}$	$3\frac{29}{32}$	$1\text{-}8\frac{3}{16}$	$4\frac{1}{8}$	$1\text{-}9\frac{7}{32}$	$4\frac{5}{16}$	$1\text{-}10\frac{1}{4}$
$\frac{7}{8}$	$3\frac{17}{32}$	$1\text{-}6\frac{7}{32}$	$3\frac{3}{4}$	$1\text{-}7\frac{1}{4}$	$3\frac{15}{16}$	$1\text{-}8\frac{1}{4}$	$4\frac{1}{8}$	$1\text{-}9\frac{9}{32}$	$4\frac{11}{32}$	$1\text{-}10\frac{5}{16}$
$\frac{15}{16}$	$3\frac{9}{16}$	$1\text{-}6\frac{9}{32}$	$3\frac{3}{4}$	$1\text{-}7\frac{5}{16}$	$3\frac{15}{16}$	$1\text{-}8\frac{5}{16}$	$4\frac{5}{32}$	$1\text{-}9\frac{11}{32}$	$4\frac{11}{32}$	$1\text{-}10\frac{3}{8}$

Feet	40′ Rise	40′ Slope	50′ Rise	50′ Slope	60′ Rise	60′ Slope	70′ Rise	70′ Slope
0	$7\text{-}11$	$40\text{-}9\frac{5}{16}$	$9\text{-}10\frac{3}{4}$	$50\text{-}11\frac{5}{8}$	$11\text{-}10\frac{1}{2}$	$61\text{-}1\frac{31}{32}$	$13\text{-}10\frac{1}{4}$	$71\text{-}4\frac{9}{32}$
1	$8\text{-}1\frac{3}{8}$	$41\text{-}9\frac{17}{32}$	$10\text{-}1\frac{1}{8}$	$51\text{-}11\frac{7}{8}$	$12\text{-}0\frac{7}{8}$	$62\text{-}2\frac{3}{16}$	$14\text{-}0\frac{5}{8}$	$72\text{-}4\frac{17}{32}$
2	$8\text{-}3\frac{3}{4}$	$42\text{-}9\frac{25}{32}$	$10\text{-}3\frac{1}{2}$	$53\text{-}0\frac{3}{32}$	$12\text{-}3\frac{1}{4}$	$63\text{-}2\frac{7}{16}$	$14\text{-}3$	$73\text{-}4\frac{3}{4}$
3	$8\text{-}6\frac{1}{8}$	$43\text{-}10$	$10\text{-}5\frac{7}{8}$	$54\text{-}0\frac{11}{32}$	$12\text{-}5\frac{5}{8}$	$64\text{-}2\frac{21}{32}$	$14\text{-}5\frac{3}{8}$	$74\text{-}5$
4	$8\text{-}8\frac{1}{2}$	$44\text{-}10\frac{1}{4}$	$10\text{-}8\frac{1}{4}$	$55\text{-}0\frac{9}{16}$	$12\text{-}8$	$65\text{-}2\frac{29}{32}$	$14\text{-}7\frac{3}{4}$	$75\text{-}5\frac{7}{32}$
5	$8\text{-}10\frac{7}{8}$	$45\text{-}10\frac{15}{32}$	$10\text{-}10\frac{5}{8}$	$56\text{-}0\frac{13}{16}$	$12\text{-}10\frac{3}{8}$	$66\text{-}3\frac{1}{8}$	$14\text{-}10\frac{1}{8}$	$76\text{-}5\frac{15}{32}$
6	$9\text{-}1\frac{1}{4}$	$46\text{-}10\frac{23}{32}$	$11\text{-}1$	$57\text{-}1\frac{1}{32}$	$13\text{-}0\frac{3}{4}$	$67\text{-}3\frac{3}{8}$	$15\text{-}0\frac{1}{2}$	$77\text{-}5\frac{11}{16}$
7	$9\text{-}3\frac{5}{8}$	$47\text{-}10\frac{15}{16}$	$11\text{-}3\frac{3}{8}$	$58\text{-}1\frac{9}{32}$	$13\text{-}3\frac{1}{8}$	$68\text{-}3\frac{19}{32}$	$15\text{-}2\frac{7}{8}$	$78\text{-}5\frac{15}{16}$
8	$9\text{-}6$	$48\text{-}11\frac{3}{16}$	$11\text{-}5\frac{3}{4}$	$59\text{-}1\frac{1}{2}$	$13\text{-}5\frac{1}{2}$	$69\text{-}3\frac{27}{32}$	$15\text{-}5\frac{1}{4}$	$79\text{-}6\frac{5}{32}$
9	$9\text{-}8\frac{3}{8}$	$49\text{-}11\frac{13}{32}$	$11\text{-}8\frac{1}{8}$	$60\text{-}1\frac{23}{32}$	$13\text{-}7\frac{7}{8}$	$70\text{-}4\frac{1}{16}$	$15\text{-}7\frac{5}{8}$	$80\text{-}6\frac{3}{8}$

natsin A=0.1941506536; natcos A=0.9809717241; nattan A=0.1979166666; natcot A=5.0526315789

Inches	0″ Rise	0″ Slope	1″ Rise	1″ Slope	2″ Rise	2″ Slope	3″ Rise	3″ Slope	4″ Rise	4″ Slope	5″ Rise	5″ Slope
0	0	0	3/16	1 1/32	13/32	2 1/32	19/32	3 1/16	13/16	4 3/32	1	5 3/32
1/16	0	1/16	7/32	1 3/32	13/32	2 3/32	5/8	3 1/8	13/16	4 5/32	1 1/32	5 5/32
1/8	1/32	1/8	7/32	1 5/32	7/16	2 5/32	5/8	3 3/16	27/32	4 7/32	1 1/32	5 7/32
3/16	1/32	3/16	1/4	1 7/32	7/16	2 7/32	21/32	3 1/4	27/32	4 9/32	1 1/16	5 9/32
1/4	1/16	1/4	1/4	1 9/32	15/32	2 9/32	21/32	3 5/16	7/8	4 11/32	1 1/16	5 11/32
5/16	1/16	5/16	9/32	1 11/32	15/32	2 3/8	11/16	3 3/8	7/8	4 13/32	1 3/32	5 13/32
3/8	1/16	3/8	9/32	1 13/32	15/32	2 7/16	11/16	3 7/16	7/8	4 15/32	1 3/32	5 1/2
7/16	3/32	7/16	9/32	1 15/32	1/2	2 1/2	11/16	3 1/2	29/32	4 17/32	1 3/32	5 9/16
1/2	3/32	1/2	5/16	1 17/32	1/2	2 9/16	23/32	3 9/16	29/32	4 19/32	1 1/8	5 5/8
9/16	1/8	9/16	5/16	1 19/32	17/32	2 5/8	23/32	3 5/8	15/16	4 21/32	1 1/8	5 11/16
5/8	1/8	5/8	11/32	1 21/32	17/32	2 11/16	3/4	3 11/16	15/16	4 23/32	1 5/32	5 3/4
11/16	1/8	11/16	11/32	1 23/32	17/32	2 3/4	3/4	3 3/4	15/16	4 25/32	1 5/32	5 13/16
3/4	5/32	3/4	11/32	1 25/32	9/16	2 13/16	3/4	3 13/16	31/32	4 27/32	1 5/32	5 7/8
13/16	5/32	27/32	3/8	1 27/32	9/16	2 7/8	25/32	3 7/8	31/32	4 29/32	1 3/16	5 15/16
7/8	3/16	29/32	3/8	1 29/32	19/32	2 15/16	25/32	3 15/16	1	4 31/32	1 3/16	6
15/16	3/16	31/32	13/32	1 31/32	19/32	3	13/16	4 1/32	1	5 1/32	1 7/32	6 1/16

Inches	6″ Rise	6″ Slope	7″ Rise	7″ Slope	8″ Rise	8″ Slope	9″ Rise	9″ Slope	10″ Rise	10″ Slope	11″ Rise	11″ Slope
0	1 7/32	6 1/8	1 13/32	7 5/32	1 5/8	8 5/32	1 13/16	9 3/16	2 1/32	10 7/32	2 7/32	11 7/32
1/16	1 7/32	6 3/16	1 7/16	7 7/32	1 5/8	8 7/32	1 27/32	9 1/4	2 1/32	10 9/32	2 1/4	11 9/32
1/8	1 1/4	6 1/4	1 7/16	7 9/32	1 21/32	8 9/32	1 27/32	9 5/16	2 1/16	10 11/32	2 1/4	11 11/32
3/16	1 1/4	6 5/16	1 15/32	7 11/32	1 21/32	8 11/32	1 7/8	9 3/8	2 1/16	10 13/32	2 9/32	11 13/32
1/4	1 9/32	6 3/8	1 15/32	7 13/32	1 11/16	8 13/32	1 7/8	9 7/16	2 3/32	10 15/32	2 9/32	11 15/32
5/16	1 9/32	6 7/16	1 1/2	7 15/32	1 11/16	8 15/32	1 29/32	9 1/2	2 3/32	10 17/32	2 5/16	11 17/32
3/8	1 9/32	6 1/2	1 1/2	7 17/32	1 11/16	8 17/32	1 29/32	9 9/16	2 3/32	10 19/32	2 5/16	11 19/32
7/16	1 5/16	6 9/16	1 1/2	7 19/32	1 23/32	8 5/8	1 29/32	9 5/8	2 1/8	10 21/32	2 5/16	11 21/32
1/2	1 5/16	6 5/8	1 17/32	7 21/32	1 23/32	8 11/16	1 15/16	9 11/16	2 1/8	10 23/32	2 11/32	11 3/4
9/16	1 11/32	6 11/16	1 17/32	7 23/32	1 3/4	8 3/4	1 15/16	9 3/4	2 5/32	10 25/32	2 11/32	11 13/16
5/8	1 11/32	6 3/4	1 9/16	7 25/32	1 3/4	8 13/16	1 31/32	9 13/16	2 5/32	10 27/32	2 3/8	11 7/8
11/16	1 11/32	6 13/16	1 9/16	7 27/32	1 3/4	8 7/8	1 31/32	9 7/8	2 5/32	10 29/32	2 3/8	11 15/16
3/4	1 3/8	6 7/8	1 9/16	7 29/32	1 25/32	8 15/16	1 31/32	9 15/16	2 3/16	10 31/32	2 3/8	1-0
13/16	1 3/8	6 15/16	1 19/32	7 31/32	1 25/32	9	2	10	2 3/16	11 1/32	2 13/32	1-0 1/16
7/8	1 13/32	7	1 19/32	8 1/32	1 13/16	9 1/16	2	10 1/16	2 7/32	11 3/32	2 13/32	1-0 1/8
15/16	1 13/32	7 3/32	1 5/8	8 3/32	1 13/16	9 1/8	2 1/32	10 1/8	2 7/32	11 5/32	2 7/16	1-0 3/16

Feet	0′ Rise	0′ Slope	10′ Rise	10′ Slope	20′ Rise	20′ Slope	30′ Rise	30′ Slope
0	0	0	2-0 3/8	10-2 7/16	4-0 3/4	20-4 29/32	6-1 1/8	30-7 11/32
1	2 7/16	1-0 1/4	2-2 13/16	11-2 11/16	4-3 3/16	21-5 5/32	6-3 9/16	31-7 19/32
2	4 7/8	2-0 1/2	2-5 1/4	12-2 15/16	4-5 5/8	22-5 13/32	6-6	32-7 27/32
3	7 5/16	3-0 3/4	2-7 11/16	13-3 3/16	4-8 1/16	23-5 5/8	6-8 7/16	33-8 3/32
4	9 3/4	4-0 31/32	2-10 1/8	14-3 7/16	4-10 1/2	24-5 7/8	6-10 7/8	34-8 11/32
5	1-0 3/16	5-1 7/32	3-0 9/16	15-3 11/16	5-0 15/16	25-6 1/8	7-1 5/16	35-8 9/16
6	1-2 5/8	6-1 15/32	3-3	16-3 15/16	5-3 3/8	26-6 3/8	7-3 3/4	36-8 13/16
7	1-5 1/16	7-1 23/32	3-5 7/16	17-4 3/16	5-5 13/16	27-6 5/8	7-6 3/16	37-9 1/16
8	1-7 1/2	8-1 31/32	3-7 7/8	18-4 13/32	5-8 1/4	28-6 7/8	7-8 5/8	38-9 5/16
9	1-9 15/16	9-2 7/32	3-10 5/16	19-4 21/32	5-10 11/16	29-7 3/32	7-11 1/16	39-9 9/16

A = 11° 28′ 55″; logsin A = 9.29898; logcos A = 9.99122; logtan A = 9.30776; logcot A = 0.69224

Ins.	12″ Rise	12″ Slope	13″ Rise	13″ Slope	14″ Rise	14″ Slope	15″ Rise	15″ Slope	16″ Rise	16″ Slope
0	$2\frac{7}{16}$	$1\text{-}0\frac14$	$2\frac58$	$1\text{-}1\frac14$	$2\frac{27}{32}$	$1\text{-}2\frac{9}{32}$	$3\frac{1}{16}$	$1\text{-}3\frac{5}{16}$	$3\frac14$	$1\text{-}4\frac{5}{16}$
$\frac1{16}$	$2\frac{7}{16}$	$1\text{-}0\frac{5}{16}$	$2\frac{21}{32}$	$1\text{-}1\frac{11}{32}$	$2\frac{27}{32}$	$1\text{-}2\frac{11}{32}$	$3\frac1{16}$	$1\text{-}3\frac38$	$3\frac14$	$1\text{-}4\frac38$
$\frac18$	$2\frac{15}{32}$	$1\text{-}0\frac38$	$2\frac{21}{32}$	$1\text{-}1\frac{13}{32}$	$2\frac78$	$1\text{-}2\frac{13}{32}$	$3\frac1{16}$	$1\text{-}3\frac7{16}$	$3\frac{9}{32}$	$1\text{-}4\frac{15}{32}$
$\frac3{16}$	$2\frac{15}{32}$	$1\text{-}0\frac7{16}$	$2\frac{11}{16}$	$1\text{-}1\frac{15}{32}$	$2\frac78$	$1\text{-}2\frac{15}{32}$	$3\frac3{32}$	$1\text{-}3\frac12$	$3\frac{9}{32}$	$1\text{-}4\frac{17}{32}$
$\frac14$	$2\frac12$	$1\text{-}0\frac12$	$2\frac{11}{16}$	$1\text{-}1\frac{17}{32}$	$2\frac{29}{32}$	$1\text{-}2\frac{17}{32}$	$3\frac3{32}$	$1\text{-}3\frac9{16}$	$3\frac5{16}$	$1\text{-}4\frac{19}{32}$
$\frac5{16}$	$2\frac12$	$1\text{-}0\frac9{16}$	$2\frac{23}{32}$	$1\text{-}1\frac{19}{32}$	$2\frac{29}{32}$	$1\text{-}2\frac{19}{32}$	$3\frac18$	$1\text{-}3\frac58$	$3\frac5{16}$	$1\text{-}4\frac{21}{32}$
$\frac38$	$2\frac12$	$1\text{-}0\frac58$	$2\frac{23}{32}$	$1\text{-}1\frac{21}{32}$	$2\frac{29}{32}$	$1\text{-}2\frac{21}{32}$	$3\frac18$	$1\text{-}3\frac{11}{16}$	$3\frac5{16}$	$1\text{-}4\frac{23}{32}$
$\frac7{16}$	$2\frac{17}{32}$	$1\text{-}0\frac{11}{16}$	$2\frac{23}{32}$	$1\text{-}1\frac{23}{32}$	$2\frac{15}{16}$	$1\text{-}2\frac{23}{32}$	$3\frac18$	$1\text{-}3\frac34$	$3\frac{11}{32}$	$1\text{-}4\frac{25}{32}$
$\frac12$	$2\frac{17}{32}$	$1\text{-}0\frac34$	$2\frac34$	$1\text{-}1\frac{25}{32}$	$2\frac{15}{16}$	$1\text{-}2\frac{25}{32}$	$3\frac5{32}$	$1\text{-}3\frac{13}{16}$	$3\frac{11}{32}$	$1\text{-}4\frac{27}{32}$
$\frac9{16}$	$2\frac9{16}$	$1\text{-}0\frac{13}{16}$	$2\frac34$	$1\text{-}1\frac{27}{32}$	$2\frac{31}{32}$	$1\text{-}2\frac78$	$3\frac5{32}$	$1\text{-}3\frac78$	$3\frac38$	$1\text{-}4\frac{29}{32}$
$\frac58$	$2\frac9{16}$	$1\text{-}0\frac78$	$2\frac{25}{32}$	$1\text{-}1\frac{29}{32}$	$2\frac{31}{32}$	$1\text{-}2\frac{15}{16}$	$3\frac3{16}$	$1\text{-}3\frac{15}{16}$	$3\frac38$	$1\text{-}4\frac{31}{32}$
$\frac{11}{16}$	$2\frac9{16}$	$1\text{-}0\frac{15}{16}$	$2\frac{25}{32}$	$1\text{-}1\frac{31}{32}$	$2\frac{31}{32}$	$1\text{-}3$	$3\frac3{16}$	$1\text{-}4$	$3\frac38$	$1\text{-}5\frac1{32}$
$\frac34$	$2\frac{19}{32}$	$1\text{-}1$	$2\frac{25}{32}$	$1\text{-}2\frac12$	3	$1\text{-}3\frac1{16}$	$3\frac3{16}$	$1\text{-}4\frac1{16}$	$3\frac{13}{32}$	$1\text{-}5\frac3{32}$
$\frac{13}{16}$	$2\frac{19}{32}$	$1\text{-}1\frac1{16}$	$2\frac{13}{16}$	$1\text{-}2\frac3{32}$	3	$1\text{-}3\frac18$	$3\frac7{32}$	$1\text{-}4\frac18$	$3\frac{13}{32}$	$1\text{-}5\frac5{32}$
$\frac78$	$2\frac58$	$1\text{-}1\frac18$	$2\frac{13}{16}$	$1\text{-}2\frac5{32}$	$3\frac1{32}$	$1\text{-}3\frac3{16}$	$3\frac7{32}$	$1\text{-}4\frac3{16}$	$3\frac7{16}$	$1\text{-}5\frac7{32}$
$\frac{15}{16}$	$2\frac58$	$1\text{-}1\frac3{16}$	$2\frac{27}{32}$	$1\text{-}2\frac7{32}$	$3\frac1{32}$	$1\text{-}3\frac14$	$3\frac14$	$1\text{-}4\frac14$	$3\frac7{16}$	$1\text{-}5\frac9{32}$

Ins.	17″ Rise	17″ Slope	18″ Rise	18″ Slope	19″ Rise	19″ Slope	20″ Rise	20″ Slope	21″ Rise	21″ Slope
0	$3\frac7{16}$	$1\text{-}5\frac{11}{32}$	$3\frac{21}{32}$	$1\text{-}6\frac38$	$3\frac78$	$1\text{-}7\frac38$	$4\frac1{16}$	$1\text{-}8\frac{13}{32}$	$4\frac14$	$1\text{-}9\frac7{16}$
$\frac1{16}$	$3\frac{15}{32}$	$1\text{-}5\frac{13}{32}$	$3\frac{21}{32}$	$1\text{-}6\frac7{16}$	$3\frac78$	$1\text{-}7\frac7{16}$	$4\frac1{16}$	$1\text{-}8\frac{15}{32}$	$4\frac9{32}$	$1\text{-}9\frac12$
$\frac18$	$3\frac{15}{32}$	$1\text{-}5\frac{15}{32}$	$3\frac{11}{16}$	$1\text{-}6\frac12$	$3\frac78$	$1\text{-}7\frac12$	$4\frac3{32}$	$1\text{-}8\frac{17}{32}$	$4\frac9{32}$	$1\text{-}9\frac9{16}$
$\frac3{16}$	$3\frac12$	$1\text{-}5\frac{17}{32}$	$3\frac{11}{16}$	$1\text{-}6\frac9{16}$	$3\frac{29}{32}$	$1\text{-}7\frac{19}{32}$	$4\frac3{32}$	$1\text{-}8\frac{19}{32}$	$4\frac5{16}$	$1\text{-}9\frac58$
$\frac14$	$3\frac12$	$1\text{-}5\frac{19}{32}$	$3\frac{23}{32}$	$1\text{-}6\frac58$	$3\frac{29}{32}$	$1\text{-}7\frac{21}{32}$	$4\frac18$	$1\text{-}8\frac{21}{32}$	$4\frac5{16}$	$1\text{-}9\frac{11}{16}$
$\frac5{16}$	$3\frac{17}{32}$	$1\text{-}5\frac{21}{32}$	$3\frac{23}{32}$	$1\text{-}6\frac{11}{16}$	$3\frac{15}{16}$	$1\text{-}7\frac{23}{32}$	$4\frac18$	$1\text{-}8\frac{23}{32}$	$4\frac{11}{32}$	$1\text{-}9\frac34$
$\frac38$	$3\frac{17}{32}$	$1\text{-}5\frac{23}{32}$	$3\frac{23}{32}$	$1\text{-}6\frac34$	$3\frac{15}{16}$	$1\text{-}7\frac{25}{32}$	$4\frac18$	$1\text{-}8\frac{25}{32}$	$4\frac{11}{32}$	$1\text{-}9\frac{13}{16}$
$\frac7{16}$	$3\frac{17}{32}$	$1\text{-}5\frac{25}{32}$	$3\frac34$	$1\text{-}6\frac{13}{16}$	$3\frac{15}{16}$	$1\text{-}7\frac{27}{32}$	$4\frac5{32}$	$1\text{-}8\frac{27}{32}$	$4\frac{11}{32}$	$1\text{-}9\frac78$
$\frac12$	$3\frac9{16}$	$1\text{-}5\frac{27}{32}$	$3\frac34$	$1\text{-}6\frac78$	$3\frac{31}{32}$	$1\text{-}7\frac{29}{32}$	$4\frac5{32}$	$1\text{-}8\frac{29}{32}$	$4\frac38$	$1\text{-}9\frac{15}{16}$
$\frac9{16}$	$3\frac9{16}$	$1\text{-}5\frac{29}{32}$	$3\frac{25}{32}$	$1\text{-}6\frac{15}{16}$	$3\frac{31}{32}$	$1\text{-}7\frac{31}{32}$	$4\frac3{16}$	$1\text{-}8\frac{31}{32}$	$4\frac38$	$1\text{-}10$
$\frac58$	$3\frac{19}{32}$	$1\text{-}6$	$3\frac{25}{32}$	$1\text{-}7$	4	$1\text{-}8\frac1{32}$	$4\frac3{16}$	$1\text{-}9\frac1{32}$	$4\frac{13}{32}$	$1\text{-}10\frac1{16}$
$\frac{11}{16}$	$3\frac{19}{32}$	$1\text{-}6\frac1{16}$	$3\frac{25}{32}$	$1\text{-}7\frac1{16}$	4	$1\text{-}8\frac3{32}$	$4\frac3{16}$	$1\text{-}9\frac18$	$4\frac{13}{32}$	$1\text{-}10\frac18$
$\frac34$	$3\frac{19}{32}$	$1\text{-}6\frac18$	$3\frac{13}{16}$	$1\text{-}7\frac18$	4	$1\text{-}8\frac5{32}$	$4\frac7{32}$	$1\text{-}9\frac3{16}$	$4\frac{13}{32}$	$1\text{-}10\frac3{16}$
$\frac{13}{16}$	$3\frac58$	$1\text{-}6\frac3{16}$	$3\frac{13}{16}$	$1\text{-}7\frac3{16}$	$4\frac1{32}$	$1\text{-}8\frac7{32}$	$4\frac7{32}$	$1\text{-}9\frac14$	$4\frac7{16}$	$1\text{-}10\frac14$
$\frac78$	$3\frac58$	$1\text{-}6\frac14$	$3\frac{27}{32}$	$1\text{-}7\frac14$	$4\frac1{32}$	$1\text{-}8\frac9{32}$	$4\frac14$	$1\text{-}9\frac5{16}$	$4\frac7{16}$	$1\text{-}10\frac5{16}$
$\frac{15}{16}$	$3\frac{21}{32}$	$1\text{-}6\frac5{16}$	$3\frac{27}{32}$	$1\text{-}7\frac5{16}$	$4\frac1{16}$	$1\text{-}8\frac{11}{32}$	$4\frac14$	$1\text{-}9\frac38$	$4\frac{15}{32}$	$1\text{-}10\frac38$

Feet	40′ Rise	40′ Slope	50′ Rise	50′ Slope	60′ Rise	60′ Slope	70′ Rise	70′ Slope
0	$8\text{-}1\frac12$	$40\text{-}9\frac{13}{16}$	$10\text{-}1\frac78$	$51\text{-}0\frac14$	$12\text{-}2\frac14$	$61\text{-}2\frac{23}{32}$	$14\text{-}2\frac58$	$71\text{-}5\frac5{32}$
1	$8\text{-}3\frac{15}{16}$	$41\text{-}10\frac1{16}$	$10\text{-}4\frac5{16}$	$52\text{-}0\frac12$	$12\text{-}4\frac{11}{16}$	$62\text{-}2\frac{15}{16}$	$14\text{-}5\frac1{16}$	$72\text{-}5\frac{13}{32}$
2	$8\text{-}6\frac38$	$42\text{-}10\frac9{32}$	$10\text{-}6\frac34$	$53\text{-}0\frac34$	$12\text{-}7\frac18$	$63\text{-}3\frac3{16}$	$14\text{-}7\frac12$	$73\text{-}5\frac{21}{32}$
3	$8\text{-}8\frac{13}{16}$	$43\text{-}10\frac{17}{32}$	$10\text{-}9\frac3{16}$	$54\text{-}1$	$12\text{-}9\frac9{16}$	$64\text{-}3\frac7{16}$	$14\text{-}9\frac{15}{16}$	$74\text{-}5\frac78$
4	$8\text{-}11\frac14$	$44\text{-}10\frac{25}{32}$	$10\text{-}11\frac58$	$55\text{-}1\frac7{32}$	$13\text{-}0$	$65\text{-}3\frac{11}{16}$	$15\text{-}0\frac38$	$75\text{-}6\frac18$
5	$9\text{-}1\frac{11}{16}$	$45\text{-}11\frac12$	$11\text{-}2\frac1{16}$	$56\text{-}1\frac{15}{32}$	$13\text{-}2\frac7{16}$	$66\text{-}3\frac{15}{16}$	$15\text{-}2\frac{13}{16}$	$76\text{-}6\frac38$
6	$9\text{-}4\frac18$	$46\text{-}11\frac9{32}$	$11\text{-}4\frac12$	$57\text{-}1\frac{23}{32}$	$13\text{-}4\frac78$	$67\text{-}4\frac3{16}$	$15\text{-}5\frac14$	$77\text{-}6\frac58$
7	$9\text{-}6\frac9{16}$	$47\text{-}11\frac{17}{32}$	$11\text{-}6\frac{15}{16}$	$58\text{-}1\frac{31}{32}$	$13\text{-}7\frac5{16}$	$68\text{-}4\frac{13}{32}$	$15\text{-}7\frac{11}{16}$	$78\text{-}6\frac78$
8	$9\text{-}9$	$48\text{-}11\frac34$	$11\text{-}9\frac38$	$59\text{-}2\frac7{32}$	$13\text{-}9\frac34$	$69\text{-}4\frac{21}{32}$	$15\text{-}10\frac18$	$79\text{-}7\frac18$
9	$9\text{-}11\frac7{16}$	$50\text{-}0$	$11\text{-}11\frac{13}{16}$	$60\text{-}2\frac{15}{32}$	$14\text{-}0\frac3{16}$	$70\text{-}4\frac{29}{32}$	$16\text{-}0\frac9{16}$	$80\text{-}7\frac38$

natsin A=0.1990599243; natcos A=0.9799873196; nattan A=0.2031250000; natcot A=4.9230769230

Inches	0" Rise	0" Slope	1" Rise	1" Slope	2" Rise	2" Slope	3" Rise	3" Slope	4" Rise	4" Slope	5" Rise	5" Slope
0	0	0	7/32	1 1/32	13/32	2 1/32	5/8	3 1/16	27/32	4 3/32	1 1/32	5 3/32
1/16	0	1/16	7/32	1 3/32	7/16	2 3/32	5/8	3 1/8	21/32	4 5/32	1 1/16	5 5/32
1/8	1/32	1/8	1/4	1 5/32	7/16	2 5/32	21/32	3 3/16	7/8	4 7/32	1 1/16	5 1/4
3/16	1/32	3/16	1/4	1 7/32	15/32	2 1/4	21/32	3 1/4	7/8	4 9/32	1 3/32	5 5/16
1/4	1/16	1/4	1/4	1 9/32	15/32	2 5/16	11/16	3 5/16	7/8	4 11/32	1 3/32	5 3/8
5/16	1/16	5/16	9/32	1 11/32	15/32	2 3/8	11/16	3 3/8	29/32	4 13/32	1 3/32	5 7/16
3/8	1/16	3/8	9/32	1 13/32	1/2	2 7/16	11/16	3 7/16	29/32	4 15/32	1 1/8	5 1/2
7/16	3/32	7/16	5/16	1 15/32	1/2	2 1/2	23/32	3 1/2	15/16	4 17/32	1 1/8	5 9/16
1/2	3/32	1/2	5/16	1 17/32	17/32	2 9/16	23/32	3 9/16	15/16	4 19/32	1 5/32	5 5/8
9/16	1/8	9/16	5/16	1 19/32	17/32	2 5/8	3/4	3 5/8	15/16	4 21/32	1 5/32	5 11/16
5/8	1/8	5/8	11/32	1 21/32	9/16	2 11/16	3/4	3 11/16	31/32	4 23/32	1 3/16	5 3/4
11/16	5/32	11/16	11/32	1 23/32	9/16	2 3/4	25/32	3 25/32	31/32	4 25/32	1 3/16	5 13/16
3/4	5/32	25/32	3/8	1 25/32	9/16	2 13/16	25/32	3 27/32	1	4 27/32	1 3/16	5 7/8
13/16	5/32	27/32	3/8	1 27/32	19/32	2 7/8	25/32	3 29/32	1	4 29/32	1 7/32	5 15/16
7/8	3/16	29/32	3/8	1 29/32	19/32	2 15/16	13/16	3 31/32	1	4 31/32	1 7/32	6
15/16	3/16	31/32	13/32	1 31/32	5/8	3	13/16	4 1/32	1 1/16	5 1/32	1 1/4	6 1/16

Inches	6" Rise	6" Slope	7" Rise	7" Slope	8" Rise	8" Slope	9" Rise	9" Slope	10" Rise	10" Slope	11" Rise	11" Slope
0	1 1/4	6 1/8	1 15/32	7 5/32	1 21/32	8 5/32	1 7/8	9 3/16	2 3/32	10 7/32	2 9/32	11 1/4
1/16	1 1/4	6 3/16	1 15/32	7 7/32	1 11/16	8 1/4	1 7/8	9 1/4	2 3/32	10 9/32	2 5/16	11 5/16
1/8	1 9/32	6 1/4	1 1/2	7 9/32	1 11/16	8 5/16	1 29/32	9 5/16	2 1/8	10 11/32	2 5/16	11 3/8
3/16	1 9/32	6 5/16	1 1/2	7 11/32	1 23/32	8 3/8	1 29/32	9 3/8	2 1/8	10 13/32	2 11/32	11 7/16
1/4	1 5/16	6 3/8	1 1/2	7 13/32	1 23/32	8 7/16	1 15/16	9 7/16	2 1/8	10 15/32	2 11/32	11 1/2
5/16	1 5/16	6 7/16	1 17/32	7 15/32	1 23/32	8 1/2	1 15/16	9 1/2	2 5/32	10 17/32	2 11/32	11 9/16
3/8	1 5/16	6 1/2	1 17/32	7 17/32	1 3/4	8 9/16	1 15/16	9 9/16	2 5/32	10 19/32	2 3/8	11 5/8
7/16	1 11/32	6 9/16	1 9/16	7 19/32	1 3/4	8 5/8	1 31/32	9 5/8	2 3/16	10 21/32	2 3/8	11 11/16
1/2	1 11/32	6 5/8	1 9/16	7 21/32	1 25/32	8 11/16	1 31/32	9 23/32	2 3/16	10 23/32	2 13/32	11 3/4
9/16	1 3/8	6 23/32	1 9/16	7 23/32	1 25/32	8 3/4	2	9 23/32	2 3/16	10 25/32	2 13/32	11 13/16
5/8	1 3/8	6 25/32	1 19/32	7 25/32	1 13/16	8 13/16	2	9 27/32	2 7/32	10 27/32	2 7/16	11 7/8
11/16	1 13/32	6 27/32	1 19/32	7 27/32	1 13/16	8 7/8	2 1/32	9 29/32	2 7/32	10 29/32	2 7/16	11 15/16
3/4	1 13/32	6 29/32	1 5/8	7 29/32	1 13/16	8 15/16	2 1/32	9 31/32	2 1/4	10 31/32	2 7/16	1-0
13/16	1 13/32	6 31/32	1 5/8	7 31/32	1 27/32	9	2 1/32	10 1/32	2 1/4	11 1/32	2 15/32	1-0 1/16
7/8	1 7/16	7 1/32	1 5/8	8 1/32	1 27/32	9 1/16	2 1/16	10 3/32	2 1/4	11 3/32	2 15/32	1-0 1/8
15/16	1 7/16	7 3/32	1 21/32	8 3/32	1 7/8	9 1/8	2 1/16	10 5/32	2 9/32	11 3/16	2 1/2	1-0 3/16

Feet	0' Rise	0' Slope	10' Rise	10' Slope	20' Rise	20' Slope	30' Rise	30' Slope
0	0		2-1	10-2 9/16	4-2	20-5 5/32	6-3	30-7 23/32
1	2½	1-0 1/4	2-3½	11-2 27/32	4-4½	21-5 13/16	6-5½	31-8
2	5	2-0 1/2	2-6	12-3 3/32	4-7	22-5 21/32	6-8	32-8 1/4
3	7½	3-0 25/32	2-8½	13-3 11/32	4-9½	23-5 15/16	6-10½	33-8 1/2
4	10	4-1 1/32	2-11	14-3 19/32	5-0	24-6 3/16	7-1	34-8 3/4
5	1-0½	5-1 9/32	3-1½	15-3 7/8	5-2½	25-6 7/16	7-3½	35-9 1/32
6	1-3	6-1 17/32	3-4	16-4 1/8	5-5	26-6 11/16	7-6	36-9 9/32
7	1-5½	7-1 13/16	3-6½	17-4 3/8	5-7½	27-6 31/32	7-8½	37-9 17/32
8	1-8	8-2 1/16	3-9	18-4 5/8	5-10	28-7 7/32	7-11	38-9 25/32
9	1-10½	9-2 5/16	3-11½	19-4 29/32	6-0½	29-7 15/32	8-1½	39-10 1/16

A = 11° 46′ 06″; logsin A = 9.30953; logcos A = 9.99077; logtan A = 9.31876; logcot A = 0.68124

Ins.	12″ Rise	12″ Slope	13″ Rise	13″ Slope	14″ Rise	14″ Slope	15″ Rise	15″ Slope	16″ Rise	16″ Slope
0	$2\frac{1}{2}$	1-0$\frac{1}{4}$	$2\frac{23}{32}$	1-1$\frac{9}{32}$	$2\frac{29}{32}$	1-2$\frac{5}{16}$	$3\frac{1}{8}$	1-3$\frac{5}{16}$	$3\frac{11}{32}$	1-4$\frac{11}{32}$
$\frac{1}{16}$	$2\frac{1}{2}$	1-0$\frac{5}{16}$	$2\frac{23}{32}$	1-1$\frac{11}{32}$	$2\frac{15}{16}$	1-2$\frac{3}{8}$	$3\frac{1}{8}$	1-3$\frac{3}{8}$	$3\frac{11}{32}$	1-4$\frac{13}{32}$
$\frac{1}{8}$	$2\frac{17}{32}$	1-0$\frac{3}{8}$	$2\frac{3}{4}$	1-1$\frac{13}{32}$	$2\frac{15}{16}$	1-2$\frac{7}{16}$	$3\frac{5}{32}$	1-3$\frac{7}{16}$	$3\frac{3}{8}$	1-4$\frac{15}{32}$
$\frac{3}{16}$	$2\frac{17}{32}$	1-0$\frac{7}{16}$	$2\frac{3}{4}$	1-1$\frac{15}{32}$	$2\frac{31}{32}$	1-2$\frac{1}{2}$	$3\frac{5}{32}$	1-3$\frac{1}{2}$	$3\frac{3}{8}$	1-4$\frac{17}{32}$
$\frac{1}{4}$	$2\frac{9}{16}$	1-0$\frac{1}{2}$	$2\frac{3}{4}$	1-1$\frac{17}{32}$	$2\frac{31}{32}$	1-2$\frac{9}{16}$	$3\frac{3}{16}$	1-3$\frac{9}{16}$	$3\frac{3}{8}$	1-4$\frac{19}{32}$
$\frac{5}{16}$	$2\frac{9}{16}$	1-0$\frac{9}{16}$	$2\frac{25}{32}$	1-1$\frac{19}{32}$	$2\frac{31}{32}$	1-2$\frac{5}{8}$	$3\frac{3}{16}$	1-3$\frac{21}{32}$	$3\frac{13}{32}$	1-4$\frac{21}{32}$
$\frac{3}{8}$	$2\frac{9}{16}$	1-0$\frac{21}{32}$	$2\frac{25}{32}$	1-1$\frac{21}{32}$	3	1-2$\frac{11}{16}$	$3\frac{3}{16}$	1-3$\frac{23}{32}$	$3\frac{13}{32}$	1-4$\frac{23}{32}$
$\frac{7}{16}$	$2\frac{19}{32}$	1-0$\frac{23}{32}$	$2\frac{13}{16}$	1-1$\frac{23}{32}$	3	1-2$\frac{3}{4}$	$3\frac{7}{32}$	1-3$\frac{25}{32}$	$3\frac{7}{16}$	1-4$\frac{25}{32}$
$\frac{1}{2}$	$2\frac{19}{32}$	1-0$\frac{25}{32}$	$2\frac{13}{16}$	1-1$\frac{25}{32}$	$3\frac{1}{32}$	1-2$\frac{13}{16}$	$3\frac{7}{32}$	1-3$\frac{27}{32}$	$3\frac{7}{16}$	1-4$\frac{27}{32}$
$\frac{9}{16}$	$2\frac{5}{8}$	1-0$\frac{27}{32}$	$2\frac{13}{16}$	1-1$\frac{27}{32}$	$3\frac{1}{32}$	1-2$\frac{7}{8}$	$3\frac{1}{4}$	1-3$\frac{29}{32}$	$3\frac{7}{16}$	1-4$\frac{29}{32}$
$\frac{5}{8}$	$2\frac{5}{8}$	1-0$\frac{29}{32}$	$2\frac{27}{32}$	1-1$\frac{29}{32}$	$3\frac{1}{16}$	1-2$\frac{15}{16}$	$3\frac{1}{4}$	1-3$\frac{31}{32}$	$3\frac{15}{32}$	1-4$\frac{31}{32}$
$\frac{11}{16}$	$2\frac{21}{32}$	1-0$\frac{31}{32}$	$2\frac{27}{32}$	1-1$\frac{31}{32}$	$3\frac{1}{16}$	1-3	$3\frac{9}{32}$	1-4$\frac{1}{32}$	$3\frac{15}{32}$	1-5$\frac{1}{2}$
$\frac{3}{4}$	$2\frac{21}{32}$	1-1$\frac{1}{32}$	$2\frac{7}{8}$	1-2$\frac{1}{32}$	$3\frac{1}{16}$	1-3$\frac{1}{16}$	$3\frac{9}{32}$	1-4$\frac{3}{32}$	$3\frac{1}{2}$	1-5$\frac{1}{8}$
$\frac{13}{16}$	$2\frac{21}{32}$	1-1$\frac{3}{32}$	$2\frac{7}{8}$	1-2$\frac{3}{32}$	$3\frac{3}{32}$	1-3$\frac{1}{8}$	$3\frac{9}{32}$	1-4$\frac{5}{32}$	$3\frac{1}{2}$	1-5$\frac{3}{16}$
$\frac{7}{8}$	$2\frac{11}{16}$	1-1$\frac{5}{32}$	$2\frac{7}{8}$	1-2$\frac{3}{16}$	$3\frac{3}{32}$	1-3$\frac{3}{16}$	$3\frac{5}{16}$	1-4$\frac{7}{32}$	$3\frac{1}{2}$	1-5$\frac{1}{4}$
$\frac{15}{16}$	$2\frac{11}{16}$	1-1$\frac{7}{32}$	$2\frac{29}{32}$	1-2$\frac{1}{4}$	$3\frac{1}{8}$	1-3$\frac{1}{4}$	$3\frac{5}{16}$	1-4$\frac{9}{32}$	$3\frac{17}{32}$	1-5$\frac{5}{16}$

Ins.	17″ Rise	17″ Slope	18″ Rise	18″ Slope	19″ Rise	19″ Slope	20″ Rise	20″ Slope	21″ Rise	21″ Slope
0	$3\frac{17}{32}$	1-5$\frac{3}{8}$	$3\frac{3}{4}$	1-6$\frac{3}{8}$	$3\frac{31}{32}$	1-7$\frac{13}{32}$	$4\frac{5}{32}$	1-8$\frac{7}{16}$	$4\frac{3}{8}$	1-9$\frac{7}{16}$
$\frac{1}{16}$	$3\frac{9}{16}$	1-5$\frac{7}{16}$	$3\frac{3}{4}$	1-6$\frac{7}{16}$	$3\frac{31}{32}$	1-7$\frac{15}{32}$	$4\frac{3}{16}$	1-8$\frac{1}{2}$	$4\frac{3}{8}$	1-9$\frac{1}{2}$
$\frac{1}{8}$	$3\frac{9}{16}$	1-5$\frac{1}{2}$	$3\frac{25}{32}$	1-6$\frac{1}{2}$	4	1-7$\frac{17}{32}$	$4\frac{3}{16}$	1-8$\frac{9}{16}$	$4\frac{13}{32}$	1-9$\frac{19}{32}$
$\frac{3}{16}$	$3\frac{19}{32}$	1-5$\frac{9}{16}$	$3\frac{25}{32}$	1-6$\frac{9}{16}$	4	1-7$\frac{19}{32}$	$4\frac{7}{32}$	1-8$\frac{5}{8}$	$4\frac{13}{32}$	1-9$\frac{21}{32}$
$\frac{1}{4}$	$3\frac{19}{32}$	1-5$\frac{5}{8}$	$3\frac{13}{16}$	1-6$\frac{21}{32}$	4	1-7$\frac{21}{32}$	$4\frac{7}{32}$	1-8$\frac{11}{16}$	$4\frac{7}{16}$	1-9$\frac{23}{32}$
$\frac{5}{16}$	$3\frac{19}{32}$	1-5$\frac{11}{16}$	$3\frac{13}{16}$	1-6$\frac{23}{32}$	$4\frac{1}{32}$	1-7$\frac{23}{32}$	$4\frac{7}{32}$	1-8$\frac{3}{4}$	$4\frac{7}{16}$	1-9$\frac{25}{32}$
$\frac{3}{8}$	$3\frac{5}{8}$	1-5$\frac{3}{4}$	$3\frac{13}{16}$	1-6$\frac{25}{32}$	$4\frac{1}{32}$	1-7$\frac{25}{32}$	$4\frac{1}{4}$	1-8$\frac{13}{16}$	$4\frac{7}{16}$	1-9$\frac{27}{32}$
$\frac{7}{16}$	$3\frac{5}{8}$	1-5$\frac{13}{16}$	$3\frac{27}{32}$	1-6$\frac{27}{32}$	$4\frac{1}{16}$	1-7$\frac{27}{32}$	$4\frac{1}{4}$	1-8$\frac{7}{8}$	$4\frac{15}{32}$	1-9$\frac{29}{32}$
$\frac{1}{2}$	$3\frac{21}{32}$	1-5$\frac{7}{8}$	$3\frac{27}{32}$	1-6$\frac{29}{32}$	$4\frac{1}{16}$	1-7$\frac{29}{32}$	$4\frac{9}{32}$	1-8$\frac{15}{16}$	$4\frac{15}{32}$	1-9$\frac{31}{32}$
$\frac{9}{16}$	$3\frac{21}{32}$	1-5$\frac{15}{16}$	$3\frac{7}{8}$	1-6$\frac{31}{32}$	$4\frac{1}{16}$	1-7$\frac{31}{32}$	$4\frac{9}{32}$	1-9	$4\frac{1}{2}$	1-10$\frac{1}{32}$
$\frac{5}{8}$	$3\frac{11}{16}$	1-6	$3\frac{7}{8}$	1-7$\frac{1}{32}$	$4\frac{3}{32}$	1-8$\frac{1}{32}$	$4\frac{5}{16}$	1-9$\frac{1}{16}$	$4\frac{1}{2}$	1-10$\frac{3}{32}$
$\frac{11}{16}$	$3\frac{11}{16}$	1-6$\frac{1}{16}$	$3\frac{29}{32}$	1-7$\frac{3}{32}$	$4\frac{3}{32}$	1-8$\frac{1}{8}$	$4\frac{5}{16}$	1-9$\frac{1}{8}$	$4\frac{17}{32}$	1-10$\frac{5}{32}$
$\frac{3}{4}$	$3\frac{11}{16}$	1-6$\frac{1}{8}$	$3\frac{29}{32}$	1-7$\frac{5}{32}$	$4\frac{1}{8}$	1-8$\frac{3}{16}$	$4\frac{5}{16}$	1-9$\frac{3}{16}$	$4\frac{17}{32}$	1-10$\frac{7}{32}$
$\frac{13}{16}$	$3\frac{23}{32}$	1-6$\frac{3}{16}$	$3\frac{29}{32}$	1-7$\frac{7}{32}$	$4\frac{1}{8}$	1-8$\frac{1}{4}$	$4\frac{11}{32}$	1-9$\frac{1}{4}$	$4\frac{17}{32}$	1-10$\frac{9}{32}$
$\frac{7}{8}$	$3\frac{23}{32}$	1-6$\frac{1}{4}$	$3\frac{15}{16}$	1-7$\frac{9}{32}$	$4\frac{1}{8}$	1-8$\frac{5}{16}$	$4\frac{11}{32}$	1-9$\frac{5}{16}$	$4\frac{9}{16}$	1-10$\frac{11}{32}$
$\frac{15}{16}$	$3\frac{3}{4}$	1-6$\frac{5}{16}$	$3\frac{15}{16}$	1-7$\frac{11}{32}$	$4\frac{5}{32}$	1-8$\frac{3}{8}$	$4\frac{3}{8}$	1-9$\frac{3}{8}$	$4\frac{9}{16}$	1-10$\frac{13}{32}$

Feet	40′ Rise	40′ Slope	50′ Rise	50′ Slope	60′ Rise	60′ Slope	70′ Rise	70′ Slope
0	8-4	40-10$\frac{5}{16}$	10-5	51-0$\frac{7}{8}$	12-6	61-3$\frac{15}{32}$	14-7	71-6$\frac{1}{2}$
1	8-6$\frac{1}{2}$	41-10$\frac{9}{16}$	10-7$\frac{1}{2}$	52-1$\frac{1}{8}$	12-8$\frac{1}{2}$	62-3$\frac{23}{32}$	14-9$\frac{1}{2}$	72-6$\frac{9}{32}$
2	8-9	42-10$\frac{13}{16}$	10-10	53-1$\frac{13}{32}$	12-11	63-3$\frac{31}{32}$	15-0	73-6$\frac{9}{16}$
3	8-11$\frac{1}{2}$	43-11$\frac{3}{32}$	11-0$\frac{1}{2}$	54-1$\frac{21}{32}$	13-1$\frac{1}{2}$	64-4$\frac{7}{32}$	15-2$\frac{1}{2}$	74-6$\frac{13}{16}$
4	9-2	44-11$\frac{11}{32}$	11-3	55-1$\frac{29}{32}$	13-4	65-4$\frac{1}{2}$	15-5	75-7$\frac{1}{16}$
5	9-4$\frac{1}{2}$	45-11$\frac{19}{32}$	11-5$\frac{1}{2}$	56-2$\frac{5}{8}$	13-6$\frac{1}{2}$	66-4$\frac{3}{4}$	15-7$\frac{1}{2}$	76-7$\frac{5}{16}$
6	9-7	46-11$\frac{27}{32}$	11-8	57-2$\frac{7}{16}$	13-9	67-5	15-10	77-7$\frac{19}{32}$
7	9-9$\frac{1}{2}$	48-0$\frac{1}{8}$	11-10$\frac{1}{2}$	58-2$\frac{11}{16}$	13-11$\frac{1}{2}$	68-5$\frac{1}{4}$	16-0$\frac{1}{2}$	78-7$\frac{27}{32}$
8	10-0	49-0$\frac{3}{8}$	12-1	59-2$\frac{15}{16}$	14-2	69-5$\frac{17}{32}$	16-3	79-8$\frac{3}{32}$
9	10-2$\frac{1}{2}$	50-0$\frac{5}{8}$	12-3$\frac{1}{2}$	60-3$\frac{3}{16}$	14-4$\frac{1}{2}$	70-5$\frac{25}{32}$	16-5$\frac{1}{2}$	80-8$\frac{11}{32}$

natsin A=0.2039542540; natcos A=0.9789804197; nattan A=0.2083333333; natcot A=4.8000000000

Inches	0" Rise	0" Slope	1" Rise	1" Slope	2" Rise	2" Slope	3" Rise	3" Slope	4" Rise	4" Slope	5" Rise	5" Slope
0	0	0	7/32	1 1/32	7/16	2 1/32	5/8	3 1/16	27/32	4 3/32	1 1/16	5 1/8
1/16	0	1/16	7/32	1 3/32	7/16	2 3/32	21/32	3 1/8	7/8	4 5/32	1 3/32	5 3/16
1/8	1/32	1/8	1/4	1 5/32	15/32	2 3/16	21/32	3 3/32	7/8	4 7/32	1 3/32	5 1/4
3/16	3/32	3/16	1/4	1 7/32	15/32	2 1/4	11/16	3 1/4	29/32	4 9/32	1 3/32	5 5/32
1/4	1/16	1/4	9/32	1 9/32	15/32	2 5/16	11/16	3 5/32	29/32	4 11/32	1 1/8	5 3/8
5/16	1/16	5/16	9/32	1 11/32	1/2	2 3/8	23/32	3 3/8	29/32	4 13/32	1 1/8	5 7/16
3/8	3/32	3/8	9/32	1 13/32	1/2	2 7/16	23/32	3 7/16	15/16	4 15/32	1 5/32	5 1/2
7/16	3/32	7/16	5/16	1 15/32	17/32	2 1/2	23/32	3 1/2	15/16	4 17/32	1 5/32	5 9/16
1/2	3/32	1/2	5/16	1 17/32	17/32	2 9/16	3/4	3 19/32	31/32	4 19/32	1 3/16	5 5/8
9/16	1/8	9/16	11/32	1 19/32	9/16	2 5/8	3/4	3 21/32	31/32	4 21/32	1 3/16	5 11/16
5/8	1/8	5/8	11/32	1 21/32	9/16	2 11/16	25/32	3 23/32	1	4 23/32	1 3/16	5 3/4
11/16	5/32	11/16	3/8	1 23/32	9/16	2 3/4	25/32	3 25/32	1	4 25/32	1 7/32	5 13/16
3/4	5/32	25/32	3/8	1 25/32	19/32	2 13/16	13/16	3 27/32	1	4 27/32	1 7/32	5 7/8
13/16	5/32	27/32	3/8	1 27/32	19/32	2 7/8	13/16	3 29/32	1 1/32	4 29/32	1 1/4	5 15/16
7/8	3/16	29/32	13/32	1 29/32	5/8	2 15/16	13/16	3 31/32	1 1/32	5	1 1/4	6
15/16	3/16	31/32	13/32	1 31/32	5/8	3	27/32	4 1/32	1 1/16	5 1/16	1 9/32	6 1/16

Inches	6" Rise	6" Slope	7" Rise	7" Slope	8" Rise	8" Slope	9" Rise	9" Slope	10" Rise	10" Slope	11" Rise	11" Slope
0	1 9/32	6 1/8	1 1/2	7 5/32	1 23/32	8 3/16	1 15/16	9 3/16	2 1/8	10 7/32	2 11/32	11 1/4
1/16	1 9/32	6 3/16	1 1/2	7 7/32	1 23/32	8 1/4	1 15/16	9 9/32	2 5/32	10 9/32	2 3/8	11 5/16
1/8	1 5/16	6 1/4	1 17/32	7 9/32	1 3/4	8 5/16	1 15/16	9 11/32	2 5/32	10 11/32	2 3/8	11 3/8
3/16	1 5/16	6 5/16	1 17/32	7 11/32	1 3/4	8 3/8	1 31/32	9 13/32	2 3/16	10 13/32	2 3/8	11 7/16
1/4	1 11/32	6 13/32	1 9/16	7 13/32	1 3/4	8 7/16	1 31/32	9 15/32	2 3/16	10 15/32	2 13/32	11 1/2
5/16	1 11/32	6 15/32	1 9/16	7 15/32	1 25/32	8 1/2	2	9 17/32	2 3/16	10 17/32	2 13/32	11 9/16
3/8	1 3/8	6 17/32	1 9/16	7 17/32	1 25/32	8 9/16	2	9 19/32	2 7/32	10 19/32	2 7/16	11 5/8
7/16	1 3/8	6 19/32	1 19/32	7 19/32	1 13/16	8 5/8	2	9 21/32	2 7/32	10 11/16	2 7/16	11 11/16
1/2	1 3/8	6 21/32	1 19/32	7 21/32	1 13/16	8 11/16	2 1/32	9 23/32	2 1/4	10 3/4	2 15/32	11 3/4
9/16	1 13/32	6 23/32	1 5/8	7 23/32	1 27/32	8 3/4	2 1/32	9 25/32	2 1/4	10 13/16	2 15/32	11 13/16
5/8	1 13/32	6 25/32	1 5/8	7 13/16	1 27/32	8 13/16	2 1/16	9 27/32	2 9/32	10 7/8	2 15/32	11 7/8
11/16	1 7/16	6 27/32	1 21/32	7 7/8	1 27/32	8 7/8	2 1/16	9 29/32	2 9/32	10 15/16	2 1/2	11 15/16
3/4	1 7/16	6 29/32	1 21/32	7 15/16	1 7/8	8 15/16	2 3/32	9 31/32	2 9/32	11	2 1/2	1-0
13/16	1 15/32	6 31/32	1 21/32	8	1 7/8	9	2 3/32	10 1/32	2 5/16	11 1/16	2 17/32	1-0 1/32
7/8	1 15/32	7 1/32	1 11/16	8 1/16	1 29/32	9 1/16	2 3/32	10 3/32	2 5/16	11 1/8	2 17/32	1-0 5/32
15/16	1 15/32	7 3/32	1 11/16	8 1/8	1 29/32	9 1/8	2 1/8	10 5/32	2 11/32	11 3/16	2 9/16	1-0 7/32

Feet	0' Rise	0' Slope	10' Rise	10' Slope	20' Rise	20' Slope	30' Rise	30' Slope
0	0	0	2-1 5/8	10-2 23/32	4-3 1/4	20-5 13/32	6-4 7/8	30-8 1/8
1	2 9/16	1-0 9/32	2-4 3/16	11-2 31/32	4-5 13/16	21-5 11/32	6-7 7/16	31-8 3/8
2	5 1/8	2-0 17/32	2-6 3/4	12-3 1/4	4-8 3/8	22-5 15/16	6-10	32-8 21/32
3	7 11/16	3-0 13/32	2-9 5/16	13-3 17/32	4-10 15/16	23-6 7/32	7-0 9/16	33-8 15/16
4	10 1/4	4-1 3/32	2-11 7/8	14-3 25/32	5-1 1/2	24-6 1/2	7-3 1/8	34-9 3/16
5	1-0 13/16	5-1 1/4	3-2 7/16	15-4 1/16	5-4 1/16	25-6 3/4	7-5 11/16	35-9 15/32
6	1-3 3/8	6-1 5/8	3-5	16-4 11/32	5-6 5/8	26-7 1/32	7-8 1/4	36-9 3/4
7	1-5 15/16	7-1 29/32	3-7 9/16	17-4 19/32	5-9 3/16	27-7 5/16	7-10 13/16	37-10
8	1-8 1/2	8-2 5/32	3-10 1/8	18-4 7/8	5-11 3/4	28-7 9/16	8-1 3/8	38-10 9/32
9	1-11 1/16	9-2 7/16	4-0 11/16	19-5 1/8	6-2 5/16	29-7 27/32	8-3 15/16	39-10 9/16

A = 12° 03' 14''; logsin A = 9.31980; logcos A = 9.99032; logtan A = 9.32948; logcot A = 0.67052

Ins.	12″ Rise	12″ Slope	13″ Rise	13″ Slope	14″ Rise	14″ Slope	15″ Rise	15″ Slope	16″ Rise	16″ Slope
0	$2\frac{9}{16}$	$1\text{-}0\frac{9}{32}$	$2\frac{25}{32}$	$1\text{-}1\frac{9}{32}$	3	$1\text{-}2\frac{5}{16}$	$3\frac{3}{16}$	$1\text{-}3\frac{11}{32}$	$3\frac{13}{16}$	$1\text{-}4\frac{3}{8}$
1/16	$2\frac{9}{16}$	$1\text{-}0\frac{11}{32}$	$2\frac{25}{32}$	$1\text{-}1\frac{11}{32}$	3	$1\text{-}2\frac{3}{8}$	$3\frac{7}{16}$	$1\text{-}3\frac{13}{32}$	$3\frac{7}{16}$	$1\text{-}4\frac{7}{16}$
1/8	$2\frac{19}{32}$	$1\text{-}0\frac{13}{32}$	$2\frac{13}{16}$	$1\text{-}1\frac{13}{32}$	$3\frac{1}{32}$	$1\text{-}2\frac{7}{16}$	$3\frac{7}{32}$	$1\text{-}3\frac{15}{32}$	$3\frac{7}{16}$	$1\text{-}4\frac{1}{2}$
3/16	$2\frac{19}{32}$	$1\text{-}0\frac{15}{32}$	$2\frac{13}{16}$	$1\text{-}1\frac{1}{2}$	$3\frac{1}{32}$	$1\text{-}2\frac{1}{2}$	$3\frac{1}{4}$	$1\text{-}3\frac{17}{32}$	$3\frac{15}{32}$	$1\text{-}4\frac{9}{16}$
1/4	$2\frac{5}{8}$	$1\text{-}0\frac{17}{32}$	$2\frac{27}{32}$	$1\text{-}1\frac{9}{16}$	$3\frac{1}{32}$	$1\text{-}2\frac{9}{16}$	$3\frac{1}{4}$	$1\text{-}3\frac{19}{32}$	$3\frac{15}{32}$	$1\text{-}4\frac{5}{8}$
5/16	$2\frac{5}{8}$	$1\text{-}0\frac{19}{32}$	$2\frac{27}{32}$	$1\text{-}1\frac{5}{8}$	$3\frac{1}{16}$	$1\text{-}2\frac{5}{8}$	$3\frac{9}{32}$	$1\text{-}3\frac{21}{32}$	$3\frac{15}{32}$	$1\text{-}4\frac{11}{16}$
3/8	$2\frac{21}{32}$	$1\text{-}0\frac{21}{32}$	$2\frac{27}{32}$	$1\text{-}1\frac{11}{16}$	$3\frac{1}{16}$	$1\text{-}2\frac{11}{16}$	$3\frac{9}{32}$	$1\text{-}3\frac{23}{32}$	$3\frac{1}{2}$	$1\text{-}4\frac{3}{4}$
7/16	$2\frac{21}{32}$	$1\text{-}0\frac{23}{32}$	$2\frac{7}{8}$	$1\text{-}1\frac{3}{4}$	$3\frac{3}{32}$	$1\text{-}2\frac{3}{4}$	$3\frac{9}{32}$	$1\text{-}3\frac{25}{32}$	$3\frac{1}{2}$	$1\text{-}4\frac{13}{16}$
1/2	$2\frac{21}{32}$	$1\text{-}0\frac{25}{32}$	$2\frac{7}{8}$	$1\text{-}1\frac{13}{16}$	$3\frac{3}{32}$	$1\text{-}2\frac{13}{16}$	$3\frac{5}{16}$	$1\text{-}3\frac{27}{32}$	$3\frac{17}{32}$	$1\text{-}4\frac{7}{8}$
9/16	$2\frac{11}{16}$	$1\text{-}0\frac{27}{32}$	$2\frac{29}{32}$	$1\text{-}1\frac{7}{8}$	$3\frac{3}{8}$	$1\text{-}2\frac{29}{32}$	$3\frac{5}{16}$	$1\text{-}3\frac{29}{32}$	$3\frac{17}{32}$	$1\text{-}4\frac{15}{16}$
5/8	$2\frac{11}{16}$	$1\text{-}0\frac{29}{32}$	$2\frac{29}{32}$	$1\text{-}1\frac{15}{16}$	$3\frac{3}{8}$	$1\text{-}2\frac{31}{32}$	$3\frac{11}{32}$	$1\text{-}3\frac{31}{32}$	$3\frac{9}{16}$	$1\text{-}5$
11/16	$2\frac{23}{32}$	$1\text{-}0\frac{31}{32}$	$2\frac{15}{16}$	$1\text{-}2$	$3\frac{1}{8}$	$1\text{-}3\frac{1}{8}$	$3\frac{11}{32}$	$1\text{-}4\frac{1}{32}$	$3\frac{9}{16}$	$1\text{-}5\frac{1}{16}$
3/4	$2\frac{23}{32}$	$1\text{-}1\frac{1}{2}$	$2\frac{15}{16}$	$1\text{-}2\frac{1}{16}$	$3\frac{5}{32}$	$1\text{-}3\frac{3}{32}$	$3\frac{3}{8}$	$1\text{-}4\frac{3}{32}$	$3\frac{9}{16}$	$1\text{-}5\frac{1}{8}$
13/16	$2\frac{3}{4}$	$1\text{-}1\frac{3}{32}$	$2\frac{15}{16}$	$1\text{-}2\frac{1}{8}$	$3\frac{5}{32}$	$1\text{-}3\frac{5}{32}$	$3\frac{3}{8}$	$1\text{-}4\frac{5}{32}$	$3\frac{19}{32}$	$1\text{-}5\frac{3}{16}$
7/8	$2\frac{3}{4}$	$1\text{-}1\frac{5}{32}$	$2\frac{31}{32}$	$1\text{-}2\frac{3}{16}$	$3\frac{3}{16}$	$1\text{-}3\frac{7}{32}$	$3\frac{3}{8}$	$1\text{-}4\frac{7}{32}$	$3\frac{19}{32}$	$1\text{-}5\frac{1}{4}$
15/16	$2\frac{3}{4}$	$1\text{-}1\frac{7}{32}$	$2\frac{31}{32}$	$1\text{-}2\frac{1}{4}$	$3\frac{3}{16}$	$1\text{-}3\frac{9}{32}$	$3\frac{13}{32}$	$1\text{-}4\frac{9}{32}$	$3\frac{5}{8}$	$1\text{-}5\frac{5}{16}$

Ins.	17″ Rise	17″ Slope	18″ Rise	18″ Slope	19″ Rise	19″ Slope	20″ Rise	20″ Slope	21″ Rise	21″ Slope
0	$3\frac{5}{8}$	$1\text{-}5\frac{3}{8}$	$3\frac{27}{32}$	$1\text{-}6\frac{13}{32}$	$4\frac{1}{16}$	$1\text{-}7\frac{7}{16}$	$4\frac{9}{32}$	$1\text{-}8\frac{7}{16}$	$4\frac{1}{2}$	$1\text{-}9\frac{15}{32}$
1/16	$3\frac{21}{32}$	$1\text{-}5\frac{7}{16}$	$3\frac{27}{32}$	$1\text{-}6\frac{15}{32}$	$4\frac{1}{16}$	$1\text{-}7\frac{1}{2}$	$4\frac{9}{32}$	$1\text{-}8\frac{1}{2}$	$4\frac{1}{2}$	$1\text{-}9\frac{17}{32}$
1/8	$3\frac{21}{32}$	$1\text{-}5\frac{1}{2}$	$3\frac{7}{8}$	$1\text{-}6\frac{17}{32}$	$4\frac{3}{32}$	$1\text{-}7\frac{9}{16}$	$4\frac{5}{16}$	$1\text{-}8\frac{9}{16}$	$4\frac{1}{2}$	$1\text{-}9\frac{19}{32}$
3/16	$3\frac{21}{32}$	$1\text{-}5\frac{9}{16}$	$3\frac{7}{8}$	$1\text{-}6\frac{19}{32}$	$4\frac{3}{32}$	$1\text{-}7\frac{5}{8}$	$4\frac{5}{16}$	$1\text{-}8\frac{21}{32}$	$4\frac{17}{32}$	$1\text{-}9\frac{21}{32}$
1/4	$3\frac{11}{16}$	$1\text{-}5\frac{5}{8}$	$3\frac{29}{32}$	$1\text{-}6\frac{21}{32}$	$4\frac{1}{8}$	$1\text{-}7\frac{11}{16}$	$4\frac{5}{16}$	$1\text{-}8\frac{23}{32}$	$4\frac{17}{32}$	$1\text{-}9\frac{23}{32}$
5/16	$3\frac{11}{16}$	$1\text{-}5\frac{11}{16}$	$3\frac{29}{32}$	$1\text{-}6\frac{23}{32}$	$4\frac{1}{8}$	$1\text{-}7\frac{3}{4}$	$4\frac{11}{32}$	$1\text{-}8\frac{25}{32}$	$4\frac{9}{16}$	$1\text{-}9\frac{25}{32}$
3/8	$3\frac{23}{32}$	$1\text{-}5\frac{25}{32}$	$3\frac{15}{16}$	$1\text{-}6\frac{25}{32}$	$4\frac{1}{8}$	$1\text{-}7\frac{13}{16}$	$4\frac{11}{32}$	$1\text{-}8\frac{27}{32}$	$4\frac{9}{16}$	$1\text{-}9\frac{27}{32}$
7/16	$3\frac{23}{32}$	$1\text{-}5\frac{27}{32}$	$3\frac{15}{16}$	$1\text{-}6\frac{27}{32}$	$4\frac{5}{32}$	$1\text{-}7\frac{7}{8}$	$4\frac{11}{32}$	$1\text{-}8\frac{29}{32}$	$4\frac{9}{16}$	$1\text{-}9\frac{29}{32}$
1/2	$3\frac{3}{4}$	$1\text{-}5\frac{29}{32}$	$3\frac{15}{16}$	$1\text{-}6\frac{29}{32}$	$4\frac{5}{32}$	$1\text{-}7\frac{15}{16}$	$4\frac{3}{8}$	$1\text{-}8\frac{31}{32}$	$4\frac{19}{32}$	$1\text{-}10$
9/16	$3\frac{3}{4}$	$1\text{-}5\frac{31}{32}$	$3\frac{31}{32}$	$1\text{-}6\frac{31}{32}$	$4\frac{3}{16}$	$1\text{-}8$	$4\frac{13}{32}$	$1\text{-}9\frac{1}{32}$	$4\frac{19}{32}$	$1\text{-}10\frac{1}{16}$
5/8	$3\frac{3}{4}$	$1\text{-}6\frac{1}{32}$	$3\frac{31}{32}$	$1\text{-}7\frac{1}{32}$	$4\frac{3}{16}$	$1\text{-}8\frac{1}{16}$	$4\frac{13}{32}$	$1\text{-}9\frac{3}{32}$	$4\frac{5}{8}$	$1\text{-}10\frac{1}{8}$
11/16	$3\frac{25}{32}$	$1\text{-}6\frac{3}{32}$	4	$1\text{-}7\frac{3}{32}$	$4\frac{7}{32}$	$1\text{-}8\frac{1}{8}$	$4\frac{13}{32}$	$1\text{-}9\frac{5}{32}$	$4\frac{5}{8}$	$1\text{-}10\frac{3}{16}$
3/4	$3\frac{25}{32}$	$1\text{-}6\frac{5}{32}$	4	$1\text{-}7\frac{3}{16}$	$4\frac{7}{32}$	$1\text{-}8\frac{3}{16}$	$4\frac{7}{16}$	$1\text{-}9\frac{7}{32}$	$4\frac{21}{32}$	$1\text{-}10\frac{1}{4}$
13/16	$3\frac{13}{16}$	$1\text{-}6\frac{7}{32}$	$4\frac{1}{32}$	$1\text{-}7\frac{1}{4}$	$4\frac{7}{32}$	$1\text{-}8\frac{1}{4}$	$4\frac{7}{16}$	$1\text{-}9\frac{9}{32}$	$4\frac{21}{32}$	$1\text{-}10\frac{5}{16}$
7/8	$3\frac{13}{16}$	$1\text{-}6\frac{9}{32}$	$4\frac{1}{32}$	$1\text{-}7\frac{5}{16}$	$4\frac{1}{4}$	$1\text{-}8\frac{5}{16}$	$4\frac{15}{32}$	$1\text{-}9\frac{11}{32}$	$4\frac{21}{32}$	$1\text{-}10\frac{3}{8}$
15/16	$3\frac{27}{32}$	$1\text{-}6\frac{11}{32}$	$4\frac{1}{32}$	$1\text{-}7\frac{3}{8}$	$4\frac{1}{4}$	$1\text{-}8\frac{3}{8}$	$4\frac{15}{32}$	$1\text{-}9\frac{13}{32}$	$4\frac{11}{32}$	$1\text{-}10\frac{7}{16}$

Feet	40′ Rise	40′ Slope	50′ Rise	50′ Slope	60′ Rise	60′ Slope	70′ Rise	70′ Slope
0	$8\text{-}6\frac{1}{2}$	$40\text{-}10\frac{13}{16}$	$10\text{-}8\frac{1}{8}$	$51\text{-}1\frac{17}{32}$	$12\text{-}9\frac{3}{4}$	$61\text{-}4\frac{7}{32}$	$14\text{-}11\frac{3}{8}$	$71\text{-}6\frac{15}{16}$
1	$8\text{-}9\frac{1}{16}$	$41\text{-}1\frac{3}{32}$	$10\text{-}10\frac{11}{16}$	$52\text{-}1\frac{13}{16}$	$13\text{-}0\frac{5}{16}$	$62\text{-}4\frac{1}{2}$	$15\text{-}1\frac{15}{16}$	$72\text{-}7\frac{7}{32}$
2	$8\text{-}11\frac{5}{8}$	$42\text{-}1\frac{3}{8}$	$11\text{-}1\frac{1}{4}$	$53\text{-}2\frac{1}{16}$	$13\text{-}2\frac{7}{8}$	$63\text{-}4\frac{25}{32}$	$15\text{-}4\frac{1}{2}$	$73\text{-}7\frac{15}{32}$
3	$9\text{-}2\frac{3}{16}$	$43\text{-}1\frac{15}{32}$	$11\text{-}3\frac{13}{32}$	$54\text{-}2\frac{11}{32}$	$13\text{-}5\frac{7}{16}$	$64\text{-}5\frac{1}{32}$	$15\text{-}7\frac{1}{16}$	$74\text{-}7\frac{3}{4}$
4	$9\text{-}4\frac{3}{4}$	$44\text{-}11\frac{29}{32}$	$11\text{-}6\frac{3}{8}$	$55\text{-}2\frac{5}{8}$	$13\text{-}8$	$65\text{-}5\frac{5}{16}$	$15\text{-}9\frac{5}{8}$	$75\text{-}8\frac{1}{32}$
5	$9\text{-}7\frac{5}{16}$	$46\text{-}0\frac{3}{16}$	$11\text{-}8\frac{15}{16}$	$56\text{-}2\frac{7}{8}$	$13\text{-}10\frac{9}{16}$	$66\text{-}5\frac{19}{32}$	$16\text{-}0\frac{3}{16}$	$76\text{-}8\frac{9}{32}$
6	$9\text{-}9\frac{7}{8}$	$47\text{-}0\frac{7}{16}$	$11\text{-}11\frac{1}{2}$	$57\text{-}3\frac{5}{32}$	$14\text{-}1\frac{1}{8}$	$67\text{-}5\frac{27}{32}$	$16\text{-}2\frac{3}{4}$	$77\text{-}8\frac{9}{32}$
7	$10\text{-}0\frac{7}{16}$	$48\text{-}0\frac{23}{32}$	$12\text{-}2\frac{1}{16}$	$58\text{-}3\frac{13}{32}$	$14\text{-}3\frac{11}{16}$	$68\text{-}6\frac{1}{8}$	$16\text{-}5\frac{5}{16}$	$78\text{-}8\frac{27}{32}$
8	$10\text{-}3$	$49\text{-}1$	$12\text{-}4\frac{5}{8}$	$59\text{-}3\frac{11}{16}$	$14\text{-}6\frac{1}{4}$	$69\text{-}6\frac{13}{32}$	$16\text{-}7\frac{7}{8}$	$79\text{-}9\frac{3}{32}$
9	$10\text{-}5\frac{9}{16}$	$50\text{-}1\frac{1}{4}$	$12\text{-}7\frac{3}{16}$	$60\text{-}3\frac{31}{32}$	$14\text{-}8\frac{13}{16}$	$70\text{-}6\frac{21}{32}$	$16\text{-}10\frac{7}{16}$	$80\text{-}9\frac{3}{8}$

natsin A = 0.2088333386; natcos A = 0.9779512445; nattan A = 0.2135416666; natcot A = 4.6829268292

Inches	0" Rise	0" Slope	1" Rise	1" Slope	2" Rise	2" Slope	3" Rise	3" Slope	4" Rise	4" Slope	5" Rise	5" Slope
0	0	0	7/32	1 1/32	7/16	2 1/16	21/32	3 1/16	7/8	4 3/32	1 3/32	5 1/8
1/16	0	1/16	7/32	1 3/32	7/16	2 1/8	21/32	3 1/8	7/8	4 5/32	1 3/32	5 3/16
1/8	1/32	1/8	1/4	1 5/32	15/32	2 3/16	11/16	3 3/16	29/32	4 7/32	1 1/8	5 1/4
3/16	1/32	3/16	1/4	1 7/32	15/32	2 1/4	11/16	3 1/4	29/32	4 9/32	1 1/8	5 5/16
1/4	1/16	1/4	9/32	1 9/32	1/2	2 5/16	23/32	3 5/16	15/16	4 11/32	1 5/32	5 3/8
5/16	1/16	5/16	9/32	1 11/32	1/2	2 3/8	23/32	3 13/32	15/16	4 13/32	1 5/32	5 7/16
3/8	3/32	3/8	5/16	1 13/32	17/32	2 7/16	3/4	3 15/32	31/32	4 15/32	1 3/16	5 1/2
7/16	3/32	7/16	5/16	1 15/32	17/32	2 1/2	3/4	3 17/32	31/32	4 17/32	1 3/16	5 9/16
1/2	1/8	1/2	5/16	1 17/32	9/16	2 9/16	3/4	3 19/32	1	4 19/32	1 3/16	5 5/8
9/16	1/8	9/16	11/32	1 19/32	9/16	2 5/8	25/32	3 21/32	1	4 21/32	1 7/32	5 11/16
5/8	1/8	5/8	11/32	1 21/32	9/16	2 11/16	25/32	3 23/32	1	4 23/32	1 7/32	5 3/4
11/16	5/32	23/32	3/8	1 23/32	19/32	2 3/4	13/16	3 25/32	1 1/32	4 13/16	1 1/4	5 13/16
3/4	5/32	25/32	3/8	1 25/32	19/32	2 13/16	13/16	3 27/32	1 1/32	4 7/8	1 1/4	5 7/8
13/16	3/16	27/32	13/32	1 27/32	5/8	2 7/8	27/32	3 29/32	1 1/16	4 15/16	1 9/32	5 15/16
7/8	3/16	29/32	13/32	1 29/32	5/8	2 15/16	27/32	3 31/32	1 1/16	5	1 9/32	6
15/16	7/32	31/32	7/16	1 31/32	21/32	3	7/8	4 1/32	1 3/32	5 1/16	1 5/16	6 1/16

Inches	6" Rise	6" Slope	7" Rise	7" Slope	8" Rise	8" Slope	9" Rise	9" Slope	10" Rise	10" Slope	11" Rise	11" Slope
0	1 5/16	6 5/32	1 17/32	7 5/32	1 3/4	8 3/16	1 31/32	9 7/32	2 3/16	10 1/4	2 13/32	11 1/4
1/16	1 5/16	6 7/32	1 17/32	7 7/32	1 3/4	8 1/4	1 31/32	9 9/32	2 3/16	10 5/16	2 13/32	11 5/16
1/8	1 11/32	6 9/32	1 9/16	7 9/32	1 25/32	8 5/16	2	9 11/32	2 7/32	10 3/8	2 7/16	11 3/8
3/16	1 11/32	6 11/32	1 9/16	7 11/32	1 25/32	8 3/8	2	9 13/32	2 7/32	10 7/16	2 7/16	11 7/16
1/4	1 3/8	6 13/32	1 19/32	7 13/32	1 13/16	8 7/16	2 1/32	9 15/32	2 1/4	10 1/2	2 15/32	11 17/32
5/16	1 3/8	6 15/32	1 19/32	7 1/2	1 13/16	8 1/2	2 1/32	9 17/32	2 1/4	10 9/16	2 15/32	11 19/32
3/8	1 13/32	6 17/32	1 5/8	7 9/16	1 27/32	8 9/16	2 1/16	9 19/32	2 9/32	10 5/8	2 1/2	11 21/32
7/16	1 13/32	6 19/32	1 5/8	7 5/8	1 27/32	8 5/8	2 1/16	9 21/32	2 9/32	10 11/16	2 1/2	11 23/32
1/2	1 7/16	6 21/32	1 5/8	7 11/16	1 7/8	8 11/16	2 1/16	9 23/32	2 5/16	10 3/4	2 1/2	11 25/32
9/16	1 7/16	6 23/32	1 21/32	7 3/4	1 7/8	8 3/4	2 3/32	9 25/32	2 5/16	10 13/16	2 17/32	11 27/32
5/8	1 15/16	6 25/32	1 21/32	7 13/16	1 7/8	8 27/32	2 3/32	9 27/32	2 5/16	10 7/8	2 17/32	11 29/32
11/16	1 15/32	6 27/32	1 11/16	7 7/8	1 29/32	8 29/32	2 1/8	9 29/32	2 11/32	10 15/16	2 9/16	11 31/32
3/4	1 15/32	6 29/32	1 11/16	7 15/16	1 29/32	8 31/32	2 1/8	9 31/32	2 11/32	11	2 9/16	1-0 1/32
13/16	1 1/2	6 31/32	1 23/32	8	1 15/16	9 1/32	2 5/32	10 1/32	2 3/8	11 1/16	2 19/32	1-0 3/32
7/8	1 1/2	7 1/32	1 23/32	8 1/8	1 15/16	9 3/32	2 5/32	10 3/32	2 3/8	11 1/8	2 19/32	1-0 5/32
15/16	1 17/32	7 3/32	1 3/4	8 1/8	1 31/32	9 5/32	2 3/16	10 3/32	2 13/32	11 3/16	2 5/8	1-0 7/32

Feet	0' Rise	0' Slope	10' Rise	10' Slope	20' Rise	20' Slope	30' Rise	30' Slope
0	0	0	2-2 1/4	10-2 27/32	4-4 1/2	20-5 11/16	6-6 3/4	30-8 1/2
1	2 5/8	1-0 9/32	2-4 7/8	11-3 1/8	4-7 1/8	21-5 31/32	6-9 3/8	31-8 25/32
2	5 1/4	2-0 9/16	2-7 1/2	12-3 13/32	4-9 3/4	22-6 1/4	7-0	32-9 3/32
3	7 7/8	3-0 27/32	2-10 1/8	13-3 11/16	5-0 3/8	23-6 17/32	7-2 5/8	33-9 3/8
4	10 1/2	4-1 1/8	3-0 3/4	14-3 31/32	5-3	24-6 13/16	7-5 1/4	34-9 21/32
5	1-1 1/8	5-1 13/32	3-3 3/8	15-4 1/4	5-5 5/8	25-7 3/32	7-7 7/8	35-9 15/16
6	1-3 3/4	6-1 11/16	3-6	16-4 17/32	5-8 1/4	26-7 3/8	7-10 1/2	36-10 3/32
7	1-6 3/8	7-2	3-8 5/8	17-4 13/16	5-10 7/8	27-7 21/32	8-1 1/8	37-10 1/2
8	1-9	8-2 9/32	3-11 1/4	18-5 3/32	6-1 1/2	28-7 15/16	8-3 3/4	38-10 25/32
9	1-11 5/8	9-2 9/16	4-1 7/8	19-5 13/32	6-4 1/8	29-8 7/32	8-6 3/8	39-11 1/16

A = 12° 20′ 21″; logsin A = 9.32980; logcos A = 9.98985; logtan A = 9.33995; logcot A = 0.66005

Ins.	12" Rise	12" Slope	13" Rise	13" Slope	14" Rise	14" Slope	15" Rise	15" Slope	16" Rise	16" Slope
0	$2\frac{5}{8}$	$1\text{-}0\frac{9}{32}$	$2\frac{27}{32}$	$1\text{-}1\frac{5}{16}$	$3\frac{1}{16}$	$1\text{-}2\frac{11}{32}$	$3\frac{9}{32}$	$1\text{-}3\frac{11}{32}$	$3\frac{1}{2}$	$1\text{-}4\frac{3}{8}$
$\frac{1}{16}$	$2\frac{5}{8}$	$1\text{-}0\frac{11}{32}$	$2\frac{27}{32}$	$1\text{-}1\frac{3}{8}$	$3\frac{1}{16}$	$1\text{-}2\frac{13}{32}$	$3\frac{9}{32}$	$1\text{-}3\frac{13}{32}$	$3\frac{1}{2}$	$1\text{-}4\frac{7}{16}$
$\frac{1}{8}$	$2\frac{21}{32}$	$1\text{-}0\frac{13}{32}$	$2\frac{7}{8}$	$1\text{-}1\frac{7}{16}$	$3\frac{3}{32}$	$1\text{-}2\frac{15}{32}$	$3\frac{5}{16}$	$1\text{-}3\frac{15}{32}$	$3\frac{17}{32}$	$1\text{-}4\frac{1}{2}$
$\frac{3}{16}$	$2\frac{21}{32}$	$1\text{-}0\frac{15}{32}$	$2\frac{7}{8}$	$1\text{-}1\frac{1}{2}$	$3\frac{3}{32}$	$1\text{-}2\frac{17}{32}$	$3\frac{5}{16}$	$1\text{-}3\frac{17}{32}$	$3\frac{17}{32}$	$1\text{-}4\frac{9}{16}$
$\frac{1}{4}$	$2\frac{11}{16}$	$1\text{-}0\frac{17}{32}$	$2\frac{29}{32}$	$1\text{-}1\frac{9}{16}$	$3\frac{1}{8}$	$1\text{-}2\frac{19}{32}$	$3\frac{11}{32}$	$1\text{-}3\frac{5}{8}$	$3\frac{9}{16}$	$1\text{-}4\frac{5}{8}$
$\frac{5}{16}$	$2\frac{11}{16}$	$1\text{-}0\frac{19}{32}$	$2\frac{29}{32}$	$1\text{-}1\frac{5}{8}$	$3\frac{1}{8}$	$1\text{-}2\frac{21}{32}$	$3\frac{11}{32}$	$1\text{-}3\frac{11}{16}$	$3\frac{9}{16}$	$1\text{-}4\frac{11}{16}$
$\frac{3}{8}$	$2\frac{23}{32}$	$1\text{-}0\frac{21}{32}$	$2\frac{15}{16}$	$1\text{-}1\frac{11}{16}$	$3\frac{5}{32}$	$1\text{-}2\frac{23}{32}$	$3\frac{3}{8}$	$1\text{-}3\frac{3}{4}$	$3\frac{19}{32}$	$1\text{-}4\frac{3}{4}$
$\frac{7}{16}$	$2\frac{23}{32}$	$1\text{-}0\frac{23}{32}$	$2\frac{15}{16}$	$1\text{-}1\frac{3}{4}$	$3\frac{5}{32}$	$1\text{-}2\frac{25}{32}$	$3\frac{3}{8}$	$1\text{-}3\frac{13}{16}$	$3\frac{19}{32}$	$1\text{-}4\frac{13}{16}$
$\frac{1}{2}$	$2\frac{3}{4}$	$1\text{-}0\frac{25}{32}$	$2\frac{15}{16}$	$1\text{-}1\frac{13}{16}$	$3\frac{3}{16}$	$1\text{-}2\frac{27}{32}$	$3\frac{3}{8}$	$1\text{-}3\frac{7}{8}$	$3\frac{5}{8}$	$1\text{-}4\frac{7}{8}$
$\frac{9}{16}$	$2\frac{3}{4}$	$1\text{-}0\frac{7}{8}$	$2\frac{31}{32}$	$1\text{-}1\frac{7}{8}$	$3\frac{3}{16}$	$1\text{-}2\frac{29}{32}$	$3\frac{13}{32}$	$1\text{-}3\frac{15}{16}$	$3\frac{5}{8}$	$1\text{-}4\frac{31}{32}$
$\frac{5}{8}$	$2\frac{3}{4}$	$1\text{-}0\frac{15}{16}$	$2\frac{31}{32}$	$1\text{-}1\frac{15}{16}$	$3\frac{3}{16}$	$1\text{-}2\frac{31}{32}$	$3\frac{13}{32}$	$1\text{-}4$	$3\frac{5}{8}$	$1\text{-}5\frac{1}{32}$
$\frac{11}{16}$	$2\frac{25}{32}$	$1\text{-}1$	3	$1\text{-}2$	$3\frac{7}{32}$	$1\text{-}3\frac{1}{32}$	$3\frac{7}{16}$	$1\text{-}4\frac{1}{16}$	$3\frac{21}{32}$	$1\text{-}5\frac{3}{32}$
$\frac{3}{4}$	$2\frac{25}{32}$	$1\text{-}1\frac{1}{16}$	3	$1\text{-}2\frac{1}{16}$	$3\frac{7}{32}$	$1\text{-}3\frac{3}{32}$	$3\frac{7}{16}$	$1\text{-}4\frac{1}{8}$	$3\frac{21}{32}$	$1\text{-}5\frac{5}{32}$
$\frac{13}{16}$	$2\frac{13}{16}$	$1\text{-}1\frac{1}{8}$	$3\frac{1}{32}$	$1\text{-}2\frac{1}{8}$	$3\frac{1}{4}$	$1\text{-}3\frac{5}{32}$	$3\frac{15}{32}$	$1\text{-}4\frac{3}{16}$	$3\frac{11}{16}$	$1\text{-}5\frac{7}{32}$
$\frac{7}{8}$	$2\frac{13}{16}$	$1\text{-}1\frac{3}{16}$	$3\frac{1}{32}$	$1\text{-}2\frac{3}{16}$	$3\frac{1}{4}$	$1\text{-}3\frac{7}{32}$	$3\frac{15}{32}$	$1\text{-}4\frac{1}{4}$	$3\frac{11}{16}$	$1\text{-}5\frac{9}{32}$
$\frac{15}{16}$	$2\frac{27}{32}$	$1\text{-}1\frac{1}{4}$	$3\frac{1}{16}$	$1\text{-}2\frac{9}{32}$	$3\frac{9}{32}$	$1\text{-}3\frac{9}{32}$	$3\frac{1}{2}$	$1\text{-}4\frac{5}{16}$	$3\frac{23}{32}$	$1\text{-}5\frac{11}{32}$

Ins.	17" Rise	17" Slope	18" Rise	18" Slope	19" Rise	19" Slope	20" Rise	20" Slope	21" Rise	21" Slope
0	$3\frac{23}{32}$	$1\text{-}5\frac{13}{32}$	$3\frac{15}{16}$	$1\text{-}6\frac{7}{16}$	$4\frac{5}{32}$	$1\text{-}7\frac{7}{16}$	$4\frac{3}{8}$	$1\text{-}8\frac{15}{32}$	$4\frac{19}{32}$	$1\text{-}9\frac{1}{2}$
$\frac{1}{16}$	$3\frac{23}{32}$	$1\text{-}5\frac{15}{32}$	$3\frac{15}{16}$	$1\text{-}6\frac{1}{2}$	$4\frac{5}{32}$	$1\text{-}7\frac{1}{2}$	$4\frac{3}{8}$	$1\text{-}8\frac{17}{32}$	$4\frac{19}{32}$	$1\text{-}9\frac{9}{16}$
$\frac{1}{8}$	$3\frac{3}{4}$	$1\text{-}5\frac{17}{32}$	$3\frac{31}{32}$	$1\text{-}6\frac{9}{16}$	$4\frac{3}{16}$	$1\text{-}7\frac{9}{16}$	$4\frac{13}{32}$	$1\text{-}8\frac{19}{32}$	$4\frac{5}{8}$	$1\text{-}9\frac{5}{8}$
$\frac{3}{16}$	$3\frac{3}{4}$	$1\text{-}5\frac{19}{32}$	$3\frac{31}{32}$	$1\text{-}6\frac{5}{8}$	$4\frac{3}{16}$	$1\text{-}7\frac{21}{32}$	$4\frac{13}{32}$	$1\text{-}8\frac{21}{32}$	$4\frac{5}{8}$	$1\text{-}9\frac{11}{16}$
$\frac{1}{4}$	$3\frac{25}{32}$	$1\text{-}5\frac{21}{32}$	4	$1\text{-}6\frac{11}{16}$	$4\frac{7}{32}$	$1\text{-}7\frac{23}{32}$	$4\frac{7}{16}$	$1\text{-}8\frac{23}{32}$	$4\frac{21}{32}$	$1\text{-}9\frac{3}{4}$
$\frac{5}{16}$	$3\frac{25}{32}$	$1\text{-}5\frac{23}{32}$	4	$1\text{-}6\frac{3}{4}$	$4\frac{7}{32}$	$1\text{-}7\frac{25}{32}$	$4\frac{7}{16}$	$1\text{-}8\frac{25}{32}$	$4\frac{21}{32}$	$1\text{-}9\frac{13}{16}$
$\frac{3}{8}$	$3\frac{13}{16}$	$1\text{-}5\frac{25}{32}$	$4\frac{1}{32}$	$1\text{-}6\frac{13}{16}$	$4\frac{1}{4}$	$1\text{-}7\frac{27}{32}$	$4\frac{15}{32}$	$1\text{-}8\frac{27}{32}$	$4\frac{11}{16}$	$1\text{-}9\frac{7}{8}$
$\frac{7}{16}$	$3\frac{13}{16}$	$1\text{-}5\frac{27}{32}$	$4\frac{1}{32}$	$1\text{-}6\frac{7}{8}$	$4\frac{1}{4}$	$1\text{-}7\frac{29}{32}$	$4\frac{15}{32}$	$1\text{-}8\frac{29}{32}$	$4\frac{11}{16}$	$1\text{-}9\frac{15}{32}$
$\frac{1}{2}$	$3\frac{13}{16}$	$1\text{-}5\frac{29}{32}$	$4\frac{1}{16}$	$1\text{-}6\frac{15}{16}$	$4\frac{1}{4}$	$1\text{-}7\frac{31}{32}$	$4\frac{1}{2}$	$1\text{-}9$	$4\frac{11}{16}$	$1\text{-}10$
$\frac{9}{16}$	$3\frac{27}{32}$	$1\text{-}5\frac{31}{32}$	$4\frac{1}{16}$	$1\text{-}7$	$4\frac{9}{32}$	$1\text{-}8\frac{1}{32}$	$4\frac{1}{2}$	$1\text{-}9\frac{1}{16}$	$4\frac{23}{32}$	$1\text{-}10\frac{1}{16}$
$\frac{5}{8}$	$3\frac{27}{32}$	$1\text{-}6\frac{1}{32}$	$4\frac{1}{16}$	$1\text{-}7\frac{1}{16}$	$4\frac{9}{32}$	$1\text{-}8\frac{3}{32}$	$4\frac{1}{2}$	$1\text{-}9\frac{1}{8}$	$4\frac{23}{32}$	$1\text{-}10\frac{1}{8}$
$\frac{11}{16}$	$3\frac{7}{8}$	$1\text{-}6\frac{3}{32}$	$4\frac{3}{32}$	$1\text{-}7\frac{1}{8}$	$4\frac{5}{16}$	$1\text{-}8\frac{5}{32}$	$4\frac{17}{32}$	$1\text{-}9\frac{3}{16}$	$4\frac{3}{4}$	$1\text{-}10\frac{3}{16}$
$\frac{3}{4}$	$3\frac{7}{8}$	$1\text{-}6\frac{5}{32}$	$4\frac{3}{32}$	$1\text{-}7\frac{3}{16}$	$4\frac{5}{16}$	$1\text{-}8\frac{7}{32}$	$4\frac{17}{32}$	$1\text{-}9\frac{1}{4}$	$4\frac{3}{4}$	$1\text{-}10\frac{1}{4}$
$\frac{13}{16}$	$3\frac{29}{32}$	$1\text{-}6\frac{7}{32}$	$4\frac{1}{8}$	$1\text{-}7\frac{1}{4}$	$4\frac{11}{32}$	$1\text{-}8\frac{9}{32}$	$4\frac{9}{16}$	$1\text{-}9\frac{5}{16}$	$4\frac{25}{32}$	$1\text{-}10\frac{11}{32}$
$\frac{7}{8}$	$3\frac{29}{32}$	$1\text{-}6\frac{9}{32}$	$4\frac{1}{8}$	$1\text{-}7\frac{5}{16}$	$4\frac{11}{32}$	$1\text{-}8\frac{11}{32}$	$4\frac{9}{16}$	$1\text{-}9\frac{3}{8}$	$4\frac{25}{32}$	$1\text{-}10\frac{13}{32}$
$\frac{15}{16}$	$3\frac{15}{16}$	$1\text{-}6\frac{3}{8}$	$4\frac{5}{32}$	$1\text{-}7\frac{3}{8}$	$4\frac{3}{8}$	$1\text{-}8\frac{13}{32}$	$4\frac{19}{32}$	$1\text{-}9\frac{7}{16}$	$4\frac{13}{16}$	$1\text{-}10\frac{15}{32}$

Feet	40' Rise	40' Slope	50' Rise	50' Slope	60' Rise	60' Slope	70' Rise	70' Slope
0	8-9	$40\text{-}11\frac{11}{32}$	$10\text{-}11\frac{1}{4}$	$51\text{-}2\frac{3}{16}$	$13\text{-}1\frac{1}{2}$	$61\text{-}5\frac{1}{32}$	$15\text{-}3\frac{3}{4}$	$71\text{-}7\frac{7}{8}$
1	$8\text{-}11\frac{5}{8}$	$41\text{-}11\frac{5}{8}$	$11\text{-}1\frac{7}{8}$	$52\text{-}2\frac{15}{32}$	$13\text{-}4\frac{1}{8}$	$62\text{-}5\frac{5}{16}$	$15\text{-}6\frac{3}{8}$	$72\text{-}8\frac{5}{32}$
2	$9\text{-}2\frac{1}{4}$	$42\text{-}11\frac{29}{32}$	$11\text{-}4\frac{1}{2}$	$53\text{-}2\frac{3}{4}$	$13\text{-}6\frac{3}{4}$	$63\text{-}5\frac{19}{32}$	15-9	$73\text{-}8\frac{7}{16}$
3	$9\text{-}4\frac{7}{8}$	$44\text{-}0\frac{3}{16}$	$11\text{-}7\frac{1}{8}$	$54\text{-}3\frac{1}{16}$	$13\text{-}9\frac{3}{8}$	$64\text{-}5\frac{7}{8}$	$15\text{-}11\frac{5}{8}$	$74\text{-}8\frac{23}{32}$
4	$9\text{-}7\frac{1}{2}$	$45\text{-}0\frac{1}{2}$	$11\text{-}9\frac{3}{4}$	$55\text{-}3\frac{5}{16}$	14-0	$65\text{-}6\frac{5}{32}$	$16\text{-}2\frac{1}{4}$	75-9
5	$9\text{-}10\frac{1}{8}$	$46\text{-}0\frac{25}{32}$	$12\text{-}0\frac{3}{8}$	$56\text{-}3\frac{19}{32}$	$14\text{-}2\frac{5}{8}$	$66\text{-}6\frac{7}{16}$	$16\text{-}4\frac{7}{8}$	$76\text{-}9\frac{9}{32}$
6	$10\text{-}0\frac{3}{4}$	$47\text{-}1\frac{1}{16}$	12-3	$57\text{-}3\frac{7}{8}$	$14\text{-}5\frac{1}{4}$	$67\text{-}6\frac{23}{32}$	$16\text{-}7\frac{1}{2}$	$77\text{-}9\frac{9}{16}$
7	$10\text{-}3\frac{3}{8}$	$48\text{-}1\frac{11}{32}$	$12\text{-}5\frac{5}{8}$	$58\text{-}4\frac{3}{16}$	$14\text{-}7\frac{7}{8}$	68-7	$16\text{-}10\frac{1}{8}$	$78\text{-}9\frac{27}{32}$
8	10-6	$49\text{-}1\frac{5}{8}$	$12\text{-}8\frac{1}{4}$	$59\text{-}4\frac{15}{32}$	$14\text{-}10\frac{1}{2}$	$69\text{-}7\frac{9}{32}$	$17\text{-}0\frac{3}{4}$	$79\text{-}10\frac{1}{8}$
9	$10\text{-}8\frac{5}{8}$	$50\text{-}1\frac{29}{32}$	$12\text{-}10\frac{7}{8}$	$60\text{-}4\frac{3}{4}$	$15\text{-}1\frac{1}{8}$	$70\text{-}7\frac{19}{32}$	$17\text{-}3\frac{3}{8}$	$80\text{-}10\frac{13}{32}$

natsin A=0.2136968788; natcos A=0.9769000174; nattan A=0.2187500000; natcot A=4.5714285714

Inches	0" Rise	0" Slope	1" Rise	1" Slope	2" Rise	2" Slope	3" Rise	3" Slope	4" Rise	4" Slope	5" Rise	5" Slope
0	0	0	7/32	1 1/32	7/16	2 1/16	11/16	3 1/16	29/32	4 3/32	1 1/8	5 1/8
1/16	0	1/16	1/4	1 3/32	15/32	2 1/8	11/16	3 1/8	29/32	4 5/32	1 1/8	5 3/16
1/8	1/32	1/8	1/4	1 5/32	15/32	2 3/16	11/16	3 3/16	15/16	4 7/32	1 5/32	5 1/4
3/16	1/32	3/16	9/32	1 7/32	1/2	2 1/4	23/32	3 9/32	15/16	4 9/32	1 9/32	5 5/16
1/4	1/16	1/4	9/32	1 9/32	1/2	2 5/16	23/32	3 11/32	15/16	4 11/32	1 3/16	5 3/8
5/16	1/16	5/16	9/32	1 11/32	17/32	2 3/8	3/4	3 13/32	31/32	4 13/32	1 3/16	5 7/16
3/8	3/32	3/8	5/16	1 13/32	17/32	2 7/16	3/4	3 15/32	31/32	4 15/32	1 7/32	5 1/2
7/16	3/32	7/16	5/16	1 15/32	17/32	2 1/2	25/32	3 17/32	1	4 9/16	1 7/32	5 9/16
1/2	1/8	1/2	11/32	1 17/32	9/16	2 9/16	25/32	3 19/32	1	4 5/8	1 7/32	5 5/8
9/16	1/8	9/16	11/32	1 19/32	9/16	2 5/8	13/16	3 21/32	1 1/32	4 11/16	1 1/4	5 11/16
5/8	1/8	5/8	3/8	1 21/32	19/32	2 11/16	13/16	3 23/32	1 1/32	4 3/4	1 1/4	5 3/4
11/16	5/32	23/32	3/8	1 23/32	19/32	2 3/4	13/16	3 25/32	1 1/16	4 13/16	1 9/32	5 27/32
3/4	5/32	25/32	13/32	1 25/32	5/8	2 13/16	27/32	3 27/32	1 1/16	4 7/8	1 9/32	5 29/32
13/16	3/16	27/32	13/32	1 27/32	5/8	2 7/8	27/32	3 29/32	1 1/16	4 15/16	1 5/16	5 31/32
7/8	3/16	29/32	13/32	1 29/32	21/32	2 15/16	7/8	3 31/32	1 3/32	5	1 5/16	6 1/32
15/16	7/32	31/32	7/16	2	21/32	3	7/8	4 1/32	1 3/32	5 1/16	1 11/32	6 3/32

Inches	6" Rise	6" Slope	7" Rise	7" Slope	8" Rise	8" Slope	9" Rise	9" Slope	10" Rise	10" Slope	11" Rise	11" Slope
0	1 11/32	6 5/32	1 9/16	7 3/16	1 25/32	8 3/16	2	9 7/32	2 1/4	10 1/4	2 15/32	11 9/32
1/16	1 11/32	6 7/32	1 19/32	7 1/4	1 13/16	8 1/4	2 1/32	9 9/32	2 1/4	10 5/16	2 15/32	11 11/32
1/8	1 3/8	6 9/32	1 19/32	7 5/16	1 13/16	8 5/16	2 1/32	9 11/32	2 9/32	10 3/8	2 1/2	11 13/32
3/16	1 3/8	6 11/32	1 5/8	7 3/8	1 27/32	8 3/8	2 1/16	9 13/32	2 9/32	10 7/16	2 1/2	11 15/32
1/4	1 13/32	6 13/32	1 5/8	7 7/16	1 27/32	8 15/32	2 1/16	9 15/32	2 9/32	10 1/2	2 17/32	11 17/32
5/16	1 13/32	6 15/32	1 5/8	7 1/2	1 7/8	8 17/32	2 3/32	9 17/32	2 5/16	10 9/16	2 17/32	11 19/32
3/8	1 7/16	6 17/32	1 21/32	7 9/16	1 7/8	8 19/32	2 3/32	9 19/32	2 5/16	10 5/8	2 9/16	11 21/32
7/16	1 7/16	6 19/32	1 21/32	7 5/8	1 7/8	8 21/32	2 1/8	9 21/32	2 11/32	10 11/16	2 9/16	11 23/32
1/2	1 15/32	6 21/32	1 11/16	7 11/16	1 29/32	8 23/32	2 1/8	9 3/4	2 11/32	10 3/4	2 9/16	11 25/32
9/16	1 15/32	6 23/32	1 11/16	7 3/4	1 29/32	8 25/32	2 5/32	9 13/16	2 3/8	10 13/16	2 19/32	11 27/32
5/8	1 15/32	6 25/32	1 23/32	7 13/16	1 15/16	8 27/32	2 5/32	9 7/8	2 3/8	10 7/8	2 19/32	11 29/32
11/16	1 1/2	6 27/32	1 23/32	7 7/8	1 15/16	8 29/32	2 5/32	9 15/16	2 13/32	10 15/16	2 5/8	11 31/32
3/4	1 1/2	6 29/32	1 3/4	7 15/16	1 31/32	8 31/32	2 3/16	10	2 13/32	11 1/32	2 5/8	1-0 1/32
13/16	1 17/32	6 31/32	1 3/4	8	1 31/32	9 1/32	2 3/16	10 1/16	2 13/32	11 3/32	2 21/32	1-0 3/32
7/8	1 17/32	7 1/32	1 3/4	8 1/16	2	9 3/32	2 7/32	10 1/8	2 7/16	11 5/32	2 21/32	1-0 5/32
15/16	1 9/16	7 3/32	1 25/32	8 1/8	2	9 5/32	2 7/32	10 3/16	2 7/16	11 7/32	2 11/16	1-0 7/32

Feet	0' Rise	0' Slope	10' Rise	10' Slope	20' Rise	20' Slope	30' Rise	30' Slope
0	0	0	2-2 7/8	10-2 31/32	4-5 3/4	20-5 15/16	6-8 5/8	30-8 29/32
1	2 11/16	1-0 5/16	2-5 9/16	11-3 9/32	4-8 7/16	21-6 1/4	6-11 5/16	31-9 7/32
2	5 3/8	2-0 19/32	2-8 1/4	12-3 9/16	4-11 1/8	22-6 17/32	7-2	32-9 1/2
3	8 1/16	3-0 29/32	2-10 15/16	13-3 7/8	5-1 13/16	23-6 27/32	7-4 11/16	33-9 13/16
4	10 3/4	4-1 3/16	3-1 5/8	14-4 5/32	5-4 1/2	24-7 1/8	7-7 3/8	34-10 3/32
5	1-1 7/16	5-1 1/2	3-4 5/16	15-4 15/32	5-7 3/16	25-7 7/16	7-10 1/16	35-10 13/32
6	1-4 1/8	6-1 25/32	3-7	16-4 3/4	5-9 7/8	26-7 23/32	8-0 3/4	36-10 11/16
7	1-6 13/16	7-2 3/32	3-9 11/16	17-5 1/16	6-0 9/16	27-8 1/32	8-3 7/16	37-11
8	1-9 1/2	8-2 3/8	4-0 3/8	18-5 11/32	6-3 1/4	28-8 5/16	8-6 1/8	38-11 9/32
9	2-0 3/16	9-2 11/16	4-3 1/16	19-5 21/32	6-5 15/16	29-8 5/8	8-8 13/16	39-11 19/32

A = 12° 37' 25''; logsin A = 9.33954; logcos A = 9.98937; logtan A = 9.35017; logcot A = 0.64983

Ins.	12″ Rise	12″ Slope	13″ Rise	13″ Slope	14″ Rise	14″ Slope	15″ Rise	15″ Slope	16″ Rise	16″ Slope
0	2 11/16	1-0 5/16	2 29/32	1-1 5/16	3 1/8	1-2 11/32	3 3/8	1-3 3/8	3 19/32	1-4 13/32
1/16	2 11/16	1-0 3/8	2 15/16	1-1 3/8	3 5/32	1-2 13/32	3 3/8	1-3 7/16	3 19/32	1-4 15/32
1/8	2 23/32	1-0 7/16	2 15/16	1-1 7/16	3 5/32	1-2 15/32	3 3/8	1-3 1/2	3 5/8	1-4 17/32
3/16	2 23/32	1-0 1/2	2 31/32	1-1 1/2	3 3/16	1-2 17/32	3 13/32	1-3 9/16	3 5/8	1-4 19/32
1/4	2 3/4	1-0 9/16	2 31/32	1-1 19/32	3 3/16	1-2 19/32	3 13/32	1-3 5/8	3 5/8	1-4 21/32
5/16	2 3/4	1-0 5/8	2 31/32	1-1 21/32	3 7/32	1-2 21/32	3 7/16	1-3 11/16	3 21/32	1-4 23/32
3/8	2 25/32	1-0 11/16	3	1-1 23/32	3 7/32	1-2 23/32	3 7/16	1-3 3/4	3 21/32	1-4 25/32
7/16	2 25/32	1-0 3/4	3	1-1 25/32	3 7/32	1-2 25/32	3 15/32	1-3 13/16	3 11/16	1-4 27/32
1/2	2 13/16	1-0 13/16	3 1/32	1-1 27/32	3 1/4	1-2 27/32	3 15/32	1-3 7/8	3 11/16	1-4 29/32
9/16	2 13/16	1-0 7/8	3 1/32	1-1 29/32	3 1/4	1-2 15/16	3 1/2	1-3 15/16	3 23/32	1-4 31/32
5/8	2 13/16	1-0 15/16	3 1/16	1-1 31/32	3 9/32	1-3	3 1/2	1-4	3 23/32	1-5 1/32
11/16	2 27/32	1-1	3 1/16	1-2 1/32	3 9/32	1-3 1/32	3 1/2	1-4 1/16	3 3/4	1-5 3/32
3/4	2 27/32	1-1 1/16	3 3/32	1-2 3/32	3 5/16	1-3 1/8	3 17/32	1-4 1/8	3 3/4	1-5 5/32
13/16	2 7/8	1-1 1/8	3 3/32	1-2 5/32	3 5/16	1-3 3/8	3 17/32	1-4 7/32	3 3/4	1-5 7/32
7/8	2 7/8	1-1 3/16	3 3/32	1-2 7/32	3 11/32	1-3 1/4	3 9/16	1-4 9/32	3 25/32	1-5 9/32
15/16	2 29/32	1-1 1/4	3 1/8	1-2 9/32	3 11/32	1-3 5/16	3 9/16	1-4 11/32	3 25/32	1-5 11/32

Ins.	17″ Rise	17″ Slope	18″ Rise	18″ Slope	19″ Rise	19″ Slope	20″ Rise	20″ Slope	21″ Rise	21″ Slope
0	3 13/16	1-5 13/32	4 1/32	1-6 7/16	4 1/4	1-7 15/32	4 15/32	1-8 1/2	4 11/16	1-9 17/32
1/16	3 13/16	1-5 1/2	4 1/32	1-6 1/2	4 9/32	1-7 17/32	4 1/2	1-8 9/16	4 23/32	1-9 19/32
1/8	3 27/32	1-5 9/16	4 1/16	1-6 9/16	4 9/32	1-7 19/32	4 1/2	1-8 5/8	4 23/32	1-9 21/32
3/16	3 27/32	1-5 5/8	4 1/16	1-6 5/8	4 1/16	1-7 21/32	4 17/32	1-8 11/16	4 3/4	1-9 23/32
1/4	3 7/8	1-5 11/16	4 3/32	1-6 11/16	4 5/16	1-7 23/32	4 17/32	1-8 3/4	4 3/4	1-9 25/32
5/16	3 7/8	1-5 3/4	4 3/32	1-6 25/32	4 5/16	1-7 25/32	4 9/16	1-8 13/16	4 25/32	1-9 27/32
3/8	3 29/32	1-5 13/16	4 1/8	1-6 27/32	4 11/32	1-7 27/32	4 9/16	1-8 7/8	4 25/32	1-9 29/32
7/16	3 29/32	1-5 7/8	4 1/8	1-6 29/32	4 11/32	1-7 29/32	4 9/16	1-8 15/16	4 13/16	1-9 31/32
1/2	3 29/32	1-5 15/16	4 5/32	1-6 31/32	4 3/8	1-7 31/32	4 19/32	1-9	4 13/16	1-10 1/2
9/16	3 15/16	1-6	4 5/32	1-7 1/32	4 3/8	1-8 1/16	4 19/32	1-9 1/16	4 27/32	1-10 3/32
5/8	3 15/16	1-6 1/16	4 5/32	1-7 3/32	4 13/32	1-8 1/8	4 5/8	1-9 1/8	4 27/32	1-10 5/32
11/16	3 31/32	1-6 1/8	4 3/16	1-7 5/32	4 13/32	1-8 3/16	4 5/8	1-9 3/16	4 27/32	1-10 7/32
3/4	3 31/32	1-6 3/16	4 3/16	1-7 7/32	4 7/16	1-8 1/4	4 21/32	1-9 1/4	4 7/8	1-10 9/32
13/16	4	1-6 1/4	4 7/32	1-7 9/32	4 7/16	1-8 5/16	4 21/32	1-9 5/16	4 7/8	1-10 11/32
7/8	4	1-6 5/16	4 7/32	1-7 11/32	4 7/16	1-8 3/8	4 11/16	1-9 13/32	4 29/32	1-10 13/32
15/16	4 1/32	1-6 3/8	4 1/4	1-7 13/32	4 15/32	1-8 7/16	4 11/16	1-9 15/32	4 29/32	1-10 15/32

Feet	40′ Rise	40′ Slope	50′ Rise	50′ Slope	60′ Rise	60′ Slope	70′ Rise	70′ Slope
0	8-11 1/2	40-11 7/8	11-2 3/8	51-2 7/8	13-5 1/4	61-5 27/32	15-8 1/8	71-8 13/16
1	9-2 3/16	42-0 3/16	11-5 1/16	52-3 5/32	13-7 15/16	62-6 1/8	15-10 13/16	72-9 3/32
2	9-4 7/8	43-0 1/32	11-7 3/4	53-3 15/32	13-10 5/8	63-6 7/16	16-1 1/2	73-9 13/32
3	9-7 9/16	44-0 25/32	11-10 7/16	54-3 3/4	14-1 5/16	64-6 23/32	16-4 3/16	74-9 11/16
4	9-10 1/4	45-1 3/32	12-1 1/8	55-4 1/16	14-4	65-7 1/32	16-6 7/8	75-10
5	10-0 15/16	46-1 3/8	12-3 13/16	56-4 11/32	14-6 11/16	66-7 5/16	16-9 9/16	76-10 9/32
6	10-3 5/8	47-1 11/16	12-6 1/2	57-4 21/32	14-9 3/8	67-7 5/8	17-0 1/4	77-10 19/32
7	10-6 5/16	48-1 31/32	12-9 3/16	58-4 15/16	15-0 1/16	68-7 29/32	17-2 15/16	78-10 7/8
8	10-9	49-2 9/32	12-11 7/8	59-5 1/4	15-2 3/4	69-8 7/32	17-5 5/8	79-11 3/16
9	10-11 11/16	50-2 9/16	13-2 9/16	60-5 17/32	15-5 7/16	70-8 1/2	17-8 5/16	80-11 15/32

natsin A=0.2185445807; natcos A=0.9758269654; nattan A=0.2239583333; natcot A=4.4651162790

Inches	0" Rise	0" Slope	1" Rise	1" Slope	2" Rise	2" Slope	3" Rise	3" Slope	4" Rise	4" Slope	5" Rise	5" Slope
0	0	0	7/32	1 1/32	15/32	2 1/16	11/16	3 1/16	29/32	4 3/32	1 5/32	5 1/8
1/16	0	1/16	1/4	1 3/32	15/32	2 1/8	11/16	3 5/32	15/16	4 5/32	1 5/32	5 5/32
1/8	1/32	1/8	1/4	1 5/32	1/2	2 3/16	23/32	3 7/32	15/16	4 7/32	1 3/16	5 1/4
3/16	3/32	3/16	9/32	1 7/32	1/2	2 1/4	23/32	3 9/32	31/32	4 9/32	1 3/16	5 9/32
1/4	1/16	1/4	9/32	1 9/32	1/2	2 5/16	3/4	3 11/32	31/32	4 3/8	1 3/16	5 3/8
5/16	1/16	5/16	5/16	1 11/32	17/32	2 3/8	3/4	3 13/32	1	4 7/16	1 7/32	5 7/16
3/8	3/32	3/8	5/16	1 13/32	17/32	2 7/16	25/32	3 15/32	1	4 1/2	1 7/32	5 1/2
7/16	3/32	7/16	11/32	1 15/32	9/16	2 1/2	25/32	3 17/32	1 1/16	4 9/16	1 1/4	5 19/32
1/2	1/8	1/2	11/32	1 17/32	9/16	2 9/16	13/16	3 19/32	1 1/16	4 5/8	1 1/4	5 21/32
9/16	1/8	9/16	11/32	1 19/32	19/32	2 5/8	13/16	3 21/32	1 1/16	4 11/16	1 9/32	5 23/32
5/8	5/32	21/32	3/8	1 21/32	19/32	2 11/16	27/32	3 23/32	1 1/16	4 3/4	1 9/32	5 25/32
11/16	5/32	23/32	3/8	1 23/32	5/8	2 3/4	27/32	3 25/32	1 1/16	4 13/16	1 5/16	5 27/32
3/4	3/16	25/32	13/32	1 25/32	5/8	2 13/16	7/8	3 27/32	1 3/32	4 7/8	1 5/16	5 29/32
13/16	3/16	27/32	13/32	1 7/8	21/32	2 7/8	7/8	3 29/32	1 3/32	4 15/16	1 11/32	5 31/32
7/8	3/16	29/32	7/16	1 15/16	21/32	2 15/16	7/8	3 31/32	1 1/8	5	1 11/32	6 1/32
15/16	7/32	31/32	7/16	2	11/16	3	29/32	4 1/32	1 1/8	5 1/16	1 3/8	6 3/32

Inches	6" Rise	6" Slope	7" Rise	7" Slope	8" Rise	8" Slope	9" Rise	9" Slope	10" Rise	10" Slope	11" Rise	11" Slope
0	1 3/8	6 5/32	1 19/32	7 3/16	1 27/32	8 7/32	2 1/16	9 7/32	2 9/32	10 1/4	2 17/32	11 9/32
1/16	1 3/8	6 7/32	1 5/8	7 1/4	1 27/32	8 9/32	2 1/16	9 5/16	2 5/16	10 5/16	2 17/32	11 11/32
1/8	1 13/32	6 9/32	1 5/8	7 5/16	1 7/8	8 11/32	2 3/32	9 3/8	2 5/16	10 3/8	2 9/16	11 13/32
3/16	1 13/32	6 11/32	1 21/32	7 3/8	1 7/8	8 13/32	2 3/32	9 7/16	2 11/32	10 7/16	2 9/16	11 15/32
1/4	1 7/16	6 13/32	1 21/32	7 7/16	1 7/8	8 15/32	2 1/8	9 1/2	2 11/32	10 1/2	2 9/16	11 17/32
5/16	1 7/16	6 15/32	1 11/16	7 1/2	1 29/32	8 17/32	2 1/8	9 9/16	2 3/8	10 19/32	2 19/32	11 19/32
3/8	1 15/32	6 17/32	1 11/16	7 9/16	1 29/32	8 19/32	2 5/32	9 5/8	2 3/8	10 21/32	2 19/32	11 21/32
7/16	1 15/32	6 19/32	1 23/32	7 5/8	1 15/16	8 21/32	2 5/32	9 11/16	2 13/32	10 23/32	2 5/8	11 23/32
1/2	1 1/2	6 21/32	1 23/32	7 11/16	1 15/16	8 23/32	2 3/16	9 3/4	2 13/32	10 25/32	2 5/8	11 13/16
9/16	1 1/2	6 23/32	1 23/32	7 3/4	1 31/32	8 25/32	2 3/16	9 13/16	2 13/32	10 27/32	2 21/32	11 7/8
5/8	1 17/32	6 25/32	1 3/4	7 13/16	1 31/32	8 27/32	2 7/32	9 7/8	2 7/16	10 29/32	2 21/32	11 15/16
11/16	1 17/32	6 7/8	1 3/4	7 7/8	2	8 29/32	2 7/32	9 15/16	2 7/16	10 31/32	2 11/16	1-0
3/4	1 9/16	6 15/16	1 25/32	7 15/16	2	8 31/32	2 1/4	10	2 15/32	11 1/32	2 11/16	1-0 1/16
13/16	1 9/16	7	1 25/32	8	2 1/16	9 1/32	2 1/4	10 1/16	2 15/32	11 3/32	2 23/32	1-0 3/32
7/8	1 9/16	7 1/16	1 13/16	8 1/16	2 1/16	9 3/32	2 1/4	10 1/8	2 1/2	11 5/32	2 23/32	1-0 3/16
15/16	1 19/32	7 1/8	1 7/8	8 1/8	2 1/16	9 5/32	2 9/32	10 3/16	2 1/2	11 7/32	2 3/4	1-0 1/4

Feet	0' Rise	0' Slope	10' Rise	10' Slope	20' Rise	20' Slope	30' Rise	30' Slope
0	0	0	2-3 1/8	10-3 1/8	4-7	20-6 1/32	6-10 1/2	30-9 11/32
1	2 3/4	1-0 5/16	2-6 1/4	11-3 13/32	4-9 3/4	21-6 17/32	7-1 1/4	31-9 21/32
2	5 1/2	2-0 5/8	2-9	12-3 23/32	5-0 1/2	22-6 27/32	7-4	32-9 31/32
3	8 1/4	3-0 15/16	2-11 3/4	13-4 1/32	5-3 1/4	23-7 5/32	7-6 3/4	33-10 1/4
4	11	4-1 1/4	3-2 1/2	14-4 11/32	5-6	24-7 15/32	7-9 1/2	34-10 9/16
5	1-1 3/4	5-1 9/16	3-5 1/4	15-4 21/32	5-8 3/4	25-7 25/32	8-0 1/4	35-10 7/8
6	1-4 1/2	6-1 7/8	3-8	16-4 31/32	5-11 1/2	26-8 3/32	8-3	36-11 3/16
7	1-7 1/4	7-2 3/16	3-10 3/4	17-5 9/32	6-2 1/4	27-8 13/32	8-5 3/4	37-11 1/2
8	1-10	8-2 1/2	4-1 1/2	18-5 19/32	6-5	28-8 23/32	8-8 1/2	38-11 13/16
9	2-0 3/4	9-2 13/16	4-4 1/4	19-5 29/32	6-7 3/4	29-9 1/32	8-11 1/4	40-0 1/8

A = 12° 54' 27''; logsin A = 9.34904; logcos A = 9.98889: logtan A = 9.36015; logcot A = 0.63985

In.	12″ Rise	12″ Slope	13″ Rise	13″ Slope	14″ Rise	14″ Slope	15″ Rise	15″ Slope	16″ Rise	16″ Slope
0	$2\frac{3}{4}$	$1\text{-}0\frac{5}{16}$	$2\frac{31}{32}$	$1\text{-}1\frac{11}{32}$	$3\frac{7}{32}$	$1\text{-}2\frac{3}{8}$	$3\frac{7}{16}$	$1\text{-}3\frac{3}{8}$	$3\frac{21}{32}$	$1\text{-}4\frac{13}{32}$
$\frac{1}{16}$	$2\frac{3}{4}$	$1\text{-}0\frac{3}{8}$	3	$1\text{-}1\frac{13}{32}$	$3\frac{7}{32}$	$1\text{-}2\frac{7}{16}$	$3\frac{7}{16}$	$1\text{-}3\frac{7}{16}$	$3\frac{11}{16}$	$1\text{-}4\frac{15}{32}$
$\frac{1}{8}$	$2\frac{25}{32}$	$1\text{-}0\frac{7}{16}$	3	$1\text{-}1\frac{15}{32}$	$3\frac{1}{4}$	$1\text{-}2\frac{1}{2}$	$3\frac{15}{32}$	$1\text{-}3\frac{17}{32}$	$3\frac{11}{16}$	$1\text{-}4\frac{17}{32}$
$\frac{3}{16}$	$2\frac{25}{32}$	$1\text{-}0\frac{1}{2}$	$3\frac{1}{32}$	$1\text{-}1\frac{17}{32}$	$3\frac{1}{4}$	$1\text{-}2\frac{9}{16}$	$3\frac{15}{32}$	$1\text{-}3\frac{19}{32}$	$3\frac{23}{32}$	$1\text{-}4\frac{19}{32}$
$\frac{1}{4}$	$2\frac{13}{16}$	$1\text{-}0\frac{9}{16}$	$3\frac{1}{32}$	$1\text{-}1\frac{19}{32}$	$3\frac{1}{4}$	$1\text{-}2\frac{5}{8}$	$3\frac{1}{2}$	$1\text{-}3\frac{21}{32}$	$3\frac{23}{32}$	$1\text{-}4\frac{21}{32}$
$\frac{5}{16}$	$2\frac{13}{16}$	$1\text{-}0\frac{5}{8}$	$3\frac{1}{16}$	$1\text{-}1\frac{21}{32}$	$3\frac{9}{32}$	$1\text{-}2\frac{11}{16}$	$3\frac{1}{2}$	$1\text{-}3\frac{23}{32}$	$3\frac{3}{4}$	$1\text{-}4\frac{3}{4}$
$\frac{3}{8}$	$2\frac{27}{32}$	$1\text{-}0\frac{11}{16}$	$3\frac{1}{16}$	$1\text{-}1\frac{23}{32}$	$3\frac{9}{32}$	$1\text{-}2\frac{3}{4}$	$3\frac{17}{32}$	$1\text{-}3\frac{25}{32}$	$3\frac{3}{4}$	$1\text{-}4\frac{13}{16}$
$\frac{7}{16}$	$2\frac{27}{32}$	$1\text{-}0\frac{3}{4}$	$3\frac{3}{32}$	$1\text{-}1\frac{25}{32}$	$3\frac{5}{16}$	$1\text{-}2\frac{13}{16}$	$3\frac{17}{32}$	$1\text{-}3\frac{27}{32}$	$3\frac{25}{32}$	$1\text{-}4\frac{7}{8}$
$\frac{1}{2}$	$2\frac{7}{8}$	$1\text{-}0\frac{13}{16}$	$3\frac{3}{32}$	$1\text{-}1\frac{27}{32}$	$3\frac{5}{16}$	$1\text{-}2\frac{7}{8}$	$3\frac{9}{16}$	$1\text{-}3\frac{29}{32}$	$3\frac{25}{32}$	$1\text{-}4\frac{15}{16}$
$\frac{9}{16}$	$2\frac{7}{8}$	$1\text{-}0\frac{7}{8}$	$3\frac{3}{32}$	$1\text{-}1\frac{29}{32}$	$3\frac{11}{32}$	$1\text{-}2\frac{15}{16}$	$3\frac{9}{16}$	$1\text{-}3\frac{31}{32}$	$3\frac{25}{32}$	$1\text{-}5$
$\frac{5}{8}$	$2\frac{29}{32}$	$1\text{-}0\frac{15}{16}$	$3\frac{1}{8}$	$1\text{-}1\frac{31}{32}$	$3\frac{11}{32}$	$1\text{-}3$	$3\frac{19}{32}$	$1\text{-}4\frac{1}{32}$	$3\frac{13}{16}$	$1\text{-}5\frac{1}{16}$
$\frac{11}{16}$	$2\frac{29}{32}$	$1\text{-}1\frac{1}{32}$	$3\frac{1}{8}$	$1\text{-}2\frac{1}{32}$	$3\frac{11}{32}$	$1\text{-}3\frac{1}{16}$	$3\frac{19}{32}$	$1\text{-}4\frac{3}{32}$	$3\frac{13}{16}$	$1\text{-}5\frac{1}{8}$
$\frac{3}{4}$	$2\frac{15}{16}$	$1\text{-}1\frac{3}{32}$	$3\frac{5}{32}$	$1\text{-}2\frac{3}{32}$	$3\frac{3}{8}$	$1\text{-}3\frac{1}{8}$	$3\frac{5}{8}$	$1\text{-}4\frac{5}{32}$	$3\frac{27}{32}$	$1\text{-}5\frac{3}{16}$
$\frac{13}{16}$	$2\frac{15}{16}$	$1\text{-}1\frac{5}{32}$	$3\frac{5}{32}$	$1\text{-}2\frac{5}{32}$	$3\frac{13}{32}$	$1\text{-}3\frac{3}{16}$	$3\frac{5}{8}$	$1\text{-}4\frac{7}{32}$	$3\frac{27}{32}$	$1\text{-}5\frac{1}{4}$
$\frac{7}{8}$	$2\frac{15}{16}$	$1\text{-}1\frac{7}{32}$	$3\frac{3}{16}$	$1\text{-}2\frac{1}{4}$	$3\frac{13}{32}$	$1\text{-}3\frac{1}{4}$	$3\frac{5}{8}$	$1\text{-}4\frac{9}{32}$	$3\frac{7}{8}$	$1\text{-}5\frac{5}{16}$
$\frac{15}{16}$	$2\frac{31}{32}$	$1\text{-}1\frac{9}{32}$	$3\frac{3}{16}$	$1\text{-}2\frac{5}{16}$	$3\frac{7}{16}$	$1\text{-}3\frac{5}{16}$	$3\frac{21}{32}$	$1\text{-}4\frac{11}{32}$	$3\frac{7}{8}$	$1\text{-}5\frac{3}{8}$

In.	17″ Rise	17″ Slope	18″ Rise	18″ Slope	19″ Rise	19″ Slope	20″ Rise	20″ Slope	21″ Rise	21″ Slope
0	$3\frac{29}{32}$	$1\text{-}5\frac{7}{16}$	$4\frac{1}{8}$	$1\text{-}6\frac{15}{32}$	$4\frac{11}{32}$	$1\text{-}7\frac{1}{2}$	$4\frac{19}{32}$	$1\text{-}8\frac{17}{32}$	$4\frac{13}{16}$	$1\text{-}9\frac{17}{32}$
$\frac{1}{16}$	$3\frac{29}{32}$	$1\text{-}5\frac{1}{2}$	$4\frac{1}{8}$	$1\text{-}6\frac{17}{32}$	$4\frac{3}{8}$	$1\text{-}7\frac{9}{16}$	$4\frac{19}{32}$	$1\text{-}8\frac{19}{32}$	$4\frac{13}{16}$	$1\text{-}9\frac{19}{32}$
$\frac{1}{8}$	$3\frac{15}{16}$	$1\text{-}5\frac{9}{16}$	$4\frac{5}{32}$	$1\text{-}6\frac{19}{32}$	$4\frac{3}{8}$	$1\text{-}7\frac{5}{8}$	$4\frac{5}{8}$	$1\text{-}8\frac{21}{32}$	$4\frac{27}{32}$	$1\text{-}9\frac{11}{16}$
$\frac{3}{16}$	$3\frac{15}{16}$	$1\text{-}5\frac{5}{8}$	$4\frac{5}{32}$	$1\text{-}6\frac{21}{32}$	$4\frac{13}{32}$	$1\text{-}7\frac{11}{16}$	$4\frac{5}{8}$	$1\text{-}8\frac{23}{32}$	$4\frac{27}{32}$	$1\text{-}9\frac{3}{4}$
$\frac{1}{4}$	$3\frac{15}{16}$	$1\text{-}5\frac{11}{16}$	$4\frac{3}{16}$	$1\text{-}6\frac{23}{32}$	$4\frac{13}{32}$	$1\text{-}7\frac{3}{4}$	$4\frac{5}{8}$	$1\text{-}8\frac{25}{32}$	$4\frac{7}{8}$	$1\text{-}9\frac{13}{16}$
$\frac{5}{16}$	$3\frac{31}{32}$	$1\text{-}5\frac{3}{4}$	$4\frac{3}{16}$	$1\text{-}6\frac{25}{32}$	$4\frac{7}{16}$	$1\text{-}7\frac{13}{16}$	$4\frac{21}{32}$	$1\text{-}8\frac{27}{32}$	$4\frac{7}{8}$	$1\text{-}9\frac{7}{8}$
$\frac{3}{8}$	$3\frac{31}{32}$	$1\text{-}5\frac{13}{16}$	$4\frac{7}{32}$	$1\text{-}6\frac{27}{32}$	$4\frac{7}{16}$	$1\text{-}7\frac{7}{8}$	$4\frac{21}{32}$	$1\text{-}8\frac{29}{32}$	$4\frac{29}{32}$	$1\text{-}9\frac{15}{16}$
$\frac{7}{16}$	4	$1\text{-}5\frac{7}{8}$	$4\frac{7}{32}$	$1\text{-}6\frac{29}{32}$	$4\frac{15}{32}$	$1\text{-}7\frac{15}{16}$	$4\frac{11}{16}$	$1\text{-}8\frac{31}{32}$	$4\frac{29}{32}$	$1\text{-}10$
$\frac{1}{2}$	4	$1\text{-}5\frac{31}{32}$	$4\frac{1}{4}$	$1\text{-}6\frac{31}{32}$	$4\frac{15}{32}$	$1\text{-}8$	$4\frac{11}{16}$	$1\text{-}9\frac{1}{32}$	$4\frac{15}{16}$	$1\text{-}10\frac{1}{16}$
$\frac{9}{16}$	$4\frac{1}{32}$	$1\text{-}6\frac{1}{32}$	$4\frac{1}{4}$	$1\text{-}7\frac{1}{32}$	$4\frac{15}{32}$	$1\text{-}8\frac{1}{16}$	$4\frac{23}{32}$	$1\text{-}9\frac{3}{32}$	$4\frac{15}{16}$	$1\text{-}10\frac{1}{8}$
$\frac{5}{8}$	$4\frac{1}{32}$	$1\text{-}6\frac{3}{32}$	$4\frac{9}{32}$	$1\text{-}7\frac{3}{32}$	$4\frac{1}{2}$	$1\text{-}8\frac{1}{8}$	$4\frac{23}{32}$	$1\text{-}9\frac{5}{32}$	$4\frac{31}{32}$	$1\text{-}10\frac{3}{16}$
$\frac{11}{16}$	$4\frac{1}{16}$	$1\text{-}6\frac{5}{32}$	$4\frac{9}{32}$	$1\text{-}7\frac{3}{16}$	$4\frac{1}{2}$	$1\text{-}8\frac{3}{16}$	$4\frac{3}{4}$	$1\text{-}9\frac{7}{32}$	$4\frac{31}{32}$	$1\text{-}10\frac{1}{4}$
$\frac{3}{4}$	$4\frac{1}{16}$	$1\text{-}6\frac{7}{32}$	$4\frac{5}{16}$	$1\text{-}7\frac{1}{4}$	$4\frac{17}{32}$	$1\text{-}8\frac{1}{4}$	$4\frac{3}{4}$	$1\text{-}9\frac{9}{32}$	5	$1\text{-}10\frac{5}{16}$
$\frac{13}{16}$	$4\frac{3}{32}$	$1\text{-}6\frac{9}{32}$	$4\frac{5}{16}$	$1\text{-}7\frac{5}{16}$	$4\frac{17}{32}$	$1\text{-}8\frac{5}{16}$	$4\frac{25}{32}$	$1\text{-}9\frac{11}{32}$	5	$1\text{-}10\frac{3}{8}$
$\frac{7}{8}$	$4\frac{3}{32}$	$1\text{-}6\frac{11}{32}$	$4\frac{5}{16}$	$1\text{-}7\frac{3}{8}$	$4\frac{9}{16}$	$1\text{-}8\frac{3}{8}$	$4\frac{25}{32}$	$1\text{-}9\frac{13}{32}$	5	$1\text{-}10\frac{7}{16}$
$\frac{15}{16}$	$4\frac{1}{8}$	$1\text{-}6\frac{13}{32}$	$4\frac{11}{32}$	$1\text{-}7\frac{7}{16}$	$4\frac{9}{16}$	$1\text{-}8\frac{15}{32}$	$4\frac{13}{16}$	$1\text{-}9\frac{15}{32}$	$5\frac{1}{32}$	$1\text{-}10\frac{1}{2}$

Feet	40′ Rise	40′ Slope	50′ Rise	50′ Slope	60′ Rise	60′ Slope	70′ Rise	70′ Slope
0	$9\text{-}2$	$41\text{-}0\frac{7}{16}$	$11\text{-}5\frac{1}{2}$	$51\text{-}3\frac{9}{16}$	$13\text{-}9$	$61\text{-}6\frac{21}{32}$	$16\text{-}0\frac{1}{2}$	$71\text{-}9\frac{25}{32}$
1	$9\text{-}4\frac{3}{4}$	$42\text{-}0\frac{3}{4}$	$11\text{-}8\frac{1}{4}$	$52\text{-}3\frac{7}{8}$	$13\text{-}11\frac{3}{4}$	$62\text{-}6\frac{31}{32}$	$16\text{-}3\frac{1}{4}$	$72\text{-}10\frac{3}{32}$
2	$9\text{-}7\frac{1}{2}$	$43\text{-}1\frac{1}{16}$	$11\text{-}11$	$53\text{-}4\frac{3}{16}$	$14\text{-}2\frac{1}{2}$	$63\text{-}7\frac{9}{32}$	$16\text{-}6$	$73\text{-}10\frac{13}{32}$
3	$9\text{-}10\frac{1}{4}$	$44\text{-}1\frac{3}{8}$	$12\text{-}1\frac{3}{4}$	$54\text{-}4\frac{1}{2}$	$14\text{-}5\frac{1}{4}$	$64\text{-}7\frac{19}{32}$	$16\text{-}8\frac{3}{4}$	$74\text{-}10\frac{23}{32}$
4	$10\text{-}1$	$45\text{-}1\frac{11}{16}$	$12\text{-}4\frac{1}{2}$	$55\text{-}4\frac{13}{16}$	$14\text{-}8$	$65\text{-}7\frac{29}{32}$	$16\text{-}11\frac{1}{2}$	$75\text{-}11\frac{1}{32}$
5	$10\text{-}3\frac{3}{4}$	$46\text{-}2$	$12\text{-}7\frac{1}{4}$	$56\text{-}5\frac{5}{32}$	$14\text{-}10\frac{3}{4}$	$66\text{-}8\frac{7}{32}$	$17\text{-}2\frac{1}{4}$	$76\text{-}11\frac{11}{32}$
6	$10\text{-}6\frac{1}{2}$	$47\text{-}2\frac{5}{16}$	$12\text{-}10$	$57\text{-}5\frac{13}{32}$	$15\text{-}1\frac{1}{2}$	$67\text{-}8\frac{17}{32}$	$17\text{-}5$	$77\text{-}11\frac{21}{32}$
7	$10\text{-}9\frac{1}{4}$	$48\text{-}2\frac{5}{8}$	$13\text{-}0\frac{3}{4}$	$58\text{-}5\frac{23}{32}$	$15\text{-}4\frac{1}{4}$	$68\text{-}8\frac{27}{32}$	$17\text{-}7\frac{3}{4}$	$78\text{-}11\frac{15}{16}$
8	$11\text{-}0$	$49\text{-}2\frac{15}{16}$	$13\text{-}3\frac{1}{2}$	$59\text{-}6\frac{1}{32}$	$15\text{-}7$	$69\text{-}9\frac{5}{32}$	$17\text{-}10\frac{1}{2}$	$80\text{-}0\frac{1}{4}$
9	$11\text{-}2\frac{3}{4}$	$50\text{-}3\frac{1}{4}$	$13\text{-}6\frac{1}{4}$	$60\text{-}6\frac{11}{32}$	$15\text{-}9\frac{3}{4}$	$70\text{-}9\frac{15}{32}$	$18\text{-}1\frac{1}{4}$	$81\text{-}0\frac{9}{16}$

natsin A=0.2233761562; **natcos** A=0.9747323186; **nattan** A=0.2291666666; **natcot** A=4.3636363636

Inches	0" Rise	0" Slope	1" Rise	1" Slope	2" Rise	2" Slope	3" Rise	3" Slope	4" Rise	4" Slope	5" Rise	5" Slope
0	0	0	1/4	1 1/2	15/32	2 1/16	11/16	3 3/32	15/16	4 3/32	1 3/16	5 1/8
1/16	0	1/16	1/4	1 3/32	15/32	2 1/8	23/32	3 5/32	15/16	4 3/16	1 3/16	5 3/16
1/8	1/16	1/8	1/4	1 5/32	1/2	2 3/16	23/32	3 7/32	31/32	4 1/4	1 3/16	5 1/4
3/16	1/32	3/16	9/32	1 7/32	1/2	2 1/4	3/4	3 9/32	31/32	4 5/16	1 7/32	5 5/16
1/4	1/16	1/4	9/32	1 9/32	17/32	2 5/16	3/4	3 11/32	1	4 3/8	1 7/32	5 13/32
5/16	3/32	5/16	5/16	1 11/32	17/32	2 3/8	25/32	3 13/32	1	4 7/16	1 1/4	5 15/32
3/8	3/32	3/8	5/16	1 13/32	9/16	2 7/16	25/32	3 15/32	1 1/32	4 1/2	1 1/4	5 17/32
7/16	3/32	7/16	11/32	1 15/32	9/16	2 1/2	13/16	3 17/32	1 1/32	4 9/16	1 9/32	5 19/32
1/2	1/8	1/2	11/32	1 17/32	19/32	2 9/16	13/16	3 19/32	1 1/16	4 5/8	1 9/32	5 21/32
9/16	1/8	9/16	3/8	1 19/32	19/32	2 5/8	27/32	3 21/32	1 1/16	4 11/16	1 5/16	5 23/32
5/8	5/32	21/32	3/8	1 21/32	5/8	2 11/16	27/32	3 23/32	1 3/32	4 3/4	1 5/16	5 25/32
11/16	5/32	23/32	13/32	1 23/32	5/8	2 3/4	7/8	3 25/32	1 3/32	4 13/16	1 11/32	5 27/32
3/4	3/16	25/32	13/32	1 13/16	21/32	2 13/16	7/8	3 27/32	1 1/8	4 7/8	1 11/32	5 29/32
13/16	3/16	27/32	7/16	1 7/8	21/32	2 7/8	29/32	3 29/32	1 1/8	4 15/16	1 3/8	5 31/32
7/8	7/32	29/32	7/16	1 15/16	11/16	2 15/16	29/32	3 31/32	1 5/32	5	1 3/8	6 1/16
15/16	7/32	31/32	15/32	2	11/16	3 1/32	15/16	4 1/32	1 5/32	5 1/16	1 13/32	6 3/32

Inches	6" Rise	6" Slope	7" Rise	7" Slope	8" Rise	8" Slope	9" Rise	9" Slope	10" Rise	10" Slope	11" Rise	11" Slope
0	1 13/32	6 5/32	1 5/8	7 3/16	1 7/8	8 7/32	2 1/8	9 1/4	2 11/32	10 9/32	2 9/16	11 5/16
1/16	1 13/32	6 7/32	1 21/32	7 1/4	1 7/8	8 9/32	2 1/8	9 5/16	2 11/32	10 11/32	2 19/32	11 3/8
1/8	1 7/16	6 9/32	1 21/32	7 5/16	1 29/32	8 11/32	2 1/8	9 3/8	2 3/8	10 13/32	2 19/32	11 7/16
3/16	1 7/16	6 11/32	1 11/16	7 3/8	1 29/32	8 13/32	2 5/32	9 7/16	2 3/8	10 15/32	2 5/8	11 1/2
1/4	1 15/32	6 13/32	1 11/16	7 7/16	1 15/16	8 15/32	2 5/32	9 1/2	2 13/32	10 17/32	2 5/8	11 9/16
5/16	1 15/32	6 15/32	1 23/32	7 1/2	1 15/16	8 17/32	2 3/16	9 9/16	2 13/32	10 19/32	2 21/32	11 5/8
3/8	1 1/2	6 9/16	1 23/32	7 9/16	1 31/32	8 19/32	2 3/16	9 5/8	2 7/16	10 21/32	2 21/32	11 11/16
7/16	1 1/2	6 5/8	1 3/4	7 5/8	1 31/32	8 21/32	2 7/32	9 11/16	2 7/16	10 23/32	2 11/16	11 3/4
1/2	1 17/32	6 11/16	1 3/4	7 23/32	2	8 23/32	2 7/32	9 3/4	2 15/32	10 25/32	2 11/16	11 13/16
9/16	1 17/32	6 3/4	1 25/32	7 25/32	2	8 25/32	2 1/4	9 13/16	2 15/32	10 27/32	2 23/32	11 7/8
5/8	1 9/16	6 13/16	1 25/32	7 27/32	2 1/32	8 27/32	2 1/4	9 7/8	2 1/2	10 29/32	2 23/32	11 15/16
11/16	1 9/16	6 7/8	1 13/16	7 29/32	2 1/32	8 15/16	2 9/32	9 15/16	2 1/2	10 31/32	2 3/4	1-0
3/4	1 19/32	6 15/16	1 13/16	7 31/32	2 1/16	9	2 9/32	10	2 17/32	11 1/2	2 3/4	1-0 1/16
13/16	1 19/32	7	1 27/32	8 1/32	2 1/16	9 1/16	2 5/16	10 3/32	2 17/32	11 3/32	2 25/32	1-0 1/8
7/8	1 5/8	7 1/16	1 27/32	8 3/32	2 3/32	9 1/8	2 5/16	10 5/32	2 9/16	11 5/32	2 25/32	1-0 3/16
15/16	1 5/8	7 1/8	1 7/8	8 5/32	2 3/32	9 3/16	2 11/32	10 7/32	2 9/16	11 7/32	2 13/16	1-0 1/4

Feet	0' Rise	0' Slope	10' Rise	10' Slope	20' Rise	20' Slope	30' Rise	30' Slope
0	0	0	2-4 1/8	10-3 1/4	4-8 1/4	20-6 1/2	7-0 3/8	30-9 3/4
1	2 13/16	1-0 5/16	2-6 15/16	11-3 9/16	4-11 11/16	21-6 27/32	7-3 3/16	31-10 3/32
2	5 5/8	2-0 21/32	2-9 3/4	12-3 29/32	5-1 7/8	22-7 5/32	7-6	32-10 13/32
3	8 7/16	3-0 31/32	3-0 9/16	13-4 7/32	5-4 11/16	23-7 15/32	7-8 13/16	33-10 23/32
4	11 1/4	4-1 5/16	3-3 3/8	14-4 9/16	5-7 1/2	24-7 13/16	7-11 5/8	34-11 1/16
5	1-2 1/16	5-1 5/8	3-6 3/16	15-4 7/8	5-10 5/16	25-8 1/8	8-2 7/16	35-11 3/8
6	1-4 7/8	6-1 15/16	3-9	16-5 3/16	6-1 1/8	26-8 15/32	8-5 1/4	36-11 23/32
7	1-7 11/16	7-2 9/32	3-11 13/16	17-5 17/32	6-3 15/16	27-8 25/32	8-8 1/16	38-0 1/32
8	1-10 1/2	8-2 19/32	4-2 5/8	18-5 27/32	6-6 3/4	28-9 3/32	8-10 7/8	39-0 11/32
9	2-1 5/16	9-2 15/16	4-5 7/16	19-6 3/16	6-9 9/16	29-9 7/16	9-1 11/16	40-0 11/16

A = 13° 11' 26"; logsin A = 9.35830; logcos A = 9.98839; logtan A = 9.36991; logcot A = 0.63009

Ins.	12″ Rise	Slope	13″ Rise	Slope	14″ Rise	Slope	15″ Rise	Slope	16″ Rise	Slope
0	$2\frac{13}{16}$	$1\text{-}0\frac{5}{16}$	$3\frac{1}{16}$	$1\text{-}1\frac{11}{32}$	$3\frac{9}{32}$	$1\text{-}2\frac{3}{8}$	$3\frac{1}{2}$	$1\text{-}3\frac{13}{32}$	$3\frac{3}{4}$	$1\text{-}4\frac{1}{16}$
$\frac{1}{16}$	$2\frac{13}{16}$	$1\text{-}0\frac{3}{8}$	$3\frac{3}{32}$	$1\text{-}1\frac{13}{32}$	$3\frac{9}{32}$	$1\text{-}2\frac{7}{16}$	$3\frac{17}{32}$	$1\text{-}3\frac{15}{32}$	$3\frac{3}{4}$	$1\text{-}4\frac{1}{4}$
$\frac{1}{8}$	$2\frac{27}{32}$	$1\text{-}0\frac{15}{32}$	$3\frac{1}{16}$	$1\text{-}1\frac{15}{32}$	$3\frac{5}{16}$	$1\text{-}2\frac{1}{2}$	$3\frac{17}{32}$	$1\text{-}3\frac{17}{32}$	$3\frac{25}{32}$	$1\text{-}4\frac{9}{16}$
$\frac{3}{16}$	$2\frac{27}{32}$	$1\text{-}0\frac{17}{32}$	$3\frac{3}{32}$	$1\text{-}1\frac{17}{32}$	$3\frac{5}{16}$	$1\text{-}2\frac{9}{16}$	$3\frac{9}{16}$	$1\text{-}3\frac{19}{32}$	$3\frac{25}{32}$	$1\text{-}4\frac{5}{8}$
$\frac{1}{4}$	$2\frac{7}{8}$	$1\text{-}0\frac{19}{32}$	$3\frac{3}{32}$	$1\text{-}1\frac{19}{32}$	$3\frac{11}{32}$	$1\text{-}2\frac{5}{8}$	$3\frac{9}{16}$	$1\text{-}3\frac{21}{32}$	$3\frac{13}{16}$	$1\text{-}4\frac{11}{16}$
$\frac{5}{16}$	$2\frac{7}{8}$	$1\text{-}0\frac{21}{32}$	$3\frac{1}{8}$	$1\text{-}1\frac{11}{16}$	$3\frac{11}{32}$	$1\text{-}2\frac{11}{16}$	$3\frac{19}{32}$	$1\text{-}3\frac{23}{32}$	$3\frac{13}{16}$	$1\text{-}4\frac{3}{4}$
$\frac{3}{8}$	$2\frac{29}{32}$	$1\text{-}0\frac{23}{32}$	$3\frac{1}{8}$	$1\text{-}1\frac{3}{4}$	$3\frac{3}{8}$	$1\text{-}2\frac{3}{4}$	$3\frac{19}{32}$	$1\text{-}3\frac{25}{32}$	$3\frac{27}{32}$	$1\text{-}4\frac{13}{16}$
$\frac{7}{16}$	$2\frac{29}{32}$	$1\text{-}0\frac{25}{32}$	$3\frac{5}{32}$	$1\text{-}1\frac{13}{16}$	$3\frac{3}{8}$	$1\text{-}2\frac{27}{32}$	$3\frac{5}{8}$	$1\text{-}3\frac{27}{32}$	$3\frac{27}{32}$	$1\text{-}4\frac{7}{8}$
$\frac{1}{2}$	$2\frac{15}{16}$	$1\text{-}0\frac{27}{32}$	$3\frac{5}{32}$	$1\text{-}1\frac{7}{8}$	$3\frac{13}{32}$	$1\text{-}2\frac{29}{32}$	$3\frac{5}{8}$	$1\text{-}3\frac{29}{32}$	$3\frac{7}{8}$	$1\text{-}4\frac{15}{16}$
$\frac{9}{16}$	$2\frac{15}{16}$	$1\text{-}0\frac{29}{32}$	$3\frac{3}{16}$	$1\text{-}1\frac{15}{16}$	$3\frac{13}{32}$	$1\text{-}2\frac{31}{32}$	$3\frac{21}{32}$	$1\text{-}3\frac{31}{32}$	$3\frac{7}{8}$	$1\text{-}5$
$\frac{5}{8}$	$2\frac{31}{32}$	$1\text{-}0\frac{31}{32}$	$3\frac{3}{16}$	$1\text{-}2$	$3\frac{7}{16}$	$1\text{-}3\frac{1}{32}$	$3\frac{21}{32}$	$1\text{-}4\frac{1}{16}$	$3\frac{29}{32}$	$1\text{-}5\frac{1}{16}$
$\frac{11}{16}$	$2\frac{31}{32}$	$1\text{-}1\frac{1}{32}$	$3\frac{7}{32}$	$1\text{-}2\frac{1}{16}$	$3\frac{7}{16}$	$1\text{-}3\frac{3}{32}$	$3\frac{11}{16}$	$1\text{-}4\frac{1}{8}$	$3\frac{29}{32}$	$1\text{-}5\frac{1}{8}$
$\frac{3}{4}$	3	$1\text{-}1\frac{3}{32}$	$3\frac{7}{32}$	$1\text{-}2\frac{1}{8}$	$3\frac{15}{32}$	$1\text{-}3\frac{5}{32}$	$3\frac{11}{16}$	$1\text{-}4\frac{3}{8}$	$3\frac{15}{16}$	$1\text{-}5\frac{7}{32}$
$\frac{13}{16}$	3	$1\text{-}1\frac{5}{32}$	$3\frac{1}{4}$	$1\text{-}2\frac{3}{16}$	$3\frac{15}{32}$	$1\text{-}3\frac{7}{32}$	$3\frac{23}{32}$	$1\text{-}4\frac{1}{4}$	$3\frac{15}{16}$	$1\text{-}5\frac{9}{32}$
$\frac{7}{8}$	$3\frac{1}{32}$	$1\text{-}1\frac{7}{32}$	$3\frac{1}{4}$	$1\text{-}2\frac{1}{4}$	$3\frac{1}{2}$	$1\text{-}3\frac{9}{32}$	$3\frac{23}{32}$	$1\text{-}4\frac{5}{16}$	$3\frac{31}{32}$	$1\text{-}5\frac{11}{32}$
$\frac{15}{16}$	$3\frac{1}{32}$	$1\text{-}1\frac{9}{32}$	$3\frac{9}{32}$	$1\text{-}2\frac{5}{16}$	$3\frac{1}{2}$	$1\text{-}3\frac{11}{32}$	$3\frac{3}{4}$	$1\text{-}4\frac{3}{8}$	$3\frac{31}{32}$	$1\text{-}5\frac{13}{32}$

Ins.	17″ Rise	Slope	18″ Rise	Slope	19″ Rise	Slope	20″ Rise	Slope	21″ Rise	Slope
0	4	$1\text{-}5\frac{15}{32}$	$4\frac{7}{32}$	$1\text{-}6\frac{1}{2}$	$4\frac{7}{16}$	$1\text{-}7\frac{1}{2}$	$4\frac{11}{16}$	$1\text{-}8\frac{17}{32}$	$4\frac{15}{16}$	$1\text{-}9\frac{9}{16}$
$\frac{1}{16}$	4	$1\text{-}5\frac{17}{32}$	$4\frac{7}{32}$	$1\text{-}6\frac{9}{16}$	$4\frac{15}{32}$	$1\text{-}7\frac{19}{32}$	$4\frac{11}{16}$	$1\text{-}8\frac{19}{32}$	$4\frac{15}{16}$	$1\text{-}9\frac{5}{8}$
$\frac{1}{8}$	4	$1\text{-}5\frac{19}{32}$	$4\frac{1}{4}$	$1\text{-}6\frac{5}{8}$	$4\frac{15}{32}$	$1\text{-}7\frac{21}{32}$	$4\frac{23}{32}$	$1\text{-}8\frac{21}{32}$	$4\frac{15}{16}$	$1\text{-}9\frac{11}{16}$
$\frac{3}{16}$	$4\frac{1}{32}$	$1\text{-}5\frac{21}{32}$	$4\frac{1}{4}$	$1\text{-}6\frac{11}{16}$	$4\frac{1}{2}$	$1\text{-}7\frac{23}{32}$	$4\frac{23}{32}$	$1\text{-}8\frac{3}{4}$	$4\frac{31}{32}$	$1\text{-}9\frac{3}{4}$
$\frac{1}{4}$	$4\frac{1}{16}$	$1\text{-}5\frac{23}{32}$	$4\frac{9}{32}$	$1\text{-}6\frac{3}{4}$	$4\frac{1}{2}$	$1\text{-}7\frac{25}{32}$	$4\frac{3}{4}$	$1\text{-}8\frac{13}{16}$	$4\frac{31}{32}$	$1\text{-}9\frac{13}{16}$
$\frac{5}{16}$	$4\frac{1}{16}$	$1\text{-}5\frac{25}{32}$	$4\frac{9}{32}$	$1\text{-}6\frac{13}{16}$	$4\frac{17}{32}$	$1\text{-}7\frac{27}{32}$	$4\frac{3}{4}$	$1\text{-}8\frac{7}{8}$	5	$1\text{-}9\frac{7}{8}$
$\frac{3}{8}$	$4\frac{1}{16}$	$1\text{-}5\frac{27}{32}$	$4\frac{5}{16}$	$1\text{-}6\frac{7}{8}$	$4\frac{17}{32}$	$1\text{-}7\frac{29}{32}$	$4\frac{25}{32}$	$1\text{-}8\frac{15}{16}$	5	$1\text{-}9\frac{31}{32}$
$\frac{7}{16}$	$4\frac{3}{32}$	$1\text{-}5\frac{29}{32}$	$4\frac{5}{16}$	$1\text{-}6\frac{15}{16}$	$4\frac{9}{16}$	$1\text{-}7\frac{31}{32}$	$4\frac{25}{32}$	$1\text{-}9$	$5\frac{1}{16}$	$1\text{-}10\frac{1}{32}$
$\frac{1}{2}$	$4\frac{3}{32}$	$1\text{-}5\frac{31}{32}$	$4\frac{11}{32}$	$1\text{-}7$	$4\frac{9}{16}$	$1\text{-}8\frac{1}{32}$	$4\frac{13}{16}$	$1\text{-}9\frac{1}{16}$	$5\frac{1}{16}$	$1\text{-}10\frac{3}{32}$
$\frac{9}{16}$	$4\frac{1}{8}$	$1\text{-}6\frac{1}{32}$	$4\frac{11}{32}$	$1\text{-}7\frac{1}{16}$	$4\frac{19}{32}$	$1\text{-}8\frac{3}{32}$	$4\frac{13}{16}$	$1\text{-}9\frac{1}{8}$	$5\frac{1}{16}$	$1\text{-}10\frac{5}{32}$
$\frac{5}{8}$	$4\frac{1}{8}$	$1\text{-}6\frac{3}{32}$	$4\frac{3}{8}$	$1\text{-}7\frac{1}{8}$	$4\frac{19}{32}$	$1\text{-}8\frac{5}{32}$	$4\frac{27}{32}$	$1\text{-}9\frac{3}{16}$	$5\frac{1}{16}$	$1\text{-}10\frac{7}{32}$
$\frac{11}{16}$	$4\frac{5}{32}$	$1\text{-}6\frac{5}{32}$	$4\frac{3}{8}$	$1\text{-}7\frac{3}{16}$	$4\frac{5}{8}$	$1\text{-}8\frac{7}{32}$	$4\frac{27}{32}$	$1\text{-}9\frac{1}{4}$	$5\frac{3}{32}$	$1\text{-}10\frac{9}{32}$
$\frac{3}{4}$	$4\frac{5}{32}$	$1\text{-}6\frac{7}{32}$	$4\frac{13}{32}$	$1\text{-}7\frac{1}{4}$	$4\frac{5}{8}$	$1\text{-}8\frac{9}{32}$	$4\frac{7}{8}$	$1\text{-}9\frac{5}{16}$	$5\frac{3}{32}$	$1\text{-}10\frac{11}{32}$
$\frac{13}{16}$	$4\frac{3}{16}$	$1\text{-}6\frac{9}{32}$	$4\frac{13}{32}$	$1\text{-}7\frac{5}{16}$	$4\frac{21}{32}$	$1\text{-}8\frac{11}{32}$	$4\frac{7}{8}$	$1\text{-}9\frac{3}{8}$	$5\frac{1}{8}$	$1\text{-}10\frac{13}{32}$
$\frac{7}{8}$	$4\frac{3}{16}$	$1\text{-}6\frac{3}{8}$	$4\frac{7}{16}$	$1\text{-}7\frac{3}{8}$	$4\frac{21}{32}$	$1\text{-}8\frac{13}{32}$	$4\frac{29}{32}$	$1\text{-}9\frac{7}{16}$	$5\frac{1}{8}$	$1\text{-}10\frac{15}{32}$
$\frac{15}{16}$	$4\frac{7}{32}$	$1\text{-}6\frac{7}{16}$	$4\frac{7}{16}$	$1\text{-}7\frac{7}{16}$	$4\frac{11}{16}$	$1\text{-}8\frac{15}{32}$	$4\frac{29}{32}$	$1\text{-}9\frac{1}{2}$	$5\frac{5}{32}$	$1\text{-}10\frac{17}{32}$

Feet	40′ Rise	Slope	50′ Rise	Slope	60′ Rise	Slope	70′ Rise	Slope
0	$9\text{-}4\frac{1}{2}$	$41\text{-}1$	$11\text{-}8\frac{5}{8}$	$51\text{-}4\frac{1}{4}$	$14\text{-}0\frac{3}{4}$	$61\text{-}7\frac{1}{2}$	$16\text{-}4\frac{7}{8}$	$71\text{-}10\frac{3}{4}$
1	$9\text{-}7\frac{5}{16}$	$42\text{-}1\frac{11}{32}$	$11\text{-}11\frac{7}{16}$	$52\text{-}4\frac{19}{32}$	$14\text{-}3\frac{9}{16}$	$62\text{-}7\frac{27}{32}$	$16\text{-}7\frac{11}{16}$	$72\text{-}11\frac{3}{32}$
2	$9\text{-}10\frac{1}{8}$	$43\text{-}1\frac{21}{32}$	$12\text{-}2\frac{1}{4}$	$53\text{-}4\frac{29}{32}$	$14\text{-}6\frac{3}{8}$	$63\text{-}8\frac{5}{32}$	$16\text{-}10\frac{1}{2}$	$73\text{-}11\frac{13}{32}$
3	$10\text{-}0\frac{15}{16}$	$44\text{-}1\frac{31}{32}$	$12\text{-}5\frac{1}{16}$	$54\text{-}5\frac{1}{4}$	$14\text{-}9\frac{3}{16}$	$64\text{-}8\frac{1}{2}$	$17\text{-}1\frac{5}{16}$	$74\text{-}11\frac{3}{4}$
4	$10\text{-}3\frac{3}{4}$	$45\text{-}2\frac{5}{16}$	$12\text{-}7\frac{7}{8}$	$55\text{-}5\frac{9}{16}$	$15\text{-}0$	$65\text{-}8\frac{13}{16}$	$17\text{-}4\frac{1}{8}$	$76\text{-}0\frac{1}{16}$
5	$10\text{-}6\frac{9}{16}$	$46\text{-}2\frac{5}{8}$	$12\text{-}10\frac{11}{16}$	$56\text{-}5\frac{7}{8}$	$15\text{-}2\frac{13}{16}$	$66\text{-}9\frac{1}{8}$	$17\text{-}6\frac{15}{16}$	$77\text{-}0\frac{3}{8}$
6	$10\text{-}9\frac{3}{8}$	$47\text{-}2\frac{31}{32}$	$13\text{-}1\frac{1}{2}$	$57\text{-}6\frac{3}{32}$	$15\text{-}5\frac{5}{8}$	$67\text{-}9\frac{15}{32}$	$17\text{-}9\frac{3}{4}$	$78\text{-}0\frac{23}{32}$
7	$11\text{-}0\frac{3}{16}$	$48\text{-}3\frac{9}{32}$	$13\text{-}4\frac{5}{16}$	$58\text{-}6\frac{11}{32}$	$15\text{-}8\frac{7}{16}$	$68\text{-}9\frac{25}{32}$	$18\text{-}0\frac{9}{16}$	$79\text{-}1\frac{1}{32}$
8	$11\text{-}3$	$49\text{-}3\frac{19}{32}$	$13\text{-}7\frac{1}{8}$	$59\text{-}6\frac{7}{8}$	$15\text{-}11\frac{1}{4}$	$69\text{-}10\frac{1}{8}$	$18\text{-}3\frac{3}{8}$	$80\text{-}1\frac{3}{8}$
9	$11\text{-}5\frac{13}{16}$	$50\text{-}3\frac{15}{16}$	$13\text{-}9\frac{15}{16}$	$60\text{-}7\frac{3}{16}$	$16\text{-}2\frac{1}{16}$	$70\text{-}10\frac{7}{16}$	$18\text{-}6\frac{3}{16}$	$81\text{-}1\frac{11}{16}$

natsin A=0.2281913227; natcos A=0.9736163105; nattan A=0.2343750000; natcot A=4.2666666666

Bevel 2 7/8" to 12"

Inches	0" Rise	0" Slope	1" Rise	1" Slope	2" Rise	2" Slope	3" Rise	3" Slope	4" Rise	4" Slope	5" Rise	5" Slope
0	0	0	1/4	1 1/32–	15/32	2 1/16	23/32	3 3/32–	31/32–	4 1/8	1 3/16	5 5/32–
1/16	0	1/16	1/4	1 3/32–	1/2	2 1/8	23/32	3 5/32–	31/32	4 3/16	1 7/32–	5 7/32–
1/8	1/32–	1/8	9/32–	1 5/32	1/2	2 3/16	3/4	3 7/32–	1	4 1/4	1 7/32	5 9/32–
3/16	1/32	3/16	9/32	1 7/32	17/32–	2 1/4	3/4	3 9/32–	1	4 5/16	1 1/4	5 11/32–
1/4	1/16	1/4	5/16	1 9/32	17/32	2 5/16	25/32–	3 11/32–	1 1/32–	4 3/8	1 1/4	5 13/32–
5/16	1/16	5/16	5/16	1 11/32	9/16	2 3/8	25/32	3 13/32–	1 1/32	4 7/16	1 9/32–	5 15/32–
3/8	3/32–	3/8	11/32–	1 13/32	9/16	2 7/16	13/16	3 15/32	1 1/16	4 1/2	1 9/32	5 17/32–
7/16	3/32	7/16	11/32	1 15/32	19/32–	2 1/2	13/16	3 17/32	1 1/16	4 9/16	1 5/16	5 19/32–
1/2	1/8	1/2	3/8	1 17/32	19/32	2 9/16	27/32–	3 19/32	1 1/16	4 5/8	1 5/16	5 21/32–
9/16	1/8	19/32–	3/8	1 19/32	5/8	2 5/8	27/32	3 21/32	1 3/32–	4 11/16	1 11/32–	5 23/32
5/8	5/32–	21/32–	3/8	1 21/32	5/8	2 11/16	7/8	3 23/32	1 3/32	4 3/4	1 11/32	5 25/32
11/16	5/32	23/32–	13/32–	1 3/4	21/32–	2 3/4	7/8	3 25/32	1 1/8	4 13/16	1 3/8	5 27/32
3/4	3/16	25/32–	13/32	1 13/16	21/32	2 13/16	29/32–	3 27/32	1 1/8	4 7/8	1 3/8	5 29/32
13/16	3/16	27/32–	7/16	1 7/8	11/16	2 29/32–	29/32	3 29/32	1 5/32–	4 15/16	1 13/32–	5 31/32
7/8	7/32–	29/32–	7/16	1 15/16	11/16	2 31/32–	15/16	4	1 5/32	5	1 13/32	6 1/32
15/16	7/32	31/32–	15/32–	2	23/32–	3 1/32–	15/16	4 1/16	1 3/16	5 1/16	1 7/16	6 3/32

Inches	6" Rise	6" Slope	7" Rise	7" Slope	8" Rise	8" Slope	9" Rise	9" Slope	10" Rise	10" Slope	11" Rise	11" Slope
0	1 7/16	6 5/32	1 11/16	7 3/16	1 29/32	8 7/32	2 5/32	9 1/4	2 13/32–	10 9/32	2 5/8	11 5/16
1/16	1 7/16	6 7/32	1 11/16	7 1/4	1 15/16	8 9/32	2 5/32	9 5/16	2 13/32	10 11/32	2 21/32–	11 3/8
1/8	1 15/32–	6 5/16	1 23/32–	7 5/16	1 15/16	8 11/32	2 3/16	9 3/8	2 7/16	10 13/32	2 21/32	11 7/16
3/16	1 15/32	6 3/8	1 23/32	7 13/32–	1 31/32–	8 13/32	2 3/16	9 7/16	2 7/16	10 15/32	2 11/16	11 1/2
1/4	1 1/2	6 7/16	1 3/4	7 15/32–	1 31/32	8 15/32	2 7/32–	9 1/2	2 15/32–	10 17/32	2 11/16	11 9/16
5/16	1 1/2	6 1/2	1 3/4	7 17/32–	2	8 9/16	2 7/32	9 9/16	2 15/32	10 19/32	2 23/32–	11 5/8
3/8	1 17/32–	6 9/16	1 25/32–	7 19/32–	2	8 5/8	2 1/4	9 5/8	2 1/2	10 21/32	2 23/32	11 11/16
7/16	1 17/32	6 5/8	1 25/32	7 21/32–	2 1/32–	8 11/16	2 1/4	9 23/32–	2 1/2	10 23/32	2 3/4	11 3/4
1/2	1 9/16	6 11/16	1 13/16	7 23/32–	2 1/32	8 3/4	2 9/32–	9 25/32–	2 1/2	10 13/16	2 3/4	11 13/16
9/16	1 9/16	6 3/4	1 13/16	7 25/32–	2 1/16	8 13/16	2 9/32	9 27/32–	2 17/32–	10 7/8	2 25/32–	11 7/8
5/8	1 19/32–	6 13/16	1 13/16	7 27/32–	2 1/16	8 7/8	2 5/16	9 29/32–	2 17/32	10 15/16	2 25/32	11 31/32–
11/16	1 19/32	6 7/8	1 27/32–	7 29/32–	2 3/32–	8 15/16	2 5/16	9 31/32–	2 9/16	11	2 13/16	1-0 1/32–
3/4	1 5/8	6 15/16	1 27/32	7 31/32	2 3/32	9	2 11/32–	10 1/32–	2 9/16	11 1/16	2 13/16	1-0 3/32–
13/16	1 5/8	7	1 7/8	8 1/32	2 1/8	9 1/16	2 11/32	10 3/32–	2 19/32–	11 1/8	2 27/32–	1-0 5/32–
7/8	1 21/32–	7 1/16	1 7/8	8 3/32	2 1/8	9 1/8	2 3/8	10 5/32–	2 19/32	11 3/16	2 27/32	1-0 7/32–
15/16	1 21/32	7 1/8	1 29/32–	8 5/32	2 5/32–	9 3/16	2 3/8	10 7/32–	2 5/8	11 1/4	2 7/8	1-0 9/32–

Feet	0' Rise	0' Slope	10' Rise	10' Slope	20' Rise	20' Slope	30' Rise	30' Slope
0	0	0	2-4 3/4	10-3 13/32–	4-9 1/2	20-6 25/32	7-2 1/4	30-10 3/16
1	2 7/8	1-0 11/32–	2-7 5/8	11-3 3/4	5-0 3/8	21-7 1/8	7-5 1/8	31-10 17/32–
2	5 3/4	2-0 11/16	2-10 1/2	12-4 1/16	5-3 1/4	22-7 15/32	7-8	32-10 7/8
3	8 5/8	3-1 1/32–	3-1 3/8	13-4 13/32	5-6 1/8	23-7 13/16	7-10 7/8	33-11 7/32–
4	11 1/2	4-1 11/32	3-4 1/4	14-4 3/4	5-9	24-8 5/32–	8-1 3/4	34-11 17/32
5	1-2 3/8	5-1 11/16	3-7 1/8	15-5 3/32	5-11 7/8	25-8 1/2	8-4 5/8	35-11 7/8
6	1-5 1/4	6-2 1/32	3-10	16-5 7/16	6-2 3/4	26-8 27/32–	8-7 1/2	37-0 7/32
7	1-8 1/8	7-2 3/8	4-0 7/8	17-5 25/32–	6-5 5/8	27-9 5/32	8-10 3/8	38-0 9/16
8	1-11	8-2 23/32–	4-3 3/4	18-6 1/8	6-8 1/2	28-9 1/2	9-1 1/4	39-0 29/32–
9	2-1 7/8	9-3 1/16	4-6 5/8	19-6 7/16	6-11 3/8	29-9 27/32	9-4 1/8	40-1 1/4

A = 13° 28′ 23″; logsin A = 9.36734; logcos A = 9.98788; logtan A = 9.37946; logcot A = 0.62054

Ins.	12″ Rise	12″ Slope	13″ Rise	13″ Slope	14″ Rise	14″ Slope	15″ Rise	15″ Slope	16″ Rise	16″ Slope
0	$2\frac{7}{8}$	$1\text{-}0\frac{11}{32}$	$3\frac{1}{8}$	$1\text{-}1\frac{3}{8}$	$3\frac{11}{32}$	$1\text{-}2\frac{13}{32}$	$3\frac{19}{32}$	$1\text{-}3\frac{7}{16}$	$3\frac{21}{32}$	$1\text{-}4\frac{7}{16}$
$\frac{1}{16}$	$2\frac{7}{8}$	$1\text{-}0\frac{13}{32}$	$3\frac{1}{8}$	$1\text{-}1\frac{7}{16}$	$3\frac{3}{8}$	$1\text{-}2\frac{15}{32}$	$3\frac{19}{32}$	$1\text{-}3\frac{1}{2}$	$3\frac{27}{32}$	$1\text{-}4\frac{17}{32}$
$\frac{1}{8}$	$2\frac{29}{32}$	$1\text{-}0\frac{15}{32}$	$3\frac{5}{32}$	$1\text{-}1\frac{1}{2}$	$3\frac{3}{8}$	$1\text{-}2\frac{17}{32}$	$3\frac{5}{8}$	$1\text{-}3\frac{9}{16}$	$3\frac{7}{8}$	$1\text{-}4\frac{19}{32}$
$\frac{3}{16}$	$2\frac{29}{32}$	$1\text{-}0\frac{17}{32}$	$3\frac{5}{32}$	$1\text{-}1\frac{9}{16}$	$3\frac{13}{32}$	$1\text{-}2\frac{19}{32}$	$3\frac{5}{8}$	$1\text{-}3\frac{5}{8}$	$3\frac{7}{8}$	$1\text{-}4\frac{21}{32}$
$\frac{1}{4}$	$2\frac{15}{16}$	$1\text{-}0\frac{19}{32}$	$3\frac{3}{16}$	$1\text{-}1\frac{5}{8}$	$3\frac{13}{32}$	$1\text{-}2\frac{21}{32}$	$3\frac{21}{32}$	$1\text{-}3\frac{11}{16}$	$3\frac{29}{32}$	$1\text{-}4\frac{23}{32}$
$\frac{5}{16}$	$2\frac{15}{16}$	$1\text{-}0\frac{21}{32}$	$3\frac{3}{16}$	$1\text{-}1\frac{11}{16}$	$3\frac{7}{16}$	$1\text{-}2\frac{23}{32}$	$3\frac{21}{32}$	$1\text{-}3\frac{3}{4}$	$3\frac{29}{32}$	$1\text{-}4\frac{25}{32}$
$\frac{3}{8}$	$2\frac{31}{32}$	$1\text{-}0\frac{23}{32}$	$3\frac{7}{32}$	$1\text{-}1\frac{3}{4}$	$3\frac{7}{16}$	$1\text{-}2\frac{25}{32}$	$3\frac{11}{16}$	$1\text{-}3\frac{13}{16}$	$3\frac{15}{16}$	$1\text{-}4\frac{27}{32}$
$\frac{7}{16}$	$2\frac{31}{32}$	$1\text{-}0\frac{25}{32}$	$3\frac{7}{32}$	$1\text{-}1\frac{13}{16}$	$3\frac{15}{32}$	$1\text{-}2\frac{27}{32}$	$3\frac{11}{16}$	$1\text{-}3\frac{7}{8}$	$3\frac{15}{16}$	$1\text{-}4\frac{29}{32}$
$\frac{1}{2}$	3	$1\text{-}0\frac{27}{32}$	$3\frac{1}{4}$	$1\text{-}1\frac{7}{8}$	$3\frac{15}{32}$	$1\text{-}2\frac{29}{32}$	$3\frac{23}{32}$	$1\text{-}3\frac{15}{16}$	$3\frac{15}{16}$	$1\text{-}4\frac{31}{32}$
$\frac{9}{16}$	3	$1\text{-}0\frac{29}{32}$	$3\frac{1}{4}$	$1\text{-}1\frac{15}{16}$	$3\frac{1}{2}$	$1\text{-}2\frac{31}{32}$	$3\frac{23}{32}$	$1\text{-}4$	$3\frac{31}{32}$	$1\text{-}5\frac{1}{32}$
$\frac{5}{8}$	$3\frac{1}{32}$	$1\text{-}0\frac{31}{32}$	$3\frac{1}{4}$	$1\text{-}2$	$3\frac{1}{2}$	$1\text{-}3\frac{1}{32}$	$3\frac{3}{4}$	$1\text{-}4\frac{1}{16}$	$3\frac{31}{32}$	$1\text{-}5\frac{3}{32}$
$\frac{11}{16}$	$3\frac{1}{32}$	$1\text{-}1\frac{1}{32}$	$3\frac{9}{32}$	$1\text{-}2\frac{1}{16}$	$3\frac{17}{32}$	$1\text{-}3\frac{3}{32}$	$3\frac{3}{4}$	$1\text{-}4\frac{1}{8}$	4	$1\text{-}5\frac{5}{32}$
$\frac{3}{4}$	$3\frac{1}{16}$	$1\text{-}1\frac{1}{8}$	$3\frac{9}{32}$	$1\text{-}2\frac{1}{8}$	$3\frac{17}{32}$	$1\text{-}3\frac{5}{32}$	$3\frac{25}{32}$	$1\text{-}4\frac{3}{16}$	4	$1\text{-}5\frac{7}{32}$
$\frac{13}{16}$	$3\frac{1}{16}$	$1\text{-}1\frac{3}{16}$	$3\frac{5}{16}$	$1\text{-}2\frac{3}{16}$	$3\frac{9}{16}$	$1\text{-}3\frac{7}{32}$	$3\frac{25}{32}$	$1\text{-}4\frac{1}{4}$	$4\frac{1}{32}$	$1\text{-}5\frac{9}{32}$
$\frac{7}{8}$	$3\frac{3}{32}$	$1\text{-}1\frac{1}{4}$	$3\frac{5}{16}$	$1\text{-}2\frac{1}{4}$	$3\frac{9}{16}$	$1\text{-}3\frac{9}{32}$	$3\frac{13}{16}$	$1\text{-}4\frac{5}{16}$	$4\frac{1}{32}$	$1\text{-}5\frac{11}{32}$
$\frac{15}{16}$	$3\frac{3}{32}$	$1\text{-}1\frac{5}{16}$	$3\frac{11}{32}$	$1\text{-}2\frac{11}{32}$	$3\frac{19}{32}$	$1\text{-}3\frac{3}{8}$	$3\frac{13}{16}$	$1\text{-}4\frac{3}{8}$	$4\frac{1}{16}$	$1\text{-}5\frac{13}{32}$

Ins.	17″ Rise	17″ Slope	18″ Rise	18″ Slope	19″ Rise	19″ Slope	20″ Rise	20″ Slope	21″ Rise	21″ Slope
0	$4\frac{1}{16}$	$1\text{-}5\frac{15}{32}$	$4\frac{5}{16}$	$1\text{-}6\frac{1}{2}$	$4\frac{9}{16}$	$1\text{-}7\frac{17}{32}$	$4\frac{25}{32}$	$1\text{-}8\frac{9}{16}$	$5\frac{1}{32}$	$1\text{-}9\frac{19}{32}$
$\frac{1}{16}$	$4\frac{3}{32}$	$1\text{-}5\frac{17}{32}$	$4\frac{5}{16}$	$1\text{-}6\frac{9}{16}$	$4\frac{9}{16}$	$1\text{-}7\frac{19}{32}$	$4\frac{13}{16}$	$1\text{-}8\frac{5}{8}$	$5\frac{1}{32}$	$1\text{-}9\frac{21}{32}$
$\frac{1}{8}$	$4\frac{3}{32}$	$1\text{-}5\frac{5}{8}$	$4\frac{11}{32}$	$1\text{-}6\frac{5}{8}$	$4\frac{19}{32}$	$1\text{-}7\frac{21}{32}$	$4\frac{13}{16}$	$1\text{-}8\frac{11}{16}$	$5\frac{1}{16}$	$1\text{-}9\frac{23}{32}$
$\frac{3}{16}$	$4\frac{1}{8}$	$1\text{-}5\frac{11}{16}$	$4\frac{11}{32}$	$1\text{-}6\frac{11}{16}$	$4\frac{19}{32}$	$1\text{-}7\frac{23}{32}$	$4\frac{27}{32}$	$1\text{-}8\frac{3}{4}$	$5\frac{1}{16}$	$1\text{-}9\frac{25}{32}$
$\frac{1}{4}$	$4\frac{1}{8}$	$1\text{-}5\frac{3}{4}$	$4\frac{3}{8}$	$1\text{-}6\frac{25}{32}$	$4\frac{5}{8}$	$1\text{-}7\frac{25}{32}$	$4\frac{27}{32}$	$1\text{-}8\frac{13}{16}$	$5\frac{3}{32}$	$1\text{-}9\frac{27}{32}$
$\frac{5}{16}$	$4\frac{5}{32}$	$1\text{-}5\frac{13}{16}$	$4\frac{3}{8}$	$1\text{-}6\frac{27}{32}$	$4\frac{5}{8}$	$1\text{-}7\frac{27}{32}$	$4\frac{7}{8}$	$1\text{-}8\frac{7}{8}$	$5\frac{3}{32}$	$1\text{-}9\frac{29}{32}$
$\frac{3}{8}$	$4\frac{5}{32}$	$1\text{-}5\frac{7}{8}$	$4\frac{13}{32}$	$1\text{-}6\frac{29}{32}$	$4\frac{21}{32}$	$1\text{-}7\frac{15}{16}$	$4\frac{7}{8}$	$1\text{-}8\frac{15}{16}$	$5\frac{1}{8}$	$1\text{-}9\frac{31}{32}$
$\frac{7}{16}$	$4\frac{3}{16}$	$1\text{-}5\frac{15}{16}$	$4\frac{13}{32}$	$1\text{-}6\frac{31}{32}$	$4\frac{21}{32}$	$1\text{-}8$	$4\frac{29}{32}$	$1\text{-}9\frac{1}{16}$	$5\frac{1}{8}$	$1\text{-}10\frac{1}{32}$
$\frac{1}{2}$	$4\frac{3}{16}$	$1\text{-}6$	$4\frac{7}{16}$	$1\text{-}7\frac{1}{32}$	$4\frac{11}{16}$	$1\text{-}8\frac{1}{32}$	$4\frac{29}{32}$	$1\text{-}9\frac{3}{32}$	$5\frac{5}{32}$	$1\text{-}10\frac{3}{32}$
$\frac{9}{16}$	$4\frac{7}{32}$	$1\text{-}6\frac{1}{16}$	$4\frac{7}{16}$	$1\text{-}7\frac{3}{32}$	$4\frac{11}{16}$	$1\text{-}8\frac{1}{8}$	$4\frac{15}{16}$	$1\text{-}9\frac{5}{32}$	$5\frac{5}{32}$	$1\text{-}10\frac{3}{16}$
$\frac{5}{8}$	$4\frac{7}{32}$	$1\text{-}6\frac{1}{8}$	$4\frac{15}{32}$	$1\text{-}7\frac{5}{32}$	$4\frac{11}{16}$	$1\text{-}8\frac{3}{16}$	$4\frac{15}{16}$	$1\text{-}9\frac{7}{32}$	$5\frac{3}{16}$	$1\text{-}10\frac{1}{4}$
$\frac{11}{16}$	$4\frac{1}{4}$	$1\text{-}6\frac{3}{16}$	$4\frac{15}{32}$	$1\text{-}7\frac{7}{32}$	$4\frac{23}{32}$	$1\text{-}8\frac{1}{4}$	$4\frac{31}{32}$	$1\text{-}9\frac{9}{32}$	$5\frac{3}{16}$	$1\text{-}10\frac{5}{32}$
$\frac{3}{4}$	$4\frac{1}{4}$	$1\text{-}6\frac{1}{4}$	$4\frac{1}{2}$	$1\text{-}7\frac{9}{32}$	$4\frac{23}{32}$	$1\text{-}8\frac{5}{16}$	$4\frac{31}{32}$	$1\text{-}9\frac{11}{32}$	$5\frac{7}{32}$	$1\text{-}10\frac{3}{8}$
$\frac{13}{16}$	$4\frac{9}{32}$	$1\text{-}6\frac{5}{16}$	$4\frac{1}{2}$	$1\text{-}7\frac{11}{32}$	$4\frac{3}{4}$	$1\text{-}8\frac{3}{8}$	5	$1\text{-}9\frac{13}{32}$	$5\frac{7}{32}$	$1\text{-}10\frac{7}{16}$
$\frac{7}{8}$	$4\frac{9}{32}$	$1\text{-}6\frac{3}{8}$	$4\frac{17}{32}$	$1\text{-}7\frac{13}{32}$	$4\frac{3}{4}$	$1\text{-}8\frac{7}{16}$	5	$1\text{-}9\frac{15}{32}$	$5\frac{1}{4}$	$1\text{-}10\frac{1}{2}$
$\frac{15}{16}$	$4\frac{5}{16}$	$1\text{-}6\frac{7}{16}$	$4\frac{17}{32}$	$1\text{-}7\frac{15}{32}$	$4\frac{25}{32}$	$1\text{-}8\frac{1}{2}$	$5\frac{1}{32}$	$1\text{-}9\frac{17}{32}$	$5\frac{1}{4}$	$1\text{-}10\frac{9}{16}$

Feet	40′ Rise	40′ Slope	50′ Rise	50′ Slope	60′ Rise	60′ Slope	70′ Rise	70′ Slope
0	$9\text{-}7$	$41\text{-}1\frac{19}{32}$	$11\text{-}11\frac{3}{4}$	$51\text{-}4\frac{31}{32}$	$14\text{-}4\frac{1}{2}$	$61\text{-}8\frac{3}{8}$	$16\text{-}9\frac{1}{4}$	$71\text{-}11\frac{25}{32}$
1	$9\text{-}9\frac{7}{8}$	$42\text{-}1\frac{15}{16}$	$12\text{-}2\frac{5}{8}$	$52\text{-}5\frac{5}{16}$	$14\text{-}7\frac{3}{8}$	$62\text{-}8\frac{23}{32}$	$17\text{-}0\frac{1}{8}$	$73\text{-}0\frac{1}{8}$
2	$10\text{-}0\frac{3}{4}$	$43\text{-}2\frac{1}{4}$	$12\text{-}5\frac{1}{2}$	$53\text{-}5\frac{21}{32}$	$14\text{-}10\frac{1}{4}$	$63\text{-}9\frac{1}{16}$	$17\text{-}3$	$74\text{-}0\frac{7}{16}$
3	$10\text{-}3\frac{5}{8}$	$44\text{-}2\frac{19}{32}$	$12\text{-}8\frac{3}{8}$	$54\text{-}6$	$15\text{-}1\frac{1}{8}$	$64\text{-}9\frac{13}{32}$	$17\text{-}5\frac{7}{8}$	$75\text{-}0\frac{25}{32}$
4	$10\text{-}6\frac{1}{2}$	$45\text{-}2\frac{15}{16}$	$12\text{-}11\frac{1}{4}$	$55\text{-}6\frac{11}{32}$	$15\text{-}4$	$65\text{-}9\frac{23}{32}$	$17\text{-}8\frac{3}{4}$	$76\text{-}1\frac{1}{8}$
5	$10\text{-}9\frac{3}{8}$	$46\text{-}3\frac{9}{32}$	$13\text{-}2\frac{1}{8}$	$56\text{-}6\frac{11}{16}$	$15\text{-}6\frac{7}{8}$	$66\text{-}10\frac{1}{16}$	$17\text{-}11\frac{5}{8}$	$77\text{-}1\frac{15}{32}$
6	$11\text{-}0\frac{1}{4}$	$47\text{-}3\frac{5}{8}$	$13\text{-}5$	$57\text{-}7\frac{1}{32}$	$15\text{-}9\frac{3}{4}$	$67\text{-}10\frac{13}{32}$	$18\text{-}2\frac{1}{2}$	$78\text{-}1\frac{13}{16}$
7	$11\text{-}3\frac{1}{8}$	$48\text{-}3\frac{31}{32}$	$13\text{-}7\frac{7}{8}$	$58\text{-}7\frac{11}{32}$	$16\text{-}0\frac{5}{8}$	$68\text{-}10\frac{3}{4}$	$18\text{-}5\frac{3}{8}$	$79\text{-}2\frac{5}{32}$
8	$11\text{-}6$	$49\text{-}4\frac{5}{16}$	$13\text{-}10\frac{3}{4}$	$59\text{-}7\frac{11}{16}$	$16\text{-}3\frac{1}{2}$	$69\text{-}11\frac{3}{32}$	$18\text{-}8\frac{1}{4}$	$80\text{-}2\frac{1}{2}$
9	$11\text{-}8\frac{7}{8}$	$50\text{-}4\frac{5}{8}$	$14\text{-}1\frac{5}{8}$	$60\text{-}8\frac{1}{32}$	$16\text{-}6\frac{3}{8}$	$70\text{-}11\frac{7}{16}$	$18\text{-}11\frac{1}{8}$	$81\text{-}2\frac{13}{16}$

natsin A=0.2329898030; natcos A=0.9724791779; nattan A=0.2395833333; natcot A=4.1739130434

Inches	0" Rise	0" Slope	1" Rise	1" Slope	2" Rise	2" Slope	3" Rise	3" Slope	4" Rise	4" Slope	5" Rise	5" Slope
0	0	0	1/4	1 1/32	1/2	2 1/16	3/4	3 3/32	31/32	4 1/8	1 17/32	5 5/32
1/16	0	1/16	1/4	1 3/32	1/2	2 1/8	3/4	3 5/32	1	4 3/16	1 1/4	5 7/32
1/8	1/32	1/8	9/32	1 5/32	17/32	2 3/16	3/4	3 7/32	1	4 1/4	1 1/4	5 9/32
3/16	1/32	3/16	9/32	1 7/32	17/32	2 1/4	25/32	3 9/32	1 1/32	4 5/16	1 9/32	5 11/32
1/4	1/16	1/4	5/16	1 9/32	9/16	2 5/16	25/32	3 11/32	1 1/32	4 3/8	1 9/32	5 13/32
5/16	1/16	5/16	5/16	1 11/32	9/16	2 3/8	13/16	3 13/32	1 1/16	4 7/16	1 5/16	5 15/32
3/8	3/32	3/8	11/32	1 13/32	19/32	2 7/16	13/16	3 15/32	1 1/16	4 1/2	1 5/16	5 17/32
7/16	3/32	7/16	11/32	1 15/32	19/32	2 1/2	27/32	3 17/32	1 3/32	4 9/16	1 11/32	5 19/32
1/2	1/8	1/2	3/8	1 17/32	5/8	2 9/16	27/32	3 19/32	1 3/32	4 5/8	1 11/32	5 21/32
9/16	1/8	19/32	3/8	1 19/32	5/8	2 5/8	7/8	3 21/32	1 1/8	4 11/16	1 3/8	5 23/32
5/8	5/32	21/32	13/32	1 11/16	21/32	2 11/16	7/8	3 23/32	1 1/8	4 3/4	1 3/8	5 25/32
11/16	5/32	23/32	13/32	1 3/4	21/32	2 25/32	29/32	3 25/32	1 5/32	4 13/16	1 13/32	5 27/32
3/4	3/16	25/32	7/16	1 13/16	11/16	2 27/32	29/32	3 7/8	1 5/32	4 7/8	1 13/32	5 29/32
13/16	3/16	27/32	7/16	1 7/8	11/16	2 29/32	15/16	3 15/16	1 3/16	4 31/32	1 7/16	5 31/32
7/8	7/32	29/32	15/32	1 15/16	23/32	2 31/32	15/16	4	1 3/16	5 1/32	1 7/16	6 1/16
15/16	7/32	31/32	15/32	2	23/32	3 1/32	31/32	4 1/16	1 7/32	5 3/32	1 15/32	6 1/8

Inches	6" Rise	6" Slope	7" Rise	7" Slope	8" Rise	8" Slope	9" Rise	9" Slope	10" Rise	10" Slope	11" Rise	11" Slope
0	1 15/32	6 3/16	1 23/32	7 7/32	1 31/32	8 1/4	2 3/16	9 9/32	2 7/16	10 9/32	2 11/16	11 5/16
1/16	1 15/32	6 1/4	1 23/32	7 9/32	1 31/32	8 5/16	2 7/32	9 11/32	2 15/32	10 3/8	2 23/32	11 3/8
1/8	1 1/2	6 5/16	1 3/4	7 11/32	2	8 3/8	2 7/32	9 13/32	2 15/32	10 7/16	2 23/32	11 15/32
3/16	1 1/2	6 3/8	1 3/4	7 13/32	2	8 7/16	2 1/4	9 15/32	2 1/2	10 1/2	2 3/4	11 17/32
1/4	1 17/32	6 7/16	1 25/32	7 15/32	2 1/32	8 1/2	2 1/4	9 17/32	2 1/2	10 9/16	2 3/4	11 19/32
5/16	1 17/32	6 1/2	1 25/32	7 17/32	2 1/32	8 9/16	2 9/32	9 19/32	2 17/32	10 5/8	2 25/32	11 21/32
3/8	1 9/16	6 9/16	1 13/16	7 19/32	2 1/16	8 5/8	2 9/32	9 21/32	2 17/32	10 11/16	2 25/32	11 23/32
7/16	1 9/16	6 5/8	1 13/16	7 21/32	2 1/16	8 11/16	2 5/16	9 23/32	2 9/16	10 3/4	2 13/16	11 25/32
1/2	1 19/32	6 11/16	1 27/32	7 23/32	2 3/32	8 3/4	2 5/16	9 25/32	2 9/16	10 13/16	2 13/16	11 27/32
9/16	1 19/32	6 3/4	1 27/32	7 25/32	2 3/32	8 13/16	2 11/32	9 27/32	2 19/32	10 7/8	2 27/32	11 29/32
5/8	1 5/8	6 13/16	1 7/8	7 27/32	2 1/8	8 7/8	2 11/32	9 29/32	2 19/32	10 15/16	2 27/32	11 31/32
11/16	1 5/8	6 7/8	1 7/8	7 29/32	2 1/8	8 15/16	2 3/8	9 31/32	2 5/8	11	2 7/8	1-0 1/32
3/4	1 21/32	6 15/16	1 29/32	7 31/32	2 5/32	9	2 3/8	10 1/32	2 5/8	11 1/16	2 7/8	1-0 3/32
13/16	1 21/32	7	1 29/32	8 1/32	2 5/32	9 1/16	2 13/32	10 3/32	2 21/32	11 1/8	2 29/32	1-0 5/32
7/8	1 11/16	7 1/16	1 15/16	8 3/32	2 3/16	9 1/8	2 13/32	10 5/32	2 21/32	11 3/16	2 29/32	1-0 7/32
15/16	1 11/16	7 5/32	1 15/16	8 3/16	2 3/16	9 3/16	2 7/16	10 7/32	2 11/16	11 1/4	2 15/16	1-0 9/32

Feet	0' Rise	0' Slope	10' Rise	10' Slope	20' Rise	20' Slope	30' Rise	30' Slope
0	0	0	2-5 3/8	10-3 17/32	4-10 3/4	20-7 3/32	7-4 1/8	30-10 5/8
1	2 15/16	1-0 11/32	2-8 5/16	11-3 29/32	5-1 11/16	21-7 7/16	7-7 1/16	31-10 31/32
2	5 7/8	2-0 23/32	2-11 1/4	12-4 1/4	5-4 5/8	22-7 25/32	7-10	32-11 11/32
3	8 13/16	3-1 1/16	3-2 3/16	13-4 19/32	5-7 9/16	23-8 5/32	8-0 15/16	33-11 11/16
4	11 3/4	4-1 13/32	3-5 1/8	14-4 31/32	5-10 1/2	24-8 1/2	8-3 7/8	35-0 1/32
5	1-2 11/16	5-1 25/32	3-8 1/16	15-5 5/16	6-1 7/16	25-8 27/32	8-6 13/16	36-0 13/32
6	1-5 5/8	6-2 1/8	3-11	16-5 21/32	6-4 3/8	26-9 7/32	8-9 3/4	37-0 3/4
7	1-8 9/16	7-2 15/32	4-1 15/16	17-6 1/32	6-7 5/16	27-9 9/16	9-0 11/16	38-1 3/8
8	1-11 1/2	8-2 27/32	4-4 7/8	18-6 3/8	6-10 1/4	28-9 29/32	9-3 5/8	39-1 15/32
9	2-2 7/16	9-3 3/16	4-7 13/16	19-6 23/32	7-1 3/16	29-10 9/32	9-6 9/16	40-1 13/16

A = 13° 45′ 18″; logsin A = 9.37616; logcos A = 9.98736; logtan A = 9.38880; logcot A = 0.61120

In.	12″ Rise	12″ Slope	13″ Rise	13″ Slope	14″ Rise	14″ Slope	15″ Rise	15″ Slope	16″ Rise	16″ Slope
0	$2\frac{15}{16}$	1-0$\frac{11}{32}$	$3\frac{3}{16}$	1-1$\frac{3}{8}$	$3\frac{7}{16}$	1-2$\frac{13}{32}$	$3\frac{11}{16}$	1-3$\frac{7}{16}$	$3\frac{29}{32}$	1-4$\frac{15}{32}$
$\frac{1}{16}$	$2\frac{15}{16}$	1-0$\frac{13}{32}$	$3\frac{3}{16}$	1-1$\frac{7}{16}$	$3\frac{7}{16}$	1-2$\frac{15}{32}$	$3\frac{11}{16}$	1-3$\frac{1}{2}$	$3\frac{15}{16}$	1-4$\frac{17}{32}$
$\frac{1}{8}$	$2\frac{31}{32}$	1-0$\frac{15}{32}$	$3\frac{7}{32}$	1-1$\frac{1}{2}$	$3\frac{15}{32}$	1-2$\frac{17}{32}$	$3\frac{11}{16}$	1-3$\frac{9}{16}$	$3\frac{15}{16}$	1-4$\frac{19}{32}$
$\frac{3}{16}$	$2\frac{31}{32}$	1-0$\frac{9}{16}$	$3\frac{7}{32}$	1-1$\frac{9}{16}$	$3\frac{15}{32}$	1-2$\frac{19}{32}$	$3\frac{23}{32}$	1-3$\frac{5}{8}$	$3\frac{31}{32}$	1-4$\frac{21}{32}$
$\frac{1}{4}$	3	1-0$\frac{5}{8}$	$3\frac{1}{4}$	1-1$\frac{21}{32}$	$3\frac{1}{2}$	1-2$\frac{21}{32}$	$3\frac{23}{32}$	1-3$\frac{11}{16}$	$3\frac{31}{32}$	1-4$\frac{23}{32}$
$\frac{5}{16}$	3	1-0$\frac{11}{16}$	$3\frac{1}{4}$	1-1$\frac{23}{32}$	$3\frac{1}{2}$	1-2$\frac{3}{4}$	$3\frac{3}{4}$	1-3$\frac{3}{4}$	4	1-4$\frac{25}{32}$
$\frac{3}{8}$	$3\frac{1}{16}$	1-0$\frac{3}{4}$	$3\frac{9}{32}$	1-1$\frac{25}{32}$	$3\frac{17}{32}$	1-2$\frac{13}{16}$	$3\frac{3}{4}$	1-3$\frac{27}{32}$	4	1-4$\frac{27}{32}$
$\frac{7}{16}$	$3\frac{1}{16}$	1-0$\frac{13}{16}$	$3\frac{9}{32}$	1-1$\frac{27}{32}$	$3\frac{17}{32}$	1-2$\frac{7}{8}$	$3\frac{25}{32}$	1-3$\frac{29}{32}$	$4\frac{1}{32}$	1-4$\frac{15}{16}$
$\frac{1}{2}$	$3\frac{1}{16}$	1-0$\frac{7}{8}$	$3\frac{5}{16}$	1-1$\frac{29}{32}$	$3\frac{9}{16}$	1-2$\frac{15}{16}$	$3\frac{25}{32}$	1-3$\frac{31}{32}$	$4\frac{1}{2}$	1-5
$\frac{9}{16}$	$3\frac{1}{16}$	1-0$\frac{15}{16}$	$3\frac{5}{16}$	1-1$\frac{31}{32}$	$3\frac{9}{16}$	1-3	$3\frac{13}{16}$	1-4$\frac{1}{32}$	$4\frac{1}{2}$	1-5$\frac{1}{16}$
$\frac{5}{8}$	$3\frac{3}{32}$	1-1	$3\frac{11}{32}$	1-2$\frac{1}{32}$	$3\frac{19}{32}$	1-3$\frac{1}{16}$	$3\frac{13}{16}$	1-4$\frac{3}{32}$	$4\frac{1}{8}$	1-5$\frac{1}{8}$
$\frac{11}{16}$	$3\frac{5}{32}$	1-1$\frac{1}{16}$	$3\frac{11}{32}$	1-2$\frac{3}{32}$	$3\frac{19}{32}$	1-3$\frac{1}{8}$	$3\frac{27}{32}$	1-4$\frac{5}{32}$	$4\frac{3}{32}$	1-5$\frac{3}{16}$
$\frac{3}{4}$	$3\frac{1}{8}$	1-1$\frac{1}{8}$	$3\frac{3}{8}$	1-2$\frac{5}{32}$	$3\frac{5}{8}$	1-3$\frac{3}{16}$	$3\frac{27}{32}$	1-4$\frac{7}{32}$	$4\frac{3}{32}$	1-5$\frac{1}{4}$
$\frac{13}{16}$	$3\frac{1}{8}$	1-1$\frac{3}{16}$	$3\frac{3}{8}$	1-2$\frac{7}{32}$	$3\frac{5}{8}$	1-3$\frac{1}{4}$	$3\frac{7}{8}$	1-4$\frac{9}{32}$	$4\frac{1}{8}$	1-5$\frac{5}{16}$
$\frac{7}{8}$	$3\frac{5}{32}$	1-1$\frac{1}{4}$	$3\frac{13}{32}$	1-2$\frac{9}{32}$	$3\frac{21}{32}$	1-3$\frac{5}{16}$	$3\frac{7}{8}$	1-4$\frac{11}{32}$	$4\frac{1}{8}$	1-5$\frac{3}{8}$
$\frac{15}{16}$	$3\frac{5}{32}$	1-1$\frac{5}{16}$	$3\frac{13}{32}$	1-2$\frac{11}{32}$	$3\frac{21}{32}$	1-3$\frac{3}{8}$	$3\frac{29}{32}$	1-4$\frac{13}{32}$	$4\frac{5}{32}$	1-5$\frac{7}{16}$

In.	17″ Rise	17″ Slope	18″ Rise	18″ Slope	19″ Rise	19″ Slope	20″ Rise	20″ Slope	21″ Rise	21″ Slope
0	$4\frac{5}{32}$	1-5$\frac{1}{2}$	$4\frac{13}{32}$	1-6$\frac{17}{32}$	$4\frac{21}{32}$	1-7$\frac{9}{16}$	$4\frac{29}{32}$	1-8$\frac{19}{32}$	$5\frac{1}{8}$	1-9$\frac{5}{8}$
$\frac{1}{16}$	$4\frac{3}{16}$	1-5$\frac{9}{16}$	$4\frac{13}{32}$	1-6$\frac{19}{32}$	$4\frac{21}{32}$	1-7$\frac{5}{8}$	$4\frac{29}{32}$	1-8$\frac{21}{32}$	$5\frac{5}{32}$	1-9$\frac{11}{16}$
$\frac{1}{8}$	$4\frac{3}{16}$	1-5$\frac{5}{8}$	$4\frac{7}{16}$	1-6$\frac{21}{32}$	$4\frac{11}{16}$	1-7$\frac{11}{16}$	$4\frac{15}{16}$	1-8$\frac{23}{32}$	$5\frac{5}{32}$	1-9$\frac{3}{4}$
$\frac{3}{16}$	$4\frac{7}{32}$	1-5$\frac{11}{16}$	$4\frac{7}{16}$	1-6$\frac{23}{32}$	$4\frac{11}{16}$	1-7$\frac{3}{4}$	$4\frac{15}{16}$	1-8$\frac{25}{32}$	$5\frac{3}{16}$	1-9$\frac{13}{16}$
$\frac{1}{4}$	$4\frac{7}{32}$	1-5$\frac{3}{4}$	$4\frac{15}{32}$	1-6$\frac{25}{32}$	$4\frac{23}{32}$	1-7$\frac{13}{16}$	$4\frac{31}{32}$	1-8$\frac{27}{32}$	$5\frac{3}{16}$	1-9$\frac{7}{8}$
$\frac{5}{16}$	$4\frac{1}{4}$	1-5$\frac{13}{16}$	$4\frac{15}{32}$	1-6$\frac{27}{32}$	$4\frac{23}{32}$	1-7$\frac{7}{8}$	$4\frac{31}{32}$	1-8$\frac{29}{32}$	$5\frac{7}{32}$	1-9$\frac{15}{16}$
$\frac{3}{8}$	$4\frac{1}{4}$	1-5$\frac{7}{8}$	$4\frac{1}{2}$	1-6$\frac{29}{32}$	$4\frac{3}{4}$	1-7$\frac{15}{16}$	5	1-8$\frac{31}{32}$	$5\frac{7}{32}$	1-10
$\frac{7}{16}$	$4\frac{9}{32}$	1-5$\frac{15}{16}$	$4\frac{1}{2}$	1-6$\frac{31}{32}$	$4\frac{3}{4}$	1-8	5	1-9$\frac{1}{32}$	$5\frac{1}{4}$	1-10$\frac{1}{16}$
$\frac{1}{2}$	$4\frac{9}{32}$	1-6$\frac{1}{32}$	$4\frac{17}{32}$	1-7$\frac{1}{32}$	$4\frac{25}{32}$	1-8$\frac{1}{16}$	$5\frac{1}{32}$	1-9$\frac{3}{32}$	$5\frac{1}{4}$	1-10$\frac{1}{8}$
$\frac{9}{16}$	$4\frac{5}{16}$	1-6$\frac{3}{32}$	$4\frac{17}{32}$	1-7$\frac{1}{8}$	$4\frac{25}{32}$	1-8$\frac{1}{8}$	$5\frac{1}{32}$	1-9$\frac{5}{32}$	$5\frac{9}{32}$	1-10$\frac{3}{16}$
$\frac{5}{8}$	$4\frac{5}{16}$	1-6$\frac{5}{32}$	$4\frac{9}{16}$	1-7$\frac{3}{16}$	$4\frac{13}{16}$	1-8$\frac{5}{32}$	$5\frac{1}{16}$	1-9$\frac{7}{32}$	$5\frac{9}{32}$	1-10$\frac{1}{4}$
$\frac{11}{16}$	$4\frac{11}{32}$	1-6$\frac{7}{32}$	$4\frac{9}{16}$	1-7$\frac{1}{4}$	$4\frac{13}{16}$	1-8$\frac{9}{32}$	$5\frac{1}{16}$	1-9$\frac{9}{32}$	$5\frac{5}{16}$	1-10$\frac{5}{16}$
$\frac{3}{4}$	$4\frac{11}{32}$	1-6$\frac{9}{32}$	$4\frac{19}{32}$	1-7$\frac{5}{16}$	$4\frac{27}{32}$	1-8$\frac{11}{32}$	$5\frac{3}{32}$	1-9$\frac{3}{8}$	$5\frac{5}{16}$	1-10$\frac{13}{32}$
$\frac{13}{16}$	$4\frac{3}{8}$	1-6$\frac{11}{32}$	$4\frac{19}{32}$	1-7$\frac{3}{8}$	$4\frac{27}{32}$	1-8$\frac{13}{32}$	$5\frac{3}{32}$	1-9$\frac{7}{16}$	$5\frac{11}{32}$	1-10$\frac{15}{32}$
$\frac{7}{8}$	$4\frac{3}{8}$	1-6$\frac{13}{32}$	$4\frac{5}{8}$	1-7$\frac{7}{16}$	$4\frac{7}{8}$	1-8$\frac{15}{32}$	$5\frac{1}{8}$	1-9$\frac{1}{2}$	$5\frac{11}{32}$	1-10$\frac{17}{32}$
$\frac{15}{16}$	$4\frac{13}{32}$	1-6$\frac{15}{32}$	$4\frac{5}{8}$	1-7$\frac{1}{2}$	$4\frac{7}{8}$	1-8$\frac{17}{32}$	$5\frac{1}{8}$	1-9$\frac{9}{16}$	$5\frac{3}{8}$	1-10$\frac{19}{32}$

Feet	40′ Rise	40′ Slope	50′ Rise	50′ Slope	60′ Rise	60′ Slope	70′ Rise	70′ Slope
0	9-9$\frac{1}{2}$	41-2$\frac{3}{16}$	12-2$\frac{7}{8}$	51-5$\frac{23}{32}$	14-8$\frac{1}{4}$	61-9$\frac{1}{4}$	17-1$\frac{5}{8}$	72-0$\frac{13}{16}$
1	10-0$\frac{7}{16}$	42-2$\frac{17}{32}$	12-5$\frac{13}{16}$	52-6$\frac{1}{16}$	14-11$\frac{3}{16}$	62-9$\frac{5}{8}$	17-4$\frac{9}{16}$	73-1$\frac{5}{32}$
2	10-3$\frac{3}{8}$	43-2$\frac{7}{8}$	12-8$\frac{3}{4}$	53-6$\frac{7}{16}$	15-2$\frac{1}{8}$	63-9$\frac{31}{32}$	17-7$\frac{1}{2}$	74-1$\frac{1}{2}$
3	10-6$\frac{5}{16}$	44-3$\frac{1}{4}$	12-11$\frac{11}{16}$	54-6$\frac{25}{32}$	15-5$\frac{1}{16}$	64-10$\frac{5}{16}$	17-10$\frac{7}{16}$	75-1$\frac{7}{8}$
4	10-9$\frac{1}{4}$	45-3$\frac{19}{32}$	13-2$\frac{5}{8}$	55-7$\frac{1}{8}$	15-8	65-10$\frac{11}{16}$	18-1$\frac{3}{8}$	76-2$\frac{1}{32}$
5	11-0$\frac{3}{16}$	46-3$\frac{15}{16}$	13-5$\frac{9}{16}$	56-7$\frac{1}{2}$	15-10$\frac{15}{16}$	66-11$\frac{1}{32}$	18-4$\frac{5}{16}$	77-2$\frac{9}{16}$
6	11-3$\frac{1}{8}$	47-4$\frac{5}{16}$	13-8$\frac{1}{2}$	57-7$\frac{27}{32}$	16-1$\frac{7}{8}$	67-11$\frac{3}{8}$	18-7$\frac{1}{4}$	78-2$\frac{15}{16}$
7	11-6$\frac{1}{16}$	48-4$\frac{21}{32}$	13-11$\frac{7}{16}$	58-8$\frac{3}{16}$	16-4$\frac{13}{16}$	68-11$\frac{3}{4}$	18-10$\frac{3}{16}$	79-3$\frac{9}{32}$
8	11-9	49-5	14-2$\frac{3}{8}$	59-8$\frac{9}{16}$	16-7$\frac{3}{4}$	70-0$\frac{3}{32}$	19-1$\frac{1}{8}$	80-3$\frac{5}{8}$
9	11-11$\frac{15}{16}$	50-5$\frac{3}{8}$	14-5$\frac{5}{16}$	60-8$\frac{29}{32}$	16-10$\frac{11}{16}$	71-0$\frac{7}{16}$	19-4$\frac{1}{16}$	81-4

natsin A=0.2377713256; natcos A=0.9713211604; nattan A=0.2447916666; natcot A=4.0851063829

Bevel 3″ to 12″

Inches	0″ Rise	0″ Slope	1″ Rise	1″ Slope	2″ Rise	2″ Slope	3″ Rise	3″ Slope	4″ Rise	4″ Slope	5″ Rise	5″ Slope
0	0	0	1/4	1 1/32	1/2	2 1/16	3/4	3 3/32	1	4 1/8	1 1/4	5 5/32
1/16	0	1/16	1/4	1 3/32	1/2	2 1/8	3/4	3 5/32	1	4 3/16	1 1/4	5 7/32
1/8	1/32	1/8	9/32	1 5/32	17/32	2 3/16	25/32	3 7/32	1 1/32	4 1/4	1 9/32	5 9/32
3/16	1/16	3/16	5/16	1 7/32	9/16	2 1/4	13/16	3 9/32	1 1/16	4 5/16	1 5/16	5 11/32
1/4	1/16	1/4	5/16	1 9/32	9/16	2 5/16	13/16	3 11/32	1 1/16	4 3/8	1 5/16	5 13/32
5/16	1/16	5/16	5/16	1 11/32	9/16	2 3/8	13/16	3 13/32	1 1/16	4 7/16	1 5/16	5 15/32
3/8	3/32	3/8	11/32	1 13/32	19/32	2 7/16	27/32	3 15/32	1 3/32	4 1/2	1 11/16	5 17/32
7/16	1/8	7/16	3/8	1 15/32	5/8	2 1/2	7/8	3 17/32	1 1/8	4 9/16	1 3/8	5 19/32
1/2	1/8	1/2	3/8	1 17/32	5/8	2 9/16	7/8	3 19/32	1 1/8	4 5/8	1 3/8	5 21/32
9/16	1/8	19/32	3/8	1 5/8	5/8	2 21/32	7/8	3 11/16	1 1/8	4 11/16	1 3/8	5 23/32
5/8	5/32	21/32	13/32	1 11/16	21/32	2 23/32	29/32	3 3/4	1 5/32	4 25/32	1 13/32	5 13/16
11/16	3/16	23/32	7/16	1 3/4	11/16	2 25/32	15/16	3 13/16	1 3/16	4 27/32	1 7/16	5 7/8
3/4	3/16	25/32	7/16	1 13/16	11/16	2 27/32	15/16	3 7/8	1 3/16	4 29/32	1 7/16	5 15/16
13/16	3/16	27/32	7/16	1 7/8	11/16	2 29/32	15/16	3 15/16	1 3/16	4 31/32	1 7/16	6
7/8	7/32	29/32	15/32	1 15/16	23/32	2 31/32	31/32	4	1 7/32	5 1/32	1 15/32	6 1/16
15/16	1/4	31/32	1/2	2	3/4	3 1/32	1	4 1/16	1 1/4	5 3/32	1 1/2	6 1/8

Inches	6″ Rise	6″ Slope	7″ Rise	7″ Slope	8″ Rise	8″ Slope	9″ Rise	9″ Slope	10″ Rise	10″ Slope	11″ Rise	11″ Slope
0	1 1/2	6 3/16	1 3/4	7 7/32	2	8 1/4	2 1/4	9 9/32	2 1/2	10 5/16	2 3/4	11 11/32
1/16	1 1/2	6 1/4	1 3/4	7 9/32	2	8 5/16	2 1/4	9 11/32	2 1/2	10 3/8	2 3/4	11 13/32
1/8	1 17/32	6 5/16	1 25/32	7 11/32	2 1/32	8 3/8	2 9/32	9 13/32	2 11/32	10 7/16	2 25/32	11 15/32
3/16	1 9/16	6 3/8	1 13/16	7 13/32	2 1/16	8 7/16	2 5/16	9 15/32	2 9/16	10 1/2	2 13/16	11 17/32
1/4	1 9/16	6 7/16	1 13/16	7 15/32	2 1/16	8 1/2	2 5/16	9 17/32	2 9/16	10 9/16	2 13/16	11 19/32
5/16	1 9/16	6 1/2	1 13/16	7 17/32	2 1/16	8 9/16	2 5/16	9 19/32	2 9/16	10 5/8	2 13/16	11 21/32
3/8	1 19/32	6 9/16	1 27/32	7 19/32	2 3/32	8 5/8	2 11/32	9 21/32	2 19/32	10 11/16	2 27/32	11 23/32
7/16	1 5/8	6 5/8	1 7/8	7 21/32	2 1/8	8 11/16	2 3/8	9 23/32	2 5/8	10 3/4	2 7/8	11 25/32
1/2	1 5/8	6 11/16	1 7/8	7 23/32	2 1/8	8 3/4	2 3/8	9 25/32	2 5/8	10 13/16	2 7/8	11 27/32
9/16	1 5/8	6 3/4	1 7/8	7 25/32	2 1/8	8 13/16	2 3/8	9 27/32	2 5/8	10 7/8	2 7/8	11 29/32
5/8	1 21/32	6 27/32	1 29/32	7 7/8	2 5/32	8 7/8	2 13/32	9 29/32	2 21/32	10 15/16	2 29/32	11 31/32
11/16	1 11/16	6 29/32	1 15/16	7 15/16	2 3/16	8 31/32	2 7/16	10	2 11/16	11 1/32	2 15/16	1-0 1/16
3/4	1 11/16	6 31/32	1 15/16	8	2 3/16	9 1/32	2 7/16	10 1/16	2 11/16	11 3/32	2 15/16	1-0 3/32
13/16	1 11/16	7 1/32	1 15/16	8 1/16	2 3/16	9 3/32	2 7/16	10 1/8	2 11/16	11 5/32	2 15/16	1-0 5/32
7/8	1 23/32	7 3/32	1 31/32	8 1/8	2 7/32	9 5/32	2 15/32	10 3/16	2 23/32	11 7/32	2 31/32	1-0 1/4
15/16	1 3/4	7 5/32	2	8 3/16	2 1/4	9 7/32	2 1/2	10 1/4	2 3/4	11 9/32	3	1-0 5/16

Feet	0′ Rise	0′ Slope	10′ Rise	10′ Slope	20′ Rise	20′ Slope	30′ Rise	30′ Slope
0	0	0	2-6	10-3 11/16	5-0	20-7 3/8	7-6	30-11 3/32
1	3	1-0 3/8	2-9	11-4 1/16	5-3	21-7 3/4	7-9	31-11 7/16
2	6	2-0 3/4	3-0	12-4 7/16	5-6	22-8 1/8	8-0	32-11 13/16
3	9	3-1 3/32	3-3	13-4 13/16	5-9	23-8 1/2	8-3	34-0 3/16
4	1-0	4-1 15/32	3-6	14-5 3/32	6-0	24-8 7/8	8-6	35-0 9/16
5	1-3	5-1 27/32	3-9	15-5 17/32	6-3	25-9 7/32	8-9	36-0 15/16
6	1-6	6-2 7/32	4-0	16-5 29/32	6-6	26-9 19/32	9-0	37-1 9/32
7	1-9	7-2 19/32	4-3	17-6 9/32	6-9	27-9 31/32	9-3	38-1 21/32
8	2-0	8-2 31/32	4-6	18-6 21/32	7-0	28-10 11/32	9-6	39-2 1/32
9	2-3	9-3 5/16	4-9	19-7 1/32	7-3	29-10 23/32	9-9	40-2 13/32

A = 14° 02′ 10″; logsin A = 9.38477; logcos A = 9.98584; logtan A = 9.39794; logcot A = 0.60206

Ins.	12″ Rise	12″ Slope	13″ Rise	13″ Slope	14″ Rise	14″ Slope	15″ Rise	15″ Slope	16″ Rise	16″ Slope
0	3	1-0 3/8	3-1/4	1-1 13/32	3-1/2	1-2 7/32	3-3/4	1-3 15/32	4	1-4 1/2
1/16	3	1-0 7/16	3-1/4	1-1 15/32	3-1/2	1-2 1/2	3-3/4	1-3 17/32	4	1-4 9/16
1/8	3-1/32	1-0 1/2	3-9/32	1-1 17/32	3-17/32	1-2 9/16	3-25/32	1-3 19/32	4-1/16	1-4 5/8
3/16	3-1/16	1-0 9/16	3-5/16	1-1 19/32	3-9/16	1-2 5/8	3-13/16	1-3 21/32	4-3/16	1-4 11/16
1/4	3-1/16	1-0 5/8	3-5/16	1-1 21/32	3-9/16	1-2 11/16	3-13/16	1-3 23/32	4-1/16	1-4 3/4
5/16	3-1/16	1-0 11/16	3-5/16	1-1 23/32	3-9/16	1-2 3/4	3-13/16	1-3 25/32	4-2/16	1-4 13/16
3/8	3-3/32	1-0 3/4	3-11/32	1-1 25/32	3-19/32	1-2 13/16	3-27/32	1-3 27/32	4-3/32	1-4 7/8
7/16	3-1/8	1-0 13/16	3-3/8	1-1 27/32	3-5/8	1-2 7/8	3-7/8	1-3 29/32	4-1/8	1-4 15/16
1/2	3-1/8	1-0 7/8	3-3/8	1-1 29/32	3-5/8	1-2 15/16	3-7/8	1-3 31/32	4-1/8	1-5
9/16	3-1/8	1-0 15/16	3-3/8	1-1 31/32	3-5/8	1-3	3-7/8	1-4 1/32	4-1/8	1-5 1/16
5/8	3-5/32	1-1	3-13/32	1-2 1/32	3-21/32	1-3 1/16	3-29/32	1-4 3/32	4-5/32	1-5 1/8
11/16	3-3/16	1-1 1/16	3-7/16	1-2 3/32	3-11/16	1-3 1/8	3-15/16	1-4 5/32	4-3/16	1-5 3/16
3/4	3-3/16	1-1 5/32	3-7/16	1-2 3/16	3-11/16	1-3 7/32	3-15/16	1-4 1/4	4-3/16	1-5 1/4
13/16	3-3/16	1-1 7/32	3-7/16	1-2 1/4	3-11/16	1-3 9/32	3-15/16	1-4 5/16	4-3/16	1-5 11/32
7/8	3-7/32	1-1 9/32	3-15/32	1-2 5/16	3-23/32	1-3 11/32	3-31/32	1-4 3/8	4-7/32	1-5 13/32
15/16	3-1/4	1-1 11/32	3-1/2	1-2 3/8	3-3/4	1-3 13/32	4	1-4 7/32	4-1/4	1-5 15/32

Ins.	17″ Rise	17″ Slope	18″ Rise	18″ Slope	19″ Rise	19″ Slope	20″ Rise	20″ Slope	21″ Rise	21″ Slope
0	4-1/4	1-5 17/32	4-1/2	1-6 9/16	4-3/4	1-7 19/32	5	1-8 5/8	5-1/4	1-9 21/32
1/16	4-1/4	1-5 19/32	4-1/2	1-6 5/8	4-3/4	1-7 21/32	5	1-8 11/16	5-1/4	1-9 23/32
1/8	4-9/32	1-5 21/32	4-17/32	1-6 11/16	4-25/32	1-7 23/32	5-1/32	1-8 3/4	5-9/32	1-9 25/32
3/16	4-5/16	1-5 23/32	4-9/16	1-6 3/4	4-13/16	1-7 25/32	5-1/16	1-8 13/16	5-5/16	1-9 27/32
1/4	4-5/16	1-5 25/32	4-9/16	1-6 13/16	4-13/16	1-7 27/32	5-1/16	1-8 7/8	5-5/16	1-9 29/32
5/16	4-5/16	1-5 27/32	4-9/16	1-6 7/8	4-13/16	1-7 29/32	5-1/16	1-8 15/16	5-5/16	1-9 31/32
3/8	4-11/32	1-5 29/32	4-19/32	1-6 15/16	4-27/32	1-7 31/32	5-3/32	1-9	5-11/32	1-10 1/32
7/16	4-3/8	1-5 31/32	4-5/8	1-7	4-7/8	1-8 1/32	5-1/8	1-9 1/16	5-3/8	1-10 3/32
1/2	4-3/8	1-6 1/32	4-5/8	1-7 1/32	4-7/8	1-8 3/32	5-1/8	1-9 1/8	5-3/8	1-10 5/32
9/16	4-3/8	1-6 3/32	4-5/8	1-7 1/8	4-7/8	1-8 5/32	5-1/8	1-9 3/16	5-3/8	1-10 7/32
5/8	4-13/32	1-6 5/32	4-21/32	1-7 3/16	4-29/32	1-8 7/32	5-5/32	1-9 1/4	5-13/32	1-10 9/32
11/16	4-7/16	1-6 7/32	4-11/16	1-7 1/4	4-15/16	1-8 9/32	5-3/16	1-9 5/16	5-7/16	1-10 11/32
3/4	4-7/16	1-6 9/32	4-11/16	1-7 5/16	4-15/16	1-8 11/32	5-3/16	1-9 3/8	5-7/16	1-10 13/32
13/16	4-7/16	1-6 11/32	4-11/16	1-7 13/32	4-15/16	1-8 7/16	5-3/16	1-9 7/16	5-7/16	1-10 15/32
7/8	4-15/32	1-6 13/32	4-23/32	1-7 15/32	4-31/32	1-8 1/2	5-7/32	1-9 17/32	5-15/32	1-10 9/16
15/16	4-1/2	1-6 1/2	4-3/4	1-7 17/32	5	1-8 9/16	5-1/4	1-9 19/32	5-1/2	1-10 5/8

Feet	40′ Rise	40′ Slope	50′ Rise	50′ Slope	60′ Rise	60′ Slope	70′ Rise	70′ Slope
0	10-0	41-2 25/32	12-6	51-6 15/32	15-0	61-10 5/32	17-6	72-1 27/32
1	10-3	42-3 5/32	12-9	52-6 27/32	15-3	62-10 17/32	17-9	73-2 7/32
2	10-6	43-3 1/2	13-0	53-7 7/32	15-6	63-10 29/32	18-0	74-2 19/32
3	10-9	44-3 7/8	13-3	54-7 9/16	15-9	64-11 9/32	18-3	75-2 31/32
4	11-0	45-4 1/4	13-6	55-7 15/16	16-0	65-11 5/8	18-6	76-3 11/32
5	11-3	46-4 5/8	13-9	56-8 5/16	16-3	67-0	18-9	77-3 11/16
6	11-6	47-5	14-0	57-8 11/16	16-6	68-0 3/8	19-0	78-4 1/16
7	11-9	48-5 11/32	14-3	58-9 1/16	16-9	69-0 3/4	19-3	79-4 7/16
8	12-0	49-5 23/32	14-6	59-9 13/32	17-0	70-1 1/8	19-6	80-4 13/16
9	12-3	50-6 3/32	14-9	60-9 25/32	17-3	71-1 15/32	19-9	81-5 3/16

natsin A=0.2425356250; **natcos** A=0.9701425000; **nattan** A=0.2500000000; **natcot** A=4.0000000000

Inches	0" Rise	Slope	1" Rise	Slope	2" Rise	Slope	3" Rise	Slope	4" Rise	Slope	5" Rise	Slope
0	0	0	1/4	1 1/32	1/2	2 1/16	3/4	3 3/32	1 1/32	4 1/8	1 9/32	5 5/32
1/16	1/32	1/16	9/32	1 3/32	17/32	2 1/8	25/32	3 5/32	1 1/32	4 3/16	1 9/32	5 7/32
1/8	1/32	1/8	9/32	1 5/32	17/32	2 3/16	13/16	3 7/32	1 1/16	4 1/4	1 5/16	5 9/32
3/16	1/16	3/16	5/16	1 7/32	9/16	2 1/4	13/16	3 9/32	1 1/16	4 5/16	1 5/16	5 11/32
1/4	1/16	1/4	5/16	1 9/32	9/16	2 5/16	27/32	3 11/32	1 3/32	4 3/8	1 11/32	5 13/32
5/16	3/32	5/16	11/32	1 11/32	19/32	2 3/8	27/32	3 13/32	1 3/32	4 7/16	1 11/32	5 15/32
3/8	3/32	3/8	11/32	1 13/32	19/32	2 7/16	7/8	3 15/32	1 1/8	4 1/2	1 3/8	5 9/16
7/16	1/8	7/16	3/8	1 15/32	5/8	2 1/2	7/8	3 9/16	1 1/8	4 19/32	1 3/8	5 5/8
1/2	1/8	17/32	3/8	1 9/16	5/8	2 19/32	29/32	3 5/8	1 5/32	4 21/32	1 13/32	5 11/16
9/16	5/32	19/32	13/32	1 5/8	21/32	2 21/32	29/32	3 11/16	1 5/32	4 23/32	1 13/32	5 3/4
5/8	5/32	21/32	13/32	1 11/16	21/32	2 23/32	15/16	3 3/4	1 3/16	4 25/32	1 7/16	5 13/16
11/16	3/16	23/32	7/16	1 3/4	11/16	2 25/32	15/16	3 13/16	1 3/16	4 27/32	1 7/16	5 7/8
3/4	3/16	25/32	7/16	1 13/16	11/16	2 27/32	31/32	3 7/8	1 7/32	4 29/32	1 15/32	5 15/16
13/16	7/32	27/32	15/32	1 7/8	23/32	2 29/32	31/32	3 15/16	1 7/32	4 31/32	1 15/32	6
7/8	7/32	29/32	15/32	1 15/16	23/32	2 31/32	1	4	1 1/4	5 1/32	1 1/2	6 1/16
15/16	1/4	31/32	1/2	2	3/4	3 1/32	1	4 1/16	1 1/4	5 3/32	1 1/2	6 1/8

Inches	6" Rise	Slope	7" Rise	Slope	8" Rise	Slope	9" Rise	Slope	10" Rise	Slope	11" Rise	Slope
0	1 17/32	6 3/16	1 25/32	7 7/32	2 1/32	8 1/4	2 5/16	9 9/32	2 9/16	10 5/16	2 13/16	11 11/32
1/16	1 9/16	6 1/4	1 13/16	7 9/32	2 1/16	8 5/16	2 5/16	9 11/32	2 9/16	10 3/8	2 13/16	11 13/32
1/8	1 9/16	6 5/16	1 13/16	7 11/32	2 1/16	8 3/8	2 11/32	9 13/32	2 19/32	10 7/16	2 27/32	11 15/32
3/16	1 19/32	6 3/8	1 27/32	7 13/32	2 3/32	8 7/16	2 11/32	9 15/32	2 19/32	10 1/2	2 27/32	11 17/32
1/4	1 19/32	6 7/16	1 27/32	7 15/32	2 3/32	8 1/2	2 3/8	9 17/32	2 5/8	10 19/32	2 7/8	11 5/8
5/16	1 5/8	6 1/2	1 7/8	7 9/16	2 1/8	8 19/32	2 3/8	9 5/8	2 5/8	10 21/32	2 7/8	11 11/16
3/8	1 5/8	6 19/32	1 7/8	7 5/8	2 1/8	8 21/32	2 13/32	9 11/16	2 21/32	10 25/32	2 29/32	11 3/4
7/16	1 21/32	6 21/32	1 29/32	7 11/16	2 5/32	8 23/32	2 13/32	9 3/4	2 21/32	10 25/32	2 29/32	11 13/16
1/2	1 21/32	6 23/32	1 29/32	7 3/4	2 5/32	8 25/32	2 7/16	9 13/16	2 11/16	10 27/32	2 15/16	11 7/8
9/16	1 11/16	6 25/32	1 15/16	7 13/16	2 3/16	8 27/32	2 7/16	9 7/8	2 11/16	10 29/32	2 15/16	11 15/16
5/8	1 11/16	6 27/32	1 15/16	7 7/8	2 3/16	8 29/32	2 15/32	9 15/16	2 23/32	10 31/32	2 31/32	1-0
11/16	1 23/32	6 29/32	1 31/32	7 15/16	2 7/32	8 31/32	2 15/32	10	2 23/32	11 1/32	2 31/32	1-0 1/16
3/4	1 23/32	6 31/32	1 31/32	8	2 7/32	9 1/32	2 1/2	10 1/16	2 3/4	11 3/32	3	1-0 1/8
13/16	1 3/4	7 1/32	2	8 1/16	2 1/4	9 3/32	2 1/2	10 1/8	2 3/4	11 5/32	3	1-0 3/16
7/8	1 3/4	7 3/32	2	8 1/8	2 1/4	9 5/32	2 17/32	10 3/16	2 25/32	11 7/32	3 1/32	1-0 1/4
15/16	1 25/32	7 5/32	2 1/32	8 3/16	2 1/4	9 7/32	2 17/32	10 1/4	2 25/32	11 9/32	3 1/32	1-0 5/16

Feet	0' Rise	Slope	10' Rise	Slope	20' Rise	Slope	30' Rise	Slope
0	0	0	2-6 5/8	10-3 27/32	5-1 1/4	20-7 11/16	7-7 7/8	30-11 17/32
1	3 1/16	1-0 3/8	2-9 11/16	11-4 5/32	5-4 5/16	21-8 1/16	7-10 15/16	31-11 15/16
2	6 1/8	2-0 25/32	3-0 3/4	12-4 5/8	5-7 3/8	22-8 15/32	8-2	33-0 5/16
3	9 3/16	3-1 5/32	3-3 13/16	13-5	5-10 7/16	23-8 27/32	8-5 1/16	34-0 11/16
4	1-0 1/4	4-1 17/32	3-6 7/8	14-5 3/8	6-1 1/2	24-9 7/32	8-8 1/8	35-1 1/16
5	1-3 5/16	5-1 15/16	3-9 15/16	15-5 25/32	6-4 9/16	25-9 5/8	8-11 3/16	36-1 15/32
6	1-6 3/8	6-2 5/16	4-1	16-6 5/32	6-7 5/8	26-10	9-2 1/4	37-1 27/32
7	1-9 7/16	7-2 11/16	4-4 1/16	17-6 17/32	6-10 11/16	27-10 3/8	9-5 5/16	38-2 7/32
8	2-0 1/2	8-3 1/16	4-7 1/8	18-6 15/16	7-1 3/4	28-10 25/32	9-8 3/8	39-2 5/8
9	2-3 9/16	9-3 15/32	4-10 3/16	19-7 5/16	7-4 13/16	29-11 5/32	9-11 7/16	40-3

A = 14° 19' 00''; log sin A = 9.39319; log cos A = 9.98630; log tan A = 9.40689; log cot A = 0.59311

Ins.	12" Rise	12" Slope	13" Rise	13" Slope	14" Rise	14" Slope	15" Rise	15" Slope	16" Rise	16" Slope
0	3 1/16	1-0 3/8	3 5/16	1-1 13/32	3 9/16	1-2 7/16	3 13/16	1-3 15/32	4 3/32	1-4 1/2
1/16	3 3/32	1-0 7/16	3 11/32	1-1 15/32	3 19/32	1-2 1/2	3 27/32	1-3 17/32	4 3/32	1-4 9/16
1/8	3 3/32	1-0 1/2	3 11/32	1-1 17/32	3 19/32	1-2 9/16	3 7/8	1-3 5/8	4 1/8	1-4 21/32
3/16	3 1/8	1-0 19/32	3 3/8	1-1 5/8	3 5/8	1-2 21/32	3 7/8	1-3 11/16	4 1/8	1-4 23/32
1/4	3 1/8	1-0 21/32	3 3/8	1-1 11/16	3 5/8	1-2 23/32	3 29/32	1-3 3/4	4 5/32	1-4 25/32
5/16	3 5/32	1-0 23/32	3 13/32	1-1 3/4	3 21/32	1-2 25/32	3 29/32	1-3 13/16	4 5/32	1-4 27/32
3/8	3 5/32	1-0 25/32	3 13/32	1-1 13/16	3 21/32	1-2 27/32	3 15/16	1-3 7/8	4 3/16	1-4 29/32
7/16	3 3/16	1-0 27/32	3 7/16	1-1 7/8	3 11/16	1-2 29/32	3 15/16	1-3 15/16	4 3/16	1-4 31/32
1/2	3 3/16	1-0 29/32	3 7/16	1-1 15/16	3 11/16	1-2 31/32	3 31/32	1-4	4 7/32	1-5 1/8
9/16	3 7/32	1-0 31/32	3 15/32	1-2	3 23/32	1-3 1/32	3 31/32	1-4 1/8	4 7/32	1-5 3/32
5/8	3 7/32	1-1 1/32	3 15/32	1-2 1/8	3 23/32	1-3 3/32	4	1-4 1/8	4 1/4	1-5 5/32
11/16	3 1/4	1-1 3/32	3 1/2	1-2 1/8	3 3/4	1-3 5/32	4	1-4 3/16	4 1/4	1-5 7/32
3/4	3 1/4	1-1 5/32	3 1/2	1-2 3/16	3 3/4	1-3 7/32	4 1/32	1-4 1/4	4 9/32	1-5 9/32
13/16	3 9/32	1-1 7/32	3 17/32	1-2 1/4	3 25/32	1-3 9/32	4 1/32	1-4 5/16	4 9/32	1-5 11/32
7/8	3 9/32	1-1 9/32	3 17/32	1-2 5/16	3 25/32	1-3 11/32	4 1/16	1-4 3/8	4 5/16	1-5 13/32
15/16	3 5/16	1-1 11/32	3 9/16	1-2 3/8	3 13/16	1-3 13/32	4 1/16	1-4 7/16	4 5/16	1-5 15/32

Ins.	17" Rise	17" Slope	18" Rise	18" Slope	19" Rise	19" Slope	20" Rise	20" Slope	21" Rise	21" Slope
0	4 11/32	1-5 17/32	4 19/32	1-6 9/16	4 27/32	1-7 19/32	5 3/32	1-8 21/32	5 3/8	1-9 11/16
1/16	4 11/32	1-5 5/8	4 5/8	1-6 21/32	4 7/8	1-7 11/16	5 1/8	1-8 23/32	5 3/8	1-9 3/4
1/8	4 3/8	1-5 11/16	4 5/8	1-6 23/32	4 7/8	1-7 3/4	5 1/8	1-8 25/32	5 13/32	1-9 13/16
3/16	4 3/8	1-5 3/4	4 21/32	1-6 25/32	4 29/32	1-7 13/16	5 5/32	1-8 27/32	5 13/32	1-9 7/8
1/4	4 13/32	1-5 13/16	4 21/32	1-6 27/32	4 29/32	1-7 7/8	5 5/32	1-8 29/32	5 7/16	1-9 15/16
5/16	4 13/32	1-5 7/8	4 11/16	1-6 29/32	4 15/16	1-7 15/16	5 3/16	1-8 31/32	5 7/16	1-10
3/8	4 7/16	1-5 15/16	4 11/16	1-6 31/32	4 15/16	1-8	5 3/16	1-9 1/32	5 15/32	1-10 1/16
7/16	4 7/16	1-6	4 23/32	1-7 1/32	4 31/32	1-8 1/16	5 7/32	1-9 3/32	5 15/32	1-10 1/16
1/2	4 15/32	1-6 1/8	4 23/32	1-7 3/32	4 31/32	1-8 1/8	5 7/32	1-9 5/32	5 1/2	1-10 3/16
9/16	4 15/32	1-6 1/8	4 3/4	1-7 5/32	5	1-8 3/16	5 1/4	1-9 7/32	5 1/2	1-10 1/4
5/8	4 1/2	1-6 3/16	4 3/4	1-7 7/32	5	1-8 1/4	5 1/4	1-9 9/32	5 17/32	1-10 5/32
11/16	4 1/2	1-6 1/4	4 25/32	1-7 9/32	5 1/32	1-8 5/16	5 9/32	1-9 11/32	5 17/32	1-10 3/8
3/4	4 17/32	1-6 5/16	4 25/32	1-7 11/32	5 1/32	1-8 3/8	5 9/32	1-9 13/32	5 9/16	1-10 7/16
13/16	4 17/32	1-6 3/8	4 13/16	1-7 13/32	5 1/16	1-8 7/16	5 5/16	1-9 15/32	5 9/16	1-10 1/2
7/8	4 9/16	1-6 7/16	4 13/16	1-7 15/32	5 1/16	1-8 1/2	5 5/16	1-9 17/32	5 19/32	1-10 9/16
15/16	4 9/16	1-6 1/2	4 27/32	1-7 17/32	5 3/32	1-8 9/16	5 11/32	1-9 19/32	5 19/32	1-10 21/32

Feet	40' Rise	40' Slope	50' Rise	50' Slope	60' Rise	60' Slope	70' Rise	70' Slope
0	10-2 1/2	41-3 3/8	12-9 1/8	51-7 7/32	15-3 3/4	61-11 11/16	17-10 3/8	72-2 15/16
1	10-5 5/16	42-3 25/32	13-0 3/16	52-7 5/8	15-6 13/16	62-11 15/32	18-1 7/16	73-3 5/16
2	10-8 5/8	43-4 5/32	13-3 1/4	53-8	15-9 7/8	63-11 27/32	18-4 1/2	74-3 11/16
3	10-11 11/16	44-4 17/32	13-6 5/8	54-8 3/8	16-0 15/16	65-0 7/32	18-7 7/8	75-4 1/16
4	11-2 3/4	45-4 15/32	13-9 3/8	55-8 25/32	16-4	66-0 5/8	18-10 5/8	76-4 15/32
5	11-5 13/16	46-5 5/16	14-0 7/16	56-9 5/32	16-7 1/16	67-1	19-1 11/16	77-4 27/32
6	11-8 7/8	47-5 11/16	14-3 1/2	57-9 17/32	16-10 1/8	68-1 3/8	19-4 3/4	78-5 7/32
7	11-11 15/16	48-6 1/16	14-6 5/8	58-9 15/16	17-1 3/16	69-1 25/32	19-7 13/16	79-5 5/8
8	12-3	49-6 15/32	14-9 5/8	59-10 5/16	17-4 1/4	70-2 5/32	19-10 7/8	80-6
9	12-6 1/16	50-6 27/32	15-0 11/16	60-10 11/16	17-7 5/16	71-2 17/32	20-1 15/16	81-6 3/8

natsin A=0.2472824410; natcos A=0.9689434424; nattan A=0.2552083333; natcot A=3.9183673469

BEVEL 3 1/8" TO 12"

Inches	0" Rise	0" Slope	1" Rise	1" Slope	2" Rise	2" Slope	3" Rise	3" Slope	4" Rise	4" Slope	5" Rise	5" Slope
0	0	0	1/4	1 1/32	17/32-	2 1/16	25/32	3 3/32	1 1/32	4 1/8	1 5/16	5 5/32
1/16	1/32-	1/16	9/32-	1 3/32	17/32	2 1/8	13/16	3 5/32	1 1/16	4 3/16	1 5/16	5 7/32
1/8	1/32	1/8	9/32	1 5/32	9/16	2 3/16	13/16	3 7/32	1 1/16	4 1/4	1 11/32-	5 9/32
3/16	1/16	3/16	5/16	1 7/32	9/16	2 1/4	27/32-	3 9/32	1 3/32-	4 5/16	1 11/32	5 3/8
1/4	1/16	1/4	5/16	1 9/32	19/32-	2 5/16	27/32	3 11/32	1 3/32	4 13/32-	1 3/8	5 7/16
5/16	3/32-	5/16	11/32-	1 11/32	19/32	2 3/8	7/8	3 7/16	1 1/8	4 15/32-	1 3/8	5 1/2
3/8	3/32	3/8	11/32	1 13/32	5/8	2 15/32-	7/8	3 1/2	1 1/8	4 17/32-	1 13/32-	5 9/16
7/16	1/8	7/16	3/8	1 1/2	5/8	2 17/32-	29/32-	3 9/16	1 5/32-	4 19/32-	1 13/32	5 5/8
1/2	1/8	17/32-	3/8	1 9/16	21/32-	2 19/32-	29/32	3 5/8	1 3/16	4 21/32-	1 7/16	5 11/16
9/16	5/32-	19/32-	13/32	1 5/8	21/32	2 21/32-	15/16	3 11/16	1 3/16	4 23/32-	1 7/16	5 3/4
5/8	5/32	21/32-	7/16	1 11/16	11/16	2 23/32-	15/16	3 3/4	1 7/32-	4 25/32-	1 15/32-	5 13/16
11/16	3/16	23/32-	7/16	1 3/4	11/16	2 25/32-	31/32-	3 13/16	1 7/32	4 27/32	1 15/32	5 7/8
3/4	3/16	25/32-	15/32-	1 13/16	23/32-	2 27/32-	31/32	3 7/8	1 1/4	4 29/32	1 1/2	5 15/16
13/16	7/32-	27/32-	15/32	1 7/8	23/32	2 29/32	1	3 15/16	1 1/4	4 31/32	1 1/2	6
7/8	7/32	29/32-	1/2	1 15/16	3/4	2 31/32	1	4	1 9/32-	5 1/32	1 17/32-	6 1/16
15/16	1/4	31/32	1/2	2	3/4	3 1/32	1 1/32-	4 1/16	1 9/32	5 3/32	1 17/32	6 1/8

Inches	6" Rise	6" Slope	7" Rise	7" Slope	8" Rise	8" Slope	9" Rise	9" Slope	10" Rise	10" Slope	11" Rise	11" Slope
0	1 9/16	6 3/16	1 13/16	7 7/32	2 3/32-	8 9/32-	2 11/32	9 5/16	2 19/32	10 11/32-	2 7/8	11 3/8
1/16	1 19/32-	6 1/4	1 27/32-	7 5/16	2 3/32	8 11/32-	2 3/8	9 3/8	2 5/8	10 13/32-	2 7/8	11 7/16
1/8	1 19/32	6 11/32-	1 27/32	7 3/8	2 1/8	8 13/32-	2 3/8	9 7/16	2 5/8	10 15/32-	2 29/32-	11 1/2
3/16	1 5/8	6 13/32-	1 7/8	7 7/16	2 1/8	8 15/32-	2 13/32-	9 1/2	2 21/32-	10 17/32-	2 29/32	11 9/16
1/4	1 5/8	6 15/32-	1 7/8	7 1/2	2 5/32-	8 17/32-	2 13/32	9 9/16	2 21/32	10 19/32-	2 15/16	11 5/8
5/16	1 21/32-	6 17/32-	1 29/32-	7 9/16	2 5/32	8 19/32-	2 7/16	9 5/8	2 11/16	10 21/32	2 15/16	11 11/16
3/8	1 21/32	6 19/32-	1 29/32	7 5/8	2 3/16	8 21/32-	2 7/16	9 11/16	2 11/16	10 23/32	2 31/32-	11 3/4
7/16	1 11/16	6 21/32-	1 15/16	7 11/16	2 3/16	8 23/32	2 15/32-	9 3/4	2 23/32-	10 25/32	2 31/32	11 13/16
1/2	1 11/16	6 23/32-	1 31/32-	7 3/4	2 7/32-	8 25/32	2 15/32	9 13/16	2 3/4	10 27/32	3	11 7/8
9/16	1 23/32-	6 25/32	1 31/32	7 13/16	2 7/32	8 27/32	2 1/2	9 7/8	2 3/4	10 29/32	3	11 15/16
5/8	1 23/32	6 27/32	2	7 7/8	2 1/4	8 29/32	2 1/2	9 15/16	2 25/32-	10 31/32	3 1/32-	1-0
11/16	1 3/4	6 29/32	2	7 15/16	2 1/4	8 31/32	2 17/32-	10	2 25/32	11 1/32	3 1/32	1-0 1/16
3/4	1 3/4	6 31/32	2 1/32-	8	2 9/32-	9 1/32	2 17/32	10 1/16	2 13/16	11 3/32	3 1/16	1-0 5/32-
13/16	1 25/32-	7 1/32	2 1/32	8 1/16	2 9/32	9 3/32	2 9/16	10 1/8	2 13/16	11 3/16	3 1/16	1-0 7/32-
7/8	1 25/32	7 3/32	2 1/16	8 1/8	2 5/16	9 5/32	2 9/16	10 7/32-	2 27/32-	11 1/4	3 3/32-	1-0 9/32-
15/16	1 13/16	7 5/32	2 1/16	8 3/16	2 5/16	9 1/4	2 19/32-	10 9/32-	2 27/32	11 5/16	3 3/32	1-0 11/32-

Feet	0' Rise	0' Slope	10' Rise	10' Slope	20' Rise	20' Slope	30' Rise	30' Slope
0	0	0	2-7 1/4	10-4	5-2 1/2	20-8	7-9 3/4	31-0
1	3 1/8	1-0 13/32-	2-10 3/8	11-4 13/32-	5-5 5/8	21-8 13/32-	8-0 7/8	32-0 13/32
2	6 1/4	2-0 13/16	3-1 1/2	12-4 13/16	5-8 3/4	22-8 13/16	8-4	33-0 13/16
3	9 3/8	3-1 3/16	3-4 5/8	13-5 3/16	5-11 7/8	23-9 7/32-	8-7 1/8	34-1 7/32-
4	1-0 1/2	4-1 19/32	3-7 3/4	14-5 19/32	6-3	24-9 19/32	8-10 1/4	35-1 19/32
5	1-3 5/8	5-2	3-10 7/8	15-6	6-6 1/8	25-10	9-1 3/8	36-2
6	1-6 3/4	6-2 13/32-	4-2	16-6 13/32-	6-9 1/4	26-10 13/32-	9-4 1/2	37-2 13/32
7	1-9 7/8	7-2 13/16	4-5 1/8	17-6 13/16	7-0 3/8	27-10 13/16	9-7 5/8	38-2 13/16
8	2-1	8-3 3/16	4-8 1/4	18-7 7/32-	7-3 1/2	28-11 7/32-	9-10 3/4	39-3 7/32-
9	2-4 1/8	9-3 19/32	4-11 3/8	19-7 19/32	7-6 5/8	29-11 19/32	10-1 7/8	40-3 19/32

A = 14° 35′ 48″; logsin A = 9.40142; logcos A = 9.98575; logtan A = 9.41567; logcot A = 0.58433

Ins.	12″ Rise	12″ Slope	13″ Rise	13″ Slope	14″ Rise	14″ Slope	15″ Rise	15″ Slope	16″ Rise	16″ Slope
0	3 1/8	1-0 13/32	3 3/8	1-1 7/16	3 21/32	1-2 15/32	3 29/32	1-3 1/2	4 5/32	1-4 17/32
1/16	3 5/32	1-0 15/32	3 13/32	1-1 1/2	3 21/32	1-2 17/32	3 15/16	1-3 9/16	4 3/16	1-4 19/32
1/8	3 5/32	1-0 17/32	3 13/32	1-1 9/16	3 11/16	1-2 19/32	3 15/16	1-3 5/8	4 3/16	1-4 21/32
3/16	3 3/16	1-0 19/32	3 7/16	1-1 5/8	3 11/16	1-2 21/32	3 31/32	1-3 11/16	4 7/32	1-4 23/32
1/4	3 3/16	1-0 21/32	3 7/16	1-1 11/16	3 23/32	1-2 23/32	3 31/32	1-3 3/4	4 7/32	1-4 25/32
5/16	3 7/32	1-0 23/32	3 15/32	1-1 3/4	3 23/32	1-2 25/32	4	1-3 13/16	4 1/4	1-4 27/32
3/8	3 7/32	1-0 25/32	3 15/32	1-1 13/16	3 3/4	1-2 27/32	4	1-3 7/8	4 1/4	1-4 29/32
7/16	3 1/4	1-0 27/32	3 1/2	1-1 7/8	3 3/4	1-2 29/32	4 1/32	1-3 15/16	4 9/32	1-5
1/2	3 1/4	1-0 29/32	3 1/2	1-1 15/16	3 25/32	1-2 31/32	4 1/32	1-4 1/32	4 5/16	1-5 1/16
9/16	3 9/32	1-0 31/32	3 17/32	1-2	3 25/32	1-3 1/32	4 1/16	1-4 3/32	4 5/16	1-5 1/8
5/8	3 9/32	1-1 1/32	3 9/16	1-2 3/32	3 13/16	1-3 1/8	4 1/16	1-4 5/32	4 11/32	1-5 3/16
11/16	3 5/16	1-1 1/8	3 9/16	1-2 5/32	3 13/16	1-3 3/16	4 3/32	1-4 7/32	4 11/32	1-5 1/4
3/4	3 5/16	1-1 3/16	3 19/32	1-2 7/32	3 27/32	1-3 1/4	4 3/32	1-4 9/32	4 3/8	1-5 5/16
13/16	3 11/32	1-1 1/4	3 19/32	1-2 9/32	3 27/32	1-3 5/16	4 1/8	1-4 11/32	4 3/8	1-5 3/8
7/8	3 11/32	1-1 5/16	3 5/8	1-2 11/32	3 7/8	1-3 3/8	4 1/8	1-4 13/32	4 13/32	1-5 7/16
15/16	3 3/8	1-1 3/8	3 5/8	1-2 13/32	3 7/8	1-3 7/16	4 5/32	1-4 15/32	4 13/32	1-5 1/2

Ins.	17″ Rise	17″ Slope	18″ Rise	18″ Slope	19″ Rise	19″ Slope	20″ Rise	20″ Slope	21″ Rise	21″ Slope
0	4 7/16	1-5 9/16	4 11/16	1-6 19/32	4 15/16	1-7 5/8	5 7/32	1-8 21/32	5 15/32	1-9 11/16
1/16	4 7/16	1-5 5/8	4 23/32	1-6 21/32	4 31/32	1-7 11/16	5 7/32	1-8 23/32	5 1/2	1-9 3/4
1/8	4 15/32	1-5 11/16	4 23/32	1-6 23/32	4 31/32	1-7 3/4	5 1/4	1-8 25/32	5 1/2	1-9 27/32
3/16	4 15/32	1-5 3/4	4 3/4	1-6 25/32	5	1-7 13/16	5 1/4	1-8 7/8	5 17/32	1-9 29/32
1/4	4 1/2	1-5 13/16	4 3/4	1-6 27/32	5	1-7 29/32	5 9/32	1-8 15/16	5 17/32	1-9 31/32
5/16	4 1/2	1-5 7/8	4 25/32	1-6 15/16	5 1/32	1-7 31/32	5 9/32	1-9	5 9/16	1-10 1/32
3/8	4 17/32	1-5 31/32	4 25/32	1-7	5 1/32	1-8 1/32	5 5/16	1-9 1/16	5 9/16	1-10 3/32
7/16	4 17/32	1-6 1/32	4 13/16	1-7 1/16	5 1/16	1-8 3/32	5 5/16	1-9 1/8	5 19/32	1-10 5/32
1/2	4 9/16	1-6 3/32	4 13/16	1-7 1/8	5 1/16	1-8 5/32	5 11/32	1-9 3/16	5 19/32	1-10 7/32
9/16	4 9/16	1-6 5/32	4 27/32	1-7 3/16	5 3/32	1-8 7/32	5 11/32	1-9 1/4	5 5/8	1-10 9/32
5/8	4 19/32	1-6 7/32	4 27/32	1-7 1/4	5 1/8	1-8 9/32	5 3/8	1-9 5/16	5 5/8	1-10 11/32
11/16	4 19/32	1-6 9/32	4 7/8	1-7 5/16	5 1/8	1-8 11/32	5 3/8	1-9 3/8	5 21/32	1-10 13/32
3/4	4 5/8	1-6 11/32	4 7/8	1-7 3/8	5 5/32	1-8 13/32	5 13/32	1-9 7/16	5 21/32	1-10 15/32
13/16	4 5/8	1-6 13/32	4 29/32	1-7 7/16	5 5/32	1-8 15/32	5 13/32	1-9 1/2	5 11/16	1-10 17/32
7/8	4 21/32	1-6 15/32	4 29/32	1-7 1/2	5 3/16	1-8 17/32	5 7/16	1-9 9/16	5 11/16	1-10 19/32
15/16	4 21/32	1-6 17/32	4 15/16	1-7 9/16	5 3/16	1-8 19/32	5 7/16	1-9 5/8	5 23/32	1-10 21/32

Feet	40′ Rise	40′ Slope	50′ Rise	50′ Slope	60′ Rise	60′ Slope	70′ Rise	70′ Slope
0	10-5	41-4	13-0 1/4	51-8	15-7 1/2	62-0	18-2 3/4	72-4 1/32
1	10-8 1/8	42-4 13/32	13-3 3/8	52-8 13/32	15-10 5/8	63-0 13/32	18-5 7/8	73-4 13/32
2	10-11 1/4	43-4 13/16	13-6 1/2	53-8 13/16	16-1 3/4	64-0 13/16	18-9	74-4 13/16
3	11-2 3/8	44-5 7/32	13-9 5/8	54-9 7/32	16-4 7/8	65-1 7/32	19-0 1/8	75-5 7/32
4	11-5 1/2	45-5 5/8	14-0 3/4	55-9 5/8	16-8	66-1 5/8	19-3 1/4	76-5 5/8
5	11-8 5/8	46-6	14-3 7/8	56-10	16-11 1/8	67-2	19-6 3/8	77-6 1/32
6	11-11 3/4	47-6 13/32	14-7	57-10 13/32	17-2 1/4	68-2 13/32	19-9 1/2	78-6 13/32
7	12-2 7/8	48-6 13/16	14-10 1/8	58-10 13/16	17-5 3/8	69-2 13/16	20-0 5/8	79-6 13/16
8	12-6	49-7 7/32	15-1 1/4	59-11 7/32	17-8 1/2	70-3 7/32	20-3 3/4	80-7 7/32
9	12-9 1/8	50-7 5/8	15-4 3/8	60-11 5/8	17-11 5/8	71-3 5/8	20-6 7/8	81-7 5/8

natsin A=0.2520115193; natcos A=0.9677242345; nattan A=0.2604166666; natcot A=3.8400000000

BEVEL 3 3/16" TO 12"

Inches	0" Rise	0" Slope	1" Rise	1" Slope	2" Rise	2" Slope	3" Rise	3" Slope	4" Rise	4" Slope	5" Rise	5" Slope
0	0	0	1/4	1 1/32	17/32	2 1/16	13/16	3 3/32	1 1/16	4 1/8	1 5/16	5 3/16
1/16	1/32	1/16	9/32	1 3/32	9/16	2 1/8	13/16	3 5/32	1 3/32	4 7/32	1 11/32	5 1/4
1/8	1/32	1/8	5/16	1 5/32	9/16	2 3/16	27/32	3 7/32	1 3/32	4 9/32	1 3/8	5 5/16
3/16	1/16	3/16	5/16	1 7/32	19/32	2 1/4	27/32	3 5/16	1 1/8	4 11/32	1 3/8	5 3/8
1/4	1/16	1/4	11/32	1 9/32	19/32	2 5/16	7/8	3 3/8	1 1/8	4 13/32	1 13/32	5 7/16
5/16	3/32	5/16	11/32	1 11/32	5/8	2 13/32	7/8	3 7/16	1 5/32	4 15/32	1 13/32	5 1/2
3/8	3/32	3/8	3/8	1 7/16	5/8	2 15/32	29/32	3 1/2	1 5/32	4 17/32	1 7/16	5 9/16
7/16	1/8	7/16	3/8	1 1/2	21/32	2 17/32	29/32	3 9/16	1 3/16	4 19/32	1 7/16	5 5/8
1/2	1/8	17/32	13/32	1 9/16	21/32	2 19/32	15/16	3 5/8	1 3/16	4 21/32	1 15/32	5 11/16
9/16	5/32	19/32	13/32	1 5/8	11/16	2 21/32	15/16	3 11/16	1 7/32	4 23/32	1 15/32	5 3/4
5/8	5/32	21/32	7/16	1 11/16	11/16	2 23/32	31/32	3 3/4	1 7/32	4 25/32	1 1/2	5 13/16
11/16	3/16	23/32	7/16	1 3/4	23/32	2 25/32	31/32	3 13/16	1 1/4	4 27/32	1 1/2	5 7/8
3/4	3/16	25/32	15/32	1 13/16	23/32	2 27/32	1	3 7/8	1 1/4	4 29/32	1 17/32	5 15/16
13/16	7/32	27/32	15/32	1 7/8	3/4	2 29/32	1	3 15/16	1 9/32	4 31/32	1 17/32	6
7/8	7/32	29/32	1/2	1 15/16	3/4	2 31/32	1 1/32	4	1 9/32	5 1/32	1 9/16	6 3/32
15/16	1/4	31/32	1/2	2	25/32	3 1/32	1 1/32	4 1/16	1 5/16	5 3/32	1 9/16	6 5/32

Inches	6" Rise	6" Slope	7" Rise	7" Slope	8" Rise	8" Slope	9" Rise	9" Slope	10" Rise	10" Slope	11" Rise	11" Slope
0	1 19/32	6 7/32	1 7/8	7 1/4	2 1/8	8 9/32	2 3/8	9 5/16	2 21/32	10 11/32	2 15/16	11 3/8
1/16	1 5/8	6 9/32	1 7/8	7 5/16	2 5/32	8 11/32	2 13/32	9 3/8	2 11/16	10 13/32	2 15/16	11 7/16
1/8	1 5/8	6 11/32	1 29/32	7 3/8	2 5/32	8 13/32	2 7/16	9 7/16	2 11/16	10 15/32	2 31/32	11 1/2
3/16	1 21/32	6 13/32	1 29/32	7 7/16	2 3/16	8 15/32	2 7/16	9 1/2	2 23/32	10 17/32	2 31/32	11 9/16
1/4	1 21/32	6 15/32	1 15/16	7 1/2	2 3/16	8 17/32	2 15/32	9 9/16	2 23/32	10 19/32	3	11 5/8
5/16	1 11/16	6 17/32	1 15/16	7 9/16	2 7/32	8 19/32	2 15/32	9 5/8	2 3/4	10 21/32	3	11 23/32
3/8	1 11/16	6 19/32	1 31/32	7 5/8	2 7/32	8 21/32	2 1/2	9 11/16	2 3/4	10 3/4	3 1/32	11 25/32
7/16	1 23/32	6 21/32	1 31/32	7 11/16	2 1/4	8 23/32	2 1/2	9 3/4	2 25/32	10 13/16	3 1/32	11 27/32
1/2	1 23/32	6 23/32	2	7 3/4	2 1/4	8 25/32	2 17/32	9 27/32	2 25/32	10 7/8	3 1/16	11 29/32
9/16	1 3/4	6 25/32	2	7 13/16	2 9/32	8 7/8	2 17/32	9 29/32	2 13/16	10 15/16	3 1/16	11 31/32
5/8	1 3/4	6 27/32	2 1/32	7 7/8	2 9/32	8 15/16	2 9/16	9 31/32	2 13/16	11	3 3/32	1-0 1/32
11/16	1 25/32	6 29/32	2 1/32	7 31/32	2 5/16	9	2 9/16	10 1/32	2 27/32	11 1/16	3 3/32	1-0 3/32
3/4	1 25/32	6 31/32	2 1/16	8 1/32	2 5/16	9 1/16	2 19/32	10 3/32	2 27/32	11 1/8	3 1/8	1-0 5/32
13/16	1 13/16	7 1/16	2 1/16	8 3/32	2 11/32	9 1/8	2 19/32	10 5/32	2 7/8	11 3/16	3 1/8	1-0 7/32
7/8	1 13/16	7 1/8	2 3/32	8 5/32	2 11/32	9 3/16	2 5/8	10 7/32	2 7/8	11 1/4	3 5/32	1-0 9/32
15/16	1 27/32	7 3/16	2 3/32	8 7/32	2 3/8	9 1/4	2 5/8	10 9/32	2 29/32	11 5/16	3 5/32	1-0 11/32

Feet	0' Rise	0' Slope	10' Rise	10' Slope	20' Rise	20' Slope	30' Rise	30' Slope
0	0	0	2-7 7/8	10-4 5/32	5-3 3/4	20-8 5/16	7-11 5/8	31-0 15/32
1	3 3/16	1-0 13/32	2-11 1/16	11-4 9/32	5-6 15/16	21-8 3/4	8-2 13/16	32-0 29/32
2	6 3/8	2-0 27/32	3-2 1/4	12-5	5-10 1/8	22-9 5/32	8-6	33-1 5/16
3	9 9/16	3-1 1/4	3-5 7/16	13-5 13/32	6-1 5/16	23-9 9/16	8-9 3/16	34-1 23/32
4	1-0 3/4	4-1 21/32	3-8 5/8	14-5 13/32	6-4 1/2	24-10	9-0 3/8	35-2 5/32
5	1-3 15/16	5-2 3/32	3-11 13/16	15-6 1/4	6-7 11/16	25-10 13/32	9-3 9/16	36-2 9/16
6	1-7 1/8	6-2 1/2	4-3	16-6 21/32	6-10 7/8	26-10 13/16	9-6 3/4	37-2 31/32
7	1-10 5/16	7-2 29/32	4-6 3/16	17-7 1/16	7-2 1/16	27-11 1/4	9-9 15/16	38-3 13/32
8	2-1 1/2	8-3 11/32	4-9 3/8	18-7 1/2	7-5 1/4	28-11 21/32	10-1 1/8	39-3 13/16
9	2-4 11/16	9-3 3/4	5-0 9/16	19-7 29/32	7-8 7/16	30-0 1/16	10-4 5/16	40-4 7/32

A = 14° 52' 32''; logsin A = 9.40946; logcos A = 9.98520; logtan A = 9.42427; logcot A = 0.57573

In.	12″ Rise	12″ Slope	13″ Rise	13″ Slope	14″ Rise	14″ Slope	15″ Rise	15″ Slope	16″ Rise	16″ Slope
0	$3\frac{3}{16}$	$1\text{-}0\frac{13}{32}$	$3\frac{7}{16}$	$1\text{-}1\frac{7}{16}$	$3\frac{23}{32}$	$1\text{-}2\frac{1}{2}$	4	$1\text{-}3\frac{17}{32}$	$4\frac{1}{4}$	$1\text{-}4\frac{9}{16}$
$\frac{1}{16}$	$3\frac{7}{32}$	$1\text{-}0\frac{15}{32}$	$3\frac{15}{32}$	$1\text{-}1\frac{1}{2}$	$3\frac{3}{4}$	$1\text{-}2\frac{9}{16}$	4	$1\text{-}3\frac{19}{32}$	$4\frac{9}{32}$	$1\text{-}4\frac{5}{8}$
$\frac{1}{8}$	$3\frac{7}{32}$	$1\text{-}0\frac{17}{32}$	$3\frac{1}{2}$	$1\text{-}1\frac{19}{32}$	$3\frac{3}{4}$	$1\text{-}2\frac{5}{8}$	$4\frac{1}{32}$	$1\text{-}3\frac{21}{32}$	$4\frac{9}{32}$	$1\text{-}4\frac{11}{16}$
$\frac{3}{16}$	$3\frac{1}{4}$	$1\text{-}0\frac{5}{8}$	$3\frac{1}{2}$	$1\text{-}1\frac{21}{32}$	$3\frac{25}{32}$	$1\text{-}2\frac{11}{16}$	$4\frac{1}{32}$	$1\text{-}3\frac{23}{32}$	$4\frac{5}{16}$	$1\text{-}4\frac{3}{4}$
$\frac{1}{4}$	$3\frac{1}{4}$	$1\text{-}0\frac{11}{16}$	$3\frac{17}{32}$	$1\text{-}1\frac{23}{32}$	$3\frac{25}{32}$	$1\text{-}2\frac{3}{4}$	$4\frac{1}{16}$	$1\text{-}3\frac{25}{32}$	$4\frac{5}{16}$	$1\text{-}4\frac{13}{16}$
$\frac{5}{16}$	$3\frac{9}{32}$	$1\text{-}0\frac{3}{4}$	$3\frac{17}{32}$	$1\text{-}1\frac{25}{32}$	$3\frac{13}{16}$	$1\text{-}2\frac{13}{16}$	$4\frac{1}{16}$	$1\text{-}3\frac{27}{32}$	$4\frac{11}{32}$	$1\text{-}4\frac{7}{8}$
$\frac{3}{8}$	$3\frac{9}{32}$	$1\text{-}0\frac{13}{16}$	$3\frac{9}{16}$	$1\text{-}1\frac{27}{32}$	$3\frac{13}{16}$	$1\text{-}2\frac{7}{8}$	$4\frac{3}{32}$	$1\text{-}3\frac{29}{32}$	$4\frac{11}{32}$	$1\text{-}4\frac{15}{16}$
$\frac{7}{16}$	$3\frac{5}{16}$	$1\text{-}0\frac{7}{8}$	$3\frac{9}{16}$	$1\text{-}1\frac{29}{32}$	$3\frac{27}{32}$	$1\text{-}2\frac{15}{16}$	$4\frac{3}{32}$	$1\text{-}3\frac{31}{32}$	$4\frac{3}{8}$	$1\text{-}5$
$\frac{1}{2}$	$3\frac{5}{16}$	$1\text{-}0\frac{15}{32}$	$3\frac{19}{32}$	$1\text{-}1\frac{31}{32}$	$3\frac{27}{32}$	$1\text{-}3$	$4\frac{1}{8}$	$1\text{-}4\frac{1}{32}$	$4\frac{3}{8}$	$1\text{-}5\frac{1}{16}$
$\frac{9}{16}$	$3\frac{11}{32}$	$1\text{-}1$	$3\frac{19}{32}$	$1\text{-}2\frac{1}{32}$	$3\frac{7}{8}$	$1\text{-}3\frac{1}{32}$	$4\frac{1}{8}$	$1\text{-}4\frac{3}{32}$	$4\frac{13}{32}$	$1\text{-}5\frac{1}{8}$
$\frac{5}{8}$	$3\frac{11}{32}$	$1\text{-}1\frac{1}{16}$	$3\frac{5}{8}$	$1\text{-}2\frac{3}{32}$	$3\frac{7}{8}$	$1\text{-}3\frac{1}{8}$	$4\frac{5}{32}$	$1\text{-}4\frac{5}{32}$	$4\frac{13}{32}$	$1\text{-}5\frac{3}{16}$
$\frac{11}{16}$	$3\frac{3}{8}$	$1\text{-}1\frac{1}{8}$	$3\frac{5}{8}$	$1\text{-}2\frac{5}{32}$	$3\frac{29}{32}$	$1\text{-}3\frac{3}{16}$	$4\frac{5}{32}$	$1\text{-}4\frac{7}{32}$	$4\frac{7}{16}$	$1\text{-}5\frac{5}{32}$
$\frac{3}{4}$	$3\frac{3}{8}$	$1\text{-}1\frac{3}{16}$	$3\frac{21}{32}$	$1\text{-}2\frac{7}{32}$	$3\frac{29}{32}$	$1\text{-}3\frac{1}{4}$	$4\frac{3}{16}$	$1\text{-}4\frac{9}{32}$	$4\frac{7}{16}$	$1\text{-}5\frac{11}{32}$
$\frac{13}{16}$	$3\frac{13}{32}$	$1\text{-}1\frac{1}{4}$	$3\frac{21}{32}$	$1\text{-}2\frac{9}{32}$	$3\frac{15}{16}$	$1\text{-}3\frac{5}{16}$	$4\frac{3}{16}$	$1\text{-}4\frac{3}{8}$	$4\frac{15}{32}$	$1\text{-}5\frac{13}{32}$
$\frac{7}{8}$	$3\frac{13}{32}$	$1\text{-}1\frac{5}{16}$	$3\frac{11}{16}$	$1\text{-}2\frac{11}{32}$	$3\frac{15}{16}$	$1\text{-}3\frac{13}{32}$	$4\frac{7}{32}$	$1\text{-}4\frac{7}{16}$	$4\frac{15}{32}$	$1\text{-}5\frac{15}{32}$
$\frac{15}{16}$	$3\frac{7}{16}$	$1\text{-}1\frac{3}{8}$	$3\frac{11}{16}$	$1\text{-}2\frac{13}{32}$	$3\frac{31}{32}$	$1\text{-}3\frac{15}{32}$	$4\frac{7}{32}$	$1\text{-}4\frac{1}{2}$	$4\frac{1}{2}$	$1\text{-}5\frac{17}{32}$

In.	17″ Rise	17″ Slope	18″ Rise	18″ Slope	19″ Rise	19″ Slope	20″ Rise	20″ Slope	21″ Rise	21″ Slope
0	$4\frac{1}{2}$	$1\text{-}5\frac{19}{32}$	$4\frac{25}{32}$	$1\text{-}6\frac{5}{8}$	$5\frac{1}{16}$	$1\text{-}7\frac{21}{32}$	$5\frac{5}{16}$	$1\text{-}8\frac{11}{16}$	$5\frac{9}{16}$	$1\text{-}9\frac{23}{32}$
$\frac{1}{16}$	$4\frac{17}{32}$	$1\text{-}5\frac{21}{32}$	$4\frac{13}{16}$	$1\text{-}6\frac{11}{16}$	$5\frac{1}{16}$	$1\text{-}7\frac{23}{32}$	$5\frac{11}{32}$	$1\text{-}8\frac{3}{4}$	$5\frac{19}{32}$	$1\text{-}9\frac{25}{32}$
$\frac{1}{8}$	$4\frac{9}{16}$	$1\text{-}5\frac{23}{32}$	$4\frac{13}{16}$	$1\text{-}6\frac{3}{4}$	$5\frac{3}{32}$	$1\text{-}7\frac{25}{32}$	$5\frac{11}{32}$	$1\text{-}8\frac{13}{16}$	$5\frac{5}{8}$	$1\text{-}9\frac{27}{32}$
$\frac{3}{16}$	$4\frac{9}{16}$	$1\text{-}5\frac{25}{32}$	$4\frac{27}{32}$	$1\text{-}6\frac{13}{16}$	$5\frac{3}{32}$	$1\text{-}7\frac{27}{32}$	$5\frac{3}{8}$	$1\text{-}8\frac{7}{8}$	$5\frac{5}{8}$	$1\text{-}9\frac{15}{16}$
$\frac{1}{4}$	$4\frac{19}{32}$	$1\text{-}5\frac{27}{32}$	$4\frac{27}{32}$	$1\text{-}6\frac{7}{8}$	$5\frac{1}{8}$	$1\text{-}7\frac{29}{32}$	$5\frac{3}{8}$	$1\text{-}8\frac{15}{16}$	$5\frac{21}{32}$	$1\text{-}10$
$\frac{5}{16}$	$4\frac{19}{32}$	$1\text{-}5\frac{29}{32}$	$4\frac{7}{8}$	$1\text{-}6\frac{15}{16}$	$5\frac{1}{8}$	$1\text{-}7\frac{31}{32}$	$5\frac{13}{32}$	$1\text{-}9\frac{1}{32}$	$5\frac{21}{32}$	$1\text{-}10\frac{1}{16}$
$\frac{3}{8}$	$4\frac{5}{8}$	$1\text{-}5\frac{31}{32}$	$4\frac{7}{8}$	$1\text{-}7$	$5\frac{5}{32}$	$1\text{-}8\frac{1}{2}$	$5\frac{13}{32}$	$1\text{-}9\frac{3}{32}$	$5\frac{11}{16}$	$1\text{-}10\frac{1}{8}$
$\frac{7}{16}$	$4\frac{5}{8}$	$1\text{-}6\frac{1}{32}$	$4\frac{29}{32}$	$1\text{-}7\frac{1}{16}$	$5\frac{5}{32}$	$1\text{-}8\frac{1}{8}$	$5\frac{7}{16}$	$1\text{-}9\frac{5}{32}$	$5\frac{11}{16}$	$1\text{-}10\frac{3}{32}$
$\frac{1}{2}$	$4\frac{21}{32}$	$1\text{-}6\frac{3}{32}$	$4\frac{29}{32}$	$1\text{-}7\frac{5}{32}$	$5\frac{3}{16}$	$1\text{-}8\frac{3}{32}$	$5\frac{7}{16}$	$1\text{-}9\frac{7}{32}$	$5\frac{23}{32}$	$1\text{-}10\frac{1}{4}$
$\frac{9}{16}$	$4\frac{21}{32}$	$1\text{-}6\frac{5}{32}$	$4\frac{15}{16}$	$1\text{-}7\frac{7}{32}$	$5\frac{3}{16}$	$1\text{-}8\frac{1}{4}$	$5\frac{15}{32}$	$1\text{-}9\frac{9}{32}$	$5\frac{23}{32}$	$1\text{-}10\frac{5}{16}$
$\frac{5}{8}$	$4\frac{11}{16}$	$1\text{-}6\frac{1}{4}$	$4\frac{15}{16}$	$1\text{-}7\frac{9}{32}$	$5\frac{7}{32}$	$1\text{-}8\frac{5}{16}$	$5\frac{15}{32}$	$1\text{-}9\frac{11}{32}$	$5\frac{3}{4}$	$1\text{-}10\frac{3}{8}$
$\frac{11}{16}$	$4\frac{11}{16}$	$1\text{-}6\frac{5}{16}$	$4\frac{31}{32}$	$1\text{-}7\frac{11}{32}$	$5\frac{7}{32}$	$1\text{-}8\frac{3}{8}$	$5\frac{1}{2}$	$1\text{-}9\frac{13}{32}$	$5\frac{3}{4}$	$1\text{-}10\frac{7}{16}$
$\frac{3}{4}$	$4\frac{23}{32}$	$1\text{-}6\frac{3}{8}$	$4\frac{31}{32}$	$1\text{-}7\frac{13}{32}$	$5\frac{1}{4}$	$1\text{-}8\frac{7}{16}$	$5\frac{1}{2}$	$1\text{-}9\frac{15}{32}$	$5\frac{25}{32}$	$1\text{-}10\frac{1}{2}$
$\frac{13}{16}$	$4\frac{23}{32}$	$1\text{-}6\frac{7}{16}$	5	$1\text{-}7\frac{15}{32}$	$5\frac{1}{4}$	$1\text{-}8\frac{1}{2}$	$5\frac{17}{32}$	$1\text{-}9\frac{17}{32}$	$5\frac{25}{32}$	$1\text{-}10\frac{9}{16}$
$\frac{7}{8}$	$4\frac{3}{4}$	$1\text{-}6\frac{1}{2}$	5	$1\text{-}7\frac{17}{32}$	$5\frac{9}{32}$	$1\text{-}8\frac{9}{16}$	$5\frac{17}{32}$	$1\text{-}9\frac{19}{32}$	$5\frac{13}{16}$	$1\text{-}10\frac{5}{8}$
$\frac{15}{16}$	$4\frac{3}{4}$	$1\text{-}6\frac{9}{16}$	$5\frac{1}{32}$	$1\text{-}7\frac{19}{32}$	$5\frac{9}{32}$	$1\text{-}8\frac{5}{8}$	$5\frac{9}{16}$	$1\text{-}9\frac{21}{32}$	$5\frac{13}{16}$	$1\text{-}10\frac{11}{16}$

Feet	40′ Rise	40′ Slope	50′ Rise	50′ Slope	60′ Rise	60′ Slope	70′ Rise	70′ Slope
0	$10\text{-}7\frac{1}{2}$	$41\text{-}4\frac{21}{32}$	$13\text{-}3\frac{3}{8}$	$51\text{-}8\frac{13}{16}$	$15\text{-}11\frac{1}{4}$	$62\text{-}0\frac{31}{32}$	$18\text{-}7\frac{1}{8}$	$72\text{-}5\frac{1}{8}$
1	$10\text{-}10\frac{11}{16}$	$42\text{-}5\frac{1}{16}$	$13\text{-}6\frac{9}{16}$	$52\text{-}9\frac{7}{32}$	$16\text{-}2\frac{7}{16}$	$63\text{-}1\frac{3}{8}$	$18\text{-}10\frac{5}{16}$	$73\text{-}5\frac{17}{32}$
2	$11\text{-}1\frac{7}{8}$	$43\text{-}5\frac{15}{32}$	$13\text{-}9\frac{3}{4}$	$53\text{-}9\frac{5}{8}$	$16\text{-}5\frac{5}{8}$	$64\text{-}1\frac{13}{16}$	$19\text{-}1\frac{1}{2}$	$74\text{-}5\frac{31}{32}$
3	$11\text{-}5\frac{1}{16}$	$44\text{-}5\frac{29}{32}$	$14\text{-}0\frac{15}{16}$	$54\text{-}10\frac{1}{16}$	$16\text{-}8\frac{13}{16}$	$65\text{-}2\frac{7}{32}$	$19\text{-}4\frac{11}{16}$	$75\text{-}6\frac{3}{8}$
4	$11\text{-}8\frac{1}{4}$	$45\text{-}6\frac{5}{16}$	$14\text{-}4\frac{1}{8}$	$55\text{-}10\frac{15}{32}$	$17\text{-}0$	$66\text{-}2\frac{5}{8}$	$19\text{-}7\frac{7}{8}$	$76\text{-}6\frac{25}{32}$
5	$11\text{-}11\frac{7}{16}$	$46\text{-}6\frac{23}{32}$	$14\text{-}7\frac{5}{16}$	$56\text{-}10\frac{7}{8}$	$17\text{-}3\frac{3}{16}$	$67\text{-}3\frac{1}{16}$	$19\text{-}11\frac{1}{16}$	$77\text{-}7\frac{1}{32}$
6	$12\text{-}2\frac{5}{8}$	$47\text{-}7\frac{5}{32}$	$14\text{-}10\frac{1}{2}$	$57\text{-}11\frac{5}{16}$	$17\text{-}6\frac{3}{8}$	$68\text{-}3\frac{15}{32}$	$20\text{-}2\frac{1}{4}$	$78\text{-}7\frac{5}{8}$
7	$12\text{-}5\frac{13}{16}$	$48\text{-}7\frac{9}{16}$	$15\text{-}1\frac{11}{16}$	$58\text{-}11\frac{23}{32}$	$17\text{-}9\frac{9}{16}$	$69\text{-}3\frac{7}{8}$	$20\text{-}5\frac{7}{16}$	$79\text{-}8\frac{1}{32}$
8	$12\text{-}9$	$49\text{-}7\frac{31}{32}$	$15\text{-}4\frac{7}{8}$	$60\text{-}0\frac{1}{8}$	$18\text{-}0\frac{3}{4}$	$70\text{-}4\frac{9}{32}$	$20\text{-}8\frac{5}{8}$	$80\text{-}8\frac{15}{32}$
9	$13\text{-}0\frac{3}{16}$	$50\text{-}8\frac{3}{8}$	$15\text{-}8\frac{1}{16}$	$61\text{-}0\frac{9}{16}$	$18\text{-}3\frac{15}{16}$	$71\text{-}4\frac{23}{32}$	$20\text{-}11\frac{13}{16}$	$81\text{-}8\frac{7}{8}$

natsin A=0.2567226118; natcos A=0.9664851269; nattan A=0.2656250000; natcot A=3.7647058823

Inches	0" Rise	0" Slope	1" Rise	1" Slope	2" Rise	2" Slope	3" Rise	3" Slope	4" Rise	4" Slope	5" Rise	5" Slope
0	0	0	9/32	1 1/32	17/32	2 1/16	13/16	3 3/32	1 3/32	4 5/32	1 11/32	5 3/16
1/16	1/32	1/16	9/32	1 3/32	9/16	2 1/8	27/32	3 3/16	1 3/32	4 7/32	1 3/8	5 1/4
1/8	1/32	1/8	5/16	1 5/32	9/16	2 3/16	27/32	3 1/4	1 1/8	4 9/32	1 3/8	5 5/16
3/16	3/32	3/16	5/16	1 7/32	19/32	2 9/32	7/8	3 5/16	1 1/8	4 11/32	1 13/32	5 3/8
1/4	1/16	1/4	11/32	1 9/32	5/8	2 11/32	7/8	3 3/8	1 5/32	4 13/32	1 7/16	5 7/16
5/16	3/32	5/16	11/32	1 3/8	5/8	2 13/32	29/32	3 7/16	1 5/32	4 15/32	1 7/16	5 1/2
3/8	3/32	3/8	3/8	1 7/16	21/32	2 15/32	29/32	3 1/2	1 3/16	4 17/32	1 15/32	5 9/16
7/16	1/8	7/16	3/8	1 1/2	21/32	2 17/32	15/16	3 9/16	1 3/16	4 19/32	1 15/32	5 5/8
1/2	1/8	17/32	13/32	1 9/16	11/16	2 19/32	15/16	3 5/8	1 7/32	4 21/32	1 1/2	5 11/16
9/16	5/32	19/32	7/16	1 5/8	11/16	2 21/32	31/32	3 11/16	1 1/4	4 23/32	1 1/2	5 3/4
5/8	5/32	21/32	7/16	1 11/16	23/32	2 23/32	31/32	3 3/4	1 1/4	4 25/32	1 17/32	5 13/16
11/16	3/16	23/32	15/32	1 3/4	23/32	2 25/32	1	3 13/16	1 9/32	4 27/32	1 17/32	5 29/32
3/4	3/16	25/32	15/32	1 13/16	3/4	2 27/32	1	3 7/8	1 9/32	4 29/32	1 9/16	5 31/32
13/16	7/32	27/32	1/2	1 7/8	3/4	2 29/32	1 1/32	3 15/16	1 5/16	5	1 9/16	6 1/32
7/8	1/4	29/32	1/2	1 15/16	25/32	2 31/32	1 1/16	4	1 5/16	5 1/16	1 19/32	6 3/32
15/16	1/4	31/32	17/32	2	25/32	2 31/32	1 1/16	4 3/32	1 11/32	5 1/8	1 19/32	6 5/32

Inches	6" Rise	6" Slope	7" Rise	7" Slope	8" Rise	8" Slope	9" Rise	9" Slope	10" Rise	10" Slope	11" Rise	11" Slope
0	1 5/8	6 7/32	1 29/32	7 1/4	2 5/32	8 9/32	2 7/16	9 5/16	2 23/32	10 3/8	2 31/32	11 13/32
1/16	1 21/32	6 9/32	1 29/32	7 5/16	2 3/16	8 11/32	2 15/32	9 3/8	2 23/32	10 7/16	3	11 15/32
1/8	1 21/32	6 11/32	1 15/16	7 3/8	2 3/16	8 13/32	2 15/32	9 15/32	2 3/4	10 1/2	3	11 17/32
3/16	1 11/16	6 13/32	1 15/16	7 7/16	2 7/32	8 15/32	2 1/2	9 17/32	2 3/4	10 9/16	3 1/32	11 19/32
1/4	1 11/16	6 15/32	1 31/32	7 1/2	2 1/4	8 9/16	2 1/2	9 19/32	2 25/32	10 5/8	3 1/16	11 21/32
5/16	1 23/32	6 17/32	1 31/32	7 9/16	2 1/4	8 5/8	2 17/32	9 21/32	2 25/32	10 11/16	3 1/16	11 23/32
3/8	1 23/32	6 19/32	2	7 21/32	2 9/32	8 11/16	2 17/32	9 23/32	2 13/16	10 3/4	3 3/32	11 25/32
7/16	1 3/4	6 21/32	2	7 23/32	2 9/32	8 3/4	2 9/16	9 25/32	2 13/16	10 13/16	3 3/32	11 27/32
1/2	1 3/4	6 23/32	2 1/32	7 25/32	2 5/16	8 13/16	2 9/16	9 27/32	2 7/8	10 7/8	3 1/8	11 29/32
9/16	1 25/32	6 13/16	2 1/16	7 27/32	2 5/16	8 7/8	2 19/32	9 29/32	2 7/8	10 15/16	3 1/8	11 31/32
5/8	1 25/32	6 7/8	2 1/16	7 29/32	2 11/32	8 15/16	2 19/32	9 31/32	2 7/8	11	3 5/32	1-0 1/32
11/16	1 13/16	6 15/16	2 3/32	7 31/32	2 11/32	9	2 5/8	10 1/32	2 29/32	11 1/16	3 5/32	1-0 3/32
3/4	1 13/16	7	2 3/32	8 1/32	2 3/8	9 1/16	2 5/8	10 3/32	2 29/32	11 1/8	3 3/16	1-0 3/32
13/16	1 27/32	7 1/16	2 1/8	8 3/32	2 3/8	9 1/8	2 21/32	10 5/32	2 15/16	11 3/16	3 3/16	1-0 1/4
7/8	1 7/8	7 1/8	2 1/8	8 5/32	2 13/32	9 3/16	2 11/16	10 7/32	2 15/16	11 9/32	3 7/32	1-0 5/16
15/16	1 7/8	7 3/16	2 5/32	8 7/32	2 13/32	9 1/4	2 11/16	10 9/32	2 31/32	11 11/32	3 7/32	1-0 3/8

Feet	0' Rise	0' Slope	10' Rise	10' Slope	20' Rise	20' Slope	30' Rise	30' Slope
0	0	0	2-8 1/2	10-4 5/16	5-5	20-8 21/32	8-1 1/2	31-0 31/32
1	3 1/4	1-0 7/16	2-11 3/4	11-4 3/4	5-8 1/4	21-9 3/32	8-4 3/4	32-1 13/32
2	6 1/2	2-0 7/8	3-3	12-5 3/16	5-11 1/2	22-9 1/2	8-8	33-1 27/32
3	9 3/4	3-1 5/16	3-6 1/4	13-5 5/8	6-2 3/4	23-9 15/16	8-11 1/4	34-2 9/32
4	1-1	4-1 23/32	3-9 1/2	14-6 1/16	6-6	24-10 3/8	9-2 1/2	35-2 11/16
5	1-4 1/4	5-2 5/32	4-0 3/4	15-6 1/2	6-9 1/4	25-10 13/16	9-5 3/4	36-3 1/8
6	1-7 1/2	6-2 19/32	4-4	16-6 29/32	7-0 1/2	26-11 1/4	9-9	37-3 9/16
7	1-10 3/4	7-3 1/32	4-7 1/4	17-7 11/32	7-3 3/4	27-11 11/16	10-0 1/4	38-4
8	2-2	8-3 15/32	4-10 1/2	18-7 25/32	7-7	29-0 3/32	10-3 1/2	39-4 7/16
9	2-5 1/4	9-3 29/32	5-1 3/4	19-8 7/32	7-10 1/4	30-0 17/32	10-6 3/4	40-4 7/8

A = 15° 09' 15"; logsin A = 9.41733; logcos A = 9 98463; logtan A = 9.43270; logcot A = 0.56730

Ins.	12″ Rise	12″ Slope	13″ Rise	13″ Slope	14″ Rise	14″ Slope	15″ Rise	15″ Slope	16″ Rise	16″ Slope
0	$3\frac14$	$1\text{-}0\frac{7}{16}$	$3\frac{17}{32}$	$1\text{-}1\frac{15}{32}$	$3\frac{25}{32}$	$1\text{-}2\frac12$	$4\frac{1}{16}$	$1\text{-}3\frac{17}{32}$	$4\frac{11}{32}$	$1\text{-}4\frac{9}{16}$
$\frac{1}{16}$	$3\frac{9}{32}$	$1\text{-}0\frac12$	$3\frac{17}{32}$	$1\text{-}1\frac{17}{32}$	$3\frac{13}{16}$	$1\text{-}2\frac{9}{16}$	$4\frac{3}{32}$	$1\text{-}3\frac{19}{32}$	$4\frac{11}{32}$	$1\text{-}4\frac{21}{32}$
$\frac18$	$3\frac{9}{32}$	$1\text{-}0\frac{9}{16}$	$3\frac{9}{16}$	$1\text{-}1\frac{19}{32}$	$3\frac{13}{16}$	$1\text{-}2\frac58$	$4\frac{3}{32}$	$1\text{-}3\frac{21}{32}$	$4\frac38$	$1\text{-}4\frac{23}{32}$
$\frac{3}{16}$	$3\frac{5}{16}$	$1\text{-}0\frac58$	$3\frac{9}{16}$	$1\text{-}1\frac{21}{32}$	$3\frac{27}{32}$	$1\text{-}2\frac{11}{16}$	$4\frac18$	$1\text{-}3\frac34$	$4\frac38$	$1\text{-}4\frac{25}{32}$
$\frac14$	$3\frac{5}{16}$	$1\text{-}0\frac{11}{16}$	$3\frac{19}{32}$	$1\text{-}1\frac{23}{32}$	$3\frac78$	$1\text{-}2\frac34$	$4\frac18$	$1\text{-}3\frac{13}{16}$	$4\frac{13}{32}$	$1\text{-}4\frac{27}{32}$
$\frac{5}{16}$	$3\frac{11}{32}$	$1\text{-}0\frac34$	$3\frac{19}{32}$	$1\text{-}1\frac{25}{32}$	$3\frac78$	$1\text{-}2\frac{27}{32}$	$4\frac{5}{32}$	$1\text{-}3\frac78$	$4\frac{13}{32}$	$1\text{-}4\frac{29}{32}$
$\frac38$	$3\frac{11}{32}$	$1\text{-}0\frac{13}{16}$	$3\frac58$	$1\text{-}1\frac{27}{32}$	$3\frac{29}{32}$	$1\text{-}2\frac{29}{32}$	$4\frac{5}{32}$	$1\text{-}3\frac{15}{16}$	$4\frac{7}{16}$	$1\text{-}4\frac{31}{32}$
$\frac{7}{16}$	$3\frac38$	$1\text{-}0\frac78$	$3\frac58$	$1\text{-}1\frac{29}{32}$	$3\frac{29}{32}$	$1\text{-}2\frac{31}{32}$	$4\frac{3}{16}$	$1\text{-}4$	$4\frac{7}{16}$	$1\text{-}5\frac{1}{32}$
$\frac12$	$3\frac38$	$1\text{-}0\frac{15}{16}$	$3\frac{21}{32}$	$1\text{-}2$	$3\frac{15}{16}$	$1\text{-}3\frac{1}{32}$	$4\frac{3}{16}$	$1\text{-}4\frac{1}{16}$	$4\frac{15}{32}$	$1\text{-}5\frac{3}{32}$
$\frac{9}{16}$	$3\frac{13}{32}$	$1\text{-}1$	$3\frac{11}{16}$	$1\text{-}2\frac{1}{16}$	$3\frac{15}{16}$	$1\text{-}3\frac{3}{32}$	$4\frac{7}{32}$	$1\text{-}4\frac18$	$4\frac12$	$1\text{-}5\frac{5}{32}$
$\frac58$	$3\frac{13}{32}$	$1\text{-}1\frac{3}{32}$	$3\frac{11}{16}$	$1\text{-}2\frac18$	$3\frac{31}{32}$	$1\text{-}3\frac{5}{32}$	$4\frac{7}{32}$	$1\text{-}4\frac{3}{16}$	$4\frac12$	$1\text{-}5\frac{7}{32}$
$\frac{11}{16}$	$3\frac{7}{16}$	$1\text{-}1\frac{5}{32}$	$3\frac{23}{32}$	$1\text{-}2\frac{3}{16}$	$3\frac{31}{32}$	$1\text{-}3\frac{7}{32}$	$4\frac14$	$1\text{-}4\frac14$	$4\frac{17}{32}$	$1\text{-}5\frac{9}{32}$
$\frac34$	$3\frac{7}{16}$	$1\text{-}1\frac{7}{32}$	$3\frac{23}{32}$	$1\text{-}2\frac14$	4	$1\text{-}3\frac{9}{32}$	$4\frac14$	$1\text{-}4\frac{5}{16}$	$4\frac{17}{32}$	$1\text{-}5\frac{11}{32}$
$\frac{13}{16}$	$3\frac{15}{32}$	$1\text{-}1\frac{9}{32}$	$3\frac34$	$1\text{-}2\frac{5}{16}$	4	$1\text{-}3\frac{11}{32}$	$4\frac{9}{32}$	$1\text{-}4\frac38$	$4\frac{9}{16}$	$1\text{-}5\frac{13}{32}$
$\frac78$	$3\frac12$	$1\text{-}1\frac{11}{32}$	$3\frac34$	$1\text{-}2\frac38$	$4\frac{1}{32}$	$1\text{-}3\frac{13}{32}$	$4\frac{5}{16}$	$1\text{-}4\frac{7}{16}$	$4\frac{9}{16}$	$1\text{-}5\frac{15}{32}$
$\frac{15}{16}$	$3\frac12$	$1\text{-}1\frac{13}{32}$	$3\frac{25}{32}$	$1\text{-}2\frac{7}{16}$	$4\frac{1}{32}$	$1\text{-}3\frac{15}{32}$	$4\frac{5}{16}$	$1\text{-}4\frac12$	$4\frac{19}{32}$	$1\text{-}5\frac{9}{16}$

Ins.	17″ Rise	17″ Slope	18″ Rise	18″ Slope	19″ Rise	19″ Slope	20″ Rise	20″ Slope	21″ Rise	21″ Slope
0	$4\frac{19}{32}$	$1\text{-}5\frac58$	$4\frac78$	$1\text{-}6\frac{21}{32}$	$5\frac{3}{32}$	$1\text{-}7\frac{11}{16}$	$5\frac{13}{32}$	$1\text{-}8\frac{23}{32}$	$5\frac{11}{16}$	$1\text{-}9\frac34$
$\frac{1}{16}$	$4\frac58$	$1\text{-}5\frac{11}{16}$	$4\frac{29}{32}$	$1\text{-}6\frac{23}{32}$	$5\frac{3}{32}$	$1\text{-}7\frac34$	$5\frac{7}{16}$	$1\text{-}8\frac{25}{32}$	$5\frac{23}{32}$	$1\text{-}9\frac{13}{16}$
$\frac18$	$4\frac58$	$1\text{-}5\frac34$	$4\frac{29}{32}$	$1\text{-}6\frac{25}{32}$	$5\frac{3}{16}$	$1\text{-}7\frac{13}{16}$	$5\frac{7}{16}$	$1\text{-}8\frac{27}{32}$	$5\frac{23}{32}$	$1\text{-}9\frac78$
$\frac{3}{16}$	$4\frac{21}{32}$	$1\text{-}5\frac{13}{16}$	$4\frac{15}{16}$	$1\text{-}6\frac{27}{32}$	$5\frac{3}{16}$	$1\text{-}7\frac78$	$5\frac{15}{32}$	$1\text{-}8\frac{29}{32}$	$5\frac34$	$1\text{-}9\frac{15}{16}$
$\frac14$	$4\frac{11}{16}$	$1\text{-}5\frac78$	$4\frac{15}{16}$	$1\text{-}6\frac{29}{32}$	$5\frac{7}{32}$	$1\text{-}7\frac{15}{16}$	$5\frac12$	$1\text{-}8\frac{31}{32}$	$5\frac34$	$1\text{-}10$
$\frac{5}{16}$	$4\frac{11}{16}$	$1\text{-}5\frac{15}{16}$	$4\frac{31}{32}$	$1\text{-}6\frac{31}{32}$	$5\frac{7}{32}$	$1\text{-}8$	$5\frac12$	$1\text{-}9\frac{1}{32}$	$5\frac{25}{32}$	$1\text{-}10\frac{3}{32}$
$\frac38$	$4\frac{23}{32}$	$1\text{-}6$	$4\frac{31}{32}$	$1\text{-}7\frac{1}{32}$	$5\frac14$	$1\text{-}8\frac{1}{16}$	$5\frac{17}{32}$	$1\text{-}9\frac{3}{32}$	$5\frac{25}{32}$	$1\text{-}10\frac{5}{32}$
$\frac{7}{16}$	$4\frac{23}{32}$	$1\text{-}6\frac{1}{16}$	5	$1\text{-}7\frac{3}{32}$	$5\frac14$	$1\text{-}8\frac18$	$5\frac{17}{32}$	$1\text{-}9\frac{3}{16}$	$5\frac{13}{16}$	$1\text{-}10\frac{7}{32}$
$\frac12$	$4\frac34$	$1\text{-}6\frac18$	5	$1\text{-}7\frac{5}{32}$	$5\frac{9}{32}$	$1\text{-}8\frac{3}{16}$	$5\frac{9}{16}$	$1\text{-}9\frac14$	$5\frac{13}{16}$	$1\text{-}10\frac{9}{32}$
$\frac{9}{16}$	$4\frac34$	$1\text{-}6\frac{3}{16}$	$5\frac{1}{32}$	$1\text{-}7\frac{7}{32}$	$5\frac{5}{16}$	$1\text{-}8\frac{9}{32}$	$5\frac{9}{16}$	$1\text{-}9\frac{5}{16}$	$5\frac{27}{32}$	$1\text{-}10\frac{11}{32}$
$\frac58$	$4\frac{25}{32}$	$1\text{-}6\frac14$	$5\frac{1}{32}$	$1\text{-}7\frac{9}{32}$	$5\frac{5}{16}$	$1\text{-}8\frac{11}{32}$	$5\frac{19}{32}$	$1\text{-}9\frac38$	$5\frac{27}{32}$	$1\text{-}10\frac{13}{32}$
$\frac{11}{16}$	$4\frac{25}{32}$	$1\text{-}6\frac{5}{16}$	$5\frac{1}{16}$	$1\text{-}7\frac38$	$5\frac{11}{32}$	$1\text{-}8\frac{13}{32}$	$5\frac{19}{32}$	$1\text{-}9\frac{7}{16}$	$5\frac78$	$1\text{-}10\frac{15}{32}$
$\frac34$	$4\frac{13}{16}$	$1\text{-}6\frac38$	$5\frac{1}{16}$	$1\text{-}7\frac{7}{16}$	$5\frac{11}{32}$	$1\text{-}8\frac{15}{32}$	$5\frac58$	$1\text{-}9\frac12$	$5\frac78$	$1\text{-}10\frac{17}{32}$
$\frac{13}{16}$	$4\frac{13}{16}$	$1\text{-}6\frac{15}{32}$	$5\frac{3}{32}$	$1\text{-}7\frac12$	$5\frac38$	$1\text{-}8\frac{17}{32}$	$5\frac58$	$1\text{-}9\frac{9}{16}$	$5\frac{29}{32}$	$1\text{-}10\frac{19}{32}$
$\frac78$	$4\frac{27}{32}$	$1\text{-}6\frac{17}{32}$	$5\frac18$	$1\text{-}7\frac{9}{16}$	$5\frac38$	$1\text{-}8\frac{19}{32}$	$5\frac{21}{32}$	$1\text{-}9\frac58$	$5\frac{15}{16}$	$1\text{-}10\frac{21}{32}$
$\frac{15}{16}$	$4\frac{27}{32}$	$1\text{-}6\frac{19}{32}$	$5\frac18$	$1\text{-}7\frac58$	$5\frac{13}{32}$	$1\text{-}8\frac{21}{32}$	$5\frac{21}{32}$	$1\text{-}9\frac{11}{16}$	$5\frac{15}{16}$	$1\text{-}10\frac{23}{32}$

Feet	40′ Rise	40′ Slope	50′ Rise	50′ Slope	60′ Rise	60′ Slope	70′ Rise	70′ Slope
0	10-10	$41\text{-}5\frac38$	$13\text{-}6\frac12$	$51\text{-}9\frac58$	16-3	$62\text{-}1\frac{15}{16}$	$18\text{-}11\frac12$	$72\text{-}6\frac14$
1	$11\text{-}1\frac14$	$42\text{-}5\frac{23}{32}$	$13\text{-}9\frac34$	$52\text{-}10\frac{1}{16}$	$16\text{-}6\frac14$	$63\text{-}2\frac38$	$19\text{-}2\frac34$	$73\text{-}6\frac{11}{16}$
2	$11\text{-}4\frac12$	$43\text{-}6\frac{5}{32}$	14-1	$53\text{-}10\frac{15}{32}$	$16\text{-}9\frac12$	$64\text{-}2\frac{13}{16}$	19-6	$74\text{-}7\frac18$
3	$11\text{-}7\frac34$	$44\text{-}6\frac{19}{32}$	$14\text{-}4\frac14$	$54\text{-}10\frac{29}{32}$	$17\text{-}0\frac34$	$65\text{-}3\frac14$	$19\text{-}9\frac14$	$75\text{-}7\frac{9}{16}$
4	11-11	$45\text{-}7\frac{1}{32}$	$14\text{-}7\frac12$	$55\text{-}11\frac{11}{32}$	17-4	$66\text{-}3\frac{21}{32}$	$20\text{-}0\frac12$	76-8
5	$12\text{-}2\frac14$	$46\text{-}7\frac{15}{32}$	$14\text{-}10\frac34$	$56\text{-}11\frac{25}{32}$	$17\text{-}7\frac14$	$67\text{-}4\frac{3}{32}$	$20\text{-}3\frac34$	$77\text{-}8\frac{7}{16}$
6	$12\text{-}5\frac12$	$47\text{-}7\frac78$	15-2	$58\text{-}0\frac{7}{32}$	$17\text{-}10\frac12$	$68\text{-}4\frac{17}{32}$	20-7	$78\text{-}8\frac{27}{32}$
7	$12\text{-}8\frac34$	$48\text{-}8\frac{5}{16}$	$15\text{-}5\frac14$	$59\text{-}0\frac{21}{32}$	$18\text{-}1\frac34$	$69\text{-}4\frac{31}{32}$	$20\text{-}10\frac14$	$79\text{-}9\frac{9}{32}$
8	13-0	$49\text{-}8\frac34$	$15\text{-}8\frac12$	$60\text{-}1\frac{1}{16}$	18-5	$70\text{-}5\frac{13}{32}$	$21\text{-}1\frac12$	$80\text{-}9\frac{23}{32}$
9	$13\text{-}3\frac14$	$50\text{-}9\frac{3}{16}$	$15\text{-}11\frac34$	$61\text{-}1\frac12$	$18\text{-}8\frac14$	$71\text{-}5\frac{27}{32}$	$21\text{-}4\frac34$	$81\text{-}10\frac{5}{32}$

natsin A$=0.2614154756$; natcos A$=0.9652263719$; nattan A$=0.2708333333$; natcot A$=3.6923076923$

Inches	0″ Rise	0″ Slope	1″ Rise	1″ Slope	2″ Rise	2″ Slope	3″ Rise	3″ Slope	4″ Rise	4″ Slope	5″ Rise	5″ Slope
0	0	0	9/32	1 1/2	9/16	2 1/16	13/16	3 1/8	1 3/32	4 5/32	1 3/8	5 3/16
1/16	1/32	1/16	9/32	1 13/32	9/16	2 1/8	27/32	3 3/16	1 1/8	4 7/32	1 13/32	5 1/4
1/8	1/32	1/8	5/16	1 5/32	19/32	2 7/32	7/8	3 1/4	1 1/8	4 9/32	1 13/32	5 5/16
3/16	1/16	3/16	5/16	1 7/32	19/32	2 9/32	7/8	3 5/16	1 5/32	4 11/32	1 7/16	5 3/8
1/4	1/16	1/4	11/32	1 9/32	5/8	2 11/32	29/32	3 3/8	1 3/16	4 13/32	1 7/16	5 7/16
5/16	3/32	5/16	3/8	1 3/8	5/8	2 13/32	29/32	3 7/16	1 3/16	4 15/32	1 15/32	5 1/2
3/8	3/32	3/8	3/8	1 7/16	21/32	2 15/32	15/16	3 1/2	1 7/32	4 17/32	1 15/32	5 9/16
7/16	3/32	15/32	13/32	1 1/2	11/16	2 17/32	15/16	3 9/16	1 7/32	4 19/32	1 1/2	5 21/32
1/2	1/8	17/32	13/32	1 9/16	11/16	2 19/32	31/32	3 5/8	1 1/4	4 21/32	1 17/32	5 23/32
9/16	5/32	19/32	7/16	1 5/8	23/32	2 21/32	31/32	3 11/16	1 1/4	4 23/32	1 17/32	5 25/32
5/8	3/16	21/32	7/16	1 11/16	23/32	2 23/32	1	3 3/4	1 9/32	4 13/16	1 9/16	5 27/32
11/16	3/16	23/32	15/32	1 3/4	3/4	2 25/32	1 1/32	3 13/16	1 9/32	4 7/8	1 9/16	5 29/32
3/4	7/32	25/32	15/32	1 13/16	3/4	2 27/32	1 1/16	3 7/8	1 5/16	4 15/16	1 19/32	5 31/32
13/16	7/32	27/32	1/2	1 7/8	25/32	2 29/32	1 1/16	3 31/32	1 11/32	5	1 19/32	6 1/32
7/8	1/4	29/32	17/32	1 15/16	25/32	2 31/32	1 1/16	4 1/32	1 11/32	5 1/16	1 5/8	6 3/32
15/16	1/4	31/32	17/32	2	13/16	3 1/16	1 3/32	4 3/32	1 3/8	5 1/8	1 5/8	6 5/32

Inches	6″ Rise	6″ Slope	7″ Rise	7″ Slope	8″ Rise	8″ Slope	9″ Rise	9″ Slope	10″ Rise	10″ Slope	11″ Rise	11″ Slope
0	1 21/32	6 7/32	1 15/16	7 1/4	2 7/32	8 5/16	2 1/2	9 11/32	2 3/4	10 3/8	3 1/32	11 13/32
1/16	1 11/16	6 9/32	1 15/16	7 5/16	2 7/32	8 3/8	2 1/2	9 13/32	2 25/32	10 7/16	3 1/16	11 15/32
1/8	1 11/16	6 11/32	1 31/32	7 13/32	2 1/4	8 7/16	2 17/32	9 15/32	2 25/32	10 1/2	3 1/16	11 17/32
3/16	1 23/32	6 13/32	1 31/32	7 15/32	2 1/4	8 1/2	2 17/32	9 17/32	2 13/16	10 9/16	3 3/32	11 19/32
1/4	1 23/32	6 15/32	2	7 17/32	2 9/32	8 9/16	2 9/16	9 19/32	2 27/32	10 5/8	3 3/32	11 21/32
5/16	1 3/4	6 9/16	2 1/32	7 19/32	2 9/32	8 5/8	2 9/16	9 21/32	2 27/32	10 11/16	3 1/8	11 3/4
3/8	1 3/4	6 5/8	2 1/32	7 21/32	2 5/16	8 11/16	2 19/32	9 23/32	2 7/8	10 3/4	3 1/8	11 13/16
7/16	1 25/32	6 11/16	2 1/16	7 23/32	2 11/32	8 3/4	2 19/32	9 25/32	2 7/8	10 13/16	3 5/32	11 7/8
1/2	1 25/32	6 3/4	2 1/16	7 25/32	2 11/32	8 13/16	2 5/8	9 27/32	2 29/32	10 29/32	3 3/16	11 15/16
9/16	1 13/16	6 13/16	2 3/32	7 27/32	2 3/8	8 7/8	2 5/8	9 29/32	2 29/32	10 31/32	3 3/16	1-0
5/8	1 27/32	6 7/8	2 3/32	7 29/32	2 3/8	8 15/16	2 21/32	10	2 15/16	11 1/32	3 7/32	1-0 1/16
11/16	1 27/32	6 15/16	2 1/8	7 31/32	2 13/32	9	2 11/16	10 1/16	2 15/16	11 3/32	3 7/32	1-0 1/8
3/4	1 7/8	7	2 1/8	8 1/16	2 13/32	9 1/16	2 11/16	10 1/8	2 31/32	11 5/32	3 1/4	1-0 3/16
13/16	1 7/8	7 1/16	2 5/32	8 3/32	2 7/16	9 5/32	2 23/32	10 3/16	3	11 7/32	3 1/4	1-0 1/4
7/8	1 29/32	7 1/8	2 5/32	8 5/32	2 7/16	9 7/32	2 23/32	10 1/4	3	11 9/32	3 9/32	1-0 5/16
15/16	1 29/32	7 3/16	2 3/16	8 7/32	2 15/32	9 9/32	2 3/4	10 5/16	3 1/32	11 11/32	3 9/32	1-0 3/8

Feet	0′ Rise	0′ Slope	10′ Rise	10′ Slope	20′ Rise	20′ Slope	30′ Rise	30′ Slope
0	0	0	2-9 1/8	10-4 1/2	5-6 1/4	20-8 31/32	8-3 3/8	31-1 15/32
1	3 5/16	1-0 7/16	3-0 7/16	11-4 15/32	5-9 9/16	21-9 7/16	8-6 11/16	32-1 29/32
2	6 5/8	2-0 29/32	3-3 3/4	12-5 3/8	6-0 7/8	22-9 7/8	8-10	33-2 3/8
3	9 15/16	3-1 11/32	3-7 1/16	13-5 27/32	6-4 3/16	23-10 5/16	9-1 5/16	34-2 13/16
4	1-1 1/4	4-1 25/32	3-10 3/8	14-6 9/32	6-7 1/2	24-10 25/32	9-4 5/8	35-3 1/4
5	1-4 9/16	5-2 1/4	4-1 11/16	15-6 23/32	6-10 13/16	25-11 7/32	9-7 15/16	36-3 23/32
6	1-7 7/8	6-2 11/16	4-5	16-7 3/16	7-2 1/8	26-11 21/32	9-11 1/4	37-4 5/32
7	1-11 3/16	7-3 5/32	4-8 5/16	17-7 5/8	7-5 7/16	28-0 1/8	10-2 9/16	38-4 19/32
8	2-2 1/2	8-3 19/32	4-11 5/8	18-8 3/32	7-8 3/4	29-0 9/16	10-5 7/8	39-5 1/16
9	2-5 13/16	9-4 1/32	5-2 15/16	19-8 17/32	8-0 1/16	30-1	10-9 3/16	40-5 1/2

A = 15° 25′ 54″; logsin A = 9.42503; logcos A = 9.98405; logtan A = 9.44097; logcot A = 0.55903

ins.	12″ Rise	12″ Slope	13″ Rise	13″ Slope	14″ Rise	14″ Slope	15″ Rise	15″ Slope	16″ Rise	16″ Slope
0	3 5/16	1-0 7/16	3 19/32	1-1 1/2	3 7/8	1-2 17/32	4 1/8	1-3 3/16	4 13/32	1-4 19/32
1/16	3 11/32	1-0 1/2	3 19/32	1-1 9/16	3 7/8	1-2 19/32	4 5/32	1-3 5/8	4 7/16	1-4 21/32
1/8	3 11/32	1-0 19/32	3 5/8	1-1 5/8	3 29/32	1-2 21/32	4 3/16	1-3 11/32	4 7/16	1-4 23/32
3/16	3 3/8	1-0 21/32	3 5/8	1-1 11/16	3 29/32	1-2 23/32	4 3/16	1-3 3/4	4 15/32	1-4 25/32
1/4	3 3/8	1-0 23/32	3 21/32	1-1 3/4	3 15/16	1-2 25/32	4 7/32	1-3 13/16	4 1/2	1-4 27/32
5/16	3 13/32	1-0 25/32	3 11/16	1-1 13/16	3 15/16	1-2 27/32	4 7/32	1-3 7/8	4 1/2	1-4 15/16
3/8	3 13/32	1-0 27/32	3 11/16	1-1 7/8	3 31/32	1-2 29/32	4 1/4	1-3 15/16	4 17/32	1-5
7/16	3 7/16	1-0 29/32	3 23/32	1-1 15/16	4	1-2 31/32	4 1/4	1-4	4 17/32	1-5 1/16
1/2	3 7/16	1-0 31/32	3 23/32	1-2	4	1-3 1/8	4 9/32	1-4 3/32	4 9/16	1-5 1/8
9/16	3 15/32	1-1 1/32	3 3/4	1-2 1/16	4 1/16	1-3 3/32	4 9/32	1-4 5/32	4 9/16	1-5 3/16
5/8	3 1/2	1-1 3/32	3 3/4	1-2 1/8	4 1/2	1-3 3/16	4 5/16	1-4 7/32	4 19/32	1-5 1/4
11/16	3 1/2	1-1 5/32	3 25/32	1-2 3/16	4 1/16	1-3 1/4	4 11/32	1-4 9/32	4 19/32	1-5 5/16
3/4	3 17/32	1-1 7/32	3 25/32	1-2 1/4	4 1/16	1-3 5/32	4 11/32	1-4 11/32	4 5/8	1-5 3/8
13/16	3 17/32	1-1 9/32	3 13/16	1-2 11/32	4 3/32	1-3 3/8	4 3/8	1-4 13/32	4 21/32	1-5 7/16
7/8	3 9/16	1-1 11/32	3 27/32	1-2 13/32	4 3/32	1-3 7/16	4 3/8	1-4 15/32	4 21/32	1-5 1/2
15/16	3 9/16	1-1 13/32	3 27/32	1-2 15/32	4 1/8	1-3 1/2	4 13/32	1-4 17/32	4 11/16	1-5 9/16

ins.	17″ Rise	17″ Slope	18″ Rise	18″ Slope	19″ Rise	19″ Slope	20″ Rise	20″ Slope	21″ Rise	21″ Slope
0	4 11/16	1-5 5/8	4 31/32	1-6 11/16	5 1/4	1-7 23/32	5 17/32	1-8 3/4	5 13/16	1-9 25/32
1/16	4 23/32	1-5 11/16	5	1-6 3/4	5 1/4	1-7 25/32	5 17/32	1-8 13/16	5 13/16	1-9 27/32
1/8	4 23/32	1-5 3/4	5	1-6 13/16	5 9/32	1-7 27/32	5 9/16	1-8 7/8	5 27/32	1-9 29/32
3/16	4 3/4	1-5 27/32	5 1/32	1-6 7/8	5 9/32	1-7 29/32	5 9/16	1-8 15/16	5 27/32	1-9 31/32
1/4	4 3/4	1-5 29/32	5 1/2	1-6 15/16	5 5/16	1-7 31/32	5 19/32	1-9	5 7/8	1-10 1/2
5/16	4 25/32	1-5 31/32	5 1/16	1-7	5 11/32	1-8 1/2	5 19/32	1-9 1/16	5 7/8	1-10 1/8
3/8	4 25/32	1-6 1/32	5 1/16	1-7 1/16	5 11/32	1-8 3/32	5 5/8	1-9 1/8	5 29/32	1-10 3/16
7/16	4 13/16	1-6 3/32	5 3/32	1-7 1/8	5 3/8	1-8 5/32	5 21/32	1-9 3/16	5 29/32	1-10 1/4
1/2	4 27/32	1-6 5/32	5 3/32	1-7 3/16	5 3/8	1-8 7/32	5 21/32	1-9 9/32	5 15/16	1-10 5/16
9/16	4 27/32	1-6 7/32	5 1/8	1-7 1/4	5 13/32	1-8 9/32	5 11/16	1-9 11/32	5 15/16	1-10 3/8
5/8	4 7/8	1-6 9/32	5 5/32	1-7 5/16	5 13/32	1-8 11/32	5 11/16	1-9 13/32	5 31/32	1-10 7/16
11/16	4 7/8	1-6 11/32	5 5/32	1-7 3/8	5 7/16	1-8 7/16	5 23/32	1-9 15/32	6	1-10 1/2
3/4	4 29/32	1-6 13/32	5 3/16	1-7 7/16	5 7/16	1-8 1/2	5 23/32	1-9 17/32	6	1-10 9/16
13/16	4 29/32	1-6 15/32	5 3/16	1-7 17/32	5 15/32	1-8 9/16	5 3/4	1-9 19/32	6 1/32	1-10 5/8
7/8	4 15/16	1-6 17/32	5 7/32	1-7 19/32	5 1/2	1-8 5/8	5 3/4	1-9 21/32	6 1/32	1-10 11/16
15/16	4 15/16	1-6 19/32	5 7/32	1-7 21/32	5 1/2	1-8 11/16	5 25/32	1-9 23/32	6 1/16	1-10 3/4

Feet	40′ Rise	40′ Slope	50′ Rise	50′ Slope	60′ Rise	60′ Slope	70′ Rise	70′ Slope
0	11-0 1/2	41-5 15/16	13-9 5/8	51-10 7/16	16-6 3/4	62-2 15/16	19-3 7/8	72-7 13/32
1	11-3 13/16	42-6 13/32	14-0 15/16	52-10 7/8	16-10 1/16	63-3 3/8	19-7 3/16	73-7 7/8
2	11-7 1/8	43-6 27/32	14-4 1/4	53-11 11/32	17-1 3/8	64-3 13/16	19-10 1/2	74-8 5/16
3	11-10 7/16	44-7 5/16	14-7 9/16	54-11 25/32	17-4 11/16	65-4 9/32	20-1 13/16	75-8 3/4
4	12-1 3/4	45-7 3/4	14-10 7/8	56-0 1/4	17-8	66-4 23/32	20-5 1/8	76-9 7/32
5	12-5 1/16	46-8 5/16	15-2 3/16	57-0 11/16	17-11 5/16	67-5 3/16	20-8 7/16	77-9 21/32
6	12-8 3/8	47-8 21/32	15-5 1/2	58-1 1/8	18-2 5/8	68-5 5/8	20-11 3/4	78-10 3/8
7	12-11 11/16	48-9 3/32	15-8 13/16	59-1 19/32	18-5 15/16	69-6 1/16	21-3 1/16	79-10 9/16
8	13-3	49-9 11/32	16-0 1/8	60-2 1/32	18-9 1/4	70-6 17/32	21-6 3/8	80-11
9	13-6 5/16	50-10	16-3 7/16	61-2 15/32	19-0 9/16	71-6 31/32	21-9 11/16	81-11 15/32

natsin A=0.2660898743; natcos A=0.9639482242; nattan A=0.2760416666; natcot A=3.6226415094

BEVEL 3⅜" TO 12"

Inches	0" Rise	0" Slope	1" Rise	1" Slope	2" Rise	2" Slope	3" Rise	3" Slope	4" Rise	4" Slope	5" Rise	5" Slope
0	0	0	9/32	1 1/32	9/16	2 1/16	27/32	3 1/8	1 1/8	4 5/32	1 13/32	5 3/16
1/16	1/32	1/16	5/16	1 3/32	19/32	2 5/32	7/8	3 3/16	1 5/32	4 7/32	1 7/16	5 1/4
1/8	1/32	1/8	5/16	1 5/32	19/32	2 7/32	7/8	3 1/4	1 5/32	4 9/32	1 7/16	5 5/16
3/16	1/16	3/16	11/32	1 7/32	5/8	2 9/32	29/32	3 5/16	1 3/16	4 11/32	1 15/32	5 3/8
1/4	1/16	1/4	11/32	1 5/16	5/8	2 11/32	29/32	3 3/8	1 3/16	4 13/32	1 15/32	5 15/32
5/16	3/32	5/16	3/8	1 3/8	21/32	2 13/32	15/16	3 7/16	1 7/32	4 15/32	1 1/2	5 17/32
3/8	3/32	3/8	3/8	1 7/16	21/32	2 15/32	15/16	3 1/2	1 7/32	4 17/32	1 1/2	5 19/32
7/16	1/8	15/32	13/32	1 1/2	11/16	2 17/32	31/32	3 9/16	1 1/4	4 5/8	1 17/32	5 21/32
1/2	1/8	17/32	7/16	1 9/16	11/16	2 19/32	1	3 5/8	1 1/4	4 11/16	1 9/16	5 23/32
9/16	5/32	19/32	7/16	1 5/8	23/32	2 21/32	1	3 11/16	1 9/32	4 3/4	1 9/16	5 25/32
5/8	3/16	21/32	15/32	1 11/16	3/4	2 23/32	1 1/32	3 25/32	1 5/16	4 13/16	1 19/32	5 27/32
11/16	3/16	23/32	15/32	1 3/4	3/4	2 25/32	1 1/32	3 27/32	1 5/16	4 7/8	1 19/32	5 29/32
3/4	7/32	25/32	1/2	1 13/16	25/32	2 27/32	1 1/16	3 29/32	1 11/32	4 15/16	1 5/8	5 31/32
13/16	7/32	27/32	1/2	1 7/8	25/32	2 29/32	1 1/16	3 31/32	1 11/32	5	1 5/8	6 1/32
7/8	1/4	29/32	17/32	1 15/16	13/16	3	1 3/32	4 1/32	1 3/8	5 1/16	1 21/32	6 3/32
15/16	1/4	31/32	17/32	2	13/16	3 1/16	1 3/32	4 3/32	1 3/8	5 1/8	1 21/32	6 5/32

Inches	6" Rise	6" Slope	7" Rise	7" Slope	8" Rise	8" Slope	9" Rise	9" Slope	10" Rise	10" Slope	11" Rise	11" Slope
0	1 11/16	6 7/32	1 31/32	7 9/32	2 1/4	8 5/16	2 17/32	9 11/32	2 13/16	10 3/8	3 3/32	11 7/16
1/16	1 23/32	6 5/16	2	7 11/32	2 9/32	8 3/8	2 9/16	9 13/32	2 27/32	10 7/16	3 1/8	11 1/2
1/8	1 23/32	6 3/8	2	7 13/32	2 9/32	8 7/16	2 9/16	9 15/32	2 27/32	10 17/32	3 1/8	11 9/16
3/16	1 3/4	6 7/16	2 1/32	7 15/32	2 5/16	8 1/2	2 19/32	9 17/32	2 7/8	10 19/32	3 5/32	11 5/8
1/4	1 3/4	6 1/2	2 1/32	7 17/32	2 5/16	8 9/16	2 19/32	9 19/32	2 7/8	10 21/32	3 5/32	11 11/16
5/16	1 25/32	6 9/16	2 1/16	7 19/32	2 11/32	8 5/8	2 5/8	9 11/16	2 29/32	10 23/32	3 3/16	11 3/4
3/8	1 25/32	6 5/8	2 1/16	7 21/32	2 11/32	8 11/16	2 5/8	9 3/4	2 29/32	10 25/32	3 3/16	11 13/16
7/16	1 13/16	6 11/16	2 3/32	7 23/32	2 3/8	8 3/4	2 21/32	9 13/16	2 15/16	10 27/32	3 7/32	11 7/8
1/2	1 13/16	6 3/4	2 1/8	7 25/32	2 3/8	8 27/32	2 11/16	9 7/8	2 15/16	10 29/32	3 1/4	11 15/16
9/16	1 27/32	6 13/16	2 1/8	7 27/32	2 13/32	8 29/32	2 11/16	9 15/16	2 31/32	10 31/32	3 1/4	1-0
5/8	1 7/8	6 7/8	2 5/32	7 29/32	2 7/16	8 31/32	2 23/32	10	3	11 1/32	3 9/32	1-0 1/16
11/16	1 7/8	6 15/16	2 5/32	8	2 7/16	9 1/32	2 23/32	10 1/16	3	11 3/32	3 9/32	1-0 5/32
3/4	1 29/32	7	2 3/16	8 1/16	2 15/32	9 3/32	2 3/4	10 1/8	3 1/32	11 5/32	3 5/16	1-0 7/32
13/16	1 29/32	7 1/16	2 3/16	8 1/8	2 15/32	9 5/32	2 3/4	10 3/16	3 1/32	11 7/32	3 5/16	1-0 9/32
7/8	1 15/16	7 5/32	2 7/32	8 3/16	2 1/2	9 7/32	2 25/32	10 1/4	3 1/16	11 9/32	3 11/32	1-0 11/32
15/16	1 15/16	7 7/32	2 7/32	8 1/4	2 1/2	9 9/32	2 25/32	10 5/16	3 1/16	11 3/8	3 11/32	1-0 13/32

Feet	0' Rise	0' Slope	10' Rise	10' Slope	20' Rise	20' Slope	30' Rise	30' Slope
0	0	0	2-9 3/4	10-4 21/32	5-7 1/2	20-9 5/16	8-5 1/4	31-1 31/32
1	3 3/8	1-0 15/32	3-1 1/8	11-5 1/8	5-10 7/8	21-9 25/32	8-8 5/8	32-2 7/16
2	6 3/4	2-0 15/32	3-4 1/2	12-5 19/32	6-2 1/4	22-10 1/4	9-0	33-2 29/32
3	10 1/8	3-1 13/32	3-7 7/8	13-6 1/16	6-5 5/8	23-10 23/32	9-3 3/8	34-3 3/8
4	1-1 1/2	4-1 7/8	3-11 1/4	14-6 17/32	6-9	24-11 3/16	9-6 3/4	35-3 27/32
5	1-4 7/8	5-2 5/16	4-2 5/8	15-6 31/32	7-0 3/8	25-11 5/8	9-10 1/8	36-4 5/16
6	1-8 1/4	6-2 25/32	4-6	16-7 7/16	7-3 3/4	27-0 3/32	10-1 1/2	37-4 3/4
7	1-11 5/8	7-3 1/4	4-9 3/4	17-7 29/32	7-7 1/8	28-0 9/16	10-4 7/8	38-5 7/32
8	2-3	8-3 23/32	5-0 3/4	18-8 3/8	7-10 1/2	29-1 1/32	10-8 1/4	39-5 11/32
9	2-6 3/8	9-4 3/16	5-4 1/8	19-8 27/32	8-1 7/8	30-1 1/2	10-11 5/8	40-6 5/32

A = 15° 42′ 31″; logsin A = 9.43256; logcos A = 9.98347; logtan A = 9.44909; logcot A = 0.55091

Ins.	12″ Rise	12″ Slope	13″ Rise	13″ Slope	14″ Rise	14″ Slope	15″ Rise	15″ Slope	16″ Rise	16″ Slope
0	$3\frac{3}{8}$	$1\text{-}0\frac{15}{32}$	$3\frac{21}{32}$	$1\text{-}1\frac{1}{2}$	$3\frac{15}{16}$	$1\text{-}2\frac{17}{32}$	$4\frac{7}{32}$	$1\text{-}3\frac{19}{32}$	$4\frac{1}{2}$	$1\text{-}4\frac{5}{8}$
$\frac{1}{16}$	$3\frac{13}{32}$	$1\text{-}0\frac{17}{32}$	$3\frac{11}{16}$	$1\text{-}1\frac{9}{16}$	$3\frac{31}{32}$	$1\text{-}2\frac{19}{32}$	$4\frac{1}{4}$	$1\text{-}3\frac{21}{32}$	$4\frac{17}{32}$	$1\text{-}4\frac{11}{16}$
$\frac{1}{8}$	$3\frac{13}{32}$	$1\text{-}0\frac{19}{32}$	$3\frac{11}{16}$	$1\text{-}1\frac{5}{8}$	$3\frac{31}{32}$	$1\text{-}2\frac{11}{16}$	$4\frac{1}{4}$	$1\text{-}3\frac{23}{32}$	$4\frac{17}{32}$	$1\text{-}4\frac{3}{4}$
$\frac{3}{16}$	$3\frac{7}{16}$	$1\text{-}0\frac{21}{32}$	$3\frac{23}{32}$	$1\text{-}1\frac{11}{16}$	4	$1\text{-}2\frac{3}{4}$	$4\frac{9}{32}$	$1\text{-}3\frac{25}{32}$	$4\frac{9}{16}$	$1\text{-}4\frac{13}{16}$
$\frac{1}{4}$	$3\frac{7}{16}$	$1\text{-}0\frac{23}{32}$	$3\frac{23}{32}$	$1\text{-}1\frac{3}{4}$	4	$1\text{-}2\frac{13}{16}$	$4\frac{9}{32}$	$1\text{-}3\frac{27}{32}$	$4\frac{9}{16}$	$1\text{-}4\frac{7}{8}$
$\frac{5}{16}$	$3\frac{15}{32}$	$1\text{-}0\frac{25}{32}$	$3\frac{3}{4}$	$1\text{-}1\frac{27}{32}$	$4\frac{1}{32}$	$1\text{-}2\frac{7}{8}$	$4\frac{5}{16}$	$1\text{-}3\frac{29}{32}$	$4\frac{19}{32}$	$1\text{-}4\frac{15}{16}$
$\frac{3}{8}$	$3\frac{15}{32}$	$1\text{-}0\frac{27}{32}$	$3\frac{3}{4}$	$1\text{-}1\frac{29}{32}$	$4\frac{1}{32}$	$1\text{-}2\frac{15}{16}$	$4\frac{5}{16}$	$1\text{-}3\frac{31}{32}$	$4\frac{19}{32}$	$1\text{-}5$
$\frac{7}{16}$	$3\frac{1}{2}$	$1\text{-}0\frac{29}{32}$	$3\frac{25}{32}$	$1\text{-}1\frac{31}{32}$	$4\frac{1}{8}$	$1\text{-}3$	$4\frac{11}{32}$	$1\text{-}4\frac{1}{32}$	$4\frac{5}{8}$	$1\text{-}5\frac{1}{16}$
$\frac{1}{2}$	$3\frac{1}{2}$	$1\text{-}1$	$3\frac{13}{16}$	$1\text{-}2\frac{1}{32}$	$4\frac{1}{16}$	$1\text{-}3\frac{1}{8}$	$4\frac{3}{8}$	$1\text{-}4\frac{3}{32}$	$4\frac{5}{8}$	$1\text{-}5\frac{1}{8}$
$\frac{9}{16}$	$3\frac{17}{32}$	$1\text{-}1\frac{1}{16}$	$3\frac{13}{16}$	$1\text{-}2\frac{3}{32}$	$4\frac{3}{32}$	$1\text{-}3\frac{1}{8}$	$4\frac{3}{8}$	$1\text{-}4\frac{5}{32}$	$4\frac{21}{32}$	$1\text{-}5\frac{7}{32}$
$\frac{5}{8}$	$3\frac{9}{16}$	$1\text{-}1\frac{1}{8}$	$3\frac{27}{32}$	$1\text{-}2\frac{5}{32}$	$4\frac{1}{8}$	$1\text{-}3\frac{3}{16}$	$4\frac{13}{32}$	$1\text{-}4\frac{7}{32}$	$4\frac{11}{16}$	$1\text{-}5\frac{9}{32}$
$\frac{11}{16}$	$3\frac{9}{16}$	$1\text{-}1\frac{3}{16}$	$3\frac{27}{32}$	$1\text{-}2\frac{7}{32}$	$4\frac{1}{8}$	$1\text{-}3\frac{1}{4}$	$4\frac{13}{32}$	$1\text{-}4\frac{9}{32}$	$4\frac{11}{16}$	$1\text{-}5\frac{11}{32}$
$\frac{3}{4}$	$3\frac{19}{32}$	$1\text{-}1\frac{1}{4}$	$3\frac{7}{8}$	$1\text{-}2\frac{9}{32}$	$4\frac{5}{32}$	$1\text{-}3\frac{5}{16}$	$4\frac{7}{16}$	$1\text{-}4\frac{3}{8}$	$4\frac{23}{32}$	$1\text{-}5\frac{13}{32}$
$\frac{13}{16}$	$3\frac{19}{32}$	$1\text{-}1\frac{5}{16}$	$3\frac{7}{8}$	$1\text{-}2\frac{11}{32}$	$4\frac{5}{32}$	$1\text{-}3\frac{3}{8}$	$4\frac{7}{16}$	$1\text{-}4\frac{7}{16}$	$4\frac{23}{32}$	$1\text{-}5\frac{15}{32}$
$\frac{7}{8}$	$3\frac{5}{8}$	$1\text{-}1\frac{3}{8}$	$3\frac{29}{32}$	$1\text{-}2\frac{13}{32}$	$4\frac{3}{16}$	$1\text{-}3\frac{7}{16}$	$4\frac{15}{32}$	$1\text{-}4\frac{1}{2}$	$4\frac{3}{4}$	$1\text{-}5\frac{17}{32}$
$\frac{15}{16}$	$3\frac{5}{8}$	$1\text{-}1\frac{7}{16}$	$3\frac{29}{32}$	$1\text{-}2\frac{15}{32}$	$4\frac{3}{16}$	$1\text{-}3\frac{17}{32}$	$4\frac{15}{32}$	$1\text{-}4\frac{9}{16}$	$4\frac{3}{4}$	$1\text{-}5\frac{19}{32}$

Ins.	17″ Rise	17″ Slope	18″ Rise	18″ Slope	19″ Rise	19″ Slope	20″ Rise	20″ Slope	21″ Rise	21″ Slope
0	$4\frac{25}{32}$	$1\text{-}5\frac{21}{32}$	$5\frac{1}{16}$	$1\text{-}6\frac{11}{16}$	$5\frac{11}{32}$	$1\text{-}7\frac{3}{4}$	$5\frac{5}{8}$	$1\text{-}8\frac{25}{32}$	$5\frac{29}{32}$	$1\text{-}9\frac{13}{16}$
$\frac{1}{16}$	$4\frac{13}{16}$	$1\text{-}5\frac{23}{32}$	$5\frac{3}{32}$	$1\text{-}6\frac{3}{4}$	$5\frac{3}{8}$	$1\text{-}7\frac{13}{16}$	$5\frac{21}{32}$	$1\text{-}8\frac{27}{32}$	$5\frac{15}{16}$	$1\text{-}9\frac{7}{8}$
$\frac{1}{8}$	$4\frac{13}{16}$	$1\text{-}5\frac{25}{32}$	$5\frac{3}{32}$	$1\text{-}6\frac{27}{32}$	$5\frac{3}{8}$	$1\text{-}7\frac{7}{8}$	$5\frac{21}{32}$	$1\text{-}8\frac{29}{32}$	$5\frac{15}{16}$	$1\text{-}9\frac{15}{16}$
$\frac{3}{16}$	$4\frac{27}{32}$	$1\text{-}5\frac{27}{32}$	$5\frac{1}{8}$	$1\text{-}6\frac{29}{32}$	$5\frac{13}{32}$	$1\text{-}7\frac{15}{16}$	$5\frac{11}{16}$	$1\text{-}8\frac{31}{32}$	$5\frac{31}{32}$	$1\text{-}10$
$\frac{1}{4}$	$4\frac{27}{32}$	$1\text{-}5\frac{29}{32}$	$5\frac{1}{8}$	$1\text{-}6\frac{31}{32}$	$5\frac{13}{32}$	$1\text{-}8$	$5\frac{11}{16}$	$1\text{-}9\frac{1}{32}$	$5\frac{31}{32}$	$1\text{-}10\frac{1}{16}$
$\frac{5}{16}$	$4\frac{7}{8}$	$1\text{-}5\frac{31}{32}$	$5\frac{5}{32}$	$1\text{-}7\frac{1}{32}$	$5\frac{7}{16}$	$1\text{-}8\frac{1}{16}$	$5\frac{23}{32}$	$1\text{-}9\frac{3}{32}$	6	$1\text{-}10\frac{1}{8}$
$\frac{3}{8}$	$4\frac{7}{8}$	$1\text{-}6\frac{1}{32}$	$5\frac{5}{32}$	$1\text{-}7\frac{3}{32}$	$5\frac{7}{16}$	$1\text{-}8\frac{1}{8}$	$5\frac{23}{32}$	$1\text{-}9\frac{5}{32}$	6	$1\text{-}10\frac{7}{32}$
$\frac{7}{16}$	$4\frac{29}{32}$	$1\text{-}6\frac{1}{8}$	$5\frac{3}{16}$	$1\text{-}7\frac{5}{32}$	$5\frac{15}{32}$	$1\text{-}8\frac{3}{16}$	$5\frac{3}{4}$	$1\text{-}9\frac{7}{32}$	$6\frac{1}{32}$	$1\text{-}10\frac{9}{32}$
$\frac{1}{2}$	$4\frac{15}{16}$	$1\text{-}6\frac{3}{16}$	$5\frac{3}{16}$	$1\text{-}7\frac{7}{32}$	$5\frac{1}{2}$	$1\text{-}8\frac{1}{4}$	$5\frac{3}{4}$	$1\text{-}9\frac{9}{32}$	$6\frac{1}{16}$	$1\text{-}10\frac{11}{32}$
$\frac{9}{16}$	$4\frac{15}{16}$	$1\text{-}6\frac{1}{4}$	$5\frac{7}{32}$	$1\text{-}7\frac{9}{32}$	$5\frac{1}{2}$	$1\text{-}8\frac{5}{16}$	$5\frac{25}{32}$	$1\text{-}9\frac{3}{8}$	$6\frac{1}{16}$	$1\text{-}10\frac{13}{32}$
$\frac{5}{8}$	$4\frac{31}{32}$	$1\text{-}6\frac{5}{16}$	$5\frac{1}{4}$	$1\text{-}7\frac{11}{32}$	$5\frac{17}{32}$	$1\text{-}8\frac{3}{8}$	$5\frac{13}{16}$	$1\text{-}9\frac{7}{16}$	$6\frac{3}{32}$	$1\text{-}10\frac{15}{32}$
$\frac{11}{16}$	$4\frac{31}{32}$	$1\text{-}6\frac{3}{8}$	$5\frac{1}{4}$	$1\text{-}7\frac{13}{32}$	$5\frac{17}{32}$	$1\text{-}8\frac{7}{16}$	$5\frac{13}{16}$	$1\text{-}9\frac{1}{2}$	$6\frac{3}{32}$	$1\text{-}10\frac{17}{32}$
$\frac{3}{4}$	5	$1\text{-}6\frac{7}{16}$	$5\frac{9}{32}$	$1\text{-}7\frac{15}{32}$	$5\frac{9}{16}$	$1\text{-}8\frac{17}{32}$	$5\frac{27}{32}$	$1\text{-}9\frac{9}{16}$	$6\frac{1}{8}$	$1\text{-}10\frac{19}{32}$
$\frac{13}{16}$	5	$1\text{-}6\frac{1}{2}$	$5\frac{9}{32}$	$1\text{-}7\frac{17}{32}$	$5\frac{9}{16}$	$1\text{-}8\frac{19}{32}$	$5\frac{27}{32}$	$1\text{-}9\frac{5}{8}$	$6\frac{1}{8}$	$1\text{-}10\frac{21}{32}$
$\frac{7}{8}$	$5\frac{1}{32}$	$1\text{-}6\frac{9}{32}$	$5\frac{5}{16}$	$1\text{-}7\frac{19}{32}$	$5\frac{19}{32}$	$1\text{-}8\frac{21}{32}$	$5\frac{7}{8}$	$1\text{-}9\frac{11}{16}$	$6\frac{5}{32}$	$1\text{-}10\frac{23}{32}$
$\frac{15}{16}$	$5\frac{1}{16}$	$1\text{-}6\frac{5}{8}$	$5\frac{5}{16}$	$1\text{-}7\frac{11}{16}$	$5\frac{19}{32}$	$1\text{-}8\frac{23}{32}$	$5\frac{7}{8}$	$1\text{-}9\frac{3}{4}$	$6\frac{5}{32}$	$1\text{-}10\frac{25}{32}$

Feet	40′ Rise	40′ Slope	50′ Rise	50′ Slope	60′ Rise	60′ Slope	70′ Rise	70′ Slope
0	$11\text{-}3$	$41\text{-}6\frac{5}{8}$	$14\text{-}0\frac{3}{4}$	$51\text{-}11\frac{9}{32}$	$16\text{-}10\frac{1}{4}$	$62\text{-}3\frac{15}{16}$	$19\text{-}8\frac{1}{4}$	$72\text{-}8\frac{19}{32}$
1	$11\text{-}6\frac{3}{8}$	$42\text{-}7\frac{3}{32}$	$14\text{-}4\frac{1}{8}$	$52\text{-}11\frac{3}{4}$	$17\text{-}1\frac{7}{8}$	$63\text{-}4\frac{13}{32}$	$19\text{-}11\frac{5}{8}$	$73\text{-}9\frac{1}{16}$
2	$11\text{-}9\frac{3}{4}$	$43\text{-}7\frac{9}{16}$	$14\text{-}7\frac{1}{2}$	$54\text{-}0\frac{7}{32}$	$17\text{-}5\frac{1}{4}$	$64\text{-}4\frac{7}{8}$	$20\text{-}3$	$74\text{-}9\frac{17}{32}$
3	$12\text{-}1\frac{1}{8}$	$44\text{-}8\frac{1}{32}$	$14\text{-}10\frac{7}{8}$	$55\text{-}0\frac{11}{16}$	$17\text{-}8\frac{5}{8}$	$65\text{-}5\frac{11}{32}$	$20\text{-}6\frac{3}{8}$	$75\text{-}10$
4	$12\text{-}4\frac{1}{2}$	$45\text{-}8\frac{1}{2}$	$15\text{-}2\frac{1}{4}$	$56\text{-}1\frac{5}{32}$	$18\text{-}0$	$66\text{-}5\frac{13}{16}$	$20\text{-}9\frac{3}{4}$	$76\text{-}10\frac{7}{16}$
5	$12\text{-}7\frac{7}{8}$	$46\text{-}8\frac{15}{16}$	$15\text{-}5\frac{5}{8}$	$57\text{-}1\frac{19}{32}$	$18\text{-}3\frac{3}{8}$	$67\text{-}6\frac{1}{4}$	$21\text{-}1\frac{1}{8}$	$77\text{-}10\frac{29}{32}$
6	$12\text{-}11\frac{1}{4}$	$47\text{-}9\frac{13}{32}$	$15\text{-}9$	$58\text{-}2\frac{1}{16}$	$18\text{-}6\frac{3}{4}$	$68\text{-}6\frac{23}{32}$	$21\text{-}4\frac{1}{2}$	$78\text{-}11\frac{3}{8}$
7	$13\text{-}2\frac{5}{8}$	$48\text{-}9\frac{7}{8}$	$16\text{-}0\frac{3}{8}$	$59\text{-}2\frac{17}{32}$	$18\text{-}10\frac{1}{8}$	$69\text{-}7\frac{3}{16}$	$21\text{-}7\frac{7}{8}$	$79\text{-}11\frac{21}{32}$
8	$13\text{-}6$	$49\text{-}10\frac{11}{32}$	$16\text{-}3\frac{3}{4}$	$60\text{-}3$	$19\text{-}1\frac{1}{2}$	$70\text{-}7\frac{21}{32}$	$21\text{-}11\frac{1}{4}$	$81\text{-}0\frac{5}{16}$
9	$13\text{-}9\frac{3}{8}$	$50\text{-}10\frac{13}{16}$	$16\text{-}7\frac{1}{8}$	$61\text{-}3\frac{15}{32}$	$19\text{-}4\frac{7}{8}$	$71\text{-}8\frac{1}{8}$	$22\text{-}2\frac{5}{8}$	$82\text{-}0\frac{25}{32}$

natsin A=0.2707455769; natcos A=0.9626509401; nattan A=0.2812500000; natcot A=3.5555555555

Inches	0" Rise	0" Slope	1" Rise	1" Slope	2" Rise	2" Slope	3" Rise	3" Slope	4" Rise	4" Slope	5" Rise	5" Slope
0	0	0	9/32	1 1/32	9/16	2 3/32	7/8	3 1/8	1 5/32	4 5/32	1 7/16	5 3/16
1/16	1/32	1/16	5/16	1 3/32	19/32	2 5/32	7/8	3 3/16	1 5/32	4 7/32	1 7/16	5 9/32
1/8	1/32	1/8	5/16	1 5/32	19/32	2 7/32	29/32	3 1/4	1 3/16	4 9/32	1 15/32	5 11/32
3/16	1/16	3/16	11/32	1 1/4	5/8	2 9/32	29/32	3 5/16	1 3/16	4 11/32	1 1/2	5 13/32
1/4	1/16	1/4	11/32	1 5/16	21/32	2 11/32	15/16	3 3/8	1 7/32	4 13/32	1 1/2	5 15/32
5/16	3/32	5/16	3/8	1 3/8	21/32	2 13/32	15/16	3 7/16	1 1/4	4 1/2	1 17/32	5 17/32
3/8	3/32	3/8	13/32	1 7/16	11/16	2 15/32	31/32	3 1/2	1 1/4	4 9/16	1 17/32	5 19/32
7/16	1/8	15/32	13/32	1 1/2	11/16	2 17/32	1	3 9/16	1 9/32	4 5/8	1 9/16	5 21/32
1/2	5/32	17/32	7/16	1 9/32	23/32	2 19/32	1	3 21/32	1 9/32	4 11/16	1 9/16	5 23/32
9/16	5/32	19/32	7/16	1 5/8	23/32	2 21/32	1 1/32	3 23/32	1 5/16	4 3/4	1 19/32	5 25/32
5/8	3/16	21/32	15/32	1 11/16	3/4	2 23/32	1 1/32	3 25/32	1 5/16	4 13/16	1 5/8	5 27/32
11/16	3/16	23/32	15/32	1 3/4	25/32	2 25/32	1 1/16	3 27/32	1 11/32	4 7/8	1 5/8	5 29/32
3/4	7/32	25/32	1/2	1 13/16	25/32	2 7/8	1 1/16	3 29/32	1 3/8	4 15/16	1 21/32	5 31/32
13/16	7/32	27/32	17/32	1 7/8	13/16	2 15/16	1 3/32	3 31/32	1 3/8	5	1 21/32	6 1/32
7/8	1/4	29/32	17/32	1 15/16	13/16	3	1 1/8	4 1/32	1 13/32	5 1/16	1 11/16	6 1/8
15/16	9/32	31/32	9/16	2	27/32	3 1/16	1 1/8	4 3/32	1 13/32	5 1/8	1 11/16	6 3/16

Inches	6" Rise	6" Slope	7" Rise	7" Slope	8" Rise	8" Slope	9" Rise	9" Slope	10" Rise	10" Slope	11" Rise	11" Slope
0	1 23/32	6 1/4	2	7 9/32	2 9/32	8 5/16	2 9/16	9 3/8	2 7/8	10 13/32	3 5/32	11 7/16
1/16	1 3/4	6 5/16	2 1/32	7 11/32	2 5/16	8 3/8	2 19/32	9 7/16	2 7/8	10 15/32	3 5/32	11 1/2
1/8	1 3/4	6 3/8	2 1/32	7 13/32	2 5/16	8 7/16	2 5/8	9 1/2	2 29/32	10 17/32	3 3/16	11 9/16
3/16	1 25/32	6 7/16	2 1/16	7 15/32	2 11/32	8 17/32	2 5/8	9 9/16	2 29/32	10 19/32	3 7/32	11 5/8
1/4	1 25/32	6 1/2	2 1/16	7 17/32	2 3/8	8 19/32	2 21/32	9 5/8	2 15/16	10 21/32	3 7/32	11 11/16
5/16	1 13/16	6 9/16	2 3/32	7 19/32	2 3/8	8 21/32	2 21/32	9 11/16	2 31/32	10 23/32	3 1/4	11 25/32
3/8	1 13/16	6 5/8	2 1/8	7 21/32	2 13/32	8 23/32	2 11/16	9 3/4	2 31/32	10 25/32	3 1/4	11 27/32
7/16	1 27/32	6 11/16	2 1/8	7 3/4	2 13/32	8 25/32	2 23/32	9 13/16	3	10 27/32	3 9/32	11 29/32
1/2	1 7/8	6 3/4	2 5/32	7 13/16	2 7/16	8 27/32	2 23/32	9 7/8	3	10 15/16	3 9/32	11 31/32
9/16	1 7/8	6 13/16	2 5/32	7 7/8	2 7/16	8 29/32	2 3/4	9 15/16	3	11	3 5/16	1-0 1/32
5/8	1 29/32	6 29/32	2 3/16	7 15/16	2 15/32	8 31/32	2 3/4	10	3 1/2	11 1/16	3 11/32	1-0 3/32
11/16	1 29/32	6 31/32	2 3/16	8	2 1/2	9 1/32	2 25/32	10 1/16	3 1/16	11 1/8	3 11/32	1-0 5/32
3/4	1 15/16	7 1/32	2 7/32	8 1/16	2 1/2	9 3/32	2 25/32	10 5/32	3 3/32	11 3/16	3 3/8	1-0 7/32
13/16	1 15/16	7 3/32	2 1/4	8 1/8	2 17/32	9 5/32	2 13/16	10 7/32	3 3/32	11 1/4	3 3/8	1-0 9/32
7/8	1 31/32	7 5/32	2 1/4	8 3/16	2 17/32	9 7/32	2 27/32	10 9/32	3 1/8	11 5/16	3 13/32	1-0 11/32
15/16	2	7 7/32	2 9/32	8 1/4	2 9/16	9 9/32	2 27/32	10 11/32	3 1/8	11 3/8	3 13/32	1-0 13/16

Feet	0' Rise	0' Slope	10' Rise	10' Slope	20' Rise	20' Slope	30' Rise	30' Slope
0	0	0	2-10 3/8	10-4 13/16	5-8 3/4	20-9 21/32	8-7 1/8	31-2 15/32
1	3 7/16	1-0 15/32	3-1 13/16	11-5 5/16	6-0 3/16	21-10 1/8	8-10 9/16	32-2 31/32
2	6 7/8	2-0 31/32	3-5 1/4	12-5 25/32	6-3 5/8	22-10 5/8	9-2	33-3 7/16
3	10 5/16	3-1 7/16	3-8 11/16	13-6 9/32	6-7 1/16	23-11 3/32	9-5 7/16	34-3 15/32
4	1-1 3/4	4-1 15/16	4-0 1/8	14-6 3/4	6-10 1/2	24-11 19/32	9-8 7/8	35-4 13/32
5	1-5 3/16	5-2 13/32	4-3 9/16	15-7 1/4	7-1 15/16	26-0 1/16	10-0 5/16	36-4 29/32
6	1-8 5/8	6-2 29/32	4-7	16-7 23/32	7-5 3/8	27-0 9/16	10-3 3/4	37-5 3/8
7	2-0 1/16	7-3 3/8	4-10 7/16	17-8 7/32	7-8 13/16	28-1 1/32	10-7 3/16	38-5 27/32
8	2-3 1/2	8-3 7/8	5-1 7/8	18-8 11/16	8-0 1/4	29-1 1/2	10-10 5/8	39-6 11/32
9	2-6 15/16	9-4 11/32	5-5 5/16	19-9 5/32	8-3 11/16	30-2	11-2 1/16	40-6 13/16

A = 15° 59′ 05″; logsin A = 9.43994; logcos A = 9.98287; logtan A = 9.45706; logcot A = 0.54294

Ins.	12″ Rise	Slope	13″ Rise	Slope	14″ Rise	Slope	15″ Rise	Slope	16″ Rise	Slope
0	3 7/16	1-0 15/32	3 23/32	1-1 17/32	4	1-2 9/16	4 5/16	1-3 19/32	4 19/32	1-4 21/32
1/16	3 15/32	1-0 9/16	3 3/4	1-1 19/32	4 1/32	1-2 5/8	4 5/16	1-3 21/32	4 19/32	1-4 23/32
1/8	3 15/32	1-0 5/8	3 3/4	1-1 21/32	4 1/32	1-2 11/16	4 11/32	1-3 23/32	4 5/8	1-4 25/32
3/16	3 1/2	1-0 11/16	3 25/32	1-1 23/32	4 1/16	1-2 3/4	4 11/32	1-3 13/16	4 5/8	1-4 27/32
1/4	3 1/2	1-0 3/4	3 25/32	1-1 25/32	4 3/32	1-2 13/16	4 3/8	1-3 7/8	4 21/32	1-4 29/32
5/16	3 17/32	1-0 13/16	3 13/16	1-1 27/32	4 3/32	1-2 7/8	4 3/8	1-3 15/16	4 11/16	1-4 31/32
3/8	3 17/32	1-0 7/8	3 27/32	1-1 29/32	4 1/8	1-2 31/32	4 13/32	1-4	4 11/16	1-5 1/32
7/16	3 9/16	1-0 15/16	3 27/32	1-1 31/32	4 1/8	1-3 1/32	4 7/32	1-4 1/32	4 23/32	1-5 3/32
1/2	3 19/32	1-1	3 7/8	1-2 1/32	4 5/32	1-3 3/32	4 7/16	1-4 1/8	4 23/32	1-5 5/32
9/16	3 19/32	1-1 1/16	3 7/8	1-2 3/32	4 5/32	1-3 5/32	4 15/32	1-4 3/16	4 3/4	1-5 7/32
5/8	3 5/8	1-1 1/8	3 29/32	1-2 3/16	4 3/16	1-3 7/32	4 15/32	1-4 1/4	4 3/4	1-5 9/32
11/16	3 5/8	1-1 3/16	3 29/32	1-2 1/4	4 7/32	1-3 9/32	4 1/2	1-4 5/16	4 25/32	1-5 11/32
3/4	3 21/32	1-1 1/4	3 15/16	1-2 5/16	4 7/32	1-3 11/32	4 1/2	1-4 3/8	4 13/16	1-5 7/16
13/16	3 21/32	1-1 5/16	3 31/32	1-2 3/8	4 1/4	1-3 13/32	4 17/32	1-4 7/16	4 13/16	1-5 1/2
7/8	3 11/16	1-1 13/32	3 31/32	1-2 7/16	4 1/4	1-3 15/32	4 9/16	1-4 1/2	4 27/32	1-5 9/16
15/16	3 23/32	1-1 15/32	4	1-2 1/2	4 9/32	1-3 17/32	4 9/16	1-4 19/32	4 27/32	1-5 5/8

Ins.	17″ Rise	Slope	18″ Rise	Slope	19″ Rise	Slope	20″ Rise	Slope	21″ Rise	Slope
0	4 7/8	1-5 11/32	5 5/8	1-6 23/32	5 7/16	1-7 3/4	5 23/32	1-8 13/16	6	1-9 27/32
1/16	4 7/8	1-5 3/4	5 3/16	1-6 25/32	5 15/32	1-7 27/32	5 3/4	1-8 7/8	6 1/2	1-9 29/32
1/8	4 29/32	1-5 13/32	5 3/16	1-6 27/32	5 15/32	1-7 29/32	5 3/4	1-8 15/16	6 1/16	1-9 31/32
3/16	4 15/16	1-5 7/8	5 7/32	1-6 29/32	5 1/2	1-7 31/32	5 25/32	1-9	6 1/16	1-10 1/32
1/4	4 15/16	1-5 15/16	5 7/32	1-6 31/32	5 1/2	1-8 1/32	5 13/16	1-9 1/16	6 3/32	1-10 3/32
5/16	4 31/32	1-6	5 1/4	1-7 1/16	5 17/32	1-8 3/32	5 13/16	1-9 1/8	6 3/32	1-10 5/32
3/8	4 31/32	1-6 1/32	5 1/4	1-7 1/8	5 9/16	1-8 5/32	5 27/32	1-9 3/16	6 1/8	1-10 1/4
7/16	5	1-6 1/8	5 9/32	1-7 3/16	5 9/16	1-8 7/32	5 27/32	1-9 1/4	6 5/32	1-10 5/32
1/2	5	1-6 7/32	5 5/16	1-7 1/4	5 19/32	1-8 9/32	5 7/8	1-9 5/16	6 5/32	1-10 3/8
9/16	5 1/32	1-6 9/32	5 5/16	1-7 5/16	5 19/32	1-8 11/32	5 7/8	1-9 3/8	6 3/16	1-10 7/16
5/8	5 1/16	1-6 11/32	5 11/32	1-7 3/8	5 5/8	1-8 13/32	5 29/32	1-9 15/32	6 3/16	1-10 1/2
11/16	5 1/16	1-6 13/32	5 11/32	1-7 7/16	5 5/8	1-8 15/32	5 15/16	1-9 17/32	6 7/32	1-10 9/16
3/4	5 3/32	1-6 15/32	5 3/8	1-7 1/2	5 21/32	1-8 17/32	5 15/16	1-9 19/32	6 7/32	1-10 5/8
13/16	5 3/32	1-6 17/32	5 3/8	1-7 9/16	5 11/16	1-8 19/32	5 31/32	1-9 21/32	6 1/4	1-10 11/16
7/8	5 1/8	1-6 19/32	5 13/32	1-7 5/8	5 11/16	1-8 11/16	5 31/32	1-9 23/32	6 9/32	1-10 3/4
15/16	5 1/8	1-6 21/32	5 7/16	1-7 11/16	5 23/32	1-8 3/4	6	1-9 25/32	6 9/32	1-10 13/16

Feet	40′ Rise	Slope	50′ Rise	Slope	60′ Rise	Slope	70′ Rise	Slope
0	11-5 1/2	41-7 5/16	14-3 7/8	52-0 1/8	17-2 1/4	62-4 31/32	20-0 5/8	72-9 25/32
1	11-8 15/16	42-7 25/32	14-7 5/16	53-0 5/8	17-5 11/16	63-5 7/16	20-4 1/16	73-10 9/32
2	12-0 3/8	43-8 9/32	14-10 3/4	54-1 3/32	17-9 1/8	64-5 15/16	20-7 1/2	74-10 3/4
3	12-3 13/16	44-8 3/4	15-2 3/16	55-1 19/32	18-0 9/16	65-6 13/32	20-10 15/16	75-11 7/32
4	12-7 1/4	45-9 1/4	15-5 5/8	56-2 1/16	18-4	66-6 7/8	21-2 3/8	76-11 23/32
5	12-10 11/16	46-9 23/32	15-9 1/16	57-2 17/32	18-7 7/16	67-7 3/8	21-5 13/16	78-0 3/16
6	13-2 1/8	47-10 3/16	16-0 1/2	58-3 1/32	18-10 7/8	68-7 27/32	21-9 1/4	79-0 11/16
7	13-5 9/16	48-10 11/16	16-3 15/16	59-3 1/2	19-2 5/16	69-8 11/32	22-0 11/16	80-1 5/32
8	13-9	49-11 5/32	16-7 3/8	60-4	19-5 3/4	70-8 13/16	22-4 1/8	81-1 21/32
9	14-0 7/16	50-11 21/32	16-10 13/16	61-4 15/32	19-9 3/16	71-9 5/16	22-7 9/16	82-2 1/8

natsin A=0.2753823584; **natcos** A=0.9613347787; **nattan** A=0.2864583333; **natcot** A=3 4909090909

Inches	0" Rise	0" Slope	1" Rise	1" Slope	2" Rise	2" Slope	3" Rise	3" Slope	4" Rise	4" Slope	5" Rise	5" Slope
0	0	0	9/32	1 1/32	19/32	2 3/32	7/8	3 1/8	1 5/32	4 5/32	1 15/32	5 7/32
1/16	1/32	1/16	5/16	1 3/32	19/32	2 5/32	29/32	3 3/16	1 5/32	4 7/32	1 15/32	5 9/32
1/8	1/32	1/8	5/16	1 5/32	5/8	2 7/32	29/32	3 1/4	1 3/16	4 9/32	1 1/2	5 11/32
3/16	1/16	3/16	11/32	1 1/4	5/8	2 9/32	15/16	3 5/16	1 7/32	4 3/8	1 1/2	5 13/32
1/4	1/16	1/4	3/8	1 5/16	21/32	2 11/32	15/16	3 3/8	1 1/4	4 7/16	1 17/32	5 15/32
5/16	3/32	5/16	3/8	1 3/8	11/16	2 13/32	31/32	3 7/16	1 1/4	4 1/2	1 9/16	5 17/32
3/8	1/8	3/8	13/32	1 7/16	11/16	2 15/32	1	3 1/2	1 9/32	4 9/16	1 9/16	5 19/32
7/16	1/8	15/32	13/32	1 1/2	23/32	2 17/32	1	3 19/32	1 9/32	4 5/8	1 19/32	5 21/32
1/2	5/32	17/32	7/16	1 9/16	23/32	2 19/32	1 1/32	3 21/32	1 5/16	4 11/16	1 19/32	5 23/32
9/16	5/32	19/32	15/32	1 5/8	3/4	2 21/32	1 1/32	3 23/32	1 11/32	4 3/4	1 5/8	5 25/32
5/8	3/16	21/32	15/32	1 11/16	3/4	2 23/32	1 1/16	3 25/32	1 11/32	4 13/16	1 5/8	5 27/32
11/16	3/16	23/32	1/2	1 3/4	25/32	2 13/16	1 1/16	3 27/32	1 3/8	4 7/8	1 21/32	5 15/16
3/4	7/32	25/32	1/2	1 13/16	13/16	2 7/8	1 3/32	3 29/32	1 3/8	4 15/16	1 11/16	6
13/16	1/4	27/32	17/32	1 7/8	13/16	2 15/16	1 1/8	3 31/32	1 13/32	5	1 11/16	6 1/16
7/8	1/4	29/32	9/16	1 15/16	27/32	3	1 1/8	4 1/32	1 7/16	5 1/16	1 23/32	6 1/8
15/16	9/32	31/32	9/16	2 1/32	27/32	3 1/16	1 5/32	4 3/32	1 7/16	5 5/32	1 23/32	6 3/32

Inches	6" Rise	6" Slope	7" Rise	7" Slope	8" Rise	8" Slope	9" Rise	9" Slope	10" Rise	10" Slope	11" Rise	11" Slope
0	1 3/4	6 1/4	2 1/32	7 9/32	2 11/32	8 11/32	2 5/8	9 3/8	2 29/32	10 13/32	3 7/32	11 15/32
1/16	1 25/32	6 5/16	2 1/16	7 11/32	2 11/32	8 13/32	2 21/32	9 7/16	2 15/16	10 15/32	3 7/32	11 17/32
1/8	1 25/32	6 3/8	2 1/16	7 13/32	2 3/8	8 15/32	2 21/32	9 1/2	2 15/16	10 17/32	3 1/4	11 19/32
3/16	1 13/16	6 7/16	2 3/32	7 1/2	2 3/8	8 17/32	2 11/16	9 9/16	2 31/32	10 5/8	3 1/4	11 21/32
1/4	1 13/16	6 1/2	2 1/8	7 9/16	2 13/32	8 19/32	2 11/16	9 5/8	3	10 11/16	3 9/32	11 23/32
5/16	1 27/32	6 9/16	2 1/8	7 5/8	2 7/16	8 21/32	2 23/32	9 11/16	3	10 3/4	3 5/16	11 25/32
3/8	1 7/8	6 5/8	2 5/32	7 11/16	2 7/16	8 23/32	2 3/4	9 3/4	3 1/32	10 13/16	3 5/16	11 27/32
7/16	1 7/8	6 23/32	2 5/32	7 3/4	2 15/32	8 25/32	2 3/4	9 27/32	3 1/32	10 7/8	3 11/32	11 29/32
1/2	1 29/32	6 25/32	2 3/16	7 13/16	2 15/32	8 27/32	2 25/32	9 29/32	3 1/16	10 15/16	3 11/32	11 31/32
9/16	1 29/32	6 27/32	2 7/32	7 7/8	2 1/2	8 29/32	2 25/32	9 31/32	3 3/32	11	3 3/8	1-0 1/32
5/8	1 15/16	6 29/32	2 7/32	7 15/16	2 1/2	8 31/32	2 13/16	10 1/32	3 3/32	11 1/16	3 3/8	1-0 3/32
11/16	1 15/16	6 31/32	2 1/4	8	2 17/32	9 1/16	2 13/16	10 3/32	3 1/8	11 1/8	3 13/32	1-0 3/16
3/4	1 31/32	7 1/32	2 1/4	8 1/16	2 9/16	9 1/8	2 27/32	10 5/32	3 1/8	11 3/16	3 7/16	1-0 1/4
13/16	2	7 3/32	2 9/32	8 1/8	2 9/16	9 3/16	2 7/8	10 7/32	3 5/32	11 1/4	3 7/16	1-0 5/16
7/8	2	7 5/32	2 9/32	8 3/16	2 19/32	9 1/4	2 7/8	10 9/32	3 3/16	11 5/16	3 15/32	1-0 3/8
15/16	2 1/32	7 7/32	2 5/16	8 9/32	2 19/32	9 5/16	2 29/32	10 11/32	3 3/16	11 13/32	3 15/32	1-0 7/16

Feet	0' Rise	0' Slope	10' Rise	10' Slope	20' Rise	20' Slope	30' Rise	30' Slope
0	0	0	2-11	10-5	5-10	20-10	8-9	31-3
1	3 1/2	1-0 1/2	3-2 1/2	11-5 1/2	6-1 1/2	21-10 1/2	9-0 1/2	32-3 1/2
2	7	2-1	3-6	12-6	6-5	22-11	9-4	33-4
3	10 1/2	3-1 1/2	3-9 1/2	13-6 1/2	6-8 1/2	23-11 1/2	9-7 1/2	34-4 1/2
4	1-2	4-2	4-1	14-7	7-0	25-0	9-11	35-5
5	1-5 1/2	5-2 1/2	4-4 1/2	15-7 1/2	7-3 1/2	26-0 1/2	10-2 1/2	36-5 1/2
6	1-9	6-3	4-8	16-8	7-7	27-1	10-6	37-6
7	2-0 1/2	7-3 1/2	4-11 1/2	17-8 1/2	7-10 1/2	28-1 1/2	10-9 1/2	38-6 1/2
8	2-4	8-4	5-3	18-9	8-2	29-2	11-1	39-7
9	2-7 1/2	9-4 1/2	5-6 1/2	19-9 1/2	8-5 1/2	30-2 1/2	11-4 1/2	40-7 1/2

A = 16° 15′ 37″; logsin A = 9.44716; logcos A = 9.98227; logtan A = 9.46489; logcot A = 0.53511

Ins.	12" Rise	12" Slope	13" Rise	13" Slope	14" Rise	14" Slope	15" Rise	15" Slope	16" Rise	16" Slope
0	3 1/2	1-0 1/2	3 25/32	1-1 17/32	4 3/32-	1-2 19/32-	4 3/8	1-3 5/8	4 21/32	1-4 21/32
1/16	3 17/32-	1-0 9/16	3 13/16	1-1 19/32	4 3/32	1-2 21/32-	4 13/32-	1-3 11/16	4 11/16	1-4 23/32
1/8	3 17/32	1-0 5/8	3 13/16	1-1 11/16	4 1/8	1-2 23/32-	4 13/32	1-3 3/4	4 11/16	1-4 13/16
3/16	3 9/16	1-0 11/16	3 27/32	1-1 3/4	4 1/8	1-2 25/32-	4 7/16	1-3 13/16	4 23/32	1-4 7/8
1/4	3 9/16	1-0 3/4	3 7/8	1-1 13/16	4 5/32	1-2 27/32	4 7/16	1-3 7/8	4 3/4	1-4 15/16
5/16	3 19/32-	1-0 13/16	3 7/8	1-1 7/8	4 3/16	1-2 29/32	4 15/32-	1-3 15/16	4 3/4	1-5
3/8	3 5/8	1-0 7/8	3 29/32-	1-1 15/16	4 3/16	1-2 31/32	4 1/2	1-4	4 25/32-	1-5 1/16
7/16	3 5/8	1-0 31/32-	3 29/32	1-2	4 7/32-	1-3 1/32	4 1/2	1-4 3/32-	4 25/32	1-5 1/8
1/2	3 21/32-	1-1 1/32-	3 15/16	1-2 1/16	4 7/32	1-3 3/32	4 17/32-	1-4 5/32-	4 13/16	1-5 3/16
9/16	3 21/32	1-1 3/32-	3 31/32-	1-2 1/8	4 1/4	1-3 5/32	4 17/32	1-4 7/32-	4 27/32-	1-5 1/4
5/8	3 11/16	1-1 5/32-	3 31/32	1-2 3/16	4 1/4	1-3 1/4	4 9/16	1-4 9/32-	4 27/32	1-5 5/16
11/16	3 11/16	1-1 7/32-	4	1-2 1/4	4 9/32	1-3 5/16	4 9/16	1-4 11/32-	4 7/8	1-5 3/8
3/4	3 23/32	1-1 9/32	4	1-2 5/16	4 5/16	1-3 3/8	4 19/32	1-4 13/32	4 7/8	1-5 7/16
13/16	3 3/4	1-1 11/32	4 1/32-	1-2 3/8	4 5/16	1-3 7/16	4 5/8	1-4 15/32	4 29/32-	1-5 1/2
7/8	3 3/4	1-1 13/32	4 1/16	1-2 7/16	4 11/32-	1-3 1/2	4 5/8	1-4 17/32	4 15/16	1-5 9/16
15/16	3 25/32-	1-1 15/32	4 1/16	1-2 17/32-	4 11/32	1-3 9/16	4 21/32-	1-4 19/32	4 15/16	1-5 21/32-

Ins.	17" Rise	17" Slope	18" Rise	18" Slope	19" Rise	19" Slope	20" Rise	20" Slope	21" Rise	21" Slope
0	4 31/32-	1-5 23/32-	5 1/4	1-6 3/4	5 17/32	1-7 25/32	5 27/32-	1-8 27/32-	6 1/8	1-9 7/8
1/16	4 31/32	1-5 25/32-	5 9/32-	1-6 13/16	5 9/16	1-7 27/32	5 27/32	1-8 29/32-	6 5/32-	1-9 15/16
1/8	5	1-5 27/32-	5 9/32	1-6 7/8	5 9/16	1-7 15/16	5 7/8	1-8 31/32-	6 5/32	1-10
3/16	5	1-5 29/32-	5 5/16	1-6 15/16	5 19/32	1-8	5 7/8	1-9 1/32-	6 3/16	1-10 1/16
1/4	5 1/32	1-5 31/32	5 5/16	1-7	5 5/8	1-8 1/16	5 29/32	1-9 3/32	6 3/16	1-10 1/8
5/16	5 1/16	1-6 1/32	5 11/32-	1-7 1/16	5 5/8	1-8 1/8	5 15/16	1-9 5/32	6 7/32-	1-10 3/16
3/8	5 1/16	1-6 3/32	5 3/8	1-7 1/8	5 21/32-	1-8 3/16	5 15/16	1-9 7/32	6 1/4	1-10 1/4
7/16	5 3/32-	1-6 5/32	5 3/8	1-7 7/32-	5 21/32	1-8 1/4	5 31/32-	1-9 9/32	6 1/4	1-10 11/32-
1/2	5 3/32	1-6 7/32	5 13/32-	1-7 9/32-	5 11/16	1-8 5/16	5 31/32	1-9 11/32	6 9/32-	1-10 13/32-
9/16	5 1/8	1-6 9/32	5 13/32	1-7 11/32-	5 23/32-	1-8 3/8	6	1-9 13/32	6 9/32	1-10 15/32-
5/8	5 1/8	1-6 3/8	5 7/16	1-7 13/32-	5 23/32	1-8 7/16	6	1-9 1/2	6 5/16	1-10 17/32-
11/16	5 5/32	1-6 7/16	5 7/16	1-7 15/32-	5 3/4	1-8 1/2	6 1/32	1-9 9/16	6 5/16	1-10 19/32-
3/4	5 3/16	1-6 1/2	5 15/32	1-7 17/32	5 3/4	1-8 9/16	6 1/16	1-9 5/8	6 11/32	1-10 21/32
13/16	5 3/16	1-6 9/16	5 1/2	1-7 19/32	5 25/32-	1-8 5/8	6 1/16	1-9 11/16	6 3/8	1-10 23/32
7/8	5 7/32-	1-6 5/8	5 1/2	1-7 21/32	5 13/16	1-8 11/16	6 3/32-	1-9 3/4	6 3/8	1-10 25/32
15/16	5 7/32	1-6 11/16	5 17/32-	1-7 23/32	5 13/16	1-8 25/32-	6 3/32	1-9 13/16	6 13/32-	1-10 27/32

Feet	40' Rise	40' Slope	50' Rise	50' Slope	60' Rise	60' Slope	70' Rise	70' Slope
0	11-8	41-8	14-7	52-1	17-6	62-6	20-5	72-11
1	11-11 1/2	42-8 1/2	14-10 1/2	53-1 1/2	17-9 1/2	63-6 1/2	20-8 1/2	73-11 1/2
2	12-3	43-9	15-2	54-2	18-1	64-7	21-0	75-0
3	12-6 1/2	44-9 1/2	15-5 1/2	55-2 1/2	18-4 1/2	65-7 1/2	21-3 1/2	76-0 1/2
4	12-10	45-10	15-9	56-3	18-8	66-8	21-7	77-1
5	13-1 1/2	46-10 1/2	16-0 1/2	57-3 1/2	18-11 1/2	67-8 1/2	21-10 1/2	78-1 1/2
6	13-5	47-11	16-4	58-4	19-3	68-9	22-2	79-2
7	13-8 1/2	48-11 1/2	16-7 1/2	59-4 1/2	19-6 1/2	69-9 1/2	22-5 1/2	80-2 1/2
8	14-0	50-0	16-11	60-5	19-10	70-10	22-9	81-3
9	14-3 1/2	51-0 1/2	17-2 1/2	61-5 1/2	20-1 1/2	71-10 1/2	23-0 1/2	82-3 1/2

natsin A=0.2800000000; natcos A=0.9600000000; nattan A=0.2916666666; natcot A=3.4285714285

Inches	0" Rise	0" Slope	1" Rise	1" Slope	2" Rise	2" Slope	3" Rise	3" Slope	4" Rise	4" Slope	5" Rise	5" Slope
0	0	0	5/16	1 1/32	19/32	2 3/32	7/8	3 1/8	1 3/16	4 3/16	1 1/2	5 1/32
1/16	1/32	1/16	5/16	1 3/32	5/8	2 5/32	29/32	3 3/16	1 7/32	4 1/4	1 1/2	5 9/32
1/8	1/32	1/8	11/32	1 3/16	5/8	2 7/32	15/16	3 1/4	1 7/32	4 5/16	1 17/32	5 11/32
3/16	3/32	3/16	11/32	1 1/4	21/32	2 9/32	15/16	3 5/16	1 1/4	4 3/8	1 17/32	5 13/32
1/4	1/16	1/4	3/8	1 5/16	21/32	2 11/32	31/32	3 3/8	1 1/4	4 7/16	1 9/16	5 15/32
5/16	3/32	5/16	3/8	1 3/8	11/16	2 13/32	31/32	3 15/32	1 9/32	4 1/2	1 9/16	5 17/32
3/8	1/8	13/32	13/32	1 7/16	23/32	2 15/32	1	3 17/32	1 9/32	4 9/16	1 19/32	5 19/32
7/16	1/8	15/32	7/16	1 1/2	23/32	2 17/32	1 1/32	3 19/32	1 5/16	4 5/8	1 5/8	5 11/16
1/2	5/32	17/32	7/16	1 9/16	3/4	2 19/32	1 1/32	3 21/32	1 11/32	4 11/16	1 5/8	5 3/4
9/16	5/32	19/32	15/32	1 5/8	3/4	2 11/16	1 1/16	3 23/32	1 11/32	4 3/4	1 21/32	5 13/16
5/8	3/16	21/32	15/32	1 11/16	25/32	2 3/4	1 1/16	3 25/32	1 3/8	4 13/16	1 21/32	5 7/8
11/16	7/32	23/32	1/2	1 3/4	13/16	2 13/16	1 3/32	3 27/32	1 13/32	4 7/8	1 11/16	5 15/16
3/4	7/32	25/32	17/32	1 13/16	13/16	2 7/8	1 1/8	3 29/32	1 13/32	4 31/32	1 23/32	6
13/16	1/4	27/32	17/32	1 29/32	27/32	2 15/16	1 1/8	3 31/32	1 7/16	5 1/32	1 23/32	6 1/16
7/8	1/4	29/32	9/16	1 31/32	27/32	3	1 5/32	4 1/32	1 7/16	5 3/32	1 3/4	6 1/8
15/16	9/32	31/32	9/16	2 1/32	7/8	3 1/16	1 5/32	4 3/32	1 15/32	5 5/32	1 3/4	6 3/16

Inches	6" Rise	6" Slope	7" Rise	7" Slope	8" Rise	8" Slope	9" Rise	9" Slope	10" Rise	10" Slope	11" Rise	11" Slope
0	1 25/32	6 1/4	2 1/16	7 5/16	2 3/8	8 11/32	2 11/16	9 3/8	2 31/32	10 7/16	3 1/4	11 15/32
1/16	1 13/16	6 5/16	2 3/32	7 3/8	2 13/32	8 13/32	2 11/16	9 15/32	3	10 1/2	3 9/32	11 17/32
1/8	1 13/16	6 3/8	2 1/8	7 7/16	2 13/32	8 15/32	2 23/32	9 17/32	3	10 9/16	3 5/16	11 19/32
3/16	1 27/32	6 15/32	2 1/8	7 1/2	2 7/16	8 17/32	2 23/32	9 19/32	3 1/32	10 5/8	3 5/16	11 21/32
1/4	1 27/32	6 17/32	2 5/32	7 9/16	2 7/16	8 19/32	2 3/4	9 21/32	3 1/16	10 11/16	3 11/32	11 3/4
5/16	1 7/8	6 19/32	2 5/32	7 5/8	2 15/32	8 21/32	2 3/4	9 23/32	3 1/16	10 3/4	3 11/32	11 13/16
3/8	1 29/32	6 21/32	2 3/16	7 11/16	2 1/2	8 3/4	2 25/32	9 25/32	3 3/32	10 13/16	3 3/8	11 7/8
7/16	1 29/32	6 23/32	2 7/32	7 3/4	2 1/2	8 13/16	2 13/16	9 27/32	3 3/32	10 7/8	3 13/32	11 15/16
1/2	1 15/16	6 25/32	2 7/32	7 13/16	2 17/32	8 7/8	2 13/16	9 29/32	3 1/8	10 15/16	3 13/32	1-0
9/16	1 15/16	6 27/32	2 1/4	7 7/8	2 17/32	8 15/16	2 27/32	9 31/32	3 1/8	11 1/32	3 7/16	1-0 1/16
5/8	1 31/32	6 29/32	2 1/4	7 31/32	2 9/16	9	2 27/32	10 1/32	3 5/32	11 3/32	3 7/16	1-0 1/8
11/16	2	6 31/32	2 9/32	8 1/32	2 19/32	9 1/16	2 7/8	10 3/32	3 3/16	11 5/32	3 15/32	1-0 3/16
3/4	2	7 1/32	2 5/16	8 3/32	2 19/32	9 1/8	2 29/32	10 5/32	3 3/16	11 7/32	3 1/2	1-0 1/4
13/16	2 1/32	7 3/32	2 5/16	8 5/32	2 5/8	9 3/16	2 29/32	10 1/4	3 7/32	11 9/32	3 1/2	1-0 5/16
7/8	2 1/32	7 5/32	2 11/32	8 7/32	2 5/8	9 1/4	2 15/16	10 5/16	3 7/32	11 11/32	3 17/32	1-0 3/8
15/16	2 1/16	7 1/4	2 11/32	8 9/32	2 21/32	9 5/16	2 15/16	10 3/8	3 1/4	11 13/32	3 17/32	1-0 7/16

Feet	0' Rise	0' Slope	10' Rise	10' Slope	20' Rise	20' Slope	30' Rise	30' Slope
0	0	0	2-11 5/8	10-5 3/16	5-11 1/4	20-10 11/32	8-10 7/8	31-3 17/32
1	3 1/4	1-0 17/32	3-3 3/8	11-5 11/16	6-2 13/32	21-10 7/8	9-2 7/16	32-4 1/8
2	7 1/8	2-1 1/2	3-6 3/4	12-6 1/2	6-6 3/8	22-11 3/8	9-6	33-4 9/16
3	10 11/16	3-1 9/16	3-10 5/16	13-6 23/32	6-9 15/16	23-11 29/32	9-9 9/16	34-5 3/32
4	1-2 1/4	4-2 1/4	4-1 7/8	14-7 1/4	7-1 1/2	25-0 7/16	10-1 1/8	35-5 19/32
5	1-5 13/16	5-2 19/32	4-5 7/16	15-7 3/4	7-5 1/16	26-0 15/16	10-4 11/16	36-6 1/8
6	1-9 3/8	6-3 3/32	4-9	16-8 9/32	7-8 5/8	27-1 15/32	10-8 1/4	37-6 5/8
7	2-0 15/16	7-3 5/8	5-0 9/16	17-8 13/16	8-0 3/16	28-1 31/32	10-11 13/16	38-7 5/32
8	2-4 1/2	8-4 5/32	5-4 1/8	18-9 5/16	8-3 3/4	29-2 1/2	11-3 3/8	39-7 21/32
9	2-8 1/16	9-4 21/32	5-7 11/16	19-9 27/32	8-7 5/16	30-3	11-6 15/16	40-8 3/16

A = 16° 32' 05"; logsin A = 9.45423; logcos A = 9.98166; logtan A = 9.47257; logcot A = 0.52743

ins.	12″ Rise	12″ Slope	13″ Rise	13″ Slope	14″ Rise	14″ Slope	15″ Rise	15″ Slope	16″ Rise	16″ Slope
0	$3\frac{9}{16}$	$1\text{-}0\frac{17}{32}$	$3\frac{7}{8}$	$1\text{-}1\frac{9}{16}$	$4\frac{5}{32}$	$1\text{-}2\frac{19}{32}$	$4\frac{7}{16}$	$1\text{-}3\frac{21}{32}$	$4\frac{3}{4}$	$1\text{-}4\frac{11}{16}$
$\frac{1}{16}$	$3\frac{19}{32}$	$1\text{-}0\frac{19}{32}$	$3\frac{7}{8}$	$1\text{-}1\frac{5}{8}$	$4\frac{3}{16}$	$1\text{-}2\frac{21}{32}$	$4\frac{15}{32}$	$1\text{-}3\frac{23}{32}$	$4\frac{25}{32}$	$1\text{-}4\frac{3}{4}$
$\frac{1}{8}$	$3\frac{19}{32}$	$1\text{-}0\frac{21}{32}$	$3\frac{29}{32}$	$1\text{-}1\frac{11}{16}$	$4\frac{3}{16}$	$1\text{-}2\frac{23}{32}$	$4\frac{1}{2}$	$1\text{-}3\frac{25}{32}$	$4\frac{25}{32}$	$1\text{-}4\frac{13}{16}$
$\frac{3}{16}$	$3\frac{5}{8}$	$1\text{-}0\frac{23}{32}$	$3\frac{29}{32}$	$1\text{-}1\frac{3}{4}$	$4\frac{7}{32}$	$1\text{-}2\frac{13}{16}$	$4\frac{1}{2}$	$1\text{-}3\frac{27}{32}$	$4\frac{13}{16}$	$1\text{-}4\frac{7}{8}$
$\frac{1}{4}$	$3\frac{5}{8}$	$1\text{-}0\frac{25}{32}$	$3\frac{15}{16}$	$1\text{-}1\frac{13}{16}$	$4\frac{7}{32}$	$1\text{-}2\frac{7}{8}$	$4\frac{17}{32}$	$1\text{-}3\frac{29}{32}$	$4\frac{13}{16}$	$1\text{-}4\frac{15}{16}$
$\frac{5}{16}$	$3\frac{21}{32}$	$1\text{-}0\frac{27}{32}$	$3\frac{15}{16}$	$1\text{-}1\frac{7}{8}$	$4\frac{1}{4}$	$1\text{-}2\frac{15}{16}$	$4\frac{17}{32}$	$1\text{-}3\frac{31}{32}$	$4\frac{27}{32}$	$1\text{-}5\frac{1}{32}$
$\frac{3}{8}$	$3\frac{11}{16}$	$1\text{-}0\frac{29}{32}$	$3\frac{31}{32}$	$1\text{-}1\frac{15}{16}$	$4\frac{9}{32}$	$1\text{-}3$	$4\frac{9}{16}$	$1\text{-}4\frac{1}{32}$	$4\frac{7}{8}$	$1\text{-}5\frac{3}{32}$
$\frac{7}{16}$	$3\frac{11}{16}$	$1\text{-}0\frac{31}{32}$	4	$1\text{-}2\frac{1}{32}$	$4\frac{9}{32}$	$1\text{-}3\frac{1}{16}$	$4\frac{19}{32}$	$1\text{-}4\frac{3}{32}$	$4\frac{7}{8}$	$1\text{-}5\frac{5}{32}$
$\frac{1}{2}$	$3\frac{23}{32}$	$1\text{-}1\frac{1}{32}$	4	$1\text{-}2\frac{3}{32}$	$4\frac{5}{16}$	$1\text{-}3\frac{1}{8}$	$4\frac{19}{32}$	$1\text{-}4\frac{5}{32}$	$4\frac{29}{32}$	$1\text{-}5\frac{7}{32}$
$\frac{9}{16}$	$3\frac{23}{32}$	$1\text{-}1\frac{3}{32}$	$4\frac{1}{32}$	$1\text{-}2\frac{5}{32}$	$4\frac{5}{16}$	$1\text{-}3\frac{3}{16}$	$4\frac{5}{8}$	$1\text{-}4\frac{7}{32}$	$4\frac{29}{32}$	$1\text{-}5\frac{9}{32}$
$\frac{5}{8}$	$3\frac{3}{4}$	$1\text{-}1\frac{5}{32}$	$4\frac{1}{32}$	$1\text{-}2\frac{7}{32}$	$4\frac{11}{32}$	$1\text{-}3\frac{1}{4}$	$4\frac{5}{8}$	$1\text{-}4\frac{5}{16}$	$4\frac{15}{16}$	$1\text{-}5\frac{11}{32}$
$\frac{11}{16}$	$3\frac{25}{32}$	$1\text{-}1\frac{1}{4}$	$4\frac{1}{16}$	$1\text{-}2\frac{9}{32}$	$4\frac{3}{8}$	$1\text{-}3\frac{5}{16}$	$4\frac{21}{32}$	$1\text{-}4\frac{3}{8}$	$4\frac{31}{32}$	$1\text{-}5\frac{13}{32}$
$\frac{3}{4}$	$3\frac{25}{32}$	$1\text{-}1\frac{5}{16}$	$4\frac{3}{32}$	$1\text{-}2\frac{11}{32}$	$4\frac{3}{8}$	$1\text{-}3\frac{3}{8}$	$4\frac{11}{16}$	$1\text{-}4\frac{7}{16}$	$4\frac{31}{32}$	$1\text{-}5\frac{15}{32}$
$\frac{13}{16}$	$3\frac{13}{16}$	$1\text{-}1\frac{3}{8}$	$4\frac{3}{32}$	$1\text{-}2\frac{13}{32}$	$4\frac{13}{32}$	$1\text{-}3\frac{7}{16}$	$4\frac{11}{16}$	$1\text{-}4\frac{1}{2}$	5	$1\text{-}5\frac{17}{32}$
$\frac{7}{8}$	$3\frac{13}{16}$	$1\text{-}1\frac{7}{16}$	$4\frac{1}{8}$	$1\text{-}2\frac{15}{32}$	$4\frac{13}{32}$	$1\text{-}3\frac{17}{32}$	$4\frac{23}{32}$	$1\text{-}4\frac{9}{16}$	5	$1\text{-}5\frac{19}{32}$
$\frac{15}{16}$	$3\frac{27}{32}$	$1\text{-}1\frac{1}{2}$	$4\frac{1}{8}$	$1\text{-}2\frac{17}{32}$	$4\frac{7}{16}$	$1\text{-}3\frac{19}{32}$	$4\frac{25}{32}$	$1\text{-}4\frac{5}{8}$	$5\frac{1}{2}$	$1\text{-}5\frac{21}{32}$

ins.	17″ Rise	17″ Slope	18″ Rise	18″ Slope	19″ Rise	19″ Slope	20″ Rise	20″ Slope	21″ Rise	21″ Slope
0	$5\frac{1}{16}$	$1\text{-}5\frac{23}{32}$	$5\frac{11}{32}$	$1\text{-}6\frac{25}{32}$	$5\frac{5}{8}$	$1\text{-}7\frac{13}{16}$	$5\frac{15}{16}$	$1\text{-}8\frac{7}{8}$	$6\frac{1}{4}$	$1\text{-}9\frac{29}{32}$
$\frac{1}{16}$	$5\frac{1}{16}$	$1\text{-}5\frac{13}{16}$	$5\frac{3}{8}$	$1\text{-}6\frac{27}{32}$	$5\frac{21}{32}$	$1\text{-}7\frac{7}{8}$	$5\frac{31}{32}$	$1\text{-}8\frac{15}{16}$	$6\frac{1}{4}$	$1\text{-}9\frac{31}{32}$
$\frac{1}{8}$	$5\frac{3}{32}$	$1\text{-}5\frac{7}{8}$	$5\frac{3}{8}$	$1\text{-}6\frac{29}{32}$	$5\frac{11}{16}$	$1\text{-}7\frac{15}{16}$	$5\frac{31}{32}$	$1\text{-}9$	$6\frac{9}{32}$	$1\text{-}10\frac{1}{32}$
$\frac{3}{16}$	$5\frac{3}{32}$	$1\text{-}5\frac{15}{16}$	$5\frac{13}{32}$	$1\text{-}6\frac{31}{32}$	$5\frac{11}{16}$	$1\text{-}8$	6	$1\text{-}9\frac{1}{16}$	$6\frac{9}{32}$	$1\text{-}10\frac{3}{32}$
$\frac{1}{4}$	$5\frac{1}{8}$	$1\text{-}6$	$5\frac{13}{32}$	$1\text{-}7\frac{1}{32}$	$5\frac{23}{32}$	$1\text{-}8\frac{3}{32}$	6	$1\text{-}9\frac{1}{8}$	$6\frac{5}{16}$	$1\text{-}10\frac{5}{32}$
$\frac{5}{16}$	$5\frac{1}{8}$	$1\text{-}6\frac{1}{16}$	$5\frac{7}{16}$	$1\text{-}7\frac{3}{32}$	$5\frac{23}{32}$	$1\text{-}8\frac{5}{32}$	$6\frac{1}{32}$	$1\text{-}9\frac{3}{16}$	$6\frac{5}{16}$	$1\text{-}10\frac{7}{32}$
$\frac{3}{8}$	$5\frac{5}{32}$	$1\text{-}6\frac{1}{8}$	$5\frac{15}{32}$	$1\text{-}7\frac{5}{32}$	$5\frac{3}{4}$	$1\text{-}8\frac{7}{32}$	$6\frac{1}{16}$	$1\text{-}9\frac{1}{4}$	$6\frac{11}{32}$	$1\text{-}10\frac{5}{16}$
$\frac{7}{16}$	$5\frac{3}{16}$	$1\text{-}6\frac{3}{16}$	$5\frac{15}{32}$	$1\text{-}7\frac{7}{32}$	$5\frac{25}{32}$	$1\text{-}8\frac{9}{32}$	$6\frac{1}{16}$	$1\text{-}9\frac{5}{16}$	$6\frac{3}{8}$	$1\text{-}10\frac{3}{8}$
$\frac{1}{2}$	$5\frac{3}{16}$	$1\text{-}6\frac{1}{4}$	$5\frac{1}{2}$	$1\text{-}7\frac{5}{16}$	$5\frac{25}{32}$	$1\text{-}8\frac{11}{32}$	$6\frac{3}{32}$	$1\text{-}9\frac{3}{8}$	$6\frac{3}{8}$	$1\text{-}10\frac{7}{16}$
$\frac{9}{16}$	$5\frac{7}{32}$	$1\text{-}6\frac{5}{16}$	$5\frac{1}{2}$	$1\text{-}7\frac{3}{8}$	$5\frac{13}{16}$	$1\text{-}8\frac{13}{32}$	$6\frac{3}{32}$	$1\text{-}9\frac{7}{16}$	$6\frac{13}{32}$	$1\text{-}10\frac{1}{2}$
$\frac{5}{8}$	$5\frac{7}{32}$	$1\text{-}6\frac{3}{8}$	$5\frac{17}{32}$	$1\text{-}7\frac{7}{16}$	$5\frac{13}{16}$	$1\text{-}8\frac{15}{32}$	$6\frac{1}{8}$	$1\text{-}9\frac{1}{2}$	$6\frac{13}{32}$	$1\text{-}10\frac{9}{16}$
$\frac{11}{16}$	$5\frac{1}{4}$	$1\text{-}6\frac{7}{16}$	$5\frac{9}{16}$	$1\text{-}7\frac{1}{2}$	$5\frac{27}{32}$	$1\text{-}8\frac{17}{32}$	$6\frac{5}{32}$	$1\text{-}9\frac{19}{32}$	$6\frac{7}{16}$	$1\text{-}10\frac{5}{8}$
$\frac{3}{4}$	$5\frac{9}{32}$	$1\text{-}6\frac{17}{32}$	$5\frac{9}{16}$	$1\text{-}7\frac{9}{16}$	$5\frac{7}{8}$	$1\text{-}8\frac{19}{32}$	$6\frac{5}{32}$	$1\text{-}9\frac{21}{32}$	$6\frac{15}{32}$	$1\text{-}10\frac{11}{16}$
$\frac{13}{16}$	$5\frac{9}{32}$	$1\text{-}6\frac{19}{32}$	$5\frac{19}{32}$	$1\text{-}7\frac{5}{8}$	$5\frac{7}{8}$	$1\text{-}8\frac{21}{32}$	$6\frac{3}{16}$	$1\text{-}9\frac{23}{32}$	$6\frac{15}{32}$	$1\text{-}10\frac{3}{4}$
$\frac{7}{8}$	$5\frac{5}{16}$	$1\text{-}6\frac{21}{32}$	$5\frac{19}{32}$	$1\text{-}7\frac{11}{16}$	$5\frac{29}{32}$	$1\text{-}8\frac{23}{32}$	$6\frac{3}{16}$	$1\text{-}9\frac{25}{32}$	$6\frac{1}{2}$	$1\text{-}10\frac{13}{16}$
$\frac{15}{16}$	$5\frac{5}{16}$	$1\text{-}6\frac{23}{32}$	$5\frac{5}{8}$	$1\text{-}7\frac{3}{4}$	$5\frac{29}{32}$	$1\text{-}8\frac{13}{16}$	$6\frac{7}{32}$	$1\text{-}9\frac{27}{32}$	$6\frac{1}{2}$	$1\text{-}10\frac{7}{8}$

Feet	40′ Rise	40′ Slope	50′ Rise	50′ Slope	60′ Rise	60′ Slope	70′ Rise	70′ Slope
0	$11\text{-}10\frac{1}{2}$	$41\text{-}8\frac{23}{32}$	$14\text{-}10\frac{1}{8}$	$52\text{-}1\frac{7}{8}$	$17\text{-}9\frac{3}{4}$	$62\text{-}7\frac{1}{16}$	$20\text{-}9\frac{3}{8}$	$73\text{-}0\frac{1}{4}$
1	$12\text{-}2\frac{1}{16}$	$42\text{-}9\frac{7}{32}$	$15\text{-}1\frac{11}{16}$	$53\text{-}2\frac{13}{32}$	$18\text{-}1\frac{5}{8}$	$63\text{-}7\frac{9}{16}$	$21\text{-}0\frac{15}{16}$	$74\text{-}0\frac{3}{4}$
2	$12\text{-}5\frac{5}{8}$	$43\text{-}9\frac{3}{4}$	$15\text{-}5\frac{1}{4}$	$54\text{-}2\frac{29}{32}$	$18\text{-}4\frac{7}{8}$	$64\text{-}8\frac{3}{32}$	$21\text{-}4\frac{1}{2}$	$75\text{-}1\frac{9}{32}$
3	$12\text{-}9\frac{3}{16}$	$44\text{-}10\frac{1}{4}$	$15\text{-}8\frac{13}{16}$	$55\text{-}3\frac{7}{16}$	$18\text{-}8\frac{7}{8}$	$65\text{-}8\frac{5}{8}$	$21\text{-}8\frac{1}{16}$	$76\text{-}1\frac{25}{32}$
4	$13\text{-}0\frac{3}{4}$	$45\text{-}10\frac{25}{32}$	$16\text{-}0\frac{3}{8}$	$56\text{-}3\frac{15}{16}$	$19\text{-}0$	$66\text{-}9\frac{1}{8}$	$21\text{-}11\frac{5}{8}$	$77\text{-}2\frac{5}{16}$
5	$13\text{-}4\frac{5}{16}$	$46\text{-}11\frac{9}{32}$	$16\text{-}3\frac{15}{16}$	$57\text{-}4\frac{15}{32}$	$19\text{-}3\frac{9}{16}$	$67\text{-}9\frac{21}{32}$	$22\text{-}3\frac{3}{16}$	$78\text{-}2\frac{13}{16}$
6	$13\text{-}7\frac{7}{8}$	$47\text{-}11\frac{13}{16}$	$16\text{-}7\frac{1}{2}$	$58\text{-}5$	$19\text{-}7\frac{1}{8}$	$68\text{-}10\frac{5}{32}$	$22\text{-}6\frac{3}{4}$	$79\text{-}3\frac{11}{32}$
7	$13\text{-}11\frac{7}{16}$	$49\text{-}0\frac{11}{32}$	$16\text{-}11\frac{1}{16}$	$59\text{-}5\frac{1}{2}$	$19\text{-}10\frac{11}{16}$	$69\text{-}10\frac{11}{16}$	$22\text{-}10\frac{5}{16}$	$80\text{-}3\frac{27}{32}$
8	$14\text{-}3$	$50\text{-}0\frac{7}{32}$	$17\text{-}2\frac{5}{8}$	$60\text{-}6\frac{1}{32}$	$20\text{-}2\frac{1}{4}$	$70\text{-}11\frac{3}{16}$	$23\text{-}1\frac{7}{8}$	$81\text{-}4\frac{3}{8}$
9	$14\text{-}6\frac{9}{16}$	$51\text{-}1\frac{3}{8}$	$17\text{-}6\frac{3}{16}$	$61\text{-}6\frac{17}{32}$	$20\text{-}5\frac{13}{16}$	$71\text{-}11\frac{23}{32}$	$23\text{-}5\frac{7}{16}$	$82\text{-}4\frac{29}{32}$

natsin A=0.2845982884; natcos A=0.9586468662; nattan A=0.2968750000; natcot A=3.3684210526

Inches	0" Rise	0" Slope	1" Rise	1" Slope	2" Rise	2" Slope	3" Rise	3" Slope	4" Rise	4" Slope	5" Rise	5" Slope
0	0	0	5/16	1 1/32	19/32	2 3/32	29/32	3 1/8	1 7/32	4 3/16	1 1/2	5 7/32
1/16	1/32	1/16	5/16	1 1/8	5/8	2 5/32	15/16	3 3/16	1 7/32	4 1/4	1 17/32	5 9/32
1/8	1/32	1/8	11/32	1 3/16	21/32	2 7/32	15/16	3 1/4	1 1/4	4 5/16	1 9/16	5 11/32
3/16	1/16	3/16	11/32	1 1/4	21/32	2 9/32	31/32	3 11/32	1 1/4	4 3/8	1 9/16	5 13/32
1/4	1/16	1/4	3/8	1 5/16	11/16	2 11/32	31/32	3 13/32	1 9/32	4 7/16	1 19/32	5 15/32
5/16	3/32	5/16	13/32	1 3/8	11/16	2 13/32	1	3 15/32	1 5/16	4 1/2	1 19/32	5 9/16
3/8	1/8	13/32	13/32	1 7/16	23/32	2 15/32	1 1/16–	3 17/32	1 5/16	4 9/16	1 5/8	5 5/8
7/16	1/8	15/32	7/16	1 1/2	3/4	2 17/32	1 1/16–	3 19/32	1 11/32–	4 5/8	1 21/32	5 11/32
1/2	5/32	17/32	7/16	1 9/16	3/4	2 5/8	1 1/16	3 21/32	1 3/8	4 11/16	1 21/32	5 3/4
9/16	5/32	19/32	15/32	1 5/8	25/32	2 11/16	1 1/16	3 23/32	1 3/8	4 25/32	1 11/16	5 13/16
5/8	3/16	21/32	1/2	1 11/16	25/32	2 3/4	1 3/32	3 25/32	1 13/32–	4 27/32	1 11/16	5 7/8
11/16	7/32	23/32	1/2	1 3/4	13/16	2 13/16	1 1/8	3 27/32	1 13/32–	4 29/32	1 23/32	5 15/16
3/4	7/32	25/32	17/32	1 13/16	27/32	2 7/8	1 1/8	3 29/32	1 7/16	4 31/32	1 3/4	6
13/16	1/4	27/32	9/16	1 29/32	27/32	2 15/16	1 5/32–	3 31/32	1 15/32–	5 1/32–	1 3/4	6 1/16
7/8	1/4	29/32	9/16	1 31/32	7/8	3	1 5/32–	4 1/16	1 15/32–	5 3/32–	1 25/32	6 1/8
15/16	9/32	31/32	19/32	2 1/32	7/8	3 1/16	1 3/16	4 1/8	1 1/2	5 5/32–	1 25/32	6 3/16

Inches	6" Rise	6" Slope	7" Rise	7" Slope	8" Rise	8" Slope	9" Rise	9" Slope	10" Rise	10" Slope	11" Rise	11" Slope
0	1 13/16	6 9/32	2 1/8	7 5/16	2 13/32	8 11/32–	2 23/32	9 13/32–	3 1/32–	10 7/16	3 5/16	11 1/2
1/16	1 27/32	6 11/32–	2 1/8	7 3/8	2 7/16	8 7/16	2 3/4	9 15/32–	3 1/32–	10 1/2	3 11/32–	11 9/32–
1/8	1 27/32	6 13/32–	2 5/32–	7 7/16	2 15/32–	8 1/2	2 3/4	9 17/32–	3 1/16	10 9/16	3 3/8	11 5/8
3/16	1 7/8	6 15/32–	2 5/32–	7 1/2	2 15/32–	8 9/16	2 25/32–	9 19/32–	3 1/16	10 21/32–	3 3/8	11 11/16
1/4	1 7/8	6 17/32–	2 3/16–	7 9/16	2 1/2	8 5/8	2 25/32–	9 21/32–	3 3/32–	10 23/32–	3 13/32–	11 3/4
5/16	1 29/32	6 19/32–	2 7/32–	7 5/8	2 1/2	8 11/16	2 13/16	9 23/32–	3 1/8	10 25/32–	3 13/32–	11 13/16
3/8	1 15/16	6 21/32–	2 7/32–	7 23/32–	2 17/32–	8 3/4	2 27/32–	9 25/32–	3 1/8	10 27/32–	3 7/16	11 7/8
7/16	1 15/16	6 23/32–	2 1/4	7 25/32–	2 9/16	8 13/16	2 27/32–	9 27/32–	3 5/32–	10 29/32–	3 15/32–	11 15/16
1/2	1 31/32	6 25/32–	2 1/4	7 27/32–	2 9/16	8 7/8	2 7/8	9 15/16	3 3/16–	10 31/32–	3 15/32–	1-0
9/16	1 31/32	6 27/32–	2 9/32–	7 29/32–	2 19/32–	8 15/16	2 7/8	10	3 3/16–	11 1/32–	3 1/2	1-0 3/32–
5/8	2	6 29/32–	2 5/16	7 31/32–	2 19/32–	9	2 29/32–	10 1/16	3 7/32–	11 3/32–	3 1/2	1-0 5/32–
11/16	2 1/32–	7	2 5/16	8 1/32–	2 5/8	9 1/16	2 15/16	10 1/8	3 7/32–	11 5/32–	3 17/32–	1-0 7/32–
3/4	2 1/32–	7 1/16	2 11/32–	8 3/32–	2 21/32–	9 1/8	2 15/16	10 3/16–	3 1/4	11 7/32–	3 9/16	1-0 9/32–
13/16	2 1/16	7 1/8	2 3/8	8 5/32–	2 21/32–	9 7/32–	2 31/32–	10 1/4	3 9/32–	11 9/32–	3 9/16	1-0 11/32–
7/8	2 1/16	7 3/16	2 3/8	8 7/32–	2 11/16	9 9/32–	2 31/32–	10 5/16	3 9/32–	11 3/8–	3 19/32–	1-0 13/32–
15/16	2 3/32	7 1/4	2 13/32–	8 9/32–	2 11/16	9 11/32–	3	10 3/8	3 5/16	11 7/16	3 19/32–	1-0 15/32–

Feet	0' Rise	0' Slope	10' Rise	10' Slope	20' Rise	20' Slope	30' Rise	30' Slope
0	0	0	3-0 1/4	10-5 11/32–	6-0 1/2	20-10 23/32–	9-0 3/4	31-4 1/32–
1	3 5/8	1-0 17/32–	3-3 7/8	11-5 29/32–	6-4 1/8	21-11 1/4	9-4 3/8	32-4 19/32–
2	7 1/4	2-1 1/16	3-7 1/2	12-6 7/16	6-7 3/4	22-11 25/32–	9-8	33-5 1/8
3	10 7/8	3-1 19/32–	3-11 1/8	13-6 31/32–	6-11 3/8	24-0 5/16	9-11 5/8	34-5 11/16
4	1-2 1/2	4-2 5/32–	4-2 3/4	14-7 1/2	7-3	25-0 27/32–	10-3 1/4	35-6 7/32–
5	1-6 1/8	5-2 11/16	4-6 3/8	15-8 1/32–	7-6 5/8	26-1 3/8	10-6 7/8	36-6 3/4
6	1-9 3/4	6-3 7/32–	4-10	16-8 9/16	7-10 1/4	27-1 15/16	10-10 1/2	37-7 9/32–
7	2-1 3/8	7-3 3/4	5-1 5/8	17-9 3/32–	8-1 7/8	28-2 15/32–	11-2 1/8	38-7 13/16
8	2-5	8-4 9/32–	5-5 1/4	18-9 5/8	8-5 1/2	29-3	11-5 3/4	39-8 11/32–
9	2-8 5/8	9-4 13/16	5-8 7/8	19-10 3/16	8-9 1/8	30-3 17/32–	11-9 3/8	40-8 7/8

A = 16° 48′ 31″; logsin A = 9.46116; logcos A = 9.98104; logtan A = 9.48013; logcot A = 0.51987

	12″		13″		14″		15″		16″	
Ins.	Rise	Slope	Rise	Slope	Rise	Slope	Rise	Slope	Rise	Slope
0	$3\frac{5}{8}$	$1\text{-}0\frac{17}{32}$	$3\frac{15}{16}$	$1\text{-}1\frac{19}{32}$	$4\frac{7}{32}$	$1\text{-}2\frac{5}{8}$	$4\frac{17}{32}$	$1\text{-}3\frac{21}{32}$	$4\frac{27}{32}$	$1\text{-}4\frac{23}{32}$
$\frac{1}{16}$	$3\frac{21}{32}$	$1\text{-}0\frac{19}{32}$	$3\frac{15}{16}$	$1\text{-}1\frac{21}{32}$	$4\frac{1}{4}$	$1\text{-}2\frac{11}{16}$	$4\frac{9}{16}$	$1\text{-}3\frac{3}{4}$	$4\frac{27}{32}$	$1\text{-}4\frac{25}{32}$
$\frac{1}{8}$	$3\frac{21}{32}$	$1\text{-}0\frac{21}{32}$	$3\frac{31}{32}$	$1\text{-}1\frac{23}{32}$	$4\frac{9}{32}$	$1\text{-}2\frac{3}{4}$	$4\frac{9}{16}$	$1\text{-}3\frac{13}{32}$	$4\frac{7}{8}$	$1\text{-}4\frac{27}{32}$
$\frac{3}{16}$	$3\frac{11}{16}$	$1\text{-}0\frac{23}{32}$	$3\frac{31}{32}$	$1\text{-}1\frac{25}{32}$	$4\frac{9}{32}$	$1\text{-}2\frac{13}{16}$	$4\frac{19}{32}$	$1\text{-}3\frac{7}{8}$	$4\frac{7}{8}$	$1\text{-}4\frac{29}{32}$
$\frac{1}{4}$	$3\frac{11}{16}$	$1\text{-}0\frac{25}{32}$	4	$1\text{-}1\frac{27}{32}$	$4\frac{5}{16}$	$1\text{-}2\frac{7}{8}$	$4\frac{19}{32}$	$1\text{-}3\frac{15}{16}$	$4\frac{29}{32}$	$1\text{-}4\frac{31}{32}$
$\frac{5}{16}$	$3\frac{23}{32}$	$1\text{-}0\frac{7}{8}$	$4\frac{1}{32}$	$1\text{-}1\frac{29}{32}$	$4\frac{5}{16}$	$1\text{-}2\frac{15}{16}$	$4\frac{5}{8}$	$1\text{-}4$	$4\frac{15}{16}$	$1\text{-}5\frac{1}{32}$
$\frac{3}{8}$	$3\frac{3}{4}$	$1\text{-}0\frac{15}{16}$	$4\frac{1}{32}$	$1\text{-}1\frac{31}{32}$	$4\frac{11}{32}$	$1\text{-}3\frac{1}{2}$	$4\frac{21}{32}$	$1\text{-}4\frac{1}{16}$	$4\frac{15}{16}$	$1\text{-}5\frac{3}{32}$
$\frac{7}{16}$	$3\frac{3}{4}$	$1\text{-}1$	$4\frac{1}{16}$	$1\text{-}2\frac{1}{32}$	$4\frac{3}{8}$	$1\text{-}3\frac{3}{32}$	$4\frac{21}{32}$	$1\text{-}4\frac{1}{8}$	$4\frac{31}{32}$	$1\text{-}5\frac{5}{32}$
$\frac{1}{2}$	$3\frac{25}{32}$	$1\text{-}1\frac{1}{16}$	$4\frac{1}{16}$	$1\text{-}2\frac{3}{32}$	$4\frac{3}{8}$	$1\text{-}3\frac{5}{32}$	$4\frac{11}{16}$	$1\text{-}4\frac{3}{16}$	5	$1\text{-}5\frac{1}{4}$
$\frac{9}{16}$	$3\frac{25}{32}$	$1\text{-}1\frac{1}{8}$	$4\frac{3}{32}$	$1\text{-}2\frac{5}{32}$	$4\frac{13}{32}$	$1\text{-}3\frac{7}{32}$	$4\frac{11}{16}$	$1\text{-}4\frac{1}{4}$	5	$1\text{-}5\frac{5}{32}$
$\frac{5}{8}$	$3\frac{13}{16}$	$1\text{-}1\frac{3}{16}$	$4\frac{1}{8}$	$1\text{-}2\frac{7}{32}$	$4\frac{13}{32}$	$1\text{-}3\frac{9}{32}$	$4\frac{23}{32}$	$1\text{-}4\frac{5}{32}$	$5\frac{1}{32}$	$1\text{-}5\frac{3}{8}$
$\frac{11}{16}$	$3\frac{27}{32}$	$1\text{-}1\frac{1}{4}$	$4\frac{1}{8}$	$1\text{-}2\frac{5}{16}$	$4\frac{7}{16}$	$1\text{-}3\frac{11}{32}$	$4\frac{3}{4}$	$1\text{-}4\frac{3}{8}$	$5\frac{1}{32}$	$1\text{-}5\frac{7}{16}$
$\frac{3}{4}$	$3\frac{27}{32}$	$1\text{-}1\frac{5}{16}$	$4\frac{5}{16}$	$1\text{-}2\frac{3}{8}$	$4\frac{15}{32}$	$1\text{-}3\frac{13}{32}$	$4\frac{3}{4}$	$1\text{-}4\frac{7}{16}$	$5\frac{1}{16}$	$1\text{-}5\frac{1}{2}$
$\frac{13}{16}$	$3\frac{7}{8}$	$1\text{-}1\frac{3}{8}$	$4\frac{9}{16}$	$1\text{-}2\frac{7}{16}$	$4\frac{15}{32}$	$1\text{-}3\frac{15}{32}$	$4\frac{25}{32}$	$1\text{-}4\frac{17}{32}$	$5\frac{3}{32}$	$1\text{-}5\frac{9}{16}$
$\frac{7}{8}$	$3\frac{7}{8}$	$1\text{-}1\frac{7}{16}$	$4\frac{3}{16}$	$1\text{-}2\frac{1}{2}$	$4\frac{1}{2}$	$1\text{-}3\frac{17}{32}$	$4\frac{25}{32}$	$1\text{-}4\frac{19}{32}$	$5\frac{3}{32}$	$1\text{-}5\frac{5}{8}$
$\frac{15}{16}$	$3\frac{29}{32}$	$1\text{-}1\frac{1}{2}$	$4\frac{7}{16}$	$1\text{-}2\frac{9}{32}$	$4\frac{1}{2}$	$1\text{-}3\frac{19}{32}$	$4\frac{13}{16}$	$1\text{-}4\frac{21}{32}$	$5\frac{1}{8}$	$1\text{-}5\frac{11}{16}$

	17″		18″		19″		20″		21″	
Ins.	Rise	Slope	Rise	Slope	Rise	Slope	Rise	Slope	Rise	Slope
0	$5\frac{1}{8}$	$1\text{-}5\frac{3}{4}$	$5\frac{7}{16}$	$1\text{-}6\frac{13}{16}$	$5\frac{3}{4}$	$1\text{-}7\frac{27}{32}$	$6\frac{1}{8}$	$1\text{-}8\frac{29}{32}$	$6\frac{11}{16}$	$1\text{-}9\frac{15}{16}$
$\frac{1}{16}$	$5\frac{5}{32}$	$1\text{-}5\frac{13}{16}$	$5\frac{15}{32}$	$1\text{-}6\frac{7}{8}$	$5\frac{3}{4}$	$1\text{-}7\frac{29}{32}$	$6\frac{1}{16}$	$1\text{-}8\frac{31}{32}$	$6\frac{3}{8}$	$1\text{-}10$
$\frac{1}{8}$	$5\frac{3}{16}$	$1\text{-}5\frac{7}{8}$	$5\frac{15}{32}$	$1\text{-}6\frac{15}{16}$	$5\frac{25}{32}$	$1\text{-}7\frac{31}{32}$	$6\frac{3}{32}$	$1\text{-}9\frac{1}{32}$	$6\frac{3}{8}$	$1\text{-}10\frac{1}{16}$
$\frac{3}{16}$	$5\frac{3}{16}$	$1\text{-}5\frac{31}{32}$	$5\frac{1}{2}$	$1\text{-}7$	$5\frac{25}{32}$	$1\text{-}8\frac{1}{32}$	$6\frac{3}{32}$	$1\text{-}9\frac{3}{32}$	$6\frac{13}{32}$	$1\text{-}10\frac{1}{8}$
$\frac{1}{4}$	$5\frac{7}{32}$	$1\text{-}6\frac{1}{32}$	$5\frac{1}{2}$	$1\text{-}7\frac{1}{16}$	$5\frac{13}{16}$	$1\text{-}8\frac{3}{32}$	$6\frac{1}{8}$	$1\text{-}9\frac{5}{32}$	$6\frac{13}{32}$	$1\text{-}10\frac{3}{16}$
$\frac{5}{16}$	$5\frac{7}{32}$	$1\text{-}6\frac{3}{32}$	$5\frac{17}{32}$	$1\text{-}7\frac{1}{8}$	$5\frac{27}{32}$	$1\text{-}8\frac{3}{32}$	$6\frac{1}{8}$	$1\text{-}9\frac{7}{32}$	$6\frac{7}{16}$	$1\text{-}10\frac{1}{4}$
$\frac{3}{8}$	$5\frac{1}{4}$	$1\text{-}6\frac{5}{32}$	$5\frac{9}{16}$	$1\text{-}7\frac{3}{16}$	$5\frac{7}{8}$	$1\text{-}8\frac{1}{4}$	$6\frac{3}{16}$	$1\text{-}9\frac{9}{32}$	$6\frac{15}{32}$	$1\text{-}10\frac{11}{32}$
$\frac{7}{16}$	$5\frac{9}{32}$	$1\text{-}6\frac{7}{32}$	$5\frac{9}{16}$	$1\text{-}7\frac{1}{4}$	$5\frac{7}{8}$	$1\text{-}8\frac{5}{32}$	$6\frac{3}{16}$	$1\text{-}9\frac{11}{32}$	$6\frac{15}{32}$	$1\text{-}10\frac{13}{32}$
$\frac{1}{2}$	$5\frac{9}{32}$	$1\text{-}6\frac{9}{32}$	$5\frac{19}{32}$	$1\text{-}7\frac{5}{32}$	$5\frac{7}{8}$	$1\text{-}8\frac{3}{8}$	$6\frac{3}{16}$	$1\text{-}9\frac{13}{32}$	$6\frac{1}{2}$	$1\text{-}10\frac{15}{32}$
$\frac{9}{16}$	$5\frac{5}{16}$	$1\text{-}6\frac{11}{32}$	$5\frac{19}{32}$	$1\text{-}7\frac{13}{32}$	$5\frac{29}{32}$	$1\text{-}8\frac{7}{16}$	$6\frac{7}{32}$	$1\text{-}9\frac{15}{32}$	$6\frac{1}{2}$	$1\text{-}10\frac{17}{32}$
$\frac{5}{8}$	$5\frac{5}{16}$	$1\text{-}6\frac{13}{32}$	$5\frac{5}{8}$	$1\text{-}7\frac{15}{32}$	$5\frac{15}{16}$	$1\text{-}8\frac{1}{2}$	$6\frac{7}{32}$	$1\text{-}9\frac{17}{32}$	$6\frac{17}{32}$	$1\text{-}10\frac{19}{32}$
$\frac{11}{16}$	$5\frac{11}{32}$	$1\text{-}6\frac{15}{32}$	$5\frac{21}{32}$	$1\text{-}7\frac{17}{32}$	$5\frac{15}{16}$	$1\text{-}8\frac{9}{16}$	$6\frac{1}{4}$	$1\text{-}9\frac{5}{8}$	$6\frac{9}{16}$	$1\text{-}10\frac{21}{32}$
$\frac{3}{4}$	$5\frac{3}{8}$	$1\text{-}6\frac{17}{32}$	$5\frac{21}{32}$	$1\text{-}7\frac{19}{32}$	$5\frac{31}{32}$	$1\text{-}8\frac{5}{8}$	$6\frac{9}{32}$	$1\text{-}9\frac{11}{16}$	$6\frac{9}{16}$	$1\text{-}10\frac{23}{32}$
$\frac{13}{16}$	$5\frac{3}{8}$	$1\text{-}6\frac{19}{32}$	$5\frac{11}{16}$	$1\text{-}7\frac{21}{32}$	6	$1\text{-}8\frac{11}{16}$	$6\frac{9}{32}$	$1\text{-}9\frac{3}{4}$	$6\frac{19}{32}$	$1\text{-}10\frac{25}{32}$
$\frac{7}{8}$	$5\frac{13}{32}$	$1\text{-}6\frac{11}{16}$	$5\frac{11}{16}$	$1\text{-}7\frac{23}{32}$	6	$1\text{-}8\frac{3}{4}$	$6\frac{5}{16}$	$1\text{-}9\frac{13}{16}$	$6\frac{19}{32}$	$1\text{-}10\frac{27}{32}$
$\frac{15}{16}$	$5\frac{13}{32}$	$1\text{-}6\frac{3}{4}$	$5\frac{23}{32}$	$1\text{-}7\frac{25}{32}$	$6\frac{1}{32}$	$1\text{-}8\frac{13}{16}$	$6\frac{5}{16}$	$1\text{-}9\frac{7}{8}$	$6\frac{5}{8}$	$1\text{-}10\frac{29}{32}$

	40′		50′		60′		70′	
Feet	Rise	Slope	Rise	Slope	Rise	Slope	Rise	Slope
0	12-1	$41\text{-}9\frac{7}{16}$	$15\text{-}1\frac{1}{4}$	$52\text{-}2\frac{25}{32}$	$18\text{-}1\frac{1}{2}$	$62\text{-}8\frac{1}{8}$	$21\text{-}1\frac{3}{4}$	$73\text{-}1\frac{1}{2}$
1	$12\text{-}4\frac{5}{8}$	$42\text{-}9\frac{31}{32}$	$15\text{-}4\frac{7}{8}$	$53\text{-}3\frac{5}{16}$	$18\text{-}5\frac{1}{8}$	$63\text{-}8\frac{21}{32}$	$21\text{-}5\frac{3}{8}$	$74\text{-}2\frac{1}{32}$
2	$12\text{-}8\frac{1}{4}$	$43\text{-}10\frac{1}{2}$	$15\text{-}8\frac{1}{2}$	$54\text{-}3\frac{27}{32}$	$18\text{-}8\frac{3}{4}$	$64\text{-}9\frac{7}{32}$	21-9	$75\text{-}2\frac{9}{16}$
3	$12\text{-}11\frac{7}{8}$	$44\text{-}11\frac{1}{32}$	$16\text{-}0\frac{1}{8}$	$55\text{-}4\frac{3}{8}$	$19\text{-}0\frac{3}{8}$	$65\text{-}9\frac{3}{4}$	$22\text{-}0\frac{5}{8}$	$76\text{-}3\frac{3}{32}$
4	$13\text{-}3\frac{1}{2}$	$45\text{-}11\frac{9}{16}$	$16\text{-}3\frac{3}{4}$	$56\text{-}4\frac{29}{32}$	19-4	$66\text{-}10\frac{9}{32}$	$22\text{-}4\frac{1}{4}$	$77\text{-}3\frac{5}{8}$
5	$13\text{-}7\frac{1}{8}$	$47\text{-}0\frac{5}{32}$	$16\text{-}7\frac{3}{8}$	$57\text{-}5\frac{15}{32}$	$19\text{-}7\frac{5}{8}$	$67\text{-}10\frac{13}{16}$	$22\text{-}7\frac{7}{8}$	$78\text{-}4\frac{5}{32}$
6	$13\text{-}10\frac{3}{4}$	$48\text{-}0\frac{5}{8}$	16-11	58-6	$19\text{-}11\frac{1}{4}$	$68\text{-}11\frac{11}{32}$	$22\text{-}11\frac{1}{2}$	$79\text{-}4\frac{23}{32}$
7	$14\text{-}2\frac{3}{8}$	$49\text{-}1\frac{3}{16}$	$17\text{-}2\frac{5}{8}$	$59\text{-}6\frac{17}{32}$	$20\text{-}2\frac{7}{8}$	$69\text{-}11\frac{7}{8}$	$23\text{-}3\frac{1}{8}$	$80\text{-}5\frac{1}{4}$
8	14-6	$50\text{-}1\frac{23}{32}$	$17\text{-}6\frac{1}{4}$	$60\text{-}7\frac{1}{16}$	$20\text{-}6\frac{1}{2}$	$71\text{-}0\frac{13}{32}$	$23\text{-}6\frac{3}{4}$	$81\text{-}5\frac{25}{32}$
9	$14\text{-}9\frac{5}{8}$	$51\text{-}2\frac{1}{4}$	$17\text{-}9\frac{7}{8}$	$61\text{-}7\frac{19}{32}$	$20\text{-}10\frac{1}{8}$	$72\text{-}0\frac{31}{32}$	$23\text{-}10\frac{3}{8}$	$82\text{-}6\frac{5}{16}$

natsin A=0.2891770165; natcos A=0.9572756412; nattan A=0.3020833333; natcot A=3.3103448275

Inches	0″ Rise	0″ Slope	1″ Rise	1″ Slope	2″ Rise	2″ Slope	3″ Rise	3″ Slope	4″ Rise	4″ Slope	5″ Rise	5″ Slope
0	0	0	5/16	1 1/32	5/8	2 3/32	15/16	3 1/8	1 7/32	4 3/16	1 17/32	5 7/32
1/16	1/32	1/16	5/16	1 1/8	5/8	2 5/32	15/16	3 7/32	1 1/4	4 1/4	1 9/16	5 9/32
1/8	1/32	1/8	11/32	1 3/16	21/32	2 7/32	31/32	3 9/32	1 9/32	4 5/16	1 9/16	5 3/8
3/16	1/16	3/16	3/8	1 1/4	11/16	2 9/32	31/32	3 11/32	1 9/32	4 3/8	1 19/32	5 7/16
1/4	1/16	1/4	3/8	1 5/16	11/16	2 11/32	1	3 13/32	1 5/16	4 7/16	1 5/8	5 1/2
5/16	3/32	5/16	13/32	1 3/8	23/32	2 13/32	1 1/32	3 15/32	1 5/16	4 1/2	1 5/8	5 9/16
3/8	1/8	13/32	7/16	1 7/16	23/32	2 1/2	1 1/32	3 17/32	1 11/32	4 9/16	1 21/32	5 5/8
7/16	1/8	15/32	7/16	1 1/2	3/4	2 9/16	1 1/16	3 19/32	1 3/8	4 21/32	1 21/32	5 11/16
1/2	5/32	17/32	15/32	1 9/16	25/32	2 5/8	1 1/16	3 21/32	1 3/8	4 23/32	1 11/16	5 3/4
9/16	3/16	19/32	15/32	1 5/8	25/32	2 11/16	1 3/32	3 23/32	1 13/32	4 25/32	1 23/32	5 13/16
5/8	3/16	21/32	1/2	1 11/16	13/16	2 3/4	1 1/8	3 25/32	1 13/32	4 27/32	1 23/32	5 7/8
11/16	7/32	23/32	17/32	1 3/4	13/16	2 13/16	1 1/8	3 27/32	1 7/16	4 29/32	1 3/4	5 15/16
3/4	7/32	25/32	17/32	1 27/32	27/32	2 7/8	1 5/32	3 15/16	1 15/32	4 31/32	1 25/32	6
13/16	1/4	27/32	9/16	1 29/32	7/8	2 15/16	1 5/32	4	1 15/32	5 1/32	1 25/32	6 3/32
7/8	9/32	29/32	19/32	1 31/32	7/8	3	1 3/16	4 1/16	1 1/2	5 3/32	1 13/16	6 5/32
15/16	9/32	31/32	19/32	2 1/32	29/32	3 1/16	1 7/32	4 1/8	1 17/32	5 5/32	1 13/16	6 7/32

Inches	6″ Rise	6″ Slope	7″ Rise	7″ Slope	8″ Rise	8″ Slope	9″ Rise	9″ Slope	10″ Rise	10″ Slope	11″ Rise	11″ Slope
0	1 27/32	6 9/32	2 5/32	7 5/16	2 15/32	8 3/8	2 3/4	9 13/32	3 1/16	10 15/32	3 3/8	11 1/2
1/16	1 7/8	6 11/32	2 5/32	7 3/8	2 15/32	8 7/16	2 25/32	9 15/32	3 3/32	10 17/32	3 13/32	11 9/16
1/8	1 7/8	6 13/32	2 3/16	7 15/32	2 1/2	8 1/2	2 13/16	9 17/32	3 1/8	10 19/32	3 13/32	11 5/8
3/16	1 29/32	6 15/32	2 7/32	7 17/32	2 17/32	8 9/16	2 13/16	9 5/8	3 1/8	10 21/32	3 7/16	11 23/32
1/4	1 29/32	6 17/32	2 7/32	7 19/32	2 17/32	8 5/8	2 27/32	9 11/16	3 5/32	10 23/32	3 15/32	11 25/32
5/16	1 15/16	6 19/32	2 1/4	7 21/32	2 9/16	8 11/16	2 7/8	9 3/4	3 5/32	10 25/32	3 15/32	11 27/32
3/8	1 31/32	6 21/32	2 9/32	7 23/32	2 9/16	8 3/4	2 7/8	9 13/16	3 3/16	10 27/32	3 1/2	11 29/32
7/16	1 31/32	6 3/4	2 9/32	7 25/32	2 19/32	8 13/16	2 29/32	9 7/8	3 7/32	10 29/32	3 1/2	11 31/32
1/2	2	6 13/16	2 5/16	7 27/32	2 5/8	8 29/32	2 29/32	9 15/16	3 7/32	11	3 17/32	1-0 1/32
9/16	2 1/32	6 7/8	2 5/16	7 29/32	2 5/8	8 31/32	2 15/16	10	3 1/4	11 1/16	3 9/16	1-0 3/32
5/8	2 1/32	6 15/16	2 11/32	7 31/32	2 21/32	9 1/32	2 31/32	10 1/16	3 1/4	11 1/8	3 9/16	1-0 5/32
11/16	2 1/16	7	2 3/8	8 1/32	2 21/32	9 3/32	2 31/32	10 1/8	3 9/32	11 3/16	3 19/32	1-0 7/32
3/4	2 1/16	7 1/16	2 3/8	8 3/32	2 11/16	9 5/32	3	10 3/16	3 5/16	11 1/4	3 5/8	1-0 9/32
13/16	2 3/32	7 1/8	2 13/32	8 3/16	2 23/32	9 7/32	3	10 1/4	3 5/16	11 5/16	3 5/8	1-0 11/32
7/8	2 1/8	7 3/16	2 13/32	8 1/4	2 23/32	9 9/32	3 1/32	10 11/32	3 11/32	11 3/8	3 21/32	1-0 7/16
15/16	2 1/8	7 1/4	2 7/16	8 5/16	2 3/4	9 11/32	3 1/16	10 13/32	3 3/8	11 7/16	3 21/32	1-0 1/2

Feet	0′ Rise	0′ Slope	10′ Rise	10′ Slope	20′ Rise	20′ Slope	30′ Rise	30′ Slope
0	0	0	3-0 7/8	10-5 17/32	6-1 3/4	20-11 1/16	9-2 5/8	31-4 5/8
1	3 11/16	1-0 9/16	3-4 9/16	11-6 3/32	6-5 7/16	21-11 5/8	9-6 5/16	32-5 5/32
2	7 3/8	2-1 3/32	3-8 1/4	12-6 21/32	6-9 1/8	23-0 3/16	9-10	33-5 23/32
3	11 1/16	3-1 21/32	3-11 15/16	13-7 3/16	7-0 13/16	24-0 3/4	10-1 11/16	34-6 9/32
4	1-2 3/4	4-2 7/32	4-3 5/8	14-7 3/4	7-4 1/2	25-1 9/32	10-5 3/8	35-6 27/32
5	1-6 7/16	5-2 25/32	4-7 5/16	15-8 5/16	7-8 3/16	26-1 27/32	10-9 1/16	36-7 3/8
6	1-10 1/8	6-3 5/16	4-11	16-8 7/8	7-11 7/8	27-2 13/32	11-0 3/4	37-7 15/16
7	2-1 13/16	7-3 7/8	5-2 11/16	17-9 13/32	8-3 9/16	28-2 15/16	11-4 7/16	38-8 1/2
8	2-5 1/2	8-4 7/16	5-6 3/8	18-9 31/32	8-7 1/4	29-3 1/2	11-8 1/8	39-9 1/32
9	2-9 3/16	9-4 31/32	5-10 1/16	19-10 17/32	8-10 15/16	30-4 1/16	11-11 13/16	40-9 19/32

A = 17° 04′ 54″; logsin A = 9.46796; logcos A = 9.98041; logtan A = 9.48755; logcot A = 0.51245

In.	12″ Rise	12″ Slope	13″ Rise	13″ Slope	14″ Rise	14″ Slope	15″ Rise	15″ Slope	16″ Rise	16″ Slope
0	3 11/16	1-0 9/16	4	1-1 19/32	4 5/16	1-2 21/32	4 5/8	1-3 11/16	4 29/32	1-4 3/4
1/16	3 23/32	1-0 5/8	4	1-1 21/32	4 5/16	1-2 23/32	4 5/8	1-3 3/4	4 15/16	1-4 13/16
1/8	3 23/32	1-0 11/16	4 1/32	1-1 23/32	4 11/32	1-2 25/32	4 21/32	1-3 13/16	4 31/32	1-4 7/8
3/16	3 3/4	1-0 3/4	4 1/16	1-1 25/32	4 3/8	1-2 27/32	4 21/32	1-3 7/8	4 31/32	1-4 15/16
1/4	3 3/4	1-0 13/16	4 1/16	1-1 7/8	4 3/8	1-2 29/32	4 11/16	1-3 31/32	5	1-5
5/16	3 25/32	1-0 7/8	4 3/32	1-1 15/16	4 13/32	1-2 31/32	4 23/32	1-4 1/32	5	1-5 1/16
3/8	3 13/16	1-0 15/16	4 1/8	1-2	4 13/32	1-3 1/32	4 23/32	1-4 3/32	5 1/8	1-5 1/8
7/16	3 13/16	1-1	4 1/8	1-2 1/16	4 7/16	1-3 3/32	4 23/32	1-4 1/4	5 1/16	1-5 3/32
1/2	3 27/32	1-1 1/32	4 5/32	1-2 1/8	4 15/32	1-3 5/32	4 3/4	1-4 7/32	5 1/8	1-5 1/4
9/16	3 7/8	1-1 5/32	4 5/32	1-2 3/16	4 15/32	1-3 1/4	4 25/32	1-4 9/32	5 3/32	1-5 5/32
5/8	3 7/8	1-1 7/32	4 3/16	1-2 1/4	4 1/2	1-3 5/16	4 13/16	1-4 11/32	5 3/32	1-5 13/32
11/16	3 29/32	1-1 9/32	4 7/32	1-2 5/16	4 1/2	1-3 3/8	4 13/16	1-4 13/32	5 1/8	1-5 15/32
3/4	3 29/32	1-1 11/32	4 7/32	1-2 3/8	4 17/32	1-3 7/16	4 27/32	1-4 15/32	5 5/32	1-5 17/32
13/16	3 15/16	1-1 13/32	4 1/4	1-2 7/16	4 9/16	1-3 1/2	4 27/32	1-4 17/32	5 5/32	1-5 19/32
7/8	3 31/32	1-1 15/32	4 1/4	1-2 1/2	4 9/16	1-3 9/16	4 7/8	1-4 19/32	5 3/16	1-5 21/32
15/16	3 31/32	1-1 17/32	4 9/32	1-2 9/16	4 19/32	1-3 5/8	4 29/32	1-4 11/16	5 7/32	1-5 23/32

In.	17″ Rise	17″ Slope	18″ Rise	18″ Slope	19″ Rise	19″ Slope	20″ Rise	20″ Slope	21″ Rise	21″ Slope
0	5 7/32	1-5 25/32	5 17/32	1-6 27/32	5 27/32	1-7 7/8	6 5/32	1-8 15/16	6 7/16	1-9 31/32
1/16	5 1/4	1-5 27/32	5 9/16	1-6 29/32	5 27/32	1-7 15/16	6 5/32	1-9	6 15/32	1-10 1/32
1/8	5 1/4	1-5 29/32	5 9/16	1-6 31/32	5 7/8	1-8	6 3/16	1-9 1/16	6 1/2	1-10 3/32
3/16	5 9/32	1-5 31/32	5 19/32	1-7 1/32	5 29/32	1-8 1/16	6 7/32	1-9 1/8	6 1/2	1-10 5/32
1/4	5 5/16	1-6 1/32	5 19/32	1-7 3/32	5 29/32	1-8 1/8	6 7/32	1-9 3/16	6 17/32	1-10 7/32
5/16	5 5/16	1-6 1/8	5 5/8	1-7 5/32	5 15/16	1-8 7/32	6 1/4	1-9 1/4	6 9/16	1-10 9/32
3/8	5 11/32	1-6 3/32	5 21/32	1-7 7/32	5 31/32	1-8 9/32	6 1/4	1-9 5/16	6 9/16	1-10 3/8
7/16	5 11/32	1-6 1/4	5 21/32	1-7 9/32	5 31/32	1-8 11/32	6 9/32	1-9 3/8	6 19/32	1-10 7/16
1/2	5 3/8	1-6 5/16	5 11/16	1-7 11/32	6	1-8 13/32	6 5/16	1-9 7/16	6 19/32	1-10 1/2
9/16	5 13/32	1-6 3/8	5 23/32	1-7 13/32	6	1-8 15/32	6 5/16	1-9 1/2	6 5/8	1-10 9/16
5/8	5 13/32	1-6 7/16	5 23/32	1-7 1/2	6 1/32	1-8 17/32	6 11/32	1-9 9/16	6 21/32	1-10 5/8
11/16	5 7/16	1-6 1/2	5 3/4	1-7 9/16	6 1/16	1-8 19/32	6 11/32	1-9 21/32	6 21/32	1-10 11/16
3/4	5 15/32	1-6 9/16	5 3/4	1-7 5/8	6 1/16	1-8 21/32	6 3/8	1-9 23/32	6 11/16	1-10 3/4
13/16	5 15/32	1-6 5/8	5 25/32	1-7 11/16	6 3/32	1-8 23/32	6 13/32	1-9 25/32	6 11/16	1-10 13/16
7/8	5 1/2	1-6 11/16	5 13/16	1-7 3/4	6 3/32	1-8 25/32	6 13/32	1-9 27/32	6 23/32	1-10 7/8
15/16	5 1/2	1-6 3/4	5 13/16	1-7 13/16	6 1/8	1-8 27/32	6 7/16	1-9 29/32	6 3/4	1-10 15/16

Feet	40′ Rise	40′ Slope	50′ Rise	50′ Slope	60′ Rise	60′ Slope	70′ Rise	70′ Slope
0	12-3 1/2	41-10 5/32	15-4 3/8	52-3 11/16	18-5 1/4	62-9 7/32	21-6 1/8	73-2 3/4
1	12-7 3/16	42-10 23/32	15-8 1/16	53-4 1/4	18-8 15/16	63-9 25/32	21-9 13/16	74-3 5/16
2	12-10 7/8	43-11 1/4	15-11 3/4	54-4 13/16	19-0 5/8	64-10 11/32	22-1 1/2	75-3 7/8
3	13-2 9/16	44-11 13/16	16-3 7/16	55-5 11/32	19-4 5/16	65-10 7/8	22-5 3/8	76-4 7/16
4	13-6 1/4	46-0 3/8	16-7 1/8	56-5 29/32	19-8	66-11 7/16	22-8 7/8	77-4 31/32
5	13-9 15/16	47-0 29/32	16-10 13/16	57-6 15/32	19-11 11/16	68-0	23-0 9/16	78-5 17/32
6	14-1 5/8	48-1 5/32	17-2 1/2	58-7	20-3 3/8	69-0 9/16	23-4 1/4	79-6 3/32
7	14-5 5/16	49-2 1/32	17-6 3/16	59-7 9/16	20-7 1/16	70-1 3/32	23-7 15/16	80-6 21/32
8	14-9	50-2 19/32	17-9 7/8	60-8 1/8	20-10 3/4	71-1 21/32	23-11 5/8	81-7 3/16
9	15-0 11/16	51-3 1/8	18-1 9/16	61-8 11/16	21-2 7/16	72-2 7/32	24-3 5/16	82-7 3/4

natsin A=0.2937359832; natcos A=0.9558865896; nattan A=0.3072916666; natcot A=3.2542372881

Inches	0" Rise	0" Slope	1" Rise	1" Slope	2" Rise	2" Slope	3" Rise	3" Slope	4" Rise	4" Slope	5" Rise	5" Slope
0	0	0	5/16	1 1/16	5/8	2 3/32	15/16	3 5/32	1 1/4	4 3/16	1 9/16	5 1/4
1/16	1/32	1/16	11/32	1 1/8	21/32	2 5/32	31/32	3 7/32	1 9/32	4 1/4	1 19/32	5 5/16
1/8	1/32	1/8	11/32	1 3/16	21/32	2 7/32	31/32	3 9/32	1 9/32	4 5/16	1 19/32	5 3/8
3/16	1/16	3/16	3/8	1 1/4	11/16	2 9/32	1	3 11/32	1 5/16	4 3/8	1 5/8	5 7/16
1/4	1/16	1/4	3/8	1 5/16	11/16	2 11/32	1	3 13/32	1 5/16	4 7/16	1 5/8	5 1/2
5/16	3/32	5/16	13/32	1 3/8	23/32	2 7/16	1 1/32	3 15/32	1 11/32	4 17/32	1 21/32	5 9/16
3/8	1/8	3/8	7/16	1 7/16	3/4	2 1/2	1 1/16	3 17/32	1 3/8	4 19/32	1 11/16	5 5/8
7/16	1/8	7/16	7/16	1 1/2	3/4	2 9/16	1 1/16	3 19/32	1 3/8	4 21/32	1 11/16	5 11/16
1/2	5/32	17/32	15/32	1 9/16	25/32	2 5/8	1 3/32	3 21/32	1 13/32	4 23/32	1 23/32	5 3/4
9/16	3/16	19/32	1/2	1 5/8	13/16	2 11/16	1 1/8	3 23/32	1 7/16	4 25/32	1 3/4	5 13/16
5/8	3/16	21/32	1/2	1 11/16	13/16	2 3/4	1 1/8	3 13/16	1 7/16	4 27/32	1 3/4	5 29/32
11/16	7/32	23/32	17/32	1 25/32	27/32	2 13/16	1 5/32	3 7/8	1 15/32	4 29/32	1 25/32	5 31/32
3/4	1/4	25/32	9/16	1 27/32	7/8	2 7/8	1 3/16	3 15/16	1 1/2	4 31/32	1 13/16	6 1/32
13/16	1/4	27/32	9/16	1 29/32	7/8	2 15/16	1 3/16	4	1 1/2	5 1/32	1 13/16	6 3/32
7/8	9/32	29/32	19/32	1 31/32	29/32	3	1 7/32	4 1/16	1 17/32	5 3/32	1 27/32	6 3/32
15/16	9/32	31/32	19/32	2 1/32	29/32	3 1/16	1 7/32	4 1/8	1 17/32	5 3/16	1 27/32	6 1/8

Inches	6" Rise	6" Slope	7" Rise	7" Slope	8" Rise	8" Slope	9" Rise	9" Slope	10" Rise	10" Slope	11" Rise	11" Slope
0	1 7/8	6 9/32	2 3/16	7 11/32	2 1/2	8 3/8	2 13/16	9 7/16	3 1/8	10 15/32	3 7/16	11 11/32
1/16	1 29/32	6 11/32	2 7/32	7 13/32	2 17/32	8 7/16	2 27/32	9 1/2	3 5/32	10 17/32	3 15/32	11 19/32
1/8	1 29/32	6 13/32	2 7/32	7 15/32	2 17/32	8 1/2	2 27/32	9 9/16	3 5/32	10 19/32	3 15/32	11 21/32
3/16	1 15/16	6 15/32	2 1/4	7 17/32	2 9/16	8 9/16	2 7/8	9 5/8	3 3/16	10 11/16	3 1/2	11 23/32
1/4	1 15/16	6 9/16	2 1/4	7 19/32	2 9/16	8 21/32	2 7/8	9 11/16	3 3/16	10 3/4	3 1/2	11 25/32
5/16	1 31/32	6 5/8	2 9/32	7 21/32	2 19/32	8 23/32	2 29/32	9 3/4	3 7/32	10 13/16	3 17/32	11 27/32
3/8	2	6 11/16	2 5/16	7 23/32	2 5/8	8 25/32	2 15/16	9 13/16	3 1/4	10 7/8	3 9/16	11 29/32
7/16	2	6 3/4	2 5/16	7 25/32	2 5/8	8 27/32	2 15/16	9 7/8	3 1/4	10 15/16	3 9/16	11 31/32
1/2	2 1/32	6 13/16	2 11/32	7 27/32	2 21/32	8 29/32	2 31/32	9 15/16	3 9/32	11	3 19/32	1-0 1/16
9/16	2 1/16	6 7/8	2 3/8	7 15/16	2 11/16	8 31/32	3	10 1/32	3 5/16	11 1/16	3 5/8	1-0 1/8
5/8	2 1/16	6 15/16	2 3/8	8	2 11/16	9 1/32	3	10 3/32	3 5/16	11 1/8	3 5/8	1-0 3/16
11/16	2 3/32	7	2 13/32	8 1/16	2 23/32	9 3/32	3 1/32	10 5/32	3 11/32	11 3/16	3 21/32	1-0 1/4
3/4	2 1/8	7 1/16	2 7/16	8 1/8	2 3/4	9 5/32	3 1/16	10 7/32	3 3/8	11 1/4	3 11/16	1-0 5/16
13/16	2 1/8	7 1/8	2 7/16	8 3/16	2 3/4	9 7/32	3 1/16	10 9/32	3 3/8	11 11/32	3 11/16	1-0 3/8
7/8	2 5/32	7 3/16	2 15/32	8 1/4	2 25/32	9 5/16	3 3/32	10 11/32	3 13/32	11 13/32	3 23/32	1-0 7/16
15/16	2 5/32	7 9/32	2 15/32	8 5/16	2 25/32	9 3/8	3 3/32	10 13/32	3 15/32	11 15/32	3 23/32	1-0 1/2

Feet	0' Rise	0' Slope	10' Rise	10' Slope	20' Rise	20' Slope	30' Rise	30' Slope
0	0	0	3-1 1/2	10-5 23/32	6-3	20-11 7/16	9-4 1/2	31-5 5/32
1	3 3/4	1-0 9/16	3-5 1/4	11-6 9/32	6-6 3/4	22-0 1/32	9-8 1/4	32-5 3/4
2	7 1/2	2-1 5/32	3-9	12-6 7/8	6-10 1/2	23-0 19/32	10-0	33-6 9/16
3	11 1/4	3-1 23/32	4-0 3/4	13-7 7/16	7-2 1/4	24-1 5/32	10-3 3/4	34-6 7/8
4	1-3	4-2 9/32	4-8	14-8	7-6	25-1 3/4	10-7 1/2	35-7 15/32
5	1-6 3/4	5-2 7/8	4-8 1/4	15-8 19/32	7-9 5/8	26-2 5/16	10-11 1/4	36-8 1/32
6	1-10 1/2	6-3 7/16	5-0	16-9 5/32	8-1 1/2	27-2 7/8	11-3	37-8 19/32
7	2-2 1/4	7-4	5-3 3/4	17-9 23/32	8-5 1/4	28-3 7/16	11-6 3/4	38-9 3/16
8	2-6	8-4 19/32	5-7 1/2	18-10 5/16	8-9	29-4 1/32	11-10 1/2	39-9 3/4
9	2-9 3/4	9-5 5/32	5-11 1/4	19-10 7/8	9-0 3/4	30-4 19/32	12-2 1/4	40-10 5/16

A=17° 21' 14"; logsin A=9.47462; logcos A=9.97977; logtan A=9.49485; logcot A=0.50515

In.	12″ Rise	12″ Slope	13″ Rise	13″ Slope	14″ Rise	14″ Slope	15″ Rise	15″ Slope	16″ Rise	16″ Slope
0	3 3/4	1-0 9/16	4 1/16	1-1 5/8	4 3/8	1-2 21/32	4 11/16	1-3 23/32	5	1-4 3/4
1/16	3 25/32	1-0 5/8	4 3/32	1-1 11/16	4 13/32	1-2 23/32	4 23/32	1-3 25/32	5 1/32	1-4 27/32
1/8	3 25/32	1-0 23/32	4 3/32	1-1 3/4	4 13/32	1-2 13/16	4 23/32	1-3 27/32	5 1/32	1-4 29/32
3/16	3 13/16	1-0 25/32	4 1/8	1-1 13/16	4 7/16	1-2 7/8	4 3/4	1-3 29/32	5 1/16	1-4 31/32
1/4	3 13/16	1-0 27/32	4 1/8	1-1 7/8	4 7/16	1-2 15/16	4 3/4	1-3 31/32	5 1/16	1-5 1/32
5/16	3 27/32	1-0 29/32	4 5/32	1-1 15/16	4 15/32	1-3	4 25/32	1-4 1/32	5 3/32	1-5 3/32
3/8	3 7/8	1-0 31/32	4 3/16	1-2	4 1/2	1-3 1/16	4 13/16	1-4 3/32	5 1/8	1-5 5/32
7/16	3 7/8	1-1 1/32	4 3/16	1-2 3/32	4 1/2	1-3 1/8	4 13/16	1-4 3/16	5 1/8	1-5 7/32
1/2	3 29/32	1-1 3/32	4 7/32	1-2 5/32	4 17/32	1-3 3/16	4 27/32	1-4 1/4	5 5/32	1-5 9/32
9/16	3 15/16	1-1 5/32	4 1/4	1-2 7/32	4 9/16	1-3 1/4	4 7/8	1-4 5/16	5 3/16	1-5 11/32
5/8	3 15/16	1-1 7/32	4 1/4	1-2 9/32	4 9/16	1-3 5/16	4 7/8	1-4 3/8	5 3/16	1-5 13/32
11/16	3 31/32	1-1 9/32	4 9/32	1-2 11/32	4 19/32	1-3 3/8	4 29/32	1-4 7/16	5 7/32	1-5 15/32
3/4	4	1-1 11/32	4 5/16	1-2 13/32	4 5/8	1-3 15/32	4 15/16	1-4 1/2	5 1/4	1-5 9/16
13/16	4	1-1 7/16	4 5/16	1-2 15/32	4 5/8	1-3 17/32	4 15/16	1-4 9/16	5 1/4	1-5 5/8
7/8	4 1/32	1-1 1/2	4 11/32	1-2 17/32	4 21/32	1-3 19/32	4 31/32	1-4 5/8	5 9/32	1-5 11/16
15/16	4 1/32	1-1 9/16	4 11/32	1-2 19/32	4 21/32	1-3 21/32	4 31/32	1-4 11/16	5 9/32	1-5 3/4

In.	17″ Rise	17″ Slope	18″ Rise	18″ Slope	19″ Rise	19″ Slope	20″ Rise	20″ Slope	21″ Rise	21″ Slope
0	5 5/16	1-5 13/16	5 5/8	1-6 27/32	5 15/16	1-7 29/32	6 1/4	1-8 31/32	6 9/16	1-10
1/16	5 11/32	1-5 7/8	5 21/32	1-6 15/16	5 31/32	1-7 31/32	6 9/32	1-9 1/32	6 19/32	1-10 1/16
1/8	5 11/32	1-5 15/16	5 21/32	1-7	5 31/32	1-8 1/32	6 9/32	1-9 3/32	6 19/32	1-10 1/8
3/16	5 3/8	1-6	5 11/16	1-7 1/16	6	1-8 3/32	6 5/16	1-9 5/32	6 5/8	1-10 3/16
1/4	5 3/8	1-6 1/16	5 11/16	1-7 1/8	6	1-8 5/32	6 5/16	1-9 7/32	6 5/8	1-10 1/4
5/16	5 13/32	1-6 1/8	5 23/32	1-7 3/16	6 1/32	1-8 7/32	6 11/32	1-9 9/32	6 21/32	1-10 11/32
3/8	5 7/16	1-6 5/32	5 3/4	1-7 1/4	6 1/16	1-8 5/16	6 3/8	1-9 11/32	6 11/16	1-10 13/32
7/16	5 7/16	1-6 9/32	5 3/4	1-7 5/16	6 1/16	1-8 3/8	6 3/8	1-9 13/32	6 11/16	1-10 15/32
1/2	5 15/32	1-6 11/32	5 25/32	1-7 3/8	6 3/32	1-8 7/16	6 13/32	1-9 15/32	6 23/32	1-10 17/32
9/16	5 1/2	1-6 13/32	5 13/16	1-7 7/16	6 1/8	1-8 1/2	6 7/16	1-9 17/32	6 3/4	1-10 19/32
5/8	5 1/2	1-6 15/32	5 13/16	1-7 1/2	6 1/8	1-8 9/16	6 7/16	1-9 19/32	6 3/4	1-10 21/32
11/16	5 17/32	1-6 17/32	5 27/32	1-7 19/32	6 5/32	1-8 5/8	6 15/32	1-9 11/16	6 25/32	1-10 23/32
3/4	5 9/16	1-6 19/32	5 7/8	1-7 21/32	6 3/16	1-8 11/16	6 1/2	1-9 3/4	6 13/16	1-10 25/32
13/16	5 9/16	1-6 21/32	5 7/8	1-7 23/32	6 3/16	1-8 3/4	6 1/2	1-9 13/16	6 13/16	1-10 27/32
7/8	5 19/32	1-6 23/32	5 29/32	1-7 25/32	6 7/32	1-8 13/16	6 17/32	1-9 7/8	6 27/32	1-10 29/32
15/16	5 19/32	1-6 25/32	5 29/32	1-7 27/32	6 7/32	1-8 7/8	6 17/32	1-9 15/16	6 27/32	1-10 31/32

Feet	40′ Rise	40′ Slope	50′ Rise	50′ Slope	60′ Rise	60′ Slope	70′ Rise	70′ Slope
0	12-6	41-10 29/32	15-7 1/2	52-4 5/8	18-9	62-10 11/32	21-10 1/2	73-4 1/16
1	12-9 3/4	42-11 15/32	15-11 1/4	53-5 3/16	19-0 3/4	63-10 29/32	22-2 1/4	74-4 5/8
2	13-1 1/2	44-0 1/32	16-3	54-5 3/4	19-4 1/2	64-11 15/32	22-6	75-5 25/32
3	13-5 1/4	45-0 19/32	16-6 3/4	55-6 11/32	19-8 1/4	66-0 1/16	22-9 3/4	76-5 25/32
4	13-9	46-1 3/32	16-10 1/2	56-6 29/32	20-0	67-0 5/8	23-1 1/2	77-6 11/32
5	14-0 3/4	47-1 3/4	17-2 1/4	57-7 15/32	20-3 3/4	68-1 3/16	23-5 1/4	78-6 29/32
6	14-4 1/2	48-2 5/16	17-6	58-8 1/16	20-7 1/2	69-1 25/32	23-9	79-7 1/2
7	14-8 1/4	49-2 29/32	17-9 3/4	59-8 5/8	20-11 1/4	70-2 11/32	24-0 3/4	80-8 1/16
8	15-0	50-3 15/32	18-1 1/2	60-9 3/16	21-3	71-2 29/32	24-4 1/2	81-8 5/8
9	15-3 3/4	51-4 1/32	18-5 1/4	61-9 3/4	21-6 3/4	72-3 1/2	24-8 1/4	82-9 11/16

natsin A=0.2982749931; natcos A=0.9544799781; nattan A=0.3125000000; natcot A=3.2000000000

Inches	0" Rise	0" Slope	1" Rise	1" Slope	2" Rise	2" Slope	3" Rise	3" Slope	4" Rise	4" Slope	5" Rise	5" Slope
0	0	0	5/16	1 1/16	5/8	2 3/32	15/16	3 5/32	1 9/32	4 3/16	1 19/32	5 1/4
1/16	1/32	1/16	11/32	1 1/8	21/32	2 5/32	31/32	3 7/32	1 9/32	4 1/4	1 19/32	5 5/16
1/8	1/32	1/8	11/32	1 3/16	11/16	2 7/32	1	3 9/32	1 5/16	4 11/32	1 5/8	5 3/8
3/16	1/16	3/16	3/8	1 1/4	11/16	2 9/32	1	3 11/32	1 11/32	4 13/32	1 21/32	5 7/16
1/4	3/32	1/4	13/32	1 5/16	23/32	2 3/8	1 1/32	3 13/32	1 11/32	4 15/32	1 21/32	5 1/2
5/16	3/32	5/16	13/32	1 3/8	3/4	2 7/16	1 1/16	3 15/32	1 3/8	4 17/32	1 11/16	5 9/16
3/8	1/8	13/32	7/16	1 7/16	3/4	2 1/2	1 1/16	3 17/32	1 3/8	4 19/32	1 23/32	5 5/8
7/16	1/8	15/32	15/32	1 1/2	25/32	2 9/16	1 3/32	3 19/32	1 13/32	4 21/32	1 23/32	5 23/32
1/2	5/32	17/32	15/32	1 9/16	25/32	2 5/8	1 1/8	3 11/16	1 7/16	4 23/32	1 3/4	5 25/32
9/16	3/16	19/32	1/2	1 5/8	13/16	2 11/16	1 1/8	3 3/4	1 7/16	4 25/32	1 25/32	5 27/32
5/8	3/16	21/32	17/32	1 23/32	27/32	2 3/4	1 5/32	3 13/16	1 15/32	4 27/32	1 25/32	5 29/32
11/16	7/32	23/32	17/32	1 25/32	27/32	2 13/16	1 5/32	3 7/8	1 1/2	4 29/32	1 13/16	5 31/32
3/4	1/4	25/32	9/16	1 27/32	7/8	2 7/8	1 3/16	3 15/16	1 1/2	4 31/32	1 13/16	6 1/32
13/16	1/4	27/32	9/16	1 29/32	29/32	2 15/16	1 7/32	4	1 17/32	5 1/16	1 27/32	6 3/32
7/8	9/32	29/32	19/32	1 31/32	29/32	3 1/32	1 7/32	4 1/16	1 9/16	5 1/8	1 7/8	6 5/32
15/16	5/16	31/32	5/8	2 1/32	15/16	3 3/32	1 1/4	4 1/8	1 9/16	5 3/16	1 7/8	6 7/32

Inches	6" Rise	6" Slope	7" Rise	7" Slope	8" Rise	8" Slope	9" Rise	9" Slope	10" Rise	10" Slope	11" Rise	11" Slope
0	1 29/32	6 9/32	2 7/32	7 11/32	2 17/32	8 13/32	2 7/8	9 7/16	3 3/16	10 1/2	3 1/2	11 17/32
1/16	1 15/16	6 3/8	2 1/4	7 13/32	2 9/16	8 15/32	2 7/8	9 1/2	3 3/16	10 9/16	3 1/2	11 19/32
1/8	1 15/16	6 7/16	2 1/4	7 15/32	2 19/32	8 17/32	2 29/32	9 9/16	3 7/32	10 5/8	3 17/32	11 11/16
3/16	1 31/32	6 1/2	2 9/32	7 17/32	2 19/32	8 19/32	2 29/32	9 5/8	3 1/4	10 11/16	3 9/16	11 3/4
1/4	2	6 9/16	2 5/16	7 19/32	2 5/8	8 21/32	2 15/16	9 23/32	3 1/4	10 3/4	3 9/16	11 13/16
5/16	2	6 5/8	2 5/16	7 11/16	2 21/32	8 23/32	2 31/32	9 25/32	3 9/32	10 13/16	3 19/32	11 7/8
3/8	2 1/16	6 11/16	2 11/32	7 3/4	2 21/32	8 25/32	2 31/32	9 27/32	3 9/32	10 7/8	3 5/8	11 15/16
7/16	2 1/32	6 3/4	2 3/8	7 13/16	2 11/16	8 27/32	3	9 29/32	3 5/16	10 15/16	3 5/8	1-0
1/2	2 1/16	6 13/16	2 3/8	7 7/8	2 11/16	8 29/32	3 1/32	9 31/32	3 11/32	11 1/32	3 21/32	1-0 1/32
9/16	2 3/32	6 7/8	2 13/32	7 15/16	2 23/32	8 31/32	3 1/32	10 1/32	3 11/32	11 3/32	3 11/16	1-0 1/16
5/8	2 3/32	6 15/16	2 7/16	8	2 3/4	9 1/16	3 1/16	10 3/32	3 3/8	11 5/32	3 11/16	1-0 3/16
11/16	2 1/8	7 1/32	2 7/16	8 1/16	2 3/4	9 1/8	3 1/16	10 5/32	3 13/32	11 7/32	3 23/32	1-0 1/4
3/4	2 5/32	7 3/32	2 15/32	8 1/8	2 25/32	9 3/16	3 3/32	10 7/32	3 13/32	11 9/32	3 23/32	1-0 11/32
13/16	2 5/32	7 5/32	2 15/32	8 3/16	2 13/16	9 1/4	3 1/8	10 9/32	3 7/16	11 11/32	3 3/4	1-0 13/32
7/8	2 3/16	7 7/32	2 1/2	8 1/4	2 13/16	9 5/16	3 1/8	10 3/8	3 15/32	11 13/32	3 25/32	1-0 15/32
15/16	2 7/32	7 9/32	2 17/32	8 11/32	2 27/32	9 3/8	3 5/32	10 7/16	3 15/32	11 15/32	3 25/32	1-0 17/32

Feet	0' Rise	0' Slope	10' Rise	10' Slope	20' Rise	20' Slope	30' Rise	30' Slope
0	0	0	3-2 1/8	10-5 29/32	6-4 1/4	20-11 13/16	9-6 3/8	31-5 23/32
1	3 13/16	1-0 19/32	3-5 15/16	11-6 1/2	6-8 1/16	22-0 13/32	9-10 3/16	32-6 5/16
2	7 5/8	2-1 3/16	3-9 3/4	12-7 3/32	6-11 7/8	23-1	10-2	33-6 29/32
3	11 7/16	3-1 25/32	4-1 9/16	13-7 11/16	7-3 11/16	24-1 19/32	10-5 13/16	34-7 1/2
4	1-3 1/4	4-2 3/8	4-5 3/8	14-8 9/32	7-7 1/2	25-2 3/16	10-9 5/8	35-8 3/32
5	1-7 1/16	5-2 31/32	4-9 3/16	15-8 7/8	7-11 5/16	26-2 25/32	11-1 7/16	36-8 11/16
6	1-10 7/8	6-3 17/32	5-1	16-9 15/32	8-3 3/8	27-3 3/8	11-5 1/4	37-9 9/32
7	2-2 11/16	7-4 1/8	5-4 13/16	17-10 1/16	8-6 15/16	28-3 31/32	11-9 1/16	38-9 7/8
8	2-6 1/2	8-4 23/32	5-8 5/8	18-10 5/8	8-10 3/4	29-4 9/16	12-0 7/8	39-10 15/32
9	2-10 5/16	9-5 5/16	6-0 7/16	19-11 7/32	9-2 9/16	30-5 5/32	12-4 11/16	40-11 1/16

A = 17° 37′ 32″; logsin A = 9.48115; logcos A = 9.97912; logtan A = 9.50203; logcot A = 0.49797

Ins.	12″ Rise	Slope	13″ Rise	Slope	14″ Rise	Slope	15″ Rise	Slope	16″ Rise	Slope
0	$3^{13}/_{16}$	$1-0^{19}/_{32}$	$4^{1}/_{8}$	$1-1^{5}/_{8}$	$4^{7}/_{16}$	$1-2^{11}/_{16}$	$4^{3}/_{4}$	$1-3^{3}/_{4}$	$5^{3}/_{32}$	$1-4^{25}/_{32}$
$^{1}/_{16}$	$3^{27}/_{32}$	$1-0^{21}/_{32}$	$4^{5}/_{32}$	$1-1^{23}/_{32}$	$4^{15}/_{32}$	$1-2^{3}/_{4}$	$4^{25}/_{32}$	$1-3^{13}/_{16}$	$5^{3}/_{32}$	$1-4^{27}/_{32}$
$^{1}/_{8}$	$3^{27}/_{32}$	$1-0^{23}/_{32}$	$4^{5}/_{32}$	$1-1^{25}/_{32}$	$4^{1}/_{2}$	$1-2^{13}/_{16}$	$4^{13}/_{16}$	$1-3^{7}/_{8}$	$5^{1}/_{8}$	$1-4^{29}/_{32}$
$^{3}/_{16}$	$3^{7}/_{8}$	$1-0^{25}/_{32}$	$4^{3}/_{16}$	$1-1^{27}/_{32}$	$4^{1}/_{2}$	$1-2^{7}/_{8}$	$4^{13}/_{16}$	$1-3^{15}/_{16}$	$5^{5}/_{32}$	$1-5$
$^{1}/_{4}$	$3^{29}/_{32}$	$1-0^{27}/_{32}$	$4^{7}/_{32}$	$1-1^{29}/_{32}$	$4^{17}/_{32}$	$1-2^{15}/_{16}$	$4^{27}/_{32}$	$1-4$	$5^{5}/_{32}$	$1-5^{1}/_{16}$
$^{5}/_{16}$	$3^{29}/_{32}$	$1-0^{29}/_{32}$	$4^{7}/_{32}$	$1-1^{31}/_{32}$	$4^{9}/_{16}$	$1-3^{1}/_{32}$	$4^{7}/_{8}$	$1-4^{1}/_{16}$	$5^{3}/_{16}$	$1-5^{1}/_{8}$
$^{3}/_{8}$	$3^{15}/_{16}$	$1-1$	$4^{1}/_{4}$	$1-2^{1}/_{32}$	$4^{9}/_{16}$	$1-3^{3}/_{32}$	$4^{7}/_{8}$	$1-4^{1}/_{8}$	$5^{3}/_{16}$	$1-5^{3}/_{16}$
$^{7}/_{16}$	$3^{15}/_{16}$	$1-1^{1}/_{16}$	$4^{9}/_{32}$	$1-2^{3}/_{32}$	$4^{19}/_{32}$	$1-3^{5}/_{32}$	$4^{29}/_{32}$	$1-4^{3}/_{16}$	$5^{7}/_{32}$	$1-5^{1}/_{4}$
$^{1}/_{2}$	$3^{31}/_{32}$	$1-1^{1}/_{8}$	$4^{9}/_{32}$	$1-2^{5}/_{32}$	$4^{19}/_{32}$	$1-3^{7}/_{32}$	$4^{15}/_{16}$	$1-4^{1}/_{4}$	$5^{1}/_{4}$	$1-5^{5}/_{16}$
$^{9}/_{16}$	4	$1-1^{3}/_{16}$	$4^{5}/_{16}$	$1-2^{7}/_{32}$	$4^{5}/_{8}$	$1-3^{9}/_{32}$	$4^{15}/_{16}$	$1-4^{11}/_{32}$	$5^{1}/_{4}$	$1-5^{3}/_{8}$
$^{5}/_{8}$	4	$1-1^{1}/_{4}$	$4^{11}/_{32}$	$1-2^{9}/_{32}$	$4^{21}/_{32}$	$1-3^{11}/_{32}$	$4^{31}/_{32}$	$1-4^{13}/_{32}$	$5^{9}/_{32}$	$1-5^{7}/_{16}$
$^{11}/_{16}$	$4^{1}/_{32}$	$1-1^{5}/_{16}$	$4^{11}/_{32}$	$1-2^{3}/_{8}$	$4^{21}/_{32}$	$1-3^{13}/_{32}$	$4^{31}/_{32}$	$1-4^{15}/_{32}$	$5^{5}/_{16}$	$1-5^{1}/_{2}$
$^{3}/_{4}$	$4^{1}/_{16}$	$1-1^{3}/_{8}$	$4^{3}/_{8}$	$1-2^{7}/_{16}$	$4^{11}/_{16}$	$1-3^{15}/_{32}$	5	$1-4^{17}/_{32}$	$5^{5}/_{16}$	$1-5^{9}/_{16}$
$^{13}/_{16}$	$4^{1}/_{16}$	$1-1^{7}/_{16}$	$4^{3}/_{8}$	$1-2^{1}/_{2}$	$4^{23}/_{32}$	$1-3^{17}/_{32}$	$5^{1}/_{32}$	$1-4^{19}/_{32}$	$5^{11}/_{32}$	$1-5^{5}/_{8}$
$^{7}/_{8}$	$4^{3}/_{32}$	$1-1^{1}/_{2}$	$4^{13}/_{32}$	$1-2^{9}/_{16}$	$4^{23}/_{32}$	$1-3^{19}/_{32}$	$5^{1}/_{32}$	$1-4^{21}/_{32}$	$5^{3}/_{8}$	$1-5^{23}/_{32}$
$^{15}/_{16}$	$4^{1}/_{8}$	$1-1^{9}/_{16}$	$4^{7}/_{16}$	$1-2^{5}/_{8}$	$4^{3}/_{4}$	$1-3^{11}/_{16}$	$5^{1}/_{16}$	$1-4^{23}/_{32}$	$5^{3}/_{8}$	$1-5^{25}/_{32}$

Ins.	17″ Rise	Slope	18″ Rise	Slope	19″ Rise	Slope	20″ Rise	Slope	21″ Rise	Slope
0	$5^{13}/_{32}$	$1-5^{27}/_{32}$	$5^{23}/_{32}$	$1-6^{7}/_{8}$	$6^{1}/_{32}$	$1-7^{15}/_{16}$	$6^{11}/_{32}$	$1-9$	$6^{11}/_{16}$	$1-10^{1}/_{32}$
$^{1}/_{16}$	$5^{13}/_{32}$	$1-5^{29}/_{32}$	$5^{3}/_{4}$	$1-6^{15}/_{16}$	$6^{1}/_{16}$	$1-8$	$6^{3}/_{8}$	$1-9^{1}/_{16}$	$6^{11}/_{16}$	$1-10^{3}/_{32}$
$^{1}/_{8}$	$5^{7}/_{16}$	$1-5^{31}/_{32}$	$5^{3}/_{4}$	$1-7^{1}/_{32}$	$6^{1}/_{16}$	$1-8^{1}/_{16}$	$6^{13}/_{32}$	$1-9^{1}/_{8}$	$6^{23}/_{32}$	$1-10^{5}/_{32}$
$^{3}/_{16}$	$5^{15}/_{32}$	$1-6^{1}/_{32}$	$5^{25}/_{32}$	$1-7^{3}/_{32}$	$6^{3}/_{32}$	$1-8^{1}/_{8}$	$6^{13}/_{32}$	$1-9^{3}/_{16}$	$6^{23}/_{32}$	$1-10^{7}/_{32}$
$^{1}/_{4}$	$5^{15}/_{32}$	$1-6^{3}/_{32}$	$5^{13}/_{16}$	$1-7^{5}/_{32}$	$6^{1}/_{8}$	$1-8^{3}/_{16}$	$6^{7}/_{16}$	$1-9^{1}/_{4}$	$6^{3}/_{4}$	$1-10^{9}/_{32}$
$^{5}/_{16}$	$5^{1}/_{2}$	$1-6^{5}/_{32}$	$5^{13}/_{16}$	$1-7^{7}/_{32}$	$6^{1}/_{8}$	$1-8^{1}/_{4}$	$6^{15}/_{32}$	$1-9^{5}/_{16}$	$6^{25}/_{32}$	$1-10^{3}/_{8}$
$^{3}/_{8}$	$5^{17}/_{32}$	$1-6^{7}/_{32}$	$5^{27}/_{32}$	$1-7^{9}/_{32}$	$6^{5}/_{32}$	$1-8^{11}/_{32}$	$6^{15}/_{32}$	$1-9^{3}/_{8}$	$6^{25}/_{32}$	$1-10^{7}/_{16}$
$^{7}/_{16}$	$5^{17}/_{32}$	$1-6^{9}/_{32}$	$5^{27}/_{32}$	$1-7^{11}/_{32}$	$6^{3}/_{16}$	$1-8^{13}/_{32}$	$6^{1}/_{2}$	$1-9^{7}/_{16}$	$6^{13}/_{16}$	$1-10^{1}/_{2}$
$^{1}/_{2}$	$5^{9}/_{16}$	$1-6^{3}/_{8}$	$5^{7}/_{8}$	$1-7^{13}/_{32}$	$6^{3}/_{16}$	$1-8^{15}/_{32}$	$6^{1}/_{2}$	$1-9^{1}/_{2}$	$6^{27}/_{32}$	$1-10^{9}/_{16}$
$^{9}/_{16}$	$5^{19}/_{32}$	$1-6^{7}/_{16}$	$5^{29}/_{32}$	$1-7^{15}/_{32}$	$6^{7}/_{32}$	$1-8^{17}/_{32}$	$6^{17}/_{32}$	$1-9^{9}/_{16}$	$6^{27}/_{32}$	$1-10^{5}/_{8}$
$^{5}/_{8}$	$5^{19}/_{32}$	$1-6^{1}/_{2}$	$5^{29}/_{32}$	$1-7^{17}/_{32}$	$6^{1}/_{4}$	$1-8^{19}/_{32}$	$6^{9}/_{16}$	$1-9^{21}/_{32}$	$6^{7}/_{8}$	$1-10^{11}/_{16}$
$^{11}/_{16}$	$5^{5}/_{8}$	$1-6^{9}/_{16}$	$5^{15}/_{16}$	$1-7^{19}/_{32}$	$6^{1}/_{4}$	$1-8^{21}/_{32}$	$6^{9}/_{16}$	$1-9^{23}/_{32}$	$6^{7}/_{8}$	$1-10^{3}/_{4}$
$^{3}/_{4}$	$5^{5}/_{8}$	$1-6^{5}/_{8}$	$5^{31}/_{32}$	$1-7^{11}/_{16}$	$6^{9}/_{32}$	$1-8^{23}/_{32}$	$6^{19}/_{32}$	$1-9^{25}/_{32}$	$6^{29}/_{32}$	$1-10^{13}/_{16}$
$^{13}/_{16}$	$5^{21}/_{32}$	$1-6^{11}/_{16}$	$5^{31}/_{32}$	$1-7^{3}/_{4}$	$6^{9}/_{32}$	$1-8^{25}/_{32}$	$6^{5}/_{8}$	$1-9^{27}/_{32}$	$6^{15}/_{16}$	$1-10^{7}/_{8}$
$^{7}/_{8}$	$5^{11}/_{16}$	$1-6^{3}/_{4}$	6	$1-7^{13}/_{16}$	$6^{5}/_{16}$	$1-8^{27}/_{32}$	$6^{5}/_{8}$	$1-9^{29}/_{32}$	$6^{15}/_{16}$	$1-10^{15}/_{16}$
$^{15}/_{16}$	$5^{11}/_{16}$	$1-6^{13}/_{16}$	$6^{1}/_{32}$	$1-7^{7}/_{8}$	$6^{11}/_{32}$	$1-8^{29}/_{32}$	$6^{21}/_{32}$	$1-9^{31}/_{32}$	$6^{31}/_{32}$	$1-11^{1}/_{32}$

Feet	40′ Rise	Slope	50′ Rise	Slope	60′ Rise	Slope	70′ Rise	Slope
0	$12-8^{1}/_{2}$	$41-11^{21}/_{32}$	$15-10^{5}/_{8}$	$52-5^{9}/_{16}$	$19-0^{3}/_{4}$	$62-11^{15}/_{32}$	$22-2^{7}/_{8}$	$73-5^{3}/_{8}$
1	$13-0^{5}/_{16}$	$43-0^{7}/_{32}$	$16-2^{7}/_{16}$	$53-6^{5}/_{32}$	$19-4^{9}/_{16}$	$64-0^{1}/_{16}$	$22-6^{11}/_{16}$	$74-5^{31}/_{32}$
2	$13-4^{1}/_{8}$	$44-0^{13}/_{16}$	$16-6^{1}/_{4}$	$54-6^{3}/_{4}$	$19-8^{3}/_{8}$	$65-0^{21}/_{32}$	$22-10^{1}/_{2}$	$75-6^{9}/_{16}$
3	$13-7^{15}/_{16}$	$45-1^{13}/_{32}$	$16-10^{1}/_{8}$	$55-7^{5}/_{16}$	$20-0^{3}/_{16}$	$66-1^{1}/_{4}$	$23-2^{5}/_{16}$	$76-7^{5}/_{32}$
4	$13-11^{3}/_{4}$	$46-2$	$17-1^{7}/_{8}$	$56-7^{29}/_{32}$	$20-4$	$67-1^{27}/_{32}$	$23-6^{1}/_{8}$	$77-7^{3}/_{4}$
5	$14-3^{9}/_{16}$	$47-2^{19}/_{32}$	$17-5^{11}/_{16}$	$57-8^{1}/_{2}$	$20-7^{13}/_{16}$	$68-2^{13}/_{32}$	$23-9^{15}/_{16}$	$78-8^{11}/_{32}$
6	$14-7^{3}/_{8}$	$48-3^{3}/_{16}$	$17-9^{1}/_{2}$	$58-9^{3}/_{32}$	$20-11^{5}/_{8}$	$69-3$	$24-1^{3}/_{4}$	$79-8^{29}/_{32}$
7	$14-11^{3}/_{16}$	$49-3^{25}/_{32}$	$18-1^{5}/_{16}$	$59-9^{11}/_{16}$	$21-3^{7}/_{16}$	$70-3^{19}/_{32}$	$24-5^{9}/_{16}$	$80-9^{1}/_{2}$
8	$15-3$	$50-4^{3}/_{8}$	$18-5^{1}/_{8}$	$60-10^{9}/_{32}$	$21-7^{1}/_{4}$	$71-4^{3}/_{16}$	$24-9^{3}/_{8}$	$81-10^{3}/_{32}$
9	$15-6^{13}/_{16}$	$51-4^{31}/_{32}$	$18-8^{15}/_{16}$	$61-10^{7}/_{8}$	$21-11^{1}/_{16}$	$72-4^{25}/_{32}$	$25-1^{3}/_{16}$	$82-10^{11}/_{16}$

natsin A=0.3027938568; natcos A=0.9530560739; nattan A=0.3177083333; natcot A=3.1475409836

Inches	0" Rise	0" Slope	1" Rise	1" Slope	2" Rise	2" Slope	3" Rise	3" Slope	4" Rise	4" Slope	5" Rise	5" Slope
0	0	0	5/16	1 1/16	21/32	2 3/32	31/32	3 5/32	1 9/32	4 7/32	1 5/8	5 1/4
1/16	1/32	1/16	11/32	1 1/8	21/32	2 5/32	1	3 7/32	1 5/16	4 9/32	1 5/8	5 5/16
1/8	1/32	1/8	3/8	1 3/16	11/16	2 7/32	1	3 9/32	1 11/32	4 11/32	1 21/32	5 3/8
3/16	1/16	3/16	3/8	1 1/4	23/32	2 5/16	1 1/32	3 11/32	1 11/32	4 13/32	1 11/16	5 7/16
1/4	3/32	1/4	13/32	1 5/16	23/32	2 3/8	1 1/16	3 13/32	1 3/8	4 15/32	1 11/16	5 17/32
5/16	3/32	11/32	7/16	1 3/8	3/4	2 7/16	1 1/16	3 15/32	1 13/32	4 17/32	1 23/32	5 19/32
3/8	1/8	13/32	7/16	1 7/16	25/32	2 1/2	1 3/32	3 17/32	1 13/32	4 19/32	1 3/4	5 21/32
7/16	5/32	15/32	15/32	1 1/2	25/32	2 9/16	1 1/8	3 5/8	1 7/16	4 21/32	1 3/4	5 23/32
1/2	5/32	17/32	1/2	1 9/16	13/16	2 5/8	1 1/8	3 11/16	1 7/16	4 23/32	1 25/32	5 25/32
9/16	3/16	19/32	1/2	1 21/32	13/16	2 11/16	1 5/32	3 3/4	1 15/32	4 25/32	1 25/32	5 27/32
5/8	3/16	21/32	17/32	1 23/32	27/32	2 3/4	1 5/32	3 13/16	1 1/2	4 7/8	1 13/16	5 29/32
11/16	7/32	23/32	17/32	1 25/32	7/8	2 13/16	1 3/16	3 7/8	1 1/2	4 15/16	1 27/32	5 31/32
3/4	1/4	25/32	9/16	1 27/32	7/8	2 7/8	1 7/32	3 15/16	1 17/32	5	1 27/32	6 1/16
13/16	1/4	27/32	19/32	1 29/32	29/32	2 31/32	1 7/32	4	1 9/16	5 1/16	1 7/8	6 3/32
7/8	9/32	29/32	19/32	1 31/32	15/16	3 1/32	1 1/4	4 1/16	1 9/16	5 1/8	1 29/32	6 3/16
15/16	5/16	1	5/8	2 1/32	15/16	3 3/32	1 9/32	4 1/8	1 19/32	5 3/16	1 29/32	6 1/4

Inches	6" Rise	6" Slope	7" Rise	7" Slope	8" Rise	8" Slope	9" Rise	9" Slope	10" Rise	10" Slope	11" Rise	11" Slope
0	1 15/16	6 5/16	2 1/4	7 11/32	2 19/32	8 13/32	2 29/32	9 15/32	3 1/2	10 1/2	3 9/16	11 9/16
1/16	1 31/32	6 3/8	2 9/32	7 13/32	2 19/32	8 15/32	2 15/16	9 17/32	3 1/4	10 9/16	3 9/16	11 5/8
1/8	1 31/32	6 7/16	2 5/16	7 1/2	2 5/8	8 17/32	2 15/16	9 19/32	3 9/32	10 5/8	3 19/32	11 11/16
3/16	2	6 1/2	2 5/16	7 9/16	2 21/32	8 19/32	2 31/32	9 21/32	3 9/32	10 23/32	3 5/8	11 3/4
1/4	2 1/32	6 9/16	2 11/32	7 5/8	2 21/32	8 21/32	3	9 23/32	3 5/16	10 25/32	3 5/8	11 13/16
5/16	2 1/32	6 5/8	2 3/8	7 11/16	2 11/16	8 3/4	3	9 25/32	3 11/32	10 27/32	3 21/32	11 7/8
3/8	2 1/16	6 11/16	2 3/8	7 3/4	2 23/32	8 13/16	3 1/32	9 27/32	3 11/32	10 29/32	3 11/16	11 31/32
7/16	2 3/32	6 3/4	2 13/32	7 13/16	2 23/32	8 7/8	3 1/16	9 29/32	3 3/8	10 31/32	3 11/16	1-0 1/32
1/2	2 3/32	6 27/32	2 7/16	7 7/8	2 3/4	8 15/16	3 1/16	9 31/32	3 3/8	11 1/32	3 23/32	1-0 3/32
9/16	2 1/8	6 29/32	2 7/16	7 15/16	2 3/4	9	3 3/32	10 1/32	3 13/32	11 3/32	3 23/32	1-0 5/32
5/8	2 1/8	6 31/32	2 15/32	8	2 25/32	9 1/16	3 3/32	10 1/8	3 7/16	11 5/32	3 3/4	1-0 7/32
11/16	2 5/32	7 1/32	2 15/32	8 3/32	2 13/16	9 1/8	3 1/8	10 3/16	3 7/16	11 7/32	3 25/32	1-0 9/32
3/4	2 3/16	7 3/32	2 1/2	8 5/32	2 13/16	9 3/16	3 5/32	10 1/4	3 15/32	11 9/32	3 25/32	1-0 11/32
13/16	2 3/16	7 5/32	2 17/32	8 7/32	2 27/32	9 1/4	3 5/32	10 5/16	3 1/2	11 3/8	3 13/16	1-0 13/32
7/8	2 7/32	7 7/32	2 17/32	8 9/32	2 7/8	9 5/16	3 3/16	10 3/8	3 1/2	11 7/16	3 27/32	1-0 15/32
15/16	2 1/4	7 9/32	2 9/16	8 11/32	2 7/8	9 13/32	3 7/32	10 7/16	3 17/32	11 1/2	3 27/32	1-0 17/32

Feet	0' Rise	0' Slope	10' Rise	10' Slope	20' Rise	20' Slope	30' Rise	30' Slope
0	0	0	3-2 3/4	10-6 3/32	6-5 1/2	21-0 3/16	9-8 1/4	31-6 5/16
1	3 7/8	1-0 5/32	3-6 5/8	11-6 23/32	6-9 3/8	22-0 13/16	10-0 1/8	32-6 29/32
2	7 3/4	2-1 7/32	3-10 1/2	12-7 5/16	7-1 1/4	23-1 7/16	10-4	33-7 17/32
3	11 5/8	3-1 27/32	4-2 3/8	13-7 15/16	7-5 1/8	24-2 1/32	10-7 7/8	34-8 1/8
4	1-3 1/2	4-2 7/16	4-6 1/4	14-8 17/32	7-9	25-2 21/32	10-11 3/4	35-8 3/4
5	1-7 3/8	5-3 1/16	4-10 1/8	15-9 5/32	8-0 7/8	26-3 1/4	11-3 5/8	36-9 11/32
6	1-11 1/4	6-3 21/32	5-2	16-9 3/4	8-4 3/4	27-3 7/8	11-7 1/2	37-9 31/32
7	2-3 1/8	7-4 9/32	5-5 7/8	17-10 3/8	8-8 5/8	28-4 15/32	11-11 3/8	38-10 9/16
8	2-7	8-4 7/8	5-9 3/4	18-10 31/32	9-0 1/2	29-5 3/32	12-3 1/4	39-11 3/16
9	2-10 7/8	9-5 1/2	6-1 5/8	19-11 19/32	9-4 3/8	30-5 11/16	12-7 1/8	40-11 25/32

A = 17° 53′ 46″; logsin A = 9.48755; logcos A = 9.97846; logtan A = 9.50909; logcot A = 0.49091

Ins.	12″ Rise	12″ Slope	13″ Rise	13″ Slope	14″ Rise	14″ Slope	15″ Rise	15″ Slope	16″ Rise	16″ Slope
0	3 7/8	1-0 5/8	4 3/16	1-1 21/32	4 17/32	1-2 23/32	4 27/32	1-3 3/4	5 5/32	1-4 13/16
1/16	3 29/32	1-0 11/16	4 7/32	1-1 23/32	4 17/32	1-2 25/32	4 7/8	1-3 27/32	5 3/16	1-4 7/8
1/8	3 29/32	1-0 3/4	4 1/4	1-1 25/32	4 9/16	1-2 27/32	4 7/8	1-3 29/32	5 7/32	1-4 15/16
3/16	3 15/16	1-0 13/16	4 1/4	1-1 27/32	4 19/32	1-2 29/32	4 29/32	1-3 31/32	5 1/4	1-5
1/4	3 31/32	1-0 7/8	4 9/32	1-1 15/16	4 19/32	1-2 31/32	4 15/16	1-4 1/32	5 1/4	1-5 1/16
5/16	3 31/32	1-0 15/16	4 5/16	1-2	4 5/8	1-3 1/32	4 15/16	1-4 3/32	5 9/32	1-5 5/32
3/8	4	1-1	4 5/16	1-2 1/16	4 21/32	1-3 3/32	4 31/32	1-4 5/32	5 9/32	1-5 7/32
7/16	4 1/32	1-1 1/16	4 11/32	1-2 1/8	4 21/32	1-3 5/32	5	1-4 7/32	5 5/16	1-5 9/32
1/2	4 1/8	1-1 1/8	4 3/8	1-2 3/16	4 11/16	1-3 3/16	5	1-4 9/32	5 5/16	1-5 11/32
9/16	4 1/16	1-1 3/16	4 3/8	1-2 1/4	4 11/16	1-3 5/16	5 1/8	1-4 11/32	5 11/32	1-5 13/32
5/8	4 1/16	1-1 9/32	4 13/32	1-2 5/16	4 23/32	1-3 3/8	5 1/8	1-4 13/32	5 5/8	1-5 15/32
11/16	4 3/32	1-1 11/32	4 13/32	1-2 3/8	4 3/4	1-3 7/16	5 1/16	1-4 1/2	5 5/8	1-5 17/32
3/4	4 1/8	1-1 13/32	4 7/16	1-2 7/16	4 3/4	1-3 1/2	5 3/32	1-4 9/16	5 13/32	1-5 19/32
13/16	4 1/8	1-1 15/32	4 15/32	1-2 1/2	4 25/32	1-3 9/16	5 3/32	1-4 5/8	5 7/16	1-5 21/32
7/8	4 5/32	1-1 17/32	4 15/32	1-2 19/32	4 13/16	1-3 5/8	5 1/8	1-4 11/16	5 7/16	1-5 23/32
15/16	4 3/16	1-1 19/32	4 1/2	1-2 21/32	4 13/16	1-3 11/16	5 5/32	1-4 3/4	5 15/32	1-5 13/16

Ins.	17″ Rise	17″ Slope	18″ Rise	18″ Slope	19″ Rise	19″ Slope	20″ Rise	20″ Slope	21″ Rise	21″ Slope
0	5 1/2	1-5 7/8	5 13/16	1-6 29/32	6 1/8	1-7 31/32	6 15/32	1-9 1/32	6 25/32	1-10 1/16
1/16	5 1/2	1-5 15/16	5 27/32	1-6 31/32	6 5/32	1-8 1/32	6 15/32	1-9 3/32	6 13/16	1-10 1/8
1/8	5 17/32	1-6	5 27/32	1-7 1/32	6 3/16	1-8 3/32	6 1/2	1-9 5/32	6 13/16	1-10 3/16
3/16	5 9/16	1-6 1/16	5 7/8	1-7 1/8	6 3/16	1-8 5/32	6 17/32	1-9 7/32	6 27/32	1-10 1/4
1/4	5 9/16	1-6 1/8	5 29/32	1-7 3/16	6 7/32	1-8 7/32	6 17/32	1-9 9/32	6 7/8	1-10 11/32
5/16	5 19/32	1-6 3/16	5 29/32	1-7 1/4	6 1/4	1-8 9/32	6 9/16	1-9 11/32	6 7/8	1-10 13/32
3/8	5 5/8	1-6 1/4	5 15/16	1-7 5/16	6 1/4	1-8 3/8	6 19/32	1-9 13/32	6 29/32	1-10 15/32
7/16	5 5/8	1-6 5/16	5 31/32	1-7 3/8	6 9/32	1-8 7/16	6 19/32	1-9 15/32	6 15/16	1-10 17/32
1/2	5 21/32	1-6 3/8	5 31/32	1-7 7/16	6 5/16	1-8 1/2	6 5/8	1-9 17/32	6 15/16	1-10 19/32
9/16	5 21/32	1-6 15/32	6	1-7 1/2	6 5/16	1-8 9/16	6 5/8	1-9 19/32	6 31/32	1-10 21/32
5/8	5 11/16	1-6 17/32	6	1-7 9/16	6 11/32	1-8 5/8	6 21/32	1-9 11/16	6 31/32	1-10 23/32
11/16	5 23/32	1-6 19/32	6 1/32	1-7 5/8	6 11/32	1-8 11/16	6 11/16	1-9 3/4	7	1-10 25/32
3/4	5 23/32	1-6 21/32	6 1/16	1-7 23/32	6 3/8	1-8 3/4	6 11/16	1-9 13/16	7 1/32	1-10 27/32
13/16	5 3/4	1-6 23/32	6 1/16	1-7 25/32	6 13/32	1-8 13/16	6 23/32	1-9 7/8	7 1/2	1-10 29/32
7/8	5 25/32	1-6 25/32	6 3/32	1-7 27/32	6 13/32	1-8 7/8	6 3/4	1-9 15/16	7 1/16	1-11
15/16	5 25/32	1-6 27/32	6 1/8	1-7 29/32	6 7/16	1-8 15/16	6 3/4	1-10	7 3/32	1-11 1/16

Feet	40′ Rise	40′ Slope	50′ Rise	50′ Slope	60′ Rise	60′ Slope	70′ Rise	70′ Slope
0	12-11	42-0 13/32	16-1 3/4	52-6 1/2	19-4 1/2	63-0 19/32	22-7 1/4	73-6 23/32
1	13-2 7/8	43-1 3/32	16-5 5/8	53-7 1/8	19-8 3/8	64-1 1/32	22-11 1/8	74-7 5/16
2	13-6 3/4	44-1 5/8	16-9 1/2	54-7 23/32	20-0 1/4	65-1 27/32	23-3	75-7 15/16
3	13-10 5/8	45-2 1/4	17-1 3/8	55-8 11/32	20-4 1/8	66-2 1/16	23-6 7/8	76-8 17/32
4	14-2 1/2	46-2 7/32	17-5 1/4	56-8 15/16	20-8	67-3 1/16	23-10 3/4	77-9 5/32
5	14-6 3/8	47-3 15/32	17-9 1/8	57-9 9/16	20-11 7/8	68-3 21/32	24-2 5/8	78-9 3/4
6	14-10 1/4	48-4 1/16	18-1	58-10 5/32	21-3 3/4	69-4 9/32	24-6 1/2	79-10 3/8
7	15-2 1/8	49-4 11/16	18-4 7/8	59-10 25/32	21-7 5/8	70-4 7/8	24-10 3/8	80-10 31/32
8	15-6	50-5 9/32	18-8 3/4	60-11 3/8	21-11 1/2	71-5 1/2	25-2 1/4	81-11 19/32
9	15-9 7/8	51-5 29/32	19-0 5/8	62-0	22-3 3/8	72-6 3/32	25-6 1/8	83-0 3/16

natsin A=0.3072923908; natcos A=0.9516151461; nattan A=0.3229166666; natcot A=3.0967741935

Inches	0" Rise	0" Slope	1" Rise	1" Slope	2" Rise	2" Slope	3" Rise	3" Slope	4" Rise	4" Slope	5" Rise	5" Slope
0	0	0	5/16	1 1/16	21/32	2 3/32	1	3 5/32	1 5/16	4 7/32	1 5/8	5 1/4
1/16	1/32	1/16	11/32	1 1/8	11/16	2 5/32	1	3 7/32	1 11/32	4 9/32	1 21/32	5 5/16
1/8	1/32	1/8	3/8	1 3/16	11/16	2 1/4	1 1/32	3 9/32	1 11/32	4 11/32	1 11/16	5 13/32
3/16	1/16	3/16	3/8	1 1/4	23/32	2 5/16	1 1/32	3 11/32	1 3/8	4 13/32	1 11/16	5 15/32
1/4	3/32	1/4	13/32	1 5/16	3/4	2 3/8	1 1/16	3 13/32	1 13/32	4 15/32	1 23/32	5 17/32
5/16	3/32	1 1/32	7/16	1 3/8	3/4	2 7/16	1 3/32	3 1/2	1 13/32	4 17/32	1 3/4	5 19/32
3/8	1/8	1 13/32	7/16	1 7/16	25/32	2 1/2	1 3/32	3 9/16	1 7/16	4 19/32	1 3/4	5 21/32
7/16	5/32	15/32	15/32	1 1/2	13/16	2 9/16	1 1/8	3 5/8	1 15/32	4 21/32	1 25/32	5 23/32
1/2	5/32	17/32	1/2	1 19/32	13/16	2 5/8	1 5/32	3 11/16	1 15/32	4 3/4	1 13/16	5 25/32
9/16	3/16	19/32	1/2	1 21/32	27/32	2 11/16	1 5/32	3 3/4	1 1/2	4 13/16	1 13/16	5 27/32
5/8	7/32	21/32	17/32	1 23/32	7/8	2 3/4	1 3/16	3 13/16	1 17/32	4 7/8	1 27/32	5 29/32
11/16	7/32	23/32	9/16	1 25/32	7/8	2 27/32	1 7/32	3 7/8	1 17/32	4 15/16	1 7/8	6
3/4	1/4	25/32	9/16	1 27/32	29/32	2 29/32	1 7/32	3 15/16	1 9/16	5	1 7/8	6 1/16
13/16	9/32	27/32	19/32	1 29/32	15/16	2 31/32	1 1/4	4	1 19/32	5 1/16	1 29/32	6 1/8
7/8	9/32	29/32	5/8	1 31/32	15/16	3 1/32	1 9/32	4 3/32	1 19/32	5 1/8	1 15/16	6 3/16
15/16	5/16	1	5/8	2 1/32	31/32	3 3/32	1 9/32	4 5/32	1 5/8	5 3/16	1 15/16	6 1/4

Inches	6" Rise	6" Slope	7" Rise	7" Slope	8" Rise	8" Slope	9" Rise	9" Slope	10" Rise	10" Slope	11" Rise	11" Slope
0	1 31/32	6 5/16	2 5/16	7 3/8	2 5/8	8 13/32	2 15/16	9 15/32	3 9/32	10 17/32	3 5/8	11 9/16
1/16	2	6 3/8	2 5/16	7 7/16	2 21/32	8 1/2	2 31/32	9 17/32	3 5/16	10 19/32	3 5/8	11 21/32
1/8	2	6 7/16	2 11/32	7 1/2	2 21/32	8 9/16	3	9 19/32	3 5/16	10 21/32	3 21/32	11 23/32
3/16	2 1/32	6 1/2	2 11/32	7 9/16	2 11/16	8 5/8	3	9 21/32	3 11/32	10 23/32	3 21/32	11 25/32
1/4	2 1/16	6 9/16	2 3/8	7 5/8	2 23/32	8 11/16	3 1/32	9 3/4	3 3/8	10 25/32	3 11/16	11 27/32
5/16	2 1/16	6 21/32	2 13/32	7 11/16	2 23/32	8 3/4	3 1/16	9 13/16	3 3/8	10 27/32	3 23/32	11 29/32
3/8	2 3/32	6 23/32	2 13/32	7 3/4	2 3/4	8 13/16	3 1/16	9 7/8	3 13/32	10 29/32	3 23/32	11 31/32
7/16	2 1/8	6 25/32	2 7/16	7 13/16	2 25/32	8 7/8	3 3/32	9 15/16	3 7/16	11	3 3/4	1-0 1/32
1/2	2 1/8	6 27/32	2 15/32	7 29/32	2 25/32	8 15/16	3 1/8	10	3 7/16	11 1/16	3 25/32	1-0 3/32
9/16	2 5/32	6 29/32	2 15/32	7 31/32	2 13/16	9	3 1/8	10 1/16	3 15/32	11 1/8	3 25/32	1-0 5/32
5/8	2 3/16	6 31/32	2 1/2	8 1/32	2 27/32	9 1/16	3 5/32	10 1/8	3 1/2	11 3/16	3 13/16	1-0 1/4
11/16	2 3/16	7 1/32	2 17/32	8 3/32	2 27/32	9 1/8	3 3/16	10 3/16	3 1/2	11 1/4	3 27/32	1-0 5/16
3/4	2 7/32	7 3/32	2 17/32	8 5/32	2 7/8	9 7/32	3 3/16	10 1/4	3 17/32	11 5/16	3 27/32	1-0 3/8
13/16	2 1/4	7 5/32	2 9/16	8 7/32	2 29/32	9 9/32	3 7/32	10 5/16	3 9/16	11 3/8	3 7/8	1-0 7/16
7/8	2 1/4	7 1/4	2 19/32	8 9/32	2 29/32	9 11/32	3 1/4	10 13/32	3 9/16	11 7/16	3 29/32	1-0 1/2
15/16	2 9/32	7 5/16	2 19/32	8 11/32	2 15/16	9 13/32	3 1/4	10 15/32	3 19/32	11 1/2	3 29/32	1-0 9/16

Feet	0' Rise	0' Slope	10' Rise	10' Slope	20' Rise	20' Slope	30' Rise	30' Slope
0	0	0	3-3 3/8	10-6 9/32	6-6 3/4	21-0 19/32	9-10 1/8	31-6 7/8
1	3 15/16	1-0 5/8	3-7 5/16	11-6 15/16	6-10 11/16	22-1 7/32	10-2 1/16	32-7 1/2
2	7 7/8	2-1 1/4	3-11 1/4	12-7 9/16	7-2 5/8	23-1 27/32	10-6	33-8 5/32
3	11 13/16	3-1 7/8	4-3 3/16	13-8 3/16	7-6 9/16	24-2 15/32	10-9 15/16	34-8 25/32
4	1-3 3/4	4-2 17/32	4-7 1/8	14-8 13/16	7-10 1/2	25-3 3/32	11-1 7/8	35-9 13/32
5	1-7 11/16	5-3 5/32	4-11 1/16	15-9 7/16	8-2 7/16	26-3 3/4	11-5 13/16	36-10 1/2
6	1-11 5/8	6-3 25/32	5-3	16-10 1/16	8-6 3/8	27-4 3/8	11-9 3/4	37-10 21/32
7	2-3 9/16	7-4 13/32	5-6 15/16	17-10 11/16	8-10 5/16	28-5	12-1 11/16	38-11 9/32
8	2-7 1/2	8-5 1/32	5-10 7/8	18-11 11/16	9-2 1/4	29-5 5/8	12-5 5/8	39-11 29/32
9	2-11 7/16	9-5 21/32	6-2 13/16	19-11 31/32	9-6 3/16	30-6 1/4	12-9 9/16	41-0 9/16

A = 18° 09' 57''; logsin = 9.49383; logcos A = 9.97780; logtan A = 9.51604; logcot A = 0.48396

In.	Rise 12″	Slope 12″	Rise 13″	Slope 13″	Rise 14″	Slope 14″	Rise 15″	Slope 15″	Rise 16″	Slope 16″
0	3 15/16	1-0 5/8	4 1/4	1-1 11/16	4 19/32	1-2 3/4	4 15/16	1-3 25/32	5 1/4	1-4 27/32
1/16	3 31/32	1-0 11/16	4 9/32	1-1 3/4	4 5/8	1-2 13/16	4 15/16	1-3 27/32	5 9/32	1-4 29/32
1/8	3 31/32	1-0 3/4	4 5/16	1-1 13/16	4 5/8	1-2 7/8	4 31/32	1-3 29/32	5 9/32	1-4 31/32
3/16	4	1-0 13/16	4 5/16	1-1 7/8	4 21/32	1-2 15/16	4 31/32	1-3 31/32	5 5/16	1-5 1/32
1/4	4 1/32	1-0 29/32	4 11/32	1-1 15/16	4 11/16	1-3	5	1-4 1/16	5 11/32	1-5 3/32
5/16	4 1/32	1-0 31/32	4 3/8	1-2	4 11/16	1-3 1/16	5 1/32	1-4 1/8	5 11/32	1-5 5/32
3/8	4 1/16	1-1 1/32	4 3/8	1-2 1/16	4 23/32	1-3 1/8	5 1/32	1-4 3/16	5 3/8	1-5 7/32
7/16	4 3/32	1-1 3/32	4 13/32	1-2 5/32	4 3/4	1-3 5/16	5 1/16	1-4 1/4	5 13/32	1-5 5/16
1/2	4 3/32	1-1 5/32	4 7/16	1-2 7/32	4 3/4	1-3 1/4	5 3/32	1-4 5/16	5 13/32	1-5 3/8
9/16	4 1/8	1-1 7/32	4 7/16	1-2 9/32	4 25/32	1-3 5/16	5 3/32	1-4 3/8	5 7/16	1-5 7/16
5/8	4 5/32	1-1 9/32	4 15/32	1-2 11/32	4 13/16	1-3 13/32	5 1/8	1-4 7/16	5 15/32	1-5 1/2
11/16	4 5/32	1-1 11/32	4 1/2	1-2 13/32	4 13/16	1-3 15/32	5 5/32	1-4 1/2	5 15/32	1-5 9/16
3/4	4 3/16	1-1 13/32	4 1/2	1-2 15/32	4 27/32	1-3 17/32	5 5/32	1-4 9/16	5 1/2	1-5 5/8
13/16	4 7/32	1-1 1/2	4 17/32	1-2 17/32	4 7/8	1-3 19/32	5 3/16	1-4 21/32	5 17/32	1-5 11/16
7/8	4 7/32	1-1 9/16	4 9/16	1-2 19/32	4 7/8	1-3 21/32	5 7/32	1-4 23/32	5 17/32	1-5 3/4
15/16	4 1/4	1-1 5/8	4 9/16	1-2 21/32	4 29/32	1-3 23/32	5 7/32	1-4 25/32	5 9/16	1-5 13/16

In.	Rise 17″	Slope 17″	Rise 18″	Slope 18″	Rise 19″	Slope 19″	Rise 20″	Slope 20″	Rise 21″	Slope 21″
0	5 9/16	1-5 29/32	5 29/32	1-6 15/16	6 1/4	1-8	6 9/16	1-9 1/16	6 7/8	1-10 3/32
1/16	5 19/32	1-5 31/32	5 15/16	1-7	6 1/4	1-8 1/16	6 19/32	1-9 1/8	6 29/32	1-10 5/32
1/8	5 5/8	1-6 1/32	5 15/16	1-7 1/16	6 9/32	1-8 1/8	6 19/32	1-9 3/16	6 15/16	1-10 7/32
3/16	5 5/8	1-6 3/32	5 31/32	1-7 5/32	6 9/32	1-8 3/16	6 5/8	1-9 1/4	6 15/16	1-10 5/16
1/4	5 21/32	1-6 5/32	6	1-7 7/32	6 5/16	1-8 1/4	6 21/32	1-9 5/16	6 31/32	1-10 3/8
5/16	5 11/16	1-6 7/32	6	1-7 9/32	6 11/32	1-8 5/16	6 21/32	1-9 3/8	7	1-10 7/16
3/8	5 11/16	1-6 9/32	6 1/16	1-7 11/32	6 11/32	1-8 13/32	6 11/16	1-9 7/16	7	1-10 1/2
7/16	5 23/32	1-6 11/32	6 1/16	1-7 13/32	6 3/8	1-8 15/32	6 23/32	1-9 1/2	7 1/32	1-10 9/16
1/2	5 3/4	1-6 13/32	6 1/16	1-7 15/32	6 13/32	1-8 17/32	6 23/32	1-9 9/16	7 1/16	1-10 5/8
9/16	5 3/4	1-6 15/32	6 3/32	1-7 17/32	6 13/32	1-8 19/32	6 3/4	1-9 21/32	7 1/16	1-10 11/16
5/8	5 25/32	1-6 9/16	6 1/8	1-7 19/32	6 7/16	1-8 21/32	6 25/32	1-9 23/32	7 3/32	1-10 3/4
11/16	5 13/16	1-6 5/8	6 1/8	1-7 21/32	6 15/32	1-8 23/32	6 25/32	1-9 25/32	7 1/8	1-10 13/16
3/4	5 13/16	1-6 11/16	6 5/32	1-7 23/32	6 15/32	1-8 25/32	6 13/16	1-9 27/32	7 1/8	1-10 29/32
13/16	5 27/32	1-6 3/4	6 3/16	1-7 13/16	6 1/2	1-8 27/32	6 27/32	1-9 29/32	7 5/32	1-10 31/32
7/8	5 7/8	1-6 13/16	6 3/16	1-7 7/8	6 17/32	1-8 29/32	6 27/32	1-9 31/32	7 3/16	1-11 1/32
15/16	5 7/8	1-6 7/8	6 7/32	1-7 15/16	6 17/32	1-8 31/32	6 7/8	1-10 1/32	7 3/16	1-11 3/32

Feet	Rise 40′	Slope 40′	Rise 50′	Slope 50′	Rise 60′	Slope 60′	Rise 70′	Slope 70′
0	13-1 1/2	42-1 3/16	16-4 7/8	52-7 15/16	19-8 1/4	63-1 25/32	22-11 5/8	73-8 1/16
1	13-5 7/16	43-1 13/16	16-8 13/16	53-8 3/32	20-0 3/16	64-2 13/32	23-3 9/16	74-8 11/16
2	13-9 3/8	44-2 7/16	17-0 3/4	54-8 23/32	20-4 1/8	65-3 1/32	23-7 1/2	75-9 5/16
3	14-1 5/16	45-3 1/16	17-4 11/16	55-9 3/8	20-8 1/16	66-3 21/32	23-11 7/16	76-9 15/16
4	14-5 1/4	46-3 11/16	17-8 5/8	56-10	21-0	67-4 9/32	24-3 3/8	77-10 19/32
5	14-9 3/16	47-4 5/16	18-0 9/16	57-10 5/8	21-3 15/16	68-4 29/32	24-7 5/16	78-11 7/32
6	15-1 1/8	48-4 31/32	18-4 1/2	58-11 1/4	21-7 7/8	69-5 17/32	24-11 1/4	79-11 27/32
7	15-5 1/16	49-5 19/32	18-8 7/16	59-11 7/8	21-11 13/16	70-6 3/16	25-3 3/16	81-0 15/32
8	15-9	50-6 7/32	19-0 3/8	61-0 1/2	22-3 3/4	71-6 13/16	25-7 1/8	82-1 3/32
9	16-0 15/16	51-6 27/32	19-4 5/16	62-1 1/8	22-7 11/16	72-7 7/16	25-11 1/16	83-1 23/32

natsin A=0.3117704178; natcos A=0.9501574640; nattan A=0.3281250000; natcot A=3.0476190476

Inches	0" Rise	0" Slope	1" Rise	1" Slope	2" Rise	2" Slope	3" Rise	3" Slope	4" Rise	4" Slope	5" Rise	5" Slope
0	0	0	11/32	1 1/16	21/32	2 3/32	1	3 5/32	1 11/32	4 7/32	1 21/32	5 9/32
1/16	1/32	1/16	11/32	1 1/8	11/16	2 3/16	1 1/32	3 7/32	1 11/32	4 9/32	1 11/16	5 11/32
1/8	1/32	1/8	3/8	1 3/16	23/32	2 1/4	1 1/32	3 9/32	1 3/8	4 11/32	1 23/32	5 13/32
3/16	1/16	3/16	13/32	1 1/4	23/32	2 5/16	1 1/16	3 3/8	1 13/32	4 13/32	1 23/32	5 15/32
1/4	3/32	1/4	13/32	1 5/16	3/4	2 3/8	1 3/32	3 7/16	1 13/32	4 15/32	1 3/4	5 17/32
5/16	3/32	11/32	13/32	1 3/8	25/32	2 7/16	1 3/32	3 1/2	1 7/16	4 17/32	1 25/32	5 19/32
3/8	1/8	13/32	15/32	1 7/16	25/32	2 1/2	1 1/8	3 9/16	1 15/32	4 5/8	1 25/32	5 21/32
7/16	5/32	15/32	15/32	1 1/2	13/16	2 9/16	1 5/32	3 5/8	1 15/32	4 11/16	1 13/16	5 23/32
1/2	5/32	17/32	1/2	1 19/32	27/32	2 5/8	1 5/32	3 11/16	1 1/2	4 3/4	1 27/32	5 13/16
9/16	3/16	19/32	17/32	1 21/32	27/32	2 11/16	1 3/16	3 3/4	1 17/32	4 13/16	1 27/32	5 7/8
5/8	7/32	21/32	17/32	1 23/32	7/8	2 25/32	1 7/32	3 13/16	1 17/32	4 7/8	1 7/8	5 15/16
11/16	7/32	23/32	9/16	1 25/32	29/32	2 27/32	1 7/32	3 7/8	1 9/16	4 15/16	1 29/32	6
3/4	1/4	25/32	19/32	1 27/32	29/32	2 29/32	1 1/4	3 15/16	1 19/32	5	1 29/32	6 1/16
13/16	9/32	27/32	19/32	1 29/32	15/16	2 31/32	1 9/32	4 1/32	1 19/32	5 1/16	1 15/16	6 1/8
7/8	9/32	15/16	5/8	1 31/32	31/32	3 1/32	1 9/32	4 3/32	1 5/8	5 1/8	1 31/32	6 3/16
15/16	5/16	1	21/32	2 1/32	31/32	3 3/32	1 5/16	4 5/32	1 21/32	5 7/32	1 31/32	6 1/4

Inches	6" Rise	6" Slope	7" Rise	7" Slope	8" Rise	8" Slope	9" Rise	9" Slope	10" Rise	10" Slope	11" Rise	11" Slope
0	2	6 5/16	2 11/32	7 3/8	2 21/32	8 7/16	3	9 1/2	3 11/32	10 17/32	3 21/32	11 19/32
1/16	2 1/32	6 3/8	2 11/32	7 7/16	2 11/16	8 1/2	3 1/32	9 9/16	3 11/32	10 19/32	3 11/16	11 21/32
1/8	2 1/32	6 15/32	2 3/8	7 1/2	2 23/32	8 9/16	3 1/32	9 5/8	3 3/8	10 11/16	3 23/32	11 23/32
3/16	2 1/16	6 17/32	2 13/32	7 9/16	2 23/32	8 5/8	3 1/16	9 11/16	3 13/32	10 3/4	3 23/32	11 25/32
1/4	2 3/32	6 19/32	2 13/32	7 21/32	2 3/4	8 11/16	3 3/32	9 3/4	3 13/32	10 13/16	3 3/4	11 27/32
5/16	2 3/32	6 21/32	2 7/16	7 23/32	2 25/32	8 3/4	3 3/32	9 13/16	3 7/16	10 7/8	3 25/32	11 15/16
3/8	2 1/8	6 23/32	2 15/32	7 25/32	2 25/32	8 13/16	3 1/8	9 7/8	3 15/32	10 15/16	3 25/32	1-0
7/16	2 5/32	6 25/32	2 15/32	7 27/32	2 13/16	8 29/32	3 5/32	9 15/16	3 15/32	11	3 13/16	1-0 1/16
1/2	2 5/32	6 27/32	2 1/2	7 29/32	2 27/32	8 31/32	3 5/32	10	3 1/2	11 1/16	3 27/32	1-0 1/8
9/16	2 3/16	6 29/32	2 17/32	7 31/32	2 27/32	9 1/32	3 3/16	10 3/32	3 17/32	11 1/8	3 27/32	1-0 3/16
5/8	2 7/32	6 31/32	2 17/32	8 1/32	2 7/8	9 3/32	3 7/32	10 5/32	3 17/32	11 3/16	3 7/8	1-0 1/4
11/16	2 7/32	7 1/32	2 9/16	8 3/32	2 29/32	9 5/32	3 7/32	10 7/32	3 9/16	11 1/4	3 29/32	1-0 5/16
3/4	2 1/4	7 1/8	2 9/16	8 5/32	2 29/32	9 7/32	3 1/4	10 9/32	3 19/32	11 11/32	3 29/32	1-0 3/8
13/16	2 9/32	7 3/16	2 19/32	8 1/4	2 15/16	9 9/32	3 9/32	10 11/32	3 19/32	11 13/32	3 31/32	1-0 7/16
7/8	2 29/32	7 1/4	2 19/32	8 5/16	2 31/32	9 11/32	3 9/32	10 13/32	3 5/8	11 15/32	3 31/32	1-0 17/32
15/16	2 5/16	7 5/16	2 21/32	8 3/8	2 31/32	9 13/32	3 5/16	10 15/32	3 21/32	11 17/32	3 31/32	1-0 19/32

Feet	0' Rise	0' Slope	10' Rise	10' Slope	20' Rise	20' Slope	30' Rise	30' Slope
0	0	0	3-4	10-6 1/2	6-8	21-0 31/32	10-0	31-7 15/32
1	4	1-0 21/32	3-8	11-7 1/8	7-0	22-1 5/8	10-4	32-8 1/8
2	8	2-1 5/16	4-0	12-7 25/32	7-4	23-2 9/32	10-8	33-8 25/32
3	1-0	3-1 15/16	4-4	13-8 7/16	7-8	24-2 15/16	11-0	34-9 13/32
4	1-4	4-2 19/32	4-8	14-9 3/32	8-0	25-3 19/32	11-4	35-10 1/16
5	1-8	5-3 1/4	5-0	15-9 3/4	8-4	26-4 7/32	11-8	36-10 23/32
6	2-0	6-3 29/32	5-4	16-10 3/8	8-8	27-4 7/8	12-0	37-11 3/8
7	2-4	7-4 17/32	5-8	17-11 1/32	9-0	28-5 17/32	12-4	39-0 1/32
8	2-8	8-5 3/16	6-0	18-11 11/16	9-4	29-6 3/16	12-8	40-0 21/32
9	3-0	9-5 27/32	6-4	20-0 11/32	9-8	30-6 13/16	13-0	41-1 5/16

A = 18° 26' 06"; logsin A = 9.50000; logcos A = 9.77712; logtan A = 9.52288; logcot A = 0.47712.

In.	12″ Rise	12″ Slope	13″ Rise	13″ Slope	14″ Rise	14″ Slope	15″ Rise	15″ Slope	16″ Rise	16″ Slope
0	4	1-0 21/32	4 11/32	1-1 23/32	4 21/32	1-2 3/4	5	1-3 13/16	5 11/32	1-4 7/8
1/16	4 1/32	1-0 23/32	4 11/32	1-1 25/32	4 11/16	1-2 13/16	5 1/32	1-3 7/8	5 11/32	1-4 15/16
1/8	4 1/32	1-0 25/32	4 3/8	1-1 27/32	4 23/32	1-2 7/8	5 1/32	1-3 15/16	5 3/8	1-5
3/16	4 1/16	1-0 27/32	4 13/32	1-1 29/32	4 23/32	1-2 31/32	5 1/16	1-4	5 13/32	1-5 1/16
1/4	4 3/32	1-0 29/32	4 13/32	1-1 31/32	4 3/4	1-3 1/32	5 3/32	1-4 1/16	5 13/32	1-5 1/8
5/16	4 3/32	1-0 31/32	4 7/16	1-2 1/32	4 25/32	1-3 3/32	5 3/32	1-4 5/32	5 7/16	1-5 3/16
3/8	4 1/8	1-1 1/32	4 15/32	1-2 3/32	4 25/32	1-3 5/32	5 1/8	1-4 7/32	5 15/32	1-5 1/4
7/16	4 5/32	1-1 1/8	4 15/32	1-2 5/32	4 13/16	1-3 7/32	5 5/32	1-4 9/32	5 15/32	1-5 5/16
1/2	4 5/32	1-1 3/16	4 1/2	1-2 7/32	4 27/32	1-3 9/32	5 5/32	1-4 11/32	5 1/2	1-5 13/32
9/16	4 3/16	1-1 1/4	4 17/32	1-2 9/32	4 27/32	1-3 11/32	5 3/16	1-4 13/32	5 17/32	1-5 15/32
5/8	4 7/32	1-1 5/16	4 17/32	1-2 3/8	4 7/8	1-3 13/32	5 7/32	1-4 15/32	5 17/32	1-5 17/32
11/16	4 7/32	1-1 3/8	4 9/16	1-2 7/16	4 29/32	1-3 15/32	5 1/4	1-4 17/32	5 9/16	1-5 19/32
3/4	4 1/4	1-1 7/16	4 19/32	1-2 1/2	4 29/32	1-3 9/16	5 1/4	1-4 19/32	5 19/32	1-5 21/32
13/16	4 9/32	1-1 1/2	4 19/32	1-2 9/16	4 15/16	1-3 5/8	5 9/32	1-4 21/32	5 19/32	1-5 23/32
7/8	4 9/32	1-1 9/16	4 5/8	1-2 5/8	4 31/32	1-3 11/16	5 9/32	1-4 23/32	5 5/8	1-5 25/32
15/16	4 5/16	1-1 5/8	4 21/32	1-2 11/16	4 31/32	1-3 3/4	5 5/16	1-4 13/16	5 21/32	1-5 27/32

In.	17″ Rise	17″ Slope	18″ Rise	18″ Slope	19″ Rise	19″ Slope	20″ Rise	20″ Slope	21″ Rise	21″ Slope
0	5 21/32	1-5 29/32	6	1-6 31/32	6 11/32	1-8 1/32	6 21/32	1-9 3/32	7	1-10 1/8
1/16	5 11/16	1-6	6 1/32	1-7 1/32	6 11/32	1-8 3/32	6 11/16	1-9 5/32	7 1/32	1-10 3/16
1/8	5 23/32	1-6 1/16	6 1/32	1-7 3/32	6 3/8	1-8 5/32	6 23/32	1-9 7/32	7 1/32	1-10 9/32
3/16	5 23/32	1-6 1/8	6 1/16	1-7 5/32	6 13/32	1-8 7/32	6 23/32	1-9 9/32	7 1/16	1-10 11/32
1/4	5 3/4	1-6 3/16	6 3/32	1-7 1/4	6 13/32	1-8 9/32	6 3/4	1-9 11/32	7 3/32	1-10 13/32
5/16	5 25/32	1-6 1/4	6 3/32	1-7 5/16	6 7/16	1-8 11/32	6 25/32	1-9 13/32	7 3/32	1-10 15/32
3/8	5 25/32	1-6 5/16	6 1/8	1-7 3/8	6 15/32	1-8 7/16	6 25/32	1-9 15/32	7 1/8	1-10 17/32
7/16	5 13/16	1-6 3/8	6 5/32	1-7 7/16	6 15/32	1-8 1/2	6 13/16	1-9 17/32	7 5/32	1-10 19/32
1/2	5 27/32	1-6 7/16	6 5/32	1-7 1/2	6 1/2	1-8 9/16	6 27/32	1-9 19/32	7 5/32	1-10 21/32
9/16	5 27/32	1-6 1/2	6 3/16	1-7 9/16	6 17/32	1-8 5/8	6 27/32	1-9 11/16	7 3/16	1-10 23/32
5/8	5 7/8	1-6 19/32	6 7/32	1-7 5/8	6 17/32	1-8 11/16	6 7/8	1-9 3/4	7 7/32	1-10 25/32
11/16	5 29/32	1-6 21/32	6 7/32	1-7 11/16	6 9/16	1-8 3/4	6 29/32	1-9 13/16	7 7/32	1-10 7/8
3/4	5 29/32	1-6 23/32	6 1/4	1-7 3/4	6 19/32	1-8 13/16	6 29/32	1-9 7/8	7 1/4	1-10 15/16
13/16	5 15/16	1-6 25/32	6 9/32	1-7 27/32	6 19/32	1-8 7/8	6 15/16	1-9 15/16	7 9/32	1-11
7/8	5 31/32	1-6 27/32	6 9/32	1-7 29/32	6 5/8	1-8 15/16	6 31/32	1-10	7 9/32	1-11 1/16
15/16	5 31/32	1-6 29/32	6 5/16	1-7 31/32	6 21/32	1-9 1/32	6 31/32	1-10 1/16	7 5/16	1-11 1/8

Feet	40′ Rise	40′ Slope	50′ Rise	50′ Slope	60′ Rise	60′ Slope	70′ Rise	70′ Slope
0	13-4	42-1 31/32	16-8	52-8 15/32	20-0	63-2 15/16	23-4	73-9 7/16
1	13-8	43-2 5/8	17-0	53-9 3/32	20-4	64-3 19/32	23-8	74-10 3/32
2	14-0	44-3 1/4	17-4	54-9 3/4	20-8	65-4 1/4	24-0	75-10 3/4
3	14-4	45-3 29/32	17-8	55-10 13/32	21-0	66-4 29/32	24-4	76-11 3/8
4	14-8	46-4 9/16	18-0	56-11 1/16	21-4	67-5 17/32	24-8	78-0 1/32
5	15-0	47-5 7/32	18-4	57-11 11/16	21-8	68-6 3/16	25-0	79-0 11/16
6	15-4	48-5 27/32	18-8	59-0 11/32	22-0	69-6 27/32	25-4	80-1 11/32
7	15-8	49-6 1/2	19-0	60-1	22-4	70-7 1/2	25-8	81-1 31/32
8	16-0	50-7 5/32	19-4	61-1 21/32	22-8	71-8 1/8	26-0	82-2 5/8
9	16-4	51-7 13/16	19-8	62-2 5/16	23-0	72-8 25/32	26-4	83-3 9/32

natsin A=0.3162277660; natcos A=0.9486832981; nattan A=0.3333333333; natcot A=3.0000000000

Inches	0" Rise	0" Slope	1" Rise	1" Slope	2" Rise	2" Slope	3" Rise	3" Slope	4" Rise	4" Slope	5" Rise	5" Slope
0	0	0	11/32−	1 1/16	11/16	2 1/8	1	3 5/32	1 11/32	4 7/32	1 11/16	5 9/32
1/16	1/32	1/16	3/8	1 1/8	11/16	2 3/16	1 1/32	3 7/32	1 3/8	4 9/32	1 23/32	5 11/32
1/8	1/32	1/8	3/8	1 3/16	23/32	2 1/4	1 1/16	3 5/16	1 13/32	4 11/32	1 3/4	5 13/32
3/16	1/16	3/16	13/32	1 1/4	3/4	2 5/16	1 3/32−	3 3/8	1 13/32	4 13/32	1 3/4	5 15/32
1/4	3/32	1/4	7/16	1 5/16	3/4	2 3/8	1 3/32	3 7/16	1 7/16	4 1/2	1 25/32−	5 17/32
5/16	3/32	11/32	7/16	1 3/8	25/32	2 7/16	1 1/8	3 1/2	1 15/32	4 9/16	1 13/16	5 19/32
3/8	1/8	13/32	15/32−	1 7/16	13/16	2 1/2	1 5/32−	3 9/16	1 15/32	4 5/8	1 13/16	5 11/16
7/16	5/32	15/32	1/2	1 17/32−	13/16	2 9/16	1 3/16	3 5/8	1 1/2	4 11/16	1 27/32−	5 3/4
1/2	5/32	17/32−	1/2	1 19/32−	27/32−	2 5/8	1 3/16	3 11/16	1 17/32−	4 3/4	1 7/8	5 13/16
9/16	3/16	19/32	17/32−	1 21/32−	7/8	2 23/32−	1 3/16	3 3/4	1 17/32	4 13/16	1 7/8	5 7/8
5/8	7/32−	21/32	9/16	1 23/32−	7/8	2 25/32−	1 7/32	3 13/16	1 9/16	4 7/8	1 29/32−	5 15/16
11/16	7/32	23/32	9/16	1 25/32−	29/32−	2 27/32−	1 1/4	3 29/32−	1 19/32	4 15/16	1 15/16	6
3/4	1/4	25/32	19/32−	1 27/32−	15/16	2 29/32−	1 9/32	3 31/32−	1 19/32	5	1 15/16	6 1/16
13/16	9/32−	27/32	5/8	1 29/32−	15/16	2 31/32−	1 9/32	4 1/32−	1 5/8	5 3/32−	1 31/32−	6 1/8
7/8	9/32	15/16	5/8	1 31/32−	31/32−	3 1/32−	1 5/16	4 3/32−	1 21/32	5 5/32−	2	6 3/16
15/16	5/16	1	21/32−	2 1/32−	1	3 3/32−	1 11/32−	4 5/32−	1 21/32	5 7/32−	2	6 9/32−

Inches	6" Rise	6" Slope	7" Rise	7" Slope	8" Rise	8" Slope	9" Rise	9" Slope	10" Rise	10" Slope	11" Rise	11" Slope
0	2 1/32	6 11/32−	2 3/8	7 3/8	2 23/32−	8 7/16	3 1/16	9 1/2	3 3/8	10 9/16	3 23/32−	11 5/8
1/16	2 1/16	6 13/32−	2 13/32−	7 15/32−	2 23/32−	8 1/2	3 1/16	9 9/16	3 13/32−	10 5/8	3 3/4	11 11/16
1/8	2 1/16	6 15/32−	2 13/32−	7 17/32−	2 3/4	8 9/16	3 3/32−	9 5/8	3 7/16	10 11/16	3 25/32−	11 3/4
3/16	2 3/32	6 17/32−	2 7/16	7 19/32−	2 25/32−	8 21/32−	3 1/8	9 11/16	3 7/16	10 3/4	3 25/32−	11 13/16
1/4	2 1/8	6 19/32−	2 15/32−	7 21/32−	2 25/32−	8 23/32−	3 1/8	9 25/32−	3 15/32−	10 13/16	3 13/16	11 7/8
5/16	2 1/8	6 21/32−	2 15/32−	7 23/32−	2 13/16	8 25/32−	3 5/32−	9 27/32−	3 1/2	10 7/8	3 27/32−	11 15/16
3/8	2 5/32−	6 23/32−	2 1/2	7 25/32−	2 27/32−	8 27/32−	3 3/16	9 29/32−	3 1/2	10 31/32−	3 27/32−	1-0
7/16	2 3/16	6 25/32−	2 17/32−	7 27/32−	2 27/32−	8 29/32−	3 3/16	9 31/32−	3 17/32−	11 1/32−	3 7/8	1-0 1/16
1/2	2 3/16	6 7/8	2 17/32−	7 29/32−	2 7/8	8 31/32−	3 7/32−	10 1/32−	3 9/16	11 3/32−	3 29/32−	1-0 5/32−
9/16	2 7/32−	6 15/16	2 9/16	7 31/32−	2 29/32−	9 1/32−	3 1/4	10 3/32−	3 9/16	11 5/32−	3 29/32−	1-0 7/32−
5/8	2 1/4	7	2 19/32−	8 1/16	2 29/32−	9 3/32−	3 1/4	10 5/32−	3 19/32−	11 7/32−	3 15/16	1-0 9/32−
11/16	2 1/4	7 1/16	2 19/32−	8 1/8	2 15/16	9 5/32−	3 9/32−	10 7/32−	3 5/8	11 9/32−	3 31/32−	1-0 11/32−
3/4	2 9/32−	7 1/8	2 5/8	8 3/16	2 31/32−	9 1/4	3 5/16	10 9/32−	3 5/8	11 11/32−	3 31/32−	1-0 13/32−
13/16	2 5/16	7 3/16	2 21/32−	8 1/4	2 31/32−	9 5/16	3 5/16	10 3/8	3 21/32−	11 13/32−	4	1-0 15/32−
7/8	2 5/16	7 1/4	2 21/32−	8 5/16	3	9 3/8	3 11/32−	10 7/16	3 11/16	11 15/32−	4 1/32−	1-0 17/32−
15/16	2 11/32−	7 5/16	2 11/16	8 3/8	3 1/32−	9 7/16	3 3/8	10 1/2	3 11/16	11 9/16	4 1/32−	1-0 19/32−

Feet	0' Rise	0' Slope	10' Rise	10' Slope	20' Rise	20' Slope	30' Rise	30' Slope
0	0	0	3-4 5/8	10-6 11/16	6-9 1/4	21-1 3/8	10-1 7/8	31-8 1/16
1	4 1/16	1-0 21/32−	3-8 11/16	11-7 11/32−	7-1 5/16	22-2 1/16	10-5 15/16	32-8 3/4
2	8 1/8	2-1 11/32−	4-0 3/4	12-8 1/32−	7-5 3/8	23-2 23/32−	10-10	33-9 13/32−
3	1-0 3/16	3-2	4-4 13/16	13-8 11/16	7-9 7/16	24-3 3/8	11-2 1/16	34-10 1/16
4	1-4 1/4	4-2 11/16	4-8 7/8	14-9 3/8	8-1 1/2	25-4 1/16	11-6 1/8	35-10 3/4
5	1-8 5/16	5-3 11/32−	5-0 15/16	15-10 1/32−	8-5 9/16	26-4 23/32−	11-10 3/16	36-11 13/32−
6	2-0 3/8	6-4	5-5	16-10 23/32−	8-9 5/8	27-5 13/32−	12-2 1/4	38-0 3/32−
7	2-4 7/16	7-4 11/16	5-9 1/16	17-11 3/8	9-1 11/16	28-6 1/16	12-6 5/16	39-0 3/4
8	2-8 1/2	8-5 11/32−	6-1 1/8	19-0 1/32−	9-5 3/4	29-6 23/32−	12-10 3/8	40-1 7/16
9	3-0 9/16	9-6 1/32−	6-5 3/16	20-0 23/32−	9-9 13/16	30-7 13/32−	13-2 7/16	41-2 3/32−

A = 18° 42′ 11″; logsin A = 9.50605; logcos A = 9.97644; logtan A = 9.52961; logcot A = 0.47039

Ins.	12" Rise	12" Slope	13" Rise	13" Slope	14" Rise	14" Slope	15" Rise	15" Slope	16" Rise	16" Slope
0	$4\frac{1}{16}$	$1\text{-}0\frac{21}{32}$	$4\frac{13}{32}$	$1\text{-}1\frac{23}{32}$	$4\frac{3}{4}$	$1\text{-}2\frac{25}{32}$	$5\frac{1}{16}$	$1\text{-}3\frac{27}{32}$	$5\frac{13}{32}$	$1\text{-}4\frac{29}{32}$
$\frac{1}{16}$	$4\frac{3}{32}$	$1\text{-}0\frac{3}{4}$	$4\frac{7}{16}$	$1\text{-}1\frac{25}{32}$	$4\frac{3}{4}$	$1\text{-}2\frac{27}{32}$	$5\frac{3}{32}$	$1\text{-}3\frac{29}{32}$	$5\frac{7}{16}$	$1\text{-}4\frac{31}{32}$
$\frac{1}{8}$	$4\frac{3}{32}$	$1\text{-}0\frac{13}{16}$	$4\frac{7}{16}$	$1\text{-}1\frac{27}{32}$	$4\frac{25}{32}$	$1\text{-}2\frac{29}{32}$	$5\frac{1}{8}$	$1\text{-}3\frac{31}{32}$	$5\frac{15}{32}$	$1\text{-}5\frac{1}{32}$
$\frac{3}{16}$	$4\frac{1}{8}$	$1\text{-}0\frac{7}{8}$	$4\frac{15}{32}$	$1\text{-}1\frac{15}{16}$	$4\frac{13}{16}$	$1\text{-}2\frac{31}{32}$	$5\frac{5}{32}$	$1\text{-}4\frac{1}{32}$	$5\frac{15}{32}$	$1\text{-}5\frac{3}{32}$
$\frac{1}{4}$	$4\frac{5}{32}$	$1\text{-}0\frac{15}{32}$	$4\frac{1}{2}$	$1\text{-}2$	$4\frac{13}{16}$	$1\text{-}3\frac{1}{32}$	$5\frac{5}{32}$	$1\text{-}4\frac{3}{32}$	$5\frac{1}{2}$	$1\text{-}5\frac{5}{32}$
$\frac{5}{16}$	$4\frac{5}{32}$	$1\text{-}1$	$4\frac{1}{2}$	$1\text{-}2\frac{1}{16}$	$4\frac{27}{32}$	$1\text{-}3\frac{1}{8}$	$5\frac{3}{16}$	$1\text{-}4\frac{5}{32}$	$5\frac{17}{32}$	$1\text{-}5\frac{7}{32}$
$\frac{3}{8}$	$4\frac{3}{16}$	$1\text{-}1\frac{1}{16}$	$4\frac{17}{32}$	$1\text{-}2\frac{1}{8}$	$4\frac{7}{8}$	$1\text{-}3\frac{3}{16}$	$5\frac{7}{32}$	$1\text{-}4\frac{7}{32}$	$5\frac{17}{32}$	$1\text{-}5\frac{9}{32}$
$\frac{7}{16}$	$4\frac{7}{32}$	$1\text{-}1\frac{1}{8}$	$4\frac{9}{16}$	$1\text{-}2\frac{3}{16}$	$4\frac{7}{8}$	$1\text{-}3\frac{1}{4}$	$5\frac{7}{32}$	$1\text{-}4\frac{5}{16}$	$5\frac{9}{16}$	$1\text{-}5\frac{11}{32}$
$\frac{1}{2}$	$4\frac{7}{32}$	$1\text{-}1\frac{3}{16}$	$4\frac{9}{16}$	$1\text{-}2\frac{1}{4}$	$4\frac{29}{32}$	$1\text{-}3\frac{5}{16}$	$5\frac{1}{4}$	$1\text{-}4\frac{3}{8}$	$5\frac{19}{32}$	$1\text{-}5\frac{13}{32}$
$\frac{9}{16}$	$4\frac{1}{4}$	$1\text{-}1\frac{1}{4}$	$4\frac{19}{32}$	$1\text{-}2\frac{5}{16}$	$4\frac{15}{16}$	$1\text{-}3\frac{3}{8}$	$5\frac{9}{32}$	$1\text{-}4\frac{7}{16}$	$5\frac{19}{32}$	$1\text{-}5\frac{1}{2}$
$\frac{5}{8}$	$4\frac{9}{32}$	$1\text{-}1\frac{11}{32}$	$4\frac{5}{8}$	$1\text{-}2\frac{3}{8}$	$4\frac{15}{16}$	$1\text{-}3\frac{7}{16}$	$5\frac{9}{32}$	$1\text{-}4\frac{1}{2}$	$5\frac{5}{8}$	$1\text{-}5\frac{9}{16}$
$\frac{11}{16}$	$4\frac{9}{32}$	$1\text{-}1\frac{13}{32}$	$4\frac{5}{8}$	$1\text{-}2\frac{7}{16}$	$4\frac{31}{32}$	$1\text{-}3\frac{1}{2}$	$5\frac{5}{16}$	$1\text{-}4\frac{9}{16}$	$5\frac{21}{32}$	$1\text{-}5\frac{5}{8}$
$\frac{3}{4}$	$4\frac{5}{16}$	$1\text{-}1\frac{15}{32}$	$4\frac{21}{32}$	$1\text{-}2\frac{17}{32}$	5	$1\text{-}3\frac{9}{16}$	$5\frac{11}{32}$	$1\text{-}4\frac{5}{8}$	$5\frac{21}{32}$	$1\text{-}5\frac{11}{16}$
$\frac{13}{16}$	$4\frac{11}{32}$	$1\text{-}1\frac{17}{32}$	$4\frac{11}{16}$	$1\text{-}2\frac{19}{32}$	5	$1\text{-}3\frac{5}{8}$	$5\frac{11}{32}$	$1\text{-}4\frac{11}{16}$	$5\frac{11}{16}$	$1\text{-}5\frac{3}{4}$
$\frac{7}{8}$	$4\frac{11}{32}$	$1\text{-}1\frac{19}{32}$	$4\frac{11}{16}$	$1\text{-}2\frac{21}{32}$	$5\frac{1}{32}$	$1\text{-}3\frac{23}{32}$	$5\frac{3}{8}$	$1\text{-}4\frac{3}{4}$	$5\frac{23}{32}$	$1\text{-}5\frac{13}{16}$
$\frac{15}{16}$	$4\frac{3}{8}$	$1\text{-}1\frac{21}{32}$	$4\frac{23}{32}$	$1\text{-}2\frac{23}{32}$	$5\frac{1}{32}$	$1\text{-}3\frac{25}{32}$	$5\frac{13}{32}$	$1\text{-}4\frac{13}{16}$	$5\frac{23}{32}$	$1\text{-}5\frac{7}{8}$

Ins.	17" Rise	17" Slope	18" Rise	18" Slope	19" Rise	19" Slope	20" Rise	20" Slope	21" Rise	21" Slope
0	$5\frac{3}{4}$	$1\text{-}5\frac{15}{16}$	$6\frac{3}{32}$	$1\text{-}7$	$6\frac{7}{16}$	$1\text{-}8\frac{1}{16}$	$6\frac{25}{32}$	$1\text{-}9\frac{1}{8}$	$7\frac{1}{8}$	$1\text{-}10\frac{5}{32}$
$\frac{1}{16}$	$5\frac{25}{32}$	$1\text{-}6$	$6\frac{1}{8}$	$1\text{-}7\frac{1}{16}$	$6\frac{15}{32}$	$1\text{-}8\frac{1}{8}$	$6\frac{25}{32}$	$1\text{-}9\frac{3}{16}$	$7\frac{1}{8}$	$1\text{-}10\frac{1}{4}$
$\frac{1}{8}$	$5\frac{13}{16}$	$1\text{-}6\frac{3}{32}$	$6\frac{1}{8}$	$1\text{-}7\frac{1}{8}$	$6\frac{15}{32}$	$1\text{-}8\frac{3}{16}$	$6\frac{13}{16}$	$1\text{-}9\frac{1}{4}$	$7\frac{5}{32}$	$1\text{-}10\frac{5}{16}$
$\frac{3}{16}$	$5\frac{13}{16}$	$1\text{-}6\frac{5}{32}$	$6\frac{5}{32}$	$1\text{-}7\frac{3}{16}$	$6\frac{1}{2}$	$1\text{-}8\frac{1}{4}$	$6\frac{27}{32}$	$1\text{-}9\frac{5}{16}$	$7\frac{3}{16}$	$1\text{-}10\frac{3}{8}$
$\frac{1}{4}$	$5\frac{27}{32}$	$1\text{-}6\frac{7}{32}$	$6\frac{3}{16}$	$1\text{-}7\frac{9}{32}$	$6\frac{17}{32}$	$1\text{-}8\frac{5}{16}$	$6\frac{27}{32}$	$1\text{-}9\frac{3}{8}$	$7\frac{3}{16}$	$1\text{-}10\frac{7}{16}$
$\frac{5}{16}$	$5\frac{7}{8}$	$1\text{-}6\frac{9}{32}$	$6\frac{3}{16}$	$1\text{-}7\frac{11}{32}$	$6\frac{17}{32}$	$1\text{-}8\frac{3}{8}$	$6\frac{7}{8}$	$1\text{-}9\frac{7}{16}$	$7\frac{7}{32}$	$1\text{-}10\frac{1}{2}$
$\frac{3}{8}$	$5\frac{7}{8}$	$1\text{-}6\frac{11}{32}$	$6\frac{7}{32}$	$1\text{-}7\frac{13}{32}$	$6\frac{9}{16}$	$1\text{-}8\frac{15}{32}$	$6\frac{29}{32}$	$1\text{-}9\frac{1}{2}$	$7\frac{1}{4}$	$1\text{-}10\frac{9}{16}$
$\frac{7}{16}$	$5\frac{29}{32}$	$1\text{-}6\frac{13}{32}$	$6\frac{1}{4}$	$1\text{-}7\frac{15}{32}$	$6\frac{19}{32}$	$1\text{-}8\frac{17}{32}$	$6\frac{29}{32}$	$1\text{-}9\frac{9}{16}$	$7\frac{1}{4}$	$1\text{-}10\frac{5}{8}$
$\frac{1}{2}$	$5\frac{15}{16}$	$1\text{-}6\frac{15}{32}$	$6\frac{1}{4}$	$1\text{-}7\frac{17}{32}$	$6\frac{19}{32}$	$1\text{-}8\frac{19}{32}$	$6\frac{15}{16}$	$1\text{-}9\frac{21}{32}$	$7\frac{9}{32}$	$1\text{-}10\frac{11}{16}$
$\frac{9}{16}$	$5\frac{15}{16}$	$1\text{-}6\frac{17}{32}$	$6\frac{9}{32}$	$1\text{-}7\frac{19}{32}$	$6\frac{5}{8}$	$1\text{-}8\frac{21}{32}$	$6\frac{31}{32}$	$1\text{-}9\frac{23}{32}$	$7\frac{5}{16}$	$1\text{-}10\frac{3}{4}$
$\frac{5}{8}$	$5\frac{31}{32}$	$1\text{-}6\frac{19}{32}$	$6\frac{5}{16}$	$1\text{-}7\frac{21}{32}$	$6\frac{21}{32}$	$1\text{-}8\frac{23}{32}$	$6\frac{31}{32}$	$1\text{-}9\frac{25}{32}$	$7\frac{5}{16}$	$1\text{-}10\frac{27}{32}$
$\frac{11}{16}$	6	$1\text{-}6\frac{11}{16}$	$6\frac{5}{16}$	$1\text{-}7\frac{23}{32}$	$6\frac{21}{32}$	$1\text{-}8\frac{25}{32}$	7	$1\text{-}9\frac{27}{32}$	$7\frac{11}{32}$	$1\text{-}10\frac{29}{32}$
$\frac{3}{4}$	6	$1\text{-}6\frac{3}{4}$	$6\frac{11}{32}$	$1\text{-}7\frac{25}{32}$	$6\frac{11}{16}$	$1\text{-}8\frac{27}{32}$	$7\frac{1}{32}$	$1\text{-}9\frac{29}{32}$	$7\frac{3}{8}$	$1\text{-}10\frac{31}{32}$
$\frac{13}{16}$	$6\frac{1}{32}$	$1\text{-}6\frac{13}{16}$	$6\frac{3}{8}$	$1\text{-}7\frac{7}{8}$	$6\frac{23}{32}$	$1\text{-}8\frac{29}{32}$	$7\frac{1}{32}$	$1\text{-}9\frac{31}{32}$	$7\frac{3}{8}$	$1\text{-}11\frac{1}{32}$
$\frac{7}{8}$	$6\frac{1}{16}$	$1\text{-}6\frac{7}{8}$	$6\frac{3}{8}$	$1\text{-}7\frac{15}{16}$	$6\frac{23}{32}$	$1\text{-}8\frac{31}{32}$	$7\frac{1}{16}$	$1\text{-}10\frac{1}{32}$	$7\frac{13}{32}$	$1\text{-}11\frac{3}{32}$
$\frac{15}{16}$	$6\frac{1}{16}$	$1\text{-}6\frac{15}{16}$	$6\frac{13}{32}$	$1\text{-}8$	$6\frac{3}{4}$	$1\text{-}9\frac{1}{16}$	$7\frac{3}{32}$	$1\text{-}10\frac{3}{32}$	$7\frac{7}{16}$	$1\text{-}11\frac{5}{32}$

Feet	40' Rise	40' Slope	50' Rise	50' Slope	60' Rise	60' Slope	70' Rise	70' Slope
0	$13\text{-}6\frac{1}{2}$	$42\text{-}2\frac{3}{4}$	$16\text{-}11\frac{1}{8}$	$52\text{-}9\frac{7}{16}$	$20\text{-}3\frac{3}{4}$	$63\text{-}4\frac{5}{32}$	$23\text{-}8\frac{3}{8}$	$73\text{-}10\frac{27}{32}$
1	$13\text{-}10\frac{9}{16}$	$43\text{-}3\frac{7}{16}$	$17\text{-}3\frac{3}{16}$	$53\text{-}10\frac{1}{16}$	$20\text{-}7\frac{13}{16}$	$64\text{-}4\frac{13}{16}$	$24\text{-}0\frac{7}{16}$	$74\text{-}11\frac{1}{2}$
2	$14\text{-}2\frac{5}{8}$	$44\text{-}4\frac{3}{32}$	$17\text{-}7\frac{1}{4}$	$54\text{-}10\frac{25}{32}$	$20\text{-}11\frac{7}{8}$	$65\text{-}5\frac{15}{32}$	$24\text{-}4\frac{1}{2}$	$76\text{-}0\frac{5}{32}$
3	$14\text{-}6\frac{11}{16}$	$45\text{-}4\frac{25}{32}$	$17\text{-}11\frac{5}{16}$	$55\text{-}11\frac{15}{32}$	$21\text{-}3\frac{15}{16}$	$66\text{-}6\frac{5}{32}$	$24\text{-}8\frac{9}{16}$	$77\text{-}0\frac{27}{32}$
4	$14\text{-}10\frac{3}{4}$	$46\text{-}5\frac{7}{16}$	$18\text{-}3\frac{3}{8}$	$57\text{-}0\frac{1}{8}$	$21\text{-}8$	$67\text{-}6\frac{13}{16}$	$25\text{-}0\frac{5}{8}$	$78\text{-}1\frac{1}{2}$
5	$15\text{-}2\frac{13}{16}$	$47\text{-}6\frac{3}{32}$	$18\text{-}7\frac{7}{16}$	$58\text{-}0\frac{25}{32}$	$22\text{-}0\frac{1}{16}$	$68\text{-}7\frac{1}{2}$	$25\text{-}4\frac{11}{16}$	$79\text{-}2\frac{3}{16}$
6	$15\text{-}6\frac{7}{8}$	$48\text{-}6\frac{25}{32}$	$18\text{-}11\frac{1}{2}$	$59\text{-}1\frac{15}{32}$	$22\text{-}4\frac{1}{8}$	$69\text{-}8\frac{5}{32}$	$25\text{-}8\frac{3}{4}$	$80\text{-}2\frac{27}{32}$
7	$15\text{-}10\frac{15}{16}$	$49\text{-}7\frac{7}{16}$	$19\text{-}3\frac{9}{16}$	$60\text{-}2\frac{1}{8}$	$22\text{-}8\frac{3}{16}$	$70\text{-}8\frac{13}{16}$	$26\text{-}0\frac{13}{16}$	$81\text{-}3\frac{1}{2}$
8	$16\text{-}3$	$50\text{-}8\frac{1}{8}$	$19\text{-}7\frac{5}{8}$	$61\text{-}2\frac{13}{16}$	$23\text{-}0\frac{1}{4}$	$71\text{-}9\frac{1}{2}$	$26\text{-}4\frac{7}{8}$	$82\text{-}4\frac{3}{16}$
9	$16\text{-}7\frac{1}{16}$	$51\text{-}8\frac{25}{32}$	$19\text{-}11\frac{11}{16}$	$62\text{-}3\frac{15}{32}$	$23\text{-}4\frac{5}{16}$	$72\text{-}10\frac{5}{32}$	$26\text{-}8\frac{15}{16}$	$83\text{-}4\frac{27}{32}$

natsin A=0.3206642694; natcos A=0.9471929193; nattan A=0.3385416666; natcot A=2.9538461538

Inches	0" Rise	0" Slope	1" Rise	1" Slope	2" Rise	2" Slope	3" Rise	3" Slope	4" Rise	4" Slope	5" Rise	5" Slope
0	0	0	11/32	1 1/16	11/16	2 1/8	1 1/32	3 3/16	1 3/8	4 7/32	1 23/32	5 9/32
1/16	1/32	1/16	3/8	1 1/8	23/32	2 3/16	1 1/16	3 1/4	1 13/32	4 9/32	1 3/4	5 11/32
1/8	1/32	1/8	3/8	1 3/16	23/32	2 1/4	1 1/16	3 5/16	1 13/32	4 3/8	1 3/4	5 13/32
3/16	1/16	3/16	13/32	1 1/4	3/4	2 5/16	1 3/32	3 3/8	1 7/16	4 7/16	1 25/32	5 1/2
1/4	3/32	1/4	7/16	1 5/16	25/32	2 3/8	1 1/8	3 7/16	1 15/32	4 1/2	1 13/16	5 9/16
5/16	3/32	11/32	7/16	1 3/8	25/32	2 7/16	1 1/8	3 1/2	1 15/32	4 9/16	1 13/16	5 5/8
3/8	1/8	13/32	15/32	1 15/32	13/16	2 1/2	1 5/32	3 9/16	1 1/2	4 5/8	1 27/32	5 11/16
7/16	5/32	15/32	1/2	1 17/32	27/32	2 9/16	1 3/16	3 5/8	1 17/32	4 11/16	1 7/8	5 3/4
1/2	3/16	17/32	1/2	1 19/32	7/8	2 21/32	1 3/16	3 11/16	1 9/16	4 3/4	1 7/8	5 13/16
9/16	3/16	19/32	17/32	1 21/32	7/8	2 23/32	1 7/32	3 25/32	1 9/16	4 13/16	1 29/32	5 7/8
5/8	7/32	21/32	9/16	1 23/32	29/32	2 25/32	1 1/4	3 27/32	1 19/32	4 29/32	1 15/16	5 15/16
11/16	1/4	23/32	19/32	1 25/32	15/16	2 27/32	1 9/32	3 29/32	1 5/8	4 31/32	1 31/32	6
3/4	1/4	25/32	19/32	1 27/32	15/16	2 29/32	1 9/32	3 31/32	1 5/8	5 1/32	1 31/32	6 3/32
13/16	9/32	27/32	5/8	1 29/32	31/32	2 31/32	1 5/16	4 1/32	1 21/32	5 3/32	2	6 5/32
7/8	5/16	15/16	21/32	1 31/32	1	3 1/32	1 11/32	4 3/32	1 11/16	5 5/32	2 1/32	6 7/32
15/16	5/16	1	21/32	2 1/16	1	3 3/32	1 11/32	4 5/32	1 11/16	5 7/32	2 1/32	6 9/32

Inches	6" Rise	6" Slope	7" Rise	7" Slope	8" Rise	8" Slope	9" Rise	9" Slope	10" Rise	10" Slope	11" Rise	11" Slope
0	2 1/16	6 11/32	2 13/32	7 13/32	2 3/4	8 15/32	3 3/32	9 17/32	3 7/16	10 9/16	3 25/32	11 5/8
1/16	2 3/32	6 13/32	2 7/16	7 15/32	2 25/32	8 17/32	3 1/8	9 19/32	3 15/32	10 5/8	3 13/16	11 11/16
1/8	2 3/32	6 15/32	2 7/16	7 17/32	2 25/32	8 19/32	3 1/8	9 21/32	3 15/32	10 23/32	3 13/16	11 3/4
3/16	2 1/8	6 17/32	2 15/32	7 19/32	2 13/16	8 21/32	3 5/32	9 23/32	3 1/2	10 25/32	3 27/32	11 27/32
1/4	2 5/32	6 19/32	2 1/2	7 21/32	2 27/32	8 23/32	3 3/16	9 25/32	3 17/32	10 27/32	3 7/8	11 29/32
5/16	2 5/32	6 11/16	2 1/2	7 23/32	2 27/32	8 25/32	3 3/16	9 27/32	3 17/32	10 29/32	3 7/8	11 31/32
3/8	2 3/16	6 3/4	2 17/32	7 13/16	2 7/8	8 27/32	3 7/32	9 29/32	3 9/16	10 31/32	3 29/32	1-0 1/32
7/16	2 7/32	6 13/16	2 9/16	7 7/8	2 29/32	8 15/16	3 1/4	9 31/32	3 19/32	11 1/32	3 15/16	1-0 3/32
1/2	2 1/4	6 7/8	2 9/16	7 15/16	2 15/16	9	3 1/4	10 1/16	3 5/8	11 3/32	3 15/16	1-0 5/32
9/16	2 1/4	6 15/16	2 19/32	8	2 15/16	9 1/16	3 9/32	10 1/8	3 5/8	11 5/32	3 31/32	1-0 7/32
5/8	2 9/32	7	2 5/8	8 1/16	2 31/32	9 1/8	3 5/16	10 3/16	3 21/32	11 1/4	4	1-0 9/32
11/16	2 5/16	7 1/16	2 21/32	8 1/8	3	9 3/16	3 11/32	10 1/4	3 11/16	11 5/16	4 1/32	1-0 11/32
3/4	2 5/16	7 1/8	2 21/32	8 3/16	3	9 1/4	3 11/32	10 5/16	3 11/16	11 3/8	4 1/32	1-0 7/16
13/16	2 11/32	7 1/8	2 11/16	8 1/4	3 1/32	9 5/16	3 3/8	10 3/8	3 23/32	11 7/16	4 1/16	1-0 1/2
7/8	2 3/8	7 9/32	2 23/32	8 5/16	3 1/16	9 3/8	3 13/32	10 7/16	3 3/4	11 1/2	4 3/32	1-0 9/16
15/16	2 3/8	7 11/32	2 23/32	8 13/32	3 1/16	9 7/16	3 13/32	10 1/2	3 3/4	11 9/16	4 3/32	1-0 5/8

Feet	0' Rise	0' Slope	10' Rise	10' Slope	20' Rise	20' Slope	30' Rise	30' Slope
0	0	0	3-5 1/4	10-6 29/32	6-10 1/2	21-1 25/32	10-3 3/4	31-8 11/16
1	4 1/8	1-0 11/16	3-9 3/8	11-7 19/32	7-2 5/8	22-2 15/32	10-7 7/8	32-9 3/8
2	8 1/4	2-1 3/8	4-1 1/2	12-8 9/32	7-6 3/4	23-3 5/32	11-0	33-10 1/16
3	1-0 3/8	3-2 1/16	4-5 5/8	13-8 31/32	7-10 7/8	24-3 27/32	11-4 1/8	34-10 3/4
4	1-4 1/2	4-2 3/4	4-9 3/4	14-9 21/32	8-3	25-4 17/32	11-8 1/4	35-11 7/16
5	1-8 5/8	5-3 7/16	5-1 7/8	15-10 11/32	8-7 1/8	26-5 7/32	12-0 3/8	37-0 1/8
6	2-0 3/4	6-4 1/8	5-6	16-11 1/32	8-11 1/4	27-5 29/32	12-4 1/2	38-0 13/16
7	2-4 7/8	7-4 13/16	5-10 1/8	17-11 23/32	9-3 3/8	28-6 19/32	12-8 5/8	39-1 1/2
8	2-9	8-5 1/2	6-2 1/4	19-0 13/32	9-7 1/2	29-7 5/16	13-0 3/4	40-2 3/16
9	3-1 1/8	9-6 3/16	6-6 3/8	20-1 3/32	9-11 5/8	30-8	13-4 7/8	41-2 7/8

A = 18° 58' 13"; logsin A = 9.51199; logcos A = 9.97575; logtan A = 9.53624; logcot A = 0.46376

Ins.	12″ Rise	12″ Slope	13″ Rise	13″ Slope	14″ Rise	14″ Slope	15″ Rise	15″ Slope	16″ Rise	16″ Slope
0	4 13/16	1-0 11/16	4 15/32	1-1 3/4	4 13/16	1-2 13/16	5 5/32	1-3 7/8	5 1/2	1-4 29/32
1/16	4 5/32	1-0 3/4	4 1/2	1-1 13/16	4 27/32	1-2 7/8	5 3/16	1-3 15/16	5 17/32	1-5
1/8	4 5/32	1-0 13/16	4 1/2	1-1 7/8	4 27/32	1-2 15/16	5 3/16	1-4	5 17/32	1-5 1/16
3/16	4 3/16	1-0 7/8	4 17/32	1-1 15/16	4 7/8	1-3	5 7/32	1-4 1/16	5 9/16	1-5 1/8
1/4	4 7/32	1-0 31/32	4 9/16	1-2	4 29/32	1-3 1/16	5 1/4	1-4 1/8	5 19/32	1-5 3/16
5/16	4 7/32	1-1 1/32	4 9/16	1-2 1/16	4 29/32	1-3 1/8	5 1/4	1-4 3/16	5 19/32	1-5 1/4
3/8	4 1/4	1-1 3/32	4 19/32	1-2 5/32	4 15/16	1-3 3/16	5 9/32	1-4 1/4	5 5/8	1-5 5/16
7/16	4 9/32	1-1 5/32	4 5/8	1-2 7/32	4 31/32	1-3 9/32	5 5/16	1-4 5/16	5 21/32	1-5 3/8
1/2	4 5/16	1-1 7/32	4 5/8	1-2 9/32	5	1-3 11/32	5 5/16	1-4 3/8	5 11/16	1-5 7/16
9/16	4 5/16	1-1 9/32	4 21/32	1-2 11/32	5	1-3 13/32	5 11/32	1-4 15/32	5 11/16	1-5 1/2
5/8	4 11/32	1-1 11/32	4 11/16	1-2 13/32	5 1/32	1-3 15/32	5 3/8	1-4 17/32	5 23/32	1-5 19/32
11/16	4 3/8	1-1 13/32	4 23/32	1-2 15/32	5 1/16	1-3 17/32	5 13/32	1-4 19/32	5 3/4	1-5 21/32
3/4	4 3/8	1-1 15/32	4 23/32	1-2 17/32	5 1/16	1-3 19/32	5 13/32	1-4 21/32	5 3/4	1-5 23/32
13/16	4 13/32	1-1 9/16	4 3/4	1-2 9/16	5 3/32	1-3 21/32	5 7/16	1-4 23/32	5 25/32	1-5 25/32
7/8	4 7/16	1-1 5/8	4 25/32	1-2 11/16	5 1/8	1-3 23/32	5 15/32	1-4 25/32	5 13/16	1-5 27/32
15/16	4 7/16	1-1 11/32	4 25/32	1-2 3/4	5 1/8	1-3 25/32	5 15/32	1-4 27/32	5 13/16	1-5 29/32

Ins.	17″ Rise	17″ Slope	18″ Rise	18″ Slope	19″ Rise	19″ Slope	20″ Rise	20″ Slope	21″ Rise	21″ Slope
0	5 27/32	1-5 31/32	6 3/16	1-7 1/32	6 17/32	1-8 3/32	6 7/8	1-9 5/32	7 1/32	1-10 7/32
1/16	5 7/8	1-6 1/32	6 7/32	1-7 3/32	6 9/16	1-8 5/32	6 29/32	1-9 7/32	7 1/4	1-10 9/32
1/8	5 7/8	1-6 3/32	6 7/32	1-7 5/32	6 9/16	1-8 7/32	6 29/32	1-9 9/32	7 1/4	1-10 11/32
3/16	5 29/32	1-6 3/16	6 1/4	1-7 7/32	6 19/32	1-8 9/32	6 15/16	1-9 11/32	7 9/32	1-10 13/32
1/4	5 15/16	1-6 1/4	6 9/32	1-7 5/16	6 5/8	1-8 11/32	6 31/32	1-9 13/32	7 5/16	1-10 15/32
5/16	5 15/16	1-6 5/16	6 9/32	1-7 3/8	6 5/8	1-8 13/32	6 31/32	1-9 15/32	7 5/16	1-10 17/32
3/8	5 31/32	1-6 3/8	6 5/16	1-7 7/16	6 21/32	1-8 1/2	7	1-9 17/32	7 11/32	1-10 19/32
7/16	6	1-6 7/16	6 11/32	1-7 1/2	6 11/16	1-8 9/16	7 1/32	1-9 5/8	7 3/8	1-10 21/32
1/2	6	1-6 1/2	6 3/8	1-7 9/16	6 11/16	1-8 5/8	7 1/16	1-9 11/16	7 3/8	1-10 3/4
9/16	6 1/32	1-6 9/16	6 3/8	1-7 5/8	6 23/32	1-8 11/16	7 1/16	1-9 3/4	7 13/32	1-10 13/16
5/8	6 1/16	1-6 5/8	6 13/32	1-7 11/16	6 3/4	1-8 3/4	7 3/32	1-9 13/16	7 7/16	1-10 7/8
11/16	6 3/32	1-6 23/32	6 7/16	1-7 3/4	6 25/32	1-8 13/16	7 1/8	1-9 7/8	7 15/32	1-10 15/16
3/4	6 3/32	1-6 25/32	6 7/16	1-7 13/16	6 25/32	1-8 7/8	7 1/8	1-9 15/16	7 15/32	1-11
13/16	6 1/8	1-6 27/32	6 15/32	1-7 29/32	6 13/16	1-8 15/16	7 5/32	1-10	7 1/2	1-11 1/16
7/8	6 5/32	1-6 29/32	6 1/2	1-7 31/32	6 27/32	1-9 1/32	7 3/16	1-10 1/16	7 17/32	1-11 1/8
15/16	6 5/32	1-6 31/32	6 1/2	1-8 1/32	6 27/32	1-9 3/32	7 3/16	1-10 1/8	7 17/32	1-11 3/16

Feet	40′ Rise	40′ Slope	50′ Rise	50′ Slope	60′ Rise	60′ Slope	70′ Rise	70′ Slope
0	13-9	42-3 9/16	17-2 1/4	52-10 15/32	20-7 1/2	63-5 11/32	24-0 3/4	74-0 1/4
1	14-1 1/8	43-4 1/4	17-6 3/8	53-11 5/32	20-11 5/8	64-6 1/32	24-4 7/8	75-0 15/16
2	14-5 1/4	44-4 15/16	17-10 1/2	54-11 27/32	21-3 3/4	65-6 23/32	24-9	76-1 5/8
3	14-9 3/8	45-5 5/8	18-2 5/8	56-0 17/32	21-7 7/8	66-7 13/32	25-1 1/8	77-2 5/16
4	15-1 1/2	46-6 5/16	18-6 3/4	57-1 7/32	22-0	67-8 3/32	25-5 1/4	78-3
5	15-5 5/8	47-7	18-10 7/8	58-1 29/32	22-4 1/8	68-8 13/16	25-9 3/8	79-3 11/16
6	15-9 3/4	48-7 11/16	19-3	59-2 19/32	22-8 1/4	69-9 1/2	26-1 1/2	80-4 3/8
7	16-1 7/8	49-8 13/32	19-7 1/8	60-3 9/32	23-0 3/8	70-10 3/16	26-5 5/8	81-5 1/16
8	16-6	50-9 3/32	19-11 1/4	61-3 31/32	23-4 1/2	71-10 7/8	26-9 3/4	82-5 3/4
9	16-10 1/8	51-9 25/32	20-3 3/8	62-4 21/32	23-8 5/8	72-11 9/16	27-1 7/8	83-6 7/16

natsin A=0.3250797685; natcos A=0.9456865993; nattan A=0.3437500000; natcot A=2.9090909090

Inches	0″ Rise	0″ Slope	1″ Rise	1″ Slope	2″ Rise	2″ Slope	3″ Rise	3″ Slope	4″ Rise	4″ Slope	5″ Rise	5″ Slope
0	0	0	11/32	1 1/32	11/32	2 1/8	1 1/16	3 3/16	1 13/32	4 1/4	1 3/4	5 9/32
1/16	1/32	1/16	3/8	1 1/8	23/32	2 3/16	1 1/16	3 1/4	1 13/32	4 5/16	1 25/32	5 3/8
1/8	1/32	1/8	13/32	1 3/16	3/4	2 1/4	1 3/32	3 5/16	1 7/16	4 3/8	1 25/32	5 7/16
3/16	1/16	3/16	13/32	1 1/4	3/4	2 5/16	1 1/8	3 3/8	1 15/32	4 7/16	1 13/16	5 1/2
1/4	3/32	1/4	7/16	1 5/16	25/32	2 3/8	1 1/8	3 7/16	1 15/32	4 1/2	1 27/32	5 9/16
5/16	3/32	11/32	15/32	1 3/8	13/16	2 7/16	1 5/32	3 1/2	1 1/2	4 9/16	1 27/32	5 5/8
3/8	1/8	13/32	15/32	1 15/32	27/32	2 1/2	1 3/16	3 9/16	1 17/32	4 5/8	1 7/8	5 11/16
7/16	5/32	15/32	1/2	1 17/32	27/32	2 19/32	1 3/16	3 21/32	1 9/16	4 11/16	1 29/32	5 3/4
1/2	3/16	17/32	17/32	1 19/32	7/8	2 21/32	1 7/32	3 23/32	1 9/16	4 25/32	1 29/32	5 13/16
9/16	3/16	19/32	17/32	1 21/32	29/32	2 23/32	1 1/4	3 25/32	1 19/32	4 27/32	1 15/16	5 29/32
5/8	7/32	21/32	9/16	1 23/32	29/32	2 25/32	1 1/4	3 27/32	1 5/8	4 29/32	1 31/32	5 31/32
11/16	1/4	23/32	19/32	1 25/32	15/16	2 27/32	1 9/32	3 29/32	1 5/8	4 31/32	2	6 1/32
3/4	1/4	25/32	5/8	1 27/32	31/32	2 29/32	1 5/16	3 31/32	1 21/32	5 1/32	2	6 3/32
13/16	9/32	7/8	5/8	1 29/32	31/32	2 31/32	1 11/32	4 1/32	1 11/16	5 3/32	2 1/16	6 5/32
7/8	5/16	15/16	21/32	2	1	3 1/32	1 11/32	4 3/32	1 11/16	5 5/32	2 1/16	6 7/32
15/16	5/16	1	11/16	2 1/16	1 1/32	3 1/8	1 3/8	4 5/32	1 23/32	5 7/32	2 1/16	6 9/32

Inches	6″ Rise	6″ Slope	7″ Rise	7″ Slope	8″ Rise	8″ Slope	9″ Rise	9″ Slope	10″ Rise	10″ Slope	11″ Rise	11″ Slope
0	2 3/32	6 11/32	2 7/16	7 13/32	2 25/32	8 15/32	3 1/8	9 17/32	3 1/2	10 19/32	3 21/32	11 21/32
1/16	2 1/16	6 13/32	2 15/32	7 15/32	2 13/16	8 17/32	3 5/32	9 19/32	3 1/2	10 21/32	3 7/8	11 23/32
1/8	2 1/8	6 1/2	2 1/2	7 17/32	2 27/32	8 19/32	3 3/16	9 21/32	3 17/32	10 23/32	3 7/8	11 25/32
3/16	2 9/32	6 9/16	2 1/2	7 5/8	2 27/32	8 21/32	3 7/32	9 23/32	3 9/16	10 25/32	3 29/32	11 27/32
1/4	2 3/16	6 5/8	2 17/32	7 11/16	2 7/8	8 3/4	3 7/32	9 13/16	3 9/16	10 27/32	3 15/16	11 29/32
5/16	2 3/16	6 11/16	2 9/16	7 3/4	2 29/32	8 13/16	3 1/4	9 7/8	3 19/32	10 15/16	3 15/16	11 31/32
3/8	2 1/4	6 3/4	2 9/16	7 13/16	2 15/16	8 7/8	3 9/32	9 15/16	3 5/8	11	3 31/32	1-0 1/16
7/16	2 1/4	6 13/16	2 19/32	7 7/8	2 15/16	8 15/16	3 9/32	10	3 21/32	11 1/16	4	1-0 1/8
1/2	2 9/32	6 7/8	2 5/8	7 15/32	2 31/32	9	3 5/16	10 1/8	3 21/32	11 1/8	4	1-0 3/16
9/16	2 9/32	6 15/16	2 5/8	8	3	9 1/16	3 11/32	10 1/8	3 11/16	11 3/16	4 1/16	1-0 1/4
5/8	2 5/16	7 1/32	2 21/32	8 1/16	3	9 1/8	3 11/32	10 3/8	3 23/32	11 1/4	4 1/16	1-0 5/16
11/16	2 11/32	7 3/32	2 11/16	8 5/32	3 1/32	9 3/16	3 3/8	10 1/4	3 23/32	11 5/16	4 3/32	1-0 3/8
3/4	2 11/32	7 5/32	2 23/32	8 7/32	3 1/16	9 9/32	3 13/32	10 5/16	3 3/4	11 3/8	4 3/32	1-0 7/32
13/16	2 3/8	7 11/32	2 23/32	8 9/32	3 1/16	9 11/32	3 7/16	10 13/32	3 25/32	11 7/16	4 1/8	1-0 1/2
7/8	2 13/32	7 9/32	2 3/4	8 11/32	3 3/32	9 13/32	3 7/16	10 15/32	3 25/32	11 17/32	4 5/32	1-0 19/32
15/16	2 13/32	7 11/32	2 25/32	8 13/32	3 1/8	9 15/32	3 15/32	10 17/32	3 13/16	11 19/32	4 5/32	1-0 21/32

Feet	0′ Rise	0′ Slope	10′ Rise	10′ Slope	20′ Rise	20′ Slope	30′ Rise	30′ Slope
0	0	0	3-5 7/8	10-7 3/8	6-11 3/4	21-2 3/16	10-5 5/8	31-9 9/32
1	4 3/16	1-0 23/32	3-10 1/16	11-7 13/16	7-3 15/16	22-2 29/32	10-9 13/16	32-10
2	8 3/8	2-1 13/32	4-2 1/4	12-8 17/32	7-8 1/8	23-3 5/8	11-2	33-10 23/32
3	1-0 9/16	3-2 1/8	4-6 7/16	13-9 7/32	8-0 5/16	24-4 5/16	11-6 3/16	34-11 13/32
4	1-4 3/4	4-2 27/32	4-10 5/8	14-9 15/16	8-4 1/2	25-5 1/32	11-10 3/8	36-0 1/8
5	1-8 15/16	5-3 9/16	5-2 13/16	15-10 21/32	8-8 11/16	26-5 3/4	12-2 9/16	37-0 27/32
6	2-1 1/8	6-4 1/4	5-7	16-11 11/32	9-0 7/8	27-6 7/16	12-6 3/4	38-1 9/16
7	2-5 5/16	7-4 31/32	5-11 3/16	18-0 1/16	9-5 1/16	28-7 5/32	12-10 15/16	39-2 1/4
8	2-9 1/2	8-5 11/16	6-3 3/8	19-0 25/32	9-9 1/4	29-7 7/8	13-3 1/8	40-2 31/32
9	3-1 11/16	9-6 3/8	6-7 9/16	20-1 15/32	10-1 7/16	30-8 19/32	13-7 5/16	41-3 11/16

A = 19° 14′ 12″; logsin A = 9.51782; logcos A = 9.97505; logtan A = 9.54277; logcot A = 0.45723

Ins.	12″ Rise	12″ Slope	13″ Rise	13″ Slope	14″ Rise	14″ Slope	15″ Rise	15″ Slope	16″ Rise	16″ Slope
0	$4\frac{3}{16}$	1-0$\frac{23}{32}$	$4\frac{17}{32}$	1-1$\frac{25}{32}$	$4\frac{7}{8}$	1-2$\frac{13}{16}$	$5\frac{1}{4}$	1-3$\frac{7}{8}$	$5\frac{19}{32}$	1-4$\frac{15}{16}$
$\frac{1}{16}$	$4\frac{7}{32}$	1-0$\frac{25}{32}$	$4\frac{9}{16}$	1-1$\frac{27}{32}$	$4\frac{29}{32}$	1-2$\frac{29}{32}$	$5\frac{1}{4}$	1-3$\frac{31}{32}$	$5\frac{19}{32}$	1-5
$\frac{1}{8}$	$4\frac{7}{32}$	1-0$\frac{27}{32}$	$4\frac{19}{32}$	1-1$\frac{29}{32}$	$4\frac{15}{16}$	1-2$\frac{31}{32}$	$5\frac{9}{32}$	1-4$\frac{1}{32}$	$5\frac{5}{8}$	1-5$\frac{3}{32}$
$\frac{3}{16}$	$4\frac{1}{4}$	1-0$\frac{29}{32}$	$4\frac{19}{32}$	1-1$\frac{31}{32}$	$4\frac{15}{16}$	1-3$\frac{1}{32}$	$5\frac{5}{16}$	1-4$\frac{3}{32}$	$5\frac{21}{32}$	1-5$\frac{5}{32}$
$\frac{1}{4}$	$4\frac{9}{32}$	1-0$\frac{31}{32}$	$4\frac{5}{8}$	1-2$\frac{1}{32}$	$4\frac{31}{32}$	1-3$\frac{3}{32}$	$5\frac{5}{16}$	1-4$\frac{5}{32}$	$5\frac{21}{32}$	1-5$\frac{7}{32}$
$\frac{5}{16}$	$4\frac{9}{32}$	1-1$\frac{1}{32}$	$4\frac{21}{32}$	1-2$\frac{3}{32}$	5	1-3$\frac{5}{32}$	$5\frac{11}{32}$	1-4$\frac{7}{32}$	$5\frac{11}{16}$	1-5$\frac{9}{32}$
$\frac{3}{8}$	$4\frac{5}{16}$	1-1$\frac{3}{32}$	$4\frac{21}{32}$	1-2$\frac{5}{32}$	$5\frac{1}{32}$	1-3$\frac{7}{32}$	$5\frac{3}{8}$	1-4$\frac{9}{32}$	$5\frac{23}{32}$	1-5$\frac{11}{32}$
$\frac{7}{16}$	$4\frac{11}{32}$	1-1$\frac{5}{32}$	$4\frac{11}{16}$	1-2$\frac{7}{32}$	$5\frac{1}{32}$	1-3$\frac{9}{32}$	$5\frac{3}{8}$	1-4$\frac{11}{32}$	$5\frac{3}{4}$	1-5$\frac{13}{32}$
$\frac{1}{2}$	$4\frac{3}{8}$	1-1$\frac{1}{4}$	$4\frac{23}{32}$	1-2$\frac{5}{16}$	$5\frac{1}{16}$	1-3$\frac{11}{32}$	$5\frac{13}{32}$	1-4$\frac{13}{32}$	$5\frac{3}{4}$	1-5$\frac{15}{32}$
$\frac{9}{16}$	$4\frac{3}{8}$	1-1$\frac{5}{16}$	$4\frac{23}{32}$	1-2$\frac{3}{8}$	$5\frac{3}{32}$	1-3$\frac{7}{16}$	$5\frac{7}{16}$	1-4$\frac{15}{32}$	$5\frac{25}{32}$	1-5$\frac{17}{32}$
$\frac{5}{8}$	$4\frac{13}{32}$	1-1$\frac{3}{8}$	$4\frac{3}{4}$	1-2$\frac{7}{16}$	$5\frac{5}{32}$	1-3$\frac{1}{2}$	$5\frac{7}{16}$	1-4$\frac{9}{16}$	$5\frac{13}{16}$	1-5$\frac{19}{32}$
$\frac{11}{16}$	$4\frac{7}{16}$	1-1$\frac{7}{16}$	$4\frac{25}{32}$	1-2$\frac{1}{2}$	$5\frac{1}{8}$	1-3$\frac{9}{16}$	$5\frac{15}{32}$	1-4$\frac{5}{8}$	$5\frac{13}{16}$	1-5$\frac{11}{16}$
$\frac{3}{4}$	$4\frac{7}{16}$	1-1$\frac{1}{2}$	$4\frac{13}{16}$	1-2$\frac{9}{16}$	$5\frac{5}{32}$	1-3$\frac{5}{8}$	$5\frac{1}{2}$	1-4$\frac{11}{16}$	$5\frac{27}{32}$	1-5$\frac{3}{4}$
$\frac{13}{16}$	$4\frac{15}{32}$	1-1$\frac{9}{16}$	$4\frac{13}{16}$	1-2$\frac{5}{8}$	$5\frac{5}{32}$	1-3$\frac{11}{16}$	$5\frac{17}{32}$	1-4$\frac{3}{4}$	$5\frac{7}{8}$	1-5$\frac{13}{16}$
$\frac{7}{8}$	$4\frac{1}{2}$	1-1$\frac{5}{8}$	$4\frac{27}{32}$	1-2$\frac{11}{16}$	$5\frac{3}{16}$	1-3$\frac{3}{4}$	$5\frac{17}{32}$	1-4$\frac{13}{16}$	$5\frac{7}{8}$	1-5$\frac{7}{8}$
$\frac{15}{16}$	$4\frac{1}{2}$	1-1$\frac{11}{16}$	$4\frac{7}{8}$	1-2$\frac{3}{4}$	$5\frac{7}{32}$	1-3$\frac{13}{16}$	$5\frac{9}{16}$	1-4$\frac{7}{8}$	$5\frac{29}{32}$	1-5$\frac{15}{16}$

Ins.	17″ Rise	17″ Slope	18″ Rise	18″ Slope	19″ Rise	19″ Slope	20″ Rise	20″ Slope	21″ Rise	21″ Slope
0	$5\frac{15}{16}$	1-6	$6\frac{9}{32}$	1-7$\frac{1}{16}$	$6\frac{5}{8}$	1-8$\frac{1}{8}$	$6\frac{31}{32}$	1-9$\frac{3}{16}$	$7\frac{5}{32}$	1-10$\frac{1}{4}$
$\frac{1}{16}$	$5\frac{31}{32}$	1-6$\frac{1}{16}$	$6\frac{5}{16}$	1-7$\frac{1}{8}$	$6\frac{21}{32}$	1-8$\frac{3}{16}$	7	1-9$\frac{1}{4}$	$7\frac{11}{32}$	1-10$\frac{5}{16}$
$\frac{1}{8}$	$5\frac{31}{32}$	1-6$\frac{1}{8}$	$6\frac{5}{16}$	1-7$\frac{3}{16}$	$6\frac{11}{16}$	1-8$\frac{1}{4}$	$7\frac{1}{32}$	1-9$\frac{5}{16}$	$7\frac{3}{8}$	1-10$\frac{3}{8}$
$\frac{3}{16}$	6	1-6$\frac{7}{32}$	$6\frac{11}{32}$	1-7$\frac{1}{4}$	$6\frac{11}{16}$	1-8$\frac{5}{16}$	$7\frac{1}{32}$	1-9$\frac{3}{8}$	$7\frac{13}{32}$	1-10$\frac{7}{16}$
$\frac{1}{4}$	$6\frac{1}{32}$	1-6$\frac{9}{32}$	$6\frac{3}{8}$	1-7$\frac{11}{32}$	$6\frac{23}{32}$	1-8$\frac{3}{8}$	$7\frac{1}{16}$	1-9$\frac{7}{16}$	$7\frac{13}{32}$	1-10$\frac{1}{2}$
$\frac{5}{16}$	$6\frac{1}{32}$	1-6$\frac{11}{32}$	$6\frac{3}{8}$	1-7$\frac{13}{32}$	$6\frac{3}{4}$	1-8$\frac{15}{32}$	$7\frac{3}{32}$	1-9$\frac{1}{2}$	$7\frac{7}{16}$	1-10$\frac{9}{16}$
$\frac{3}{8}$	$6\frac{1}{16}$	1-6$\frac{13}{32}$	$6\frac{13}{32}$	1-7$\frac{15}{32}$	$6\frac{3}{4}$	1-8$\frac{17}{32}$	$7\frac{1}{8}$	1-9$\frac{19}{32}$	$7\frac{15}{32}$	1-10$\frac{5}{8}$
$\frac{7}{16}$	$6\frac{3}{32}$	1-6$\frac{15}{32}$	$6\frac{7}{16}$	1-7$\frac{17}{32}$	$6\frac{25}{32}$	1-8$\frac{19}{32}$	$7\frac{1}{8}$	1-9$\frac{21}{32}$	$7\frac{15}{32}$	1-10$\frac{23}{32}$
$\frac{1}{2}$	$6\frac{3}{32}$	1-6$\frac{17}{32}$	$6\frac{15}{32}$	1-7$\frac{19}{32}$	$6\frac{13}{16}$	1-8$\frac{21}{32}$	$7\frac{5}{32}$	1-9$\frac{23}{32}$	$7\frac{1}{2}$	1-10$\frac{25}{32}$
$\frac{9}{16}$	$6\frac{1}{8}$	1-6$\frac{19}{32}$	$6\frac{15}{32}$	1-7$\frac{21}{32}$	$6\frac{13}{16}$	1-8$\frac{23}{32}$	$7\frac{3}{16}$	1-9$\frac{25}{32}$	$7\frac{17}{32}$	1-10$\frac{27}{32}$
$\frac{5}{8}$	$6\frac{5}{32}$	1-6$\frac{21}{32}$	$6\frac{1}{2}$	1-7$\frac{23}{32}$	$6\frac{27}{32}$	1-8$\frac{25}{32}$	$7\frac{3}{16}$	1-9$\frac{27}{32}$	$7\frac{17}{32}$	1-10$\frac{29}{32}$
$\frac{11}{16}$	$6\frac{3}{16}$	1-6$\frac{23}{32}$	$6\frac{17}{32}$	1-7$\frac{25}{32}$	$6\frac{7}{8}$	1-8$\frac{27}{32}$	$7\frac{7}{32}$	1-9$\frac{29}{32}$	$7\frac{9}{16}$	1-10$\frac{31}{32}$
$\frac{3}{4}$	$6\frac{3}{16}$	1-6$\frac{13}{16}$	$6\frac{17}{32}$	1-7$\frac{27}{32}$	$6\frac{29}{32}$	1-8$\frac{29}{32}$	$7\frac{1}{4}$	1-9$\frac{31}{32}$	$7\frac{19}{32}$	1-11$\frac{1}{4}$
$\frac{13}{16}$	$6\frac{7}{32}$	1-6$\frac{7}{8}$	$6\frac{9}{16}$	1-7$\frac{15}{16}$	$6\frac{29}{32}$	1-8$\frac{31}{32}$	$7\frac{1}{4}$	1-10$\frac{1}{16}$	$7\frac{5}{8}$	1-11$\frac{3}{32}$
$\frac{7}{8}$	$6\frac{1}{4}$	1-6$\frac{15}{16}$	$6\frac{19}{32}$	1-8	$6\frac{15}{16}$	1-9$\frac{1}{16}$	$7\frac{9}{32}$	1-10$\frac{1}{8}$	$7\frac{5}{8}$	1-11$\frac{5}{32}$
$\frac{15}{16}$	$6\frac{1}{4}$	1-7	$6\frac{19}{32}$	1-8$\frac{1}{16}$	$6\frac{31}{32}$	1-9$\frac{1}{8}$	$7\frac{5}{16}$	1-10$\frac{3}{16}$	$7\frac{21}{32}$	1-11$\frac{1}{4}$

Feet	40′ Rise	40′ Slope	50′ Rise	50′ Slope	60′ Rise	60′ Slope	70′ Rise	70′ Slope
0	13-11$\frac{1}{2}$	42-4$\frac{3}{8}$	17-5$\frac{3}{8}$	52-11$\frac{15}{16}$	20-11$\frac{1}{4}$	63-6$\frac{19}{32}$	24-5$\frac{1}{8}$	74-1$\frac{11}{16}$
1	14-3$\frac{11}{16}$	43-5$\frac{3}{32}$	17-9$\frac{9}{16}$	54-0$\frac{5}{16}$	21-3$\frac{7}{16}$	64-7$\frac{9}{32}$	24-9$\frac{5}{16}$	75-2$\frac{3}{8}$
2	14-7$\frac{7}{8}$	44-5$\frac{13}{16}$	18-1$\frac{3}{4}$	55-0$\frac{29}{32}$	21-7$\frac{5}{8}$	65-8	25-1$\frac{1}{2}$	76-3$\frac{3}{32}$
3	15-0$\frac{1}{16}$	45-6$\frac{1}{2}$	18-5$\frac{15}{16}$	56-1$\frac{5}{8}$	21-11$\frac{13}{16}$	66-8$\frac{23}{32}$	25-5$\frac{11}{16}$	77-3$\frac{13}{16}$
4	15-4$\frac{1}{4}$	46-7$\frac{7}{32}$	18-10$\frac{1}{8}$	57-2$\frac{5}{16}$	22-4	67-9$\frac{13}{32}$	25-9$\frac{7}{8}$	78-4$\frac{1}{2}$
5	15-8$\frac{7}{16}$	47-7$\frac{15}{16}$	19-2$\frac{5}{16}$	58-3$\frac{1}{32}$	22-8$\frac{3}{16}$	68-10$\frac{1}{8}$	26-2$\frac{1}{16}$	79-5$\frac{7}{32}$
6	16-0$\frac{5}{8}$	48-8$\frac{21}{32}$	19-6$\frac{1}{2}$	59-3$\frac{3}{4}$	23-0$\frac{3}{8}$	69-10$\frac{27}{32}$	26-6$\frac{1}{4}$	80-5$\frac{15}{16}$
7	16-4$\frac{13}{16}$	49-9$\frac{11}{32}$	19-10$\frac{11}{16}$	60-4$\frac{7}{16}$	23-4$\frac{9}{16}$	70-11$\frac{17}{32}$	26-10$\frac{7}{16}$	81-6$\frac{21}{32}$
8	16-9	50-10$\frac{1}{16}$	20-2$\frac{7}{8}$	61-5$\frac{5}{32}$	23-8$\frac{3}{4}$	72-0$\frac{1}{4}$	27-2$\frac{5}{8}$	82-7$\frac{11}{32}$
9	17-1$\frac{3}{16}$	51-10$\frac{25}{32}$	20-7$\frac{1}{16}$	62-5$\frac{7}{8}$	24-0$\frac{15}{16}$	73-0$\frac{31}{32}$	27-6$\frac{13}{16}$	83-8$\frac{1}{16}$

natsin A=0.3294741088; natcos A=0.9441646104; nattan A=0.3489583333; natcot A=2.8656716417

Inches	0" Rise	0" Slope	1" Rise	1" Slope	2" Rise	2" Slope	3" Rise	3" Slope	4" Rise	4" Slope	5" Rise	5" Slope
0	0	0	11/32	1 1/16	23/32	2 1/8	1 1/16	3 3/16	1 13/32	4 1/4	1 25/32	5 5/16
1/16	1/32	1/16	3/8	1 1/8	23/32	2 3/16	1 3/32	3 1/4	1 7/16	4 5/16	1 25/32	5 3/8
1/8	1/32	1/8	13/32	1 3/16	3/4	2 1/4	1 3/32	3 5/16	1 15/32	4 3/8	1 13/16	5 7/16
3/16	1/16	3/16	13/32	1 1/4	25/32	2 5/16	1 1/8	3 3/8	1 15/32	4 7/16	1 27/32	5 1/2
1/4	3/32	1/4	7/16	1 5/16	13/16	2 3/8	1 5/32	3 7/16	1 1/2	4 1/2	1 7/8	5 9/16
5/16	1/8	11/32	15/32	1 13/32	13/16	2 15/32	1 3/16	3 1/2	1 17/32	4 9/16	1 7/8	5 5/8
3/8	1/8	13/32	1/2	1 15/32	27/32	2 17/32	1 3/16	3 19/32	1 9/16	4 21/32	1 29/32	5 11/16
7/16	5/32	15/32	1/2	1 17/32	7/8	2 19/32	1 7/32	3 21/32	1 9/16	4 23/32	1 15/16	5 25/32
1/2	3/16	17/32	17/32	1 19/32	7/8	2 21/32	1 1/4	3 23/32	1 19/32	4 25/32	1 15/16	5 27/32
9/16	3/16	19/32	9/16	1 21/32	29/32	2 23/32	1 1/4	3 25/32	1 5/8	4 27/32	1 31/32	5 29/32
5/8	7/32	21/32	9/16	1 23/32	15/16	2 25/32	1 9/32	3 27/32	1 5/8	4 29/32	2	5 31/32
11/16	1/4	23/32	19/32	1 25/32	15/16	2 27/32	1 5/16	3 29/32	1 21/32	4 31/32	2	6 1/32
3/4	1/4	25/32	5/8	1 27/32	31/32	2 29/32	1 5/16	3 31/32	1 11/16	5 1/32	2 1/2	6 3/32
13/16	9/32	7/8	21/32	1 15/16	1	2 31/32	1 11/32	4 1/32	1 23/32	5 3/32	2 1/16	6 5/32
7/8	5/16	15/16	21/32	2	1 1/32	3 1/16	1 3/8	4 1/8	1 23/32	5 5/32	2 3/32	6 7/32
15/16	11/32	1	11/16	2 1/16	1 1/32	3 1/8	1 13/32	4 3/16	1 3/4	5 1/4	2 3/32	6 5/16

Inches	6" Rise	6" Slope	7" Rise	7" Slope	8" Rise	8" Slope	9" Rise	9" Slope	10" Rise	10" Slope	11" Rise	11" Slope
0	2 1/8	6 3/8	2 15/32	7 7/16	2 27/32	8 1/2	3 3/16	9 9/16	3 17/32	10 19/32	3 29/32	11 21/32
1/16	2 5/32	6 7/16	2 1/2	7 1/2	2 27/32	8 9/16	3 7/32	9 5/8	3 9/16	10 11/16	3 29/32	11 3/4
1/8	2 5/32	6 1/2	2 17/32	7 9/16	2 7/8	8 5/8	3 7/32	9 11/16	3 19/32	10 3/4	3 15/16	11 13/16
3/16	2 3/16	6 9/16	2 17/32	7 5/8	2 29/32	8 11/16	3 1/4	9 3/4	3 19/32	10 13/16	3 31/32	11 7/8
1/4	2 7/32	6 5/8	2 9/16	7 11/16	2 15/16	8 3/4	3 9/32	9 13/16	3 5/8	10 7/8	4	11 15/16
5/16	2 1/4	6 11/16	2 19/32	7 3/4	2 15/16	8 13/16	3 5/16	9 7/8	3 21/32	10 15/16	4	1-0
3/8	2 1/4	6 3/4	2 5/8	7 13/16	2 31/32	8 7/8	3 5/16	9 15/16	3 11/16	11	4 1/32	1-0 1/16
7/16	2 9/32	6 27/32	2 5/8	7 7/8	3	8 15/16	3 11/32	10	3 11/16	11 1/16	4 1/16	1-0 1/8
1/2	2 5/16	6 29/32	2 21/32	7 31/32	3	9 1/32	3 3/8	10 3/32	3 23/32	11 1/8	4 1/16	1-0 3/16
9/16	2 5/16	6 31/32	2 11/16	8 1/32	3 1/32	9 3/32	3 3/8	10 5/32	3 3/4	11 7/32	4 3/32	1-0 9/32
5/8	2 11/32	7 1/32	2 11/16	8 3/32	3 1/16	9 5/32	3 13/32	10 7/32	3 3/4	11 9/32	4 1/8	1-0 11/32
11/16	2 3/8	7 3/32	2 23/32	8 5/32	3 1/16	9 7/32	3 7/16	10 9/32	3 25/32	11 11/32	4 1/8	1-0 13/32
3/4	2 3/8	7 5/32	2 3/4	8 7/32	3 3/32	9 9/32	3 7/16	10 11/32	3 13/16	11 13/32	4 5/32	1-0 15/32
13/16	2 13/32	7 7/32	2 25/32	8 9/32	3 1/8	9 11/32	3 15/32	10 13/32	3 27/32	11 15/32	4 3/16	1-0 17/32
7/8	2 7/16	7 9/32	2 25/32	8 11/32	3 5/32	9 13/32	3 1/2	10 15/32	3 27/32	11 17/32	4 7/32	1-0 19/32
15/16	2 15/32	7 3/8	2 13/16	8 13/32	3 5/32	9 15/32	3 17/32	10 17/32	3 7/8	11 19/32	4 7/32	1-0 21/32

Feet	0' Rise	0' Slope	10' Rise	10' Slope	20' Rise	20' Slope	30' Rise	30' Slope
0	0	0	3-6 1/2	10-7 5/16	7-1	21-2 19/32	10-7 1/2	31-9 29/32
1	4 1/4	1-0 23/32	3-10 3/4	11-8 1/32	7-5 1/4	22-3 11/32	10-11 3/4	32-10 21/32
2	8 1/2	2-1 15/32	4-3	12-8 3/4	7-9 1/2	23-4 1/16	11-4	33-11 3/8
3	1-0 3/4	3-2 3/16	4-7 1/4	13-9 1/2	8-1 3/4	24-4 13/16	11-8 1/4	35-0 3/32
4	1-5	4-2 29/32	4-11 1/2	14-10 7/32	8-6	25-5 17/32	12-0 1/2	36-0 27/32
5	1-9 1/4	5-3 21/32	5-3 3/4	15-10 31/32	8-10 1/4	26-6 1/4	12-4 3/4	37-1 9/16
6	2-1 1/2	6-4 3/8	5-8	16-11 11/16	9-2 1/2	27-7	12-9	38-2 9/32
7	2-5 3/4	7-5 1/8	6-0 1/4	18-0 13/32	9-6 3/4	28-7 23/32	13-1 1/4	39-3 1/32
8	2-10	8-5 27/32	6-4 1/2	19-1 5/32	9-11	29-8 7/16	13-5 1/2	40-3 3/4
9	3-2 1/4	9-6 9/16	6-8 3/4	20-1 7/8	10-3 1/4	30-9 3/16	13-9 3/4	41-4 1/2

A = 19° 30′ 09″; logsin A = 9.52355; logcos A = 9.97434; logtan A = 9.54921; logcot A = 0.45079

Ins.	12″ Rise	12″ Slope	13″ Rise	13″ Slope	14″ Rise	14″ Slope	15″ Rise	15″ Slope	16″ Rise	16″ Slope
0	$4\frac{1}{4}$	$1\text{-}0\frac{23}{32}$	$4\frac{19}{32}$	$1\text{-}1\frac{25}{32}$	$4\frac{31}{32}$	$1\text{-}2\frac{27}{32}$	$5\frac{5}{16}$	$1\text{-}3\frac{29}{32}$	$5\frac{21}{32}$	$1\text{-}4\frac{31}{32}$
$\frac{1}{16}$	$4\frac{9}{32}$	$1\text{-}0\frac{25}{32}$	$4\frac{5}{8}$	$1\text{-}1\frac{27}{32}$	$4\frac{31}{32}$	$1\text{-}2\frac{29}{32}$	$5\frac{11}{32}$	$1\text{-}3\frac{31}{32}$	$5\frac{11}{16}$	$1\text{-}5\frac{1}{32}$
$\frac{1}{8}$	$4\frac{9}{32}$	$1\text{-}0\frac{7}{8}$	$4\frac{21}{32}$	$1\text{-}1\frac{15}{16}$	5	$1\text{-}3$	$5\frac{11}{32}$	$1\text{-}4\frac{1}{32}$	$5\frac{23}{32}$	$1\text{-}5\frac{3}{32}$
$\frac{3}{16}$	$4\frac{5}{16}$	$1\text{-}0\frac{15}{16}$	$4\frac{21}{32}$	$1\text{-}2$	$5\frac{1}{32}$	$1\text{-}3\frac{1}{32}$	$5\frac{3}{8}$	$1\text{-}4\frac{1}{8}$	$5\frac{23}{32}$	$1\text{-}5\frac{3}{16}$
$\frac{1}{4}$	$4\frac{11}{32}$	$1\text{-}1$	$4\frac{11}{16}$	$1\text{-}2\frac{1}{16}$	$5\frac{1}{32}$	$1\text{-}3\frac{1}{8}$	$5\frac{13}{32}$	$1\text{-}4\frac{3}{16}$	$5\frac{3}{4}$	$1\text{-}5\frac{1}{4}$
$\frac{5}{16}$	$4\frac{3}{8}$	$1\text{-}1\frac{1}{16}$	$4\frac{23}{32}$	$1\text{-}2\frac{1}{8}$	$5\frac{1}{16}$	$1\text{-}3\frac{3}{16}$	$5\frac{7}{16}$	$1\text{-}4\frac{1}{4}$	$5\frac{25}{32}$	$1\text{-}5\frac{5}{16}$
$\frac{3}{8}$	$4\frac{3}{8}$	$1\text{-}1\frac{1}{8}$	$4\frac{3}{4}$	$1\text{-}2\frac{3}{16}$	$5\frac{3}{32}$	$1\text{-}3\frac{1}{4}$	$5\frac{7}{16}$	$1\text{-}4\frac{5}{16}$	$5\frac{13}{16}$	$1\text{-}5\frac{3}{8}$
$\frac{7}{16}$	$4\frac{13}{32}$	$1\text{-}1\frac{3}{16}$	$4\frac{3}{4}$	$1\text{-}2\frac{1}{4}$	$5\frac{1}{8}$	$1\text{-}3\frac{5}{16}$	$5\frac{15}{32}$	$1\text{-}4\frac{3}{8}$	$5\frac{13}{16}$	$1\text{-}5\frac{7}{16}$
$\frac{1}{2}$	$4\frac{7}{16}$	$1\text{-}1\frac{1}{4}$	$4\frac{25}{32}$	$1\text{-}2\frac{5}{16}$	$5\frac{1}{8}$	$1\text{-}3\frac{3}{8}$	$5\frac{1}{2}$	$1\text{-}4\frac{7}{16}$	$5\frac{27}{32}$	$1\text{-}5\frac{1}{2}$
$\frac{9}{16}$	$4\frac{7}{16}$	$1\text{-}1\frac{5}{16}$	$4\frac{13}{16}$	$1\text{-}2\frac{3}{8}$	$5\frac{3}{16}$	$1\text{-}3\frac{7}{16}$	$5\frac{1}{2}$	$1\text{-}4\frac{1}{2}$	$5\frac{7}{8}$	$1\text{-}5\frac{9}{16}$
$\frac{5}{8}$	$4\frac{15}{32}$	$1\text{-}1\frac{13}{32}$	$4\frac{13}{16}$	$1\text{-}2\frac{15}{32}$	$5\frac{3}{16}$	$1\text{-}3\frac{1}{2}$	$5\frac{17}{32}$	$1\text{-}4\frac{9}{16}$	$5\frac{7}{8}$	$1\text{-}5\frac{5}{8}$
$\frac{11}{16}$	$4\frac{1}{2}$	$1\text{-}1\frac{15}{32}$	$4\frac{27}{32}$	$1\text{-}2\frac{17}{32}$	$5\frac{3}{16}$	$1\text{-}3\frac{19}{32}$	$5\frac{9}{16}$	$1\text{-}4\frac{21}{32}$	$5\frac{29}{32}$	$1\text{-}5\frac{23}{32}$
$\frac{3}{4}$	$4\frac{1}{2}$	$1\text{-}1\frac{17}{32}$	$4\frac{7}{8}$	$1\text{-}2\frac{19}{32}$	$5\frac{7}{32}$	$1\text{-}3\frac{21}{32}$	$5\frac{9}{16}$	$1\text{-}4\frac{23}{32}$	$5\frac{15}{16}$	$1\text{-}5\frac{25}{32}$
$\frac{13}{16}$	$4\frac{17}{32}$	$1\text{-}1\frac{19}{32}$	$4\frac{29}{32}$	$1\text{-}2\frac{21}{32}$	$5\frac{1}{4}$	$1\text{-}3\frac{23}{32}$	$5\frac{19}{32}$	$1\text{-}4\frac{25}{32}$	$5\frac{31}{32}$	$1\text{-}5\frac{27}{32}$
$\frac{7}{8}$	$4\frac{9}{16}$	$1\text{-}1\frac{21}{32}$	$4\frac{29}{32}$	$1\text{-}2\frac{23}{32}$	$5\frac{9}{32}$	$1\text{-}3\frac{25}{32}$	$5\frac{5}{8}$	$1\text{-}4\frac{27}{32}$	$5\frac{31}{32}$	$1\text{-}5\frac{29}{32}$
$\frac{15}{16}$	$4\frac{19}{32}$	$1\text{-}1\frac{23}{32}$	$4\frac{15}{16}$	$1\text{-}2\frac{25}{32}$	$5\frac{9}{32}$	$1\text{-}3\frac{27}{32}$	$5\frac{21}{32}$	$1\text{-}4\frac{29}{32}$	6	$1\text{-}5\frac{31}{32}$

Ins.	17″ Rise	17″ Slope	18″ Rise	18″ Slope	19″ Rise	19″ Slope	20″ Rise	20″ Slope	21″ Rise	21″ Slope
0	$6\frac{1}{32}$	$1\text{-}6\frac{1}{32}$	$6\frac{3}{8}$	$1\text{-}7\frac{3}{32}$	$6\frac{23}{32}$	$1\text{-}8\frac{5}{32}$	$7\frac{3}{32}$	$1\text{-}9\frac{7}{32}$	$7\frac{7}{16}$	$1\text{-}10\frac{9}{32}$
$\frac{1}{16}$	$6\frac{1}{32}$	$1\text{-}6\frac{3}{32}$	$6\frac{13}{32}$	$1\text{-}7\frac{5}{32}$	$6\frac{3}{4}$	$1\text{-}8\frac{7}{32}$	$7\frac{3}{32}$	$1\text{-}9\frac{9}{32}$	$7\frac{15}{32}$	$1\text{-}10\frac{11}{32}$
$\frac{1}{8}$	$6\frac{1}{16}$	$1\text{-}6\frac{5}{32}$	$6\frac{13}{32}$	$1\text{-}7\frac{7}{32}$	$6\frac{25}{32}$	$1\text{-}8\frac{9}{32}$	$7\frac{1}{8}$	$1\text{-}9\frac{11}{32}$	$7\frac{15}{32}$	$1\text{-}10\frac{13}{32}$
$\frac{3}{16}$	$6\frac{3}{32}$	$1\text{-}6\frac{7}{32}$	$6\frac{1}{16}$	$1\text{-}7\frac{9}{32}$	$6\frac{25}{32}$	$1\text{-}8\frac{11}{32}$	$7\frac{5}{32}$	$1\text{-}9\frac{13}{32}$	$7\frac{1}{2}$	$1\text{-}10\frac{15}{32}$
$\frac{1}{4}$	$6\frac{1}{8}$	$1\text{-}6\frac{5}{16}$	$6\frac{15}{32}$	$1\text{-}7\frac{3}{8}$	$6\frac{13}{16}$	$1\text{-}8\frac{13}{32}$	$7\frac{3}{16}$	$1\text{-}9\frac{15}{32}$	$7\frac{17}{32}$	$1\text{-}10\frac{17}{32}$
$\frac{5}{16}$	$6\frac{1}{8}$	$1\text{-}6\frac{3}{8}$	$6\frac{1}{2}$	$1\text{-}7\frac{7}{16}$	$6\frac{27}{32}$	$1\text{-}8\frac{1}{2}$	$7\frac{3}{16}$	$1\text{-}9\frac{9}{16}$	$7\frac{9}{16}$	$1\text{-}10\frac{5}{8}$
$\frac{3}{8}$	$6\frac{5}{32}$	$1\text{-}6\frac{7}{16}$	$6\frac{1}{2}$	$1\text{-}7\frac{1}{2}$	$6\frac{7}{8}$	$1\text{-}8\frac{9}{16}$	$7\frac{1}{4}$	$1\text{-}9\frac{5}{8}$	$7\frac{9}{16}$	$1\text{-}10\frac{11}{16}$
$\frac{7}{16}$	$6\frac{3}{16}$	$1\text{-}6\frac{1}{2}$	$6\frac{17}{32}$	$1\text{-}7\frac{9}{16}$	$6\frac{7}{8}$	$1\text{-}8\frac{5}{8}$	$7\frac{1}{4}$	$1\text{-}9\frac{11}{16}$	$7\frac{19}{32}$	$1\text{-}10\frac{3}{4}$
$\frac{1}{2}$	$6\frac{3}{16}$	$1\text{-}6\frac{9}{16}$	$6\frac{9}{16}$	$1\text{-}7\frac{5}{8}$	$6\frac{29}{32}$	$1\text{-}8\frac{11}{16}$	$7\frac{1}{4}$	$1\text{-}9\frac{3}{4}$	$7\frac{5}{8}$	$1\text{-}10\frac{13}{16}$
$\frac{9}{16}$	$6\frac{7}{32}$	$1\text{-}6\frac{5}{8}$	$6\frac{9}{16}$	$1\text{-}7\frac{11}{16}$	$6\frac{15}{16}$	$1\text{-}8\frac{3}{4}$	$7\frac{9}{32}$	$1\text{-}9\frac{13}{16}$	$7\frac{5}{8}$	$1\text{-}10\frac{7}{8}$
$\frac{5}{8}$	$6\frac{1}{4}$	$1\text{-}6\frac{11}{16}$	$6\frac{19}{32}$	$1\text{-}7\frac{3}{4}$	$6\frac{15}{16}$	$1\text{-}8\frac{13}{16}$	$7\frac{5}{16}$	$1\text{-}9\frac{7}{8}$	$7\frac{21}{32}$	$1\text{-}10\frac{15}{16}$
$\frac{11}{16}$	$6\frac{1}{4}$	$1\text{-}6\frac{3}{4}$	$6\frac{5}{8}$	$1\text{-}7\frac{13}{16}$	$6\frac{31}{32}$	$1\text{-}8\frac{7}{8}$	$7\frac{5}{16}$	$1\text{-}9\frac{15}{16}$	$7\frac{11}{16}$	$1\text{-}11$
$\frac{3}{4}$	$6\frac{9}{32}$	$1\text{-}6\frac{27}{32}$	$6\frac{5}{8}$	$1\text{-}7\frac{29}{32}$	7	$1\text{-}8\frac{15}{16}$	$7\frac{11}{32}$	$1\text{-}10$	$7\frac{11}{16}$	$1\text{-}11\frac{1}{16}$
$\frac{13}{16}$	$6\frac{5}{16}$	$1\text{-}6\frac{29}{32}$	$6\frac{21}{32}$	$1\text{-}7\frac{31}{32}$	$7\frac{1}{32}$	$1\text{-}9\frac{1}{32}$	$7\frac{3}{8}$	$1\text{-}10\frac{3}{32}$	$7\frac{23}{32}$	$1\text{-}11\frac{1}{8}$
$\frac{7}{8}$	$6\frac{11}{32}$	$1\text{-}6\frac{31}{32}$	$6\frac{11}{16}$	$1\text{-}8\frac{1}{32}$	$7\frac{1}{32}$	$1\text{-}9\frac{3}{32}$	$7\frac{13}{32}$	$1\text{-}10\frac{5}{32}$	$7\frac{3}{4}$	$1\text{-}11\frac{3}{32}$
$\frac{15}{16}$	$6\frac{11}{32}$	$1\text{-}7\frac{1}{32}$	$6\frac{23}{32}$	$1\text{-}8\frac{3}{32}$	$7\frac{1}{16}$	$1\text{-}9\frac{5}{32}$	$7\frac{13}{32}$	$1\text{-}10\frac{7}{32}$	$7\frac{25}{32}$	$1\text{-}11\frac{9}{32}$

Feet	40′ Rise	40′ Slope	50′ Rise	50′ Slope	60′ Rise	60′ Slope	70′ Rise	70′ Slope
0	14-2	$42\text{-}5\frac{7}{32}$	$17\text{-}8\frac{1}{2}$	$53\text{-}0\frac{17}{32}$	21-3	$63\text{-}7\frac{13}{16}$	$24\text{-}9\frac{1}{2}$	$74\text{-}3\frac{1}{8}$
1	$14\text{-}6\frac{1}{4}$	$43\text{-}5\frac{15}{16}$	$18\text{-}0\frac{3}{4}$	$54\text{-}1\frac{3}{4}$	$21\text{-}7\frac{1}{4}$	$64\text{-}8\frac{9}{16}$	$25\text{-}1\frac{3}{4}$	$75\text{-}3\frac{27}{32}$
2	$14\text{-}10\frac{1}{2}$	$44\text{-}6\frac{11}{16}$	18-5	$55\text{-}1\frac{31}{32}$	$21\text{-}11\frac{1}{2}$	$65\text{-}9\frac{9}{32}$	25-6	$76\text{-}4\frac{19}{32}$
3	$15\text{-}2\frac{3}{4}$	$45\text{-}7\frac{13}{32}$	$18\text{-}9\frac{1}{4}$	$56\text{-}2\frac{3}{32}$	$22\text{-}3\frac{3}{4}$	66-10	$25\text{-}10\frac{1}{4}$	$77\text{-}5\frac{5}{16}$
4	15-7	$46\text{-}8\frac{1}{8}$	$19\text{-}1\frac{1}{2}$	$57\text{-}3\frac{7}{16}$	22-8	$67\text{-}10\frac{3}{4}$	$26\text{-}2\frac{1}{2}$	$78\text{-}6\frac{1}{16}$
5	$15\text{-}11\frac{1}{4}$	$47\text{-}8\frac{7}{8}$	$19\text{-}5\frac{3}{4}$	$58\text{-}4\frac{5}{32}$	$23\text{-}0\frac{1}{4}$	$68\text{-}11\frac{15}{32}$	$26\text{-}6\frac{3}{4}$	$79\text{-}6\frac{25}{32}$
6	$16\text{-}3\frac{1}{2}$	$48\text{-}9\frac{19}{32}$	19-10	$59\text{-}4\frac{29}{32}$	$23\text{-}4\frac{1}{2}$	$70\text{-}0\frac{7}{32}$	26-11	$80\text{-}7\frac{1}{2}$
7	$16\text{-}7\frac{3}{4}$	$49\text{-}10\frac{5}{16}$	$20\text{-}2\frac{1}{4}$	$60\text{-}5\frac{5}{8}$	$23\text{-}8\frac{3}{4}$	$71\text{-}0\frac{15}{16}$	$27\text{-}3\frac{1}{4}$	$81\text{-}8\frac{1}{4}$
8	17-0	$50\text{-}11\frac{1}{16}$	$20\text{-}6\frac{1}{2}$	$61\text{-}6\frac{3}{8}$	24-1	$72\text{-}1\frac{21}{32}$	$27\text{-}7\frac{1}{2}$	$82\text{-}8\frac{31}{32}$
9	$17\text{-}4\frac{1}{4}$	$51\text{-}11\frac{25}{32}$	$20\text{-}10\frac{3}{4}$	$62\text{-}7\frac{3}{32}$	$24\text{-}5\frac{1}{4}$	$73\text{-}2\frac{13}{32}$	$27\text{-}11\frac{3}{4}$	$83\text{-}9\frac{11}{16}$

natsin A=0.3338471422; natcos A=0.9426272252; nattan A=0.3541666666; natcot A=2.8235294117

Inches	0"		1"		2"		3"		4"		5"	
	Rise	Slope	Rise	Slope	Rise	Slope	Rise	Slope	Rise	Slope	Rise	Slope
0	0	0	$3/8$	$1\,1/16$	$23/32$	$2\,1/8$	$1\,1/16$	$3\,3/16$	$1\,7/16$	$4\,1/4$	$1\,13/16$	$5\,5/16$
$1/16$	$1/32$	$1/16$	$3/8$	$1\,1/8$	$3/4$	$2\,3/16$	$1\,3/32$	$3\,1/4$	$1\,15/32$	$4\,5/16$	$1\,13/16$	$5\,3/8$
$1/8$	$1/32$	$1/8$	$13/32$	$1\,3/16$	$3/4$	$2\,1/4$	$1\,1/8$	$3\,5/16$	$1\,15/32$	$4\,3/8$	$1\,27/32$	$5\,7/16$
$3/16$	$1/16$	$3/16$	$7/16$	$1\,1/4$	$25/32$	$2\,5/16$	$1\,5/32$	$3\,3/8$	$1\,1/2$	$4\,7/16$	$1\,7/8$	$5\,1/2$
$1/4$	$3/32$	$9/32$	$7/16$	$1\,11/32$	$13/16$	$2\,13/32$	$1\,5/32$	$3\,15/32$	$1\,17/32$	$4\,17/32$	$1\,7/8$	$5\,19/32$
$5/16$	$1/8$	$11/32$	$15/32$	$1\,13/32$	$27/32$	$2\,15/32$	$1\,3/16$	$3\,17/32$	$1\,9/16$	$4\,19/32$	$1\,29/32$	$5\,21/32$
$3/8$	$13/32$	$13/32$	$1/2$	$1\,15/32$	$27/32$	$2\,17/32$	$1\,3/16$	$3\,19/32$	$1\,9/16$	$4\,21/32$	$1\,15/16$	$5\,23/32$
$7/16$	$5/32$	$15/32$	$17/32$	$1\,17/32$	$7/8$	$2\,19/32$	$1\,1/4$	$3\,21/32$	$1\,19/32$	$4\,23/32$	$1\,31/32$	$5\,25/32$
$1/2$	$3/32$	$17/32$	$17/32$	$1\,19/32$	$29/32$	$2\,21/32$	$1\,1/4$	$3\,23/32$	$1\,5/8$	$4\,25/32$	$1\,31/32$	$5\,27/32$
$9/16$	$3/16$	$19/32$	$9/16$	$1\,21/32$	$29/32$	$2\,23/32$	$1\,9/32$	$3\,25/32$	$1\,5/8$	$4\,27/32$	2	$5\,29/32$
$5/8$	$7/32$	$21/32$	$19/32$	$1\,23/32$	$15/16$	$2\,25/32$	$1\,5/16$	$3\,27/32$	$1\,21/32$	$4\,29/32$	$2\,1/32$	$5\,31/32$
$11/16$	$1/4$	$23/32$	$19/32$	$1\,25/32$	$31/32$	$2\,27/32$	$1\,5/16$	$3\,29/32$	$1\,11/16$	$4\,31/32$	$2\,1/32$	$6\,1/32$
$3/4$	$9/32$	$13/16$	$5/8$	$1\,7/8$	1	$2\,15/16$	$1\,11/32$	4	$1\,23/32$	$5\,1/16$	$2\,1/16$	$6\,1/8$
$13/16$	$9/32$	$7/8$	$21/32$	$1\,15/16$	1	3	$1\,3/8$	$4\,1/16$	$1\,23/32$	$5\,1/8$	$2\,3/32$	$6\,3/16$
$7/8$	$5/16$	$15/16$	$11/16$	2	$1\,1/32$	$3\,1/16$	$1\,13/32$	$4\,1/8$	$1\,3/4$	$5\,3/16$	$2\,1/8$	$6\,1/4$
$15/16$	$11/32$	1	$11/16$	$2\,1/16$	$1\,1/16$	$3\,1/8$	$1\,13/32$	$4\,3/16$	$1\,25/32$	$5\,1/4$	$2\,1/8$	$6\,5/16$

Inches	6"		7"		8"		9"		10"		11"	
	Rise	Slope	Rise	Slope	Rise	Slope	Rise	Slope	Rise	Slope	Rise	Slope
0	$2\,5/32$	$6\,3/8$	$2\,1/2$	$7\,7/16$	$2\,7/8$	$8\,1/2$	$3\,1/4$	$9\,9/16$	$3\,19/32$	$10\,5/8$	$3\,15/16$	$11\,11/16$
$1/16$	$2\,3/16$	$6\,7/16$	$2\,17/32$	$7\,1/2$	$2\,29/32$	$8\,9/16$	$3\,1/4$	$9\,5/8$	$3\,5/8$	$10\,11/16$	$3\,31/32$	$11\,3/4$
$1/8$	$2\,3/16$	$6\,1/2$	$2\,9/16$	$7\,9/16$	$2\,29/32$	$8\,5/8$	$3\,9/32$	$9\,11/16$	$3\,5/8$	$10\,3/4$	4	$11\,13/16$
$3/16$	$2\,7/32$	$6\,9/16$	$2\,19/32$	$7\,5/8$	$2\,15/16$	$8\,11/16$	$3\,5/16$	$9\,3/4$	$3\,21/32$	$10\,13/16$	$4\,1/32$	$11\,7/8$
$1/4$	$2\,1/4$	$6\,21/32$	$2\,19/32$	$7\,23/32$	$2\,31/32$	$8\,25/32$	$3\,5/16$	$9\,27/32$	$3\,11/16$	$10\,29/32$	$4\,1/32$	$11\,31/32$
$5/16$	$2\,9/32$	$6\,23/32$	$2\,5/8$	$7\,25/32$	3	$8\,27/32$	$3\,11/32$	$9\,29/32$	$3\,23/32$	$10\,31/32$	$4\,1/16$	$1\text{-}0\,1/32$
$3/8$	$2\,9/32$	$6\,25/32$	$2\,21/32$	$7\,27/32$	3	$8\,29/32$	$3\,3/8$	$9\,31/32$	$3\,23/32$	$11\,1/32$	$4\,1/16$	$1\text{-}0\,3/32$
$7/16$	$2\,5/16$	$6\,27/32$	$2\,11/16$	$7\,29/32$	$3\,1/32$	$8\,31/32$	$3\,13/32$	$10\,1/32$	$3\,3/4$	$11\,3/32$	$4\,1/8$	$1\text{-}0\,5/32$
$1/2$	$2\,11/32$	$6\,29/32$	$2\,11/16$	$7\,31/32$	$3\,1/16$	$9\,1/32$	$3\,13/32$	$10\,3/32$	$3\,25/32$	$11\,5/32$	$4\,1/8$	$1\text{-}0\,7/32$
$9/16$	$2\,11/32$	$6\,31/32$	$2\,23/32$	$8\,1/32$	$3\,1/16$	$9\,3/32$	$3\,7/16$	$10\,5/32$	$3\,13/16$	$11\,7/32$	$4\,5/32$	$1\text{-}0\,9/32$
$5/8$	$2\,3/8$	$7\,1/32$	$2\,3/4$	$8\,3/32$	$3\,3/32$	$9\,5/32$	$3\,15/32$	$10\,7/32$	$3\,13/16$	$11\,9/32$	$4\,3/16$	$1\text{-}0\,11/32$
$11/16$	$2\,13/32$	$7\,3/32$	$2\,3/4$	$8\,5/32$	$3\,1/8$	$9\,7/32$	$3\,15/32$	$10\,9/32$	$3\,27/32$	$11\,11/32$	$4\,3/16$	$1\text{-}0\,13/32$
$3/4$	$2\,7/16$	$7\,3/16$	$2\,25/32$	$8\,1/4$	$3\,5/32$	$9\,5/16$	$3\,1/2$	$10\,3/8$	$3\,7/8$	$11\,7/16$	$4\,7/32$	$1\text{-}0\,1/2$
$13/16$	$2\,7/16$	$7\,1/4$	$2\,13/16$	$8\,5/16$	$3\,5/32$	$9\,3/8$	$3\,17/32$	$10\,7/16$	$3\,7/8$	$11\,1/2$	$4\,1/4$	$1\text{-}0\,9/16$
$7/8$	$2\,15/32$	$7\,5/16$	$2\,27/32$	$8\,3/8$	$3\,3/16$	$9\,7/16$	$3\,9/16$	$10\,1/2$	$3\,29/32$	$11\,9/16$	$4\,9/32$	$1\text{-}0\,5/8$
$15/16$	$2\,1/2$	$7\,3/8$	$2\,27/32$	$8\,7/16$	$3\,7/32$	$9\,1/2$	$3\,9/16$	$10\,9/16$	$3\,15/16$	$11\,5/8$	$4\,9/32$	$1\text{-}0\,11/16$

Feet	0'		10'		20'		30'	
	Rise	Slope	Rise	Slope	Rise	Slope	Rise	Slope
0	0	0	$3\text{-}7\,1/8$	$10\text{-}7\,1/2$	$7\text{-}2\,1/4$	$21\text{-}3\,1/32$	$10\text{-}9\,3/8$	$31\text{-}10\,17/32$
1	$4\,5/16$	$1\text{-}0\,3/4$	$3\text{-}11\,7/16$	$11\text{-}8\,1/4$	$7\text{-}6\,9/16$	$22\text{-}3\,25/32$	$11\text{-}1\,11/16$	$32\text{-}11\,9/32$
2	$8\,5/8$	$2\text{-}1\,1/2$	$4\text{-}3\,3/4$	$12\text{-}9\,1/32$	$7\text{-}10\,7/8$	$23\text{-}4\,17/32$	$11\text{-}6$	$34\text{-}0\,1/32$
3	$1\text{-}0\,15/16$	$3\text{-}2\,1/4$	$4\text{-}8\,1/16$	$13\text{-}9\,25/32$	$8\text{-}3\,3/16$	$24\text{-}5\,9/32$	$11\text{-}10\,5/16$	$35\text{-}0\,25/32$
4	$1\text{-}5\,1/4$	$4\text{-}3$	$5\text{-}0\,3/8$	$14\text{-}10\,17/32$	$8\text{-}7\,1/2$	$25\text{-}6\,1/32$	$12\text{-}2\,5/8$	$36\text{-}1\,17/32$
5	$1\text{-}9\,9/16$	$5\text{-}3\,3/4$	$5\text{-}4\,11/16$	$15\text{-}11\,9/32$	$8\text{-}11\,13/16$	$26\text{-}6\,25/32$	$12\text{-}6\,15/16$	$37\text{-}2\,5/16$
6	$2\text{-}1\,7/8$	$6\text{-}4\,1/2$	$5\text{-}9$	$17\text{-}0\,1/32$	$9\text{-}4\,1/8$	$27\text{-}7\,17/32$	$12\text{-}11\,1/4$	$38\text{-}3\,1/16$
7	$2\text{-}6\,3/16$	$7\text{-}5\,1/4$	$6\text{-}1\,5/16$	$18\text{-}0\,25/32$	$9\text{-}8\,7/16$	$28\text{-}8\,9/32$	$13\text{-}3\,9/16$	$39\text{-}3\,13/16$
8	$2\text{-}10\,1/2$	$8\text{-}6$	$6\text{-}5\,5/8$	$19\text{-}1\,17/32$	$10\text{-}0\,3/4$	$29\text{-}9\,1/32$	$13\text{-}7\,7/8$	$40\text{-}4\,9/16$
9	$3\text{-}2\,13/16$	$9\text{-}6\,3/4$	$6\text{-}9\,15/16$	$20\text{-}2\,9/32$	$10\text{-}5\,1/16$	$30\text{-}9\,25/32$	$14\text{-}0\,3/16$	$41\text{-}5\,5/16$

A = 19° 46′ 02″; logsin A = 9.52917; logcos A = 9.97362; logtan A = 9.55555; logcot A = 0.44445

Ins.	12″ Rise	12″ Slope	13″ Rise	13″ Slope	14″ Rise	14″ Slope	15″ Rise	15″ Slope	16″ Rise	16″ Slope
0	4 5/16	1-0 3/4	4 11/16	1-1 13/16	5 1/32	1-2 7/8	5 3/8	1-3 15/16	5 3/4	1-5
1/16	4 11/32	1-0 13/16	4 11/16	1-1 7/8	5 1/16	1-2 15/16	5 13/32	1-4	5 25/32	1-5 1/16
1/8	4 11/32	1-0 7/8	4 23/32	1-1 15/16	5 1/16	1-3	5 7/16	1-4 1/16	5 25/32	1-5 1/8
3/16	4 3/8	1-0 15/16	4 3/4	1-2	5 3/8	1-3 1/16	5 15/32	1-4 1/8	5 13/16	1-5 3/16
1/4	4 13/32	1-1 1/32	4 3/4	1-2 3/32	5 1/8	1-3 5/32	5 15/32	1-4 7/32	5 27/32	1-5 9/32
5/16	4 7/16	1-1 3/32	4 25/32	1-2 5/32	5 5/32	1-3 7/32	5 1/2	1-4 9/32	5 7/8	1-5 11/32
3/8	4 7/16	1-1 5/32	4 13/16	1-2 7/32	5 5/32	1-3 9/32	5 17/32	1-4 11/32	5 7/8	1-5 13/32
7/16	4 15/32	1-1 7/32	4 27/32	1-2 9/32	5 3/16	1-3 11/32	5 9/16	1-4 13/32	5 29/32	1-5 15/32
1/2	4 1/2	1-1 9/32	4 27/32	1-2 11/32	5 7/32	1-3 13/32	5 9/16	1-4 15/32	5 15/16	1-5 17/32
9/16	4 1/2	1-1 11/32	4 7/8	1-2 13/32	5 7/32	1-3 15/32	5 19/32	1-4 17/32	5 15/16	1-5 19/32
5/8	4 17/32	1-1 13/32	4 29/32	1-2 15/32	5 1/4	1-3 17/32	5 5/8	1-4 19/32	5 31/32	1-5 21/32
11/16	4 9/16	1-1 15/32	4 29/32	1-2 17/32	5 9/32	1-3 19/32	5 5/8	1-4 21/32	6	1-5 23/32
3/4	4 19/32	1-1 9/16	4 15/16	1-2 5/8	5 5/16	1-3 11/16	5 21/32	1-4 3/4	6 1/32	1-5 13/16
13/16	4 19/32	1-1 5/8	4 31/32	1-2 11/16	5 5/16	1-3 3/4	5 11/16	1-4 13/16	6 1/32	1-5 7/8
7/8	4 5/8	1-1 11/16	5	1-2 3/4	5 11/32	1-3 13/16	5 23/32	1-4 7/8	6 1/16	1-5 15/16
15/16	4 21/32	1-1 3/4	5	1-2 13/16	5 3/8	1-3 7/8	5 23/32	1-4 15/16	6 3/32	1-6

Ins.	17″ Rise	17″ Slope	18″ Rise	18″ Slope	19″ Rise	19″ Slope	20″ Rise	20″ Slope	21″ Rise	21″ Slope
0	6 1/8	1-6 1/16	6 15/32	1-7 1/8	6 13/16	1-8 3/16	7 3/16	1-9 1/4	7 9/16	1-10 5/16
1/16	6 1/8	1-6 1/8	6 1/2	1-7 3/16	6 27/32	1-8 1/4	7 7/32	1-9 5/16	7 9/16	1-10 3/8
1/8	6 5/32	1-6 3/16	6 1/2	1-7 1/4	6 7/8	1-8 5/16	7 7/32	1-9 3/8	7 19/32	1-10 7/16
3/16	6 3/16	1-6 1/4	6 17/32	1-7 5/16	6 29/32	1-8 3/8	7 1/4	1-9 7/16	7 5/8	1-10 1/2
1/4	6 3/16	1-6 11/32	6 9/16	1-7 13/32	6 29/32	1-8 15/32	7 9/32	1-9 17/32	7 5/8	1-10 19/32
5/16	6 7/32	1-6 13/32	6 19/32	1-7 15/32	6 15/16	1-8 17/32	7 5/16	1-9 19/32	7 21/32	1-10 21/32
3/8	6 1/4	1-6 15/32	6 19/32	1-7 17/32	6 31/32	1-8 19/32	7 5/16	1-9 21/32	7 11/16	1-10 23/32
7/16	6 9/32	1-6 17/32	6 5/8	1-7 19/32	7	1-8 21/32	7 11/32	1-9 23/32	7 23/32	1-10 25/32
1/2	6 9/32	1-6 19/32	6 21/32	1-7 21/32	7	1-8 23/32	7 3/8	1-9 25/32	7 23/32	1-10 27/32
9/16	6 5/16	1-6 21/32	6 21/32	1-7 23/32	7 1/32	1-8 25/32	7 3/8	1-9 27/32	7 3/4	1-10 29/32
5/8	6 11/32	1-6 23/32	6 11/16	1-7 25/32	7 1/16	1-8 27/32	7 13/32	1-9 29/32	7 25/32	1-10 31/32
11/16	6 11/32	1-6 25/32	6 23/32	1-7 27/32	7 1/16	1-8 29/32	7 7/16	1-9 31/32	7 25/32	1-11 1/32
3/4	6 3/8	1-6 7/8	6 3/4	1-7 15/16	7 3/32	1-9	7 15/32	1-10 1/16	7 13/16	1-11 1/8
13/16	6 13/32	1-6 15/16	6 3/4	1-8	7 1/8	1-9 1/16	7 15/32	1-10 1/8	7 27/32	1-11 3/16
7/8	6 7/16	1-7	6 25/32	1-8 1/16	7 5/32	1-9 1/8	7 1/2	1-10 3/16	7 7/8	1-11 1/4
15/16	6 7/16	1-7 1/16	6 13/16	1-8 1/8	7 5/32	1-9 3/16	7 17/32	1-10 1/4	7 7/8	1-11 5/16

Feet	40′ Rise	40′ Slope	50′ Rise	50′ Slope	60′ Rise	60′ Slope	70′ Rise	70′ Slope
0	14-4 1/2	42-6 1/16	17-11 5/8	53-1 9/16	21-6 3/4	63-9 3/32	25-1 7/8	74-4 19/32
1	14-8 13/16	43-6 13/16	18-3 15/16	54-2 5/16	21-11 1/16	64-9 27/32	25-6 3/16	75-5 11/32
2	15-1 1/8	44-7 9/16	18-8 1/4	55-3 1/16	22-3 3/8	65-10 19/32	25-10 1/2	76-6 3/32
3	15-5 7/16	45-8 5/16	19-0 9/16	56-3 13/16	22-7 11/16	66-11 11/32	26-2 13/16	77-6 27/32
4	15-9 3/4	46-9 1/16	19-4 7/8	57-4 9/16	23-0		26-7 1/8	78-7 19/32
5	16-2 1/16	47-9 13/16	19-9 3/16	58-5 5/16	23-4 5/16	69-0 27/32	26-11 7/16	79-8 11/32
6	16-6 3/8	48-10 9/16	20-1 1/2	59-6 1/16	23-8 5/8	70-1 19/32	27-3 3/4	80-9 3/32
7	16-10 11/16	49-11 5/16	20-5 13/16	60-6 27/32	24-0 15/16	71-2 11/32	27-8 1/16	81-9 27/32
8	17-3	51-0 1/16	20-10 1/8	61-7 19/32	24-5 1/4	72-3 3/32	28-0 3/8	82-10 19/32
9	17-7 5/16	52-0 13/16	21-2 7/16	62-8 11/32	24-9 9/16	73-3 27/32	28-4 11/16	83-11 11/32

natsin A=0.3381987261; natcos A=0.9410747162; nattan A=0.3593750000; natcot A=2.7826086956

Inches	0" Rise	0" Slope	1" Rise	1" Slope	2" Rise	2" Slope	3" Rise	3" Slope	4" Rise	4" Slope	5" Rise	5" Slope
0	0	0	3/8	1 1/16	23/32	2 1/8	1 3/32	3 3/16	1 15/32	4 1/4	1 13/16	5 5/16
1/16	1/32	1/16	3/8	1 1/8	3/4	2 3/16	1 1/8	3 1/4	1 15/32	4 5/16	1 27/32	5 3/8
1/8	1/32	1/8	13/32	1 3/16	25/32	2 1/4	1 1/8	3 5/16	1 1/2	4 3/8	1 7/8	5 15/32
3/16	1/16	3/16	7/16	1 1/4	13/16	2 11/32	1 5/32	3 13/32	1 17/32	4 15/32	1 29/32	5 17/32
1/4	3/32	9/32	15/32	1 11/32	13/16	2 13/32	1 3/16	3 15/32	1 9/16	4 17/32	1 29/32	5 19/32
5/16	1/8	11/32	15/32	1 13/32	27/32	2 15/32	1 7/32	3 17/32	1 9/16	4 19/32	1 15/16	5 21/32
3/8	1/8	13/32	1/2	1 15/32	7/8	2 17/32	1 7/32	3 19/32	1 19/32	4 21/32	1 31/32	5 23/32
7/16	5/32	15/32	17/32	1 17/32	7/8	2 19/32	1 1/4	3 21/32	1 5/8	4 23/32	1 31/32	5 25/32
1/2	3/16	17/32	9/16	1 19/32	29/32	2 21/32	1 9/32	3 28/32	1 5/8	4 25/32	2	5 27/32
9/16	7/32	19/32	9/16	1 21/32	15/16	2 23/32	1 5/16	3 25/32	1 21/32	4 27/32	2 1/32	5 29/32
5/8	7/32	21/32	19/32	1 23/32	31/32	2 25/32	1 5/16	3 27/32	1 11/16	4 15/16	2 1/16	6
11/16	1/4	23/32	5/8	1 25/32	31/32	2 7/8	1 11/32	3 15/16	1 23/32	5	2 1/16	6 1/16
3/4	9/32	13/16	5/8	1 7/8	1	2 15/16	1 3/8	4	1 23/32	5 1/16	2 3/32	6 1/8
13/16	9/32	7/8	21/32	1 15/16	1 1/32	3	1 3/8	4 1/16	1 3/4	5 1/8	2 1/8	6 3/16
7/8	5/16	15/16	11/16	2	1 1/16	3 1/16	1 13/32	4 1/8	1 25/32	5 3/16	2 5/32	6 1/4
15/16	11/32	1	23/32	2 1/16	1 1/16	3 1/8	1 7/16	4 3/16	1 13/16	5 1/4	2 5/32	6 5/16

Inches	6" Rise	6" Slope	7" Rise	7" Slope	8" Rise	8" Slope	9" Rise	9" Slope	10" Rise	10" Slope	11" Rise	11" Slope
0	2 3/16	6 3/8	2 9/16	7 7/16	2 29/32	8 1/2	3 9/32	9 19/32	3 21/32	10 21/32	4	11 23/32
1/16	2 7/32	6 7/16	2 9/16	7 17/32	2 15/16	8 19/32	3 5/16	9 21/32	3 21/32	10 23/32	4 1/32	11 25/32
1/8	2 7/32	6 17/32	2 19/32	7 19/32	2 31/32	8 21/32	3 5/16	9 23/32	3 11/16	10 25/32	4 1/16	11 27/32
3/16	2 1/4	6 19/32	2 5/8	7 21/32	3	8 23/32	3 11/32	9 25/32	3 23/32	10 27/32	4 3/32	11 29/32
1/4	2 9/32	6 21/32	2 21/32	7 23/32	3	8 25/32	3 3/8	9 27/32	3 3/4	10 29/32	4 3/32	11 31/32
5/16	2 5/16	6 23/32	2 21/32	7 25/32	3 1/32	8 27/32	3 13/32	9 29/32	3 3/4	10 31/32	4 1/8	1-0 1/32
3/8	2 5/16	6 25/32	2 11/16	7 27/32	3 1/16	8 31/32	3 13/32	9 31/32	3 25/32	11 1/32	4 5/32	1-0 3/32
7/16	2 11/32	6 27/32	2 23/32	7 29/32	3 1/16	8 31/32	3 7/16	10 1/32	3 13/16	11 1/8	4 5/32	1-0 3/16
1/2	2 3/8	6 29/32	2 3/4	7 31/32	3 3/32	9 1/16	3 15/32	10 1/8	3 13/16	11 3/16	4 3/16	1-0 1/4
9/16	2 13/32	7	2 3/4	8 1/16	3 1/8	9 1/8	3 1/2	10 3/32	3 27/32	11 1/4	4 7/32	1-0 5/16
5/8	2 13/32	7 1/16	2 25/32	8 1/8	3 5/32	9 3/16	3 1/2	10 1/4	3 7/8	11 5/16	4 1/4	1-0 3/8
11/16	2 7/16	7 1/8	2 13/16	8 3/16	3 5/32	9 1/4	3 17/32	10 5/16	3 29/32	11 3/8	4 1/4	1-0 7/16
3/4	2 15/32	7 3/16	2 13/16	8 1/4	3 3/16	9 5/16	3 9/16	10 3/8	3 29/32	11 7/16	4 9/32	1-0 1/2
13/16	2 15/32	7 1/4	2 27/32	8 5/16	3 7/32	9 3/8	3 9/16	10 7/16	3 15/16	11 1/2	4 5/16	1-0 9/16
7/8	2 1/2	7 5/16	2 7/8	8 3/8	3 1/4	9 7/16	3 19/32	10 1/2	3 31/32	11 9/16	4 11/32	1-0 5/8
15/16	2 17/32	7 3/8	2 29/32	8 7/16	3 1/4	9 1/2	3 5/8	10 9/16	4	11 21/32	4 11/32	1-0 23/32

Feet	0' Rise	0' Slope	10' Rise	10' Slope	20' Rise	20' Slope	30' Rise	30' Slope
0			3-7 3/4	10-7 23/32	7-3 1/2	21-3 7/16	10-11 1/4	31-11 3/16
1	4 3/8	1-0 25/32	4-0 1/8	11-8 1/2	7-7 7/8	22-4 7/32	11-3 5/8	32-11 15/16
2	8 3/4	2-1 17/32	4-4 1/2	12-9 9/32	8-0 1/4	23-5	11-8	34-0 23/32
3	1-1 1/8	3-2 5/16	4-8 7/8	13-10 1/32	8-4 5/8	24-5 25/32	12-0 3/8	35-1 1/2
4	1-5 1/2	4-3 3/32	5-1 1/4	14-10 13/16	8-9	25-6 17/32	12-4 3/4	36-2 9/32
5	1-9 7/8	5-3 7/8	5-5 5/8	15-11 19/32	9-1 3/8	26-7 5/16	12-9 1/8	37-3 1/32
6	2-2 1/4	6-4 5/8	5-10	17-0 3/8	9-5 3/4	27-8 3/32	13-1 1/2	38-3 13/16
7	2-6 5/8	7-5 13/32	6-2 3/8	18-1 1/8	9-10 1/8	28-8 7/8	13-5 7/8	39-4 19/32
8	2-11	8-6 3/16	6-6 3/4	19-1 29/32	10-2 1/2	29-9 5/8	13-10 1/4	40-5 3/8
9	3-3 3/8	9-6 31/32	6-11 1/8	20-2 11/16	10-6 7/8	30-10 13/32	14-2 5/8	41-6 1/8

A = 20° 01′ 52″; logsin A = 9.53470; logcos A = 9.97290; logtan A = 9.56180; logcot A = 0.43820

Ins.	12″ Rise	12″ Slope	13″ Rise	13″ Slope	14″ Rise	14″ Slope	15″ Rise	15″ Slope	16″ Rise	16″ Slope
0	$4\frac{3}{8}$	$1\text{-}0\frac{25}{32}$	$4\frac{3}{4}$	$1\text{-}1\frac{27}{32}$	$5\frac{3}{32}$	$1\text{-}2\frac{29}{32}$	$5\frac{15}{32}$	$1\text{-}3\frac{31}{32}$	$5\frac{27}{32}$	$1\text{-}5\frac{1}{32}$
1/16	$4\frac{13}{32}$	$1\text{-}0\frac{27}{32}$	$4\frac{3}{4}$	$1\text{-}1\frac{29}{32}$	$5\frac{1}{8}$	$1\text{-}2\frac{31}{32}$	$5\frac{1}{2}$	$1\text{-}4\frac{1}{32}$	$5\frac{27}{32}$	$1\text{-}5\frac{3}{32}$
1/8	$4\frac{13}{32}$	$1\text{-}0\frac{29}{32}$	$4\frac{25}{32}$	$1\text{-}1\frac{31}{32}$	$5\frac{5}{32}$	$1\text{-}3\frac{1}{32}$	$5\frac{1}{2}$	$1\text{-}4\frac{3}{32}$	$5\frac{7}{8}$	$1\text{-}5\frac{5}{32}$
3/16	$4\frac{7}{16}$	$1\text{-}0\frac{31}{32}$	$4\frac{13}{16}$	$1\text{-}2\frac{1}{32}$	$5\frac{9}{16}$	$1\text{-}3\frac{3}{32}$	$5\frac{17}{32}$	$1\text{-}4\frac{5}{32}$	$5\frac{29}{32}$	$1\text{-}5\frac{7}{32}$
1/4	$4\frac{15}{32}$	$1\text{-}1\frac{1}{32}$	$4\frac{27}{32}$	$1\text{-}2\frac{3}{32}$	$5\frac{3}{16}$	$1\text{-}3\frac{5}{32}$	$5\frac{9}{16}$	$1\text{-}4\frac{7}{32}$	$5\frac{15}{16}$	$1\text{-}5\frac{9}{32}$
5/16	$4\frac{1}{2}$	$1\text{-}1\frac{3}{32}$	$4\frac{27}{32}$	$1\text{-}2\frac{5}{32}$	$5\frac{7}{32}$	$1\text{-}3\frac{7}{32}$	$5\frac{19}{32}$	$1\text{-}4\frac{5}{16}$	$5\frac{15}{16}$	$1\text{-}5\frac{3}{8}$
3/8	$4\frac{1}{2}$	$1\text{-}1\frac{5}{32}$	$4\frac{7}{8}$	$1\text{-}2\frac{1}{4}$	$5\frac{1}{4}$	$1\text{-}3\frac{5}{16}$	$5\frac{19}{32}$	$1\text{-}4\frac{3}{8}$	$5\frac{31}{32}$	$1\text{-}5\frac{7}{16}$
7/16	$4\frac{17}{32}$	$1\text{-}1\frac{1}{4}$	$4\frac{29}{32}$	$1\text{-}2\frac{5}{16}$	$5\frac{1}{4}$	$1\text{-}3\frac{3}{8}$	$5\frac{5}{8}$	$1\text{-}4\frac{7}{16}$	6	$1\text{-}5\frac{1}{2}$
1/2	$4\frac{9}{16}$	$1\text{-}1\frac{5}{16}$	$4\frac{15}{16}$	$1\text{-}2\frac{3}{8}$	$5\frac{9}{32}$	$1\text{-}3\frac{7}{16}$	$5\frac{21}{32}$	$1\text{-}4\frac{1}{2}$	6	$1\text{-}5\frac{9}{16}$
9/16	$4\frac{19}{32}$	$1\text{-}1\frac{3}{8}$	$4\frac{15}{16}$	$1\text{-}2\frac{7}{16}$	$5\frac{5}{16}$	$1\text{-}3\frac{1}{2}$	$5\frac{11}{16}$	$1\text{-}4\frac{9}{16}$	$6\frac{1}{16}$	$1\text{-}5\frac{5}{8}$
5/8	$4\frac{19}{32}$	$1\text{-}1\frac{7}{16}$	$4\frac{31}{32}$	$1\text{-}2\frac{1}{2}$	$5\frac{11}{32}$	$1\text{-}3\frac{9}{16}$	$5\frac{11}{16}$	$1\text{-}4\frac{5}{8}$	$6\frac{1}{16}$	$1\text{-}5\frac{11}{16}$
11/16	$4\frac{5}{8}$	$1\text{-}1\frac{1}{2}$	5	$1\text{-}2\frac{9}{16}$	$5\frac{11}{32}$	$1\text{-}3\frac{5}{8}$	$5\frac{23}{32}$	$1\text{-}4\frac{11}{16}$	$6\frac{3}{32}$	$1\text{-}5\frac{3}{4}$
3/4	$4\frac{21}{32}$	$1\text{-}1\frac{9}{16}$	5	$1\text{-}2\frac{5}{8}$	$5\frac{3}{8}$	$1\text{-}3\frac{11}{16}$	$5\frac{3}{4}$	$1\text{-}4\frac{3}{4}$	$6\frac{3}{32}$	$1\text{-}5\frac{27}{32}$
13/16	$4\frac{21}{32}$	$1\text{-}1\frac{5}{8}$	$5\frac{1}{32}$	$1\text{-}2\frac{11}{16}$	$5\frac{13}{32}$	$1\text{-}3\frac{25}{32}$	$5\frac{3}{4}$	$1\text{-}4\frac{27}{32}$	$6\frac{1}{8}$	$1\text{-}5\frac{29}{32}$
7/8	$4\frac{11}{16}$	$1\text{-}1\frac{23}{32}$	$5\frac{1}{16}$	$1\text{-}2\frac{25}{32}$	$5\frac{7}{16}$	$1\text{-}3\frac{27}{32}$	$5\frac{25}{32}$	$1\text{-}4\frac{29}{32}$	$6\frac{5}{32}$	$1\text{-}5\frac{31}{32}$
15/16	$4\frac{23}{32}$	$1\text{-}1\frac{25}{32}$	$5\frac{3}{32}$	$1\text{-}2\frac{27}{32}$	$5\frac{7}{16}$	$1\text{-}3\frac{29}{32}$	$5\frac{13}{16}$	$1\text{-}4\frac{31}{32}$	$6\frac{3}{16}$	$1\text{-}6\frac{1}{32}$

Ins.	17″ Rise	17″ Slope	18″ Rise	18″ Slope	19″ Rise	19″ Slope	20″ Rise	20″ Slope	21″ Rise	21″ Slope
0	$6\frac{3}{16}$	$1\text{-}6\frac{3}{32}$	$6\frac{9}{16}$	$1\text{-}7\frac{5}{32}$	$6\frac{15}{16}$	$1\text{-}8\frac{7}{32}$	$7\frac{9}{32}$	$1\text{-}9\frac{9}{32}$	$7\frac{21}{32}$	$1\text{-}10\frac{11}{32}$
1/16	$6\frac{7}{32}$	$1\text{-}6\frac{5}{32}$	$6\frac{19}{32}$	$1\text{-}7\frac{7}{32}$	$6\frac{15}{16}$	$1\text{-}8\frac{9}{32}$	$7\frac{5}{16}$	$1\text{-}9\frac{11}{32}$	$7\frac{11}{16}$	$1\text{-}10\frac{13}{32}$
1/8	$6\frac{1}{4}$	$1\text{-}6\frac{7}{32}$	$6\frac{19}{32}$	$1\text{-}7\frac{9}{32}$	$6\frac{31}{32}$	$1\text{-}8\frac{11}{32}$	$7\frac{11}{32}$	$1\text{-}9\frac{13}{32}$	$7\frac{11}{16}$	$1\text{-}10\frac{1}{2}$
3/16	$6\frac{9}{32}$	$1\text{-}6\frac{9}{32}$	$6\frac{5}{8}$	$1\text{-}7\frac{11}{32}$	7	$1\text{-}8\frac{7}{16}$	$7\frac{3}{8}$	$1\text{-}9\frac{1}{2}$	$7\frac{23}{32}$	$1\text{-}10\frac{9}{16}$
1/4	$6\frac{9}{32}$	$1\text{-}6\frac{3}{8}$	$6\frac{21}{32}$	$1\text{-}7\frac{7}{16}$	$7\frac{1}{32}$	$1\text{-}8\frac{1}{2}$	$7\frac{3}{8}$	$1\text{-}9\frac{9}{16}$	$7\frac{3}{4}$	$1\text{-}10\frac{5}{8}$
5/16	$6\frac{5}{16}$	$1\text{-}6\frac{7}{16}$	$6\frac{11}{16}$	$1\text{-}7\frac{1}{2}$	$7\frac{1}{32}$	$1\text{-}8\frac{9}{16}$	$7\frac{13}{32}$	$1\text{-}9\frac{5}{8}$	$7\frac{25}{32}$	$1\text{-}10\frac{11}{16}$
3/8	$6\frac{11}{32}$	$1\text{-}6\frac{1}{2}$	$6\frac{11}{16}$	$1\text{-}7\frac{9}{16}$	$7\frac{1}{16}$	$1\text{-}8\frac{5}{8}$	$7\frac{7}{16}$	$1\text{-}9\frac{11}{16}$	$7\frac{25}{32}$	$1\text{-}10\frac{3}{4}$
7/16	$6\frac{11}{32}$	$1\text{-}6\frac{9}{16}$	$6\frac{23}{32}$	$1\text{-}7\frac{5}{8}$	$7\frac{3}{32}$	$1\text{-}8\frac{11}{16}$	$7\frac{17}{32}$	$1\text{-}9\frac{3}{4}$	$7\frac{13}{16}$	$1\text{-}10\frac{13}{16}$
1/2	$6\frac{3}{8}$	$1\text{-}6\frac{5}{8}$	$6\frac{3}{4}$	$1\text{-}7\frac{11}{16}$	$7\frac{1}{8}$	$1\text{-}8\frac{3}{4}$	$7\frac{15}{32}$	$1\text{-}9\frac{13}{16}$	$7\frac{27}{32}$	$1\text{-}10\frac{7}{8}$
9/16	$6\frac{13}{32}$	$1\text{-}6\frac{11}{16}$	$6\frac{25}{32}$	$1\text{-}7\frac{3}{4}$	$7\frac{1}{8}$	$1\text{-}8\frac{13}{16}$	$7\frac{1}{2}$	$1\text{-}9\frac{7}{8}$	$7\frac{7}{8}$	$1\text{-}10\frac{15}{16}$
5/8	$6\frac{7}{16}$	$1\text{-}6\frac{3}{4}$	$6\frac{25}{32}$	$1\text{-}7\frac{13}{16}$	$7\frac{5}{32}$	$1\text{-}8\frac{7}{8}$	$7\frac{17}{32}$	$1\text{-}9\frac{15}{16}$	$7\frac{7}{8}$	$1\text{-}11\frac{1}{32}$
11/16	$6\frac{7}{16}$	$1\text{-}6\frac{13}{16}$	$6\frac{13}{16}$	$1\text{-}7\frac{29}{32}$	$7\frac{3}{16}$	$1\text{-}8\frac{31}{32}$	$7\frac{17}{32}$	$1\text{-}10\frac{1}{32}$	$7\frac{29}{32}$	$1\text{-}11\frac{3}{32}$
3/4	$6\frac{15}{32}$	$1\text{-}6\frac{29}{32}$	$6\frac{27}{32}$	$1\text{-}7\frac{31}{32}$	$7\frac{3}{16}$	$1\text{-}9\frac{1}{32}$	$7\frac{9}{16}$	$1\text{-}10\frac{3}{32}$	$7\frac{15}{16}$	$1\text{-}11\frac{5}{32}$
13/16	$6\frac{1}{2}$	$1\text{-}6\frac{31}{32}$	$6\frac{27}{32}$	$1\text{-}8\frac{1}{32}$	$7\frac{7}{32}$	$1\text{-}9\frac{3}{32}$	$7\frac{19}{32}$	$1\text{-}10\frac{5}{32}$	$7\frac{15}{16}$	$1\text{-}11\frac{7}{32}$
7/8	$6\frac{17}{32}$	$1\text{-}7\frac{1}{16}$	$6\frac{7}{8}$	$1\text{-}8\frac{3}{32}$	$7\frac{1}{4}$	$1\text{-}9\frac{5}{32}$	$7\frac{5}{8}$	$1\text{-}10\frac{7}{32}$	$7\frac{31}{32}$	$1\text{-}11\frac{9}{32}$
15/16	$6\frac{17}{32}$	$1\text{-}7\frac{3}{32}$	$6\frac{29}{32}$	$1\text{-}8\frac{5}{32}$	$7\frac{9}{32}$	$1\text{-}9\frac{7}{32}$	$7\frac{5}{8}$	$1\text{-}10\frac{9}{32}$	8	$1\text{-}11\frac{11}{32}$

Fret	40′ Rise	40′ Slope	50′ Rise	50′ Slope	60′ Rise	60′ Slope	70′ Rise	70′ Slope
0	14-7	$42\text{-}6\frac{29}{32}$	$18\text{-}2\frac{3}{4}$	$53\text{-}2\frac{5}{8}$	$21\text{-}10\frac{1}{2}$	$63\text{-}10\frac{11}{32}$	$25\text{-}6\frac{1}{4}$	$74\text{-}6\frac{3}{32}$
1	$14\text{-}11\frac{3}{8}$	$43\text{-}7\frac{11}{16}$	$18\text{-}7\frac{1}{8}$	$54\text{-}3\frac{13}{32}$	$22\text{-}2\frac{7}{8}$	$64\text{-}11\frac{1}{8}$	$25\text{-}10\frac{5}{8}$	$75\text{-}6\frac{27}{32}$
2	$15\text{-}3\frac{3}{4}$	$44\text{-}8\frac{7}{16}$	$18\text{-}11\frac{1}{2}$	$55\text{-}4\frac{3}{16}$	$22\text{-}7\frac{1}{4}$	$65\text{-}11\frac{29}{32}$	$26\text{-}3$	$76\text{-}7\frac{5}{8}$
3	$15\text{-}8\frac{1}{8}$	$45\text{-}9\frac{7}{32}$	$19\text{-}3\frac{7}{8}$	$56\text{-}4\frac{15}{16}$	$22\text{-}11\frac{5}{8}$	$67\text{-}0\frac{11}{16}$	$26\text{-}7\frac{3}{8}$	$77\text{-}8\frac{13}{32}$
4	$16\text{-}0\frac{1}{2}$	46-10	$19\text{-}8\frac{1}{4}$	$57\text{-}5\frac{23}{32}$	$23\text{-}4$	$68\text{-}1\frac{7}{16}$	$26\text{-}11\frac{3}{4}$	$78\text{-}9\frac{3}{32}$
5	$16\text{-}4\frac{7}{8}$	$47\text{-}10\frac{25}{32}$	$20\text{-}0\frac{5}{8}$	$58\text{-}6\frac{1}{2}$	$23\text{-}8\frac{3}{8}$	$69\text{-}2\frac{1}{4}$	$27\text{-}4\frac{1}{8}$	$79\text{-}9\frac{15}{16}$
6	$16\text{-}9\frac{1}{4}$	$48\text{-}11\frac{17}{32}$	20-5	$59\text{-}7\frac{9}{32}$	$24\text{-}0\frac{3}{4}$	70-3	$27\text{-}8\frac{1}{2}$	$80\text{-}10\frac{23}{32}$
7	$17\text{-}1\frac{5}{8}$	$50\text{-}0\frac{5}{16}$	$20\text{-}9\frac{3}{8}$	$60\text{-}8\frac{1}{32}$	$24\text{-}5\frac{1}{8}$	$71\text{-}3\frac{25}{32}$	$28\text{-}0\frac{7}{8}$	$81\text{-}11\frac{1}{2}$
8	17-6	$51\text{-}1\frac{3}{32}$	$21\text{-}1\frac{3}{4}$	$61\text{-}8\frac{13}{16}$	$24\text{-}9\frac{1}{2}$	$72\text{-}4\frac{17}{32}$	$28\text{-}5\frac{1}{4}$	$83\text{-}0\frac{9}{32}$
9	$17\text{-}10\frac{3}{8}$	$52\text{-}1\frac{7}{8}$	$21\text{-}6\frac{1}{8}$	$62\text{-}9\frac{19}{32}$	$25\text{-}1\frac{7}{8}$	$73\text{-}5\frac{5}{16}$	$28\text{-}9\frac{5}{8}$	$84\text{-}1\frac{1}{32}$

natsin A=0.3425287237; natcos A=0.9395073566; nattan A=0.3645833333; natcot A=2.7428571428

Inches	0" Rise	0" Slope	1" Rise	1" Slope	2" Rise	2" Slope	3" Rise	3" Slope	4" Rise	4" Slope	5" Rise	5" Slope
0	0	0	3/8	1 1/16	3/4	2 1/8	1 1/8	3 3/16	1 15/32	4 1/4	1 27/32	5 11/32
1/16	1/2	1/16	13/32	1 1/8	3/4	2 3/16	1 1/8	3 1/4	1 1/2	4 11/32	1 7/8	5 13/32
1/8	1/32	1/8	13/32	1 3/16	25/32	2 9/32	1 5/32	3 11/32	1 17/32	4 13/32	1 29/32	5 15/32
3/16	1/16	3/16	7/16	1 9/32	13/16	2 11/32	1 3/16	3 13/32	1 9/16	4 15/32	1 29/32	5 17/32
1/4	3/32	9/32	15/32	1 11/32	27/32	2 13/32	1 3/16	3 15/32	1 9/16	4 17/32	1 15/16	5 19/32
5/16	1/8	11/32	1/2	1 13/32	27/32	2 15/32	1 7/32	3 17/32	1 19/32	4 19/32	1 31/32	5 21/32
3/8	1/8	13/32	1/2	1 15/32	7/8	2 17/32	1 1/4	3 19/32	1 5/8	4 21/32	2	5 23/32
7/16	5/32	15/32	17/32	1 17/32	29/32	2 19/32	1 9/32	3 21/32	1 21/32	4 23/32	2	5 13/16
1/2	3/16	17/32	9/16	1 19/32	15/16	2 21/32	1 9/32	3 23/32	1 21/32	4 13/16	2 1/32	5 7/8
9/16	7/32	19/32	9/16	1 21/32	15/16	2 23/32	1 5/16	3 13/16	1 11/16	4 7/8	2 1/32	5 15/16
5/8	7/32	21/32	21/32	1 23/32	31/32	2 13/16	1 11/32	3 7/8	1 23/32	4 15/16	2 3/32	6
11/16	1/4	23/32	5/8	1 13/16	1	2 7/8	1 3/8	3 15/16	1 23/32	5	2 3/32	6 1/16
3/4	9/32	13/16	21/32	1 7/8	1 1/32	2 15/16	1 3/8	4	1 3/4	5 1/16	2 1/8	6 1/8
13/16	5/16	7/8	21/32	1 15/16	1 1/32	3	1 13/32	4 1/16	1 25/32	5 1/8	2 5/32	6 3/16
7/8	5/16	15/16	11/16	2	1 1/16	3 1/16	1 7/16	4 1/8	1 13/16	5 3/16	2 5/32	6 1/4
15/16	11/32	1	23/32	2 1/16	1 1/16	3 1/8	1 15/32	4 3/16	1 13/16	5 1/4	2 3/16	6 11/32

Inches	6" Rise	6" Slope	7" Rise	7" Slope	8" Rise	8" Slope	9" Rise	9" Slope	10" Rise	10" Slope	11" Rise	11" Slope
0	2 7/32	6 13/32	2 19/32	7 15/32	2 31/32	8 17/32	3 5/16	9 19/32	3 11/16	10 21/32	4 1/16	11 23/32
1/16	2 1/4	6 15/32	2 5/8	7 17/32	2 31/32	8 19/32	3 11/32	9 21/32	3 23/32	10 23/32	4 3/32	11 25/32
1/8	2 1/4	6 17/32	2 5/8	7 19/32	3	8 21/32	3 3/8	9 23/32	3 3/4	10 25/32	4 1/8	11 7/8
3/16	2 9/32	6 19/32	2 21/32	7 21/32	3 1/32	8 23/32	3 13/32	9 25/32	3 25/32	10 7/8	4 1/8	11 15/16
1/4	2 5/16	6 21/32	2 11/16	7 23/32	3 1/16	8 25/32	3 13/32	9 7/8	3 25/32	10 15/16	4 5/32	1-0
5/16	2 11/32	6 23/32	2 23/32	7 25/32	3 1/16	8 7/8	3 7/16	9 15/16	3 13/16	11	4 3/16	1-0 1/16
3/8	2 11/32	6 13/16	2 23/32	7 7/8	3 3/32	8 15/16	3 15/32	10	3 27/32	11 1/16	4 7/32	1-0 1/8
7/16	2 3/8	6 7/8	2 3/4	7 15/16	3 1/8	9	3 1/2	10 1/16	3 7/8	11 1/8	4 7/32	1-0 3/16
1/2	2 13/32	6 15/16	2 25/32	8	3 5/32	9 1/16	3 1/2	10 1/8	3 7/8	11 3/16	4 1/4	1-0 1/4
9/16	2 7/16	7	2 25/32	8 1/16	3 5/32	9 1/8	3 17/32	10 3/16	3 29/32	11 1/4	4 9/32	1-0 5/16
5/8	2 7/16	7 1/16	2 13/16	8 1/8	3 3/16	9 3/16	3 9/16	10 1/4	3 15/16	11 11/32	4 5/16	1-0 13/32
11/16	2 15/32	7 1/8	2 27/32	8 3/16	3 7/32	9 1/4	3 19/32	10 11/32	3 15/16	11 13/32	4 5/16	1-0 15/32
3/4	2 1/2	7 3/16	2 7/8	8 1/4	3 1/4	9 11/32	3 19/32	10 13/32	3 31/32	11 15/32	4 11/32	1-0 17/32
13/16	2 17/32	7 1/4	2 7/8	8 11/32	3 1/4	9 13/32	3 5/8	10 15/32	4	11 17/32	4 3/8	1-0 19/32
7/8	2 17/32	7 11/32	2 29/32	8 13/32	3 9/32	9 15/32	3 21/32	10 17/32	4 1/32	11 19/32	4 13/32	1-0 21/32
15/16	2 9/16	7 13/32	2 15/16	8 15/32	3 5/16	9 17/32	3 11/16	10 19/32	4 1/32	11 21/32	4 13/32	1-0 23/32

Feet	0' Rise	0' Slope	10' Rise	10' Slope	20' Rise	20' Slope	30' Rise	30' Slope
0	0	0	3-8 3/8	10-7 15/16	7-4 3/4	21-3 7/8	11-1 1/8	31-11 13/16
1	4 7/16	1-0 25/32	4-0 13/16	10-8 3/4	7-9 3/16	22-4 11/16	11-5 9/16	33-0 5/8
2	8 7/8	2-1 19/32	4-5 1/4	12-9 17/32	8-1 5/8	23-5 15/32	11-10	34-1 13/32
3	1-1 5/16	3-2 3/8	4-9 11/16	13-10 5/16	8-6 1/16	24-6 9/32	12-2 7/16	35-2 7/32
4	1-5 3/4	4-3 3/16	5-2 1/8	14-11 1/8	8-10 1/2	25-7 1/16	12-6 7/8	36-3
5	1-10 3/16	5-3 31/32	5-6 9/16	15-11 29/32	9-2 15/16	26-7 27/32	12-11 5/16	37-3 25/32
6	2-2 5/8	6-4 3/4	5-11	17-0 23/32	9-7 3/8	27-8 21/32	13-3 3/4	38-4 19/32
7	2-7 1/16	7-5 9/16	6-3 7/16	18-1 1/2	9-11 13/16	28-9 7/16	13-8 3/16	39-5 3/8
8	2-11 1/2	8-6 11/32	6-7 7/8	19-2 9/32	10-4 1/4	29-10 1/4	14-0 5/8	40-6 3/16
9	3-3 15/16	9-7 5/32	7-0 5/16	20-3 3/32	10-8 11/16	30-11 1/32	14-5 1/16	41-6 31/32

A = 20° 17' 38"; logsin A = 9.54013; logcos A = 9.97217; logtan A = 9.56796; logcot A = 0.43204

In.	12″ Rise	Slope	13″ Rise	Slope	14″ Rise	Slope	15″ Rise	Slope	16″ Rise	Slope
0	4 7/16	1-0 25/32	4 13/16	1-1 1/8	5 3/16	1-2 15/16	5 9/16	1-4	5 29/32	1-5 1/16
1/16	4 15/32	1-0 7/8	4 27/32	1-1 15/16	5 3/16	1-3	5 9/16	1-4 1/16	5 15/16	1-5 1/8
1/8	4 15/32	1-0 15/16	4 27/32	1-2	5 7/32	1-3 1/16	5 19/32	1-4 1/8	5 31/32	1-5 3/16
3/16	4 1/2	1-1	4 7/8	1-2 1/16	5 1/4	1-3 1/8	5 5/8	1-4 3/16	6	1-5 1/4
1/4	4 17/32	1-1 1/16	4 29/32	1-2 1/8	5 9/32	1-3 3/16	5 5/8	1-4 1/4	6	1-5 5/16
5/16	4 9/16	1-1 1/8	4 15/16	1-2 3/16	5 9/32	1-3 1/4	5 21/32	1-4 5/16	6 1/32	1-5 13/32
3/8	4 9/16	1-1 3/16	4 15/16	1-2 1/4	5 5/16	1-3 5/16	5 11/16	1-4 13/32	6 1/16	1-5 15/32
7/16	4 19/32	1-1 1/4	4 31/32	1-2 5/16	5 11/32	1-3 13/32	5 23/32	1-4 15/32	6 3/32	1-5 17/32
1/2	4 5/8	1-1 5/16	5	1-2 13/32	5 3/8	1-3 15/32	5 23/32	1-4 17/32	6 3/32	1-5 19/32
9/16	4 21/32	1-1 13/32	5	1-2 15/32	5 3/8	1-3 17/32	5 3/4	1-4 19/32	6 1/8	1-5 21/32
5/8	4 21/32	1-1 15/32	5 1/16	1-2 17/32	5 13/32	1-3 19/32	5 25/32	1-4 21/32	6 5/32	1-5 23/32
11/16	4 11/16	1-1 17/32	5 1/16	1-2 19/32	5 7/16	1-3 21/32	5 13/16	1-4 23/32	6 5/32	1-5 25/32
3/4	4 23/32	1-1 19/32	5 3/32	1-2 21/32	5 15/32	1-3 23/32	5 13/16	1-4 25/32	6 3/16	1-5 27/32
13/16	4 3/4	1-1 21/32	5 3/32	1-2 23/32	5 15/32	1-3 25/32	5 27/32	1-4 27/32	6 7/32	1-5 15/32
7/8	4 3/4	1-1 23/32	5 1/8	1-2 25/32	5 1/2	1-3 7/8	5 7/8	1-4 15/16	6 1/4	1-6
15/16	4 25/32	1-1 25/32	5 5/32	1-2 7/8	5 17/32	1-3 15/16	5 29/32	1-5	6 1/4	1-6 1/16

In.	17″ Rise	Slope	18″ Rise	Slope	19″ Rise	Slope	20″ Rise	Slope	21″ Rise	Slope
0	6 9/32	1-6 1/8	6 21/32	1-7 3/32	7 1/16	1-8 1/4	7 13/32	1-9 5/32	7 3/4	1-10 3/8
1/16	6 5/16	1-6 3/16	6 11/16	1-7 1/4	7 1/16	1-8 5/16	7 13/32	1-9 3/8	7 25/32	1-10 15/32
1/8	6 11/32	1-6 1/4	6 11/16	1-7 5/16	7 3/32	1-8 13/32	7 7/16	1-9 15/32	7 13/16	1-10 17/32
3/16	6 11/32	1-6 5/16	6 23/32	1-7 13/32	7 3/32	1-8 15/32	7 15/32	1-9 17/32	7 27/32	1-10 19/32
1/4	6 3/8	1-6 13/32	6 3/4	1-7 15/32	7 1/8	1-8 17/32	7 1/2	1-9 19/32	7 27/32	1-10 21/32
5/16	6 13/32	1-6 15/32	6 25/32	1-7 17/32	7 5/32	1-8 19/32	7 1/2	1-9 21/32	7 7/8	1-10 23/32
3/8	6 7/16	1-6 17/32	6 25/32	1-7 19/32	7 5/32	1-8 21/32	7 17/32	1-9 23/32	7 29/32	1-10 25/32
7/16	6 7/16	1-6 19/32	6 13/16	1-7 21/32	7 3/16	1-8 23/32	7 9/16	1-9 25/32	7 15/16	1-10 27/32
1/2	6 15/32	1-6 21/32	6 27/32	1-7 23/32	7 7/32	1-8 25/32	7 19/32	1-9 27/32	7 15/16	1-10 15/16
9/16	6 1/2	1-6 23/32	6 7/8	1-7 25/32	7 7/32	1-8 27/32	7 19/32	1-9 15/16	7 31/32	1-11
5/8	6 17/32	1-6 25/32	6 7/8	1-7 27/32	7 1/4	1-8 15/16	7 5/8	1-10	8	1-11 1/16
11/16	6 17/32	1-6 27/32	6 29/32	1-7 15/16	7 9/32	1-9	7 21/32	1-10 1/16	8 1/32	1-11 1/8
3/4	6 9/16	1-6 15/16	6 15/16	1-8	7 5/16	1-9 1/16	7 11/16	1-10 1/8	8 1/32	1-11 3/16
13/16	6 19/32	1-7	6 31/32	1-8 1/16	7 5/16	1-9 1/8	7 11/16	1-10 3/16	8 1/16	1-11 1/4
7/8	6 5/8	1-7 1/16	6 31/32	1-8 1/8	7 11/32	1-9 3/16	7 23/32	1-10 1/4	8 3/32	1-11 5/16
15/16	6 5/8	1-7 1/8	7	1-8 3/16	7 3/8	1-9 1/4	7 3/4	1-10 5/16	8 1/8	1-11 3/8

Feet	40′ Rise	Slope	50′ Rise	Slope	60′ Rise	Slope	70′ Rise	Slope
0	14-9 1/2	42-7 25/32	18-5 7/8	53-3 23/32	22-2 1/4	63-11 21/32	25-10 5/8	74-7 19/32
1	15-1 15/16	43-8 9/16	18-10 5/8	54-4 1/2	22-6 11/16	65-0 7/16	26-3 1/16	75-8 3/8
2	15-6 3/8	44-9 11/32	19-2 3/4	55-5 5/16	22-11 1/8	66-1 1/4	26-7 1/2	76-9 3/16
3	15-10 13/16	45-10 5/32	19-7 3/16	56-6 3/32	23-3 9/16	67-2 1/32	26-11 15/16	77-9 31/32
4	16-3 1/4	46-10 15/16	19-11 5/8	57-6 7/8	23-8	68-2 27/32	27-4 3/8	78-10 25/32
5	16-7 11/16	47-11 3/4	20-4 1/16	58-7 11/16	24-0 7/16	69-3 5/8	27-8 13/16	79-11 9/16
6	17-0 1/8	49-0 17/32	20-8 1/2	59-8 15/32	24-4 7/8	70-4 13/32	28-1 1/4	81-0 11/32
7	17-4 9/16	50-1 5/16	21-0 15/16	60-9 9/32	24-9 5/16	71-5 7/32	28-5 11/16	82-1 5/32
8	17-9	51-2 1/8	21-5 3/8	61-10 1/16	25-1 3/4	72-6	28-10 1/8	83-1 15/16
9	18-1 7/16	52-2 29/32	21-9 13/16	62-10 27/32	25-6 3/16	73-6 13/16	29-2 9/16	84-2 3/4

natsin A=0.3468370040; natcos A=0.9379254196; nattan A=0.3697916666; natcot A=2.7042253521

Inches	0" Rise	0" Slope	1" Rise	1" Slope	2" Rise	2" Slope	3" Rise	3" Slope	4" Rise	4" Slope	5" Rise	5" Slope
0	0	0	3/8	1 1/16	3/4	2 1/8	1 1/8	3 7/32	1 1/2	4 9/32	1 7/8	5 11/32
1/16	1/32	1/16	13/32	1 1/8	25/32	2 3/16	1 5/32	3 9/32	1 17/32	4 11/32	1 29/32	5 13/32
1/8	1/16	1/8	7/16	1 3/16	13/16	2 9/32	1 3/16	3 11/32	1 9/16	4 13/32	1 15/16	5 15/32
3/16	1/16	3/16	7/16	1 9/32	13/16	2 11/32	1 3/16	3 13/32	1 9/16	4 15/32	1 15/16	5 17/32
1/4	3/32	9/32	15/32	1 11/32	27/32	2 13/32	1 7/32	3 15/32	1 19/32	4 17/32	1 31/32	5 19/32
5/16	1/8	11/32	1/2	1 13/32	7/8	2 15/32	1 1/4	3 17/32	1 5/8	4 19/32	2	5 11/16
3/8	1/8	13/32	1/2	1 15/32	7/8	2 17/32	1 1/4	3 19/32	1 5/8	4 11/16	2	5 3/4
7/16	5/32	15/32	17/32	1 17/32	29/32	2 19/32	1 9/32	3 21/32	1 21/32	4 3/4	2 1/32	5 13/16
1/2	3/16	17/32	9/16	1 19/32	15/16	2 21/32	1 5/16	3 3/4	1 11/16	4 13/16	2 1/16	5 7/8
9/16	7/32	19/32	9/16	1 21/32	31/32	2 3/4	1 11/32	3 13/16	1 23/32	4 7/8	2 3/32	5 15/16
5/8	7/32	21/32	5/8	1 3/4	1	2 13/16	1 3/8	3 7/8	1 3/4	4 15/16	2 1/8	6
11/16	1/4	23/32	5/8	1 13/16	1	2 7/8	1 3/8	3 15/16	1 3/4	5	2 1/8	6 1/16
3/4	9/32	13/16	21/32	1 7/8	1 1/32	2 15/16	1 13/32	4	1 25/32	5 1/16	2 5/32	6 5/32
13/16	5/16	7/8	11/16	1 15/16	1 1/16	3	1 7/16	4 1/16	1 13/16	5 1/8	2 3/16	6 7/32
7/8	5/16	15/16	11/16	2	1 1/16	3 1/16	1 7/16	4 1/8	1 13/16	5 7/32	2 3/16	6 9/32
15/16	11/32	1	23/32	2 1/16	1 3/32	3 1/8	1 15/32	4 7/32	1 27/32	5 9/32	2 7/32	6 11/32

Inches	6" Rise	6" Slope	7" Rise	7" Slope	8" Rise	8" Slope	9" Rise	9" Slope	10" Rise	10" Slope	11" Rise	11" Slope
0	2 1/4	6 13/32	2 5/8	7 15/32	3	8 17/32	3 3/8	9 5/8	3 3/4	10 11/16	4 1/8	11 3/4
1/16	2 9/32	6 15/32	2 21/32	7 17/32	3 1/32	8 5/8	3 13/32	9 11/16	3 25/32	10 3/4	4 5/32	11 13/16
1/8	2 5/16	6 17/32	2 11/16	7 5/8	3 1/16	8 11/16	3 7/16	9 3/4	3 13/16	10 13/16	4 3/16	11 7/8
3/16	2 5/16	6 19/32	2 11/16	7 11/16	3 1/16	8 3/4	3 7/16	9 13/16	3 13/16	10 7/8	4 3/16	11 15/16
1/4	2 11/32	6 11/16	2 23/32	7 3/4	3 3/32	8 13/16	3 15/32	9 7/8	3 27/32	10 15/16	4 7/32	1-0
5/16	2 3/8	6 3/4	2 3/4	7 13/16	3 1/8	8 7/8	3 1/2	9 15/16	3 7/8	11	4 1/4	1-0 3/32
3/8	2 3/8	6 13/16	2 3/4	7 7/8	3 1/8	8 15/16	3 1/2	10	3 7/8	11 3/32	4 1/4	1-0 5/32
7/16	2 13/32	6 7/8	2 25/32	7 15/16	3 5/32	9	3 17/32	10 3/32	3 29/32	11 5/32	4 9/32	1-0 7/32
1/2	2 7/16	6 15/16	2 13/16	8	3 3/16	9 1/16	3 9/16	10 5/32	3 15/16	11 7/32	4 5/16	1-0 9/32
9/16	2 15/32	7	2 27/32	8 1/16	3 7/32	9 5/32	3 19/32	10 7/32	3 31/32	11 9/32	4 11/32	1-0 11/32
5/8	2 1/2	7 1/16	2 7/8	8 5/32	3 1/4	9 7/32	3 5/8	10 9/32	4	11 11/32	4 3/8	1-0 13/32
11/16	2 1/2	7 5/32	2 7/8	8 7/32	3 1/4	9 9/32	3 5/8	10 11/32	4	11 13/32	4 3/8	1-0 15/32
3/4	2 17/32	7 7/32	2 29/32	8 9/32	3 9/32	9 11/32	3 21/32	10 13/32	4 1/32	11 15/32	4 13/32	1-0 9/32
13/16	2 9/16	7 9/32	2 15/16	8 11/32	3 5/16	9 13/32	3 11/16	10 15/32	4 1/16	11 9/16	4 7/16	1-0 5/8
7/8	2 9/16	7 11/32	2 15/16	8 13/32	3 5/16	9 15/32	3 11/16	10 17/32	4 1/16	11 5/8	4 7/16	1-0 11/16
15/16	2 19/32	7 13/32	2 31/32	8 15/32	3 11/32	9 17/32	3 23/32	10 5/8	4 3/32	11 11/16	4 15/32	1-0 3/4

Feet	0' Rise	0' Slope	10' Rise	10' Slope	20' Rise	20' Slope	30' Rise	30' Slope
0	0	0	3-9	10-8 5/32	7-6	21-4 5/16	11-3	32-0 15/32
1	4 1/2	1-0 13/32	4-1 1/2	11-8 5/32	7-10 1/2	22-5 1/8	11-7 1/2	33-1 9/32
2	9	2-1 5/32	4-6	12-9 25/32	8-3	23-5 15/16	12-0	34-2 1/8
3	1-1 1/2	3-2 7/16	4-10 1/2	13-10 19/32	8-7 1/2	24-6 25/32	12-4 1/2	35-2 15/16
4	1-6	4-3 1/4	5-3	14-11 7/16	9-0	25-7 19/32	12-9	36-3 3/4
5	1-10 1/2	5-4 3/32	5-7 1/2	16-0 1/4	9-4 1/2	26-8 13/32	13-1 1/2	37-4 9/16
6	2-3	6-4 29/32	6-0	17-1 1/16	9-9	27-9 7/32	13-6	38-5 3/8
7	2-7 1/2	7-5 25/32	6-4 1/2	18-1 7/8	10-1 1/2	28-10 1/32	13-10 1/2	39-6 3/16
8	3-0	8-6 17/32	6-9	19-2 11/16	10-6	29-10 27/32	14-3	40-7
9	3-4 1/2	9-7 11/32	7-1 1/2	20-3 1/2	10-10 1/2	30-11 21/32	14-7 1/2	41-7 13/16

A = 20° 33′ 22″; logsin A = 9.54546; logcos A = 9.97143; logtan A = 9.57403; logcot A = 0.42597

Ins.	12″ Rise	12″ Slope	13″ Rise	13″ Slope	14″ Rise	14″ Slope	15″ Rise	15″ Slope	16″ Rise	16″ Slope
0	4 1/2	1-0 13/16	4 7/8	1-1 7/8	5 1/4	1-2 15/16	5 5/8	1-4 1/32−	6	1-5 3/32−
1/16	4 17/32−	1-0 7/8	4 29/32−	1-1 15/16	5 9/32−	1-3 1/32−	5 21/32−	1-4 3/32−	6 1/32−	1-5 5/32−
1/8	4 9/16	1-0 15/16	4 15/16	1-2 1/32−	5 5/16	1-3 3/32−	5 11/16	1-4 5/32−	6 1/16	1-5 7/32
3/16	4 9/16	1-1 1/32−	4 15/16	1-2 3/32−	5 5/16	1-3 5/32−	5 11/16	1-4 7/32	6 1/16	1-5 9/32
1/4	4 19/32	1-1 3/32−	4 31/32	1-2 5/32−	5 11/32	1-3 7/32	5 23/32	1-4 9/32	6 3/32	1-5 11/32
5/16	4 5/8	1-1 5/32−	5	1-2 7/32−	5 3/8	1-3 9/32	5 3/4	1-4 11/32	6 1/8	1-5 13/32
3/8	4 5/8	1-1 7/32−	5	1-2 9/32	5 3/8	1-3 11/32	5 3/4	1-4 13/32	6 1/8	1-5 1/2
7/16	4 21/32	1-1 9/32	5 1/32	1-2 11/32	5 13/32	1-3 13/32	5 25/32	1-4 1/2	6 5/32	1-5 9/16
1/2	4 11/16	1-1 11/32	5 1/16	1-2 13/32	5 7/16	1-3 1/2	5 13/16	1-4 9/16	6 3/16	1-5 5/8
9/16	4 23/32−	1-1 13/32	5 3/32−	1-2 1/2	5 15/32−	1-3 9/16	5 27/32−	1-4 5/8	6 7/32−	1-5 11/16
5/8	4 3/4	1-1 15/32	5 1/8	1-2 9/16	5 1/2	1-3 5/8	5 7/8	1-4 11/16	6 1/4	1-5 3/4
11/16	4 3/4	1-1 9/16	5 1/8	1-2 5/8	5 1/2	1-3 11/16	5 7/8	1-4 3/4	6 1/4	1-5 13/16
3/4	4 25/32	1-1 5/8	5 5/32	1-2 11/16	5 17/32	1-3 3/4	5 29/32	1-4 13/16	6 9/32	1-5 7/8
13/16	4 13/16	1-1 11/16	5 3/16	1-2 3/4	5 9/16	1-3 13/16	5 15/16	1-4 7/8	6 5/16	1-5 31/32−
7/8	4 13/16	1-1 3/4	5 3/16	1-2 13/16	5 9/16	1-3 7/8	5 15/16	1-4 31/32−	6 5/16	1-6 1/32−
15/16	4 27/32	1-1 13/16	5 7/32	1-2 7/8	5 19/32	1-3 31/32−	5 31/32	1-5 1/32−	6 11/32	1-6 3/32−

Ins.	17″ Rise	17″ Slope	18″ Rise	18″ Slope	19″ Rise	19″ Slope	20″ Rise	20″ Slope	21″ Rise	21″ Slope
0	6 3/8	1-6 5/32−	6 3/4	1-7 7/32	7 1/8	1-8 9/32	7 1/2	1-9 3/8	7 7/8	1-10 7/16
1/16	6 13/32−	1-6 7/32	6 25/32−	1-7 9/32	7 5/32−	1-8 11/32	7 17/32−	1-9 7/16	7 29/32−	1-10 1/2
1/8	6 7/16	1-6 9/32	6 13/16	1-7 11/32	7 3/16	1-8 7/16	7 9/16	1-9 1/2	7 15/16	1-10 9/16
3/16	6 7/16	1-6 11/32	6 13/16	1-7 7/16	7 3/16	1-8 1/2	7 9/16	1-9 9/16	7 15/16	1-10 5/8
1/4	6 15/32	1-6 7/16	6 27/32	1-7 1/2	7 7/32	1-8 9/16	7 19/32	1-9 5/8	7 31/32	1-10 11/16
5/16	6 1/2	1-6 1/2	6 7/8	1-7 9/16	7 1/4	1-8 5/8	7 5/8	1-9 11/16	8	1-10 3/4
3/8	6 1/2	1-6 9/16	6 7/8	1-7 5/8	7 1/4	1-8 11/16	7 5/8	1-9 3/4	8	1-10 27/32−
7/16	6 17/32	1-6 5/8	6 29/32	1-7 11/16	7 9/32	1-8 3/4	7 21/32	1-9 13/16	8 1/32	1-10 29/32−
1/2	6 9/16	1-6 11/16	6 15/16	1-7 3/4	7 5/16	1-8 13/16	7 11/16	1-9 29/32−	8 1/16	1-10 31/32−
9/16	6 19/32−	1-6 3/4	6 31/32−	1-7 13/16	7 11/32−	1-8 29/32−	7 23/32−	1-9 31/32−	8 3/32−	1-11 1/32−
5/8	6 5/8	1-6 13/16	7	1-7 29/32−	7 3/8	1-8 31/32−	7 3/4	1-10 1/32−	8 1/8	1-11 3/32
11/16	6 5/8	1-6 7/8	7	1-7 31/32−	7 3/8	1-9 1/32−	7 3/4	1-10 3/32	8 1/8	1-11 5/32
3/4	6 21/32	1-6 31/32−	7 1/32	1-8 1/32−	7 13/32	1-9 3/32−	7 25/32	1-10 5/32	8 5/32	1-11 7/32
13/16	6 11/16	1-7 1/32−	7 1/16	1-8 3/32−	7 7/16	1-9 5/32	7 13/16	1-10 7/32	8 3/16	1-11 9/32
7/8	6 11/16	1-7 3/32−	7 1/16	1-8 5/32	7 7/16	1-9 7/32	7 13/16	1-10 9/32	8 3/16	1-11 3/8
15/16	6 23/32	1-7 5/32	7 3/32	1-8 7/32	7 15/32	1-9 9/32	7 27/32	1-10 3/8	8 7/32	1-11 7/16

Feet	40′ Rise	40′ Slope	50′ Rise	50′ Slope	60′ Rise	60′ Slope	70′ Rise	70′ Slope
0	15-0	42-8 5/8	18-9	53-4 13/16	22-6	64-0 31/32−	26-3	74-9 1/8
1	15-4 1/2	43-9 15/32−	19-1 1/2	54-5 5/8	22-10 1/2	65-1 25/32−	26-7 1/2	75-9 15/16
2	15-9	44-10 9/32−	19-6	55-6 7/16	23-3	66-2 19/32−	27-0	76-10 3/4
3	16-1 1/2	45-11 3/32−	19-10 1/2	56-7 1/4	23-7 1/2	67-3 13/32	27-4 1/2	77-11 9/16
4	16-6	46-11 29/32−	20-3	57-8 1/16	24-0	68-4 7/32	27-9	79-0 3/8
5	16-10 1/2	48-0 23/32	20-7 1/2	58-8 7/8	24-4 1/2	69-5 1/32	28-1 1/2	80-1 3/16
6	17-3	49-1 17/32	21-0	59-9 11/16	24-9	70-5 27/32	28-6	81-2 1/32−
7	17-7 1/2	50-2 11/32	21-4 1/2	60-10 1/2	25-1 1/2	71-6 11/16	28-10 1/2	82-2 27/32−
8	18-0	51-3 5/32	21-9	61-11 11/32−	25-6	72-7 1/2	29-3	83-3 21/32−
9	18-4 1/2	52-3 31/32	22-1 1/2	63-0 5/32−	25-10 1/2	73-8 5/16	29-7 1/2	84-4 15/32−

natsin A=0.3511234416; natcos A=0.9363291776; nattan A=0.3750000000; natcot A=2.6666666666

Inches	0" Rise	0" Slope	1" Rise	1" Slope	2" Rise	2" Slope	3" Rise	3" Slope	4" Rise	4" Slope	5" Rise	5" Slope
0	0	0	3/8	1 1/16	3/4	2 1/8	1 1/8	3 1/32	1 17/32	4 9/32	1 29/32	5 11/32
1/16	1/32	1/16	13/32	1 1/8	25/32	2 7/32	1 5/32	3 9/32	1 17/32	4 11/32	1 15/16	5 13/32
1/8	1/16	1/8	7/16	1 17/32	13/16	2 9/32	1 3/16	3 11/32	1 9/16	4 13/32	1 15/16	5 15/32
3/16	1/16	3/16	7/16	1 9/32	27/32	2 11/32	1 7/32	3 13/32	1 19/32	4 15/32	1 31/32	5 9/16
1/4	3/32	9/32	15/32	1 11/32	27/32	2 13/32	1 1/4	3 15/32	1 5/8	4 17/32	2	5 5/8
5/16	1/8	11/32	1/2	1 13/32	7/8	2 15/32	1 1/4	3 17/32	1 5/8	4 5/8	2 1/32	5 11/16
3/8	5/32	13/32	17/32	1 15/32	29/32	2 17/32	1 9/32	3 5/8	1 21/32	4 11/16	2 1/32	5 3/4
7/16	5/32	15/32	17/32	1 17/32	15/16	2 19/32	1 5/16	3 11/16	1 11/16	4 3/4	2 1/16	5 13/16
1/2	3/16	17/32	9/16	1 19/32	15/16	2 11/16	1 11/32	3 3/4	1 23/32	4 13/16	2 3/32	5 7/8
9/16	7/32	19/32	19/32	1 21/32	31/32	2 3/4	1 11/32	3 13/16	1 3/4	4 7/8	2 1/8	5 15/16
5/8	1/4	21/32	5/8	1 3/4	1	2 13/16	1 3/8	3 7/8	1 3/4	4 15/16	2 1/8	6 1/32
11/16	1/4	3/4	21/32	1 13/16	1 1/16	2 7/8	1 13/32	3 15/16	1 25/32	5	2 5/32	6 3/32
3/4	9/32	13/16	21/32	1 7/8	1 1/16	2 15/16	1 7/16	4	1 13/16	5 3/32	2 3/16	6 5/32
13/16	5/16	7/8	11/16	1 15/16	1 1/16	3	1 7/16	4 3/32	1 27/32	5 5/32	2 7/32	6 7/32
7/8	11/32	15/16	23/32	2	1 3/32	3 1/16	1 15/32	4 5/32	1 27/32	5 1/4	2 7/32	6 9/32
15/16	11/32	1	3/4	2 1/16	1 1/8	3 5/32	1 1/2	4 7/32	1 7/8	5 9/32	2 1/4	6 11/32

Inches	6" Rise	6" Slope	7" Rise	7" Slope	8" Rise	8" Slope	9" Rise	9" Slope	10" Rise	10" Slope	11" Rise	11" Slope
0	2 9/32	6 13/32	2 21/32	7 1/2	3 1/32	8 9/16	3 7/16	9 5/8	3 13/16	10 11/16	4 3/16	11 25/32
1/16	2 5/16	6 1/2	2 11/16	7 9/16	3 1/16	8 5/8	3 7/16	9 11/16	3 13/16	10 3/4	4 7/32	11 27/32
1/8	2 11/32	6 9/16	2 23/32	7 5/8	3 3/32	8 11/16	3 15/32	9 3/4	3 27/32	10 27/32	4 7/32	11 29/32
3/16	2 11/32	6 5/8	2 23/32	7 11/16	3 1/8	8 3/4	3 1/2	9 27/32	3 7/8	10 29/32	4 1/4	11 31/32
1/4	2 3/8	6 11/16	2 3/4	7 3/4	3 1/8	8 13/16	3 17/32	9 29/32	3 29/32	10 31/32	4 9/32	1-0 1/32
5/16	2 13/32	6 3/4	2 25/32	7 13/16	3 5/32	8 29/32	3 17/32	9 31/32	3 29/32	11 1/32	4 5/16	1-0 3/32
3/8	2 7/16	6 13/16	2 13/16	7 7/8	3 3/16	8 31/32	3 9/16	10 1/32	3 15/16	11 3/32	4 5/16	1-0 5/32
7/16	2 7/16	6 7/8	2 13/16	7 31/32	3 7/32	9 1/32	3 19/32	10 3/32	3 31/32	11 5/32	4 11/32	1-0 1/4
1/2	2 15/32	6 31/32	2 27/32	8 1/32	3 7/32	9 3/32	3 5/8	10 5/32	4	11 7/32	4 3/8	1-0 5/16
9/16	2 1/2	7 1/32	2 7/8	8 3/32	3 1/4	9 5/32	3 5/8	10 7/32	4 1/32	11 9/32	4 13/32	1-0 3/8
5/8	2 17/32	7 3/32	2 29/32	8 5/32	3 9/32	9 7/32	3 21/32	10 9/32	4 1/32	11 3/8	4 13/32	1-0 7/16
11/16	2 17/32	7 5/32	2 15/16	8 7/32	3 5/16	9 9/32	3 11/16	10 3/8	4 1/16	11 7/16	4 7/16	1-0 1/2
3/4	2 9/16	7 7/32	2 15/16	8 9/32	3 5/16	9 3/8	3 23/32	10 7/16	4 3/32	11 1/2	4 15/32	1-0 9/16
13/16	2 19/32	7 9/32	2 31/32	8 11/32	3 11/32	9 7/16	3 23/32	10 1/2	4 1/8	11 9/16	4 1/2	1-0 5/8
7/8	2 5/8	7 11/32	3	8 7/16	3 3/8	9 1/2	3 3/4	10 9/16	4 1/8	11 5/8	4 1/2	1-0 23/32
15/16	2 5/8	7 7/16	3 1/32	8 1/2	3 13/32	9 9/16	3 25/32	10 5/8	4 5/32	11 11/16	4 17/32	1-0 25/32

Feet	0' Rise	0' Slope	10' Rise	10' Slope	20' Rise	20' Slope	30' Rise	30' Slope
0	0	0	3-9 5/8	10-8 3/8	7-7 1/4	21-4 3/4	11-4 7/8	32-1 5/32
1	4 9/16	1-0 27/32	4-2 3/16	11-9 7/32	7-11 13/16	22-5 19/32	11-9 7/16	33-1 13/32
2	9 1/8	2-1 11/16	4-6 3/4	12-10 1/16	8-4 3/8	23-6 7/16	12-2	34-2 13/16
3	1-1 11/16	3-2 1/2	4-11 5/16	13-10 29/32	8-8 15/16	24-7 9/32	12-6 9/16	35-3 21/32
4	1-6 1/4	4-3 11/32	5-3 7/8	14-11 23/32	9-1 1/2	25-8 1/8	12-11 1/8	36-4 1/2
5	1-10 13/16	5-4 3/16	5-8 7/16	16-0 9/16	9-6 1/16	26-8 15/16	13-3 11/16	37-5 11/32
6	2-3 3/8	6-5 1/32	6-1	17-1 13/32	9-10 5/8	27-9 25/32	13-8 1/4	38-6 5/32
7	2-7 15/16	7-5 7/8	6-5 9/16	18-2 1/4	10-3 3/16	28-10 5/8	14-0 13/16	39-7
8	3-0 1/2	8-6 23/32	6-10 1/8	19-3 3/32	10-7 3/4	29-11 15/32	14-5 3/8	40-7 27/32
9	3-5 1/16	9-7 17/32	7-2 11/16	20-3 15/16	11-0 5/16	31-0 5/16	14-9 15/16	41-8 11/16

A = 20° 49' 02"; logsin A = 9.55070; logcos A = 9.97068; logtan A = 9.58002; logcot A = 0.41998

Ins.	12″ Rise	Slope	13″ Rise	Slope	14″ Rise	Slope	15″ Rise	Slope	16″ Rise	Slope
0	4 9/16	1-0 27/32	4 15/16	1-1 29/32	5 5/16	1-2 31/32	5 11/16	1-4 1/16	6 3/32	1-5 1/8
1/16	4 19/32	1-0 29/32	4 31/32	1-1 31/32	5 11/32	1-3 1/32	5 23/32	1-4 1/8	6 3/32	1-5 3/16
1/8	4 5/8	1-0 31/32	5	1-2 1/32	5 3/8	1-3 1/16	5 3/4	1-4 3/16	6 1/8	1-5 1/4
3/16	4 5/8	1-1 1/32	5	1-2 3/32	5 13/32	1-3 3/16	5 25/32	1-4 1/4	6 5/32	1-5 5/16
1/4	4 21/32	1-1 3/32	5 1/32	1-2 3/16	5 13/32	1-3 1/4	5 13/16	1-4 5/16	6 3/16	1-5 3/8
5/16	4 11/16	1-1 3/16	5 1/16	1-2 1/4	5 7/16	1-3 5/16	5 13/16	1-4 3/8	6 3/16	1-5 7/16
3/8	4 23/32	1-1 1/4	5 3/32	1-2 5/16	5 15/32	1-3 3/8	5 27/32	1-4 7/16	6 7/32	1-5 17/32
7/16	4 23/32	1-1 5/16	5 3/32	1-2 3/8	5 1/2	1-3 7/16	5 7/8	1-4 17/32	6 1/4	1-5 19/32
1/2	4 3/4	1-1 3/8	5 1/8	1-2 7/16	5 1/2	1-3 1/2	5 29/32	1-4 19/32	6 9/32	1-5 21/32
9/16	4 25/32	1-1 7/16	5 5/32	1-2 1/2	5 17/32	1-3 9/16	5 29/32	1-4 21/32	6 5/16	1-5 23/32
5/8	4 13/16	1-1 1/2	5 3/16	1-2 9/16	5 9/16	1-3 21/32	5 15/16	1-4 23/32	6 5/16	1-5 25/32
11/16	4 13/16	1-1 9/16	5 7/32	1-2 21/32	5 19/32	1-3 23/32	5 31/32	1-4 25/32	6 11/32	1-5 27/32
3/4	4 27/32	1-1 5/8	5 7/32	1-2 23/32	5 19/32	1-3 25/32	6	1-4 27/32	6 3/8	1-5 29/32
13/16	4 7/8	1-1 23/32	5 1/4	1-2 25/32	5 5/8	1-3 27/32	6	1-4 29/32	6 13/32	1-6
7/8	4 29/32	1-1 25/32	5 9/32	1-2 27/32	5 21/32	1-3 29/32	6 1/32	1-4 31/32	6 13/32	1-6 1/16
15/16	4 29/32	1-1 27/32	5 5/16	1-2 29/32	5 11/16	1-3 31/32	6 1/16	1-5 1/16	6 7/16	1-6 1/8

Ins.	17″ Rise	Slope	18″ Rise	Slope	19″ Rise	Slope	20″ Rise	Slope	21″ Rise	Slope
0	6 15/32	1-6 3/16	6 27/32	1-7 1/4	7 7/32	1-8 5/16	7 19/32	1-9 13/32	8	1-10 15/32
1/16	6 1/2	1-6 1/4	6 7/8	1-7 5/16	7 1/4	1-8 13/32	7 5/8	1-9 15/32	8	1-10 17/32
1/8	6 1/2	1-6 5/16	6 29/32	1-7 13/32	7 9/32	1-8 15/32	7 21/32	1-9 17/32	8 1/16	1-10 19/32
3/16	6 17/32	1-6 3/8	6 29/32	1-7 15/32	7 9/32	1-8 17/32	7 11/16	1-9 19/32	8 1/16	1-10 21/32
1/4	6 9/16	1-6 15/32	6 15/16	1-7 17/32	7 5/16	1-8 19/32	7 11/16	1-9 21/32	8 3/32	1-10 23/32
5/16	6 19/32	1-6 17/32	6 31/32	1-7 19/32	7 11/32	1-8 21/32	7 23/32	1-9 23/32	8 3/32	1-10 13/16
3/8	6 19/32	1-6 19/32	7	1-7 21/32	7 3/8	1-8 23/32	7 3/4	1-9 13/16	8 1/8	1-10 7/8
7/16	6 5/8	1-6 21/32	7	1-7 23/32	7 3/8	1-8 25/32	7 25/32	1-9 7/8	8 5/32	1-10 15/16
1/2	6 21/32	1-6 23/32	7 1/32	1-7 25/32	7 13/32	1-8 7/8	7 25/32	1-9 15/16	8 3/16	1-11
9/16	6 11/16	1-6 25/32	7 1/16	1-7 27/32	7 7/16	1-8 15/16	7 13/16	1-10	8 3/16	1-11 1/16
5/8	6 11/16	1-6 27/32	7 3/32	1-7 15/16	7 15/32	1-9	7 27/32	1-10 1/16	8 7/32	1-11 1/8
11/16	6 23/32	1-6 15/16	7 3/32	1-8	7 1/2	1-9 1/16	7 7/8	1-10 1/8	8 1/4	1-11 3/16
3/4	6 3/4	1-7	7 1/8	1-8 1/16	7 1/2	1-9 1/8	7 7/8	1-10 3/16	8 9/32	1-11 9/32
13/16	6 25/32	1-7 1/16	7 5/32	1-8 1/8	7 17/32	1-9 3/16	7 29/32	1-10 9/32	8 9/32	1-11 11/32
7/8	6 25/32	1-7 1/8	7 3/16	1-8 3/16	7 9/16	1-9 1/4	7 15/16	1-10 11/32	8 5/16	1-11 13/32
15/16	6 13/16	1-7 3/16	7 3/16	1-8 1/4	7 19/32	1-9 11/32	7 31/32	1-10 13/32	8 11/32	1-11 15/32

Feet	40′ Rise	Slope	50′ Rise	Slope	60′ Rise	Slope	70′ Rise	Slope
0	15-2 1/2	42-9 17/32	19-0 1/8	53-5 29/32	22-9 3/4	64-2 9/32	26-7 3/8	74-10 21/32
1	15-7 1/16	43-10 3/8	19-4 11/16	54-6 3/4	23-2 5/16	65-3 1/8	26-11 15/16	75-11 1/2
2	15-11 5/8	44-11 3/16	19-9 1/4	55-7 19/32	23-6 7/8	66-3 31/32	27-4 1/2	77-0 11/32
3	16-4 3/16	46-0 1/32	20-1 13/16	56-8 13/32	23-11 7/16	67-4 13/16	27-9 1/16	78-1 3/16
4	16-8 3/4	47-0 7/8	20-6 3/8	57-9 1/4	24-4	68-5 5/8	28-1 5/8	79-2 1/32
5	17-1 5/16	48-1 23/32	20-10 15/16	58-10 3/32	24-8 9/16	69-6 15/32	28-6 3/16	80-2 27/32
6	17-5 7/8	49-2 9/16	21-3 1/2	59-10 15/32	25-1 1/8	70-7 5/16	28-10 3/4	81-3 11/16
7	17-10 7/16	50-3 3/8	21-8 1/8	60-11 25/32	25-5 11/16	71-8 5/32	29-3 5/16	82-4 17/32
8	18-3	51-4 7/32	22-0 5/8	62-0 19/32	25-10 1/4	72-9	29-7 7/8	83-5 3/8
9	18-7 9/16	52-5 1/16	22-5 3/16	63-1 7/16	26-2 13/16	73-9 13/16	30-0 7/16	84-6 1/4

natsin A=0.3553879164; natcos A=0.9347189036; nattan A=0.3802083333; natcot A=2.6301369863

Inches	0" Rise	0" Slope	1" Rise	1" Slope	2" Rise	2" Slope	3" Rise	3" Slope	4" Rise	4" Slope	5" Rise	5" Slope
0	0	0	3/8	1 1/16	25/32	2 5/32	1 5/32	3 7/32	1 17/32	4 9/32	1 15/16	5 11/32
1/16	1/32	1/16	13/32	1 1/8	25/32	2 7/32	1 3/16	3 9/32	1 9/16	4 11/32	1 15/16	5 7/16
1/8	1/16	1/8	7/16	1 7/32	13/16	2 9/32	1 7/32	3 11/32	1 19/32	4 13/32	1 31/32	5 1/2
3/16	1/16	3/16	15/32	1 9/32	27/32	2 11/32	1 7/32	3 13/32	1 5/8	4 1/2	2	5 9/16
1/4	3/32	9/32	15/32	1 11/32	7/8	2 13/32	1 1/4	3 15/32	1 5/8	4 9/16	2 1/32	5 5/8
5/16	1/8	11/32	1/2	1 13/32	29/32	2 15/32	1 9/32	3 9/16	1 21/32	4 5/8	2 1/16	5 11/16
3/8	5/32	13/32	17/32	1 15/32	29/32	2 17/32	1 5/16	3 5/8	1 11/16	4 11/16	2 1/16	5 3/4
7/16	5/32	15/32	9/16	1 17/32	15/16	2 5/8	1 5/16	3 11/16	1 23/32	4 3/4	2 3/32	5 13/16
1/2	3/16	17/32	9/16	1 19/32	31/32	2 11/16	1 11/32	3 3/4	1 3/4	4 13/16	2 1/8	5 29/32
9/16	7/32	19/32	19/32	1 11/16	1	2 3/4	1 3/8	3 13/16	1 3/4	4 7/8	2 5/32	5 31/32
5/8	1/4	21/32	5/8	1 3/4	1	2 13/16	1 13/32	3 7/8	1 25/32	4 31/32	2 5/32	6 1/32
11/16	1/4	3/4	21/32	1 13/16	1 1/32	2 7/8	1 13/32	3 15/16	1 13/16	5 1/32	2 3/16	6 3/32
3/4	9/32	13/16	11/16	1 7/8	1 1/16	2 15/16	1 7/16	4 1/32	1 27/32	5 3/32	2 7/32	6 5/32
13/16	5/16	7/8	11/16	1 15/16	1 3/32	3	1 15/32	4 3/32	1 27/32	5 5/32	2 1/4	6 7/32
7/8	11/32	15/16	23/32	2	1 3/32	3 3/32	1 1/2	4 5/32	1 7/8	5 7/32	2 1/4	6 9/32
15/16	3/8	1	3/4	2 1/16	1 1/8	3 5/32	1 17/32	4 7/32	1 29/32	5 9/32	2 9/32	6 3/8

Inches	6" Rise	6" Slope	7" Rise	7" Slope	8" Rise	8" Slope	9" Rise	9" Slope	10" Rise	10" Slope	11" Rise	11" Slope
0	2 5/16	6 7/16	2 11/16	7 1/2	3 3/32	8 9/16	3 15/32	9 21/32	3 27/32	10 23/32	4 1/4	11 25/32
1/16	2 11/32	6 1/2	2 23/32	7 9/16	3 3/32	8 5/8	3 1/2	9 23/32	3 7/8	10 25/32	4 1/4	11 27/32
1/8	2 3/8	6 9/16	2 3/4	7 5/8	3 1/8	8 23/32	3 17/32	9 25/32	3 29/32	10 27/32	4 9/32	11 15/16
3/16	2 3/8	6 5/8	2 25/32	7 11/16	3 5/32	8 25/32	3 17/32	9 27/32	3 15/16	10 29/32	4 5/16	1-0
1/4	2 13/32	6 11/16	2 25/32	7 25/32	3 3/16	8 27/32	3 9/16	9 29/32	3 15/16	11	4 11/32	1-0 1/16
5/16	2 7/16	6 3/4	2 13/16	7 27/32	3 7/32	8 29/32	3 19/32	9 31/32	3 31/32	11 1/16	4 3/8	1-0 1/8
3/8	2 15/32	6 27/32	2 27/32	7 29/32	3 7/32	8 31/32	3 5/8	10 1/16	4	11 1/8	4 3/8	1-0 3/16
7/16	2 15/32	6 29/32	2 7/8	7 31/32	3 1/4	9 1/32	3 5/8	10 1/8	4 1/32	11 3/16	4 13/32	1-0 1/4
1/2	2 1/2	6 31/32	2 7/8	8 1/32	3 9/32	9 1/8	3 21/32	10 3/16	4 1/16	11 1/4	4 7/16	1-0 5/16
9/16	2 17/32	7 1/32	2 29/32	8 3/32	3 5/16	9 3/16	3 11/16	10 1/4	4 1/16	11 5/16	4 15/32	1-0 13/32
5/8	2 9/16	7 3/32	2 15/16	8 5/32	3 5/16	9 1/4	3 23/32	10 5/16	4 3/32	11 3/8	4 15/32	1-0 15/32
11/16	2 9/16	7 5/32	2 31/32	8 1/4	3 11/32	9 5/16	3 23/32	10 3/8	4 1/8	11 15/32	4 1/2	1-0 17/32
3/4	2 19/32	7 7/32	3	8 5/16	3 3/8	9 3/8	3 3/4	10 7/16	4 5/32	11 17/32	4 17/32	1-0 19/32
13/16	2 5/8	7 5/16	3	8 3/8	3 13/32	9 7/16	3 25/32	10 17/32	4 5/32	11 19/32	4 9/16	1-0 21/32
7/8	2 21/32	7 3/8	3 1/16	8 7/16	3 13/32	9 1/2	3 13/16	10 19/32	4 3/16	11 21/32	4 9/16	1-0 23/32
15/16	2 11/16	7 7/16	3 1/16	8 1/2	3 7/16	9 9/16	3 27/32	10 21/32	4 7/32	11 23/32	4 19/32	1-0 25/32

Feet	0' Rise	0' Slope	10' Rise	10' Slope	20' Rise	20' Slope	30' Rise	30' Slope
0	0	0	3-10 1/4	10-8 19/32	7-8 1/2	21-5 7/32	11-6 3/4	32-1 13/16
1	4 5/8	1-0 7/8	4-2 7/8	11-9 15/32	8-1 1/8	22-6 1/16	11-11 3/8	33-2 11/16
2	9 1/4	2-1 23/32	4-7 1/2	12-10 5/16	8-5 3/4	23-6 15/16	12-4	34-3 17/32
3	1-1 7/8	3-2 19/32	5-0 1/2	13-11 3/16	8-10 3/8	24-7 25/32	12-8 5/8	35-4 13/32
4	1-6 1/2	4-3 7/16	5-4 3/4	15-0 1/32	9-3	25-8 21/32	13-1 1/4	36-5 1/4
5	1-11 1/8	5-4 5/16	5-9 3/8	16-0 29/32	9-7 5/8	26-9 1/2	13-5 7/8	37-6 1/8
6	2-3 3/4	6-5 5/32	6-2	17-1 25/32	10-0 1/4	27-10 3/8	13-10 1/2	38-6 31/32
7	2-8 3/8	7-6 1/32	6-6 5/8	18-2 5/8	10-4 7/8	28-11 7/32	14-3 1/8	39-7 27/32
8	3-1	8-6 7/8	6-11 1/4	19-3 1/2	10-9 1/2	30-0 3/32	14-7 3/4	40-8 11/16
9	3-5 5/8	9-7 3/4	7-3 7/8	20-4 11/32	11-2 1/8	31-0 15/16	15-0 3/8	41-9 9/16

A = 21° 04′ 39″; logsin A = 9.55586; logcos A = 9.96993; logtan A = 9.58593; logcot A = 0.41407

Ins.	12" Rise	Slope	13" Rise	Slope	14" Rise	Slope	15" Rise	Slope	16" Rise	Slope
0	$4\frac{5}{8}$	$1\text{-}0\frac{7}{8}$	5	$1\text{-}1\frac{15}{16}$	$5\frac{13}{32}$	$1\text{-}3$	$5\frac{25}{32}$	$1\text{-}4\frac{1}{16}$	$6\frac{5}{32}$	$1\text{-}5\frac{5}{32}$
$\frac{1}{16}$	$4\frac{21}{32}$	$1\text{-}0\frac{15}{16}$	$5\frac{1}{32}$	$1\text{-}2$	$5\frac{13}{32}$	$1\text{-}3\frac{1}{16}$	$5\frac{13}{16}$	$1\text{-}4\frac{5}{32}$	$6\frac{3}{16}$	$1\text{-}5\frac{7}{32}$
$\frac{1}{8}$	$4\frac{11}{16}$	$1\text{-}1$	$5\frac{1}{16}$	$1\text{-}2\frac{1}{16}$	$5\frac{7}{16}$	$1\text{-}3\frac{1}{8}$	$5\frac{27}{32}$	$1\text{-}4\frac{7}{32}$	$6\frac{7}{32}$	$1\text{-}5\frac{9}{32}$
$\frac{3}{16}$	$4\frac{11}{16}$	$1\text{-}1\frac{1}{16}$	$5\frac{3}{32}$	$1\text{-}2\frac{1}{8}$	$5\frac{15}{32}$	$1\text{-}3\frac{7}{32}$	$5\frac{27}{32}$	$1\text{-}4\frac{9}{32}$	$6\frac{1}{4}$	$1\text{-}5\frac{11}{32}$
$\frac{1}{4}$	$4\frac{23}{32}$	$1\text{-}1\frac{1}{8}$	$5\frac{3}{32}$	$1\text{-}2\frac{3}{16}$	$5\frac{1}{2}$	$1\text{-}3\frac{9}{32}$	$5\frac{7}{8}$	$1\text{-}4\frac{11}{32}$	$6\frac{1}{4}$	$1\text{-}5\frac{13}{32}$
$\frac{5}{16}$	$4\frac{3}{4}$	$1\text{-}1\frac{3}{16}$	$5\frac{1}{8}$	$1\text{-}2\frac{9}{32}$	$5\frac{17}{32}$	$1\text{-}3\frac{11}{32}$	$5\frac{29}{32}$	$1\text{-}4\frac{13}{32}$	$6\frac{9}{32}$	$1\text{-}5\frac{15}{32}$
$\frac{3}{8}$	$4\frac{25}{32}$	$1\text{-}1\frac{1}{4}$	$5\frac{5}{32}$	$1\text{-}2\frac{11}{32}$	$5\frac{17}{32}$	$1\text{-}3\frac{13}{32}$	$5\frac{15}{16}$	$1\text{-}4\frac{15}{32}$	$6\frac{5}{16}$	$1\text{-}5\frac{9}{16}$
$\frac{7}{16}$	$4\frac{25}{32}$	$1\text{-}1\frac{11}{32}$	$5\frac{3}{16}$	$1\text{-}2\frac{13}{32}$	$5\frac{9}{16}$	$1\text{-}3\frac{15}{32}$	$5\frac{15}{16}$	$1\text{-}4\frac{17}{32}$	$6\frac{11}{32}$	$1\text{-}5\frac{5}{8}$
$\frac{1}{2}$	$4\frac{13}{16}$	$1\text{-}1\frac{13}{32}$	$5\frac{3}{16}$	$1\text{-}2\frac{15}{32}$	$5\frac{19}{32}$	$1\text{-}3\frac{17}{32}$	$5\frac{31}{32}$	$1\text{-}4\frac{5}{8}$	$6\frac{3}{8}$	$1\text{-}5\frac{11}{16}$
$\frac{9}{16}$	$4\frac{27}{32}$	$1\text{-}1\frac{15}{32}$	$5\frac{7}{32}$	$1\text{-}2\frac{17}{32}$	$5\frac{5}{8}$	$1\text{-}3\frac{19}{32}$	6	$1\text{-}4\frac{11}{16}$	$6\frac{3}{8}$	$1\text{-}5\frac{3}{4}$
$\frac{5}{8}$	$4\frac{7}{8}$	$1\text{-}1\frac{17}{32}$	$5\frac{1}{4}$	$1\text{-}2\frac{19}{32}$	$5\frac{5}{8}$	$1\text{-}3\frac{11}{16}$	$6\frac{1}{32}$	$1\text{-}4\frac{3}{4}$	$6\frac{13}{32}$	$1\text{-}5\frac{13}{16}$
$\frac{11}{16}$	$4\frac{7}{8}$	$1\text{-}1\frac{19}{32}$	$5\frac{9}{32}$	$1\text{-}2\frac{21}{32}$	$5\frac{21}{32}$	$1\text{-}3\frac{3}{4}$	$6\frac{1}{32}$	$1\text{-}4\frac{13}{16}$	$6\frac{7}{16}$	$1\text{-}5\frac{7}{8}$
$\frac{3}{4}$	$4\frac{29}{32}$	$1\text{-}1\frac{21}{32}$	$5\frac{5}{16}$	$1\text{-}2\frac{3}{4}$	$5\frac{11}{16}$	$1\text{-}3\frac{13}{16}$	$6\frac{1}{16}$	$1\text{-}4\frac{7}{8}$	$6\frac{15}{32}$	$1\text{-}5\frac{15}{16}$
$\frac{13}{16}$	$4\frac{15}{16}$	$1\text{-}1\frac{23}{32}$	$5\frac{5}{16}$	$1\text{-}2\frac{13}{16}$	$5\frac{23}{32}$	$1\text{-}3\frac{7}{8}$	$6\frac{3}{32}$	$1\text{-}4\frac{15}{16}$	$6\frac{15}{32}$	$1\text{-}6\frac{1}{32}$
$\frac{7}{8}$	$4\frac{31}{32}$	$1\text{-}1\frac{13}{16}$	$5\frac{11}{32}$	$1\text{-}2\frac{7}{8}$	$5\frac{23}{32}$	$1\text{-}3\frac{15}{16}$	$6\frac{1}{8}$	$1\text{-}5$	$6\frac{1}{2}$	$1\text{-}6\frac{3}{32}$
$\frac{15}{16}$	5	$1\text{-}1\frac{7}{8}$	$5\frac{3}{8}$	$1\text{-}2\frac{15}{16}$	$5\frac{3}{4}$	$1\text{-}4$	$6\frac{5}{32}$	$1\text{-}5\frac{3}{32}$	$6\frac{17}{32}$	$1\text{-}6\frac{5}{32}$

Ins.	17" Rise	Slope	18" Rise	Slope	19" Rise	Slope	20" Rise	Slope	21" Rise	Slope
0	$6\frac{9}{16}$	$1\text{-}6\frac{7}{32}$	$6\frac{15}{16}$	$1\text{-}7\frac{9}{32}$	$7\frac{5}{16}$	$1\text{-}8\frac{3}{8}$	$7\frac{23}{32}$	$1\text{-}9\frac{7}{16}$	$8\frac{3}{32}$	$1\text{-}10\frac{1}{2}$
$\frac{1}{16}$	$6\frac{9}{16}$	$1\text{-}6\frac{9}{32}$	$6\frac{31}{32}$	$1\text{-}7\frac{11}{32}$	$7\frac{11}{32}$	$1\text{-}8\frac{7}{16}$	$7\frac{23}{32}$	$1\text{-}9\frac{1}{2}$	$8\frac{1}{8}$	$1\text{-}10\frac{9}{16}$
$\frac{1}{8}$	$6\frac{19}{32}$	$1\text{-}6\frac{11}{32}$	7	$1\text{-}7\frac{7}{16}$	$7\frac{3}{8}$	$1\text{-}8\frac{1}{2}$	$7\frac{3}{4}$	$1\text{-}9\frac{9}{16}$	$8\frac{5}{32}$	$1\text{-}10\frac{5}{8}$
$\frac{3}{16}$	$6\frac{5}{8}$	$1\text{-}6\frac{13}{32}$	7	$1\text{-}7\frac{1}{2}$	$7\frac{13}{32}$	$1\text{-}8\frac{9}{16}$	$7\frac{25}{32}$	$1\text{-}9\frac{5}{8}$	$8\frac{5}{32}$	$1\text{-}10\frac{23}{32}$
$\frac{1}{4}$	$6\frac{21}{32}$	$1\text{-}6\frac{1}{2}$	$7\frac{1}{32}$	$1\text{-}7\frac{9}{16}$	$7\frac{13}{32}$	$1\text{-}8\frac{5}{8}$	$7\frac{13}{16}$	$1\text{-}9\frac{11}{16}$	$8\frac{3}{16}$	$1\text{-}10\frac{25}{32}$
$\frac{5}{16}$	$6\frac{11}{16}$	$1\text{-}6\frac{9}{16}$	$7\frac{1}{16}$	$1\text{-}7\frac{5}{8}$	$7\frac{7}{16}$	$1\text{-}8\frac{11}{16}$	$7\frac{27}{32}$	$1\text{-}9\frac{25}{32}$	$8\frac{7}{32}$	$1\text{-}10\frac{27}{32}$
$\frac{3}{8}$	$6\frac{11}{16}$	$1\text{-}6\frac{5}{8}$	$7\frac{3}{32}$	$1\text{-}7\frac{11}{16}$	$7\frac{15}{32}$	$1\text{-}8\frac{3}{4}$	$7\frac{27}{32}$	$1\text{-}9\frac{27}{32}$	$8\frac{1}{4}$	$1\text{-}10\frac{29}{32}$
$\frac{7}{16}$	$6\frac{23}{32}$	$1\text{-}6\frac{11}{16}$	$7\frac{3}{32}$	$1\text{-}7\frac{3}{4}$	$7\frac{1}{2}$	$1\text{-}8\frac{27}{32}$	$7\frac{7}{8}$	$1\text{-}9\frac{29}{32}$	$8\frac{1}{4}$	$1\text{-}10\frac{31}{32}$
$\frac{1}{2}$	$6\frac{3}{4}$	$1\text{-}6\frac{3}{4}$	$7\frac{1}{8}$	$1\text{-}7\frac{13}{16}$	$7\frac{1}{2}$	$1\text{-}8\frac{29}{32}$	$7\frac{29}{32}$	$1\text{-}9\frac{31}{32}$	$8\frac{9}{32}$	$1\text{-}11\frac{1}{32}$
$\frac{9}{16}$	$6\frac{25}{32}$	$1\text{-}6\frac{13}{16}$	$7\frac{5}{32}$	$1\text{-}7\frac{29}{32}$	$7\frac{17}{32}$	$1\text{-}8\frac{31}{32}$	$7\frac{15}{16}$	$1\text{-}10\frac{1}{32}$	$8\frac{5}{16}$	$1\text{-}11\frac{3}{32}$
$\frac{5}{8}$	$6\frac{25}{32}$	$1\text{-}6\frac{7}{8}$	$7\frac{3}{16}$	$1\text{-}7\frac{31}{32}$	$7\frac{9}{16}$	$1\text{-}9\frac{1}{32}$	$7\frac{15}{16}$	$1\text{-}10\frac{3}{32}$	$8\frac{11}{32}$	$1\text{-}11\frac{3}{16}$
$\frac{11}{16}$	$6\frac{13}{16}$	$1\text{-}6\frac{31}{32}$	$7\frac{3}{16}$	$1\text{-}8\frac{1}{32}$	$7\frac{19}{32}$	$1\text{-}9\frac{3}{32}$	$7\frac{31}{32}$	$1\text{-}10\frac{5}{32}$	$8\frac{11}{32}$	$1\text{-}11\frac{1}{4}$
$\frac{3}{4}$	$6\frac{27}{32}$	$1\text{-}7\frac{1}{32}$	$7\frac{7}{32}$	$1\text{-}8\frac{3}{32}$	$7\frac{5}{8}$	$1\text{-}9\frac{5}{32}$	8	$1\text{-}10\frac{1}{4}$	$8\frac{3}{8}$	$1\text{-}11\frac{5}{16}$
$\frac{13}{16}$	$6\frac{7}{8}$	$1\text{-}7\frac{3}{32}$	$7\frac{1}{4}$	$1\text{-}8\frac{5}{32}$	$7\frac{5}{8}$	$1\text{-}9\frac{7}{32}$	$8\frac{1}{32}$	$1\text{-}10\frac{5}{16}$	$8\frac{13}{32}$	$1\text{-}11\frac{3}{8}$
$\frac{7}{8}$	$6\frac{7}{8}$	$1\text{-}7\frac{5}{32}$	$7\frac{9}{32}$	$1\text{-}8\frac{7}{32}$	$7\frac{21}{32}$	$1\text{-}9\frac{5}{16}$	$8\frac{1}{32}$	$1\text{-}10\frac{3}{8}$	$8\frac{7}{16}$	$1\text{-}11\frac{7}{16}$
$\frac{15}{16}$	$6\frac{29}{32}$	$1\text{-}7\frac{7}{32}$	$7\frac{5}{16}$	$1\text{-}8\frac{9}{32}$	$7\frac{11}{16}$	$1\text{-}9\frac{3}{8}$	$8\frac{1}{16}$	$1\text{-}10\frac{7}{16}$	$8\frac{15}{32}$	$1\text{-}11\frac{1}{2}$

Feet	40' Rise	Slope	50' Rise	Slope	60' Rise	Slope	70' Rise	Slope
0	15-5	$42\text{-}10\frac{13}{32}$	$19\text{-}3\frac{1}{4}$	$53\text{-}7\frac{1}{32}$	$23\text{-}1\frac{1}{2}$	$64\text{-}3\frac{5}{8}$	$26\text{-}11\frac{3}{4}$	$75\text{-}0\frac{1}{32}$
1	$15\text{-}9\frac{5}{8}$	$43\text{-}11\frac{9}{32}$	$19\text{-}7\frac{1}{8}$	$54\text{-}7\frac{1}{8}$	$23\text{-}6\frac{1}{8}$	$65\text{-}4\frac{1}{2}$	$27\text{-}4\frac{3}{8}$	$76\text{-}1\frac{3}{32}$
2	$16\text{-}2\frac{1}{4}$	$45\text{-}0\frac{1}{8}$	$20\text{-}0\frac{1}{2}$	$55\text{-}8\frac{3}{4}$	$23\text{-}10\frac{3}{4}$	$66\text{-}5\frac{11}{32}$	27-9	$77\text{-}1\frac{15}{16}$
3	$16\text{-}6\frac{7}{8}$	46-1	$20\text{-}5\frac{1}{8}$	$56\text{-}9\frac{19}{32}$	$24\text{-}3\frac{3}{8}$	$67\text{-}6\frac{7}{32}$	$28\text{-}1\frac{5}{8}$	$78\text{-}2\frac{13}{16}$
4	$16\text{-}11\frac{1}{2}$	$47\text{-}1\frac{27}{32}$	$20\text{-}9\frac{3}{4}$	$57\text{-}10\frac{15}{32}$	24-8	$68\text{-}7\frac{1}{16}$	$28\text{-}6\frac{1}{4}$	$79\text{-}3\frac{21}{32}$
5	$17\text{-}4\frac{1}{8}$	$48\text{-}2\frac{23}{32}$	$21\text{-}2\frac{3}{8}$	$58\text{-}11\frac{5}{16}$	$25\text{-}0\frac{5}{8}$	$69\text{-}7\frac{15}{16}$	$28\text{-}10\frac{7}{8}$	$80\text{-}4\frac{17}{32}$
6	$17\text{-}8\frac{3}{4}$	$49\text{-}3\frac{19}{32}$	21-7	$60\text{-}0\frac{3}{16}$	$25\text{-}5\frac{1}{4}$	$70\text{-}8\frac{25}{32}$	$29\text{-}3\frac{1}{2}$	$81\text{-}5\frac{13}{32}$
7	$18\text{-}1\frac{3}{8}$	$50\text{-}4\frac{7}{16}$	$21\text{-}11\frac{5}{8}$	$61\text{-}1\frac{1}{32}$	$25\text{-}9\frac{7}{8}$	$71\text{-}9\frac{21}{32}$	$29\text{-}8\frac{1}{8}$	$82\text{-}6\frac{1}{4}$
8	18-6	$51\text{-}5\frac{5}{16}$	$22\text{-}4\frac{1}{4}$	$62\text{-}1\frac{29}{32}$	$26\text{-}2\frac{1}{2}$	$72\text{-}10\frac{1}{2}$	$30\text{-}0\frac{3}{4}$	$83\text{-}7\frac{1}{8}$
9	$18\text{-}10\frac{5}{8}$	$52\text{-}6\frac{5}{32}$	$22\text{-}8\frac{7}{8}$	$63\text{-}2\frac{3}{4}$	$26\text{-}7\frac{1}{8}$	$73\text{-}11\frac{3}{8}$	$30\text{-}5\frac{3}{8}$	$84\text{-}7\frac{31}{32}$

natsin A=0.3596303145; natcos A=0.9330948703; nattan A=0.3854166666; natcot A=2.5945945945

Inches	0" Rise	0" Slope	1" Rise	1" Slope	2" Rise	2" Slope	3" Rise	3" Slope	4" Rise	4" Slope	5" Rise	5" Slope
0	0	0	3/8	1 1/16	25/32	2 5/32	1 3/16	3 7/32	1 9/16	4 9/32	1 15/16	5 3/8
1/16	1/32	1/16	13/32	1 5/32	13/16	2 7/32	1 3/16	3 9/32	1 19/32	4 3/8	1 31/32	5 7/16
1/8	1/16	1/8	7/16	1 7/32	27/32	2 9/32	1 7/32	3 11/32	1 5/8	4 7/16	2	5 1/2
3/16	1/16	3/16	15/32	1 9/32	27/32	2 11/32	1 1/4	3 7/16	1 5/8	4 1/2	2 1/32	5 9/16
1/4	3/32	9/32	1/2	1 11/32	7/8	2 13/32	1 9/32	3 1/2	1 21/32	4 9/16	2 1/16	5 5/8
5/16	1/8	11/32	1/2	1 13/32	29/32	2 15/32	1 9/32	3 9/16	1 11/16	4 5/8	2 1/16	5 23/32
3/8	5/32	13/32	17/32	1 15/32	15/16	2 9/16	1 5/16	3 5/8	1 23/32	4 11/16	2 3/32	5 25/32
7/16	5/32	15/32	9/16	1 17/32	15/16	2 5/8	1 11/32	3 11/16	1 23/32	4 3/4	2 1/8	5 27/32
1/2	3/16	17/32	19/32	1 5/8	31/32	2 11/16	1 3/8	3 3/4	1 3/4	4 27/32	2 5/32	5 29/32
9/16	7/32	19/32	5/8	1 11/16	1	2 3/4	1 13/32	3 13/16	1 25/32	4 29/32	2 3/16	5 31/32
5/8	1/4	21/32	5/8	1 3/4	1 1/32	2 13/16	1 13/32	3 29/32	1 13/16	4 31/32	2 3/16	6 1/32
11/16	9/32	3/4	21/32	1 13/16	1 1/16	2 7/8	1 7/16	3 31/32	1 27/32	5 1/32	2 7/32	6 3/32
3/4	9/32	13/16	11/16	1 7/8	1 1/16	2 15/16	1 15/32	4 1/32	1 27/32	5 3/32	2 1/4	6 3/16
13/16	5/16	7/8	23/32	1 15/16	1 3/32	3 1/32	1 1/2	4 3/32	1 7/8	5 5/32	2 9/32	6 1/4
7/8	11/32	15/16	23/32	2	1 1/8	3 3/32	1 1/2	4 5/32	1 29/32	5 7/32	2 9/32	6 5/16
15/16	3/8	1	3/4	2 3/32	1 5/32	3 5/32	1 17/32	4 7/32	1 15/16	5 5/16	2 5/16	6 3/8

Inches	6" Rise	6" Slope	7" Rise	7" Slope	8" Rise	8" Slope	9" Rise	9" Slope	10" Rise	10" Slope	11" Rise	11" Slope
0	2 11/32	6 7/16	2 3/4	7 1/2	3 1/8	8 19/32	3 1/2	9 21/32	3 29/32	10 3/4	4 5/16	11 13/16
1/16	2 3/8	6 1/2	2 3/4	7 19/32	3 5/32	8 21/32	3 17/32	9 23/32	3 15/16	10 13/16	4 5/16	11 7/8
1/8	2 13/32	6 9/16	2 25/32	7 21/32	3 3/16	8 23/32	3 9/16	9 25/32	3 31/32	10 7/8	4 11/32	11 15/16
3/16	2 13/32	6 21/32	2 13/16	7 23/32	3 3/16	8 25/32	3 19/32	9 7/8	3 31/32	10 15/16	4 3/8	1-0
1/4	2 7/16	6 23/32	2 27/32	7 25/32	3 7/32	8 27/32	3 5/8	9 15/16	4	11	4 13/32	1-0 1/16
5/16	2 15/32	6 25/32	2 27/32	7 27/32	3 1/4	8 15/16	3 5/8	10	4 1/32	11 1/16	4 13/32	1-0 5/32
3/8	2 1/2	6 27/32	2 7/8	7 29/32	3 9/32	9	3 21/32	10 1/16	4 1/16	11 1/8	4 7/16	1-0 7/32
7/16	2 1/2	6 29/32	2 29/32	8	3 9/32	9 1/16	3 11/16	10 1/8	4 1/16	11 7/32	4 15/32	1-0 9/32
1/2	2 17/32	6 31/32	2 15/16	8 1/16	3 5/16	9 1/8	3 23/32	10 3/16	4 3/32	11 9/32	4 1/2	1-0 11/32
9/16	2 9/16	7 1/32	2 31/32	8 1/8	3 11/32	9 3/16	3 3/4	10 9/32	4 1/8	11 11/32	4 17/32	1-0 13/32
5/8	2 19/32	7 1/8	2 31/32	8 3/16	3 3/8	9 1/4	3 3/4	10 11/32	4 5/32	11 13/32	4 17/32	1-0 15/32
11/16	2 5/8	7 3/16	3	8 1/4	3 13/32	9 5/16	3 25/32	10 13/32	4 3/16	11 15/32	4 9/16	1-0 9/16
3/4	2 5/8	7 1/4	3 1/32	8 5/16	3 13/32	9 13/32	3 13/16	10 15/32	4 3/16	11 17/32	4 19/32	1-0 5/8
13/16	2 21/32	7 5/16	3 1/16	8 3/8	3 7/16	9 15/32	3 27/32	10 17/32	4 7/32	11 19/32	4 5/8	1-0 11/16
7/8	2 11/16	7 3/8	3 1/16	8 15/32	3 15/32	9 17/32	3 27/32	10 19/32	4 1/4	11 11/16	4 5/8	1-0 3/4
15/16	2 23/32	7 7/16	3 3/32	8 17/32	3 1/2	9 19/32	3 7/8	10 21/32	4 9/32	11 3/4	4 21/32	1-0 13/16

Feet	0' Rise	0' Slope	10' Rise	10' Slope	20' Rise	20' Slope	30' Rise	30' Slope
0	0	0	3-10 7/8	10-8 27/32	7-9 3/4	21-5 21/32	11-8 5/8	32-2 1/2
1	4 11/16	1-0 7/8	4-3 9/16	11-9 23/32	8-2 7/16	22-6 17/32	12-1 5/16	33-3 3/8
2	9 3/8	2-1 25/32	4-8 1/4	12-10 19/32	8-7 1/8	23-7 7/16	12-6	34-4 1/4
3	1-2 1/16	3-2 21/32	5-0 15/16	13-11 15/32	8-11 13/16	24-8 5/16	12-10 11/16	35-5 1/8
4	1-6 3/4	4-3 17/32	5-5 5/8	15-0 3/8	9-4 1/2	25-9 3/16	13-3 3/8	36-6 1/32
5	1-11 7/16	5-4 13/32	5-10 5/16	16-1 1/4	9-9 3/16	26-10 1/16	13-8 1/16	37-6 29/32
6	2-4 1/8	6-5 5/16	6-3	17-2 1/8	10-1 7/8	27-10 31/32	14-0 3/4	38-7 25/32
7	2-8 13/16	7-6 3/16	6-7 11/16	18-3	10-6 9/16	28-11 27/32	14-5 1/2	39-8 11/16
8	3-1 1/2	8-7 1/16	7-0 3/8	19-3 29/32	10-11 1/4	30-0 23/32	14-10 3/16	40-9 9/16
9	3-6 3/16	9-7 15/16	7-5 1/16	20-4 25/32	11-3 15/16	31-1 19/32	15-2 13/16	41-10 7/16

A = 21° 20′ 13″; logsin A = 9.55092; logcos A = 9.96916; logtan A = 9.59176; logcot A = 0.40824

Ins.	12″		13″		14″		15″		16″	
	Rise	Slope	Rise	Slope	Rise	Slope	Rise	Slope	Rise	Slope
0	4^{11}/$_{16}$	1-0^7/$_8$	5^1/$_{16}$	1-1^{31}/$_{32}$	5^{15}/$_{32}$	1-3^1/$_{32}$	5^7/$_8$	1-4^3/$_{32}$	6^1/$_4$	1-5^3/$_{16}$
^{1}/$_{16}$	4^{23}/$_{32}$	1-0^{15}/$_{16}$	5^3/$_{32}$	1-2^1/$_{32}$	5^1/$_2$	1-3^3/$_{32}$	5^7/$_8$	1-4^5/$_{32}$	6^9/$_{32}$	1-5^1/$_4$
^{1}/$_8$	4^3/$_4$	1-1^1/$_{32}$	5^1/$_8$	1-2^3/$_{32}$	5^{17}/$_{32}$	1-3^5/$_{32}$	5^{29}/$_{32}$	1-4^1/$_4$	6^5/$_{16}$	1-5^5/$_{16}$
^{3}/$_{16}$	4^3/$_4$	1-1^3/$_{32}$	5^5/$_{32}$	1-2^5/$_{32}$	5^{17}/$_{32}$	1-3^7/$_{32}$	5^{15}/$_{16}$	1-4^5/$_{16}$	6^5/$_{16}$	1-5^3/$_8$
^{1}/$_4$	4^{25}/$_{32}$	1-1^5/$_{32}$	5^3/$_{16}$	1-2^7/$_{32}$	5^9/$_{16}$	1-3^5/$_{16}$	5^{31}/$_{32}$	1-4^3/$_8$	6^{11}/$_{32}$	1-5^7/$_{16}$
^{5}/$_{16}$	4^{13}/$_{16}$	1-1^7/$_{32}$	5^3/$_{16}$	1-2^9/$_{32}$	5^{19}/$_{32}$	1-3^3/$_8$	5^{31}/$_{32}$	1-4^7/$_{16}$	6^3/$_8$	1-5^1/$_2$
^{3}/$_8$	4^{27}/$_{32}$	1-1^9/$_{32}$	5^7/$_{32}$	1-2^{11}/$_{32}$	5^5/$_8$	1-3^7/$_{16}$	6	1-4^1/$_2$	6^{13}/$_{32}$	1-5^{19}/$_{32}$
^{7}/$_{16}$	4^{27}/$_{32}$	1-1^{11}/$_{32}$	5^1/$_4$	1-2^7/$_{16}$	5^5/$_8$	1-3^1/$_2$	6^1/$_{32}$	1-4^9/$_{16}$	6^{13}/$_{32}$	1-5^{21}/$_{32}$
^{1}/$_2$	4^7/$_8$	1-1^{13}/$_{32}$	5^9/$_{32}$	1-2^1/$_2$	5^{21}/$_{32}$	1-3^9/$_{16}$	6^1/$_{16}$	1-4^5/$_8$	6^7/$_{16}$	1-5^{23}/$_{32}$
^{9}/$_{16}$	4^{29}/$_{32}$	1-1^1/$_2$	5^5/$_{16}$	1-2^9/$_{16}$	5^{11}/$_{16}$	1-3^5/$_8$	6^3/$_{32}$	1-4^{23}/$_{32}$	6^{15}/$_{32}$	1-5^{25}/$_{32}$
^{5}/$_8$	4^{15}/$_{16}$	1-1^9/$_{16}$	5^5/$_{16}$	1-2^5/$_8$	5^{23}/$_{32}$	1-3^{11}/$_{16}$	6^3/$_{32}$	1-4^{25}/$_{32}$	6^1/$_2$	1-5^{27}/$_{32}$
^{11}/$_{16}$	4^{31}/$_{32}$	1-1^5/$_8$	5^{11}/$_{32}$	1-2^{11}/$_{16}$	5^3/$_4$	1-3^{25}/$_{32}$	6^1/$_8$	1-4^{27}/$_{32}$	6^{17}/$_{32}$	1-5^{29}/$_{32}$
^{3}/$_4$	4^{31}/$_{32}$	1-1^{11}/$_{16}$	5^3/$_8$	1-2^3/$_4$	5^3/$_4$	1-3^{27}/$_{32}$	6^5/$_{32}$	1-4^{29}/$_{32}$	6^{17}/$_{32}$	1-5^{31}/$_{32}$
^{13}/$_{16}$	5	1-1^3/$_4$	5^{13}/$_{32}$	1-2^{27}/$_{32}$	5^{25}/$_{32}$	1-3^{29}/$_{32}$	6^5/$_{16}$	1-4^{31}/$_{32}$	6^9/$_{16}$	1-6^1/$_{16}$
^{7}/$_8$	5^1/$_{32}$	1-1^{13}/$_{16}$	5^{13}/$_{32}$	1-2^{29}/$_{32}$	5^{13}/$_{16}$	1-3^{31}/$_{32}$	6^3/$_8$	1-5^1/$_{32}$	6^{19}/$_{32}$	1-6^1/$_8$
^{15}/$_{16}$	5^1/$_{16}$	1-1^7/$_8$	5^7/$_{16}$	1-2^{31}/$_{32}$	5^{27}/$_{32}$	1-4^1/$_{32}$	6^7/$_{32}$	1-5^1/$_8$	6^5/$_8$	1-6^3/$_{16}$

Ins.	17″		18″		19″		20″		21″	
	Rise	Slope	Rise	Slope	Rise	Slope	Rise	Slope	Rise	Slope
0	6^5/$_8$	1-6^1/$_4$	7^1/$_{32}$	1-7^5/$_{16}$	7^7/$_{16}$	1-8^{13}/$_{32}$	7^{13}/$_{16}$	1-9^{15}/$_{32}$	8^3/$_{16}$	1-10^{17}/$_{32}$
^{1}/$_{16}$	6^{21}/$_{32}$	1-6^5/$_{16}$	7^1/$_{16}$	1-7^{13}/$_{32}$	7^7/$_{16}$	1-8^{15}/$_{32}$	7^{27}/$_{32}$	1-9^{17}/$_{32}$	8^7/$_{32}$	1-10^5/$_8$
^{1}/$_8$	6^{11}/$_{16}$	1-6^3/$_8$	7^3/$_{32}$	1-7^{15}/$_{32}$	7^{15}/$_{32}$	1-8^{17}/$_{32}$	7^7/$_8$	1-9^{19}/$_{32}$	8^1/$_4$	1-10^{11}/$_{16}$
^{3}/$_{16}$	6^{23}/$_{32}$	1-6^7/$_{16}$	7^3/$_8$	1-7^{17}/$_{32}$	7^1/$_2$	1-8^{19}/$_{32}$	7^7/$_8$	1-9^{11}/$_{16}$	8^9/$_{32}$	1-10^3/$_4$
^{1}/$_4$	6^3/$_4$	1-6^{17}/$_{32}$	7^1/$_8$	1-7^{19}/$_{32}$	7^{17}/$_{32}$	1-8^{21}/$_{32}$	7^{29}/$_{32}$	1-9^3/$_4$	8^5/$_{16}$	1-10^{13}/$_{16}$
^{5}/$_{16}$	6^3/$_4$	1-6^{19}/$_{32}$	7^1/$_8$	1-7^{21}/$_{32}$	7^{17}/$_{32}$	1-8^{23}/$_{32}$	7^{15}/$_{16}$	1-9^{13}/$_{16}$	8^5/$_{16}$	1-10^7/$_8$
^{3}/$_8$	6^{25}/$_{32}$	1-6^{21}/$_{32}$	7^3/$_{16}$	1-7^{23}/$_{32}$	7^9/$_{16}$	1-8^{13}/$_{16}$	7^{31}/$_{32}$	1-9^7/$_8$	8^{11}/$_{32}$	1-10^{15}/$_{16}$
^{7}/$_{16}$	6^{13}/$_{16}$	1-6^{23}/$_{32}$	7^3/$_{16}$	1-7^{25}/$_{32}$	7^{19}/$_{32}$	1-8^7/$_8$	7^{31}/$_{32}$	1-9^{15}/$_{16}$	8^3/$_8$	1-11
^{1}/$_2$	6^{27}/$_{32}$	1-6^{25}/$_{32}$	7^7/$_{32}$	1-7^7/$_8$	7^5/$_8$	1-8^{15}/$_{16}$	8	1-10	8^{13}/$_{32}$	1-11^3/$_{32}$
^{9}/$_{16}$	6^7/$_8$	1-6^{27}/$_{32}$	7^1/$_4$	1-7^{15}/$_{16}$	7^{21}/$_{32}$	1-9	8^1/$_{32}$	1-10^1/$_{16}$	8^7/$_{16}$	1-11^5/$_{32}$
^{5}/$_8$	6^7/$_8$	1-6^{15}/$_{16}$	7^9/$_{32}$	1-8	7^{21}/$_{32}$	1-9^1/$_{16}$	8^1/$_{16}$	1-10^5/$_{32}$	8^7/$_{16}$	1-11^7/$_{32}$
^{11}/$_{16}$	6^{29}/$_{32}$	1-7	7^5/$_{16}$	1-8^1/$_{16}$	7^{11}/$_{16}$	1-9^1/$_8$	8^3/$_{32}$	1-10^7/$_{32}$	8^{15}/$_{32}$	1-11^9/$_{32}$
^{3}/$_4$	6^{15}/$_{16}$	1-7^1/$_{16}$	7^5/$_{16}$	1-8^1/$_8$	7^{23}/$_{32}$	1-9^7/$_{32}$	8^3/$_{32}$	1-10^9/$_{32}$	8^1/$_2$	1-11^{11}/$_{32}$
^{13}/$_{16}$	6^{31}/$_{32}$	1-7^1/$_8$	7^{11}/$_{16}$	1-8^3/$_{16}$	7^3/$_4$	1-9^9/$_{32}$	8^1/$_8$	1-10^{11}/$_{32}$	8^{17}/$_{32}$	1-11^{13}/$_{32}$
^{7}/$_8$	6^{31}/$_{32}$	1-7^3/$_{16}$	7^3/$_8$	1-8^1/$_4$	7^3/$_4$	1-9^{11}/$_{32}$	8^5/$_{32}$	1-10^{13}/$_{32}$	8^{17}/$_{32}$	1-11^1/$_2$
^{15}/$_{16}$	7	1-7^1/$_4$	7^{13}/$_{16}$	1-8^{11}/$_{16}$	7^{25}/$_{32}$	1-9^{13}/$_{32}$	8^3/$_{16}$	1-10^{15}/$_{32}$	8^9/$_{16}$	1-11^9/$_{16}$

Feet	40′		50′		60′		70′	
	Rise	Slope	Rise	Slope	Rise	Slope	Rise	Slope
0	15-7^1/$_2$	42-11^5/$_{16}$	19-6^3/$_8$	53-8^5/$_{32}$	23-5^1/$_4$	64-4^{31}/$_{32}$	27-4^1/$_8$	75-1^{13}/$_{16}$
1	16-0^3/$_{16}$	44-0^7/$_{32}$	19-11^3/$_{16}$	54-9^1/$_{32}$	23-9^{15}/$_{16}$	65-5^7/$_8$	27-8^{13}/$_{16}$	76-2^{11}/$_{16}$
2	16-4^7/$_8$	45-1^3/$_{32}$	20-3^3/$_4$	55-9^{29}/$_{32}$	24-2^5/$_8$	66-6^3/$_4$	28-1^1/$_2$	77-3^{19}/$_{32}$
3	16-9^9/$_{16}$	46-1^{31}/$_{32}$	20-8^7/$_{16}$	56-10^{13}/$_{16}$	24-7^5/$_{16}$	67-7^5/$_8$	28-6^3/$_{16}$	78-4^{15}/$_{32}$
4	17-2^1/$_4$	47-2^{27}/$_{32}$	21-1^1/$_8$	57-11^{11}/$_{16}$	25-0	68-8^1/$_2$	28-10^7/$_8$	79-5^{11}/$_{32}$
5	17-6^{15}/$_{16}$	48-3^3/$_4$	21-5^{13}/$_{16}$	59-0^9/$_{16}$	25-4^{11}/$_{16}$	69-9^{13}/$_{32}$	29-3^9/$_{16}$	80-6^7/$_{32}$
6	17-11^5/$_8$	49-4^5/$_8$	21-10^1/$_2$	60-1^7/$_{16}$	25-9^3/$_8$	70-10^9/$_{32}$	29-8^1/$_4$	81-7^1/$_8$
7	18-4^5/$_{16}$	50-5^1/$_2$	22-3^3/$_{16}$	61-2^{11}/$_{32}$	26-2^1/$_{16}$	71-11^5/$_{32}$	30-0^{15}/$_{16}$	82-8
8	18-9	51-6^3/$_8$	22-7^7/$_8$	62-3^7/$_{32}$	26-6^3/$_4$	73-0^1/$_{32}$	30-5^5/$_8$	83-8^7/$_8$
9	19-1^{11}/$_{16}$	52-7^9/$_{32}$	23-0^9/$_{16}$	63-4^3/$_{32}$	26-11^7/$_{16}$	74-0^{15}/$_{16}$	30-10^5/$_{16}$	84-9^3/$_4$

natsin A=0.3638505271; natcos A=0.9314573494; nattan A=0.3906250000; natcot A=2.5600000000

Inches	0" Rise	0" Slope	1" Rise	1" Slope	2" Rise	2" Slope	3" Rise	3" Slope	4" Rise	4" Slope	5" Rise	5" Slope
0	0	0	13/32	1 1/16	25/32	2 5/32	1 3/16	3 7/32	1 19/32	4 5/16	1 31/32	5 3/8
1/16	1/32	1/16	13/32	1 5/32	13/16	2 7/32	1 7/32	3 9/32	1 19/32	4 3/8	2	5 7/16
1/8	1/16	1/8	7/16	1 7/32	27/32	2 9/32	1 1/4	3 3/8	1 5/8	4 7/16	2 1/32	5 1/2
3/16	1/16	3/16	15/32	1 9/32	7/8	2 11/32	1 1/4	3 7/16	1 21/32	4 1/2	2 1/16	5 19/32
1/4	3/32	9/32	1/2	1 11/32	7/8	2 13/32	1 9/32	3 1/2	1 11/16	4 9/16	2 1/16	5 21/32
5/16	1/8	11/32	17/32	1 13/32	29/32	2 1/2	1 5/16	3 9/16	1 23/32	4 5/8	2 3/32	5 23/32
3/8	5/32	13/32	17/32	1 15/32	15/16	2 5/8	1 11/32	3 5/8	1 23/32	4 23/32	2 1/8	5 25/32
7/16	3/16	15/32	9/16	1 17/32	31/32	2 5/8	1 3/8	3 11/16	1 3/4	4 25/32	2 5/32	5 27/32
1/2	3/16	17/32	19/32	1 5/8	1	2 11/32	1 3/8	3 3/4	1 25/32	4 27/32	2 3/16	5 29/32
9/16	7/32	19/32	5/8	1 11/16	1	2 3/4	1 13/32	3 27/32	1 13/16	4 29/32	2 3/16	5 31/32
5/8	1/4	11/16	21/32	1 3/4	1 1/32	2 13/16	1 7/16	3 29/32	1 27/32	4 31/32	2 7/32	6 1/16
11/16	9/32	3/4	21/32	1 13/16	1 1/16	2 29/32	1 15/32	3 31/32	1 27/32	5 1/32	2 1/4	6 1/8
3/4	5/16	13/16	11/16	1 7/8	1 3/32	2 31/32	1 1/2	4 1/16	1 7/8	5 3/32	2 9/32	6 3/16
13/16	5/16	7/8	23/32	1 15/16	1 1/8	3 1/32	1 1/2	4 3/32	1 29/32	5 3/16	2 5/16	6 1/4
7/8	11/32	15/16	3/4	2 1/32	1 1/8	3 3/32	1 17/32	4 5/32	1 15/16	5 1/4	2 5/16	6 5/16
15/16	3/8	1	25/32	2 3/32	1 5/32	3 3/32	1 9/16	4 1/4	1 31/32	5 5/16	2 11/32	6 3/8

Inches	6" Rise	6" Slope	7" Rise	7" Slope	8" Rise	8" Slope	9" Rise	9" Slope	10" Rise	10" Slope	11" Rise	11" Slope
0	2 3/8	6 7/16	2 25/32	7 17/32	3 5/32	8 19/32	3 9/16	9 11/16	3 31/32	10 3/4	4 11/32	11 27/32
1/16	2 13/32	6 17/32	2 25/32	7 19/32	3 3/16	8 21/32	3 19/32	9 3/4	3 31/32	10 13/16	4 3/8	11 29/32
1/8	2 7/16	6 19/32	2 13/16	7 21/32	3 7/32	8 3/4	3 5/8	9 13/16	4	10 7/8	4 13/32	11 31/32
3/16	2 7/16	6 21/32	2 27/32	7 23/32	3 1/4	8 13/16	3 5/8	9 7/8	4 1/32	10 31/32	4 7/16	1-0 1/32
1/4	2 15/32	6 23/32	2 7/8	7 13/16	3 1/4	8 7/8	3 21/32	9 15/16	4 1/16	11 1/32	4 7/16	1-0 3/32
5/16	2 1/2	6 25/32	2 29/32	7 7/8	3 9/32	8 15/16	3 11/16	10	4 3/32	11 3/32	4 15/32	1-0 5/32
3/8	2 17/32	6 27/32	2 29/32	7 15/16	3 5/16	9	3 23/32	10 3/32	4 3/32	11 5/32	4 1/2	1-0 7/32
7/16	2 9/16	6 15/16	2 15/16	8	3 11/32	9 1/16	3 3/4	10 5/32	4 1/8	11 7/32	4 17/32	1-0 5/16
1/2	2 9/16	7	2 31/32	8 1/16	3 3/8	9 5/32	3 3/4	10 7/32	4 5/32	11 9/32	4 9/16	1-0 3/8
9/16	2 19/32	7 1/16	3	8 1/8	3 3/8	9 7/32	3 25/32	10 9/32	4 3/16	11 3/8	4 9/16	1-0 7/16
5/8	2 5/8	7 1/8	3 1/32	8 3/16	3 13/32	9 9/32	3 13/16	10 11/32	4 7/32	11 7/16	4 19/32	1-0 1/2
11/16	2 21/32	7 3/16	3 1/32	8 9/32	3 7/16	9 11/32	3 27/32	10 13/32	4 7/32	11 1/2	4 5/8	1-0 9/16
3/4	2 11/16	7 1/4	3 1/16	8 11/32	3 15/32	9 13/32	3 7/8	10 1/2	4 1/4	11 9/16	4 21/32	1-0 5/8
13/16	2 11/16	7 5/16	3 3/32	8 13/32	3 1/2	9 15/32	3 7/8	10 9/16	4 9/32	11 5/8	4 11/16	1-0 23/32
7/8	2 23/32	7 13/32	3 1/8	8 15/32	3 1/2	9 17/32	3 29/32	10 5/8	4 5/16	11 11/16	4 11/16	1-0 25/32
15/16	2 3/4	7 15/32	3 5/32	8 17/32	3 17/32	9 5/8	3 15/16	10 11/16	4 11/32	11 3/4	4 23/32	1-0 27/32

Feet	0' Rise	0' Slope	10' Rise	10' Slope	20' Rise	20' Slope	30' Rise	30' Slope
0	0	0	3-11 1/2	10-9 1/16	7-11	21-6 1/8	11-10 1/2	32-3 3/16
1	4 3/4	1-0 29/32	4-4 1/4	11-9 31/32	8-3 3/4	22-7 1/32	12-3 1/4	33-4 3/32
2	9 1/2	2-1 13/16	4-9	12-10 7/8	8-8 1/2	23-7 15/16	12-8	34-5
3	1-2 1/4	3-2 23/32	5-1 3/4	13-11 25/32	9-1 1/4	24-8 27/32	13-0 3/4	35-5 29/32
4	1-7	4-3 5/8	5-6 1/2	15-0 11/16	9-6	25-9 3/4	13-5 1/2	36-6 13/16
5	1-11 3/4	5-4 17/32	5-11 1/4	16-1 19/32	9-10 3/4	26-10 21/32	13-10 1/4	37-7 23/32
6	2-4 1/2	6-5 7/16	6-4	17-2 1/2	10-3 1/2	27-11 9/16	14-3	38-8 5/8
7	2-9 1/4	7-6 11/32	6-8 3/4	18-3 13/32	10-8 1/4	29-0 15/32	14-7 3/4	39-9 17/32
8	3-2	8-7 1/4	7-1 1/2	19-4 5/16	11-1	30-1 3/8	15-0 1/2	40-10 7/16
9	3-6 3/4	9-8 5/32	7-6 1/4	20-5 1/2	11-5 3/4	31-2 9/32	15-5 1/4	41-11 11/32

A = 21° 35′ 43″; logsin A = 9.56591; logcos A = 9.96839; logtan A = 9.59751; logcot A = 0.40249

In.	Rise (12″)	Slope (12″)	Rise (13″)	Slope (13″)	Rise (14″)	Slope (14″)	Rise (15″)	Slope (15″)	Rise (16″)	Slope (16″)
0	$4\frac{3}{4}$	$1\text{-}0\frac{29}{32}$	$5\frac{5}{8}$	$1\text{-}1\frac{31}{32}$	$5\frac{17}{32}$	$1\text{-}3\frac{1}{16}$	$5\frac{15}{16}$	$1\text{-}4\frac{1}{8}$	$6\frac{11}{32}$	$1\text{-}5\frac{7}{32}$
1/16	$4\frac{25}{32}$	$1\text{-}0\frac{31}{32}$	$5\frac{5}{32}$	$1\text{-}2\frac{1}{16}$	$5\frac{9}{16}$	$1\text{-}3\frac{1}{8}$	$5\frac{31}{32}$	$1\text{-}4\frac{3}{16}$	$6\frac{11}{32}$	$1\text{-}5\frac{9}{32}$
1/8	$4\frac{13}{16}$	$1\text{-}1\frac{1}{32}$	$5\frac{3}{32}$	$1\text{-}2\frac{1}{8}$	$5\frac{19}{32}$	$1\text{-}3\frac{3}{16}$	6	$1\text{-}4\frac{9}{32}$	$6\frac{3}{8}$	$1\text{-}5\frac{11}{32}$
3/16	$4\frac{13}{16}$	$1\text{-}1\frac{3}{32}$	$5\frac{7}{32}$	$1\text{-}2\frac{3}{16}$	$5\frac{5}{8}$	$1\text{-}3\frac{1}{4}$	6	$1\text{-}4\frac{11}{32}$	$6\frac{13}{32}$	$1\text{-}5\frac{13}{32}$
1/4	$4\frac{27}{32}$	$1\text{-}1\frac{3}{16}$	$5\frac{1}{4}$	$1\text{-}2\frac{1}{4}$	$5\frac{5}{8}$	$1\text{-}3\frac{5}{32}$	$6\frac{1}{32}$	$1\text{-}4\frac{13}{32}$	$6\frac{7}{16}$	$1\text{-}5\frac{15}{32}$
5/16	$4\frac{7}{8}$	$1\text{-}1\frac{1}{4}$	$5\frac{9}{32}$	$1\text{-}2\frac{5}{16}$	$5\frac{21}{32}$	$1\text{-}3\frac{13}{32}$	$6\frac{1}{16}$	$1\text{-}4\frac{15}{32}$	$6\frac{15}{32}$	$1\text{-}5\frac{17}{32}$
3/8	$4\frac{29}{32}$	$1\text{-}1\frac{5}{16}$	$5\frac{9}{32}$	$1\text{-}2\frac{3}{8}$	$5\frac{11}{16}$	$1\text{-}3\frac{15}{32}$	$6\frac{3}{32}$	$1\text{-}4\frac{17}{32}$	$6\frac{15}{32}$	$1\text{-}5\frac{5}{8}$
7/16	$4\frac{15}{16}$	$1\text{-}1\frac{3}{8}$	$5\frac{5}{16}$	$1\text{-}2\frac{7}{16}$	$5\frac{23}{32}$	$1\text{-}3\frac{17}{32}$	$6\frac{1}{8}$	$1\text{-}4\frac{19}{32}$	$6\frac{1}{2}$	$1\text{-}5\frac{11}{16}$
1/2	$4\frac{15}{16}$	$1\text{-}1\frac{7}{16}$	$5\frac{11}{32}$	$1\text{-}2\frac{17}{32}$	$5\frac{3}{4}$	$1\text{-}3\frac{19}{32}$	$6\frac{1}{8}$	$1\text{-}4\frac{21}{32}$	$6\frac{17}{32}$	$1\text{-}5\frac{3}{4}$
9/16	$4\frac{31}{32}$	$1\text{-}1\frac{1}{2}$	$5\frac{3}{8}$	$1\text{-}2\frac{19}{32}$	$5\frac{3}{4}$	$1\text{-}3\frac{21}{32}$	$6\frac{5}{32}$	$1\text{-}4\frac{3}{4}$	$6\frac{9}{16}$	$1\text{-}5\frac{13}{16}$
5/8	5	$1\text{-}1\frac{9}{16}$	$5\frac{13}{32}$	$1\text{-}2\frac{21}{32}$	$5\frac{25}{32}$	$1\text{-}3\frac{23}{32}$	$6\frac{3}{16}$	$1\text{-}4\frac{13}{16}$	$6\frac{19}{32}$	$1\text{-}5\frac{7}{8}$
11/16	$5\frac{1}{32}$	$1\text{-}1\frac{21}{32}$	$5\frac{13}{32}$	$1\text{-}2\frac{23}{32}$	$5\frac{13}{16}$	$1\text{-}3\frac{25}{32}$	$6\frac{7}{32}$	$1\text{-}4\frac{7}{8}$	$6\frac{19}{32}$	$1\text{-}5\frac{15}{16}$
3/4	$5\frac{1}{16}$	$1\text{-}1\frac{23}{32}$	$5\frac{7}{16}$	$1\text{-}2\frac{25}{32}$	$5\frac{27}{32}$	$1\text{-}3\frac{7}{8}$	$6\frac{1}{4}$	$1\text{-}4\frac{15}{16}$	$6\frac{5}{8}$	$1\text{-}6$
13/16	$5\frac{1}{16}$	$1\text{-}1\frac{25}{32}$	$5\frac{15}{32}$	$1\text{-}2\frac{27}{32}$	$5\frac{7}{8}$	$1\text{-}3\frac{15}{16}$	$6\frac{1}{4}$	$1\text{-}5$	$6\frac{21}{32}$	$1\text{-}6\frac{3}{32}$
7/8	$5\frac{3}{32}$	$1\text{-}1\frac{27}{32}$	$5\frac{1}{2}$	$1\text{-}2\frac{15}{16}$	$5\frac{7}{8}$	$1\text{-}4$	$6\frac{9}{32}$	$1\text{-}5\frac{1}{16}$	$6\frac{11}{16}$	$1\text{-}6\frac{5}{32}$
15/16	$5\frac{1}{8}$	$1\text{-}1\frac{29}{32}$	$5\frac{17}{32}$	$1\text{-}3$	$5\frac{29}{32}$	$1\text{-}4\frac{1}{16}$	$6\frac{5}{16}$	$1\text{-}5\frac{5}{32}$	$6\frac{23}{32}$	$1\text{-}6\frac{7}{32}$

In.	Rise (17″)	Slope (17″)	Rise (18″)	Slope (18″)	Rise (19″)	Slope (19″)	Rise (20″)	Slope (20″)	Rise (21″)	Slope (21″)
0	$6\frac{23}{32}$	$1\text{-}6\frac{3}{8}$	$7\frac{1}{8}$	$1\text{-}7\frac{11}{32}$	$7\frac{17}{32}$	$1\text{-}8\frac{7}{16}$	$7\frac{29}{32}$	$1\text{-}9\frac{1}{2}$	$8\frac{5}{16}$	$1\text{-}10\frac{19}{32}$
1/16	$6\frac{3}{4}$	$1\text{-}6\frac{11}{32}$	$7\frac{5}{32}$	$1\text{-}7\frac{7}{16}$	$7\frac{17}{32}$	$1\text{-}8\frac{1}{2}$	$7\frac{15}{16}$	$1\text{-}9\frac{9}{16}$	$8\frac{11}{32}$	$1\text{-}10\frac{21}{32}$
1/8	$6\frac{25}{32}$	$1\text{-}6\frac{13}{32}$	$7\frac{3}{16}$	$1\text{-}7\frac{1}{2}$	$7\frac{9}{16}$	$1\text{-}8\frac{9}{16}$	$7\frac{31}{32}$	$1\text{-}9\frac{21}{32}$	$8\frac{3}{8}$	$1\text{-}10\frac{23}{32}$
3/16	$6\frac{13}{16}$	$1\text{-}6\frac{1}{2}$	$7\frac{3}{16}$	$1\text{-}7\frac{9}{16}$	$7\frac{19}{32}$	$1\text{-}8\frac{5}{8}$	8	$1\text{-}9\frac{23}{32}$	$8\frac{3}{8}$	$1\text{-}10\frac{25}{32}$
1/4	$6\frac{13}{16}$	$1\text{-}6\frac{9}{16}$	$7\frac{7}{32}$	$1\text{-}7\frac{5}{8}$	$7\frac{5}{8}$	$1\text{-}8\frac{23}{32}$	8	$1\text{-}9\frac{25}{32}$	$8\frac{13}{32}$	$1\text{-}10\frac{27}{32}$
5/16	$6\frac{27}{32}$	$1\text{-}6\frac{5}{8}$	$7\frac{1}{4}$	$1\text{-}7\frac{11}{16}$	$7\frac{21}{32}$	$1\text{-}8\frac{25}{32}$	$8\frac{1}{32}$	$1\text{-}9\frac{27}{32}$	$8\frac{7}{16}$	$1\text{-}10\frac{29}{32}$
3/8	$6\frac{7}{8}$	$1\text{-}6\frac{11}{32}$	$7\frac{9}{32}$	$1\text{-}7\frac{3}{4}$	$7\frac{11}{16}$	$1\text{-}8\frac{27}{32}$	$8\frac{1}{16}$	$1\text{-}9\frac{29}{32}$	$8\frac{15}{32}$	$1\text{-}11$
7/16	$6\frac{29}{32}$	$1\text{-}6\frac{3}{4}$	$7\frac{5}{16}$	$1\text{-}7\frac{21}{32}$	$7\frac{11}{16}$	$1\text{-}8\frac{29}{32}$	$8\frac{3}{32}$	$1\text{-}9\frac{31}{32}$	$8\frac{1}{2}$	$1\text{-}11\frac{1}{16}$
1/2	$6\frac{15}{16}$	$1\text{-}6\frac{7}{8}$	$7\frac{5}{16}$	$1\text{-}7\frac{29}{32}$	$7\frac{23}{32}$	$1\text{-}8\frac{31}{32}$	$8\frac{1}{8}$	$1\text{-}10\frac{1}{16}$	$8\frac{1}{2}$	$1\text{-}11\frac{1}{8}$
9/16	$6\frac{15}{16}$	$1\text{-}6\frac{7}{8}$	$7\frac{11}{32}$	$1\text{-}7\frac{31}{32}$	$7\frac{3}{4}$	$1\text{-}9\frac{1}{32}$	$8\frac{1}{8}$	$1\text{-}10\frac{1}{8}$	$8\frac{17}{32}$	$1\text{-}11\frac{3}{16}$
5/8	$6\frac{31}{32}$	$1\text{-}6\frac{31}{32}$	$7\frac{3}{8}$	$1\text{-}8\frac{1}{32}$	$7\frac{25}{32}$	$1\text{-}9\frac{3}{32}$	$8\frac{5}{32}$	$1\text{-}10\frac{3}{16}$	$8\frac{9}{16}$	$1\text{-}11\frac{1}{4}$
11/16	7	$1\text{-}7\frac{1}{32}$	$7\frac{13}{32}$	$1\text{-}8\frac{3}{32}$	$7\frac{25}{32}$	$1\text{-}9\frac{3}{16}$	$8\frac{3}{16}$	$1\text{-}10\frac{1}{4}$	$8\frac{19}{32}$	$1\text{-}11\frac{5}{16}$
3/4	$7\frac{1}{32}$	$1\text{-}7\frac{3}{32}$	$7\frac{7}{16}$	$1\text{-}8\frac{5}{32}$	$7\frac{13}{16}$	$1\text{-}9\frac{1}{4}$	$8\frac{7}{32}$	$1\text{-}10\frac{5}{16}$	$8\frac{5}{8}$	$1\text{-}11\frac{13}{32}$
13/16	$7\frac{1}{16}$	$1\text{-}7\frac{5}{32}$	$7\frac{7}{16}$	$1\text{-}8\frac{7}{32}$	$7\frac{27}{32}$	$1\text{-}9\frac{5}{16}$	$8\frac{1}{4}$	$1\text{-}10\frac{3}{8}$	$8\frac{5}{8}$	$1\text{-}11\frac{15}{32}$
7/8	$7\frac{1}{16}$	$1\text{-}7\frac{7}{32}$	$7\frac{15}{32}$	$1\text{-}8\frac{5}{16}$	$7\frac{7}{8}$	$1\text{-}9\frac{3}{8}$	$8\frac{1}{4}$	$1\text{-}10\frac{7}{16}$	$8\frac{21}{32}$	$1\text{-}11\frac{17}{32}$
15/16	$7\frac{3}{32}$	$1\text{-}7\frac{9}{32}$	$7\frac{1}{2}$	$1\text{-}8\frac{3}{8}$	$7\frac{29}{32}$	$1\text{-}9\frac{7}{16}$	$8\frac{9}{32}$	$1\text{-}10\frac{17}{32}$	$8\frac{11}{16}$	$1\text{-}11\frac{19}{32}$

Feet	Rise (40′)	Slope (40′)	Rise (50′)	Slope (50′)	Rise (60′)	Slope (60′)	Rise (70′)	Slope (70′)
0	15-10	$43\text{-}0\frac{1}{4}$	$19\text{-}9\frac{1}{2}$	$53\text{-}9\frac{9}{32}$	23-9	$64\text{-}6\frac{11}{32}$	$27\text{-}8\frac{1}{2}$	$75\text{-}3\frac{13}{32}$
1	$16\text{-}2\frac{3}{4}$	$44\text{-}1\frac{5}{32}$	$20\text{-}2\frac{1}{4}$	$54\text{-}10\frac{3}{16}$	$24\text{-}1\frac{3}{4}$	$65\text{-}7\frac{1}{4}$	$28\text{-}1\frac{1}{4}$	$76\text{-}4\frac{5}{16}$
2	$16\text{-}7\frac{1}{2}$	$45\text{-}2\frac{1}{16}$	20-7	$55\text{-}11\frac{3}{32}$	$24\text{-}6\frac{1}{2}$	$66\text{-}8\frac{5}{32}$	28-6	$77\text{-}5\frac{7}{32}$
3	$17\text{-}0\frac{1}{4}$	$46\text{-}2\frac{31}{32}$	$20\text{-}11\frac{3}{4}$	57-0	$24\text{-}11\frac{1}{4}$	$67\text{-}9\frac{1}{16}$	$28\text{-}10\frac{3}{4}$	$78\text{-}6\frac{1}{8}$
4	17-5	$47\text{-}3\frac{7}{8}$	$21\text{-}4\frac{1}{2}$	$58\text{-}0\frac{29}{32}$	25-4	$68\text{-}9\frac{31}{32}$	$29\text{-}3\frac{1}{2}$	$79\text{-}7\frac{1}{32}$
5	$17\text{-}9\frac{3}{4}$	$48\text{-}4\frac{25}{32}$	$21\text{-}9\frac{1}{4}$	$59\text{-}1\frac{13}{16}$	$25\text{-}8\frac{3}{4}$	$69\text{-}10\frac{7}{8}$	$29\text{-}8\frac{1}{4}$	$80\text{-}7\frac{15}{16}$
6	$18\text{-}2\frac{1}{2}$	$49\text{-}5\frac{21}{32}$	22-2	$60\text{-}2\frac{23}{32}$	$26\text{-}1\frac{1}{2}$	$70\text{-}11\frac{25}{32}$	30-1	$81\text{-}8\frac{27}{32}$
7	$18\text{-}7\frac{1}{4}$	$50\text{-}6\frac{9}{16}$	$22\text{-}6\frac{3}{4}$	$61\text{-}3\frac{5}{8}$	$26\text{-}6\frac{1}{4}$	$72\text{-}0\frac{11}{16}$	$30\text{-}5\frac{3}{4}$	$82\text{-}9\frac{3}{4}$
8	19-0	$51\text{-}7\frac{15}{32}$	$22\text{-}11\frac{1}{2}$	$62\text{-}4\frac{17}{32}$	26-11	$73\text{-}1\frac{19}{32}$	$30\text{-}10\frac{1}{2}$	$83\text{-}10\frac{21}{32}$
9	$19\text{-}4\frac{3}{4}$	$52\text{-}8\frac{3}{8}$	$23\text{-}4\frac{1}{4}$	$63\text{-}5\frac{7}{16}$	$27\text{-}3\frac{3}{4}$	$74\text{-}2\frac{1}{2}$	$31\text{-}3\frac{1}{4}$	$84\text{-}11\frac{9}{16}$

natsin A=0.3680484509; natcos A=0.9298066131; nattan A=0.3958333333; natcot A=2.5263157894

Inches	0" Rise	0" Slope	1" Rise	1" Slope	2" Rise	2" Slope	3" Rise	3" Slope	4" Rise	4" Slope	5" Rise	5" Slope
0	0	0	13/32	1 1/16	13/16	2 5/32	1 3/16	3 7/32	1 19/32	4 5/16	2	5 3/8
1/16	1/32	1/16	7/16	1 5/32	13/16	2 7/32	1 7/32	3 5/16	1 5/8	4 3/8	2 1/32	5 15/32
1/8	1/16	1/8	7/16	1 7/32	27/32	2 9/32	1 1/4	3 3/8	1 21/32	4 7/16	2 1/16	5 17/32
3/16	1/16	3/16	15/32	1 9/32	7/8	2 11/32	1 9/32	3 7/16	1 11/16	4 1/2	2 3/32	5 19/32
1/4	3/32	9/32	1/2	1 11/32	29/32	2 7/16	1 5/16	3 1/2	1 23/32	4 19/32	2 1/8	5 21/32
5/16	1/8	11/32	17/32	1 13/32	15/16	2 1/2	1 11/32	3 9/16	1 23/32	4 21/32	2 1/8	5 23/32
3/8	5/32	13/32	9/16	1 15/32	15/16	2 9/16	1 11/32	3 5/8	1 3/4	4 23/32	2 5/32	5 25/32
7/16	3/16	15/32	19/32	1 9/16	31/32	2 5/8	1 3/8	3 23/32	1 25/32	4 25/32	2 3/16	5 27/32
1/2	3/16	17/32	19/32	1 5/8	1	2 11/16	1 13/32	3 25/32	1 13/16	4 27/32	2 7/32	5 15/16
9/16	7/32	19/32	5/8	1 11/16	1 1/16	2 3/4	1 7/16	3 27/32	1 27/32	4 29/32	2 1/4	6
5/8	1/4	11/16	21/32	1 3/4	1 1/16	2 27/32	1 15/32	3 29/32	1 27/32	4 31/32	2 1/4	6 1/16
11/16	9/32	3/4	11/16	1 13/16	1 1/16	2 29/32	1 15/32	3 31/32	1 7/8	5 1/16	2 9/32	6 1/8
3/4	5/16	13/16	11/16	1 7/8	1 3/32	2 31/32	1 1/2	4 1/16	1 29/32	5 1/8	2 5/16	6 3/16
13/16	5/16	7/8	23/32	1 15/16	1 1/8	3 1/32	1 17/32	4 3/32	1 15/16	5 3/16	2 11/32	6 1/4
7/8	11/32	15/16	3/4	2 1/32	1 5/32	3 3/32	1 9/16	4 3/16	1 31/32	5 1/4	2 11/32	6 11/32
15/16	3/8	1	25/32	2 3/32	1 3/16	3 5/32	1 19/32	4 1/4	1 31/32	5 5/16	2 3/8	6 13/32

Inches	6" Rise	6" Slope	7" Rise	7" Slope	8" Rise	8" Slope	9" Rise	9" Slope	10" Rise	10" Slope	11" Rise	11" Slope
0	2 13/32	6 15/32	2 13/16	7 17/32	3 7/32	8 5/8	3 5/8	9 11/16	4	10 25/32	4 13/32	11 27/32
1/16	2 7/16	6 17/32	2 27/32	7 19/32	3 7/32	8 11/16	3 5/8	9 3/4	4 1/32	10 27/32	4 7/16	11 29/32
1/8	2 15/32	6 19/32	2 27/32	7 11/16	3 1/4	8 3/4	3 21/32	9 27/32	4 1/16	10 29/32	4 15/32	1-0
3/16	2 15/32	6 21/32	2 7/8	7 3/4	3 9/32	8 13/16	3 11/16	9 29/32	4 3/32	10 31/32	4 1/2	1-0 1/16
1/4	2 1/2	6 23/32	2 29/32	7 13/16	3 5/16	8 7/8	3 23/32	9 31/32	4 1/8	11 1/16	4 1/2	1-0 1/8
5/16	2 17/32	6 13/16	2 15/16	7 7/8	3 11/32	8 31/32	3 3/4	10 1/32	4 1/8	11 1/8	4 17/32	1-0 3/16
3/8	2 9/16	6 7/8	2 31/32	7 15/16	3 11/32	9 1/32	3 3/4	10 3/32	4 5/32	11 3/16	4 9/16	1-0 1/4
7/16	2 19/32	6 31/32	3	8	3 3/8	9 3/32	3 25/32	10 5/32	4 3/16	11 1/4	4 19/32	1-0 5/16
1/2	2 19/32	7	3	8 3/32	3 13/32	9 5/32	3 13/16	10 1/4	4 7/32	11 5/16	4 5/8	1-0 3/8
9/16	2 5/8	7 1/16	3 1/32	8 5/32	3 7/16	9 7/32	3 27/32	10 5/16	4 1/4	11 3/8	4 5/8	1-0 7/16
5/8	2 21/32	7 1/8	3 1/16	8 7/32	3 15/32	9 9/32	3 7/8	10 3/8	4 1/4	11 7/16	4 21/32	1-0 17/32
11/16	2 11/16	7 7/32	3 3/32	8 9/32	3 15/32	9 3/8	3 7/8	10 7/16	4 9/32	11 1/2	4 11/16	1-0 19/32
3/4	2 23/32	7 9/32	3 3/32	8 11/32	3 1/2	9 7/16	3 29/32	10 1/2	4 5/16	11 19/32	4 23/32	1-0 21/32
13/16	2 23/32	7 11/32	3 1/8	8 13/32	3 17/32	9 1/2	3 15/16	10 9/16	4 11/32	11 21/32	4 3/4	1-0 23/32
7/8	2 3/4	7 13/32	3 5/32	8 1/2	3 9/16	9 9/16	3 31/32	10 5/8	4 3/8	11 23/32	4 3/4	1-0 25/32
15/16	2 25/32	7 15/32	3 3/16	8 9/16	3 19/32	9 5/8	4	10 23/32	4 3/8	11 25/32	4 25/32	1-0 7/8

Feet	0' Rise	0' Slope	10' Rise	10' Slope	20' Rise	20' Slope	30' Rise	30' Slope
0	0	0	4-0 1/8	10-9 9/32	8-0 1/4	21-6 19/32	12-0 3/8	32-3 7/8
1	4 13/16	1-0 15/16	4-4 15/16	11-10 7/32	8-5 1/16	22-7 1/2	12-5 3/16	33-4 13/16
2	9 5/8	2-1 27/32	4-9 3/4	12-11 5/32	8-9 7/8	23-8 7/16	12-10	34-5 23/32
3	1-2 7/16	3-2 25/32	5-2 9/16	14-0 1/16	9-2 11/16	24-9 3/8	13-2 13/16	35-6 21/32
4	1-7 1/4	4-3 23/32	5-7 3/8	15-1	9-7 1/2	25-10 5/16	13-7 5/8	36-7 19/32
5	2-0 1/16	5-4 21/32	6-0 3/4	16-1 15/16	10-0 5/16	26-11 7/32	14-0 7/16	37-8 17/32
6	2-4 7/8	6-5 9/16	6-5	17-2 7/8	10-5 1/8	28-0 5/32	14-5 1/4	38-9 7/16
7	2-9 11/16	7-6 1/2	6-9 13/16	18-3 25/32	10-9 15/16	29-1 3/32	14-10 1/16	39-10 3/8
8	3-2 1/2	8-7 7/16	7-2 5/8	19-4 23/32	11-2 3/4	30-2	15-2 7/8	40-11 5/16
9	3-7 5/16	9-8 3/8	7-7 11/16	20-5 21/32	11-7 9/16	31-2 15/32	15-7 11/16	42-0 7/32

A = 21° 51' 10"; logsin A = 9.57080; logcos A = 9.96761; logtan A = 9.60319; logcot A = 0.39681

Ins.	12" Rise	12" Slope	13" Rise	13" Slope	14" Rise	14" Slope	15" Rise	15" Slope	16" Rise	16" Slope
0	4 13/16	1-0 15/16	5 7/32	1-2	5 5/8	1-3 3/32	6	1-4 5/32	6 13/32	1-5 1/4
1/16	4 27/32	1-1	5 1/4	1-2 1/32	5 5/8	1-3 5/32	6 1/32	1-4 7/32	6 7/16	1-5 5/16
1/8	4 7/8	1-1 1/16	5 1/4	1-2 5/32	5 21/32	1-3 7/32	6 1/16	1-4 9/32	6 15/32	1-5 3/8
3/16	4 7/8	1-1 1/8	5 9/32	1-2 7/32	5 11/16	1-3 9/32	6 3/32	1-4 3/8	6 1/2	1-5 7/16
1/4	4 29/32	1-1 3/16	5 5/16	1-2 9/32	5 23/32	1-3 11/32	6 1/8	1-4 7/16	6 17/32	1-5 1/2
5/16	4 15/16	1-1 9/32	5 11/32	1-2 11/32	5 3/4	1-3 13/32	6 5/32	1-4 1/2	6 17/32	1-5 9/16
3/8	4 31/32	1-1 11/32	5 3/8	1-2 13/32	5 3/4	1-3 1/2	6 5/32	1-4 9/16	6 9/16	1-5 21/32
7/16	5	1-1 13/32	5 3/8	1-2 15/32	5 25/32	1-3 9/16	6 3/16	1-4 5/8	6 19/32	1-5 23/32
1/2	5	1-1 15/32	5 13/32	1-2 17/32	5 13/16	1-3 5/8	6 7/32	1-4 11/16	6 5/8	1-5 25/32
9/16	5 1/32	1-1 17/32	5 7/16	1-2 5/8	5 27/32	1-3 11/16	6 1/4	1-4 25/32	6 21/32	1-5 27/32
5/8	5 1/16	1-1 19/32	5 15/32	1-2 11/16	5 7/8	1-3 3/4	6 9/32	1-4 27/32	6 21/32	1-5 29/32
11/16	5 3/32	1-1 21/32	5 1/2	1-2 3/4	5 7/8	1-3 13/16	6 9/32	1-4 29/32	6 11/16	1-5 31/32
3/4	5 1/8	1-1 3/4	5 1/2	1-2 13/16	5 29/32	1-3 29/32	6 5/16	1-4 31/32	6 23/32	1-6 1/32
13/16	5 1/8	1-1 13/16	5 17/32	1-2 7/8	5 15/16	1-3 31/32	6 11/32	1-5 1/32	6 3/4	1-6 1/8
7/8	5 5/32	1-1 7/8	5 9/16	1-2 15/16	5 31/32	1-4 1/32	6 3/8	1-5 3/32	6 25/32	1-6 3/16
15/16	5 3/16	1-1 15/16	5 19/32	1-3 1/32	6	1-4 3/32	6 13/32	1-5 5/32	6 25/32	1-6 1/4

Ins.	17" Rise	17" Slope	18" Rise	18" Slope	19" Rise	19" Slope	20" Rise	20" Slope	21" Rise	21" Slope
0	6 13/16	1-6 5/16	7 7/32	1-7 13/32	7 5/8	1-8 15/32	8 1/32	1-9 9/16	8 7/16	1-10 5/8
1/16	6 27/32	1-6 3/8	7 1/4	1-7 15/32	7 21/32	1-8 17/32	8 1/32	1-9 5/8	8 7/16	1-10 11/16
1/8	6 7/8	1-6 7/16	7 9/32	1-7 17/32	7 21/32	1-8 19/32	8 1/16	1-9 11/16	8 15/32	1-10 3/4
3/16	6 29/32	1-6 17/32	7 9/32	1-7 19/32	7 11/16	1-8 11/16	8 3/32	1-9 3/4	8 1/2	1-10 13/16
1/4	6 29/32	1-6 19/32	7 5/16	1-7 21/32	7 23/32	1-8 3/4	8 1/8	1-9 13/16	8 17/32	1-10 29/32
5/16	6 15/16	1-6 21/32	7 11/32	1-7 23/32	7 3/4	1-8 13/16	8 5/32	1-9 7/8	8 9/16	1-10 31/32
3/8	6 31/32	1-6 23/32	7 3/8	1-7 13/16	7 25/32	1-8 7/8	8 5/32	1-9 15/16	8 9/16	1-11 1/32
7/16	7	1-6 25/32	7 13/32	1-7 7/8	7 25/32	1-8 15/16	8 3/16	1-10 1/32	8 19/32	1-11 3/32
1/2	7 1/32	1-6 27/32	7 13/32	1-7 15/16	7 13/16	1-9	8 7/32	1-10 3/32	8 5/8	1-11 5/32
9/16	7 1/32	1-6 15/16	7 7/16	1-8	7 27/32	1-9 1/16	8 1/4	1-10 5/32	8 21/32	1-11 7/32
5/8	7 1/16	1-7	7 15/32	1-8 1/16	7 7/8	1-9 5/32	8 9/32	1-10 7/32	8 11/16	1-11 5/16
11/16	7 3/32	1-7 1/16	7 1/2	1-8 1/8	7 29/32	1-9 7/32	8 9/32	1-10 9/32	8 11/16	1-11 3/8
3/4	7 1/8	1-7 1/8	7 17/32	1-8 3/16	7 29/32	1-9 9/32	8 5/16	1-10 11/32	8 23/32	1-11 7/16
13/16	7 5/32	1-7 3/16	7 17/32	1-8 9/32	7 15/16	1-9 11/32	8 11/32	1-10 7/16	8 3/4	1-11 1/2
7/8	7 5/32	1-7 1/4	7 9/16	1-8 11/32	7 31/32	1-9 13/32	8 3/8	1-10 1/2	8 25/32	1-11 9/16
15/16	7 3/16	1-7 5/16	7 19/32	1-8 13/32	8	1-9 15/32	8 13/32	1-10 9/16	8 13/16	1-11 5/8

Feet	40' Rise	40' Slope	50' Rise	50' Slope	60' Rise	60' Slope	70' Rise	70' Slope
0	16-0 1/2	43-15 5/32	20-0 5/8	53-10 7/16	24-0 3/4	64-7 3/4	28-0 7/8	75-5 1/32
1	16-5 5/16	44-2 3/32	20-5 7/16	54-11 3/8	24-5 9/16	65-8 21/32	28-5 11/16	76-5 31/32
2	16-10 1/8	45-3 1/32	20-10 1/4	56-0 5/16	24-10 3/8	66-9 19/32	28-10 1/2	77-6 29/32
3	17-2 15/16	46-3 15/16	21-3 1/16	57-1 1/4	25-3 3/16	67-10 17/32	29-3 5/16	78-7 13/16
4	17-7 3/4	47-4 7/8	21-7 7/8	58-2 5/32	25-8	68-11 15/32	29-8 1/8	79-8 3/4
5	18-0 9/16	48-5 13/16	22-0 11/16	59-3 3/32	26-0 13/16	70-0 3/8	30-0 15/16	80-9 11/32
6	18-5 3/8	49-6 3/4	22-5 1/2	60-4 1/32	26-5 5/8	71-1 5/16	30-5 3/4	81-10 19/32
7	18-10 3/16	50-7 21/32	22-10 5/16	61-4 31/32	26-10 7/16	72-2 1/4	30-10 9/16	82-11 17/32
8	19-3	51-8 19/32	23-3 1/8	62-5 7/8	27-3 1/4	73-3 3/16	31-3 3/8	84-0 15/32
9	19-7 13/16	52-9 17/32	23-7 15/16	63-6 13/16	27-8 1/16	74-4 3/32	31-8 3/16	85-1 13/32

natsin A=0.3722239884; natcos A=0.9281429322; nattan A=0.4010416666; natcot A=2.4935064935

Inches	0" Rise	0" Slope	1" Rise	1" Slope	2" Rise	2" Slope	3" Rise	3" Slope	4" Rise	4" Slope	5" Rise	5" Slope
0	0	0	13/32	1 3/32	13/16	2 5/32	1 7/32	3 1/4	1 5/8	4 5/16	2 1/32	5 13/32
1/16	1/32	1/16	7/16	1 5/32	27/32	2 7/32	1 1/4	3 5/16	1 21/32	4 3/8	2 1/16	5 15/32
1/8	1/16	1/8	15/32	1 7/32	7/8	2 9/32	1 9/32	3 3/8	1 11/16	4 7/16	2 3/32	5 17/32
3/16	1/16	3/16	15/32	1 9/32	7/8	2 3/8	1 9/32	3 7/16	1 11/16	4 17/32	2 3/32	5 19/32
1/4	3/32	9/32	1/2	1 11/32	29/32	2 7/16	1 5/16	3 1/2	1 23/32	4 19/32	2 1/8	5 21/32
5/16	1/8	11/32	17/32	1 13/32	15/16	2 1/2	1 11/32	3 9/16	1 3/4	4 21/32	2 5/32	5 23/32
3/8	5/32	13/32	9/16	1 15/32	31/32	2 9/16	1 3/8	3 21/32	1 25/32	4 23/32	2 3/16	5 13/16
7/16	3/16	15/32	19/32	1 9/16	1	2 5/8	1 13/32	3 23/32	1 13/16	4 25/32	2 7/32	5 7/8
1/2	3/16	17/32	5/8	1 5/8	1	2 11/16	1 13/32	3 25/32	1 13/16	4 27/32	2 1/4	5 15/16
9/16	7/32	19/32	5/8	1 11/16	1 1/32	2 25/32	1 7/16	3 27/32	1 27/32	4 15/16	2 1/4	6
5/8	1/4	11/16	21/32	1 3/4	1 1/16	2 27/32	1 15/32	3 29/32	1 7/8	5	2 9/32	6 1/16
11/16	9/32	3/4	11/16	1 13/16	1 3/32	2 29/32	1 1/2	3 31/32	1 29/32	5 1/16	2 5/16	6 1/8
3/4	5/16	13/16	23/32	1 7/8	1 1/8	2 31/32	1 17/32	4 1/16	1 15/16	5 1/8	2 11/32	6 7/32
13/16	11/32	7/8	3/4	1 31/32	1 5/32	3 1/32	1 9/16	4 1/8	1 31/32	5 3/16	2 3/8	6 9/32
7/8	11/32	15/16	3/4	2 1/32	1 5/32	3 3/32	1 9/16	4 3/16	1 31/32	5 1/4	2 3/8	6 11/32
15/16	3/8	1	25/32	2 3/32	1 3/16	3 5/32	1 19/32	4 1/4	2	5 11/32	2 13/32	6 13/32

Inches	6" Rise	6" Slope	7" Rise	7" Slope	8" Rise	8" Slope	9" Rise	9" Slope	10" Rise	10" Slope	11" Rise	11" Slope
0	2 7/16	6 15/32	2 27/32	7 9/16	3 1/4	8 5/8	3 21/32	9 23/32	4 1/16	10 25/32	4 15/32	11 7/8
1/16	2 15/32	6 17/32	2 7/8	7 5/8	3 9/32	8 11/16	3 11/16	9 25/32	4 3/32	10 7/8	4 1/2	11 15/16
1/8	2 1/2	6 5/8	2 29/32	7 11/16	3 5/16	8 25/32	3 23/32	9 27/32	4 1/8	10 15/16	4 17/32	1-0
3/16	2 1/2	6 11/16	2 29/32	7 3/4	3 5/16	8 27/32	3 23/32	9 29/32	4 1/8	11	4 17/32	1-0 1/16
1/4	2 17/32	6 3/4	2 15/16	7 13/16	3 11/32	8 29/32	3 3/4	9 31/32	4 5/32	11 1/16	4 9/16	1-0 5/32
5/16	2 9/16	6 13/16	2 31/32	7 29/32	3 3/8	8 31/32	3 25/32	10 1/32	4 3/16	11 1/8	4 19/32	1-0 7/32
3/8	2 19/32	6 7/8	3	7 31/32	3 13/32	9 1/32	3 13/16	10 1/8	4 7/32	11 3/16	4 5/8	1-0 9/32
7/16	2 5/8	6 15/16	3 1/32	8 1/32	3 7/16	9 3/32	3 27/32	10 3/16	4 1/4	11 9/32	4 21/32	1-0 11/32
1/2	2 5/8	7 1/32	3 1/16	8 3/32	3 7/16	9 3/16	3 7/8	10 1/4	4 1/4	11 11/32	4 11/16	1-0 13/32
9/16	2 21/32	7 3/32	3 1/16	8 5/32	3 15/32	9 1/4	3 7/8	10 5/16	4 9/32	11 13/32	4 11/16	1-0 15/32
5/8	2 11/16	7 5/32	3 3/32	8 7/32	3 1/2	9 5/16	3 29/32	10 3/8	4 5/16	11 15/32	4 23/32	1-0 9/16
11/16	2 23/32	7 7/32	3 1/8	8 5/16	3 17/32	9 3/8	3 15/16	10 15/32	4 11/32	11 17/32	4 3/4	1-0 5/8
3/4	2 3/4	7 9/32	3 5/32	8 3/8	3 9/16	9 7/16	3 31/32	10 17/32	4 3/8	11 19/32	4 25/32	1-0 11/16
13/16	2 25/32	7 11/32	3 3/16	8 7/16	3 19/32	9 1/2	4	10 19/32	4 13/32	11 21/32	4 13/16	1-0 3/4
7/8	2 25/32	7 13/32	3 3/16	8 1/2	3 19/32	9 19/32	4	10 21/32	4 13/32	11 3/4	4 13/16	1-0 13/16
15/16	2 13/16	7 1/2	3 7/32	8 9/16	3 5/8	9 21/32	4 1/32	10 23/32	4 7/16	11 13/16	4 27/32	1-0 7/8

Feet	0' Rise	0' Slope	10' Rise	10' Slope	20' Rise	20' Slope	30' Rise	30' Slope
0	0	0	4-0 3/4	10-9 17/32	8-1 1/2	21-7 1/16	12-2 1/4	32-4 9/16
1	4 7/8	1-0 15/16	4-5 5/8	11-10 15/32	8-6 3/8	22-8	12-7 1/8	33-5 17/32
2	9 3/4	2-1 29/32	4-10 1/2	12-11 7/16	8-11 1/4	23-8 31/32	13-0	34-6 15/32
3	1-2 5/8	3-2 27/32	5-3 3/8	14-0 3/8	9-4 1/8	24-9 29/32	13-4 7/8	35-7 1/16
4	1-7 1/2	4-3 13/16	5-8 1/4	15-1 11/32	9-9	25-10 27/32	13-9 3/4	36-8 3/8
5	2-0 3/8	5-4 3/4	6-1 1/8	16-2 9/32	10-1 7/8	26-11 13/16	14-2 5/8	37-9 11/32
6	2-5 1/4	6-5 23/32	6-6	17-3 1/4	10-6 3/4	28-0 3/4	14-7 1/2	38-10 9/32
7	2-10 1/8	7-6 21/32	6-10 7/8	18-4 3/16	10-11 5/8	29-1 23/32	15-0 3/8	39-11 1/4
8	3-3	8-7 5/8	7-3 3/4	19-5 5/32	11-4 1/2	30-2 21/32	15-5 1/4	41-0 3/16
9	3-7 7/8	9-8 9/16	7-8 5/8	20-6 3/32	11-9 3/8	31-3 5/8	15-10 1/8	42-1 5/32

A = 22° 06′ 34″; logsin A = 9.57562; logcos A = 9.96683; logtan A = 9.60879; logcot A = 0.39121

12″ – 16″

In.	12″ Rise	12″ Slope	13″ Rise	13″ Slope	14″ Rise	14″ Slope	15″ Rise	15″ Slope	16″ Rise	16″ Slope
0	4 7/8	1-0 15/16	5 5/32	1-2 1/32	5 11/16	1-3 1/8	6 3/32	1-4 3/32	6 1/2	1-5 9/32
1/16	4 29/32	1-1 1/32	5 5/16	1-2 3/32	5 23/32	1-3 3/16	6 1/8	1-4 1/4	6 17/32	1-5 11/32
1/8	4 15/16	1-1 3/32	5 11/32	1-2 5/32	5 3/4	1-3 1/4	6 5/32	1-4 5/16	6 9/16	1-5 13/32
3/16	4 15/16	1-1 5/32	5 11/32	1-2 7/32	5 3/4	1-3 5/16	6 5/32	1-4 13/32	6 9/16	1-5 15/32
1/4	4 31/32	1-1 7/32	5 3/8	1-2 5/16	5 25/32	1-3 3/8	6 3/16	1-4 15/32	6 19/32	1-5 17/32
5/16	5	1-1 9/32	5 13/32	1-2 3/8	5 13/16	1-3 7/16	6 7/32	1-4 17/32	6 5/8	1-5 19/32
3/8	5 1/32	1-1 11/32	5 7/16	1-2 7/16	5 27/32	1-3 17/32	6 1/4	1-4 19/32	6 21/32	1-5 11/16
7/16	5 1/16	1-1 7/32	5 15/32	1-2 1/2	5 7/8	1-3 19/32	6 9/32	1-4 21/32	6 11/16	1-5 3/4
1/2	5 1/8	1-1 1/2	5 1/2	1-2 9/32	5 7/8	1-3 21/32	6 5/16	1-4 23/32	6 11/16	1-5 13/16
9/16	5 3/32	1-1 9/16	5 1/2	1-2 5/8	5 29/32	1-3 23/32	6 5/16	1-4 13/16	6 23/32	1-5 7/8
5/8	5 1/8	1-1 5/8	5 17/32	1-2 23/32	5 15/16	1-3 25/32	6 11/32	1-4 7/8	6 3/4	1-5 15/16
11/16	5 5/32	1-1 11/16	5 9/16	1-2 25/32	5 31/32	1-3 27/32	6 3/8	1-4 15/32	6 25/32	1-6
3/4	5 3/16	1-1 3/4	5 19/32	1-2 27/32	6	1-3 29/32	6 13/32	1-5	6 13/16	1-6 1/32
13/16	5 7/32	1-1 27/32	5 5/8	1-2 29/32	6 1/16	1-4	6 7/16	1-5 1/16	6 27/32	1-6 5/32
7/8	5 7/32	1-1 29/32	5 5/8	1-2 31/32	6 1/2	1-4 1/8	6 7/16	1-5 1/2	6 27/32	1-6 7/32
15/16	5 1/4	1-1 31/32	5 21/32	1-3 1/32	6 1/16	1-4 1/8	6 15/32	1-5 3/16	6 7/8	1-6 9/32

17″ – 21″

In.	17″ Rise	17″ Slope	18″ Rise	18″ Slope	19″ Rise	19″ Slope	20″ Rise	20″ Slope	21″ Rise	21″ Slope
0	6 29/32	1-6 11/32	7 5/16	1-7 7/16	7 23/32	1-8 1/2	8 1/8	1-9 19/32	8 17/32	1-10 21/32
1/16	6 15/16	1-6 13/32	7 11/32	1-7 1/2	7 3/4	1-8 9/16	8 5/32	1-9 21/32	8 9/16	1-10 23/32
1/8	6 31/32	1-6 15/32	7 3/8	1-7 9/16	7 25/32	1-8 21/32	8 3/16	1-9 23/32	8 19/32	1-10 13/16
3/16	6 31/32	1-6 9/16	7 3/8	1-7 5/8	7 25/32	1-8 23/32	8 3/16	1-9 25/32	8 19/32	1-10 7/8
1/4	7	1-6 5/8	7 13/32	1-7 11/32	7 13/16	1-8 25/32	8 7/32	1-9 27/32	8 5/8	1-10 15/16
5/16	7 1/32	1-6 11/16	7 7/16	1-7 25/32	7 27/32	1-8 27/32	8 1/4	1-9 15/32	8 21/32	1-11
3/8	7 1/16	1-6 3/4	7 15/32	1-7 27/32	7 7/8	1-8 29/32	8 9/32	1-10	8 11/16	1-11 1/16
7/16	7 3/32	1-6 13/16	7 1/2	1-7 29/32	7 29/32	1-8 31/32	8 5/16	1-10 1/16	8 23/32	1-11 1/8
1/2	7 1/8	1-6 7/8	7 1/2	1-7 31/32	7 15/16	1-9 1/16	8 5/16	1-10 1/8	8 3/4	1-11 7/32
9/16	7 1/8	1-6 31/32	7 17/32	1-8 1/2	7 15/16	1-9 1/8	8 11/32	1-10 3/16	8 3/4	1-11 9/32
5/8	7 5/32	1-7 1/32	7 9/16	1-8 3/8	7 31/32	1-9 3/16	8 3/8	1-10 1/4	8 25/32	1-11 11/32
11/16	7 3/16	1-7 3/32	7 9/16	1-8 5/16	8	1-9 1/4	8 13/32	1-10 11/32	8 13/16	1-11 13/32
3/4	7 7/32	1-7 5/32	7 5/8	1-8 1/4	8 1/8	1-9 5/16	8 7/16	1-10 13/32	8 27/32	1-11 15/32
13/16	7 1/4	1-7 7/32	7 21/32	1-8 5/16	8 1/16	1-9 3/8	8 15/32	1-10 15/32	8 7/8	1-11 17/32
7/8	7 1/4	1-7 9/32	7 21/32	1-8 3/8	8 1/16	1-9 7/16	8 15/32	1-10 17/32	8 7/8	1-11 5/8
15/16	7 9/32	1-7 3/8	7 11/16	1-8 7/16	8 3/32	1-9 17/32	8 1/2	1-10 19/32	8 29/32	1-11 11/16

40′ – 70′

Feet	40′ Rise	40′ Slope	50′ Rise	50′ Slope	60′ Rise	60′ Slope	70′ Rise	70′ Slope
0	16-3	43-2 3/32	20-3 3/4	53-11 5/8	24-4 1/2	64-9 5/32	28-5 1/4	75-6 21/32
1	16-7 7/8	44-3 1/16	20-8 5/8	55-0 9/16	24-9 3/8	65-10 3/32	28-10 1/8	76-7 5/8
2	17-0 3/4	45-4	21-1 1/2	56-1 17/32	25-2 1/4	66-11 1/16	29-3	77-8 9/16
3	17-5 5/8	46-4 31/32	21-6 3/8	57-2 15/32	25-7 1/8	68-0	29-7 7/8	78-9 17/32
4	17-10 1/2	47-5 29/32	21-11 1/4	58-3 7/16	26-0	69-0 31/32	30-0 3/4	79-10 15/32
5	18-3 3/8	48-6 7/8	22-4 1/8	59-4 3/8	26-4 7/8	70-1 29/32	30-5 5/8	80-11 7/16
6	18-8 1/4	49-7 13/16	22-9	60-5 11/32	26-9 3/4	71-2 7/8	30-10 1/2	82-0 3/8
7	19-1 1/8	50-8 3/4	23-1 7/8	61-6 9/32	27-2 5/8	72-3 13/16	31-3 3/8	83-1 11/16
8	19-6	51-9 23/32	23-6 3/4	62-7 1/4	27-7 1/2	73-4 25/32	31-8 1/4	84-2 9/32
9	19-10 7/8	52-10 21/32	23-11 5/8	63-8 3/16	28-0 3/8	74-5 23/32	32-1 1/8	85-3 1/4

natsin A=0.3763770469; natcos A=0.9264665770; nattan A=0.4062500000; natcot A=2.4615384615

Inches	0" Rise	0" Slope	1" Rise	1" Slope	2" Rise	2" Slope	3" Rise	3" Slope	4" Rise	4" Slope	5" Rise	5" Slope
0	0	0	13/32	13/32	13/16	25/32	1 1/4	3 1/4	1 21/32	4 5/16	2 1/16	5 13/32
1/16	1/32	1/16	7/16	15/32	27/32	27/32	1 1/4	3 5/16	1 21/32	4 13/32	2 3/32	5 15/32
1/8	1/16	1/8	15/32	17/32	7/8	2 5/16	1 9/32	3 3/8	1 11/16	4 15/32	2 3/32	5 17/32
3/16	1/16	3/16	1/2	19/32	29/32	2 3/8	1 5/16	3 7/16	1 23/32	4 17/32	2 1/8	5 5/8
1/4	3/32	9/32	1/2	1 11/32	15/16	2 7/16	1 11/32	3 1/2	1 3/4	4 19/32	2 5/32	5 11/16
5/16	1/8	11/32	17/32	1 13/32	15/16	2 1/2	1 3/8	3 19/32	1 25/32	4 21/32	2 3/16	5 3/4
3/8	5/32	3/8	9/16	1 1/2	31/32	2 9/16	1 3/8	3 21/32	1 13/16	4 23/32	2 7/32	5 13/16
7/16	3/16	15/32	19/32	1 9/16	1	2 5/8	1 13/32	3 23/32	1 13/16	4 13/16	2 1/4	5 7/8
1/2	7/32	17/32	5/8	1 5/8	1 1/32	2 23/32	1 7/16	3 25/32	1 27/32	4 7/8	2 1/4	5 15/32
9/16	7/32	19/32	21/32	1 11/16	1 1/16	2 25/32	1 15/32	3 27/32	1 7/8	4 15/16	2 9/32	6
5/8	1/4	11/16	21/32	1 3/4	1 3/32	2 27/32	1 1/2	3 29/32	1 29/32	5	2 5/16	6 3/4
11/16	9/32	3/4	11/16	1 13/16	1 3/32	2 29/32	1 17/32	4	1 15/16	5 1/16	2 11/32	6 5/32
3/4	5/16	13/16	23/32	1 29/32	1 1/8	2 31/32	1 17/32	4 1/16	1 31/32	5 1/8	2 3/8	6 7/32
13/16	11/32	7/8	3/4	1 31/32	1 5/32	3 1/32	1 9/16	4 1/8	1 31/32	5 7/32	2 13/32	6 9/32
7/8	3/8	15/16	25/32	2 1/32	1 3/16	3 3/32	1 19/32	4 3/16	2	5 9/32	2 13/32	6 11/32
15/16	3/8	1	13/16	2 3/32	1 7/32	3 3/32	1 5/8	4 1/4	2 1/32	5 11/32	2 7/16	6 13/32

Inches	6" Rise	6" Slope	7" Rise	7" Slope	8" Rise	8" Slope	9" Rise	9" Slope	10" Rise	10" Slope	11" Rise	11" Slope
0	2 15/32	6 1/2	2 7/8	7 9/16	3 9/32	8 21/32	3 11/16	9 23/32	4 1/8	10 13/32	4 17/32	11 29/32
1/16	2 1/2	6 9/16	2 29/32	7 5/8	3 5/16	8 23/32	3 23/32	9 13/16	4 1/8	10 7/8	4 9/16	11 31/32
1/8	2 17/32	6 5/8	2 15/16	7 23/32	3 11/32	8 25/32	3 3/4	9 7/8	4 5/32	10 15/32	4 9/16	1-0 1/32
3/16	2 17/32	6 11/16	2 31/32	7 25/32	3 3/8	8 27/32	3 25/32	9 15/16	4 3/16	11 1/32	4 19/32	1-0 3/32
1/4	2 9/16	6 3/4	2 31/32	7 27/32	3 13/32	8 29/32	3 13/16	10	4 7/32	11 3/32	4 5/8	1-0 5/32
5/16	2 19/32	6 13/16	3	7 29/32	3 13/32	9	3 27/32	10 1/16	4 1/4	11 5/32	4 21/32	1-0 7/32
3/8	2 5/8	6 29/32	3 1/32	7 31/32	3 7/16	9 1/16	3 27/32	10 1/8	4 9/32	11 7/32	4 11/16	1-0 9/32
7/16	2 21/32	6 31/32	3 1/32	8 1/32	3 15/32	9 1/8	3 7/8	10 7/32	4 9/32	11 9/32	4 23/32	1-0 3/8
1/2	2 11/16	7 1/32	3 3/32	8 1/8	3 1/2	9 3/32	3 29/32	10 3/8	4 5/16	11 11/32	4 23/32	1-0 7/16
9/16	2 11/16	7 3/32	3 1/8	8 3/16	3 17/32	9 1/4	3 15/16	10 11/32	4 11/32	11 13/32	4 3/4	1-0 1/2
5/8	2 23/32	7 5/32	3 1/8	8 1/4	3 9/16	9 5/16	3 31/32	10 13/32	4 3/8	11 1/2	4 25/32	1-0 9/16
11/16	2 3/4	7 7/32	3 5/32	8 5/16	3 9/16	9 13/32	4	10 15/32	4 13/32	11 9/16	4 13/32	1-0 5/8
3/4	2 25/32	7 5/16	3 3/16	8 3/8	3 19/32	9 15/32	4	10 17/32	4 7/16	11 5/8	4 27/32	1-0 23/32
13/16	2 13/16	7 3/8	3 7/32	8 7/16	3 5/8	9 17/32	4 1/32	10 5/8	4 7/16	11 11/16	4 7/8	1-0 25/32
7/8	2 27/32	7 7/16	3 1/4	8 1/2	3 21/32	9 19/32	4 1/16	10 11/16	4 15/32	11 3/4	4 7/8	1-0 27/32
15/16	2 27/32	7 1/2	3 9/32	8 19/32	3 11/16	9 21/32	4 3/32	10 3/4	4 1/2	11 13/16	4 29/32	1-0 29/32

Feet	0' Rise	0' Slope	10' Rise	10' Slope	20' Rise	20' Slope	30' Rise	30' Slope
0	0	0	4-1 3/8	10-9 3/4	8-2 3/4	21-7 11/32	12-4 1/8	32-5 9/32
1	4 15/16	1-0 31/32	4-6 5/16	11-10 3/4	8-7 11/16	22-8 1/2	12-9 1/16	33-6 1/4
2	9 7/8	2-1 15/16	4-11 1/4	12-11 23/32	9-0 5/8	23-9 15/32	13-2	34-7 1/4
3	1-2 13/16	3-2 15/16	5-4 3/16	14-0 11/16	9-5 9/16	24-10 7/16	13-6 15/16	35-8 7/32
4	1-7 3/4	4-3 29/32	5-9 1/8	15-1 21/32	9-10 1/2	25-11 7/16	13-11 7/8	36-9 3/16
5	2-0 11/16	5-4 7/8	6-2 1/16	16-2 21/32	10-3 7/16	27-0 13/32	14-4 13/16	37-10 5/32
6	2-5 5/8	6-5 27/32	6-7	17-3 5/8	10-8 3/8	28-1 3/8	14-9 3/4	38-11 1/8
7	2-10 9/16	7-6 27/32	6-11 15/16	18-4 19/32	11-1 5/16	29-2 11/32	15-2 11/16	40-0 1/8
8	3-3 1/2	8-7 13/16	7-4 7/8	19-5 9/16	11-6 1/4	30-3 11/32	15-7 5/8	41-1 3/32
9	3-8 7/16	9-8 25/32	7-9 13/16	20-6 11/32	11-11 3/16	31-4 5/16	16-0 9/16	42-2 1/16

A = 22° 21′ 54″; logsin A = 9.58036: logcos A = 9.96604; logtan A = 9.61433; logcot A = 0.38567

Ins.	12″ Rise	12″ Slope	13″ Rise	13″ Slope	14″ Rise	14″ Slope	15″ Rise	15″ Slope	16″ Rise	16″ Slope
0	$4\frac{15}{16}$	1-0$\frac{31}{32}$	$5\frac{11}{32}$	1-2$\frac{1}{32}$	$5\frac{3}{4}$	1-3$\frac{1}{8}$	$6\frac{3}{16}$	1-4$\frac{7}{32}$	$6\frac{19}{32}$	1-5$\frac{5}{16}$
$\frac{1}{16}$	$4\frac{31}{32}$	1-1$\frac{1}{32}$	$5\frac{3}{8}$	1-2$\frac{1}{8}$	$5\frac{25}{32}$	1-3$\frac{7}{32}$	$6\frac{3}{16}$	1-4$\frac{9}{32}$	$6\frac{19}{32}$	1-5$\frac{3}{8}$
$\frac{1}{8}$	5	1-1$\frac{1}{8}$	$5\frac{13}{32}$	1-2$\frac{3}{16}$	$5\frac{13}{16}$	1-3$\frac{9}{32}$	$6\frac{7}{32}$	1-4$\frac{11}{32}$	$6\frac{5}{8}$	1-5$\frac{7}{16}$
$\frac{3}{16}$	5	1-1$\frac{3}{16}$	$5\frac{7}{16}$	1-2$\frac{1}{4}$	$5\frac{27}{32}$	1-3$\frac{11}{32}$	$6\frac{1}{4}$	1-4$\frac{7}{16}$	$6\frac{21}{32}$	1-5$\frac{1}{2}$
$\frac{1}{4}$	$5\frac{1}{32}$	1-1$\frac{1}{4}$	$5\frac{7}{16}$	1-2$\frac{5}{16}$	$5\frac{7}{8}$	1-3$\frac{13}{32}$	$6\frac{9}{32}$	1-4$\frac{1}{2}$	$6\frac{11}{16}$	1-5$\frac{9}{16}$
$\frac{5}{16}$	$5\frac{1}{32}$	1-1$\frac{5}{16}$	$5\frac{15}{32}$	1-2$\frac{3}{8}$	$5\frac{7}{8}$	1-3$\frac{15}{32}$	$6\frac{5}{16}$	1-4$\frac{9}{16}$	$6\frac{23}{32}$	1-5$\frac{5}{8}$
$\frac{3}{8}$	$5\frac{3}{32}$	1-1$\frac{3}{8}$	$5\frac{1}{2}$	1-2$\frac{15}{32}$	$5\frac{29}{32}$	1-3$\frac{17}{32}$	$6\frac{5}{16}$	1-4$\frac{5}{8}$	$6\frac{3}{4}$	1-5$\frac{23}{32}$
$\frac{7}{16}$	$5\frac{1}{8}$	1-1$\frac{7}{16}$	$5\frac{17}{32}$	1-2$\frac{17}{32}$	$5\frac{15}{16}$	1-3$\frac{5}{8}$	$6\frac{11}{32}$	1-4$\frac{11}{16}$	$6\frac{3}{4}$	1-5$\frac{25}{32}$
$\frac{1}{2}$	$5\frac{5}{32}$	1-1$\frac{17}{32}$	$5\frac{9}{16}$	1-2$\frac{19}{32}$	$5\frac{31}{32}$	1-3$\frac{11}{16}$	$6\frac{3}{8}$	1-4$\frac{3}{4}$	$6\frac{25}{32}$	1-5$\frac{27}{32}$
$\frac{9}{16}$	$5\frac{5}{32}$	1-1$\frac{19}{32}$	$5\frac{19}{32}$	1-2$\frac{21}{32}$	6	1-3$\frac{3}{4}$	$6\frac{13}{32}$	1-4$\frac{27}{32}$	$6\frac{13}{16}$	1-5$\frac{29}{32}$
$\frac{5}{8}$	$5\frac{3}{16}$	1-1$\frac{21}{32}$	$5\frac{19}{32}$	1-2$\frac{23}{32}$	$6\frac{1}{8}$	1-3$\frac{13}{16}$	$6\frac{7}{16}$	1-4$\frac{29}{32}$	$6\frac{27}{32}$	1-5$\frac{31}{32}$
$\frac{11}{16}$	$5\frac{7}{32}$	1-1$\frac{23}{32}$	$5\frac{5}{8}$	1-2$\frac{13}{16}$	$6\frac{1}{8}$	1-3$\frac{7}{8}$	$6\frac{15}{32}$	1-4$\frac{31}{32}$	$6\frac{7}{8}$	1-6$\frac{1}{32}$
$\frac{3}{4}$	$5\frac{1}{4}$	1-1$\frac{25}{32}$	$5\frac{21}{32}$	1-2$\frac{7}{8}$	$6\frac{1}{16}$	1-3$\frac{15}{16}$	$6\frac{15}{32}$	1-5$\frac{1}{32}$	$6\frac{29}{32}$	1-6$\frac{1}{8}$
$\frac{13}{16}$	$5\frac{9}{32}$	1-1$\frac{27}{32}$	$5\frac{11}{16}$	1-2$\frac{15}{16}$	$6\frac{3}{32}$	1-4$\frac{1}{32}$	$6\frac{1}{2}$	1-5$\frac{3}{32}$	$6\frac{29}{32}$	1-6$\frac{3}{16}$
$\frac{7}{8}$	$5\frac{5}{32}$	1-1$\frac{15}{16}$	$5\frac{23}{32}$	1-3	$6\frac{1}{8}$	1-4$\frac{3}{32}$	$6\frac{17}{32}$	1-5$\frac{5}{32}$	$6\frac{15}{16}$	1-6$\frac{1}{4}$
$\frac{15}{16}$	$5\frac{5}{16}$	1-2	$5\frac{3}{4}$	1-3$\frac{1}{16}$	$6\frac{5}{32}$	1-4$\frac{5}{32}$	$6\frac{9}{16}$	1-5$\frac{7}{32}$	$6\frac{31}{32}$	1-6$\frac{5}{16}$

Ins.	17″ Rise	17″ Slope	18″ Rise	18″ Slope	19″ Rise	19″ Slope	20″ Rise	20″ Slope	21″ Rise	21″ Slope
0	7	1-6$\frac{3}{8}$	$7\frac{13}{32}$	1-7$\frac{15}{32}$	$7\frac{13}{16}$	1-8$\frac{17}{32}$	$8\frac{7}{32}$	1-9$\frac{5}{8}$	$8\frac{5}{8}$	1-10$\frac{23}{32}$
$\frac{1}{16}$	$7\frac{1}{32}$	1-6$\frac{7}{16}$	$7\frac{1}{16}$	1-7$\frac{17}{32}$	$7\frac{27}{32}$	1-8$\frac{5}{8}$	$8\frac{1}{4}$	1-9$\frac{11}{16}$	$8\frac{21}{32}$	1-10$\frac{25}{32}$
$\frac{1}{8}$	$7\frac{1}{8}$	1-6$\frac{17}{32}$	$7\frac{15}{32}$	1-7$\frac{19}{32}$	$7\frac{7}{8}$	1-8$\frac{11}{16}$	$8\frac{9}{32}$	1-9$\frac{3}{4}$	$8\frac{11}{16}$	1-10$\frac{27}{32}$
$\frac{3}{16}$	$7\frac{1}{16}$	1-6$\frac{19}{32}$	$7\frac{15}{32}$	1-7$\frac{21}{32}$	$7\frac{29}{32}$	1-8$\frac{3}{4}$	$8\frac{5}{16}$	1-9$\frac{27}{32}$	$8\frac{23}{32}$	1-10$\frac{29}{32}$
$\frac{1}{4}$	$7\frac{3}{32}$	1-6$\frac{21}{32}$	$7\frac{1}{2}$	1-7$\frac{3}{4}$	$7\frac{29}{32}$	1-8$\frac{13}{16}$	$8\frac{11}{32}$	1-9$\frac{29}{32}$	$8\frac{3}{4}$	1-10$\frac{31}{32}$
$\frac{5}{16}$	$7\frac{1}{8}$	1-6$\frac{23}{32}$	$7\frac{17}{32}$	1-7$\frac{13}{16}$	$7\frac{15}{16}$	1-8$\frac{7}{8}$	$8\frac{11}{32}$	1-9$\frac{31}{32}$	$8\frac{25}{32}$	1-11$\frac{1}{32}$
$\frac{3}{8}$	$7\frac{5}{32}$	1-6$\frac{25}{32}$	$7\frac{9}{16}$	1-7$\frac{7}{8}$	$7\frac{31}{32}$	1-8$\frac{15}{16}$	$8\frac{3}{8}$	1-10$\frac{1}{32}$	$8\frac{25}{32}$	1-11$\frac{1}{8}$
$\frac{7}{16}$	$7\frac{3}{16}$	1-6$\frac{27}{32}$	$7\frac{19}{32}$	1-7$\frac{15}{16}$	8	1-9$\frac{1}{32}$	$8\frac{13}{32}$	1-10$\frac{3}{32}$	$8\frac{13}{16}$	1-11$\frac{3}{16}$
$\frac{1}{2}$	$7\frac{3}{16}$	1-6$\frac{15}{16}$	$7\frac{5}{8}$	1-8	$8\frac{1}{32}$	1-9$\frac{3}{32}$	$8\frac{7}{16}$	1-10$\frac{5}{32}$	$8\frac{27}{32}$	1-11$\frac{1}{4}$
$\frac{9}{16}$	$7\frac{7}{32}$	1-7	$7\frac{5}{8}$	1-8$\frac{1}{16}$	$8\frac{1}{8}$	1-9$\frac{5}{32}$	$8\frac{15}{32}$	1-10$\frac{1}{4}$	$8\frac{7}{8}$	1-11$\frac{5}{16}$
$\frac{5}{8}$	$7\frac{1}{4}$	1-7$\frac{1}{16}$	$7\frac{21}{32}$	1-8$\frac{1}{8}$	$8\frac{1}{8}$	1-9$\frac{7}{32}$	$8\frac{1}{2}$	1-10$\frac{5}{16}$	$8\frac{29}{32}$	1-11$\frac{3}{8}$
$\frac{11}{16}$	$7\frac{9}{32}$	1-7$\frac{1}{8}$	$7\frac{11}{16}$	1-8$\frac{7}{32}$	$8\frac{3}{32}$	1-9$\frac{9}{32}$	$8\frac{1}{2}$	1-10$\frac{3}{8}$	$8\frac{15}{16}$	1-11$\frac{7}{16}$
$\frac{3}{4}$	$7\frac{5}{16}$	1-7$\frac{3}{16}$	$7\frac{23}{32}$	1-8$\frac{9}{32}$	$8\frac{1}{8}$	1-9$\frac{11}{16}$	$8\frac{17}{32}$	1-10$\frac{7}{16}$	$8\frac{15}{16}$	1-11$\frac{17}{32}$
$\frac{13}{16}$	$7\frac{11}{32}$	1-7$\frac{1}{4}$	$7\frac{3}{4}$	1-8$\frac{11}{32}$	$8\frac{5}{32}$	1-9$\frac{7}{16}$	$8\frac{9}{16}$	1-10$\frac{1}{2}$	$8\frac{31}{32}$	1-11$\frac{19}{32}$
$\frac{7}{8}$	$7\frac{11}{32}$	1-7$\frac{11}{32}$	$7\frac{25}{32}$	1-8$\frac{13}{32}$	$8\frac{5}{16}$	1-9$\frac{1}{2}$	$8\frac{19}{32}$	1-10$\frac{9}{16}$	9	1-11$\frac{21}{32}$
$\frac{15}{16}$	$7\frac{3}{8}$	1-7$\frac{13}{32}$	$7\frac{25}{32}$	1-8$\frac{15}{32}$	$8\frac{7}{32}$	1-9$\frac{9}{16}$	$8\frac{5}{8}$	1-10$\frac{5}{8}$	$9\frac{1}{32}$	1-11$\frac{23}{32}$

Feet	40′ Rise	40′ Slope	50′ Rise	50′ Slope	60′ Rise	60′ Slope	70′ Rise	70′ Slope
0	16-5$\frac{1}{2}$	43-3$\frac{1}{32}$	20-6$\frac{7}{8}$	54-0$\frac{13}{16}$	24-8$\frac{1}{4}$	64-10$\frac{9}{16}$	28-9$\frac{5}{8}$	75-8$\frac{5}{16}$
1	16-10$\frac{7}{16}$	44-4$\frac{1}{32}$	20-11$\frac{13}{32}$	55-1$\frac{25}{32}$	25-1$\frac{3}{8}$	65-11$\frac{17}{32}$	29-2$\frac{9}{16}$	76-9$\frac{5}{32}$
2	17-3$\frac{3}{8}$	45-5	21-4$\frac{3}{4}$	56-2$\frac{3}{4}$	25-6$\frac{1}{8}$	67-0$\frac{17}{32}$	29-7$\frac{1}{2}$	77-10$\frac{9}{32}$
3	17-8$\frac{5}{16}$	46-5$\frac{31}{32}$	21-9$\frac{11}{16}$	57-3$\frac{23}{32}$	25-11$\frac{1}{16}$	68-11$\frac{1}{2}$	30-0$\frac{7}{16}$	78-11$\frac{1}{4}$
4	18-1$\frac{1}{4}$	47-6$\frac{15}{16}$	22-2$\frac{5}{8}$	58-4$\frac{23}{32}$	26-4	69-2$\frac{15}{32}$	30-5$\frac{3}{8}$	80-0$\frac{1}{32}$
5	18-6$\frac{3}{16}$	48-7$\frac{15}{32}$	22-7$\frac{9}{16}$	59-5$\frac{11}{16}$	26-8$\frac{15}{16}$	70-3$\frac{7}{16}$	30-10$\frac{5}{16}$	81-1$\frac{7}{32}$
6	18-11$\frac{1}{8}$	49-8$\frac{29}{32}$	23-0$\frac{1}{2}$	60-6$\frac{21}{32}$	27-1$\frac{7}{8}$	71-4$\frac{7}{16}$	31-3$\frac{1}{4}$	82-2$\frac{3}{16}$
7	19-4$\frac{1}{16}$	50-9$\frac{7}{8}$	23-5$\frac{7}{16}$	61-7$\frac{5}{8}$	27-6$\frac{13}{16}$	72-5$\frac{13}{32}$	31-8$\frac{3}{16}$	83-3$\frac{5}{32}$
8	19-9	51-10$\frac{27}{32}$	23-10$\frac{3}{8}$	62-8$\frac{5}{8}$	27-11$\frac{3}{4}$	73-6$\frac{3}{8}$	32-1$\frac{1}{8}$	84-4$\frac{1}{8}$
9	20-1$\frac{15}{16}$	52-11$\frac{27}{32}$	24-3$\frac{5}{16}$	63-9$\frac{19}{32}$	28-4$\frac{11}{16}$	74-7$\frac{11}{32}$	32-6$\frac{1}{16}$	85-5$\frac{1}{8}$

natsin A=0.3805075396; natcos A=0.9247778178; nattan A=0.4114583333; natcot A=2.4303797468

Inches	0" Rise	0" Slope	1" Rise	1" Slope	2" Rise	2" Slope	3" Rise	3" Slope	4" Rise	4" Slope	5" Rise	5" Slope
0	0	0	13/32	1 3/32	27/32	2 5/32	1 1/4	3 1/4	1 21/32	4 11/32	2 3/32	5 13/32
1/16	1/32	1/16	7/16	1 5/32	7/8	2 1/4	1 9/32	3 5/16	1 11/16	4 13/32	2 1/8	5 1/2
1/8	1/16	1/8	15/32	1 7/32	7/8	2 5/16	1 5/16	3 3/8	1 23/32	4 15/32	2 1/8	5 9/16
3/16	1/16	3/16	1/2	1 9/32	29/32	2 3/8	1 5/16	3 7/16	1 3/4	4 17/32	2 5/32	5 5/8
1/4	3/32	9/32	17/32	1 11/32	15/16	2 7/16	1 11/32	3 17/32	1 25/32	4 19/32	2 3/16	5 11/16
5/16	1/8	11/32	9/16	1 7/16	31/32	2 1/2	1 3/8	3 19/32	1 13/16	4 11/16	2 7/32	5 3/4
3/8	5/32	13/32	9/16	1 1/2	1	2 9/16	1 13/32	3 21/32	1 13/16	4 3/4	2 1/4	5 13/16
7/16	3/16	15/32	19/32	1 9/16	1	2 5/8	1 7/16	3 23/32	1 27/32	4 13/16	2 1/4	5 7/8
1/2	7/32	17/32	5/8	1 5/8	1 1/32	2 23/32	1 15/32	3 25/32	1 7/8	4 7/8	2 9/32	5 31/32
9/16	1/4	5/8	21/32	1 11/16	1 1/16	2 25/32	1 1/2	3 7/8	1 29/32	4 15/16	2 5/16	6 1/32
5/8	1/4	11/16	11/16	1 3/4	1 3/32	2 27/32	1 1/2	3 15/16	1 15/16	5	2 11/32	6 3/32
11/16	9/32	3/4	11/16	1 13/16	1 1/8	2 29/32	1 17/32	4	1 15/16	5 1/16	2 3/8	6 5/32
3/4	5/16	13/16	23/32	1 29/32	1 5/32	2 31/32	1 9/16	4 1/16	1 31/32	5 5/32	2 13/32	6 7/32
13/16	11/32	7/8	3/4	1 31/32	1 3/16	3 1/16	1 19/32	4 1/8	2	5 7/32	2 7/16	6 5/16
7/8	3/8	15/16	25/32	2 1/32	1 3/16	3 1/8	1 5/8	4 3/16	2 1/32	5 9/32	2 7/16	6 3/8
15/16	3/8	1	13/16	2 3/32	1 7/32	3 3/16	1 5/8	4 1/4	2 1/16	5 11/32	2 15/32	6 7/16

Inches	6" Rise	6" Slope	7" Rise	7" Slope	8" Rise	8" Slope	9" Rise	9" Slope	10" Rise	10" Slope	11" Rise	11" Slope
0	2 1/2	6 1/2	2 29/32	7 19/32	3 11/32	8 21/32	3 3/4	9 3/4	4 5/32	10 27/32	4 19/32	11 29/32
1/16	2 17/32	6 9/16	2 15/16	7 21/32	3 3/8	8 3/4	3 25/32	9 13/16	4 3/16	10 29/32	4 5/8	1-0
1/8	2 9/16	6 5/8	2 31/32	7 23/32	3 3/8	8 13/16	3 13/16	9 7/8	4 7/32	10 31/32	4 5/8	1-0 1/16
3/16	2 9/16	6 11/16	3	7 25/32	3 13/32	8 7/8	3 13/16	9 15/16	4 1/4	11 1/32	4 21/32	1-0 1/8
1/4	2 19/32	6 25/32	3 1/32	7 27/32	3 7/16	8 15/16	3 27/32	10 1/32	4 9/32	11 3/32	4 11/16	1-0 3/16
5/16	2 5/8	6 27/32	3 1/16	7 15/16	3 15/32	9	3 7/8	10 3/32	4 5/16	11 3/16	4 23/32	1-0 1/4
3/8	2 21/32	6 29/32	3 1/16	8	3 1/2	9 1/16	3 29/32	10 5/32	4 5/16	11 1/4	4 3/4	1-0 5/16
7/16	2 11/16	6 31/32	3 3/32	8 1/16	3 1/2	9 1/8	3 15/16	10 7/32	4 11/32	11 5/16	4 3/4	1-0 3/8
1/2	2 23/32	7 1/32	3 1/8	8 1/8	3 17/32	9 7/32	3 31/32	10 9/32	4 3/8	11 3/8	4 25/32	1-0 15/32
9/16	2 3/4	7 1/8	3 5/32	8 3/16	3 9/16	9 9/32	4	10 3/8	4 13/32	11 7/16	4 13/16	1-0 17/32
5/8	2 3/4	7 3/16	3 3/16	8 1/4	3 19/32	9 11/32	4	10 7/16	4 7/16	11 1/2	4 27/32	1-0 19/32
11/16	2 25/32	7 1/4	3 3/16	8 5/16	3 5/8	9 13/32	4 1/32	10 1/2	4 7/16	11 9/16	4 7/8	1-0 21/32
3/4	2 13/16	7 5/16	3 7/32	8 13/32	3 21/32	9 15/32	4 1/16	10 9/16	4 15/32	11 21/32	4 29/32	1-0 23/32
13/16	2 27/32	7 3/8	3 1/4	8 15/32	3 11/16	9 9/16	4 3/32	10 5/8	4 1/2	11 23/32	4 15/16	1-0 13/16
7/8	2 7/8	7 7/16	3 9/32	8 17/32	3 11/16	9 5/8	4 1/8	10 11/16	4 17/32	11 25/32	4 15/16	1-0 7/8
15/16	2 7/8	7 1/2	3 5/16	8 19/32	3 23/32	9 11/16	4 1/8	10 3/4	4 9/16	11 27/32	4 31/32	1-0 15/16

Feet	0' Rise	0' Slope	10' Rise	10' Slope	20' Rise	20' Slope	30' Rise	30' Slope
0	0	0	4-2	10-10	8-4	21-8	12-6	32-6
1	5	1-1	4-7	11-11	8-9	22-9	12-11	33-7
2	10	2-2	5-0	13-0	9-2	23-10	13-4	34-8
3	1-3	3-3	5-5	14-1	9-7	24-11	13-9	35-9
4	1-8	4-4	5-10	15-2	10-0	26-0	14-2	36-10
5	2-1	5-5	6-3	16-3	10-5	27-1	14-7	37-11
6	2-6	6-6	6-8	17-4	10-10	28-2	15-0	39-0
7	2-11	7-7	7-1	18-5	11-3	29-3	15-5	40-1
8	3-4	8-8	7-6	19-6	11-8	30-4	15-10	41-2
9	3-9	9-9	7-11	20-7	12-1	31-5	16-3	42-3

A = 22° 37′ 12″; log sin A = 9.58503; log cos A = 9.96524; log tan A = 9.61979; log cot A = 0.38021.

Ins.	12″ Rise	12″ Slope	13″ Rise	13″ Slope	14″ Rise	14″ Slope	15″ Rise	15″ Slope	16″ Rise	16″ Slope
0	5	1-1	$5\frac{13}{32}$	1-2$\frac{3}{32}$	$5\frac{27}{32}$	1-3$\frac{5}{32}$	$6\frac{1}{4}$	1-4$\frac{1}{4}$	$6\frac{21}{32}$	1-5$\frac{11}{32}$
$\frac{1}{16}$	$5\frac{1}{32}$	1-1$\frac{1}{16}$	$5\frac{7}{16}$	1-2$\frac{5}{32}$	$5\frac{7}{8}$	1-3$\frac{1}{4}$	$6\frac{9}{32}$	1-4$\frac{5}{16}$	$6\frac{11}{16}$	1-5$\frac{13}{32}$
$\frac{1}{8}$	$5\frac{1}{16}$	1-1$\frac{1}{8}$	$5\frac{15}{32}$	1-2$\frac{7}{32}$	$5\frac{7}{8}$	1-3$\frac{5}{16}$	$6\frac{5}{16}$	1-4$\frac{3}{8}$	$6\frac{23}{32}$	1-5$\frac{15}{32}$
$\frac{3}{16}$	$5\frac{1}{16}$	1-1$\frac{3}{16}$	$5\frac{1}{2}$	1-2$\frac{9}{32}$	$5\frac{29}{32}$	1-3$\frac{3}{8}$	$6\frac{5}{16}$	1-4$\frac{7}{16}$	$6\frac{3}{4}$	1-5$\frac{17}{32}$
$\frac{1}{4}$	$5\frac{3}{32}$	1-1$\frac{9}{32}$	$5\frac{17}{32}$	1-2$\frac{11}{32}$	$5\frac{15}{16}$	1-3$\frac{7}{16}$	$6\frac{11}{32}$	1-4$\frac{17}{32}$	$6\frac{25}{32}$	1-5$\frac{19}{32}$
$\frac{5}{16}$	$5\frac{1}{8}$	1-1$\frac{11}{32}$	$5\frac{9}{16}$	1-2$\frac{7}{16}$	$5\frac{31}{32}$	1-3$\frac{1}{2}$	$6\frac{3}{8}$	1-4$\frac{19}{32}$	$6\frac{13}{16}$	1-5$\frac{11}{16}$
$\frac{3}{8}$	$5\frac{5}{32}$	1-1$\frac{13}{32}$	$5\frac{9}{16}$	1-2$\frac{1}{2}$	6	1-3$\frac{9}{16}$	$6\frac{13}{32}$	1-4$\frac{21}{32}$	$6\frac{13}{16}$	1-5$\frac{3}{4}$
$\frac{7}{16}$	$5\frac{3}{16}$	1-1$\frac{15}{32}$	$5\frac{19}{32}$	1-2$\frac{9}{16}$	6	1-3$\frac{5}{8}$	$6\frac{7}{16}$	1-4$\frac{23}{32}$	$6\frac{27}{32}$	1-5$\frac{13}{16}$
$\frac{1}{2}$	$5\frac{7}{32}$	1-1$\frac{17}{32}$	$5\frac{5}{8}$	1-2$\frac{5}{8}$	$6\frac{1}{32}$	1-3$\frac{23}{32}$	$6\frac{15}{32}$	1-4$\frac{25}{32}$	$6\frac{7}{8}$	1-5$\frac{7}{8}$
$\frac{9}{16}$	$5\frac{1}{4}$	1-1$\frac{5}{8}$	$5\frac{21}{32}$	1-2$\frac{11}{16}$	$6\frac{1}{16}$	1-3$\frac{25}{32}$	$6\frac{1}{2}$	1-4$\frac{7}{8}$	$6\frac{29}{32}$	1-5$\frac{15}{16}$
$\frac{5}{8}$	$5\frac{1}{4}$	1-1$\frac{11}{16}$	$5\frac{11}{16}$	1-2$\frac{3}{4}$	$6\frac{3}{32}$	1-3$\frac{27}{32}$	$6\frac{1}{2}$	1-4$\frac{15}{16}$	$6\frac{15}{16}$	1-6
$\frac{11}{16}$	$5\frac{9}{32}$	1-1$\frac{3}{4}$	$5\frac{11}{16}$	1-2$\frac{13}{16}$	$6\frac{1}{8}$	1-3$\frac{29}{32}$	$6\frac{17}{32}$	1-5	$6\frac{15}{16}$	1-6$\frac{1}{16}$
$\frac{3}{4}$	$5\frac{5}{16}$	1-1$\frac{13}{16}$	$5\frac{23}{32}$	1-2$\frac{29}{32}$	$6\frac{5}{32}$	1-3$\frac{31}{32}$	$6\frac{9}{16}$	1-5$\frac{1}{16}$	$6\frac{31}{32}$	1-6$\frac{5}{32}$
$\frac{13}{16}$	$5\frac{11}{32}$	1-1$\frac{7}{8}$	$5\frac{3}{4}$	1-2$\frac{31}{32}$	$6\frac{3}{16}$	1-4$\frac{1}{16}$	$6\frac{19}{32}$	1-5$\frac{1}{8}$	7	1-6$\frac{7}{32}$
$\frac{7}{8}$	$5\frac{3}{8}$	1-1$\frac{15}{16}$	$5\frac{25}{32}$	1-3$\frac{1}{32}$	$6\frac{3}{16}$	1-4$\frac{1}{8}$	$6\frac{5}{8}$	1-5$\frac{3}{16}$	$7\frac{1}{32}$	1-6$\frac{9}{32}$
$\frac{15}{16}$	$5\frac{3}{8}$	1-2	$5\frac{13}{16}$	1-3$\frac{3}{32}$	$6\frac{7}{32}$	1-4$\frac{3}{16}$	$6\frac{5}{8}$	1-5$\frac{1}{4}$	$7\frac{1}{16}$	1-6$\frac{11}{32}$

Ins.	17″ Rise	17″ Slope	18″ Rise	18″ Slope	19″ Rise	19″ Slope	20″ Rise	20″ Slope	21″ Rise	21″ Slope
0	$7\frac{3}{32}$	1-6$\frac{13}{32}$	$7\frac{1}{2}$	1-7$\frac{1}{2}$	$7\frac{29}{32}$	1-8$\frac{19}{32}$	$8\frac{11}{32}$	1-9$\frac{21}{32}$	$8\frac{3}{4}$	1-10$\frac{3}{4}$
$\frac{1}{16}$	$7\frac{1}{8}$	1-6$\frac{1}{2}$	$7\frac{17}{32}$	1-7$\frac{9}{16}$	$7\frac{15}{16}$	1-8$\frac{21}{32}$	$8\frac{3}{8}$	1-9$\frac{3}{4}$	$8\frac{25}{32}$	1-10$\frac{13}{16}$
$\frac{1}{8}$	$7\frac{1}{8}$	1-6$\frac{9}{16}$	$7\frac{9}{16}$	1-7$\frac{5}{8}$	$7\frac{31}{32}$	1-8$\frac{23}{32}$	$8\frac{3}{8}$	1-9$\frac{13}{16}$	$8\frac{13}{16}$	1-10$\frac{7}{8}$
$\frac{3}{16}$	$7\frac{5}{32}$	1-6$\frac{5}{8}$	$7\frac{9}{16}$	1-7$\frac{11}{16}$	8	1-8$\frac{25}{32}$	$8\frac{13}{32}$	1-9$\frac{7}{8}$	$8\frac{13}{16}$	1-10$\frac{15}{16}$
$\frac{1}{4}$	$7\frac{3}{16}$	1-6$\frac{11}{16}$	$7\frac{19}{32}$	1-7$\frac{25}{32}$	$8\frac{1}{32}$	1-8$\frac{27}{32}$	$8\frac{7}{16}$	1-9$\frac{15}{16}$	$8\frac{27}{32}$	1-11$\frac{1}{32}$
$\frac{5}{16}$	$7\frac{7}{32}$	1-6$\frac{3}{4}$	$7\frac{5}{8}$	1-7$\frac{27}{32}$	$8\frac{1}{16}$	1-8$\frac{15}{16}$	$8\frac{15}{32}$	1-10	$8\frac{7}{8}$	1-11$\frac{3}{32}$
$\frac{3}{8}$	$7\frac{1}{4}$	1-6$\frac{13}{16}$	$7\frac{21}{32}$	1-7$\frac{29}{32}$	$8\frac{1}{16}$	1-9	$8\frac{1}{2}$	1-10$\frac{1}{16}$	$8\frac{29}{32}$	1-11$\frac{5}{32}$
$\frac{7}{16}$	$7\frac{1}{4}$	1-6$\frac{7}{8}$	$7\frac{11}{16}$	1-7$\frac{31}{32}$	$8\frac{3}{32}$	1-9$\frac{1}{16}$	$8\frac{1}{2}$	1-10$\frac{1}{8}$	$8\frac{15}{16}$	1-11$\frac{7}{32}$
$\frac{1}{2}$	$7\frac{9}{32}$	1-6$\frac{31}{32}$	$7\frac{23}{32}$	1-8$\frac{1}{32}$	$8\frac{1}{8}$	1-9$\frac{1}{8}$	$8\frac{17}{32}$	1-10$\frac{7}{32}$	$8\frac{31}{32}$	1-11$\frac{9}{32}$
$\frac{9}{16}$	$7\frac{5}{16}$	1-7$\frac{1}{32}$	$7\frac{3}{4}$	1-8$\frac{1}{8}$	$8\frac{5}{32}$	1-9$\frac{3}{16}$	$8\frac{9}{16}$	1-10$\frac{9}{32}$	9	1-11$\frac{3}{8}$
$\frac{5}{8}$	$7\frac{11}{32}$	1-7$\frac{3}{32}$	$7\frac{3}{4}$	1-8$\frac{3}{16}$	$8\frac{3}{16}$	1-9$\frac{1}{4}$	$8\frac{19}{32}$	1-10$\frac{11}{32}$	9	1-11$\frac{7}{16}$
$\frac{11}{16}$	$7\frac{3}{8}$	1-7$\frac{5}{32}$	$7\frac{25}{32}$	1-8$\frac{1}{4}$	$8\frac{3}{16}$	1-9$\frac{5}{16}$	$8\frac{5}{8}$	1-10$\frac{13}{32}$	$9\frac{1}{32}$	1-11$\frac{1}{2}$
$\frac{3}{4}$	$7\frac{13}{32}$	1-7$\frac{7}{32}$	$7\frac{13}{16}$	1-8$\frac{5}{16}$	$8\frac{7}{32}$	1-9$\frac{13}{32}$	$8\frac{21}{32}$	1-10$\frac{15}{32}$	$9\frac{1}{16}$	1-11$\frac{9}{16}$
$\frac{13}{16}$	$7\frac{7}{16}$	1-7$\frac{5}{16}$	$7\frac{27}{32}$	1-8$\frac{3}{8}$	$8\frac{1}{4}$	1-9$\frac{15}{32}$	$8\frac{11}{16}$	1-10$\frac{9}{16}$	$9\frac{3}{32}$	1-11$\frac{5}{8}$
$\frac{7}{8}$	$7\frac{7}{16}$	1-7$\frac{3}{8}$	$7\frac{7}{8}$	1-8$\frac{7}{16}$	$8\frac{9}{32}$	1-9$\frac{17}{32}$	$8\frac{11}{16}$	1-10$\frac{5}{8}$	$9\frac{1}{8}$	1-11$\frac{11}{16}$
$\frac{15}{16}$	$7\frac{15}{32}$	1-7$\frac{7}{16}$	$7\frac{7}{8}$	1-8$\frac{1}{2}$	$8\frac{5}{16}$	1-9$\frac{19}{32}$	$8\frac{23}{32}$	1-10$\frac{11}{16}$	$9\frac{1}{8}$	1-11$\frac{3}{4}$

Feet	40′ Rise	40′ Slope	50′ Rise	50′ Slope	60′ Rise	60′ Slope	70′ Rise	70′ Slope
0	16-8	43-4	20-10	54-2	25-0	65-0	29-2	75-10
1	17-1	44-5	21-3	55-3	25-5	66-1	29-7	76-11
2	17-6	45-6	21-8	56-4	25-10	67-2	30-0	78-0
3	17-11	46-7	22-1	57-5	26-3	68-3	30-5	79-1
4	18-4	47-8	22-6	58-6	26-8	69-4	30-10	80-2
5	18-9	48-9	22-11	59-7	27-1	70-5	31-3	81-3
6	19-2	49-10	23-4	60-8	27-6	71-6	31-8	82-4
7	19-7	50-11	23-9	61-9	27-11	72-7	32-1	83-5
8	20-0	52-0	24-2	62-10	28-4	73-8	32-6	84-6
9	20-5	53-1	24-7	63-11	28-9	74-9	32-11	85-7

natsin A=0.3846153846; natcos A=0.9230769231; nattan A=0.4166666666; natcot A=2.4000000000

Inches	0" Rise	0" Slope	1" Rise	1" Slope	2" Rise	2" Slope	3" Rise	3" Slope	4" Rise	4" Slope	5" Rise	5" Slope
0	0	0	7/16	1 3/32	27/32	2 5/32	1 1/4	3 1/4	1 11/16	4 11/32	2 1/8	5 7/16
1/16	1/32	1/16	7/16	1 5/32	7/8	2 1/4	1 9/32	3 5/16	1 23/32	4 13/32	2 1/8	5 1/2
1/8	1/16	1/8	15/32	1 7/32	29/32	2 5/16	1 5/16	3 13/32	1 3/4	4 15/32	2 5/32	5 9/16
3/16	3/32	7/32	1/2	1 9/32	15/16	2 3/8	1 11/32	3 15/32	1 25/32	4 17/32	2 3/16	5 5/8
1/4	3/32	9/32	17/32	1 11/32	15/16	2 7/16	1 3/8	3 17/32	1 25/32	4 5/8	2 7/32	5 11/16
5/16	1/8	11/32	9/16	1 7/16	31/32	2 1/2	1 13/32	3 19/32	1 13/16	4 11/16	2 1/4	5 25/32
3/8	5/32	13/32	19/32	1 1/2	1	2 9/16	1 7/16	3 21/32	1 27/32	4 3/4	2 9/32	5 27/32
7/16	3/16	15/32	19/32	1 9/16	1 1/32	2 21/32	1 7/16	3 23/32	1 7/8	4 13/16	2 9/32	5 29/32
1/2	7/32	17/32	5/8	1 5/8	1 1/16	2 23/32	1 15/32	3 13/16	1 29/32	4 7/8	2 5/16	5 31/32
9/16	1/4	5/8	21/32	1 11/16	1 3/32	2 25/32	1 1/2	3 7/8	1 15/16	4 15/16	2 11/32	6 1/32
5/8	1/4	11/16	11/16	1 3/4	1 3/32	2 27/32	1 17/32	3 15/16	1 15/16	5 1/32	2 3/8	6 3/32
11/16	9/32	3/4	23/32	1 27/32	1 1/8	2 29/32	1 9/16	4	1 31/32	5 3/32	2 13/32	6 3/16
3/4	5/16	13/16	3/4	1 29/32	1 5/32	3	1 19/32	4 1/16	2	5 5/32	2 7/16	6 1/4
13/16	11/32	7/8	3/4	1 31/32	1 3/16	3 1/16	1 19/32	4 1/8	2 1/32	5 7/32	2 7/16	6 5/16
7/8	3/8	15/16	25/32	2 1/32	1 7/32	3 1/8	1 5/8	4 7/32	2 1/16	5 9/32	2 15/32	6 3/8
15/16	13/32	1 1/32	13/16	2 3/32	1 1/4	3 3/16	1 21/32	4 9/32	2 3/32	5 11/32	2 1/2	6 7/16

Inches	6" Rise	6" Slope	7" Rise	7" Slope	8" Rise	8" Slope	9" Rise	9" Slope	10" Rise	10" Slope	11" Rise	11" Slope
0	2 17/32	6 1/2	2 15/16	7 19/32	3 3/8	8 11/16	3 13/16	9 25/32	4 7/32	10 27/32	4 5/8	11 15/16
1/16	2 9/16	6 19/32	2 31/32	7 21/32	3 13/32	8 3/4	3 13/16	9 27/32	4 1/4	10 29/32	4 21/32	1-0
1/8	2 19/32	6 21/32	3	7 23/32	3 7/16	8 13/16	3 27/32	9 29/32	4 9/32	11	4 11/16	1-0 1/16
3/16	2 5/8	6 23/32	3 1/32	7 13/16	3 15/32	8 7/8	3 7/8	9 31/32	4 5/16	11 1/16	4 23/32	1-0 5/32
1/4	2 5/8	6 25/32	3 1/16	7 7/8	3 15/32	8 31/32	3 29/32	10 1/32	4 5/16	11 1/8	4 3/4	1-0 7/32
5/16	2 21/32	6 27/32	3 3/32	7 15/16	3 1/2	9 1/32	3 15/16	10 3/32	4 11/32	11 3/16	4 25/32	1-0 9/32
3/8	2 11/16	6 29/32	3 1/8	8	3 17/32	9 3/32	3 31/32	10 3/16	4 3/8	11 1/4	4 13/16	1-0 11/32
7/16	2 23/32	7	3 1/8	8 1/8	3 9/16	9 5/32	3 31/32	10 1/4	4 13/32	11 11/32	4 13/16	1-0 13/32
1/2	2 3/4	7 1/16	3 5/32	8 1/8	3 19/32	9 7/32	4	10 5/16	4 7/16	11 13/32	4 27/32	1-0 15/32
9/16	2 25/32	7 1/8	3 3/16	8 7/32	3 5/8	9 9/32	4 1/32	10 3/8	4 15/32	11 15/32	4 7/8	1-0 9/16
5/8	2 25/32	7 3/16	3 7/32	8 9/32	3 5/8	9 3/8	4 1/16	10 7/16	4 15/32	11 17/32	4 29/32	1-0 5/8
11/16	2 13/16	7 1/4	3 1/4	8 11/32	3 21/32	9 7/16	4 3/32	10 1/2	4 1/2	11 19/32	4 15/16	1-0 11/16
3/4	2 27/32	7 5/16	3 9/32	8 13/32	3 11/16	9 1/2	4 1/8	10 19/32	4 17/32	11 21/32	4 31/32	1-0 3/4
13/16	2 7/8	7 13/32	3 9/32	8 15/32	3 23/32	9 9/16	4 1/8	10 21/32	4 9/16	11 3/4	4 31/32	1-0 13/16
7/8	2 29/32	7 15/32	3 5/16	8 9/16	3 3/4	9 5/8	4 5/32	10 23/32	4 19/32	11 13/16	5	1-0 7/8
15/16	2 15/16	7 17/32	3 11/32	8 5/8	3 25/32	9 11/16	4 3/16	10 25/32	4 5/8	11 7/8	5 1/32	1-0 31/32

Feet	0' Rise	0' Slope	10' Rise	10' Slope	20' Rise	20' Slope	30' Rise	30' Slope
0	0	0	4-2 5/8	10-10 1/4	8-5 1/4	21-8 15/16	12-7 7/8	32-6 23/32
1	5 1/16	1-1 1/2	4-7 11/16	11-1 19/32	8-10 5/16	22-9 1/2	13-0 15/16	33-7 3/4
2	10 1/8	2-2 1/16	5-0 3/4	13-0 9/32	9-3 3/8	23-10 17/32	13-6	34-8 25/32
3	1-3 3/16	3-3 11/16	5-5 13/16	14-1 5/16	9-8 7/16	24-11 9/16	13-11 11/16	35-9 13/16
4	1-8 1/4	4-4 3/32	5-10 7/8	15-2 11/32	10-1 1/2	26-0 19/32	14-4 1/8	36-10 13/16
5	2-1 5/16	5-5 1/8	6-3 15/16	16-3 3/8	10-6 9/16	27-1 19/32	14-9 3/16	37-11 27/32
6	2-6 3/8	6-6 5/32	6-9	17-4 3/8	10-11 5/8	28-2 5/8	15-2 1/4	39-0 7/8
7	2-11 7/16	7-7 5/32	7-2 1/16	18-5 13/32	11-4 11/16	29-3 21/32	15-7 5/16	40-1 29/32
8	3-4 1/2	8-8 3/16	7-7 1/8	19-6 7/16	11-9 3/4	30-4 11/16	16-0 3/8	41-2 29/32
9	3-9 9/16	9-9 7/32	8-0 3/16	20-7 15/32	12-2 13/16	31-5 11/16	16-5 7/16	42-3 15/16

A = 22° 52′ 25″; logsin A = 9.58962; logcos A = 9.96443; logtan A = 9.62518; logcot A = 0.37482

Ins.	12″ Rise	12″ Slope	13″ Rise	13″ Slope	14″ Rise	14″ Slope	15″ Rise	15″ Slope	16″ Rise	16″ Slope
0	5 1/16	1-1 1/32	5 1/2	1-2 1/8	5 29/32	1-3 3/32	6 5/16	1-4 9/32	6 3/4	1-5 3/8
1/16	5 3/32	1-1 3/32	5 1/2	1-2 3/16	5 15/16	1-3 1/4	6 11/32	1-4 11/32	6 25/32	1-5 7/16
1/8	5 1/8	1-1 5/32	5 17/32	1-2 1/4	5 31/32	1-3 11/32	6 3/8	1-4 13/32	6 13/16	1-5 1/2
3/16	5 5/32	1-1 7/32	5 9/16	1-2 5/16	6	1-3 13/32	6 13/32	1-4 15/32	6 27/32	1-5 9/16
1/4	5 5/32	1-1 9/32	5 19/32	1-2 3/8	6	1-3 15/32	6 7/16	1-4 9/16	6 27/32	1-5 5/8
5/16	5 3/16	1-1 3/8	5 5/8	1-2 7/16	6 1/32	1-3 17/32	6 15/32	1-4 5/8	6 7/8	1-5 23/32
3/8	5 7/32	1-1 7/16	5 21/32	1-2 17/32	6 1/16	1-3 19/32	6 1/2	1-4 11/32	6 29/32	1-5 25/32
7/16	5 1/4	1-1 1/2	5 21/32	1-2 19/32	6 3/32	1-3 21/32	6 1/2	1-4 3/4	6 15/16	1-5 27/32
1/2	5 9/32	1-1 9/16	5 11/16	1-2 21/32	6 1/8	1-3 3/4	6 17/32	1-4 13/16	6 31/32	1-5 29/32
9/16	5 5/16	1-1 5/8	5 23/32	1-2 23/32	6 5/32	1-3 13/16	6 9/16	1-4 29/32	7	1-5 31/32
5/8	5 5/16	1-1 11/16	5 3/4	1-2 25/32	6 5/32	1-3 7/8	6 19/32	1-4 31/32	7	1-6 1/32
11/16	5 11/32	1-1 25/32	5 25/32	1-2 27/32	6 3/16	1-3 15/16	6 5/8	1-5 1/32	7 1/32	1-6 1/8
3/4	5 3/8	1-1 27/32	5 13/16	1-2 15/16	6 7/32	1-4	6 21/32	1-5 3/32	7 1/16	1-6 3/16
13/16	5 13/32	1-1 29/32	5 13/16	1-3	6 1/4	1-4 1/16	6 21/32	1-5 5/32	7 3/32	1-6 1/4
7/8	5 7/16	1-1 31/32	5 27/32	1-3 1/16	6 9/32	1-4 5/32	6 11/16	1-5 7/32	7 1/8	1-6 5/16
15/16	5 15/32	1-2 1/32	5 7/8	1-3 1/8	6 5/16	1-4 7/32	6 23/32	1-5 5/16	7 5/32	1-6 3/8

Ins.	17″ Rise	17″ Slope	18″ Rise	18″ Slope	19″ Rise	19″ Slope	20″ Rise	20″ Slope	21″ Rise	21″ Slope
0	7 3/16	1-6 7/16	7 19/32	1-7 17/32	8	1-8 5/8	8 7/16	1-9 23/32	8 7/8	1-10 25/32
1/16	7 3/16	1-6 17/32	7 5/8	1-7 19/32	8 1/32	1-8 11/16	8 15/32	1-9 25/32	8 7/8	1-10 7/8
1/8	7 7/32	1-6 19/32	7 21/32	1-7 11/16	8 1/16	1-8 3/4	8 1/2	1-9 27/32	8 29/32	1-10 15/16
3/16	7 1/4	1-6 21/32	7 11/16	1-7 3/4	8 3/32	1-8 13/16	8 17/32	1-9 29/32	8 15/32	1-11
1/4	7 9/32	1-6 23/32	7 11/16	1-7 13/16	8 1/8	1-8 29/32	8 17/32	1-9 31/32	8 31/32	1-11 1/16
5/16	7 5/16	1-6 25/32	7 23/32	1-7 7/8	8 5/32	1-8 31/32	8 9/16	1-10 1/32	9	1-11 1/8
3/8	7 11/32	1-6 27/32	7 3/4	1-7 15/16	8 3/16	1-9 1/32	8 19/32	1-10 1/8	9 1/32	1-11 3/16
7/16	7 11/32	1-6 15/16	7 25/32	1-8	8 3/16	1-9 3/32	8 5/8	1-10 3/16	9 1/32	1-11 9/32
1/2	7 3/8	1-7	7 13/16	1-8 3/32	8 7/32	1-9 5/32	8 21/32	1-10 1/4	9 1/16	1-11 11/32
9/16	7 13/32	1-7 1/16	7 27/32	1-8 5/32	8 1/4	1-9 7/32	8 11/16	1-10 5/16	9 3/32	1-11 13/32
5/8	7 7/16	1-7 1/8	7 27/32	1-8 7/32	8 9/32	1-9 5/16	8 11/16	1-10 3/8	9 1/8	1-11 15/32
11/16	7 15/32	1-7 3/16	7 7/8	1-8 9/32	8 5/16	1-9 3/8	8 23/32	1-10 7/16	9 5/32	1-11 17/32
3/4	7 1/2	1-7 1/4	7 29/32	1-8 11/32	8 11/32	1-9 7/16	8 3/4	1-10 17/32	9 3/16	1-11 19/32
13/16	7 1/2	1-7 11/32	7 15/16	1-8 13/32	8 11/32	1-9 1/2	8 25/32	1-10 19/32	9 3/16	1-11 11/16
7/8	7 17/32	1-7 13/32	7 31/32	1-8 1/2	8 3/8	1-9 9/16	8 13/16	1-10 21/32	9 7/32	1-11 3/4
15/16	7 9/16	1-7 15/32	8	1-8 9/16	8 13/32	1-9 5/8	8 27/32	1-10 23/32	9 1/4	1-11 15/16

Feet	40′ Rise	40′ Slope	50′ Rise	50′ Slope	60′ Rise	60′ Slope	70′ Rise	70′ Slope
0	16-10 1/2	43-4 31/32	21-1 1/8	54-3 7/32	25-3 3/4	65-1 7/16	29-6 3/8	75-11 11/16
1	17-3 9/16	44-6	21-6 3/16	55-4 7/32	25-8 13/16	66-2 15/32	29-11 1/16	77-0 23/32
2	17-8 5/8	45-7	21-11 1/4	56-5 1/4	26-1 7/8	67-3 1/2	30-4 1/2	78-1 3/4
3	18-1 11/16	46-8 1/32	22-4 5/16	57-6 9/32	26-6 15/16	68-4 17/32	30-9 9/16	79-2 3/4
4	18-6 3/4	47-9 1/16	22-9 3/8	58-7 5/16	27-0		31-2 5/8	80-3 25/32
5	18-11 13/16	48-10 3/32	23-2 7/16	59-8 11/32	27-5 1/16	70-6 9/16	31-7 11/16	81-4 13/16
6	19-4 7/8	49-11 1/8	23-7 1/2	60-9 11/32	27-10 1/8	71-7 19/32	32-0 3/4	82-5 27/32
7	19-9 15/16	51-0 1/8	24-0 9/16	61-10 3/8	28-3 3/16	72-8 5/8	32-5 13/16	83-6 7/8
8	20-3	52-1 5/32	24-5 5/8	62-11 13/32	28-8 1/4	73-9 21/32	32-10 7/8	84-7 7/8
9	20-8 1/16	53-2 3/16	24-10 11/16	64-0 7/16	29-1 5/16	74-10 21/32	33-3 15/16	85-8 29/32

natsin A=0.3887005053; natcos A=0.9213641609; nattan A=0.4218750000; natcot A=2.3703703703

Inches	0" Rise	0" Slope	1" Rise	1" Slope	2" Rise	2" Slope	3" Rise	3" Slope	4" Rise	4" Slope	5" Rise	5" Slope
0	0	0	7/16	13/32	27/32	2 3/16	1 9/32	3 1/4	1 23/32	4 11/32	2 1/8	5 7/16
1/16	1/32	1/16	15/32	15/32	7/8	2 1/4	1 5/16	3 11/32	1 3/4	4 13/32	2 5/32	5 1/2
1/8	1/16	1/8	15/32	17/32	29/32	2 5/16	1 11/32	3 13/32	1 3/4	4 1/2	2 3/16	5 9/16
3/16	3/32	7/32	1/2	19/32	15/16	2 3/8	1 3/8	3 15/32	1 25/32	4 9/16	2 7/32	5 21/32
1/4	3/32	9/32	17/32	1 11/32	31/32	2 7/16	1 3/8	3 17/32	1 13/16	4 5/8	2 1/4	5 23/32
5/16	1/8	11/32	9/16	1 7/16	1	2 1/2	1 13/32	3 19/32	1 27/32	4 11/16	2 9/32	5 25/32
3/8	5/32	13/32	19/32	1 1/2	1	2 19/32	1 7/16	3 21/32	1 7/8	4 3/4	2 5/16	5 27/32
7/16	3/16	15/32	5/8	1 9/16	1 1/32	2 21/32	1 15/32	3 3/4	1 29/32	4 13/16	2 11/32	5 29/32
1/2	7/32	17/32	5/8	1 5/8	1 1/16	2 23/32	1 1/2	3 13/16	1 15/16	4 29/32	2 11/32	5 31/32
9/16	1/4	5/8	21/32	1 11/16	1 3/32	2 25/32	1 17/32	3 7/8	1 15/16	4 31/32	2 3/8	6 1/16
5/8	9/32	11/16	11/16	1 25/32	1 1/8	2 27/32	1 9/16	3 15/16	1 31/32	5 1/32	2 13/32	6 1/8
11/16	9/32	3/4	23/32	1 27/32	1 5/32	2 15/16	1 9/16	4	2	5 3/32	2 7/16	6 3/16
3/4	5/16	13/16	3/4	1 29/32	1 3/16	3	1 19/32	4 1/16	2 1/32	5 5/32	2 15/32	6 1/4
13/16	11/32	7/8	25/32	1 31/32	1 3/16	3 1/16	1 5/8	4 5/32	2 1/16	5 7/32	2 15/32	6 5/16
7/8	3/8	15/16	13/16	2 1/32	1 7/32	3 1/8	1 21/32	4 7/32	2 3/32	5 5/16	2 1/2	6 3/8
15/16	13/32	1 1/32	13/16	2 3/32	1 1/4	3 3/16	1 11/16	4 9/32	2 3/32	5 3/8	2 17/32	6 15/32

Inches	6" Rise	6" Slope	7" Rise	7" Slope	8" Rise	8" Slope	9" Rise	9" Slope	10" Rise	10" Slope	11" Rise	11" Slope
0	2 9/16	6 17/32	3	7 5/8	3 13/32	8 11/16	3 27/32	9 25/32	4 9/32	10 7/8	4 11/16	11 31/32
1/16	2 19/32	6 19/32	3 1/32	7 11/16	3 7/16	8 25/32	3 7/8	9 27/32	4 5/16	10 15/16	4 23/32	1-0 1/32
1/8	2 5/8	6 21/32	3 1/32	7 3/4	3 15/32	8 27/32	3 29/32	9 15/16	4 5/16	11	4 3/4	1-0 3/32
3/16	2 21/32	6 23/32	3 1/16	7 13/16	3 1/2	8 29/32	3 15/16	10	4 11/32	11 1/16	4 25/32	1-0 5/32
1/4	2 21/32	6 25/32	3 3/8	7 7/8	3 17/32	8 31/32	3 15/16	10 1/16	4 3/8	11 5/32	4 13/16	1-0 7/32
5/16	2 11/16	6 7/8	3 1/8	7 15/16	3 9/16	9 1/32	3 31/32	10 1/8	4 13/32	11 7/32	4 27/32	1-0 5/16
3/8	2 23/32	6 15/16	3 5/32	8	3 9/16	9 3/32	4	10 3/16	4 7/16	11 9/32	4 27/32	1-0 3/8
7/16	2 3/4	7	3 3/16	8 3/32	3 19/32	9 3/16	4 1/32	10 1/4	4 15/32	11 11/32	4 7/8	1-0 7/16
1/2	2 25/32	7 1/16	3 3/8	8 5/32	3 5/8	9 1/4	4 1/16	10 11/32	4 1/2	11 13/32	4 29/32	1-0 1/2
9/16	2 13/16	7 1/8	3 7/32	8 7/32	3 21/32	9 5/16	4 3/32	10 13/32	4 1/2	11 1/2	4 15/16	1-0 9/16
5/8	2 27/32	7 7/32	3 1/4	8 9/32	3 11/16	9 3/8	4 1/8	10 15/32	4 17/32	11 9/16	4 31/32	1-0 21/32
11/16	2 27/32	7 9/32	3 9/32	8 11/32	3 23/32	9 7/16	4 1/8	10 17/32	4 9/16	11 5/8	5	1-0 23/32
3/4	2 7/8	7 11/32	3 5/16	8 7/16	3 3/4	9 1/2	4 5/32	10 19/32	4 19/32	11 11/16	5 1/32	1-0 25/32
13/16	2 29/32	7 13/32	3 11/32	8 1/2	3 3/4	9 19/32	4 3/16	10 21/32	4 5/8	11 3/4	5 1/32	1-0 27/32
7/8	2 15/16	7 15/32	3 3/8	8 9/16	3 25/32	9 21/32	4 7/32	10 3/4	4 21/32	11 13/16	5 1/16	1-0 29/32
15/16	2 31/32	7 17/32	3 3/8	8 5/8	3 13/16	9 23/32	4 1/4	10 13/16	4 21/32	11 29/32	5 3/32	1-0 31/32

Feet	0' Rise	0' Slope	10' Rise	10' Slope	20' Rise	20' Slope	30' Rise	30' Slope
0	0	0	4-3 1/4	10-10 1/2	8-6 1/2	21-8 31/32	12-9 3/4	32-7 15/32
1	5 1/8	1-1 1/16	4-8 3/8	11-11 17/32	8-11 5/8	22-10 1/2	13-2 7/8	33-8 1/2
2	10 1/4	2-2 3/32	5-1 1/2	13-0 19/32	9-4 3/4	23-11 1/16	13-8	34-9 9/16
3	1-3 3/8	3-3 5/32	5-6 5/8	14-1 5/8	9-9 7/8	25-0 1/8	14-1 1/8	35-10 19/32
4	1-8 1/2	4-4 3/16	5-11 3/4	15-2 11/16	10-3	26-1 5/32	14-6 1/4	36-11 21/32
5	2-1 5/8	5-5 1/4	6-4 7/8	16-3 23/32	10-8 1/8	27-2 7/32	14-11 3/8	38-0 11/16
6	2-6 3/4	6-6 9/32	6-10	17-4 25/32	11-1 1/4	28-3 1/4	15-4 1/2	39-1 3/4
7	2-11 7/8	7-7 11/32	7-3 1/8	18-5 13/16	11-6 3/8	29-4 5/16	15-9 5/8	40-2 13/16
8	3-5	8-8 3/8	7-8 1/4	19-6 7/8	11-11 1/2	30-5 3/8	16-2 3/4	41-3 27/32
9	3-10 1/8	9-9 7/16	8-1 3/8	20-7 15/16	12-4 5/8	31-6 13/32	16-7 7/8	42-4 29/32

A = 23° 07′ 35″; logsin A = 9.59413; logcos A = 9.96362; logtan A = 9.63051; logcot A = 0.36949

Ins.	12″ Rise	12″ Slope	13″ Rise	13″ Slope	14″ Rise	14″ Slope	15″ Rise	15″ Slope	16″ Rise	16″ Slope
0	5 1/8	1-1 1/16	5 9/16	1-2 1/8	5 31/32	1-3 7/32	6 13/32	1-4 5/16	6 27/32−	1-5 13/32−
1/16	5 5/32−	1-1 1/8	5 19/32−	1-2 7/32−	6	1-3 9/32	6 7/16	1-4 3/8	6 7/8	1-5 15/32−
1/8	5 3/16	1-1 3/16	5 19/32	1-2 9/32−	6 1/32	1-3 11/32	6 15/32−	1-4 7/16	6 7/8	1-5 17/32
3/16	5 7/32−	1-1 1/4	5 5/8	1-2 11/32−	6 1/16	1-3 7/16	6 1/2	1-4 1/2	6 29/32	1-5 19/32
1/4	5 7/32	1-1 5/16	5 21/32	1-2 13/32	6 3/32−	1-3 1/2	6 1/2	1-4 19/32−	6 15/16	1-5 21/32
5/16	5 1/4	1-1 3/8	5 11/16	1-2 15/32	6 1/8	1-3 9/16	6 17/32	1-4 21/32−	6 31/32−	1-5 3/4
3/8	5 9/32	1-1 15/32−	5 23/32−	1-2 17/32	6 1/8	1-3 5/8	6 9/16	1-4 23/32−	7	1-5 13/16
7/16	5 5/16	1-1 17/32−	5 3/4	1-2 5/8	6 5/32	1-3 11/16	6 19/32−	1-4 25/32	7 1/32−	1-5 7/8
1/2	5 11/32−	1-1 19/32−	5 3/4	1-2 11/16	6 3/16	1-3 25/32−	6 5/8	1-4 27/32	7 1/16	1-5 15/16
9/16	5 3/8	1-1 21/32	5 25/32	1-2 3/4	6 7/32	1-3 27/32−	6 21/32−	1-4 15/16	7 1/16	1-6
5/8	5 13/32−	1-1 23/32	5 13/16	1-2 13/16	6 1/4	1-3 29/32−	6 11/16	1-5	7 3/32	1-6 1/16
11/16	5 13/32	1-1 25/32	5 27/32	1-2 7/8	6 9/32−	1-3 31/32	6 11/16	1-5 1/16	7 1/8	1-6 5/32−
3/4	5 7/16	1-1 7/8	5 7/8	1-2 15/16	6 5/16	1-4 1/32	6 23/32	1-5 1/8	7 5/32−	1-6 7/32−
13/16	5 15/32	1-1 15/16	5 29/32−	1-3 1/32−	6 5/16	1-4 3/32	6 3/4	1-5 3/16	7 3/16	1-6 9/32
7/8	5 1/2	1-2	5 15/16	1-3 3/32−	6 11/32	1-4 3/16	6 25/32−	1-5 1/4	7 7/32−	1-6 11/32
15/16	5 17/32−	1-2 1/16	5 15/16	1-3 5/32−	6 3/8	1-4 1/4	6 13/16	1-5 11/32−	7 7/32	1-6 13/32

Ins.	17″ Rise	17″ Slope	18″ Rise	18″ Slope	19″ Rise	19″ Slope	20″ Rise	20″ Slope	21″ Rise	21″ Slope
0	7 1/4	1-6 1/2	7 11/16	1-7 9/16	8 1/8	1-8 21/32	8 17/32	1-9 3/4	8 31/32	1-10 27/32−
1/16	7 9/32	1-6 9/16	7 23/32−	1-7 21/32−	8 5/32−	1-8 23/32	8 9/16	1-9 13/16	9	1-10 29/32−
1/8	7 5/16	1-6 5/8	7 3/4	1-7 23/32−	8 5/32	1-8 25/32	8 19/32	1-9 7/8	9 1/32−	1-10 31/32
3/16	7 11/32−	1-6 11/16	7 25/32−	1-7 25/32−	8 3/16	1-8 7/8	8 5/8	1-9 15/16	9 1/16	1-11 1/32
1/4	7 3/8	1-6 3/4	7 25/32	1-7 27/32	8 7/32	1-8 15/16	8 21/32−	1-10 1/32−	9 1/16	1-11 3/32
5/16	7 13/32−	1-6 13/16	7 13/16	1-7 29/32	8 1/4	1-9	8 11/16	1-10 3/32−	9 3/32	1-11 3/16
3/8	7 13/32	1-6 29/32−	7 27/32	1-7 31/32	8 9/32−	1-9 1/16	8 11/16	1-10 5/32−	9 1/8	1-11 1/4
7/16	7 7/16	1-6 31/32−	7 7/8	1-8 1/16	8 5/16	1-9 1/8	8 23/32	1-10 7/32	9 5/32−	1-11 5/16
1/2	7 15/32	1-7 1/32−	7 29/32−	1-8 1/8	8 5/16	1-9 7/32−	8 3/4	1-10 9/32	9 3/16	1-11 3/8
9/16	7 1/2	1-7 3/32	7 15/16	1-8 3/16	8 11/32	1-9 9/32−	8 25/32	1-10 11/32	9 7/32−	1-11 7/16
5/8	7 17/32−	1-7 5/32	7 31/32−	1-8 1/4	8 3/8	1-9 11/32−	8 13/16	1-10 7/16	9 1/4	1-11 1/2
11/16	7 9/16	1-7 7/32	7 31/32	1-8 5/16	8 13/32	1-9 13/32	8 27/32−	1-10 1/2	9 1/4	1-11 19/32−
3/4	7 19/32−	1-7 5/16	8	1-8 3/8	8 7/16	1-9 15/32	8 7/8	1-10 9/16	9 9/32	1-11 21/32−
13/16	7 19/32	1-7 3/8	8 1/32	1-8 15/32−	8 15/32−	1-9 17/32	8 7/8	1-10 5/8	9 5/16	1-11 23/32−
7/8	7 5/8	1-7 7/16	8 1/16	1-8 17/32−	8 1/2	1-9 5/8	8 29/32	1-10 11/16	9 11/32−	1-11 25/32
15/16	7 21/32	1-7 1/2	8 3/32−	1-8 19/32−	8 1/2	1-9 11/16	8 15/16	1-10 25/32−	9 3/8	1-11 27/32

Feet	40′ Rise	40′ Slope	50′ Rise	50′ Slope	60′ Rise	60′ Slope	70′ Rise	70′ Slope
0	17-1	43-5 15/16	21-4 1/4	54-4 7/16	25-7 1/2	65-2 29/32	29-10 3/4	76-1 13/32−
1	17-6 1/8	44-7	21-9 3/8	55-5 15/32	26-0 5/8	66-3 31/32−	30-3 7/8	77-2 7/16
2	17-11 1/4	45-8 1/32	22-2 1/2	56-6 17/32−	26-5 3/4	67-5	30-9	78-3 1/2
3	18-4 3/8	46-9 3/32−	22-7 5/8	57-7 9/16	26-10 7/8	68-6 1/16	31-2 1/8	79-4 17/32
4	18-9 1/2	47-10 1/8	23-0 3/4	58-8 5/8	27-4	69-7 1/8	31-7 1/4	80-5 19/32
5	19-2 5/8	48-11 3/16	23-5 7/8	59-9 11/16	27-9 1/8	70-8 5/32	32-0 3/8	81-6 21/32−
6	19-7 3/4	50-0 1/4	23-11	60-10 23/32	28-2 1/4	71-9 7/32−	32-5 1/2	82-7 11/16
7	20-0 7/8	51-1 9/32	24-4 1/8	61-11 25/32−	28-7 3/8	72-10 1/4	32-10 5/8	83-8 3/4
8	20-6	52-2 11/32−	24-9 1/4	63-0 13/16	29-0 1/2	73-11 5/16	33-3 3/4	84-9 25/32
9	20-11 1/8	53-3 3/8	25-2 3/8	64-1 7/8	29-5 5/8	75-0 11/32	33-8 7/8	85-10 27/32−

natsin A=0.3927628305; natcos A=0.9196397985; nattan A=0.4270833333; natcot A=2.3414634146

Inches	0" Rise	0" Slope	1" Rise	1" Slope	2" Rise	2" Slope	3" Rise	3" Slope	4" Rise	4" Slope	5" Rise	5" Slope
0	0	0	7/16	1 3/32	7/8	2 3/16	1 5/16	3 9/32	1 23/32	4 11/32	2 5/32	5 7/16
1/16	1/32	1/16	15/32	1 5/32	29/32	2 1/4	1 5/16	3 11/32	1 3/4	4 7/16	2 3/16	5 1/2
1/8	1/16	1/8	1/2	1 7/32	29/32	2 5/16	1 11/32	3 13/32	1 25/32	4 1/2	2 7/32	5 19/32
3/16	3/32	7/32	1/2	1 9/32	15/16	2 3/8	1 3/8	3 15/32	1 13/16	4 9/16	2 1/4	5 21/32
1/4	3/32	9/32	17/32	1 3/8	31/32	2 7/16	1 13/32	3 17/32	1 27/32	4 5/8	2 9/32	5 23/32
5/16	1/8	11/32	9/16	1 7/16	1	2 17/32	1 7/16	3 19/32	1 7/8	4 11/16	2 9/32	5 25/32
3/8	5/32	13/32	19/32	1 1/2	1 1/32	2 19/32	1 15/32	3 11/16	1 29/32	4 25/32	2 5/16	5 27/32
7/16	3/16	15/32	5/8	1 9/16	1 1/16	2 21/32	1 1/2	3 3/4	1 29/32	4 27/32	2 11/32	5 15/16
1/2	7/32	17/32	21/32	1 5/8	1 3/32	2 23/32	1 1/2	3 13/16	1 15/16	4 29/32	2 3/8	6
9/16	1/4	5/8	11/16	1 11/16	1 3/32	2 25/32	1 17/32	3 7/8	1 31/32	4 31/32	2 13/32	6 1/16
5/8	9/32	11/16	11/16	1 25/32	1 1/8	2 7/8	1 9/16	3 15/16	2	5 1/32	2 7/16	6 1/8
11/16	5/16	3/4	23/32	1 27/32	1 5/32	2 15/16	1 19/32	4 1/32	2 1/32	5 3/32	2 15/32	6 3/16
3/4	5/16	13/16	3/4	1 29/32	1 3/16	3	1 5/8	4 3/32	2 1/16	5 3/16	2 1/2	6 1/4
13/16	11/32	7/8	25/32	1 31/32	1 7/32	3 1/16	1 21/32	4 5/32	2 3/32	5 1/4	2 1/2	6 11/32
7/8	3/8	31/32	13/16	2 1/32	1 1/4	3 1/8	1 11/16	4 7/32	2 3/32	5 5/16	2 17/32	6 13/32
15/16	13/32	1 1/32	27/32	2 1/8	1 9/32	3 3/16	1 11/16	4 9/32	2 1/8	5 3/8	2 9/16	6 15/32

Inches	6" Rise	6" Slope	7" Rise	7" Slope	8" Rise	8" Slope	9" Rise	9" Slope	10" Rise	10" Slope	11" Rise	11" Slope
0	2 19/32	6 17/32	3 1/32	7 5/8	3 15/32	8 23/32	3 7/8	9 13/16	4 5/16	10 29/32	4 3/4	11 31/32
1/16	2 5/8	6 19/32	3 1/16	7 11/16	3 1/2	8 25/32	3 29/32	9 7/8	4 11/32	10 31/32	4 25/32	1-0 1/32
1/8	2 21/32	6 11/16	3 3/32	7 3/4	3 1/2	8 27/32	3 15/16	9 15/16	4 3/8	11 1/32	4 13/16	1-0 1/8
3/16	2 11/16	6 3/4	3 3/32	7 27/32	3 17/32	8 29/32	3 31/32	10	4 13/32	11 3/32	4 27/32	1-0 3/16
1/4	2 11/16	6 13/16	3 1/8	7 29/32	3 9/16	9	4	10 1/16	4 7/16	11 5/32	4 7/8	1-0 1/4
5/16	2 23/32	6 7/8	3 5/32	7 31/32	3 19/32	9 1/16	4 1/32	10 5/32	4 15/32	11 1/4	4 7/8	1-0 5/16
3/8	2 3/4	6 15/16	3 3/16	8 1/32	3 5/8	9 1/8	4 1/16	10 7/32	4 1/2	11 5/16	4 29/32	1-0 13/32
7/16	2 25/32	7	3 7/32	8 3/32	3 21/32	9 3/16	4 3/32	10 9/32	4 1/2	11 3/8	4 15/16	1-0 15/32
1/2	2 13/16	7 3/32	3 1/4	8 5/32	3 11/16	9 1/4	4 3/32	10 11/32	4 17/32	11 7/16	4 31/32	1-0 17/32
9/16	2 27/32	7 5/32	3 9/32	8 1/4	3 11/16	9 11/32	4 1/8	10 13/32	4 9/16	11 1/2	5	1-0 19/32
5/8	2 7/8	7 7/32	3 9/32	8 5/16	3 23/32	9 13/32	4 5/32	10 1/2	4 19/32	11 9/16	5 1/32	1-0 21/32
11/16	2 29/32	7 9/32	3 5/16	8 3/8	3 3/4	9 15/32	4 3/16	10 9/16	4 5/8	11 21/32	5 1/16	1-0 23/32
3/4	2 29/32	7 11/32	3 11/32	8 7/16	3 25/32	9 17/32	4 7/32	10 5/8	4 21/32	11 23/32	5 3/32	1-0 13/16
13/16	2 15/16	7 13/32	3 3/8	8 1/2	3 13/16	9 19/32	4 1/4	10 11/16	4 11/16	11 25/32	5 3/32	1-0 7/8
7/8	2 31/32	7 1/2	3 13/32	8 19/32	3 27/32	9 21/32	4 9/32	10 3/4	4 11/16	11 27/32	5 1/8	1-0 15/16
15/16	3	7 9/16	3 7/16	8 21/32	3 7/8	9 3/4	4 9/32	10 13/16	4 23/32	11 29/32	5 5/32	1-1

Feet	0' Rise	0' Slope	10' Rise	10' Slope	20' Rise	20' Slope	30' Rise	30' Slope
0	0	0	4-3 7/8	10-10 23/32	8-7 3/4	21-9 15/32	12-11 5/8	32-8 3/16
1	5 3/16	1-1 1/16	4-9 1/16	11-11 13/16	9-0 15/16	22-10 17/32	13-4 13/16	33-9 9/32
2	10 3/8	2-2 5/32	5-2 1/4	13-0 7/8	9-6 1/8	23-11 5/8	13-10	34-10 11/32
3	1-3 9/16	3-3 7/32	5-7 7/16	14-1 15/16	9-11 5/16	25-0 11/16	14-3 3/16	35-11 13/32
4	1-8 3/4	4-4 9/32	6-0 5/8	15-3 1/32	10-4 1/2	26-1 3/4	14-8 3/8	37-0 1/2
5	2-1 15/16	5-5 3/8	6-5 13/16	16-4 3/32	10-9 11/16	27-2 27/32	15-1 9/16	38-1 9/16
6	2-7 1/8	6-6 7/16	6-11	17-5 5/32	11-2 7/8	28-3 29/32	15-6 3/4	39-2 5/8
7	3-0 5/16	7-7 1/2	7-4 3/16	18-6 1/4	11-8 1/16	29-4 31/32	15-11 15/16	40-3 3/4
8	3-5 1/2	8-8 19/32	7-9 3/8	19-7 5/16	12-1 1/4	30-6 1/16	16-5 1/8	41-4 25/32
9	3-10 11/16	9-9 21/32	8-2 9/16	20-8 13/32	12-6 7/16	31-7 1/8	16-10 5/16	42-5 27/32

A = 23° 22′ 42″; logsin A = 9.59857; logcos A = 9.96280; logtan A = 9.63578; logcot A = 0.36422

In.	12″ Rise	12″ Slope	13″ Rise	13″ Slope	14″ Rise	14″ Slope	15″ Rise	15″ Slope	16″ Rise	16″ Slope
0	5 3/16	1-1 1/16	5 5/8	1-2 5/32	6 1/16	1-3 1/4	6 1/2	1-4 11/32	6 29/32	1-5 7/16
1/16	5 7/32	1-1 5/32	5 21/32	1-2 7/32	6 3/32	1-3 5/16	6 1/2	1-4 13/32	6 15/16	1-5 1/2
1/8	5 1/4	1-1 7/32	5 11/32	1-2 5/16	6 5/32	1-3 3/8	6 17/32	1-4 15/32	6 31/32	1-5 9/16
3/16	5 9/32	1-1 9/32	5 11/16	1-2 3/8	6 1/8	1-3 15/32	6 9/16	1-4 17/32	7	1-5 5/8
1/4	5 9/32	1-1 11/32	5 23/32	1-2 7/16	6 5/32	1-3 17/32	6 19/32	1-4 5/8	7 1/32	1-5 23/32
5/16	5 5/16	1-1 13/32	5 3/4	1-2 1/2	6 6/32	1-3 19/32	6 5/8	1-4 11/32	7 1/32	1-5 25/32
3/8	5 11/32	1-1 15/32	5 25/32	1-2 9/16	6 1/4	1-3 21/32	6 21/32	1-4 3/4	7 3/32	1-5 27/32
7/16	5 3/8	1-1 9/16	5 13/16	1-2 5/8	6 1/4	1-3 23/32	6 11/16	1-4 13/32	7 3/32	1-5 29/32
1/2	5 13/32	1-1 5/8	5 27/32	1-2 23/32	6 9/32	1-3 25/32	6 11/16	1-4 7/8	7 1/8	1-5 31/32
9/16	5 7/32	1-1 11/16	5 7/8	1-2 25/32	6 9/32	1-3 7/8	6 23/32	1-4 31/32	7 5/32	1-6 1/32
5/8	5 15/32	1-1 3/4	5 7/8	1-2 27/32	6 9/16	1-3 15/16	6 3/4	1-5 1/32	7 3/16	1-6 1/8
11/16	5 1/2	1-1 13/16	5 29/32	1-2 29/32	6 11/32	1-4	6 25/32	1-5 3/32	7 7/32	1-6 3/16
3/4	5 1/2	1-1 7/8	5 15/16	1-2 31/32	6 3/8	1-4 1/16	6 13/16	1-5 5/32	7 1/4	1-6 1/4
13/16	5 17/32	1-1 31/32	5 31/32	1-3 1/16	6 3/8	1-4 1/16	6 27/32	1-5 7/32	7 9/32	1-6 5/16
7/8	5 9/16	1-2 1/32	6	1-3 1/8	6 7/16	1-4 7/32	6 7/8	1-5 9/32	7 9/32	1-6 3/8
15/16	5 19/32	1-2 3/32	6 1/8	1-3 3/16	6 15/32	1-4 9/32	6 7/8	1-5 3/8	7 5/16	1-6 7/16

In.	17″ Rise	17″ Slope	18″ Rise	18″ Slope	19″ Rise	19″ Slope	20″ Rise	20″ Slope	21″ Rise	21″ Slope
0	7 11/32	1-6 17/32	7 25/32	1-7 5/8	8 7/32	1-8 11/16	8 21/32	1-9 25/32	9 1/16	1-10 7/8
1/16	7 3/8	1-6 19/32	7 13/16	1-7 11/16	8 1/4	1-8 25/32	8 11/16	1-9 27/32	9 3/32	1-10 15/16
1/8	7 13/32	1-6 21/32	7 27/32	1-7 3/4	8 9/32	1-8 27/32	8 11/16	1-9 15/16	9 1/8	1-11
3/16	7 7/16	1-6 23/32	7 7/8	1-7 13/16	8 9/32	1-8 29/32	8 23/32	1-10	9 5/32	1-11 3/32
1/4	7 15/32	1-6 25/32	7 7/8	1-7 7/8	8 5/16	1-8 31/32	8 3/4	1-10 1/32	9 3/16	1-11 5/32
5/16	7 15/32	1-6 7/8	7 29/32	1-7 15/16	8 11/32	1-9 1/32	8 25/32	1-10 1/8	9 7/32	1-11 7/32
3/8	7 1/2	1-6 15/16	7 15/16	1-8 1/32	8 3/8	1-9 3/32	8 13/16	1-10 3/16	9 1/4	1-11 9/32
7/16	7 17/32	1-7	7 31/32	1-8 3/32	8 13/32	1-9 3/16	8 27/32	1-10 1/4	9 9/32	1-11 11/32
1/2	7 9/16	1-7 1/16	8	1-8 5/32	8 7/16	1-9 1/4	8 7/8	1-10 11/32	9 9/32	1-11 7/16
9/16	7 19/32	1-7 1/8	8 1/32	1-8 7/32	8 15/32	1-9 5/16	8 7/8	1-10 13/32	9 5/16	1-11 1/2
5/8	7 5/8	1-7 3/32	8 1/8	1-8 9/32	8 15/32	1-9 3/8	8 29/32	1-10 15/32	9 11/32	1-11 9/16
11/16	7 21/32	1-7 9/32	8 3/32	1-8 11/32	8 1/2	1-9 7/16	8 15/16	1-10 17/32	9 3/8	1-11 5/8
3/4	7 11/16	1-7 11/32	8 3/8	1-8 1/8	8 17/32	1-9 17/32	8 31/32	1-10 19/32	9 13/32	1-11 11/16
13/16	7 11/16	1-7 13/32	8 1/8	1-8 1/2	8 9/16	1-9 19/32	9	1-10 11/16	9 7/16	1-11 3/4
7/8	7 23/32	1-7 15/32	8 5/32	1-8 9/16	8 19/32	1-9 21/32	9 1/32	1-10 3/4	9 15/32	1-11 21/32
15/16	7 3/4	1-7 17/32	8 3/16	1-8 5/8	8 5/8	1-9 23/32	9 1/16	1-10 13/32	9 15/32	1-11 29/32

Feet	40′ Rise	40′ Slope	50′ Rise	50′ Slope	60′ Rise	60′ Slope	70′ Rise	70′ Slope
0	17-3 1/2	43-6 15/32	21-7 3/8	54-5 21/32	25-11 1/4	65-4 13/32	30-3 1/8	76-3 1/8
1	17-8 11/16	44-8	22-0 9/16	55-6 3/4	26-4 7/16	66-5 15/32	30-8 5/8	77-4 3/16
2	18-1 7/8	45-9 1/16	22-5 3/4	56-7 13/16	26-9 5/8	67-6 17/32	31-1 1/2	78-5 9/32
3	18-7 1/16	46-10 5/32	22-10 15/16	57-8 7/8	27-2 13/16	68-7 5/8	31-6 11/16	79-6 11/32
4	19-0 1/4	47-11 7/32	23-4 1/8	58-9 31/32	27-8	69-8 11/16	31-11 7/8	80-7 13/32
5	19-5 7/16	49-0 9/32	23-9 5/16	59-11 1/32	28-1 3/8	70-9 3/4	32-5 1/16	81-8 1/2
6	19-10 5/8	50-1 3/8	24-2 1/2	61-0 3/32	28-6 3/8	71-10 27/32	32-10 1/4	82-9 9/16
7	20-3 13/16	51-2 7/16	24-7 11/16	62-1 3/16	28-11 1/2	72-11 29/32	33-3 7/16	83-10 21/32
8	20-9	52-3 17/32	25-0 7/8	63-2 1/4	29-4 3/4	74-0 31/32	33-8 5/8	84-11 23/32
9	21-2 3/16	53-4 19/32	25-6 1/16	64-3 5/16	29-9 15/16	75-2 1/4	34-1 13/16	86-0 25/32

natsin A=0.3968022938; natcos A=0.9179041014; nattan A=0.4322916666; natcot A=2.3132530120

Inches	0" Rise	0" Slope	1" Rise	1" Slope	2" Rise	2" Slope	3" Rise	3" Slope	4" Rise	4" Slope	5" Rise	5" Slope
0	0	0	7/16	1 3/32	7/8	2 3/16	15/16	3 9/32	1 3/4	4 3/8	2 3/16	5 15/32
1/16	1/32	1/16	15/32	1 5/32	29/32	2 1/4	1 11/32	3 11/32	1 25/32	4 7/16	2 7/32	5 17/32
1/8	1/16	1/8	1/2	1 7/32	15/16	2 5/16	1 3/8	3 13/32	1 13/16	4 1/2	2 1/4	5 19/32
3/16	3/32	7/32	17/32	1 9/32	31/32	2 3/8	1 13/32	3 15/32	1 27/32	4 9/16	2 9/32	5 21/32
1/4	1/8	9/32	9/16	1 3/8	1	2 15/32	1 7/16	3 9/16	1 7/8	4 5/8	2 5/16	5 23/32
5/16	1/8	11/32	9/16	1 7/16	1	2 17/32	1 7/16	3 5/8	1 7/8	4 23/32	2 5/16	5 13/16
3/8	5/32	13/32	9/16	1 1/2	1 1/32	2 19/32	1 15/32	3 11/16	1 29/32	4 25/32	2 11/32	5 7/8
7/16	3/16	15/32	5/8	1 9/16	1 1/16	2 21/32	1 1/2	3 3/4	1 15/16	4 27/32	2 3/8	5 15/16
1/2	7/32	17/32	21/32	1 5/8	1 3/32	2 23/32	1 17/32	3 13/16	1 31/32	4 29/32	2 13/32	6
9/16	1/4	5/8	11/16	1 23/32	1 1/8	2 13/16	1 9/16	3 7/8	2	4 31/32	2 7/16	6 1/4
5/8	9/32	11/16	23/32	1 25/32	1 5/32	2 7/8	1 19/32	3 31/32	2 1/32	5 1/16	2 15/32	6 1/8
11/16	5/16	3/4	3/4	1 27/32	1 3/16	2 15/16	1 5/8	4 1/32	2 1/16	5 1/8	2 1/2	6 7/32
3/4	5/16	13/16	3/4	1 29/32	1 3/16	3	1 5/8	4 3/32	2 1/16	5 3/16	2 1/2	6 9/32
13/16	11/32	7/8	25/32	1 31/32	1 7/32	3 1/16	1 21/32	4 5/32	2 3/32	5 1/4	2 17/32	6 11/32
7/8	3/8	15/16	13/16	2 1/32	1 1/4	3 1/8	1 11/32	4 7/32	2 1/8	5 5/16	2 9/16	6 13/32
15/16	13/32	1 1/32	27/32	2 1/8	1 9/32	3 7/32	1 23/32	4 5/16	2 5/32	5 3/8	2 19/32	6 15/32

Inches	6" Rise	6" Slope	7" Rise	7" Slope	8" Rise	8" Slope	9" Rise	9" Slope	10" Rise	10" Slope	11" Rise	11" Slope
0	2 5/8	6 9/16	3 1/16	7 5/8	3 1/2	8 23/32	3 15/16	9 13/16	4 3/8	10 29/32	4 13/16	1-0
1/16	2 21/32	6 5/8	3 3/32	7 23/32	3 17/32	8 13/16	3 31/32	9 29/32	4 13/32	10 31/32	4 27/32	1-0 1/16
1/8	2 11/16	6 11/16	3 1/8	7 25/32	3 9/16	8 7/8	4	9 31/32	4 7/16	11 1/16	4 7/8	1-0 5/32
3/16	2 23/32	6 3/4	3 5/32	7 27/32	3 19/32	8 15/16	4 1/32	10 1/16	4 15/32	11 1/8	4 29/32	1-0 7/32
1/4	2 3/4	6 13/16	3 3/16	7 29/32	3 5/8	9	4 1/16	10 3/32	4 1/2	11 3/16	4 15/16	1-0 9/32
5/16	2 3/4	6 7/8	3 3/16	7 31/32	3 5/8	9 1/16	4 1/16	10 5/32	4 1/2	11 1/4	4 15/16	1-0 11/32
3/8	2 25/32	6 31/32	3 7/32	8 1/16	3 21/32	9 5/32	4 3/32	10 7/32	4 17/32	11 5/16	4 31/32	1-0 13/32
7/16	2 13/16	7 1/32	3 1/4	8 1/8	3 11/16	9 7/32	4 1/8	10 5/16	4 9/16	11 13/32	5	1-0 15/32
1/2	2 27/32	7 3/32	3 9/32	8 3/16	3 23/32	9 9/32	4 5/32	10 3/8	4 19/32	11 15/32	5 1/32	1-0 9/16
9/16	2 7/8	7 5/32	3 5/16	8 1/4	3 3/4	9 11/32	4 3/16	10 7/16	4 5/8	11 17/32	5 1/16	1-0 5/8
5/8	2 29/32	7 7/32	3 11/32	8 5/16	3 25/32	9 13/32	4 7/32	10 1/2	4 21/32	11 19/32	5 3/32	1-0 11/16
11/16	2 15/16	7 5/16	3 3/8	8 13/32	3 13/16	9 15/32	4 1/4	10 9/16	4 11/16	11 21/32	5 1/8	1-0 3/4
3/4	2 15/16	7 3/8	3 3/8	8 15/32	3 13/16	9 9/16	4 1/4	10 21/32	4 11/16	11 23/32	5 1/8	1-0 13/16
13/16	2 31/32	7 7/16	3 13/32	8 17/32	3 27/32	9 5/8	4 9/32	10 23/32	4 23/32	11 13/16	5 5/32	1-0 29/32
7/8	3	7 1/2	3 7/16	8 19/32	3 7/8	9 11/16	4 5/16	10 25/32	4 3/4	11 7/8	5 3/16	1-0 31/32
15/16	3 1/16	7 9/16	3 15/32	8 21/32	3 29/32	9 3/4	4 11/32	10 27/32	4 25/32	11 15/16	5 7/32	1-1 1/32

Feet	0' Rise	0' Slope	10' Rise	10' Slope	20' Rise	20' Slope	30' Rise	30' Slope
0	0	0	4-4 1/2	10-10 31/32	8-9	21-9 31/32	13-1 1/2	32-8 15/16
1	5 1/4	1-1 3/32	4-9 3/4	12-0 3/32	9-2 1/4	22-11 11/16	13-6 3/4	33-10 1/32
2	10 1/2	2-2 3/16	5-3	13-1 3/16	9-7 1/2	24-0 5/32	14-0	34-11 5/32
3	1-3 3/4	3-3 9/32	5-8 1/4	14-2 9/32	10-0 3/4	25-1 1/4	14-5 1/4	36-0 1/4
4	1-9	4-4 13/32	6-1 1/2	15-3 3/8	10-6	26-2 11/32	14-10 1/2	37-1 11/32
5	2-2 1/4	5-5 1/2	6-6 3/4	16-4 15/32	10-11 1/4	27-3 15/32	15-3 3/4	38-2 7/16
6	2-7 1/2	6-6 19/32	7-0	17-5 9/16	11-4 1/4	28-4 9/16	15-9	39-3 17/32
7	3-0 3/4	7-7 11/16	7-5 1/4	18-6 21/32	11-9 3/4	29-5 21/32	16-2 1/4	40-4 5/8
8	3-6	8-8 25/32	7-10 1/2	19-7 25/32	12-3	30-6 3/4	16-7 1/2	41-5 23/32
9	3-11 1/4	9-9 7/8	8-3 3/4	20-8 7/8	12-8 1/4	31-7 27/32	17-0 3/4	42-6 27/32

A = 23° 37' 46"; logsin A = 9.60295; logcos A = 9.96197; logtan A = 9.64098; logcot A = 0.35902

Ins.	12″ Rise	12″ Slope	13″ Rise	13″ Slope	14″ Rise	14″ Slope	15″ Rise	15″ Slope	16″ Rise	16″ Slope
0	5 1/4	1-1 3/32	5 11/16	1-2 3/16	6 1/8	1-3 9/32−	6 9/16	1-4 3/8	7	1-5 15/32−
1/16	5 9/32−	1-1 5/32	5 23/32−	1-2 1/4	6 5/32−	1-3 11/32	6 19/32−	1-4 7/16	7 1/32−	1-5 17/32
1/8	5 5/16	1-1 1/4	5 3/4	1-2 5/16	6 3/16	1-3 13/32	6 5/8	1-4 1/2	7 1/16	1-5 19/32
3/16	5 11/32−	1-1 5/16	5 25/32−	1-2 13/32−	6 7/32−	1-3 1/2	6 21/32−	1-4 9/16	7 3/32−	1-5 21/32
1/4	5 3/8	1-1 3/8	5 13/16	1-2 15/32−	6 1/4	1-3 9/16	6 11/16	1-4 21/32−	7 1/8	1-5 3/4
5/16	5 3/8	1-1 7/16	5 13/16	1-2 17/32−	6 1/4	1-3 5/8	6 11/16	1-4 23/32−	7 1/8	1-5 13/16
3/8	5 13/32	1-1 1/2	5 27/32	1-2 19/32	6 9/32	1-3 11/16	6 23/32	1-4 25/32	7 5/32	1-5 7/8
7/16	5 7/16	1-1 9/16	5 7/8	1-2 21/32	6 5/16	1-3 3/4	6 3/4	1-4 27/32	7 3/16	1-5 15/16
1/2	5 15/32	1-1 21/32−	5 29/32	1-2 3/4	6 11/32	1-3 13/16	6 25/32	1-4 29/32	7 7/32	1-6
9/16	5 1/2	1-1 23/32−	5 15/16	1-2 13/16	6 3/8	1-3 29/32−	6 13/16	1-5	7 1/4	1-6 3/32−
5/8	5 17/32−	1-1 25/32−	5 31/32−	1-2 7/8	6 13/32−	1-3 31/32−	6 27/32−	1-5 1/16	7 9/32−	1-6 5/32−
11/16	5 9/16	1-1 27/32	6	1-2 15/16	6 7/16	1-4 1/32	6 7/8	1-5 1/8	7 5/16	1-6 7/32−
3/4	5 9/16	1-1 29/32	6	1-3	6 7/16	1-4 3/32	6 7/8	1-5 3/16	7 5/16	1-6 9/32
13/16	5 19/32	1-2	6 1/32	1-3 1/16	6 15/32	1-4 5/32	6 29/32	1-5 1/4	7 11/32	1-6 11/32
7/8	5 5/8	1-2 1/16	6 1/16	1-3 5/32−	6 1/2	1-4 1/4	6 15/16	1-5 5/16	7 3/8	1-6 13/32
15/16	5 21/32	1-2 1/8	6 3/32	1-3 7/32−	6 17/32	1-4 5/16	6 31/32	1-5 13/32−	7 13/32	1-6 1/2

Ins.	17″ Rise	17″ Slope	18″ Rise	18″ Slope	19″ Rise	19″ Slope	20″ Rise	20″ Slope	21″ Rise	21″ Slope
0	7 7/16	1-6 9/16	7 7/8	1-7 21/32−	8 5/16	1-8 3/4	8 3/4	1-9 27/32−	9 3/16	1-10 29/32
1/16	7 15/32−	1-6 5/8	7 29/32−	1-7 23/32−	8 11/32−	1-8 13/16	8 25/32−	1-9 29/32−	9 7/32−	1-11
1/8	7 1/2	1-6 11/16	7 15/16	1-7 25/32	8 3/8	1-8 7/8	8 13/16	1-9 31/32−	9 1/4	1-11 1/16
3/16	7 17/32−	1-6 3/4	7 31/32−	1-7 27/32	8 13/32−	1-8 15/16	8 27/32−	1-10 1/32	9 9/32−	1-11 1/8
1/4	7 9/16	1-6 27/32−	8	1-7 29/32	8 7/16	1-9	8 7/8	1-10 3/32	9 5/16	1-11 3/16
5/16	7 9/16	1-6 29/32−	8	1-8	8 7/16	1-9 3/32−	8 7/8	1-10 5/32	9 5/16	1-11 1/4
3/8	7 19/32	1-6 31/32−	8 1/32	1-8 1/16	8 15/32	1-9 5/32−	8 29/32	1-10 1/4	9 11/32	1-11 11/32−
7/16	7 5/8	1-7 1/32	8 1/16	1-8 1/8	8 1/2	1-9 7/32−	8 15/16	1-10 5/16	9 3/8	1-11 13/32−
1/2	7 21/32	1-7 3/32	8 3/32	1-8 3/16	8 17/32	1-9 9/32	8 31/32	1-10 3/8	9 13/32	1-11 15/32−
9/16	7 11/16	1-7 5/32	8 1/8	1-8 1/4	8 9/16	1-9 11/32	9	1-10 7/16	9 7/16	1-11 17/32
5/8	7 23/32−	1-7 1/4	8 5/32−	1-8 11/32−	8 19/32−	1-9 13/32	9 1/32−	1-10 1/2	9 15/32−	1-11 19/32
11/16	7 3/4	1-7 5/16	8 3/16	1-8 13/32−	8 5/8	1-9 1/2	9 1/16	1-10 19/32−	9 1/2	1-11 11/16
3/4	7 3/4	1-7 3/8	8 3/16	1-8 15/32−	8 5/8	1-9 9/16	9 1/16	1-10 21/32−	9 1/2	1-11 3/4
13/16	7 25/32	1-7 7/16	8 7/32	1-8 17/32	8 21/32	1-9 5/8	9 3/32	1-10 23/32−	9 17/32	1-11 13/16
7/8	7 13/16	1-7 1/2	8 1/4	1-8 19/32	8 11/16	1-9 11/16	9 1/8	1-10 25/32	9 9/16	1-11 7/8
15/16	7 27/32	1-7 19/32−	8 9/32	1-8 21/32	8 23/32	1-9 3/4	9 5/32	1-10 27/32	9 19/32	1-11 15/16

Feet	40′ Rise	40′ Slope	50′ Rise	50′ Slope	60′ Rise	60′ Slope	70′ Rise	70′ Slope
0	17-6	43-7 15/16	21-10 1/2	54-6 29/32	26-3	65-5 29/32−	30-7 1/2	76-4 7/8
1	17-11 1/4	44-9 1/32−	22-3 3/4	55-8	26-8 1/4	66-7	31-0 3/4	77-5 31/32
2	18-4 1/2	45-10 1/8	22-9	56-9 3/32	27-1 1/2	67-8 3/32−	31-6	78-7 1/16
3	18-9 3/4	46-11 7/32	23-2 1/4	57-10 7/32−	27-6 3/4	68-9 3/16	31-11 1/4	79-8 5/32
4	19-3	48-0 5/16	23-7 1/2	58-11 5/16	28-0	69-10 9/32	32-4 1/2	80-9 9/32−
5	19-8 1/4	49-1 13/32	24-0 3/4	60-0 13/32−	28-5 1/4	70-11 3/8	32-9 3/4	81-10 3/8
6	20-1 1/2	50-2 17/32−	24-6	61-1 1/2	28-10 1/2	72-0 15/32	33-3	82-11 15/32−
7	20-6 3/4	51-3 5/8	24-11 1/4	62-2 19/32	29-3 3/4	73-1 19/32−	33-8 1/4	84-0 9/16
8	21-0	52-4 23/32−	25-4 1/2	63-3 11/16	29-9	74-2 11/16	34-1 1/2	85-1 21/32
9	21-5 1/4	53-5 13/16	25-9 3/4	64-4 25/32	30-2 1/4	75-3 25/32−	34-6 3/4	86-2 3/4

natsin A=0.4008188340; natcos A=0.9161573348; nattan A=0.4375000000; natcot A=2.2857142857

Inches	0" Rise	0" Slope	1" Rise	1" Slope	2" Rise	2" Slope	3" Rise	3" Slope	4" Rise	4" Slope	5" Rise	5" Slope
0	0	0	7/16	1 3/32	7/8	2 3/16	1 5/16	3 9/32	1 25/32	4 3/8	2 7/32	5 15/32
1/16	1/32	1/16	15/16	1 5/32	29/32	2 1/4	1 11/32	3 11/32	1 13/16	4 7/16	2 1/4	5 17/32
1/8	1/16	1/8	1/2	1 7/32	15/16	2 5/16	1 3/8	3 13/32	1 13/16	4 1/2	2 9/32	5 19/32
3/16	3/32	7/32	17/32	1 5/16	31/32	2 13/32	1 13/32	3 1/2	1 27/32	4 19/32	2 9/32	5 11/16
1/4	1/8	9/32	9/16	1 3/8	1	2 15/32	1 7/16	3 9/16	1 7/8	4 21/32	2 5/16	5 3/4
5/16	1/8	11/32	19/32	1 7/16	1 1/32	2 17/32	1 15/32	3 5/8	1 29/32	4 23/32	2 11/32	5 13/16
3/8	5/32	13/32	19/32	1 1/2	1 1/16	2 19/32	1 1/2	3 11/16	1 15/16	4 25/32	2 3/8	5 7/8
7/16	3/16	15/32	5/8	1 9/16	1 3/32	2 21/32	1 17/32	3 3/4	1 31/32	4 27/32	2 13/32	5 15/16
1/2	7/32	17/32	21/32	1 5/8	1 3/32	2 23/32	1 9/16	3 13/16	2	4 29/32	2 7/16	6
9/16	1/4	5/8	11/16	1 23/32	1 1/8	2 13/16	1 9/16	3 29/32	2 1/32	5	2 15/32	6 3/32
5/8	9/32	11/16	23/32	1 25/32	1 5/32	2 7/8	1 19/32	3 31/32	2 1/16	5 1/16	2 1/2	6 5/32
11/16	5/16	3/4	3/4	1 27/32	1 3/16	2 15/16	1 5/8	4 1/32	2 1/16	5 1/8	2 17/32	6 1/4
3/4	11/32	13/16	25/32	1 29/32	1 7/32	3	1 21/32	4 3/32	2 3/32	5 3/16	2 17/32	6 9/32
13/16	3/8	7/8	13/16	1 31/32	1 1/4	3 1/16	1 11/16	4 5/32	2 1/8	5 1/4	2 9/16	6 11/32
7/8	3/8	31/32	27/32	2 1/16	1 9/32	3 5/32	1 23/32	4 1/4	2 5/32	5 11/32	2 19/32	6 7/16
15/16	13/32	1 1/32	27/32	2 1/8	1 5/16	3 7/32	1 3/4	4 5/16	2 3/16	5 13/32	2 5/8	6 1/2

Inches	6" Rise	6" Slope	7" Rise	7" Slope	8" Rise	8" Slope	9" Rise	9" Slope	10" Rise	10" Slope	11" Rise	11" Slope
0	2 21/32	6 9/16	3 3/32	7 21/32	3 17/32	8 3/4	4	9 27/32	4 7/16	10 15/16	4 7/8	1-0 1/32
1/16	2 11/16	6 5/8	3 1/8	7 23/32	3 9/16	8 13/16	4	9 29/32	4 15/32	11	4 29/32	1-0 3/32
1/8	2 23/32	6 11/16	3 5/32	7 25/32	3 19/32	8 7/8	4 1/32	9 31/32	4 15/32	11 1/16	4 15/16	1-0 5/32
3/16	2 3/4	6 25/32	3 3/16	7 7/8	3 5/8	8 31/32	4 1/16	10 1/16	4 1/2	11 5/32	4 15/16	1-0 1/4
1/4	2 25/32	6 27/32	3 7/32	7 15/16	3 21/32	9 1/32	4 3/32	10 1/8	4 17/32	11 7/32	4 31/32	1-0 5/16
5/16	2 25/32	6 29/32	3 1/4	8	3 11/16	9 3/32	4 1/8	10 3/16	4 9/16	11 9/32	5	1-0 3/8
3/8	2 13/16	6 31/32	3 1/4	8 1/16	3 23/32	9 5/32	4 5/32	10 1/4	4 19/32	11 11/32	5 1/32	1-0 7/16
7/16	2 27/32	7 1/32	3 9/32	8 1/8	3 3/4	9 7/32	4 3/16	10 5/16	4 5/8	11 13/32	5 1/16	1-0 1/2
1/2	2 7/8	7 3/32	3 5/16	8 3/16	3 3/4	9 9/32	4 7/32	10 3/8	4 21/32	11 15/32	5 3/32	1-0 9/16
9/16	2 29/32	7 3/16	3 11/32	8 9/32	3 25/32	9 3/8	4 7/32	10 15/32	4 11/16	11 9/16	5 1/8	1-0 21/32
5/8	2 15/16	7 1/4	3 3/8	8 11/32	3 13/16	9 7/16	4 1/4	10 17/32	4 23/32	11 5/8	5 5/32	1-0 23/32
11/16	2 31/32	7 5/16	3 13/32	8 13/32	3 27/32	9 1/2	4 9/32	10 19/32	4 23/32	11 11/16	5 3/16	1-0 25/32
3/4	3	7 3/8	3 7/16	8 15/32	3 7/8	9 9/32	4 5/16	10 21/32	4 3/4	11 3/4	5 3/16	1-0 27/32
13/16	3 1/32	7 7/16	3 15/32	8 17/32	3 29/32	9 5/8	4 11/32	10 23/32	4 25/32	11 13/16	5 7/32	1-0 29/32
7/8	3 1/32	7 17/32	3 1/2	8 5/8	3 15/16	9 23/32	4 3/8	10 13/16	4 13/16	11 29/32	5 1/4	1-1
15/16	3 1/16	7 19/32	3 1/2	8 11/16	3 31/32	9 25/32	4 13/32	10 7/8	4 27/32	11 31/32	5 9/32	1-1 1/16

Feet	0' Rise	0' Slope	10' Rise	10' Slope	20' Rise	20' Slope	30' Rise	30' Slope
0	0	0	4-5 1/8	10-1 17/32	8-10 1/4	21-1 15/32	13-3 3/8	32-9 11/16
1	5 5/16	1-1 1/8	4-10 7/16	12-0 11/32	9-3 9/16	22-1 19/32	13-8 11/16	33-10 13/16
2	10 5/8	2-2 1/4	5-3 3/4	13-1 15/32	9-8 7/8	24-0 23/32	14-2	34-11 15/16
3	1-3 15/16	3-3 3/8	5-9 1/16	14-2 19/32	10-2 3/16	25-1 27/32	14-7 5/16	36-1 1/16
4	1-9 1/4	4-4 1/2	6-2 3/8	15-3 23/32	10-7 1/2	26-2 31/32	15-0 5/8	37-2 3/16
5	2-2 9/16	5-5 5/8	6-7 11/16	16-4 27/32	11-0 13/16	27-4 3/32	15-5 15/16	38-3 5/16
6	2-7 7/8	6-6 3/4	7-1	17-5 31/32	11-6 1/8	28-5 7/32	15-11 1/4	39-4 7/16
7	3-1 3/16	7-7 7/8	7-6 5/16	18-7 3/32	11-11 7/16	29-6 11/32	16-4 9/16	40-5 9/16
8	3-6 1/2	8-9	7-11 5/8	19-8 7/32	12-4 3/4	30-7 15/32	16-9 7/8	41-6 11/16
9	3-11 13/16	9-10 1/8	8-4 15/16	20-9 11/32	12-10 1/16	31-8 9/16	17-3 3/16	42-7 13/16

A = 23° 52′ 46″; logsin A = 9.60725; logcos A = 9.96114; logtan A = 9.64612; logcot A = 0.35388

Ins.	12" Rise	12" Slope	13" Rise	13" Slope	14" Rise	14" Slope	15" Rise	15" Slope	16" Rise	16" Slope
0	5 5/16	1-1 1/8	5 3/4	1-2 7/32–	6 3/16	1-3 5/16	6 5/8	1-4 13/32–	7 3/32–	1-5 1/2
1/16	5 11/32–	1-1 3/16	5 25/32	1-2 9/32	6 7/32	1-3 3/8	6 21/32	1-4 15/32	7 1/8	1-5 9/16
1/8	5 3/8	1-1 1/4	5 13/16	1-2 11/32	6 1/4	1-3 7/16	6 11/16	1-4 17/32	7 1/8	1-5 5/8
3/16	5 13/32–	1-1 11/32–	5 27/32–	1-2 7/16	6 9/32–	1-3 17/32–	6 23/32	1-4 19/32	7 5/32	1-5 11/16
1/4	5 7/16	1-1 13/32–	5 7/8	1-2 1/2	6 5/16	1-3 19/32–	6 3/4	1-4 11/16	7 3/16	1-5 25/32–
5/16	5 7/16	1-1 15/32–	5 29/32–	1-2 9/16	6 11/32–	1-3 21/32–	6 25/32–	1-4 3/4	7 7/32	1-5 27/32–
3/8	5 15/32	1-1 17/32	5 29/32	1-2 5/8	6 3/8	1-3 23/32	6 13/16	1-4 13/16	7 1/4	1-5 29/32
7/16	5 1/2	1-1 19/32	5 15/16	1-2 11/16	6 13/32–	1-3 25/32	6 27/32–	1-4 7/8	7 9/32–	1-5 31/32
1/2	5 17/32	1-1 21/32	5 31/32	1-2 3/4	6 13/32	1-3 27/32	6 7/8	1-4 15/16	7 5/16	1-6 1/32
9/16	5 9/16	1-1 3/4	6	1-2 27/32–	6 7/16	1-3 15/16	6 7/8	1-5 1/32–	7 11/32–	1-6 1/8
5/8	5 19/32–	1-1 13/16	6 1/32	1-2 29/32–	6 15/32	1-4	6 29/32	1-5 3/32–	7 3/8	1-6 3/16
11/16	5 5/8	1-1 7/8	6 1/16	1-2 31/32	6 1/2	1-4 1/16	6 15/16	1-5 5/32–	7 3/8	1-6 1/4
3/4	5 21/32–	1-1 15/16	6 3/32–	1-3 1/32	6 17/32–	1-4 1/8	6 31/32	1-5 7/32	7 13/32	1-6 5/16
13/16	5 11/16	1-2	6 1/8	1-3 3/32	6 9/16	1-4 3/16	7	1-5 9/32	7 7/16	1-6 3/8
7/8	5 11/16	1-2 3/32–	6 5/32–	1-3 3/16	6 19/32–	1-4 9/32–	7 1/32–	1-5 3/8	7 15/32	1-6 15/32–
15/16	5 23/32	1-2 5/32–	6 5/32	1-3 1/4	6 5/8	1-4 11/32–	7 1/16	1-5 7/16	7 1/2	1-6 17/32–

Ins.	17" Rise	17" Slope	18" Rise	18" Slope	19" Rise	19" Slope	20" Rise	20" Slope	21" Rise	21" Slope
0	7 17/32–	1-6 19/32–	7 31/32	1-7 11/16	8 13/32	1-8 25/32–	8 27/32	1-9 7/8	9 5/16	1-10 31/32–
1/16	7 9/16	1-6 21/32	8	1-7 3/4	8 7/16	1-8 27/32	8 7/8	1-9 15/16	9 5/16	1-11 1/32
1/8	7 19/32–	1-6 23/32	8 1/32–	1-7 13/16	8 15/32–	1-8 29/32	8 29/32	1-10	9 11/32	1-11 3/32
3/16	7 19/32	1-6 25/32	8 1/16	1-7 7/8	8 1/2	1-8 31/32	8 15/16	1-10 1/16	9 3/8	1-11 5/32
1/4	7 5/8	1-6 7/8	8 3/32–	1-7 31/32–	8 17/32–	1-9 1/16	8 31/32–	1-10 5/32–	9 13/32	1-11 1/4
5/16	7 21/32	1-6 15/16	8 3/32	1-8 1/32–	8 9/16	1-9 1/8	9	1-10 7/32–	9 7/16	1-11 5/16
3/8	7 11/16	1-7	8 1/8	1-8 3/32	8 9/16	1-9 3/16	9 1/32–	1-10 9/32	9 15/32–	1-11 3/8
7/16	7 23/32	1-7 1/16	8 5/32	1-8 5/32	8 19/32	1-9 1/4	9 1/16	1-10 11/32	9 1/2	1-11 7/16
1/2	7 3/4	1-7 1/8	8 3/16	1-8 7/32	8 5/8	1-9 5/16	9 1/16	1-10 13/32	9 17/32–	1-11 1/2
9/16	7 25/32–	1-7 7/32–	8 7/32–	1-8 5/16	8 21/32	1-9 13/32–	9 3/32	1-10 1/2	9 17/32	1-11 19/32–
5/8	7 13/16	1-7 9/32–	8 1/4	1-8 3/8	8 11/16	1-9 15/32–	9 1/8	1-10 9/16	9 9/16	1-11 21/32–
11/16	7 27/32–	1-7 11/32–	8 9/32–	1-8 7/16	8 23/32–	1-9 17/32–	9 5/32	1-10 5/8	9 19/32	1-11 23/32–
3/4	7 27/32	1-7 13/32	8 5/16	1-8 1/2	8 3/4	1-9 19/32	9 3/16	1-10 11/16	9 5/8	1-11 25/32
13/16	7 7/8	1-7 15/32	8 11/32–	1-8 9/16	8 25/32–	1-9 21/32	9 7/32–	1-10 3/4	9 21/32	1-11 27/32
7/8	7 29/32	1-7 9/16	8 11/32	1-8 21/32–	8 13/16	1-9 3/4	9 1/4	1-10 27/32–	9 11/16	1-11 15/16
15/16	7 15/16	1-7 5/8	8 3/8	1-8 23/32–	8 13/16	1-9 13/16	9 9/32–	1-10 29/32–	9 23/32–	2-0

Feet	40' Rise	40' Slope	50' Rise	50' Slope	60' Rise	60' Slope	70' Rise	70' Slope
0	17-8 1/2	43-8 15/16	22-1 5/8	54-8 5/32	26-6 3/4	65-7 13/32–	30-11 7/8	76-6 5/8
1	18-1 13/16	44-10 1/16	22-6 15/16	55-9 9/32	27-0 1/16	66-8 17/32–	31-5 3/16	77-7 3/4
2	18-7 1/8	45-11 3/16	23-0 1/4	56-10 13/32	27-5 3/8	67-9 21/32–	31-10 1/2	78-8 7/8
3	19-0 7/16	47-0 5/16	23-5 9/16	57-11 17/32	27-10 11/16	68-10 25/32–	32-3 13/16	79-10
4	19-5 3/4	48-1 7/16	23-10 7/8	59-0 21/32	28-4	69-11 29/32–	32-9 1/8	80-11 1/8
5	19-11 1/16	49-2 9/16	24-4 3/16	60-1 25/32	28-9 5/16	71-1 1/32–	33-2 7/16	82-0 1/4
6	20-4 3/8	50-3 11/16	24-9 1/2	61-2 29/32	29-2 5/8	72-2 5/32–	33-7 3/4	83-1 3/8
7	20-9 11/16	51-4 13/16	25-2 13/16	62-4 1/32	29-7 15/16	73-3 1/4	34-1 1/16	84-2 1/2
8	21-3	52-5 29/32	25-8 1/8	63-5 5/32–	30-1 1/4	74-4 3/8	34-6 3/8	85-3 5/8
9	21-8 5/16	53-7 1/32	26-1 7/16	64-6 9/32–	30-6 9/16	75-5 1/2	34-11 11/16	86-4 3/4

natsin A=0.4048123947; natcos A=0.9143997622; nattan A=0.4427083333; natcot A=2.2588235294

BEVEL 5⅜" TO 12"

Inches	0" Rise	0" Slope	1" Rise	1" Slope	2" Rise	2" Slope	3" Rise	3" Slope	4" Rise	4" Slope	5" Rise	5" Slope
0	0	0	7/16	13/32	29/32	2 3/16	1 11/32	3 9/32	1 25/32	4 3/8	2 1/4	5 15/32
1/16	1/32	1/16	15/32	15/32	15/16	2 1/4	1 3/8	3 11/32	1 13/16	4 7/16	2 9/32	5 9/16
1/8	1/16	1/8	1/2	17/32	15/16	2 11/32	1 13/32	3 7/16	1 27/32	4 17/32	2 9/32	5 5/8
3/16	3/32	7/32	17/32	15/16	31/32	2 13/32	1 7/16	3 1/2	1 7/8	4 19/32	2 5/16	5 11/16
1/4	1/8	9/32	9/16	1 3/8	1	2 15/32	1 15/32	3 9/16	1 29/32	4 21/32	2 11/32	5 3/4
5/16	1/8	11/32	19/32	1 7/16	1 1/32	2 17/32	1 15/32	3 5/8	1 15/16	4 23/32	2 3/8	5 13/16
3/8	5/32	13/32	5/8	1 1/2	1 1/16	2 19/32	1 1/2	3 11/16	1 31/32	4 25/32	2 13/32	5 7/8
7/16	3/16	15/32	21/32	1 9/16	1 3/32	2 21/32	1 17/32	3 25/32	2	4 7/8	2 7/16	5 31/32
1/2	7/32	9/16	11/16	1 21/32	1 1/8	2 3/4	1 9/16	3 27/32	2	4 15/16	2 15/32	6 1/32
9/16	1/4	5/8	11/16	1 23/32	1 5/32	2 13/16	1 19/32	3 29/32	2 1/32	5	2 1/2	6 3/32
5/8	9/32	11/16	23/32	1 25/32	1 3/16	2 7/8	1 5/8	3 31/32	2 1/16	5 1/16	2 17/32	6 5/32
11/16	5/16	3/4	3/4	1 27/32	1 7/32	2 15/16	1 21/32	4 1/32	2 3/32	5 1/8	2 9/16	6 7/32
3/4	11/32	13/16	25/32	1 29/32	1 7/32	3	1 11/16	4 3/32	2 1/8	5 7/32	2 9/16	6 5/16
13/16	3/8	7/8	13/16	2	1 1/4	3 3/32	1 23/32	4 3/16	2 5/32	5 9/32	2 19/32	6 3/8
7/8	13/32	31/32	27/32	2 1/16	1 9/32	3 5/32	1 3/4	4 1/4	2 3/16	5 11/32	2 5/8	6 7/16
15/16	13/32	1 1/32	7/8	2 1/8	1 5/16	3 7/32	1 3/4	4 5/16	2 7/32	5 13/32	2 21/32	6 1/2

Inches	6" Rise	6" Slope	7" Rise	7" Slope	8" Rise	8" Slope	9" Rise	9" Slope	10" Rise	10" Slope	11" Rise	11" Slope
0	2 11/16	6 9/16	3 1/8	7 21/32	3 19/32	8 25/32	4 1/32	9 7/8	4 15/32	10 31/32	4 15/16	1-0 1/16
1/16	2 23/32	6 21/32	3 5/32	7 3/4	3 5/8	8 27/32	4 1/16	9 15/16	4 1/2	11 1/32	4 31/32	1-0 1/8
1/8	2 3/4	6 23/32	3 3/16	7 13/16	3 5/8	8 29/32	4 3/32	10	4 17/32	11 3/32	4 31/32	1-0 3/16
3/16	2 25/32	6 25/32	3 7/32	7 7/8	3 21/32	8 31/32	4 1/8	10 1/16	4 9/16	11 5/32	5	1-0 1/4
1/4	2 13/16	6 27/32	3 1/4	7 15/16	3 11/16	9 1/32	4 5/32	10 1/8	4 19/32	11 7/32	5 1/32	1-0 5/16
5/16	2 13/16	6 29/32	3 9/32	8	3 23/32	9 3/32	4 5/32	10 7/32	4 5/8	11 5/16	5 1/16	1-0 13/32
3/8	2 27/32	7	3 5/16	8 3/32	3 3/4	9 3/16	4 3/16	10 9/32	4 21/32	11 3/8	5 3/32	1-0 15/32
7/16	2 7/8	7 1/16	3 11/32	8 5/32	3 25/32	9 1/4	4 7/32	10 11/32	4 11/16	11 7/16	5 1/8	1-0 17/32
1/2	2 29/32	7 1/8	3 3/8	8 7/32	3 13/16	9 5/16	4 1/4	10 13/32	4 11/16	11 1/2	5 5/32	1-0 19/32
9/16	2 15/16	7 3/16	3 3/8	8 9/32	3 27/32	9 3/8	4 9/32	10 15/32	4 23/32	11 9/16	5 3/16	1-0 21/32
5/8	2 31/32	7 1/4	3 13/32	8 11/32	3 7/8	9 7/16	4 5/16	10 17/32	4 3/4	11 21/32	5 7/32	1-0 3/4
11/16	3	7 5/16	3 7/16	8 7/16	3 29/32	9 17/32	4 11/32	10 5/8	4 25/32	11 23/32	5 1/4	1-0 13/16
3/4	3 1/32	7 13/32	3 15/32	8 1/2	3 29/32	9 19/32	4 3/8	10 11/16	4 13/16	11 25/32	5 1/4	1-0 7/8
13/16	3 1/16	7 15/32	3 1/2	8 9/16	3 15/16	9 21/32	4 13/32	10 3/4	4 27/32	11 27/32	5 9/32	1-0 15/16
7/8	3 3/32	7 17/32	3 17/32	8 5/8	3 31/32	9 23/32	4 7/16	10 13/16	4 7/8	11 29/32	5 5/16	1-1
15/16	3 3/32	7 19/32	3 9/16	8 11/16	4	9 25/32	4 7/16	10 7/8	4 29/32	1-0	5 11/32	1-1 3/32

Feet	0' Rise	0' Slope	10' Rise	10' Slope	20' Rise	20' Slope	30' Rise	30' Slope
0	0	0	4-5 3/4	10-11 1/2	8-11 1/2	21-10 31/32	13-5 1/4	32-10 15/32
1	5 3/8	1-1 5/32	4-11 1/8	12-0 5/8	9-4 7/8	23-0 1/8	13-10 5/8	33-11 5/8
2	10 3/4	2-2 5/16	5-4 1/2	13-1 25/32	9-10 1/4	24-1 9/32	14-4	35-0 3/4
3	1-4 1/8	3-3 1/2	5-9 7/8	14-2 15/16	10-3 5/8	25-2 7/16	14-9 3/8	36-1 29/32
4	1-9 1/2	4-4 19/32	6-3 1/4	15-4 3/32	10-9	26-3 9/16	15-2 3/4	37-3 1/16
5	2-2 7/8	5-5 3/4	6-8 5/8	16-5 7/32	11-2 3/8	27-4 23/32	15-8 1/8	38-4 7/32
6	2-8 1/4	6-6 29/32	7-2	17-6 3/8	11-7 3/4	28-5 7/8	16-1 1/2	39-5 11/32
7	3-1 5/8	7-8 1/32	7-7 3/8	18-7 17/32	12-1 1/8	29-7 1/32	16-6 7/8	40-6 1/2
8	3-7	8-9 3/16	8-0 3/4	19-8 11/16	12-6 1/2	30-8 5/32	17-0 1/4	41-7 21/32
9	4-0 3/8	9-10 11/32	8-6 1/8	20-9 13/16	12-11 7/8	31-9 5/16	17-5 5/8	42-8 13/16

A = 24° 07′ 42″; logsin A = 9.61149; logcos A = 9.96030; logtan A = 9.65120; logcot A = 0.34880

ins.	12″ Rise	12″ Slope	13″ Rise	13″ Slope	14″ Rise	14″ Slope	15″ Rise	15″ Slope	16″ Rise	16″ Slope
0	5 3/8	1-1 5/32	5 13/16	1-2 1/4	6 7/8	1-3 11/32	6 23/32	1-4 7/32	7 5/32	1-5 17/32
1/16	5 13/32	1-1 7/32	5 27/32	1-2 5/16	6 5/16	1-3 13/32	6 3/4	1-4 1/2	7 3/16	1-5 19/32
1/8	5 7/16	1-1 9/32	5 7/8	1-2 3/8	6 5/16	1-3 15/32	6 25/32	1-4 9/32	7 7/32	1-5 21/32
3/16	5 15/32	1-1 11/32	5 29/32	1-2 7/16	6 11/32	1-3 17/32	6 13/16	1-4 21/32	7 1/4	1-5 3/4
1/4	5 1/2	1-1 7/16	5 15/16	1-2 17/32	6 3/8	1-3 5/8	6 27/32	1-4 23/32	7 9/32	1-5 13/16
5/16	5 1/2	1-1 1/2	5 31/32	1-2 19/32	6 13/32	1-3 11/16	6 27/32	1 4 25/32	7 5/16	1-5 7/8
3/8	5 17/32	1-1 9/16	6	1-2 21/32	6 7/16	1-3 3/4	6 7/8	1-4 27/32	7 11/32	1-5 15/16
7/16	5 9/16	1-1 5/8	6 1/32	1-2 23/32	6 15/32	1-3 13/16	6 29/32	1-4 29/32	7 3/8	1-6
1/2	5 19/32	1-1 11/16	6 1/16	1-2 25/32	6 1/2	1-3 7/8	6 15/16	1-4 31/32	7 3/8	1-6 3/32
9/16	5 5/8	1-1 3/4	6 1/16	1-2 7/8	6 17/32	1-3 31/32	6 31/32	1-5 1/16	7 13/32	1-6 5/32
5/8	5 21/32	1-1 27/32	6 3/32	1-2 15/16	6 9/16	1-4 1/32	7	1-5 1/8	7 7/16	1-6 7/32
11/16	5 11/16	1-1 29/32	6 1/8	1-3	6 19/32	1-4 3/32	7 1/2	1-5 3/32	7 15/32	1-6 9/32
3/4	5 23/32	1-1 31/32	6 5/32	1-3 1/16	6 19/32	1-4 5/32	7 1/16	1-5 1/4	7 1/2	1-6 11/32
13/16	5 3/4	1-2 1/32	6 3/16	1-3 1/8	6 5/8	1-4 7/32	7 3/32	1-5 5/16	7 17/32	1-6 7/16
7/8	5 25/32	1-2 3/32	6 7/32	1-3 3/32	6 21/32	1-4 5/16	7 1/8	1-5 13/32	7 9/16	1-6 1/2
15/16	5 25/32	1-2 3/16	6 1/4	1-3 9/32	6 11/16	1-4 3/8	7 1/8	1-5 15/32	7 19/32	1-6 9/16

ins.	17″ Rise	17″ Slope	18″ Rise	18″ Slope	19″ Rise	19″ Slope	20″ Rise	20″ Slope	21″ Rise	21″ Slope
0	7 5/8	1-6 5/8	8 1/16	1-7 23/32	8 1/2	1-8 13/16	8 31/32	1-9 29/32	9 13/32	1-11
1/16	7 21/32	1-6 11/16	8 3/32	1-7 25/32	8 17/32	1-8 7/8	9	1-9 31/32	9 7/16	1-11 3/32
1/8	7 21/32	1-6 3/4	8 1/8	1-7 7/8	8 9/16	1-8 31/32	9	1-10 1/16	9 15/32	1-11 5/32
3/16	7 11/16	1-6 27/32	8 5/32	1-7 15/16	8 19/32	1-9 1/32	9 1/2	1-10 1/8	9 1/2	1-11 7/32
1/4	7 23/32	1-6 29/32	8 3/16	1-8	8 5/8	1-9 3/32	9 1/16	1-10 3/32	9 17/32	1-11 9/32
5/16	7 3/4	1-6 31/32	8 3/16	1-8 1/8	8 21/32	1-9 5/32	9 3/32	1-10 1/4	9 17/32	1-11 11/32
3/8	7 25/32	1-7 1/32	8 7/32	1-8 1/8	8 11/16	1-9 7/32	9 1/8	1-10 5/32	9 9/16	1-11 13/32
7/16	7 13/16	1-7 3/32	8 1/4	1-8 3/16	8 23/32	1-9 5/16	9 5/32	1-10 13/32	9 19/32	1-11 1/2
1/2	7 27/32	1-7 3/16	8 9/32	1-8 9/32	8 3/4	1-9 3/8	9 3/16	1-10 15/32	9 5/8	1-11 1/2
9/16	7 7/8	1-7 1/4	8 5/16	1-8 11/32	8 3/4	1-9 7/16	9 7/32	1-10 17/32	9 21/32	1-11 5/8
5/8	7 29/32	1-7 5/16	8 11/32	1-8 13/32	8 25/32	1-9 1/2	9 1/4	1-10 19/32	9 11/16	1-11 11/16
11/16	7 15/16	1-7 3/8	8 3/8	1-8 15/32	8 13/16	1-9 5/8	9 9/32	1-10 21/32	9 23/32	1-11 3/4
3/4	7 15/16	1-7 7/16	8 13/32	1-8 17/32	8 27/32	1-9 21/32	9 9/32	1-10 3/4	9 3/4	1-11 27/32
13/16	7 31/32	1-7 17/32	8 7/16	1-8 5/8	8 7/8	1-9 23/32	9 5/16	1-10 13/16	9 25/32	1-11 29/32
7/8	8	1-7 19/32	8 15/32	1-8 11/16	8 29/32	1-9 25/32	9 11/32	1-10 7/8	9 13/16	1-11 31/32
15/16	8 1/2	1-7 21/32	8 15/32	1-8 3/4	8 15/16	1-9 27/32	9 3/8	1-10 15/16	9 13/16	2-0 1/32

Feet	40′ Rise	40′ Slope	50′ Rise	50′ Slope	60′ Rise	60′ Slope	70′ Rise	70′ Slope
0	17-11	43-9 15/16	22-4 3/4	54-9 7/16	26-10 1/2	65-8 15/16	31-4 1/4	76-8 13/32
1	18-4 3/8	44-11 3/4	22-10 1/8	55-10 19/32	27-3 7/8	66-10 1/16	31-9 5/8	77-9 9/16
2	18-9 3/4	46-0 1/4	23-3 1/2	56-11 3/4	27-9 1/4	67-11 7/32	32-3	78-10 23/32
3	19-3 1/8	47-1 13/32	23-8 7/8	58-0 7/8	28-2 5/8	69-0 3/8	32-8 3/8	79-11 7/8
4	19-8 1/2	48-2 17/32	24-2 1/4	59-2 1/32	28-8	70-1 7/32	33-1 3/4	81-1
5	20-1 7/8	49-3 11/32	24-7 5/8	60-3 3/16	29-1 3/8	71-2 21/32	33-7 1/8	82-2 5/32
6	20-7 1/4	50-4 27/32	25-1	61-4 11/32	29-6 3/4	72-3 13/16	34-0 1/2	83-3 5/16
7	21-0 5/8	51-6	25-6 3/8	62-5 15/32	30-0 1/8	73-4 31/32	34-5 7/8	84-4 15/32
8	21-6	52-7 5/32	25-11 3/4	63-6 5/8	30-5 1/2	74-6 1/8	34-11 1/4	85-5 19/32
9	21-11 3/8	53-8 9/32	26-5 1/8	64-7 25/32	30-10 7/8	75-7 9/32	35-4 5/8	86-6 3/4

natsin A=0.4087829245; natcos A=0.9126316456; nattan A=0.4479166666; natcot A=2.2325581395

Inches	0" Rise	0" Slope	1" Rise	1" Slope	2" Rise	2" Slope	3" Rise	3" Slope	4" Rise	4" Slope	5" Rise	5" Slope
0	0	0	7/16	1 3/32	29/32	2 3/16	1 3/8	3 9/32	1 13/16	4 13/32	2 1/4	5 1/2
1/16	1/32	1/16	15/32	1 5/32	15/16	2 1/4	1 3/8	3 3/8	1 27/32	4 15/32	2 9/32	5 9/16
1/8	1/16	1/8	1/2	1 1/4	31/32	2 11/16	1 13/32	3 7/16	1 7/8	4 17/32	2 5/16	5 5/8
3/16	3/32	3/32	17/32	1 5/16	1	2 13/32	1 7/16	3 1/2	1 29/32	4 19/32	2 11/32	5 11/16
1/4	1/8	9/32	9/16	1 3/8	1 1/32	2 15/32	1 15/32	3 9/16	1 15/16	4 21/32	2 3/8	5 3/4
5/16	5/32	9/32	19/32	1 7/16	1 1/16	2 17/32	1 1/2	3 5/8	1 31/32	4 3/4	2 13/32	5 27/32
3/8	3/16	13/32	5/8	1 1/2	1 1/16	2 19/32	1 17/32	3 23/32	1 31/32	4 13/16	2 7/16	5 29/32
7/16	3/16	15/32	21/32	1 19/32	1 3/32	2 11/16	1 9/16	3 25/32	2	4 7/8	2 15/32	5 31/32
1/2	7/32	9/16	11/16	1 21/32	1 1/8	2 3/4	1 19/32	3 27/32	2 1/16	4 15/16	2 1/2	6 1/16
9/16	1/4	5/8	23/32	1 23/32	1 5/32	2 13/16	1 5/8	3 29/32	2 1/16	5	2 17/32	6 3/32
5/8	9/32	11/16	3/4	1 25/32	1 3/16	2 7/8	1 21/32	3 31/32	2 3/32	5 1/16	2 9/16	6 3/16
11/16	5/16	3/4	3/4	1 27/32	1 7/32	2 15/16	1 21/32	4 1/16	2 1/8	5 5/32	2 9/16	6 1/4
3/4	11/32	13/16	25/32	1 29/32	1 1/4	3 1/32	1 11/16	4 1/8	2 5/32	5 7/32	2 19/32	6 5/16
13/16	3/8	29/32	13/16	2	1 9/32	3 3/32	1 23/32	4 3/16	2 3/16	5 9/32	2 5/8	6 3/8
7/8	13/32	31/32	27/32	2 1/16	1 5/16	3 5/32	1 3/4	4 1/4	2 7/32	5 11/32	2 21/32	6 7/16
15/16	7/16	1 1/32	7/8	2 1/8	1 11/32	3 7/32	1 25/32	4 5/16	2 1/4	5 13/32	2 11/32	6 17/32

Inches	6" Rise	6" Slope	7" Rise	7" Slope	8" Rise	8" Slope	9" Rise	9" Slope	10" Rise	10" Slope	11" Rise	11" Slope
0	2 23/32	6 19/32	3 3/16	7 11/16	3 5/8	8 25/32	4 1/16	9 7/8	4 17/32	10 31/32	5	1-0 1/16
1/16	2 3/4	6 21/32	3 3/16	7 3/4	3 21/32	8 27/32	4 3/32	9 15/16	4 9/16	11 1/16	5	1-0 5/32
1/8	2 25/32	6 23/32	3 7/32	7 13/16	3 11/16	8 29/32	4 1/8	10 1/32	4 19/32	11 1/8	5 1/32	1-0 7/32
3/16	2 13/16	6 25/32	3 1/4	7 29/32	3 23/32	9	4 5/32	10 3/32	4 5/8	11 3/16	5 1/16	1-0 9/32
1/4	2 27/32	6 7/8	3 9/32	7 31/32	3 3/4	9 1/16	4 3/16	10 5/32	4 21/32	11 1/4	5 3/32	1-0 11/32
5/16	2 7/8	6 15/16	3 5/16	8 1/2	3 25/32	9 1/8	4 7/32	10 7/32	4 11/16	11 5/16	5 1/8	1-0 13/32
3/8	2 7/8	7	3 11/32	8 3/32	3 25/32	9 3/16	4 1/4	10 9/32	4 11/16	11 3/8	5 5/32	1-0 1/2
7/16	2 29/32	7 1/16	3 3/8	8 5/32	3 13/16	9 1/4	4 9/32	10 3/8	4 23/32	11 15/32	5 3/16	1-0 9/32
1/2	2 15/16	7 1/8	3 13/32	8 7/32	3 27/32	9 11/32	4 5/16	10 7/16	4 3/4	11 17/32	5 7/32	1-0 5/8
9/16	2 31/32	7 7/32	3 7/16	8 5/16	3 7/8	9 13/32	4 11/32	10 1/2	4 25/32	11 19/32	5 1/4	1-0 11/16
5/8	3	7 9/32	3 15/32	8 3/8	3 29/32	9 15/32	4 3/8	10 9/16	4 13/16	11 21/32	5 9/32	1-0 3/4
11/16	3 1/32	7 11/32	3 15/32	8 7/16	3 15/16	9 17/32	4 3/8	10 5/8	4 27/32	11 23/32	5 9/32	1-0 27/32
3/4	3 1/16	7 13/32	3 1/2	8 1/2	3 31/32	9 19/32	4 13/32	10 23/32	4 7/8	11 13/16	5 5/16	1-0 29/32
13/16	3 3/32	7 15/32	3 17/32	8 9/16	4	9 11/16	4 7/16	10 25/32	4 29/32	11 7/8	5 11/32	1-0 31/32
7/8	3 1/8	7 9/16	3 9/16	8 21/32	4 1/32	9 11/16	4 15/32	10 27/32	4 15/16	11 15/16	5 3/8	1-1 1/32
15/16	3 5/32	7 5/8	3 19/32	8 23/32	4 1/16	9 13/16	4 1/2	10 29/32	4 31/32	1-0	5 13/32	1-1 3/32

Feet	0' Rise	0' Slope	10' Rise	10' Slope	20' Rise	20' Slope	30' Rise	30' Slope
0	0	0	4-6 3/8	10-11 3/4	9-0 3/4	21-11 1/2	13-7 1/8	32-11 7/8
1	5 7/16	1-1 3/16	4-11 13/16	12-0 29/32	9-6 3/16	23-0 21/32	14-0 9/16	34-0 13/32
2	10 7/8	2-2 11/32	5-5 1/4	13-2 3/32	9-11 5/8	24-1 27/32	14-6	35-1 19/32
3	1-4 5/16	3-3 17/32	5-10 11/16	14-3 9/32	10-5 1/16	25-3	14-11 7/16	36-2 3/4
4	1-9 3/4	4-4 11/16	6-4 1/8	15-4 7/16	10-10 1/2	26-4 3/16	15-4 7/8	37-3 15/16
5	2-3 3/16	5-5 7/8	6-9 9/16	16-5 5/8	11-3 15/16	27-5 3/8	15-10 5/16	38-5 3/32
6	2-8 5/8	6-7 1/32	7-3	17-6 25/32	11-9 3/8	28-6 17/32	16-3 3/4	39-6 9/32
7	3-2 1/16	7-8 7/32	7-8 7/16	18-7 31/32	12-2 13/16	29-7 23/32	16-9 3/16	40-7 15/32
8	3-7 1/2	8-9 13/32	8-1 7/8	19-9 1/8	12-8 1/4	30-8 7/8	17-2 5/8	41-8 5/8
9	4-0 15/16	9-10 9/16	8-7 5/16	20-10 5/16	13-1 11/16	31-10 1/16	17-8 1/16	42-9 13/16

A = 24° 22′ 35″; logsin A = 9.61567; logcos A = 9.95945; logtan A = 9.65622; logcot A = 0.34378

Ins.	12″ Rise	12″ Slope	13″ Rise	13″ Slope	14″ Rise	14″ Slope	15″ Rise	15″ Slope	16″ Rise	16″ Slope
0	5 7/16	1-1 3/16	5 7/8	1-2 9/32	6 11/32	1-3 3/8	6 13/16	1-4 15/32	7 1/4	1-5 9/16
1/16	5 15/32	1-1 1/4	5 29/32	1-2 11/32	6 3/8	1-3 7/16	6 13/16	1-4 17/32	7 9/32	1-5 5/8
1/8	5 1/2	1-1 5/16	5 15/16	1-2 13/32	6 13/32	1-3 1/2	6 27/32	1-4 19/32	7 5/16	1-5 23/32
3/16	5 17/32	1-1 3/8	5 31/32	1-2 15/32	6 7/16	1-3 9/16	6 7/8	1-4 11/16	7 11/32	1-5 25/32
1/4	5 9/16	1-1 7/16	6	1-2 17/32	6 15/32	1-3 21/32	6 29/32	1-4 3/4	7 3/8	1-5 27/32
5/16	5 19/32	1-1 17/32	6 1/32	1-2 5/8	6 1/2	1-3 23/32	6 15/16	1-4 13/16	7 13/32	1-5 29/32
3/8	5 19/32	1-1 19/32	6 1/16	1-2 11/16	6 1/2	1-3 25/32	6 31/32	1-4 7/8	7 13/32	1-5 31/32
7/16	5 5/8	1-1 21/32	6 3/32	1-2 3/4	6 17/32	1-3 27/32	7	1-4 15/16	7 7/16	1-6 1/32
1/2	5 21/32	1-1 23/32	6 1/8	1-2 13/16	6 9/16	1-3 29/32	7 1/32	1-5 1/32	7 15/32	1-6 1/8
9/16	5 11/16	1-1 25/32	6 5/32	1-2 7/8	6 19/32	1-4	7 1/16	1-5 3/32	7 1/2	1-6 3/16
5/8	5 23/32	1-1 7/8	6 3/16	1-2 31/32	6 5/8	1-4 1/16	7 3/32	1-5 5/32	7 17/32	1-6 1/4
11/16	5 3/4	1-1 15/16	6 3/16	1-3 1/32	6 21/32	1-4 1/8	7 3/32	1-5 7/32	7 9/16	1-6 5/16
3/4	5 25/32	1-2	6 7/32	1-3 3/32	6 11/16	1-4 3/16	7 1/8	1-5 9/32	7 19/32	1-6 3/8
13/16	5 13/16	1-2 1/16	6 1/4	1-3 5/32	6 23/32	1-4 1/4	7 5/32	1-5 3/8	7 5/8	1-6 15/32
7/8	5 27/32	1-2 1/8	6 9/32	1-3 7/32	6 3/4	1-4 11/32	7 3/16	1-5 7/16	7 21/32	1-6 17/32
15/16	5 7/8	1-2 7/32	6 5/16	1-3 5/16	6 25/32	1-4 13/32	7 7/32	1-5 1/2	7 11/16	1-6 19/32

Ins.	17″ Rise	17″ Slope	18″ Rise	18″ Slope	19″ Rise	19″ Slope	20″ Rise	20″ Slope	21″ Rise	21″ Slope
0	7 11/16	1-6 21/32	8 5/32	1-7 3/4	8 5/8	1-8 7/8	9 1/16	1-9 31/32	9 1/2	1-11 1/16
1/16	7 23/32	1-6 23/32	8 3/16	1-7 27/32	8 5/8	1-8 15/16	9 3/32	1-10 1/32	9 17/32	1-11 1/8
1/8	7 3/4	1-6 13/16	8 7/32	1-7 29/32	8 21/32	1-9	9 1/8	1-10 3/32	9 9/16	1-11 3/16
3/16	7 25/32	1-6 7/8	8 1/4	1-7 31/32	8 11/16	1-9 1/16	9 5/32	1-10 5/32	9 19/32	1-11 1/4
1/4	7 13/16	1-6 15/16	8 9/32	1-8 1/32	8 23/32	1-9 1/8	9 3/16	1-10 7/32	9 5/8	1-11 11/32
5/16	7 27/32	1-7	8 5/16	1-8 3/32	8 3/4	1-9 3/16	9 7/32	1-10 5/16	9 21/32	1-11 13/32
3/8	7 7/8	1-7 1/16	8 5/16	1-8 3/16	8 25/32	1-9 9/32	9 7/32	1-10 3/8	9 11/16	1-11 15/32
7/16	7 29/32	1-7 5/32	8 11/32	1-8 1/4	8 13/16	1-9 11/32	9 1/4	1-10 7/16	9 23/32	1-11 17/32
1/2	7 15/16	1-7 7/32	8 3/8	1-8 5/16	8 27/32	1-9 13/32	9 9/32	1-10 1/2	9 3/4	1-11 19/32
9/16	7 31/32	1-7 9/32	8 13/32	1-8 3/8	8 7/8	1-9 15/32	9 5/16	1-10 9/16	9 25/32	1-11 11/16
5/8	8	1-7 11/32	8 7/16	1-8 7/16	8 29/32	1-9 17/32	9 11/32	1-10 21/32	9 13/16	1-11 3/4
11/16	8	1-7 13/32	8 15/32	1-8 17/32	8 29/32	1-9 5/8	9 3/8	1-10 23/32	9 13/16	1-11 13/16
3/4	8 1/8	1-7 1/2	8 1/2	1-8 19/32	8 15/16	1-9 11/16	9 13/32	1-10 25/32	9 27/32	1-11 7/8
13/16	8 1/8	1-7 9/16	8 17/32	1-8 21/32	8 31/32	1-9 3/4	9 7/16	1-10 27/32	9 7/8	1-11 15/16
7/8	8 3/32	1-7 5/8	8 9/16	1-8 23/32	9	1-9 13/16	9 15/32	1-10 29/32	9 29/32	2-0 1/32
15/16	8 1/8	1-7 11/16	8 19/32	1-8 25/32	9 1/32	1-9 7/8	9 1/2	1-11	9 15/16	2-0 3/32

Feet	40′ Rise	40′ Slope	50′ Rise	50′ Slope	60′ Rise	60′ Slope	70′ Rise	70′ Slope
0	18-1 1/2	43-10 31/32	22-7 7/8	54-10 23/32	27-2 1/4	65-10 15/32	31-8 5/8	76-10 7/32
1	18-6 15/16	45-0 5/32	23-1 5/16	55-11 29/32	27-7 11/16	66-11 21/32	32-2 1/16	77-11 3/8
2	19-0 3/8	46-1 5/16	23-6 3/4	57-1 1/16	28-1 1/8	68-0 13/16	32-7 1/2	79-0 9/16
3	19-5 13/16	47-2 1/2	24-0 3/16	58-2 1/4	28-6 9/16	69-2	33-0 15/16	80-1 3/4
4	19-11 1/4	48-3 11/16	24-5 5/8	59-3 13/32	29-0	70-3 5/32	33-6 3/8	81-2 29/32
5	20-4 11/16	49-4 27/32	24-11 1/16	60-4 19/32	29-5 7/16	71-4 11/32	33-11 13/16	82-4 3/32
6	20-10 1/8	50-6 1/32	25-4 1/2	61-5 25/32	29-10 7/8	72-5 1/2	34-5 1/4	83-5 1/4
7	21-3 9/16	51-7 3/16	25-9 15/16	62-6 15/16	30-4 5/16	73-6 11/16	34-10 11/16	84-6 7/16
8	21-9	52-8 3/8	26-3 3/8	63-8 1/8	30-9 3/4	74-7 7/8	35-4 1/8	85-7 19/32
9	22-2 7/16	53-9 9/16	26-8 13/16	64-9 9/32	31-3 3/16	75-9 1/32	35-9 9/16	86-8 25/32

natsin A=0.4127303771; natcos A=0.9108532460; nattan A=0.4531250000; natcot A=2.2068965517

BEVEL 5½" TO 12"

Inches	0" Rise	0" Slope	1" Rise	1" Slope	2" Rise	2" Slope	3" Rise	3" Slope	4" Rise	4" Slope	5" Rise	5" Slope
0	0	0	15/32	1 3/32	29/32	2 3/16	1 3/8	3 5/16	1 27/32	4 13/32	2 9/32	5 1/2
1/16	1/32	1/16	1/2	1 5/32	15/16	2 9/32	1 13/32	3 3/8	1 7/8	4 15/32	2 5/16	5 9/16
1/8	1/16	1/8	1/2	1 1/4	31/32	2 11/32	1 7/16	3 7/16	1 7/8	4 17/32	2 11/32	5 5/8
3/16	3/32	7/32	17/32	1 5/16	1	2 13/32	1 15/32	3 1/2	1 29/32	4 19/32	2 3/8	5 23/32
1/4	1/8	9/32	9/16	1 3/8	1 1/32	2 15/32	1 1/2	3 9/16	1 15/16	4 11/16	2 13/32	5 25/32
5/16	5/32	11/32	19/32	1 7/16	1 1/16	2 17/32	1 17/32	3 21/32	1 31/32	4 3/4	2 7/16	5 27/32
3/8	3/16	13/32	5/8	1 1/2	1 3/32	2 5/8	1 9/16	3 23/32	2	4 13/16	2 15/32	5 29/32
7/16	3/16	15/32	21/32	1 19/32	1 1/8	2 11/16	1 9/16	3 25/32	2 1/32	4 7/8	2 1/2	5 31/32
1/2	7/32	9/16	11/16	1 21/32	1 5/32	2 3/4	1 19/32	3 27/32	2 1/16	4 15/16	2 17/32	6 1/16
9/16	1/4	5/8	23/32	1 23/32	1 3/16	2 13/16	1 5/8	3 29/32	2 3/32	5 1/32	2 9/16	6 1/8
5/8	9/32	11/16	3/4	1 25/32	1 3/16	2 7/8	1 21/32	4	2 1/8	5 3/32	2 9/16	6 3/16
11/16	5/16	3/4	25/32	1 27/32	1 7/32	2 31/32	1 11/16	4 1/16	2 5/32	5 5/32	2 19/32	6 1/4
3/4	11/32	13/16	13/16	1 15/16	1 1/4	3 1/32	1 23/32	4 1/8	2 3/16	5 7/32	2 5/8	6 5/16
13/16	3/8	29/32	27/32	2	1 9/32	3 3/32	1 3/4	4 3/16	2 7/32	5 9/32	2 21/32	6 13/32
7/8	13/32	31/32	7/8	2 1/16	1 5/16	3 5/32	1 25/32	4 1/4	2 1/4	5 3/8	2 11/16	6 15/32
15/16	7/16	1 1/32	7/8	2 1/8	1 11/32	3 7/32	1 13/16	4 11/32	2 1/4	5 7/16	2 23/32	6 17/32

Inches	6" Rise	6" Slope	7" Rise	7" Slope	8" Rise	8" Slope	9" Rise	9" Slope	10" Rise	10" Slope	11" Rise	11" Slope
0	2 3/4	6 19/32	3 7/32	7 11/16	3 21/32	8 13/16	4 1/8	9 29/32	4 19/32	11	5 1/32	1-0 3/32
1/16	2 25/32	6 21/32	3 1/4	7 25/32	3 11/16	8 7/8	4 5/32	9 31/32	4 5/8	11 1/16	5 1/16	1-0 5/32
1/8	2 13/16	6 3/4	3 1/4	7 27/32	3 23/32	8 15/16	4 3/16	10 1/32	4 5/8	11 1/8	5 3/32	1-0 1/4
3/16	2 27/32	6 13/16	3 9/32	7 29/32	3 3/4	9	4 7/32	10 3/32	4 21/32	11 7/32	5 1/8	1-0 5/16
1/4	2 7/8	6 7/8	3 5/16	7 31/32	3 25/32	9 1/16	4 1/4	10 3/16	4 11/16	11 9/32	5 5/32	1-0 3/8
5/16	2 29/32	6 15/16	3 11/32	8 1/32	3 13/16	9 5/32	4 9/32	10 1/4	4 23/32	11 11/32	5 3/16	1-0 7/16
3/8	2 15/16	7	3 3/8	8 1/8	3 27/32	9 7/32	4 5/16	10 5/16	4 3/4	11 13/32	5 7/32	1-0 1/2
7/16	2 15/16	7 3/32	3 13/32	8 3/16	3 7/8	9 9/32	4 5/16	10 3/8	4 25/32	11 15/32	5 1/4	1-0 19/32
1/2	2 31/32	7 5/32	3 7/16	8 1/4	3 29/32	9 11/32	4 11/32	10 7/16	4 13/16	11 9/16	5 9/32	1-0 21/32
9/16	3	7 7/32	3 15/32	8 5/16	3 15/16	9 13/32	4 3/8	10 17/32	4 27/32	11 5/8	5 5/16	1-0 23/32
5/8	3 1/32	7 9/32	3 1/2	8 3/8	3 15/16	9 1/2	4 13/32	10 19/32	4 7/8	11 11/16	5 5/16	1-0 25/32
11/16	3 1/16	7 11/32	3 17/32	8 15/32	3 31/32	9 9/16	4 7/16	10 21/32	4 29/32	11 3/4	5 11/32	1-0 27/32
3/4	3 3/32	7 7/16	3 9/16	8 17/32	4	9 5/8	4 15/32	10 23/32	4 15/16	11 13/16	5 3/8	1-0 15/16
13/16	3 1/8	7 1/2	3 19/32	8 19/32	4 1/32	9 11/16	4 1/2	10 25/32	4 31/32	11 29/32	5 13/32	1-1
7/8	3 5/32	7 9/16	3 5/8	8 21/32	4 1/16	9 3/4	4 17/32	10 7/8	5	11 31/32	5 7/16	1-1 1/16
15/16	3 3/16	7 5/8	3 5/8	8 23/32	4 3/32	9 27/32	4 9/16	10 15/16	5	1-0 1/32	5 15/32	1-1 1/8

Feet	0' Rise	0' Slope	10' Rise	10' Slope	20' Rise	20' Slope	30' Rise	30' Slope
0	0	0	4-7	11-0	9-2	22-0	13-9	33-0
1	5 1/2	1-1 3/16	5-0 1/2	12-1 7/32	9-7 1/2	23-1 7/32	14-2 1/2	34-1 7/32
2	11	2-2 13/32	5-6	13-2 13/32	10-1	24-2 13/32	14-8	35-2 13/32
3	1-4 1/2	3-3 19/32	5-11 1/2	14-3 19/32	10-6 1/2	25-3 19/32	15-1 1/2	36-3 5/8
4	1-10	4-4 13/16	6-5	15-4 13/16	11-0	26-4 13/16	15-7	37-4 13/16
5	2-3 1/2	5-6	6-10 1/2	16-6	11-5 1/2	27-6	16-0 1/2	38-6
6	2-9	6-7 7/32	7-4	17-7 7/32	11-11	28-7 7/32	16-6	39-7 7/32
7	3-2 1/2	7-8 13/32	7-9 1/2	18-8 13/32	12-4 1/2	29-8 13/32	16-11 1/2	40-8 13/32
8	3-8	8-9 19/32	8-3	19-9 19/32	12-10	30-9 5/8	17-5	41-9 5/8
9	4-1 1/2	9-10 13/16	8-8 1/2	20-10 13/16	13-3 1/2	31-10 13/16	17-10 1/2	42-10 13/16

A = 24° 37′ 25″; logsin A = 9.61978; logcos A = 9.95859; logtan A = 9.66118; logcot A = 0.33882

In.	12″ Rise	Slope	13″ Rise	Slope	14″ Rise	Slope	15″ Rise	Slope	16″ Rise	Slope
0	5 1/2	1-13/16	5 31/32	1-2 5/32	6 13/32	1-3 13/32	6 7/8	1-4 1/2	7 11/32	1-5 19/32
1/16	5 17/32	1-1 19/32	6	1-2 3/8	6 7/16	1-3 15/32	6 29/32	1-4 9/16	7 3/8	1-5 21/32
1/8	5 9/16	1-1 11/32	6	1-2 7/16	6 15/32	1-3 17/32	6 15/16	1-4 5/8	7 3/8	1-5 3/4
3/16	5 19/32	1-1 13/32	6 1/32	1-2 1/2	6 1/2	1-3 19/32	6 31/32	1-4 23/32	7 13/32	1-5 13/16
1/4	5 5/8	1-1 15/32	6 1/16	1-2 9/16	6 17/32	1-3 11/16	7	1-4 25/32	7 7/16	1-5 7/8
5/16	5 21/32	1-1 17/32	6 3/32	1-2 21/32	6 9/16	1-3 3/4	7 1/32	1-4 27/32	7 15/32	1-5 15/16
3/8	5 11/16	1-1 5/8	6 1/8	1-2 23/32	6 19/32	1-3 13/16	7 1/16	1-4 29/32	7 1/2	1-6
7/16	5 11/16	1-1 11/16	6 5/32	1-2 25/32	6 5/8	1-3 7/8	7 1/16	1-4 31/32	7 17/32	1-6 3/32
1/2	5 23/32	1-1 3/4	6 3/16	1-2 27/32	6 21/32	1-3 15/16	7 3/32	1-5 1/16	7 9/16	1-6 5/32
9/16	5 3/4	1-1 13/16	6 7/32	1-2 29/32	6 11/16	1-4 1/16	7 1/8	1-5 1/8	7 19/32	1-6 7/32
5/8	5 25/32	1-1 7/8	6 1/4	1-3	6 11/16	1-4 3/32	7 5/32	1-5 3/16	7 5/8	1-6 9/32
11/16	5 13/16	1-1 31/32	6 9/32	1-3 1/16	6 23/32	1-4 5/32	7 3/16	1-5 1/4	7 21/32	1-6 11/32
3/4	5 27/32	1-2 1/32	6 5/16	1-3 1/8	6 3/4	1-4 7/32	7 7/32	1-5 5/16	7 11/16	1-6 7/16
13/16	5 7/8	1-2 3/32	6 11/32	1-3 3/16	6 25/32	1-4 9/32	7 1/4	1-5 13/32	7 23/32	1-6 1/2
7/8	5 29/32	1-2 5/32	6 3/8	1-3 1/4	6 13/16	1-4 3/8	7 9/32	1-5 15/32	7 3/4	1-6 9/16
15/16	5 15/16	1-2 7/32	6 3/8	1-3 11/32	6 27/32	1-4 7/16	7 5/16	1-5 17/32	7 3/4	1-6 5/8

In.	17″ Rise	Slope	18″ Rise	Slope	19″ Rise	Slope	20″ Rise	Slope	21″ Rise	Slope
0	7 25/32	1-6 11/16	8 1/4	1-7 13/16	8 23/32	1-8 29/32	9 5/32	1-10	9 5/8	1-11 3/32
1/16	7 13/16	1-6 25/32	8 9/32	1-7 7/8	8 3/4	1-8 31/32	9 3/16	1-10 1/16	9 21/32	1-11 5/32
1/8	7 27/32	1-6 27/32	8 5/16	1-7 15/16	8 3/4	1-9 1/32	9 7/32	1-10 1/8	9 11/16	1-11 1/4
3/16	7 7/8	1-6 29/32	8 11/32	1-8	8 25/32	1-9 3/32	9 1/4	1-10 7/32	9 23/32	1-11 5/16
1/4	7 29/32	1-6 31/32	8 3/8	1-8 1/16	8 13/16	1-9 3/16	9 9/32	1-10 9/32	9 3/4	1-11 3/8
5/16	7 15/16	1-7 1/32	8 13/32	1-8 1/8	8 27/32	1-9 1/4	9 5/16	1-10 11/32	9 25/32	1-11 7/16
3/8	7 31/32	1-7 1/8	8 7/16	1-8 7/32	8 7/8	1-9 5/16	9 11/32	1-10 13/32	9 13/16	1-11 1/2
7/16	8	1-7 3/16	8 7/16	1-8 9/32	8 29/32	1-9 3/8	9 3/8	1-10 15/32	9 13/16	1-11 19/32
1/2	8 1/32	1-7 1/4	8 15/32	1-8 11/32	8 15/16	1-9 7/16	9 13/32	1-10 9/16	9 27/32	1-11 21/32
9/16	8 1/16	1-7 5/16	8 1/2	1-8 13/32	8 31/32	1-9 17/32	9 7/16	1-10 5/8	9 7/8	1-11 23/32
5/8	8 1/16	1-7 3/8	8 17/32	1-8 1/2	9	1-9 19/32	9 7/16	1-10 11/16	9 29/32	1-11 25/32
11/16	8 3/32	1-7 15/32	8 9/16	1-8 9/16	9 1/32	1-9 21/32	9 15/32	1-10 3/4	9 15/16	1-11 27/32
3/4	8 1/8	1-7 17/32	8 19/32	1-8 5/8	9 1/16	1-9 23/32	9 1/2	1-10 13/16	9 31/32	1-11 15/16
13/16	8 5/32	1-7 19/32	8 5/8	1-8 11/16	9 3/32	1-9 25/32	9 17/32	1-10 29/32	10	2-0
7/8	8 3/16	1-7 21/32	8 21/32	1-8 3/4	9 1/8	1-9 7/8	9 9/16	1-10 31/32	10 1/32	2-0 1/16
15/16	8 7/32	1-7 23/32	8 11/16	1-8 27/32	9 1/8	1-9 15/16	9 19/32	1-11 1/32	10 1/16	2-0 1/8

Feet	40′ Rise	Slope	50′ Rise	Slope	60′ Rise	Slope	70′ Rise	Slope
0	18-4	44-0	22-11	55-0 1/32	27-6	66-0 1/32	32-1	77-0 1/32
1	18-9½	45-1 7/32	23-4½	56-1 7/32	27-11½	67-1 7/32	32-6½	78-1 7/32
2	19-3	46-2 13/32	23-10	57-2 13/32	28-5	68-2 7/16	33-0	79-2 7/16
3	19-8½	47-3 5/8	24-3½	58-3 5/8	28-10½	69-3 5/8	33-5½	80-3 5/8
4	20-2	48-4 13/16	24-9	59-4 13/16	29-4	70-4 13/16	33-11	81-4 13/16
5	20-7½	49-6 1/32	25-2½	60-6 1/32	29-9½	71-6 1/32	34-4½	82-6 1/32
6	21-1	50-7 7/32	25-8	61-7 7/32	30-3	72-7 7/32	34-10	83-7 7/32
7	21-6½	51-8 13/32	26-1½	62-8 13/32	30-8½	73-8 7/16	35-3½	84-8 7/16
8	22-0	52-9 5/8	26-7	63-9 5/8	31-2	74-9 5/8	35-9	85-9 5/8
9	22-5½	53-10 13/16	27-0½	64-10 13/16	31-7½	75-10 13/16	36-2½	86-10 27/32

natsin A=0.4166547105; natcos A=0.9090648229; nattan A=0.4583333333; natcot A=2.1818181818

Inches	0" Rise	0" Slope	1" Rise	1" Slope	2" Rise	2" Slope	3" Rise	3" Slope	4" Rise	4" Slope	5" Rise	5" Slope
0	0	0	15/32	13/32	15/16	27/32	1 3/8	3 5/16	1 27/32	4 13/32	2 5/16	5 1/2
1/16	1/32	1/16	1/2	15/32	31/32	29/32	1 13/32	3 3/8	1 7/8	4 15/32	2 11/32	5 19/32
1/8	1/16	1/8	17/32	1 1/4	1	2 11/32	1 7/16	3 7/16	1 29/32	4 17/32	2 3/8	5 21/32
3/16	3/32	7/32	9/16	15/16	1	2 13/32	1 15/32	3 1/2	1 15/16	4 5/8	2 13/32	5 23/32
1/4	1/8	9/32	19/32	1 3/8	1 1/16	2 15/32	1 1/2	3 19/32	1 31/32	4 11/16	2 7/16	5 25/32
5/16	5/32	11/32	19/32	1 7/16	1 1/16	2 9/16	1 17/32	3 21/32	2	4 3/4	2 15/32	5 27/32
3/8	3/16	13/32	5/8	1 1/2	1 3/32	2 5/8	1 9/16	3 23/32	2 1/32	4 13/16	2 1/2	5 15/16
7/16	3/16	15/32	21/32	1 19/32	1 3/8	2 11/16	1 19/32	3 25/32	2 1/16	4 29/32	2 17/32	6
1/2	7/32	9/16	11/16	1 21/32	1 5/32	2 3/4	1 5/8	3 27/32	2 3/32	4 31/32	2 9/16	6 1/16
9/16	1/4	5/8	23/32	1 23/32	1 3/16	2 13/16	1 21/32	3 15/16	2 1/8	5 1/32	2 19/32	6 1/8
5/8	9/32	11/16	3/4	1 25/32	1 7/32	2 29/32	1 11/16	4	2 5/32	5 3/32	2 19/32	6 3/16
11/16	5/16	3/4	25/32	1 7/8	1 1/4	2 31/32	1 23/32	4 1/16	2 3/16	5 5/32	2 5/8	6 9/32
3/4	11/32	13/16	13/16	1 15/16	1 9/32	3 1/32	1 3/4	4 1/8	2 7/16	5 1/4	2 21/32	6 11/32
13/16	3/8	29/32	27/32	2	1 5/16	3 3/32	1 25/32	4 3/16	2 7/32	5 5/16	2 11/16	6 13/32
7/8	13/32	31/32	7/8	2 1/16	1 11/32	3 5/32	1 25/32	4 9/32	2 1/4	5 3/8	2 23/32	6 15/32
15/16	7/16	1 1/32	29/32	2 1/8	1 3/8	3 1/4	1 13/16	4 11/32	2 9/32	5 7/16	2 3/4	6 17/32

Inches	6" Rise	6" Slope	7" Rise	7" Slope	8" Rise	8" Slope	9" Rise	9" Slope	10" Rise	10" Slope	11" Rise	11" Slope
0	2 25/32	6 5/8	3 1/4	7 23/32	3 23/32	8 13/16	4 3/16	9 29/32	4 5/8	11 1/32	5 3/32	1-0 1/8
1/16	2 13/16	6 11/16	3 9/32	7 25/32	3 3/4	8 7/8	4 3/16	10	4 21/32	11 3/32	5 1/8	1-0 3/16
1/8	2 27/32	6 3/4	3 5/16	7 27/32	3 25/32	8 31/32	4 7/32	10 1/16	4 11/16	11 5/32	5 5/32	1-0 1/4
3/16	2 7/8	6 13/16	3 11/32	7 15/16	3 25/32	9 1/32	4 1/4	10 1/8	4 25/32	11 7/32	5 7/32	1-0 11/32
1/4	2 29/32	6 7/8	3 3/8	8	3 13/16	9 3/32	4 9/32	10 3/16	4 3/4	11 5/16	5 7/32	1-0 13/32
5/16	2 15/16	6 31/32	3 3/8	8 1/16	3 27/32	9 5/32	4 5/16	10 1/4	4 25/32	11 3/8	5 1/4	1-0 15/32
3/8	2 31/32	7 1/32	3 13/32	8 1/8	3 7/8	9 7/32	4 11/32	10 11/32	4 13/16	11 7/16	5 9/32	1-0 17/32
7/16	2 31/32	7 3/32	3 7/16	8 3/16	3 29/32	9 5/16	4 3/8	10 13/32	4 27/32	11 1/2	5 5/16	1-0 19/32
1/2	3	7 5/32	3 15/32	8 9/32	3 15/16	9 3/8	4 13/32	10 15/32	4 7/8	11 9/16	5 11/32	1-0 11/16
9/16	3 1/32	7 7/32	3 1/2	8 11/32	3 31/32	9 7/16	4 7/16	10 17/32	4 29/32	11 21/32	5 3/8	1-0 3/4
5/8	3 1/16	7 5/16	3 17/32	8 13/32	4	9 1/2	4 15/32	10 19/32	4 15/16	11 23/32	5 3/8	1-0 13/16
11/16	3 3/32	7 3/8	3 9/16	8 15/32	4 1/32	9 9/16	4 1/2	10 11/16	4 31/32	11 25/32	5 13/32	1-0 7/8
3/4	3 1/8	7 7/16	3 19/32	8 17/32	4 1/16	9 21/32	4 17/32	10 3/4	4 31/32	11 27/32	5 7/16	1-0 15/16
13/16	3 5/32	7 1/2	3 5/8	8 5/8	4 3/32	9 23/32	4 9/16	10 13/16	5	11 29/32	5 15/32	1-1 1/32
7/8	3 3/16	7 9/16	3 21/32	8 11/16	4 1/8	9 25/32	4 9/16	10 7/8	5 1/32	1-0	5 1/2	1-1 3/32
15/16	3 7/32	7 21/32	3 11/16	8 3/4	4 5/32	9 27/32	4 19/32	10 31/32	5 1/16	1-0 1/16	5 17/32	1-1 5/32

Feet	0' Rise	0' Slope	10' Rise	10' Slope	20' Rise	20' Slope	30' Rise	30' Slope
0	0	0	4-7 5/8	11-0 1/4	9-3 1/4	22-0 17/32	13-10 7/8	33-0 25/32
1	5 9/16	1-1 7/32	5-1 3/16	12-1 1/2	9-8 13/16	23-1 3/4	14-4 7/16	34-2 1/32
2	11 1/8	2-2 7/16	5-6 3/4	13-2 23/32	10-2 3/8	24-2 31/32	14-10	35-3 1/4
3	1-4 11/16	3-3 11/16	6-0 5/16	14-3 15/16	10-7 15/16	25-4 7/32	15-3 9/16	36-4 15/32
4	1-10 1/4	4-4 29/32	6-5 7/8	15-5 5/32	11-1 1/2	26-5 7/16	15-9 1/8	37-5 11/16
5	2-3 13/16	5-6 1/8	6-11 7/16	16-6 13/32	11-7 1/16	27-6 21/32	16-2 11/16	38-6 15/16
6	2-9 3/8	6-7 11/32	7-5	17-7 5/8	12-0 5/8	28-7 7/8	16-8 1/4	39-8 5/32
7	3-2 15/16	7-8 19/32	7-10 9/16	18-8 27/32	12-6 3/16	29-9 1/8	17-1 13/16	40-9 3/8
8	3-8 1/2	8-9 13/16	8-4 1/8	19-10 1/16	12-11 3/4	30-10 11/32	17-7 3/8	41-10 19/32
9	4-2 1/16	9-11 1/32	8-9 11/16	20-11 5/16	13-5 5/16	31-11 9/16	18-0 15/16	42-11 27/32

A = 24° 52' 11"; logsin A = 9.62382; logcos A = 9.95773; logtan A = 9.66609; logcot A = 0.33391

Ins.	12″ Rise	12″ Slope	13″ Rise	13″ Slope	14″ Rise	14″ Slope	15″ Rise	15″ Slope	16″ Rise	16″ Slope
0	5 9/16	1-1 7/32	6 1/2	1-2 11/32	6 1/2	1-3 7/16	6 15/16	1-4 17/32	7 13/32	1-5 5/8
1/16	5 19/32	1-1 9/32	6 1/16	1-2 13/32	6 17/32	1-3 1/2	6 31/32	1-4 19/32	7 7/16	1-5 23/32
1/8	5 5/8	1-1 3/8	6 3/32	1-2 15/32	6 9/16	1-3 9/16	7	1-4 21/32	7 15/32	1-5 25/32
3/16	5 21/32	1-1 7/16	6 1/8	1-2 17/32	6 9/16	1-3 5/8	7 1/32	1-4 3/4	7 1/2	1-5 27/32
1/4	5 11/16	1-1 1/2	6 5/32	1-2 19/32	6 19/32	1-3 23/32	7 1/16	1-4 13/16	7 17/32	1-5 29/32
5/16	5 23/32	1-1 9/16	6 5/32	1-2 11/16	6 5/8	1-3 25/32	7 3/32	1-4 7/8	7 9/16	1-5 31/32
3/8	5 3/4	1-1 5/8	6 3/16	1-2 3/4	6 21/32	1-3 27/32	7 1/8	1-4 15/16	7 19/32	1-6 1/16
7/16	5 3/4	1-1 23/32	6 7/32	1-2 13/16	6 11/16	1-3 29/32	7 5/32	1-5	7 5/8	1-6 1/8
1/2	5 25/32	1-1 25/32	6 1/4	1-2 7/8	6 23/32	1-3 31/32	7 3/16	1-5 3/32	7 21/32	1-6 3/16
9/16	5 13/16	1-1 27/32	6 9/32	1-2 15/16	6 3/4	1-4 1/16	7 7/32	1-5 5/32	7 11/16	1-6 1/4
5/8	5 27/32	1-1 29/32	6 5/16	1-3 1/32	6 25/32	1-4 1/8	7 1/4	1-5 7/32	7 23/32	1-6 5/16
11/16	5 7/8	1-1 31/32	6 11/32	1-3 3/32	6 13/16	1-4 3/16	7 9/32	1-5 9/32	7 3/4	1-6 13/32
3/4	5 29/32	1-2 1/16	6 3/8	1-3 5/32	6 27/32	1-4 1/4	7 5/16	1-5 3/8	7 3/4	1-6 15/32
13/16	5 15/16	1-2 1/8	6 13/32	1-3 7/32	6 7/8	1-4 5/16	7 11/32	1-5 7/16	7 25/32	1-6 17/32
7/8	5 31/32	1-2 3/16	6 7/16	1-3 9/32	6 29/32	1-4 13/32	7 11/32	1-5 1/2	7 13/16	1-6 19/32
15/16	6	1-2 1/4	6 15/32	1-3 3/8	6 15/16	1-4 15/32	7 3/8	1-5 9/16	7 27/32	1-6 21/32

Ins.	17″ Rise	17″ Slope	18″ Rise	18″ Slope	19″ Rise	19″ Slope	20″ Rise	20″ Slope	21″ Rise	21″ Slope
0	7 7/8	1-6 3/4	8 11/32	1-7 27/32	8 13/16	1-8 15/16	9 9/32	1-10 1/32	9 3/4	1-11 5/32
1/16	7 29/32	1-6 13/16	8 3/8	1-7 29/32	8 27/32	1-9	9 5/16	1-10 1/8	9 3/4	1-11 7/32
1/8	7 15/16	1-6 7/8	8 13/32	1-7 31/32	8 7/8	1-9 3/32	9 11/32	1-10 3/16	9 25/32	1-11 9/32
3/16	7 31/32	1-6 15/16	8 7/16	1-8 1/32	8 29/32	1-9 5/32	9 11/32	1-10 1/4	9 13/16	1-11 11/32
1/4	8	1-7	8 15/32	1-8 1/8	8 15/16	1-9 7/32	9 3/8	1-10 5/16	9 27/32	1-11 7/16
5/16	8 1/32	1-7 3/32	8 1/2	1-8 3/16	8 15/16	1-9 9/32	9 13/32	1-10 3/8	9 7/8	1-11 1/2
3/8	8 1/16	1-7 5/32	8 17/32	1-8 1/4	8 31/32	1-9 11/32	9 7/16	1-10 15/32	9 29/32	1-11 9/16
7/16	8 3/32	1-7 7/32	8 17/32	1-8 5/16	9	1-9 7/16	9 15/32	1-10 17/32	9 15/16	1-11 5/8
1/2	8 1/8	1-7 9/32	8 9/16	1-8 13/32	9 1/32	1-9 1/2	9 1/2	1-10 19/32	9 31/32	1-11 11/16
9/16	8 5/32	1-7 11/32	8 19/32	1-8 15/32	9 1/16	1-9 9/16	9 17/32	1-10 21/32	10	1-11 25/32
5/8	8 5/32	1-7 7/16	8 5/8	1-8 17/32	9 3/32	1-9 5/8	9 9/16	1-10 23/32	10 1/32	1-11 27/32
11/16	8 3/16	1-7 1/2	8 21/32	1-8 19/32	9 1/8	1-9 11/16	9 19/32	1-10 13/16	10 1/16	1-11 29/32
3/4	8 7/32	1-7 9/16	8 11/16	1-8 21/32	9 5/32	1-9 25/32	9 5/8	1-10 7/8	10 3/32	1-11 31/32
13/16	8 1/4	1-7 5/8	8 23/32	1-8 3/4	9 3/16	1-9 27/32	9 21/32	1 10 15/32	10 1/8	2-0 1/32
7/8	8 9/32	1-7 11/16	8 3/4	1-8 13/16	9 7/32	1-9 29/32	9 11/16	1-11	10 1/8	2-0 1/8
15/16	8 5/16	1-7 25/32	8 25/32	1-8 7/8	9 1/4	1-9 31/32	9 23/32	1-11 1/16	10 5/32	2-0 3/16

Feet	40′ Rise	40′ Slope	50′ Rise	50′ Slope	60′ Rise	60′ Slope	70′ Rise	70′ Slope
0	18-6 1/2	44-1 1/16	23-2 1/8	55-1 5/16	27-9 3/4	66-1 19/32	32-5 3/8	77-1 27/32
1	19-0 1/16	45-2 9/32	23-7 11/16	56-2 9/16	28-3 5/16	67-2 13/16	32-10 15/16	78-3 3/32
2	19-5 5/8	46-3 1/2	24-1 1/4	57-3 25/32	28-8 7/8	68-4 1/32	33-4 1/2	79-4 5/16
3	19-11 3/16	47-4 3/4	24-6 13/16	58-5	29-2 7/16	69-5 9/32	33-10 1/16	80-5 17/32
4	20-4 3/4	48-5 31/32	25-0 3/8	59-6 7/32	29-8	70-6 1/2	34-3 5/8	81-6 3/4
5	20-10 5/16	49-7 3/16	25-5 15/16	60-7 15/32	30-1 9/16	71-7 23/32	34-9 3/16	82-8
6	21-3 7/8	50-8 13/32	25-11 1/2	61-8 11/16	30-7 1/8	72-8 15/16	35-2 3/4	83-9 7/32
7	21-9 7/16	51-9 21/32	26-5 1/16	62-9 29/32	31-0 11/16	73-10 3/16	35-8 5/16	84-10 7/16
8	22-3	52-10 7/8	26-10 5/8	63-11 1/8	31-6 1/4	74-11 13/32	36-1 7/8	85-11 21/32
9	22-8 9/16	54-0 3/32	27-4 3/16	65-0 3/8	31-11 13/16	76-0 5/8	36-7 7/16	87-0 29/32

natsin A=0.4205558876; natcos A=0.9072666341; nattan A=0.4635416666; natcot A=2.1573033707

Inches	0" Rise	0" Slope	1" Rise	1" Slope	2" Rise	2" Slope	3" Rise	3" Slope	4" Rise	4" Slope	5" Rise	5" Slope
0	0	0	15/32	1 3/32	15/16	2 7/32	1 13/32	3 5/16	1 7/8	4 13/32	2 11/32	5 17/32
1/16	1/32	1/16	1/2	1 3/16	31/32	2 9/32	1 7/16	3 3/8	1 29/32	4 1/2	2 3/8	5 19/32
1/8	1/16	1/8	17/32	1 1/4	1	2 11/32	1 15/32	3 7/16	1 15/16	4 9/16	2 13/32	5 21/32
3/16	3/32	7/32	9/16	1 5/16	1 1/32	2 13/32	1 1/2	3 17/32	1 31/32	4 5/8	2 7/16	5 23/32
1/4	1/8	9/32	19/32	1 3/8	1 1/16	2 1/2	1 17/32	3 19/32	2	4 11/16	2 15/32	5 13/16
5/16	5/32	11/32	5/8	1 7/16	1 3/32	2 9/16	1 9/16	3 21/32	2 1/16	4 3/4	2 1/2	5 7/8
3/8	3/16	13/32	21/32	1 17/32	1 1/8	2 5/8	1 19/32	3 23/32	2 1/16	4 27/32	2 17/32	5 15/16
7/16	7/32	15/32	11/16	1 19/32	1 5/32	2 11/16	1 5/8	3 25/32	2 3/32	4 29/32	2 9/16	6
1/2	1/4	9/16	11/16	1 21/32	1 3/16	2 3/4	1 5/8	3 7/8	2 1/8	4 31/32	2 9/16	6 1/16
9/16	1/4	5/8	23/32	1 23/32	1 3/16	2 27/32	1 21/32	3 15/16	2 1/8	5 1/32	2 19/32	6 5/32
5/8	9/32	11/16	3/4	1 25/32	1 7/32	2 29/32	1 11/16	4	2 5/32	5 3/32	2 5/8	6 7/32
11/16	5/16	3/4	25/32	1 7/8	1 1/4	2 31/32	1 23/32	4 1/16	2 3/16	5 3/16	2 21/32	6 9/32
3/4	11/32	27/32	13/16	1 15/16	1 9/32	3 1/32	1 3/4	4 5/32	2 7/32	5 1/4	2 11/16	6 11/32
13/16	3/8	29/32	27/32	2	1 5/16	3 3/32	1 25/32	4 7/32	2 1/4	5 5/16	2 23/32	6 13/32
7/8	13/32	31/32	7/8	2 1/16	1 11/32	3 3/16	1 13/16	4 9/32	2 9/32	5 3/8	2 3/4	6 1/2
15/16	7/16	1 1/32	29/32	2 1/8	1 3/8	3 1/4	1 27/32	4 11/32	2 5/16	5 7/16	2 25/32	6 9/16

Inches	6" Rise	6" Slope	7" Rise	7" Slope	8" Rise	8" Slope	9" Rise	9" Slope	10" Rise	10" Slope	11" Rise	11" Slope
0	2 13/16	6 5/8	3 9/32	7 23/32	3 3/4	8 27/32	4 7/32	9 15/16	4 11/16	11 1/32	5 5/32	1-0 5/32
1/16	2 27/32	6 11/16	3 5/16	7 13/16	3 25/32	8 29/32	4 1/4	10	4 23/32	11 1/8	5 3/16	1-0 7/32
1/8	2 7/8	6 3/4	3 11/32	7 7/8	3 13/16	8 31/32	4 9/32	10 1/16	4 3/4	11 3/16	5 7/32	1-0 9/32
3/16	2 29/32	6 27/32	3 3/8	7 15/16	3 27/32	9 1/32	4 5/16	10 5/32	4 25/32	11 1/4	5 1/4	1-0 11/32
1/4	2 15/16	6 29/32	3 13/32	8	3 7/8	9 1/8	4 11/32	10 7/32	4 13/16	11 5/16	5 9/32	1-0 7/16
5/16	2 31/32	6 31/32	3 7/16	8 1/16	3 29/32	9 3/16	4 3/8	10 9/32	4 27/32	11 3/8	5 5/16	1-0 1/2
3/8	3	7 1/32	3 15/32	8 5/32	3 15/16	9 1/4	4 13/32	10 11/32	4 7/8	11 15/32	5 11/32	1-0 9/16
7/16	3 1/32	7 1/8	3 1/2	8 7/32	3 31/32	9 5/16	4 7/16	10 7/16	4 29/32	11 17/32	5 3/8	1-0 5/8
1/2	3 1/16	7 3/16	3 1/2	8 9/32	4	9 3/8	4 15/32	10 1/2	4 15/16	11 19/32	5 3/8	1-0 11/16
9/16	3 1/16	7 1/4	3 17/32	8 11/32	4	9 15/32	4 15/32	10 9/16	4 15/16	11 21/32	5 13/32	1-0 25/32
5/8	3 3/32	7 5/16	3 9/16	8 13/32	4 1/32	9 17/32	4 1/2	10 5/8	4 31/32	11 3/4	5 7/16	1-0 27/32
11/16	3 1/8	7 3/8	3 19/32	8 1/2	4 1/16	9 19/32	4 17/32	10 11/16	5	11 13/16	5 15/32	1-0 29/32
3/4	3 5/32	7 15/32	3 5/8	8 9/16	4 3/32	9 21/32	4 9/16	10 25/32	5 1/16	11 7/8	5 1/2	1-0 31/32
13/16	3 3/16	7 17/32	3 21/32	8 5/8	4 1/8	9 23/32	4 19/32	10 27/32	5 1/16	11 15/16	5 17/32	1-1 1/32
7/8	3 7/32	7 19/32	3 11/16	8 11/16	4 5/32	9 13/16	4 5/8	10 29/32	5 1/8	1-0	5 9/16	1-1 1/8
15/16	3 1/4	7 21/32	3 23/32	8 25/32	4 3/16	9 7/8	4 21/32	10 31/32	5 1/8	1-0 3/32	5 19/32	1-1 3/16

Feet	0' Rise	0' Slope	10' Rise	10' Slope	20' Rise	20' Slope	30' Rise	30' Slope
0	0	0	4-8 1/4	11-0 1/32	9-4 1/2	22-1 1/16	14-0 3/4	33-1 19/32
1	5 5/8	1-1 1/4	5-1 7/8	12-1 25/32	9-10 1/8	23-2 5/16	14-6 3/8	34-2 27/32
2	11 1/4	2-2 1/2	5-7 1/2	13-3 1/32	10-3 3/4	24-3 9/16	15-0	35-4 3/32
3	1-4 7/8	3-3 3/4	6-1 1/8	14-4 9/32	10-9 3/8	25-4 13/16	15-5 5/8	36-5 11/32
4	1-10 1/2	4-5	6-6 3/4	15-5 17/32	11-3	26-6 1/16	15-11 1/4	37-6 19/32
5	2-4 1/8	5-6 1/4	7-0 3/8	16-6 25/32	11-8 5/8	27-7 5/16	16-4 7/8	38-7 27/32
6	2-9 3/4	6-7 17/32	7-6	17-8 1/16	12-2 1/4	28-8 9/16	16-10 1/2	39-9 3/32
7	3-3 3/8	7-8 25/32	7-11 5/8	18-9 5/16	12-7 7/8	29-9 27/32	17-4 1/8	40-10 11/32
8	3-9	8-10 1/32	8-5 1/4	19-10 9/16	13-1 1/2	30-11 3/32	17-9 3/4	41-11 5/8
9	4-2 5/8	9-11 9/32	8-10 7/8	20-11 13/16	13-7 1/8	32-0 11/32	18-3 3/8	43-0 7/8

A = 25° 06' 53''; logsin A = 9.62781; logcos A = 9.95687; logtan A = 9.67094; logcot A = 0.32906

Ins.	12″ Rise	12″ Slope	13″ Rise	13″ Slope	14″ Rise	14″ Slope	15″ Rise	15″ Slope	16″ Rise	16″ Slope
0	5 5/8	1-1 1/4	6 3/32	1-2 11/32	6 9/16	1-3 15/32−	7 1/32	1-4 9/16	7 1/2	1-5 21/32
1/16	5 21/32−	1-1 5/16	6 1/8	1-2 7/16	6 19/32−	1-3 17/32−	7 1/16	1-4 5/8	7 17/32−	1-5 3/4
1/8	5 11/16	1-1 13/32−	6 5/32−	1-2 1/2	6 5/8	1-3 19/32	7 3/32−	1-4 23/32−	7 9/16	1-5 13/16
3/16	5 23/32−	1-1 15/32−	6 3/16	1-2 9/16	6 21/32−	1-3 21/32	7 1/8	1-4 25/32−	7 19/32−	1-5 7/8
1/4	5 3/4	1 1 17/32−	6 7/32−	1-2 5/8	6 11/16	1-3 3/4	7 5/32−	1-4 27/32−	7 5/8	1-5 15/16
5/16	5 25/32−	1-1 19/32	6 1/4	1-2 11/16	6 23/32−	1-3 13/16	7 3/16	1-4 29/32	7 21/32−	1-6 1/32−
3/8	5 13/16	1-1 21/32	6 9/32−	1-2 25/32−	6 3/4	1-3 7/8	7 7/32−	1-4 31/32	7 11/16	1-6 3/32−
7/16	5 27/32−	1-1 3/4	6 5/16	1-2 27/32−	6 25/32−	1-3 15/16	7 1/4	1-5 1/16	7 23/32−	1-6 5/32−
1/2	5 7/8	1-1 13/16	6 5/16	1-2 29/32	6 13/16	1-4	7 1/4	1-5 1/8	7 3/4	1-6 7/32
9/16	5 7/8	1-1 7/8	6 11/32	1-2 31/32	6 13/16	1-4 3/32−	7 9/32	1-5 3/16	7 3/4	1-6 9/32
5/8	5 29/32	1-1 15/16	6 3/8	1-3 1/16	6 27/32	1-4 5/32−	7 5/16	1-5 1/4	7 25/32	1-6 3/8
11/16	5 15/16	1-2	6 13/32	1-3 1/8	6 7/8	1-4 7/32	7 11/32	1-5 5/16	7 13/16	1-6 7/16
3/4	5 31/32	1-2 3/32−	6 7/16	1-3 3/16	6 29/32	1-4 9/32	7 3/8	1-5 13/32−	7 27/32	1-6 1/2
13/16	6	1-2 5/32−	6 15/32	1-3 1/4	6 15/16	1-4 11/32	7 13/32	1-5 15/32−	7 7/8	1-6 9/16
7/8	6 1/32	1-2 7/32	6 1/2	1-3 5/16	6 31/32	1-4 7/16	7 7/16	1-5 17/32	7 29/32	1-6 5/8
15/16	6 1/16	1-2 9/32	6 17/32	1-3 13/32−	7	1-4 1/2	7 15/32	1-5 19/32	7 15/16	1-6 23/32−

Ins.	17″ Rise	17″ Slope	18″ Rise	18″ Slope	19″ Rise	19″ Slope	20″ Rise	20″ Slope	21″ Rise	21″ Slope
0	7 31/32	1-6 25/32−	8 7/16	1-7 7/8	8 29/32	1-8 31/32	9 3/8	1-10 3/32−	9 27/32	1-11 3/16
1/16	8	1-6 27/32	8 15/32−	1-7 15/16	8 15/16	1-9 1/16	9 13/32−	1-10 5/32	9 7/8	1-11 1/4
1/8	8 1/32−	1-6 29/32	8 1/2	1-8 1/32−	8 31/32−	1-9 1/8	9 7/16	1-10 7/32	9 29/32−	1-11 11/32−
3/16	8 1/16	1-6 31/32	8 17/32−	1-8 3/32−	9	1-9 3/16	9 15/32−	1-10 9/32	9 15/16	1-11 13/32−
1/4	8 3/32−	1-7 1/16	8 9/16	1-8 5/32−	9 1/32−	1-9 1/4	9 1/2	1-10 3/8	9 31/32−	1-11 15/32
5/16	8 1/8	1-7 1/8	8 19/32−	1-8 7/32	9 1/16	1-9 11/32−	9 17/32−	1-10 7/16	10	1-11 17/32
3/8	8 5/32−	1-7 3/16	8 5/8	1-8 9/32	9 3/32−	1-9 13/32−	9 9/16	1-10 1/2	10 1/32−	1-11 19/32
7/16	8 3/16	1-7 1/4	8 21/32−	1-8 3/8	9 1/8	1-9 15/32−	9 19/32−	1-10 9/16	10 1/16	1-11 11/16
1/2	8 3/16	1-7 5/16	8 11/16	1-8 7/16	9 1/8	1-9 17/32	9 5/8	1-10 5/8	10 1/16	1-11 3/4
9/16	8 7/32	1-7 13/32−	8 11/16	1-8 1/2	9 5/32	1-9 19/32	9 5/8	1-10 23/32−	10 3/32	1-11 13/16
5/8	8 1/4	1-7 15/32−	8 23/32	1-8 9/16	9 3/16	1-9 11/16	9 21/32	1-10 25/32−	10 1/8	1-11 7/8
11/16	8 9/32	1-7 17/32	8 3/4	1-8 5/8	9 7/32	1-9 3/4	9 11/16	1-10 27/32	10 5/32	1-11 15/16
3/4	8 5/16	1-7 19/32	8 25/32	1-8 23/32−	9 1/4	1-9 13/16	9 23/32	1-10 29/32	10 3/16	2-0 1/32−
13/16	8 11/32	1-7 11/16	8 13/16	1-8 25/32−	9 9/32	1-9 7/8	9 3/4	1-11	10 7/32	2-0 3/32−
7/8	8 3/8	1-7 3/4	8 27/32	1-8 27/32	9 5/16	1-9 15/16	9 25/32	1-11 1/16	10 1/4	2-0 5/32
15/16	8 13/32	1-7 13/16	8 7/8	1-8 29/32	9 11/32	1-10 1/32−	9 13/16	1-11 1/8	10 9/32	2-0 7/32

Feet	40′ Rise	40′ Slope	50′ Rise	50′ Slope	60′ Rise	60′ Slope	70′ Rise	70′ Slope
0	18-9	44-2 1/8	23-5 1/4	55-2 21/32−	28-1 1/2	66-3 3/16	32-9 3/4	77-3 23/32−
1	19-2 5/8	45-3 3/8	23-10 7/8	56-3 29/32−	28-7 1/8	67-4 7/16	33-3 3/8	78-4 31/32−
2	19-8 1/4	46-4 5/8	24-4 1/2	57-5 5/32−	29-0 3/4	68-5 11/16	33-9	79-6 7/32−
3	20-1 7/8	47-5 7/8	24-10 1/8	58-6 13/32−	29-6 3/8	69-6 15/16	34-2 5/8	80-7 15/32−
4	20-7 1/2	48-7 1/8	25-3 3/4	59-7 21/32	30-0	70-8 3/16	34-8 1/4	81-8 23/32−
5	21-1 1/8	49-8 3/8	25-9 3/8	60-8 29/32	30-5 5/8	71-9 7/16	35-1 7/8	82-9 31/32
6	21-6 3/4	50-9 5/8	26-3	61-10 5/32	30-11 1/4	72-10 11/16	35-7 1/2	83-11 7/32
7	22-0 3/8	51-10 7/8	26-8 5/8	62-11 13/32	31-4 7/8	73-11 15/16	36-1 1/8	85-0 15/32
8	22-6	53-0 5/32−	27-2 1/4	64-0 21/32	31-10 1/2	75-1 3/16	36-6 3/4	86-1 23/32
9	22-11 5/8	54-1 13/32−	27-7 7/8	65-1 15/16	32-4 1/8	76-2 15/32−	37-0 3/8	87-2 31/32

natsin A=0.4244338762; natcos A=0.9054589359; nattan A=0.4687500000; natcot A=2.1333333333

Inches	0" Rise	0" Slope	1" Rise	1" Slope	2" Rise	2" Slope	3" Rise	3" Slope	4" Rise	4" Slope	5" Rise	5" Slope
0	0	0	15/32	1 3/32	15/16	2 1/32	1 7/16	3 5/16	1 29/32	4 7/16	2 3/8	5 17/32
1/16	1/32	1/16	1/2	1 3/16	31/32	2 9/32	1 7/16	3 3/8	1 15/16	4 1/2	2 13/32	5 19/32
1/8	1/16	1/8	17/32	1 1/4	1	2 11/32	1 15/32	3 15/32	1 31/32	4 9/16	2 7/16	5 21/32
3/16	3/32	7/32	9/16	1 5/16	1 1/32	2 13/32	1 1/2	3 17/32	2	4 5/8	2 15/32	5 3/4
1/4	1/8	9/32	19/32	1 3/8	1 1/16	2 1/2	1 17/32	3 19/32	2	4 23/32	2 1/2	5 13/16
5/16	5/32	11/32	5/8	1 7/16	1 3/32	2 9/16	1 9/16	3 21/32	2 1/16	4 25/32	2 17/32	5 7/8
3/8	3/16	13/32	21/32	1 17/32	1 1/8	2 5/8	1 19/32	3 3/4	2 1/16	4 27/32	2 9/16	5 15/16
7/16	7/32	15/32	11/16	1 19/32	1 5/32	2 11/16	1 5/8	3 13/16	2 3/32	4 29/32	2 9/16	6 1/32
1/2	1/4	9/16	23/32	1 21/32	1 3/16	2 25/32	1 21/32	3 7/8	2 1/8	4 31/32	2 19/32	6 3/32
9/16	9/32	5/8	3/4	1 23/32	1 7/32	2 27/32	1 11/16	3 15/16	2 5/32	5 1/16	2 5/8	6 5/32
5/8	9/32	11/16	25/32	1 13/16	1 1/4	2 29/32	1 23/32	4	2 3/16	5 1/8	2 21/32	6 7/32
11/16	5/16	3/4	13/16	1 7/8	1 9/32	2 31/32	1 3/4	4 3/32	2 7/32	5 3/16	2 11/16	6 9/32
3/4	11/32	27/32	27/32	1 15/16	1 5/16	3 1/32	1 25/32	4 5/32	2 1/4	5 1/4	2 23/32	6 3/8
13/16	3/8	29/32	27/32	2	1 11/32	3 1/8	1 13/16	4 7/32	2 9/32	5 5/16	2 3/4	6 7/16
7/8	13/32	31/32	7/8	2 1/16	1 3/8	3 3/16	1 27/32	4 9/32	2 5/16	5 13/32	2 25/32	6 1/2
15/16	7/16	1 1/32	29/32	2 5/32	1 13/32	3 1/4	1 7/8	4 11/32	2 11/32	5 15/32	2 13/16	6 9/16

Inches	6" Rise	6" Slope	7" Rise	7" Slope	8" Rise	8" Slope	9" Rise	9" Slope	10" Rise	10" Slope	11" Rise	11" Slope
0	2 27/32	6 5/8	3 5/16	7 3/4	3 25/32	8 27/32	4 1/4	9 31/32	4 3/4	11 1/16	5 7/32	1-0 3/8
1/16	2 7/8	6 23/32	3 11/32	7 13/16	3 13/16	8 15/16	4 9/32	10 1/32	4 25/32	11 1/8	5 1/4	1-0 1/4
1/8	2 29/32	6 25/32	3 3/8	7 7/8	3 27/32	9	4 5/16	10 3/32	4 13/16	11 7/8	5 9/32	1-0 5/32
3/16	2 15/16	6 27/32	3 13/32	7 31/32	3 7/8	9 1/16	4 11/32	10 5/32	4 27/32	11 9/32	5 5/16	1-0 3/8
1/4	2 31/32	6 29/32	3 7/16	8 1/32	3 29/32	9 1/8	4 3/8	10 1/4	4 27/32	11 11/32	5 11/32	1-0 7/16
5/16	3	7	3 15/32	8 3/32	3 15/16	9 3/16	4 13/32	10 5/16	4 7/8	11 13/32	5 3/8	1-0 17/32
3/8	3 1/32	7 1/16	3 1/2	8 5/32	3 31/32	9 9/32	4 7/16	10 3/8	4 29/32	11 15/32	5 13/32	1-0 19/32
7/16	3 1/16	7 1/8	3 17/32	8 7/32	4	9 11/32	4 15/32	10 7/16	4 15/16	11 9/16	5 13/32	1-0 21/32
1/2	3 3/32	7 3/16	3 9/16	8 5/16	4	9 13/32	4 1/2	10 1/2	4 31/32	11 5/8	5 7/16	1-0 23/32
9/16	3 1/8	7 1/4	3 19/32	8 3/8	4 1/16	9 15/32	4 17/32	10 19/32	5	11 11/16	5 15/32	1-0 25/32
5/8	3 1/8	7 11/32	3 5/8	8 7/16	4 3/32	9 17/32	4 9/16	10 21/32	5 1/32	11 3/4	5 1/2	1-0 7/8
11/16	3 5/32	7 13/32	3 21/32	8 1/2	4 1/8	9 5/8	4 19/32	10 23/32	5 1/16	11 13/16	5 17/32	1-0 15/16
3/4	3 3/16	7 15/32	3 11/16	8 9/16	4 5/32	9 11/16	4 5/8	10 25/32	5 3/32	11 29/32	5 9/16	1-1
13/16	3 7/32	7 17/32	3 11/16	8 21/32	4 3/16	9 3/4	4 21/32	10 27/32	5 1/8	11 31/32	5 19/32	1-1 1/16
7/8	3 7/32	7 19/32	3 23/32	8 23/32	4 7/32	9 13/16	4 11/16	10 15/16	5 5/32	1-0 1/32	5 5/8	1-1 5/32
15/16	3 9/32	7 11/16	3 3/4	8 25/32	4 1/4	9 7/8	4 23/32	11	5 3/8	1-0 3/32	5 21/32	1-1 7/32

Feet	0' Rise	0' Slope	10' Rise	10' Slope	20' Rise	20' Slope	30' Rise	30' Slope
0	0	0	4-8 7/8	11-0 25/32	9-5 3/4	22-1 19/32	14-2 5/8	33-2 3/8
1	5 11/16	1-1 9/16	5-2 9/16	12-2 1/16	9-11 7/16	23-2 7/8	14-8 5/16	34-3 21/32
2	11 3/8	2-2 9/16	5-8 1/4	13-3 11/32	10-5 1/8	24-4 5/32	15-2	35-4 15/16
3	1-5 1/16	3-3 27/32	6-1 15/16	14-4 5/8	10-10 13/16	25-5 7/16	15-7 11/16	36-6 7/32
4	1-10 3/4	4-5 1/8	6-7 5/8	15-5 29/32	11-4 1/2	26-6 23/32	16-1 3/8	37-7 1/2
5	2-4 7/16	5-6 13/32	7-1 9/16	16-7 3/8	11-10 5/16	27-8	16-7 1/16	38-8 25/32
6	2-10 1/8	6-7 11/16	7-7	17-8 15/32	12-3 7/8	28-9 9/32	17-0 3/4	39-10 1/16
7	3-3 13/16	7-8 31/32	8-0 11/16	18-9 3/4	12-9 9/16	29-10 9/16	17-6 7/16	40-11 11/32
8	3-9 1/2	8-10 1/4	8-6 3/8	19-11 1/32	13-3 1/4	30-11 27/32	18-0 1/8	42-0 5/8
9	4-3 3/16	9-11 17/32	9-0 1/16	21-0 5/16	13-8 15/16	32-1 3/32	18-5 13/16	43-1 29/32

A = 25° 21' 32"; logsin A = 9.63174: logcos A = 9.95600; logtan A = 9.67574; logcot A = 0.32426

Ins.	12″		13″		14″		15″		16″	
	Rise	Slope	Rise	Slope	Rise	Slope	Rise	Slope	Rise	Slope
0	5 11/16	1-1 9/32	6 5/32	1-2 3/8	6 5/8	1-3 1/2	7 1/8	1-4 19/32	7 19/32	1-5 23/32
1/16	5 23/32	1-1 11/32	6 3/16	1-2 15/32	6 21/32	1-3 9/16	7 1/8	1-4 21/32	7 5/8	1-5 25/32
1/8	5 3/4	1-1 13/32	6 7/32	1-2 17/32	6 11/16	1-3 5/8	7 5/32	1-4 3/4	7 21/32	1-5 27/32
3/16	5 25/32	1-1 1/2	6 1/4	1-2 19/32	6 23/32	1-3 11/16	7 3/16	1-4 13/16	7 11/16	1-5 29/32
1/4	5 13/16	1-1 9/16	6 9/32	1-2 21/32	6 3/4	1-3 25/32	7 7/32	1-4 7/8	7 11/16	1-5 31/32
5/16	5 27/32	1-1 5/8	6 5/16	1-2 23/32	6 25/32	1-3 27/32	7 1/4	1-4 15/16	7 23/32	1-6 1/16
3/8	5 7/8	1-1 11/16	6 11/32	1-2 13/16	6 13/16	1-3 29/32	7 9/32	1-5	7 3/4	1-6 1/8
7/16	5 29/32	1-1 3/4	6 3/8	1-2 7/8	6 27/32	1-3 31/32	7 5/16	1-5 3/32	7 25/32	1-6 3/16
1/2	5 15/16	1-1 27/32	6 13/32	1-2 15/16	6 7/8	1-4 1/32	7 11/32	1-5 5/32	7 13/16	1-6 1/4
9/16	5 31/32	1-1 29/32	6 7/16	1-3	6 29/32	1-4 1/8	7 3/8	1-5 7/32	7 27/32	1-6 11/32
5/8	5 31/32	1-1 31/32	6 15/32	1-3 1/16	6 15/16	1-4 3/16	7 13/32	1-5 9/32	7 7/8	1-6 13/32
11/16	6	1-2 1/32	6 1/2	1-3 5/32	6 31/32	1-4 1/4	7 7/16	1-5 3/8	7 29/32	1-6 15/32
3/4	6 1/32	1-2 1/8	6 17/32	1-3 7/32	7	1-4 5/16	7 15/32	1-5 7/16	7 15/16	1-6 17/32
13/16	6 1/16	1-2 3/16	6 17/32	1-3 9/32	7 1/32	1-4 13/32	7 1/2	1-5 1/2	7 31/32	1-6 19/32
7/8	6 3/32	1-2 1/4	6 9/16	1-3 11/32	7 1/16	1-4 15/32	7 17/32	1-5 9/16	8	1-6 11/16
15/16	6 1/8	1-2 5/16	6 19/32	1-3 7/16	7 3/32	1-4 17/32	7 9/16	1-5 5/8	8 1/32	1-6 3/4

Ins.	17″		18″		19″		20″		21″	
	Rise	Slope	Rise	Slope	Rise	Slope	Rise	Slope	Rise	Slope
0	8 1/16	1-6 13/16	8 17/32	1-7 29/32	9	1-9 1/32	9 15/32	1-10 1/8	9 15/16	1-11 1/4
1/16	8 3/32	1-6 7/8	8 9/16	1-8	9 1/32	1-9 3/32	9 1/2	1-10 3/16	9 31/32	1-11 5/16
1/8	8 1/8	1-6 15/16	8 19/32	1-8 1/16	9 1/16	1-9 5/32	9 17/32	1-10 9/32	10	1-11 3/8
3/16	8 5/32	1-7 1/32	8 5/8	1-8 1/8	9 3/32	1-9 7/32	9 9/16	1-10 11/32	10 1/32	1-11 7/16
1/4	8 3/16	1-7 3/32	8 21/32	1-8 3/16	9 1/8	1-9 5/16	9 19/32	1-10 13/32	10 1/16	1-11 17/32
5/16	8 7/32	1-7 5/32	8 11/16	1-8 1/4	9 5/32	1-9 3/8	9 5/8	1-10 15/32	10 3/32	1-11 19/32
3/8	8 1/4	1-7 7/32	8 23/32	1-8 11/32	9 3/16	1-9 7/16	9 21/32	1-10 9/16	10 1/8	1-11 21/32
7/16	8 1/4	1-7 5/16	8 3/4	1-8 13/32	9 7/32	1-9 1/2	9 11/16	1-10 5/8	10 5/32	1-11 23/32
1/2	8 9/32	1-7 3/8	8 25/32	1-8 15/32	9 1/4	1-9 19/32	9 23/32	1-10 11/16	10 3/16	1-11 25/32
9/16	8 5/16	1-7 7/16	8 13/16	1-8 17/32	9 9/32	1-9 21/32	9 3/4	1-10 3/4	10 7/32	1-11 7/8
5/8	8 11/32	1-7 1/2	8 13/16	1-8 5/8	9 5/16	1-9 23/32	9 25/32	1-10 13/16	10 1/4	1-11 15/16
11/16	8 3/8	1-7 9/16	8 27/32	1-8 11/16	9 11/32	1-9 25/32	9 13/16	1-10 29/32	10 9/32	2-0
3/4	8 13/32	1-7 21/32	8 7/8	1-8 3/4	9 3/8	1-9 27/32	9 27/32	1-10 31/32	10 5/16	2-0 1/16
13/16	8 7/16	1-7 23/32	8 29/32	1-8 13/16	9 3/8	1-9 15/16	9 7/8	1-11 1/32	10 11/32	2-0 1/8
7/8	8 15/32	1-7 25/32	8 15/16	1-8 7/8	9 13/32	1-10	9 29/32	1-11 3/32	10 3/8	2-0 7/32
15/16	8 1/2	1-7 27/32	8 31/32	1-8 31/32	9 7/16	1-10 1/16	9 15/16	1-11 5/32	10 13/32	2-0 9/32

Feet	40′		50′		60′		70′	
	Rise	Slope	Rise	Slope	Rise	Slope	Rise	Slope
0	18-11 1/2	44-3 3/16	23-8 3/8	55-3 31/32	28-5 1/4	66-4 25/32	33-2 1/8	77-5 9/16
1	19-5 3/16	45-4 15/32	24-2 1/16	56-5 1/4	28-10 15/16	67-6 1/16	33-7 13/16	78-6 27/32
2	19-10 7/8	46-5 3/4	24-7 3/4	57-6 17/32	29-4 5/8	68-7 11/32	34-1 1/2	79-8 1/8
3	20-4 9/16	47-7 1/32	25-1 7/16	58-7 13/16	29-10 5/16	69-8 5/8	34-7 3/16	80-9 13/32
4	20-10 1/4	48-8 5/16	25-7 1/8	59-9 3/32	30-4	70-9 29/32	35-0 7/8	81-10 11/16
5	21-3 15/16	49-9 19/32	26-0 13/16	60-10 3/8	30-9 11/16	71-11 3/16	35-6 9/16	82-11 31/32
6	21-9 5/8	50-10 7/8	26-6 1/2	61-11 21/32	31-3 3/8	73-0 15/32	36-0 1/4	84-1 1/4
7	22-3 5/16	52-0 5/32	27-0 3/16	63-0 15/16	31-9 1/16	74-1 23/32	36-5 15/16	85-2 17/32
8	22-9	53-1 13/32	27-5 7/8	64-2 7/32	32-2 3/4	75-3	36-11 5/8	86-3 13/16
9	23-2 11/16	54-2 11/16	27-11 9/16	65-3 1/2	32-8 7/16	76-4 9/32	37-5 5/16	87-5 3/32

natsin A=0.4282886482; natcos A=0.9036419833; nattan A=0.4739583333; natcot A=2.1098901098

Inches	0" Rise	0" Slope	1" Rise	1" Slope	2" Rise	2" Slope	3" Rise	3" Slope	4" Rise	4" Slope	5" Rise	5" Slope
0	0	0	15/32	1-3/32	31/32	2-7/32	1-7/16	3-5/16	1-29/32	4-7/16	2-13/32	5-17/32
1/16	1/32	1/16	1/2	1-3/16	1	2-9/32	1-15/32	3-13/32	1-15/16	4-1/2	2-7/16	5-5/8
1/8	1/16	1/8	17/32	1-1/4	1-1/32	2-11/32	1-1/2	3-15/32	1-31/32	4-9/16	2-15/32	5-11/16
3/16	3/32	7/32	9/16	1-5/16	1-1/16	2-7/16	1-17/32	3-17/32	2	4-21/32	2-1/2	5-3/4
1/4	1/8	9/32	19/32	1-3/8	1-1/16	2-1/2	1-9/16	3-19/32	2-1/32	4-23/32	2-1/2	5-13/16
5/16	5/32	11/32	5/8	1-15/32	1-3/32	2-9/16	1-19/32	3-11/16	2-1/16	4-25/32	2-17/32	5-29/32
3/8	3/16	13/32	21/32	1-17/32	1-1/8	2-5/8	1-5/8	3-3/4	2-3/32	4-27/32	2-9/16	5-31/32
7/16	7/32	1/2	11/16	1-19/32	1-5/32	2-11/16	1-21/32	3-13/16	2-1/8	4-29/32	2-19/32	6-1/32
1/2	1/4	9/16	23/32	1-21/32	1-3/16	2-25/32	1-11/16	3-7/8	2-5/32	5	2-5/8	6-3/32
9/16	9/32	5/8	3/4	1-23/32	1-7/32	2-27/32	1-23/32	3-15/16	2-3/16	5-1/16	2-21/32	6-5/32
5/8	5/16	11/16	25/32	1-13/16	1-1/4	2-29/32	1-3/4	4-1/32	2-7/32	5-1/8	2-11/16	6-1/4
11/16	11/32	3/4	13/16	1-7/8	1-9/32	2-31/32	1-25/32	4-3/32	2-1/4	5-3/16	2-23/32	6-5/16
3/4	3/8	27/32	27/32	1-15/16	1-5/16	3-1/16	1-13/16	4-5/32	2-9/32	5-9/32	2-3/4	6-3/8
13/16	3/8	29/32	7/8	2	1-11/32	3-1/8	1-13/16	4-7/32	2-5/16	5-11/32	2-25/32	6-7/16
7/8	13/32	31/32	29/32	2-3/32	1-3/8	3-3/16	1-27/32	4-9/32	2-11/32	5-13/32	2-13/16	6-1/2
15/16	7/16	1-1/32	15/16	2-5/32	1-13/32	3-1/4	1-7/8	4-3/8	2-3/8	5-15/32	2-27/32	6-19/32

Inches	6" Rise	6" Slope	7" Rise	7" Slope	8" Rise	8" Slope	9" Rise	9" Slope	10" Rise	10" Slope	11" Rise	11" Slope
0	2-7/8	6-21/32	3-11/32	7-3/4	3-27/32	8-7/8	4-5/16	9-31/32	4-25/32	11-3/32	5-9/32	1-0-3/32
1/16	2-29/32	6-23/32	3-3/8	7-27/32	3-7/8	8-15/16	4-11/32	10-1/16	4-13/16	11-5/32	5-5/16	1-0-9/32
1/8	2-15/16	6-25/32	3-13/32	7-29/32	3-29/32	9	4-3/8	10-1/8	4-27/32	11-7/32	5-11/32	1-0-11/32
3/16	2-31/32	6-7/8	3-7/16	7-31/32	3-15/16	9-3/32	4-13/32	10-3/16	4-7/8	11-9/32	5-3/8	1-0-13/32
1/4	3	6-15/16	3-15/32	8-1/16	3-15/16	9-5/32	4-7/16	10-1/4	4-29/32	11-3/8	5-3/8	1-0-15/32
5/16	3-1/32	7	3-1/2	8-3/32	3-31/32	9-7/32	4-15/32	10-5/16	4-15/16	11-7/16	5-13/32	1-0-17/32
3/8	3-1/16	7-1/16	3-17/32	8-5/32	4	9-9/32	4-1/2	10-13/32	4-31/32	11-1/2	5-7/16	1-0-5/8
7/16	3-3/32	7-1/8	3-9/16	8-1/4	4-1/32	9-11/32	4-17/32	10-15/32	5	11-9/16	5-15/32	1-0-11/16
1/2	3-1/8	7-7/32	3-19/32	8-5/16	4-1/16	9-7/16	4-9/16	10-17/32	5-1/32	11-21/32	5-1/2	1-0-3/4
9/16	3-5/32	7-9/32	3-5/8	8-3/8	4-3/32	9-1/2	4-19/32	10-19/32	5-1/16	11-23/32	5-17/32	1-0-13/16
5/8	3-3/16	7-11/32	3-21/32	8-15/32	4-1/8	9-9/16	4-5/8	10-11/16	5-3/32	11-25/32	5-9/16	1-0-29/32
11/16	3-7/32	7-13/32	3-11/16	8-17/32	4-5/32	9-5/8	4-21/32	10-3/4	5-1/8	11-27/32	5-19/32	1-0-31/32
3/4	3-1/4	7-1/2	3-23/32	8-19/32	4-3/16	9-11/16	4-11/16	10-13/16	5-5/32	11-29/32	5-5/8	1-1-1/32
13/16	3-1/4	7-9/16	3-3/4	8-21/32	4-7/32	9-25/32	4-11/16	10-7/8	5-3/16	1-0	5-21/32	1-1-3/32
7/8	3-9/32	7-5/8	3-25/32	8-23/32	4-1/4	9-27/32	4-23/32	10-15/16	5-7/32	1-0-1/16	5-11/16	1-1-5/32
15/16	3-5/16	7-11/16	3-13/16	8-13/16	4-9/32	9-29/32	4-3/4	11-1/32	5-1/4	1-0-1/8	5-23/32	1-1-1/4

Feet	0' Rise	0' Slope	10' Rise	10' Slope	20' Rise	20' Slope	30' Rise	30' Slope
0	0	0	4-9½	11-1-11/16	9-7	22-2-1/8	14-4½	33-3-3/16
1	5-3/4	1-1-5/16	5-3-1/4	12-2-3/8	10-0-3/4	23-3-7/16	14-10-1/4	34-4½
2	11-1/2	2-2-5/8	5-9	13-3-11/16	10-6½	24-4-3/4	15-4	35-5-13/16
3	1-5-1/4	3-3-29/32	6-2-3/4	14-4-31/32	11-0-1/4	25-6-1/16	15-9-3/4	36-7-1/8
4	1-11	4-5-7/32	6-8½	15-6-9/32	11-6	26-7-11/32	16-3½	37-8-13/32
5	2-4-3/4	5-6-17/32	7-2-1/4	16-7-19/32	11-11-3/4	27-8-21/32	16-9-1/4	38-9-23/32
6	2-10-1/2	6-7-21/32	7-8	17-8-29/32	12-5½	28-9-31/32	17-3	39-11-1/32
7	3-4-1/4	7-9-5/32	8-1-3/4	18-10-1/4	12-11-1/4	29-11-9/32	17-8-3/4	41-0-11/32
8	3-10	8-10-7/16	8-7½	19-11-17/32	13-5	31-0-19/32	18-2½	42-1-21/32
9	4-3-3/4	9-11-3/4	9-1-1/4	21-0-13/16	13-10-3/4	32-1-7/8	18-8-1/4	43-2-15/16

A = 25° 36′ 08″; logsin A = 9.63560; logcos A = 9.95512; logtan A = 9.68049; logcot A = 0.31951

Ins.	12″ Rise	12″ Slope	13″ Rise	13″ Slope	14″ Rise	14″ Slope	15″ Rise	15″ Slope	16″ Rise	16″ Slope
0	5 3/4	1-15/16	6 1/2	1-2 13/32	6 23/32	1-3 17/32	7 3/16	1-4 5/8	7 21/32	1-5 3/4
1/16	5 25/32	1-1 3/8	6 1/4	1-2 1/2	6 3/4	1-3 19/32	7 7/32	1-4 11/16	7 11/16	1-5 13/16
1/8	5 13/16	1-1 7/16	6 9/32	1-2 9/16	6 25/32	1-3 21/32	7 1/4	1-4 25/32	7 23/32	1-5 7/8
3/16	5 27/32	1-1 1/2	6 5/16	1-2 5/8	6 13/16	1-3 23/32	7 9/32	1-4 27/32	7 3/4	1-5 15/16
1/4	5 7/8	1-1 19/32	6 11/32	1-2 11/16	6 13/16	1-3 13/16	7 5/16	1-4 29/32	7 25/32	1-6 1/32
5/16	5 29/32	1-1 21/32	6 3/8	1-2 3/4	6 27/32	1-3 7/8	7 11/32	1-4 31/32	7 13/16	1-6 3/32
3/8	5 15/16	1-1 23/32	6 13/32	1-2 27/32	6 7/8	1-3 15/16	7 3/8	1-5 1/16	7 27/32	1-6 5/32
7/16	5 31/32	1-1 25/32	6 7/16	1-2 29/32	6 29/32	1-4	7 13/32	1-5 1/8	7 7/8	1-6 7/32
1/2	6	1-1 7/8	6 15/32	1-2 31/32	6 15/32	1-4 3/32	7 7/16	1-5 3/16	7 29/32	1-6 9/32
9/16	6 1/32	1-1 15/16	6 1/2	1-3 1/32	6 31/32	1-4 5/32	7 15/32	1-5 1/4	7 15/16	1-6 3/8
5/8	6 1/16	1-2	6 17/32	1-3 3/32	7	1-4 7/32	7 1/2	1-5 5/16	7 31/32	1-6 7/16
11/16	6 3/32	1-2 1/16	6 9/16	1-3 3/16	7 1/32	1-4 9/32	7 17/32	1-5 13/32	8	1-6 1/2
3/4	6 1/8	1-2 1/8	6 19/32	1-3 1/4	7 1/16	1-4 11/32	7 9/16	1-5 15/32	8 1/32	1-6 9/16
13/16	6 1/8	1-2 7/32	6 5/8	1-3 5/32	7 3/32	1-4 7/16	7 9/16	1-5 17/32	8 1/16	1-6 21/32
7/8	6 5/32	1-2 9/32	6 21/32	1-3 3/8	7 1/8	1-4 1/2	7 19/32	1-5 19/32	8 3/32	1-6 23/32
15/16	6 3/16	1-2 11/32	6 11/16	1-3 15/32	7 5/32	1-4 9/16	7 5/8	1-5 11/16	8 1/8	1-6 25/32

Ins.	17″ Rise	17″ Slope	18″ Rise	18″ Slope	19″ Rise	19″ Slope	20″ Rise	20″ Slope	21″ Rise	21″ Slope
0	8 5/32	1-6 27/32	8 5/8	1-7 31/32	9 3/8	1-9 1/16	9 19/32	1-10 3/8	10 1/16	1-11 9/32
1/16	8 3/16	1-6 29/32	8 21/32	1-8 1/32	9 1/8	1-9 1/8	9 5/8	1-10 1/4	10 3/32	1-11 11/32
1/8	8 7/32	1-7	8 11/16	1-8 3/32	9 5/32	1-9 7/32	9 21/32	1-10 5/16	10 1/8	1-11 7/16
3/16	8 1/4	1-7 1/16	8 23/32	1-8 5/32	9 3/16	1-9 9/32	9 11/16	1-10 3/8	10 5/32	1-11 1/2
1/4	8 1/4	1-7 1/8	8 3/4	1-8 1/4	9 7/32	1-9 11/32	9 11/16	1-10 15/32	10 3/16	1-11 9/16
5/16	8 9/32	1-7 3/16	8 25/32	1-8 5/16	9 1/4	1-9 13/32	9 23/32	1-10 17/32	10 7/32	1-11 5/8
3/8	8 5/16	1-7 9/32	8 13/16	1-8 3/8	9 3/4	1-9 1/2	9 3/4	1-10 19/32	10 1/4	1-11 11/16
7/16	8 11/32	1-7 11/32	8 27/32	1-8 7/16	9 5/16	1-9 9/16	9 25/32	1-10 21/32	10 9/32	1-11 25/32
1/2	8 3/8	1-7 13/32	8 7/8	1-8 1/2	9 11/32	1-9 5/8	9 13/16	1-10 23/32	10 5/16	1-11 27/32
9/16	8 13/32	1-7 15/32	8 29/32	1-8 19/32	9 3/8	1-9 11/16	9 27/32	1-10 13/16	10 11/32	1-11 29/32
5/8	8 7/16	1-7 17/32	8 15/16	1-8 21/32	9 13/32	1-9 3/4	9 7/8	1-10 7/8	10 3/8	1-11 31/32
11/16	8 15/32	1-7 5/8	8 31/32	1-8 23/32	9 7/16	1-9 27/32	9 29/32	1-10 15/16	10 13/32	2-0 1/16
3/4	8 1/2	1-7 11/16	9	1-8 25/32	9 15/32	1-9 29/32	9 15/16	1-11	10 7/16	2-0 1/8
13/16	8 17/32	1-7 3/4	9	1-8 7/8	9 1/2	1-9 31/32	9 31/32	1-11 3/32	10 7/16	2-0 3/16
7/8	8 9/16	1-7 13/16	9 1/16	1-8 15/16	9 17/32	1-10 3/32	10	1-11 5/32	10 15/32	2-0 1/4
15/16	8 19/32	1-7 7/8	9 1/16	1-9	9 9/16	1-10 3/32	10 1/32	1-11 7/32	10 1/2	2-0 5/16

Feet	40′ Rise	40′ Slope	50′ Rise	50′ Slope	60′ Rise	60′ Slope	70′ Rise	70′ Slope
0	19-2	44-4 1/4	23-11 1/2	55-5 5/16	28-9	66-6 3/8	33-6 1/2	77-7 15/32
1	19-7 3/4	45-5 9/16	24-5 1/4	56-6 5/8	29-2 3/4	67-7 11/16	34-0 1/4	78-8 3/4
2	20-1 1/2	46-6 7/8	24-11	57-7 15/16	29-8 1/2	68-9	34-6	79-10 1/16
3	20-7 1/4	47-8 3/16	25-4 3/4	58-9 1/4	30-2 1/4	69-10 5/16	34-11 3/4	80-11 3/8
4	21-1	48-9 1/2	25-10 1/2	59-10 9/16	30-8	70-11 5/8	35-5 1/2	82-0 11/16
5	21-6 3/4	49-10 25/32	26-4 1/4	60-11 27/32	31-1 3/4	72-0 29/32	35-11 1/4	83-2
6	22-0 1/2	51-0 3/32	26-10	62-1 5/32	31-7 1/2	73-2 7/32	36-5	84-3 9/32
7	22-6 1/4	52-1 13/32	27-3 3/4	63-2 15/32	32-1 1/4	74-3 17/32	36-10 3/4	85-4 19/32
8	23-0	53-2 23/32	27-9 1/2	64-3 25/32	32-7	75-4 27/32	37-4 1/2	86-5 29/32
9	23-5 3/4	54-4 1/32	28-3 1/4	65-5 5/32	33-0 3/4	76-6 5/32	37-10 1/4	87-7 1/32

natsin A=0.4321201804; natcos A=0.9018160287; nattan A=0.4791666666; natcot A=2.0869565217

Inches	0" Rise	0" Slope	1" Rise	1" Slope	2" Rise	2" Slope	3" Rise	3" Slope	4" Rise	4" Slope	5" Rise	5" Slope
0	0	0	1/2	1 1/8	31/32	2 7/32	1 7/16	3 11/32	1 15/16	4 7/16	2 7/16	5 9/16
1/16	1/32	1/16	1/2	1 3/16	1	2 9/32	1 15/32	3 13/32	1 31/32	4 1/2	2 7/16	5 5/8
1/8	1/16	1/8	17/32	1 1/4	1 1/32	2 3/8	1 1/2	3 15/32	2	4 19/32	2 15/32	5 11/16
3/16	3/32	7/32	9/16	1 5/16	1 1/16	2 7/16	1 17/32	3 17/32	2 1/32	4 21/32	2 1/2	5 3/4
1/4	1/8	9/32	19/32	1 3/8	1 3/32	2 1/2	1 9/16	3 5/8	2 1/16	4 23/32	2 17/32	5 27/32
5/16	5/32	11/32	5/8	1 15/32	1 1/8	2 9/16	1 19/32	3 11/16	2 3/32	4 25/32	2 9/16	5 29/32
3/8	3/16	13/32	21/32	1 17/32	1 5/32	2 5/8	1 5/8	3 3/4	2 1/8	4 7/8	2 19/32	5 31/32
7/16	7/32	1/2	11/16	1 19/32	1 3/16	2 23/32	1 21/32	3 13/16	2 5/32	4 15/16	2 5/8	6 1/32
1/2	1/4	9/16	23/32	1 21/32	1 7/32	2 25/32	1 11/16	3 7/8	2 3/16	5	2 21/32	6 1/8
9/16	9/32	5/8	3/4	1 3/4	1 1/4	2 27/32	1 23/32	3 31/32	2 7/32	5 1/16	2 11/16	6 3/16
5/8	5/16	11/16	25/32	1 13/16	1 9/32	2 29/32	1 3/4	4 1/32	2 1/4	5 1/8	2 23/32	6 1/4
11/16	11/32	3/4	13/16	1 7/8	1 5/16	3	1 25/32	4 3/32	2 9/32	5 7/32	2 3/4	6 5/16
3/4	3/8	27/32	27/32	1 15/16	1 11/32	3 1/16	1 13/16	4 5/32	2 5/16	5 9/32	2 25/32	6 3/8
13/16	13/32	29/32	7/8	2	1 3/8	3 1/8	1 27/32	4 1/4	2 11/32	5 11/32	2 13/16	6 15/32
7/8	7/16	31/32	29/32	2 3/32	1 13/32	3 3/16	1 7/8	4 5/16	2 3/8	5 13/32	2 27/32	6 17/32
15/16	15/32	1 1/32	15/16	2 5/32	1 7/16	3 1/4	1 29/32	4 3/8	2 13/32	5 1/2	2 7/8	6 19/32

Inches	6" Rise	6" Slope	7" Rise	7" Slope	8" Rise	8" Slope	9" Rise	9" Slope	10" Rise	10" Slope	11" Rise	11" Slope
0	2 29/32	6 21/32	3 3/8	7 25/32	3 7/8	8 7/8	4 3/8	10	4 27/32	11 1/8	5 5/16	1-0 7/32
1/16	2 15/16	6 3/4	3 13/32	7 27/32	3 29/32	8 31/32	4 13/32	10 1/16	4 7/8	11 3/16	5 11/32	1-0 9/32
1/8	2 31/32	6 13/16	3 7/16	7 29/32	3 15/16	9 1/32	4 7/16	10 1/8	4 29/32	11 1/4	5 3/8	1-0 3/8
3/16	3	6 7/8	3 15/32	8	3 31/32	9 3/32	4 15/32	10 7/32	4 15/16	11 5/16	5 13/32	1-0 7/16
1/4	3 1/32	6 15/16	3 1/2	8 1/16	4	9 5/32	4 1/2	10 9/32	4 31/32	11 3/8	5 7/16	1-0 1/2
5/16	3 1/16	7	3 17/32	8 1/8	4 1/32	9 1/4	4 17/32	10 11/32	5	11 15/32	5 15/32	1-0 9/16
3/8	3 3/32	7 3/32	3 9/16	8 3/16	4 1/16	9 5/16	4 9/16	10 13/32	5 1/32	11 17/32	5 1/2	1-0 21/32
7/16	3 1/8	7 5/32	3 19/32	8 1/4	4 3/32	9 3/8	4 19/32	10 1/2	5 1/16	11 19/32	5 17/32	1-0 23/32
1/2	3 5/32	7 7/32	3 5/8	8 11/32	4 1/8	9 7/16	4 5/8	10 9/16	5 3/32	11 21/32	5 9/16	1-0 25/32
9/16	3 3/16	7 9/32	3 21/32	8 13/32	4 5/32	9 1/2	4 21/32	10 5/8	5 1/8	11 3/4	5 19/32	1-0 27/32
5/8	3 7/32	7 3/8	3 11/16	8 15/32	4 3/16	9 19/32	4 11/16	10 11/16	5 5/32	11 13/16	5 5/8	1-0 29/32
11/16	3 1/4	7 7/16	3 23/32	8 17/32	4 7/32	9 21/32	4 23/32	10 3/4	5 3/16	11 7/8	5 21/32	1-0 31/32
3/4	3 9/32	7 1/2	3 3/4	8 5/8	4 1/4	9 23/32	4 3/4	10 27/32	5 7/32	11 15/16	5 11/16	1-1 1/16
13/16	3 5/16	7 9/16	3 25/32	8 11/16	4 9/32	9 25/32	4 25/32	10 29/32	5 1/4	1-0	5 23/32	1-1 1/8
7/8	3 11/32	7 5/8	3 13/16	8 3/4	4 5/16	9 7/8	4 13/16	10 31/32	5 9/32	1-0 3/32	5 3/4	1-1 3/16
15/16	3 3/8	7 23/32	3 27/32	8 13/16	4 11/32	9 15/16	4 27/32	11 1/32	5 5/16	1-0 5/32	5 25/32	1-1 1/4

Feet	0' Rise	0' Slope	10' Rise	10' Slope	20' Rise	20' Slope	30' Rise	30' Slope
0	0	0	4-10 1/8	11-1 11/32	9-8 1/4	22-2 11/16	14-6 3/8	33-4
1	5 13/16	1-1 11/32	5-3 15/16	12-2 21/32	10-2 1/16	23-4	15-0 3/16	34-5 11/32
2	11 5/8	2-2 21/32	5-9 3/4	13-4	10-7 7/8	24-5 11/32	15-6	35-6 11/16
3	1-5 7/16	3-4	6-3 9/16	14-5 11/32	11-1 11/16	25-6 11/16	15-11 13/16	36-8
4	1-11 1/4	4-5 11/32	6-9 3/8	15-6 21/32	11-7 1/2	26-8	16-5 5/8	37-9 11/32
5	2-5 1/16	5-6 21/32	7-3 3/16	16-8	12-1 5/16	27-9 11/32	16-11 7/16	38-10 11/16
6	2-10 7/8	6-8	7-9	17-9 11/32	12-7 1/8	28-10 11/16	17-5 1/4	40-0
7	3-4 11/16	7-9 11/32	8-2 13/16	18-10 21/32	13-0 15/16	30-0	17-11 1/16	41-1 11/32
8	3-10 1/2	8-10 21/32	8-8 5/8	20-0	13-6 3/4	31-1 11/32	18-4 7/8	42-2 11/16
9	4-4 5/16	10-0	9-2 7/16	21-1 11/32	14-0 9/16	32-2 11/16	18-10 11/16	43-4

A = 25° 50′ 40″; logsin A = 9.63942; logcos A = 9.95423; logtan A = 9.68518; logcot A = 0.31482

In.	12″ Rise	12″ Slope	13″ Rise	13″ Slope	14″ Rise	14″ Slope	15″ Rise	15″ Slope	16″ Rise	16″ Slope
0	5 13/32	1-1 11/32	6 5/16	1-2 7/16	6 25/32	1-3 9/32	7 1/4	1-4 21/32	7 3/4	1-5 25/32
1/16	5 27/32	1-1 13/32	6 5/16	1-2 1/2	6 13/16	1-3 5/8	7 9/32	1-4 3/4	7 25/32	1-5 27/32
1/8	5 7/8	1-1 15/32	6 11/32	1-2 19/32	6 27/32	1-3 11/16	7 5/16	1-4 13/16	7 13/16	1-5 29/32
3/16	5 29/32	1-1 17/32	6 3/8	1-2 21/32	6 7/8	1-3 3/4	7 11/32	1-4 7/8	7 27/32	1-6
1/4	5 15/32	1-1 5/8	6 13/16	1-2 23/32	6 29/32	1-3 27/32	7 3/8	1-4 15/16	7 7/8	1-6 1/16
5/16	5 31/32	1-1 11/16	7 1/16	1-2 25/32	6 15/16	1-3 29/32	7 13/32	1-5	7 29/32	1-6 1/8
3/8	6	1-1 3/4	6 15/16	1-2 7/8	6 31/32	1-3 31/32	7 7/16	1-5 3/32	7 15/16	1-6 3/16
7/16	6 1/32	1-1 13/16	6 1/2	1-2 15/16	7	1-4 1/32	7 15/32	1-5 5/32	7 31/32	1-6 1/4
1/2	6 1/16	1-1 7/8	6 17/32	1-3	7 1/32	1-4 1/8	7 1/2	1-5 7/32	8	1-6 11/32
9/16	6 3/32	1-1 31/32	6 9/16	1-3 1/16	7 1/16	1-4 3/16	7 17/32	1-5 9/32	8 1/32	1-6 13/32
5/8	6 1/8	1-2 1/32	6 19/32	1-3 1/8	7 3/32	1-4 1/4	7 9/16	1-5 3/8	8 1/16	1-6 15/32
11/16	6 5/32	1-2 3/32	6 5/8	1-3 7/32	7 1/8	1-4 5/16	7 19/32	1-5 7/32	8 3/32	1-6 17/32
3/4	6 3/16	1-2 5/32	6 21/32	1-3 9/32	7 5/32	1-4 3/8	7 5/8	1-5 1/2	8 1/8	1-6 5/8
13/16	6 7/32	1-2 1/4	6 11/16	1-3 11/32	7 3/16	1-4 15/32	7 21/32	1-5 9/32	8 5/32	1-6 11/16
7/8	6 1/4	1-2 5/16	6 23/32	1-3 13/32	7 7/32	1-4 17/32	7 11/16	1-5 5/8	8 3/16	1-6 3/4
15/16	6 9/32	1-2 3/8	6 3/4	1-3 1/2	7 1/4	1-4 19/32	7 23/32	1-5 23/32	8 7/32	1-6 13/16

In.	17″ Rise	17″ Slope	18″ Rise	18″ Slope	19″ Rise	19″ Slope	20″ Rise	20″ Slope	21″ Rise	21″ Slope
0	8 1/4	1-6 7/8	8 23/32	1-8	9 3/16	1-9 1/8	9 11/16	1-10 7/32	10 3/16	1-11 11/32
1/16	8 1/4	1-6 31/32	8 3/4	1-8 1/16	9 7/32	1-9 3/16	9 23/32	1-10 9/32	10 3/16	1-11 13/32
1/8	8 9/32	1-7 1/32	8 25/32	1-8 1/8	9 1/4	1-9 1/4	9 3/4	1-10 3/8	10 7/32	1-11 15/32
3/16	8 5/32	1-7 3/32	8 13/16	1-8 7/32	9 9/32	1-9 5/16	9 25/32	1-10 7/16	10 1/4	1-11 17/32
1/4	8 11/32	1-7 5/32	8 27/32	1-8 9/32	9 5/16	1-9 3/8	9 13/16	1-10 1/2	10 9/32	1-11 5/8
5/16	8 3/8	1-7 1/4	8 7/8	1-8 11/32	9 11/32	1-9 15/32	9 27/32	1-10 9/16	10 5/16	1-11 11/16
3/8	8 13/32	1-7 5/32	8 29/32	1-8 13/32	9 3/8	1-9 17/32	9 7/8	1-10 5/8	10 11/32	1-11 3/4
7/16	8 7/16	1-7 3/8	8 15/32	1-8 1/2	9 13/32	1-9 19/32	9 29/32	1-10 23/32	10 3/8	1-11 13/16
1/2	8 15/32	1-7 7/16	8 31/32	1-8 9/32	9 7/32	1-9 21/32	9 15/16	1-10 25/32	10 13/32	1-11 7/8
9/16	8 1/2	1-7 1/2	9	1-8 5/8	9 15/32	1-9 3/4	9 31/32	1-10 27/32	10 7/16	1-11 31/32
5/8	8 17/32	1-7 19/32	9 1/32	1-8 11/16	9 1/2	1-9 15/32	10	1-10 29/32	10 15/32	2-0 1/32
11/16	8 9/16	1-7 21/32	9 1/16	1-8 3/4	9 17/32	1-9 7/8	10 1/32	1-11	10 1/2	2-0 3/32
3/4	8 19/32	1-7 23/32	9 3/32	1-8 27/32	9 9/16	1-9 15/16	10 1/16	1-11 1/16	10 17/32	2-0 5/32
13/16	8 5/8	1-7 25/32	9 1/8	1-8 29/32	9 19/32	1-10	10 3/32	1-11 1/8	10 9/16	2-0 1/4
7/8	8 21/32	1-7 7/8	9 5/32	1-8 31/32	9 5/8	1-10 3/32	10 1/8	1-11 3/8	10 19/32	2-0 5/16
15/16	8 11/16	1-7 15/32	9 3/16	1-9 1/32	9 21/32	1-10 5/32	10 5/32	1-11 1/4	10 5/8	2-0 3/8

Feet	40′ Rise	40′ Slope	50′ Rise	50′ Slope	60′ Rise	60′ Slope	70′ Rise	70′ Slope
0	19-4 1/2	44-5 11/32	24-2 5/8	55-6 11/16	29-0 3/4	66-8 1/32	33-10 7/8	77-9 11/32
1	19-10 5/16	45-6 11/16	24-8 1/16	56-8	29-6 9/16	67-9 11/32	34-4 11/16	78-10 11/16
2	20-4 1/8	46-8	25-2 1/4	57-9 11/32	30-0 3/8	68-10 11/16	34-10 1/2	80-0 1/32
3	20-9 15/16	47-9 11/32	25-8 1/16	58-10 11/16	30-6 3/8	70-0 1/32	35-4 5/16	81-1 11/32
4	21-3 3/4	48-10 11/16	26-1 7/8	60-0	31-0	71-1 11/32	35-10 1/8	82-2 11/16
5	21-9 9/16	50-0	26-7 11/16	61-1 11/16	31-5 13/16	72-2 11/16	36-3 15/16	83-4 1/32
6	22-3 3/8	51-1 11/32	27-1 1/2	62-2 11/16	31-11 5/8	73-4 1/32	36-9 3/4	84-5 11/32
7	22-9 3/16	52-2 11/16	27-7 5/16	63-4 11/32	32-5 7/16	74-5 11/32	37-3 9/16	85-6 11/16
8	23-3	53-4	28-1 1/8	64-5 11/32	32-11 1/4	75-6 11/16	37-9 3/8	86-8 1/32
9	23-8 13/16	54-5 11/32	28-6 15/16	65-6 11/16	33-5 1/16	76-8 1/32	38-3 3/16	87-9 11/32

natsin A=0.4359284537; natcos A=0.8999813239; nattan A=0.4843750000; natcot A=2.0645161290

Inches	0" Rise	0" Slope	1" Rise	1" Slope	2" Rise	2" Slope	3" Rise	3" Slope	4" Rise	4" Slope	5" Rise	5" Slope
0	0	0	1/2	1 1/8	31/32	2 7/32	1 15/32	3 11/32–	1 31/32–	4 15/32–	2 7/16	5 9/16
1/16	1/32–	1/16	17/32–	1 3/16	1	2 9/32	1 1/2	3 13/32	2	4 17/32–	2 15/32	5 5/8
1/8	1/16	1/8	9/16	1 1/4	1 1/32	2 3/8	1 17/32–	3 15/32	2 1/32–	4 19/32–	2 1/2	5 23/32–
3/16	3/32–	7/32–	19/32–	1 5/16	1 1/16	2 7/16	1 9/16	3 9/16	2 1/16	4 21/32	2 17/32	5 25/32–
1/4	1/8	9/32–	5/8	1 13/32–	1 3/32	2 1/2	1 19/32–	3 5/8	2 3/32–	4 23/32	2 9/16	5 27/32
5/16	5/32–	11/32	21/32–	1 15/32–	1 1/8	2 9/16	1 5/8	3 11/16	2 1/8	4 13/16	2 19/32	5 29/32
3/8	3/16	13/32	11/16	1 17/32–	1 5/32	2 21/32–	1 21/32–	3 3/4	2 5/32–	4 7/8	2 5/8	6
7/16	7/32–	1/2	23/32–	1 19/32	1 3/16	2 23/32–	1 11/16	3 13/16	2 3/16	4 15/16	2 21/32	6 1/16
1/2	1/4	9/16	3/4	1 21/32	1 7/32	2 25/32	1 23/32–	3 29/32–	2 3/16	5	2 11/16	6 1/8
9/16	9/32–	5/8	3/4	1 3/4	1 1/4	2 27/32	1 3/4	3 31/32–	2 7/32	5 3/32–	2 23/32	6 3/16
5/8	5/16	11/16	25/32	1 13/16	1 9/32	2 15/16	1 25/32–	4 1/32	2 1/4	5 5/32–	2 3/4	6 1/4
11/16	11/32–	3/4	13/16	1 7/8	1 5/16	3	1 13/16	4 3/32	2 9/32	5 7/32	2 25/32	6 11/32–
3/4	3/8	27/32–	27/32	1 15/16	1 11/32	3 1/16	1 27/32–	4 3/16	2 5/16	5 9/32	2 13/16	6 13/32–
13/16	13/32–	29/32–	7/8	2 1/32–	1 3/8	3 1/8	1 7/8	4 1/4	2 11/32	5 11/32	2 27/32	6 15/32
7/8	7/16	31/32	29/32	2 3/32	1 13/32	3 3/16	1 29/32–	4 5/16	2 3/8	5 7/16	2 7/8	6 17/32
15/16	15/32–	1 1/32	15/16	2 5/32	1 7/16	3 9/32–	1 15/16	4 3/8	2 13/32	5 1/2	2 29/32	6 5/8

Inches	6" Rise	6" Slope	7" Rise	7" Slope	8" Rise	8" Slope	9" Rise	9" Slope	10" Rise	10" Slope	11" Rise	11" Slope
0	2 15/16	6 11/16	3 7/16	7 25/32	3 29/32	8 29/32	4 13/32	10 1/32–	4 29/32–	11 1/8	5 3/8	1-0 1/4
1/16	2 31/32–	6 3/4	3 15/32–	7 7/8	3 15/16	8 31/32	4 7/16	10 3/32–	4 15/16	11 7/32–	5 13/32	1-0 5/16
1/8	3	6 13/16	3 1/2	7 15/16	3 31/32	9 1/32	4 15/32–	10 5/32	4 31/32–	11 9/32–	5 7/16	1-0 3/8
3/16	3 1/32–	6 7/8	3 17/32–	8	4	9 1/8	4 1/2	10 7/32	5	11 11/32–	5 15/32	1-0 15/32–
1/4	3 1/16	6 31/32–	3 9/16	8 1/16	4 1/32	9 3/16	4 17/32–	10 5/16	5 1/32–	11 13/32	5 1/2	1-0 17/32–
5/16	3 3/32–	7 1/32–	3 19/32–	8 5/32–	4 1/16	9 1/4	4 9/16	10 3/8	5 1/16	11 15/32	5 17/32	1-0 19/32
3/8	3 1/8	7 3/32	3 5/8	8 7/32–	4 3/32	9 5/16	4 19/32–	10 7/16	5 3/32–	11 9/16	5 9/16	1-0 21/32
7/16	3 5/32–	7 5/32	3 21/32–	8 9/32–	4 1/8	9 13/32–	4 5/8	10 1/2	5 1/8	11 5/8	5 19/32	1-0 3/4
1/2	3 3/16	7 1/4	3 11/16	8 11/32	4 5/32	9 15/32–	4 21/32–	10 9/16	5 1/8	11 11/16	5 5/8	1-0 13/16
9/16	3 7/32–	7 5/16	3 11/16	8 13/32	4 3/16	9 17/32	4 11/16	10 21/32–	5 5/32	11 3/4	5 21/32	1-0 7/8
5/8	3 1/4	7 3/8	3 23/32	8 1/2	4 7/32	9 19/32	4 23/32–	10 23/32–	5 3/16	11 27/32–	5 11/16	1-0 15/16
11/16	3 9/32–	7 7/16	3 3/4	8 9/16	4 1/4	9 11/16	4 3/4	10 25/32	5 7/32	11 29/32–	5 23/32	1-1
3/4	3 5/16	7 1/2	3 25/32	8 5/8	4 9/32	9 3/4	4 25/32–	10 27/32	5 1/4	11 31/32	5 3/4	1-1 3/32–
13/16	3 11/32–	7 19/32–	3 13/16	8 11/16	4 5/16	9 13/16	4 13/16	10 15/16	5 9/32	1-0 1/32	5 25/32	1-1 5/32–
7/8	3 3/8	7 21/32–	3 27/32	8 25/32–	4 11/32	9 7/8	4 27/32–	11	5 5/16	1-0 3/32	5 13/16	1-1 7/32
15/16	3 13/32–	7 23/32	3 7/8	8 27/32–	4 3/8	9 15/16	4 7/8	11 1/16	5 11/32	1-0 3/16	5 27/32	1-1 9/32

Feet	0' Rise	0' Slope	10' Rise	10' Slope	20' Rise	20' Slope	30' Rise	30' Slope
0	0	0	4-10 3/4	11-1 5/8	9-9 1/2	22-3 7/32	14-8 1/4	33-4 27/32–
1	5 7/8	1-1 3/8	5-4 5/8	12-2 31/32	10-3 3/8	23-4 19/32–	15-2 1/8	34-6 3/16
2	11 3/4	2-2 23/32	5-10 1/2	13-4 11/32–	10-9 1/4	24-5 15/16	15-8	35-7 9/16
3	1-5 5/8	3-4 3/32–	6-4 3/8	14-5 11/16	11-3 1/8	25-7 5/16	16-1 7/8	36-8 29/32
4	1-11 1/2	4-5 7/16	6-10 1/4	15-7 1/16	11-9	26-8 21/32	16-7 3/4	37-10 9/32–
5	2-5 3/8	5-6 13/16	7-4 1/8	16-8 13/32	12-2 7/8	27-10 1/32–	17-1 5/8	38-11 5/8
6	2-11 1/4	6-8 5/32	7-10	17-9 25/32–	12-8 3/4	28-11 3/8	17-7 1/2	40-1
7	3-5 1/8	7-9 17/32–	8-3 7/8	18-11 1/8	13-2 5/8	30-0 3/4	18-1 3/8	41-2 11/32
8	3-11	8-10 7/8	8-9 3/4	20-0 1/2	13-8 1/2	31-2 3/32	18-7 1/4	42-3 23/32–
9	4-4 7/8	10-0 1/4	9-3 5/8	21-1 27/32	14-2 3/8	32-3 15/32–	19-1 1/8	43-5 1/16

A = 26° 05′ 08″; logsin A = **9.64317**; logcos A = **9.95334**; logtan A = **9.68983**; logcot A = **0.31017**

In.	12″ Rise	12″ Slope	13″ Rise	13″ Slope	14″ Rise	14″ Slope	15″ Rise	15″ Slope	16″ Rise	16″ Slope
0	5 7/8	1-1 3/8	6 3/8	1-2 15/32	6 27/32	1-3 19/32	7 11/32	1-4 11/16	7 27/32	1-5 13/16
1/16	5 29/32	1-1 7/16	6 13/32	1-2 17/32	6 7/8	1-3 21/32	7 3/8	1-4 25/32	7 7/8	1-5 7/8
1/8	5 15/16	1-1 1/2	6 7/16	1-2 5/8	6 29/32	1-3 23/32	7 13/32	1-4 27/32	7 29/32	1-5 31/32
3/16	5 31/32	1-1 9/16	6 15/32	1-2 11/16	6 15/16	1-3 25/32	7 7/16	1-4 29/32	7 15/16	1-6 1/32
1/4	6	1-1 5/8	6 1/2	1-2 3/4	6 31/32	1-3 7/8	7 15/32	1-4 31/32	7 31/32	1-6 3/32
5/16	6 1/32	1-1 23/32	6 17/32	1-2 13/16	7	1-3 15/16	7 1/2	1-5 1/16	8	1-6 5/32
3/8	6 1/16	1-1 25/32	6 9/16	1-2 29/32	7 1/32	1-4	7 17/32	1-5 1/8	8 1/32	1-6 7/32
7/16	6 3/32	1-1 27/32	6 19/32	1-2 31/32	7 1/16	1-4 1/16	7 9/16	1-5 3/16	8 1/16	1-6 5/16
1/2	6 1/8	1-1 29/32	6 5/8	1-3 1/32	7 3/32	1-4 5/32	7 19/32	1-5 1/4	8 1/16	1-6 3/8
9/16	6 5/32	1-2	6 5/8	1-3 3/32	7 1/8	1-4 7/32	7 5/8	1-5 5/16	8 3/32	1-6 7/32
5/8	6 3/16	1-2 1/16	6 21/32	1-3 5/32	7 5/32	1-4 9/32	7 21/32	1-5 13/32	8 1/8	1 6 1/2
11/16	6 7/32	1-2 1/8	6 11/16	1-3 1/4	7 3/16	1-4 11/32	7 11/16	1-5 15/32	8 5/32	1-6 19/32
3/4	6 1/4	1-2 3/16	6 23/32	1 3 5/16	7 7/32	1-4 7/16	7 23/32	1-5 17/32	8 3/16	1-6 21/32
13/16	6 9/32	1-2 1/4	6 3/4	1-3 3/8	7 1/4	1-4 1/2	7 3/4	1-5 19/32	8 7/32	1-6 23/32
7/8	6 5/16	1-2 11/32	6 25/32	1-3 7/16	7 9/32	1-4 9/16	7 25/32	1-5 11/16	8 1/4	1-6 25/32
15/16	6 11/32	1-2 13/32	6 13/16	1-3 17/32	7 5/16	1-4 5/8	7 13/16	1-5 3/4	8 9/32	1-6 27/32

In.	17″ Rise	17″ Slope	18″ Rise	18″ Slope	19″ Rise	19″ Slope	20″ Rise	20″ Slope	21″ Rise	21″ Slope
0	8 5/16	1-6 15/16	8 13/16	1-8 1/32	9 5/16	1-9 5/32	9 25/32	1-10 9/32	10 9/32	1-11 3/8
1/16	8 11/32	1-7	8 27/32	1-8 1/8	9 11/32	1-9 7/32	9 13/16	1-10 11/32	10 5/16	1-11 7/16
1/8	8 3/8	1-7 1/16	8 7/8	1-8 3/16	9 3/8	1-9 9/32	9 27/32	1-10 13/32	10 11/32	1-11 17/32
3/16	8 13/32	1-7 1/8	8 29/32	1-8 1/4	9 13/32	1-9 3/8	9 7/8	1-10 15/32	10 3/8	1-11 19/32
1/4	8 7/16	1-7 7/8	8 15/16	1-8 5/16	9 7/16	1-9 7/16	9 29/32	1-10 17/32	10 13/32	1-11 21/32
5/16	8 15/32	1-7 9/32	8 31/32	1-8 3/8	9 15/32	1-9 1/2	9 15/16	1-10 5/8	10 7/16	1-11 23/32
3/8	8 1/2	1-7 11/32	9	1-8 15/32	9 1/2	1-9 9/16	9 31/32	1-10 11/16	10 15/32	1-11 13/16
7/16	8 17/32	1-7 13/32	9 1/32	1-8 17/32	9 17/32	1-9 21/32	10	1-10 3/4	10 1/2	1-11 7/8
1/2	8 9/16	1-7 1/2	9 1/16	1-8 19/32	9 9/16	1-9 23/32	10 1/32	1-10 13/16	10 17/32	1-11 15/16
9/16	8 19/32	1-7 9/16	9 3/32	1-8 21/32	9 9/16	1-9 25/32	10 1/16	1-10 29/32	10 9/16	2-0
5/8	8 5/8	1-7 5/8	9 1/8	1-8 3/4	9 19/32	1-9 27/32	10 3/32	1-10 31/32	10 19/32	2-0 1/16
11/16	8 21/32	1-7 11/16	9 5/32	1-8 13/16	9 5/8	1-9 29/32	10 1/8	1-11 1/32	10 5/8	2-0 5/32
3/4	8 11/16	1-7 3/4	9 3/16	1-8 7/8	9 21/32	1-10	10 5/32	1-11 3/32	10 21/32	2-0 7/32
13/16	8 23/32	1-7 27/32	9 7/32	1-8 15/16	9 11/16	1-10 1/16	10 3/16	1-11 3/32	10 11/16	2-0 9/32
7/8	8 3/4	1-7 29/32	9 1/4	1-9 1/32	9 23/32	1-10 1/8	10 7/32	1-11 1/4	10 23/32	2-0 11/32
15/16	8 25/32	1-7 31/32	9 9/32	1-9 3/32	9 3/4	1-10 3/16	10 1/4	1-11 5/16	10 3/4	2-0 7/16

Feet	40′ Rise	40′ Slope	50′ Rise	50′ Slope	60′ Rise	60′ Slope	70′ Rise	70′ Slope
0	19-7	44-6 7/16	24-5 3/4	55-8 1/16	29-4 1/2	66-9 21/32	34-3 1/4	77-11 9/32
1	20-0 7/8	45-7 13/16	24-11 5/8	56-9 13/32	29-10 3/8	67-11 1/32	34-9 1/8	79-0 5/8
2	20-6 3/4	46-9 5/32	25-5 1/2	57-10 25/32	30-4 1/4	69-0 3/8	35-3	80-2
3	21-0 5/8	47-10 17/32	25-11 3/8	59-0 1/8	30-10 1/8	70-1 3/4	35-8 7/8	81-3 11/32
4	21-6 1/2	48-11 7/8	26-5 1/4	60-1 1/2	31-4	71-3 3/32	36-2 3/4	82-4 23/32
5	22-0 3/8	50-1 1/4	26-11 1/8	61-2 27/32	31-9 7/8	72-4 15/32	36-8 5/8	83-6 1/16
6	22-6 1/4	51-2 9/32	27-5	62-4 7/32	32-3 3/4	73-5 13/16	37-2 1/2	84-7 7/16
7	23-0 1/8	52-3 31/32	27-10 7/8	63-5 9/16	32-9 5/8	74-7 3/16	37-8 3/8	85-8 25/32
8	23-6	53-5 5/16	28-4 3/4	64-6 15/16	33-3 1/2	75-8 17/32	38-2 1/4	86-10 5/32
9	23-11 7/8	54-6 11/16	28-10 5/8	65-8 5/16	33-9 3/8	76-9 29/32	38-8 1/8	87-11 11/32

natsin A=0.4397134535; natcos A=0.8981381179; nattan A=0.4895833333; natcot A=2.0425531914

Inches	0″ Rise	0″ Slope	1″ Rise	1″ Slope	2″ Rise	2″ Slope	3″ Rise	3″ Slope	4″ Rise	4″ Slope	5″ Rise	5″ Slope
0	0	0	1/2	1 1/8	1	2 7/32	1 1/2	3 11/32	1 31/32	4 15/32	2 15/32	5 19/32
1/16	1/32	1/16	17/32	1 3/16	1 1/32	2 5/16	1 17/32	3 13/32	2	4 17/32	2 1/2	5 21/32
1/8	1/16	1/8	9/16	1 1/4	1 1/16	2 3/8	1 17/32	3 1/2	2 1/16	4 19/32	2 17/32	5 23/32
3/16	3/32	7/32	19/32	1 5/16	1 3/32	2 7/16	1 9/16	—	2 1/16	4 11/32	2 9/16	5 25/32
1/4	1/8	9/32	5/8	1 13/32	1 1/8	2 1/2	1 19/32	3 5/8	2 3/32	4 3/4	2 19/32	5 27/32
5/16	5/32	11/32	21/32	1 15/32	1 5/32	2 19/32	1 5/8	3 11/16	2 1/8	4 13/16	2 5/8	5 15/16
3/8	3/16	13/32	11/16	1 17/32	1 3/16	2 21/32	1 21/32	3 3/4	2 5/32	4 7/8	2 21/32	6
7/16	7/32	1/2	23/32	1 19/32	1 7/32	2 23/32	1 11/16	3 27/32	2 3/16	4 15/16	2 11/16	6 1/16
1/2	1/4	9/16	3/4	1 11/16	1 1/4	2 25/32	1 23/32	3 29/32	2 7/32	5 1/32	2 23/32	6 1/8
9/16	9/32	5/8	25/32	1 3/4	1 9/32	2 27/32	1 3/4	3 31/32	2 1/4	5 3/32	2 3/4	6 1/4
5/8	5/16	11/16	13/16	1 13/16	1 5/16	2 15/16	1 25/32	4 1/32	2 9/32	5 5/32	2 25/32	6 9/32
11/16	11/32	25/32	27/32	1 7/8	1 11/32	3	1 13/16	4 1/8	2 5/16	5 7/32	2 13/16	6 11/32
3/4	3/8	27/32	7/8	1 15/16	1 3/8	3 1/16	1 27/32	4 3/16	2 11/32	5 5/16	2 27/32	6 13/32
13/16	13/32	29/32	29/32	2 1/32	1 13/32	3 1/8	1 7/8	4 1/4	2 3/8	5 3/8	2 7/8	6 1/2
7/8	7/16	31/32	15/16	2 3/32	1 7/16	3 7/32	1 29/32	4 5/16	2 13/32	5 7/16	2 29/32	6 9/16
15/16	15/32	1 1/32	31/32	2 5/32	1 15/32	3 9/32	1 15/16	4 13/32	2 7/16	5 1/2	2 15/16	6 5/8

Inches	6″ Rise	6″ Slope	7″ Rise	7″ Slope	8″ Rise	8″ Slope	9″ Rise	9″ Slope	10″ Rise	10″ Slope	11″ Rise	11″ Slope
0	2 31/32	6 11/16	3 15/32	7 13/16	3 31/32	8 15/16	4 7/16	10 1/32	4 15/16	11 5/32	5 7/16	1-0 9/32
1/16	3	6 3/4	3 1/2	7 7/8	4	9	4 15/32	10 1/8	4 31/32	11 7/32	5 15/32	1-0 11/32
1/8	3 1/32	6 27/32	3 17/32	7 15/16	4 1/32	9 1/16	4 1/2	10 3/16	5	11 9/32	5 1/2	1-0 13/32
3/16	3 1/16	6 29/32	3 9/16	8 1/32	4 1/16	9 1/8	4 17/32	10 1/4	5 1/32	11 3/8	5 17/32	1-0 15/32
1/4	3 3/32	6 31/32	3 19/32	8 3/32	4 3/32	9 7/32	4 9/16	10 5/16	5 1/16	11 7/16	5 9/16	1-0 9/16
5/16	3 1/8	7 1/32	3 5/8	8 5/32	4 1/8	9 9/32	4 19/32	10 3/8	5 3/32	11 1/2	5 19/32	1-0 5/8
3/8	3 5/32	7 1/8	3 21/32	8 1/4	4 5/32	9 11/32	4 5/8	10 15/32	5 1/8	11 9/16	5 5/8	1-0 11/16
7/16	3 3/16	7 3/16	3 11/16	8 5/16	4 3/16	9 13/32	4 21/32	10 17/32	5 5/32	11 21/32	5 21/32	1-0 3/4
1/2	3 7/32	7 1/4	3 23/32	8 3/8	4 7/32	9 15/32	4 11/16	10 19/32	5 3/16	11 23/32	5 11/16	1-0 27/32
9/16	3 1/4	7 5/16	3 3/4	8 7/16	4 1/4	9 9/16	4 23/32	10 21/32	5 7/32	11 25/32	5 23/32	1-0 29/32
5/8	3 9/32	7 13/32	3 25/32	8 1/2	4 9/32	9 5/8	4 3/4	10 3/4	5 1/4	11 27/32	5 3/4	1-0 31/32
11/16	3 5/16	7 15/32	3 13/16	8 9/16	4 5/16	9 11/16	4 25/32	10 13/16	5 9/32	11 15/16	5 25/32	1-1 1/32
3/4	3 11/32	7 17/32	3 27/32	8 21/32	4 11/32	9 3/4	4 13/16	10 7/8	5 5/16	1-0	5 13/16	1-1 1/8
13/16	3 3/8	7 19/32	3 7/8	8 23/32	4 3/8	9 27/32	4 27/32	10 15/16	5 11/32	1-0 1/16	5 27/32	1-1 3/16
7/8	3 13/32	7 21/32	3 29/32	8 25/32	4 13/32	9 29/32	4 7/8	11 1/32	5 3/8	1-0 1/8	5 7/8	1-1 1/4
15/16	3 7/16	7 3/4	3 15/16	8 27/32	4 7/16	9 31/32	4 29/32	11 3/32	5 13/32	1-0 7/32	5 29/32	1-1 5/16

Feet	0′ Rise	0′ Slope	10′ Rise	10′ Slope	20′ Rise	20′ Slope	30′ Rise	30′ Slope
0	0	0	4-11 3/8	11-1 7/8	9-10 3/4	22-3 25/32	14-10 1/8	33-5 21/32
1	5 15/16	1-1 3/8	5-5 5/16	12-3 9/32	10-4 11/16	23-5 5/32	15-4 1/16	34-7 1/32
2	11 7/8	2-2 25/32	5-11 1/4	13-4 21/32	10-10 5/8	24-6 9/16	15-10	35-8 7/16
3	1-5 13/16	3-4 5/32	6-5 3/16	14-6 1/16	11-4 9/16	25-7 15/16	16-3 15/16	36-9 13/16
4	1-11 3/4	4-5 9/16	6-11 1/8	15-7 7/16	11-10 1/2	26-9 5/16	16-9 7/8	37-11 1/2
5	2-5 11/16	5-6 15/16	7-5 1/16	16-8 27/32	12-4 7/16	27-10 23/32	17-3 13/16	39-0 19/32
6	2-11 5/8	6-8 11/32	7-11	17-10 7/32	12-10 3/8	29-0 3/32	17-9 3/4	40-2
7	3-5 9/16	7-9 23/32	8-4 15/16	18-11 19/32	13-4 5/16	30-1 1/2	18-3 11/16	41-3 3/8
8	3-11 1/2	8-11 3/32	8-10 7/8	20-1	13-10 1/4	31-2 7/8	18-9 5/8	42-4 25/32
9	4-5 7/16	10-0 1/2	9-4 13/16	21-2 3/8	14-4 3/16	32-4 9/32	19-3 9/16	43-6 5/32

A = 26° 19′ 33″; logsin A = 9.64687; logcos A = 9.95245; logtan A = 9.69442; logcot A = 0.30558

Ins.	12″ Rise	12″ Slope	13″ Rise	13″ Slope	14″ Rise	14″ Slope	15″ Rise	15″ Slope	16″ Rise	16″ Slope
0	5 15/16	1-1 3/8	6 7/16	1-2 1/2	6 15/16	1-3 5/8	7 7/16	1-4 3/4	7 29/32	1-5 27/32
1/16	5 31/32–	1-1 15/32–	6 15/32–	1-2 9/16	6 31/32–	1-3 11/16	7 7/16	1-4 13/16	7 15/16	1-5 29/32
1/8	6	1-1 17/32–	6 1/2	1-2 21/32–	7	1-3 3/4	7 15/32	1-4 7/8	7 31/32	1-6
3/16	6 1/32–	1-1 19/32	6 17/32–	1-2 23/32–	7 1/32–	1-3 27/32–	7 1/2	1-4 15/16	8	1-6 1/16
1/4	6 1/16	1-1 21/32	6 9/16	1-2 25/32	7 1/16	1-3 29/32–	7 17/32	1-5	8 1/32	1-6 1/8
5/16	6 3/32–	1-1 3/4	6 19/32–	1-2 27/32	7 3/32–	1-3 31/32–	7 9/16	1-5 3/32–	8 1/16	1-6 3/16
3/8	6 1/8	1-1 13/16	6 5/8	1-2 15/16	7 1/8	1-4 1/32	7 19/32	1-5 5/32–	8 3/32	1-6 9/32–
7/16	6 5/32–	1-1 7/8	6 21/32–	1-3	7 5/32–	1-4 3/32	7 5/8	1-5 7/32	8 1/8	1-6 11/32–
1/2	6 3/16	1-1 15/16	6 11/16	1-3 1/16	7 3/16	1-4 3/16	7 21/32	1-5 9/32	8 5/32	1-6 13/32
9/16	6 7/32–	1-2 1/32–	6 23/32–	1-3 1/8	7 7/32–	1-4 1/4	7 11/16	1-5 3/8	8 3/16	1-6 15/32
5/8	6 1/4	1-2 3/32–	6 3/4	1-3 3/16	7 1/4	1-4 5/16	7 23/32	1-5 7/16	8 7/32	1-6 9/16
11/16	6 9/32–	1-2 5/32–	6 25/32–	1-3 9/32–	7 9/32–	1-4 3/8	7 3/4	1-5 1/2	8 1/4	1-6 5/8
3/4	6 5/16	1-2 7/32	6 13/16	1-3 11/32–	7 5/16	1-4 15/32–	7 25/32	1-5 9/16	8 9/32	1-6 11/16
13/16	6 11/32–	1-2 9/32	6 27/32–	1-3 13/32	7 11/32–	1-4 17/32–	7 13/16	1-5 21/32–	8 5/16	1-6 3/4
7/8	6 3/8	1-2 3/8	6 7/8	1-3 15/32	7 3/8	1-4 19/32	7 27/32	1-5 23/32–	8 11/32	1-6 13/16
15/16	6 13/32–	1-2 7/16	6 29/32–	1-3 9/16	7 13/32–	1-4 21/32	7 7/8	1-5 25/32	8 3/8	1-6 29/32–

Ins.	17″ Rise	17″ Slope	18″ Rise	18″ Slope	19″ Rise	19″ Slope	20″ Rise	20″ Slope	21″ Rise	21″ Slope
0	8 13/32	1-6 31/32–	8 29/32	1-8 3/32–	9 13/32–	1-9 3/16	9 29/32–	1-10 5/16	10 3/8	1-11 7/16
1/16	8 7/16	1-7 1/32	8 15/16	1-8 5/32–	9 7/16	1-9 9/32–	9 15/16	1-10 3/8	10 13/32	1-11 1/2
1/8	8 15/32	1-7 3/32	8 31/32–	1-8 7/32	9 15/32–	1-9 11/32–	9 31/32–	1-10 15/32–	10 7/16	1-11 9/16
3/16	8 1/2	1-7 3/16	9	1-8 9/32	9 1/2	1-9 13/32	10	1-10 17/32–	10 15/32	1-11 5/8
1/4	8 17/32	1-7 1/4	9 1/32–	1-8 3/8	9 17/32–	1-9 15/32	10 1/32–	1-10 19/32–	10 1/2	1-11 23/32–
5/16	8 9/16	1-7 5/16	9 1/16	1-8 7/16	9 9/16	1-9 9/16	10 1/16	1-10 21/32	10 17/32	1-11 25/32–
3/8	8 19/32	1-7 3/8	9 3/32–	1-8 1/2	9 19/32–	1-9 5/8	10 3/32–	1-10 23/32	10 9/16	1-11 27/32
7/16	8 5/8	1-7 15/32–	9 1/8	1-8 9/16	9 5/8	1-9 11/16	10 1/8	1-10 13/16	10 19/32	1-11 29/32
1/2	8 21/32	1-7 17/32–	9 5/32–	1-8 21/32–	9 21/32–	1-9 3/4	10 5/32–	1-10 7/8	10 5/8	2-0
9/16	8 11/16	1-7 19/32	9 3/16	1-8 23/32–	9 11/16	1-9 13/16	10 3/16	1-10 15/16	10 21/32	2-0 1/16
5/8	8 23/32	1-7 21/32	9 7/32–	1-8 25/32–	9 23/32–	1-9 29/32–	10 7/32–	1-11	10 11/16	2-0 1/8
11/16	8 3/4	1-7 23/32	9 1/4	1-8 27/32	9 3/4	1-9 31/32–	10 1/4	1-11 3/32–	10 23/32	2-0 3/16
3/4	8 25/32	1-7 13/16	9 9/32–	1-8 29/32	9 25/32–	1-10 1/32	10 9/32–	1-11 5/32–	10 3/4	2-0 9/32–
13/16	8 13/16	1-7 7/8	9 5/16	1-9	9 13/16	1-10 3/32	10 5/16	1-11 7/32	10 25/32	2-0 11/32–
7/8	8 27/32	1-7 15/16	9 11/32–	1-9 1/16	9 27/32–	1-10 3/16	10 11/32–	1-11 9/32	10 13/16	2-0 13/32
15/16	8 7/8	1-8	9 3/8	1-9 1/8	9 7/8	1-10 1/4	10 3/8	1-11 3/8	10 27/32	2-0 15/32

Feet	40′ Rise	40′ Slope	50′ Rise	50′ Slope	60′ Rise	60′ Slope	70′ Rise	70′ Slope
0	19-9 1/2	44-7 17/32	24-8 7/8	55-9 7/16	29-8 1/4	66-11 5/16	34-7 5/8	78-1 3/16
1	20-3 7/16	45-8 15/16	25-2 13/16	56-10 13/16	30-2 3/16	68-0 11/16	35-1 9/16	79-2 19/32–
2	20-9 3/8	46-10 5/16	25-8 3/4	58-0 7/32–	30-8 1/8	69-2 3/32–	35-7 1/2	80-3 31/32
3	21-3 5/16	47-11 23/32–	26-2 11/16	59-1 19/32	31-2 1/16	70-3 15/32	36-1 7/16	81-5 3/8
4	21-9 1/4	49-1 3/32	26-8 5/8	60-2 31/32	31-8	71-4 7/8	36-7 3/8	82-6 3/4
5	22-3 3/16	50-2 1/2	27-2 9/16	61-4 3/8	32-1 15/16	72-6 1/4	37-1 5/16	83-8 5/32–
6	22-9 1/8	51-3 7/8	27-8 1/2	62-5 3/4	32-7 7/8	73-7 21/32–	37-7 1/4	84-9 17/32
7	23-3 1/16	52-5 1/4	28-2 7/16	63-7 5/32–	33-1 13/16	74-9 1/32	38-1 3/16	85-10 29/32
8	23-9	53-6 21/32–	28-8 3/8	64-8 17/32	33-7 3/4	75-10 7/16	38-7 1/8	87-0 5/16
9	24-2 15/16	54-8 1/32	29-2 5/16	65-9 15/16	34-1 11/16	76-11 13/16	39-1 1/16	88-1 11/16

natsin A = 0.4434751694; natcos A = 0.8962866584; nattan A = 0.4947916666; natcot A = 2.0210526315

BEVEL 6" TO 12" — (¼ PITCH)

Inches	0" Rise	0" Slope	1" Rise	1" Slope	2" Rise	2" Slope	3" Rise	3" Slope	4" Rise	4" Slope	5" Rise	5" Slope
0	0	0	1/2	1 1/8	1	2 1/4	1 1/2	3 11/32	2	4 15/32	2 1/2	5 19/32
1/16	1/16	1/16	17/32	1 3/16	1 1/32	2 5/16	1 17/32	3 7/16	2 1/32	4 17/32	2 17/32	5 21/32
1/8	1/8	1/8	9/16	1 1/4	1 1/16	2 3/8	1 9/16	3 1/2	2 1/16	4 5/8	2 9/16	5 23/32
3/16	3/16	7/32	19/32	1 5/16	1 3/32	2 7/16	1 19/32	3 9/16	2 3/32	4 11/16	2 19/32	5 13/16
1/4	1/8	9/32	5/8	1 13/32	1 1/8	2 1/2	1 5/8	3 5/8	2 1/8	4 3/4	2 5/8	5 7/8
5/16	5/32	11/32	21/32	1 15/32	1 5/32	2 19/32	1 21/32	3 23/32	2 5/32	4 13/16	2 21/32	5 15/16
3/8	3/16	13/32	11/16	1 17/32	1 3/16	2 21/32	1 11/16	3 25/32	2 3/16	4 29/32	2 11/16	6
7/16	7/32	1/2	23/32	1 19/32	1 7/32	2 23/32	1 23/32	3 27/32	2 7/32	4 31/32	2 23/32	6 1/32
1/2	1/4	9/16	3/4	1 11/16	1 1/4	2 25/32	1 3/4	3 29/32	2 1/4	5 1/32	2 3/4	6 5/32
9/16	9/32	5/8	25/32	1 3/4	1 9/32	2 7/8	1 25/32	3 31/32	2 9/32	5 3/32	2 25/32	6 7/32
5/8	5/16	11/16	13/16	1 13/16	1 5/16	2 15/16	1 13/16	4 1/16	2 5/16	5 5/32	2 13/16	6 9/32
11/16	11/32	25/32	27/32	1 7/8	1 11/32	3	1 27/32	4 1/8	2 11/32	5 1/4	2 27/32	6 11/32
3/4	3/8	27/32	7/8	1 31/32	1 3/8	3 1/16	1 7/8	4 3/16	2 3/8	5 5/16	2 7/8	6 7/16
13/16	13/32	29/32	29/32	2 1/32	1 13/32	3 5/32	1 29/32	4 1/4	2 13/32	5 3/8	2 29/32	6 1/2
7/8	7/16	31/32	15/16	2 3/32	1 7/16	3 7/32	1 15/16	4 11/32	2 7/16	5 7/16	2 15/16	6 9/16
15/16	15/32	1 1/16	31/32	2 5/32	1 15/32	3 9/32	1 31/32	4 13/32	2 15/32	5 17/32	2 31/32	6 5/8

Inches	6" Rise	6" Slope	7" Rise	7" Slope	8" Rise	8" Slope	9" Rise	9" Slope	10" Rise	10" Slope	11" Rise	11" Slope
0	3	6 23/32	3 1/2	7 13/16	4	8 15/16	4 1/2	10 1/16	5	11 3/16	5 1/2	1-0 5/16
1/16	3 1/32	6 25/32	3 17/32	7 29/32	4 1/32	9	4 17/32	10 1/8	5 1/32	11 1/4	5 17/32	1-0 3/8
1/8	3 1/16	6 27/32	3 9/16	7 31/32	4 1/16	9 3/32	4 9/16	10 3/16	5 1/16	11 5/16	5 9/16	1-0 7/16
3/16	3 3/32	6 29/32	3 19/32	8 1/32	4 3/32	9 5/32	4 19/32	10 9/32	5 3/32	11 3/8	5 19/32	1-0 1/2
1/4	3 1/8	7	3 5/8	8 3/32	4 1/8	9 1/4	4 5/8	10 11/32	5 1/8	11 15/32	5 5/8	1-0 9/16
5/16	3 5/32	7 1/16	3 21/32	8 3/16	4 5/32	9 9/32	4 21/32	10 13/32	5 5/32	11 17/32	5 21/32	1-0 21/32
3/8	3 3/16	7 1/8	3 11/16	8 1/4	4 3/16	9 3/8	4 11/16	10 15/32	5 3/16	11 19/32	5 11/16	1-0 23/32
7/16	3 7/32	7 3/16	3 23/32	8 5/16	4 7/32	9 7/16	4 23/32	10 9/16	5 7/32	11 21/32	5 23/32	1-0 25/32
1/2	3 1/4	7 9/32	3 3/4	8 3/8	4 1/4	9 1/2	4 3/4	10 5/8	5 1/4	11 3/4	5 3/4	1-0 27/32
9/16	3 9/32	7 11/32	3 25/32	8 15/32	4 9/32	9 9/16	4 25/32	10 11/16	5 9/32	11 13/16	5 25/32	1-0 15/16
5/8	3 5/16	7 13/32	3 13/16	8 17/32	4 5/16	9 21/32	4 13/16	10 3/4	5 5/16	11 7/8	5 13/16	1-1
11/16	3 11/32	7 15/32	3 27/32	8 19/32	4 11/32	9 23/32	4 27/32	10 27/32	5 11/32	11 15/16	5 27/32	1-1 1/16
3/4	3 3/8	7 17/32	3 7/8	8 21/32	4 3/8	9 25/32	4 7/8	10 29/32	5 3/8	1-0 1/32	5 7/8	1-1 1/8
13/16	3 13/32	7 5/8	3 29/32	8 3/4	4 13/32	9 27/32	4 29/32	10 31/32	5 13/32	1-0 3/32	5 29/32	1-1 7/32
7/8	3 7/16	7 11/16	3 15/16	8 13/16	4 7/16	9 15/16	4 15/16	11 1/32	5 7/16	1-0 5/32	5 15/16	1-1 9/32
15/16	3 15/32	7 3/4	3 31/32	8 7/8	4 15/32	10	4 31/32	11 1/8	5 15/32	1-0 7/32	5 31/32	1-1 11/32

Feet	0' Rise	0' Slope	10' Rise	10' Slope	20' Rise	20' Slope	30' Rise	30' Slope
0	0	0	5-0	11-2 5/32	10-0	22-4 11/32	15-0	33-6 1/2
1	-6	1-1 13/32	5-6	12-3 19/32	10-6	23-5 3/4	15-6	34-7 29/32
2	1-0	2-2 27/32	6-0	13-5	11-0	24-7 5/32	16-0	35-9 5/16
3	1-6	3-4 1/4	6-6	14-6 13/32	11-6	25-8 9/16	16-6	36-10 3/4
4	2-0	4-5 21/32	7-0	15-7 27/32	12-0	26-10	17-0	38-0 5/32
5	2-6	5-7 3/32	7-6	16-9 1/4	12-6	27-11 13/32	17-6	39-1 9/16
6	3-0	6-8 1/2	8-0	17-10 21/32	13-0	29-0 13/16	18-0	40-3
7	3-6	7-9 29/32	8-6	19-0 3/32	13-6	30-2 1/4	18-6	41-4 13/32
8	4-0	8-11 11/32	9-0	20-1 1/2	14-0	31-3 21/32	19-0	42-5 13/16
9	4-6	10-0 3/4	9-6	21-2 29/32	14-6	32-5 1/16	19-6	43-7 1/4

A = 26° 33' 54"; logsin A = 9.65051; logcos A = 9.95154; logtan A = 9.69897; logcot A = 0.30103

Ins.	12″ Rise	12″ Slope	13″ Rise	13″ Slope	14″ Rise	14″ Slope	15″ Rise	15″ Slope	16″ Rise	16″ Slope
0	6	$1\text{-}1\frac{13}{32}$	$6\frac{1}{2}$	$1\text{-}2\frac{17}{32}$	7	$1\text{-}3\frac{21}{32}$	$7\frac{1}{2}$	$1\text{-}4\frac{25}{32}$	8	$1\text{-}5\frac{7}{8}$
$\frac{1}{16}$	$6\frac{1}{32}$	$1\text{-}1\frac{1}{2}$	$6\frac{17}{32}$	$1\text{-}2\frac{19}{32}$	$7\frac{1}{32}$	$1\text{-}3\frac{23}{32}$	$7\frac{17}{32}$	$1\text{-}4\frac{27}{32}$	$8\frac{1}{32}$	$1\text{-}5\frac{31}{32}$
$\frac{1}{8}$	$6\frac{1}{16}$	$1\text{-}1\frac{9}{16}$	$6\frac{9}{16}$	$1\text{-}2\frac{11}{16}$	$7\frac{1}{16}$	$1\text{-}3\frac{25}{32}$	$7\frac{9}{16}$	$1\text{-}4\frac{29}{32}$	$8\frac{1}{16}$	$1\text{-}6\frac{1}{32}$
$\frac{3}{16}$	$6\frac{3}{32}$	$1\text{-}1\frac{5}{8}$	$6\frac{19}{32}$	$1\text{-}2\frac{3}{4}$	$7\frac{3}{32}$	$1\text{-}3\frac{7}{8}$	$7\frac{19}{32}$	$1\text{-}4\frac{31}{32}$	$8\frac{3}{32}$	$1\text{-}6\frac{3}{32}$
$\frac{1}{4}$	$6\frac{1}{8}$	$1\text{-}1\frac{11}{16}$	$6\frac{5}{8}$	$1\text{-}2\frac{13}{16}$	$7\frac{1}{8}$	$1\text{-}3\frac{15}{16}$	$7\frac{5}{8}$	$1\text{-}5\frac{1}{16}$	$8\frac{1}{8}$	$1\text{-}6\frac{5}{32}$
$\frac{5}{16}$	$6\frac{5}{32}$	$1\text{-}1\frac{25}{32}$	$6\frac{21}{32}$	$1\text{-}2\frac{7}{8}$	$7\frac{5}{32}$	$1\text{-}4$	$7\frac{21}{32}$	$1\text{-}5\frac{1}{8}$	$8\frac{5}{32}$	$1\text{-}6\frac{1}{4}$
$\frac{3}{8}$	$6\frac{3}{16}$	$1\text{-}1\frac{27}{32}$	$6\frac{11}{16}$	$1\text{-}2\frac{31}{32}$	$7\frac{3}{16}$	$1\text{-}4\frac{1}{16}$	$7\frac{11}{16}$	$1\text{-}5\frac{3}{16}$	$8\frac{3}{16}$	$1\text{-}6\frac{5}{16}$
$\frac{7}{16}$	$6\frac{7}{32}$	$1\text{-}1\frac{29}{32}$	$6\frac{23}{32}$	$1\text{-}3\frac{1}{32}$	$7\frac{7}{32}$	$1\text{-}4\frac{1}{8}$	$7\frac{23}{32}$	$1\text{-}5\frac{1}{4}$	$8\frac{7}{32}$	$1\text{-}6\frac{3}{8}$
$\frac{1}{2}$	$6\frac{1}{4}$	$1\text{-}1\frac{31}{32}$	$6\frac{3}{4}$	$1\text{-}3\frac{3}{32}$	$7\frac{1}{4}$	$1\text{-}4\frac{7}{32}$	$7\frac{3}{4}$	$1\text{-}5\frac{11}{32}$	$8\frac{1}{4}$	$1\text{-}6\frac{7}{16}$
$\frac{9}{16}$	$6\frac{9}{32}$	$1\text{-}2\frac{1}{32}$	$6\frac{25}{32}$	$1\text{-}3\frac{5}{32}$	$7\frac{9}{32}$	$1\text{-}4\frac{9}{32}$	$7\frac{25}{32}$	$1\text{-}5\frac{13}{32}$	$8\frac{9}{32}$	$1\text{-}6\frac{17}{32}$
$\frac{5}{8}$	$6\frac{5}{16}$	$1\text{-}2\frac{1}{8}$	$6\frac{13}{16}$	$1\text{-}3\frac{7}{32}$	$7\frac{5}{16}$	$1\text{-}4\frac{11}{32}$	$7\frac{13}{16}$	$1\text{-}5\frac{15}{32}$	$8\frac{5}{16}$	$1\text{-}6\frac{19}{32}$
$\frac{11}{16}$	$6\frac{11}{32}$	$1\text{-}2\frac{3}{16}$	$6\frac{27}{32}$	$1\text{-}3\frac{5}{16}$	$7\frac{11}{32}$	$1\text{-}4\frac{13}{32}$	$7\frac{27}{32}$	$1\text{-}5\frac{17}{32}$	$8\frac{11}{32}$	$1\text{-}6\frac{21}{32}$
$\frac{3}{4}$	$6\frac{3}{8}$	$1\text{-}2\frac{1}{4}$	$6\frac{7}{8}$	$1\text{-}3\frac{3}{8}$	$7\frac{3}{8}$	$1\text{-}4\frac{1}{2}$	$7\frac{7}{8}$	$1\text{-}5\frac{19}{32}$	$8\frac{3}{8}$	$1\text{-}6\frac{23}{32}$
$\frac{13}{16}$	$6\frac{13}{32}$	$1\text{-}2\frac{5}{16}$	$6\frac{29}{32}$	$1\text{-}3\frac{7}{16}$	$7\frac{13}{32}$	$1\text{-}4\frac{9}{16}$	$7\frac{29}{32}$	$1\text{-}5\frac{11}{16}$	$8\frac{13}{32}$	$1\text{-}6\frac{13}{16}$
$\frac{7}{8}$	$6\frac{7}{16}$	$1\text{-}2\frac{13}{32}$	$6\frac{15}{16}$	$1\text{-}3\frac{1}{2}$	$7\frac{7}{16}$	$1\text{-}4\frac{5}{8}$	$7\frac{15}{16}$	$1\text{-}5\frac{3}{4}$	$8\frac{7}{16}$	$1\text{-}6\frac{7}{8}$
$\frac{15}{16}$	$6\frac{15}{32}$	$1\text{-}2\frac{15}{32}$	$6\frac{31}{32}$	$1\text{-}3\frac{19}{32}$	$7\frac{15}{32}$	$1\text{-}4\frac{11}{16}$	$7\frac{31}{32}$	$1\text{-}5\frac{13}{16}$	$8\frac{15}{32}$	$1\text{-}6\frac{15}{16}$

Ins.	17″ Rise	17″ Slope	18″ Rise	18″ Slope	19″ Rise	19″ Slope	20″ Rise	20″ Slope	21″ Rise	21″ Slope
0	$8\frac{1}{2}$	$1\text{-}7$	9	$1\text{-}8\frac{1}{8}$	$9\frac{1}{2}$	$1\text{-}9\frac{1}{4}$	10	$1\text{-}10\frac{3}{8}$	$10\frac{1}{2}$	$1\text{-}11\frac{15}{32}$
$\frac{1}{16}$	$8\frac{17}{32}$	$1\text{-}7\frac{1}{16}$	$9\frac{1}{32}$	$1\text{-}8\frac{3}{16}$	$9\frac{17}{32}$	$1\text{-}9\frac{5}{16}$	$10\frac{1}{32}$	$1\text{-}10\frac{7}{16}$	$10\frac{17}{32}$	$1\text{-}11\frac{9}{16}$
$\frac{1}{8}$	$8\frac{9}{16}$	$1\text{-}7\frac{5}{32}$	$9\frac{1}{16}$	$1\text{-}8\frac{1}{4}$	$9\frac{9}{16}$	$1\text{-}9\frac{3}{8}$	$10\frac{1}{16}$	$1\text{-}10\frac{1}{2}$	$10\frac{9}{16}$	$1\text{-}11\frac{5}{8}$
$\frac{3}{16}$	$8\frac{19}{32}$	$1\text{-}7\frac{7}{32}$	$9\frac{3}{32}$	$1\text{-}8\frac{11}{32}$	$9\frac{19}{32}$	$1\text{-}9\frac{7}{16}$	$10\frac{3}{32}$	$1\text{-}10\frac{9}{16}$	$10\frac{19}{32}$	$1\text{-}11\frac{11}{16}$
$\frac{1}{4}$	$8\frac{5}{8}$	$1\text{-}7\frac{9}{32}$	$9\frac{1}{8}$	$1\text{-}8\frac{13}{32}$	$9\frac{5}{8}$	$1\text{-}9\frac{17}{32}$	$10\frac{1}{8}$	$1\text{-}10\frac{5}{8}$	$10\frac{5}{8}$	$1\text{-}11\frac{3}{4}$
$\frac{5}{16}$	$8\frac{21}{32}$	$1\text{-}7\frac{11}{32}$	$9\frac{5}{32}$	$1\text{-}8\frac{15}{32}$	$9\frac{21}{32}$	$1\text{-}9\frac{19}{32}$	$10\frac{5}{32}$	$1\text{-}10\frac{23}{32}$	$10\frac{21}{32}$	$1\text{-}11\frac{13}{16}$
$\frac{3}{8}$	$8\frac{11}{16}$	$1\text{-}7\frac{7}{16}$	$9\frac{3}{16}$	$1\text{-}8\frac{17}{32}$	$9\frac{11}{16}$	$1\text{-}9\frac{21}{32}$	$10\frac{3}{16}$	$1\text{-}10\frac{25}{32}$	$10\frac{11}{16}$	$1\text{-}11\frac{29}{32}$
$\frac{7}{16}$	$8\frac{23}{32}$	$1\text{-}7\frac{1}{2}$	$9\frac{7}{32}$	$1\text{-}8\frac{5}{8}$	$9\frac{23}{32}$	$1\text{-}9\frac{23}{32}$	$10\frac{7}{32}$	$1\text{-}10\frac{27}{32}$	$10\frac{23}{32}$	$1\text{-}11\frac{31}{32}$
$\frac{1}{2}$	$8\frac{3}{4}$	$1\text{-}7\frac{9}{16}$	$9\frac{1}{4}$	$1\text{-}8\frac{11}{16}$	$9\frac{3}{4}$	$1\text{-}9\frac{13}{16}$	$10\frac{1}{4}$	$1\text{-}10\frac{29}{32}$	$10\frac{3}{4}$	$2\text{-}0\frac{1}{32}$
$\frac{9}{16}$	$8\frac{25}{32}$	$1\text{-}7\frac{5}{8}$	$9\frac{9}{32}$	$1\text{-}8\frac{3}{4}$	$9\frac{25}{32}$	$1\text{-}9\frac{7}{8}$	$10\frac{9}{32}$	$1\text{-}11$	$10\frac{25}{32}$	$2\text{-}0\frac{3}{32}$
$\frac{5}{8}$	$8\frac{13}{16}$	$1\text{-}7\frac{23}{32}$	$9\frac{5}{16}$	$1\text{-}8\frac{13}{16}$	$9\frac{13}{16}$	$1\text{-}9\frac{15}{16}$	$10\frac{5}{16}$	$1\text{-}11\frac{1}{16}$	$10\frac{13}{16}$	$2\text{-}0\frac{3}{16}$
$\frac{11}{16}$	$8\frac{27}{32}$	$1\text{-}7\frac{25}{32}$	$9\frac{11}{32}$	$1\text{-}8\frac{29}{32}$	$9\frac{27}{32}$	$1\text{-}10$	$10\frac{11}{32}$	$1\text{-}11\frac{1}{8}$	$10\frac{27}{32}$	$2\text{-}0\frac{1}{4}$
$\frac{3}{4}$	$8\frac{7}{8}$	$1\text{-}7\frac{27}{32}$	$9\frac{3}{8}$	$1\text{-}8\frac{31}{32}$	$9\frac{7}{8}$	$1\text{-}10\frac{3}{32}$	$10\frac{3}{8}$	$1\text{-}11\frac{3}{16}$	$10\frac{7}{8}$	$2\text{-}0\frac{5}{16}$
$\frac{13}{16}$	$8\frac{29}{32}$	$1\text{-}7\frac{29}{32}$	$9\frac{13}{32}$	$1\text{-}9\frac{1}{32}$	$9\frac{29}{32}$	$1\text{-}10\frac{5}{32}$	$10\frac{13}{32}$	$1\text{-}11\frac{9}{32}$	$10\frac{29}{32}$	$2\text{-}0\frac{3}{8}$
$\frac{7}{8}$	$8\frac{15}{16}$	$1\text{-}8$	$9\frac{7}{16}$	$1\text{-}9\frac{3}{32}$	$9\frac{15}{16}$	$1\text{-}10\frac{7}{32}$	$10\frac{7}{16}$	$1\text{-}11\frac{11}{32}$	$10\frac{15}{16}$	$2\text{-}0\frac{15}{32}$
$\frac{15}{16}$	$8\frac{31}{32}$	$1\text{-}8\frac{1}{16}$	$9\frac{15}{32}$	$1\text{-}9\frac{3}{16}$	$9\frac{31}{32}$	$1\text{-}10\frac{9}{32}$	$10\frac{15}{32}$	$1\text{-}11\frac{13}{32}$	$10\frac{31}{32}$	$2\text{-}0\frac{17}{32}$

Feet	40′ Rise	40′ Slope	50′ Rise	50′ Slope	60′ Rise	60′ Slope	70′ Rise	70′ Slope
0	20-0	$44\text{-}8\frac{21}{32}$	25-0	$55\text{-}10\frac{13}{16}$	30-0	$67\text{-}1$	35-0	$78\text{-}3\frac{5}{32}$
1	20-6	$45\text{-}10\frac{1}{16}$	25-6	$57\text{-}0\frac{1}{4}$	30-6	$68\text{-}2\frac{13}{32}$	35-6	$79\text{-}4\frac{9}{16}$
2	21-0	$46\text{-}11\frac{1}{2}$	26-0	$58\text{-}1\frac{21}{32}$	31-0	$69\text{-}3\frac{13}{16}$	36-0	$80\text{-}5\frac{31}{32}$
3	21-6	$48\text{-}0\frac{29}{32}$	26-6	$59\text{-}3\frac{3}{32}$	31-6	$70\text{-}5\frac{7}{32}$	36-6	$81\text{-}7\frac{13}{32}$
4	22-0	$49\text{-}2\frac{5}{16}$	27-0	$60\text{-}4\frac{1}{2}$	32-0	$71\text{-}6\frac{21}{32}$	37-0	$82\text{-}8\frac{13}{16}$
5	22-6	$50\text{-}3\frac{3}{4}$	27-6	$61\text{-}5\frac{29}{32}$	32-6	$72\text{-}8\frac{1}{16}$	37-6	$83\text{-}10\frac{7}{32}$
6	23-0	$51\text{-}5\frac{5}{32}$	28-0	$62\text{-}7\frac{5}{16}$	33-0	$73\text{-}9\frac{15}{32}$	38-0	$84\text{-}11\frac{21}{32}$
7	23-6	$52\text{-}6\frac{9}{16}$	28-6	$63\text{-}8\frac{3}{4}$	33-6	$74\text{-}10\frac{29}{32}$	38-6	$86\text{-}1\frac{1}{16}$
8	24-0	$53\text{-}8$	29-0	$64\text{-}10\frac{5}{32}$	34-0	$76\text{-}0\frac{5}{16}$	39-0	$87\text{-}2\frac{15}{32}$
9	24-6	$54\text{-}9\frac{13}{32}$	29-6	$65\text{-}11\frac{9}{16}$	34-6	$77\text{-}1\frac{23}{32}$	39-6	$88\text{-}3\frac{29}{32}$

natsin A=0.4472135955; natcos A=0.8944271910; nattan A=0.5000000000; natcot A=2.0000000000

See page 97b (located page 215) for angle and trigonometric functions.

Inches	0" Rise	0" Slope	1" Rise	1" Slope	2" Rise	2" Slope	3" Rise	3" Slope	4" Rise	4" Slope	5" Rise	5" Slope
0	0	0	1/2	1 1/8	1	2 1/4	1 1/2	3 3/8	2 1/32	4 15/32	2 17/32	5 19/32
1/16	1/32	1/16	17/32	1 3/16	1 1/32	2 5/16	1 9/16	3 7/16	2 1/16	4 9/16	2 9/16	5 11/16
1/8	1/16	1/8	9/16	1 1/4	1 1/16	2 3/8	1 19/32	3 1/2	2 3/32	4 5/8	2 19/32	5 3/4
3/16	3/32	7/32	19/32	1 11/32	1 3/32	2 7/16	1 5/8	3 9/16	2 1/8	4 11/16	2 5/8	5 13/16
1/4	1/8	9/32	5/8	1 13/32	1 1/8	2 17/32	1 21/32	3 21/32	2 5/32	4 3/4	2 21/32	5 7/8
5/16	5/32	11/32	21/32	1 15/32	1 5/32	2 19/32	1 11/16	3 23/32	2 3/16	4 27/32	2 11/16	5 15/16
3/8	3/16	13/32	11/16	1 17/32	1 3/16	2 21/32	1 23/32	3 25/32	2 7/32	4 29/32	2 23/32	6 1/32
7/16	7/32	1/2	23/32	1 5/8	1 7/32	2 23/32	1 3/4	3 27/32	2 1/4	4 31/32	2 3/4	6 3/32
1/2	1/4	9/16	3/4	1 11/16	1 1/4	2 13/32	1 25/32	3 29/32	2 9/32	5 1/32	2 25/32	6 5/32
9/16	9/32	5/8	25/32	1 3/4	1 9/32	2 7/8	1 13/16	4	2 5/16	5 1/8	2 13/16	6 7/32
5/8	5/16	11/16	13/16	1 13/16	1 5/16	2 15/16	1 27/32	4 1/16	2 11/32	5 3/16	2 27/32	6 5/16
11/16	11/32	25/32	27/32	1 7/8	1 11/32	3	1 7/8	4 1/8	2 3/8	5 1/4	2 7/8	6 3/8
3/4	3/8	27/32	7/8	1 31/32	1 3/8	3 3/32	1 29/32	4 3/16	2 13/32	5 5/16	2 29/32	6 7/16
13/16	13/32	29/32	29/32	2 1/32	1 13/32	3 5/32	1 15/16	4 9/32	2 7/16	5 13/32	2 15/16	6 1/2
7/8	7/16	31/32	15/16	2 3/32	1 7/16	3 7/32	1 31/32	4 11/32	2 15/32	5 15/32	2 31/32	6 19/32
15/16	15/32	1 1/16	31/32	2 5/32	1 15/32	3 9/32	2	4 13/32	2 1/2	5 17/32	3	6 21/32

Inches	6" Rise	6" Slope	7" Rise	7" Slope	8" Rise	8" Slope	9" Rise	9" Slope	10" Rise	10" Slope	11" Rise	11" Slope
0	3 1/32	6 23/32	3 17/32	7 27/32	4 1/32	8 31/32	4 9/16	10 3/32	5 1/16	11 7/32	5 9/16	1-0 5/16
1/16	3 1/16	6 25/32	3 9/16	7 29/32	4 1/16	9 1/32	4 19/32	10 5/32	5 3/32	11 9/32	5 19/32	1-0 13/32
1/8	3 3/32	6 7/8	3 19/32	7 31/32	4 3/32	9 3/32	4 5/8	10 7/32	5 1/8	11 11/32	5 5/8	1-0 15/32
3/16	3 1/8	6 15/16	3 5/8	8 1/16	4 1/8	9 3/16	4 21/32	10 9/32	5 5/32	11 13/32	5 21/32	1-0 17/32
1/4	3 5/32	7	3 21/32	8 1/8	4 5/32	9 1/4	4 11/16	10 3/8	5 3/16	11 15/32	5 11/16	1-0 19/32
5/16	3 3/16	7 1/16	3 11/16	8 3/16	4 3/16	9 5/16	4 23/32	10 7/16	5 7/32	11 9/16	5 23/32	1-0 11/16
3/8	3 7/32	7 5/32	3 23/32	8 1/4	4 7/32	9 3/8	4 3/4	10 1/2	5 1/4	11 5/8	5 3/4	1-0 3/4
7/16	3 1/4	7 7/32	3 3/4	8 11/32	4 11/32	9 15/32	4 25/32	10 9/16	5 9/32	11 11/16	5 25/32	1-0 13/16
1/2	3 9/32	7 9/32	3 25/32	8 13/32	4 9/32	9 17/32	4 13/16	10 21/32	5 5/16	11 3/4	5 13/16	1-0 7/8
9/16	3 5/16	7 11/32	3 13/16	8 15/32	4 5/16	9 19/32	4 27/32	10 23/32	5 11/32	11 27/32	5 27/32	1-0 31/32
5/8	3 11/32	7 7/16	3 27/32	8 17/32	4 11/32	9 21/32	4 7/8	10 25/32	5 3/8	11 29/32	5 7/8	1-1 1/32
11/16	3 3/8	7 1/2	3 7/8	8 5/8	4 3/8	9 23/32	4 29/32	10 27/32	5 13/32	11 31/32	5 29/32	1-1 3/32
3/4	3 13/32	7 9/16	3 29/32	8 11/16	4 13/32	9 13/16	4 15/16	10 15/16	5 7/16	1-0 1/32	5 15/16	1-1 5/32
13/16	3 7/16	7 5/8	3 15/16	8 3/4	4 7/16	9 7/8	4 31/32	11	5 15/32	1-0 1/8	5 31/32	1-1 1/4
7/8	3 15/32	7 11/16	3 31/32	8 13/16	4 15/32	9 15/16	5	11 1/16	5 1/2	1-0 3/16	6	1-1 5/16
15/16	3 1/2	7 25/32	4	8 29/32	4 1/2	10	5 1/32	11 1/8	5 17/32	1-0 1/4	6 1/32	1-1 3/8

Feet	0' Rise	0' Slope	10' Rise	10' Slope	20' Rise	20' Slope	30' Rise	30' Slope
0	0	0	5-0 5/8	11-2 7/16	10-1 1/4	22-4 7/8	15-1 7/8	33-7 11/32
1	6 1/16	1-1 7/16	5-6 11/16	12-3 7/8	10-7 5/16	23-6 11/32	15-7 15/16	34-8 25/32
2	1-0 1/8	2-2 7/8	6-0 3/4	13-5 11/32	11-1 3/8	24-7 25/32	16-2	35-10 7/32
3	1-6 3/16	3-4 11/32	6-6 13/16	14-6 25/32	11-7 7/16	25-9 7/32	16-8 1/16	36-11 21/32
4	2-0 1/4	4-5 25/32	7-0 7/8	15-8 7/32	12-1 1/2	26-10 21/32	17-2 1/8	38-1 1/8
5	2-6 5/16	5-7 7/32	7-6 15/16	16-9 21/32	12-7 9/16	28-0 1/8	17-8 3/16	39-2 9/16
6	3-0 3/8	6-8 21/32	8-1	17-11 1/8	13-1 5/8	29-1 9/16	18-2 1/4	40-4
7	3-6 7/16	7-10 1/32	8-7 1/16	19-0 9/16	13-7 11/16	30-3	18-8 5/16	41-5 7/16
8	4-0 1/2	8-11 9/16	9-1 1/8	20-2	14-1 3/4	31-4 7/16	19-2 3/8	42-6 7/8
9	4-6 9/16	10-1	9-7 3/16	21-3 7/16	14-7 13/16	32-5 7/8	19-8 7/16	43-8 11/32

A = 26° 48′ 12″; logsin A = **9.65411**; logcos A = **9.95064**; logtan A = **9.70347**; logcot A = **0.29653**

Ins.	12″ Rise	12″ Slope	13″ Rise	13″ Slope	14″ Rise	14″ Slope	15″ Rise	15″ Slope	16″ Rise	16″ Slope
0	6 1/16	1-1 7/16	6 9/16	1-2 9/16	7 1/16	1-3 11/16	7 9/16	1-4 13/16	8 3/32	1-5 15/16
1/16	6 3/32	1-1 1/2	6 19/32	1-2 5/8	7 3/32	1-3 3/4	7 5/8	1-4 7/8	8 1/8	1-6
1/8	6 1/8	1-1 19/32	6 5/8	1-2 23/32	7 1/8	1-3 13/16	7 21/32	1-4 15/16	8 5/32	1-6 1/16
3/16	6 5/32	1-1 21/32	6 21/32	1-2 25/32	7 5/32	1-3 29/32	7 11/16	1-5 1/32	8 3/16	1-6 1/8
1/4	6 3/16	1-1 23/32	6 11/16	1-2 27/32	7 3/16	1-3 31/32	7 23/32	1-5 3/32	8 7/32	1-6 7/32
5/16	6 7/32	1-1 25/32	6 23/32	1-2 29/32	7 7/32	1-4 1/32	7 3/4	1-5 5/32	8 1/4	1-6 9/32
3/8	6 1/4	1-1 7/8	6 3/4	1-3	7 1/4	1-4 3/32	7 25/32	1-5 7/32	8 9/32	1-6 11/32
7/16	6 9/32	1-1 15/16	6 25/32	1-3 1/16	7 9/32	1-4 3/16	7 13/16	1-5 9/32	8 5/16	1-6 13/32
1/2	6 5/16	1-2	6 13/16	1-3 1/8	7 5/16	1-4 1/4	7 27/32	1-5 3/8	8 11/32	1-6 1/2
9/16	6 11/32	1-2 1/16	6 27/32	1-3 3/16	7 11/32	1-4 5/16	7 7/8	1-5 7/16	8 3/8	1-6 9/16
5/8	6 3/8	1-2 5/32	6 7/8	1-3 1/4	7 3/8	1-4 3/8	7 29/32	1-5 1/2	8 13/32	1-6 5/8
11/16	6 13/32	1-2 7/32	6 29/32	1-3 11/32	7 13/32	1-4 15/32	7 15/16	1-5 9/16	8 7/16	1-6 11/16
3/4	6 7/16	1-2 9/32	6 15/16	1-3 13/32	7 7/16	1-4 17/32	7 31/32	1-5 21/32	8 15/32	1-6 25/32
13/16	6 15/32	1-2 11/32	6 31/32	1-3 15/32	7 15/32	1-4 19/32	8	1-5 23/32	8 1/2	1-6 27/32
7/8	6 1/2	1-2 7/16	7	1-3 17/32	7 1/2	1-4 21/32	8 1/32	1-5 25/32	8 17/32	1-6 29/32
15/16	6 17/32	1-2 1/2	7 1/2	1-3 5/8	7 17/32	1-4 3/4	8 1/16	1-5 27/32	8 9/16	1-6 31/32

Ins.	17″ Rise	17″ Slope	18″ Rise	18″ Slope	19″ Rise	19″ Slope	20″ Rise	20″ Slope	21″ Rise	21″ Slope
0	8 19/32	1-7 1/32	9 3/32	1-8 5/32	9 19/32	1-9 9/32	10 3/32	1-10 13/32	10 5/8	1-11 17/32
1/16	8 5/8	1-7 1/8	9 1/8	1-8 1/4	9 5/8	1-9 11/32	10 1/8	1-10 15/32	10 21/32	1-11 19/32
1/8	8 21/32	1-7 3/16	9 5/32	1-8 5/16	9 21/32	1-9 7/16	10 5/32	1-10 9/16	10 11/16	1-11 21/32
3/16	8 11/16	1-7 1/4	9 3/16	1-8 3/8	9 11/16	1-9 1/2	10 3/16	1-10 5/8	10 23/32	1-11 3/4
1/4	8 23/32	1-7 5/16	9 7/32	1-8 7/16	9 23/32	1-9 9/16	10 7/32	1-10 11/16	10 3/4	1-11 13/16
5/16	8 3/4	1-7 13/32	9 1/4	1-8 17/32	9 3/4	1-9 5/8	10 1/4	1-10 3/4	10 25/32	1-11 7/8
3/8	8 25/32	1-7 15/32	9 9/32	1-8 19/32	9 25/32	1-9 23/32	10 9/32	1-10 13/16	10 13/16	1-11 15/16
7/16	8 13/16	1-7 17/32	9 5/16	1-8 21/32	9 13/16	1-9 25/32	10 5/16	1-10 29/32	10 27/32	2-0 1/32
1/2	8 27/32	1-7 19/32	9 11/32	1-8 23/32	9 27/32	1-9 27/32	10 11/32	1-10 31/32	10 7/8	2-0 3/32
9/16	8 7/8	1-7 11/16	9 3/8	1-8 13/16	9 7/8	1-9 29/32	10 3/8	1-11 1/32	10 29/32	2-0 5/32
5/8	8 29/32	1-7 3/4	9 13/32	1-8 7/8	9 29/32	1-10	10 13/32	1-11 3/32	10 15/16	2-0 7/32
11/16	8 15/16	1-7 13/16	9 7/16	1-8 15/16	9 15/16	1-10 1/16	10 7/16	1-11 3/16	10 31/32	2-0 5/16
3/4	8 31/32	1-7 7/8	9 15/32	1-9	9 31/32	1-10 1/8	10 15/32	1-11 1/4	11	2-0 3/8
13/16	9	1-7 31/32	9 1/2	1-9 1/16	10	1-10 3/16	10 1/2	1-11 5/16	11 1/2	2-0 7/16
7/8	9 1/32	1-8 1/32	9 17/32	1-9 5/32	10 1/2	1-10 9/32	10 17/32	1-11 3/8	11 1/16	2-0 1/2
15/16	9 1/16	1-8 3/32	9 9/16	1-9 7/32	10 1/16	1-10 11/32	10 9/16	1-11 15/32	11 3/32	2-0 19/32

Feet	40' Rise	40' Slope	50' Rise	50' Slope	60' Rise	60' Slope	70' Rise	70' Slope
0	20-2 1/2	44-9 25/32	25-3 1/8	56-0 7/32	30-3 3/4	67-2 21/32	35-4 3/8	78-5 1/8
1	20-8 9/16	45-11 7/8	25-9 3/16	57-1 21/32	30-9 13/16	68-4 1/8	35-10 7/16	79-6 9/16
2	21-2 5/8	47-0 21/32	26-3 1/4	58-3 1/8	31-3 7/8	69-5 9/16	36-4 1/2	80-8
3	21-8 11/16	48-2 1/8	26-9 5/16	59-4 9/16	31-9 15/16	70-7	36-10 9/16	81-9 7/16
4	22-2 3/4	49-3 9/16	27-3 3/8	60-6	32-4	71-8 7/16	37-4 5/8	82-10 29/32
5	22-8 13/16	50-5	27-9 7/16	61-7 7/16	32-10 1/16	72-9 29/32	37-10 11/16	84-0 11/32
6	23-2 7/8	51-6 7/16	28-3 1/2	62-8 7/8	33-4 1/8	73-11 11/32	38-4 3/4	85-1 25/32
7	23-8 15/16	52-7 7/8	28-9 9/16	63-10 11/32	33-10 3/16	75-0 25/32	38-10 13/16	86-3 7/32
8	24-3	53-9 11/32	29-3 5/8	64-11 25/32	34-4 1/4	76-2 7/32	39-4 7/8	87-4 21/32
9	24-9 1/16	54-10 25/32	29-9 11/16	66-1 7/32	34-10 5/16	77-3 21/32	39-10 15/16	88-6 1/8

natsin A=0.4509287294; natcos A=0.8925599593; nattan A=0.5052083333; natcot A=1.9793814432

Inches	0" Rise	0" Slope	1" Rise	1" Slope	2" Rise	2" Slope	3" Rise	3" Slope	4" Rise	4" Slope	5" Rise	5" Slope
0	0	0	1/2	1 1/8	1 1/32	2 1/4	1 17/32	3 3/8	2 1/32	4 1/2	2 9/16	5 5/8
1/16	1/32	1/16	17/32	1 3/16	1 1/16	2 5/16	1 9/16	3 7/16	2 1/16	4 9/16	2 19/32	5 11/16
1/8	1/16	1/8	9/16	1 1/4	1 3/32	2 3/8	1 19/32	3 1/2	2 3/32	4 5/8	2 5/8	5 3/4
3/16	3/32	7/32	19/32	1 11/32	1 1/8	2 15/32	1 5/8	3 19/32	2 1/8	4 11/16	2 21/32	5 13/16
1/4	1/8	9/32	5/8	1 13/32	1 5/32	2 17/32	1 21/32	3 21/32	2 5/32	4 25/32	2 11/16	5 29/32
5/16	5/32	11/32	21/32	1 15/32	1 3/16	2 19/32	1 11/16	3 23/32	2 3/16	4 27/32	2 23/32	5 31/32
3/8	3/16	13/32	11/16	1 17/32	1 7/32	2 21/32	1 23/32	3 25/32	2 7/32	4 29/32	2 3/4	6 1/32
7/16	7/32	1/2	23/32	1 5/8	1 1/4	2 3/4	1 3/4	3 7/8	2 1/4	4 31/32	2 25/32	6 3/32
1/2	1/4	9/16	3/4	1 11/16	1 9/32	2 13/16	1 25/32	3 15/16	2 5/16	5 1/16	2 13/16	6 3/16
9/16	9/32	5/8	13/16	1 3/4	1 5/16	2 7/8	1 13/16	4	2 11/32	5 1/8	2 27/32	6 1/4
5/8	5/16	11/16	27/32	1 13/16	1 11/32	2 15/16	1 27/32	4 1/16	2 3/8	5 3/16	2 7/8	6 5/16
11/16	11/32	25/32	7/8	1 29/32	1 3/8	3 1/32	1 7/8	4 1/8	2 13/32	5 1/4	2 29/32	6 3/8
3/4	3/8	27/32	29/32	1 31/32	1 13/32	3 3/32	1 29/32	4 7/32	2 7/16	5 11/32	2 15/16	6 15/32
13/16	13/32	29/32	15/16	2 1/16	1 7/16	3 5/32	1 15/16	4 9/32	2 15/32	5 13/32	2 31/32	6 17/32
7/8	7/16	31/32	31/32	2 3/32	1 15/32	3 7/32	1 31/32	4 11/32	2 1/2	5 15/32	3	6 19/32
15/16	15/32	1 1/16	1	2 3/16	1 1/2	3 5/16	2	4 13/32	2 17/32	5 17/32	3 1/32	6 21/32

Inches	6" Rise	6" Slope	7" Rise	7" Slope	8" Rise	8" Slope	9" Rise	9" Slope	10" Rise	10" Slope	11" Rise	11" Slope
0	3 1/16	6 3/4	3 9/16	7 27/32	4 3/32	8 31/32	4 19/32	10 3/32	5 3/32	11 7/32	5 5/8	1-0 11/32
1/16	3 3/32	6 13/16	3 19/32	7 15/16	4 1/8	9 1/16	4 5/8	10 3/16	5 1/8	11 5/16	5 21/32	1-0 13/32
1/8	3 1/8	6 7/8	3 5/8	8	4 5/32	9 1/8	4 21/32	10 1/4	5 5/32	11 3/8	5 11/16	1-0 1/2
3/16	3 5/32	6 15/16	3 21/32	8 1/16	4 3/16	9 3/16	4 11/16	10 5/16	5 3/16	11 7/16	5 23/32	1-0 9/16
1/4	3 3/16	7 1/32	3 11/16	8 1/8	4 7/32	9 1/4	4 23/32	10 3/8	5 7/32	11 1/2	5 3/4	1-0 5/8
5/16	3 7/32	7 3/32	3 23/32	8 7/32	4 1/4	9 11/32	4 3/4	10 15/32	5 1/4	11 19/32	5 25/32	1-0 11/16
3/8	3 1/4	7 5/32	3 3/4	8 9/32	4 9/32	9 13/32	4 25/32	10 17/32	5 9/32	11 21/32	5 13/16	1-0 25/32
7/16	3 9/32	7 7/32	3 25/32	8 11/32	4 5/16	9 15/32	4 13/16	10 19/32	5 5/16	11 23/32	5 27/32	1-0 27/32
1/2	3 5/16	7 5/16	3 13/16	8 13/32	4 11/32	9 17/32	4 27/32	10 21/32	5 3/8	11 25/32	5 7/8	1-0 29/32
9/16	3 11/32	7 3/8	3 7/8	8 1/2	4 3/8	9 5/8	4 7/8	10 3/4	5 13/32	11 27/32	5 29/32	1-0 31/32
5/8	3 3/8	7 7/16	3 29/32	8 9/16	4 13/32	9 11/16	4 29/32	10 13/16	5 7/16	11 15/16	5 15/16	1-1 1/16
11/16	3 13/32	7 1/2	3 15/16	8 5/8	4 7/16	9 3/4	4 15/16	10 7/8	5 15/32	1-0	5 31/32	1-1 1/8
3/4	3 7/16	7 19/32	3 31/32	8 11/16	4 15/32	9 13/16	4 31/32	10 15/16	5 1/2	1-0 1/16	6	1-1 3/16
13/16	3 15/32	7 21/32	4	8 25/32	4 1/2	9 29/32	5	11 1/32	5 17/32	1-0 1/8	6 1/16	1-1 1/4
7/8	3 1/2	7 23/32	4 1/16	8 27/32	4 17/32	9 31/32	5 1/32	11 3/32	5 9/16	1-0 7/32	6 1/16	1-1 11/32
15/16	3 17/32	7 25/32	4 1/16	8 29/32	4 9/16	10 1/32	5 1/16	11 5/32	5 19/32	1-0 9/32	6 3/32	1-1 13/32

Feet	0' Rise	0' Slope	10' Rise	10' Slope	20' Rise	20' Slope	30' Rise	30' Slope
0	0	0	5-1 1/4	11-2 23/32	10-2 1/2	22-5 15/32	15-3 3/4	33-8 3/16
1	6 1/8	1-1 15/32	5-7 3/8	12-4 3/16	10-8 5/8	23-6 15/16	15-9 7/8	34-9 21/32
2	1-0 1/4	2-2 15/16	6-1 1/2	13-5 11/16	11-2 3/4	24-8 13/32	16-4	35-11 1/8
3	1-6 3/8	3-4 13/32	6-7 5/8	14-7 5/32	11-8 7/8	25-9 7/8	16-10 1/8	37-0 19/32
4	2-0 1/2	4-5 29/32	7-1 3/4	15-8 5/8	12-3	26-11 11/32	17-4 1/4	38-2 1/16
5	2-6 5/8	5-7 3/8	7-7 7/8	16-10 3/32	12-9 1/8	28-0 13/16	17-10 3/8	39-3 9/16
6	3-0 3/4	6-8 27/32	8-2	17-11 9/16	13-3 1/4	29-2 9/32	18-4 1/2	40-5 1/32
7	3-6 7/8	7-10 5/16	8-8 1/8	19-1 1/32	13-9 3/8	30-3 3/4	18-10 5/8	41-6 1/2
8	4-1	8-11 25/32	9-2 1/4	20-2 1/2	14-3 1/2	31-5 1/4	19-4 3/4	42-7 31/32
9	4-7 1/8	10-1 1/4	9-8 3/8	21-3 31/32	14-9 5/8	32-6 23/32	19-10 7/8	43-9 7/16

A = 27° 02' 26''; logsin A = 9.65765; logcos A = 9.94972; logtan A = 9.70792; logcot A = 0.29208

Ins.	12″ Rise	12″ Slope	13″ Rise	13″ Slope	14″ Rise	14″ Slope	15″ Rise	15″ Slope	16″ Rise	16″ Slope
0	$6\frac{1}{8}$	$1\text{-}1\frac{15}{32}$	$6\frac{5}{8}$	$1\text{-}2\frac{19}{32}$	$7\frac{5}{32}$	$1\text{-}3\frac{23}{32}$	$7\frac{21}{32}$	$1\text{-}4\frac{27}{32}$	$8\frac{5}{32}$	$1\text{-}5\frac{31}{32}$
1/16	$6\frac{5}{32}$	$1\text{-}1\frac{17}{32}$	$6\frac{21}{32}$	$1\text{-}2\frac{21}{32}$	$7\frac{3}{16}$	$1\text{-}3\frac{25}{32}$	$7\frac{11}{16}$	$1\text{-}4\frac{29}{32}$	$8\frac{3}{16}$	$1\text{-}6\frac{1}{32}$
1/8	$6\frac{3}{16}$	$1\text{-}1\frac{5}{8}$	$6\frac{11}{16}$	$1\text{-}2\frac{3}{4}$	$7\frac{7}{32}$	$1\text{-}3\frac{27}{32}$	$7\frac{23}{32}$	$1\text{-}4\frac{31}{32}$	$8\frac{7}{32}$	$1\text{-}6\frac{3}{32}$
3/16	$6\frac{7}{32}$	$1\text{-}1\frac{11}{16}$	$6\frac{23}{32}$	$1\text{-}2\frac{13}{16}$	$7\frac{1}{4}$	$1\text{-}3\frac{15}{16}$	$7\frac{3}{4}$	$1\text{-}5\frac{1}{16}$	$8\frac{1}{4}$	$1\text{-}6\frac{3}{16}$
1/4	$6\frac{1}{4}$	$1\text{-}1\frac{3}{4}$	$6\frac{3}{4}$	$1\text{-}2\frac{7}{8}$	$7\frac{9}{32}$	$1\text{-}4$	$7\frac{25}{32}$	$1\text{-}5\frac{1}{8}$	$8\frac{9}{32}$	$1\text{-}6\frac{1}{4}$
5/16	$6\frac{9}{32}$	$1\text{-}1\frac{13}{16}$	$6\frac{25}{32}$	$1\text{-}2\frac{15}{16}$	$7\frac{5}{16}$	$1\text{-}4\frac{1}{16}$	$7\frac{13}{16}$	$1\text{-}5\frac{3}{16}$	$8\frac{5}{16}$	$1\text{-}6\frac{5}{16}$
3/8	$6\frac{5}{16}$	$1\text{-}1\frac{29}{32}$	$6\frac{13}{16}$	$1\text{-}3\frac{1}{32}$	$7\frac{11}{32}$	$1\text{-}4\frac{1}{8}$	$7\frac{27}{32}$	$1\text{-}5\frac{1}{4}$	$8\frac{11}{32}$	$1\text{-}6\frac{3}{8}$
7/16	$6\frac{11}{32}$	$1\text{-}1\frac{31}{32}$	$6\frac{27}{32}$	$1\text{-}3\frac{3}{32}$	$7\frac{3}{8}$	$1\text{-}4\frac{7}{32}$	$7\frac{7}{8}$	$1\text{-}5\frac{11}{32}$	$8\frac{3}{8}$	$1\text{-}6\frac{15}{32}$
1/2	$6\frac{3}{8}$	$1\text{-}2\frac{1}{32}$	$6\frac{7}{8}$	$1\text{-}3\frac{5}{32}$	$7\frac{13}{32}$	$1\text{-}4\frac{9}{32}$	$7\frac{29}{32}$	$1\text{-}5\frac{13}{32}$	$8\frac{7}{16}$	$1\text{-}6\frac{17}{32}$
9/16	$6\frac{13}{32}$	$1\text{-}2\frac{1}{8}$	$6\frac{15}{16}$	$1\text{-}3\frac{7}{32}$	$7\frac{7}{16}$	$1\text{-}4\frac{11}{32}$	$7\frac{15}{16}$	$1\text{-}5\frac{15}{32}$	$8\frac{15}{32}$	$1\text{-}6\frac{19}{32}$
5/8	$6\frac{7}{16}$	$1\text{-}2\frac{3}{16}$	$6\frac{31}{32}$	$1\text{-}3\frac{5}{16}$	$7\frac{15}{32}$	$1\text{-}4\frac{13}{32}$	$7\frac{31}{32}$	$1\text{-}5\frac{17}{32}$	$8\frac{1}{2}$	$1\text{-}6\frac{21}{32}$
11/16	$6\frac{15}{32}$	$1\text{-}2\frac{1}{4}$	7	$1\text{-}3\frac{3}{8}$	$7\frac{1}{2}$	$1\text{-}4\frac{1}{2}$	8	$1\text{-}5\frac{5}{8}$	$8\frac{17}{32}$	$1\text{-}6\frac{3}{4}$
3/4	$6\frac{1}{2}$	$1\text{-}2\frac{5}{16}$	$7\frac{1}{32}$	$1\text{-}3\frac{7}{16}$	$7\frac{17}{32}$	$1\text{-}4\frac{9}{16}$	$8\frac{1}{32}$	$1\text{-}5\frac{11}{16}$	$8\frac{9}{16}$	$1\text{-}6\frac{13}{16}$
13/16	$6\frac{17}{32}$	$1\text{-}2\frac{3}{8}$	$7\frac{1}{16}$	$1\text{-}3\frac{1}{2}$	$7\frac{9}{16}$	$1\text{-}4\frac{5}{8}$	$8\frac{1}{16}$	$1\text{-}5\frac{3}{4}$	$8\frac{19}{32}$	$1\text{-}6\frac{7}{8}$
7/8	$6\frac{9}{16}$	$1\text{-}2\frac{15}{32}$	$7\frac{3}{32}$	$1\text{-}3\frac{9}{16}$	$7\frac{19}{32}$	$1\text{-}4\frac{11}{16}$	$8\frac{3}{32}$	$1\text{-}5\frac{13}{16}$	$8\frac{5}{8}$	$1\text{-}6\frac{15}{16}$
15/16	$6\frac{19}{32}$	$1\text{-}2\frac{17}{32}$	$7\frac{1}{8}$	$1\text{-}3\frac{21}{32}$	$7\frac{5}{8}$	$1\text{-}4\frac{25}{32}$	$8\frac{1}{8}$	$1\text{-}5\frac{29}{32}$	$8\frac{21}{32}$	$1\text{-}7\frac{1}{32}$

Ins.	17″ Rise	17″ Slope	18″ Rise	18″ Slope	19″ Rise	19″ Slope	20″ Rise	20″ Slope	21″ Rise	21″ Slope
0	$8\frac{11}{16}$	$1\text{-}7\frac{3}{32}$	$9\frac{3}{16}$	$1\text{-}8\frac{7}{32}$	$9\frac{11}{16}$	$1\text{-}9\frac{11}{32}$	$10\frac{7}{32}$	$1\text{-}10\frac{15}{32}$	$10\frac{23}{32}$	$1\text{-}11\frac{9}{16}$
1/16	$8\frac{23}{32}$	$1\text{-}7\frac{5}{32}$	$9\frac{7}{32}$	$1\text{-}8\frac{9}{32}$	$9\frac{23}{32}$	$1\text{-}9\frac{13}{32}$	$10\frac{1}{4}$	$1\text{-}10\frac{17}{32}$	$10\frac{3}{4}$	$1\text{-}11\frac{21}{32}$
1/8	$8\frac{3}{4}$	$1\text{-}7\frac{7}{32}$	$9\frac{1}{4}$	$1\text{-}8\frac{11}{32}$	$9\frac{3}{4}$	$1\text{-}9\frac{15}{32}$	$10\frac{9}{32}$	$1\text{-}10\frac{19}{32}$	$10\frac{25}{32}$	$1\text{-}11\frac{23}{32}$
3/16	$8\frac{25}{32}$	$1\text{-}7\frac{5}{16}$	$9\frac{9}{32}$	$1\text{-}8\frac{13}{32}$	$9\frac{25}{32}$	$1\text{-}9\frac{17}{32}$	$10\frac{5}{16}$	$1\text{-}10\frac{21}{32}$	$10\frac{13}{16}$	$1\text{-}11\frac{25}{32}$
1/4	$8\frac{13}{16}$	$1\text{-}7\frac{3}{8}$	$9\frac{5}{16}$	$1\text{-}8\frac{1}{2}$	$9\frac{13}{16}$	$1\text{-}9\frac{5}{8}$	$10\frac{11}{32}$	$1\text{-}10\frac{3}{4}$	$10\frac{27}{32}$	$1\text{-}11\frac{27}{32}$
5/16	$8\frac{27}{32}$	$1\text{-}7\frac{7}{16}$	$9\frac{11}{32}$	$1\text{-}8\frac{9}{16}$	$9\frac{27}{32}$	$1\text{-}9\frac{11}{16}$	$10\frac{3}{8}$	$1\text{-}10\frac{13}{16}$	$10\frac{7}{8}$	$1\text{-}11\frac{15}{16}$
3/8	$8\frac{7}{8}$	$1\text{-}7\frac{1}{2}$	$9\frac{3}{8}$	$1\text{-}8\frac{5}{8}$	$9\frac{7}{8}$	$1\text{-}9\frac{3}{4}$	$10\frac{13}{32}$	$1\text{-}10\frac{7}{8}$	$10\frac{29}{32}$	$2\text{-}0$
7/16	$8\frac{29}{32}$	$1\text{-}7\frac{9}{16}$	$9\frac{13}{32}$	$1\text{-}8\frac{11}{16}$	$9\frac{29}{32}$	$1\text{-}9\frac{13}{16}$	$10\frac{7}{16}$	$1\text{-}10\frac{15}{16}$	$10\frac{15}{16}$	$2\text{-}0\frac{1}{16}$
1/2	$8\frac{15}{16}$	$1\text{-}7\frac{21}{32}$	$9\frac{7}{16}$	$1\text{-}8\frac{25}{32}$	$9\frac{15}{16}$	$1\text{-}9\frac{29}{32}$	$10\frac{15}{32}$	$1\text{-}11\frac{1}{32}$	$10\frac{31}{32}$	$2\text{-}0\frac{1}{8}$
9/16	$8\frac{31}{32}$	$1\text{-}7\frac{23}{32}$	$9\frac{15}{32}$	$1\text{-}8\frac{27}{32}$	10	$1\text{-}9\frac{31}{32}$	$10\frac{1}{2}$	$1\text{-}11\frac{3}{32}$	11	$2\text{-}0\frac{7}{32}$
5/8	9	$1\text{-}7\frac{25}{32}$	$9\frac{1}{2}$	$1\text{-}8\frac{29}{32}$	$10\frac{1}{32}$	$1\text{-}10\frac{1}{32}$	$10\frac{17}{32}$	$1\text{-}11\frac{5}{32}$	$11\frac{1}{4}$	$2\text{-}0\frac{9}{32}$
11/16	$9\frac{1}{32}$	$1\text{-}7\frac{27}{32}$	$9\frac{17}{32}$	$1\text{-}8\frac{31}{32}$	$10\frac{1}{16}$	$1\text{-}10\frac{3}{32}$	$10\frac{9}{16}$	$1\text{-}11\frac{7}{32}$	$11\frac{1}{16}$	$2\text{-}0\frac{11}{32}$
3/4	$9\frac{1}{16}$	$1\text{-}7\frac{15}{16}$	$9\frac{9}{16}$	$1\text{-}9\frac{1}{16}$	$10\frac{3}{32}$	$1\text{-}10\frac{3}{16}$	$10\frac{19}{32}$	$1\text{-}11\frac{9}{32}$	$11\frac{3}{32}$	$2\text{-}0\frac{13}{32}$
13/16	$9\frac{3}{32}$	$1\text{-}8$	$9\frac{19}{32}$	$1\text{-}9\frac{1}{8}$	$10\frac{1}{8}$	$1\text{-}10\frac{1}{4}$	$10\frac{5}{8}$	$1\text{-}11\frac{3}{8}$	$11\frac{1}{8}$	$2\text{-}0\frac{1}{2}$
7/8	$9\frac{1}{8}$	$1\text{-}8\frac{1}{8}$	$9\frac{5}{8}$	$1\text{-}9\frac{3}{16}$	$10\frac{5}{32}$	$1\text{-}10\frac{5}{16}$	$10\frac{21}{32}$	$1\text{-}11\frac{7}{16}$	$11\frac{5}{32}$	$2\text{-}0\frac{9}{16}$
15/16	$9\frac{5}{32}$	$1\text{-}8\frac{1}{8}$	$9\frac{21}{32}$	$1\text{-}9\frac{1}{4}$	$10\frac{3}{16}$	$1\text{-}10\frac{3}{8}$	$10\frac{11}{16}$	$1\text{-}11\frac{1}{2}$	$11\frac{3}{16}$	$2\text{-}0\frac{5}{8}$

Feet	40′ Rise	40′ Slope	50′ Rise	50′ Slope	60′ Rise	60′ Slope	70′ Rise	70′ Slope
0	20-5	$44\text{-}10\frac{29}{32}$	$25\text{-}6\frac{1}{4}$	$56\text{-}1\frac{5}{8}$	$30\text{-}7\frac{1}{2}$	$67\text{-}4\frac{3}{8}$	$35\text{-}8\frac{3}{4}$	$78\text{-}7\frac{3}{32}$
1	$20\text{-}11\frac{1}{8}$	$46\text{-}0\frac{3}{8}$	$26\text{-}0\frac{3}{8}$	$57\text{-}3\frac{1}{8}$	$31\text{-}1\frac{5}{8}$	$68\text{-}5\frac{27}{32}$	$36\text{-}2\frac{7}{8}$	$79\text{-}8\frac{9}{16}$
2	$21\text{-}5\frac{1}{4}$	$47\text{-}1\frac{27}{32}$	$26\text{-}6\frac{1}{2}$	$58\text{-}4\frac{19}{32}$	$31\text{-}7\frac{3}{4}$	$69\text{-}7\frac{5}{16}$	$36\text{-}9$	$80\text{-}10\frac{1}{32}$
3	$21\text{-}11\frac{3}{8}$	$48\text{-}3\frac{11}{32}$	$27\text{-}0\frac{5}{8}$	$59\text{-}6\frac{1}{16}$	$32\text{-}1\frac{7}{8}$	$70\text{-}8\frac{25}{32}$	$37\text{-}3\frac{1}{8}$	$81\text{-}11\frac{1}{2}$
4	$22\text{-}5\frac{1}{2}$	$49\text{-}4\frac{13}{16}$	$27\text{-}6\frac{3}{4}$	$60\text{-}7\frac{17}{32}$	$32\text{-}8$	$71\text{-}10\frac{1}{4}$	$37\text{-}9\frac{1}{4}$	$83\text{-}1$
5	$22\text{-}11\frac{5}{8}$	$50\text{-}6\frac{9}{32}$	$28\text{-}0\frac{7}{8}$	$61\text{-}9$	$33\text{-}2\frac{1}{8}$	$72\text{-}11\frac{23}{32}$	$38\text{-}3\frac{3}{8}$	$84\text{-}2\frac{15}{32}$
6	$23\text{-}5\frac{3}{4}$	$51\text{-}7\frac{3}{4}$	$28\text{-}7$	$62\text{-}10\frac{15}{32}$	$33\text{-}8\frac{1}{4}$	$74\text{-}1\frac{3}{16}$	$38\text{-}9\frac{1}{2}$	$85\text{-}3\frac{15}{16}$
7	$23\text{-}11\frac{7}{8}$	$52\text{-}9\frac{7}{32}$	$29\text{-}1\frac{1}{8}$	$63\text{-}11\frac{15}{16}$	$34\text{-}2\frac{3}{8}$	$75\text{-}2\frac{11}{16}$	$39\text{-}3\frac{5}{8}$	$86\text{-}5\frac{13}{32}$
8	$24\text{-}6$	$53\text{-}10\frac{11}{16}$	$29\text{-}7\frac{1}{4}$	$65\text{-}1\frac{13}{32}$	$34\text{-}8\frac{1}{2}$	$76\text{-}4\frac{5}{32}$	$39\text{-}9\frac{3}{4}$	$87\text{-}6\frac{7}{8}$
9	$25\text{-}0\frac{1}{8}$	$55\text{-}0\frac{5}{32}$	$30\text{-}1\frac{3}{8}$	$66\text{-}2\frac{29}{32}$	$35\text{-}2\frac{5}{8}$	$77\text{-}5\frac{5}{8}$	$40\text{-}3\frac{7}{8}$	$88\text{-}8\frac{11}{32}$

natsin A=0.4546205733; natcos A=0.8906852049; nattan A=0.5104166666; natcot A=1.9591836734

Inches	0" Rise	0" Slope	1" Rise	1" Slope	2" Rise	2" Slope	3" Rise	3" Slope	4" Rise	4" Slope	5" Rise	5" Slope
0	0	0	1/2	1 1/8	1 1/32	2 1/4	1 9/16	3 3/8	2 1/16	4 1/2	2 9/16	5 5/8
1/16	1/16	1/16	9/16	1 3/16	1 1/16	2 5/16	1 19/32	3 7/16	2 3/32	4 9/16	2 5/8	5 11/16
1/8	1/16	5/32	19/32	1 9/32	1 3/32	2 13/32	1 5/8	3 17/32	2 1/8	4 21/32	2 21/32	5 25/32
3/16	3/32	7/32	5/8	1 11/32	1 1/8	2 15/32	1 21/32	3 19/32	2 5/32	4 23/32	2 11/16	5 27/32
1/4	1/8	9/32	21/32	1 13/32	1 5/32	2 17/32	1 11/16	3 21/32	2 3/16	4 25/32	2 23/32	5 29/32
5/16	5/32	11/32	11/16	1 15/32	1 3/16	2 19/32	1 23/32	3 23/32	2 7/32	4 27/32	2 3/4	5 31/32
3/8	3/16	7/16	23/32	1 9/16	1 7/32	2 11/16	1 3/4	3 13/16	2 1/4	4 15/16	2 25/32	6 1/16
7/16	7/32	1/2	3/4	1 5/8	1 1/4	2 3/4	1 25/32	3 7/8	2 9/32	5	2 13/16	6 1/8
1/2	1/4	9/16	25/32	1 11/16	1 9/32	2 13/16	1 13/16	3 15/16	2 5/16	5 1/16	2 27/32	6 3/16
9/16	9/32	5/8	13/16	1 3/4	1 5/16	2 7/8	1 27/32	4	2 11/32	5 1/8	2 7/8	6 1/4
5/8	5/16	23/32	27/32	1 27/32	1 11/32	2 31/32	1 7/8	4 3/32	2 3/8	5 7/32	2 29/32	6 11/32
11/16	11/32	25/32	7/8	1 29/32	1 3/8	3 1/32	1 29/32	4 5/32	2 13/32	5 9/32	2 15/16	6 13/32
3/4	3/8	27/32	29/32	1 31/32	1 13/32	3 3/32	1 15/16	4 7/32	2 7/16	5 11/32	2 31/32	6 15/32
13/16	13/32	29/32	15/16	2 1/32	1 7/16	3 5/32	1 31/32	4 9/32	2 15/32	5 13/32	3	6 17/32
7/8	7/16	1	31/32	2 1/8	1 15/32	3 1/4	2	4 3/8	2 1/2	5 1/2	3 1/32	6 5/8
15/16	15/32	1 1/16	1	2 3/16	1 1/2	3 5/16	2 1/32	4 7/16	2 17/32	5 9/16	3 1/16	6 11/16

Inches	6" Rise	6" Slope	7" Rise	7" Slope	8" Rise	8" Slope	9" Rise	9" Slope	10" Rise	10" Slope	11" Rise	11" Slope
0	3 3/32	6 3/4	3 5/8	7 7/8	4 1/8	9	4 5/8	10 1/8	5 5/32	11 1/4	5 11/16	1-0 3/8
1/16	3 1/8	6 13/16	3 21/32	7 15/16	4 5/32	9 1/16	4 11/16	10 3/16	5 3/16	11 5/16	5 23/32	1-0 7/16
1/8	3 5/32	6 29/32	3 11/16	8 1/32	4 3/16	9 5/32	4 23/32	10 9/32	5 7/32	11 13/32	5 3/4	1-0 17/32
3/16	3 3/16	6 31/32	3 23/32	8 3/32	4 7/32	9 7/32	4 3/4	10 11/32	5 1/4	11 15/32	5 25/32	1-0 19/32
1/4	3 7/32	7 1/32	3 3/4	8 5/32	4 1/4	9 9/32	4 25/32	10 13/32	5 9/32	11 17/32	5 13/16	1-0 21/32
5/16	3 1/4	7 3/32	3 25/32	8 7/32	4 9/32	9 11/32	4 13/16	10 15/32	5 5/16	11 19/32	5 27/32	1-0 23/32
3/8	3 9/32	7 3/16	3 13/16	8 5/16	4 5/16	9 7/16	4 27/32	10 9/16	5 11/32	11 11/16	5 7/8	1-0 13/16
7/16	3 5/16	7 1/4	3 27/32	8 3/8	4 11/32	9 1/2	4 7/8	10 5/8	5 3/8	11 3/4	5 29/32	1-0 7/8
1/2	3 11/32	7 5/16	3 7/8	8 7/16	4 3/8	9 9/16	4 29/32	10 11/16	5 13/32	11 13/16	5 15/16	1-0 15/16
9/16	3 3/8	7 3/8	3 29/32	8 1/2	4 13/32	9 5/8	4 15/16	10 3/4	5 7/16	11 7/8	5 31/32	1-1
5/8	3 13/32	7 15/32	3 15/16	8 19/32	4 7/16	9 23/32	4 31/32	10 27/32	5 15/32	11 31/32	6	1-1 3/32
11/16	3 7/16	7 17/32	3 31/32	8 21/32	4 15/32	9 25/32	5	10 29/32	5 1/2	1-0 1/32	6 1/32	1-1 5/32
3/4	3 15/32	7 19/32	4	8 23/32	4 1/2	9 27/32	5 1/32	10 31/32	5 17/32	1-0 3/32	6 1/16	1-1 7/32
13/16	3 1/2	7 21/32	4 1/32	8 25/32	4 17/32	9 29/32	5 1/16	11 1/32	5 9/16	1-0 5/32	6 3/32	1-1 9/32
7/8	3 17/32	7 3/4	4 1/16	8 7/8	4 9/16	10	5 3/32	11 1/8	5 19/32	1-0 1/4	6 1/8	1-1 3/8
15/16	3 9/16	7 13/16	4 3/32	8 15/16	4 19/32	10 1/16	5 1/8	11 3/16	5 5/8	1-0 5/16	6 5/32	1-1 7/16

Feet	0' Rise	0' Slope	10' Rise	10' Slope	20' Rise	20' Slope	30' Rise	30' Slope
0	0	0	5-1 7/8	11-3	10-3 3/4	22-6 1/32	15-5 5/8	33-9 1/32
1	6 3/16	1-1 1/2	5-8 1/16	12-4 1/2	10-9 15/16	23-7 17/32	15-11 13/16	34-10 17/32
2	1-0 3/8	2-3	6-2 1/4	13-6	11-4 1/8	24-9 1/32	16-6	36-0 1/32
3	1-6 9/16	3-4 1/2	6-8 7/16	14-7 17/32	11-10 5/16	25-10 17/32	17-0 3/16	37-1 17/32
4	2-0 3/4	4-6	7-2 5/8	15-9 1/32	12-4 1/2	27-0 1/32	17-6 3/8	38-3 1/32
5	2-6 15/16	5-7 1/2	7-8 13/16	16-10 17/32	12-10 11/16	28-1 17/32	18-0 9/16	39-4 17/32
6	3-1 1/8	6-9	8-3	18-0 1/32	13-4 7/8	29-3 1/32	18-6 3/4	40-6 1/32
7	3-7 5/16	7-10 1/2	8-9 3/16	19-1 17/32	13-11 1/16	30-4 17/32	19-0 15/16	41-7 17/32
8	4-1 1/2	9-0	9-3 3/8	20-3 1/32	14-5 1/4	31-6 1/32	19-7 1/8	42-9 1/16
9	4-7 11/16	10-1 1/2	9-9 9/16	21-4 17/32	14-11 7/16	32-7 17/32	20-1 5/16	43-10 9/16

A = 27° 16′ 36″; logsin A = 9.66114; logcos A = 9.94881; logtan A = 9.71233; logcot A = 0.28767

In.	$12''$ Rise	Slope	$13''$ Rise	Slope	$14''$ Rise	Slope	$15''$ Rise	Slope	$16''$ Rise	Slope
0	$6\frac{3}{16}$	1-$1\frac{1}{2}$	$6\frac{11}{16}$	1-$2\frac{5}{8}$	$7\frac{7}{32}$	1-$3\frac{3}{4}$	$7\frac{3}{4}$	1-$4\frac{7}{8}$	$8\frac{1}{4}$	1-6
$\frac{1}{16}$	$6\frac{7}{32}$	1-$1\frac{9}{16}$	$6\frac{3}{4}$	1-$2\frac{11}{16}$	$7\frac{1}{4}$	1-$3\frac{13}{16}$	$7\frac{25}{32}$	1-$4\frac{15}{16}$	$8\frac{9}{32}$	1-$6\frac{1}{16}$
$\frac{1}{8}$	$6\frac{1}{4}$	1-$1\frac{21}{32}$	$6\frac{25}{32}$	1-$2\frac{25}{32}$	$7\frac{9}{32}$	1-$3\frac{29}{32}$	$7\frac{13}{16}$	1-$5\frac{1}{32}$	$8\frac{5}{16}$	1-$6\frac{5}{32}$
$\frac{3}{16}$	$6\frac{9}{32}$	1-$1\frac{23}{32}$	$6\frac{13}{16}$	1-$2\frac{27}{32}$	$7\frac{5}{16}$	1-$3\frac{31}{32}$	$7\frac{27}{32}$	1-$5\frac{3}{32}$	$8\frac{11}{32}$	1-$6\frac{7}{32}$
$\frac{1}{4}$	$6\frac{5}{16}$	1-$1\frac{25}{32}$	$6\frac{27}{32}$	1-$2\frac{29}{32}$	$7\frac{11}{32}$	1-$4\frac{1}{32}$	$7\frac{7}{8}$	1-$5\frac{5}{32}$	$8\frac{3}{8}$	1-$6\frac{9}{32}$
$\frac{5}{16}$	$6\frac{11}{32}$	1-$1\frac{27}{32}$	$6\frac{7}{8}$	1-$2\frac{31}{32}$	$7\frac{3}{8}$	1-$4\frac{3}{32}$	$7\frac{29}{32}$	1-$5\frac{7}{32}$	$8\frac{13}{32}$	1-$6\frac{11}{32}$
$\frac{3}{8}$	$6\frac{3}{8}$	1-$1\frac{15}{16}$	$6\frac{29}{32}$	1-$3\frac{1}{16}$	$7\frac{13}{32}$	1-$4\frac{3}{16}$	$7\frac{15}{16}$	1-$5\frac{5}{16}$	$8\frac{7}{16}$	1-$6\frac{7}{16}$
$\frac{7}{16}$	$6\frac{13}{32}$	1-2	$6\frac{15}{16}$	1-$3\frac{1}{8}$	$7\frac{7}{16}$	1-$4\frac{1}{4}$	$7\frac{31}{32}$	1-$5\frac{3}{8}$	$8\frac{15}{32}$	1-$6\frac{1}{2}$
$\frac{1}{2}$	$6\frac{7}{16}$	1-$2\frac{1}{16}$	$6\frac{31}{32}$	1-$3\frac{3}{16}$	$7\frac{15}{32}$	1-$4\frac{5}{16}$	8	1-$5\frac{7}{16}$	$8\frac{1}{2}$	1-$6\frac{9}{16}$
$\frac{9}{16}$	$6\frac{15}{32}$	1-$2\frac{1}{8}$	7	1-$3\frac{1}{4}$	$7\frac{1}{2}$	1-$4\frac{3}{8}$	$8\frac{1}{16}$	1-$5\frac{1}{2}$	$8\frac{17}{32}$	1-$6\frac{5}{8}$
$\frac{5}{8}$	$6\frac{1}{2}$	1-$2\frac{7}{32}$	$7\frac{1}{32}$	1-$3\frac{11}{32}$	$7\frac{17}{32}$	1-$4\frac{15}{32}$	$8\frac{1}{16}$	1-$5\frac{19}{32}$	$8\frac{9}{16}$	1-$6\frac{23}{32}$
$\frac{11}{16}$	$6\frac{17}{32}$	1-$2\frac{9}{32}$	$7\frac{1}{16}$	1-$3\frac{13}{32}$	$7\frac{9}{16}$	1-$4\frac{17}{32}$	$8\frac{3}{32}$	1-$5\frac{21}{32}$	$8\frac{19}{32}$	1-$6\frac{25}{32}$
$\frac{3}{4}$	$6\frac{9}{16}$	1-$2\frac{11}{32}$	$7\frac{3}{32}$	1-$3\frac{15}{32}$	$7\frac{19}{32}$	1-$4\frac{19}{32}$	$8\frac{1}{8}$	1-$5\frac{23}{32}$	$8\frac{5}{8}$	1-$6\frac{27}{32}$
$\frac{13}{16}$	$6\frac{19}{32}$	1-$2\frac{13}{32}$	$7\frac{1}{8}$	1-$3\frac{17}{32}$	$7\frac{5}{8}$	1-$4\frac{21}{32}$	$8\frac{5}{32}$	1-$5\frac{25}{32}$	$8\frac{21}{32}$	1-$6\frac{29}{32}$
$\frac{7}{8}$	$6\frac{5}{8}$	1-$2\frac{1}{2}$	$7\frac{5}{32}$	1-$3\frac{5}{8}$	$7\frac{21}{32}$	1-$4\frac{3}{4}$	$8\frac{3}{16}$	1-$5\frac{7}{8}$	$8\frac{11}{16}$	1-7
$\frac{15}{16}$	$6\frac{21}{32}$	1-$2\frac{9}{16}$	$7\frac{3}{16}$	1-$3\frac{11}{16}$	$7\frac{11}{16}$	1-$4\frac{13}{16}$	$8\frac{7}{32}$	1-$5\frac{15}{16}$	$8\frac{23}{32}$	1-$7\frac{1}{16}$

In.	$17''$ Rise	Slope	$18''$ Rise	Slope	$19''$ Rise	Slope	$20''$ Rise	Slope	$21''$ Rise	Slope
0	$8\frac{3}{4}$	1-$7\frac{1}{8}$	$9\frac{9}{32}$	1-$8\frac{1}{4}$	$9\frac{13}{16}$	1-$9\frac{3}{8}$	$10\frac{5}{16}$	1-$10\frac{1}{2}$	$10\frac{13}{16}$	1-$11\frac{5}{8}$
$\frac{1}{16}$	$8\frac{13}{16}$	1-$7\frac{3}{16}$	$9\frac{5}{16}$	1-$8\frac{5}{32}$	$9\frac{27}{32}$	1-$9\frac{7}{16}$	$10\frac{11}{32}$	1-$10\frac{9}{16}$	$10\frac{7}{8}$	1-$11\frac{11}{16}$
$\frac{1}{8}$	$8\frac{27}{32}$	1-$7\frac{9}{32}$	$9\frac{11}{32}$	1-$8\frac{13}{32}$	$9\frac{7}{8}$	1-$9\frac{17}{32}$	$10\frac{3}{8}$	1-$10\frac{21}{32}$	$10\frac{29}{32}$	1-$11\frac{25}{32}$
$\frac{3}{16}$	$8\frac{7}{8}$	1-$7\frac{11}{32}$	$9\frac{3}{8}$	1-$8\frac{15}{32}$	$9\frac{29}{32}$	1-$9\frac{19}{32}$	$10\frac{13}{32}$	1-$10\frac{23}{32}$	$10\frac{15}{16}$	1-$11\frac{27}{32}$
$\frac{1}{4}$	$8\frac{29}{32}$	1-$7\frac{13}{32}$	$9\frac{13}{32}$	1-$8\frac{17}{32}$	$9\frac{15}{16}$	1-$9\frac{21}{32}$	$10\frac{7}{16}$	1-$10\frac{25}{32}$	$10\frac{31}{32}$	1-$11\frac{29}{32}$
$\frac{5}{16}$	$8\frac{15}{16}$	1-$7\frac{15}{32}$	$9\frac{7}{16}$	1-$8\frac{19}{32}$	$9\frac{31}{32}$	1-$9\frac{23}{32}$	$10\frac{15}{32}$	1-$10\frac{27}{32}$	11	1-$11\frac{31}{32}$
$\frac{3}{8}$	$8\frac{31}{32}$	1-$7\frac{9}{16}$	$9\frac{15}{32}$	1-$8\frac{11}{16}$	10	1-$9\frac{13}{16}$	$10\frac{1}{2}$	1-$10\frac{15}{16}$	$11\frac{1}{32}$	2-$0\frac{1}{16}$
$\frac{7}{16}$	9	1-$7\frac{5}{8}$	$9\frac{1}{2}$	1-$8\frac{3}{4}$	$10\frac{1}{32}$	1-$9\frac{7}{8}$	$10\frac{17}{32}$	1-11	$11\frac{1}{16}$	2-$0\frac{1}{8}$
$\frac{1}{2}$	$9\frac{1}{32}$	1-$7\frac{11}{16}$	$9\frac{17}{32}$	1-$8\frac{13}{16}$	$10\frac{1}{16}$	1-$9\frac{15}{16}$	$10\frac{9}{16}$	1-$11\frac{1}{16}$	$11\frac{3}{32}$	2-$0\frac{3}{16}$
$\frac{9}{16}$	$9\frac{1}{16}$	1-$7\frac{3}{4}$	$9\frac{9}{16}$	1-$8\frac{7}{8}$	$10\frac{3}{32}$	1-10	$10\frac{19}{32}$	1-$11\frac{1}{8}$	$11\frac{1}{8}$	2-$0\frac{1}{4}$
$\frac{5}{8}$	$9\frac{3}{32}$	1-$7\frac{27}{32}$	$9\frac{19}{32}$	1-$8\frac{31}{32}$	$10\frac{1}{8}$	1-$10\frac{3}{32}$	$10\frac{5}{8}$	1-$11\frac{7}{32}$	$11\frac{5}{32}$	2-$0\frac{11}{32}$
$\frac{11}{16}$	$9\frac{1}{8}$	1-$7\frac{29}{32}$	$9\frac{5}{8}$	1-$9\frac{1}{32}$	$10\frac{5}{32}$	1-$10\frac{5}{32}$	$10\frac{21}{32}$	1-$11\frac{9}{32}$	$11\frac{3}{16}$	2-$0\frac{13}{32}$
$\frac{3}{4}$	$9\frac{5}{32}$	1-$7\frac{31}{32}$	$9\frac{21}{32}$	1-$9\frac{3}{32}$	$10\frac{3}{16}$	1-$10\frac{7}{32}$	$10\frac{11}{16}$	1-$11\frac{11}{32}$	$11\frac{7}{32}$	2-$0\frac{15}{32}$
$\frac{13}{16}$	$9\frac{3}{16}$	1-$8\frac{1}{32}$	$9\frac{11}{16}$	1-$9\frac{5}{32}$	$10\frac{7}{32}$	1-$10\frac{9}{32}$	$10\frac{23}{32}$	1-$11\frac{13}{32}$	$11\frac{1}{4}$	2-$0\frac{17}{32}$
$\frac{7}{8}$	$9\frac{7}{32}$	1-$8\frac{1}{8}$	$9\frac{23}{32}$	1-$9\frac{1}{4}$	$10\frac{1}{4}$	1-$10\frac{3}{8}$	$10\frac{3}{4}$	1-$11\frac{1}{2}$	$11\frac{9}{32}$	2-$0\frac{5}{8}$
$\frac{15}{16}$	$9\frac{1}{4}$	1-$8\frac{3}{16}$	$9\frac{3}{4}$	1-$9\frac{5}{16}$	$10\frac{9}{32}$	1-$10\frac{7}{16}$	$10\frac{25}{32}$	1-$11\frac{9}{16}$	$11\frac{5}{16}$	2-$0\frac{11}{16}$

Feet	$40'$ Rise	Slope	$50'$ Rise	Slope	$60'$ Rise	Slope	$70'$ Rise	Slope
0	20-$7\frac{1}{2}$	45-$0\frac{1}{16}$	25-$9\frac{3}{8}$	56-$3\frac{1}{16}$	30-$11\frac{1}{4}$	67-$6\frac{1}{16}$	36-$1\frac{1}{8}$	78-$9\frac{3}{32}$
1	21-$1\frac{11}{16}$	46-$1\frac{9}{16}$	26-$3\frac{9}{16}$	57-$4\frac{9}{16}$	31-$5\frac{7}{16}$	68-$7\frac{19}{32}$	36-$7\frac{5}{16}$	79-$10\frac{19}{32}$
2	21-$7\frac{7}{8}$	47-$3\frac{1}{16}$	26-$9\frac{3}{4}$	58-$6\frac{1}{16}$	31-$11\frac{5}{8}$	69-$9\frac{3}{32}$	37-$1\frac{1}{2}$	81-$0\frac{3}{32}$
3	22-$2\frac{1}{16}$	48-$4\frac{9}{16}$	27-$3\frac{15}{16}$	59-$7\frac{9}{16}$	32-$5\frac{13}{16}$	70-$10\frac{19}{32}$	37-$7\frac{11}{16}$	82-$1\frac{19}{32}$
4	22-$8\frac{1}{4}$	49-$6\frac{1}{16}$	27-$10\frac{1}{8}$	60-$9\frac{1}{16}$	33-0	72-$0\frac{3}{32}$	38-$1\frac{7}{8}$	83-$3\frac{3}{32}$
5	23-$2\frac{7}{16}$	50-$7\frac{9}{16}$	28-$4\frac{5}{16}$	61-$10\frac{9}{16}$	33-$6\frac{3}{16}$	73-$1\frac{19}{32}$	38-$8\frac{1}{16}$	84-$4\frac{19}{32}$
6	23-$8\frac{5}{8}$	51-$9\frac{1}{16}$	28-$10\frac{1}{2}$	63-$0\frac{1}{16}$	34-$0\frac{3}{8}$	74-$3\frac{3}{32}$	39-$2\frac{1}{4}$	85-$6\frac{3}{32}$
7	24-$2\frac{13}{16}$	52-$10\frac{3}{8}$	29-$4\frac{11}{16}$	64-$1\frac{9}{16}$	34-$6\frac{9}{16}$	75-$4\frac{19}{32}$	39-$8\frac{7}{16}$	86-$7\frac{19}{32}$
8	24-9	54-$0\frac{1}{16}$	29-$10\frac{7}{8}$	65-$3\frac{1}{16}$	35-$0\frac{3}{4}$	76-$6\frac{3}{32}$	40-$2\frac{5}{8}$	87-$9\frac{3}{32}$
9	25-$3\frac{3}{16}$	55-$1\frac{9}{16}$	30-$5\frac{1}{16}$	66-$4\frac{9}{16}$	35-$6\frac{15}{16}$	77-$7\frac{19}{32}$	40-$8\frac{13}{16}$	88-$10\frac{19}{32}$

natsin A=0.4582891331; natcos A=0.8888031673; nattan A=0.5156250000; natcot A=1.9393939393

Bevel 6¼" to 12"

Inches	0" Rise	0" Slope	1" Rise	1" Slope	2" Rise	2" Slope	3" Rise	3" Slope	4" Rise	4" Slope	5" Rise	5" Slope
0	0	0	17/32−	1 1/8	1 1/32	2 1/4	1 9/16	3 3/8	2 3/32−	4 1/2	2 19/32	5 5/8
1/16	1/32	1/16	9/16	1 3/16	1 1/16	2 5/16	1 19/32	3 7/16	2 1/8	4 19/32−	2 5/8	5 23/32−
1/8	1/16	5/32−	19/32−	1 9/32−	1 3/32	2 13/32−	1 5/8	3 17/32−	2 5/32−	4 21/32−	2 21/32	5 25/32−
3/16	3/32	7/32−	5/8	1 11/32−	1 1/8	2 15/32−	1 21/32	3 19/32	2 3/16	4 23/32	2 11/16	5 27/32
1/4	1/8	9/32	21/32−	1 13/32	1 3/16	2 17/32	1 11/16	3 21/32	2 7/32−	4 25/32	2 3/4	5 29/32
5/16	5/32	11/32	11/16	1 15/32	1 7/32−	2 19/32	1 23/32	3 3/4	2 1/4	4 7/8	2 25/32−	6
3/8	3/16	7/16	23/32−	1 9/16	1 1/4	2 11/16	1 3/4	3 13/16	2 9/32−	4 15/16	2 13/16	6 1/16
7/16	7/32	1/2	3/4	1 5/8	1 9/32−	2 3/4	1 25/32	3 7/8	2 5/16	5	2 27/32−	6 1/8
1/2	1/4	9/16	25/32	1 11/16	1 5/16	2 13/16	1 13/16	3 15/16	2 11/32	5 1/16	2 7/8	6 3/16
9/16	9/32	5/8	13/16	1 3/4	1 11/32−	2 7/8	1 27/32	4 1/32−	2 3/8	5 5/32−	2 29/32−	6 9/32−
5/8	5/16	23/32−	27/32	1 27/32−	1 3/8	2 31/32−	1 7/8	4 3/32−	2 13/32	5 7/32−	2 15/16	6 11/32−
11/16	11/32	25/32−	7/8	1 29/32−	1 13/32−	3 1/32−	1 29/32	4 5/32	2 7/16	5 9/32	2 31/32−	6 13/32
3/4	3/8	27/32	29/32	1 31/32	1 7/16	3 3/32	1 15/16	4 7/32	2 15/32	5 11/32	3	6 15/32
13/16	13/32	29/32	15/16	2 1/32	1 15/32−	3 5/32	2	4 5/16	2 1/2	5 7/16	3 1/32−	6 9/16
7/8	15/32−	1	31/32	2 1/8	1 1/2	3 1/4	2 1/32−	4 3/8	2 17/32	5 1/2	3 1/16	6 5/8
15/16	1/2	1 1/16	1	2 3/16	1 17/32−	3 5/16	2 1/16	4 7/16	2 9/16	5 9/16	3 3/32−	6 11/16

Inches	6" Rise	6" Slope	7" Rise	7" Slope	8" Rise	8" Slope	9" Rise	9" Slope	10" Rise	10" Slope	11" Rise	11" Slope
0	3 1/8	6 3/4	3 21/32−	7 29/32−	4 5/32	9 1/32−	4 11/16	10 5/32−	5 7/32−	11 9/32−	5 23/32	1-0 13/32−
1/16	3 5/32	6 27/32−	3 11/16	7 31/32−	4 3/16	9 3/32−	4 23/32	10 7/32−	5 1/4	11 11/32	5 3/4	1-0 15/32
1/8	3 3/16	6 29/32−	3 23/32−	8 1/32	4 7/32	9 5/32	4 3/4	10 9/32	5 9/32−	11 13/32	5 25/32	1-0 17/32
3/16	3 7/32	6 31/32	3 3/4	8 3/32	4 1/4	9 7/32	4 25/32	10 11/32	5 5/16	11 1/2	5 13/16	1-0 5/8
1/4	3 1/4	7 1/16	3 25/32−	8 3/16	4 5/16	9 5/16	4 13/16	10 7/16	5 11/32−	11 9/16	5 7/8	1-0 11/16
5/16	3 9/32	7 1/8	3 13/16	8 1/4	4 11/32−	9 3/8	4 27/32	10 1/2	5 3/8	11 5/8	5 29/32−	1-0 3/4
3/8	3 5/16	7 3/16	3 27/32−	8 5/16	4 3/8	9 7/16	4 7/8	10 9/16	5 13/32−	11 11/16	5 15/16	1-0 13/16
7/16	3 11/32	7 1/4	3 7/8	8 3/8	4 13/32−	9 1/2	4 29/32	10 21/32−	5 7/16	11 25/32−	5 31/32−	1-0 29/32−
1/2	3 3/8	7 11/32−	3 29/32	8 15/32−	4 7/16	9 19/32−	4 15/16	10 23/32−	5 15/32	11 27/32−	6	1-0 31/32−
9/16	3 13/32	7 13/32−	3 15/16	8 17/32−	4 15/32−	9 21/32−	4 31/32	10 25/32	5 1/2	11 29/32	6 1/32−	1-1 1/32
5/8	3 7/16	7 15/32	3 31/32	8 19/32	4 1/2	9 23/32	5	10 27/32	5 17/32	11 31/32	6 1/16	1-1 3/32
11/16	3 15/32	7 17/32	4	8 21/32	4 17/32−	9 25/32	5 1/32	10 15/16	5 9/16	1-0 1/16	6 3/32−	1-1 3/16
3/4	3 1/2	7 5/8	4 1/32	8 3/4	4 9/16	9 7/8	5 1/16	11	5 19/32	1-0 1/8	6 1/8	1-1 1/4
13/16	3 9/16	7 11/16	4 1/16	8 13/16	4 19/32−	9 15/16	5 1/8	11 1/16	5 5/8	1-0 3/16	6 5/32−	1-1 5/16
7/8	3 19/32−	7 3/4	4 3/32	8 7/8	4 5/8	10	5 5/32−	11 1/8	5 21/32	1-0 1/4	6 3/16	1-1 3/8
15/16	3 5/8	7 13/16	4 1/8	8 15/16	4 21/32−	10 1/16	5 3/16	11 7/32−	5 11/16	1-0 11/32−	6 7/32−	1-1 15/32−

Feet	0' Rise	0' Slope	10' Rise	10' Slope	20' Rise	20' Slope	30' Rise	30' Slope
0	0	0	5-2 1/2	11-3 5/16	10-5	22-6 19/32	15-7 1/2	33-9 29/32−
1	6 1/4	1-1 17/32−	5-8 3/4	12-4 27/32−	10-11 1/4	23-8 1/8	16-1 3/4	34-11 7/16
2	1-0 1/2	2-3 1/16	6-3	13-6 3/8	11-5 1/2	24-9 21/32	16-8	36-0 31/32−
3	1-6 3/4	3-4 19/32−	6-9 1/4	14-7 29/32−	11-11 3/4	25-11 3/16	17-2 1/4	37-2 1/2
4	2-1	4-6 1/8	7-3 1/2	15-9 13/32	12-6	27-0 23/32	17-8 1/2	38-4 1/32−
5	2-7 1/4	5-7 21/32−	7-9 3/4	16-10 15/16	13-0 1/4	28-2 1/4	13-2 3/4	39-5 9/16
6	3-1 1/2	6-9 3/16	8-4	18-0 15/32	13-6 1/2	29-3 25/32	18-9	40-7 3/32−
7	3-7 3/4	7-10 23/32−	8-10 1/4	19-2	14-0 3/4	30-5 5/16	19-3 1/4	41-8 5/8
8	4-2	9-0 1/4	9-4 1/2	20-3 17/32	14-7	31-6 27/32−	19-9 1/2	42-10 5/32−
9	4-8 1/4	10-1 25/32−	9-10 3/4	21-5 1/16	15-1 1/4	32-8 3/8	20-3 3/4	43-11 11/16

A = 27° 30′ 43″; logsin A = **9.66458**; logcos A = **9.94789**: logtan A = **9.71670**: logcot A = **0.28330**

Ins.	12″ Rise	12″ Slope	13″ Rise	13″ Slope	14″ Rise	14″ Slope	15″ Rise	15″ Slope	16″ Rise	16″ Slope
0	$6\frac14$	$1\text{-}1\frac{17}{32}$	$6\frac{25}{32}$	$1\text{-}2\frac{21}{32}$	$7\frac{9}{32}$	$1\text{-}3\frac{25}{32}$	$7\frac{13}{16}$	$1\text{-}4\frac{29}{32}$	$8\frac{11}{32}$	$1\text{-}6\frac12$
$\frac{1}{16}$	$6\frac{9}{32}$	$1\text{-}1\frac{19}{32}$	$6\frac{13}{16}$	$1\text{-}2\frac{23}{32}$	$7\frac{5}{16}$	$1\text{-}3\frac{27}{32}$	$7\frac{27}{32}$	$1\text{-}4\frac{31}{32}$	$8\frac38$	$1\text{-}6\frac18$
$\frac{1}{8}$	$6\frac{5}{16}$	$1\text{-}1\frac{21}{32}$	$6\frac{27}{32}$	$1\text{-}2\frac{13}{16}$	$7\frac{11}{32}$	$1\text{-}3\frac{15}{16}$	$7\frac78$	$1\text{-}5\frac{1}{16}$	$8\frac{13}{32}$	$1\text{-}6\frac{3}{16}$
$\frac{3}{16}$	$6\frac{11}{32}$	$1\text{-}1\frac34$	$6\frac78$	$1\text{-}2\frac78$	$7\frac38$	$1\text{-}4$	$7\frac{29}{32}$	$1\text{-}5\frac18$	$8\frac{7}{16}$	$1\text{-}6\frac14$
$\frac{1}{4}$	$6\frac38$	$1\text{-}1\frac{13}{16}$	$6\frac{29}{32}$	$1\text{-}2\frac{15}{16}$	$7\frac{7}{16}$	$1\text{-}4\frac{1}{16}$	$7\frac{15}{32}$	$1\text{-}5\frac{3}{16}$	$8\frac{15}{32}$	$1\text{-}6\frac{5}{16}$
$\frac{5}{16}$	$6\frac{13}{32}$	$1\text{-}1\frac78$	$6\frac{15}{16}$	$1\text{-}3$	$7\frac{15}{32}$	$1\text{-}4\frac18$	$7\frac{31}{32}$	$1\text{-}5\frac14$	$8\frac12$	$1\text{-}6\frac{13}{32}$
$\frac{3}{8}$	$6\frac{7}{16}$	$1\text{-}1\frac{15}{16}$	$6\frac{31}{32}$	$1\text{-}3\frac{3}{32}$	$7\frac12$	$1\text{-}4\frac{7}{32}$	8	$1\text{-}5\frac{11}{32}$	$8\frac{17}{32}$	$1\text{-}6\frac{15}{32}$
$\frac{7}{16}$	$6\frac{15}{32}$	$1\text{-}2\frac{1}{32}$	7	$1\text{-}3\frac{5}{32}$	$7\frac{17}{32}$	$1\text{-}4\frac{9}{32}$	$8\frac14$	$1\text{-}5\frac{13}{32}$	$8\frac{9}{16}$	$1\text{-}6\frac{17}{32}$
$\frac{1}{2}$	$6\frac12$	$1\text{-}2\frac{3}{32}$	$7\frac{1}{32}$	$1\text{-}3\frac{7}{32}$	$7\frac{9}{16}$	$1\text{-}4\frac{11}{32}$	$8\frac{1}{16}$	$1\text{-}5\frac{15}{32}$	$8\frac{19}{32}$	$1\text{-}6\frac{19}{32}$
$\frac{9}{16}$	$6\frac{17}{32}$	$1\text{-}2\frac{5}{32}$	$7\frac{1}{16}$	$1\text{-}3\frac{9}{32}$	$7\frac{19}{32}$	$1\text{-}4\frac{13}{32}$	$8\frac{3}{32}$	$1\text{-}5\frac{17}{32}$	$8\frac58$	$1\text{-}6\frac{11}{16}$
$\frac{5}{8}$	$6\frac{9}{16}$	$1\text{-}2\frac14$	$7\frac{3}{32}$	$1\text{-}3\frac38$	$7\frac58$	$1\text{-}4\frac12$	$8\frac18$	$1\text{-}5\frac58$	$8\frac{21}{32}$	$1\text{-}6\frac34$
$\frac{11}{16}$	$6\frac{19}{32}$	$1\text{-}2\frac{5}{16}$	$7\frac18$	$1\text{-}3\frac{17}{32}$	$7\frac{21}{32}$	$1\text{-}4\frac{9}{16}$	$8\frac{5}{32}$	$1\text{-}5\frac{11}{16}$	$8\frac{11}{16}$	$1\text{-}6\frac{13}{16}$
$\frac{3}{4}$	$6\frac58$	$1\text{-}2\frac38$	$7\frac{5}{32}$	$1\text{-}3\frac12$	$7\frac{11}{16}$	$1\text{-}4\frac58$	$8\frac{3}{16}$	$1\text{-}5\frac34$	$8\frac{23}{32}$	$1\text{-}6\frac78$
$\frac{13}{16}$	$6\frac{11}{16}$	$1\text{-}2\frac{7}{16}$	$7\frac{3}{16}$	$1\text{-}3\frac{9}{16}$	$7\frac{23}{32}$	$1\text{-}4\frac{11}{16}$	$8\frac14$	$1\text{-}5\frac{27}{32}$	$8\frac34$	$1\text{-}6\frac{31}{32}$
$\frac{7}{8}$	$6\frac{23}{32}$	$1\text{-}2\frac{17}{32}$	$7\frac{7}{32}$	$1\text{-}3\frac{21}{32}$	$7\frac34$	$1\text{-}4\frac{25}{32}$	$8\frac{9}{32}$	$1\text{-}5\frac{29}{32}$	$8\frac{25}{32}$	$1\text{-}7\frac{1}{32}$
$\frac{15}{16}$	$6\frac34$	$1\text{-}2\frac{19}{32}$	$7\frac14$	$1\text{-}3\frac{23}{32}$	$7\frac{25}{32}$	$1\text{-}4\frac{27}{32}$	$8\frac{5}{16}$	$1\text{-}5\frac{31}{32}$	$8\frac{13}{16}$	$1\text{-}7\frac{3}{32}$

Ins.	17″ Rise	17″ Slope	18″ Rise	18″ Slope	19″ Rise	19″ Slope	20″ Rise	20″ Slope	21″ Rise	21″ Slope
0	$8\frac{27}{32}$	$1\text{-}7\frac{5}{32}$	$9\frac38$	$1\text{-}8\frac{9}{32}$	$9\frac{29}{32}$	$1\text{-}9\frac{7}{16}$	$10\frac{13}{32}$	$1\text{-}10\frac{9}{32}$	$10\frac{15}{16}$	$1\text{-}11\frac{11}{16}$
$\frac{1}{16}$	$8\frac78$	$1\text{-}7\frac14$	$9\frac{13}{32}$	$1\text{-}8\frac38$	$9\frac{15}{16}$	$1\text{-}9\frac12$	$10\frac{7}{16}$	$1\text{-}10\frac58$	$10\frac{31}{32}$	$1\text{-}11\frac34$
$\frac{1}{8}$	$8\frac{29}{32}$	$1\text{-}7\frac{5}{16}$	$9\frac{7}{16}$	$1\text{-}8\frac{7}{16}$	$9\frac{31}{32}$	$1\text{-}9\frac{9}{16}$	$10\frac{15}{32}$	$1\text{-}10\frac{11}{16}$	11	$1\text{-}11\frac{13}{16}$
$\frac{3}{16}$	$8\frac{15}{16}$	$1\text{-}7\frac38$	$9\frac{15}{32}$	$1\text{-}8\frac12$	10	$1\text{-}9\frac58$	$10\frac12$	$1\text{-}10\frac34$	$11\frac{1}{32}$	$1\text{-}11\frac78$
$\frac{1}{4}$	9	$1\text{-}7\frac{7}{16}$	$9\frac12$	$1\text{-}8\frac{9}{16}$	$10\frac{1}{16}$	$1\text{-}9\frac{23}{32}$	$10\frac{9}{16}$	$1\text{-}10\frac{27}{32}$	$11\frac{1}{16}$	$1\text{-}11\frac{31}{32}$
$\frac{5}{16}$	$9\frac{1}{32}$	$1\text{-}7\frac{17}{32}$	$9\frac{17}{32}$	$1\text{-}8\frac{21}{32}$	$10\frac{1}{16}$	$1\text{-}9\frac{25}{32}$	$10\frac{19}{32}$	$1\text{-}10\frac{29}{32}$	$11\frac{3}{32}$	$2\text{-}0\frac{1}{32}$
$\frac{3}{8}$	$9\frac{1}{16}$	$1\text{-}7\frac{19}{32}$	$9\frac{9}{16}$	$1\text{-}8\frac{23}{32}$	$10\frac18$	$1\text{-}9\frac{27}{32}$	$10\frac58$	$1\text{-}10\frac{31}{32}$	$11\frac18$	$2\text{-}0\frac{3}{32}$
$\frac{7}{16}$	$9\frac{3}{32}$	$1\text{-}7\frac{21}{32}$	$9\frac{19}{32}$	$1\text{-}8\frac{25}{32}$	$10\frac{1}{32}$	$1\text{-}9\frac{29}{32}$	$10\frac{21}{32}$	$1\text{-}11\frac{1}{32}$	$11\frac{5}{32}$	$2\text{-}0\frac{5}{32}$
$\frac{1}{2}$	$9\frac18$	$1\text{-}7\frac{23}{32}$	$9\frac58$	$1\text{-}8\frac{27}{32}$	$10\frac{5}{32}$	$1\text{-}10$	$10\frac{11}{16}$	$1\text{-}11\frac18$	$11\frac{3}{16}$	$2\text{-}0\frac14$
$\frac{9}{16}$	$9\frac{5}{32}$	$1\text{-}7\frac{13}{16}$	$9\frac{21}{32}$	$1\text{-}8\frac{15}{16}$	$10\frac{3}{16}$	$1\text{-}10\frac{1}{16}$	$10\frac{23}{32}$	$1\text{-}11\frac{3}{16}$	$11\frac{7}{32}$	$2\text{-}0\frac{5}{16}$
$\frac{5}{8}$	$9\frac{3}{16}$	$1\text{-}7\frac78$	$9\frac{11}{16}$	$1\text{-}9$	$10\frac{7}{32}$	$1\text{-}10\frac18$	$10\frac34$	$1\text{-}11\frac14$	$11\frac14$	$2\text{-}0\frac38$
$\frac{11}{16}$	$9\frac{7}{32}$	$1\text{-}7\frac{15}{16}$	$9\frac{23}{32}$	$1\text{-}9\frac{1}{16}$	$10\frac14$	$1\text{-}10\frac{3}{16}$	$10\frac{25}{32}$	$1\text{-}11\frac{5}{16}$	$11\frac{9}{32}$	$2\text{-}0\frac{7}{16}$
$\frac{3}{4}$	$9\frac14$	$1\text{-}8$	$9\frac34$	$1\text{-}9\frac{5}{32}$	$10\frac{9}{32}$	$1\text{-}10\frac{9}{32}$	$10\frac{13}{16}$	$1\text{-}11\frac{13}{32}$	$11\frac{5}{16}$	$2\text{-}0\frac{17}{32}$
$\frac{13}{16}$	$9\frac{9}{32}$	$1\text{-}8\frac{3}{32}$	$9\frac{13}{16}$	$1\text{-}9\frac{7}{32}$	$10\frac{5}{16}$	$1\text{-}10\frac{11}{32}$	$10\frac{27}{32}$	$1\text{-}11\frac{15}{32}$	$11\frac38$	$2\text{-}0\frac{19}{32}$
$\frac{7}{8}$	$9\frac{5}{16}$	$1\text{-}8\frac{5}{32}$	$9\frac{27}{32}$	$1\text{-}9\frac{9}{32}$	$10\frac{11}{32}$	$1\text{-}10\frac{13}{32}$	$10\frac78$	$1\text{-}11\frac{17}{32}$	$11\frac{13}{32}$	$2\text{-}0\frac{21}{32}$
$\frac{15}{16}$	$9\frac{11}{32}$	$1\text{-}8\frac{7}{32}$	$9\frac78$	$1\text{-}9\frac{11}{32}$	$10\frac38$	$1\text{-}10\frac{15}{32}$	$10\frac{29}{32}$	$1\text{-}11\frac{19}{32}$	$11\frac{7}{16}$	$2\text{-}0\frac34$

Feet	40′ Rise	40′ Slope	50′ Rise	50′ Slope	60′ Rise	60′ Slope	70′ Rise	70′ Slope
0	20-10	$45\text{-}1\frac{3}{16}$	$26\text{-}0\frac12$	$56\text{-}4\frac12$	31-3	$67\text{-}7\frac{13}{16}$	$36\text{-}5\frac12$	$78\text{-}11\frac34$
1	$21\text{-}4\frac14$	$46\text{-}2\frac{23}{32}$	$26\text{-}6\frac34$	$57\text{-}6\frac12$	$31\text{-}9\frac14$	$68\text{-}9\frac{11}{32}$	$36\text{-}11\frac34$	$80\text{-}0\frac58$
2	$21\text{-}10\frac12$	$47\text{-}4\frac14$	27-1	$58\text{-}7\frac{9}{16}$	$32\text{-}3\frac12$	$69\text{-}10\frac78$	37-6	$81\text{-}2\frac{5}{32}$
3	$22\text{-}4\frac34$	$48\text{-}5\frac{25}{32}$	$27\text{-}7\frac14$	$59\text{-}9\frac{3}{32}$	$32\text{-}9\frac34$	$71\text{-}0\frac{13}{32}$	$38\text{-}0\frac14$	$82\text{-}3\frac{11}{16}$
4	22-11	$49\text{-}7\frac{5}{32}$	$28\text{-}1\frac12$	$60\text{-}10\frac58$	33-4	$72\text{-}1\frac{15}{32}$	$38\text{-}6\frac12$	$83\text{-}5\frac{7}{32}$
5	$23\text{-}5\frac14$	$50\text{-}8\frac{27}{32}$	$28\text{-}7\frac34$	$62\text{-}0\frac{5}{32}$	$33\text{-}10\frac14$	$73\text{-}3\frac{15}{32}$	$39\text{-}0\frac34$	$84\text{-}6\frac{3}{32}$
6	$23\text{-}11\frac12$	$51\text{-}10\frac38$	29-2	$63\text{-}1\frac{11}{16}$	$34\text{-}4\frac12$	$74\text{-}4\frac{31}{32}$	39-7	$85\text{-}8\frac{9}{32}$
7	$24\text{-}5\frac34$	$52\text{-}11\frac{29}{32}$	$29\text{-}8\frac14$	$64\text{-}3\frac{1}{16}$	$34\text{-}10\frac34$	$75\text{-}6\frac12$	$40\text{-}1\frac14$	$86\text{-}9\frac{13}{16}$
8	25-0	$54\text{-}1\frac{7}{16}$	$30\text{-}2\frac12$	$65\text{-}4\frac34$	35-5	$76\text{-}8\frac{1}{32}$	$40\text{-}7\frac12$	$87\text{-}11\frac{11}{16}$
9	$25\text{-}6\frac14$	$55\text{-}2\frac{31}{32}$	$30\text{-}8\frac34$	$66\text{-}6\frac{9}{32}$	$35\text{-}11\frac14$	$77\text{-}9\frac{9}{16}$	$41\text{-}1\frac34$	$89\text{-}0\frac78$

natsin A=0.4619344188; natcos A=0.8869140841; nattan A=0.5208333333; natcot A=1.9200000000

Inches	0" Rise	0" Slope	1" Rise	1" Slope	2" Rise	2" Slope	3" Rise	3" Slope	4" Rise	4" Slope	5" Rise	5" Slope
0	0	0	17/32	1 1/8	1 1/16	2 1/4	1 9/16	3 3/8	2 3/32	4 11/32	2 5/8	5 21/32
1/16	1/32	1/16	9/16	1 3/16	1 3/32	2 11/32	1 5/8	3 15/32	2 1/8	4 19/32	2 21/32	5 23/32
1/8	1/16	5/32	19/32	1 9/32	1 1/8	2 13/32	1 21/32	3 17/32	2 5/32	4 21/32	2 11/16	5 25/32
3/16	3/32	7/32	5/8	1 11/32	1 5/32	2 15/32	1 11/16	3 19/32	2 3/16	4 23/32	2 23/32	5 7/8
1/4	1/8	9/32	21/32	1 13/32	1 3/16	2 17/32	1 23/32	3 11/16	2 1/4	4 13/16	2 3/4	5 15/16
5/16	5/32	11/32	11/16	1 15/32	1 7/32	2 5/8	1 3/4	3 3/4	2 9/32	4 7/8	2 25/32	6
3/8	3/16	7/16	23/32	1 9/16	1 1/4	2 11/16	1 25/32	3 13/16	2 5/16	4 15/16	2 13/16	6 1/16
7/16	7/32	1/2	3/4	1 5/8	1 9/32	2 3/4	1 13/16	3 7/8	2 11/32	5	2 7/8	6 5/32
1/2	1/4	9/16	25/32	1 11/16	1 5/16	2 13/16	1 27/32	3 31/32	2 3/8	5 3/32	2 29/32	6 7/32
9/16	9/32	5/8	13/16	1 3/4	1 11/32	2 29/32	1 7/8	4 1/32	2 13/32	5 5/32	2 15/16	6 9/32
5/8	11/32	23/32	27/32	1 27/32	1 3/8	2 31/32	1 29/32	4 3/32	2 7/16	5 7/32	2 31/32	6 11/32
11/16	3/8	25/32	7/8	1 29/32	1 13/32	3 1/32	1 15/16	4 5/32	2 15/32	5 9/32	3	6 7/16
3/4	13/32	27/32	29/32	1 31/32	1 7/16	3 3/32	1 31/32	4 1/4	2 1/2	5 3/8	3 1/32	6 1/2
13/16	7/16	29/32	31/32	2 1/16	1 15/32	3 3/16	2	4 5/16	2 17/32	5 7/16	3 1/16	6 9/16
7/8	15/32	1	1	2 1/8	1 1/2	3 1/4	2 1/16	4 3/8	2 9/16	5 1/2	3 3/32	6 5/8
15/16	1/2	1 1/16	1 1/32	2 3/16	1 17/32	3 5/16	2 1/16	4 7/16	2 19/32	5 19/32	3 1/8	6 23/32

Inches	6" Rise	6" Slope	7" Rise	7" Slope	8" Rise	8" Slope	9" Rise	9" Slope	10" Rise	10" Slope	11" Rise	11" Slope
0	3 5/32	6 25/32	3 11/16	7 29/32	4 7/32	9 1/32	4 3/4	10 5/32	5 1/4	11 5/16	5 25/32	1-0 7/16
1/16	3 3/16	6 27/32	3 23/32	7 31/32	4 1/4	9 1/8	4 25/32	10 1/4	5 9/32	11 3/8	5 13/16	1-0 1/2
1/8	3 7/32	6 29/32	3 3/4	8	4 9/32	9 3/16	4 13/16	10 5/16	5 5/16	11 7/16	5 27/32	1-0 9/16
3/16	3 1/4	7	3 25/32	8 1/8	4 5/16	9 1/4	4 27/32	10 3/8	5 11/32	11 1/2	5 7/8	1-0 21/32
1/4	3 9/32	7 1/16	3 13/16	8 3/16	4 11/32	9 5/16	4 7/8	10 7/16	5 13/32	11 19/32	5 29/32	1-0 23/32
5/16	3 5/16	7 1/8	3 7/8	8 1/4	4 3/8	9 13/32	4 29/32	10 17/32	5 7/16	11 21/32	5 15/16	1-0 25/32
3/8	3 11/32	7 7/32	3 7/8	8 11/32	4 13/32	9 15/32	4 15/16	10 19/32	5 15/32	11 23/32	5 31/32	1-0 27/32
7/16	3 3/8	7 9/32	3 29/32	8 13/32	4 15/32	9 17/32	4 31/32	10 21/32	5 1/2	11 25/32	6 1/32	1-0 15/16
1/2	3 13/32	7 11/32	3 15/16	8 15/32	4 15/32	9 19/32	5	10 23/32	5 17/32	11 7/8	6 1/16	1-1
9/16	3 7/16	7 13/32	3 31/32	8 17/32	4 1/2	9 11/16	5 1/32	10 13/16	5 9/16	11 15/16	6 3/32	1-1 1/16
5/8	3 1/2	7 1/2	4	8 5/8	4 17/32	9 3/4	5 1/16	10 7/8	5 19/32	1-0	6 1/8	1-1 1/8
11/16	3 17/32	7 9/16	4 1/16	8 11/16	4 9/16	9 13/16	5 3/32	10 15/16	5 5/8	1-0 1/16	6 5/32	1-1 7/32
3/4	3 9/16	7 5/8	4 1/16	8 3/4	4 19/32	9 7/8	5 1/8	11 1/32	5 21/32	1-0 5/32	6 3/16	1-1 9/32
13/16	3 19/32	7 11/16	4 1/8	8 13/16	4 5/8	9 31/32	5 5/32	11 3/32	5 11/16	1-0 7/32	6 7/32	1-1 11/32
7/8	3 5/8	7 25/32	4 5/32	8 29/32	4 21/32	10 1/32	5 3/16	11 5/32	5 23/32	1-0 9/32	6 1/4	1-1 13/32
15/16	3 21/32	7 27/32	4 3/16	8 31/32	4 11/16	10 3/32	5 7/32	11 7/32	5 3/4	1-0 11/32	6 9/32	1-1 1/2

Feet	0' Rise	0' Slope	10' Rise	10' Slope	20' Rise	20' Slope	30' Rise	30' Slope
0	0	0	5-3 1/8	11-3 19/32	10-6 1/4	22-7 3/16	15-9 3/8	33-10 25/32
1	6 5/16	1-1 9/16	5-9 7/16	12-5 5/32	11-0 9/16	23-8 3/4	16-3 11/16	35-0 11/32
2	1-0 5/8	2-3 1/8	6-3 3/4	13-6 23/32	11-6 7/8	24-10 5/16	16-10	36-1 7/8
3	1-6 15/16	3-4 11/16	6-10 1/16	14-8 9/32	12-1 3/16	25-11 27/32	17-4 5/16	37-3 7/16
4	2-1 1/4	4-6 1/4	7-4 3/8	15-9 13/16	12-7 1/2	27-1 13/32	17-10 5/8	38-5
5	2-7 9/16	5-7 25/32	7-10 11/16	16-11 3/8	13-1 13/16	28-2 31/32	18-4 15/16	39-6 9/16
6	3-1 7/8	6-9 11/32	8-5	18-0 15/16	13-8 1/8	29-4 17/32	18-11 1/4	40-8 1/8
7	3-8 3/16	7-10 29/32	8-11 5/16	19-2 1/2	14-2 7/16	30-6 3/32	19-5 9/16	41-9 11/16
8	4-2 1/2	9-0 15/32	9-5 5/8	20-4 1/16	14-8 3/4	31-7 21/32	19-11 7/8	42-11 1/4
9	4-8 13/16	10-2 1/32	9-11 15/16	21-5 5/8	15-3 1/16	32-9 7/32	20-6 3/16	44-0 13/16

A = 27° 44' 46"; logsin A = 9.66797; logcos A = 9.94695; logtan A = 9.72102; logcot A = 0.27898

Ins.	12″ Rise	12″ Slope	13″ Rise	13″ Slope	14″ Rise	14″ Slope	15″ Rise	15″ Slope	16″ Rise	16″ Slope
0	6 5/16	1-1 9/16	6 27/32	1-2 11/16	7 3/8	1-3 13/16	7 7/8	1-4 15/16	8 13/32	1-6 3/32
1/16	6 11/32	1-1 5/8	6 7/8	1-2 3/4	7 13/32	1-3 7/8	7 15/16	1-5 1/32	8 7/16	1-6 5/32
1/8	6 3/8	1-1 11/16	6 29/32	1-2 27/32	7 7/16	1-3 31/32	7 31/32	1-5 3/32	8 15/32	1-6 7/32
3/16	6 13/32	1-1 25/32	6 15/16	1-2 29/32	7 15/32	1-4 1/32	8	1-5 5/32	8 1/2	1-6 9/32
1/4	6 7/16	1-1 27/32	6 31/32	1-2 31/32	7 1/2	1-4 3/32	8 1/32	1-5 7/32	8 9/16	1-6 3/8
5/16	6 15/32	1-1 29/32	7	1-3 1/32	7 17/32	1-4 3/16	8 1/16	1-5 5/16	8 19/32	1-6 7/16
3/8	6 1/2	1-1 31/32	7 1/32	1-3 1/8	7 9/16	1-4 1/4	8 3/32	1-5 3/8	8 5/8	1-6 1/2
7/16	6 17/32	1-2 1/16	7 1/16	1-3 3/16	7 19/32	1-4 5/16	8 1/8	1-5 7/16	8 21/32	1-6 9/16
1/2	6 9/16	1-2 1/8	7 3/32	1-3 1/4	7 5/8	1-4 3/8	8 5/32	1-5 1/2	8 11/16	1-6 21/32
9/16	6 19/32	1-2 3/16	7 1/8	1-3 5/16	7 21/32	1-4 15/32	8 3/16	1-5 19/32	8 23/32	1-6 23/32
5/8	6 21/32	1-2 1/4	7 5/32	1-3 13/32	7 11/16	1-4 17/32	8 7/32	1-5 21/32	8 3/4	1-6 25/32
11/16	6 11/16	1-2 11/32	7 3/16	1-3 15/32	7 23/32	1-4 19/32	8 1/4	1-5 23/32	8 25/32	1-6 27/32
3/4	6 23/32	1-2 13/32	7 7/32	1-3 17/32	7 3/4	1-4 21/32	8 9/32	1-5 25/32	8 13/16	1-6 15/16
13/16	6 3/4	1-2 15/32	7 9/32	1-3 19/32	7 25/32	1-4 3/4	8 5/16	1-5 7/8	8 27/32	1-7
7/8	6 25/32	1-2 9/16	7 5/16	1-3 11/16	7 13/16	1-4 13/16	8 11/32	1-5 15/16	8 7/8	1-7 1/16
15/16	6 13/16	1-2 5/8	7 11/32	1-3 3/4	7 27/32	1-4 7/8	8 3/8	1-6	8 29/32	1-7 1/8

Ins.	17″ Rise	17″ Slope	18″ Rise	18″ Slope	19″ Rise	19″ Slope	20″ Rise	20″ Slope	21″ Rise	21″ Slope
0	8 15/16	1-7 7/32	9 15/32	1-8 11/32	10	1-9 15/32	10 17/32	1-10 19/32	11 1/16	1-11 23/32
1/16	8 31/32	1-7 9/32	9 1/2	1-8 13/32	10 1/32	1-9 17/32	10 9/16	1-10 21/32	11 3/32	1-11 13/16
1/8	9	1-7 11/32	9 17/32	1-8 15/32	10 1/16	1-9 5/8	10 19/32	1-10 3/4	11 1/8	1-11 7/8
3/16	9 1/32	1-7 13/32	9 9/16	1-8 9/16	10 3/32	1-9 11/16	10 5/8	1-10 13/16	11 5/32	1-11 15/16
1/4	9 1/16	1-7 1/2	9 19/32	1-8 5/8	10 1/8	1-9 3/4	10 21/32	1-10 7/8	11 3/16	2-0
5/16	9 3/32	1-7 9/16	9 5/8	1-8 11/16	10 5/32	1-9 13/16	10 11/16	1-10 15/16	11 7/32	2-0 3/32
3/8	9 1/8	1-7 5/8	9 21/32	1-8 3/4	10 3/16	1-9 29/32	10 23/32	1-11 1/32	11 1/4	2-0 5/32
7/16	9 3/16	1-7 11/16	9 11/16	1-8 27/32	10 7/32	1-9 31/32	10 3/4	1-11 3/32	11 9/32	2-0 7/32
1/2	9 7/32	1-7 25/32	9 23/32	1-8 29/32	10 1/4	1-10 1/32	10 25/32	1-11 5/32	11 5/16	2-0 9/32
9/16	9 1/4	1-7 27/32	9 3/4	1-8 31/32	10 9/32	1-10 3/32	10 13/16	1-11 7/32	11 11/32	2-0 3/8
5/8	9 9/32	1-7 29/32	9 13/16	1-9 1/32	10 5/16	1-10 3/16	10 27/32	1-11 5/16	11 3/8	2-0 7/16
11/16	9 5/16	1-8	9 27/32	1-9 1/8	10 11/32	1-10 1/4	10 7/8	1-11 3/8	11 13/32	2-0 1/2
3/4	9 11/32	1-8 1/16	9 7/8	1-9 3/16	10 3/8	1-10 5/16	10 29/32	1-11 7/16	11 7/16	2-0 9/16
13/16	9 3/8	1-8 1/8	9 29/32	1-9 1/4	10 7/16	1-10 3/8	10 15/16	1-11 17/32	11 15/32	2-0 21/32
7/8	9 13/32	1-8 3/16	9 15/16	1-9 5/16	10 15/32	1-10 15/32	10 31/32	1-11 19/32	11 1/2	2-0 23/32
15/16	9 7/16	1-8 9/32	9 31/32	1-9 13/32	10 1/2	1-10 17/32	11	1-11 21/32	11 17/32	2-0 25/32

Feet	40′ Rise	40′ Slope	50′ Rise	50′ Slope	60′ Rise	60′ Slope	70′ Rise	70′ Slope
0	21-0 1/2	45-2 3/8	26-3 5/8	56-5 15/16	31-6 3/4	67-9 17/32	36-9 7/8	79-1 1/8
1	21-6 13/16	46-3 29/32	26-9 15/16	57-7 1/2	32-1 1/16	68-11 3/32	37-4 3/16	80-2 11/16
2	22-1 1/8	47-5 15/32	27-4 1/4	58-9 1/16	32-7 3/8	70-0 21/32	37-10 1/2	81-4 1/4
3	22-7 7/16	48-7 1/32	27-10 5/8	59-10 5/8	33-1 11/16	71-2 7/32	38-4 13/16	82-5 13/16
4	23-1 3/4	49-8 19/32	28-4 7/8	61-0 3/16	33-8	72-3 25/32	38-11 1/8	83-7 3/8
5	23-8 1/32	50-10 5/32	28-11 3/16	62-1 3/4	34-2 5/16	73-5 11/32	39-5 7/16	84-8 15/16
6	24-2 3/8	51-11 23/32	29-5 1/2	63-3 5/16	34-8 5/8	74-6 29/32	39-11 3/4	85-10 1/2
7	24-8 11/16	53-1 9/32	29-11 13/16	64-4 7/8	35-2 15/16	75-8 15/32	40-6 1/16	87-0 1/2
8	25-3	54-2 27/32	30-6 1/8	65-6 7/16	35-9 1/4	76-10	41-0 3/8	88-1 19/32
9	25-9 5/16	55-4 13/32	31-0 7/16	66-7 31/32	36-3 9/16	77-11 9/16	41-6 11/16	89-3 5/32

natsin A=0.4655564439; natcos A=0.8850181905; nattan A=0.5260416666; natcot A=1.9009900990

Inches	0" Rise	0" Slope	1" Rise	1" Slope	2" Rise	2" Slope	3" Rise	3" Slope	4" Rise	4" Slope	5" Rise	5" Slope
0	0	0	17/32	1 1/8	1 1/16	2 1/4	1 19/32	3 13/32-	2 1/8	4 17/32-	2 21/32	5 21/32
1/16	1/32	1/16	9/16	1 7/32-	1 3/32	2 11/32-	1 5/8	3 15/32-	2 5/32	4 19/32	2 11/16	5 23/32
1/8	1/16	5/32-	19/32	1 9/32-	1 1/8	2 13/32	1 21/32	3 17/32	2 3/16	4 21/32	2 23/32	5 13/16
3/16	3/32	7/32-	5/8	1 11/32	1 5/32	2 15/32	1 11/16	3 5/8	2 7/32	4 3/4	2 3/4	5 7/8
1/4	1/8	9/32	21/32	1 13/32	1 3/16	2 9/16	1 23/32	3 11/16	2 1/4	4 13/16	2 25/32	5 15/16
5/16	5/32	11/32	11/16	1 1/2	1 7/32	2 5/8	1 3/4	3 3/4	2 9/32	4 7/8	2 13/16	6 1/32-
3/8	3/16	7/16	23/32	1 9/16	1 1/4	2 11/16	1 25/32	3 13/16	2 5/16	4 31/32-	2 27/32	6 3/32-
7/16	7/32	1/2	3/4	1 5/8	1 9/32	2 3/4	1 13/16	3 29/32-	2 11/32	5 1/32-	2 7/8	6 5/32
1/2	1/4	9/16	13/16	1 11/16	1 5/16	2 27/32-	1 7/8	3 31/32-	2 3/8	5 3/32	2 15/16	6 7/32
9/16	5/16	5/8	27/32-	1 25/32-	1 3/8	2 29/32-	1 29/32-	4 1/32	2 7/16	5 5/32	2 31/32-	6 5/16
5/8	11/32-	23/32-	7/8	1 27/32-	1 13/32-	2 31/32	1 15/16	4 3/32	2 15/32-	5 1/4	3	6 3/8
11/16	3/8	25/32-	29/32-	1 29/32	1 7/16	3 1/32	1 31/32-	4 3/16	2 1/2	5 5/16	3 1/32-	6 7/16
3/4	13/32-	27/32	15/16	1 31/32	1 15/32-	3 1/8	2	4 1/4	2 17/32-	5 3/8	3 1/16	6 1/2
13/16	7/16	29/32	31/32-	2 1/16	1 1/2	3 3/16	2 1/32-	4 5/16	2 9/16	5 7/16	3 3/32-	6 19/32-
7/8	15/32-	1	1	2 1/8	1 17/32-	3 1/4	2 1/16	4 3/8	2 19/32-	5 17/32-	3 1/8	6 21/32-
15/16	1/2	1 1/16	1 1/32-	2 3/16	1 9/16	3 5/16	2 3/32-	4 15/32-	2 5/8	5 19/32-	3 5/32-	6 23/32

Inches	6" Rise	6" Slope	7" Rise	7" Slope	8" Rise	8" Slope	9" Rise	9" Slope	10" Rise	10" Slope	11" Rise	11" Slope
0	3 3/16	6 25/32	3 23/32	7 15/16	4 1/4	9 1/16	4 25/32	10 3/16	5 5/16	11 5/16	5 27/32	1-0 15/32-
1/16	3 7/32	6 7/8	3 3/4	8	4 9/32	9 1/8	4 13/16	10 1/4	5 11/32	11 13/32-	5 7/8	1-0 17/32-
1/8	3 1/4	6 15/16	3 25/32	8 1/16	4 5/16	9 3/16	4 27/32	10 11/32-	5 3/8	11 15/32-	5 29/32	1-0 19/32
3/16	3 9/32	7	3 13/16	8 1/8	4 11/32	9 9/32-	4 7/8	10 13/32-	5 13/32	11 17/32	5 15/16	1-0 21/32
1/4	3 5/16	7 1/16	3 27/32	8 7/32-	4 3/8	9 11/32-	4 29/32	10 15/32	5 7/16	11 19/32	5 31/32	1-0 3/4
5/16	3 11/32	7 5/32-	3 7/8	8 9/32-	4 13/32	9 13/32	4 15/16	10 17/32	5 15/32	11 11/16	6	1-0 13/16
3/8	3 3/8	7 7/32	3 29/32	8 11/32	4 7/16	9 15/32	4 31/32	10 5/8	5 1/2	11 3/4	6 1/32	1-0 7/8
7/16	3 13/32	7 9/32	3 15/16	8 7/16	4 15/32	9 9/16	5	10 11/16	5 17/32	11 13/16	6 1/16	1-0 15/16
1/2	3 7/16	7 3/8	4	8 1/2	4 1/2	9 5/8	5 1/16	10 3/4	5 9/16	11 7/8	6 1/8	1-1 1/32-
9/16	3 1/2	7 7/16	4 1/32-	8 9/16	4 9/16	9 11/16	5 3/32-	10 13/16	5 5/8	11 31/32-	6 5/32-	1-1 3/32-
5/8	3 17/32-	7 1/2	4 1/16	8 5/8	4 19/32-	9 25/32-	5 1/8	10 29/32-	5 21/32-	1-0 1/32	6 3/16	1-1 5/32
11/16	3 9/16	7 9/16	4 3/32-	8 23/32-	4 5/8	9 27/32-	5 5/32-	10 31/32	5 11/16	1-0 3/32	6 7/32-	1-1 1/4
3/4	3 19/32-	7 21/32-	4 1/8	8 25/32-	4 21/32-	9 29/32	5 3/16	11 1/32	5 23/32-	1-0 3/16	6 1/4	1-1 5/16
13/16	3 5/8	7 23/32-	4 5/32-	8 27/32	4 11/16	9 31/32	5 7/32-	11 1/8	5 3/4	1-0 1/4	6 9/32-	1-1 3/8
7/8	3 21/32-	7 25/32	4 3/16	8 29/32	4 23/32-	10 1/16	5 1/4	11 3/16	5 25/32-	1-0 5/16	6 5/16	1-1 7/16
15/16	3 11/16	7 27/32	4 7/32-	9	4 3/4	10 1/8	5 9/32-	11 1/4	5 13/16	1-0 3/8	6 11/32-	1-1 17/32-

Feet	0' Rise	0' Slope	10' Rise	10' Slope	20' Rise	20' Slope	30' Rise	30' Slope
0	0	0	5-3 3/4	11-3 7/8	10-7 1/2	22-7 3/4	15-11 1/4	33-11 21/32-
1	6 3/8	1-1 19/32-	5-10 1/8	12-5 15/32	11-1 7/8	23-9 11/32	16-5 5/8	35-1 1/4
2	1-0 3/4	2-3 3/16	6-4 1/2	13-7 1/16	11-8 1/4	24-10 15/16	17-0	36-2 13/16
3	1-7 1/8	3-4 3/4	6-10 7/8	14-8 21/32-	12-2 5/8	26-0 17/32-	17-6 3/8	37-4 13/32
4	2-1 1/2	4-6 11/32	7-5 1/4	15-10 1/4	12-9	27-2 1/8	18-0 3/4	38-6
5	2-7 7/8	5-7 15/16	7-11 5/8	16-11 13/16	13-3 3/8	28-3 23/32-	18-7 1/8	39-7 19/32-
6	3-2 1/4	6-9 17/32-	8-6	18-1 13/32	13-9 3/4	29-5 9/32	19-1 1/2	40-9 3/16
7	3-8 5/8	7-11 1/8	9-0 3/8	19-3	14-4 1/8	30-6 7/8	19-7 7/8	41-10 3/4
8	4-3	9-0 23/32-	9-6 3/4	20-4 19/32-	14-10 1/2	31-8 15/32	20-2 1/4	43-0 11/32
9	4-9 3/8	10-2 9/32	10-1 1/8	21-6 3/16	15-4 7/8	32-10 1/16	20-8 5/8	44-1 15/16

A = 27° 58′ 46″; logsin A = 9.67132; logcos A = 9.94602; logtan A = 9.72530; logcot A = 0.27470

Ins.	$12''$ Rise	$12''$ Slope	$13''$ Rise	$13''$ Slope	$14''$ Rise	$14''$ Slope	$15''$ Rise	$15''$ Slope	$16''$ Rise	$16''$ Slope
0	$6\frac{3}{8}$	$1\text{-}1\frac{19}{32}$	$6\frac{29}{32}$	$1\text{-}2\frac{23}{32}$	$7\frac{7}{16}$	$1\text{-}3\frac{27}{32}$	$7\frac{31}{32}$	$1\text{-}5$	$8\frac{1}{2}$	$1\text{-}6\frac{1}{8}$
$\frac{1}{16}$	$6\frac{13}{32}$	$1\text{-}1\frac{21}{32}$	$6\frac{15}{16}$	$1\text{-}2\frac{25}{32}$	$7\frac{15}{16}$	$1\text{-}3\frac{15}{16}$	8	$1\text{-}5\frac{1}{16}$	$8\frac{17}{32}$	$1\text{-}6\frac{3}{16}$
$\frac{1}{8}$	$6\frac{7}{16}$	$1\text{-}1\frac{23}{32}$	$6\frac{31}{32}$	$1\text{-}2\frac{7}{8}$	$7\frac{1}{2}$	$1\text{-}4$	$8\frac{1}{32}$	$1\text{-}5\frac{1}{8}$	$8\frac{9}{16}$	$1\text{-}6\frac{1}{4}$
$\frac{3}{16}$	$6\frac{15}{32}$	$1\text{-}1\frac{13}{16}$	7	$1\text{-}2\frac{15}{16}$	$7\frac{17}{32}$	$1\text{-}4\frac{1}{16}$	$8\frac{1}{16}$	$1\text{-}5\frac{3}{16}$	$8\frac{19}{32}$	$1\text{-}6\frac{11}{32}$
$\frac{1}{4}$	$6\frac{1}{2}$	$1\text{-}1\frac{7}{8}$	$7\frac{1}{32}$	$1\text{-}3$	$7\frac{9}{16}$	$1\text{-}4\frac{1}{8}$	$8\frac{3}{32}$	$1\text{-}5\frac{9}{32}$	$8\frac{5}{8}$	$1\text{-}6\frac{13}{32}$
$\frac{5}{16}$	$6\frac{17}{32}$	$1\text{-}1\frac{15}{16}$	$7\frac{1}{16}$	$1\text{-}3\frac{1}{16}$	$7\frac{19}{32}$	$1\text{-}4\frac{7}{32}$	$8\frac{1}{8}$	$1\text{-}5\frac{11}{32}$	$8\frac{21}{32}$	$1\text{-}6\frac{15}{32}$
$\frac{3}{8}$	$6\frac{9}{16}$	$1\text{-}2$	$7\frac{3}{32}$	$1\text{-}3\frac{5}{32}$	$7\frac{5}{8}$	$1\text{-}4\frac{9}{32}$	$8\frac{5}{32}$	$1\text{-}5\frac{13}{32}$	$8\frac{11}{16}$	$1\text{-}6\frac{17}{32}$
$\frac{7}{16}$	$6\frac{19}{32}$	$1\text{-}2\frac{3}{32}$	$7\frac{1}{8}$	$1\text{-}3\frac{7}{32}$	$7\frac{21}{32}$	$1\text{-}4\frac{11}{32}$	$8\frac{3}{16}$	$1\text{-}5\frac{15}{32}$	$8\frac{23}{32}$	$1\text{-}6\frac{5}{8}$
$\frac{1}{2}$	$6\frac{5}{8}$	$1\text{-}2\frac{5}{32}$	$7\frac{3}{16}$	$1\text{-}3\frac{9}{32}$	$7\frac{11}{16}$	$1\text{-}4\frac{13}{32}$	$8\frac{1}{4}$	$1\text{-}5\frac{9}{16}$	$8\frac{3}{4}$	$1\text{-}6\frac{11}{16}$
$\frac{9}{16}$	$6\frac{11}{16}$	$1\text{-}2\frac{7}{32}$	$7\frac{7}{32}$	$1\text{-}3\frac{11}{32}$	$7\frac{3}{4}$	$1\text{-}4\frac{1}{2}$	$8\frac{9}{32}$	$1\text{-}5\frac{5}{8}$	$8\frac{13}{16}$	$1\text{-}6\frac{3}{4}$
$\frac{5}{8}$	$6\frac{23}{32}$	$1\text{-}2\frac{9}{32}$	$7\frac{1}{4}$	$1\text{-}3\frac{13}{32}$	$7\frac{25}{32}$	$1\text{-}4\frac{9}{16}$	$8\frac{5}{16}$	$1\text{-}5\frac{11}{16}$	$8\frac{27}{32}$	$1\text{-}6\frac{13}{16}$
$\frac{11}{16}$	$6\frac{3}{4}$	$1\text{-}2\frac{3}{8}$	$7\frac{9}{32}$	$1\text{-}3\frac{1}{2}$	$7\frac{13}{16}$	$1\text{-}4\frac{5}{8}$	$8\frac{11}{32}$	$1\text{-}5\frac{3}{4}$	$8\frac{7}{8}$	$1\text{-}6\frac{29}{32}$
$\frac{3}{4}$	$6\frac{25}{32}$	$1\text{-}2\frac{7}{16}$	$7\frac{5}{16}$	$1\text{-}3\frac{9}{16}$	$7\frac{27}{32}$	$1\text{-}4\frac{11}{16}$	$8\frac{3}{8}$	$1\text{-}5\frac{27}{32}$	$8\frac{29}{32}$	$1\text{-}6\frac{31}{32}$
$\frac{13}{16}$	$6\frac{13}{16}$	$1\text{-}2\frac{1}{2}$	$7\frac{11}{32}$	$1\text{-}3\frac{21}{32}$	$7\frac{7}{8}$	$1\text{-}4\frac{25}{32}$	$8\frac{13}{32}$	$1\text{-}5\frac{29}{32}$	$8\frac{15}{16}$	$1\text{-}7\frac{1}{32}$
$\frac{7}{8}$	$6\frac{27}{32}$	$1\text{-}2\frac{19}{32}$	$7\frac{3}{8}$	$1\text{-}3\frac{23}{32}$	$7\frac{29}{32}$	$1\text{-}4\frac{27}{32}$	$8\frac{7}{16}$	$1\text{-}5\frac{31}{32}$	$8\frac{31}{32}$	$1\text{-}7\frac{3}{32}$
$\frac{15}{16}$	$6\frac{7}{8}$	$1\text{-}2\frac{21}{32}$	$7\frac{13}{32}$	$1\text{-}3\frac{25}{32}$	$7\frac{15}{16}$	$1\text{-}4\frac{29}{32}$	$8\frac{15}{32}$	$1\text{-}6\frac{1}{16}$	9	$1\text{-}7\frac{3}{16}$

Ins.	$17''$ Rise	$17''$ Slope	$18''$ Rise	$18''$ Slope	$19''$ Rise	$19''$ Slope	$20''$ Rise	$20''$ Slope	$21''$ Rise	$21''$ Slope
0	$9\frac{1}{32}$	$1\text{-}7\frac{1}{4}$	$9\frac{9}{16}$	$1\text{-}8\frac{3}{8}$	$10\frac{3}{32}$	$1\text{-}9\frac{1}{2}$	$10\frac{5}{8}$	$1\text{-}10\frac{21}{32}$	$11\frac{5}{32}$	$1\text{-}11\frac{25}{32}$
$\frac{1}{16}$	$9\frac{1}{16}$	$1\text{-}7\frac{5}{16}$	$9\frac{19}{32}$	$1\text{-}8\frac{15}{32}$	$10\frac{1}{8}$	$1\text{-}9\frac{19}{32}$	$10\frac{21}{32}$	$1\text{-}10\frac{23}{32}$	$11\frac{3}{16}$	$1\text{-}11\frac{27}{32}$
$\frac{1}{8}$	$9\frac{3}{32}$	$1\text{-}7\frac{13}{32}$	$9\frac{5}{8}$	$1\text{-}8\frac{17}{32}$	$10\frac{5}{32}$	$1\text{-}9\frac{21}{32}$	$10\frac{11}{16}$	$1\text{-}10\frac{25}{32}$	$11\frac{7}{32}$	$1\text{-}11\frac{29}{32}$
$\frac{3}{16}$	$9\frac{1}{8}$	$1\text{-}7\frac{15}{32}$	$9\frac{21}{32}$	$1\text{-}8\frac{19}{32}$	$10\frac{3}{16}$	$1\text{-}9\frac{23}{32}$	$10\frac{23}{32}$	$1\text{-}10\frac{7}{8}$	$11\frac{1}{4}$	$2\text{-}0$
$\frac{1}{4}$	$9\frac{5}{32}$	$1\text{-}7\frac{17}{32}$	$9\frac{11}{16}$	$1\text{-}8\frac{21}{32}$	$10\frac{7}{32}$	$1\text{-}9\frac{13}{16}$	$10\frac{3}{4}$	$1\text{-}10\frac{15}{16}$	$11\frac{9}{32}$	$2\text{-}0\frac{1}{16}$
$\frac{5}{16}$	$9\frac{3}{16}$	$1\text{-}7\frac{19}{32}$	$9\frac{23}{32}$	$1\text{-}8\frac{3}{4}$	$10\frac{1}{4}$	$1\text{-}9\frac{7}{8}$	$10\frac{25}{32}$	$1\text{-}11$	$11\frac{5}{16}$	$2\text{-}0\frac{1}{8}$
$\frac{3}{8}$	$9\frac{7}{32}$	$1\text{-}7\frac{11}{16}$	$9\frac{3}{4}$	$1\text{-}8\frac{13}{16}$	$10\frac{9}{32}$	$1\text{-}9\frac{15}{16}$	$10\frac{13}{16}$	$1\text{-}11\frac{1}{16}$	$11\frac{11}{32}$	$2\text{-}0\frac{7}{32}$
$\frac{7}{16}$	$9\frac{1}{4}$	$1\text{-}7\frac{3}{4}$	$9\frac{25}{32}$	$1\text{-}8\frac{7}{8}$	$10\frac{5}{16}$	$1\text{-}10$	$10\frac{27}{32}$	$1\text{-}11\frac{5}{32}$	$11\frac{3}{8}$	$2\text{-}0\frac{9}{32}$
$\frac{1}{2}$	$9\frac{5}{16}$	$1\text{-}7\frac{13}{16}$	$9\frac{13}{16}$	$1\text{-}8\frac{15}{16}$	$10\frac{3}{8}$	$1\text{-}10\frac{3}{32}$	$10\frac{7}{8}$	$1\text{-}11\frac{7}{32}$	$11\frac{7}{16}$	$2\text{-}0\frac{11}{32}$
$\frac{9}{16}$	$9\frac{11}{32}$	$1\text{-}7\frac{7}{8}$	$9\frac{7}{8}$	$1\text{-}9\frac{1}{32}$	$10\frac{13}{32}$	$1\text{-}10\frac{5}{32}$	$10\frac{15}{16}$	$1\text{-}11\frac{9}{32}$	$11\frac{15}{32}$	$2\text{-}0\frac{13}{32}$
$\frac{5}{8}$	$9\frac{3}{8}$	$1\text{-}7\frac{31}{32}$	$9\frac{29}{32}$	$1\text{-}9\frac{3}{32}$	$10\frac{7}{16}$	$1\text{-}10\frac{7}{32}$	$10\frac{31}{32}$	$1\text{-}11\frac{11}{32}$	$11\frac{1}{2}$	$2\text{-}0\frac{1}{2}$
$\frac{11}{16}$	$9\frac{13}{32}$	$1\text{-}8\frac{1}{32}$	$9\frac{15}{16}$	$1\text{-}9\frac{5}{32}$	$10\frac{15}{32}$	$1\text{-}10\frac{9}{32}$	11	$1\text{-}11\frac{7}{16}$	$11\frac{17}{32}$	$2\text{-}0\frac{9}{16}$
$\frac{3}{4}$	$9\frac{7}{16}$	$1\text{-}8\frac{3}{32}$	$9\frac{31}{32}$	$1\text{-}9\frac{7}{32}$	$10\frac{1}{2}$	$1\text{-}10\frac{3}{8}$	$11\frac{1}{32}$	$1\text{-}11\frac{1}{2}$	$11\frac{9}{16}$	$2\text{-}0\frac{5}{8}$
$\frac{13}{16}$	$9\frac{15}{32}$	$1\text{-}8\frac{5}{32}$	10	$1\text{-}9\frac{5}{16}$	$10\frac{17}{32}$	$1\text{-}10\frac{7}{16}$	$11\frac{1}{16}$	$1\text{-}11\frac{9}{16}$	$11\frac{19}{32}$	$2\text{-}0\frac{11}{16}$
$\frac{7}{8}$	$9\frac{1}{2}$	$1\text{-}8\frac{1}{4}$	$10\frac{1}{32}$	$1\text{-}9\frac{3}{8}$	$10\frac{9}{16}$	$1\text{-}10\frac{1}{2}$	$11\frac{3}{32}$	$1\text{-}11\frac{5}{8}$	$11\frac{5}{8}$	$2\text{-}0\frac{25}{32}$
$\frac{15}{16}$	$9\frac{17}{32}$	$1\text{-}8\frac{5}{16}$	$10\frac{1}{16}$	$1\text{-}9\frac{7}{16}$	$10\frac{19}{32}$	$1\text{-}10\frac{9}{16}$	$11\frac{1}{8}$	$1\text{-}11\frac{23}{32}$	$11\frac{21}{32}$	$2\text{-}0\frac{27}{32}$

Feet	$40'$ Rise	$40'$ Slope	$50'$ Rise	$50'$ Slope	$60'$ Rise	$60'$ Slope	$70'$ Rise	$70'$ Slope
0	$21\text{-}3$	$45\text{-}3\frac{17}{32}$	$26\text{-}6\frac{3}{4}$	$56\text{-}7\frac{13}{32}$	$31\text{-}10\frac{1}{2}$	$67\text{-}11\frac{9}{32}$	$37\text{-}2\frac{1}{4}$	$79\text{-}3\frac{3}{16}$
1	$21\text{-}9\frac{3}{8}$	$46\text{-}5\frac{1}{8}$	$27\text{-}1\frac{1}{8}$	$57\text{-}9$	$32\text{-}4\frac{7}{8}$	$69\text{-}0\frac{7}{8}$	$37\text{-}8\frac{5}{8}$	$80\text{-}4\frac{25}{32}$
2	$22\text{-}3\frac{3}{4}$	$47\text{-}6\frac{23}{32}$	$27\text{-}7\frac{1}{2}$	$58\text{-}10\frac{19}{32}$	$32\text{-}11\frac{1}{4}$	$70\text{-}2\frac{15}{32}$	$38\text{-}3$	$81\text{-}6\frac{11}{32}$
3	$22\text{-}10\frac{1}{8}$	$48\text{-}8\frac{9}{32}$	$28\text{-}1\frac{7}{8}$	$60\text{-}0\frac{3}{16}$	$33\text{-}5\frac{5}{8}$	$71\text{-}4\frac{1}{16}$	$38\text{-}9\frac{3}{8}$	$82\text{-}7\frac{15}{16}$
4	$23\text{-}4\frac{1}{2}$	$49\text{-}9\frac{7}{8}$	$28\text{-}8\frac{1}{4}$	$61\text{-}1\frac{25}{32}$	$34\text{-}0$	$72\text{-}5\frac{21}{32}$	$39\text{-}3\frac{3}{4}$	$83\text{-}9\frac{17}{32}$
5	$23\text{-}10\frac{7}{8}$	$50\text{-}11\frac{15}{32}$	$29\text{-}2\frac{5}{8}$	$62\text{-}3\frac{11}{32}$	$34\text{-}6\frac{3}{8}$	$73\text{-}7\frac{1}{4}$	$39\text{-}10\frac{1}{8}$	$84\text{-}11\frac{1}{8}$
6	$24\text{-}5\frac{1}{4}$	$52\text{-}1\frac{1}{16}$	$29\text{-}9$	$63\text{-}4\frac{15}{16}$	$35\text{-}0\frac{3}{4}$	$74\text{-}8\frac{13}{16}$	$40\text{-}4\frac{1}{2}$	$86\text{-}0\frac{23}{32}$
7	$24\text{-}11\frac{5}{8}$	$53\text{-}2\frac{21}{32}$	$30\text{-}3\frac{3}{8}$	$64\text{-}6\frac{17}{32}$	$35\text{-}7\frac{1}{8}$	$75\text{-}10\frac{13}{32}$	$40\text{-}10\frac{7}{8}$	$87\text{-}2\frac{29}{32}$
8	$25\text{-}6$	$54\text{-}4\frac{1}{4}$	$30\text{-}9\frac{3}{4}$	$65\text{-}8\frac{1}{8}$	$36\text{-}1\frac{1}{2}$	$77\text{-}0$	$41\text{-}5\frac{1}{4}$	$88\text{-}3\frac{7}{8}$
9	$26\text{-}0\frac{3}{8}$	$55\text{-}5\frac{13}{32}$	$31\text{-}4\frac{1}{8}$	$66\text{-}9\frac{23}{32}$	$36\text{-}7\frac{7}{8}$	$78\text{-}1\frac{19}{32}$	$41\text{-}11\frac{5}{8}$	$89\text{-}5\frac{15}{32}$

natsin A=0.4691552259; natcos A=0.8831157194; nattan A=0.5312500000; natcot A=1.8823529411

Inches	0" Rise	0" Slope	1" Rise	1" Slope	2" Rise	2" Slope	3" Rise	3" Slope	4" Rise	4" Slope	5" Rise	5" Slope
0	0	0	17/32	1 1/8	1 1/16	2 9/32	1 5/8	3 13/32	2 5/32	4 17/32	2 11/16	5 11/16
1/16	1/16	1/16	9/16	1 17/32	1 3/32	2 11/32	1 21/32	3 15/32	2 3/16	4 5/8	2 23/32	5 3/4
1/8	1/16	5/32	19/32	1 9/32	1 1/8	2 13/32	1 11/16	3 17/32	2 7/32	4 11/16	2 3/4	5 13/16
3/16	2/32	7/32	5/8	1 11/32	1 3/16	2 15/32	1 23/32	3 5/8	2 1/4	4 3/4	2 25/32	5 7/8
1/4	1/6	9/32	21/32	1 13/32	1 7/32	2 9/16	1 3/4	3 11/16	2 9/32	4 13/16	2 13/16	5 31/32
5/16	5/32	11/32	23/32	1 1/2	1 1/4	2 5/8	1 25/32	3 3/4	2 5/16	4 29/32	2 27/32	6 1/32
3/8	3/16	7/16	3/4	1 9/16	1 9/32	2 11/16	1 13/16	3 27/32	2 11/32	4 31/32	2 7/8	6 3/32
7/16	1/4	1/2	25/32	1 5/8	1 5/16	2 25/32	1 27/32	3 29/32	2 3/8	5 1/32	2 29/32	6 9/32
1/2	9/32	9/16	13/16	1 11/16	1 11/32	2 27/32	1 7/8	3 31/32	2 13/32	5 3/32	2 15/16	6 1/4
9/16	5/16	5/8	27/32	1 25/32	1 3/8	2 29/32	1 29/32	4 1/32	2 7/16	5 3/16	2 31/32	6 11/32
5/8	11/32	23/32	7/8	1 27/32	1 13/32	2 31/32	1 15/16	4 1/8	2 15/32	5 1/4	3 1/32	6 3/8
11/16	3/8	25/32	29/32	1 29/32	1 7/16	3 1/16	1 31/32	4 3/16	2 1/2	5 5/16	3 1/16	6 15/32
3/4	13/32	27/32	15/16	2	1 15/32	3 1/8	2	4 1/4	2 9/16	5 3/8	3 3/32	6 17/32
13/16	7/16	15/16	31/32	2 1/16	1 1/2	3 3/16	2 1/32	4 5/16	2 19/32	5 15/32	3 1/8	6 19/32
7/8	15/32	1	1	2 1/8	1 17/32	3 1/4	2 3/32	4 13/32	2 5/8	5 17/32	3 5/32	6 21/32
15/16	1/2	1 1/16	1 1/32	2 3/16	1 9/16	3 11/32	2 1/8	4 15/32	2 21/32	5 19/32	3 3/16	6 3/4

Inches	6" Rise	6" Slope	7" Rise	7" Slope	8" Rise	8" Slope	9" Rise	9" Slope	10" Rise	10" Slope	11" Rise	11" Slope
0	3 7/32	6 13/16	3 3/4	7 15/16	4 9/32	9 3/32	4 13/16	10 7/32	5 3/8	11 11/32	5 29/32	1-0 15/32
1/16	3 1/4	6 7/8	3 25/32	8	4 5/16	9 5/32	4 7/8	10 9/32	5 13/32	11 13/32	5 15/16	1-0 9/16
1/8	3 9/32	6 15/16	3 13/16	8 3/32	4 11/32	9 7/32	4 29/32	10 11/32	5 7/16	11 1/2	5 31/32	1-0 5/8
3/16	3 5/16	7 1/32	3 27/32	8 5/32	4 13/32	9 9/32	4 15/16	10 7/16	5 15/32	11 9/16	6	1-0 11/16
1/4	3 11/32	7 3/32	3 7/8	8 7/32	4 7/16	9 3/8	4 31/32	10 1/2	5 1/2	11 5/8	6 1/32	1-0 25/32
5/16	3 3/8	7 5/32	3 15/16	8 5/16	4 15/32	9 7/16	5	10 9/16	5 17/32	11 11/16	6 1/16	1-0 27/32
3/8	3 13/32	7 1/4	3 31/32	8 3/8	4 1/2	9 1/2	5 1/32	10 5/8	5 9/16	11 25/32	6 3/32	1-0 29/32
7/16	3 15/32	7 5/16	4	8 7/16	4 17/32	9 9/16	5 1/16	10 23/32	5 19/32	11 27/32	6 1/8	1-0 31/32
1/2	3 1/2	7 3/8	4 1/32	8 1/2	4 9/16	9 21/32	5 3/32	10 25/32	5 5/8	11 29/32	6 5/32	1-1 1/16
9/16	3 17/32	7 7/16	4 1/16	8 19/32	4 19/32	9 23/32	5 1/8	10 27/32	5 21/32	1-0	6 3/16	1-1 1/8
5/8	3 9/16	7 17/32	4 3/32	8 21/32	4 5/8	9 25/32	5 3/16	10 15/16	5 11/16	1-0 1/16	6 1/4	1-1 3/16
11/16	3 19/32	7 19/32	4 1/8	8 23/32	4 21/32	9 27/32	5 3/16	11	5 23/32	1-0 1/8	6 9/32	1-1 1/4
3/4	3 5/8	7 21/32	4 5/32	8 25/32	4 11/16	9 15/16	5 7/32	11 1/16	5 25/32	1-0 3/16	6 5/16	1-1 5/16
13/16	3 21/32	7 23/32	4 3/16	8 7/8	4 23/32	10	5 1/4	11 1/8	5 13/16	1-0 9/32	6 11/32	1-1 13/32
7/8	3 11/16	7 13/16	4 7/32	8 15/16	4 3/4	10 1/16	5 5/16	11 7/32	5 27/32	1-0 11/32	6 3/8	1-1 15/32
15/16	3 23/32	7 7/8	4 1/4	9	4 25/32	10 5/32	5 11/32	11 9/32	5 7/8	1-0 13/32	6 13/32	1-1 17/32

Feet	0' Rise	0' Slope	10' Rise	10' Slope	20' Rise	20' Slope	30' Rise	30' Slope
0	0	0	5-4 3/8	11-4 3/16	10-8 3/4	22-8 11/32	16-1 1/8	34-0 17/32
1	6 1/16	1-1 5/8	5-10 13/16	12-5 25/32	11-3 3/8	23-9 31/32	16-7 9/16	35-2 5/32
2	1-0 7/8	2-3 1/4	6-5 1/4	13-7 13/32	11-9 5/8	24-11 19/32	17-2	36-3 25/32
3	1-7 5/16	3-4 27/32	6-11 11/16	14-9 1/32	12-4 1/16	26-1 7/32	17-8 7/16	37-5 3/8
4	2-1 3/4	4-6 15/32	7-6 1/8	15-10 21/32	12-10 1/2	27-2 13/16	18-2 7/8	38-7
5	2-8 3/16	5-8 3/4	8-0 9/16	17-0 1/4	13-4 15/16	28-4 7/16	18-9 5/16	39-8 5/8
6	3-2 5/8	6-9 23/32	8-7	18-1 7/8	13-11 3/8	29-6 1/16	19-3 3/4	40-10 1/4
7	3-9 1/16	7-11 5/16	9-1 7/16	19-3 1/2	14-5 13/16	30-7 11/16	19-10 3/16	41-11 27/32
8	4-3 1/2	9-0 15/16	9-7 7/8	20-5 1/8	15-0 1/4	31-9 9/32	20-4 5/8	43-1 15/32
9	4-9 15/16	10-2 9/16	10-2 5/16	21-6 3/4	15-6 11/16	32-10 29/32	20-11 1/16	44-3 3/32

A = 28° 12' 42''; logsin A = 9.67461; logcos A = 9.94508; logtan A = 9.72954; logcot A = 0.27046

in.	12″ Rise	12″ Slope	13″ Rise	13″ Slope	14″ Rise	14″ Slope	15″ Rise	15″ Slope	16″ Rise	16″ Slope
0	6 7/16	1-1 5/8	6 31/32	1-2 3/4	7 1/2	1-3 7/8	8 1/16	1-5 1/32	8 19/32	1-6 5/32
1/16	6 15/32	1-1 11/16	7	1-2 13/16	7 17/32	1-3 31/32	8 3/32	1-5 3/32	8 5/8	1-6 1/32
1/8	6 1/2	1-1 3/4	7 1/32	1-2 29/32	7 9/16	1-4 1/32	8 1/8	1-5 5/32	8 21/32	1-6 5/16
3/16	6 17/32	1-1 27/32	7 1/16	1-2 31/32	7 5/8	1-4 3/32	8 5/32	1-5 1/4	8 11/16	1-6 3/8
1/4	6 9/16	1-1 29/32	7 3/32	1-3 1/2	7 21/32	1-4 5/32	8 3/16	1-5 5/16	8 23/32	1-6 7/16
5/16	6 19/32	1-1 31/32	7 5/32	1-3 3/32	7 11/16	1-4 1/4	8 7/32	1-5 3/8	8 1/4	1-6 1/2
3/8	6 5/8	1-2 1/32	7 3/16	1-3 3/16	7 23/32	1-4 5/16	8 1/4	1-5 7/16	8 25/32	1-6 19/32
7/16	6 11/16	1-2 1/8	7 7/32	1-3 1/4	7 3/4	1-4 3/8	8 9/32	1-5 17/32	8 13/16	1-6 21/32
1/2	6 23/32	1-2 3/16	7 1/4	1-3 5/16	7 25/32	1-4 15/32	8 5/16	1-5 19/32	8 27/32	1-6 23/32
9/16	6 3/4	1-2 1/4	7 9/32	1-3 13/32	7 13/16	1-4 17/32	8 11/32	1-5 21/32	8 7/8	1-6 25/32
5/8	6 25/32	1-2 5/16	7 5/16	1-3 15/32	7 27/32	1-4 19/32	8 3/8	1-5 23/32	8 29/32	1-6 7/8
11/16	6 13/16	1-2 13/32	7 11/32	1-3 17/32	7 7/8	1-4 21/32	8 13/32	1-5 13/16	8 15/16	1-6 15/16
3/4	6 27/32	1-2 15/32	7 3/8	1-3 19/32	7 29/32	1-4 3/4	8 7/16	1-5 7/8	9	1-7
13/16	6 7/8	1-2 17/32	7 13/32	1-3 11/32	7 15/16	1-4 13/16	8 15/32	1-5 15/16	9 1/32	1-7 3/32
7/8	6 29/32	1-2 5/8	7 7/16	1-3 3/4	7 31/32	1-4 7/8	8 17/32	1-6	9 1/16	1-7 5/32
15/16	6 15/16	1-2 11/16	7 15/32	1-3 13/16	8	1-4 15/16	8 9/16	1-6 3/32	9 3/32	1-7 7/32

ins.	17″ Rise	17″ Slope	18″ Rise	18″ Slope	19″ Rise	19″ Slope	20″ Rise	20″ Slope	21″ Rise	21″ Slope
0	9 1/8	1-7 3/32	9 21/32	1-8 7/16	10 3/16	1-9 9/16	10 23/32	1-10 11/16	11 1/4	1-11 27/32
1/16	9 5/32	1-7 3/32	9 11/16	1-8 1/2	10 7/32	1-9 5/8	10 3/4	1-10 25/32	11 5/32	1-11 29/32
1/8	9 3/16	1-7 7/16	9 23/32	1-8 9/16	10 1/4	1-9 23/32	10 25/32	1-10 27/32	11 11/32	1-11 31/32
3/16	9 7/32	1-7 1/2	9 3/4	1-8 5/8	10 9/32	1-9 25/32	10 27/32	1-10 29/32	11 3/8	2-0 1/32
1/4	9 1/4	1-7 9/16	9 25/32	1-8 23/32	10 5/16	1-9 27/32	10 7/8	1-10 31/32	11 13/32	2-0 1/8
5/16	9 9/32	1-7 21/32	9 13/16	1-8 25/32	10 3/8	1-9 29/32	10 29/32	1-11 1/16	11 7/16	2-0 3/16
3/8	9 5/16	1-7 23/32	9 27/32	1-8 27/32	10 13/32	1-10	10 15/16	1-11 1/8	11 15/32	2-0 1/4
7/16	9 11/32	1-7 25/32	9 29/32	1-8 15/16	10 7/16	1-10 1/16	10 31/32	1-11 3/16	11 1/2	2-0 5/16
1/2	9 3/8	1-7 27/32	9 15/16	1-9	10 15/32	1-10 1/8	11	1-11 1/4	11 17/32	2-0 13/32
9/16	9 13/32	1-7 15/16	9 31/32	1-9 1/16	10 1/2	1-10 3/16	11 1/32	1-11 11/32	11 9/16	2-0 15/32
5/8	9 15/32	1-8	10	1-9 1/8	10 17/32	1-10 9/32	11 1/16	1-11 13/32	11 19/32	2-0 17/32
11/16	9 1/2	1-8 1/16	10 1/32	1-9 7/32	10 9/16	1-10 11/32	11 3/32	1-11 15/32	11 5/8	2-0 5/8
3/4	9 17/32	1-8 5/32	10 1/16	1-9 9/32	10 19/32	1-10 13/32	11 1/8	1-11 9/16	11 21/32	2-0 11/16
13/16	9 9/16	1-8 7/32	10 3/32	1-9 11/32	10 5/8	1-10 15/32	11 5/32	1-11 5/8	11 11/16	2-0 3/4
7/8	9 19/32	1-8 3/8	10 1/8	1-9 13/32	10 21/32	1-10 9/16	11 3/16	1-11 11/16	11 3/4	2-0 13/16
15/16	9 5/8	1-8 11/32	10 5/32	1-9 1/2	10 11/16	1-10 5/8	11 7/32	1-11 3/4	11 25/32	2-0 29/32

Feet	40′ Rise	40′ Slope	50′ Rise	50′ Slope	60′ Rise	60′ Slope	70′ Rise	70′ Slope
0	21-5 1/2	45-4 23/32	26-9 7/8	56-8 7/8	32-2 1/4	68-1 1/16	37-6 5/8	79-5 1/4
1	21-11 15/16	46-6 5/16	27-4 5/16	57-10 1/2	32-8 11/16	69-2 11/16	38-1 1/16	80-6 27/32
2	22-6 3/8	47-7 15/16	27-10 3/4	59-0 1/8	33-3 1/8	70-4 9/32	38-7 1/2	81-8 15/32
3	23-0 13/16	48-9 9/16	28-5 3/16	60-1 3/4	33-9 9/16	71-5 29/32	39-1 15/16	82-10 3/32
4	23-7 1/4	49-11 3/16	28-11 5/8	61-3 11/32	34-4	72-7 17/32	39-8 3/8	83-11 23/32
5	24-1 11/16	51-0 25/32	29-6 1/16	62-4 31/32	34-10 7/32	73-9 5/32	40-2 13/16	85-1 5/16
6	24-8 1/8	52-2 13/32	30-0 1/2	63-6 19/32	35-4 5/8	74-10 25/32	40-9 1/4	86-2 15/16
7	25-2 9/16	53-4 1/32	30-6 15/16	64-8 7/32	35-11 5/16	76-0 3/8	41-3 11/16	87-4 9/16
8	25-9	54-5 21/32	31-1 3/8	65-9 13/16	36-5 3/4	77-2	41-10 1/8	88-6 3/16
9	26-3 1/16	55-7 9/32	31-7 13/16	66-11 7/16	37-0 3/16	78-3 5/8	42-4 9/16	89-7 13/16

natsin A=0.4727307858; **natcos** A=0.8812069019; **nattan** A=0.5364583333; **natcot** A=1.8640776699

BEVEL 6½" TO 12"

Inches	0" Rise	0" Slope	1" Rise	1" Slope	2" Rise	2" Slope	3" Rise	3" Slope	4" Rise	4" Slope	5" Rise	5" Slope
0	0	0	17/32	1 1/8	1 3/32–	2 9/32–	1 5/8	3 13/32	2 5/32	4 9/16	2 23/32–	5 11/16
1/16	1/32	1/16	9/16	1 7/32–	1 1/8	2 11/32	1 21/32	3 15/32	2 3/16	4 5/8	2 3/4	5 3/4
1/8	1/16	5/32–	5/8	1 9/32–	1 5/32–	2 13/32	1 11/16	3 9/16	2 1/4	4 11/16	2 25/32–	5 27/32–
3/16	3/32	7/32–	21/32–	1 11/32	1 3/16	2 1/2	1 23/32	3 5/8	2 9/32–	4 3/4	2 13/16	5 29/32–
1/4	1/8	9/32	11/16	1 13/32	1 7/32	2 9/16	1 3/4	3 11/16	2 5/16	4 27/32–	2 27/32	5 31/32
5/16	5/32	11/32	23/32–	1 1/2	1 1/4	2 5/8	1 25/32	3 25/32–	2 11/32–	4 29/32–	2 7/8	6 1/32
3/8	3/16	7/16	3/4	1 9/16	1 9/32	2 11/16	1 13/16	3 27/32–	2 3/8	4 31/32	2 29/32	6 1/8
7/16	1/4	1/2	25/32–	1 5/8	1 5/16	2 25/32–	1 7/8	3 29/32	2 13/32–	5 1/32	2 15/16	6 3/16
1/2	9/32–	9/16	13/16	1 23/32–	1 11/32	2 27/32–	1 29/32–	3 31/32	2 7/16	5 1/8	2 31/32	6 1/4
9/16	5/16	5/8	27/32	1 25/32–	1 3/8	2 29/32	1 15/16	4 1/16	2 15/32	5 3/16	3	6 5/16
5/8	11/32–	23/32–	7/8	1 27/32	1 7/16	3	1 31/32–	4 1/8	2 1/2	5 1/4	3 1/16	6 13/32–
11/16	3/8	25/32	29/32	1 29/32	1 15/32–	3 1/16	2	4 3/16	2 17/32	5 11/32–	3 3/32–	6 15/32–
3/4	13/32	27/32	15/16	2	1 1/2	3 1/8	2 1/32	4 1/4	2 9/16	5 13/32–	3 1/8	6 17/32
13/16	7/16	15/16	31/32	2 1/16	1 17/32–	3 3/16	2 1/16	4 11/32–	2 19/32	5 15/32	3 5/32–	6 5/8
7/8	15/32	1	1	2 1/8	1 9/16	3 9/32–	2 3/32	4 13/32	2 5/8	5 17/32	3 3/16	6 11/16
15/16	1/2	1 1/16	1 1/16	2 7/32–	1 19/32–	3 11/32–	2 1/8	4 15/32	2 11/16	5 5/8	3 7/32–	6 3/4

Inches	6" Rise	6" Slope	7" Rise	7" Slope	8" Rise	8" Slope	9" Rise	9" Slope	10" Rise	10" Slope	11" Rise	11" Slope
0	3 1/4	6 13/16	3 25/32	7 31/32–	4 11/32–	9 3/32	4 7/8	10 1/4	5 13/32	11 3/8	5 31/32–	1-0 1/2
1/16	3 9/32	6 29/32–	3 13/16	8 1/32	4 3/8	9 5/32	4 29/32	10 5/16	5 7/16	11 7/16	6	1-0 19/32–
1/8	3 5/16	6 31/32–	3 7/8	8 3/32	4 13/32–	9 1/4	4 15/16	10 3/8	5 1/2	11 1/2	6 1/32–	1-0 21/32–
3/16	3 11/32	7 1/32	3 29/32–	8 3/16	4 7/16	9 5/16	4 31/32	10 7/16	5 17/32–	11 19/32–	6 1/16	1-0 23/32
1/4	3 3/8	7 3/32	3 15/16	8 1/4	4 15/32	9 3/8	5	10 17/32–	5 9/16	11 21/32	6 3/32	1-0 25/32
5/16	3 13/32	7 3/16	3 31/32–	8 5/16	4 1/2	9 15/32–	5 1/32	10 19/32–	5 19/32–	11 23/32	6 1/8	1-0 7/8
3/8	3 7/16	7 1/4	4	8 3/8	4 17/32	9 17/32–	5 1/16	10 21/32	5 5/8	11 13/16	6 5/32	1-0 15/16
7/16	3 1/2	7 5/16	4 1/32–	8 15/32–	4 9/16	9 19/32	5 1/8	10 23/32	5 21/32–	11 7/8	6 3/16	1-1
1/2	3 17/32–	7 13/32–	4 1/16	8 17/32–	4 19/32	9 21/32	5 5/32–	10 13/16	5 11/16	11 15/16	6 7/32	1-1 3/32–
9/16	3 9/16	7 15/32–	4 3/32	8 19/32	4 5/8	9 3/4	5 3/16	10 7/8	5 23/32	1-0	6 1/4	1-1 5/32–
5/8	3 19/32–	7 17/32	4 1/8	8 21/32	4 11/16	9 13/16	5 7/32–	10 15/16	5 3/4	1-0 3/32–	6 5/16	1-1 7/32
11/16	3 5/8	7 19/32	4 5/32	8 3/4	4 23/32–	9 7/8	5 1/4	11 1/32–	5 25/32	1-0 5/32–	6 11/32–	1-1 9/32
3/4	3 21/32	7 11/16	4 3/16	8 13/16	4 3/4	9 15/16	5 9/32	11 3/32–	5 13/16	1-0 7/32	6 3/8	1-1 3/8
13/16	3 11/16	7 3/4	4 7/32	8 7/8	4 25/32–	10 1/32–	5 5/16	11 5/32	5 27/32	1-0 9/32	6 13/32–	1-1 7/16
7/8	3 23/32	7 13/16	4 1/4	8 31/32–	4 13/16	10 3/32–	5 11/32	11 7/32	5 7/8	1-0 3/8	6 7/16	1-1 1/2
15/16	3 3/4	7 7/8	4 5/16	9 1/32–	4 27/32–	10 5/32	5 3/8	11 5/16	5 15/16	1-0 7/16	6 15/32–	1-1 9/16

Feet	0' Rise	0' Slope	10' Rise	10' Slope	20' Rise	20' Slope	30' Rise	30' Slope
0	0	0	5-5	11-4 15/32	10-10	22-8 15/16	16-3	34-1 13/32
1	6 1/2	1-1 21/32–	5-11 1/2	12-6 1/8	11-4 1/2	23-10 19/32	16-9 1/2	35-3 1/16
2	1-1	2-3 9/32	6-6	13-7 25/32–	11-11	25-0 1/4	17-4	36-4 23/32–
3	1-7 1/2	3-4 15/16	7-0 1/2	14-9 13/32	12-5 1/2	26-1 7/8	17-10 1/2	37-6 3/8
4	2-2	4-6 19/32–	7-7	15-11 1/16	13-0	27-3 17/32	18-5	38-8
5	2-8 1/2	5-8 1/4	8-1 1/2	17-0 23/32–	13-6 1/2	28-5 3/16	18-11 1/2	39-9 21/32
6	3-3	6-9 7/8	8-8	18-2 11/32	14-1	29-6 27/32–	19-6	40-11 5/16
7	3-9 1/2	7-11 17/32	9-2 1/2	19-4	14-7 1/2	30-8 15/32	20-0 1/2	42-0 15/16
8	4-4	9-1 3/16	9-9	20-5 21/32–	15-2	31-10 1/8	20-7	43-2 19/32
9	4-10 1/2	10-2 13/16	10-3 1/2	21-7 5/16	15-8 1/2	32-11 25/32–	21-1 1/2	44-4 1/4

A = 28° 26′ 35″; logsin A = 9.67787; logcos A = 9.94413; logtan A = 9.73373; logcot A = 0.26627

Ins.	12″ Rise	12″ Slope	13″ Rise	13″ Slope	14″ Rise	14″ Slope	15″ Rise	15″ Slope	16″ Rise	16″ Slope
0	6 1/2	1-1 21/32—	7 1/32	1-2 25/32	7 19/32—	1-3 15/16	8 1/8	1-5 1/16	8 21/32	1-6 3/16
1/16	6 17/32	1-1 23/32—	7 1/16	1-2 27/32	7 5/8	1-4	8 5/32	1-5 1/8	8 11/16	1-6 9/32—
1/8	6 9/16	1-1 25/32	7 1/8	1-2 15/16	7 21/32—	1-4 1/16	8 3/16	1-5 3/16	8 3/4	1-6 11/32—
3/16	6 19/32	1-1 7/8	7 5/32—	1-3	7 11/16	1-4 1/8	8 7/32	1-5 9/32—	8 25/32—	1-6 13/32
1/4	6 5/8	1-1 15/16	7 3/16	1-3 1/16	7 23/32	1-4 7/32—	8 1/4	1-5 11/32—	8 13/16	1-6 15/32
5/16	6 21/32	1-2	7 7/32—	1-3 1/8	7 3/4	1-4 9/32—	8 9/32	1-5 13/32	8 27/32—	1-6 9/16
3/8	6 11/16	1-2 1/16	7 1/4	1-3 7/32—	7 25/32	1-4 11/32	8 5/16	1-5 1/2	8 7/8	1-6 5/8
7/16	6 3/4	1-2 5/32—	7 9/32—	1-3 9/32	7 13/16	1-4 13/32	8 3/8	1-5 9/16	8 29/32—	1-6 11/16
1/2	6 25/32—	1-2 7/32—	7 5/16	1-3 11/32	7 27/32	1-4 1/2	8 13/32—	1-5 5/8	8 15/16	1-6 3/4
9/16	6 13/16	1-2 9/32	7 11/32	1-3 7/16	7 7/8	1-4 9/16	8 7/16	1-5 11/16	8 31/32	1-6 27/32—
5/8	6 27/32—	1-2 11/32	7 3/8	1-3 1/2	7 15/16	1-4 5/8	8 15/32—	1-5 25/32—	9	1-6 29/32
11/16	6 7/8	1-2 7/16	7 13/32	1-3 9/16	7 31/32—	1-4 23/32—	8 1/2	1-5 27/32—	9 1/32	1-6 31/32
3/4	6 29/32	1-2 1/2	7 7/16	1-3 5/8	8	1-4 25/32—	8 17/32	1-5 29/32	9 1/16	1-7 1/16
13/16	6 15/16	1-2 9/16	7 15/32	1-3 23/32—	8 1/32—	1-4 27/32	8 9/16	1-5 31/32	9 3/32	1-7 1/8
7/8	6 31/32	1-2 21/32—	7 1/2	1-3 25/32—	8 1/16	1-4 29/32	8 19/32	1-6 1/16	9 1/8	1-7 3/16
15/16	7	1-2 23/32—	7 9/16	1-3 27/32	8 3/32—	1-5	8 5/8	1-6 1/8	9 3/16	1-7 1/4

Ins.	17″ Rise	17″ Slope	18″ Rise	18″ Slope	19″ Rise	19″ Slope	20″ Rise	20″ Slope	21″ Rise	21″ Slope
0	9 7/32—	1-7 11/32—	9 3/4	1-8 15/32	10 9/32	1-9 19/32	10 27/32—	1-10 3/4	11 3/8	1-11 7/8
1/16	9 1/4	1-7 13/32—	9 25/32	1-8 17/32	10 5/16	1-9 11/16	10 7/8	1-10 13/16	11 13/32	1-11 31/32—
1/8	9 9/32—	1-7 15/32	9 13/16	1-8 5/8	10 3/8	1-9 3/4	10 29/32—	1-10 7/8	11 7/16	2-0 1/32—
3/16	9 5/16	1-7 9/16	9 27/32	1-8 11/16	10 13/32—	1-9 13/16	10 15/16	1-10 31/32—	11 15/32	2-0 3/32
1/4	9 11/32	1-7 5/8	9 7/8	1-8 3/4	10 7/16	1-9 29/32—	10 31/32	1-11 1/32—	11 1/2	2-0 5/32
5/16	9 3/8	1-7 11/16	9 29/32	1-8 13/16	10 15/32—	1-9 31/32—	11	1-11 3/32	11 17/32	2-0 1/4
3/8	9 13/32	1-7 3/4	9 15/16	1-8 29/32—	10 1/2	1-10 1/32	11 1/32	1-11 3/16	11 9/16	2-0 5/16
7/16	9 7/16	1-7 27/32—	10	1-8 31/32—	10 17/32—	1-10 3/32	11 1/16	1-11 1/4	11 5/8	2-0 3/8
1/2	9 15/32	1-7 29/32—	10 1/32—	1-9 1/32	10 9/16	1-10 3/16	11 3/32	1-11 5/16	11 21/32—	2-0 7/16
9/16	9 1/2	1-7 31/32	10 1/16	1-9 1/8	10 19/32	1-10 1/4	11 1/8	1-11 3/8	11 11/16	2-0 17/32—
5/8	9 9/16	1-8 1/32	10 3/32—	1-9 3/16	10 5/8	1-10 5/16	11 3/16	1-11 15/32—	11 23/32—	2-0 19/32—
11/16	9 19/32—	1-8 1/8	10 1/8	1-9 1/4	10 21/32	1-10 3/8	11 7/32—	1-11 17/32—	11 3/4	2-0 21/32
3/4	9 5/8	1-8 3/16	10 5/32	1-9 5/16	10 11/16	1-10 15/32—	11 1/4	1-11 19/32	11 25/32	2-0 3/4
13/16	9 21/32—	1-8 1/4	10 3/16	1-9 13/32—	10 23/32	1-10 17/32	11 9/32—	1-11 21/32	11 13/16	2-0 13/16
7/8	9 11/16	1-8 11/32—	10 7/32	1-9 15/32—	10 3/4	1-10 19/32	11 5/16	1-11 3/4	11 27/32	2-0 7/8
15/16	9 23/32—	1-8 13/32—	10 1/4	1-9 17/32	10 13/16	1-10 11/16	11 11/32—	1-11 13/16	11 7/8	2-0 15/16

Feet	40′ Rise	40′ Slope	50′ Rise	50′ Slope	60′ Rise	60′ Slope	70′ Rise	70′ Slope
0	21-8	45-5 29/32—	27-1	56-10 3/8	32-6	68-2 27/32—	37-11	79-7 5/16
1	22-2 1/2	46-7 17/32	27-7 1/2	58-0	33-0 1/2	69-4 1/2	38-5 1/2	80-8 31/32—
2	22-9	47-9 3/16	28-2	59-1 21/32	33-7	70-6 1/8	39-0	81-10 19/32
3	23-3 1/2	48-10 27/32—	28-8 1/2	60-3 5/16	34-1 1/2	71-7 25/32	39-6 1/2	83-0 1/4
4	23-10	50-0 15/32	29-3	61-4 31/32—	34-8	72-9 7/16	40-1	84-1 29/32—
5	24-4 1/2	51-2 1/8	29-9 1/2	62-6 19/32	35-2 1/2	73-11 1/16	40-7 1/2	85-3 9/16
6	24-11	52-3 25/32—	30-4	63-8 1/4	35-9	75-0 23/32	41-2	86-5 3/16
7	25-5 1/2	53-5 7/16	30-10 1/2	64-9 29/32—	36-3 1/2	76-2 3/8	41-8 1/2	87-6 27/32
8	26-0	54-7 1/16	31-5	65-11 17/32	36-10	77-4 1/32—	42-3	88-8 1/2
9	26-6 1/2	55-8 23/32	31-11 1/2	67-1 3/16	37-4 1/2	78-5 21/32	42-9 1/2	89-10 1/8

natsin A=0.4762831484; natcos A=0.8792919666; nattan A=0.5416666666; natcot A=1.8461538461

Inches	0" Rise	0" Slope	1" Rise	1" Slope	2" Rise	2" Slope	3" Rise	3" Slope	4" Rise	4" Slope	5" Rise	5" Slope
0	0	0	9/16	1 1/8	1 3/32	2 9/32	1 5/8	3 13/32	2 3/16	4 9/16	2 3/4	5 11/16
1/16	1/32	1/16	19/32	1 7/32	1 1/8	2 11/32	1 11/16	3 1/2	2 7/32	4 5/8	2 25/32	5 25/32
1/8	1/16	5/32	5/8	1 9/32	1 5/32	2 7/16	1 23/32	3 9/16	2 1/4	4 11/16	2 13/16	5 27/32
3/16	3/32	7/32	21/32	1 11/32	1 3/16	2 1/2	1 3/4	3 5/8	2 9/32	4 25/32	2 27/32	5 29/32
1/4	1/8	9/32	11/16	1 7/16	1 7/32	2 9/16	1 25/32	3 23/32	2 5/16	4 27/32	2 7/8	5 31/32
5/16	5/32	11/32	23/32	1 1/2	1 1/4	2 5/8	1 13/16	3 25/32	2 11/32	4 29/32	2 29/32	6 1/16
3/8	7/32	7/16	3/4	1 9/16	1 5/16	2 23/32	1 27/32	3 27/32	2 13/32	5	2 15/16	6 1/8
7/16	1/4	1/2	25/32	1 5/8	1 11/32	2 25/32	1 7/8	3 29/32	2 7/16	5 1/16	2 31/32	6 3/16
1/2	9/32	9/16	13/16	1 23/32	1 3/8	2 27/32	1 29/32	4	2 15/32	5 1/8	3	6 9/32
9/16	5/16	21/32	27/32	1 25/32	1 13/32	2 29/32	1 15/16	4 1/8	2 1/2	5 3/16	3 1/32	6 11/32
5/8	11/32	23/32	7/8	1 27/32	1 7/16	3	1 31/32	4 1/8	2 17/32	5 9/32	3 1/16	6 13/32
11/16	3/8	25/32	15/16	1 15/16	1 15/32	3 1/16	2 1/32	4 3/16	2 9/16	5 11/32	3 1/8	6 15/32
3/4	13/32	27/32	31/32	2	1 1/2	3 1/8	2 1/16	4 9/32	2 19/32	5 13/32	3 5/32	6 9/16
13/16	7/16	15/16	1	2 1/16	1 17/32	3 7/32	2 3/32	4 11/32	2 5/8	5 1/2	3 3/16	6 5/8
7/8	15/32	1	1 1/32	2 1/8	1 9/16	3 9/32	2 1/8	4 13/32	2 21/32	5 9/16	3 7/32	6 11/16
15/16	1/2	1 1/16	1 1/16	2 7/32	1 19/32	3 11/32	2 5/32	4 1/2	2 11/16	5 5/8	3 1/4	6 25/32

Inches	6" Rise	6" Slope	7" Rise	7" Slope	8" Rise	8" Slope	9" Rise	9" Slope	10" Rise	10" Slope	11" Rise	11" Slope
0	3 9/32	6 27/32	3 13/16	7 31/32	4 3/8	9 1/8	4 15/16	10 1/4	5 15/32	11 13/32	6	1-0 17/32
1/16	3 5/16	6 29/32	3 7/8	8 1/32	4 13/32	9 3/16	4 31/32	10 11/32	5 1/2	11 15/32	6 1/16	1-0 19/32
1/8	3 11/32	6 31/32	3 29/32	8 1/8	4 7/16	9 1/4	5	10 13/32	5 17/32	11 17/32	6 1/8	1-0 11/16
3/16	3 3/8	7 1/16	3 15/16	8 3/16	4 15/32	9 11/32	5 1/32	10 15/32	5 9/16	11 5/8	6 1/8	1-0 3/4
1/4	3 13/32	7 1/8	3 31/32	8 1/4	4 1/2	9 13/32	5 1/16	10 17/32	5 19/32	11 11/16	6 5/32	1-0 13/16
5/16	3 7/16	7 3/16	4	8 11/32	4 17/32	9 15/32	5 3/32	10 5/8	5 5/8	11 3/4	6 3/16	1-0 29/32
3/8	3 1/2	7 9/32	4 1/32	8 13/32	4 19/32	9 17/32	5 1/8	10 11/16	5 11/16	11 13/16	6 7/32	1-0 31/32
7/16	3 17/32	7 11/32	4 1/16	8 15/32	4 5/8	9 5/8	5 5/32	10 3/4	5 23/32	11 29/32	6 1/4	1-1 1/32
1/2	3 9/16	7 13/32	4 3/32	8 9/16	4 21/32	9 11/16	5 3/16	10 13/16	5 3/4	11 31/32	6 9/32	1-1 3/32
9/16	3 19/32	7 15/32	4 1/8	8 5/8	4 11/16	9 3/4	5 7/32	10 29/32	5 25/32	1-0 1/32	6 5/16	1-1 3/16
5/8	3 5/8	7 9/16	4 5/32	8 11/16	4 23/32	9 27/32	5 1/4	10 31/32	5 13/16	1-0 1/8	6 11/32	1-1 1/4
11/16	3 21/32	7 5/8	4 7/32	8 3/4	4 3/4	9 29/32	5 5/16	11 1/32	5 27/32	1-0 3/16	6 13/32	1-1 5/16
3/4	3 11/16	7 11/16	4 1/4	8 27/32	4 25/32	9 31/32	5 11/32	11 1/8	5 7/8	1-0 1/4	6 7/32	1-1 13/32
13/16	3 23/32	7 3/4	4 9/32	8 29/32	4 13/16	10 1/32	5 3/8	11 3/16	5 29/32	1-0 5/16	6 15/32	1-1 15/32
7/8	3 3/4	7 27/32	4 5/16	8 31/32	4 27/32	10 1/8	5 13/32	11 1/4	5 15/16	1-0 13/32	6 1/2	1-1 17/32
15/16	3 25/32	7 29/32	4 11/32	9 1/16	4 7/8	10 3/16	5 7/16	11 5/16	5 31/32	1-0 15/32	6 17/32	1-1 19/32

Feet	0' Rise	0' Slope	10' Rise	10' Slope	20' Rise	20' Slope	30' Rise	30' Slope
0	0	0	5-5 5/8	11-4 25/32	10-11 1/4	22-9 17/32	16-4 7/8	34-2 5/16
1	6 9/16	1-1 11/16	6-0 3/16	12-6 7/16	11-5 13/16	23-11 1/2	16-11 7/16	35-4
2	1-1 1/8	2-3 11/16	6-6 3/4	13-8 1/8	12-0 3/8	25-0 29/32	17-6	36-5 21/32
3	1-7 11/16	3-5 1/32	7-1 5/16	14-9 13/16	12-6 15/16	26-2 9/32	18-0 9/16	37-7 11/32
4	2-2 1/4	4-6 23/32	7-7 7/8	15-11 15/32	13-1 1/2	27-4 1/4	18-7 1/8	38-9 1/32
5	2-8 13/16	5-8 3/8	8-2 7/16	17-1 5/32	13-8 1/4	28-5 15/16	19-1 11/16	39-10 11/16
6	3-3 3/8	6-10 1/16	8-9	18-2 27/32	14-2 5/8	29-7 19/32	19-8 1/4	41-0 3/8
7	3-9 15/16	7-11 3/4	9-3 9/16	19-4 1/2	14-9 3/16	30-9 9/32	20-2 13/16	42-2 1/16
8	4-4 1/2	9-1 13/32	9-10 1/8	20-6 3/16	15-3 3/4	31-10 31/32	20-9 3/8	43-3 3/4
9	4-11 1/16	10-3 3/32	10-4 11/16	21-7 7/8	15-10 5/16	33-0 5/8	21-3 15/16	44-5 13/32

A=28° 40′ 23″; logsin A=9.68107; logcos A=9.94318; logtan A=9.73789; logcot A=0.26211

ins.	12″ Rise	12″ Slope	13″ Rise	13″ Slope	14″ Rise	14″ Slope	15″ Rise	15″ Slope	16″ Rise	16″ Slope
0	6 9/16	1-1 11/16	7 1/8	1-2 13/16	7 21/32	1-3 31/32	8 3/16	1-5 3/32	8 3/4	1-6 1/4
1/16	6 19/32	1-1 3/4	7 5/32	1-2 7/8	7 11/16	1-4 1/32	8 1/4	1-5 5/32	8 25/32	1-6 5/16
1/8	6 5/8	1-1 13/16	7 3/16	1-2 31/32	7 23/32	1-4 3/32	8 9/32	1-5 1/4	8 13/16	1-6 3/8
3/16	6 21/32	1-1 29/32	7 7/32	1-3 1/32	7 3/4	1-4 5/32	8 5/16	1-5 5/16	8 27/32	1-6 7/16
1/4	6 11/16	1-1 31/32	7 1/4	1-3 3/32	7 25/32	1-4 1/4	8 11/32	1-5 3/8	8 7/8	1-6 17/32
5/16	6 23/32	1-2 1/32	7 9/32	1-3 3/16	7 13/16	1-4 5/16	8 3/8	1-5 7/16	8 29/32	1-6 19/32
3/8	6 25/32	1-2 3/32	7 5/16	1-3 1/4	7 7/8	1-4 3/8	8 13/32	1-5 17/32	8 31/32	1-6 21/32
7/16	6 13/16	1-2 3/16	7 11/32	1-3 5/16	7 29/32	1-4 15/32	8 7/16	1-5 19/32	9	1-6 3/4
1/2	6 27/32	1-2 1/4	7 3/8	1-3 3/8	7 15/16	1-4 17/32	8 15/32	1-5 21/32	9 1/8	1-6 13/16
9/16	6 7/8	1-2 5/16	7 13/32	1-3 15/32	7 31/32	1-4 19/32	8 1/2	1-5 3/4	9 1/16	1-6 7/8
5/8	6 29/32	1-2 3/8	7 7/16	1-3 17/32	8	1-4 21/32	8 17/32	1-5 13/16	9 3/32	1-6 15/16
11/16	6 15/16	1-2 15/32	7 1/2	1-3 19/32	8 1/32	1-4 3/4	8 19/32	1-5 7/8	9 1/8	1-7 1/32
3/4	6 31/32	1-2 17/32	7 17/32	1-3 21/32	8 1/16	1-4 13/16	8 5/8	1-5 15/16	9 5/32	1-7 3/32
13/16	7	1-2 19/32	7 9/16	1-3 3/4	8 3/32	1-4 7/8	8 21/32	1-6 1/32	9 3/16	1-7 5/32
7/8	7 1/32	1-2 11/16	7 19/32	1-3 13/16	8 1/8	1-4 31/32	8 11/16	1-6 3/32	9 7/32	1-7 7/32
15/16	7 1/16	1-2 3/4	7 5/8	1-3 7/8	8 5/32	1-5 1/32	8 23/32	1-6 5/32	9 1/4	1-7 5/16

ins.	17″ Rise	17″ Slope	18″ Rise	18″ Slope	19″ Rise	19″ Slope	20″ Rise	20″ Slope	21″ Rise	21″ Slope
0	9 5/16	1-7 3/8	9 27/32	1-8 17/32	10 3/8	1-9 21/32	10 15/16	1-10 25/32	11 1/2	1-11 15/16
1/16	9 11/32	1-7 7/16	9 7/8	1-8 19/32	10 7/16	1-9 23/32	10 31/32	1-10 7/8	11 17/32	2-0
1/8	9 3/8	1-7 17/32	9 29/32	1-8 21/32	10 15/32	1-9 13/16	11	1-10 15/16	11 9/16	2-0 1/16
3/16	9 13/32	1-7 19/32	9 15/16	1-8 23/32	10 1/2	1-9 7/8	11 1/32	1-11	11 19/32	2-0 5/32
1/4	9 7/16	1-7 21/32	9 31/32	1-8 13/16	10 17/32	1-9 15/16	11 1/16	1-11 3/32	11 5/8	2-0 7/32
5/16	9 15/32	1-7 23/32	10	1-8 7/8	10 9/16	1-10	11 3/32	1-11 5/32	11 21/32	2-0 9/32
3/8	9 1/2	1-7 13/16	10 1/16	1-8 15/16	10 19/32	1-10 3/32	11 5/32	1-11 7/32	11 11/16	2-0 3/8
7/16	9 17/32	1-7 7/8	10 3/32	1-9	10 5/8	1-10 5/32	11 3/16	1-11 9/32	11 23/32	2-0 7/16
1/2	9 9/16	1-7 15/16	10 1/8	1-9 3/32	10 21/32	1-10 7/32	11 7/32	1-11 3/8	11 3/4	2-0 1/2
9/16	9 19/32	1-8 1/32	10 5/32	1-9 5/32	10 11/16	1-10 9/32	11 1/4	1-11 7/16	11 25/32	2-0 9/16
5/8	9 5/8	1-8 3/32	10 3/16	1-9 7/32	10 23/32	1-10 3/8	11 9/32	1-11 1/2	11 13/16	2-0 21/32
11/16	9 11/16	1-8 5/32	10 7/32	1-9 5/16	10 25/32	1-10 7/16	11 5/16	1-11 19/32	11 7/8	2-0 23/32
3/4	9 23/32	1-8 7/32	10 1/4	1-9 3/8	10 13/16	1-10 1/2	11 11/32	1-11 21/32	11 29/32	2-0 25/32
13/16	9 3/4	1-8 5/16	10 9/32	1-9 7/16	10 27/32	1-10 19/32	11 3/8	1-11 23/32	11 15/16	2-0 7/8
7/8	9 25/32	1-8 3/8	10 5/16	1-9 1/2	10 7/8	1-10 21/32	11 13/32	1-11 25/32	11 31/32	2-0 15/16
15/16	9 13/16	1-8 7/16	10 11/32	1-9 19/32	10 29/32	1-10 23/32	11 7/16	1-11 7/8	1-0	2-1

Feet	40′ Rise	40′ Slope	50′ Rise	50′ Slope	60′ Rise	60′ Slope	70′ Rise	70′ Slope
0	21-10 1/2	45-7 3/32	27-4 1/8	56-11 7/8	32-9 3/4	68-4 5/8	38-3 3/8	79-9 13/16
1	22-5 1/16	46-8 25/32	27-10 11/16	58-1 17/32	33-4 5/16	69-6 5/16	38-9 15/16	80-11 3/32
2	22-11 5/8	47-10 7/16	28-5 1/4	59-3 7/32	33-10 7/8	70-8	39-4 1/2	82-0 3/4
3	23-6 3/16	49-0 1/8	28-11 13/16	60-4 29/32	34-5 7/16	71-9 21/32	39-11 1/16	83-2 1/16
4	24-0 3/4	50-1 13/16	29-6 3/8	61-6 9/16	35-0	72-11 11/16	40-5 5/8	84-4 1/8
5	24-7 5/16	51-3 15/32	30-0 15/16	62-8 1/4	35-6 9/16	74-1 1/32	41-0 3/16	85-5 25/32
6	25-1 7/8	52-5 5/32	30-7 1/2	63-9 15/16	36-1 1/8	75-2 11/16	41-6 3/4	86-7 15/32
7	25-8 7/16	53-6 27/32	31-2 1/16	64-11 19/32	36-7 11/16	76-4 3/8	42-1 5/16	87-9 5/32
8	26-3	54-8 1/2	31-8 5/8	66-1 9/32	37-2 1/4	77-6 1/16	42-7 7/8	88-10 13/16
9	26-9 5/16	55-10 3/16	32-3 3/16	67-2 31/32	37-8 13/16	78-7 23/32	43-2 7/16	90-0 1/2

natsin A=0.4798123419; natcos A=0.8773711395; nattan A=0.5468750000; natcot A=1.8285714285

Inches	0" Rise	0" Slope	1" Rise	1" Slope	2" Rise	2" Slope	3" Rise	3" Slope	4" Rise	4" Slope	5" Rise	5" Slope
0	0	0	9/16	15/32	1 3/32	2 9/32	1 21/32	3 7/16	2 1/32	4 9/16	2 3/4	5 23/32
1/16	1/32	1/16	19/32	17/32	1 1/8	2 11/32	1 11/16	3 1/2	2 1/4	4 5/8	2 25/32	5 25/32
1/8	1/16	5/32	5/8	19/32	1 3/16	2 7/16	1 23/32	3 9/16	2 9/32	4 23/32	2 27/32	5 27/32
3/16	3/32	7/32	21/32	1 11/32	1 7/32	2 1/2	1 3/4	3 21/32	2 5/16	4 25/32	2 7/8	5 15/16
1/4	1/8	9/32	11/16	17/16	1 1/4	2 9/16	1 25/32	3 23/32	2 11/32	4 27/32	2 29/32	6
5/16	3/16	11/32	23/32	1 1/2	1 9/32	2 21/32	1 27/32	3 25/32	2 3/8	4 15/16	2 15/16	6 1/16
3/8	7/32	7/16	3/4	1 9/16	1 5/16	2 25/32	1 7/8	3 27/32	2 13/32	5	2 31/32	6 1/8
7/16	1/4	1/2	25/32	1 21/32	1 11/32	2 25/32	1 29/32	3 15/16	2 7/16	5 1/16	3	6 7/32
1/2	9/32	9/16	13/16	1 23/32	1 3/8	2 27/32	1 15/16	4	2 1/2	5 1/8	3 1/32	6 9/32
9/16	5/16	21/32	7/8	1 25/32	1 13/32	2 15/16	1 31/32	4 1/16	2 17/32	5 7/32	3 1/16	6 11/32
5/8	11/32	23/32	29/32	1 27/32	1 7/16	3	2	4 5/32	2 9/16	5 9/32	3 3/32	6 7/16
11/16	3/8	25/32	15/16	1 15/16	1 15/32	3 1/16	2 1/32	4 7/32	2 19/32	5 11/32	3 1/8	6 1/2
3/4	13/32	27/32	31/32	2	1 17/32	3 5/32	2 1/16	4 9/32	2 5/8	5 7/16	3 3/16	6 9/16
13/16	7/16	15/16	1	2 1/16	1 9/16	3 7/32	2 3/32	4 11/32	2 21/32	5 1/2	3 7/32	6 5/8
7/8	15/32	1	1 1/32	2 5/32	1 19/32	3 9/32	2 1/8	4 7/16	2 11/16	5 9/16	3 1/4	6 23/32
15/16	17/32	1 1/16	1 3/16	2 7/32	1 5/8	3 11/32	2 3/16	4 1/2	2 23/32	5 5/8	3 9/32	6 25/32

Inches	6" Rise	6" Slope	7" Rise	7" Slope	8" Rise	8" Slope	9" Rise	9" Slope	10" Rise	10" Slope	11" Rise	11" Slope
0	3 5/16	6 27/32	3 7/8	8	4 13/32	9 1/8	4 31/32	10 9/32	5 17/32	11 7/16	6 1/16	1-0 9/16
1/16	3 11/32	6 15/16	3 29/32	8 1/16	4 7/32	9 7/32	5	10 11/32	5 9/16	11 1/2	6 3/32	1-0 5/8
1/8	3 3/8	7	3 15/16	8 1/8	4 1/2	9 9/32	5 1/32	10 7/16	5 19/32	11 9/16	6 5/32	1-0 23/32
3/16	3 13/32	7 1/16	3 31/32	8 7/32	4 17/32	9 11/32	5 1/16	10 1/2	5 5/8	11 5/8	6 3/16	1-0 25/32
1/4	3 7/16	7 1/8	4	8 9/32	4 9/16	9 7/16	5 3/32	10 9/16	5 21/32	11 23/32	6 7/32	1-0 27/32
5/16	3 1/2	7 7/32	4 1/32	8 11/32	4 19/32	9 1/2	5 5/32	10 5/8	5 11/16	11 25/32	6 1/4	1-0 15/16
3/8	3 17/32	7 9/32	4 3/32	8 7/16	4 5/8	9 9/16	5 3/16	10 23/32	5 23/32	11 27/32	6 9/32	1-1
7/16	3 9/16	7 11/32	4 3/32	8 1/2	4 21/32	9 5/8	5 7/32	10 25/32	5 3/4	11 15/16	6 5/16	1-1 1/16
1/2	3 19/32	7 7/16	4 1/8	8 9/16	4 11/16	9 23/32	5 1/4	10 27/32	5 13/16	1-0	6 11/32	1-1 1/8
9/16	3 5/8	7 1/2	4 3/16	8 5/8	4 23/32	9 25/32	5 9/32	10 15/16	5 27/32	1-0 1/16	6 3/8	1-1 7/32
5/8	3 21/32	7 9/16	4 7/32	8 23/32	4 3/4	9 27/32	5 5/16	11	5 7/8	1-0 1/8	6 13/32	1-1 9/32
11/16	3 11/16	7 5/8	4 1/4	8 25/32	4 25/32	9 15/16	5 11/32	11 1/16	5 29/32	1-0 7/32	6 7/16	1-1 11/32
3/4	3 23/32	7 23/32	4 9/32	8 27/32	4 27/32	10	5 3/8	11 1/8	5 15/16	1-0 9/32	6 1/2	1-1 13/32
13/16	3 3/4	7 25/32	4 5/16	8 15/16	4 7/8	10 1/16	5 13/32	11 7/32	5 31/32	1-0 11/32	6 17/32	1-1 1/2
7/8	3 25/32	7 27/32	4 11/32	9	4 29/32	10 1/8	5 7/16	11 9/32	6	1-0 7/16	6 9/16	1-1 9/16
15/16	3 27/32	7 15/16	4 3/8	9 1/16	4 15/16	10 7/32	5 1/2	11 11/32	6 1/32	1-0 1/2	6 19/32	1-1 5/8

Feet	0' Rise	0' Slope	10' Rise	10' Slope	20' Rise	20' Slope	30' Rise	30' Slope
0	0	0	5-6 1/4	11-5 1/16	11-0 1/2	22-10 5/32	16-6 3/4	34-3 7/32
1	6 5/8	1-1 23/32	6-0 7/8	12-6 25/32	11-7 1/8	23-11 27/32	17-1 3/8	35-4 15/16
2	1-1 1/4	2-3 13/32	6-7 1/2	13-8 1/2	12-1 3/4	25-1 9/16	17-8	36-6 5/8
3	1-7 7/8	3-5 1/8	7-2 1/8	14-10 3/16	12-8 3/8	26-3 9/32	18-2 5/8	37-8 11/32
4	2-2 1/2	4-6 27/32	7-8 3/4	15-11 29/32	13-3	27-4 31/32	18-9 1/4	38-10 1/16
5	2-9 1/8	5-8 17/32	8-3 3/8	17-1 5/8	13-9 5/8	28-6 11/16	19-3 7/8	39-11 3/4
6	3-3 3/4	6-10 1/4	8-10	18-3 5/16	14-4 1/4	29-8 3/8	19-10 1/2	41-1 15/32
7	3-10 3/8	7-11 15/16	9-4 5/8	19-5 1/32	14-10 7/8	30-10 3/32	20-5 1/8	42-3 5/32
8	4-5	9-1 21/32	9-11 1/4	20-6 23/32	15-5 1/2	31-11 13/16	20-11 3/4	43-4 7/8
9	4-11 5/8	10-3 3/8	10-5 7/8	21-8 7/16	16-0 1/8	33-1 1/2	21-6 3/8	44-6 19/32

A = 28° 54′ 09″; logsin A = 9.68423; logcos A = 9.94223; logtan A = 9.74200; logcot A = 0.25800

In.	12″ Rise	12″ Slope	13″ Rise	13″ Slope	14″ Rise	14″ Slope	15″ Rise	15″ Slope	16″ Rise	16″ Slope
0	$6\tfrac{5}{8}$	$1\text{-}1\tfrac{23}{32}$	$7\tfrac{3}{16}$	$1\text{-}2\tfrac{27}{32}$	$7\tfrac{23}{32}$	$1\text{-}4$	$8\tfrac{9}{32}$	$1\text{-}5\tfrac{1}{8}$	$8\tfrac{27}{32}$	$1\text{-}6\tfrac{9}{32}$
1/16	$6\tfrac{21}{32}$	$1\text{-}1\tfrac{25}{32}$	$7\tfrac{7}{32}$	$1\text{-}2\tfrac{29}{32}$	$7\tfrac{3}{4}$	$1\text{-}4\tfrac{1}{16}$	$8\tfrac{5}{16}$	$1\text{-}5\tfrac{7}{32}$	$8\tfrac{7}{8}$	$1\text{-}6\tfrac{11}{32}$
1/8	$6\tfrac{11}{16}$	$1\text{-}1\tfrac{27}{32}$	$7\tfrac{1}{4}$	$1\text{-}3$	$7\tfrac{13}{16}$	$1\text{-}4\tfrac{1}{8}$	$8\tfrac{11}{32}$	$1\text{-}5\tfrac{9}{32}$	$8\tfrac{29}{32}$	$1\text{-}6\tfrac{13}{32}$
3/16	$6\tfrac{23}{32}$	$1\text{-}1\tfrac{29}{32}$	$7\tfrac{9}{32}$	$1\text{-}3\tfrac{1}{16}$	$7\tfrac{27}{32}$	$1\text{-}4\tfrac{7}{32}$	$8\tfrac{3}{8}$	$1\text{-}5\tfrac{11}{32}$	$8\tfrac{15}{16}$	$1\text{-}6\tfrac{1}{2}$
1/4	$6\tfrac{3}{4}$	$1\text{-}2$	$7\tfrac{5}{16}$	$1\text{-}3\tfrac{1}{8}$	$7\tfrac{7}{8}$	$1\text{-}4\tfrac{9}{32}$	$8\tfrac{13}{32}$	$1\text{-}5\tfrac{13}{32}$	$8\tfrac{31}{32}$	$1\text{-}6\tfrac{9}{16}$
5/16	$6\tfrac{13}{16}$	$1\text{-}2\tfrac{1}{16}$	$7\tfrac{11}{32}$	$1\text{-}3\tfrac{7}{32}$	$7\tfrac{29}{32}$	$1\text{-}4\tfrac{11}{32}$	$8\tfrac{15}{32}$	$1\text{-}5\tfrac{1}{2}$	9	$1\text{-}6\tfrac{5}{8}$
3/8	$6\tfrac{27}{32}$	$1\text{-}2\tfrac{1}{8}$	$7\tfrac{3}{8}$	$1\text{-}3\tfrac{9}{32}$	$7\tfrac{15}{16}$	$1\text{-}4\tfrac{13}{32}$	$8\tfrac{1}{2}$	$1\text{-}5\tfrac{9}{16}$	$9\tfrac{1}{16}$	$1\text{-}6\tfrac{23}{32}$
7/16	$6\tfrac{7}{8}$	$1\text{-}2\tfrac{7}{32}$	$7\tfrac{13}{32}$	$1\text{-}3\tfrac{11}{32}$	$7\tfrac{31}{32}$	$1\text{-}4\tfrac{1}{2}$	$8\tfrac{17}{32}$	$1\text{-}5\tfrac{5}{8}$	$9\tfrac{1}{16}$	$1\text{-}6\tfrac{25}{32}$
1/2	$6\tfrac{29}{32}$	$1\text{-}2\tfrac{9}{32}$	$7\tfrac{7}{16}$	$1\text{-}3\tfrac{13}{32}$	8	$1\text{-}4\tfrac{9}{32}$	$8\tfrac{9}{16}$	$1\text{-}5\tfrac{23}{32}$	$9\tfrac{1}{8}$	$1\text{-}6\tfrac{27}{32}$
9/16	$6\tfrac{15}{16}$	$1\text{-}2\tfrac{11}{32}$	$7\tfrac{1}{2}$	$1\text{-}3\tfrac{1}{2}$	$8\tfrac{1}{2}$	$1\text{-}4\tfrac{5}{8}$	$8\tfrac{19}{32}$	$1\text{-}5\tfrac{25}{32}$	$9\tfrac{5}{32}$	$1\text{-}6\tfrac{29}{32}$
5/8	$6\tfrac{31}{32}$	$1\text{-}2\tfrac{13}{32}$	$7\tfrac{17}{32}$	$1\text{-}3\tfrac{9}{16}$	$8\tfrac{1}{16}$	$1\text{-}4\tfrac{23}{32}$	$8\tfrac{5}{8}$	$1\text{-}5\tfrac{27}{32}$	$9\tfrac{3}{16}$	$1\text{-}7$
11/16	7	$1\text{-}2\tfrac{1}{2}$	$7\tfrac{9}{16}$	$1\text{-}3\tfrac{5}{8}$	$8\tfrac{3}{32}$	$1\text{-}4\tfrac{25}{32}$	$8\tfrac{21}{32}$	$1\text{-}5\tfrac{29}{32}$	$9\tfrac{7}{32}$	$1\text{-}7\tfrac{1}{16}$
3/4	$7\tfrac{1}{32}$	$1\text{-}2\tfrac{9}{16}$	$7\tfrac{19}{32}$	$1\text{-}3\tfrac{23}{32}$	$8\tfrac{5}{32}$	$1\text{-}4\tfrac{27}{32}$	$8\tfrac{11}{16}$	$1\text{-}6$	$9\tfrac{1}{4}$	$1\text{-}7\tfrac{1}{8}$
13/16	$7\tfrac{1}{16}$	$1\text{-}2\tfrac{5}{8}$	$7\tfrac{5}{8}$	$1\text{-}3\tfrac{25}{32}$	$8\tfrac{3}{16}$	$1\text{-}4\tfrac{29}{32}$	$8\tfrac{23}{32}$	$1\text{-}6\tfrac{1}{16}$	$9\tfrac{9}{32}$	$1\text{-}7\tfrac{7}{32}$
7/8	$7\tfrac{3}{32}$	$1\text{-}2\tfrac{23}{32}$	$7\tfrac{21}{32}$	$1\text{-}3\tfrac{27}{32}$	$8\tfrac{7}{32}$	$1\text{-}5$	$8\tfrac{3}{4}$	$1\text{-}6\tfrac{1}{8}$	$9\tfrac{5}{16}$	$1\text{-}7\tfrac{9}{32}$
15/16	$7\tfrac{5}{32}$	$1\text{-}2\tfrac{25}{32}$	$7\tfrac{11}{16}$	$1\text{-}3\tfrac{29}{32}$	$8\tfrac{1}{4}$	$1\text{-}5\tfrac{1}{16}$	$8\tfrac{13}{16}$	$1\text{-}6\tfrac{7}{32}$	$9\tfrac{11}{32}$	$1\text{-}7\tfrac{11}{32}$

In.	17″ Rise	17″ Slope	18″ Rise	18″ Slope	19″ Rise	19″ Slope	20″ Rise	20″ Slope	21″ Rise	21″ Slope
0	$9\tfrac{3}{8}$	$1\text{-}7\tfrac{13}{32}$	$9\tfrac{15}{16}$	$1\text{-}8\tfrac{9}{16}$	$10\tfrac{1}{2}$	$1\text{-}9\tfrac{23}{32}$	$11\tfrac{9}{32}$	$1\text{-}10\tfrac{27}{32}$	$11\tfrac{19}{32}$	$2\text{-}0$
1/16	$9\tfrac{13}{32}$	$1\text{-}7\tfrac{1}{2}$	$9\tfrac{31}{32}$	$1\text{-}8\tfrac{5}{8}$	$10\tfrac{17}{32}$	$1\text{-}9\tfrac{25}{32}$	$11\tfrac{11}{32}$	$1\text{-}10\tfrac{29}{32}$	$11\tfrac{5}{8}$	$2\text{-}0\tfrac{1}{16}$
1/8	$9\tfrac{15}{32}$	$1\text{-}7\tfrac{9}{16}$	10	$1\text{-}8\tfrac{23}{32}$	$10\tfrac{9}{16}$	$1\text{-}9\tfrac{27}{32}$	$11\tfrac{1}{8}$	$1\text{-}11$	$11\tfrac{21}{32}$	$2\text{-}0\tfrac{1}{8}$
3/16	$9\tfrac{1}{2}$	$1\text{-}7\tfrac{5}{8}$	$10\tfrac{1}{32}$	$1\text{-}8\tfrac{25}{32}$	$10\tfrac{19}{32}$	$1\text{-}9\tfrac{29}{32}$	$11\tfrac{5}{32}$	$1\text{-}11\tfrac{1}{16}$	$11\tfrac{11}{16}$	$2\text{-}0\tfrac{3}{16}$
1/4	$9\tfrac{17}{32}$	$1\text{-}7\tfrac{23}{32}$	$10\tfrac{1}{16}$	$1\text{-}8\tfrac{27}{32}$	$10\tfrac{5}{8}$	$1\text{-}10$	$11\tfrac{3}{16}$	$1\text{-}11\tfrac{1}{8}$	$11\tfrac{23}{32}$	$2\text{-}0\tfrac{9}{32}$
5/16	$9\tfrac{9}{16}$	$1\text{-}7\tfrac{25}{32}$	$10\tfrac{1}{8}$	$1\text{-}8\tfrac{29}{32}$	$10\tfrac{11}{16}$	$1\text{-}10\tfrac{1}{16}$	$11\tfrac{7}{32}$	$1\text{-}11\tfrac{3}{32}$	$11\tfrac{25}{32}$	$2\text{-}0\tfrac{11}{32}$
3/8	$9\tfrac{19}{32}$	$1\text{-}7\tfrac{27}{32}$	$10\tfrac{5}{32}$	$1\text{-}9$	$10\tfrac{23}{32}$	$1\text{-}10\tfrac{1}{8}$	$11\tfrac{1}{4}$	$1\text{-}11\tfrac{9}{32}$	$11\tfrac{13}{16}$	$2\text{-}0\tfrac{13}{32}$
7/16	$9\tfrac{5}{8}$	$1\text{-}7\tfrac{29}{32}$	$10\tfrac{3}{16}$	$1\text{-}9\tfrac{1}{16}$	$10\tfrac{23}{32}$	$1\text{-}10\tfrac{3}{32}$	$11\tfrac{9}{32}$	$1\text{-}11\tfrac{11}{32}$	$11\tfrac{27}{32}$	$2\text{-}0\tfrac{1}{2}$
1/2	$9\tfrac{21}{32}$	$1\text{-}8$	$10\tfrac{7}{32}$	$1\text{-}9\tfrac{1}{8}$	$10\tfrac{3}{4}$	$1\text{-}10\tfrac{9}{32}$	$11\tfrac{5}{16}$	$1\text{-}11\tfrac{13}{32}$	$11\tfrac{7}{8}$	$2\text{-}0\tfrac{9}{16}$
9/16	$9\tfrac{11}{16}$	$1\text{-}8\tfrac{1}{16}$	$10\tfrac{1}{4}$	$1\text{-}9\tfrac{7}{32}$	$10\tfrac{13}{16}$	$1\text{-}10\tfrac{11}{32}$	$11\tfrac{11}{32}$	$1\text{-}11\tfrac{1}{2}$	$11\tfrac{29}{32}$	$2\text{-}0\tfrac{5}{8}$
5/8	$9\tfrac{23}{32}$	$1\text{-}8\tfrac{1}{8}$	$10\tfrac{9}{32}$	$1\text{-}9\tfrac{9}{32}$	$10\tfrac{27}{32}$	$1\text{-}10\tfrac{13}{32}$	$11\tfrac{3}{8}$	$1\text{-}11\tfrac{9}{16}$	$11\tfrac{15}{16}$	$2\text{-}0\tfrac{11}{16}$
11/16	$9\tfrac{3}{4}$	$1\text{-}8\tfrac{7}{32}$	$10\tfrac{5}{16}$	$1\text{-}9\tfrac{11}{32}$	$10\tfrac{7}{8}$	$1\text{-}10\tfrac{1}{2}$	$11\tfrac{13}{32}$	$1\text{-}11\tfrac{5}{8}$	$11\tfrac{31}{32}$	$2\text{-}0\tfrac{25}{32}$
3/4	$9\tfrac{13}{16}$	$1\text{-}8\tfrac{9}{32}$	$10\tfrac{11}{32}$	$1\text{-}9\tfrac{13}{32}$	$10\tfrac{29}{32}$	$1\text{-}10\tfrac{9}{16}$	$11\tfrac{15}{32}$	$1\text{-}11\tfrac{11}{16}$	$1\text{-}0$	$2\text{-}0\tfrac{27}{32}$
13/16	$9\tfrac{27}{32}$	$1\text{-}8\tfrac{11}{32}$	$10\tfrac{3}{8}$	$1\text{-}9\tfrac{1}{2}$	$10\tfrac{31}{32}$	$1\text{-}10\tfrac{5}{8}$	$11\tfrac{1}{2}$	$1\text{-}11\tfrac{25}{32}$	$1\text{-}0\tfrac{1}{32}$	$2\text{-}0\tfrac{29}{32}$
7/8	$9\tfrac{7}{8}$	$1\text{-}8\tfrac{13}{32}$	$10\tfrac{13}{32}$	$1\text{-}9\tfrac{9}{16}$	$10\tfrac{31}{32}$	$1\text{-}10\tfrac{11}{16}$	$11\tfrac{17}{32}$	$1\text{-}11\tfrac{27}{32}$	$1\text{-}0\tfrac{1}{16}$	$2\text{-}1$
15/16	$9\tfrac{29}{32}$	$1\text{-}8\tfrac{1}{2}$	$10\tfrac{15}{32}$	$1\text{-}9\tfrac{5}{8}$	11	$1\text{-}10\tfrac{25}{32}$	$11\tfrac{9}{16}$	$1\text{-}11\tfrac{29}{32}$	$1\text{-}0\tfrac{1}{8}$	$2\text{-}1\tfrac{1}{16}$

Feet	40′ Rise	40′ Slope	50′ Rise	50′ Slope	60′ Rise	60′ Slope	70′ Rise	70′ Slope
0	$22\text{-}1$	$45\text{-}8\tfrac{9}{32}$	$27\text{-}7\tfrac{1}{4}$	$57\text{-}1\tfrac{3}{8}$	$33\text{-}1\tfrac{1}{2}$	$68\text{-}6\tfrac{7}{16}$	$38\text{-}7\tfrac{3}{4}$	$79\text{-}11\tfrac{1}{2}$
1	$22\text{-}7\tfrac{5}{8}$	$46\text{-}10$	$28\text{-}1\tfrac{7}{8}$	$58\text{-}3\tfrac{1}{16}$	$33\text{-}8\tfrac{1}{8}$	$69\text{-}8\tfrac{5}{32}$	$39\text{-}2\tfrac{3}{8}$	$81\text{-}1\tfrac{1}{32}$
2	$23\text{-}2\tfrac{1}{4}$	$47\text{-}11\tfrac{23}{32}$	$28\text{-}8\tfrac{1}{2}$	$59\text{-}4\tfrac{25}{32}$	$34\text{-}2\tfrac{3}{4}$	$70\text{-}9\tfrac{27}{32}$	$39\text{-}9$	$82\text{-}2\tfrac{15}{16}$
3	$23\text{-}8\tfrac{7}{8}$	$49\text{-}1\tfrac{13}{32}$	$29\text{-}3\tfrac{1}{8}$	$60\text{-}6\tfrac{1}{2}$	$34\text{-}9\tfrac{3}{8}$	$71\text{-}11\tfrac{9}{16}$	$40\text{-}3\tfrac{5}{8}$	$83\text{-}4\tfrac{5}{8}$
4	$24\text{-}3\tfrac{1}{2}$	$50\text{-}3\tfrac{1}{2}$	$29\text{-}9\tfrac{3}{4}$	$61\text{-}8\tfrac{3}{16}$	$35\text{-}4$	$73\text{-}1\tfrac{9}{32}$	$40\text{-}10\tfrac{1}{4}$	$84\text{-}6\tfrac{11}{32}$
5	$24\text{-}10\tfrac{1}{8}$	$51\text{-}4\tfrac{27}{32}$	$30\text{-}4\tfrac{3}{8}$	$62\text{-}9\tfrac{29}{32}$	$35\text{-}10\tfrac{5}{8}$	$74\text{-}2\tfrac{31}{32}$	$41\text{-}4\tfrac{7}{8}$	$85\text{-}8\tfrac{1}{16}$
6	$25\text{-}4\tfrac{3}{4}$	$52\text{-}6\tfrac{17}{32}$	$30\text{-}11$	$63\text{-}11\tfrac{5}{8}$	$36\text{-}5\tfrac{1}{4}$	$75\text{-}4\tfrac{11}{16}$	$41\text{-}11\tfrac{1}{2}$	$86\text{-}9\tfrac{3}{4}$
7	$25\text{-}11\tfrac{3}{8}$	$53\text{-}8\tfrac{1}{4}$	$31\text{-}5\tfrac{5}{8}$	$65\text{-}1\tfrac{5}{16}$	$36\text{-}11\tfrac{7}{8}$	$76\text{-}6\tfrac{3}{8}$	$42\text{-}6\tfrac{1}{8}$	$87\text{-}11\tfrac{15}{32}$
8	$26\text{-}6$	$54\text{-}9\tfrac{15}{16}$	$32\text{-}0\tfrac{1}{4}$	$66\text{-}3\tfrac{1}{32}$	$37\text{-}6\tfrac{1}{2}$	$77\text{-}8\tfrac{3}{8}$	$43\text{-}0\tfrac{3}{4}$	$89\text{-}1\tfrac{5}{32}$
9	$27\text{-}0\tfrac{5}{8}$	$55\text{-}11\tfrac{21}{32}$	$32\text{-}6\tfrac{7}{8}$	$67\text{-}4\tfrac{23}{32}$	$38\text{-}1\tfrac{1}{8}$	$78\text{-}9\tfrac{13}{16}$	$43\text{-}7\tfrac{3}{8}$	$90\text{-}2\tfrac{7}{8}$

natsin A=0.4833183976; natcos A=0.8754446449; nattan A=0.5520833333; natcot A=1.8113207547

Inches	0" Rise	0" Slope	1" Rise	1" Slope	2" Rise	2" Slope	3" Rise	3" Slope	4" Rise	4" Slope	5" Rise	5" Slope
0	0	0	9/16	15/32	1 1/8	29/32	1 11/16	3 7/16	2 7/32	4 19/32	2 25/32	5 23/32
1/16	1/32	1/16	19/32	17/32	1 5/32	2 3/8	1 23/32	3 1/2	2 1/4	4 21/32	2 13/16	5 25/32
1/8	1/16	5/32	5/8	19/32	1 3/16	2 7/16	1 3/4	3 9/16	2 5/16	4 23/32	2 27/32	5 7/8
3/16	3/32	7/32	21/32	1 3/8	1 7/32	2 1/2	1 25/32	3 21/32	2 11/32	4 25/32	2 29/32	5 15/16
1/4	1/8	9/32	11/16	1 7/16	1 1/4	2 9/16	1 13/16	3 23/32	2 3/8	4 7/8	2 15/16	6
5/16	3/16	11/32	23/32	1 1/2	1 9/32	2 21/32	1 27/32	3 25/32	2 13/32	4 15/16	2 31/32	6 3/32
3/8	7/32	7/16	25/32	1 9/16	1 5/16	2 23/32	1 7/8	3 7/8	2 7/16	5	3	6 5/32
7/16	1/4	1/2	13/16	1 21/32	1 11/32	2 25/32	1 29/32	3 15/16	2 15/32	5 3/32	3 1/32	6 7/32
1/2	9/32	9/16	27/32	1 23/32	1 13/32	2 7/8	1 15/16	4	2 1/2	5 5/32	3 1/16	6 9/32
9/16	5/16	21/32	7/8	1 25/32	1 7/16	2 15/16	2	4 3/32	2 17/32	5 7/32	3 3/32	6 3/8
5/8	11/32	23/32	29/32	1 7/8	1 15/32	3	2 1/32	4 5/32	2 9/16	5 9/32	3 1/8	6 7/16
11/16	3/8	25/32	15/16	1 15/16	1 1/2	3 1/16	2 1/16	4 7/32	2 5/8	5 3/8	3 5/32	6 1/2
3/4	13/32	27/32	31/32	2	1 17/32	3 5/32	2 3/32	4 9/32	2 21/32	5 7/16	3 7/32	6 19/32
13/16	7/16	15/16	1	2 1/16	1 9/16	3 7/32	2 1/8	4 3/8	2 11/16	5 1/2	3 1/4	6 21/32
7/8	1/2	1	1 1/16	2 5/32	1 19/32	3 9/32	2 5/32	4 7/16	2 23/32	5 19/32	3 9/32	6 23/32
15/16	17/32	1 1/16	1 3/32	2 7/32	1 5/8	3 3/8	2 3/16	4 1/2	2 3/4	5 21/32	3 5/16	6 13/16

Inches	6" Rise	6" Slope	7" Rise	7" Slope	8" Rise	8" Slope	9" Rise	9" Slope	10" Rise	10" Slope	11" Rise	11" Slope
0	3 11/32	6 7/8	3 29/32	8	4 15/32	9 5/32	5	10 5/16	5 9/16	11 7/16	6 1/8	1-0 19/32
1/16	3 3/8	6 15/16	3 15/16	8 3/32	4 1/2	9 7/32	5 1/16	10 3/8	5 19/32	11 17/32	6 9/32	1-0 21/32
1/8	3 13/32	7	3 31/32	8 5/32	4 17/32	9 5/16	5 3/32	10 7/16	5 21/32	11 19/32	6 3/16	1-0 3/4
3/16	3 7/16	7 3/32	4	8 7/32	4 9/16	9 3/8	5 1/8	10 17/32	5 11/16	11 21/32	6 1/4	1-0 13/16
1/4	3 15/32	7 5/32	4 1/32	8 5/16	4 19/32	9 7/16	5 5/32	10 19/32	5 23/32	11 23/32	6 9/32	1-0 7/8
5/16	3 17/32	7 7/32	4 1/16	8 3/8	4 5/8	9 17/32	5 3/16	10 21/32	5 3/4	11 13/16	6 5/16	1-0 15/16
3/8	3 9/16	7 5/16	4 1/8	8 7/16	4 21/32	9 19/32	5 7/32	10 23/32	5 25/32	11 7/8	6 11/32	1-1 1/32
7/16	3 19/32	7 3/8	4 5/32	8 1/2	4 11/16	9 21/32	5 1/4	10 13/16	5 13/16	11 15/16	6 3/8	1-1 3/32
1/2	3 5/8	7 7/16	4 3/16	8 19/32	4 3/4	9 23/32	5 9/32	10 7/8	5 27/32	1-0 1/32	6 13/32	1-1 5/32
9/16	3 21/32	7 1/2	4 7/32	8 21/32	4 25/32	9 13/16	5 11/32	10 15/16	5 7/8	1-0 3/32	6 7/16	1-1 1/4
5/8	3 11/16	7 19/32	4 1/4	8 23/32	4 13/16	9 7/8	5 3/8	11 1/32	5 29/32	1-0 5/32	6 15/16	1-1 5/16
11/16	3 23/32	7 21/32	4 9/32	8 13/16	4 27/32	9 15/16	5 13/32	11 3/32	5 31/32	1-0 1/4	6 1/2	1-1 3/8
3/4	3 3/4	7 23/32	4 5/16	8 7/8	4 7/8	10 1/32	5 7/16	11 5/32	6	1-0 5/16	6 9/16	1-1 7/16
13/16	3 25/32	7 13/16	4 11/32	8 15/16	4 29/32	10 3/32	5 15/32	11 7/32	6 1/32	1-0 3/8	6 19/32	1-1 17/32
7/8	3 27/32	7 7/8	4 3/8	9	4 15/16	10 5/32	5 1/2	11 5/16	6 1/16	1-0 7/16	6 5/8	1-1 19/32
15/16	3 7/8	7 15/16	4 7/16	9 3/32	4 31/32	10 7/32	5 17/32	11 3/8	6 3/32	1-0 17/32	6 21/32	1-1 21/32

Feet	0' Rise	0' Slope	10' Rise	10' Slope	20' Rise	20' Slope	30' Rise	30' Slope
0	0	0	5-6 7/8	11-5 3/8	11-1 3/4	22-10 3/4	16-8 5/8	34-4 1/8
1	6 11/16	1-1 3/4	6-1 9/16	12-7 1/8	11-8 7/16	24-0 1/2	17-3 5/16	35-5 7/8
2	1-1 3/8	2-3 15/32	6-8 1/4	13-8 27/32	12-3 1/8	25-2 1/2	17-10	36-7 19/32
3	1-8 1/16	3-5 7/32	7-2 15/16	14-10 19/32	12-9 13/16	26-3 31/32	18-4 11/16	37-9 11/32
4	2-2 3/4	4-6 15/16	7-9 5/8	16-0 5/16	13-4 1/2	27-5 23/32	18-11 3/8	38-11 3/32
5	2-9 7/16	5-8 11/16	8-4 5/16	17-2 1/16	13-11 3/16	28-7 7/16	19-6 1/16	40-0 13/16
6	3-4 1/8	6-10 7/16	8-11	18-3 13/16	14-5 7/8	29-9 3/16	20-0 3/4	41-2 9/16
7	3-10 13/16	8-0 5/32	9-5 11/16	19-5 17/32	15-0 9/16	30-10 29/32	20-7 7/16	42-4 9/32
8	4-5 1/2	9-1 29/32	10-0 3/8	20-7 9/32	15-7 1/4	32-0 21/32	21-2 1/8	43-6 1/32
9	5-0 3/16	10-3 5/8	10-7 1/16	21-9	16-1 15/16	33-2 13/32	21-8 13/16	44-7 25/32

A = 29° 07' 50''; logsin A = 9.68735; logcos A = 9.94127; logtan A = 9.74608; logcot A = 0.25392

Ins.	12″ Rise	12″ Slope	13″ Rise	13″ Slope	14″ Rise	14″ Slope	15″ Rise	15″ Slope	16″ Rise	16″ Slope
0	6 11/16	1-1 3/4	7 1/4	1-2 7/8	7 13/16	1-4 1/32	8 3/8	1-5 5/16	8 29/32	1-6 5/16
1/16	6 23/32	1-1 13/16	7 9/32	1-2 31/32	7 27/32	1-4 3/32	8 13/32	1-5 1/4	8 15/16	1-6 3/8
1/8	6 3/4	1-1 7/8	7 5/16	1-3 1/32	7 7/8	1-4 5/32	8 7/16	1-5 5/16	9	1-6 15/32
3/16	6 25/32	1-1 15/16	7 11/32	1-3 3/32	7 29/32	1-4 1/4	8 15/32	1-5 3/8	9 1/32	1-6 17/32
1/4	6 13/16	1-2 1/32	7 3/8	1-3 5/32	7 15/16	1-4 5/16	8 1/2	1-5 15/32	9 1/16	1-6 19/32
5/16	6 7/8	1-2 3/32	7 13/32	1-3 1/4	7 31/32	1-4 3/8	8 17/32	1-5 17/32	9 3/32	1-6 11/16
3/8	6 29/32	1-2 5/32	7 15/32	1-3 5/16	8	1-4 15/32	8 9/16	1-5 19/32	9 1/8	1-6 3/4
7/16	6 15/16	1-2 1/4	7 1/2	1-3 3/8	8 1/32	1-4 17/32	8 19/32	1-5 11/16	9 5/32	1-6 13/16
1/2	6 31/32	1-2 5/16	7 17/32	1-3 15/32	8 3/32	1-4 19/32	8 5/8	1-5 3/4	9 3/16	1-6 7/8
9/16	7	1-2 3/8	7 9/16	1-3 17/32	8 1/8	1-4 21/32	8 11/16	1-5 13/16	9 7/32	1-6 31/32
5/8	7 1/32	1-2 15/32	7 19/32	1-3 19/32	8 5/32	1-4 3/4	8 23/32	1-5 7/8	9 1/4	1-7 1/32
11/16	7 1/16	1-2 17/32	7 5/8	1-3 21/32	8 3/16	1-4 13/16	8 3/4	1-5 31/32	9 5/16	1-7 3/32
3/4	7 3/32	1-2 19/32	7 21/32	1-3 3/4	8 7/32	1-4 7/8	8 25/32	1-6 1/32	9 11/32	1-7 3/16
13/16	7 1/8	1-2 21/32	7 11/16	1-3 13/16	8 1/4	1-4 31/32	8 13/16	1-6 3/32	9 3/8	1-7 1/4
7/8	7 3/16	1-2 3/4	7 23/32	1-3 7/8	8 9/32	1-5 1/32	8 27/32	1-6 3/16	9 13/32	1-7 5/16
15/16	7 7/32	1-2 13/16	7 25/32	1-3 31/32	8 5/16	1-5 3/32	8 7/8	1-6 1/4	9 7/16	1-7 3/8

Ins.	17″ Rise	17″ Slope	18″ Rise	18″ Slope	19″ Rise	19″ Slope	20″ Rise	20″ Slope	21″ Rise	21″ Slope
0	9 15/32	1-7 5/32	10 1/32	1-8 19/32	10 19/32	1-9 3/4	11 5/32	1-10 29/32	11 11/16	2-0 1/32
1/16	9 1/2	1-7 17/32	10 1/16	1-8 11/16	10 5/8	1-9 13/16	11 3/16	1-10 31/32	11 3/4	2-0 1/8
1/8	9 17/32	1-7 19/32	10 3/32	1-8 3/4	10 21/32	1-9 29/32	11 7/32	1-11 1/32	11 25/32	2-0 3/16
3/16	9 19/32	1-7 11/16	10 1/8	1-8 13/16	10 11/16	1-9 31/32	11 1/4	1-11 1/8	11 13/32	2-0 1/4
1/4	9 5/8	1-7 3/4	10 5/32	1-8 29/32	10 23/32	1-10 1/32	11 9/32	1-11 3/16	11 27/32	2-0 5/16
5/16	9 21/32	1-7 13/16	10 7/32	1-8 31/32	10 3/4	1-10 3/32	11 5/16	1-11 1/4	11 7/8	2-0 13/32
3/8	9 11/16	1-7 29/32	10 1/4	1-9 1/32	10 13/16	1-10 3/16	11 11/32	1-11 5/16	11 29/32	2-0 15/32
7/16	9 23/32	1-7 31/32	10 9/32	1-9 3/32	10 27/32	1-10 1/4	11 3/8	1-11 13/32	11 15/16	2-0 17/32
1/2	9 3/4	1-8 1/32	10 5/16	1-9 3/16	10 7/8	1-10 5/16	11 7/16	1-11 15/32	11 31/32	2-0 5/8
9/16	9 25/32	1-8 3/32	10 11/32	1-9 1/4	10 29/32	1-10 13/32	11 15/32	1-11 17/32	1-0 1/32	2-0 11/16
5/8	9 13/16	1-8 3/16	10 3/8	1-9 5/16	10 15/16	1-10 15/32	11 1/2	1-11 5/8	1-0 1/16	2-0 3/4
11/16	9 27/32	1-8 1/4	10 13/32	1-9 13/32	10 31/32	1-10 17/32	11 17/32	1-11 11/16	1-0 3/32	2-0 13/16
3/4	9 29/32	1-8 5/16	10 7/16	1-9 15/32	11	1-10 5/8	11 9/16	1-11 3/4	1-0 1/8	2-0 29/32
13/16	9 15/16	1-8 13/32	10 15/32	1-9 17/32	11 1/32	1-10 11/16	11 19/32	1-11 13/16	1-0 5/32	2-0 31/32
7/8	9 31/32	1-8 15/32	10 17/32	1-9 19/32	11 1/16	1-10 3/4	11 5/8	1-11 29/32	1-0 3/16	2-1 1/32
15/16	10	1-8 17/32	10 9/16	1-9 11/16	11 1/8	1-10 13/16	11 21/32	1-11 31/32	1-0 7/32	2-1 1/8

Feet	40′ Rise	40′ Slope	50′ Rise	50′ Slope	60′ Rise	60′ Slope	70′ Rise	70′ Slope
0	22-3 1/2	45-9 1/2	27-10 3/8	57-2 7/8	33-5 1/4	68-8 1/4	39-0 1/8	80-1 5/8
1	22-10 3/16	46-11 1/4	28-5 1/16	58-4 5/8	33-11 15/16	69-10	39-6 13/16	81-3 3/8
2	23-4 7/8	48-0 31/32	28-11 3/4	59-6 11/16	34-6 5/8	70-11 23/32	40-1 1/2	82-5 1/8
3	23-11 9/16	49-2 23/32	29-6 7/16	60-8 3/32	35-1 5/16	72-1 15/32	40-8 3/16	83-6 27/32
4	24-6 1/4	50-4 15/32	30-1 3/8	61-9 27/32	35-8	73-3 1/32	41-2 7/8	84-8 19/32
5	25-0 15/16	51-6 3/16	30-7 13/16	62-11 9/16	36-2 11/16	74-4 15/16	41-9 9/16	85-10 5/16
6	25-7 5/8	52-7 15/16	31-2 1/2	64-1 5/16	36-9 3/8	75-6 11/16	42-4 1/4	87-0 1/16
7	26-2 5/16	53-9 21/32	31-9 3/16	65-3 1/32	37-4 1/16	76-8 13/32	42-10 15/16	88-1 13/16
8	26-9	54-11 13/32	32-3 7/8	66-4 25/32	37-10 3/4	77-10 5/32	43-5 5/8	89-3 17/32
9	27-3 11/16	56-1 5/32	32-10 9/16	67-6 17/32	38-5 7/16	78-11 29/32	44-0 5/16	90-5 9/32

natsin A=0.4868013508; natcos A=0.8735127044; nattan A=0.5572916666; natcot A=1.7943925233

Inches	0" Rise	0" Slope	1" Rise	1" Slope	2" Rise	2" Slope	3" Rise	3" Slope	4" Rise	4" Slope	5" Rise	5" Slope
0	0	0	9/16	1 5/32−	1 1/8	2 9/32	1 11/16	3 7/16	2 1/4	4 19/32−	2 13/16	5 3/4
1/16	1/32	1/16	19/32	1 7/32	1 5/32	2 3/8	1 23/32	3 1/2	2 9/32	4 21/32	2 27/32	5 13/16
1/8	1/16	5/32−	5/8	1 9/32	1 3/16	2 7/16	1 3/4	3 19/32−	2 5/16	4 23/32	2 7/8	5 7/8
3/16	3/32	7/32−	21/32	1 3/8	1 7/32	2 1/2	1 25/32	3 21/32	2 11/32	4 13/16	2 29/32	5 15/16
1/4	1/8	9/32	11/16	1 7/16	1 1/4	2 19/32−	1 13/16	3 23/32	2 3/8	4 7/8	2 15/16	6 1/32−
5/16	3/16	11/32	3/4	1 1/2	1 5/16	2 21/32−	1 7/8	3 13/16	2 7/16	4 15/16	3	6 3/32
3/8	7/32−	7/16	25/32−	1 9/16	1 11/32−	2 23/32	1 29/32−	3 7/8	2 15/32−	5 1/32−	3 1/32−	6 5/32
7/16	1/4	1/2	13/16	1 21/32−	1 3/8	2 25/32	1 15/16	3 15/16	2 1/2	5 3/32−	3 1/16	6 1/4
1/2	9/32	9/16	27/32	1 23/32	1 13/32	2 7/8	1 31/32	4 1/32−	2 17/32	5 5/32	3 3/32	6 5/16
9/16	5/16	21/32−	7/8	1 25/32	1 7/16	2 15/16	2	4 3/32−	2 9/16	5 1/4	3 1/8	6 3/8
5/8	11/32	23/32−	29/32	1 7/8	1 15/32	3	2 1/32	4 5/32	2 19/32	5 5/16	3 5/32	6 15/32−
11/16	3/8	25/32	15/16	1 15/16	1 1/2	3 3/32−	2 1/16	4 7/32	2 5/8	5 3/8	3 3/16	6 17/32−
3/4	7/16	7/8	1	2	1 9/16	3 5/32−	2 1/8	4 5/16	2 11/16	5 7/16	3 1/4	6 19/32
13/16	15/32−	15/16	1 1/32−	2 3/32−	1 19/32−	3 7/32	2 5/32−	4 3/8	2 23/32−	5 17/32−	3 9/32−	6 21/32
7/8	1/2	1	1 1/16	2 5/32−	1 5/8	3 5/16	2 3/16	4 7/16	2 3/4	5 19/32−	3 5/16	6 3/4
15/16	17/32−	1 1/16	1 3/32−	2 7/32	1 21/32−	3 3/8	2 7/32−	4 17/32−	2 25/32−	5 21/32	3 11/32−	6 13/16

Inches	6" Rise	6" Slope	7" Rise	7" Slope	8" Rise	8" Slope	9" Rise	9" Slope	10" Rise	10" Slope	11" Rise	11" Slope
0	3 3/8	6 7/8	3 15/16	8 1/32	4 1/2	9 3/16	5 1/16	10 5/16	5 5/8	11 15/32	6 3/16	1-0 5/8
1/16	3 13/32	6 31/32−	3 31/32	8 3/32	4 17/32	9 1/4	5 3/32	10 13/32−	5 21/32	11 17/32	6 7/32	1-0 11/16
1/8	3 7/16	7 1/32−	4	8 3/16	4 9/16	9 5/16	5 1/8	10 15/32	5 11/16	11 5/8	6 1/4	1-0 3/4
3/16	3 15/32	7 3/32	4 1/32	8 1/4	4 19/32	9 13/32−	5 5/32	10 17/32	5 23/32	11 11/16	6 9/32	1-0 27/32−
1/4	3 1/2	7 5/32	4 1/16	8 5/16	4 5/8	9 15/32−	5 3/16	10 5/8	5 3/4	11 3/4	6 5/16	1-0 29/32
5/16	3 9/16	7 1/4	4 1/8	8 3/8	4 11/16	9 17/32	5 1/4	10 11/16	5 13/16	11 27/32−	6 3/8	1-0 31/32
3/8	3 19/32−	7 5/16	4 5/32−	8 15/32−	4 23/32−	9 19/32	5 9/32−	10 3/4	5 27/32−	11 29/32−	6 13/32−	1-1 1/16
7/16	3 5/8	7 3/8	4 3/16	8 17/32	4 3/4	9 11/16	5 5/16	10 13/16	5 7/8	11 31/32	6 7/16	1-1 1/8
1/2	3 21/32	7 15/32−	4 7/32	8 19/32	4 25/32	9 3/4	5 11/32	10 29/32−	5 29/32	1-0 1/16	6 15/32	1-1 3/16
9/16	3 11/16	7 17/32−	4 1/4	8 11/16	4 13/16	9 13/16	5 3/8	10 31/32	5 15/16	1-0 1/8	6 1/2	1-1 9/32−
5/8	3 23/32	7 19/32	4 9/32	8 3/4	4 27/32	9 29/32−	5 13/32	11 1/32	5 31/32	1-0 3/16	6 17/32	1-1 11/32−
11/16	3 3/4	7 11/16	4 5/16	8 13/16	4 7/8	9 31/32−	5 7/16	11 1/8	6	1-0 1/4	6 9/16	1-1 13/32
3/4	3 13/16	7 3/4	4 3/8	8 29/32−	4 15/16	10 1/32	5 1/2	11 3/16	6 1/16	1-0 11/32−	6 5/8	1-1 15/32
13/16	3 27/32−	7 13/16	4 13/32−	8 31/32−	4 31/32−	10 1/8	5 17/32−	11 1/4	6 3/32−	1-0 13/32−	6 21/32−	1-1 9/16
7/8	3 7/8	7 7/8	4 7/16	9 1/32	5	10 3/16	5 9/16	11 11/32−	6 1/8	1-0 15/32	6 11/16	1-1 5/8
15/16	3 29/32−	7 31/32−	4 15/32−	9 3/32	5 1/32−	10 1/4	5 19/32−	11 13/32−	6 5/32−	1-0 9/16	6 23/32−	1-1 11/16

Feet	0' Rise	0' Slope	10' Rise	10' Slope	20' Rise	20' Slope	30' Rise	30' Slope
0	0	0	5-7 1/2	11-5 11/16	11-3	22-11 3/8	16-10 1/2	34-5 1/32
1	6 3/4	1-1 25/32−	6-2 1/4	12-7 7/16	11-9 3/4	24-1 1/8	17-5 1/4	35-6 13/16
2	1-1 1/2	2-3 17/32	6-9	13-9 7/32−	12-4 1/2	25-2 29/32−	18-0	36-8 19/32−
3	1-8 1/4	3-5 5/16	7-3 3/4	14-11	12-11 1/4	26-4 21/32	18-6 3/4	37-10 11/32
4	2-3	4-7 1/16	7-10 1/2	16-0 3/4	13-6	27-6 7/16	19-1 1/2	39-0 1/8
5	2-9 3/4	5-8 27/32−	8-5 1/4	17-2 17/32−	14-0 3/4	28-8 7/32−	19-8 1/4	40-1 7/8
6	3-4 1/2	6-10 19/32	9-0	18-4 9/32	14-7 1/2	29-9 31/32	20-3	41-3 21/32−
7	3-11 1/4	8-0 3/8	9-6 3/4	19-6 1/16	15-2 1/4	30-11 3/4	20-9 3/4	42-5 7/16
8	4-6	9-2 5/32−	10-1 1/2	20-7 13/16	15-9	32-1 1/2	21-4 1/2	43-7 3/16
9	5-0 3/4	10-3 29/32	10-8 1/4	21-9 19/32	16-3 3/4	33-3 9/32−	21-11 1/4	44-8 31/32−

A = 29° 21′ 28″; logsin A = 9.69043; logcos A = 9.94031; logtan A = 9.75012; logcot A = 0.24988

Ins.	12″ Rise	12″ Slope	13″ Rise	13″ Slope	14″ Rise	14″ Slope	15″ Rise	15″ Slope	16″ Rise	16″ Slope
0	$6\frac{3}{4}$	$1\text{-}1\frac{25}{32}$	$7\frac{5}{16}$	$1\text{-}2\frac{29}{32}$	$7\frac{7}{8}$	$1\text{-}4\frac{1}{16}$	$8\frac{7}{16}$	$1\text{-}5\frac{7}{32}$	9	$1\text{-}6\frac{11}{32}$
$\frac{1}{16}$	$6\frac{25}{32}$	$1\text{-}1\frac{27}{32}$	$7\frac{11}{32}$	$1\text{-}3$	$7\frac{29}{32}$	$1\text{-}4\frac{1}{8}$	$8\frac{15}{32}$	$1\text{-}5\frac{9}{32}$	$9\frac{1}{32}$	$1\text{-}6\frac{7}{16}$
$\frac{1}{8}$	$6\frac{13}{16}$	$1\text{-}1\frac{29}{32}$	$7\frac{3}{8}$	$1\text{-}3\frac{1}{16}$	$7\frac{15}{16}$	$1\text{-}4\frac{7}{32}$	$8\frac{1}{2}$	$1\text{-}5\frac{11}{32}$	$9\frac{1}{16}$	$1\text{-}6\frac{1}{2}$
$\frac{3}{16}$	$6\frac{27}{32}$	$1\text{-}1\frac{31}{32}$	$7\frac{13}{32}$	$1\text{-}3\frac{1}{8}$	$7\frac{31}{32}$	$1\text{-}4\frac{9}{32}$	$8\frac{17}{32}$	$1\text{-}5\frac{7}{16}$	$9\frac{3}{32}$	$1\text{-}6\frac{9}{16}$
$\frac{1}{4}$	$6\frac{7}{8}$	$1\text{-}2\frac{1}{16}$	$7\frac{7}{16}$	$1\text{-}3\frac{3}{16}$	8	$1\text{-}4\frac{11}{32}$	$8\frac{9}{16}$	$1\text{-}5\frac{1}{2}$	$9\frac{1}{8}$	$1\text{-}6\frac{21}{32}$
$\frac{5}{16}$	$6\frac{15}{16}$	$1\text{-}2\frac{1}{8}$	$7\frac{1}{2}$	$1\text{-}3\frac{9}{32}$	$8\frac{1}{16}$	$1\text{-}4\frac{13}{32}$	$8\frac{5}{8}$	$1\text{-}5\frac{9}{16}$	$9\frac{3}{16}$	$1\text{-}6\frac{23}{32}$
$\frac{3}{8}$	$6\frac{31}{32}$	$1\text{-}2\frac{3}{16}$	$7\frac{17}{32}$	$1\text{-}3\frac{11}{32}$	$8\frac{3}{32}$	$1\text{-}4\frac{1}{2}$	$8\frac{21}{32}$	$1\text{-}5\frac{5}{8}$	$9\frac{7}{32}$	$1\text{-}6\frac{25}{32}$
$\frac{7}{16}$	7	$1\text{-}2\frac{9}{32}$	$7\frac{9}{16}$	$1\text{-}3\frac{13}{32}$	$8\frac{1}{8}$	$1\text{-}4\frac{9}{16}$	$8\frac{11}{16}$	$1\text{-}5\frac{23}{32}$	$9\frac{1}{4}$	$1\text{-}6\frac{7}{8}$
$\frac{1}{2}$	$7\frac{1}{32}$	$1\text{-}2\frac{11}{32}$	$7\frac{19}{32}$	$1\text{-}3\frac{1}{2}$	$8\frac{5}{32}$	$1\text{-}4\frac{5}{8}$	$8\frac{23}{32}$	$1\text{-}5\frac{25}{32}$	$9\frac{9}{32}$	$1\text{-}6\frac{15}{16}$
$\frac{9}{16}$	$7\frac{1}{16}$	$1\text{-}2\frac{13}{32}$	$7\frac{5}{8}$	$1\text{-}3\frac{9}{16}$	$8\frac{3}{16}$	$1\text{-}4\frac{23}{32}$	$8\frac{3}{4}$	$1\text{-}5\frac{27}{32}$	$9\frac{5}{16}$	$1\text{-}7$
$\frac{5}{8}$	$7\frac{3}{32}$	$1\text{-}2\frac{1}{2}$	$7\frac{21}{32}$	$1\text{-}3\frac{5}{8}$	$8\frac{7}{32}$	$1\text{-}4\frac{25}{32}$	$8\frac{25}{32}$	$1\text{-}5\frac{15}{16}$	$9\frac{11}{32}$	$1\text{-}7\frac{1}{16}$
$\frac{11}{16}$	$7\frac{1}{8}$	$1\text{-}2\frac{9}{16}$	$7\frac{11}{16}$	$1\text{-}3\frac{23}{32}$	$8\frac{1}{4}$	$1\text{-}4\frac{27}{32}$	$8\frac{13}{16}$	$1\text{-}6$	$9\frac{3}{8}$	$1\text{-}7\frac{5}{32}$
$\frac{3}{4}$	$7\frac{5}{32}$	$1\text{-}2\frac{5}{8}$	$7\frac{3}{4}$	$1\text{-}3\frac{25}{32}$	$8\frac{5}{16}$	$1\text{-}4\frac{15}{16}$	$8\frac{7}{8}$	$1\text{-}6\frac{1}{16}$	$9\frac{7}{16}$	$1\text{-}7\frac{7}{32}$
$\frac{13}{16}$	$7\frac{3}{16}$	$1\text{-}2\frac{11}{16}$	$7\frac{25}{32}$	$1\text{-}3\frac{27}{32}$	$8\frac{11}{32}$	$1\text{-}5$	$8\frac{29}{32}$	$1\text{-}6\frac{5}{32}$	$9\frac{15}{32}$	$1\text{-}7\frac{9}{32}$
$\frac{7}{8}$	$7\frac{1}{4}$	$1\text{-}2\frac{25}{32}$	$7\frac{13}{16}$	$1\text{-}3\frac{29}{32}$	$8\frac{3}{8}$	$1\text{-}5\frac{1}{16}$	$8\frac{15}{16}$	$1\text{-}6\frac{7}{32}$	$9\frac{1}{2}$	$1\text{-}7\frac{3}{8}$
$\frac{15}{16}$	$7\frac{9}{32}$	$1\text{-}2\frac{27}{32}$	$7\frac{27}{32}$	$1\text{-}4$	$8\frac{13}{32}$	$1\text{-}5\frac{1}{8}$	$8\frac{31}{32}$	$1\text{-}6\frac{9}{32}$	$9\frac{17}{32}$	$1\text{-}7\frac{7}{16}$

Ins.	17″ Rise	17″ Slope	18″ Rise	18″ Slope	19″ Rise	19″ Slope	20″ Rise	20″ Slope	21″ Rise	21″ Slope
0	$9\frac{9}{16}$	$1\text{-}7\frac{1}{2}$	$10\frac{1}{8}$	$1\text{-}8\frac{21}{32}$	$10\frac{11}{16}$	$1\text{-}9\frac{13}{16}$	$11\frac{1}{4}$	$1\text{-}10\frac{15}{16}$	$11\frac{13}{16}$	$2\text{-}0\frac{3}{32}$
$\frac{1}{16}$	$9\frac{19}{32}$	$1\text{-}7\frac{9}{16}$	$10\frac{5}{32}$	$1\text{-}8\frac{23}{32}$	$10\frac{23}{32}$	$1\text{-}9\frac{7}{8}$	$11\frac{9}{32}$	$1\text{-}11\frac{1}{32}$	$11\frac{27}{32}$	$2\text{-}0\frac{5}{32}$
$\frac{1}{8}$	$9\frac{5}{8}$	$1\text{-}7\frac{21}{32}$	$10\frac{3}{16}$	$1\text{-}8\frac{25}{32}$	$10\frac{3}{4}$	$1\text{-}9\frac{15}{16}$	$11\frac{5}{16}$	$1\text{-}11\frac{3}{32}$	$11\frac{7}{8}$	$2\text{-}0\frac{1}{4}$
$\frac{3}{16}$	$9\frac{21}{32}$	$1\text{-}7\frac{23}{32}$	$10\frac{7}{32}$	$1\text{-}8\frac{7}{8}$	$10\frac{25}{32}$	$1\text{-}10$	$11\frac{11}{32}$	$1\text{-}11\frac{5}{32}$	$11\frac{29}{32}$	$2\text{-}0\frac{5}{16}$
$\frac{1}{4}$	$9\frac{11}{16}$	$1\text{-}7\frac{25}{32}$	$10\frac{1}{4}$	$1\text{-}8\frac{15}{16}$	$10\frac{13}{16}$	$1\text{-}10\frac{3}{32}$	$11\frac{3}{8}$	$1\text{-}11\frac{7}{32}$	$11\frac{15}{16}$	$2\text{-}0\frac{3}{8}$
$\frac{5}{16}$	$9\frac{3}{4}$	$1\text{-}7\frac{7}{8}$	$10\frac{5}{16}$	$1\text{-}9$	$10\frac{7}{8}$	$1\text{-}10\frac{5}{32}$	$11\frac{7}{16}$	$1\text{-}11\frac{15}{16}$	$1\text{-}0$	$2\text{-}0\frac{7}{16}$
$\frac{3}{8}$	$9\frac{25}{32}$	$1\text{-}7\frac{15}{16}$	$10\frac{11}{32}$	$1\text{-}9\frac{3}{32}$	$10\frac{29}{32}$	$1\text{-}10\frac{7}{32}$	$11\frac{15}{32}$	$1\text{-}11\frac{3}{8}$	$1\text{-}0\frac{1}{32}$	$2\text{-}0\frac{17}{32}$
$\frac{7}{16}$	$9\frac{13}{16}$	$1\text{-}8$	$10\frac{3}{8}$	$1\text{-}9\frac{5}{32}$	$10\frac{15}{16}$	$1\text{-}10\frac{5}{16}$	$11\frac{1}{2}$	$1\text{-}11\frac{7}{16}$	$1\text{-}0\frac{1}{16}$	$2\text{-}0\frac{19}{32}$
$\frac{1}{2}$	$9\frac{27}{32}$	$1\text{-}8\frac{3}{32}$	$10\frac{13}{32}$	$1\text{-}9\frac{7}{32}$	$10\frac{31}{32}$	$1\text{-}10\frac{3}{8}$	$11\frac{17}{32}$	$1\text{-}11\frac{17}{32}$	$1\text{-}0\frac{3}{32}$	$2\text{-}0\frac{21}{32}$
$\frac{9}{16}$	$9\frac{7}{8}$	$1\text{-}8\frac{5}{32}$	$10\frac{7}{16}$	$1\text{-}9\frac{5}{16}$	11	$1\text{-}10\frac{7}{16}$	$11\frac{9}{16}$	$1\text{-}11\frac{19}{32}$	$1\text{-}0\frac{1}{8}$	$2\text{-}0\frac{3}{4}$
$\frac{5}{8}$	$9\frac{29}{32}$	$1\text{-}8\frac{7}{32}$	$10\frac{15}{32}$	$1\text{-}9\frac{3}{8}$	$11\frac{1}{32}$	$1\text{-}10\frac{17}{32}$	$11\frac{19}{32}$	$1\text{-}11\frac{21}{32}$	$1\text{-}0\frac{5}{32}$	$2\text{-}0\frac{13}{16}$
$\frac{11}{16}$	$9\frac{15}{16}$	$1\text{-}8\frac{9}{32}$	$10\frac{1}{2}$	$1\text{-}9\frac{7}{16}$	$11\frac{1}{16}$	$1\text{-}10\frac{19}{32}$	$11\frac{5}{8}$	$1\text{-}11\frac{3}{4}$	$1\text{-}0\frac{3}{16}$	$2\text{-}0\frac{7}{8}$
$\frac{3}{4}$	10	$1\text{-}8\frac{3}{8}$	$10\frac{9}{16}$	$1\text{-}9\frac{1}{2}$	$11\frac{1}{8}$	$1\text{-}10\frac{21}{32}$	$11\frac{11}{16}$	$1\text{-}11\frac{13}{16}$	$1\text{-}0\frac{1}{4}$	$2\text{-}0\frac{31}{32}$
$\frac{13}{16}$	$10\frac{1}{32}$	$1\text{-}8\frac{7}{16}$	$10\frac{19}{32}$	$1\text{-}9\frac{19}{32}$	$11\frac{5}{32}$	$1\text{-}10\frac{23}{32}$	$11\frac{23}{32}$	$1\text{-}11\frac{7}{8}$	$1\text{-}0\frac{9}{32}$	$2\text{-}1\frac{1}{32}$
$\frac{7}{8}$	$10\frac{1}{16}$	$1\text{-}8\frac{1}{2}$	$10\frac{5}{8}$	$1\text{-}9\frac{21}{32}$	$11\frac{3}{16}$	$1\text{-}10\frac{13}{16}$	$11\frac{3}{4}$	$1\text{-}11\frac{15}{16}$	$1\text{-}0\frac{5}{16}$	$2\text{-}1\frac{3}{32}$
$\frac{15}{16}$	$10\frac{3}{32}$	$1\text{-}8\frac{19}{32}$	$10\frac{21}{32}$	$1\text{-}9\frac{23}{32}$	$11\frac{7}{32}$	$1\text{-}10\frac{7}{8}$	$11\frac{25}{32}$	$2\text{-}0\frac{1}{16}$	$1\text{-}0\frac{11}{32}$	$2\text{-}1\frac{5}{32}$

Feet	40′ Rise	40′ Slope	50′ Rise	50′ Slope	60′ Rise	60′ Slope	70′ Rise	70′ Slope
0	$22\text{-}6$	$45\text{-}10\frac{23}{32}$	$28\text{-}1\frac{1}{2}$	$57\text{-}4\frac{13}{32}$	$33\text{-}9$	$68\text{-}10\frac{3}{32}$	$39\text{-}4\frac{1}{2}$	$80\text{-}3\frac{25}{32}$
1	$23\text{-}0\frac{3}{4}$	$47\text{-}0\frac{1}{2}$	$28\text{-}8\frac{1}{4}$	$58\text{-}6\frac{3}{16}$	$34\text{-}3\frac{3}{4}$	$69\text{-}11\frac{27}{32}$	$39\text{-}11\frac{1}{4}$	$81\text{-}5\frac{17}{32}$
2	$23\text{-}7\frac{1}{2}$	$48\text{-}2\frac{1}{4}$	$29\text{-}3$	$59\text{-}7\frac{15}{16}$	$34\text{-}10\frac{1}{2}$	$71\text{-}1\frac{5}{8}$	$40\text{-}6$	$82\text{-}7\frac{5}{16}$
3	$24\text{-}2\frac{1}{4}$	$49\text{-}4\frac{1}{32}$	$29\text{-}9\frac{3}{4}$	$60\text{-}9\frac{23}{32}$	$35\text{-}5\frac{1}{4}$	$72\text{-}3\frac{13}{32}$	$41\text{-}0\frac{3}{4}$	$83\text{-}9\frac{1}{16}$
4	$24\text{-}9$	$50\text{-}5\frac{13}{16}$	$30\text{-}4\frac{1}{2}$	$61\text{-}11\frac{15}{32}$	$36\text{-}0$	$73\text{-}5\frac{5}{32}$	$41\text{-}7\frac{1}{2}$	$84\text{-}10\frac{27}{32}$
5	$25\text{-}3\frac{3}{4}$	$51\text{-}7\frac{9}{16}$	$30\text{-}11\frac{1}{4}$	$63\text{-}1\frac{1}{4}$	$36\text{-}6\frac{3}{4}$	$74\text{-}6\frac{15}{16}$	$42\text{-}2\frac{1}{4}$	$86\text{-}0\frac{5}{8}$
6	$25\text{-}10\frac{1}{2}$	$52\text{-}9\frac{11}{32}$	$31\text{-}6$	$64\text{-}3\frac{1}{32}$	$37\text{-}1\frac{1}{2}$	$75\text{-}8\frac{11}{16}$	$42\text{-}9$	$87\text{-}2\frac{3}{8}$
7	$26\text{-}5\frac{1}{4}$	$53\text{-}11\frac{3}{32}$	$32\text{-}0\frac{3}{4}$	$65\text{-}4\frac{25}{32}$	$37\text{-}8\frac{1}{4}$	$76\text{-}10\frac{15}{32}$	$43\text{-}3\frac{3}{4}$	$88\text{-}4\frac{5}{32}$
8	$27\text{-}0$	$55\text{-}0\frac{7}{8}$	$32\text{-}7\frac{1}{2}$	$66\text{-}6\frac{9}{16}$	$38\text{-}3$	$78\text{-}0\frac{1}{4}$	$43\text{-}10\frac{1}{2}$	$89\text{-}5\frac{29}{32}$
9	$27\text{-}6\frac{3}{4}$	$56\text{-}2\frac{5}{8}$	$33\text{-}2\frac{1}{4}$	$67\text{-}8\frac{5}{16}$	$38\text{-}9\frac{3}{4}$	$79\text{-}2$	$44\text{-}5\frac{1}{4}$	$90\text{-}7\frac{11}{16}$

natsin A=0.4902612395; natcos A=0.8715755370; nattan A=0.5625000000; natcot A=1.7777777777

Inches	0" Rise	0" Slope	1" Rise	1" Slope	2" Rise	2" Slope	3" Rise	3" Slope	4" Rise	4" Slope	5" Rise	5" Slope
0	0	0	9/16	1 5/32	1 1/8	2 5/16	1 11/16	3 7/16	2 9/32	4 19/32	2 27/32	5 3/4
1/16	1/32	1/16	19/32	1 7/32	1 5/32	2 3/8	1 3/4	3 17/32	2 5/16	4 21/32	2 7/8	5 13/16
1/8	1/16	5/32	5/8	1 9/32	1 7/32	2 7/16	1 25/32	3 19/32	2 11/32	4 3/4	2 29/32	5 29/32
3/16	3/32	7/32	11/16	1 3/8	1 1/4	2 1/2	1 13/16	3 21/32	2 3/8	4 13/16	2 15/16	5 31/32
1/4	5/32	9/32	23/32	1 7/16	1 9/32	2 19/32	1 27/32	3 3/4	2 13/32	4 7/8	2 31/32	6 1/32
5/16	3/16	11/32	3/4	1 1/2	1 5/16	2 21/32	1 7/8	3 13/16	2 7/16	4 31/32	3 1/32	6 3/32
3/8	7/32	7/16	25/32	1 19/32	1 11/32	2 23/32	1 29/32	3 7/8	2 15/32	5 1/32	3 1/16	6 3/16
7/16	1/4	1/2	13/16	1 21/32	1 3/8	2 13/16	1 15/16	3 15/16	2 17/32	5 3/32	3 3/32	6 1/4
1/2	9/32	9/16	27/32	1 23/32	1 13/32	2 7/8	2	4 1/32	2 9/16	5 3/16	3 1/8	6 5/16
9/16	5/16	21/32	7/8	1 25/32	1 15/32	2 15/16	2 1/32	4 3/32	2 19/32	5 1/4	3 5/32	6 13/32
5/8	11/32	23/32	15/16	1 7/8	1 1/2	3 1/32	2 1/16	4 3/16	2 5/8	5 5/16	3 3/16	6 15/32
11/16	3/8	25/32	31/32	1 15/16	1 17/32	3 3/32	2 3/32	4 1/4	2 21/32	5 3/8	3 7/32	6 17/32
3/4	7/16	7/8	1	2	1 9/16	3 5/32	2 1/8	4 5/16	2 11/16	5 15/32	3 1/4	6 5/8
13/16	15/32	15/16	1 1/32	2 3/32	1 19/32	3 7/32	2 5/32	4 3/8	2 23/32	5 17/32	3 5/16	6 11/16
7/8	1/2	1	1 1/16	2 5/32	1 5/8	3 5/16	2 3/16	4 15/32	2 25/32	5 19/32	3 11/32	6 3/4
15/16	17/32	1 1/16	1 3/32	2 7/32	1 21/32	3 3/8	2 1/4	4 17/32	2 13/16	5 11/16	3 3/8	6 13/16

Inches	6" Rise	6" Slope	7" Rise	7" Slope	8" Rise	8" Slope	9" Rise	9" Slope	10" Rise	10" Slope	11" Rise	11" Slope
0	3 13/32	6 29/32	3 31/32	8 1/16	4 17/32	9 3/16	5 1/8	10 11/32	5 11/16	11 1/2	6 1/4	1-0 21/32
1/16	3 7/16	6 31/32	4	8 1/8	4 9/16	9 9/32	5 5/32	10 13/32	5 23/32	11 9/16	6 9/32	1-0 23/32
1/8	3 15/32	7 1/32	4 1/32	8 3/16	4 19/32	9 11/32	5 3/16	10 1/2	5 3/4	11 21/32	6 5/16	1-0 25/32
3/16	3 1/2	7 1/8	4 3/32	8 1/4	4 21/32	9 13/32	5 7/32	10 9/16	5 25/32	11 23/32	6 11/32	1-0 7/8
1/4	3 9/16	7 3/16	4 1/8	8 11/32	4 11/16	9 1/2	5 1/4	10 5/8	5 13/16	11 25/32	6 3/8	1-0 15/16
5/16	3 19/32	7 1/4	4 5/32	8 13/32	4 23/32	9 9/16	5 9/32	10 23/32	5 27/32	11 27/32	6 7/16	1-1
3/8	3 5/8	7 11/32	4 3/16	8 15/32	4 3/4	9 5/8	5 5/16	10 25/32	5 7/8	11 15/16	6 15/32	1-1 1/16
7/16	3 21/32	7 13/32	4 7/32	8 9/16	4 25/32	9 11/16	5 11/32	10 27/32	5 15/16	1-0	6 1/2	1-1 5/32
1/2	3 11/16	7 15/32	4 1/4	8 5/8	4 13/16	9 25/32	5 13/32	10 15/16	5 31/32	1-0 1/16	6 17/32	1-1 7/32
9/16	3 23/32	7 17/32	4 5/16	8 11/16	4 27/32	9 27/32	5 7/16	11	6	1-0 5/32	6 9/16	1-1 9/32
5/8	3 3/4	7 5/8	4 11/32	8 25/32	4 7/8	9 29/32	5 15/32	11 1/16	6 1/32	1-0 7/32	6 19/32	1-1 3/8
11/16	3 25/32	7 11/16	4 3/8	8 27/32	4 15/16	10	5 1/2	11 1/8	6 1/16	1-0 9/32	6 5/8	1-1 7/16
3/4	3 27/32	7 3/4	4 13/32	8 29/32	4 31/32	10 1/16	5 17/32	11 7/32	6 3/32	1-0 3/8	6 21/32	1-1 1/2
13/16	3 7/8	7 27/32	4 7/16	8 31/32	5	10 1/8	5 9/16	11 9/32	6 1/8	1-0 7/16	6 23/32	1-1 19/32
7/8	3 29/32	7 29/32	4 15/32	9 1/32	5 1/32	10 7/32	5 19/32	11 11/32	6 5/32	1-0 1/2	6 3/4	1-1 21/32
15/16	3 15/16	7 31/32	4 1/2	9 1/8	5 1/16	10 9/32	5 21/32	11 7/16	6 3/16	1-0 9/16	6 25/32	1-1 23/32

Feet	0' Rise	0' Slope	10' Rise	10' Slope	20' Rise	20' Slope	30' Rise	30' Slope
0	0	0	5-8 1/8	11-6	11-4 1/4	22-11 31/32	17-0 3/8	34-5 31/32
1	6 13/16	1-1 13/16	6-2 15/16	12-7 25/32	11-11 1/16	24-1 25/32	17-7 3/16	35-7 25/32
2	1-1 5/8	2-3 19/32	6-9 3/4	13-9 19/32	12-5 7/8	25-3 9/16	18-2	36-9 9/16
3	1-8 7/16	3-5 13/32	7-4 9/16	14-11 3/8	13-0 11/16	26-5 3/8	18-8 13/16	37-11 11/32
4	2-3 1/4	4-7 3/16	7-11 3/8	16-1 3/16	13-7 1/2	27-7 3/16	19-3 5/8	39-1 5/32
5	2-10 1/16	5-9	8-6 3/16	17-2 31/32	14-2 5/16	28-8 31/32	19-10 7/16	40-2 31/32
6	3-4 7/8	6-10 25/32	9-1	18-4 25/32	14-9 1/8	29-10 25/32	20-5 1/4	41-4 3/4
7	3-11 11/16	8-0 19/32	9-7 13/16	19-6 9/16	15-3 15/16	31-0 9/16	21-0 1/16	42-6 9/16
8	4-6 1/2	9-2 13/32	10-2 5/8	20-8 3/8	15-10 3/4	32-2 3/8	21-6 7/8	43-8 11/32
9	5-1 5/16	10-4 3/16	10-9 7/16	21-10 3/16	16-5 9/16	33-4 5/32	22-1 11/16	44-10 5/32

A = 29° 35' 02"; logsin A = 9.69346; logcos A = 9.93934; logtan A = 9.75413; logcot A = 0.24587

ins.	12″ Rise	12″ Slope	13″ Rise	13″ Slope	14″ Rise	14″ Slope	15″ Rise	15″ Slope	16″ Rise	16″ Slope
0	6 13/16	1-1 13/16	7 3/8	1-2 15/32	7 15/16	1-4 3/32	8 1/2	1-5 1/4	9 3/32	1-6 13/32
1/16	6 27/32	1-1 7/8	7 13/32	1-3 1/32	7 31/32	1-4 5/32	8 9/16	1-5 5/16	9 1/8	1-6 15/32
1/8	6 7/8	1-1 15/16	7 7/16	1-3 3/32	8 1/32	1-4 1/4	8 19/32	1-5 13/32	9 5/32	1-6 17/32
3/16	6 29/32	1-2	7 1/2	1-3 5/32	8 1/16	1-4 5/16	8 5/8	1-5 15/32	9 3/16	1-6 5/8
1/4	6 31/32	1-2 3/32	7 17/32	1-3 1/4	8 3/32	1-4 3/8	8 21/32	1-5 17/32	9 7/32	1-6 11/16
5/16	7	1-2 5/32	7 9/16	1-3 5/16	8 1/8	1-4 15/32	8 11/16	1-5 19/32	9 1/4	1-6 3/4
3/8	7 1/32	1-2 7/32	7 19/32	1-3 3/8	8 5/32	1-4 17/32	8 23/32	1-5 11/16	9 9/32	1-6 27/32
7/16	7 1/16	1-2 5/32	7 5/8	1-3 7/16	8 3/16	1-4 19/32	8 3/4	1-5 3/4	9 11/32	1-6 29/32
1/2	7 3/32	1-2 3/8	7 21/32	1-3 17/32	8 7/32	1-4 11/16	8 13/16	1-5 13/16	9 3/8	1-6 31/32
9/16	7 1/8	1-2 7/16	7 11/16	1-3 19/32	8 9/32	1-4 3/4	8 27/32	1-5 29/32	9 13/32	1-7 1/32
5/8	7 5/32	1-2 17/32	7 3/4	1-3 21/32	8 5/16	1-4 13/16	8 7/8	1-5 31/32	9 7/16	1-7 1/8
11/16	7 3/16	1-2 19/32	7 25/32	1-3 3/4	8 11/32	1-4 7/8	8 29/32	1-6 1/32	9 15/32	1-7 3/16
3/4	7 1/4	1-2 21/32	7 13/16	1-3 13/16	8 3/8	1-4 31/32	8 15/16	1-6 1/8	9 1/2	1-7 1/4
13/16	7 9/32	1-2 23/32	7 27/32	1-3 7/8	8 13/32	1-5 1/32	8 31/32	1-6 3/16	9 17/32	1-7 11/32
7/8	7 5/16	1-2 13/16	7 7/8	1-3 31/32	8 7/16	1-5 3/32	9	1-6 1/4	9 19/32	1-7 13/32
15/16	7 11/32	1-2 7/8	7 29/32	1-4 1/32	8 15/32	1-5 5/32	9 1/16	1-6 5/16	9 5/8	1-7 15/32

ins.	17″ Rise	17″ Slope	18″ Rise	18″ Slope	19″ Rise	19″ Slope	20″ Rise	20″ Slope	21″ Rise	21″ Slope
0	9 21/32	1-7 9/32	10 7/32	1-8 11/32	10 25/32	1-9 27/32	11 11/32	1-11	11 15/32	2-0 5/32
1/16	9 11/16	1-7 5/8	10 1/4	1-8 25/32	10 13/16	1-9 29/32	11 3/8	1-11 1/16	11 31/32	2-0 7/32
1/8	9 23/32	1-7 11/16	10 9/32	1-8 27/32	10 27/32	1-10	11 7/16	1-11 5/32	1-0	2-0 9/32
3/16	9 3/4	1-7 3/4	10 5/16	1-8 29/32	10 29/32	1-10 1/16	11 15/32	1-11 7/32	1-0 1/32	2-0 3/8
1/4	9 25/32	1-7 27/32	10 3/8	1-9	10 15/16	1-10 1/8	11 1/2	1-11 9/32	1-0 1/16	2-0 7/16
5/16	9 27/32	1-7 29/32	10 13/32	1-9 1/16	10 31/32	1-10 1/4	11 17/32	1-11 11/32	1-0 3/32	2-0 1/2
3/8	9 7/8	1-7 31/32	10 7/16	1-9 1/8	11	1-10 9/32	11 9/16	1-11 13/32	1-0 1/8	2-0 19/32
7/16	9 29/32	1-8 1/32	10 15/32	1-9 3/16	11 1/32	1-10 11/32	11 19/32	1-11 1/2	1-0 5/32	2-0 21/32
1/2	9 15/16	1-8 1/8	10 1/2	1-9 9/32	11 1/16	1-10 7/16	11 5/8	1-11 9/16	1-0 7/32	2-0 23/32
9/16	9 31/32	1-8 3/16	10 17/32	1-9 11/32	11 3/32	1-10 1/2	11 11/16	1-11 21/32	1-0 1/4	2-0 25/32
5/8	10	1-8 9/32	10 9/16	1-9 13/32	11 5/32	1-10 9/16	11 23/32	1-11 23/32	1-0 9/32	2-0 7/8
11/16	10 1/32	1-8 11/32	10 19/32	1-9 1/2	11 3/16	1-10 5/8	11 3/4	1-11 25/32	1-0 5/16	2-0 15/16
3/4	10 1/16	1-8 13/32	10 21/32	1-9 9/16	11 7/32	1-10 23/32	11 25/32	1-11 7/8	1-0 11/32	2-1
13/16	10 1/8	1-8 15/32	10 11/16	1-9 5/8	11 1/4	1-10 25/32	11 13/16	1-11 15/16	1-0 3/8	2-1 3/32
7/8	10 5/32	1-8 9/16	10 23/32	1-9 23/32	11 9/32	1-10 27/32	11 27/32	2-0	1-0 13/32	2-1 5/32
15/16	10 3/16	1-8 5/8	10 3/4	1-9 25/32	11 5/16	1-10 15/16	11 7/8	2-0 1/16	1-0 15/32	2-1 7/32

Feet	40′ Rise	40′ Slope	50′ Rise	50′ Slope	60′ Rise	60′ Slope	70′ Rise	70′ Slope
0	22-8 1/2	45-11 31/32	28-4 5/8	57-5 15/16	34-0 3/4	68-11 15/16	39-8 7/8	80-5 15/16
1	23-3 5/16	47-1 3/4	28-11 7/16	58-7 3/4	34-7 5/8	70-1 23/32	40-3 11/16	81-7 25/32
2	23-10 1/8	48-3 9/16	29-6 1/4	59-9 17/32	35-2 3/8	71-3 17/32	40-10 1/2	82-9 17/32
3	24-4 15/16	49-5 11/32	30-1 1/16	60-11 11/32	35-9 3/16	72-5 11/32	41-5 5/16	83-11 3/16
4	24-11 3/4	50-7 5/32	30-7 7/8	62-1 5/32	36-4	73-7 1/8	42-0 1/8	85-1 1/8
5	25-6 9/16	51-8 15/16	31-2 11/16	63-2 15/16	36-10 13/16	74-8 15/16	42-6 15/16	86-2 29/32
6	26-1 3/8	52-10 3/4	31-9 1/2	64-4 3/4	37-5 5/8	75-10 23/32	43-1 3/4	87-4 23/32
7	26-8 3/16	54-0 9/16	32-4 5/16	65-6 17/32	38-0 7/16	77-0 17/32	43-8 9/16	88-6 17/32
8	27-3	55-2 11/32	32-11 1/8	66-8 11/32	38-7 1/4	78-2 5/16	44-3 3/8	89-8 5/16
9	27-9 13/16	56-4 5/32	33-5 15/16	67-10 1/8	39-2 1/16	79-4 1/8	44-10 3/16	90-10 1/8

natsin A=0.4936981053; natcos A=0.8696333599; nattan A=0.5677083333; natcot A=1.7614678899

Inches	0" Rise	0" Slope	1" Rise	1" Slope	2" Rise	2" Slope	3" Rise	3" Slope	4" Rise	4" Slope	5" Rise	5" Slope
0	0	0	9/16	1 5/32	1 5/32	2 5/16	1 23/32	3 15/32	2 9/32	4 5/8	2 7/8	5 3/4
1/16	1/32	1/16	19/32	1 7/32	1 3/16	2 3/8	1 3/4	3 17/32	2 5/16	4 11/16	2 29/32	5 27/32
1/8	1/16	5/32	21/32	1 9/32	1 7/32	2 7/16	1 25/32	3 19/32	2 3/8	4 3/4	2 15/16	5 29/32
3/16	3/32	7/32	11/16	1 3/8	1 1/4	2 17/32	1 13/16	3 11/16	2 13/32	4 13/16	2 31/32	5 31/32
1/4	5/32	9/32	23/32	1 7/16	1 9/32	2 19/32	1 7/8	3 3/4	2 7/16	4 29/32	3	6 1/16
5/16	3/16	3/8	3/4	1 1/2	1 5/16	2 21/32	1 29/32	3 13/16	2 15/32	4 31/32	3 1/8	6 1/8
3/8	7/32	7/16	25/32	1 19/32	1 3/8	2 3/4	1 15/16	3 7/8	2 1/2	5 1/32	3 3/32	6 3/16
7/16	1/4	1/2	13/16	1 21/32	1 13/32	2 13/16	1 31/32	3 31/32	2 17/32	5 1/8	3 1/8	6 9/32
1/2	9/32	9/16	7/8	1 23/32	1 7/16	2 7/8	2	4 1/32	2 9/16	5 3/16	3 5/32	6 11/32
9/16	5/16	21/32	29/32	1 13/16	1 15/32	2 31/32	2 1/32	4 3/32	2 5/8	5 1/4	3 3/16	6 13/32
5/8	11/32	23/32	15/16	1 7/8	1 1/2	3 1/32	2 1/16	4 3/16	2 21/32	5 11/32	3 7/32	6 15/32
11/16	13/32	25/32	31/32	1 15/16	1 17/32	3 3/32	2 1/8	4 1/4	2 11/16	5 13/32	3 1/4	6 9/16
3/4	7/16	7/8	1	2 1/32	1 9/16	3 5/32	2 5/32	4 5/16	2 23/32	5 15/32	3 9/32	6 5/8
13/16	15/32	15/16	1 1/32	2 3/32	1 5/8	3 1/4	2 3/16	4 13/32	2 3/4	5 17/32	3 11/32	6 11/16
7/8	1/2	1	1 1/16	2 5/32	1 21/32	3 5/32	2 7/32	4 15/32	2 25/32	5 5/8	3 3/8	6 25/32
15/16	17/32	1 3/32	1 1/8	2 7/32	1 11/16	3 3/8	2 1/4	4 17/32	2 27/32	5 11/16	3 13/32	6 27/32

Inches	6" Rise	6" Slope	7" Rise	7" Slope	8" Rise	8" Slope	9" Rise	9" Slope	10" Rise	10" Slope	11" Rise	11" Slope
0	3 7/16	6 29/32	4	8 1/16	4 19/32	9 7/32	5 5/32	10 3/8	5 23/32	11 17/32	6 5/16	1-0 11/16
1/16	3 15/32	7	4 1/32	8 1/8	4 5/8	9 9/32	5 3/16	10 7/16	5 3/4	11 19/32	6 11/32	1-0 3/4
1/8	3 1/2	7 1/16	4 3/32	8 7/32	4 21/32	9 3/8	5 7/32	10 17/32	5 13/16	11 21/32	6 3/8	1-0 13/16
3/16	3 17/32	7 1/8	4 1/8	8 9/32	4 11/16	9 7/16	5 1/4	10 19/32	5 27/32	11 3/4	6 13/32	1-0 29/32
1/4	3 19/32	7 3/16	4 5/32	8 11/32	4 23/32	9 1/2	5 5/16	10 21/32	5 7/8	11 13/16	6 7/16	1-0 31/32
5/16	3 5/8	7 9/32	4 3/16	8 7/16	4 3/4	9 19/32	5 11/32	10 23/32	5 29/32	11 7/8	6 15/32	1-1 1/32
3/8	3 21/32	7 11/32	4 7/32	8 1/2	4 13/16	9 21/32	5 3/8	10 13/16	5 15/16	11 31/32	6 17/32	1-1 1/8
7/16	3 11/16	7 13/32	4 1/4	8 9/16	4 27/32	9 23/32	5 13/32	10 7/8	5 31/32	1-0 1/32	6 9/16	1-1 3/16
1/2	3 23/32	7 1/2	4 5/16	8 21/32	4 7/8	9 25/32	5 7/16	10 15/16	6	1-0 3/32	6 19/32	1-1 1/4
9/16	3 3/4	7 9/16	4 11/32	8 23/32	4 29/32	9 7/8	5 15/32	11 1/32	6 1/16	1-0 3/16	6 5/8	1-1 5/16
5/8	3 25/32	7 5/8	4 3/8	8 25/32	4 15/16	9 15/16	5 1/2	11 3/32	6 3/32	1-0 1/4	6 21/32	1-1 3/8
11/16	3 27/32	7 23/32	4 13/32	8 7/8	4 31/32	10	5 9/16	11 5/32	6 1/8	1-0 5/16	6 11/16	1-1 15/32
3/4	3 7/8	7 25/32	4 7/16	8 15/16	5	10 3/32	5 19/32	11 1/4	6 5/32	1-0 3/8	6 23/32	1-1 17/32
13/16	3 29/32	7 27/32	4 15/32	9	5 1/16	10 5/32	5 5/8	11 5/16	6 3/16	1-0 15/32	6 25/32	1-1 5/8
7/8	3 15/16	7 29/32	4 1/2	9 1/16	5 3/32	10 7/32	5 21/32	11 3/8	6 7/32	1-0 17/32	6 13/16	1-1 11/16
15/16	3 31/32	8	4 9/16	9 5/32	5 1/8	10 5/16	5 11/16	11 17/32	6 9/32	1-0 19/32	6 27/32	1-1 3/4

Feet	0' Rise	0' Slope	10' Rise	10' Slope	20' Rise	20' Slope	30' Rise	30' Slope
0	0	0	5-8 3/4	11-6 5/16	11-5 1/2	23-0 19/32	17-2 1/4	34-6 29/32
1	6 7/8	1-1 27/32	6-3 5/8	12-8 1/8	12-0 3/8	24-2 7/16	17-9 1/8	35-8 23/32
2	1-1 3/4	2-3 21/32	6-10 1/2	13-9 31/32	12-7 1/4	25-4 1/4	18-4	36-10 9/16
3	1-8 5/8	3-5 1/2	7-5 3/8	14-11 25/32	13-2 1/8	26-6 3/32	18-10 7/8	38-0 3/8
4	2-3 1/2	4-7 5/16	8-0 1/4	16-1 5/8	13-9	27-7 29/32	19-5 3/4	39-2 7/32
5	2-10 3/8	5-9 5/32	8-7 1/8	17-3 7/16	14-3 7/8	28-9 3/4	20-0 5/8	40-4 1/4
6	3-5 1/4	6-10 31/32	9-2	18-5 5/32	14-10 3/4	29-11 9/16	20-7 1/2	41-5 7/8
7	4-0 1/8	8-0 13/16	9-8 7/8	19-7 3/32	15-5 5/8	31-1 13/32	21-2 3/8	42-7 23/32
8	4-7	9-2 5/8	10-3 3/4	20-8 15/16	16-0 1/2	32-3 1/4	21-9 1/4	43-9 17/32
9	5-1 7/8	10-4 15/32	10-10 5/8	21-10 25/32	16-7 3/8	33-5 1/16	22-4 1/8	44-11 3/8

A = 29° 48′ 33″; logsin A = 9.69645; logcos A = 9.93836; logtan A = 9.75809; logcot A = 0.24191

In.	12″ Rise	Slope	13″ Rise	Slope	14″ Rise	Slope	15″ Rise	Slope	16″ Rise	Slope
0	$6\frac{7}{8}$	$1\text{-}1\frac{27}{32}$	$7\frac{1}{16}$	$1\text{-}2\frac{31}{32}$	$8\frac{1}{32}$	$1\text{-}4\frac{1}{8}$	$8\frac{19}{32}$	$1\text{-}5\frac{9}{32}$	$9\frac{5}{32}$	$1\text{-}6\frac{7}{16}$
$\frac{1}{16}$	$6\frac{29}{32}$	$1\text{-}1\frac{29}{32}$	$7\frac{15}{32}$	$1\text{-}3\frac{1}{16}$	$8\frac{1}{16}$	$1\text{-}4\frac{7}{32}$	$8\frac{5}{8}$	$1\text{-}5\frac{3}{8}$	$9\frac{3}{16}$	$1\text{-}6\frac{1}{2}$
$\frac{1}{8}$	$6\frac{15}{16}$	$1\text{-}1\frac{31}{32}$	$7\frac{17}{32}$	$1\text{-}3\frac{1}{8}$	$8\frac{3}{32}$	$1\text{-}4\frac{9}{32}$	$8\frac{21}{32}$	$1\text{-}5\frac{7}{16}$	$9\frac{1}{4}$	$1\text{-}6\frac{19}{32}$
$\frac{3}{16}$	$6\frac{31}{32}$	$1\text{-}2\frac{1}{32}$	$7\frac{9}{16}$	$1\text{-}3\frac{3}{16}$	$8\frac{1}{8}$	$1\text{-}4\frac{11}{32}$	$8\frac{11}{16}$	$1\text{-}5\frac{1}{2}$	$9\frac{9}{32}$	$1\text{-}6\frac{21}{32}$
$\frac{1}{4}$	$7\frac{1}{32}$	$1\text{-}2\frac{1}{8}$	$7\frac{19}{32}$	$1\text{-}3\frac{9}{32}$	$8\frac{5}{32}$	$1\text{-}4\frac{7}{16}$	$8\frac{3}{4}$	$1\text{-}5\frac{9}{16}$	$9\frac{5}{16}$	$1\text{-}6\frac{23}{32}$
$\frac{5}{16}$	$7\frac{1}{16}$	$1\text{-}2\frac{3}{16}$	$7\frac{5}{8}$	$1\text{-}3\frac{11}{32}$	$8\frac{3}{16}$	$1\text{-}4\frac{1}{2}$	$8\frac{25}{32}$	$1\text{-}5\frac{21}{32}$	$9\frac{11}{32}$	$1\text{-}6\frac{13}{16}$
$\frac{3}{8}$	$7\frac{3}{32}$	$1\text{-}2\frac{1}{4}$	$7\frac{21}{32}$	$1\text{-}3\frac{13}{32}$	$8\frac{1}{4}$	$1\text{-}4\frac{9}{16}$	$8\frac{13}{16}$	$1\text{-}5\frac{23}{32}$	$9\frac{3}{8}$	$1\text{-}6\frac{7}{8}$
$\frac{7}{16}$	$7\frac{1}{8}$	$1\text{-}2\frac{11}{32}$	$7\frac{11}{16}$	$1\text{-}3\frac{1}{2}$	$8\frac{9}{32}$	$1\text{-}4\frac{5}{8}$	$8\frac{27}{32}$	$1\text{-}5\frac{25}{32}$	$9\frac{13}{32}$	$1\text{-}6\frac{15}{16}$
$\frac{1}{2}$	$7\frac{5}{32}$	$1\text{-}2\frac{13}{32}$	$7\frac{3}{4}$	$1\text{-}3\frac{9}{16}$	$8\frac{5}{16}$	$1\text{-}4\frac{23}{32}$	$8\frac{7}{8}$	$1\text{-}5\frac{7}{8}$	$9\frac{7}{16}$	$1\text{-}7\frac{1}{2}$
$\frac{9}{16}$	$7\frac{3}{16}$	$1\text{-}2\frac{15}{32}$	$7\frac{25}{32}$	$1\text{-}3\frac{5}{8}$	$8\frac{11}{32}$	$1\text{-}4\frac{25}{32}$	$8\frac{29}{32}$	$1\text{-}5\frac{15}{16}$	$9\frac{1}{2}$	$1\text{-}7\frac{3}{32}$
$\frac{5}{8}$	$7\frac{7}{32}$	$1\text{-}2\frac{9}{16}$	$7\frac{13}{16}$	$1\text{-}3\frac{11}{16}$	$8\frac{3}{8}$	$1\text{-}4\frac{27}{32}$	$8\frac{15}{16}$	$1\text{-}6$	$9\frac{17}{32}$	$1\text{-}7\frac{5}{32}$
$\frac{11}{16}$	$7\frac{9}{32}$	$1\text{-}2\frac{5}{8}$	$7\frac{27}{32}$	$1\text{-}3\frac{25}{32}$	$8\frac{13}{32}$	$1\text{-}4\frac{15}{16}$	9	$1\text{-}6\frac{3}{32}$	$9\frac{9}{16}$	$1\text{-}7\frac{7}{32}$
$\frac{3}{4}$	$7\frac{5}{16}$	$1\text{-}2\frac{11}{16}$	$7\frac{7}{8}$	$1\text{-}3\frac{27}{32}$	$8\frac{7}{16}$	$1\text{-}5$	$9\frac{1}{32}$	$1\text{-}6\frac{5}{32}$	$9\frac{19}{32}$	$1\text{-}7\frac{5}{16}$
$\frac{13}{16}$	$7\frac{11}{32}$	$1\text{-}2\frac{25}{32}$	$7\frac{29}{32}$	$1\text{-}3\frac{29}{32}$	$8\frac{1}{2}$	$1\text{-}5\frac{1}{16}$	$9\frac{1}{16}$	$1\text{-}6\frac{7}{32}$	$9\frac{5}{8}$	$1\text{-}7\frac{3}{8}$
$\frac{7}{8}$	$7\frac{3}{8}$	$1\text{-}2\frac{27}{32}$	$7\frac{15}{16}$	$1\text{-}4$	$8\frac{17}{32}$	$1\text{-}5\frac{5}{32}$	$9\frac{3}{32}$	$1\text{-}6\frac{9}{32}$	$9\frac{21}{32}$	$1\text{-}7\frac{7}{16}$
$\frac{15}{16}$	$7\frac{13}{32}$	$1\text{-}2\frac{29}{32}$	8	$1\text{-}4\frac{1}{16}$	$8\frac{9}{16}$	$1\text{-}5\frac{7}{32}$	$9\frac{1}{8}$	$1\text{-}6\frac{3}{8}$	$9\frac{23}{32}$	$1\text{-}7\frac{17}{32}$

In.	17″ Rise	Slope	18″ Rise	Slope	19″ Rise	Slope	20″ Rise	Slope	21″ Rise	Slope
0	$9\frac{3}{4}$	$1\text{-}7\frac{19}{32}$	$10\frac{5}{16}$	$1\text{-}8\frac{3}{4}$	$10\frac{7}{8}$	$1\text{-}9\frac{29}{32}$	$11\frac{15}{32}$	$1\text{-}11\frac{1}{16}$	$1\text{-}0\frac{1}{2}$	$2\text{-}0\frac{3}{16}$
$\frac{1}{16}$	$9\frac{25}{32}$	$1\text{-}7\frac{21}{32}$	$10\frac{11}{32}$	$1\text{-}8\frac{13}{16}$	$10\frac{29}{32}$	$1\text{-}9\frac{31}{32}$	$11\frac{1}{2}$	$1\text{-}11\frac{1}{8}$	$1\text{-}0\frac{1}{2}$	$2\text{-}0\frac{9}{32}$
$\frac{1}{8}$	$9\frac{13}{16}$	$1\text{-}7\frac{3}{4}$	$10\frac{3}{8}$	$1\text{-}8\frac{7}{8}$	$10\frac{31}{32}$	$1\text{-}10\frac{1}{32}$	$11\frac{17}{32}$	$1\text{-}11\frac{3}{16}$	$1\text{-}0\frac{3}{32}$	$2\text{-}0\frac{11}{32}$
$\frac{3}{16}$	$9\frac{27}{32}$	$1\text{-}7\frac{13}{16}$	$10\frac{13}{32}$	$1\text{-}8\frac{31}{32}$	11	$1\text{-}10\frac{1}{8}$	$11\frac{9}{16}$	$1\text{-}11\frac{9}{32}$	$1\text{-}0\frac{1}{8}$	$2\text{-}0\frac{13}{32}$
$\frac{1}{4}$	$9\frac{7}{8}$	$1\text{-}7\frac{7}{8}$	$10\frac{15}{32}$	$1\text{-}9\frac{1}{32}$	$11\frac{1}{32}$	$1\text{-}10\frac{3}{16}$	$11\frac{19}{32}$	$1\text{-}11\frac{11}{32}$	$1\text{-}0\frac{3}{16}$	$2\text{-}0\frac{1}{2}$
$\frac{5}{16}$	$9\frac{29}{32}$	$1\text{-}7\frac{15}{16}$	$10\frac{1}{2}$	$1\text{-}9\frac{3}{32}$	$11\frac{1}{16}$	$1\text{-}10\frac{1}{4}$	$11\frac{5}{8}$	$1\text{-}11\frac{13}{32}$	$1\text{-}0\frac{7}{32}$	$2\text{-}0\frac{9}{16}$
$\frac{3}{8}$	$9\frac{31}{32}$	$1\text{-}8\frac{1}{32}$	$10\frac{17}{32}$	$1\text{-}9\frac{3}{16}$	$11\frac{3}{32}$	$1\text{-}10\frac{11}{32}$	$11\frac{11}{16}$	$1\text{-}11\frac{15}{32}$	$1\text{-}0\frac{1}{4}$	$2\text{-}0\frac{5}{8}$
$\frac{7}{16}$	10	$1\text{-}8\frac{3}{32}$	$10\frac{9}{16}$	$1\text{-}9\frac{1}{4}$	$11\frac{1}{8}$	$1\text{-}10\frac{13}{32}$	$11\frac{27}{32}$	$1\text{-}11\frac{9}{16}$	$1\text{-}0\frac{9}{32}$	$2\text{-}0\frac{23}{32}$
$\frac{1}{2}$	$10\frac{1}{32}$	$1\text{-}8\frac{5}{32}$	$10\frac{19}{32}$	$1\text{-}9\frac{5}{16}$	$11\frac{3}{16}$	$1\text{-}10\frac{15}{32}$	$11\frac{3}{4}$	$1\text{-}11\frac{5}{8}$	$1\text{-}0\frac{5}{16}$	$2\text{-}0\frac{25}{32}$
$\frac{9}{16}$	$10\frac{1}{16}$	$1\text{-}8\frac{1}{4}$	$10\frac{5}{8}$	$1\text{-}9\frac{13}{32}$	$11\frac{7}{32}$	$1\text{-}10\frac{17}{32}$	$11\frac{25}{32}$	$1\text{-}11\frac{11}{16}$	$1\text{-}0\frac{11}{32}$	$2\text{-}0\frac{27}{32}$
$\frac{5}{8}$	$10\frac{3}{32}$	$1\text{-}8\frac{5}{16}$	$10\frac{21}{32}$	$1\text{-}9\frac{15}{32}$	$11\frac{1}{4}$	$1\text{-}10\frac{5}{8}$	$11\frac{13}{16}$	$1\text{-}11\frac{25}{32}$	$1\text{-}0\frac{3}{8}$	$2\text{-}0\frac{15}{16}$
$\frac{11}{16}$	$10\frac{1}{8}$	$1\text{-}8\frac{3}{8}$	$10\frac{23}{32}$	$1\text{-}9\frac{17}{32}$	$11\frac{9}{32}$	$1\text{-}10\frac{11}{16}$	$11\frac{27}{32}$	$1\text{-}11\frac{27}{32}$	$1\text{-}0\frac{7}{16}$	$2\text{-}1$
$\frac{3}{4}$	$10\frac{5}{32}$	$1\text{-}8\frac{15}{32}$	$10\frac{3}{4}$	$1\text{-}9\frac{19}{32}$	$11\frac{5}{16}$	$1\text{-}10\frac{3}{4}$	$11\frac{7}{8}$	$1\text{-}11\frac{29}{32}$	$1\text{-}0\frac{15}{32}$	$2\text{-}1\frac{1}{16}$
$\frac{13}{16}$	$10\frac{7}{32}$	$1\text{-}8\frac{17}{32}$	$10\frac{25}{32}$	$1\text{-}9\frac{11}{16}$	$11\frac{11}{32}$	$1\text{-}10\frac{27}{32}$	$11\frac{15}{16}$	$2\text{-}0$	$1\text{-}0\frac{1}{2}$	$2\text{-}1\frac{1}{8}$
$\frac{7}{8}$	$10\frac{1}{4}$	$1\text{-}8\frac{19}{32}$	$10\frac{13}{16}$	$1\text{-}9\frac{3}{4}$	$11\frac{3}{8}$	$1\text{-}10\frac{29}{32}$	$11\frac{31}{32}$	$2\text{-}0\frac{1}{8}$	$1\text{-}0\frac{17}{32}$	$2\text{-}1\frac{7}{32}$
$\frac{15}{16}$	$10\frac{9}{32}$	$1\text{-}8\frac{11}{16}$	$10\frac{27}{32}$	$1\text{-}9\frac{13}{16}$	$11\frac{7}{16}$	$1\text{-}10\frac{31}{32}$	$1\text{-}0$	$2\text{-}0\frac{1}{8}$	$1\text{-}0\frac{9}{16}$	$2\text{-}1\frac{9}{32}$

Feet	40′ Rise	Slope	50′ Rise	Slope	60′ Rise	Slope	70′ Rise	Slope
0	$22\text{-}11$	$46\text{-}1\frac{3}{16}$	$28\text{-}7\frac{3}{4}$	$57\text{-}7\frac{1}{2}$	$34\text{-}4\frac{1}{2}$	$69\text{-}1\frac{25}{32}$	$40\text{-}1\frac{1}{4}$	$80\text{-}8\frac{3}{32}$
1	$23\text{-}5\frac{7}{8}$	$47\text{-}3\frac{1}{32}$	$29\text{-}2\frac{5}{8}$	$58\text{-}9\frac{5}{16}$	$34\text{-}11\frac{3}{8}$	$70\text{-}3\frac{5}{8}$	$40\text{-}8\frac{1}{8}$	$81\text{-}9\frac{29}{32}$
2	$24\text{-}0\frac{3}{4}$	$48\text{-}4\frac{27}{32}$	$29\text{-}9\frac{1}{2}$	$59\text{-}11\frac{15}{32}$	$35\text{-}6\frac{1}{4}$	$71\text{-}5\frac{7}{16}$	$41\text{-}3$	$82\text{-}11\frac{3}{4}$
3	$24\text{-}7\frac{5}{8}$	$49\text{-}6\frac{11}{16}$	$30\text{-}4\frac{3}{8}$	$61\text{-}0\frac{31}{32}$	$36\text{-}1\frac{1}{8}$	$72\text{-}7\frac{3}{8}$	$41\text{-}9\frac{7}{8}$	$84\text{-}1\frac{19}{32}$
4	$25\text{-}2\frac{1}{2}$	$50\text{-}8\frac{1}{2}$	$30\text{-}11\frac{1}{4}$	$62\text{-}2\frac{13}{16}$	$36\text{-}8$	$73\text{-}9\frac{1}{8}$	$42\text{-}4\frac{3}{4}$	$85\text{-}3\frac{13}{32}$
5	$25\text{-}9\frac{3}{8}$	$51\text{-}10\frac{11}{32}$	$31\text{-}6\frac{1}{8}$	$63\text{-}4\frac{21}{32}$	$37\text{-}2\frac{7}{8}$	$74\text{-}10\frac{15}{16}$	$42\text{-}11\frac{5}{8}$	$86\text{-}5\frac{1}{4}$
6	$26\text{-}4\frac{1}{4}$	$53\text{-}0\frac{3}{16}$	$32\text{-}1$	$64\text{-}6\frac{15}{32}$	$37\text{-}9\frac{3}{4}$	$76\text{-}0\frac{25}{32}$	$43\text{-}6\frac{1}{2}$	$87\text{-}7\frac{1}{16}$
7	$26\text{-}11\frac{1}{8}$	$54\text{-}2$	$32\text{-}7\frac{7}{8}$	$65\text{-}8\frac{5}{16}$	$38\text{-}4\frac{5}{8}$	$77\text{-}2\frac{19}{32}$	$44\text{-}1\frac{3}{8}$	$88\text{-}8\frac{29}{32}$
8	$27\text{-}6$	$55\text{-}3\frac{27}{32}$	$33\text{-}2\frac{3}{4}$	$66\text{-}10\frac{1}{8}$	$38\text{-}11\frac{1}{2}$	$78\text{-}4\frac{7}{16}$	$44\text{-}8\frac{1}{4}$	$89\text{-}10\frac{23}{32}$
9	$28\text{-}0\frac{7}{8}$	$56\text{-}5\frac{21}{32}$	$33\text{-}9\frac{5}{8}$	$67\text{-}11\frac{31}{32}$	$39\text{-}6\frac{3}{8}$	$79\text{-}6\frac{1}{4}$	$45\text{-}3\frac{1}{8}$	$91\text{-}0\frac{9}{16}$

natsin A=0.4971119928; natcos A=0.8676863873; nattan A=0.5729166666; natcot A=1.7454545454

Inches	0″ Rise	0″ Slope	1″ Rise	1″ Slope	2″ Rise	2″ Slope	3″ Rise	3″ Slope	4″ Rise	4″ Slope	5″ Rise	5″ Slope
0	0	0	9/16	1 5/32	1 5/32	2 5/16	1 23/32	3 15/32	2 5/16	4 5/8	2 7/8	5 25/32
1/16	1/32	1/16	5/8	1 7/32	1 3/16	2 3/8	1 25/32	3 17/32	2 11/32	4 11/16	2 15/16	5 27/32
1/8	1/16	5/32	21/32	1 5/16	1 7/32	2 15/32	1 13/16	3 5/8	2 3/8	4 3/4	2 31/32	5 29/32
3/16	3/32	7/32	11/16	1 3/8	1 1/4	2 17/32	1 27/32	3 11/16	2 13/32	4 27/32	3	6
1/4	5/32	9/32	23/32	1 7/16	1 5/16	2 19/32	1 7/8	3 3/4	2 15/32	4 29/32	3 1/32	6 1/16
5/16	3/16	3/8	3/4	1 17/32	1 11/32	2 21/32	1 29/32	3 13/16	2 1/2	4 31/32	3 1/16	6 1/8
3/8	7/32	7/16	25/32	1 19/32	1 3/8	2 3/4	1 15/16	3 29/32	2 17/32	5 1/16	3 3/32	6 7/32
7/16	1/4	1/2	27/32	1 21/32	1 13/32	2 13/16	2	3 31/32	2 9/16	5 1/8	3 5/32	6 9/32
1/2	9/32	9/16	7/8	1 23/32	1 7/16	2 7/8	2 1/32	4 1/32	2 19/32	5 3/16	3 3/16	6 11/32
9/16	5/16	21/32	29/32	1 13/16	1 15/32	2 31/32	2 1/16	4 1/8	2 5/8	5 9/32	3 7/32	6 7/16
5/8	3/8	23/32	15/16	1 7/8	1 17/32	3 1/32	2 3/32	4 3/16	2 11/16	5 11/32	3 1/4	6 1/2
11/16	13/32	25/32	31/32	1 15/16	1 9/16	3 3/32	2 1/8	4 1/4	2 23/32	5 13/32	3 9/32	6 9/16
3/4	7/16	7/8	1	2 1/32	1 19/32	3 3/16	2 5/32	4 11/32	2 3/4	5 1/2	3 5/16	6 21/32
13/16	15/32	15/16	1 1/16	2 3/32	1 5/8	3 1/4	2 7/32	4 13/32	2 25/32	5 9/16	3 3/8	6 23/32
7/8	1/2	1	1 3/32	2 5/32	1 21/32	3 5/16	2 1/4	4 15/32	2 13/16	5 5/8	3 13/32	6 25/32
15/16	17/32	1 3/32	1 1/8	2 1/4	1 11/16	3 13/32	2 9/32	4 9/16	2 27/32	5 23/32	3 7/16	6 27/32

Inches	6″ Rise	6″ Slope	7″ Rise	7″ Slope	8″ Rise	8″ Slope	9″ Rise	9″ Slope	10″ Rise	10″ Slope	11″ Rise	11″ Slope
0	3 15/32	6 15/16	4 1/16	8 3/32	4 5/8	9 1/4	5 3/16	10 13/32	5 25/32	11 9/16	6 3/8	1-0 23/32
1/16	3 1/2	7	4 3/32	8 5/32	4 21/32	9 5/16	5 1/4	10 15/32	5 13/16	11 5/8	6 13/32	1-0 25/32
1/8	3 17/32	7 1/16	4 1/8	8 7/32	4 11/16	9 3/8	5 9/32	10 17/32	5 27/32	11 11/16	6 7/16	1-0 27/32
3/16	3 9/16	7 5/32	4 5/32	8 5/16	4 23/32	9 15/32	5 5/16	10 5/8	5 7/8	11 25/32	6 15/32	1-0 15/16
1/4	3 5/8	7 7/32	4 3/16	8 3/8	4 25/32	9 17/32	5 11/32	10 11/16	5 15/16	11 27/32	6 1/2	1-1
5/16	3 21/32	7 9/32	4 7/32	8 7/16	4 13/16	9 19/32	5 3/8	10 3/4	5 31/32	11 29/32	6 17/32	1-1 1/16
3/8	3 11/16	7 3/8	4 1/4	8 17/32	4 27/32	9 11/16	5 13/32	10 27/32	6	11 31/32	6 9/16	1-1 1/8
7/16	3 23/32	7 7/16	4 5/16	8 19/32	4 7/8	9 3/4	5 15/32	10 29/32	6 1/32	1-0 1/16	6 5/8	1-1 7/32
1/2	3 3/4	7 1/2	4 11/32	8 21/32	4 29/32	9 13/16	5 1/2	10 31/32	6 1/16	1-0 1/8	6 21/32	1-1 9/32
9/16	3 25/32	7 19/32	4 3/8	8 3/4	4 15/16	9 7/8	5 17/32	11 1/2	6 3/32	1-0 3/16	6 11/16	1-1 11/32
5/8	3 27/32	7 21/32	4 13/32	8 13/16	5	9 31/32	5 9/16	11 1/8	6 5/32	1-0 9/32	6 23/32	1-1 7/16
11/16	3 7/8	7 23/32	4 7/16	8 7/8	5 1/32	10 1/32	5 19/32	11 3/16	6 3/16	1-0 11/32	6 3/4	1-1 1/2
3/4	3 29/32	7 25/32	4 15/32	8 15/16	5 1/16	10 3/32	5 5/8	11 1/4	6 7/32	1-0 13/32	6 25/32	1-1 9/16
13/16	3 15/16	7 7/8	4 17/32	9 1/32	5 3/32	10 3/16	5 21/32	11 11/32	6 1/4	1-0 1/2	6 13/16	1-1 21/32
7/8	3 31/32	7 15/16	4 9/16	9 3/32	5 1/8	10 1/4	5 23/32	11 13/32	6 9/32	1-0 9/16	6 7/8	1-1 23/32
15/16	4	8	4 19/32	9 5/32	5 5/32	10 5/16	5 3/4	11 15/32	6 5/16	1-0 5/8	6 29/32	1-1 25/32

Feet	0′ Rise	0′ Slope	10′ Rise	10′ Slope	20′ Rise	20′ Slope	30′ Rise	30′ Slope
0	0	0	5-9 3/8	11-6 5/8	11-6 3/4	23-1 7/32	17-4 1/8	34-7 27/32
1	6 15/16	1-1 7/8	6-4 5/16	12-8 15/32	12-1 11/16	24-3 3/32	17-11 1/16	35-9 11/16
2	1-1 7/8	2-3 23/32	6-11 1/4	13-10 11/32	12-8 5/8	25-4 15/16	18-6	36-11 9/16
3	1-8 13/16	3-5 19/32	7-6 3/16	15-0 3/16	13-3 9/16	26-6 13/16	19-0 15/16	38-1 13/32
4	2-3 3/4	4-7 7/16	8-1 1/8	16-2 1/16	13-10 1/2	27-8 21/32	19-7 7/8	39-3 9/32
5	2-10 11/16	5-9 5/16	8-8 1/16	17-3 29/32	14-5 7/16	28-10 17/32	20-2 13/16	40-5 1/8
6	3-5 5/8	6-11 5/32	9-3	18-5 25/32	15-0 3/8	30-0 3/8	20-9 3/4	41-7
7	4-0 9/16	8-1 1/32	9-9 15/16	19-7 5/8	15-7 5/16	31-2 1/4	21-4 11/16	42-8 27/32
8	4-7 1/2	9-2 7/8	10-4 13/16	20-9 1/2	16-2 1/4	32-4 1/8	21-11 5/8	43-10 23/32
9	5-2 7/16	10-4 3/4	10-11 13/16	21-11 3/8	16-9 1/8	33-5 31/32	22-6 9/16	45-0 19/32

A = 30° 02′ 00″; logsin A = 9.69941; logcos A = 9.93738; logtan A = 9.76202; logcot A = 0.23798

Ins.	12″ Rise	12″ Slope	13″ Rise	13″ Slope	14″ Rise	14″ Slope	15″ Rise	15″ Slope	16″ Rise	16″ Slope
0	$6\frac{15}{16}$	$1\text{-}1\frac{7}{8}$	$7\frac{1}{2}$	$1\text{-}3\frac{1}{32}$	$8\frac{3}{32}$	$1\text{-}4\frac{5}{32}$	$8\frac{11}{16}$	$1\text{-}5\frac{5}{16}$	$9\frac{1}{4}$	$1\text{-}6\frac{15}{32}$
$\frac{1}{16}$	$6\frac{31}{32}$	$1\text{-}1\frac{15}{16}$	$7\frac{9}{16}$	$1\text{-}3\frac{3}{32}$	$8\frac{1}{8}$	$1\text{-}4\frac{1}{4}$	$8\frac{23}{32}$	$1\text{-}5\frac{13}{32}$	$9\frac{9}{32}$	$1\text{-}6\frac{9}{16}$
$\frac{1}{8}$	7	$1\text{-}2$	$7\frac{19}{32}$	$1\text{-}3\frac{5}{32}$	$8\frac{5}{32}$	$1\text{-}4\frac{5}{16}$	$8\frac{3}{4}$	$1\text{-}5\frac{15}{32}$	$9\frac{5}{16}$	$1\text{-}6\frac{5}{8}$
$\frac{3}{16}$	$7\frac{1}{32}$	$1\text{-}2\frac{1}{16}$	$7\frac{5}{8}$	$1\text{-}3\frac{7}{32}$	$8\frac{3}{16}$	$1\text{-}4\frac{3}{8}$	$8\frac{25}{32}$	$1\text{-}5\frac{17}{32}$	$9\frac{11}{32}$	$1\text{-}6\frac{11}{16}$
$\frac{1}{4}$	$7\frac{3}{32}$	$1\text{-}2\frac{5}{32}$	$7\frac{21}{32}$	$1\text{-}3\frac{5}{16}$	$8\frac{1}{4}$	$1\text{-}4\frac{15}{32}$	$8\frac{13}{16}$	$1\text{-}5\frac{5}{8}$	$9\frac{13}{32}$	$1\text{-}6\frac{25}{32}$
$\frac{5}{16}$	$7\frac{1}{8}$	$1\text{-}2\frac{7}{32}$	$7\frac{11}{16}$	$1\text{-}3\frac{3}{8}$	$8\frac{9}{32}$	$1\text{-}4\frac{17}{32}$	$8\frac{27}{32}$	$1\text{-}5\frac{11}{16}$	$9\frac{7}{16}$	$1\text{-}6\frac{27}{32}$
$\frac{3}{8}$	$7\frac{5}{32}$	$1\text{-}2\frac{9}{32}$	$7\frac{23}{32}$	$1\text{-}3\frac{7}{16}$	$8\frac{5}{16}$	$1\text{-}4\frac{19}{32}$	$8\frac{7}{8}$	$1\text{-}5\frac{3}{4}$	$9\frac{15}{32}$	$1\text{-}6\frac{29}{32}$
$\frac{7}{16}$	$7\frac{3}{16}$	$1\text{-}2\frac{3}{8}$	$7\frac{25}{32}$	$1\text{-}3\frac{17}{32}$	$8\frac{11}{32}$	$1\text{-}4\frac{11}{16}$	$8\frac{15}{16}$	$1\text{-}5\frac{27}{32}$	$9\frac{1}{2}$	$1\text{-}7$
$\frac{1}{2}$	$7\frac{7}{32}$	$1\text{-}2\frac{7}{16}$	$7\frac{13}{16}$	$1\text{-}3\frac{19}{32}$	$8\frac{3}{8}$	$1\text{-}4\frac{3}{4}$	$8\frac{31}{32}$	$1\text{-}5\frac{29}{32}$	$9\frac{17}{32}$	$1\text{-}7\frac{1}{16}$
$\frac{9}{16}$	$7\frac{1}{4}$	$1\text{-}2\frac{1}{2}$	$7\frac{27}{32}$	$1\text{-}3\frac{21}{32}$	$8\frac{13}{32}$	$1\text{-}4\frac{13}{16}$	9	$1\text{-}5\frac{31}{32}$	$9\frac{9}{16}$	$1\text{-}7\frac{1}{8}$
$\frac{5}{8}$	$7\frac{5}{16}$	$1\text{-}2\frac{19}{32}$	$7\frac{7}{8}$	$1\text{-}3\frac{3}{4}$	$8\frac{15}{32}$	$1\text{-}4\frac{29}{32}$	$9\frac{1}{16}$	$1\text{-}6\frac{1}{16}$	$9\frac{5}{8}$	$1\text{-}7\frac{7}{32}$
$\frac{11}{16}$	$7\frac{11}{32}$	$1\text{-}2\frac{21}{32}$	$7\frac{29}{32}$	$1\text{-}3\frac{13}{16}$	$8\frac{1}{2}$	$1\text{-}4\frac{31}{32}$	$9\frac{1}{8}$	$1\text{-}6\frac{1}{8}$	$9\frac{21}{32}$	$1\text{-}7\frac{9}{32}$
$\frac{3}{4}$	$7\frac{3}{8}$	$1\text{-}2\frac{23}{32}$	$7\frac{15}{16}$	$1\text{-}3\frac{7}{8}$	$8\frac{17}{32}$	$1\text{-}5\frac{1}{2}$	$9\frac{3}{16}$	$1\text{-}6\frac{3}{16}$	$9\frac{11}{16}$	$1\text{-}7\frac{11}{32}$
$\frac{13}{16}$	$7\frac{13}{32}$	$1\text{-}2\frac{13}{16}$	8	$1\text{-}3\frac{31}{32}$	$8\frac{9}{16}$	$1\text{-}5\frac{1}{8}$	$9\frac{5}{32}$	$1\text{-}6\frac{1}{4}$	$9\frac{23}{32}$	$1\text{-}7\frac{13}{32}$
$\frac{7}{8}$	$7\frac{7}{16}$	$1\text{-}2\frac{7}{8}$	$8\frac{1}{32}$	$1\text{-}4\frac{1}{32}$	$8\frac{19}{32}$	$1\text{-}5\frac{3}{16}$	$9\frac{3}{16}$	$1\text{-}6\frac{11}{32}$	$9\frac{3}{4}$	$1\text{-}7\frac{1}{2}$
$\frac{15}{16}$	$7\frac{15}{32}$	$1\text{-}2\frac{15}{16}$	$8\frac{1}{8}$	$1\text{-}4\frac{3}{32}$	$8\frac{5}{8}$	$1\text{-}5\frac{1}{4}$	$9\frac{7}{32}$	$1\text{-}6\frac{13}{32}$	$9\frac{25}{32}$	$1\text{-}7\frac{9}{16}$

Ins.	17″ Rise	17″ Slope	18″ Rise	18″ Slope	19″ Rise	19″ Slope	20″ Rise	20″ Slope	21″ Rise	21″ Slope
0	$9\frac{13}{16}$	$1\text{-}7\frac{5}{8}$	$10\frac{3}{32}$	$1\text{-}8\frac{25}{32}$	11	$1\text{-}9\frac{15}{16}$	$11\frac{9}{16}$	$1\text{-}11\frac{3}{32}$	$1\text{-}0\frac{1}{4}$	$2\text{-}0\frac{1}{4}$
$\frac{1}{16}$	$9\frac{7}{8}$	$1\text{-}7\frac{23}{32}$	$10\frac{7}{16}$	$1\text{-}8\frac{7}{8}$	$11\frac{1}{32}$	$1\text{-}10\frac{1}{32}$	$11\frac{19}{32}$	$1\text{-}11\frac{3}{16}$	$1\text{-}0\frac{3}{16}$	$2\text{-}0\frac{11}{32}$
$\frac{1}{8}$	$9\frac{29}{32}$	$1\text{-}7\frac{25}{32}$	$10\frac{15}{32}$	$1\text{-}8\frac{15}{16}$	$11\frac{1}{16}$	$1\text{-}10\frac{3}{32}$	$11\frac{5}{8}$	$1\text{-}11\frac{1}{4}$	$1\text{-}0\frac{7}{32}$	$2\text{-}0\frac{13}{32}$
$\frac{3}{16}$	$9\frac{15}{16}$	$1\text{-}7\frac{27}{32}$	$10\frac{1}{2}$	$1\text{-}9$	$11\frac{3}{32}$	$1\text{-}10\frac{5}{32}$	$11\frac{21}{32}$	$1\text{-}11\frac{5}{16}$	$1\text{-}0\frac{1}{4}$	$2\text{-}0\frac{15}{32}$
$\frac{1}{4}$	$9\frac{31}{32}$	$1\text{-}7\frac{15}{16}$	$10\frac{9}{16}$	$1\text{-}9\frac{3}{32}$	$11\frac{1}{8}$	$1\text{-}10\frac{1}{4}$	$11\frac{23}{32}$	$1\text{-}11\frac{3}{8}$	$1\text{-}0\frac{9}{32}$	$2\text{-}0\frac{17}{32}$
$\frac{5}{16}$	10	$1\text{-}8$	$10\frac{19}{32}$	$1\text{-}9\frac{5}{32}$	$11\frac{5}{32}$	$1\text{-}10\frac{5}{16}$	$11\frac{3}{4}$	$1\text{-}11\frac{15}{32}$	$1\text{-}0\frac{5}{16}$	$2\text{-}0\frac{5}{8}$
$\frac{3}{8}$	$10\frac{1}{32}$	$1\text{-}8\frac{1}{16}$	$10\frac{5}{8}$	$1\text{-}9\frac{7}{32}$	$11\frac{3}{16}$	$1\text{-}10\frac{3}{8}$	$11\frac{25}{32}$	$1\text{-}11\frac{17}{32}$	$1\text{-}0\frac{11}{32}$	$2\text{-}0\frac{11}{16}$
$\frac{7}{16}$	$10\frac{3}{32}$	$1\text{-}8\frac{5}{32}$	$10\frac{21}{32}$	$1\text{-}9\frac{5}{16}$	$11\frac{1}{4}$	$1\text{-}10\frac{7}{16}$	$11\frac{13}{16}$	$1\text{-}11\frac{19}{32}$	$1\text{-}0\frac{13}{32}$	$2\text{-}0\frac{3}{4}$
$\frac{1}{2}$	$10\frac{1}{8}$	$1\text{-}8\frac{7}{32}$	$10\frac{11}{16}$	$1\text{-}9\frac{3}{8}$	$11\frac{9}{32}$	$1\text{-}10\frac{17}{32}$	$11\frac{27}{32}$	$1\text{-}11\frac{11}{16}$	$1\text{-}0\frac{7}{16}$	$2\text{-}0\frac{27}{32}$
$\frac{9}{16}$	$10\frac{5}{32}$	$1\text{-}8\frac{9}{32}$	$10\frac{23}{32}$	$1\text{-}9\frac{7}{16}$	$11\frac{5}{16}$	$1\text{-}10\frac{19}{32}$	$11\frac{7}{8}$	$1\text{-}11\frac{3}{4}$	$1\text{-}0\frac{15}{32}$	$2\text{-}0\frac{29}{32}$
$\frac{5}{8}$	$10\frac{3}{16}$	$1\text{-}8\frac{11}{32}$	$10\frac{25}{32}$	$1\text{-}9\frac{1}{2}$	$11\frac{11}{32}$	$1\text{-}10\frac{21}{32}$	$11\frac{15}{16}$	$1\text{-}11\frac{13}{16}$	$1\text{-}0\frac{1}{2}$	$2\text{-}0\frac{31}{32}$
$\frac{11}{16}$	$10\frac{7}{32}$	$1\text{-}8\frac{7}{16}$	$10\frac{13}{16}$	$1\text{-}9\frac{19}{32}$	$11\frac{3}{8}$	$1\text{-}10\frac{3}{4}$	$11\frac{31}{32}$	$1\text{-}11\frac{29}{32}$	$1\text{-}0\frac{17}{32}$	$2\text{-}1\frac{1}{16}$
$\frac{3}{4}$	$10\frac{1}{4}$	$1\text{-}8\frac{1}{2}$	$10\frac{27}{32}$	$1\text{-}9\frac{21}{32}$	$11\frac{13}{32}$	$1\text{-}10\frac{13}{16}$	$1\text{-}0$	$1\text{-}11\frac{31}{32}$	$1\text{-}0\frac{9}{16}$	$2\text{-}1\frac{1}{8}$
$\frac{13}{16}$	$10\frac{5}{16}$	$1\text{-}8\frac{9}{16}$	$10\frac{7}{8}$	$1\text{-}9\frac{23}{32}$	$11\frac{15}{32}$	$1\text{-}10\frac{7}{8}$	$1\text{-}0\frac{1}{16}$	$2\text{-}0\frac{1}{32}$	$1\text{-}0\frac{5}{8}$	$2\text{-}1\frac{3}{16}$
$\frac{7}{8}$	$10\frac{11}{32}$	$1\text{-}8\frac{21}{32}$	$10\frac{29}{32}$	$1\text{-}9\frac{13}{16}$	$11\frac{1}{2}$	$1\text{-}10\frac{31}{32}$	$1\text{-}0\frac{1}{8}$	$2\text{-}0\frac{1}{8}$	$1\text{-}0\frac{21}{32}$	$2\text{-}1\frac{9}{32}$
$\frac{15}{16}$	$10\frac{3}{8}$	$1\text{-}8\frac{23}{32}$	$10\frac{15}{16}$	$1\text{-}9\frac{7}{8}$	$11\frac{17}{32}$	$1\text{-}11\frac{1}{32}$	$1\text{-}0\frac{3}{16}$	$2\text{-}0\frac{3}{16}$	$1\text{-}0\frac{11}{16}$	$2\text{-}1\frac{11}{32}$

Feet	40′ Rise	40′ Slope	50′ Rise	50′ Slope	60′ Rise	60′ Slope	70′ Rise	70′ Slope
0	$23\text{-}1\frac{1}{2}$	$46\text{-}2\frac{7}{16}$	$28\text{-}10\frac{7}{8}$	$57\text{-}9\frac{1}{16}$	$34\text{-}8\frac{1}{4}$	$69\text{-}3\frac{21}{32}$	$40\text{-}5\frac{5}{8}$	$80\text{-}10\frac{9}{32}$
1	$23\text{-}8\frac{7}{16}$	$47\text{-}4\frac{5}{16}$	$29\text{-}5\frac{13}{16}$	$58\text{-}10\frac{29}{32}$	$35\text{-}3\frac{3}{16}$	$70\text{-}5\frac{17}{32}$	$41\text{-}0\frac{9}{16}$	$82\text{-}0\frac{1}{8}$
2	$24\text{-}3\frac{3}{8}$	$48\text{-}6\frac{5}{32}$	$30\text{-}0\frac{3}{4}$	$60\text{-}0\frac{25}{32}$	$35\text{-}10\frac{1}{8}$	$71\text{-}7\frac{3}{8}$	$41\text{-}7\frac{1}{2}$	$83\text{-}2$
3	$24\text{-}10\frac{5}{16}$	$49\text{-}8\frac{1}{32}$	$30\text{-}7\frac{11}{16}$	$61\text{-}2\frac{5}{8}$	$36\text{-}5\frac{1}{16}$	$72\text{-}9\frac{1}{4}$	$42\text{-}2\frac{7}{16}$	$84\text{-}3\frac{27}{32}$
4	$25\text{-}5\frac{1}{4}$	$50\text{-}9\frac{7}{8}$	$31\text{-}2\frac{5}{8}$	$62\text{-}4\frac{1}{2}$	$37\text{-}0$	$73\text{-}11\frac{3}{32}$	$42\text{-}9\frac{3}{8}$	$85\text{-}5\frac{23}{32}$
5	$26\text{-}0\frac{3}{16}$	$51\text{-}11\frac{3}{4}$	$31\text{-}9\frac{9}{16}$	$63\text{-}6\frac{11}{32}$	$37\text{-}6\frac{15}{16}$	$75\text{-}0\frac{31}{32}$	$43\text{-}4\frac{5}{16}$	$86\text{-}7\frac{19}{32}$
6	$26\text{-}7\frac{1}{8}$	$53\text{-}1\frac{19}{32}$	$32\text{-}4\frac{1}{2}$	$64\text{-}8\frac{7}{32}$	$38\text{-}1\frac{7}{8}$	$76\text{-}2\frac{27}{32}$	$43\text{-}11\frac{1}{4}$	$87\text{-}9\frac{7}{16}$
7	$27\text{-}2\frac{1}{16}$	$54\text{-}3\frac{15}{32}$	$32\text{-}11\frac{7}{16}$	$65\text{-}10\frac{3}{32}$	$38\text{-}8\frac{13}{16}$	$77\text{-}4\frac{11}{16}$	$44\text{-}6\frac{3}{16}$	$88\text{-}11\frac{5}{16}$
8	$27\text{-}9$	$55\text{-}5\frac{11}{32}$	$33\text{-}6\frac{3}{8}$	$66\text{-}11\frac{15}{16}$	$39\text{-}3\frac{3}{4}$	$78\text{-}6\frac{9}{16}$	$45\text{-}1\frac{1}{8}$	$90\text{-}1\frac{5}{32}$
9	$28\text{-}3\frac{15}{16}$	$56\text{-}7\frac{3}{16}$	$34\text{-}1\frac{5}{16}$	$68\text{-}1\frac{13}{16}$	$39\text{-}10\frac{11}{16}$	$79\text{-}8\frac{13}{32}$	$45\text{-}8\frac{1}{16}$	$91\text{-}3\frac{1}{32}$

natsin $A=0.5005029492$; natcos $A=0.8657348310$; nattan $A=0.5781250000$; natcot $A=1.7297297297$

Inches	0″ Rise	0″ Slope	1″ Rise	1″ Slope	2″ Rise	2″ Slope	3″ Rise	3″ Slope	4″ Rise	4″ Slope	5″ Rise	5″ Slope
0	0	0	19/32	15/32	15/32	2 5/16	1 3/4	3 15/32	2 11/32	4 5/8	2 29/32	5 25/32
1/16	1/32	1/16	5/8	17/32	1 3/16	2 3/8	1 25/32	3 17/32	2 3/8	4 23/32	2 15/16	5 7/8
1/8	1/16	5/32	21/32	1 5/16	1 1/4	2 15/32	1 13/16	3 5/8	2 13/32	4 25/32	3	5 15/16
3/16	1/8	7/32	11/16	1 3/8	1 9/32	2 17/32	1 7/8	3 11/16	2 7/16	4 27/32	3 1/32	6
1/4	5/32	9/32	23/32	1 7/16	1 5/16	2 19/32	1 29/32	3 3/4	2 15/32	4 29/32	3 1/16	6 1/16
5/16	3/16	3/8	3/4	1 17/32	1 11/32	2 11/16	1 15/16	3 27/32	2 1/2	5	3 3/32	6 5/32
3/8	7/32	7/16	13/16	1 19/32	1 3/8	2 3/4	1 31/32	3 29/32	2 9/16	5 1/16	3 1/8	6 7/32
7/16	1/4	1/2	27/32	1 21/32	1 7/16	2 13/16	2	3 31/32	2 19/32	5 1/8	3 3/16	6 9/32
1/2	9/32	19/32	7/8	1 3/4	1 15/32	2 29/32	2 1/32	4 1/16	2 5/8	5 7/32	3 7/32	6 3/8
9/16	5/16	21/32	29/32	1 13/16	1 1/2	2 31/32	2 1/16	4 1/8	2 21/32	5 9/32	3 1/4	6 7/32
5/8	3/8	23/32	15/16	1 7/8	1 17/32	3 1/32	2 1/8	4 3/16	2 11/16	5 11/32	3 9/32	6 1/2
11/16	13/32	25/32	1	1 31/32	1 9/16	3 1/8	2 5/32	4 9/32	2 3/4	5 7/16	3 5/16	6 19/32
3/4	7/16	7/8	1 1/32	2 1/32	1 19/32	3 3/16	2 3/16	4 11/32	2 25/32	5 1/2	3 11/32	6 21/32
13/16	15/32	15/16	1 1/16	2 3/32	1 5/8	3 1/4	2 7/32	4 13/32	2 13/16	5 9/16	3 3/8	6 23/32
7/8	1/2	1	1 3/32	2 5/32	1 11/16	3 11/32	2 1/4	4 1/2	2 27/32	5 21/32	3 7/16	6 13/16
15/16	9/16	1 3/32	1 1/8	2 1/4	1 23/32	3 13/32	2 5/16	4 9/16	2 7/8	5 23/32	3 15/32	6 7/8

Inches	6″ Rise	6″ Slope	7″ Rise	7″ Slope	8″ Rise	8″ Slope	9″ Rise	9″ Slope	10″ Rise	10″ Slope	11″ Rise	11″ Slope
0	3 1/2	6 15/16	4 3/32	8 3/32	4 21/32	9 1/4	5 1/4	10 13/32	5 27/32	11 9/16	6 13/32	1-0 3/4
1/16	3 17/32	7 1/32	4 1/8	8 3/16	4 11/16	9 11/32	5 9/32	10 1/2	5 7/8	11 21/32	6 7/16	1-0 13/16
1/8	3 9/16	7 3/32	4 5/32	8 1/4	4 3/4	9 13/32	5 5/16	10 9/16	5 29/32	11 23/32	6 1/2	1-0 7/8
3/16	3 5/8	7 5/32	4 3/16	8 5/16	4 25/32	9 15/32	5 3/8	10 5/8	5 15/16	11 25/32	6 17/32	1-0 15/16
1/4	3 21/32	7 1/4	4 7/32	8 13/32	4 13/16	9 9/16	5 13/32	10 23/32	5 31/32	11 7/8	6 9/16	1-1 1/32
5/16	3 11/16	7 5/16	4 1/4	8 15/32	4 27/32	9 5/8	5 7/16	10 25/32	6	11 15/16	6 19/32	1-1 3/32
3/8	3 23/32	7 3/8	4 5/16	8 17/32	4 7/8	9 11/16	5 15/32	10 27/32	6 1/16	1-0	6 5/8	1-1 5/32
7/16	3 3/4	7 7/16	4 11/32	8 5/8	4 15/16	9 25/32	5 1/2	10 15/16	6 3/32	1-0 3/32	6 11/16	1-1 1/4
1/2	3 25/32	7 17/32	4 3/8	8 11/16	4 31/32	9 27/32	5 17/32	11	6 1/8	1-0 5/32	6 23/32	1-1 5/16
9/16	3 13/16	7 19/32	4 13/32	8 3/4	5	9 29/32	5 9/16	11 1/16	6 5/32	1-0 7/32	6 3/4	1-1 3/8
5/8	3 7/8	7 21/32	4 7/16	8 13/16	5 1/32	10	5 5/8	11 15/32	6 3/16	1-0 5/16	6 25/32	1-1 15/32
11/16	3 29/32	7 3/4	4 1/2	8 29/32	5 1/16	10 1/16	5 21/32	11 17/32	6 1/4	1-0 3/8	6 13/16	1-1 17/32
3/4	3 15/16	7 13/16	4 17/32	8 31/32	5 3/32	10 1/8	5 11/16	11 9/32	6 9/32	1-0 7/16	6 27/32	1-1 19/32
13/16	3 31/32	7 7/8	4 9/16	9 1/32	5 1/8	10 3/16	5 23/32	11 3/8	6 5/16	1-0 17/32	6 7/8	1-1 11/16
7/8	4	7 31/32	4 19/32	9 1/8	5 3/16	10 9/32	5 3/4	11 7/16	6 11/32	1-0 19/32	6 15/16	1-1 3/4
15/16	4 1/16	8 1/32	4 5/8	9 3/16	5 7/32	10 11/32	5 13/16	11 1/2	6 3/8	1-0 21/32	6 31/32	1-1 13/16

Feet	0′ Rise	0′ Slope	10′ Rise	10′ Slope	20′ Rise	20′ Slope	30′ Rise	30′ Slope
0	0	0	5-10	11-6 15/16	11-8	23-1 27/32	17-6	34-8 25/32
1	7	1-1 29/32	6-5	12-8 13/16	12-3	24-3 3/4	18-1	35-10 21/32
2	1-2	2-3 25/32	7-0	13-10 23/32	12-10	25-5 5/8	18-8	37-0 9/16
3	1-9	3-5 11/16	7-7	15-0 19/32	13-5	26-7 17/32	19-3	38-2 7/16
4	2-4	4-7 9/16	8-2	16-2 1/2	14-0	27-9 13/32	19-10	39-4 11/32
5	2-11	5-9 15/32	8-9	17-4 3/8	14-7	28-11 5/16	20-5	40-6 1/4
6	3-6	6-11 11/32	9-4	18-6 9/32	15-2	30-1 7/32	21-0	41-8 1/8
7	4-1	8-1 1/4	9-11	19-8 5/32	15-9	31-3 3/32	21-7	42-10 1/32
8	4-8	9-3 1/8	10-6	20-10 1/16	16-4	32-5	22-2	43-11 29/32
9	5-3	10-5 1/32	11-1	21-11 31/32	16-11	33-6 7/8	22-9	45-1 13/16

A = 30° 15′ 23″; logsin A = 9.70232; logcos A = 9.93640; logtan A = 9.76592; logcot A = 0.23408

Ins.	12″ Rise	Slope	13″ Rise	Slope	14″ Rise	Slope	15″ Rise	Slope	16″ Rise	Slope
0	7	$1\text{-}1\frac{29}{32}$	$7\frac{19}{32}$	$1\text{-}3\frac{1}{16}$	$8\frac{5}{32}$	$1\text{-}4\frac{7}{32}$	$8\frac34$	$1\text{-}5\frac38$	$9\frac{11}{32}$	$1\text{-}6\frac{17}{32}$
$\frac{1}{16}$	$7\frac{1}{32}$	$1\text{-}1\frac{31}{32}$	$7\frac58$	$1\text{-}3\frac18$	$8\frac{3}{16}$	$1\text{-}4\frac{9}{32}$	$8\frac{25}{32}$	$1\text{-}5\frac{7}{16}$	$9\frac38$	$1\text{-}6\frac{19}{32}$
$\frac18$	$7\frac{1}{16}$	$1\text{-}2\frac{1}{32}$	$7\frac{21}{32}$	$1\text{-}3\frac{3}{16}$	$8\frac14$	$1\text{-}4\frac{11}{32}$	$8\frac{13}{16}$	$1\text{-}5\frac12$	$9\frac{13}{32}$	$1\text{-}6\frac{21}{32}$
$\frac{3}{16}$	$7\frac18$	$1\text{-}2\frac18$	$7\frac{11}{16}$	$1\text{-}3\frac{9}{32}$	$8\frac{9}{32}$	$1\text{-}4\frac{7}{16}$	$8\frac78$	$1\text{-}5\frac{19}{32}$	$9\frac{7}{16}$	$1\text{-}6\frac34$
$\frac14$	$7\frac{5}{32}$	$1\;2\frac{3}{16}$	$7\frac{23}{32}$	$1\text{-}3\frac{11}{32}$	$8\frac{5}{16}$	$1\text{-}4\frac12$	$8\frac{29}{32}$	$1\text{-}5\frac{21}{32}$	$9\frac{15}{32}$	$1\text{-}6\frac{13}{16}$
$\frac{5}{16}$	$7\frac{3}{16}$	$1\text{-}2\frac14$	$7\frac34$	$1\text{-}3\frac{13}{32}$	$8\frac{11}{32}$	$1\text{-}4\frac{9}{16}$	$8\frac{15}{16}$	$1\text{-}5\frac{23}{32}$	$9\frac12$	$1\text{-}6\frac78$
$\frac38$	$7\frac{7}{32}$	$1\text{-}2\frac{5}{16}$	$7\frac{13}{16}$	$1\text{-}3\frac{15}{32}$	$8\frac38$	$1\text{-}4\frac{21}{32}$	$8\frac{31}{32}$	$1\text{-}5\frac{13}{16}$	$9\frac{9}{16}$	$1\text{-}6\frac{31}{32}$
$\frac{7}{16}$	$7\frac14$	$1\text{-}2\frac{13}{32}$	$7\frac{27}{32}$	$1\text{-}3\frac{9}{16}$	$8\frac{7}{16}$	$1\text{-}4\frac{23}{32}$	9	$1\text{-}5\frac78$	$9\frac{19}{32}$	$1\text{-}7\frac{1}{32}$
$\frac12$	$7\frac{9}{32}$	$1\text{-}2\frac{15}{32}$	$7\frac78$	$1\text{-}3\frac58$	$8\frac{15}{32}$	$1\text{-}4\frac{25}{32}$	$9\frac{1}{32}$	$1\text{-}5\frac{15}{16}$	$9\frac58$	$1\text{-}7\frac{3}{32}$
$\frac{9}{16}$	$7\frac{5}{16}$	$1\text{-}2\frac{17}{32}$	$7\frac{29}{32}$	$1\text{-}3\frac{11}{16}$	$8\frac12$	$1\text{-}4\frac{27}{32}$	$9\frac{1}{16}$	$1\text{-}6\frac{1}{32}$	$9\frac{21}{32}$	$1\text{-}7\frac{3}{16}$
$\frac58$	$7\frac38$	$1\text{-}2\frac58$	$7\frac{15}{32}$	$1\text{-}3\frac{25}{32}$	$8\frac{17}{32}$	$1\text{-}4\frac{15}{16}$	$9\frac18$	$1\text{-}6\frac{3}{32}$	$9\frac{11}{16}$	$1\text{-}7\frac14$
$\frac{11}{16}$	$7\frac{13}{32}$	$1\text{-}2\frac{11}{16}$	8	$1\text{-}3\frac{27}{32}$	$8\frac{9}{32}$	$1\text{-}5$	$9\frac{5}{32}$	$1\text{-}6\frac{5}{32}$	$9\frac34$	$1\text{-}7\frac{5}{16}$
$\frac34$	$7\frac{7}{16}$	$1\text{-}2\frac34$	$8\frac{1}{32}$	$1\text{-}3\frac{29}{32}$	$8\frac{19}{32}$	$1\text{-}5\frac{1}{16}$	$9\frac{3}{16}$	$1\text{-}6\frac{1}{32}$	$9\frac{25}{32}$	$1\text{-}7\frac{13}{32}$
$\frac{13}{16}$	$7\frac{15}{32}$	$1\text{-}2\frac{27}{32}$	$8\frac{1}{16}$	$1\text{-}4$	$8\frac58$	$1\text{-}5\frac{5}{32}$	$9\frac{7}{32}$	$1\text{-}6\frac{5}{16}$	$9\frac{13}{16}$	$1\text{-}7\frac{15}{32}$
$\frac78$	$7\frac12$	$1\text{-}2\frac{29}{32}$	$8\frac{3}{32}$	$1\text{-}4\frac{1}{16}$	$8\frac{11}{16}$	$1\text{-}5\frac{7}{32}$	$9\frac14$	$1\text{-}6\frac38$	$9\frac{27}{32}$	$1\text{-}7\frac{17}{32}$
$\frac{15}{16}$	$7\frac{9}{16}$	$1\text{-}2\frac{31}{32}$	$8\frac18$	$1\text{-}4\frac18$	$8\frac{23}{32}$	$1\text{-}5\frac{9}{32}$	$9\frac{5}{16}$	$1\text{-}6\frac{7}{16}$	$9\frac78$	$1\text{-}7\frac{19}{32}$

Ins.	17″ Rise	Slope	18″ Rise	Slope	19″ Rise	Slope	20″ Rise	Slope	21″ Rise	Slope
0	$9\frac{29}{32}$	$1\text{-}7\frac{11}{16}$	$10\frac12$	$1\text{-}8\frac{27}{32}$	$11\frac{3}{32}$	$1\text{-}10$	$11\frac{21}{32}$	$1\text{-}11\frac{5}{32}$	$1\text{-}0\frac14$	$2\text{-}0\frac{5}{16}$
$\frac{1}{16}$	$9\frac{15}{16}$	$1\text{-}7\frac34$	$10\frac{17}{32}$	$1\text{-}8\frac{29}{32}$	$11\frac18$	$1\text{-}10\frac{1}{16}$	$11\frac{11}{16}$	$1\text{-}11\frac{7}{32}$	$1\text{-}0\frac{9}{32}$	$2\text{-}0\frac38$
$\frac18$	10	$1\text{-}7\frac{13}{16}$	$10\frac{9}{16}$	$1\text{-}8\frac{31}{32}$	$11\frac{5}{32}$	$1\text{-}10\frac{5}{32}$	$11\frac34$	$1\text{-}11\frac{5}{16}$	$1\text{-}0\frac{5}{16}$	$2\text{-}0\frac{15}{32}$
$\frac{3}{16}$	$10\frac{1}{32}$	$1\text{-}7\frac{29}{32}$	$10\frac58$	$1\text{-}9\frac{1}{16}$	$11\frac{3}{16}$	$1\text{-}10\frac{7}{32}$	$11\frac{25}{32}$	$1\text{-}11\frac38$	$1\text{-}0\frac38$	$2\text{-}0\frac{17}{32}$
$\frac14$	$10\frac{1}{16}$	$1\text{-}7\frac{31}{32}$	$10\frac{21}{32}$	$1\text{-}9\frac18$	$11\frac{7}{32}$	$1\text{-}10\frac{9}{32}$	$11\frac{13}{16}$	$1\text{-}11\frac{7}{16}$	$1\text{-}0\frac{13}{32}$	$2\text{-}0\frac{19}{32}$
$\frac{5}{16}$	$10\frac{3}{32}$	$1\text{-}8\frac{1}{32}$	$10\frac{11}{16}$	$1\text{-}9\frac{3}{16}$	$11\frac14$	$1\text{-}10\frac{11}{32}$	$11\frac{27}{32}$	$1\text{-}11\frac{17}{32}$	$1\text{-}0\frac{7}{16}$	$2\text{-}0\frac{11}{16}$
$\frac38$	$10\frac18$	$1\text{-}8\frac18$	$10\frac{23}{32}$	$1\text{-}9\frac{9}{32}$	$11\frac{5}{16}$	$1\text{-}10\frac{7}{16}$	$11\frac78$	$1\text{-}11\frac{19}{32}$	$1\text{-}0\frac{15}{32}$	$2\text{-}0\frac34$
$\frac{7}{16}$	$10\frac{3}{16}$	$1\text{-}8\frac{3}{16}$	$10\frac34$	$1\text{-}9\frac{11}{32}$	$11\frac{11}{32}$	$1\text{-}10\frac12$	$11\frac{15}{16}$	$1\text{-}11\frac{21}{32}$	$1\text{-}0\frac12$	$2\text{-}0\frac{13}{16}$
$\frac12$	$10\frac{7}{32}$	$1\text{-}8\frac14$	$10\frac{25}{32}$	$1\text{-}9\frac{13}{32}$	$11\frac38$	$1\text{-}10\frac{9}{16}$	$11\frac{31}{32}$	$1\text{-}11\frac{23}{32}$	$1\text{-}0\frac{17}{32}$	$2\text{-}0\frac{29}{32}$
$\frac{9}{16}$	$10\frac14$	$1\text{-}8\frac{11}{32}$	$10\frac{13}{16}$	$1\text{-}9\frac12$	$11\frac{13}{32}$	$1\text{-}10\frac{21}{32}$	$1\text{-}0$	$1\text{-}11\frac{13}{16}$	$1\text{-}0\frac{9}{16}$	$2\text{-}0\frac{31}{32}$
$\frac58$	$10\frac{9}{32}$	$1\text{-}8\frac{13}{32}$	$10\frac78$	$1\text{-}9\frac{9}{16}$	$11\frac{7}{16}$	$1\text{-}10\frac{23}{32}$	$1\text{-}0\frac{1}{32}$	$1\text{-}11\frac78$	$1\text{-}0\frac58$	$2\text{-}1\frac{1}{32}$
$\frac{11}{16}$	$10\frac{5}{16}$	$1\text{-}8\frac{15}{32}$	$10\frac{29}{32}$	$1\text{-}9\frac58$	$11\frac12$	$1\text{-}10\frac{25}{32}$	$1\text{-}0\frac{1}{16}$	$1\text{-}11\frac{15}{16}$	$1\text{-}0\frac{21}{32}$	$2\text{-}1\frac{3}{32}$
$\frac34$	$10\frac{11}{32}$	$1\text{-}8\frac{9}{16}$	$10\frac{15}{16}$	$1\text{-}9\frac{23}{32}$	$11\frac{17}{32}$	$1\text{-}10\frac78$	$1\text{-}0\frac{3}{32}$	$2\text{-}0\frac{1}{32}$	$1\text{-}0\frac{11}{16}$	$2\text{-}1\frac{3}{16}$
$\frac{13}{16}$	$10\frac38$	$1\text{-}8\frac58$	$10\frac{31}{32}$	$1\text{-}9\frac{25}{32}$	$11\frac{9}{16}$	$1\text{-}10\frac{15}{16}$	$1\text{-}0\frac18$	$2\text{-}0\frac{3}{32}$	$1\text{-}0\frac{23}{32}$	$2\text{-}1\frac14$
$\frac78$	$10\frac{7}{16}$	$1\text{-}8\frac{11}{16}$	11	$1\text{-}9\frac{27}{32}$	$11\frac{19}{32}$	$1\text{-}11$	$1\text{-}0\frac{3}{16}$	$2\text{-}0\frac{5}{32}$	$1\text{-}0\frac34$	$2\text{-}1\frac{5}{16}$
$\frac{15}{16}$	$10\frac{15}{32}$	$1\text{-}8\frac{25}{32}$	$11\frac{1}{16}$	$1\text{-}9\frac{15}{16}$	$11\frac58$	$1\text{-}11\frac{3}{32}$	$1\text{-}0\frac{7}{32}$	$2\text{-}0\frac14$	$1\text{-}0\frac{13}{16}$	$2\text{-}1\frac{13}{32}$

Feet	40′ Rise	Slope	50′ Rise	Slope	60′ Rise	Slope	70′ Rise	Slope
0	23-4	$46\text{-}3\frac{11}{16}$	29-2	$57\text{-}10\frac58$	35-0	$69\text{-}5\frac{17}{32}$	40-10	$81\text{-}0\frac{15}{32}$
1	23-11	$47\text{-}5\frac{19}{32}$	29-9	$59\text{-}0\frac12$	35-7	$70\text{-}7\frac{7}{16}$	41-5	$82\text{-}2\frac38$
2	24-6	$48\text{-}7\frac{15}{32}$	30-4	$60\text{-}2\frac{13}{32}$	36-2	$71\text{-}9\frac{11}{32}$	42-0	$83\text{-}4\frac14$
3	25-1	$49\text{-}9\frac38$	30-11	$61\text{-}4\frac{5}{32}$	36-9	$72\text{-}11\frac{7}{32}$	42-7	$84\text{-}6\frac{5}{32}$
4	25-8	$50\text{-}11\frac{1}{32}$	31-6	$62\text{-}6\frac{3}{16}$	37-4	$74\text{-}1\frac18$	43-2	$85\text{-}8\frac{1}{32}$
5	26-3	$52\text{-}1\frac{5}{32}$	32-1	$63\text{-}8\frac{3}{32}$	37-11	$75\text{-}3$	43-9	$86\text{-}9\frac{15}{32}$
6	26-10	$53\text{-}3\frac{1}{16}$	32-8	$64\text{-}9\frac{31}{32}$	38-6	$76\text{-}4\frac{29}{32}$	44-4	$87\text{-}11\frac{13}{16}$
7	27-5	$54\text{-}4\frac{15}{16}$	33-3	$65\text{-}11\frac78$	39-1	$77\text{-}6\frac{25}{32}$	44-11	$89\text{-}1\frac{23}{32}$
8	28-0	$55\text{-}6\frac{27}{32}$	33-10	$67\text{-}1\frac34$	39-8	$78\text{-}8\frac{11}{16}$	45-6	$90\text{-}3\frac58$
9	28-7	$56\text{-}8\frac{23}{32}$	34-5	$68\text{-}3\frac{21}{32}$	40-3	$79\text{-}10\frac{19}{32}$	46-1	$91\text{-}5\frac12$

natsin A=0.5038710255; natcos A=0.8637789009; nattan A=0.5833333333; natcot A=1.7142857142

Inches	0" Rise	Slope	1" Rise	Slope	2" Rise	Slope	3" Rise	Slope	4" Rise	Slope	5" Rise	Slope
0	0	0	19/32	1 5/32	1 3/16	2 5/16	1 3/4	3 15/32	2 11/32	4 21/32	2 15/16	5 13/16
1/16	1/32	1/16	5/8	1 7/32	1 7/32	2 13/32	1 13/16	3 9/16	2 13/32	4 23/32	2 31/32	5 7/8
1/8	1/16	5/32	21/32	1 5/16	1 1/4	2 15/32	1 27/32	3 5/8	2 7/16	4 25/32	3 1/32	5 15/16
3/16	1/8	7/32	11/16	1 3/8	1 9/32	2 17/32	1 7/8	3 11/16	2 15/32	4 27/32	3 1/16	6 1/32
1/4	5/32	9/32	3/4	1 7/16	1 5/16	2 5/8	1 29/32	3 25/32	2 1/2	4 15/16	3 3/32	6 3/32
5/16	3/16	3/8	25/32	1 17/32	1 3/8	2 11/16	1 15/16	3 27/32	2 17/32	5	3 1/8	6 5/32
3/8	7/32	7/16	13/16	1 19/32	1 13/32	2 3/4	2	3 29/32	2 9/16	5 1/16	3 5/32	6 1/4
7/16	1/4	1/2	27/32	1 21/32	1 7/16	2 27/32	2 1/32	4	2 5/8	5 5/32	3 3/16	6 5/16
1/2	9/32	19/32	7/8	1 3/4	1 15/32	2 29/32	2 1/16	4 1/16	2 21/32	5 7/32	3 1/4	6 3/8
9/16	11/32	21/32	29/32	1 13/16	1 1/2	2 31/32	2 1/8	4 1/8	2 11/16	5 9/32	3 9/32	6 15/32
5/8	3/8	23/32	31/32	1 7/8	1 17/32	3 1/32	2 3/16	4 7/32	2 23/32	5 3/8	3 5/16	6 17/32
11/16	13/32	13/16	1	1 31/32	1 19/32	3 1/8	2 1/4	4 9/32	2 3/4	5 7/16	3 11/32	6 19/32
3/4	7/16	7/8	1 1/16	2 1/32	1 5/8	3 3/16	2 7/32	4 11/32	2 25/32	5 1/2	3 3/8	6 11/16
13/16	15/32	15/16	1 1/16	2 3/32	1 21/32	3 1/4	2 1/4	4 7/16	2 27/32	5 19/32	3 13/32	6 3/4
7/8	1/2	1	1 3/32	2 3/16	1 11/16	3 11/32	2 9/32	4 1/2	2 7/8	5 21/32	3 15/32	6 13/16
15/16	9/16	1 3/32	1 1/8	2 1/4	1 23/32	3 13/32	2 5/16	4 9/32	2 29/32	5 23/32	3 1/2	6 7/8

Inches	6" Rise	Slope	7" Rise	Slope	8" Rise	Slope	9" Rise	Slope	10" Rise	Slope	11" Rise	Slope
0	3 17/32	6 31/32	4 1/8	8 1/8	4 23/32	9 9/32	5 5/16	10 7/16	5 7/8	11 19/32	6 15/16	1-0 3/4
1/16	3 9/16	7 1/32	4 5/32	8 3/16	4 3/4	9 11/32	5 11/32	10 1/2	5 15/16	11 11/16	6 1/2	1-0 27/32
1/8	3 19/32	7 3/32	4 3/16	8 9/32	4 25/32	9 7/16	5 3/8	10 19/32	5 31/32	11 3/4	6 9/16	1-0 29/32
3/16	3 21/32	7 3/16	4 7/32	8 11/32	4 13/16	9 1/2	5 13/32	10 21/32	6	11 13/16	6 19/32	1-0 31/32
1/4	3 11/16	7 1/4	4 9/32	8 13/32	4 27/32	9 9/16	5 7/16	10 23/32	6 1/32	11 29/32	6 5/8	1-1 1/16
5/16	3 23/32	7 5/16	4 5/16	8 1/2	4 29/32	9 21/32	5 15/32	10 13/16	6 1/16	11 31/32	6 21/32	1-1 1/8
3/8	3 3/4	7 13/32	4 11/32	8 9/16	4 15/16	9 23/32	5 17/32	10 7/8	6 3/32	1-0 1/32	6 11/16	1-1 3/16
7/16	3 25/32	7 15/32	4 3/8	8 5/8	4 31/32	9 25/32	5 9/16	10 15/16	6 5/32	1-0 1/8	6 23/32	1-1 9/32
1/2	3 13/16	7 17/32	4 13/32	8 11/16	5	9 7/8	5 19/32	11 1/32	6 3/16	1-0 3/16	6 25/32	1-1 11/32
9/16	3 7/8	7 5/8	4 7/16	8 25/32	5 1/32	9 15/16	5 5/8	11 3/32	6 7/32	1-0 1/4	6 13/16	1-1 13/32
5/8	3 29/32	7 11/16	4 1/2	8 27/32	5 1/16	10	5 21/32	11 5/32	6 1/4	1-0 11/32	6 27/32	1-1 1/2
11/16	3 15/16	7 3/4	4 17/32	8 29/32	5 1/8	10 3/32	5 11/16	11 1/4	6 9/32	1-0 13/32	6 7/8	1-1 9/16
3/4	3 31/32	7 27/32	4 9/16	9	5 5/32	10 5/32	5 3/4	11 3/8	6 3/8	1-0 15/32	6 29/32	1-1 5/8
13/16	4	7 29/32	4 19/32	9 1/16	5 3/16	10 7/32	5 25/32	11 3/8	6 3/8	1-0 17/32	6 15/16	1-1 23/32
7/8	4 1/16	7 31/32	4 5/8	9 1/8	5 7/32	10 5/16	5 13/16	11 15/32	6 13/32	1-0 5/8	7	1-1 25/32
15/16	4 3/32	8 1/16	4 21/32	9 7/32	5 1/4	10 3/8	5 27/32	11 17/32	6 7/16	1-0 11/16	7 1/32	1-1 27/32

Feet	0' Rise	Slope	10' Rise	Slope	20' Rise	Slope	30' Rise	Slope
0	0	0	5-10 5/8	11-7 1/4	11-9 1/4	23-2 15/32	17-7 7/8	34-9 23/32
1	7 1/16	1-1 15/16	6-5 11/16	12-9 5/32	12-4 5/16	24-4 13/32	18-2 15/16	35-11 21/32
2	1-2 1/8	2-3 27/32	7-0 3/4	13-11 3/32	12-11 3/8	25-6 11/32	18-10	37-1 3/8
3	1-9 3/16	3-5 25/32	7-7 13/16	15-1	13-6 7/16	26-8 1/4	19-5 1/16	38-3 1/2
4	2-4 1/4	4-7 11/16	8-2 7/8	16-2 15/16	14-1 1/2	27-10 5/16	20-0 1/8	39-5 13/32
5	2-11 5/16	5-9 5/8	8-9 15/16	17-4 7/8	14-8 9/16	29-0 9/32	20-7 3/16	40-7 11/32
6	3-6 3/8	6-11 17/32	9-5	18-6 25/32	15-3 5/8	30-2 1/32	21-2 1/4	41-9 1/4
7	4-1 7/16	8-1 15/32	10-0 1/16	19-8 23/32	15-10 11/16	31-3 15/16	21-9 5/16	42-11 3/16
8	4-8 1/2	9-3 13/32	10-7 1/8	20-10 5/16	16-5 3/4	32-5 7/32	22-4 3/8	44-1 1/8
9	5-3 9/16	10-5 5/16	11-2 3/16	22-0 9/16	17-0 13/16	33-7 13/16	22-11 7/16	45-3 1/32

A = 30° 28′ 43″; logsin A = 9.70519; logcos A = 9.93542; logtan A = 9.76978; logcot A = 0.23022

Ins.	12″ Rise	12″ Slope	13″ Rise	13″ Slope	14″ Rise	14″ Slope	15″ Rise	15″ Slope	16″ Rise	16″ Slope
0	7 1/16	1-1 15/16	7 21/32	1-3 3/32	8 1/4	1-4 1/4	8 13/16	1-5 13/32	9 13/16	1-6 9/16
1/16	7 3/32	1-2	7 11/16	1-3 5/32	8 9/32	1-4 5/16	8 7/8	1-5 15/32	9 15/32	1-6 5/8
1/8	7 1/8	1-2 1/16	7 23/32	1-3 7/32	8 5/16	1-4 3/8	8 29/32	1-5 9/16	9 1/2	1-6 23/32
3/16	7 3/16	1-2 5/32	7 3/4	1-3 5/16	8 11/32	1-4 15/32	8 15/16	1-5 5/8	9 17/32	1-6 25/32
1/4	7 7/32	1-2 7/32	7 13/16	1-3 3/8	8 3/8	1-4 17/32	8 31/32	1-5 11/16	9 9/16	1-6 27/32
5/16	7 1/4	1-2 9/32	7 27/32	1-3 7/16	8 7/16	1-4 19/32	9	1-5 25/32	9 19/32	1-6 15/16
3/8	7 9/32	1-2 11/32	7 7/8	1-3 17/32	8 15/32	1-4 11/16	9 1/16	1-5 27/32	9 5/8	1-7
7/16	7 5/16	1-2 7/16	7 29/32	1-3 19/32	8 1/2	1-4 3/4	9 3/32	1-5 29/32	9 11/16	1-7 1/16
1/2	7 11/32	1-2 1/2	7 15/16	1-3 21/32	8 17/32	1-4 13/16	9 1/8	1-6	9 23/32	1-7 5/32
9/16	7 13/32	1-2 9/16	7 31/32	1-3 3/4	8 9/16	1-4 29/32	9 5/32	1-6 1/16	9 3/4	1-7 7/32
5/8	7 7/16	1-2 21/32	8 1/32	1-3 13/16	8 19/32	1-4 31/32	9 3/16	1-6 1/8	9 25/32	1 7 9/32
11/16	7 15/32	1-2 23/32	8 1/16	1-3 7/8	8 21/32	1-5 1/2	9 7/32	1-6 3/16	9 13/16	1-7 3/8
3/4	7 1/2	1-2 25/32	8 3/32	1-3 31/32	8 11/16	1-5 1/8	9 9/32	1-6 9/32	9 27/32	1-7 7/16
13/16	7 17/32	1-2 7/8	8 1/8	1-4 1/2	8 23/32	1-5 3/16	9 5/16	1-6 11/32	9 29/32	1-7 1/2
7/8	7 9/16	1-2 15/16	8 5/32	1-4 3/32	8 3/4	1-5 1/4	9 11/32	1-6 13/32	9 15/16	1-7 19/32
15/16	7 5/8	1-3	8 3/16	1-4 3/16	8 25/32	1-5 11/32	9 3/8	1-6 1/2	9 31/32	1-7 21/32

Ins.	17″ Rise	17″ Slope	18″ Rise	18″ Slope	19″ Rise	19″ Slope	20″ Rise	20″ Slope	21″ Rise	21″ Slope
0	10	1-7 23/32	10 19/32	1-8 7/8	11 3/16	1-10 1/32	11 25/32	1-11 7/32	1-0 3/8	2-0 3/8
1/16	10 1/32	1-7 13/16	10 5/8	1-8 31/32	11 7/32	1-10 1/8	11 13/16	1-11 9/32	1-0 13/32	2-0 7/16
1/8	10 3/32	1-7 7/8	10 21/32	1-9 1/32	11 1/4	1-10 3/16	11 27/32	1-11 11/32	1-0 7/16	2-0 1/2
3/16	10 1/8	1-7 15/16	10 23/32	1-9 3/32	11 9/32	1-10 1/4	11 7/8	1-11 7/16	1-0 15/32	2-0 19/32
1/4	10 5/32	1-8 1/32	10 3/4	1-9 3/16	11 11/32	1-10 11/32	11 29/32	1-11 1/2	1-0 1/2	2-0 21/32
5/16	10 3/16	1-8 3/32	10 25/32	1-9 1/4	11 3/8	1-10 13/32	11 31/32	1-11 9/16	1-0 17/32	2-0 23/32
3/8	10 7/32	1-8 5/32	10 13/16	1-9 5/16	11 13/32	1-10 15/32	1-0	1-11 21/32	1-0 19/32	2-0 13/16
7/16	10 1/4	1-8 7/32	10 27/32	1-9 13/32	11 7/16	1-10 9/16	1-0 1/32	1-11 23/32	1-0 5/8	2-0 7/8
1/2	10 5/16	1-8 5/16	10 7/8	1-9 15/32	11 15/32	1-10 5/8	1-0 1/16	1-11 25/32	1-0 21/32	2-0 15/16
9/16	10 11/32	1-8 3/8	10 15/16	1-9 17/32	11 1/2	1-10 11/16	1-0 3/32	1-11 7/8	1-0 11/16	2-1 1/32
5/8	10 3/8	1-8 7/16	10 31/32	1-9 5/8	11 9/16	1-10 25/32	1-0 1/8	1-11 15/16	1-0 23/32	2-1 3/32
11/16	10 13/32	1-8 17/32	11	1-9 11/16	11 19/32	1-10 27/32	1-0 3/16	2-0	1-0 3/4	2-1 5/32
3/4	10 7/16	1-8 19/32	11 1/32	1-9 3/4	11 5/8	1-10 29/32	1-0 7/32	2-0 1/16	1-0 13/16	2-1 1/4
13/16	10 15/32	1-8 21/32	11 1/16	1-9 27/32	11 21/32	1-11	1-0 1/4	2-0 5/32	1-0 27/32	2-1 5/16
7/8	10 17/32	1-8 3/4	11 3/32	1-9 29/32	11 11/16	1-11 1/16	1-0 9/32	2-0 7/32	1-0 7/8	2-1 3/8
15/16	10 9/16	1-8 13/16	11 5/32	1-9 31/32	11 23/32	1-11 1/8	1-0 5/16	2-0 9/32	1-0 29/32	2-1 15/32

Feet	40′ Rise	40′ Slope	50′ Rise	50′ Slope	60′ Rise	60′ Slope	70′ Rise	70′ Slope
0	23-6 1/2	46-4 31/32	29-5 1/8	58-0 3/16	35-3 3/4	69-7 7/16	41-2 3/8	81-2 11/16
1	24-1 9/16	47-6 7/8	30-0 3/16	59-2 1/8	35-10 13/16	70-9 3/8	41-9 7/16	82-4 19/32
2	24-8 5/8	48-8 13/16	30-7 1/4	60-4 1/16	36-5 7/8	71-11 9/32	42-4 1/2	83-6 17/32
3	25-3 11/16	49-10 23/32	31-2 5/16	61-5 31/32	37-0 15/16	73-1 7/32	42-11 9/16	84-8 15/32
4	25-10 3/4	51-0 21/32	31-9 3/8	62-7 29/32	37-8	74-3 1/4	43-6 5/8	85-10 3/8
5	26-5 13/16	52-2 19/32	32-4 7/16	63-9 13/16	38-3 1/16	75-5 3/16	44-1 11/16	87-0 5/16
6	27-0 7/8	53-4 1/2	32-11 1/2	64-11 3/4	38-10 1/8	76-7	44-8 3/4	88-2 7/32
7	27-7 15/16	54-6 7/16	33-6 9/16	66-1 21/32	39-5 3/16	77-8 29/32	45-3 13/16	89-4 5/32
8	28-3	55-8 11/32	34-1 5/8	67-3 19/32	40-0 1/4	78-10 27/32	45-10 7/8	90-6 1/16
9	28-10 1/16	56-10 9/32	34-8 11/16	68-5 17/32	40-7 5/16	80-0 3/4	46-5 15/16	91-8

natsin A=0.5072162750; natcos A=0.8618188036; nattan A=0.5885416666; natcot A=1.6991150442

Inches	0" Rise	0" Slope	1" Rise	1" Slope	2" Rise	2" Slope	3" Rise	3" Slope	4" Rise	4" Slope	5" Rise	5" Slope
0	0	0	19/32	15/32	1 3/16	2 5/16	1 25/32	3 1/2	2 3/8	4 21/32	2 31/32	5 13/16
1/16	1/16	1/16	5/8	1 1/4	1 7/32	2 13/32	1 13/16	3 9/16	2 13/32	4 23/32	3	5 7/8
1/8	1/16	5/32	21/32	1 5/16	1 1/4	2 15/32	1 27/32	3 5/8	2 7/16	4 13/16	3 1/32	5 31/32
3/16	1/8	7/32	23/32	1 3/8	1 5/16	2 17/32	1 29/32	3 23/32	2 1/2	4 7/8	3 3/32	6 1/32
1/4	5/32	9/32	3/4	1 15/32	1 11/32	2 5/8	1 15/16	3 25/32	2 17/32	4 15/16	3 1/8	6 3/32
5/16	3/16	3/8	25/32	1 17/32	1 3/8	2 11/16	1 31/32	3 27/32	2 9/16	5	3 5/32	6 3/16
3/8	7/32	7/16	13/16	1 19/32	1 13/32	2 3/4	2	3 15/16	2 19/32	5 3/32	3 3/16	6 1/4
7/16	1/4	1/2	27/32	1 21/32	1 7/16	2 27/32	2 1/32	4	2 5/8	5 5/32	3 7/32	6 5/16
1/2	5/16	19/32	7/8	1 3/4	1 1/2	2 29/32	2 1/16	4 1/16	2 11/16	5 7/32	3 1/4	6 13/32
9/16	11/32	21/32	15/16	1 13/16	1 17/32	2 31/32	2 1/8	4 5/32	2 23/32	5 5/16	3 5/16	6 15/32
5/8	3/8	23/32	31/32	1 7/8	1 9/16	3 1/16	2 5/32	4 7/32	2 3/4	5 3/8	3 11/32	6 17/32
11/16	13/32	13/16	1	1 31/32	1 19/32	3 1/8	2 3/16	4 9/32	2 25/32	5 7/16	3 3/8	6 5/8
3/4	7/16	7/8	1 1/32	2 1/32	1 5/8	3 3/16	2 7/32	4 3/8	2 13/16	5 17/32	3 13/32	6 11/16
13/16	15/32	15/16	1 1/16	2 3/32	1 21/32	3 9/32	2 1/4	4 7/16	2 27/32	5 19/32	3 7/16	6 3/4
7/8	17/32	1 1/32	1 1/8	2 3/16	1 23/32	3 11/32	2 5/16	4 1/2	2 29/32	5 21/32	3 1/2	6 27/32
15/16	9/16	1 3/32	1 5/32	2 1/4	1 3/4	3 13/32	2 11/32	4 19/32	2 15/16	5 3/4	3 17/32	6 29/32

Inches	6" Rise	6" Slope	7" Rise	7" Slope	8" Rise	8" Slope	9" Rise	9" Slope	10" Rise	10" Slope	11" Rise	11" Slope
0	3 9/16	6 31/32	4 5/32	8 5/32	4 3/4	9 5/16	5 11/32	10 15/32	5 15/16	11 5/8	6 17/32	1-0 25/32
1/16	3 19/32	7 1/8	4 3/16	8 7/32	4 25/32	9 3/8	5 3/8	10 17/32	5 31/32	11 11/16	6 9/16	1-0 7/8
1/8	3 5/8	7 1/8	4 7/32	8 9/32	4 13/16	9 7/16	5 13/32	10 5/8	6	11 25/32	6 19/32	1-0 15/16
3/16	3 11/16	7 3/16	4 9/32	8 11/32	4 7/8	9 17/32	5 15/32	10 11/16	6 1/16	11 27/32	6 21/32	1-1
1/4	3 23/32	7 9/32	4 5/16	8 7/16	4 29/32	9 19/32	5 1/2	10 3/4	6 3/32	11 29/32	6 11/16	1-1 3/32
5/16	3 3/4	7 11/32	4 11/32	8 1/2	4 15/16	9 21/32	5 17/32	10 27/32	6 1/8	1-0	6 23/32	1-1 5/32
3/8	3 25/32	7 13/32	4 3/8	8 9/16	4 31/32	9 3/4	5 9/16	10 29/32	6 5/32	1-0 1/16	6 3/4	1-1 7/32
7/16	3 13/16	7 1/2	4 13/32	8 21/32	5	9 13/16	5 19/32	10 31/32	6 3/16	1-0 1/8	6 25/32	1-1 5/16
1/2	3 7/8	7 9/16	4 7/16	8 23/32	5 1/16	9 7/8	5 5/8	11 1/16	6 1/4	1-0 7/32	6 13/16	1-1 3/8
9/16	3 29/32	7 5/8	4 1/2	8 25/32	5 3/32	9 31/32	5 11/16	11 1/8	6 9/32	1-0 9/32	6 7/8	1-1 7/16
5/8	3 15/16	7 23/32	4 17/32	8 7/8	5 1/8	10 1/2	5 23/32	11 3/16	6 5/16	1-0 11/32	6 29/32	1-1 17/32
11/16	3 31/32	7 25/32	4 9/16	8 15/16	5 5/32	10 3/32	5 3/4	11 9/32	6 11/32	1-0 7/16	6 15/16	1-1 19/32
3/4	4	7 27/32	4 19/32	9	5 3/16	10 3/16	5 25/32	11 11/32	6 3/8	1-0 1/2	6 31/32	1-1 21/32
13/16	4 1/16	7 15/16	4 5/8	9 3/32	5 7/32	10 1/4	5 13/16	11 13/32	6 13/32	1-0 9/16	7	1-1 3/4
7/8	4 3/32	8	4 11/16	9 5/32	5 9/32	10 5/16	5 7/8	11 1/2	6 15/32	1-0 21/32	7 1/16	1-1 13/16
15/16	4 1/8	8 1/16	4 23/32	9 7/32	5 5/16	10 13/32	5 29/32	11 9/16	6 1/2	1-0 25/32	7 3/32	1-1 7/8

Feet	0' Rise	0' Slope	10' Rise	10' Slope	20' Rise	20' Slope	30' Rise	30' Slope
0	0	0	5-11 1/4	11-7 9/16	11-10 1/2	23-3 1/8	17-9 3/4	34-10 11/16
1	7 1/8	1-1 31/32	6-6 3/8	12-9 1/2	12-5 5/8	24-5 1/16	18-4 7/8	36-0 5/8
2	1-2 1/4	2-3 29/32	7-1 1/2	13-11 15/32	13-0 3/4	25-7 1/32	19-0	37-2 19/32
3	1-9 3/8	3-5 7/8	7-8 5/8	15-1 7/16	13-7 7/8	26-9	19-7 1/8	38-4 17/32
4	2-4 1/2	4-7 13/16	8-3 3/4	16-3 3/8	14-3	27-10 15/16	20-2 1/4	39-6 1/2
5	2-11 5/8	5-9 25/32	8-10 7/8	17-5 11/32	14-10 1/8	29-0 29/32	20-9 3/8	40-8 15/32
6	3-6 3/4	6-11 3/4	9-6	18-7 9/32	15-5 1/4	30-2 7/8	21-4 1/2	41-10 13/32
7	4-1 7/8	8-1 11/16	10-1 1/8	19-9 1/4	16-0 3/8	31-4 13/16	21-11 5/8	43-0 3/8
8	4-9	9-3 21/32	10-8 1/4	20-11 7/32	16-7 1/2	32-6 3/4	22-6 3/4	44-2 5/16
9	5-4 1/8	10-5 19/32	11-3 3/8	22-1 5/32	17-2 5/8	33-8 23/32	23-1 7/8	45-4 9/32

A = 30° 41' 59''; logsin A = 9.70803; logcos A = 9.93443; logtan A = 9.77360; logcot A = 0.22640

Ins.	12″ Rise	12″ Slope	13″ Rise	13″ Slope	14″ Rise	14″ Slope	15″ Rise	15″ Slope	16″ Rise	16″ Slope
0	7 1/8	1-1 31/32	7 23/32	1-3 1/8	8 5/16	1-4 9/32	8 29/32	1-5 7/16	9 1/2	1-6 19/32
1/16	7 5/32	1-2 1/32	7 3/4	1-3 3/16	8 11/32	1-4 11/32	8 15/16	1-5 17/32	9 17/32	1-6 11/16
1/8	7 3/16	1-2 3/32	7 25/32	1-3 1/4	8 3/8	1-4 7/16	8 31/32	1-5 19/32	9 9/16	1-6 3/4
3/16	7 1/4	1-2 3/16	7 27/32	1-3 11/32	8 7/16	1-4 1/2	9 1/32	1-5 21/32	9 5/8	1-6 13/16
1/4	7 9/32	1-2 1/4	7 7/8	1-3 13/32	8 15/32	1-4 9/16	9 1/16	1-5 3/4	9 21/32	1-6 29/32
5/16	7 5/16	1-2 5/16	7 29/32	1-3 15/32	8 1/2	1-4 21/32	9 3/32	1-5 13/16	9 11/16	1-6 31/32
3/8	7 11/32	1-2 13/32	7 15/16	1-3 9/16	8 17/32	1-4 23/32	9 1/8	1-5 7/8	9 23/32	1-7 1/2
7/16	7 3/8	1-2 15/32	7 31/32	1-3 5/8	8 9/16	1-4 25/32	9 5/32	1-5 31/32	9 3/4	1-7 1/8
1/2	7 7/16	1-2 17/32	8	1-3 11/16	8 5/8	1-4 7/8	9 3/16	1-6 1/32	9 13/16	1-7 3/16
9/16	7 15/32	1-2 5/8	8 1/16	1-3 25/32	8 21/32	1-4 15/16	9 1/4	1-6 3/32	9 27/32	1-7 1/4
5/8	7 1/2	1-2 11/16	8 3/32	1-3 27/32	8 11/16	1-5	9 9/32	1-6 5/32	9 7/8	1-7 11/32
11/16	7 17/32	1-2 3/4	8 1/8	1-3 29/32	8 23/32	1-5 3/32	9 5/16	1-6 1/4	9 29/32	1-7 13/32
3/4	7 9/16	1-2 27/32	8 5/32	1-4	8 3/4	1-5 5/32	9 11/32	1-6 5/16	9 15/16	1-7 15/32
13/16	7 19/32	1-2 29/32	8 3/16	1-4 1/16	8 25/32	1-5 7/32	9 3/8	1-6 3/8	9 31/32	1-7 9/16
7/8	7 21/32	1-2 31/32	8 1/4	1-4 1/8	8 27/32	1-5 5/16	9 7/16	1-6 15/32	10 1/32	1-7 5/8
15/16	7 11/16	1-3 1/32	8 9/32	1-4 7/32	8 7/8	1-5 3/8	9 15/32	1-6 17/32	10 1/16	1-7 11/16

Ins.	17″ Rise	17″ Slope	18″ Rise	18″ Slope	19″ Rise	19″ Slope	20″ Rise	20″ Slope	21″ Rise	21″ Slope
0	10 3/32	1-7 25/32	10 11/16	1-8 15/16	11 9/32	1-10 3/32	11 7/8	1-11 1/4	1-0 15/32	2-0 7/16
1/16	10 1/8	1-7 27/32	10 23/32	1-9	11 5/16	1-10 5/32	11 29/32	1-11 11/32	1-0 1/2	2-0 1/2
1/8	10 5/32	1-7 29/32	10 3/4	1-9 3/32	11 11/32	1-10 1/4	11 15/16	1-11 13/32	1-0 17/32	2-0 9/16
3/16	10 7/32	1-8	10 13/16	1-9 5/32	11 13/32	1-10 5/16	1-0	1-11 15/32	1-0 19/32	2-0 21/32
1/4	10 1/4	1-8 1/16	10 27/32	1-9 7/32	11 7/16	1-10 3/8	1-0 1/32	1-11 9/16	1-0 5/8	2-0 23/32
5/16	10 9/32	1-8 1/8	10 7/8	1-9 5/16	11 15/32	1-10 15/32	1-0 1/16	1-11 5/8	1-0 21/32	2-0 25/32
3/8	10 5/16	1-8 7/32	10 29/32	1-9 3/8	11 1/2	1-10 17/32	1-0 3/32	1-11 11/16	1-0 11/16	2-0 27/32
7/16	10 11/32	1-8 9/32	10 15/16	1-9 7/16	11 17/32	1-10 19/32	1-0 1/8	1-11 25/32	1-0 23/32	2-0 15/16
1/2	10 3/8	1-8 11/32	11	1-9 1/2	11 9/16	1-10 11/16	1-0 3/16	1-11 27/32	1-0 3/4	2-1
9/16	10 7/16	1-8 7/16	11 1/32	1-9 19/32	11 5/8	1-10 3/4	1-0 7/32	1-11 29/32	1-0 13/16	2-1 1/16
5/8	10 15/32	1-8 1/2	11 1/16	1-9 21/32	11 21/32	1-10 13/16	1-0 1/4	2-0	1-0 27/32	2-1 5/32
11/16	10 1/2	1-8 9/16	11 3/32	1-9 23/32	11 11/16	1-10 29/32	1-0 9/32	2-0 1/16	1-0 7/8	2-1 7/32
3/4	10 17/32	1-8 21/32	11 1/8	1-9 13/16	11 23/32	1-10 31/32	1-0 5/16	2-0 1/8	1-0 29/32	2-1 9/32
13/16	10 9/16	1-8 23/32	11 5/32	1-9 7/8	11 3/4	1-11 1/32	1-0 11/32	2-0 7/32	1-0 15/16	2-1 3/8
7/8	10 5/8	1-8 25/32	11 3/16	1-9 15/16	11 13/16	1-11 1/8	1-0 13/32	2-0 9/32	1-1	2-1 7/16
15/16	10 21/32	1-8 7/8	11 1/4	1-10 1/32	11 27/32	1-11 3/16	1-0 7/16	2-0 11/32	1-1 1/32	2-1 1/2

Feet	40′ Rise	40′ Slope	50′ Rise	50′ Slope	60′ Rise	60′ Slope	70′ Rise	70′ Slope
0	23-9	46-6 7/32	29-8 1/4	58-1 25/32	35-7 1/2	69-9 11/32	41-6 3/4	81-4 29/32
1	24-4 1/8	47-8 3/16	30-3 3/8	59-3 3/4	36-2 5/8	70-11 5/16	42-1 7/8	82-6 7/8
2	24-11 1/4	48-10 5/32	30-10 1/2	60-5 23/32	36-9 3/4	72-1 1/4	42-9	83-8 13/16
3	25-6 3/8	50-0 3/32	31-5 5/8	61-7 21/32	37-4 7/8	73-3 7/32	43-4 1/8	84-10 25/32
4	26-1 1/2	51-2 1/16	32-0 3/4	62-9 5/8	38-0	74-5 3/16	43-11 1/4	86-0 23/32
5	26-8 5/8	52-4	32-7 7/8	63-11 9/16	38-7 1/8	75-7 1/8	44-6 3/8	87-2 11/16
6	27-3 3/4	53-5 31/32	33-3	65-1 17/32	39-2 1/4	76-9 3/32	45-1 1/2	88-4 21/32
7	27-10 7/8	54-7 15/16	33-10 1/8	66-3 15/32	39-9 3/8	77-11 1/32	45-8 5/8	89-6 19/32
8	28-6	55-9 7/8	34-5 1/4	67-5 7/16	40-4 1/2	79-1	46-3 3/4	90-8 9/16
9	29-1 1/8	56-11 27/32	35-0 3/8	68-7 13/32	40-11 5/8	80-2 31/32	46-10 7/8	91-10 1/2

natsin A=0.5105387541; natcos A=0.8598547437; nattan A=0.5937500000; natcot A=1.6842105263

Inches	0" Rise	0" Slope	1" Rise	1" Slope	2" Rise	2" Slope	3" Rise	3" Slope	4" Rise	4" Slope	5" Rise	5" Slope
0	0	0	19/32	1-5/32	1-3/16	2-11/32	1-13/16	3-1/2	2-13/32	4-21/32	3	5-27/32
1/16	1/16	1/16	5/8	1-1/4	1-1/4	2-13/32	1-27/32	3-9/16	2-7/16	4-3/4	3-1/32	5-29/32
1/8	1/16	5/32	11/16	1-5/16	1-9/32	2-15/32	1-7/8	3-21/32	2-15/32	4-13/16	3-1/16	5-31/32
3/16	1/8	7/32	23/32	1-3/8	1-5/16	2-9/16	1-29/32	3-23/32	2-1/2	4-7/8	3-3/32	6-1/32
1/4	5/32	9/32	3/4	1-15/32	1-11/32	2-5/8	1-15/16	3-25/32	2-17/32	4-31/32	3-5/32	6-1/8
5/16	3/16	3/8	25/32	1-17/32	1-3/8	2-11/16	1-31/32	3-7/8	2-19/32	5-1/32	3-3/16	6-3/16
3/8	7/32	7/16	13/16	1-19/32	1-13/32	2-25/32	2	3-15/16	2-5/8	5-3/32	3-7/32	6-1/4
7/16	1/4	1/2	7/8	1-11/16	1-15/32	2-27/32	2-1/16	4	2-21/32	5-3/16	3-1/4	6-11/32
1/2	5/16	19/32	29/32	1-3/4	1-1/2	2-29/32	2-3/32	4-3/32	2-11/16	5-1/4	3-9/32	6-13/32
9/16	11/32	21/32	15/16	1-13/16	1-17/32	3	2-1/8	4-5/32	2-23/32	5-5/16	3-11/32	6-15/32
5/8	3/8	23/32	31/32	1-29/32	1-9/16	3-1/16	2-5/32	4-7/32	2-25/32	5-13/32	3-3/8	6-9/16
11/16	13/32	13/16	1	1-31/32	1-5/8	3-1/8	2-7/32	4-5/16	2-13/16	5-15/32	3-13/32	6-5/8
3/4	7/16	7/8	1-1/16	2-1/32	1-21/32	3-7/32	2-1/4	4-3/8	2-27/32	5-17/32	3-7/16	6-11/16
13/16	1/2	15/16	1-3/32	2-1/8	1-11/16	3-9/32	2-9/32	4-7/16	2-7/8	5-5/8	3-15/32	6-25/32
7/8	17/32	1-1/32	1-1/8	2-3/16	1-23/32	3-11/32	2-5/16	4-17/32	2-29/32	5-11/16	3-17/32	6-27/32
15/16	9/16	1-3/32	1-5/32	2-1/4	1-3/4	3-7/16	2-11/32	4-19/32	2-31/32	5-3/4	3-9/16	6-29/32

Inches	6" Rise	6" Slope	7" Rise	7" Slope	8" Rise	8" Slope	9" Rise	9" Slope	10" Rise	10" Slope	11" Rise	11" Slope
0	3-19/32	7	4-3/16	8-5/32	4-25/32	9-5/16	5-3/8	10-1/2	6	11-21/32	6-19/32	1-0-13/16
1/16	3-5/8	7-1/16	4-7/32	8-7/32	4-27/32	9-13/32	5-7/16	10-9/16	6-1/16	11-23/32	6-5/8	1-0-29/32
1/8	3-21/32	7-1/8	4-9/32	8-5/16	4-7/8	9-15/32	5-15/32	10-5/8	6-1/16	11-13/16	6-21/32	1-0-31/32
3/16	3-23/32	7-7/32	4-5/16	8-3/8	4-29/32	9-17/32	5-1/2	10-23/32	6-3/32	11-7/8	6-11/16	1-1-1/32
1/4	3-3/4	7-9/32	4-11/32	8-7/16	4-15/16	9-5/8	5-17/32	10-25/32	6-1/8	11-15/16	6-3/4	1-1-1/8
5/16	3-25/32	7-11/32	4-3/8	8-17/32	4-31/32	9-11/16	5-9/16	10-27/32	6-3/16	1-0-1/32	6-25/32	1-1-3/16
3/8	3-13/16	7-7/16	4-13/32	8-19/32	5-1/32	9-3/4	5-5/8	10-15/16	6-7/32	1-0-3/32	6-13/16	1-1-1/4
7/16	3-27/32	7-1/2	4-15/32	8-21/32	5-1/16	9-27/32	5-21/32	11	6-1/4	1-0-5/32	6-27/32	1-1-11/32
1/2	3-29/32	7-9/16	4-1/2	8-3/4	5-3/32	9-29/32	5-11/16	11-1/16	6-9/32	1-0-1/4	6-7/8	1-1-13/32
9/16	3-15/16	7-21/32	4-17/32	8-13/16	5-1/8	9-31/32	5-23/32	11-5/32	6-5/16	1-0-5/16	6-15/16	1-1-15/32
5/8	3-31/32	7-23/32	4-9/16	8-7/8	5-5/32	10-1/16	5-3/4	11-7/32	6-3/8	1-0-3/8	6-31/32	1-1-9/16
11/16	4	7-25/32	4-19/32	8-31/32	5-7/32	10-1/8	5-13/16	11-9/32	6-13/32	1-0-15/32	7	1-1-5/8
3/4	4-1/32	7-7/8	4-21/32	9-1/32	5-1/4	10-3/16	5-27/32	11-3/8	6-7/16	1-0-17/32	7-1/32	1-1-11/16
13/16	4-3/32	7-15/16	4-11/16	9-3/32	5-9/32	10-9/32	5-7/8	11-7/16	6-15/32	1-0-19/32	7-1/16	1-1-25/32
7/8	4-1/8	8	4-23/32	9-3/16	5-5/16	10-11/32	5-29/32	11-1/2	6-1/2	1-0-11/16	7-1/8	1-1-27/32
15/16	4-5/32	8-3/32	4-3/4	9-1/4	5-11/32	10-13/32	5-15/16	11-19/32	6-9/16	1-0-3/4	7-5/32	1-1-29/32

Feet	0' Rise	0' Slope	10' Rise	10' Slope	20' Rise	20' Slope	30' Rise	30' Slope
0	0	0	5-11-7/8	11-7-7/8	11-11-3/4	23-3-3/4	17-11-5/8	34-11-5/8
1	7-3/16	1-2	6-7-1/16	12-9-7/8	12-6-15/16	24-5-3/4	18-6-13/16	36-1-5/8
2	1-2-3/8	2-3-31/32	7-2-1/4	13-11-27/32	13-2-1/8	25-7-23/32	19-2	37-3-5/8
3	1-9-9/16	3-5-31/32	7-9-7/16	15-1-27/32	13-9-5/16	26-9-23/32	19-9-3/16	38-5-19/32
4	2-4-3/4	4-7-15/16	8-4-5/8	16-3-27/32	14-4-1/2	27-11-23/32	20-4-3/8	39-7-19/32
5	2-11-15/16	5-9-15/16	8-11-13/16	17-5-13/16	14-11-11/16	29-1-11/16	20-11-9/16	40-9-9/16
6	3-7-1/8	6-11-15/16	9-7	18-7-13/16	15-6-7/8	30-3-11/16	21-6-3/4	41-11-9/16
7	4-2-5/16	8-1-29/32	10-2-3/16	19-9-25/32	16-2-1/16	31-5-11/16	22-1-15/16	43-1-9/16
8	4-9-1/2	9-3-29/32	10-9-3/8	20-11-25/32	16-9-1/4	32-7-21/32	22-9-1/8	44-3-17/32
9	5-4-11/16	10-5-29/32	11-4-9/16	22-1-25/32	17-4-7/16	33-9-21/32	23-4-5/16	45-5-17/32

A = 30° 55′ 11″; logsin A = 9.71083; logcos A = 9.93343; logtan A = 9.77740; logcot A = 0.22260

Ins.	12″ Rise	12″ Slope	13″ Rise	13″ Slope	14″ Rise	14″ Slope	15″ Rise	15″ Slope	16″ Rise	16″ Slope
0	7 3/16	1-2	7 25/32	1-3 5/32–	8 3/8	1-4 5/16	9	1-5 1/2	9 19/32–	1-6 21/32–
1/16	7 7/32	1-2 1/16	7 13/16	1-3 7/32	8 7/16	1-4 13/32–	9 1/32–	1-5 9/16	9 5/8	1-6 23/32
1/8	7 1/4	1-2 1/8	7 7/8	1-3 5/16	8 15/32–	1-4 15/32–	9 1/16	1-5 5/8	9 21/32	1-6 25/32
3/16	7 5/16	1-2 7/32–	7 29/32–	1-3 3/8	8 1/2	1-4 17/32	9 3/32	1-5 23/32–	9 11/16	1-6 7/8
1/4	7 11/32–	1-2 9/32–	7 15/16	1-3 7/16	8 17/32	1-4 5/8	9 1/8	1-5 25/32–	9 23/32	1-6 15/16
5/16	7 3/8	1-2 11/32	7 31/32	1-3 17/32–	8 9/16	1-4 11/16	9 5/32	1-5 27/32	9 25/32–	1-7
3/8	7 13/32	1-2 7/16	8	1-3 19/32–	8 5/8	1-4 3/4	9 7/32–	1-5 15/16	9 13/16	1-7 3/32–
7/16	7 7/16	1-2 1/2	8 1/16	1-3 21/32	8 21/32–	1-4 27/32–	9 1/4	1-6	9 27/32	1-7 5/32
1/2	7 1/2	1-2 9/16	8 3/32–	1-3 3/4	8 11/16	1-4 29/32–	9 9/32	1-6 1/16	9 7/8	1-7 7/32
9/16	7 17/32–	1-2 21/32–	8 1/8	1-3 13/16	8 23/32	1-4 31/32	9 5/16	1-6 1/8	9 29/32	1-7 5/16
5/8	7 9/16	1-2 23/32–	8 5/32	1-3 7/8	8 3/4	1-5 1/16	9 11/32	1-6 7/32–	9 31/32–	1-7 3/8
11/16	7 19/32	1-2 25/32	8 3/16	1-3 31/32–	8 13/16	1-5 1/8	9 13/32–	1-6 9/32	10	1-7 7/16
3/4	7 5/8	1-2 7/8	8 1/4	1-4 1/32–	8 27/32–	1-5 3/16	9 7/16	1-6 11/32	10 1/32	1-7 17/32–
13/16	7 11/16	1-2 15/16	8 9/32–	1-4 3/32	8 7/8	1-5 9/32–	9 15/32	1-6 7/16	10 1/16	1-7 19/32
7/8	7 23/32–	1-3	8 5/16	1-4 3/16	8 29/32	1-5 11/32–	9 1/2	1-6 1/2	10 3/32	1-7 21/32
15/16	7 3/4	1-3 3/32–	8 11/32	1-4 1/4	8 15/16	1-5 13/32	9 17/32	1-6 9/16	10 5/32–	1-7 3/4

Ins.	17″ Rise	17″ Slope	18″ Rise	18″ Slope	19″ Rise	19″ Slope	20″ Rise	20″ Slope	21″ Rise	21″ Slope
0	10 3/16	1-7 13/16	10 25/32	1-8 31/32	11 3/8	1-10 5/32–	11 31/32	1-11 5/16	1-0 9/16	2-0 15/32
1/16	10 7/32	1-7 7/8	10 13/16	1-9 1/16	11 13/32	1-10 7/32	1-0 1/32–	1-11 3/8	1-0 5/8	2-0 9/16
1/8	10 1/4	1-7 31/32–	10 27/32	1-9 1/8	11 15/32–	1-10 9/32	1-0 1/16	1-11 15/32–	1-0 21/32–	2-0 5/8
3/16	10 9/32	1-8 1/32	10 29/32–	1-9 3/16	11 1/2	1-10 3/8	1-0 3/32–	1-11 17/32	1-0 11/16	2-0 11/16
1/4	10 11/32–	1-8 3/32	10 15/16	1-9 9/32–	11 17/32–	1-10 7/16	1-0 1/8	1-11 19/32	1-0 23/32	2-0 25/32–
5/16	10 3/8	1-8 3/16	10 31/32–	1-9 11/32	11 9/16	1-10 1/2	1-0 5/32	1-11 11/16	1-0 3/4	2-0 27/32–
3/8	10 13/32	1-8 1/4	11	1-9 13/32	11 19/32	1-10 19/32–	1-0 7/32–	1-11 3/4	1-0 13/16	2-0 29/32
7/16	10 7/16	1-8 5/16	11 1/32	1-9 1/2	11 21/32–	1-10 21/32	1-0 1/4	1-11 13/16	1-0 27/32–	2-1
1/2	10 15/32	1-8 13/32–	11 3/32–	1-9 9/16	11 11/16	1-10 23/32	1-0 9/32–	1-11 29/32–	1-0 7/8	2-1 1/16
9/16	10 17/32–	1-8 15/32	11 1/8	1-9 5/8	11 23/32–	1-10 13/16	1-0 5/16	1-11 31/32	1-0 29/32	2-1 1/8
5/8	10 9/16	1-8 17/32	11 5/32–	1-9 23/32–	11 3/4	1-10 7/8	1-0 11/32	2-0 1/32	1-0 15/16	2-1 7/32–
11/16	10 19/32	1-8 5/8	11 3/16	1-9 25/32	11 25/32	1-10 15/16	1-0 13/32–	2-0 1/8	1-1	2-1 9/32–
3/4	10 5/8	1-8 11/16	11 7/32	1-9 27/32	11 27/32–	1-11 1/32–	1-0 7/16	2-0 3/16	1-1 1/32–	2-1 11/32
13/16	10 21/32	1-8 3/4	11 9/32–	1-9 15/16	11 7/8	1-11 3/32	1-0 15/32–	2-0 1/4	1-1 1/16	2-1 7/16
7/8	10 23/32–	1-8 27/32–	11 5/16	1-10	11 29/32–	1-11 5/32	1-0 1/2	2-0 11/32–	1-1 3/32	2-1 1/2
15/16	10 3/4	1-8 29/32	11 11/32–	1-10 1/16	11 15/16	1-11 1/4	1-0 17/32	2-0 13/32–	1-1 1/8	2-1 9/16

Feet	40′ Rise	40′ Slope	50′ Rise	50′ Slope	60′ Rise	60′ Slope	70′ Rise	70′ Slope
0	23-11 1/2	46-7 1/2	29-11 3/8	58-3 13/32–	35-11 1/4	69-11 9/32–	41-11 1/8	81-7 5/32–
1	24-6 11/16	47-9 1/2	30-6 9/16	59-5 3/8	36-6 7/16	71-1 1/4	42-6 5/16	82-9 1/8
2	25-1 7/8	48-11 1/2	31-1 3/4	60-7 3/8	37-1 5/8	72-3 1/4	43-1 1/2	83-11 1/8
3	25-9 1/16	50-1 15/32	31-8 15/16	61-9 11/32	37-8 13/16	73-5 1/4	43-8 11/16	85-1 1/8
4	26-4 1/4	51-3 15/32–	32-4 1/8	62-11 11/32	38-4	74-7 7/32	44-3 7/8	86-3 3/32
5	26-11 7/16	52-5 15/32–	32-11 5/16	64-1 11/32–	38-11 3/16	75-9 7/32–	44-11 1/16	87-5 3/32–
6	27-6 5/8	53-7 7/16	33-6 1/2	65-3 5/16	39-6 3/8	76-11 3/16	45-6 1/4	88-7 1/16
7	28-1 13/16	54-9 7/16	34-1 11/16	66-5 5/16	40-1 9/16	78-1 3/16	46-1 7/16	89-9 1/16
8	28-9	55-11 13/32	34-8 7/8	67-7 9/32	40-8 3/4	79-3 3/16	46-8 5/8	90-11 1/16
9	29-4 3/16	57-1 13/32–	35-4 1/16	68-9 9/32	41-3 15/16	80-5 5/32	47-3 13/16	92-1 1/32

natsin A=0.5138385218; natcos A=0.8578869234; nattan A=0.5989583333; natcot A=1.6695652173

Inches	0" Rise	0" Slope	1" Rise	1" Slope	2" Rise	2" Slope	3" Rise	3" Slope	4" Rise	4" Slope	5" Rise	5" Slope
0	0	0	19/32	1 5/32	1 7/32	2 11/32	1 13/16	3 1/2	2 13/32	4 11/16	3 1/32	5 27/32
1/16	1/32	1/16	21/32	1 1/4	1 1/4	2 13/32	1 27/32	3 9/16	2 15/32	4 3/4	3 1/16	5 29/32
1/8	1/16	5/32	11/16	1 5/16	1 9/32	2 15/32	1 7/8	3 21/32	2 1/2	4 13/16	3 3/32	6
3/16	1/8	7/32	23/32	1 3/8	1 5/16	2 9/16	1 15/16	3 23/32	2 17/32	4 29/32	3 1/8	6 1/16
1/4	5/32	9/32	3/4	1 15/32	1 3/8	2 5/8	1 31/32	3 13/16	2 9/16	4 31/32	3 3/16	6 1/8
5/16	3/16	3/8	25/32	1 17/32	1 13/32	2 11/16	2	3 7/8	2 19/32	5 1/32	3 7/32	6 1/4
3/8	7/32	7/16	27/32	1 19/32	1 7/16	2 25/32	2 1/16	3 15/16	2 21/32	5 1/8	3 1/4	6 9/32
7/16	1/4	1/2	7/8	1 11/16	1 15/32	2 27/32	2 1/16	4 1/32	2 11/16	5 3/16	3 9/32	6 11/32
1/2	5/16	19/32	29/32	1 3/4	1 1/2	2 29/32	2 1/8	4 3/32	2 23/32	5 1/4	3 5/16	6 7/16
9/16	11/32	21/32	15/16	1 13/16	1 9/16	3	2 5/32	4 5/32	2 3/4	5 11/32	3 3/8	6 1/2
5/8	3/8	23/32	31/32	1 29/32	1 19/32	3 1/16	2 3/16	4 1/4	2 25/32	5 13/32	3 13/32	6 9/16
11/16	13/32	13/16	1 1/32	1 31/32	1 5/8	3 1/8	2 1/4	4 5/16	2 27/32	5 15/32	3 7/16	6 21/32
3/4	7/16	7/8	1 1/16	2 1/32	1 21/32	3 7/32	2 1/4	4 3/8	2 7/8	5 9/16	3 15/32	6 23/32
13/16	1/2	15/16	1 3/32	2 1/8	1 11/16	3 9/32	2 5/16	4 15/32	2 29/32	5 5/8	3 1/2	6 25/32
7/8	17/32	1 1/32	1 1/8	2 3/16	1 3/4	3 11/32	2 11/32	4 17/32	2 15/16	5 11/16	3 9/16	6 7/8
15/16	9/16	1 3/32	1 5/32	2 1/4	1 25/32	3 7/16	2 3/8	4 19/32	2 31/32	5 25/32	3 19/32	6 15/16

Inches	6" Rise	6" Slope	7" Rise	7" Slope	8" Rise	8" Slope	9" Rise	9" Slope	10" Rise	10" Slope	11" Rise	11" Slope
0	3 5/8	7	4 7/32	8 3/16	4 27/32	9 11/32	5 7/16	10 1/2	6 1/32	11 11/16	6 21/32	1-0 27/32
1/16	3 21/32	7 3/32	4 9/32	8 1/4	4 7/8	9 13/32	5 15/32	10 19/32	6 3/32	11 3/4	6 11/16	1-0 15/16
1/8	3 11/16	7 5/32	4 5/16	8 5/16	4 29/32	9 1/2	5 1/2	10 21/32	6 1/8	11 27/32	6 23/32	1-1
3/16	3 3/4	7 7/32	4 11/32	8 13/32	4 15/16	9 9/16	5 9/16	10 23/32	6 5/32	11 29/32	6 3/4	1-1 1/16
1/4	3 25/32	7 5/16	4 3/8	8 15/32	5	9 5/8	5 19/32	10 13/16	6 3/16	11 31/32	6 13/16	1-1 5/32
5/16	3 13/16	7 3/8	4 13/32	8 17/32	5 1/32	9 23/32	5 5/8	10 7/8	6 7/32	1-0 1/16	6 27/32	1-1 7/32
3/8	3 27/32	7 7/16	4 15/32	8 5/8	5 1/16	9 25/32	5 21/32	10 31/32	6 1/4	1-0 1/8	6 7/8	1-1 9/32
7/16	3 7/8	7 17/32	4 1/2	8 11/16	5 3/32	9 27/32	5 11/16	11 1/32	6 5/16	1-0 3/16	6 29/32	1-1 3/8
1/2	3 15/16	7 19/32	4 17/32	8 3/4	5 1/8	9 15/16	5 3/4	11 3/32	6 11/32	1-0 9/32	6 15/16	1-1 7/16
9/16	3 31/32	7 21/32	4 9/16	8 27/32	5 3/16	10	5 25/32	11 3/16	6 3/8	1-0 11/32	7	1-1 1/2
5/8	4	7 3/4	4 19/32	8 29/32	5 7/32	10 1/16	5 13/16	11 1/4	6 13/32	1-0 13/32	7 1/32	1-1 19/32
11/16	4 1/32	7 13/16	4 21/32	8 31/32	5 1/4	10 5/32	5 27/32	11 5/16	6 15/32	1-0 1/2	7 1/16	1-1 21/32
3/4	4 1/16	7 7/8	4 11/16	9 1/16	5 9/32	10 7/32	5 7/8	11 13/32	6 1/2	1-0 9/16	7 3/32	1-1 23/32
13/16	4 1/8	7 31/32	4 23/32	9 1/8	5 5/16	10 9/32	5 15/16	11 15/32	6 17/32	1-0 5/8	7 1/8	1-1 13/16
7/8	4 5/32	8 1/32	4 3/4	9 3/16	5 3/8	10 3/8	5 31/32	11 17/32	6 9/16	1-0 23/32	7 3/16	1-1 7/8
15/16	4 3/16	8 3/32	4 25/32	9 9/32	5 13/32	10 7/16	6	11 5/8	6 19/32	1-0 25/32	7 7/32	1-1 15/16

Feet	0' Rise	0' Slope	10' Rise	10' Slope	20' Rise	20' Slope	30' Rise	30' Slope
0	0	0	6-0 1/2	11-8 3/16	12-1	23-4 13/32	18-1 1/2	35-0 19/32
1	7 1/4	1-2 1/2	6-7 3/4	12-10 7/32	12-8 1/4	24-6 13/32	18-8 3/4	36-2 5/8
2	1-2 1/2	2-4 1/2	7-3	14-0 1/4	13-3 1/2	25-8 7/16	19-4	37-4 21/32
3	1-9 3/4	3-6 1/16	7-10 1/4	15-2 1/4	13-10 3/4	26-10 15/32	19-11 1/4	38-6 21/32
4	2-5	4-8 3/32	8-5 1/2	16-4 9/32	14-6	28-0 15/32	20-6 1/2	39-8 11/16
5	3-0 1/4	5-10 3/32	9-0 3/4	17-6 5/16	15-1 1/4	29-2 1/2	21-1 3/4	40-10 11/16
6	3-7 1/2	7-0 1/8	9-8	18-8 5/16	15-8 1/2	30-4 17/32	21-9	42-0 23/32
7	4-2 3/4	8-2 1/8	10-3 1/4	19-10 11/32	16-3 3/4	31-6 17/32	22-4 1/4	43-2 3/4
8	4-10	9-4 5/32	10-10 1/2	21-0 3/8	16-11	32-8 9/16	22-11 1/2	44-4 3/4
9	5-5 1/4	10-6 3/16	11-5 3/4	22-2 3/8	17-6 1/4	33-10 19/32	23-6 3/4	45-6 25/32

A = 31° 08' 20''; logsin A = 9.71359; logcos A = 9.93243; logtan A = 9.78116; logcot A = 0.21884

Ins.	12″ Rise	12″ Slope	13″ Rise	13″ Slope	14″ Rise	14″ Slope	15″ Rise	15″ Slope	16″ Rise	16″ Slope
0	$7\frac{1}{4}$	$1\text{-}2\frac{1}{8}$	$7\frac{27}{32}$	$1\text{-}3\frac{3}{16}$	$8\frac{15}{32}$	$1\text{-}4\frac{11}{32}$	$9\frac{1}{16}$	$1\text{-}5\frac{17}{32}$	$9\frac{21}{32}$	$1\text{-}6\frac{11}{16}$
1/16	$7\frac{9}{32}$	$1\text{-}2\frac{3}{32}$	$7\frac{29}{32}$	$1\text{-}3\frac{1}{4}$	$8\frac{1}{2}$	$1\text{-}4\frac{7}{16}$	$9\frac{3}{32}$	$1\text{-}5\frac{19}{32}$	$9\frac{23}{32}$	$1\text{-}6\frac{25}{32}$
1/8	$7\frac{5}{16}$	$1\text{-}2\frac{5}{32}$	$7\frac{15}{16}$	$1\text{-}3\frac{11}{32}$	$8\frac{17}{32}$	$1\text{-}4\frac{1}{2}$	$9\frac{1}{8}$	$1\text{-}5\frac{21}{32}$	$9\frac{3}{4}$	$1\text{-}6\frac{27}{32}$
3/16	$7\frac{3}{8}$	$1\text{-}2\frac{1}{4}$	$7\frac{31}{32}$	$1\text{-}3\frac{13}{32}$	$8\frac{9}{16}$	$1\text{-}4\frac{9}{16}$	$9\frac{3}{16}$	$1\text{-}5\frac{3}{4}$	$9\frac{25}{32}$	$1\text{-}6\frac{29}{32}$
1/4	$7\frac{13}{32}$	$1\text{-}2\frac{5}{16}$	8	$1\text{-}3\frac{15}{32}$	$8\frac{5}{8}$	$1\text{-}4\frac{21}{32}$	$9\frac{7}{32}$	$1\text{-}5\frac{13}{16}$	$9\frac{13}{16}$	$1\text{-}7$
5/16	$7\frac{7}{16}$	$1\text{-}2\frac{3}{8}$	$8\frac{1}{32}$	$1\text{-}3\frac{9}{16}$	$8\frac{21}{32}$	$1\text{-}4\frac{23}{32}$	$9\frac{1}{4}$	$1\text{-}5\frac{7}{8}$	$9\frac{27}{32}$	$1\text{-}7\frac{1}{16}$
3/8	$7\frac{15}{32}$	$1\text{-}2\frac{15}{32}$	$8\frac{3}{32}$	$1\text{-}3\frac{5}{8}$	$8\frac{11}{16}$	$1\text{-}4\frac{25}{32}$	$9\frac{9}{32}$	$1\text{-}5\frac{31}{32}$	$9\frac{29}{32}$	$1\text{-}7\frac{1}{8}$
7/16	$7\frac{1}{2}$	$1\text{-}2\frac{17}{32}$	$8\frac{1}{8}$	$1\text{-}3\frac{11}{16}$	$8\frac{23}{32}$	$1\text{-}4\frac{7}{8}$	$9\frac{5}{16}$	$1\text{-}6\frac{1}{32}$	$9\frac{15}{16}$	$1\text{-}7\frac{7}{32}$
1/2	$7\frac{9}{16}$	$1\text{-}2\frac{19}{32}$	$8\frac{5}{32}$	$1\text{-}3\frac{25}{32}$	$8\frac{3}{4}$	$1\text{-}4\frac{15}{16}$	$9\frac{3}{8}$	$1\text{-}6\frac{3}{32}$	$9\frac{31}{32}$	$1\text{-}7\frac{9}{32}$
9/16	$7\frac{19}{32}$	$1\text{-}2\frac{11}{16}$	$8\frac{3}{16}$	$1\text{-}3\frac{27}{32}$	$8\frac{13}{16}$	$1\text{-}5$	$9\frac{13}{32}$	$1\text{-}6\frac{3}{16}$	10	$1\text{-}7\frac{11}{16}$
5/8	$7\frac{5}{8}$	$1\text{-}2\frac{3}{4}$	$8\frac{7}{32}$	$1\text{-}3\frac{29}{32}$	$8\frac{27}{32}$	$1\text{-}5\frac{3}{32}$	$9\frac{7}{16}$	$1\text{-}6\frac{1}{4}$	$10\frac{1}{32}$	$1\text{-}7\frac{7}{16}$
11/16	$7\frac{21}{32}$	$1\text{-}2\frac{13}{16}$	$8\frac{9}{32}$	$1\text{-}4$	$8\frac{7}{8}$	$1\text{-}5\frac{5}{32}$	$9\frac{15}{32}$	$1\text{-}6\frac{11}{32}$	$10\frac{3}{32}$	$1\text{-}7\frac{1}{2}$
3/4	$7\frac{11}{16}$	$1\text{-}2\frac{29}{32}$	$8\frac{5}{16}$	$1\text{-}4\frac{1}{16}$	$8\frac{29}{32}$	$1\text{-}5\frac{7}{32}$	$9\frac{1}{2}$	$1\text{-}6\frac{13}{32}$	$10\frac{1}{8}$	$1\text{-}7\frac{5}{8}$
13/16	$7\frac{3}{4}$	$1\text{-}2\frac{31}{32}$	$8\frac{11}{32}$	$1\text{-}4\frac{1}{8}$	$8\frac{15}{16}$	$1\text{-}5\frac{5}{16}$	$9\frac{9}{16}$	$1\text{-}6\frac{15}{32}$	$10\frac{5}{32}$	$1\text{-}7\frac{21}{32}$
7/8	$7\frac{25}{32}$	$1\text{-}3\frac{1}{16}$	$8\frac{3}{8}$	$1\text{-}4\frac{7}{32}$	9	$1\text{-}5\frac{3}{8}$	$9\frac{19}{32}$	$1\text{-}6\frac{9}{16}$	$10\frac{3}{16}$	$1\text{-}7\frac{23}{32}$
15/16	$7\frac{13}{16}$	$1\text{-}3\frac{1}{8}$	$8\frac{13}{32}$	$1\text{-}4\frac{9}{32}$	$9\frac{1}{32}$	$1\text{-}5\frac{7}{16}$	$9\frac{5}{8}$	$1\text{-}6\frac{5}{8}$	$10\frac{7}{32}$	$1\text{-}7\frac{25}{32}$

Ins.	17″ Rise	17″ Slope	18″ Rise	18″ Slope	19″ Rise	19″ Slope	20″ Rise	20″ Slope	21″ Rise	21″ Slope
0	$10\frac{9}{32}$	$1\text{-}7\frac{7}{8}$	$10\frac{7}{8}$	$1\text{-}9\frac{1}{16}$	$11\frac{15}{32}$	$1\text{-}10\frac{3}{16}$	$1\text{-}0\frac{3}{32}$	$1\text{-}11\frac{3}{8}$	$1\text{-}0\frac{11}{16}$	$2\text{-}0\frac{17}{32}$
1/16	$10\frac{5}{16}$	$1\text{-}7\frac{15}{16}$	$10\frac{29}{32}$	$1\text{-}9\frac{3}{32}$	$11\frac{17}{32}$	$1\text{-}10\frac{9}{32}$	$1\text{-}0\frac{1}{8}$	$1\text{-}11\frac{7}{16}$	$1\text{-}0\frac{23}{32}$	$2\text{-}0\frac{19}{32}$
1/8	$10\frac{11}{32}$	$1\text{-}8$	$10\frac{15}{16}$	$1\text{-}9\frac{3}{16}$	$11\frac{9}{16}$	$1\text{-}10\frac{11}{32}$	$1\text{-}0\frac{5}{32}$	$1\text{-}11\frac{1}{2}$	$1\text{-}0\frac{3}{4}$	$2\text{-}0\frac{11}{16}$
3/16	$10\frac{3}{8}$	$1\text{-}8\frac{3}{32}$	11	$1\text{-}9\frac{1}{4}$	$11\frac{19}{32}$	$1\text{-}10\frac{13}{32}$	$1\text{-}0\frac{3}{16}$	$1\text{-}11\frac{19}{32}$	$1\text{-}0\frac{13}{16}$	$2\text{-}0\frac{3}{4}$
1/4	$10\frac{7}{16}$	$1\text{-}8\frac{5}{32}$	$11\frac{1}{32}$	$1\text{-}9\frac{5}{16}$	$11\frac{5}{8}$	$1\text{-}10\frac{1}{2}$	$1\text{-}0\frac{1}{4}$	$1\text{-}11\frac{21}{32}$	$1\text{-}0\frac{27}{32}$	$2\text{-}0\frac{13}{16}$
5/16	$10\frac{15}{32}$	$1\text{-}8\frac{7}{32}$	$11\frac{1}{16}$	$1\text{-}9\frac{13}{32}$	$11\frac{21}{32}$	$1\text{-}10\frac{9}{16}$	$1\text{-}0\frac{9}{32}$	$1\text{-}11\frac{23}{32}$	$1\text{-}0\frac{7}{8}$	$2\text{-}0\frac{29}{32}$
3/8	$10\frac{1}{2}$	$1\text{-}8\frac{5}{16}$	$11\frac{3}{32}$	$1\text{-}9\frac{15}{32}$	$11\frac{23}{32}$	$1\text{-}10\frac{5}{8}$	$1\text{-}0\frac{5}{16}$	$1\text{-}11\frac{13}{16}$	$1\text{-}0\frac{29}{32}$	$2\text{-}0\frac{31}{32}$
7/16	$10\frac{17}{32}$	$1\text{-}8\frac{3}{8}$	$11\frac{1}{8}$	$1\text{-}9\frac{17}{32}$	$11\frac{3}{4}$	$1\text{-}10\frac{23}{32}$	$1\text{-}0\frac{11}{32}$	$1\text{-}11\frac{7}{8}$	$1\text{-}0\frac{15}{16}$	$2\text{-}1\frac{1}{32}$
1/2	$10\frac{9}{16}$	$1\text{-}8\frac{7}{16}$	$11\frac{3}{16}$	$1\text{-}9\frac{5}{8}$	$11\frac{25}{32}$	$1\text{-}10\frac{25}{32}$	$1\text{-}0\frac{3}{8}$	$1\text{-}11\frac{15}{16}$	$1\text{-}1$	$2\text{-}1\frac{1}{8}$
9/16	$10\frac{5}{8}$	$1\text{-}8\frac{17}{32}$	$11\frac{7}{32}$	$1\text{-}9\frac{11}{16}$	$11\frac{13}{16}$	$1\text{-}10\frac{27}{32}$	$1\text{-}0\frac{7}{16}$	$2\text{-}0\frac{1}{32}$	$1\text{-}1\frac{1}{32}$	$2\text{-}1\frac{3}{16}$
5/8	$10\frac{21}{32}$	$1\text{-}8\frac{19}{32}$	$11\frac{1}{4}$	$1\text{-}9\frac{3}{4}$	$11\frac{27}{32}$	$1\text{-}10\frac{15}{16}$	$1\text{-}0\frac{15}{32}$	$2\text{-}0\frac{3}{32}$	$1\text{-}1\frac{1}{16}$	$2\text{-}1\frac{1}{4}$
11/16	$10\frac{11}{16}$	$1\text{-}8\frac{21}{32}$	$11\frac{9}{32}$	$1\text{-}9\frac{27}{32}$	$11\frac{29}{32}$	$1\text{-}11$	$1\text{-}0\frac{1}{2}$	$2\text{-}0\frac{5}{32}$	$1\text{-}1\frac{3}{32}$	$2\text{-}1\frac{11}{32}$
3/4	$10\frac{23}{32}$	$1\text{-}8\frac{3}{4}$	$11\frac{5}{16}$	$1\text{-}9\frac{29}{32}$	$11\frac{15}{16}$	$1\text{-}11\frac{1}{16}$	$1\text{-}0\frac{17}{32}$	$2\text{-}0\frac{1}{4}$	$1\text{-}1\frac{1}{8}$	$2\text{-}1\frac{13}{32}$
13/16	$10\frac{3}{4}$	$1\text{-}8\frac{13}{16}$	$11\frac{3}{8}$	$1\text{-}9\frac{31}{32}$	$11\frac{31}{32}$	$1\text{-}11\frac{5}{32}$	$1\text{-}0\frac{9}{16}$	$2\text{-}0\frac{5}{16}$	$1\text{-}1\frac{3}{16}$	$2\text{-}1\frac{1}{2}$
7/8	$10\frac{13}{16}$	$1\text{-}8\frac{7}{8}$	$11\frac{13}{32}$	$1\text{-}10\frac{1}{16}$	$1\text{-}0$	$1\text{-}11\frac{3}{32}$	$1\text{-}0\frac{5}{8}$	$2\text{-}0\frac{3}{8}$	$1\text{-}1\frac{7}{32}$	$2\text{-}1\frac{9}{16}$
15/16	$10\frac{27}{32}$	$1\text{-}8\frac{31}{32}$	$11\frac{7}{16}$	$1\text{-}10\frac{1}{8}$	$1\text{-}0\frac{1}{32}$	$1\text{-}11\frac{9}{32}$	$1\text{-}0\frac{21}{32}$	$2\text{-}0\frac{15}{32}$	$1\text{-}1\frac{1}{4}$	$2\text{-}1\frac{5}{8}$

Feet	40′ Rise	40′ Slope	50′ Rise	50′ Slope	60′ Rise	60′ Slope	70′ Rise	70′ Slope
0	24-2	$46\text{-}8\frac{13}{16}$	$30\text{-}2\frac{1}{2}$	58-5	36-3	$70\text{-}1\frac{7}{32}$	$42\text{-}3\frac{1}{2}$	$81\text{-}9\frac{13}{32}$
1	$24\text{-}9\frac{1}{4}$	$47\text{-}10\frac{13}{16}$	$30\text{-}9\frac{3}{4}$	$59\text{-}7\frac{1}{32}$	$36\text{-}10\frac{1}{4}$	$71\text{-}3\frac{7}{32}$	$42\text{-}10\frac{3}{4}$	$82\text{-}11\frac{7}{16}$
2	$25\text{-}4\frac{1}{2}$	$49\text{-}0\frac{27}{32}$	31-5	$60\text{-}9\frac{1}{32}$	$37\text{-}5\frac{1}{2}$	$72\text{-}5\frac{1}{4}$	43-6	$84\text{-}1\frac{7}{16}$
3	$25\text{-}11\frac{3}{4}$	$50\text{-}2\frac{7}{8}$	$32\text{-}0\frac{1}{4}$	$61\text{-}11\frac{1}{16}$	$38\text{-}0\frac{3}{4}$	$73\text{-}7\frac{1}{4}$	$44\text{-}1\frac{1}{4}$	$85\text{-}3\frac{15}{32}$
4	26-7	$51\text{-}4\frac{7}{8}$	$32\text{-}7\frac{1}{2}$	$63\text{-}1\frac{3}{32}$	38-8	$74\text{-}9\frac{9}{32}$	$44\text{-}8\frac{1}{2}$	$86\text{-}5\frac{1}{2}$
5	$27\text{-}2\frac{1}{4}$	$52\text{-}6\frac{29}{32}$	$33\text{-}2\frac{3}{4}$	$64\text{-}3\frac{3}{32}$	$39\text{-}3\frac{1}{4}$	$75\text{-}11\frac{5}{16}$	$45\text{-}3\frac{3}{4}$	$87\text{-}7\frac{1}{2}$
6	$27\text{-}9\frac{1}{2}$	$53\text{-}8\frac{15}{16}$	33-10	$65\text{-}5\frac{1}{8}$	$39\text{-}10\frac{1}{2}$	$77\text{-}1\frac{5}{16}$	45-11	$88\text{-}9\frac{17}{32}$
7	$28\text{-}4\frac{3}{4}$	$54\text{-}10\frac{15}{16}$	$34\text{-}5\frac{1}{4}$	$66\text{-}7\frac{5}{32}$	$40\text{-}5\frac{3}{4}$	$78\text{-}3\frac{11}{32}$	$46\text{-}6\frac{1}{4}$	$89\text{-}11\frac{17}{32}$
8	29-0	$56\text{-}0\frac{31}{32}$	$35\text{-}0\frac{1}{2}$	$67\text{-}9\frac{5}{32}$	41-1	$79\text{-}5\frac{3}{8}$	$47\text{-}1\frac{1}{2}$	$91\text{-}1\frac{9}{16}$
9	$29\text{-}7\frac{1}{4}$	$57\text{-}2\frac{31}{32}$	$35\text{-}7\frac{3}{4}$	$68\text{-}11\frac{3}{16}$	$41\text{-}8\frac{1}{4}$	$80\text{-}7\frac{3}{8}$	$47\text{-}8\frac{3}{4}$	$92\text{-}3\frac{19}{32}$

natsin A=0.5171156398; natcos A=0.8559155419; nattan A=0.6041666666; natcot A=1.6551724137

Inches	0″ Rise	0″ Slope	1″ Rise	1″ Slope	2″ Rise	2″ Slope	3″ Rise	3″ Slope	4″ Rise	4″ Slope	5″ Rise	5″ Slope
0	0	0	5/8	1 5/32	1 7/32	2 11/32	1 13/16	3 1/2	2 7/16	4 11/16	3 1/16	5 27/32
1/16	1/32	1/16	21/32	1 1/4	1 1/4	2 13/32	1 7/8	3 19/32	2 15/32	4 3/4	3 3/32	5 15/16
1/8	1/16	5/32	11/16	1 5/16	1 9/32	2 1/2	1 29/32	3 21/32	2 1/2	4 27/32	3 1/8	6
3/16	1/8	7/32	23/32	1 3/8	1 11/32	2 9/16	1 15/16	3 23/32	2 9/16	4 29/32	3 5/32	6 1/16
1/4	5/32	9/32	3/4	1 15/32	1 3/8	2 5/8	1 31/32	3 13/16	2 19/32	4 31/32	3 3/16	6 5/32
5/16	3/16	3/8	13/16	1 17/32	1 13/32	2 23/32	2 1/32	3 7/8	2 5/8	5 1/16	3 1/4	6 7/32
3/8	7/32	7/16	27/32	1 5/8	1 7/16	2 25/32	2 1/16	3 15/16	2 21/32	5 1/8	3 9/32	6 9/32
7/16	9/32	1/2	7/8	1 11/16	1 1/2	2 27/32	2 3/32	4 1/32	2 23/32	5 3/16	3 5/16	6 3/8
1/2	5/16	19/32	29/32	1 3/4	1 17/32	2 15/16	2 1/8	4 3/32	2 3/4	5 9/32	3 11/32	6 7/16
9/16	11/32	21/32	15/16	1 27/32	1 9/16	3	2 5/32	4 5/32	2 25/32	5 11/32	3 3/8	6 1/2
5/8	3/8	23/32	1	1 29/32	1 19/32	3 1/16	2 7/32	4 1/4	2 13/16	5 13/32	3 7/16	6 19/32
11/16	13/32	13/16	1 1/32	1 31/32	1 5/8	3 5/32	2 1/4	4 5/16	2 27/32	5 1/2	3 15/32	6 21/32
3/4	15/32	7/8	1 1/16	2 1/16	1 11/16	3 7/32	2 9/32	4 13/32	2 29/32	5 9/16	3 1/2	6 23/32
13/16	1/2	15/16	1 3/32	2 1/8	1 23/32	3 9/32	2 5/16	4 15/32	2 15/16	5 5/8	3 17/32	6 13/16
7/8	17/32	1 1/32	1 5/32	2 3/16	1 3/4	3 3/8	2 3/8	4 17/32	2 31/32	5 23/32	3 19/32	6 7/8
15/16	9/16	1 3/32	1 3/16	2 9/32	1 25/32	3 7/16	2 13/32	4 5/8	3	5 25/32	3 5/8	6 15/16

Inches	6″ Rise	6″ Slope	7″ Rise	7″ Slope	8″ Rise	8″ Slope	9″ Rise	9″ Slope	10″ Rise	10″ Slope	11″ Rise	11″ Slope
0	3 21/32	7 1/32	4 1/4	8 3/16	4 7/8	9 3/8	5 1/2	10 17/32	6 3/32	11 23/32	6 11/16	1-0 7/8
1/16	3 11/16	7 3/32	4 5/16	8 9/32	4 29/32	9 7/16	5 17/32	10 5/8	6 1/8	11 25/32	6 3/4	1-0 31/32
1/8	3 23/32	7 3/16	4 11/32	8 11/32	4 15/16	9 1/2	5 9/16	10 11/16	6 5/32	11 27/32	6 25/32	1-1 1/32
3/16	3 25/32	7 1/4	4 3/8	8 15/32	5	9 19/32	5 19/32	10 3/4	6 7/32	11 15/16	6 13/16	1-1 3/32
1/4	3 13/16	7 5/16	4 13/32	8 1/2	5 1/32	9 21/32	5 5/8	10 27/32	6 1/4	1-0	6 27/32	1-1 3/16
5/16	3 27/32	7 13/32	4 15/32	8 9/16	5 1/16	9 23/32	5 11/16	10 29/32	6 9/32	1-0 1/16	6 29/32	1-1 1/4
3/8	3 7/8	7 15/32	4 1/2	8 5/8	5 3/32	9 13/16	5 23/32	10 31/32	6 5/16	1-0 5/32	6 15/16	1-1 5/16
7/16	3 15/16	7 17/32	4 17/32	8 23/32	5 5/32	9 7/8	5 3/4	11 1/16	6 3/8	1-0 7/32	6 31/32	1-1 13/32
1/2	3 31/32	7 5/8	4 9/16	8 25/32	5 3/16	9 31/32	5 25/32	11 1/8	6 13/32	1-0 9/32	7	1-1 15/32
9/16	4	7 11/16	4 19/32	8 27/32	5 7/32	10 1/32	5 13/16	11 3/16	6 7/16	1-0 3/8	7 1/32	1-1 17/32
5/8	4 1/32	7 3/4	4 21/32	8 15/16	5 1/4	10 3/32	5 7/8	11 9/32	6 15/32	1-0 7/16	7 3/32	1-1 5/8
11/16	4 1/16	7 27/32	4 11/16	9	5 9/32	10 3/16	5 29/32	11 11/32	6 1/2	1-0 1/2	7 1/8	1-1 11/16
3/4	4 1/8	7 29/32	4 23/32	9 1/16	5 11/32	10 1/4	5 15/16	11 13/32	6 9/16	1-0 19/32	7 5/32	1-1 3/4
13/16	4 5/32	7 31/32	4 3/4	9 5/32	5 3/8	10 5/16	5 31/32	11 1/2	6 19/32	1-0 21/32	7 3/16	1-1 27/32
7/8	4 3/16	8 1/16	4 13/16	9 7/32	5 13/32	10 13/32	6 1/32	11 9/16	6 5/8	1-0 3/4	7 1/4	1-1 29/32
15/16	4 7/32	8 1/8	4 27/32	9 9/32	5 7/16	10 15/32	6 1/16	11 5/8	6 21/32	1-0 13/16	7 9/32	1-1 31/32

Feet	0′ Rise	0′ Slope	10′ Rise	10′ Slope	20′ Rise	20′ Slope	30′ Rise	30′ Slope
0	0	0	6-1 1/8	11-8 17/32	12-2 1/4	23-5 1/16	18-3 3/8	35-1 9/16
1	7 5/16	1-2 1/16	6-8 7/16	12-10 9/16	12-9 9/16	24-7 9/32	18-10 11/16	36-3 5/8
2	1-2 5/8	2-4 3/32	7-3 3/4	14-0 5/8	13-4 7/8	25-9 5/32	19-6	37-5 11/16
3	1-9 15/16	3-6 5/32	7-11 1/16	15-2 11/16	14-0 3/16	26-11 7/32	20-1 5/16	38-7 23/32
4	2-5 1/4	4-8 7/32	8-6 3/8	16-4 3/4	14-7 1/2	28-1 1/4	20-8 5/8	39-9 25/32
5	3-0 9/16	5-10 1/4	9-1 11/16	17-6 25/32	15-2 13/16	29-3 5/16	21-3 15/16	40-11 27/32
6	3-7 7/8	7-0 5/16	9-9	18-8 27/32	15-10 1/8	30-5 3/8	21-11 1/4	42-1 7/8
7	4-3 3/16	8-2 3/8	10-4 5/16	19-10 29/32	16-5 7/16	31-7 3/8	22-6 9/16	43-3 15/16
8	4-10 1/2	9-4 13/32	10-11 5/8	21-0 15/16	17-0 3/4	32-9 15/32	23-1 7/8	44-6
9	5-5 13/16	10-6 15/32	11-6 15/16	22-3	17-8 1/16	33-11 17/32	23-9 3/16	45-8 1/16

A = 31° 21′ 26″; logsin A = 9.71631; logcos A = 9.93143; logtan A = 9.78488; logcot A = 0.21512

Ins.	12" Rise	12" Slope	13" Rise	13" Slope	14" Rise	14" Slope	15" Rise	15" Slope	16" Rise	16" Slope
0	$7\frac{5}{16}$	$1\text{-}2\frac{1}{16}$	$7\frac{15}{16}$	$1\text{-}3\frac{7}{32}$	$8\frac{17}{32}$	$1\text{-}4\frac{13}{32}$	$9\frac{1}{8}$	$1\text{-}5\frac{9}{16}$	$9\frac{3}{4}$	$1\text{-}6\frac{3}{4}$
$\frac{1}{16}$	$7\frac{11}{32}$	$1\text{-}2\frac{1}{8}$	$7\frac{31}{32}$	$1\text{-}3\frac{9}{32}$	$8\frac{9}{16}$	$1\text{-}4\frac{15}{32}$	$9\frac{3}{16}$	$1\text{-}5\frac{5}{8}$	$9\frac{25}{32}$	$1\text{-}6\frac{13}{16}$
$\frac{1}{8}$	$7\frac{3}{8}$	$1\text{-}2\frac{3}{16}$	8	$1\text{-}3\frac{3}{8}$	$8\frac{19}{32}$	$1\text{-}4\frac{17}{32}$	$9\frac{7}{32}$	$1\text{-}5\frac{23}{32}$	$9\frac{13}{16}$	$1\text{-}6\frac{7}{8}$
$\frac{3}{16}$	$7\frac{7}{16}$	$1\text{-}2\frac{9}{32}$	$8\frac{1}{32}$	$1\text{-}3\frac{7}{16}$	$8\frac{21}{32}$	$1\text{-}4\frac{5}{8}$	$9\frac{1}{4}$	$1\text{-}5\frac{25}{32}$	$9\frac{7}{8}$	$1\text{-}6\frac{31}{32}$
$\frac{1}{4}$	$7\frac{15}{32}$	$1\text{-}2\frac{11}{32}$	$8\frac{1}{16}$	$1\text{-}3\frac{17}{32}$	$8\frac{11}{16}$	$1\text{-}4\frac{11}{16}$	$9\frac{9}{32}$	$1\text{-}5\frac{27}{32}$	$9\frac{29}{32}$	$1\text{-}7\frac{1}{32}$
$\frac{5}{16}$	$7\frac{1}{2}$	$1\text{-}2\frac{13}{32}$	$8\frac{1}{8}$	$1\text{-}3\frac{19}{32}$	$8\frac{23}{32}$	$1\text{-}4\frac{3}{4}$	$9\frac{11}{32}$	$1\text{-}5\frac{15}{16}$	$9\frac{15}{16}$	$1\text{-}7\frac{3}{32}$
$\frac{3}{8}$	$7\frac{17}{32}$	$1\text{-}2\frac{1}{2}$	$8\frac{5}{32}$	$1\text{-}3\frac{21}{32}$	$8\frac{3}{4}$	$1\text{-}4\frac{27}{32}$	$9\frac{3}{8}$	$1\text{-}6$	$9\frac{31}{32}$	$1\text{-}7\frac{3}{16}$
$\frac{7}{16}$	$7\frac{19}{32}$	$1\text{-}2\frac{9}{16}$	$8\frac{3}{16}$	$1\text{-}3\frac{3}{4}$	$8\frac{13}{16}$	$1\text{-}4\frac{29}{32}$	$9\frac{13}{32}$	$1\text{-}6\frac{1}{16}$	$10\frac{1}{32}$	$1\text{-}7\frac{1}{4}$
$\frac{1}{2}$	$7\frac{5}{8}$	$1\text{-}2\frac{5}{8}$	$8\frac{7}{32}$	$1\text{-}3\frac{13}{16}$	$8\frac{27}{32}$	$1\text{-}4\frac{31}{32}$	$9\frac{7}{16}$	$1\text{-}6\frac{5}{32}$	$10\frac{1}{16}$	$1\text{-}7\frac{5}{16}$
$\frac{9}{16}$	$7\frac{21}{32}$	$1\text{-}2\frac{23}{32}$	$8\frac{1}{4}$	$1\text{-}3\frac{7}{8}$	$8\frac{7}{8}$	$1\text{-}5\frac{1}{16}$	$9\frac{15}{32}$	$1\text{-}6\frac{7}{32}$	$10\frac{3}{32}$	$1\text{-}7\frac{13}{32}$
$\frac{5}{8}$	$7\frac{11}{16}$	$1\text{-}2\frac{25}{32}$	$8\frac{5}{16}$	$1\text{-}3\frac{31}{32}$	$8\frac{29}{32}$	$1\text{-}5\frac{1}{8}$	$9\frac{17}{32}$	$1\text{-}6\frac{5}{16}$	$10\frac{1}{8}$	$1\text{-}7\frac{15}{32}$
$\frac{11}{16}$	$7\frac{23}{32}$	$1\text{-}2\frac{27}{32}$	$8\frac{11}{32}$	$1\text{-}4\frac{1}{32}$	$8\frac{15}{16}$	$1\text{-}5\frac{3}{16}$	$9\frac{9}{16}$	$1\text{-}6\frac{3}{8}$	$10\frac{5}{32}$	$1\text{-}7\frac{17}{32}$
$\frac{3}{4}$	$7\frac{25}{32}$	$1\text{-}2\frac{15}{16}$	$8\frac{3}{8}$	$1\text{-}4\frac{3}{32}$	9	$1\text{-}5\frac{9}{32}$	$9\frac{19}{32}$	$1\text{-}6\frac{7}{16}$	$10\frac{7}{32}$	$1\text{-}7\frac{5}{8}$
$\frac{13}{16}$	$7\frac{13}{16}$	$1\text{-}3$	$8\frac{13}{32}$	$1\text{-}4\frac{3}{16}$	$9\frac{1}{32}$	$1\text{-}5\frac{11}{32}$	$9\frac{5}{8}$	$1\text{-}6\frac{11}{32}$	$10\frac{1}{4}$	$1\text{-}7\frac{11}{16}$
$\frac{7}{8}$	$7\frac{27}{32}$	$1\text{-}3\frac{1}{16}$	$8\frac{15}{32}$	$1\text{-}4\frac{1}{4}$	$9\frac{1}{16}$	$1\text{-}5\frac{13}{32}$	$9\frac{11}{16}$	$1\text{-}6\frac{15}{32}$	$10\frac{9}{32}$	$1\text{-}7\frac{3}{4}$
$\frac{15}{16}$	$7\frac{7}{8}$	$1\text{-}3\frac{5}{32}$	$8\frac{1}{2}$	$1\text{-}4\frac{5}{16}$	$9\frac{3}{32}$	$1\text{-}5\frac{1}{2}$	$9\frac{23}{32}$	$1\text{-}6\frac{21}{32}$	$10\frac{5}{16}$	$1\text{-}7\frac{27}{32}$

Ins.	17" Rise	17" Slope	18" Rise	18" Slope	19" Rise	19" Slope	20" Rise	20" Slope	21" Rise	21" Slope
0	$10\frac{3}{8}$	$1\text{-}7\frac{29}{32}$	$10\frac{31}{32}$	$1\text{-}9\frac{3}{32}$	$11\frac{9}{16}$	$1\text{-}10\frac{1}{4}$	$1\text{-}0\frac{3}{16}$	$1\text{-}11\frac{13}{32}$	$1\text{-}0\frac{13}{16}$	$2\text{-}0\frac{19}{32}$
$\frac{1}{16}$	$10\frac{13}{32}$	$1\text{-}7\frac{31}{32}$	11	$1\text{-}9\frac{5}{32}$	$11\frac{5}{8}$	$1\text{-}10\frac{5}{16}$	$1\text{-}0\frac{7}{32}$	$1\text{-}11\frac{1}{2}$	$1\text{-}0\frac{27}{32}$	$2\text{-}0\frac{21}{32}$
$\frac{1}{8}$	$10\frac{7}{16}$	$1\text{-}8\frac{1}{16}$	$11\frac{1}{4}$	$1\text{-}9\frac{7}{32}$	$11\frac{21}{32}$	$1\text{-}10\frac{13}{32}$	$1\text{-}0\frac{1}{4}$	$1\text{-}11\frac{5}{8}$	$1\text{-}0\frac{7}{8}$	$2\text{-}0\frac{3}{4}$
$\frac{3}{16}$	$10\frac{15}{32}$	$1\text{-}8\frac{1}{8}$	$11\frac{3}{32}$	$1\text{-}9\frac{9}{16}$	$11\frac{11}{16}$	$1\text{-}10\frac{15}{32}$	$1\text{-}0\frac{5}{16}$	$1\text{-}11\frac{5}{8}$	$1\text{-}0\frac{29}{32}$	$2\text{-}0\frac{13}{16}$
$\frac{1}{4}$	$10\frac{1}{2}$	$1\text{-}8\frac{3}{16}$	$11\frac{1}{8}$	$1\text{-}9\frac{3}{8}$	$11\frac{23}{32}$	$1\text{-}10\frac{17}{32}$	$1\text{-}0\frac{11}{32}$	$1\text{-}11\frac{23}{32}$	$1\text{-}0\frac{15}{16}$	$2\text{-}0\frac{7}{8}$
$\frac{5}{16}$	$10\frac{9}{16}$	$1\text{-}8\frac{9}{32}$	$11\frac{5}{32}$	$1\text{-}9\frac{7}{16}$	$11\frac{25}{32}$	$1\text{-}10\frac{5}{8}$	$1\text{-}0\frac{3}{8}$	$1\text{-}11\frac{25}{32}$	$1\text{-}1$	$2\text{-}0\frac{31}{32}$
$\frac{3}{8}$	$10\frac{19}{32}$	$1\text{-}8\frac{11}{32}$	$11\frac{3}{16}$	$1\text{-}9\frac{17}{32}$	$11\frac{13}{16}$	$1\text{-}10\frac{11}{16}$	$1\text{-}0\frac{13}{32}$	$1\text{-}11\frac{7}{8}$	$1\text{-}1\frac{1}{16}$	$2\text{-}1\frac{1}{32}$
$\frac{7}{16}$	$10\frac{5}{8}$	$1\text{-}8\frac{13}{32}$	$11\frac{1}{4}$	$1\text{-}9\frac{19}{32}$	$11\frac{27}{32}$	$1\text{-}10\frac{3}{4}$	$1\text{-}0\frac{15}{32}$	$1\text{-}11\frac{15}{16}$	$1\text{-}1\frac{1}{16}$	$2\text{-}1\frac{3}{32}$
$\frac{1}{2}$	$10\frac{21}{32}$	$1\text{-}8\frac{1}{2}$	$11\frac{9}{32}$	$1\text{-}9\frac{21}{32}$	$11\frac{7}{8}$	$1\text{-}10\frac{27}{32}$	$1\text{-}0\frac{1}{2}$	$2\text{-}0$	$1\text{-}1\frac{3}{32}$	$2\text{-}1\frac{3}{16}$
$\frac{9}{16}$	$10\frac{11}{16}$	$1\text{-}8\frac{9}{16}$	$11\frac{5}{16}$	$1\text{-}9\frac{3}{4}$	$11\frac{29}{32}$	$1\text{-}10\frac{29}{32}$	$1\text{-}0\frac{17}{32}$	$2\text{-}0\frac{3}{32}$	$1\text{-}1\frac{1}{8}$	$2\text{-}1\frac{1}{4}$
$\frac{5}{8}$	$10\frac{3}{4}$	$1\text{-}8\frac{5}{8}$	$11\frac{11}{32}$	$1\text{-}9\frac{13}{16}$	$11\frac{31}{32}$	$1\text{-}10\frac{31}{32}$	$1\text{-}0\frac{9}{16}$	$2\text{-}0\frac{5}{32}$	$1\text{-}1\frac{3}{16}$	$2\text{-}1\frac{5}{16}$
$\frac{11}{16}$	$10\frac{25}{32}$	$1\text{-}8\frac{23}{32}$	$11\frac{3}{8}$	$1\text{-}9\frac{7}{8}$	$1\text{-}0$	$1\text{-}11\frac{1}{16}$	$1\text{-}0\frac{19}{32}$	$2\text{-}0\frac{7}{32}$	$1\text{-}1\frac{7}{32}$	$2\text{-}1\frac{13}{32}$
$\frac{3}{4}$	$10\frac{13}{32}$	$1\text{-}8\frac{25}{32}$	$11\frac{7}{16}$	$1\text{-}9\frac{31}{32}$	$1\text{-}0\frac{1}{32}$	$1\text{-}11\frac{1}{8}$	$1\text{-}0\frac{21}{32}$	$2\text{-}0\frac{5}{16}$	$1\text{-}1\frac{1}{4}$	$2\text{-}1\frac{15}{32}$
$\frac{13}{16}$	$10\frac{27}{32}$	$1\text{-}8\frac{27}{32}$	$11\frac{15}{32}$	$1\text{-}10\frac{1}{32}$	$1\text{-}0\frac{1}{16}$	$1\text{-}11\frac{3}{16}$	$1\text{-}0\frac{11}{16}$	$2\text{-}0\frac{3}{8}$	$1\text{-}1\frac{9}{32}$	$2\text{-}1\frac{17}{32}$
$\frac{7}{8}$	$10\frac{29}{32}$	$1\text{-}8\frac{15}{16}$	$11\frac{1}{2}$	$1\text{-}10\frac{3}{32}$	$1\text{-}0\frac{1}{8}$	$1\text{-}11\frac{9}{32}$	$1\text{-}0\frac{23}{32}$	$2\text{-}0\frac{7}{16}$	$1\text{-}1\frac{11}{32}$	$2\text{-}1\frac{5}{8}$
$\frac{15}{16}$	$10\frac{15}{16}$	$1\text{-}9$	$11\frac{17}{32}$	$1\text{-}10\frac{3}{16}$	$1\text{-}0\frac{5}{32}$	$1\text{-}11\frac{11}{32}$	$1\text{-}0\frac{3}{4}$	$2\text{-}0\frac{17}{32}$	$1\text{-}1\frac{3}{8}$	$2\text{-}1\frac{11}{16}$

Feet	40' Rise	40' Slope	50' Rise	50' Slope	60' Rise	60' Slope	70' Rise	70' Slope
0	$24\text{-}4\frac{1}{2}$	$46\text{-}10\frac{3}{32}$	$30\text{-}5\frac{5}{8}$	$58\text{-}6\frac{5}{8}$	$36\text{-}6\frac{3}{4}$	$70\text{-}3\frac{5}{32}$	$42\text{-}7\frac{7}{8}$	$81\text{-}11\frac{11}{16}$
1	$24\text{-}11\frac{13}{16}$	$48\text{-}0\frac{5}{32}$	$31\text{-}0\frac{15}{16}$	$59\text{-}8\frac{11}{16}$	$37\text{-}2\frac{1}{16}$	$71\text{-}5\frac{3}{16}$	$43\text{-}3\frac{3}{16}$	$83\text{-}1\frac{23}{32}$
2	$25\text{-}7\frac{1}{8}$	$49\text{-}2\frac{7}{32}$	$31\text{-}8\frac{1}{4}$	$60\text{-}10\frac{23}{32}$	$37\text{-}9\frac{3}{8}$	$72\text{-}7\frac{1}{4}$	$43\text{-}10\frac{1}{2}$	$84\text{-}3\frac{25}{32}$
3	$26\text{-}2\frac{11}{16}$	$50\text{-}4\frac{1}{4}$	$32\text{-}3\frac{9}{16}$	$62\text{-}0\frac{25}{32}$	$38\text{-}4\frac{11}{16}$	$73\text{-}9\frac{5}{16}$	$44\text{-}5\frac{13}{16}$	$85\text{-}5\frac{27}{32}$
4	$26\text{-}9\frac{3}{4}$	$51\text{-}6\frac{5}{16}$	$32\text{-}10\frac{7}{8}$	$63\text{-}2\frac{27}{32}$	$39\text{-}0$	$74\text{-}11\frac{3}{8}$	$45\text{-}1\frac{1}{8}$	$86\text{-}7\frac{7}{8}$
5	$27\text{-}5\frac{1}{16}$	$52\text{-}8\frac{3}{8}$	$33\text{-}6\frac{3}{16}$	$64\text{-}4\frac{7}{8}$	$39\text{-}7\frac{5}{16}$	$76\text{-}1\frac{13}{32}$	$45\text{-}8\frac{7}{16}$	$87\text{-}9\frac{15}{16}$
6	$28\text{-}0\frac{3}{8}$	$53\text{-}10\frac{13}{32}$	$34\text{-}1\frac{1}{2}$	$65\text{-}6\frac{15}{16}$	$40\text{-}2\frac{5}{8}$	$77\text{-}3\frac{15}{32}$	$46\text{-}3\frac{3}{4}$	$89\text{-}0$
7	$28\text{-}7\frac{11}{16}$	$55\text{-}0\frac{15}{32}$	$34\text{-}8\frac{13}{16}$	$66\text{-}9$	$40\text{-}9\frac{15}{16}$	$78\text{-}5\frac{17}{32}$	$46\text{-}11\frac{1}{16}$	$90\text{-}2\frac{1}{32}$
8	$29\text{-}3$	$56\text{-}2\frac{17}{32}$	$35\text{-}4\frac{1}{8}$	$67\text{-}11\frac{1}{32}$	$41\text{-}5\frac{1}{4}$	$79\text{-}7\frac{9}{16}$	$47\text{-}6\frac{3}{8}$	$91\text{-}4\frac{3}{32}$
9	$29\text{-}10\frac{5}{16}$	$57\text{-}4\frac{9}{16}$	$35\text{-}11\frac{7}{16}$	$69\text{-}1\frac{3}{32}$	$42\text{-}0\frac{9}{16}$	$80\text{-}9\frac{5}{8}$	$48\text{-}1\frac{11}{16}$	$92\text{-}6\frac{5}{32}$

natsin A=0.5203701727; natcos A=0.8539407962; nattan A=0.6093750000; natcot A=1.6410256410

Inches	0" Rise	0" Slope	1" Rise	1" Slope	2" Rise	2" Slope	3" Rise	3" Slope	4" Rise	4" Slope	5" Rise	5" Slope
0	0	0	5/8	1 3/16	1 7/32	2 11/32	1 27/32	3 17/32	2 15/32	4 11/16	3 1/16	5 7/8
1/16	1/32	1/16	21/32	1 1/4	1 9/32	2 13/32	1 7/8	3 19/32	2 1/2	4 25/32	3 1/8	5 15/16
1/8	1/16	5/32	11/16	1 5/16	1 5/16	2 1/2	1 29/32	3 21/32	2 17/32	4 27/32	3 5/32	6
3/16	1/8	7/32	23/32	1 13/32	1 11/32	2 9/16	1 31/32	3 3/4	2 9/16	4 29/32	3 3/16	6 3/32
1/4	5/32	9/32	25/32	1 15/32	1 3/8	2 21/32	2	3 13/16	2 5/8	5	3 7/32	6 5/32
5/16	3/16	3/8	13/16	1 17/32	1 13/32	2 23/32	2 1/32	3 7/8	2 21/32	5 1/16	3 1/4	6 1/4
3/8	7/32	7/16	27/32	1 5/8	1 15/32	2 25/32	2 1/16	3 31/32	2 11/16	5 1/8	3 5/16	6 5/16
7/16	9/32	1/2	7/8	1 11/16	1 1/2	2 7/8	2 1/8	4 1/32	2 23/32	5 7/32	3 11/32	6 3/8
1/2	5/16	19/32	15/16	1 3/4	1 17/32	2 15/16	2 5/32	4 3/32	2 3/4	5 9/32	3 3/8	6 15/32
9/16	11/32	21/32	31/32	1 27/32	1 9/32	3	2 3/16	4 3/16	2 13/16	5 11/32	3 13/32	6 17/32
5/8	3/8	23/32	1	1 29/32	1 5/8	3 3/32	2 7/32	4 1/4	2 27/32	5 7/16	3 15/32	6 19/32
11/16	7/16	13/16	1 1/32	1 31/32	1 21/32	3 5/32	2 9/32	4 11/32	2 7/8	5 1/2	3 1/2	6 11/16
3/4	15/32	7/8	1 1/16	2 1/16	1 11/16	3 7/32	2 5/16	4 13/32	2 29/32	5 9/16	3 17/32	6 3/4
13/16	1/2	31/32	1 1/8	2 1/8	1 23/32	3 5/16	2 11/32	4 15/32	2 31/32	5 21/32	3 9/16	6 13/16
7/8	17/32	1 1/32	1 5/32	2 3/16	1 25/32	3 3/8	2 3/8	4 9/16	3	5 23/32	3 5/8	6 29/32
15/16	9/16	1 3/32	1 3/16	2 9/32	1 13/16	3 7/16	2 13/32	4 5/8	3 1/32	5 25/32	3 21/32	6 31/32

Inches	6" Rise	6" Slope	7" Rise	7" Slope	8" Rise	8" Slope	9" Rise	9" Slope	10" Rise	10" Slope	11" Rise	11" Slope
0	3 11/16	7 1/2	4 5/16	8 7/32	4 29/32	9 3/8	5 17/32	10 9/16	6 5/32	11 3/4	6 3/4	1-0 29/32
1/16	3 23/32	7 1/2	4 11/32	8 9/32	4 31/32	9 15/32	5 9/16	10 5/8	6 3/16	11 13/16	6 13/16	1-1
1/8	3 3/4	7 9/16	4 3/8	8 3/8	5	9 17/32	5 19/32	10 23/32	6 7/32	11 7/8	6 27/32	1-1 1/32
3/16	3 13/16	7 1/4	4 13/32	8 7/16	5 1/32	9 5/8	5 21/32	10 23/32	6 1/4	11 31/32	6 7/8	1-1 1/8
1/4	3 27/32	7 11/32	4 15/32	8 1/2	5 1/16	9 11/16	5 11/16	10 27/32	6 5/16	1-0 1/32	6 29/32	1-1 7/32
5/16	3 7/8	7 13/32	4 1/2	8 19/32	5 3/32	9 3/4	5 23/32	10 15/16	6 11/32	1-0 3/32	6 15/16	1-1 9/32
3/8	3 29/32	7 15/32	4 17/32	8 21/32	5 5/32	9 27/32	5 3/4	11	6 3/8	1-0 3/16	7	1-1 11/32
7/16	3 31/32	7 9/16	4 9/16	8 23/32	5 3/16	9 29/32	5 13/16	11 1/16	6 13/32	1-0 1/4	7 1/32	1-1 7/16
1/2	4	7 5/8	4 5/8	8 13/16	5 7/32	9 31/32	5 27/32	11 1/2	6 7/16	1-0 5/16	7 1/16	1-1 1/2
9/16	4 1/16	7 11/32	4 21/32	8 7/8	5 1/4	10 1/16	5 7/8	11 17/32	6 1/2	1-0 13/32	7 3/32	1-1 9/16
5/8	4 1/8	7 25/32	4 11/16	8 31/32	5 5/16	10 1/8	5 29/32	11 15/32	6 17/32	1-0 15/32	7 5/32	1-1 21/32
11/16	4 1/8	7 27/32	4 23/32	9 1/32	5 11/32	10 3/16	5 31/32	11 3/8	6 9/16	1-0 17/32	7 3/16	1-1 23/32
3/4	4 5/32	7 15/16	4 3/4	9 3/32	5 3/8	10 9/32	6	11 7/16	6 19/32	1-0 5/8	7 7/32	1-1 25/32
13/16	4 3/16	8	4 13/16	9 3/16	5 13/32	10 11/32	6 1/32	11 17/32	6 21/32	1-0 11/16	7 1/4	1-1 7/8
7/8	4 7/32	8 1/16	4 27/32	9 1/4	5 15/32	10 13/32	6 1/16	11 19/32	6 11/16	1-0 3/4	7 5/16	1-1 15/16
15/16	4 1/4	8 5/32	4 7/8	9 5/16	5 1/2	10 1/2	6 3/32	11 21/32	6 23/32	1-0 27/32	7 11/32	1-2

Feet	0' Rise	0' Slope	10' Rise	10' Slope	20' Rise	20' Slope	30' Rise	30' Slope
0	0	0	6-1 3/4	11-8 27/32	12-3 1/2	23-5 11/16	18-5 1/4	35-2 9/16
1	7 3/8	1-2 3/32	6-9 1/8	12-10 15/16	12-10 7/8	24-7 25/32	19-0 5/8	36-4 5/8
2	1-2 3/4	2-4 5/32	7-4 1/2	14-1 1/16	13-6 1/4	25-9 7/8	19-8	37-6 23/32
3	1-10 1/8	3-6 1/4	7-11 7/8	15-3 3/32	14-1 5/8	26-11 31/32	20-3 3/8	38-8 13/16
4	2-5 1/2	4-8 11/32	8-7 1/4	16-5 3/16	14-9	28-2 1/32	20-10 3/4	39-10 29/32
5	3-0 7/8	5-10 7/16	9-2 5/8	17-7 9/32	15-4 3/8	29-4 1/8	21-6 1/8	41-0 31/32
6	3-8 1/4	7-0 1/2	9-10	18-9 3/8	15-11 3/4	30-6 7/32	22-1 1/2	42-3 1/16
7	4-3 5/8	8-2 19/32	10-5 3/8	19-11 7/16	16-7 1/8	31-8 5/16	22-8 7/8	43-5 5/32
8	4-11	9-4 11/32	11-0 3/4	21-1 17/32	17-2 1/2	32-10 3/8	23-4 1/4	44-7 1/4
9	5-6 3/8	10-6 25/32	11-8 1/8	22-3 5/8	17-9 7/8	34-0 15/32	23-11 5/8	45-9 5/16

A = 31° 34′ 27″; logsin A = 9.71900; logcos A = 9.93042; logtan A = 9.78858; logcot A = 0.21142

Ins.	12″ Rise	12″ Slope	13″ Rise	13″ Slope	14″ Rise	14″ Slope	15″ Rise	15″ Slope	16″ Rise	16″ Slope
0	7 3/8	1-2 3/32	8	1-3 1/4	8 19/32	1-4 7/16	9 7/32	1-5 19/32	9 27/32	1-6 25/32
1/16	7 13/32	1-2 5/32	8 1/32	1-3 11/32	8 21/32	1-4 1/2	9 1/4	1-5 11/16	9 7/8	1-6 27/32
1/8	7 7/16	1-2 7/32	8 1/16	1-3 13/32	8 11/16	1-4 19/32	9 9/32	1-5 3/4	9 29/32	1-6 15/16
3/16	7 1/2	1-2 5/16	8 3/32	1-3 15/32	8 23/32	1-4 21/32	9 11/32	1-5 13/16	9 15/16	1-7
1/4	7 17/32	1-2 3/8	8 5/32	1-3 9/16	8 3/4	1-4 23/32	9 3/8	1-5 29/32	10	1-7 1/16
5/16	7 9/16	1-2 7/16	8 3/16	1-3 5/8	8 25/32	1-4 13/16	9 13/32	1-5 31/32	10 1/32	1-7 5/32
3/8	7 19/32	1-2 17/32	8 7/32	1-3 11/16	8 27/32	1-4 7/8	9 7/16	1-6 1/32	10 1/16	1-7 7/32
7/16	7 21/32	1-2 19/32	8 1/4	1-3 25/32	8 7/8	1-4 15/16	9 1/2	1-6 1/8	10 3/32	1-7 9/32
1/2	7 11/16	1-2 11/16	8 5/16	1-3 27/32	8 29/32	1-5 1/8	9 17/32	1-6 3/16	10 1/8	1-7 3/8
9/16	7 23/32	1-2 3/4	8 11/32	1-3 29/32	8 15/16	1-5 3/32	9 9/16	1-6 9/32	10 5/32	1-7 11/16
5/8	7 3/4	1-2 13/16	8 3/8	1-4	9	1-5 5/32	9 19/32	1-6 11/32	10 7/32	1-7 1/2
11/16	7 13/16	1-2 29/32	8 13/32	1-4 1/16	9 1/32	1-5 1/4	9 21/32	1-6 13/32	10 1/4	1-7 19/32
3/4	7 27/32	1-2 31/32	8 7/16	1-4 1/8	9 1/16	1-5 5/16	9 11/16	1-6 1/2	10 9/32	1-7 21/32
13/16	7 7/8	1-3 1/32	8 1/2	1-4 7/32	9 3/32	1-5 3/8	9 23/32	1-6 9/16	10 11/32	1-7 23/32
7/8	7 29/32	1-3 1/8	8 17/32	1-4 9/32	9 5/32	1-5 15/32	9 3/4	1-6 5/8	10 3/8	1-7 13/16
15/16	7 15/16	1-3 3/32	8 9/16	1-4 11/32	9 3/16	1-5 17/32	9 25/32	1-6 23/32	10 13/32	1-7 7/8

Ins.	17″ Rise	17″ Slope	18″ Rise	18″ Slope	19″ Rise	19″ Slope	20″ Rise	20″ Slope	21″ Rise	21″ Slope
0	10 7/16	1-7 31/32	11 1/16	1-9 1/8	11 11/16	1-10 5/16	1-0 9/32	1-11 15/32	1-0 29/32	2-0 21/32
1/16	10 1/2	1-8 1/32	11 3/32	1-9 3/16	11 23/32	1-10 3/8	1-0 11/32	1-11 9/16	1-0 15/32	2-0 23/32
1/8	10 17/32	1-8 3/32	11 1/8	1-9 9/32	11 3/4	1-10 7/16	1-0 3/8	1-11 5/8	1-0 31/32	2-0 25/32
3/16	10 9/16	1-8 3/16	11 3/16	1-9 11/32	11 25/32	1-10 17/32	1-0 13/32	1-11 11/16	1-1 1/2	2-0 7/8
1/4	10 19/32	1-8 1/4	11 7/32	1-9 13/32	11 27/32	1-10 19/32	1-0 7/16	1-11 25/32	1-1 1/16	2-0 15/16
5/16	10 5/8	1-8 5/16	11 1/4	1-9 1/2	11 7/8	1-10 21/32	1-0 15/32	1-11 27/32	1-1 3/32	2-1 1/32
3/8	10 11/16	1-8 13/32	11 9/32	1-9 9/16	11 29/32	1-10 3/4	1-0 17/32	1-11 29/32	1-1 1/8	2-1 3/32
7/16	10 23/32	1-8 15/32	11 11/32	1-9 21/32	11 15/16	1-10 13/16	1-0 9/16	2-0	1-1 3/16	2-1 5/32
1/2	10 3/4	1-8 17/32	11 3/8	1-9 23/32	1-0	1-10 7/8	1-0 19/32	2-0 1/8	1-1 7/32	2-1 1/4
9/16	10 25/32	1-8 5/8	11 13/32	1-9 25/32	1-0 1/2	1-10 31/32	1-0 5/8	2-0 1/8	1-1 1/4	2-1 5/16
5/8	10 27/32	1-8 11/16	11 7/16	1-9 7/8	1-0 1/16	1-11 3/32	1-0 11/16	2-0 7/32	1-1 9/32	2-1 3/8
11/16	10 7/8	1-8 3/4	11 1/2	1-9 15/16	1-0 3/32	1-11 3/16	1-0 23/32	2-0 9/32	1-1 11/32	2-1 15/32
3/4	10 29/32	1-8 27/32	11 17/32	1-10	1-0 1/8	1-11 3/16	1-0 3/4	2-0 11/32	1-1 3/8	2-1 17/32
13/16	10 15/16	1-8 29/32	11 9/16	1-10 3/32	1-0 3/16	1-11 1/4	1-0 25/32	2-0 7/16	1-1 13/32	2-1 19/32
7/8	11	1-8 31/32	11 19/32	1-10 5/32	1-0 7/32	1-11 11/32	1-0 27/32	2-0 1/2	1-1 7/16	2-1 11/16
15/16	11 1/32	1-9 1/32	11 5/8	1-10 7/32	1-0 1/4	1-11 13/32	1-0 7/8	2-0 9/32	1-1 15/32	2-1 3/4

Feet	40′ Rise	40′ Slope	50′ Rise	50′ Slope	60′ Rise	60′ Slope	70′ Rise	70′ Slope
0	24-7	46-11 3/32	30-8 3/4	58-8 1/4	36-10 1/2	70-5 3/32	43-0 1/4	82-1 31/32
1	25-2 3/8	48-1 1/2	31-4 1/8	59-10 11/32	37-5 7/8	71-7 3/16	43-7 5/8	83-4 1/32
2	25-9 3/4	49-3 9/16	31-11 1/2	61-0 7/16	38-1 1/4	72-9 9/32	44-3	84-6 1/8
3	26-5 1/8	50-5 21/32	32-6 7/8	62-2 1/2	38-8 5/8	73-11 3/8	44-10 3/8	85-8 7/32
4	27-0 1/2	51-7 3/4	33-2 1/4	63-4 19/32	39-4	75-1 7/16	45-5 3/4	86-10 5/16
5	27-7 7/8	52-9 27/32	33-9 5/8	64-6 11/16	39-11 3/8	76-3 17/32	46-1 1/8	88-0 3/8
6	28-3 1/4	53-11 29/32	34-5	65-8 25/32	40-6 3/4	77-5 5/8	46-8 1/2	89-2 15/32
7	28-10 5/8	55-2	35-0 3/8	66-10 27/32	41-2 1/4	78-7 11/16	47-3 7/8	90-4 9/16
8	29-6	56-4 3/32	35-7 3/4	68-0 15/16	41-9 1/2	79-9 25/32	47-11 1/4	91-6 5/8
9	30-1 3/8	57-6 5/32	36-3 1/8	69-3 1/32	42-4 7/8	80-11 7/8	48-6 5/8	92-8 23/32

natsin A=0.5236021870; natcos A=0.8519628806; nattan A=0.6145833333; natcot A=1.6271186440

Inches	0″ Rise	0″ Slope	1″ Rise	1″ Slope	2″ Rise	2″ Slope	3″ Rise	3″ Slope	4″ Rise	4″ Slope	5″ Rise	5″ Slope
0	0	0	5/8	1 3/16	1 1/4	2 11/32	1 7/8	3 17/32	2 15/32	4 23/32	3 3/32	5 7/8
1/16	1/2	1/16	21/32	1 1/4	1 9/32	2 7/16	1 29/32	3 19/32	2 17/32	4 25/32	3 1/8	5 31/32
1/8	1/16	5/32	11/16	1 5/16	1 5/16	2 1/2	1 15/16	3 11/16	2 9/16	4 27/32	3 3/16	6 1/32
3/16	1/8	7/32	3/4	1 13/32	1 11/32	2 9/16	1 31/32	3 3/4	2 19/32	4 15/16	3 7/32	6 3/32
1/4	5/32	9/32	25/32	1 15/32	1 13/32	2 21/32	2	3 13/16	2 5/8	5	3 1/4	6 3/16
5/16	3/16	3/8	13/16	1 17/32	1 7/16	2 23/32	2 1/16	3 29/32	2 11/16	5 1/16	3 9/32	6 1/4
3/8	7/32	7/16	27/32	1 5/8	1 15/32	2 25/32	2 3/32	3 31/32	2 23/32	5 5/32	3 11/32	6 5/16
7/16	9/32	1/2	29/32	1 11/16	1 1/2	2 7/8	2 1/8	4 1/32	2 3/4	5 7/32	3 3/8	6 13/32
1/2	5/16	19/32	15/16	1 3/4	1 9/16	2 15/16	2 5/32	4 1/8	2 25/32	5 9/32	3 13/32	6 15/32
9/16	11/32	21/32	31/32	1 27/32	1 19/32	3	2 7/32	4 3/16	2 13/16	5 3/8	3 7/16	6 17/32
5/8	3/8	3/4	1	1 29/32	1 5/8	3 3/32	2 1/4	4 1/4	2 7/8	5 7/16	3 1/2	6 5/8
11/16	7/16	13/16	1 1/32	2	1 21/32	3 5/32	2 9/32	4 11/32	2 29/32	5 1/2	3 17/32	6 11/16
3/4	15/32	7/8	1 3/32	2 1/16	1 23/32	3 1/4	2 5/32	4 13/32	2 15/32	5 19/32	3 9/16	6 3/4
13/16	1/2	31/32	1 1/8	2 1/8	1 3/4	3 5/16	2 3/8	4 1/2	2 31/32	5 21/32	3 19/32	6 27/32
7/8	17/32	1 1/32	1 5/32	2 7/32	1 25/32	3 3/8	2 13/32	4 9/16	3 1/32	5 3/4	3 21/32	6 29/32
15/16	19/32	1 3/32	1 3/16	2 9/32	1 13/16	3 15/32	2 7/16	4 5/8	3 1/16	5 13/16	3 11/16	7

Inches	6″ Rise	6″ Slope	7″ Rise	7″ Slope	8″ Rise	8″ Slope	9″ Rise	9″ Slope	10″ Rise	10″ Slope	11″ Rise	11″ Slope
0	3 23/32	7 1/16	4 11/32	8 1/4	4 31/32	9 13/32	5 9/16	10 19/32	6 3/16	11 3/4	6 13/16	1-0 15/16
1/16	3 3/4	7 1/8	4 3/8	8 5/16	5	9 1/2	5 5/8	10 21/32	6 1/4	11 27/32	6 27/32	1-1
1/8	3 25/32	7 7/32	4 13/32	8 3/8	5 1/32	9 9/16	5 21/32	10 3/4	6 9/32	11 29/32	6 29/32	1-1 3/32
3/16	3 27/32	7 9/32	4 15/32	8 15/32	5 1/16	9 5/8	5 11/16	10 13/16	6 5/16	1-0	6 15/16	1-1 5/32
1/4	3 7/8	7 11/32	4 1/2	8 17/32	5 1/8	9 23/32	5 23/32	10 7/8	6 11/32	1-0 1/16	6 31/32	1-1 1/4
5/16	3 29/32	7 7/16	4 17/32	8 19/32	5 5/32	9 25/32	5 25/32	10 31/32	6 13/32	1-0 1/8	7	1-1 5/16
3/8	3 15/16	7 1/2	4 9/16	8 11/16	5 3/16	9 27/32	5 13/16	11 1/32	6 7/16	1-0 7/32	7 1/16	1-1 3/8
7/16	4	7 9/16	4 5/8	8 3/4	5 7/32	9 15/16	5 27/32	11 3/32	6 15/32	1-0 9/32	7 3/32	1-1 15/32
1/2	4 1/32	7 21/32	4 21/32	8 13/16	5 9/32	10	5 7/8	11 3/16	6 1/2	1-0 11/32	7 1/8	1-1 17/32
9/16	4 1/16	7 23/32	4 11/16	8 29/32	5 5/16	10 1/16	5 15/16	11 1/4	6 17/32	1-0 7/16	7 5/32	1-1 19/32
5/8	4 3/32	7 25/32	4 23/32	8 31/32	5 11/32	10 5/32	5 31/32	11 5/16	6 19/32	1-0 1/2	7 7/32	1-1 11/16
11/16	4 5/32	7 7/8	4 3/4	9 1/32	5 3/8	10 7/32	6	11 13/32	6 5/8	1-0 9/16	7 1/4	1-1 3/4
3/4	4 3/16	7 15/16	4 13/16	9 1/8	5 7/16	10 9/32	6 1/32	11 15/32	6 21/32	1-0 21/32	7 9/32	1-1 13/16
13/16	4 7/32	8	4 27/32	9 3/16	5 15/32	10 3/8	6 3/32	11 17/32	6 11/16	1-0 23/32	7 5/16	1-1 29/32
7/8	4 1/4	8 3/32	4 7/8	9 1/4	5 1/2	10 7/16	6 1/8	11 5/8	6 3/4	1-0 25/32	7 3/8	1-1 31/32
15/16	4 5/16	8 5/32	4 29/32	9 11/32	5 17/32	10 1/2	6 5/32	11 11/16	6 25/32	1-0 7/8	7 13/32	1-2 1/32

Feet	0′ Rise	0′ Slope	10′ Rise	10′ Slope	20′ Rise	20′ Slope	30′ Rise	30′ Slope
0	0	0	6-2 3/8	11-9 9/16	12-4 3/4	23-6 11/32	18-7 1/8	35-3 17/32
1	7 7/16	1-2 1/8	6-9 13/16	12-11 5/16	13-0 3/16	24-8 15/32	19-2 9/16	36-5 21/32
2	1-2 7/8	2-4 1/4	7-5 1/4	14-1 13/32	13-7 5/8	25-10 19/32	19-10	37-7 25/32
3	1-10 5/16	3-6 11/32	8-0 11/16	15-3 17/32	14-3 1/16	27-0 23/32	20-5 7/16	38-9 29/32
4	2-5 3/4	4-8 15/32	8-8 1/8	16-5 21/32	14-10 1/2	28-2 27/32	21-0 7/8	40-0
5	3-1 3/16	5-10 19/32	9-3 9/16	17-7 25/32	15-5 15/16	29-4 15/32	21-8 5/16	41-2 1/8
6	3-8 5/8	7-0 23/32	9-11	18-9 7/8	16-1 3/8	30-7 1/16	22-3 3/4	42-4 1/4
7	4-4 1/16	8-2 13/16	10-6 7/16	20-0	16-8 13/16	31-9 3/16	22-11 3/16	43-6 3/8
8	4-11 1/2	9-4 15/16	11-1 7/8	21-2 1/8	17-4 1/4	32-11 5/16	23-6 5/8	44-8 15/32
9	5-6 15/16	10-7 1/16	11-9 5/16	22-4 1/4	17-11 11/16	34-1 13/32	24-2 1/4	45-10 19/32

A = 31° 47′ 25″; logsin A = 9.72166; logcos A = 9.92941; logtan A = 9.79225; logcot A = 0.20775

Ins.	12″ Rise	12″ Slope	13″ Rise	13″ Slope	14″ Rise	14″ Slope	15″ Rise	15″ Slope	16″ Rise	16″ Slope
0	7 7/16	1-2 1/8	8 1/16	1-3 9/32	8 11/16	1-4 15/32	9 5/16	1-5 21/32	9 29/32	1-6 13/16
1/16	7 15/32	1-2 3/32	8 3/32	1-3 3/8	8 23/32	1-4 17/32	9 11/32	1-5 23/32	9 31/32	1-6 29/32
1/8	7 1/2	1-2 1/4	8 1/8	1-3 7/16	8 3/4	1-4 5/8	9 3/8	1-5 25/32	10	1-6 31/32
3/16	7 9/16	1-2 11/32	8 5/32	1-3 1/2	8 25/32	1-4 11/16	9 13/32	1-5 7/8	10 1/32	1-7 1/32
1/4	7 19/32	1-2 13/32	8 7/32	1-3 19/32	8 27/32	1-4 3/4	9 7/16	1-5 15/16	10 1/16	1-7 1/8
5/16	7 5/8	1-2 1/2	8 1/4	1-3 21/32	8 7/8	1-4 27/32	9 1/2	1-6	10 1/8	1-7 3/16
3/8	7 21/32	1-2 9/16	8 9/32	1-3 3/4	8 29/32	1-4 29/32	9 17/32	1-6 3/32	10 5/32	1-7 1/4
7/16	7 23/32	1-2 5/8	8 11/32	1-3 13/16	8 15/16	1-5	9 9/16	1-6 5/32	10 3/16	1-7 11/32
1/2	7 3/4	1-2 23/32	8 3/8	1-3 7/8	9	1-5 1/16	9 19/32	1-6 1/4	10 7/32	1-7 13/32
9/16	7 25/32	1-2 25/32	8 13/32	1-3 31/32	9 1/2	1-5 1/8	9 21/32	1-6 5/16	10 1/4	1-7 1/2
5/8	7 13/16	1-2 27/32	8 7/16	1-4 1/32	9 1/16	1-5 7/32	9 11/32	1-6 3/8	10 5/16	1-7 9/16
11/16	7 7/8	1-2 15/16	8 15/32	1-4 3/32	9 3/32	1-5 9/32	9 23/32	1-6 15/32	10 11/32	1-7 5/8
3/4	7 29/32	1-3	8 17/32	1-4 3/16	9 5/32	1-5 11/32	9 3/4	1-6 17/32	10 3/8	1-7 23/32
13/16	7 15/16	1-3 1/16	8 9/16	1-4 1/4	9 3/16	1-5 7/16	9 13/16	1-6 19/32	10 13/32	1-7 25/32
7/8	7 31/32	1-3 5/32	8 19/32	1-4 5/16	9 7/32	1-5 1/2	9 27/32	1-6 11/16	10 15/32	1-7 27/32
15/16	8 1/32	1-3 7/32	8 5/8	1-4 13/32	9 1/4	1-5 9/16	9 7/8	1-6 3/4	10 1/2	1-7 15/16

Ins.	17″ Rise	17″ Slope	18″ Rise	18″ Slope	19″ Rise	19″ Slope	20″ Rise	20″ Slope	21″ Rise	21″ Slope
0	10 17/32	1-8	11 5/32	1-9 3/16	11 25/32	1-10 11/32	1-0 13/32	1-11 17/32	1-1	2-0 23/32
1/16	10 9/16	1-8 1/16	11 3/16	1-9 1/4	11 13/16	1-10 7/16	1-0 7/16	1-11 19/32	1-1 1/16	2-0 25/32
1/8	10 5/8	1-8 5/32	11 7/32	1-9 5/16	11 27/32	1-10 1/2	1-0 15/32	1-11 11/16	1-1 3/32	2-0 27/32
3/16	10 21/32	1-8 7/32	11 9/32	1-9 13/32	11 29/32	1-10 9/16	1-0 1/2	1-11 3/4	1-1 1/8	2-0 15/16
1/4	10 11/16	1-8 9/32	11 5/16	1-9 15/32	11 15/16	1-10 21/32	1-0 9/16	1-11 13/16	1-1 5/32	2-1
5/16	10 23/32	1-8 3/8	11 11/32	1-9 17/32	11 31/32	1-10 23/32	1-0 19/32	1-11 29/32	1-1 7/32	2-1 1/16
3/8	10 25/32	1-8 7/16	11 3/8	1-9 5/8	1-0	1-10 25/32	1-0 5/8	1-11 31/32	1-1 1/4	2-1 5/32
7/16	10 13/16	1-8 1/2	11 7/16	1-9 11/16	1-0 1/16	1-10 7/8	1-0 21/32	2-0 1/32	1-1 9/32	2-1 7/32
1/2	10 27/32	1-8 19/32	11 15/32	1-9 3/4	1-0 3/32	1-10 15/16	1-0 23/32	2-0 1/8	1-1 5/16	2-1 9/32
9/16	10 7/8	1-8 21/32	11 1/2	1-9 27/32	1-0 1/8	1-11	1-0 3/4	2-0 3/16	1-1 3/8	2-1 3/8
5/8	10 15/16	1-8 3/4	11 17/32	1-9 29/32	1-0 5/32	1-11 3/32	1-0 25/32	2-0 1/4	1-1 13/32	2-1 7/16
11/16	10 31/32	1-8 13/16	11 19/32	1-10	1-0 3/16	1-11 5/32	1-0 13/16	2-0 11/32	1-1 7/16	2-1 1/2
3/4	11	1-8 7/8	11 5/8	1-10 1/16	1-0 1/4	1-11 1/4	1-0 7/8	2-0 13/32	1-1 15/32	2-1 19/32
13/16	11 1/32	1-8 31/32	11 21/32	1-10 1/8	1-0 9/32	1-11 5/16	1-0 29/32	2-0 1/2	1-1 17/32	2-1 21/32
7/8	11 3/32	1-9 1/32	11 11/16	1-10 3/16	1-0 7/16	1-11 3/8	1-0 15/16	2-0 9/16	1-1 9/16	2-1 3/4
15/16	11 1/8	1-9 3/32	11 3/4	1-10 9/32	1-0 11/32	1-11 15/32	1-0 31/32	2-0 5/8	1-1 19/32	2-1 13/16

Feet	40′ Rise	40′ Slope	50′ Rise	50′ Slope	60′ Rise	60′ Slope	70′ Rise	70′ Slope
0	24-9 1/2	47-0 23/32	30-11 7/8	58-9 29/32	37-2 1/4	70-7 1/16	43-4 5/8	82-4 1/4
1	25-4 15/16	48-2 27/32	31-7 5/16	60-0	37-9 11/16	71-9 3/16	44-0 1/16	83-6 3/8
2	26-0 3/8	49-4 31/32	32-2 3/4	61-2 1/8	38-5 1/8	72-11 5/16	44-7 1/2	84-8 1/2
3	26-7 13/16	50-7 1/16	32-10 3/32	62-4 1/4	39-0 9/16	74-1 1/16	45-2 15/16	85-10 5/8
4	27-3 1/4	51-9 3/16	33-5 5/8	63-6 3/8	39-8	75-3 9/16	45-10 3/8	87-0 23/32
5	27-10 11/16	52-11 5/16	34-1 1/16	64-8 1/2	40-3 7/16	76-5 21/32	46-5 13/16	88-2 27/32
6	28-6 1/8	54-1 7/16	34-8 1/2	65-10 19/32	40-10 7/8	77-7 25/32	47-1 1/4	89-4 31/32
7	29-1 9/16	55-3 17/32	35-3 15/16	67-0 23/32	41-6 5/16	78-9 29/32	47-8 11/16	90-7 3/32
8	29-9	56-5 21/32	35-11 3/8	68-2 27/32	42-1 3/4	80-0 1/32	48-4 1/8	91-9 3/16
9	30-4 7/16	57-7 25/32	36-6 13/16	69-4 31/32	42-9 3/16	81-2 1/8	48-11 9/16	92-11 5/16

natsin A=0.5268117521; natcos A=0.8499819868; nattan A=0.6197916666; natcot A=1.6134453781

Inches	0" Rise	0" Slope	1" Rise	1" Slope	2" Rise	2" Slope	3" Rise	3" Slope	4" Rise	4" Slope	5" Rise	5" Slope
0	0	0	5/8	1 3/16	1 1/4	2 11/32	1 7/8	3 17/32	2 1/2	4 23/32	3 1/8	5 29/32
1/16	1/32	1/16	21/32	1 1/4	1 9/32	2 7/16	1 29/32	3 5/8	2 17/32	4 25/32	3 5/32	5 31/32
1/8	1/16	5/32	11/16	1 5/16	1 5/16	2 1/2	1 15/16	3 11/16	2 9/16	4 7/8	3 3/16	6 1/32
3/16	3/32	7/32	3/4	1 13/32	1 3/8	2 19/32	2	3 3/4	2 5/8	4 15/16	3 1/4	6 1/8
1/4	5/32	9/32	25/32	1 15/32	1 13/32	2 21/32	2 1/32	3 27/32	2 21/32	5	3 9/32	6 3/16
5/16	3/16	3/8	13/16	1 9/16	1 7/16	2 23/32	2 1/16	3 29/32	2 11/16	5 3/32	3 5/16	6 1/4
3/8	1/4	7/16	7/8	1 5/8	1 1/2	2 13/16	2 1/8	3 31/32	2 3/4	5 5/32	3 3/8	6 11/32
7/16	9/32	17/32	29/32	1 11/16	1 17/32	2 7/8	2 5/32	4 1/32	2 25/32	5 7/32	3 13/32	6 13/32
1/2	5/16	19/32	15/16	1 25/32	1 9/16	2 15/16	2 3/16	4 1/8	2 13/16	5 5/16	3 7/16	6 1/2
9/16	11/32	21/32	31/32	1 27/32	1 19/32	3 1/32	2 1/4	4 3/16	2 27/32	5 3/8	3 15/32	6 9/16
5/8	3/8	3/4	1	1 29/32	1 5/8	3 3/32	2 1/4	4 9/32	2 7/8	5 15/32	3 1/2	6 5/8
11/16	7/16	13/16	1 1/16	2	1 11/16	3 5/32	2 5/16	4 11/32	2 15/16	5 17/32	3 9/16	6 23/32
3/4	15/32	7/8	1 3/32	2 1/16	1 23/32	3 1/4	2 11/32	4 7/16	2 31/32	5 19/32	3 19/32	6 25/32
13/16	1/2	31/32	1 1/8	2 1/8	1 3/4	3 5/16	2 3/8	4 1/2	3	5 11/16	3 5/8	6 27/32
7/8	9/16	1 1/32	1 3/16	2 7/32	1 13/16	3 3/8	2 7/16	4 9/16	3 1/16	5 3/4	3 11/16	6 15/16
15/16	19/32	1 3/32	1 7/32	2 9/32	1 27/32	3 15/32	2 15/32	4 21/32	3 3/32	5 13/16	3 23/32	7

Inches	6" Rise	6" Slope	7" Rise	7" Slope	8" Rise	8" Slope	9" Rise	9" Slope	10" Rise	10" Slope	11" Rise	11" Slope
0	3 3/4	7 1/16	4 3/8	8 1/4	5	9 7/16	5 5/8	10 5/8	6 1/4	11 25/32	6 7/8	1-0 31/32
1/16	3 25/32	7 5/32	4 13/32	8 11/32	5 1/16	9 1/2	5 21/32	10 11/16	6 9/32	11 7/8	6 29/32	1-1 1/32
1/8	3 13/16	7 7/32	4 7/16	8 13/32	5 1/8	9 19/32	5 11/16	10 3/4	6 5/16	11 15/16	6 15/16	1-1 1/8
3/16	3 7/8	7 9/32	4 1/2	8 15/32	5 1/8	9 21/32	5 3/4	10 27/32	6 3/8	1-0	7	1-1 13/16
1/4	3 29/32	7 3/8	4 17/32	8 9/16	5 5/8	9 23/32	5 25/32	10 29/32	6 13/32	1-0 3/8	7 1/32	1-1 9/32
5/16	3 15/16	7 7/16	4 9/16	8 5/8	5 3/16	9 13/16	5 13/16	10 31/32	6 7/16	1-0 5/32	7 1/16	1-1 11/32
3/8	4	7 17/32	4 5/8	8 11/16	5 1/4	9 7/8	5 7/8	11 1/16	6 1/2	1-0 1/4	7 1/8	1-1 13/32
7/16	4 1/32	7 19/32	4 21/32	8 25/32	5 9/32	9 15/16	5 29/32	11 1/8	6 17/32	1-0 5/16	7 5/32	1-1 1/2
1/2	4 1/16	7 21/32	4 11/16	8 27/32	5 5/16	10 1/32	5 15/16	11 3/16	6 9/16	1-0 3/8	7 3/16	1-1 9/32
9/16	4 3/32	7 3/4	4 23/32	8 29/32	5 11/32	10 3/32	5 31/32	11 9/32	6 19/32	1-0 15/32	7 7/32	1-1 5/8
5/8	4 1/8	7 13/16	4 3/4	9	5 3/8	10 5/32	6	11 11/32	6 5/8	1-0 17/32	7 1/4	1-1 23/32
11/16	4 3/16	7 7/8	4 13/16	9 1/16	5 7/16	10 1/4	6 1/16	11 7/16	6 11/16	1-0 19/32	7 5/16	1-1 25/32
3/4	4 7/8	7 31/32	4 27/32	9 1/8	5 15/32	10 5/32	6 3/32	11 1/2	6 23/32	1-0 11/32	7 11/32	1-1 27/32
13/16	4 1/4	8 1/32	4 7/8	9 27/32	5 1/2	10 13/32	6 1/8	11 9/16	6 3/4	1-0 3/4	7 3/8	1-1 15/16
7/8	4 5/16	8 3/32	4 15/16	9 31/32	5 9/16	10 15/32	6 3/16	11 21/32	6 13/16	1-0 13/16	7 7/16	1-2
15/16	4 11/32	8 5/16	4 31/32	9 3/8	5 19/32	10 17/32	6 7/32	11 23/32	6 27/32	1-0 29/32	7 15/32	1-2 1/16

Feet	0' Rise	0' Slope	10' Rise	10' Slope	20' Rise	20' Slope	30' Rise	30' Slope
0	0	0	6-3	11-9 1/2	12-6	23-7 1/32	18-9	35-4 17/32
1	7 1/2	1-2 5/32	6-10 1/2	12-11 21/32	13-1 1/2	24-9 5/32	19-4 1/2	36-6 11/16
2	1-3	2-4 5/16	7-6	14-1 13/16	13-9	25-11 15/16	20-0	37-8 27/32
3	1-10 1/2	3-6 7/16	8-1 1/2	15-3 31/32	14-4 1/2	27-1 15/32	20-7 1/2	38-10 31/32
4	2-6	4-8 19/32	8-9	16-6 1/8	15-0	28-3 5/8	21-3	40-1 1/8
5	3-1 1/2	5-10 3/4	9-4 1/2	17-8 1/4	15-7 1/2	29-5 25/32	21-10 1/2	41-3 9/16
6	3-9	7-0 29/32	10-0	18-10 13/32	16-3	30-7 15/16	22-6	42-5 7/16
7	4-4 1/2	8-3 1/16	10-7 1/2	20-0 9/16	16-10 1/2	31-10 1/16	23-1 1/2	43-7 19/32
8	5-0	9-5 7/32	11-3	21-2 23/32	17-6	33-0 7/32	23-9	44-9 3/4
9	5-7 1/2	10-7 11/32	11-10 1/2	22-4 7/8	18-1 1/2	34-2 3/8	24-4 1/2	45-11 7/8

A = 32° 00′ 19″; logsin A = 9.72427; logcos A = 9.92839; logtan A = 9.79588; logcot A = 0.20412

Ins.	12″ Rise	12″ Slope	13″ Rise	13″ Slope	14″ Rise	14″ Slope	15″ Rise	15″ Slope	16″ Rise	16″ Slope
0	$7\frac{1}{2}$	$1\text{-}2\frac{5}{32}$	$8\frac{1}{8}$	$1\text{-}3\frac{11}{32}$	$8\frac{3}{4}$	$1\text{-}4\frac{1}{2}$	$9\frac{3}{8}$	$1\text{-}5\frac{11}{16}$	10	$1\text{-}6\frac{7}{8}$
$\frac{1}{16}$	$7\frac{17}{32}$	$1\text{-}2\frac{7}{32}$	$8\frac{5}{32}$	$1\text{-}3\frac{13}{32}$	$8\frac{25}{32}$	$1\text{-}4\frac{19}{32}$	$9\frac{13}{32}$	$1\text{-}5\frac{3}{4}$	$10\frac{1}{32}$	$1\text{-}6\frac{15}{16}$
$\frac{1}{8}$	$7\frac{9}{16}$	$1\text{-}2\frac{5}{32}$	$8\frac{3}{16}$	$1\text{-}3\frac{15}{32}$	$8\frac{13}{16}$	$1\text{-}4\frac{21}{32}$	$9\frac{7}{16}$	$1\text{-}5\frac{27}{32}$	$10\frac{1}{16}$	$1\text{-}7$
$\frac{3}{16}$	$7\frac{5}{8}$	$1\text{-}2\frac{3}{8}$	$8\frac{1}{4}$	$1\text{-}3\frac{9}{16}$	$8\frac{7}{8}$	$1\text{-}4\frac{23}{32}$	$9\frac{1}{2}$	$1\text{-}5\frac{29}{32}$	$10\frac{1}{8}$	$1\text{-}7\frac{3}{32}$
$\frac{1}{4}$	$7\frac{21}{32}$	$1\text{-}2\frac{7}{16}$	$8\frac{9}{32}$	$1\text{-}3\frac{5}{8}$	$8\frac{29}{32}$	$1\text{-}4\frac{13}{16}$	$9\frac{17}{32}$	$1\text{-}5\frac{31}{32}$	$10\frac{5}{32}$	$1\text{-}7\frac{5}{32}$
$\frac{5}{16}$	$7\frac{11}{16}$	$1\text{-}2\frac{17}{32}$	$8\frac{5}{16}$	$1\text{-}3\frac{11}{16}$	$8\frac{15}{16}$	$1\text{-}4\frac{7}{8}$	$9\frac{9}{16}$	$1\text{-}6\frac{1}{16}$	$10\frac{3}{16}$	$1\text{-}7\frac{1}{4}$
$\frac{3}{8}$	$7\frac{3}{4}$	$1\text{-}2\frac{19}{32}$	$8\frac{3}{8}$	$1\text{-}3\frac{25}{32}$	9	$1\text{-}4\frac{15}{16}$	$9\frac{5}{8}$	$1\text{-}6\frac{1}{8}$	$10\frac{1}{4}$	$1\text{-}7\frac{5}{16}$
$\frac{7}{16}$	$7\frac{25}{32}$	$1\text{-}2\frac{21}{32}$	$8\frac{13}{32}$	$1\text{-}3\frac{27}{32}$	$9\frac{1}{32}$	$1\text{-}5\frac{1}{32}$	$9\frac{21}{32}$	$1\text{-}6\frac{7}{32}$	$10\frac{9}{32}$	$1\text{-}7\frac{3}{8}$
$\frac{1}{2}$	$7\frac{13}{16}$	$1\text{-}2\frac{3}{4}$	$8\frac{7}{16}$	$1\text{-}3\frac{29}{32}$	$9\frac{1}{16}$	$1\text{-}5\frac{3}{32}$	$9\frac{11}{16}$	$1\text{-}6\frac{9}{32}$	$10\frac{5}{16}$	$1\text{-}7\frac{15}{32}$
$\frac{9}{16}$	$7\frac{27}{32}$	$1\text{-}2\frac{13}{16}$	$8\frac{15}{32}$	$1\text{-}4$	$9\frac{3}{32}$	$1\text{-}5\frac{3}{16}$	$9\frac{23}{32}$	$1\text{-}6\frac{11}{32}$	$10\frac{11}{32}$	$1\text{-}7\frac{17}{32}$
$\frac{5}{8}$	$7\frac{7}{8}$	$1\text{-}2\frac{7}{8}$	$8\frac{1}{2}$	$1\text{-}4\frac{1}{32}$	$9\frac{1}{8}$	$1\text{-}5\frac{1}{4}$	$9\frac{3}{4}$	$1\text{-}6\frac{7}{16}$	$10\frac{3}{8}$	$1\text{-}7\frac{19}{32}$
$\frac{11}{16}$	$7\frac{15}{16}$	$1\text{-}2\frac{31}{32}$	$8\frac{9}{16}$	$1\text{-}4\frac{5}{32}$	$9\frac{3}{16}$	$1\text{-}5\frac{5}{16}$	$9\frac{13}{16}$	$1\text{-}6\frac{1}{2}$	$10\frac{7}{16}$	$1\text{-}7\frac{11}{16}$
$\frac{3}{4}$	$7\frac{31}{32}$	$1\text{-}3\frac{1}{32}$	$8\frac{19}{32}$	$1\text{-}4\frac{7}{32}$	$9\frac{7}{32}$	$1\text{-}5\frac{13}{32}$	$9\frac{27}{32}$	$1\text{-}6\frac{9}{16}$	$10\frac{15}{32}$	$1\text{-}7\frac{3}{4}$
$\frac{13}{16}$	8	$1\text{-}3\frac{3}{32}$	$8\frac{5}{8}$	$1\text{-}4\frac{9}{32}$	$9\frac{1}{4}$	$1\text{-}5\frac{15}{32}$	$9\frac{7}{8}$	$1\text{-}6\frac{21}{32}$	$10\frac{1}{2}$	$1\text{-}7\frac{13}{16}$
$\frac{7}{8}$	$8\frac{1}{16}$	$1\text{-}3\frac{3}{16}$	$8\frac{11}{16}$	$1\text{-}4\frac{3}{8}$	$9\frac{5}{16}$	$1\text{-}5\frac{17}{32}$	$9\frac{15}{16}$	$1\text{-}6\frac{23}{32}$	$10\frac{9}{16}$	$1\text{-}7\frac{29}{32}$
$\frac{15}{16}$	$8\frac{3}{32}$	$1\text{-}3\frac{1}{4}$	$8\frac{23}{32}$	$1\text{-}4\frac{7}{16}$	$9\frac{11}{32}$	$1\text{-}5\frac{5}{8}$	$9\frac{31}{32}$	$1\text{-}6\frac{25}{32}$	$10\frac{19}{32}$	$1\text{-}7\frac{31}{32}$

Ins.	17″ Rise	17″ Slope	18″ Rise	18″ Slope	19″ Rise	19″ Slope	20″ Rise	20″ Slope	21″ Rise	21″ Slope
0	$10\frac{5}{8}$	$1\text{-}8\frac{1}{16}$	$11\frac{1}{4}$	$1\text{-}9\frac{7}{32}$	$11\frac{7}{8}$	$1\text{-}10\frac{13}{32}$	$1\text{-}0\frac{1}{2}$	$1\text{-}11\frac{19}{32}$	$1\text{-}1\frac{1}{8}$	$2\text{-}0\frac{3}{4}$
$\frac{1}{16}$	$10\frac{21}{32}$	$1\text{-}8\frac{1}{8}$	$11\frac{9}{32}$	$1\text{-}9\frac{5}{16}$	$11\frac{29}{32}$	$1\text{-}10\frac{15}{32}$	$1\text{-}0\frac{17}{32}$	$1\text{-}11\frac{21}{32}$	$1\text{-}1\frac{5}{32}$	$2\text{-}0\frac{27}{32}$
$\frac{1}{8}$	$10\frac{11}{16}$	$1\text{-}8\frac{3}{16}$	$11\frac{5}{16}$	$1\text{-}9\frac{3}{8}$	$11\frac{15}{16}$	$1\text{-}10\frac{9}{16}$	$1\text{-}0\frac{9}{16}$	$1\text{-}11\frac{23}{32}$	$1\text{-}1\frac{3}{16}$	$2\text{-}0\frac{29}{32}$
$\frac{3}{16}$	$10\frac{3}{4}$	$1\text{-}8\frac{9}{32}$	$11\frac{3}{8}$	$1\text{-}9\frac{7}{16}$	$1\text{-}0$	$1\text{-}10\frac{5}{8}$	$1\text{-}0\frac{5}{8}$	$1\text{-}11\frac{13}{16}$	$1\text{-}1\frac{1}{4}$	$2\text{-}1$
$\frac{1}{4}$	$10\frac{25}{32}$	$1\text{-}8\frac{11}{32}$	$11\frac{13}{32}$	$1\text{-}9\frac{17}{32}$	$1\text{-}0\frac{1}{32}$	$1\text{-}10\frac{11}{16}$	$1\text{-}0\frac{21}{32}$	$1\text{-}11\frac{7}{8}$	$1\text{-}1\frac{9}{32}$	$2\text{-}1\frac{1}{16}$
$\frac{5}{16}$	$10\frac{13}{16}$	$1\text{-}8\frac{13}{32}$	$11\frac{7}{16}$	$1\text{-}9\frac{19}{32}$	$1\text{-}0\frac{1}{16}$	$1\text{-}10\frac{25}{32}$	$1\text{-}0\frac{11}{16}$	$1\text{-}11\frac{31}{32}$	$1\text{-}1\frac{5}{16}$	$2\text{-}1\frac{1}{8}$
$\frac{3}{8}$	$10\frac{7}{8}$	$1\text{-}8\frac{1}{2}$	$11\frac{1}{2}$	$1\text{-}9\frac{21}{32}$	$1\text{-}0\frac{1}{8}$	$1\text{-}10\frac{27}{32}$	$1\text{-}0\frac{3}{4}$	$2\text{-}0\frac{1}{32}$	$1\text{-}1\frac{3}{8}$	$2\text{-}1\frac{7}{32}$
$\frac{7}{16}$	$10\frac{29}{32}$	$1\text{-}8\frac{9}{16}$	$11\frac{17}{32}$	$1\text{-}9\frac{3}{4}$	$1\text{-}0\frac{5}{32}$	$1\text{-}10\frac{29}{32}$	$1\text{-}0\frac{25}{32}$	$2\text{-}0\frac{3}{32}$	$1\text{-}1\frac{13}{32}$	$2\text{-}1\frac{9}{32}$
$\frac{1}{2}$	$10\frac{15}{16}$	$1\text{-}8\frac{5}{8}$	$11\frac{9}{16}$	$1\text{-}9\frac{13}{16}$	$1\text{-}0\frac{3}{16}$	$1\text{-}11$	$1\text{-}0\frac{13}{16}$	$2\text{-}0\frac{3}{16}$	$1\text{-}1\frac{7}{16}$	$2\text{-}1\frac{11}{32}$
$\frac{9}{16}$	$10\frac{31}{32}$	$1\text{-}8\frac{23}{32}$	$11\frac{19}{32}$	$1\text{-}9\frac{7}{8}$	$1\text{-}0\frac{7}{32}$	$1\text{-}11\frac{1}{16}$	$1\text{-}0\frac{27}{32}$	$2\text{-}0\frac{1}{4}$	$1\text{-}1\frac{15}{32}$	$2\text{-}1\frac{7}{16}$
$\frac{5}{8}$	11	$1\text{-}8\frac{25}{32}$	$11\frac{5}{8}$	$1\text{-}9\frac{31}{32}$	$1\text{-}0\frac{1}{4}$	$1\text{-}11\frac{5}{32}$	$1\text{-}0\frac{7}{8}$	$2\text{-}0\frac{5}{16}$	$1\text{-}1\frac{1}{2}$	$2\text{-}1\frac{1}{2}$
$\frac{11}{16}$	$11\frac{1}{16}$	$1\text{-}8\frac{27}{32}$	$11\frac{11}{16}$	$1\text{-}10\frac{1}{32}$	$1\text{-}0\frac{5}{16}$	$1\text{-}11\frac{7}{32}$	$1\text{-}0\frac{15}{16}$	$2\text{-}0\frac{13}{32}$	$1\text{-}1\frac{9}{16}$	$2\text{-}1\frac{9}{16}$
$\frac{3}{4}$	$11\frac{3}{32}$	$1\text{-}8\frac{15}{16}$	$11\frac{23}{32}$	$1\text{-}10\frac{1}{8}$	$1\text{-}0\frac{11}{32}$	$1\text{-}11\frac{9}{32}$	$1\text{-}0\frac{31}{32}$	$2\text{-}0\frac{15}{32}$	$1\text{-}1\frac{19}{32}$	$2\text{-}1\frac{21}{32}$
$\frac{13}{16}$	$11\frac{1}{8}$	$1\text{-}9$	$11\frac{3}{4}$	$1\text{-}10\frac{3}{16}$	$1\text{-}0\frac{3}{8}$	$1\text{-}11\frac{3}{8}$	$1\text{-}1$	$2\text{-}0\frac{17}{32}$	$1\text{-}1\frac{5}{8}$	$2\text{-}1\frac{23}{32}$
$\frac{7}{8}$	$11\frac{13}{32}$	$1\text{-}9\frac{3}{32}$	$11\frac{13}{16}$	$1\text{-}10\frac{1}{4}$	$1\text{-}0\frac{7}{16}$	$1\text{-}11\frac{7}{16}$	$1\text{-}1\frac{1}{4}$	$2\text{-}0\frac{5}{8}$	$1\text{-}1\frac{11}{16}$	$2\text{-}1\frac{25}{32}$
$\frac{15}{16}$	$11\frac{7}{32}$	$1\text{-}9\frac{5}{32}$	$11\frac{27}{32}$	$1\text{-}10\frac{11}{32}$	$1\text{-}0\frac{15}{32}$	$1\text{-}11\frac{1}{2}$	$1\text{-}1\frac{3}{32}$	$2\text{-}0\frac{11}{32}$	$1\text{-}1\frac{23}{32}$	$2\text{-}1\frac{7}{8}$

Feet	40′ Rise	40′ Slope	50′ Rise	50′ Slope	60′ Rise	60′ Slope	70′ Rise	70′ Slope
0	25-0	$47\text{-}2\frac{1}{32}$	31-3	$58\text{-}11\frac{9}{16}$	37-6	$70\text{-}9\frac{1}{16}$	43-9	$82\text{-}6\frac{9}{16}$
1	$25\text{-}7\frac{1}{2}$	$48\text{-}4\frac{3}{16}$	$31\text{-}10\frac{1}{2}$	$60\text{-}1\frac{11}{16}$	$38\text{-}1\frac{1}{2}$	$71\text{-}11\frac{7}{32}$	$44\text{-}4\frac{1}{2}$	$83\text{-}8\frac{23}{32}$
2	26-3	$49\text{-}6\frac{11}{32}$	32-6	$61\text{-}3\frac{27}{32}$	38-9	$73\text{-}1\frac{3}{8}$	45-0	$84\text{-}10\frac{7}{8}$
3	$26\text{-}10\frac{1}{2}$	$50\text{-}8\frac{1}{2}$	$33\text{-}1\frac{1}{2}$	62-6	$39\text{-}4\frac{1}{2}$	$74\text{-}3\frac{1}{2}$	$45\text{-}7\frac{1}{2}$	$86\text{-}1\frac{1}{32}$
4	27-6	$51\text{-}10\frac{21}{32}$	33-9	$63\text{-}8\frac{5}{32}$	40-0	$75\text{-}5\frac{21}{32}$	46-3	$87\text{-}3\frac{3}{16}$
5	$28\text{-}1\frac{1}{2}$	$53\text{-}0\frac{25}{32}$	$34\text{-}4\frac{1}{2}$	$64\text{-}10\frac{5}{16}$	$40\text{-}7\frac{1}{2}$	$76\text{-}7\frac{13}{16}$	$46\text{-}10\frac{1}{2}$	$88\text{-}5\frac{5}{16}$
6	28-9	$54\text{-}2\frac{15}{16}$	35-0	$66\text{-}0\frac{15}{32}$	41-3	$77\text{-}9\frac{31}{32}$	47-6	$89\text{-}7\frac{15}{32}$
7	$29\text{-}4\frac{1}{2}$	$55\text{-}5\frac{3}{32}$	$35\text{-}7\frac{1}{2}$	$67\text{-}2\frac{19}{32}$	$41\text{-}10\frac{1}{2}$	$79\text{-}0\frac{1}{16}$	$48\text{-}1\frac{1}{2}$	$90\text{-}9\frac{5}{8}$
8	30-0	$56\text{-}7\frac{1}{4}$	36-3	$68\text{-}4\frac{3}{4}$	42-6	$80\text{-}2\frac{9}{32}$	48-9	$91\text{-}11\frac{25}{32}$
9	$30\text{-}7\frac{1}{2}$	$57\text{-}9\frac{13}{32}$	$36\text{-}10\frac{1}{2}$	$69\text{-}6\frac{29}{32}$	$43\text{-}1\frac{1}{2}$	$81\text{-}4\frac{13}{32}$	$49\text{-}4\frac{1}{2}$	$93\text{-}1\frac{15}{16}$

natsin A=0.5299989399; natcos A=0.8479983039; nattan A=0.6250000000; natcot A=1.6000000000

Inches	0" Rise	0" Slope	1" Rise	1" Slope	2" Rise	2" Slope	3" Rise	3" Slope	4" Rise	4" Slope	5" Rise	5" Slope
0	0	0	5/8	1 3/16	1 1/4	2 3/8	1 7/8	3 17/32	2 17/32	4 23/32	3 5/32	5 29/32
1/16	1/32	1/16	21/32	1 1/4	1 5/16	2 7/16	1 15/16	3 5/8	2 9/16	4 13/16	3 3/16	5 31/32
1/8	3/32	5/32	23/32	1 11/32	1 11/32	2 1/2	1 31/32	3 11/16	2 19/32	4 7/8	3 7/32	6 1/16
3/16	1/8	7/32	3/4	1 13/32	1 3/8	2 19/32	2	3 25/32	2 5/8	4 15/16	3 9/32	6 1/8
1/4	5/32	9/32	25/32	1 15/32	1 13/32	2 21/32	2 1/16	3 27/32	2 11/16	5 1/32	3 5/16	6 7/32
5/16	3/16	3/8	13/16	1 9/16	1 15/32	2 23/32	2 3/32	3 29/32	2 23/32	5 3/32	3 11/32	6 9/32
3/8	1/4	7/16	7/8	1 5/8	1 1/2	2 13/16	2 1/8	4	2 3/4	5 5/32	3 3/8	6 11/32
7/16	9/32	17/32	29/32	1 11/16	1 17/32	2 7/8	2 5/32	4 1/16	2 25/32	5 1/4	3 7/16	6 7/16
1/2	5/16	19/32	15/16	1 25/32	1 9/16	2 31/32	2 7/32	4 1/8	2 27/32	5 5/16	3 15/32	6 1/2
9/16	11/32	21/32	1	1 27/32	1 5/8	3 1/32	2 1/4	4 7/32	2 7/8	5 13/32	3 1/2	6 9/16
5/8	13/32	3/4	1 1/32	1 29/32	1 21/32	3 3/32	2 9/32	4 9/32	2 29/32	5 15/32	3 17/32	6 21/32
11/16	7/16	13/16	1 1/16	2	1 11/16	3 3/16	2 5/16	4 11/32	2 31/32	5 17/32	3 19/32	6 23/32
3/4	15/32	7/8	1 3/32	2 1/16	1 23/32	3 1/4	2 3/8	4 7/16	3	5 5/8	3 5/8	6 25/32
13/16	1/2	31/32	1 5/32	2 5/32	1 25/32	3 5/16	2 13/32	4 1/2	3 1/32	5 11/16	3 21/32	6 7/8
7/8	9/16	1 1/32	1 3/16	2 7/32	1 13/16	3 13/32	2 7/16	4 19/32	3 1/16	5 3/4	3 11/16	6 15/16
15/16	19/32	1 3/32	1 7/32	2 9/32	1 27/32	3 15/32	2 15/32	4 21/32	3 1/8	5 27/32	3 3/4	7 1/32

Inches	6" Rise	6" Slope	7" Rise	7" Slope	8" Rise	8" Slope	9" Rise	9" Slope	10" Rise	10" Slope	11" Rise	11" Slope
0	3 25/32	7 3/32	4 13/32	8 9/32	5 1/32	9 15/32	5 11/16	10 5/8	6 5/16	11 13/16	6 15/16	1-1
1/16	3 13/16	7 5/32	4 7/16	8 11/32	5 3/32	9 17/32	5 23/32	10 23/32	6 11/32	11 29/32	6 31/32	1-1 1/16
1/8	3 7/8	7 1/4	4 1/2	8 13/32	5 1/8	9 19/32	5 3/4	10 25/32	6 3/8	11 31/32	7	1-1 5/32
3/16	3 29/32	7 5/16	4 17/32	8 1/2	5 5/32	9 11/16	5 25/32	10 7/8	6 13/32	1-0 1/32	7 1/16	1-1 7/32
1/4	3 15/16	7 3/8	4 9/16	8 9/16	5 3/16	9 3/4	5 27/32	10 15/16	6 15/32	1-0 1/8	7 3/32	1-1 5/16
5/16	3 31/32	7 15/32	4 19/32	8 21/32	5 1/4	9 13/16	5 7/8	11	6 1/2	1-0 3/16	7 1/8	1-1 3/8
3/8	4 1/32	7 17/32	4 21/32	8 23/32	5 9/32	9 29/32	5 29/32	11 3/32	6 17/32	1-0 1/4	7 5/32	1-1 7/16
7/16	4 1/16	7 19/32	4 11/16	8 25/32	5 5/16	9 31/32	5 15/16	11 5/32	6 9/16	1-0 11/32	7 7/32	1-1 17/32
1/2	4 3/32	7 11/16	4 23/32	8 7/8	5 11/32	10 1/16	6	11 7/32	6 5/8	1-0 13/32	7 1/4	1-1 19/32
9/16	4 1/8	7 3/4	4 25/32	8 15/16	5 13/32	10 1/8	6 1/32	11 5/16	6 21/32	1-0 1/2	7 9/32	1-1 21/32
5/8	4 3/16	7 27/32	4 13/16	9	5 7/16	10 3/16	6 1/16	11 3/8	6 11/16	1-0 9/16	7 5/16	1-1 3/4
11/16	4 7/32	7 29/32	4 27/32	9 3/32	5 15/32	10 9/32	6 3/32	11 7/16	6 3/4	1-0 5/8	7 3/8	1-1 13/16
3/4	4 1/4	7 31/32	4 7/8	9 5/32	5 1/2	10 11/32	6 5/32	11 17/32	6 25/32	1-0 23/32	7 13/32	1-1 7/8
13/16	4 9/32	8 1/16	4 15/16	9 1/4	5 9/16	10 13/32	6 3/16	11 19/32	6 13/16	1-0 25/32	7 7/16	1-1 31/32
7/8	4 11/32	8 1/8	4 31/32	9 5/16	5 19/32	10 1/2	6 7/32	11 11/16	6 27/32	1-0 27/32	7 15/32	1-2 1/32
15/16	4 3/8	8 3/16	5	9 3/8	5 5/8	10 9/16	6 1/4	11 3/4	6 29/32	1-0 15/16	7 17/32	1-2 1/8

Feet	0' Rise	0' Slope	10' Rise	10' Slope	20' Rise	20' Slope	30' Rise	30' Slope
0	0	0	6-3 5/8	11-9 27/32	12-7 1/4	23-7 11/16	18-10 7/8	35-5 17/32
1	7 9/16	1-2 3/16	6-11 3/16	13-0 1/32	13-2 13/16	24-9 7/8	19-6 7/16	36-7 23/32
2	1-3 1/8	2-4 3/8	7-6 3/4	14-2 7/32	13-10 3/8	26-0 1/16	20-2	37-9 29/32
3	1-10 11/16	3-6 9/16	8-2 5/16	15-4 13/32	14-5 15/16	27-2 1/4	20-9 9/16	39-0 3/32
4	2-6 1/4	4-8 3/4	8-9 7/8	16-6 19/32	15-1 1/2	28-4 13/32	21-5 1/8	40-2 1/4
5	3-1 13/16	5-10 29/32	9-5 7/16	17-8 3/4	15-9 1/16	29-6 19/32	22-0 11/16	41-4 7/16
6	3-9 3/8	7-1 3/32	10-1	18-10 15/16	16-4 5/8	30-8 25/32	22-8 1/4	42-6 5/8
7	4-4 15/16	8-3 9/32	10-8 9/16	20-1 1/8	17-0 3/16	31-10 31/32	23-3 13/16	43-8 13/16
8	5-0 1/2	9-5 15/32	11-4 1/8	21-3 5/16	17-7 3/4	33-1 5/32	23-11 3/8	44-11
9	5-8 1/16	10-7 21/32	11-11 11/16	22-5 1/2	18-3 5/16	34-3 11/32	24-6 15/16	46-1 3/16

A = 32° 13' 10"; logsin A = 9.72686; logcos A = 9.92738; logtan A = 9.79948; logcot A = 0.20052.

Ins.	12″ Rise	12″ Slope	13″ Rise	13″ Slope	14″ Rise	14″ Slope	15″ Rise	15″ Slope	16″ Rise	16″ Slope
0	7 9/16	1-2 3/16	8 3/16	1-3 3/8	8 13/16	1-4 9/16	9 7/16	1-5 23/32	10 3/32	1-6 29/32
1/16	7 19/32	1-2 1/4	8 7/32	1-3 7/16	8 7/8	1-4 5/8	9 1/2	1-5 13/16	10 1/8	1-7
1/8	7 21/32	1-2 11/32	8 9/32	1-3 1/2	8 29/32	1-4 11/16	9 17/32	1-5 7/8	10 5/32	1-7 1/16
3/16	7 11/16	1-2 13/32	8 5/16	1-3 19/32	8 15/16	1-4 25/32	9 9/16	1-5 15/16	10 3/16	1-7 1/8
1/4	7 23/32	1-2 15/32	8 11/32	1-3 21/32	8 31/32	1-4 27/32	9 5/8	1-6 1/32	10 1/4	1-7 7/32
5/16	7 3/4	1-2 9/16	8 3/8	1-3 3/4	9 1/32	1-4 29/32	9 21/32	1-6 3/32	10 9/32	1-7 9/32
3/8	7 13/16	1-2 5/8	8 7/16	1-3 13/16	9 1/16	1-5	9 11/16	1-6 3/16	10 5/16	1-7 11/32
7/16	7 27/32	1-2 11/16	8 15/32	1-3 7/8	9 3/32	1-5 1/16	9 23/32	1-6 1/4	10 11/32	1-7 7/16
1/2	7 7/8	1-2 25/32	8 1/2	1-3 31/32	9 1/8	1-5 1/8	9 25/32	1-6 5/16	10 13/32	1-7 1/2
9/16	7 29/32	1-2 27/32	8 9/16	1-4 1/32	9 3/16	1-5 7/32	9 13/16	1-6 13/32	10 7/16	1-7 9/16
5/8	7 31/32	1-2 15/16	8 19/32	1-4 3/32	9 7/32	1-5 9/32	9 27/32	1-6 15/32	10 15/32	1-7 21/32
11/16	8	1-3	8 5/8	1-4 3/16	9 1/4	1-5 3/8	9 7/8	1-6 17/32	10 17/32	1-7 23/32
3/4	8 1/32	1-3 1/16	8 21/32	1-4 1/4	9 9/32	1-5 7/16	9 15/16	1-6 5/8	10 9/16	1-7 13/16
13/16	8 1/16	1-3 5/32	8 23/32	1-4 5/16	9 11/32	1-5 1/2	9 31/32	1-6 11/16	10 19/32	1-7 7/8
7/8	8 1/8	1-3 7/32	8 3/4	1-4 13/32	9 3/8	1-5 19/32	10	1-6 3/4	10 5/8	1-7 15/16
15/16	8 5/32	1-3 9/32	8 25/32	1-4 15/32	9 13/32	1-5 21/32	10 1/32	1-6 27/32	10 11/16	1-8 1/32

Ins.	17″ Rise	17″ Slope	18″ Rise	18″ Slope	19″ Rise	19″ Slope	20″ Rise	20″ Slope	21″ Rise	21″ Slope
0	10 23/32	1-8 3/32	11 11/32	1-9 9/32	11 31/32	1-10 15/32	1-0 19/32	1-11 5/8	1-1 1/4	2-0 13/16
1/16	10 3/4	1-8 5/32	11 3/8	1-9 11/32	1-0	1-10 17/32	1-0 21/32	1-11 23/32	1-1 9/32	2-0 29/32
1/8	10 25/32	1-8 1/4	11 7/16	1-9 7/16	1-0 1/16	1-10 19/32	1-0 11/16	1-11 25/32	1-1 5/16	2-0 31/32
3/16	10 27/32	1-8 5/16	11 15/32	1-9 1/2	1-0 3/32	1-10 11/16	1-0 23/32	1-11 7/8	1-1 11/32	2-1 1/32
1/4	10 7/8	1-8 3/8	11 1/2	1-9 9/16	1-0 1/8	1-10 3/4	1-0 3/4	1-11 15/16	1-1 13/32	2-1 1/8
5/16	10 29/32	1-8 15/32	11 17/32	1-9 21/32	1-0 5/32	1-10 13/16	1-0 13/16	2-0	1-1 7/16	2-1 3/16
3/8	10 15/16	1-8 17/32	11 19/32	1-9 23/32	1-0 7/32	1-10 29/32	1-0 27/32	2-0 3/32	1-1 15/32	2-1 1/4
7/16	11	1-8 5/8	11 5/8	1-9 25/32	1-0 1/4	1-10 31/32	1-0 7/8	2-0 5/32	1-1 1/2	2-1 11/32
1/2	11 1/32	1-8 11/16	11 21/32	1-9 7/8	1-0 9/32	1-11 1/16	1-0 29/32	2-0 7/32	1-1 9/16	2-1 13/32
9/16	11 1/16	1-8 3/4	11 11/16	1-9 15/16	1-0 11/32	1-11 1/8	1-0 31/32	2-0 5/16	1-1 19/32	2-1 1/2
5/8	11 3/32	1-8 27/32	11 3/4	1-10	1-0 3/8	1-11 3/16	1-1	2-0 3/8	1-1 5/8	2-1 9/16
11/16	11 5/32	1-8 29/32	11 25/32	1-10 3/32	1-0 13/32	1-11 9/32	1-1 1/32	2-0 7/16	1-1 21/32	2-1 5/8
3/4	11 3/16	1-8 31/32	11 13/16	1-10 5/32	1-0 7/16	1-11 11/32	1-1 1/16	2-0 17/32	1-1 23/32	2-1 23/32
13/16	11 7/32	1-9 1/16	11 27/32	1-10 1/4	1-0 1/2	1-11 13/32	1-1 1/8	2-0 19/32	1-1 3/4	2-1 25/32
7/8	11 1/4	1-9 1/8	11 29/32	1-10 5/16	1-0 17/32	1-11 1/2	1-1 5/32	2-0 11/16	1-1 25/32	2-1 27/32
15/16	11 5/16	1-9 3/16	11 15/16	1-10 3/8	1-0 9/16	1-11 9/16	1-1 3/16	2-0 3/4	1-1 13/16	2-1 15/16

Feet	40′ Rise	40′ Slope	50′ Rise	50′ Slope	60′ Rise	60′ Slope	70′ Rise	70′ Slope
0	25-2 1/2	47-3 3/8	31-6 1/8	59-1 7/32	37-9 3/4	70-11 1/16	44-1 3/8	82-8 29/32
1	25-10 1/16	48-5 9/16	32-1 11/16	60-3 13/32	38-5 5/16	72-1 1/4	44-8 15/16	83-11 1/16
2	26-5 5/8	49-7 3/4	32-9 1/4	61-5 19/32	39-0 7/8	73-3 13/32	45-4 1/2	85-1 1/4
3	27-1 3/16	50-9 29/32	33-4 13/16	62-7 3/4	39-8 7/16	74-5 19/32	46-0 1/16	86-3 7/16
4	27-8 3/4	52-0 3/32	34-0 3/8	63-9 15/16	40-4	75-7 25/32	46-7 5/8	87-5 5/8
5	28-4 5/16	53-2 9/32	34-7 15/16	65-0 1/8	40-11 9/16	76-9 31/32	47-3 3/16	88-7 13/16
6	28-11 7/8	54-4 15/32	35-3 1/2	66-2 5/16	41-7 1/8	78-0 5/32	47-10 3/4	89-10
7	29-7 7/16	55-6 21/32	35-11 1/16	67-4 1/2	42-2 11/16	79-2 11/32	48-6 5/16	91-0 3/16
8	30-3	56-8 27/32	36-6 5/8	68-6 11/16	42-10 1/4	80-4 17/32	49-1 7/8	92-2 3/8
9	30-10 9/16	57-11 1/32	37-2 3/16	69-8 7/8	43-5 13/16	81-6 23/32	49-9 7/16	93-4 9/16

natsin A=0.5331638244; natcos A=0.8460120189; nattan A=0.6302083333; natcot A=1.5867768595

Inches	0" Rise	0" Slope	1" Rise	1" Slope	2" Rise	2" Slope	3" Rise	3" Slope	4" Rise	4" Slope	5" Rise	5" Slope
0	0	0	5/8	13/16	1 9/32	2 3/8	1 29/32	3 9/16	2 17/32	4 3/4	3 3/16	5 15/16
1/16	1/32	1/16	11/16	1 1/4	1 5/16	2 7/16	1 15/16	3 5/8	2 19/32	4 13/16	3 7/32	6
1/8	3/32	5/32	23/32	1 11/32	1 11/32	2 17/32	2	3 11/16	2 5/8	4 7/8	3 1/4	6 1/16
3/16	1/8	7/32	3/4	1 13/32	1 3/8	2 19/32	2 1/32	3 25/32	2 21/32	4 31/32	3 9/32	6 5/32
1/4	5/32	9/32	25/32	1 15/32	1 7/16	2 21/32	2 1/16	3 27/32	2 11/16	5 1/16	3 11/32	6 7/32
5/16	3/16	3/8	27/32	1 9/16	1 15/32	2 3/4	2 3/32	3 15/16	2 3/4	5 1/8	3 3/8	6 9/32
3/8	1/4	7/16	7/8	1 5/8	1 1/2	2 13/16	2 1/8	4	2 25/32	5 3/16	3 13/32	6 3/8
7/16	9/32	17/32	29/32	1 23/32	1 9/16	2 7/8	2 3/16	4 1/16	2 13/16	5 1/4	3 15/32	6 7/16
1/2	5/16	19/32	15/16	1 25/32	1 19/32	2 31/32	2 7/32	4 5/32	2 7/8	5 11/32	3 1/2	6 17/32
9/16	11/32	21/32	1	1 27/32	1 5/8	3 1/32	2 1/4	4 7/32	2 29/32	5 13/32	3 17/32	6 19/32
5/8	13/32	3/4	1 1/32	1 15/16	1 21/32	3 1/8	2 5/16	4 9/32	2 15/16	5 15/32	3 9/16	6 21/32
11/16	7/16	13/16	1 1/16	2	1 23/32	3 3/16	2 11/32	4 3/8	2 31/32	5 9/16	3 5/8	6 3/4
3/4	15/32	7/8	1 1/8	2 1/16	1 3/4	3 1/4	2 3/8	4 7/16	3 1/32	5 5/8	3 21/32	6 13/16
13/16	17/32	31/32	1 5/32	2 5/32	1 25/32	3 11/32	2 7/16	4 17/32	3 1/16	5 11/16	3 11/16	6 7/8
7/8	9/16	1 1/32	1 3/16	2 7/32	1 13/16	3 13/32	2 15/32	4 19/32	3 3/32	5 25/32	3 23/32	6 31/32
15/16	19/32	1 1/8	1 7/32	2 9/32	1 7/8	3 15/32	2 1/2	4 21/32	3 1/8	5 27/32	3 25/32	7 1/32

Inches	6" Rise	6" Slope	7" Rise	7" Slope	8" Rise	8" Slope	9" Rise	9" Slope	10" Rise	10" Slope	11" Rise	11" Slope
0	3 13/16	7 3/32	4 7/16	8 9/32	5 3/32	9 15/32	5 23/32	10 21/32	6 11/32	11 27/32	7	1-1 1/32
1/16	3 27/32	7 3/16	4 1/2	8 3/8	5 1/8	9 9/16	5 3/4	10 3/4	6 13/32	11 15/16	7 1/32	1-1 3/32
1/8	3 29/32	7 1/4	4 17/32	8 7/16	5 5/32	9 5/8	5 13/16	10 13/16	6 7/16	1-0	7 1/16	1-1 3/16
3/16	3 15/16	7 11/32	4 9/16	8 17/32	5 3/16	9 11/16	5 27/32	10 7/8	6 15/32	1-0 1/16	7 3/32	1-1 1/4
1/4	3 31/32	7 13/32	4 19/32	8 19/32	5 1/4	9 25/32	5 7/8	10 31/32	6 1/2	1-0 5/32	7 5/32	1-1 11/32
5/16	4	7 15/32	4 21/32	8 21/32	5 9/32	9 27/32	5 29/32	11 1/32	6 9/16	1-0 7/32	7 3/16	1-1 13/32
3/8	4 1/16	7 17/32	4 11/16	8 3/4	5 5/16	9 15/16	5 31/32	11 3/32	6 19/32	1-0 9/32	7 7/32	1-1 15/32
7/16	4 3/32	7 5/8	4 23/32	8 13/16	5 3/8	10	6	11 3/16	6 5/8	1-0 3/8	7 9/32	1-1 9/16
1/2	4 1/8	7 11/16	4 3/4	8 7/8	5 13/32	10 1/16	6 1/16	11 1/4	6 11/16	1-0 7/16	7 5/16	1-1 5/8
9/16	4 5/32	7 25/32	4 13/16	8 31/32	5 7/16	10 5/32	6 1/16	11 11/32	6 23/32	1-0 1/2	7 11/32	1-1 11/16
5/8	4 7/32	7 27/32	4 27/32	9 1/32	5 15/32	10 7/32	6 1/8	11 13/32	6 3/4	1-0 19/32	7 3/8	1-1 25/32
11/16	4 1/4	7 15/16	4 7/8	9 3/32	5 1/2	10 9/32	6 9/32	11 15/32	6 25/32	1-0 21/32	7 7/16	1-1 27/32
3/4	4 9/32	8	4 15/16	9 3/16	5 9/16	10 3/8	6 3/16	11 9/16	6 27/32	1-0 3/4	7 15/32	1-1 29/32
13/16	4 11/32	8 1/16	4 31/32	9 1/4	5 19/32	10 7/16	6 1/4	11 5/8	6 7/8	1-0 13/16	7 1/2	1-2
7/8	4 3/8	8 5/32	5	9 11/32	5 5/8	10 1/2	6 9/32	11 11/16	6 29/32	1-0 7/8	7 17/32	1-2 1/16
15/16	4 13/32	8 7/32	5 1/32	9 13/32	5 11/16	10 19/32	6 5/16	11 25/32	6 15/16	1-0 31/32	7 9/16	1-2 5/32

Feet	0' Rise	0' Slope	10' Rise	10' Slope	20' Rise	20' Slope	30' Rise	30' Slope
0	0	0	6-4 1/4	11-10 3/8	12-8 1/2	23-8 11/32	19-0 3/4	35-6 17/32
1	7 5/8	1-2 7/32	6-11 7/8	13-0 13/32	13-4 1/8	24-10 9/16	19-8 3/8	36-8 3/4
2	1-3 1/4	2-4 7/16	7-7 1/2	14-2 5/8	13-11 3/4	26-0 25/32	20-4	37-10 31/32
3	1-10 7/8	3-6 21/32	8-3 1/8	15-4 27/32	14-7 3/8	27-3	20-11 5/8	39-1 3/16
4	2-6 1/2	4-8 7/8	8-10 3/4	16-7 1/32	15-3	28-5 7/32	21-7 1/4	40-3 13/32
5	3-2 1/8	5-11 3/32	9-6 3/8	17-9 1/4	15-10 5/8	29-7 7/16	22-2 7/8	41-5 5/8
6	3-7 3/4	7-1 5/16	10-2	18-11 15/32	16-6 1/4	30-9 21/32	22-10 1/2	42-7 27/32
7	4-5 3/8	8-3 17/32	10-9 5/8	20-1 11/16	17-1 7/8	31-11 7/8	23-6 1/8	43-10 1/16
8	5-1	9-5 3/4	11-5 1/4	21-3 29/32	17-9 1/2	33-2 3/32	24-1 3/4	45-0 9/32
9	5-8 5/8	10-7 31/32	12-0 7/8	22-6 1/8	18-5 1/8	34-4 5/16	24-9 3/8	46-2 1/2

A = 32° 25' 57"; logsin A = 9.72941; logcos A = 9.92635; logtan A = 9.80306; logcot A = 0.19694

Ins.	12″ Rise	Slope	13″ Rise	Slope	14″ Rise	Slope	15″ Rise	Slope	16″ Rise	Slope
0	$7\tfrac{5}{8}$	$1\text{-}2\tfrac{7}{32}$	$8\tfrac{1}{4}$	$1\text{-}3\tfrac{13}{32}$	$8\tfrac{29}{32}$	$1\text{-}4\tfrac{19}{32}$	$9\tfrac{17}{32}$	$1\text{-}5\tfrac{25}{32}$	$10\tfrac{5}{32}$	$1\text{-}6\tfrac{31}{32}$
$\tfrac{1}{16}$	$7\tfrac{21}{32}$	$1\text{-}2\tfrac{9}{32}$	$8\tfrac{5}{16}$	$1\text{-}3\tfrac{15}{32}$	$8\tfrac{15}{16}$	$1\text{-}4\tfrac{21}{32}$	$9\tfrac{9}{16}$	$1\text{-}5\tfrac{27}{32}$	$10\tfrac{7}{32}$	$1\text{-}7\tfrac{1}{32}$
$\tfrac{1}{8}$	$7\tfrac{23}{32}$	$1\text{-}2\tfrac{3}{8}$	$8\tfrac{11}{32}$	$1\text{-}3\tfrac{9}{32}$	$8\tfrac{31}{32}$	$1\text{-}4\tfrac{3}{4}$	$9\tfrac{5}{8}$	$1\text{-}5\tfrac{29}{32}$	$10\tfrac{1}{4}$	$1\text{-}7\tfrac{3}{32}$
$\tfrac{3}{16}$	$7\tfrac{3}{4}$	$1\text{-}2\tfrac{7}{16}$	$8\tfrac{3}{8}$	$1\text{-}3\tfrac{5}{8}$	9	$1\text{-}4\tfrac{13}{16}$	$9\tfrac{21}{32}$	$1\text{-}6$	$10\tfrac{9}{32}$	$1\text{-}7\tfrac{3}{16}$
$\tfrac{1}{4}$	$7\tfrac{25}{32}$	$1\text{-}2\tfrac{1}{2}$	$8\tfrac{13}{32}$	$1\text{-}3\tfrac{11}{16}$	$9\tfrac{1}{16}$	$1\text{-}4\tfrac{7}{8}$	$9\tfrac{11}{16}$	$1\text{-}6\tfrac{1}{16}$	$10\tfrac{5}{16}$	$1\text{-}7\tfrac{1}{4}$
$\tfrac{5}{16}$	$7\tfrac{13}{16}$	$1\text{-}2\tfrac{19}{32}$	$8\tfrac{15}{32}$	$1\text{-}3\tfrac{25}{32}$	$9\tfrac{3}{32}$	$1\text{-}4\tfrac{31}{32}$	$9\tfrac{23}{32}$	$1\text{-}6\tfrac{5}{32}$	$10\tfrac{3}{8}$	$1\text{-}7\tfrac{5}{16}$
$\tfrac{3}{8}$	$7\tfrac{7}{8}$	$1\text{-}2\tfrac{21}{32}$	$8\tfrac{1}{2}$	$1\text{-}3\tfrac{27}{32}$	$9\tfrac{1}{8}$	$1\text{-}5\tfrac{1}{32}$	$9\tfrac{25}{32}$	$1\text{-}6\tfrac{7}{32}$	$10\tfrac{13}{32}$	$1\text{-}7\tfrac{13}{32}$
$\tfrac{7}{16}$	$7\tfrac{29}{32}$	$1\text{-}2\tfrac{3}{4}$	$8\tfrac{17}{32}$	$1\text{-}3\tfrac{29}{32}$	$9\tfrac{3}{16}$	$1\text{-}5\tfrac{3}{32}$	$9\tfrac{13}{16}$	$1\text{-}6\tfrac{9}{32}$	$10\tfrac{7}{16}$	$1\text{-}7\tfrac{15}{32}$
$\tfrac{1}{2}$	$7\tfrac{15}{16}$	$1\text{-}2\tfrac{13}{16}$	$8\tfrac{9}{16}$	$1\text{-}4$	$9\tfrac{7}{32}$	$1\text{-}5\tfrac{3}{16}$	$9\tfrac{27}{32}$	$1\text{-}6\tfrac{3}{8}$	$10\tfrac{1}{2}$	$1\text{-}7\tfrac{9}{16}$
$\tfrac{9}{16}$	$7\tfrac{31}{32}$	$1\text{-}2\tfrac{7}{8}$	$8\tfrac{5}{8}$	$1\text{-}4\tfrac{1}{16}$	$9\tfrac{1}{4}$	$1\text{-}5\tfrac{1}{4}$	$9\tfrac{7}{8}$	$1\text{-}6\tfrac{7}{16}$	$10\tfrac{17}{32}$	$1\text{-}7\tfrac{5}{8}$
$\tfrac{5}{8}$	$8\tfrac{1}{32}$	$1\text{-}2\tfrac{31}{32}$	$8\tfrac{21}{32}$	$1\text{-}4\tfrac{5}{32}$	$9\tfrac{9}{32}$	$1\text{-}5\tfrac{5}{16}$	$9\tfrac{15}{16}$	$1\text{-}6\tfrac{1}{2}$	$10\tfrac{9}{16}$	$1\text{-}7\tfrac{11}{16}$
$\tfrac{11}{16}$	$8\tfrac{1}{16}$	$1\text{-}3\tfrac{1}{32}$	$8\tfrac{11}{16}$	$1\text{-}4\tfrac{7}{32}$	$9\tfrac{11}{32}$	$1\text{-}5\tfrac{13}{32}$	$9\tfrac{31}{32}$	$1\text{-}6\tfrac{19}{32}$	$10\tfrac{19}{32}$	$1\text{-}7\tfrac{25}{32}$
$\tfrac{3}{4}$	$8\tfrac{3}{32}$	$1\text{-}3\tfrac{3}{32}$	$8\tfrac{3}{4}$	$1\text{-}4\tfrac{9}{32}$	$9\tfrac{3}{8}$	$1\text{-}5\tfrac{15}{32}$	10	$1\text{-}6\tfrac{21}{32}$	$10\tfrac{21}{32}$	$1\text{-}7\tfrac{27}{32}$
$\tfrac{13}{16}$	$8\tfrac{5}{32}$	$1\text{-}3\tfrac{5}{32}$	$8\tfrac{25}{32}$	$1\text{-}4\tfrac{3}{8}$	$9\tfrac{13}{32}$	$1\text{-}5\tfrac{9}{16}$	$10\tfrac{1}{16}$	$1\text{-}6\tfrac{3}{4}$	$10\tfrac{11}{16}$	$1\text{-}7\tfrac{29}{32}$
$\tfrac{7}{8}$	$8\tfrac{3}{16}$	$1\text{-}3\tfrac{1}{4}$	$8\tfrac{13}{16}$	$1\text{-}4\tfrac{7}{16}$	$9\tfrac{7}{16}$	$1\text{-}5\tfrac{5}{8}$	$10\tfrac{3}{32}$	$1\text{-}6\tfrac{13}{16}$	$10\tfrac{23}{32}$	$1\text{-}8$
$\tfrac{15}{16}$	$8\tfrac{7}{16}$	$1\text{-}3\tfrac{11}{32}$	$8\tfrac{27}{32}$	$1\text{-}4\tfrac{1}{2}$	$9\tfrac{1}{2}$	$1\text{-}5\tfrac{11}{32}$	$10\tfrac{1}{8}$	$1\text{-}6\tfrac{7}{8}$	$10\tfrac{3}{4}$	$1\text{-}8\tfrac{1}{16}$

Ins.	17″ Rise	Slope	18″ Rise	Slope	19″ Rise	Slope	20″ Rise	Slope	21″ Rise	Slope
0	$10\tfrac{13}{16}$	$1\text{-}8\tfrac{5}{32}$	$11\tfrac{7}{16}$	$1\text{-}9\tfrac{5}{32}$	$1\text{-}0\tfrac{1}{16}$	$1\text{-}10\tfrac{1}{2}$	$1\text{-}0\tfrac{23}{32}$	$1\text{-}11\tfrac{11}{16}$	$1\text{-}1\tfrac{11}{32}$	$2\text{-}0\tfrac{7}{8}$
$\tfrac{1}{16}$	$10\tfrac{27}{32}$	$1\text{-}8\tfrac{7}{32}$	$11\tfrac{15}{32}$	$1\text{-}9\tfrac{13}{32}$	$1\text{-}0\tfrac{1}{8}$	$1\text{-}10\tfrac{19}{32}$	$1\text{-}0\tfrac{3}{4}$	$1\text{-}11\tfrac{25}{32}$	$1\text{-}1\tfrac{3}{8}$	$2\text{-}0\tfrac{31}{32}$
$\tfrac{1}{8}$	$10\tfrac{7}{8}$	$1\text{-}8\tfrac{9}{32}$	$11\tfrac{17}{32}$	$1\text{-}9\tfrac{15}{32}$	$1\text{-}0\tfrac{5}{32}$	$1\text{-}10\tfrac{21}{32}$	$1\text{-}0\tfrac{25}{32}$	$1\text{-}11\tfrac{27}{32}$	$1\text{-}1\tfrac{7}{16}$	$2\text{-}1\tfrac{1}{32}$
$\tfrac{3}{16}$	$10\tfrac{29}{32}$	$1\text{-}8\tfrac{3}{8}$	$11\tfrac{9}{16}$	$1\text{-}9\tfrac{9}{16}$	$1\text{-}0\tfrac{3}{16}$	$1\text{-}10\tfrac{23}{32}$	$1\text{-}0\tfrac{13}{16}$	$1\text{-}11\tfrac{29}{32}$	$1\text{-}1\tfrac{15}{32}$	$2\text{-}1\tfrac{3}{32}$
$\tfrac{1}{4}$	$10\tfrac{31}{32}$	$1\text{-}8\tfrac{7}{16}$	$11\tfrac{19}{32}$	$1\text{-}9\tfrac{5}{8}$	$1\text{-}0\tfrac{7}{32}$	$1\text{-}10\tfrac{13}{16}$	$1\text{-}0\tfrac{7}{8}$	$2\text{-}0$	$1\text{-}1\tfrac{1}{2}$	$2\text{-}1\tfrac{3}{16}$
$\tfrac{5}{16}$	11	$1\text{-}8\tfrac{1}{2}$	$11\tfrac{5}{8}$	$1\text{-}9\tfrac{11}{16}$	$1\text{-}0\tfrac{9}{32}$	$1\text{-}10\tfrac{7}{8}$	$1\text{-}0\tfrac{29}{32}$	$2\text{-}0\tfrac{1}{16}$	$1\text{-}1\tfrac{17}{32}$	$2\text{-}1\tfrac{1}{4}$
$\tfrac{3}{8}$	$11\tfrac{1}{16}$	$1\text{-}8\tfrac{19}{32}$	$11\tfrac{11}{16}$	$1\text{-}9\tfrac{25}{32}$	$1\text{-}0\tfrac{5}{16}$	$1\text{-}10\tfrac{31}{32}$	$1\text{-}0\tfrac{15}{16}$	$2\text{-}0\tfrac{1}{8}$	$1\text{-}1\tfrac{19}{32}$	$2\text{-}1\tfrac{5}{16}$
$\tfrac{7}{16}$	$11\tfrac{3}{32}$	$1\text{-}8\tfrac{21}{32}$	$11\tfrac{23}{32}$	$1\text{-}9\tfrac{27}{32}$	$1\text{-}0\tfrac{11}{32}$	$1\text{-}11\tfrac{1}{32}$	$1\text{-}1$	$2\text{-}0\tfrac{7}{32}$	$1\text{-}1\tfrac{5}{8}$	$2\text{-}1\tfrac{13}{32}$
$\tfrac{1}{2}$	$11\tfrac{1}{8}$	$1\text{-}8\tfrac{23}{32}$	$11\tfrac{3}{4}$	$1\text{-}9\tfrac{29}{32}$	$1\text{-}0\tfrac{3}{8}$	$1\text{-}11\tfrac{3}{32}$	$1\text{-}1\tfrac{1}{16}$	$2\text{-}0\tfrac{9}{32}$	$1\text{-}1\tfrac{21}{32}$	$2\text{-}1\tfrac{15}{32}$
$\tfrac{9}{16}$	$11\tfrac{5}{32}$	$1\text{-}8\tfrac{13}{16}$	$11\tfrac{25}{32}$	$1\text{-}10$	$1\text{-}0\tfrac{7}{16}$	$1\text{-}11\tfrac{3}{16}$	$1\text{-}1\tfrac{1}{16}$	$2\text{-}0\tfrac{3}{8}$	$1\text{-}1\tfrac{11}{16}$	$2\text{-}1\tfrac{9}{16}$
$\tfrac{5}{8}$	$11\tfrac{3}{16}$	$1\text{-}8\tfrac{7}{8}$	$11\tfrac{27}{32}$	$1\text{-}10\tfrac{1}{16}$	$1\text{-}0\tfrac{15}{32}$	$1\text{-}11\tfrac{1}{4}$	$1\text{-}1\tfrac{3}{32}$	$2\text{-}0\tfrac{7}{16}$	$1\text{-}1\tfrac{3}{4}$	$2\text{-}1\tfrac{5}{8}$
$\tfrac{11}{16}$	$11\tfrac{1}{4}$	$1\text{-}8\tfrac{31}{32}$	$11\tfrac{7}{8}$	$1\text{-}10\tfrac{5}{32}$	$1\text{-}0\tfrac{1}{2}$	$1\text{-}11\tfrac{5}{16}$	$1\text{-}1\tfrac{5}{32}$	$2\text{-}0\tfrac{1}{2}$	$1\text{-}1\tfrac{25}{32}$	$2\text{-}1\tfrac{11}{16}$
$\tfrac{3}{4}$	$11\tfrac{9}{32}$	$1\text{-}9\tfrac{1}{32}$	$11\tfrac{29}{32}$	$1\text{-}10\tfrac{7}{32}$	$1\text{-}0\tfrac{9}{16}$	$1\text{-}11\tfrac{13}{32}$	$1\text{-}1\tfrac{3}{16}$	$2\text{-}0\tfrac{19}{32}$	$1\text{-}1\tfrac{13}{16}$	$2\text{-}1\tfrac{25}{32}$
$\tfrac{13}{16}$	$11\tfrac{5}{16}$	$1\text{-}9\tfrac{3}{32}$	$11\tfrac{31}{32}$	$1\text{-}10\tfrac{9}{32}$	$1\text{-}0\tfrac{19}{32}$	$1\text{-}11\tfrac{15}{32}$	$1\text{-}1\tfrac{7}{32}$	$2\text{-}0\tfrac{21}{32}$	$1\text{-}1\tfrac{7}{8}$	$2\text{-}1\tfrac{27}{32}$
$\tfrac{7}{8}$	$11\tfrac{11}{32}$	$1\text{-}9\tfrac{3}{16}$	$1\text{-}0$	$1\text{-}10\tfrac{3}{8}$	$1\text{-}0\tfrac{5}{8}$	$1\text{-}11\tfrac{9}{16}$	$1\text{-}1\tfrac{1}{4}$	$2\text{-}0\tfrac{23}{32}$	$1\text{-}1\tfrac{29}{32}$	$2\text{-}1\tfrac{29}{32}$
$\tfrac{15}{16}$	$11\tfrac{13}{32}$	$1\text{-}9\tfrac{1}{4}$	$1\text{-}0\tfrac{1}{16}$	$1\text{-}10\tfrac{7}{16}$	$1\text{-}0\tfrac{21}{32}$	$1\text{-}11\tfrac{5}{8}$	$1\text{-}1\tfrac{9}{32}$	$2\text{-}0\tfrac{13}{16}$	$1\text{-}1\tfrac{15}{16}$	$2\text{-}2$

Feet	40′ Rise	Slope	50′ Rise	Slope	60′ Rise	Slope	70′ Rise	Slope
0	$25\text{-}5$	$47\text{-}4\tfrac{23}{32}$	$31\text{-}9\tfrac{1}{4}$	$59\text{-}2\tfrac{7}{8}$	$38\text{-}1\tfrac{1}{2}$	$71\text{-}1\tfrac{1}{16}$	$44\text{-}5\tfrac{3}{4}$	$82\text{-}11\tfrac{7}{8}$
1	$26\text{-}0\tfrac{5}{8}$	$48\text{-}6\tfrac{15}{32}$	$32\text{-}4\tfrac{7}{8}$	$60\text{-}5\tfrac{3}{32}$	$38\text{-}9\tfrac{1}{8}$	$72\text{-}3\tfrac{9}{32}$	$45\text{-}1\tfrac{3}{8}$	$84\text{-}1\tfrac{7}{16}$
2	$26\text{-}8\tfrac{1}{4}$	$49\text{-}9\tfrac{1}{8}$	$33\text{-}0\tfrac{1}{2}$	$61\text{-}7\tfrac{5}{16}$	$39\text{-}4\tfrac{3}{4}$	$73\text{-}5\tfrac{1}{2}$	$45\text{-}9$	$85\text{-}3\tfrac{21}{32}$
3	$27\text{-}3\tfrac{7}{8}$	$50\text{-}11\tfrac{11}{32}$	$33\text{-}8\tfrac{1}{8}$	$62\text{-}9\tfrac{17}{32}$	$40\text{-}0\tfrac{3}{8}$	$74\text{-}7\tfrac{23}{32}$	$46\text{-}4\tfrac{5}{8}$	$86\text{-}5\tfrac{7}{8}$
4	$27\text{-}11\tfrac{1}{2}$	$52\text{-}1\tfrac{9}{16}$	$34\text{-}3\tfrac{3}{4}$	$63\text{-}11\tfrac{3}{4}$	$40\text{-}8$	$75\text{-}9\tfrac{15}{16}$	$47\text{-}0\tfrac{1}{4}$	$87\text{-}8\tfrac{3}{32}$
5	$28\text{-}7\tfrac{1}{8}$	$53\text{-}3\tfrac{25}{32}$	$34\text{-}11\tfrac{3}{8}$	$65\text{-}1\tfrac{31}{32}$	$41\text{-}3\tfrac{5}{8}$	$77\text{-}0\tfrac{5}{32}$	$47\text{-}7\tfrac{7}{8}$	$88\text{-}10\tfrac{5}{16}$
6	$29\text{-}2\tfrac{3}{4}$	$54\text{-}6$	$35\text{-}7$	$66\text{-}4\tfrac{3}{16}$	$41\text{-}11\tfrac{1}{4}$	$78\text{-}2\tfrac{3}{8}$	$48\text{-}3\tfrac{1}{2}$	$90\text{-}0\tfrac{17}{32}$
7	$29\text{-}10\tfrac{3}{8}$	$55\text{-}8\tfrac{7}{32}$	$36\text{-}2\tfrac{5}{8}$	$67\text{-}6\tfrac{13}{32}$	$42\text{-}6\tfrac{7}{8}$	$79\text{-}4\tfrac{19}{32}$	$48\text{-}11\tfrac{1}{8}$	$91\text{-}2\tfrac{3}{4}$
8	$30\text{-}6$	$56\text{-}10\tfrac{7}{16}$	$36\text{-}10\tfrac{1}{4}$	$68\text{-}8\tfrac{5}{8}$	$43\text{-}2\tfrac{1}{2}$	$80\text{-}6\tfrac{13}{16}$	$49\text{-}6\tfrac{3}{4}$	$92\text{-}4\tfrac{31}{32}$
9	$31\text{-}1\tfrac{5}{8}$	$58\text{-}0\tfrac{21}{32}$	$37\text{-}5\tfrac{7}{8}$	$69\text{-}10\tfrac{27}{32}$	$43\text{-}10\tfrac{1}{8}$	$81\text{-}9$	$50\text{-}2\tfrac{3}{8}$	$93\text{-}7\tfrac{3}{16}$

natsin A=0.5363064818; natcos A=0.8440233158; nattan A=0.6354166666; natcot A=1.5737704918

Inches	0" Rise	0" Slope	1" Rise	1" Slope	2" Rise	2" Slope	3" Rise	3" Slope	4" Rise	4" Slope	5" Rise	5" Slope
0	0	0	5/8	13/16	1 9/32	2 3/8	1 15/16	3 9/16	2 9/16	4 3/4	3 3/8	5 15/16
1/16	1/16	1/32	11/16	1 1/4	1 5/16	2 7/16	1 31/32	3 5/8	2 19/32	4 13/16	3 1/4	6
1/8	3/32	5/32	23/32	1 11/32	1 3/8	2 17/32	2	3 23/32	2 21/32	4 29/32	3 9/32	6 3/32
3/16	1/8	7/32	3/4	1 13/32	1 13/32	2 19/32	2 1/32	3 25/32	2 11/16	4 31/32	3 5/16	6 5/32
1/4	5/32	5/16	13/16	1 1/2	1 7/16	2 11/16	2 3/32	3 7/8	2 23/32	5 1/16	3 3/8	6 1/4
5/16	3/16	3/8	27/32	1 9/16	1 15/32	2 3/4	2 1/8	3 15/16	2 3/4	5 1/8	3 13/32	6 5/16
3/8	1/4	7/16	7/8	1 5/8	1 17/32	2 13/16	2 5/32	4	2 13/16	5 3/16	3 7/16	6 3/8
7/16	9/32	17/32	29/32	1 23/32	1 9/16	2 29/32	2 7/32	4 3/32	2 27/32	5 9/32	3 15/32	6 15/32
1/2	5/16	19/32	31/32	1 25/32	1 19/32	2 31/32	2 1/4	4 5/32	2 7/8	5 11/32	3 17/32	6 17/32
9/16	3/8	21/32	1	1 27/32	1 21/32	3 1/32	2 9/32	4 7/32	2 15/16	5 13/32	3 9/16	6 19/32
5/8	13/32	3/4	1 1/32	1 15/16	1 11/16	3 1/8	2 5/16	4 5/16	2 31/32	5 1/2	3 19/32	6 11/16
11/16	7/16	13/16	1 3/32	2	1 23/32	3 3/16	2 3/8	4 3/8	3	5 9/16	3 21/32	6 3/4
3/4	15/32	29/32	1 1/8	2 3/32	1 3/4	3 9/32	2 13/32	4 15/32	3 1/2	5 21/32	3 11/16	6 27/32
13/16	17/32	31/32	1 5/32	2 5/32	1 13/16	3 11/32	2 7/16	4 17/32	3 3/32	5 23/32	3 23/32	6 29/32
7/8	9/16	1 1/32	1 3/16	2 7/32	1 27/32	3 13/32	2 15/32	4 19/32	3 1/8	5 25/32	3 3/4	6 31/32
15/16	19/32	1 1/8	1 1/4	2 5/16	1 7/8	3 1/2	2 17/32	4 11/16	3 5/32	5 7/8	3 13/16	7 1/16

Inches	6" Rise	6" Slope	7" Rise	7" Slope	8" Rise	8" Slope	9" Rise	9" Slope	10" Rise	10" Slope	11" Rise	11" Slope
0	3 27/32	7 1/8	4 1/2	8 5/16	5 1/8	9 1/2	5 3/4	10 11/16	6 13/32	11 7/8	7 1/16	1-1 1/16
1/16	3 7/8	7 3/16	4 17/32	8 3/8	5 5/32	9 9/16	5 13/16	10 3/4	6 7/16	11 15/16	7 3/32	1-1 1/8
1/8	3 15/16	7 9/32	4 9/16	8 15/32	5 7/32	9 21/32	5 27/32	10 27/32	6 1/2	1-0 1/32	7 1/8	1-1 7/32
3/16	3 31/32	7 11/32	4 19/32	8 17/32	5 1/4	9 23/32	5 7/8	10 29/32	6 17/32	1-0 3/32	7 5/32	1-1 9/32
1/4	4	7 7/16	4 21/32	8 5/8	5 9/32	9 13/16	5 15/16	11	6 9/16	1-0 3/16	7 7/32	1-1 3/8
5/16	4 1/32	7 1/2	4 11/16	8 11/16	5 5/16	9 7/8	5 31/32	11 1/16	6 19/32	1-0 1/4	7 1/4	1-1 7/16
3/8	4 3/32	7 9/16	4 23/32	8 3/4	5 3/8	9 15/16	6	11 1/8	6 21/32	1-0 5/16	7 9/32	1-1 1/2
7/16	4 1/8	7 21/32	4 3/4	8 27/32	5 13/32	10 1/32	6 1/32	11 7/32	6 11/16	1-0 13/32	7 5/16	1-1 19/32
1/2	4 5/32	7 23/32	4 13/16	8 29/32	5 7/16	10 3/32	6 3/32	11 9/32	6 23/32	1-0 15/32	7 3/8	1-1 21/32
9/16	4 7/32	7 25/32	4 27/32	8 31/32	5 1/2	10 5/32	6 1/8	11 11/32	6 25/32	1-0 17/32	7 13/32	1-1 23/32
5/8	4 1/4	7 7/8	4 7/8	9 1/16	5 17/32	10 1/4	6 5/32	11 7/16	6 13/16	1-0 5/8	7 7/16	1-1 13/16
11/16	4 9/32	7 15/16	4 15/16	9 1/8	5 9/16	10 5/16	6 7/32	11 1/2	6 27/32	1-0 11/16	7 1/2	1-1 7/8
3/4	4 5/16	8 1/32	4 31/32	9 7/32	5 19/32	10 3/8	6 1/4	11 19/32	6 7/8	1-0 25/32	7 17/32	1-1 31/32
13/16	4 3/8	8 3/32	5	9 9/32	5 21/32	10 15/32	6 9/32	11 21/32	6 15/16	1-0 27/32	7 9/16	1-2 1/2
7/8	4 13/32	8 5/32	5 1/32	9 11/32	5 11/16	10 17/32	6 5/16	11 23/32	6 31/32	1-0 29/32	7 19/32	1-2 3/32
15/16	4 7/16	8 1/4	5 3/32	9 7/16	5 23/32	10 5/8	6 3/8	11 13/16	7	1-1	7 21/32	1-2 3/16

Feet	0' Rise	0' Slope	10' Rise	10' Slope	20' Rise	20' Slope	30' Rise	30' Slope
0	0	0	6-4 7/8	11-10 1/2	12-9 3/4	23-9 1/4	19-2 5/8	35-7 1/2
1	7 11/16	1-2 1/4	7-0 9/16	13-0 3/4	13-5 7/16	24-11 9/32	19-10 5/16	36-9 25/32
2	1-3 3/8	2-4 1/2	7-8 1/4	14-3	14-1 1/8	26-1 17/32	20-6	38-0 1/32
3	1-11 1/16	3-6 3/4	8-3 15/16	15-5 9/32	14-8 13/16	27-3 25/32	21-1 11/16	39-2 9/32
4	2-6 3/4	4-9	8-11 5/8	16-7 17/32	15-4 1/2	28-6 1/32	21-9 3/8	40-4 17/32
5	3-2 7/16	5-11 1/4	9-7 5/16	17-9 25/32	16-0 3/16	29-8 9/32	22-5 1/16	41-6 25/32
6	3-10 1/8	7-1 1/2	10-3	19-0 1/32	16-7 7/8	30-10 17/32	23-0 3/4	42-9 1/32
7	4-5 13/16	8-3 3/4	10-10 11/16	20-2 9/32	17-3 9/16	32-0 25/32	23-8 7/16	43-11 9/32
8	5-1 1/2	9-6	11-6 3/8	21-4 17/32	17-11 1/4	33-3 1/32	24-4 1/8	45-1 9/16
9	5-9 3/16	10-8 1/4	12-2 1/16	22-6 25/32	18-6 15/16	34-5 9/32	24-11 13/16	46-3 13/16

A = 32° 38′ 41″; logsin A = 9.73193; logcos A = 9.92533; logtan A = 9.80660; logcot A = 0.19340

In.	12″ Rise	12″ Slope	13″ Rise	13″ Slope	14″ Rise	14″ Slope	15″ Rise	15″ Slope	16″ Rise	16″ Slope
0	7 11/16	1-2 1/4	8 5/16	1-3 7/16	8 31/32	1-4 5/8	9 5/8	1-5 13/16	10 1/4	1-7
1/16	7 23/32	1-2 5/16	8 3/8	1-3 1/2	9	1-4 11/16	9 21/32	1-5 7/8	10 9/32	1-7 1/16
1/8	7 25/32	1-2 13/32	8 13/32	1-3 19/32	9 1/16	1-4 25/32	9 11/16	1-5 31/32	10 11/32	1-7 5/32
3/16	7 13/16	1-2 15/32	8 7/16	1-3 21/32	9 3/32	1-4 27/32	9 23/32	1-6 1/32	10 3/8	1-7 7/32
1/4	7 27/32	1-2 9/16	8 1/2	1-3 3/4	9 1/8	1-4 15/16	9 25/32	1-6 1/8	10 13/32	1-7 5/16
5/16	7 7/8	1-2 5/8	8 17/32	1-3 13/16	9 5/32	1-5	9 13/16	1-6 3/16	10 7/16	1-7 3/8
3/8	7 15/16	1-2 11/16	8 9/16	1-3 7/8	9 7/32	1-5 1/16	9 27/32	1-6 1/4	10 1/2	1-7 7/16
7/16	7 31/32	1-2 25/32	8 19/32	1-3 31/32	9 1/4	1-5 5/32	9 7/8	1-6 11/32	10 17/32	1-7 17/32
1/2	8	1-2 27/32	8 21/32	1-4 1/32	9 9/32	1-5 7/32	9 15/16	1-6 13/32	10 9/16	1-7 19/32
9/16	8 1/16	1-2 29/32	8 11/16	1-4 3/32	9 11/32	1-5 9/32	9 31/32	1-6 15/32	10 5/8	1-7 21/32
5/8	8 3/32	1-3	8 23/32	1-4 3/16	9 3/8	1-5 3/8	10	1-6 9/16	10 21/32	1-7 3/4
11/16	8 1/8	1-3 1/16	8 25/32	1-4 1/4	9 13/32	1-5 7/16	10 1/16	1-6 5/8	10 11/16	1-7 13/16
3/4	8 5/32	1-3 5/32	8 13/16	1-4 11/32	9 7/16	1-5 17/32	10 3/32	1-6 23/32	10 23/32	1-7 29/32
13/16	8 7/32	1-3 7/32	8 27/32	1-4 13/32	9 1/2	1-5 19/32	10 1/8	1-6 25/32	10 25/32	1-7 31/32
7/8	8 1/4	1-3 9/32	8 7/8	1-4 15/32	9 17/32	1-5 21/32	10 5/32	1-6 27/32	10 13/16	1-8 1/32
15/16	8 9/32	1-3 3/8	8 15/16	1-4 9/16	9 9/16	1-5 3/4	10 7/32	1-6 15/16	10 27/32	1-8 1/8

In.	17″ Rise	17″ Slope	18″ Rise	18″ Slope	19″ Rise	19″ Slope	20″ Rise	20″ Slope	21″ Rise	21″ Slope
0	10 7/8	1-8 3/16	11 17/32	1-9 3/8	1-0 3/16	1-10 9/16	1-0 13/16	1-11 3/4	1-1 7/16	2-0 15/16
1/16	10 15/16	1-8 1/4	11 9/16	1-9 7/16	1-0 7/32	1-10 5/8	1-0 27/32	1-11 13/16	1-1 1/2	2-1
1/8	10 31/32	1-8 11/32	11 5/8	1-9 17/32	1-0 1/4	1-10 23/32	1-0 29/32	1-11 29/32	1-1 17/32	2-1 3/32
3/16	11	1-8 13/32	11 21/32	1-9 19/32	1-0 9/32	1-10 25/32	1-0 15/16	1-11 31/32	1-1 9/16	2-1 5/32
1/4	11 1/16	1-8 1/2	11 11/16	1-9 11/16	1-0 11/32	1-10 7/8	1-0 31/32	2-0 1/16	1-1 5/8	2-1 1/4
5/16	11 3/32	1-8 9/16	11 23/32	1-9 3/4	1-0 3/8	1-10 15/16	1-1	2-0 1/8	1-1 21/32	2-1 5/16
3/8	11 1/8	1-8 5/8	11 25/32	1-9 13/16	1-0 13/32	1-11	1-1 1/16	2-0 3/16	1-1 11/16	2-1 3/8
7/16	11 5/32	1-8 23/32	11 13/16	1-9 29/32	1-0 7/16	1-11 3/32	1-1 3/32	2-0 9/32	1-1 23/32	2-1 15/32
1/2	11 7/32	1-8 25/32	11 27/32	1-9 31/32	1-0 1/2	1-11 5/32	1-1 1/8	2-0 11/32	1-1 25/32	2-1 17/32
9/16	11 1/4	1-8 27/32	11 29/32	1-10 1/32	1-0 17/32	1-11 7/32	1-1 3/16	2-0 13/32	1-1 13/16	2-1 19/32
5/8	11 9/32	1-8 15/16	11 15/16	1-10 1/8	1-0 9/16	1-11 5/16	1-1 7/32	2-0 1/2	1-1 27/32	2-1 11/16
11/16	11 11/32	1-9	11 31/32	1-10 3/16	1-0 5/8	1-11 3/8	1-1 1/4	2-0 9/16	1-1 29/32	2-1 3/4
3/4	11 3/8	1-9 3/32	1-0	1-10 9/32	1-0 21/32	1-11 15/32	1-1 9/32	2-0 21/32	1-1 15/16	2-1 27/32
13/16	11 13/32	1-9 5/32	1-0 1/16	1-10 11/32	1-0 11/16	1-11 17/32	1-1 11/32	2-0 23/32	1-1 31/32	2-1 29/32
7/8	11 7/16	1-9 7/32	1-0 3/32	1-10 13/32	1-0 23/32	1-11 19/32	1-1 3/8	2-0 25/32	1-2	2-1 31/32
15/16	11 1/2	1-9 5/32	1-0 1/8	1-10 1/2	1-0 25/32	1-11 11/16	1-1 13/32	2-0 7/8	1-2 1/16	2-2 1/16

Feet	40′ Rise	40′ Slope	50′ Rise	50′ Slope	60′ Rise	60′ Slope	70′ Rise	70′ Slope
0	25-7 1/2	47-6 1/16	32-0 3/8	59-4 9/16	38-5 1/4	71-3 1/16	44-10 1/8	83-1 19/32
1	26-3 3/16	48-8 5/16	32-8 1/16	60-6 13/16	39-0 15/16	72-5 9/16	45-5 13/16	84-3 27/32
2	26-10 7/8	49-10 9/16	33-3 3/4	61-9 1/16	39-8 5/8	73-7 9/16	46-1 1/2	85-6 3/32
3	27-6 9/16	51-0 13/16	33-11 7/16	62-11 5/16	40-4 5/16	74-9 13/16	46-9 3/16	86-8 11/32
4	28-2 1/4	52-3 1/16	34-7 1/8	64-1 9/16	41-0	76-0 3/32	47-4 7/8	87-10 19/32
5	28-9 15/16	53-5 5/16	35-2 13/16	65-3 13/16	41-7 11/16	77-2 11/32	48-0 9/16	89-0 27/32
6	29-5 5/8	54-7 9/16	35-10 1/2	66-6 1/16	42-3 3/8	78-4 9/32	48-8 1/4	90-3 3/32
7	30-1 5/16	55-9 13/16	36-6 3/16	67-8 5/16	42-11 1/16	79-6 27/32	49-3 15/16	91-5 11/32
8	30-9	57-0 1/16	37-1 7/8	68-10 9/16	43-6 3/4	80-9 3/32	49-11 5/8	92-7 19/32
9	31-4 11/16	58-2 5/16	37-9 9/16	70-0 13/16	44-2 7/16	81-11 11/32	50-7 5/16	93-9 27/32

natsin A=0.5394269908; natcos A=0.8420323757; nattan A=0.6406250000; natcot A=1.5609756097

Inches	0" Rise	0" Slope	1" Rise	1" Slope	2" Rise	2" Slope	3" Rise	3" Slope	4" Rise	4" Slope	5" Rise	5" Slope
0	0	0	21/32	13/16	19/32	2 3/8	1 15/16	3 9/16	2 19/32	4 3/4	3 1/2	5 15/16
1/16	1/32	1/16	11/16	1 1/4	1 11/32	2 15/32	1 31/32	3 21/32	2 5/8	4 27/32	3 9/32	6 1/32
1/8	3/32	5/32	23/32	1 11/32	1 3/8	2 17/32	2 1/32	3 23/32	2 21/32	4 29/32	3 5/16	6 3/32
3/16	1/8	7/32	25/32	1 13/32	1 13/32	2 19/32	2 1/16	3 25/32	2 23/32	5	3 11/32	6 3/16
1/4	5/32	5/16	13/16	1 1/2	1 7/16	2 11/16	2 3/32	3 7/8	2 3/4	5 1/16	3 3/8	6 1/4
5/16	3/16	3/8	27/32	1 9/16	1 1/2	2 3/4	2 1/8	3 15/16	2 25/32	5 1/8	3 7/16	6 5/16
3/8	1/4	7/16	7/8	1 5/8	1 17/32	2 13/16	2 3/16	4 1/32	2 13/16	5 7/32	3 15/32	6 13/32
7/16	9/32	17/32	15/16	1 23/32	1 9/16	2 29/32	2 7/32	4 3/32	2 7/8	5 9/32	3 1/2	6 15/32
1/2	5/16	19/32	31/32	1 25/32	1 5/8	2 31/32	2 1/4	4 5/32	2 29/32	5 11/32	3 9/16	6 9/16
9/16	3/8	21/32	1	1 7/8	1 21/32	3 1/16	2 5/16	4 1/4	2 15/16	5 7/16	3 19/32	6 5/8
5/8	13/32	3/4	1 1/16	1 15/16	1 11/16	3 1/8	2 11/32	4 5/16	3	5 1/2	3 5/8	6 11/16
11/16	7/16	13/16	1 3/32	2	1 3/4	3 3/16	2 3/8	4 3/8	3 1/32	5 19/32	3 11/16	6 25/32
3/4	1/2	29/32	1 1/8	2 3/32	1 25/32	3 9/32	2 7/16	4 15/32	3 1/16	5 21/32	3 23/32	6 27/32
13/16	17/32	31/32	1 5/32	2 5/32	1 13/16	3 11/32	2 15/32	4 17/32	3 3/32	5 23/32	3 3/4	6 29/32
7/8	9/16	1 1/32	1 7/32	2 1/4	1 27/32	3 7/16	2 1/2	4 5/8	3 5/32	5 13/16	3 25/32	7
15/16	19/32	1 1/8	1 1/4	2 5/16	1 29/32	3 1/2	2 17/32	4 11/16	3 3/16	5 7/8	3 27/32	7 1/16

Inches	6" Rise	6" Slope	7" Rise	7" Slope	8" Rise	8" Slope	9" Rise	9" Slope	10" Rise	10" Slope	11" Rise	11" Slope
0	3 7/8	7 5/32	4 17/32	8 11/32	5 5/32	9 17/32	5 13/16	10 23/32	6 15/32	11 29/32	7 3/32	1-1 3/32
1/16	3 29/32	7 7/32	4 9/16	8 13/32	5 7/32	9 19/32	5 27/32	10 25/32	6 1/2	11 31/32	7 5/32	1-1 5/32
1/8	3 31/32	7 9/32	4 19/32	8 15/32	5 1/4	9 11/16	5 29/32	10 7/8	6 17/32	1-0 1/16	7 3/16	1-1 1/4
3/16	4	7 3/8	4 21/32	8 9/16	5 9/32	9 3/4	5 15/16	10 15/16	6 19/32	1-0 1/8	7 7/32	1-1 5/16
1/4	4 1/32	7 7/16	4 11/16	8 5/8	5 5/16	9 13/16	5 31/32	11	6 5/8	1-0 3/16	7 1/4	1-1 13/32
5/16	4 1/16	7 1/2	4 23/32	8 23/32	5 3/8	9 29/32	6	11 3/32	6 21/32	1-0 9/32	7 5/16	1-1 15/32
3/8	4 1/8	7 19/32	4 3/4	8 25/32	5 13/32	9 31/32	6 1/16	11 5/32	6 11/16	1-0 11/32	7 11/32	1-1 17/32
7/16	4 5/32	7 21/32	4 13/16	8 27/32	5 7/16	10 1/32	6 3/32	11 1/4	6 3/4	1-0 7/16	7 3/8	1-1 5/8
1/2	4 3/16	7 3/4	4 27/32	8 15/16	5 1/2	10 1/8	6 1/8	11 5/16	6 25/32	1-0 1/2	7 7/16	1-1 11/16
9/16	4 1/4	7 13/16	4 7/8	9	5 17/32	10 3/16	6 3/16	11 3/8	6 13/16	1-0 9/16	7 15/32	1-1 3/4
5/8	4 9/32	7 7/8	4 15/16	9 1/16	5 9/16	10 9/32	6 7/32	11 15/32	6 7/8	1-0 21/32	7 1/2	1-1 27/32
11/16	4 5/16	7 31/32	4 31/32	9 5/32	5 5/8	10 11/32	6 1/4	11 17/32	6 29/32	1-0 23/32	7 9/16	1-1 29/32
3/4	4 3/8	8 1/32	5	9 7/32	5 21/32	10 13/32	6 5/16	11 19/32	6 15/32	1-0 13/16	7 19/32	1-2
13/16	4 13/32	8 1/8	5 1/32	9 5/16	5 11/16	10 1/2	6 11/32	11 11/16	6 31/32	1-0 7/8	7 5/8	1-2 1/16
7/8	4 7/16	8 3/16	5 3/32	9 3/8	5 23/32	10 9/16	6 3/8	11 3/4	7 1/32	1-0 15/16	7 21/32	1-2 1/8
15/16	4 15/32	8 1/4	5 1/8	9 7/16	5 25/32	10 5/8	6 13/32	11 27/32	7 1/16	1-1 1/32	7 23/32	1-2 7/32

Feet	0' Rise	0' Slope	10' Rise	10' Slope	20' Rise	20' Slope	30' Rise	30' Slope
0	0	0	6-5 1/2	11-10 27/32	12-11	23-9 11/16	19-4 1/2	35-8 9/16
1	7 3/4	1-2 9/32	7-1 1/4	13-1 1/8	13-6 3/4	25-0	20-0 1/4	36-10 27/32
2	1-3 1/2	2-4 9/16	7-9	14-3 13/32	14-2 1/2	26-2 9/32	20-8	38-1 1/8
3	1-11 1/4	3-6 27/32	8-4 3/4	15-5 23/32	14-10 1/4	27-4 9/16	21-3 3/4	39-3 13/32
4	2-7	4-9 1/8	9-0 1/2	16-8	15-6	28-6 27/32	21-11 1/2	40-5 11/16
5	3-2 3/4	5-11 7/16	9-8 1/4	17-10 9/32	16-1 3/4	29-9 1/8	22-7 1/4	41-7 31/32
6	3-10 1/2	7-1 23/32	10-4	19-0 9/16	16-9 1/2	30-11 13/32	23-3	42-10 1/4
7	4-6 1/4	8-4	10-11 3/4	20-2 27/32	17-5 1/4	32-1 11/16	23-10 3/4	44-0 17/32
8	5-2	9-6 9/32	11-7 1/2	21-5 1/8	18-1	33-3 31/32	24-6 1/2	45-2 27/32
9	5-9 3/4	10-8 9/16	12-3 1/4	22-7 13/32	18-8 3/4	34-6 9/32	25-2 1/4	46-5 1/8

A = 32° 51′ 21″; logsin A = 9.73442; logcos A = 9.92430; logtan A = 9.81012; logcot A = 0.18988

Ins.	12" Rise	12" Slope	13" Rise	13" Slope	14" Rise	14" Slope	15" Rise	15" Slope	16" Rise	16" Slope
0	7 3/4	1-2 9/32	8 13/32—	1-3 15/32	9 1/32	1-4 21/32	9 11/16	1-5 27/32	10 11/32—	1-7 1/32
1/16	7 25/32	1-2 3/8	8 7/16	1-3 9/16	9 3/32—	1-4 3/4	9 23/32	1-5 15/16	10 3/8	1-7 1/8
1/8	7 27/32—	1-2 7/16	8 15/32	1-3 5/8	9 1/8	1-4 13/16	9 25/32—	1-6	10 13/32	1-7 3/16
3/16	7 7/8	1-2 1/2	8 17/32—	1-3 11/16	9 5/32	1-4 7/8	9 13/16	1-6 3/32—	10 15/32—	1-7 9/32—
1/4	7 29/32	1-2 19/32—	8 9/16	1-3 25/32—	9 3/16	1-4 31/32—	9 27/32	1-6 5/32—	10 1/2	1-7 11/32
5/16	7 15/16	1-2 21/32	8 19/32	1-3 27/32	9 1/4	1-5 1/32	9 7/8	1-6 7/32	10 17/32	1-7 13/32
3/8	8	1-2 23/32	8 5/8	1-3 29/32	9 9/32	1-5 1/8	9 15/16	1-6 5/16	10 9/16	1-7 1/2
7/16	8 1/32	1-2 13/16	8 11/16	1-4	9 5/16	1-5 3/16	9 31/32	1-6 3/8	10 5/8	1-7 9/16
1/2	8 1/16	1-2 7/8	8 23/32	1-4 1/16	9 3/8	1-5 1/4	10	1-6 7/16	10 21/32	1-7 21/32—
9/16	8 1/8	1-2 31/32—	8 3/4	1-4 5/32—	9 13/32—	1-5 11/32—	10 1/16	1-6 17/32—	10 11/16	1-7 23/32—
5/8	8 5/32—	1-3 1/32—	8 13/16	1-4 7/32	9 7/16	1-5 13/32	10 3/32—	1-6 19/32	10 3/4	1-7 25/32
11/16	8 3/16	1-3 3/32	8 27/32—	1-4 9/32	9 1/2	1-5 15/32	10 1/8	1-6 11/16	10 25/32—	1-7 7/8
3/4	8 1/4	1-3 3/16	8 7/8	1-4 3/8	9 17/32—	1-5 9/16	10 3/16	1-6 3/4	10 13/16	1-7 15/16
13/16	8 9/32—	1-3 1/4	8 29/32	1-4 7/16	9 9/16	1-5 5/8	10 7/32—	1-6 13/16	10 27/32	1-8
7/8	8 5/16	1-3 5/16	8 31/32—	1-4 17/32—	9 19/32	1-5 23/32—	10 1/4	1-6 29/32—	10 29/32—	1-8 3/32—
15/16	8 11/32	1-3 13/32—	9	1-4 19/32—	9 21/32—	1-5 25/32	10 9/32	1-6 31/32	10 15/16	1-8 5/32

Ins.	17" Rise	17" Slope	18" Rise	18" Slope	19" Rise	19" Slope	20" Rise	20" Slope	21" Rise	21" Slope
0	10 31/32	1-8 1/4	11 5/8	1-9 7/16	1-0 9/32—	1-10 5/8	1-0 29/32	1-11 13/16	1-1 9/16	2-1
1/16	11 1/32—	1-8 5/16	11 21/32	1-9 1/2	1-0 5/16	1-10 11/16	1-0 31/32—	1-11 7/8	1-1 19/32	2-1 1/16
1/8	11 1/16	1-8 3/8	11 23/32—	1-9 9/16	1-0 11/32	1-10 25/32—	1-1	1-11 31/32—	1-1 21/32—	2-1 5/32—
3/16	11 3/32	1-8 15/32—	11 3/4	1-9 21/32—	1-0 13/32—	1-10 27/32—	1-1 1/32	2-0 1/32	1-1 11/16	2-1 7/32
1/4	11 1/8	1-8 17/32	11 25/32	1-9 23/32	1-0 7/16	1-10 29/32	1-1 1/16	2-0 3/32	1-1 23/32	2-1 9/32
5/16	11 3/16	1-8 19/32	11 13/16	1-9 13/16	1-0 15/32	1-11	1-1 1/8	2-0 3/16	1-1 3/4	2-1 3/8
3/8	11 7/32	1-8 11/16	11 7/8	1-9 7/8	1-0 1/2	1-11 1/16	1-1 5/32	2-0 1/4	1-1 13/16	2-1 7/16
7/16	11 1/4	1-8 3/4	11 29/32	1-9 15/16	1-0 9/16	1-11 1/8	1-1 3/16	2-0 11/32—	1-1 27/32	2-1 17/32—
1/2	11 5/16	1-8 27/32—	11 15/16	1-10 1/32—	1-0 19/32	1-11 7/32—	1-1 1/4	2-0 13/32—	1-1 7/8	2-1 19/32
9/16	11 11/32—	1-8 29/32	1-0	1-10 3/32	1-0 5/8	1-11 9/32	1-1 9/32—	2-0 15/32	1-1 15/16	2-1 21/32
5/8	11 3/8	1-8 31/32	1-0 1/32—	1-10 5/32	1-0 11/16	1-11 3/8	1-1 5/16	2-0 9/16	1-1 31/32—	2-1 3/4
11/16	11 7/16	1-9 1/16	1-0 1/16	1-10 1/4	1-0 23/32—	1-11 7/16	1-1 3/8	2-0 5/8	1-2	2-1 13/16
3/4	11 15/32—	1-9 1/8	1-0 1/8	1-10 5/16	1-0 3/4	1-11 1/2	1-1 13/32—	2-0 11/16	1-2 1/16	2-1 29/32—
13/16	11 1/2	1-9 7/32—	1-0 5/32—	1-10 13/32—	1-0 25/32	1-11 19/32—	1-1 7/16	2-0 25/32—	1-2 3/32—	2-1 31/32—
7/8	11 17/32	1-9 9/32—	1-0 3/16	1-10 15/32	1-0 27/32—	1-11 21/32	1-1 15/32	2-0 27/32	1-2 1/8	2-2 1/32
15/16	11 19/32—	1-9 11/32	1-0 7/32	1-10 17/32	1-0 7/8	1-11 23/32	1-1 17/32—	2-0 15/16	1-2 5/32	2-2 1/8

Feet	40' Rise	40' Slope	50' Rise	50' Slope	60' Rise	60' Slope	70' Rise	70' Slope
0	25-10	47-7 13/32—	32-3 1/2	59-6 1/4	38-9	71-5 3/32	45-2 1/2	83-3 15/16
1	26-5 3/4	48-9 11/16	32-11 1/4	60-8 17/32	39-4 3/4	72-7 3/8	45-10 1/4	84-6 1/4
2	27-1 1/2	49-11 31/32	33-7	61-10 13/16	40-0 1/2	73-9 11/16	46-6	85-8 17/32—
3	27-9 1/4	51-2 1/4	34-2 3/4	63-1 3/32	40-8 1/4	74-11 31/32—	47-1 3/4	86-10 13/16
4	28-5	52-4 17/32	34-10 1/2	64-3 13/32—	41-4	76-2 1/4	47-9 1/2	88-1 3/32—
5	29-0 3/4	53-6 13/16	35-6 1/4	65-5 11/16	41-11 3/4	77-4 17/32—	48-5 1/4	89-3 3/8
6	29-8 1/2	54-9 1/8	36-2	66-7 31/32—	42-7 1/2	78-6 13/16	49-1	90-5 21/32
7	30-4 1/4	55-11 13/32—	36-9 3/4	67-10 1/4	43-3 1/4	79-9 3/32	49-8 3/4	91-7 15/16
8	31-0	57-1 11/16	37-5 1/2	69-0 17/32	43-11	80-11 3/8	50-4 1/2	92-10 7/32
9	31-7 3/4	58-3 31/32—	38-1 1/4	70-2 13/16	44-6 3/4	82-1 21/32	51-0 1/4	94-0 17/32—

natsin A=0.5425254314; natcos A=0.8400393778; nattan A=0.6458333333; natcot A=1.5483870967

Inches	0" Rise	Slope	1" Rise	Slope	2" Rise	Slope	3" Rise	Slope	4" Rise	Slope	5" Rise	Slope
0	0	0	21/32	13/16	15/16	2 3/8	1 15/16	3 19/32	2 19/32	4 25/32	3 1/4	5 31/32
1/16	1/32	1/16	11/16	1 9/32	1 11/32	2 15/32	2	3 21/32	2 21/32	4 27/32	3 9/32	6 1/32
1/8	3/32	5/32	23/32	1 11/32	1 3/8	2 17/32	2 1/32	3 23/32	2 11/16	4 15/16	3 11/32	6 1/32
3/16	1/8	7/32	25/32	1 13/32	1 7/16	2 5/8	2 1/16	3 13/16	2 23/32	5	3 3/8	6 3/16
1/4	5/32	5/16	13/16	1 1/2	1 15/32	2 11/16	2 1/8	3 7/8	2 25/32	5 1/16	3 13/32	6 1/4
5/16	7/32	3/8	27/32	1 9/16	1 1/2	2 3/4	2 5/32	3 15/16	2 13/16	5 5/32	3 15/32	6 11/32
3/8	1/4	7/16	29/32	1 21/32	1 17/32	2 27/32	2 3/16	4 1/32	2 27/32	5 7/32	3 1/2	6 13/32
7/16	9/32	17/32	15/16	1 23/32	1 19/32	2 29/32	2 1/4	4 3/32	2 7/8	5 9/32	3 17/32	6 1/2
1/2	5/16	19/32	31/32	1 25/32	1 5/8	2 31/32	2 9/32	4 3/16	2 15/16	5 3/8	3 19/32	6 9/16
9/16	3/8	21/32	1 1/32	1 7/8	1 21/32	3 1/16	2 5/16	4 1/4	2 31/32	5 7/16	3 5/8	6 5/8
5/8	13/32	3/4	1 1/16	1 15/16	1 23/32	3 1/8	2 3/8	4 5/16	3	5 17/32	3 21/32	6 23/32
11/16	7/16	13/16	1 3/32	2	1 3/4	3 7/32	2 13/32	4 13/32	3 1/16	5 19/32	3 11/16	6 25/32
3/4	1/2	29/32	1 1/8	2 3/32	1 25/32	3 9/32	2 7/16	4 15/32	3 3/32	5 21/32	3 3/4	6 7/8
13/16	17/32	31/32	1 3/16	2 5/32	1 27/32	3 11/32	2 15/32	4 9/16	3 1/8	5 3/4	3 25/32	6 15/16
7/8	9/16	1 1/32	1 7/32	2 1/4	1 7/8	3 7/16	2 17/32	4 5/8	3 3/16	5 13/16	3 13/16	7
15/16	5/8	1 3/32	1 1/4	2 5/16	1 29/32	3 1/2	2 9/16	4 11/16	3 7/32	5 29/32	3 7/8	7 3/32

Inches	6" Rise	Slope	7" Rise	Slope	8" Rise	Slope	9" Rise	Slope	10" Rise	Slope	11" Rise	Slope
0	3 29/32	7 5/32	4 9/16	8 11/32	5 7/32	9 17/32	5 7/8	10 3/4	6 1/2	11 15/16	7 5/32	1-1 1/8
1/16	3 15/16	7 7/32	4 19/32	8 7/16	5 1/4	9 5/8	5 29/32	10 13/16	6 9/16	1-0	7 3/16	1-1 3/16
1/8	4	7 5/16	4 5/8	8 1/2	5 9/32	9 11/16	5 15/16	10 7/8	6 19/32	1-0 3/32	7 1/4	1-1 9/32
3/16	4 1/32	7 3/8	4 11/16	8 9/16	5 11/32	9 25/32	5 31/32	10 31/32	6 5/8	1-0 5/32	7 9/32	1-1 11/32
1/4	4 1/16	7 15/32	4 23/32	8 21/32	5 3/8	9 27/32	6 1/32	11 1/32	6 11/16	1-0 7/32	7 5/16	1-1 7/16
5/16	4 1/8	7 17/32	4 3/4	8 23/32	5 13/32	9 29/32	6 1/16	11 1/8	6 23/32	1-0 5/16	7 3/8	1-1 1/2
3/8	4 5/32	7 19/32	4 13/16	8 13/16	5 7/16	10	6 3/32	11 3/16	6 3/4	1-0 3/8	7 13/32	1-1 9/16
7/16	4 3/16	7 11/16	4 27/32	8 7/8	5 1/2	10 1/16	6 5/32	11 1/4	6 25/32	1-0 15/32	7 7/16	1-1 21/32
1/2	4 7/32	7 3/4	4 7/8	8 15/16	5 17/32	10 5/32	6 3/16	11 11/32	6 27/32	1-0 17/32	7 1/2	1-1 23/32
9/16	4 9/32	7 27/32	4 15/16	9 1/32	5 9/16	10 7/32	6 7/32	11 13/32	6 7/8	1-0 19/32	7 17/32	1-1 13/16
5/8	4 5/16	7 29/32	4 31/32	9 3/32	5 5/8	10 9/32	6 9/32	11 1/2	6 29/32	1-0 11/16	7 9/16	1-1 7/8
11/16	4 11/32	7 31/32	5	9 9/16	5 21/32	10 3/8	6 5/16	11 9/16	6 31/32	1-0 3/4	7 19/32	1-1 15/16
3/4	4 13/32	8 1/16	5 1/32	9 1/4	5 11/16	10 7/16	6 11/32	11 5/8	7	1-0 13/16	7 21/32	1-2 1/16
13/16	4 7/16	8 1/8	5 3/32	9 5/16	5 3/4	10 1/2	6 3/8	11 23/32	7 1/32	1-0 29/32	7 11/16	1-2 3/32
7/8	4 15/32	8 7/32	5 1/8	9 13/32	5 25/32	10 19/32	6 7/16	11 25/32	7 3/32	1-0 31/32	7 23/32	1-2 5/32
15/16	4 17/32	8 9/32	5 5/32	9 15/32	5 13/16	10 21/32	6 15/32	11 27/32	7 1/8	1-1 1/16	7 25/32	1-2 1/4

Feet	0' Rise	Slope	10' Rise	Slope	20' Rise	Slope	30' Rise	Slope
0	0	0	6-6 1/8	11-11 3/8	13-0 1/4	23-10 3/8	19-6 3/8	35-9 9/16
1	7 13/16	1-2 5/16	7-1 15/16	13-1 1/2	13-8 1/16	25-0 11/16	20-2 3/16	36-11 7/8
2	1-3 5/8	2-4 5/8	7-9 3/4	14-3 27/32	14-3 7/8	25-3 1/2	20-10	38-2 7/32
3	1-11 7/16	3-6 31/32	8-5 9/16	15-6 5/32	14-11 11/16	27-5 11/32	21-5 13/16	39-4 17/32
4	2-7 1/4	4-9 9/32	9-1 3/8	16-8 15/32	15-7 1/2	28-7 21/32	22-1 5/8	40-6 27/32
5	3-3 1/16	5-11 19/32	9-9 3/16	17-10 25/32	16-3 5/16	29-9 31/32	22-9 7/16	41-9 5/32
6	3-10 7/8	7-1 29/32	10-5	19-1 3/32	16-11 1/8	31-0 9/32	23-5 1/4	42-11 1/2
7	4-6 11/16	8-4 7/32	11-0 13/16	20-3 7/16	17-6 15/16	32-2 5/8	24-1 1/16	44-1 13/16
8	5-2 1/2	9-6 9/16	11-8 5/8	21-5 3/4	18-2 3/4	33-4 15/16	24-8 7/8	45-4 1/8
9	5-10 5/16	10-8 7/8	12-4 7/16	22-8 1/16	18-10 9/16	34-7 1/4	25-4 11/16	46-6 7/16

A = 33° 03′ 57″; logsin A = 9.73688; logcos A = 9.92327; logtan A = 9.81361; logcot A = 0.18639

ins.	12″ Rise	Slope	13″ Rise	Slope	14″ Rise	Slope	15″ Rise	Slope	16″ Rise	Slope
0	7 13/16	1-2 5/16	8 15/32	1-3 1/2	9 1/8	1-4 23/32	9 3/4	1-5 29/32	10 13/32	1-7 3/32
1/16	7 27/32	1-2 13/32	8 1/2	1-3 19/32	9 5/32	1-4 25/32	9 13/16	1-5 31/32	10 15/32	1-7 5/32
1/8	7 29/32	1-2 15/32	8 17/32	1-3 21/32	9 3/16	1-4 27/32	9 27/32	1-6 1/16	10 1/2	1-7 1/4
3/16	7 15/16	1-2 17/32	8 19/32	1-3 3/4	9 1/4	1-4 15/16	9 7/8	1-6 1/8	10 17/32	1-7 5/16
1/4	7 31/32	1-2 5/8	8 5/8	1-3 13/16	9 9/32	1-5	9 15/16	1-6 3/32	10 19/32	1-7 3/8
5/16	8 1/32	1-2 11/32	8 21/32	1-3 7/8	9 5/16	1-5 3/32	9 31/32	1-6 9/32	10 5/8	1-7 15/32
3/8	8 1/16	1-2 25/32	8 23/32	1-3 31/32	9 11/32	1-5 5/32	10	1-6 11/32	10 21/32	1-7 17/32
7/16	8 3/32	1-2 27/32	8 3/4	1-4 1/32	9 13/32	1-5 7/32	10 1/16	1-6 13/32	10 11/16	1-7 5/8
1/2	8 1/8	1-2 29/32	8 25/32	1-4 3/32	9 7/16	1-5 5/16	10 3/32	1-6 1/2	10 3/4	1-7 11/16
9/16	8 3/16	1-3	8 27/32	1-4 3/16	9 15/32	1-5 3/8	10 1/8	1-6 9/16	10 25/32	1-7 3/4
5/8	8 7/32	1-3 1/16	8 7/8	1-4 1/4	9 17/32	1-5 7/16	10 3/16	1-6 21/32	10 13/16	1-7 27/32
11/16	8 1/4	1-3 1/8	8 29/32	1-4 11/32	9 9/16	1-5 17/32	10 7/32	1-6 23/32	10 7/8	1-7 29/32
3/4	8 5/16	1-3 7/32	8 15/16	1-4 13/32	9 19/32	1-5 19/32	10 1/4	1-6 25/32	10 29/32	1-8
13/16	8 11/32	1-3 9/32	9	1-4 15/32	9 21/32	1-5 11/16	10 9/32	1-6 7/8	10 15/16	1-8 1/16
7/8	8 3/8	1-3 3/8	9 1/8	1-4 9/16	9 11/16	1-5 3/4	10 11/32	1-6 15/16	11	1-8 1/8
15/16	8 7/16	1-3 7/16	9 1/16	1-4 5/8	9 23/32	1-5 13/16	10 3/8	1-7 1/32	11 1/16	1-8 1/4

ins.	17″ Rise	Slope	18″ Rise	Slope	19″ Rise	Slope	20″ Rise	Slope	21″ Rise	Slope
0	11 1/16	1-8 9/32	11 23/32	1-9 15/32	1-0 3/8	1-10 21/32	1-1 1/2	1-11 7/8	1-1 11/16	2-1 1/4
1/16	11 3/32	1-8 3/8	11 3/4	1-9 9/16	1-0 13/32	1-10 3/4	1-1 1/2	1-11 15/16	1-1 23/32	2-1 1/8
1/8	11 5/32	1-8 7/16	11 13/16	1-9 5/8	1-0 7/16	1-10 13/16	1-1 3/32	2-0	1-1 3/4	2-1 7/32
3/16	11 3/16	1-8 1/2	11 27/32	1-9 11/16	1-0 1/2	1-10 29/32	1-1 5/32	2-0 3/32	1-1 25/32	2-1 9/32
1/4	11 7/32	1-8 19/32	11 7/8	1-9 25/32	1-0 17/32	1-10 31/32	1-1 3/16	2-0 5/32	1-1 27/32	2-1 11/32
5/16	11 9/32	1-8 21/32	11 15/16	1-9 27/32	1-0 9/16	1-11 1/32	1-1 7/32	2-0 1/4	1-1 7/8	2-1 7/16
3/8	11 5/16	1-8 23/32	11 31/32	1-9 15/16	1-0 5/8	1-11 1/8	1-1 1/4	2-0 5/16	1-1 29/32	2-1 1/2
7/16	11 11/32	1-8 13/16	1-0	1-10	1-0 21/32	1-11 3/16	1-1 5/16	2-0 3/8	1-1 31/32	2-1 19/32
1/2	11 13/32	1-8 7/8	1-0 1/32	1-10 1/32	1-0 11/16	1-11 9/32	1-1 11/32	2-0 15/32	1-2	2-1 21/32
9/16	11 7/16	1-8 31/32	1-0 3/32	1-10 5/32	1-0 3/4	1-11 11/32	1-1 3/8	2-0 17/32	1-2 1/32	2-1 23/32
5/8	11 15/32	1-9 1/32	1-0 1/8	1-10 7/32	1-0 25/32	1-11 13/32	1-1 7/16	2-0 5/8	1-2 3/32	2-1 13/16
11/16	11 1/2	1-9 3/32	1-0 5/32	1-10 5/16	1-0 13/16	1-11 1/2	1-1 15/32	2-0 11/16	1-2 1/8	2-1 7/8
3/4	11 9/16	1-9 3/16	1-0 7/32	1-10 3/8	1-0 27/32	1-11 9/16	1-1 1/2	2-0 3/4	1-2 5/32	2-1 31/32
13/16	11 19/32	1-9 1/4	1-0 1/4	1-10 7/16	1-0 29/32	1-11 21/32	1-1 9/16	2-0 27/32	1-2 3/16	2-2 1/32
7/8	11 5/8	1-9 11/32	1-0 9/32	1-10 17/32	1-0 17/32	1-11 23/32	1-1 19/32	2-0 29/32	1-2 1/4	2-2 3/32
15/16	11 11/16	1-9 13/32	1-0 11/32	1-10 19/32	1-0 31/32	1-11 25/32	1-1 5/8	2-0 31/32	1-2 9/32	2-2 3/16

Feet	40′ Rise	Slope	50′ Rise	Slope	60′ Rise	Slope	70′ Rise	Slope
0	26-0 1/2	47-8 3/4	32-6 5/8	59-7 15/16	39-0 3/4	71-7 5/32	45-6 7/8	83-6 11/32
1	26-8 5/16	48-11 3/32	33-2 7/16	60-10 5/32	39-8 9/16	72-9 15/32	46-2 11/16	84-8 21/32
2	27-4 1/8	50-1 13/32	33-10 1/4	62-0 19/32	40-4 3/8	73-11 25/32	46-10 1/2	85-10 31/32
3	27-11 15/16	51-3 23/32	34-6 1/16	63-2 29/32	41-0 3/16	75-2 3/32	47-6 5/16	87-1 9/32
4	28-7 3/4	52-6 1/32	35-1 7/8	64-5 7/32	41-8	76-4 13/32	48-2 1/8	88-3 5/8
5	29-3 3/8	53-8 11/32	35-9 11/16	65-7 9/16	42-3 13/16	77-6 3/4	48-9 15/16	89-5 15/16
6	29-11 3/8	54-10 11/16	36-5 1/2	66-9 7/8	42-11 5/8	78-9 1/16	49-5 3/4	90-8 1/4
7	30-7 3/4	56-1	37-1 5/16	68-0 3/16	43-7 7/16	79-11 3/8	50-1 9/16	91-10 9/16
8	31-3	57-3 5/16	37-9 1/8	69-2 1/2	44-3 1/4	81-1 11/16	50-9 3/8	93-0 7/8
9	31-10 13/16	58-5 5/8	38-4 15/16	70-4 13/16	44-11 1/16	82-4	51-5 3/16	94-3 7/32

natsin A=0.5456018868; natcos A=0.8380444983; nattan A=0.6510416666; natcot A=1.5360000000

Inches	0″ Rise	0″ Slope	1″ Rise	1″ Slope	2″ Rise	2″ Slope	3″ Rise	3″ Slope	4″ Rise	4″ Slope	5″ Rise	5″ Slope
0	0	0	21/32	1 3/16	1 5/16	2 13/32–	1 31/32	3 19/32–	2 5/8	4 25/32	3 9/32	5 31/32
1/16	1/32	1/16	11/16	1 9/32–	1 11/32	2 15/32–	2	3 21/32	2 21/32	4 27/32	3 5/16	6 1/16
1/8	3/32–	5/32–	3/4	1 11/32	1 13/32–	2 17/32	2 1/16	3 3/4	2 23/32–	4 15/16	3 3/8	6 1/8
3/16	1/8	7/32	25/32–	1 13/32	1 7/16	2 5/8	2 3/32–	3 13/16	2 3/4	5	3 13/32–	6 7/32–
1/4	5/32	5/16	13/16	1 1/2	1 15/32	2 11/16	2 1/8	3 7/8	2 25/32	5 3/32–	3 7/16	6 9/32–
5/16	7/32–	3/8	7/8	1 9/16	1 17/32–	2 25/32–	2 3/16	3 31/32–	2 27/32–	5 5/32	3 1/2	6 11/32
3/8	1/4	7/16	29/32–	1 21/32–	1 9/16	2 27/32–	2 7/32–	4 1/32	2 7/8	5 7/32	3 17/32–	6 7/16
7/16	9/32	17/32–	15/16	1 23/32	1 19/32	2 29/32	2 1/4	4 1/8	2 29/32	5 5/16	3 9/16	6 1/2
1/2	5/16	19/32	1	1 25/32	1 5/8	3	2 5/16	4 3/16	2 15/16	5 3/8	3 5/8	6 19/32–
9/16	3/8	11/16	1 1/32–	1 7/8	1 11/16	3 1/16	2 11/32–	4 1/4	3	5 15/32–	3 21/32–	6 21/32–
5/8	13/32	3/4	1 1/16	1 15/16	1 23/32	3 1/8	2 3/8	4 11/32–	3 1/32	5 17/32	3 11/16	6 23/32
11/16	7/16	13/16	1 3/32	2 1/32–	1 3/4	3 7/32–	2 13/32	4 13/32	3 1/16	5 19/32	3 23/32	6 13/16
3/4	1/2	29/32–	1 5/32–	2 3/32–	1 13/16	3 9/32	2 15/32–	4 1/2	3 1/8	5 11/16	3 25/32–	6 7/8
13/16	17/32	31/32	1 3/16	2 5/32	1 27/32	3 3/8	2 1/2	4 9/16	3 5/32	5 3/4	3 13/16	6 15/16
7/8	9/16	1 1/32	1 7/32	2 1/4	1 7/8	3 7/16	2 17/32	4 5/8	3 3/16	5 27/32–	3 27/32	7 1/32–
15/16	5/8	1 1/8	1 9/32–	2 5/16	1 15/16	3 1/2	2 19/32–	4 23/32–	3 1/4	5 29/32–	3 29/32–	7 3/32

Inches	6″ Rise	6″ Slope	7″ Rise	7″ Slope	8″ Rise	8″ Slope	9″ Rise	9″ Slope	10″ Rise	10″ Slope	11″ Rise	11″ Slope
0	3 15/16	7 3/16	4 19/32	8 3/8	5 1/4	9 9/16	5 29/32	10 3/4	6 9/16	11 31/32–	7 7/32	1-1 5/32
1/16	3 31/32	7 1/4	4 5/8	8 7/16	5 9/32	9 21/32–	5 15/16	10 27/32–	6 19/32	1-0 1/32	7 1/4	1-1 7/32
1/8	4 1/32–	7 5/16	4 11/16	8 17/32–	5 11/32–	9 23/32–	6	10 29/32	6 21/32–	1-0 1/8	7 5/16	1-1 5/16
3/16	4 1/16	7 13/32–	4 23/32–	8 19/32	5 3/8	9 25/32	6 1/32–	11	6 11/16	1-0 3/16	7 11/32–	1-1 3/8
1/4	4 3/32	7 15/32	4 3/4	8 21/32	5 13/32	9 7/8	6 1/16	11 1/16	6 23/32	1-0 1/4	7 3/8	1-1 15/32–
5/16	4 5/32–	7 9/16	4 13/16	8 3/4	5 15/32–	9 15/16	6 1/8	11 1/8	6 25/32–	1-0 11/32–	7 7/16	1-1 17/32–
3/8	4 3/16	7 5/8	4 27/32–	8 13/16	5 1/2	10 1/32–	6 5/32–	11 7/32–	6 13/16	1-0 13/32	7 15/32–	1-1 19/32
7/16	4 7/32	7 11/16	4 7/8	8 29/32–	5 17/32	10 3/32–	6 3/16	11 9/32	6 27/32	1-0 15/32	7 1/2	1-1 11/16
1/2	4 1/4	7 25/32–	4 15/16	8 31/32	5 9/16	10 5/32	6 1/4	11 3/8	6 7/8	1-0 9/16	7 9/16	1-1 3/4
9/16	4 5/16	7 27/32	4 31/32–	9 1/32	5 5/8	10 1/4	6 9/32–	11 7/16	6 15/16	1-0 5/8	7 19/32–	1-1 27/32–
5/8	4 11/32	7 15/16	5	9 1/8	5 21/32	10 5/16	6 5/16	11 1/2	6 31/32	1-0 23/32–	7 5/8	1-1 29/32–
11/16	4 3/8	8	5 1/32	9 3/16	5 11/16	10 13/32–	6 11/32	11 19/32–	7	1-0 25/32	7 21/32	1-1 31/32
3/4	4 7/16	8 1/16	5 3/32–	9 9/32–	5 3/4	10 15/32–	6 13/32–	11 21/32	7 1/16	1-0 27/32	7 23/32–	1-2 1/16
13/16	4 15/32	8 5/32–	5 1/8	9 11/32	5 25/32	10 17/32	6 7/16	11 3/4	7 3/32	1-0 15/16	7 3/4	1-2 1/8
7/8	4 1/2	8 7/32	5 5/32	9 13/32	5 13/16	10 5/8	6 15/32	11 13/16	7 1/8	1-1	7 25/32	1-2 7/32–
15/16	4 9/16	8 5/16	5 7/32–	9 1/2	5 7/8	10 11/16	6 17/32–	11 7/8	7 3/16	1-1 3/32–	7 27/32–	1-2 9/32–

Feet	0′ Rise	0′ Slope	10′ Rise	10′ Slope	20′ Rise	20′ Slope	30′ Rise	30′ Slope
0	0	0	6-6 3/4	11-11 17/32	13-1 1/2	23-11 1/16	19-8 1/4	35-10 19/32
1	7 7/8	1-2 11/32	7-2 5/8	13-1 7/8	13-9 3/8	25-1 13/32	20-4 1/8	37-0 15/16
2	1-3 3/4	2-4 23/32–	7-10 1/2	14-4 1/4	14-5 1/4	26-3 25/32–	21-0	38-3 5/16
3	1-11 5/8	3-7 1/16	8-6 3/8	15-6 19/32–	15-1 1/8	27-6 1/8	21-7 7/8	39-5 21/32
4	2-7 1/2	4-9 13/32	9-2 1/4	16-8 15/16	15-9	28-8 15/32	22-3 3/4	40-8
5	3-3 3/8	5-11 25/32–	9-10 1/8	17-11 5/16	16-4 7/8	29-10 27/32–	22-11 5/8	41-10 3/8
6	3-11 1/4	7-2 1/8	10-6	19-1 21/32–	17-0 3/4	31-1 3/16	23-7 1/2	43-0 23/32–
7	4-7 1/8	8-4 15/32	11-1 7/8	20-4	17-8 5/8	32-3 17/32	24-3 3/8	44-3 1/16
8	5-3	9-6 13/16	11-9 3/4	21-6 11/32	18-4 1/2	33-5 29/32–	24-11 1/4	45-5 7/16
9	5-10 7/8	10-9 3/16	12-5 5/8	22-8 23/32–	19-0 3/8	34-8 1/4	25-7 1/8	46-7 25/32–

A = 33° 16′ 30″; logsin A = 9.73930; logcos A = 9.92223; logtan A = 9.81707; logcot A = 0.18293

In.	12″ Rise	12″ Slope	13″ Rise	13″ Slope	14″ Rise	14″ Slope	15″ Rise	15″ Slope	16″ Rise	16″ Slope
0	$7\frac{7}{8}$	$1\text{-}2\frac{11}{32}$	$8\frac{17}{32}$	$1\text{-}3\frac{9}{16}$	$9\frac{3}{16}$	$1\text{-}4\frac{3}{4}$	$9\frac{27}{32}$	$1\text{-}5\frac{15}{16}$	$10\frac{1}{2}$	$1\text{-}7\frac{1}{8}$
$\frac{1}{16}$	$7\frac{29}{32}$	$1\text{-}2\frac{7}{16}$	$8\frac{9}{16}$	$1\text{-}3\frac{5}{8}$	$9\frac{7}{32}$	$1\text{-}4\frac{13}{16}$	$9\frac{7}{8}$	$1\text{-}6\frac{1}{32}$	$10\frac{17}{32}$	$1\text{-}7\frac{7}{32}$
$\frac{1}{8}$	$7\frac{31}{32}$	$1\text{-}2\frac{1}{2}$	$8\frac{5}{8}$	$1\text{-}3\frac{11}{32}$	$9\frac{9}{32}$	$1\text{-}4\frac{29}{32}$	$9\frac{15}{16}$	$1\text{-}6\frac{5}{32}$	$10\frac{19}{32}$	$1\text{-}7\frac{9}{32}$
$\frac{3}{16}$	8	$1\text{-}2\frac{9}{16}$	$8\frac{21}{32}$	$1\text{-}3\frac{25}{32}$	$9\frac{5}{16}$	$1\text{-}4\frac{31}{32}$	$9\frac{31}{32}$	$1\text{-}6\frac{9}{32}$	$10\frac{5}{8}$	$1\text{-}7\frac{3}{8}$
$\frac{1}{4}$	$8\frac{1}{2}$	$1\text{-}2\frac{21}{32}$	$8\frac{11}{16}$	$1\text{-}3\frac{27}{32}$	$9\frac{11}{32}$	$1\text{-}5\frac{1}{32}$	10	$1\text{-}6\frac{1}{4}$	$10\frac{21}{32}$	$1\text{-}7\frac{7}{16}$
$\frac{5}{16}$	$8\frac{3}{32}$	$1\text{-}2\frac{23}{32}$	$8\frac{3}{4}$	$1\text{-}3\frac{15}{16}$	$9\frac{13}{32}$	$1\text{-}5\frac{1}{8}$	$10\frac{1}{16}$	$1\text{-}6\frac{5}{16}$	$10\frac{23}{32}$	$1\text{-}7\frac{1}{2}$
$\frac{3}{8}$	$8\frac{1}{8}$	$1\text{-}2\frac{13}{16}$	$8\frac{25}{32}$	$1\text{-}4$	$9\frac{7}{16}$	$1\text{-}5\frac{3}{16}$	$10\frac{3}{32}$	$1\text{-}6\frac{3}{8}$	$10\frac{3}{4}$	$1\text{-}7\frac{19}{32}$
$\frac{7}{16}$	$8\frac{5}{32}$	$1\text{-}2\frac{7}{8}$	$8\frac{13}{16}$	$1\text{-}4\frac{1}{16}$	$9\frac{15}{32}$	$1\text{-}5\frac{9}{32}$	$10\frac{1}{8}$	$1\text{-}6\frac{15}{32}$	$10\frac{25}{32}$	$1\text{-}7\frac{21}{32}$
$\frac{1}{2}$	$8\frac{3}{16}$	$1\text{-}2\frac{15}{16}$	$8\frac{7}{8}$	$1\text{-}4\frac{5}{32}$	$9\frac{1}{2}$	$1\text{-}5\frac{11}{32}$	$10\frac{3}{16}$	$1\text{-}6\frac{17}{32}$	$10\frac{13}{16}$	$1\text{-}7\frac{3}{4}$
$\frac{9}{16}$	$8\frac{1}{4}$	$1\text{-}3\frac{1}{32}$	$8\frac{29}{32}$	$1\text{-}4\frac{7}{32}$	$9\frac{9}{16}$	$1\text{-}5\frac{13}{32}$	$10\frac{7}{32}$	$1\text{-}6\frac{5}{8}$	$10\frac{7}{8}$	$1\text{-}7\frac{13}{16}$
$\frac{5}{8}$	$8\frac{9}{32}$	$1\text{-}3\frac{3}{32}$	$8\frac{15}{16}$	$1\text{-}4\frac{5}{16}$	$9\frac{19}{32}$	$1\text{-}5\frac{1}{2}$	$10\frac{1}{4}$	$1\text{-}6\frac{11}{16}$	$10\frac{29}{32}$	$1\text{-}7\frac{7}{8}$
$\frac{11}{16}$	$8\frac{5}{16}$	$1\text{-}3\frac{3}{16}$	$8\frac{31}{32}$	$1\text{-}4\frac{3}{8}$	$9\frac{5}{8}$	$1\text{-}5\frac{9}{16}$	$10\frac{9}{32}$	$1\text{-}6\frac{3}{4}$	$10\frac{15}{16}$	$1\text{-}7\frac{31}{32}$
$\frac{3}{4}$	$8\frac{3}{8}$	$1\text{-}3\frac{1}{4}$	$9\frac{1}{32}$	$1\text{-}4\frac{7}{16}$	$9\frac{11}{16}$	$1\text{-}5\frac{21}{32}$	$10\frac{11}{32}$	$1\text{-}6\frac{27}{32}$	11	$1\text{-}8\frac{1}{2}$
$\frac{13}{16}$	$8\frac{13}{32}$	$1\text{-}3\frac{5}{16}$	$9\frac{1}{16}$	$1\text{-}4\frac{17}{32}$	$9\frac{23}{32}$	$1\text{-}5\frac{25}{32}$	$10\frac{3}{8}$	$1\text{-}6\frac{29}{32}$	$11\frac{1}{32}$	$1\text{-}8\frac{1}{8}$
$\frac{7}{8}$	$8\frac{7}{16}$	$1\text{-}3\frac{13}{32}$	$9\frac{3}{32}$	$1\text{-}4\frac{19}{32}$	$9\frac{3}{4}$	$1\text{-}5\frac{25}{32}$	$10\frac{13}{32}$	$1\text{-}7$	$11\frac{1}{16}$	$1\text{-}8\frac{3}{16}$
$\frac{15}{16}$	$8\frac{1}{2}$	$1\text{-}3\frac{15}{32}$	$9\frac{5}{32}$	$1\text{-}4\frac{21}{32}$	$9\frac{13}{16}$	$1\text{-}5\frac{7}{8}$	$10\frac{15}{32}$	$1\text{-}7\frac{1}{16}$	$11\frac{1}{8}$	$1\text{-}8\frac{1}{4}$

In.	17″ Rise	17″ Slope	18″ Rise	18″ Slope	19″ Rise	19″ Slope	20″ Rise	20″ Slope	21″ Rise	21″ Slope
0	$11\frac{5}{32}$	$1\text{-}8\frac{11}{32}$	$11\frac{13}{16}$	$1\text{-}9\frac{17}{32}$	$1\text{-}0\frac{15}{32}$	$1\text{-}10\frac{23}{32}$	$1\text{-}1\frac{1}{8}$	$1\text{-}11\frac{15}{16}$	$1\text{-}1\frac{25}{32}$	$2\text{-}1\frac{1}{8}$
$\frac{1}{16}$	$11\frac{13}{32}$	$1\text{-}8\frac{13}{32}$	$11\frac{27}{32}$	$1\text{-}9\frac{19}{32}$	$1\text{-}0\frac{1}{2}$	$1\text{-}10\frac{13}{16}$	$1\text{-}1\frac{5}{32}$	$2\text{-}0$	$1\text{-}1\frac{13}{16}$	$2\text{-}1\frac{3}{32}$
$\frac{1}{8}$	$11\frac{1}{4}$	$1\text{-}8\frac{15}{32}$	$11\frac{29}{32}$	$1\text{-}9\frac{11}{16}$	$1\text{-}0\frac{9}{16}$	$1\text{-}10\frac{7}{8}$	$1\text{-}1\frac{7}{32}$	$2\text{-}0\frac{1}{16}$	$1\text{-}1\frac{7}{8}$	$2\text{-}1\frac{9}{32}$
$\frac{3}{16}$	$11\frac{9}{32}$	$1\text{-}8\frac{9}{16}$	$11\frac{15}{16}$	$1\text{-}9\frac{3}{4}$	$1\text{-}0\frac{19}{32}$	$1\text{-}10\frac{15}{16}$	$1\text{-}1\frac{1}{4}$	$2\text{-}0\frac{5}{32}$	$1\text{-}1\frac{29}{32}$	$2\text{-}1\frac{11}{32}$
$\frac{1}{4}$	$11\frac{5}{16}$	$1\text{-}8\frac{5}{8}$	$11\frac{31}{32}$	$1\text{-}9\frac{27}{32}$	$1\text{-}0\frac{5}{8}$	$1\text{-}11\frac{1}{2}$	$1\text{-}1\frac{9}{32}$	$2\text{-}0\frac{7}{32}$	$1\text{-}1\frac{15}{16}$	$2\text{-}1\frac{13}{32}$
$\frac{5}{16}$	$11\frac{3}{8}$	$1\text{-}8\frac{23}{32}$	$1\text{-}0\frac{1}{32}$	$1\text{-}9\frac{29}{32}$	$1\text{-}0\frac{11}{16}$	$1\text{-}11\frac{3}{32}$	$1\text{-}1\frac{11}{32}$	$2\text{-}0\frac{9}{32}$	$1\text{-}2$	$2\text{-}1\frac{1}{2}$
$\frac{3}{8}$	$11\frac{13}{32}$	$1\text{-}8\frac{25}{32}$	$1\text{-}0\frac{1}{16}$	$1\text{-}9\frac{31}{32}$	$1\text{-}0\frac{23}{32}$	$1\text{-}11\frac{3}{32}$	$1\text{-}1\frac{3}{8}$	$2\text{-}0\frac{3}{8}$	$1\text{-}2\frac{1}{16}$	$2\text{-}1\frac{9}{16}$
$\frac{7}{16}$	$11\frac{7}{16}$	$1\text{-}8\frac{27}{32}$	$1\text{-}0\frac{3}{32}$	$1\text{-}10\frac{1}{16}$	$1\text{-}0\frac{3}{4}$	$1\text{-}11\frac{1}{4}$	$1\text{-}1\frac{13}{32}$	$2\text{-}0\frac{7}{16}$	$1\text{-}2\frac{1}{16}$	$2\text{-}1\frac{21}{32}$
$\frac{1}{2}$	$11\frac{1}{2}$	$1\text{-}8\frac{15}{16}$	$1\text{-}0\frac{1}{8}$	$1\text{-}10\frac{1}{8}$	$1\text{-}0\frac{13}{16}$	$1\text{-}11\frac{5}{16}$	$1\text{-}1\frac{7}{16}$	$2\text{-}0\frac{17}{32}$	$1\text{-}2\frac{1}{8}$	$2\text{-}1\frac{23}{32}$
$\frac{9}{16}$	$11\frac{17}{32}$	$1\text{-}9$	$1\text{-}0\frac{3}{16}$	$1\text{-}10\frac{3}{16}$	$1\text{-}0\frac{27}{32}$	$1\text{-}11\frac{13}{32}$	$1\text{-}1\frac{1}{2}$	$2\text{-}0\frac{19}{32}$	$1\text{-}2\frac{5}{32}$	$2\text{-}1\frac{25}{32}$
$\frac{5}{8}$	$11\frac{9}{16}$	$1\text{-}9\frac{3}{32}$	$1\text{-}0\frac{7}{32}$	$1\text{-}10\frac{9}{32}$	$1\text{-}0\frac{7}{8}$	$1\text{-}11\frac{15}{32}$	$1\text{-}1\frac{17}{32}$	$2\text{-}0\frac{21}{32}$	$1\text{-}2\frac{3}{16}$	$2\text{-}1\frac{7}{8}$
$\frac{11}{16}$	$11\frac{19}{32}$	$1\text{-}9\frac{5}{32}$	$1\text{-}0\frac{1}{4}$	$1\text{-}10\frac{11}{32}$	$1\text{-}0\frac{29}{32}$	$1\text{-}11\frac{9}{16}$	$1\text{-}1\frac{9}{16}$	$2\text{-}0\frac{3}{4}$	$1\text{-}2\frac{7}{32}$	$2\text{-}1\frac{15}{16}$
$\frac{3}{4}$	$11\frac{21}{32}$	$1\text{-}9\frac{7}{32}$	$1\text{-}0\frac{5}{16}$	$1\text{-}10\frac{7}{16}$	$1\text{-}0\frac{31}{32}$	$1\text{-}11\frac{5}{8}$	$1\text{-}1\frac{5}{8}$	$2\text{-}0\frac{13}{16}$	$1\text{-}2\frac{9}{32}$	$2\text{-}2$
$\frac{13}{16}$	$11\frac{11}{16}$	$1\text{-}9\frac{5}{16}$	$1\text{-}0\frac{11}{32}$	$1\text{-}10\frac{1}{2}$	$1\text{-}1$	$1\text{-}11\frac{11}{16}$	$1\text{-}1\frac{21}{32}$	$2\text{-}0\frac{29}{32}$	$1\text{-}2\frac{5}{16}$	$2\text{-}2\frac{3}{32}$
$\frac{7}{8}$	$11\frac{23}{32}$	$1\text{-}9\frac{3}{8}$	$1\text{-}0\frac{3}{8}$	$1\text{-}10\frac{9}{16}$	$1\text{-}1\frac{1}{16}$	$1\text{-}11\frac{25}{32}$	$1\text{-}1\frac{11}{16}$	$2\text{-}0\frac{31}{32}$	$1\text{-}2\frac{11}{32}$	$2\text{-}2\frac{5}{32}$
$\frac{15}{16}$	$11\frac{25}{32}$	$1\text{-}9\frac{15}{32}$	$1\text{-}0\frac{7}{16}$	$1\text{-}10\frac{21}{32}$	$1\text{-}1\frac{3}{32}$	$1\text{-}11\frac{27}{32}$	$1\text{-}1\frac{3}{4}$	$2\text{-}1\frac{1}{32}$	$1\text{-}2\frac{13}{32}$	$2\text{-}2\frac{1}{4}$

Feet	40′ Rise	40′ Slope	50′ Rise	50′ Slope	60′ Rise	60′ Slope	70′ Rise	70′ Slope
0	$26\text{-}3$	$47\text{-}10\frac{1}{8}$	$32\text{-}9\frac{3}{4}$	$59\text{-}9\frac{21}{32}$	$39\text{-}4\frac{1}{2}$	$71\text{-}9\frac{3}{16}$	$45\text{-}11\frac{1}{4}$	$83\text{-}8\frac{23}{32}$
1	$26\text{-}10\frac{7}{8}$	$49\text{-}0\frac{15}{32}$	$33\text{-}5\frac{5}{8}$	$61\text{-}0$	$40\text{-}0\frac{3}{8}$	$72\text{-}11\frac{5}{16}$	$46\text{-}7\frac{1}{8}$	$84\text{-}11\frac{3}{32}$
2	$27\text{-}6\frac{3}{4}$	$50\text{-}2\frac{21}{32}$	$34\text{-}1\frac{1}{2}$	$62\text{-}2\frac{3}{8}$	$40\text{-}8\frac{1}{4}$	$74\text{-}1\frac{29}{32}$	$47\text{-}3$	$86\text{-}1\frac{11}{16}$
3	$28\text{-}2\frac{5}{8}$	$51\text{-}5\frac{3}{16}$	$34\text{-}9\frac{3}{8}$	$63\text{-}4\frac{23}{32}$	$41\text{-}4\frac{1}{8}$	$75\text{-}4\frac{1}{4}$	$47\text{-}10\frac{7}{8}$	$87\text{-}3\frac{25}{32}$
4	$28\text{-}10\frac{1}{2}$	$52\text{-}7\frac{17}{32}$	$35\text{-}5\frac{1}{4}$	$64\text{-}7\frac{1}{16}$	$42\text{-}0$	$76\text{-}6\frac{19}{32}$	$48\text{-}6\frac{3}{4}$	$88\text{-}6\frac{1}{8}$
5	$29\text{-}6\frac{3}{8}$	$53\text{-}9\frac{29}{32}$	$36\text{-}1\frac{1}{8}$	$65\text{-}9\frac{7}{16}$	$42\text{-}7\frac{7}{8}$	$77\text{-}8\frac{31}{32}$	$49\text{-}2\frac{5}{8}$	$89\text{-}8\frac{1}{2}$
6	$30\text{-}2\frac{1}{4}$	$55\text{-}0\frac{1}{4}$	$36\text{-}9$	$66\text{-}11\frac{25}{32}$	$43\text{-}3\frac{3}{4}$	$78\text{-}11\frac{5}{16}$	$49\text{-}10\frac{1}{2}$	$90\text{-}10\frac{27}{32}$
7	$30\text{-}10\frac{1}{8}$	$56\text{-}2\frac{19}{32}$	$37\text{-}4\frac{7}{8}$	$68\text{-}2\frac{1}{8}$	$43\text{-}11\frac{5}{8}$	$80\text{-}1\frac{21}{32}$	$50\text{-}6\frac{3}{8}$	$92\text{-}1\frac{3}{16}$
8	$31\text{-}6$	$57\text{-}4\frac{31}{32}$	$38\text{-}0\frac{3}{4}$	$69\text{-}4\frac{1}{2}$	$44\text{-}7\frac{1}{2}$	$81\text{-}4\frac{1}{32}$	$51\text{-}2\frac{1}{4}$	$93\text{-}3\frac{9}{16}$
9	$32\text{-}1\frac{7}{8}$	$58\text{-}7\frac{5}{16}$	$38\text{-}8\frac{5}{8}$	$70\text{-}6\frac{27}{32}$	$45\text{-}3\frac{3}{8}$	$82\text{-}6\frac{3}{8}$	$51\text{-}10\frac{1}{8}$	$94\text{-}5\frac{29}{32}$

natsin A=0.5486564415; natcos A=0.8360479108; nattan A=0.6562500000; natcot A=1.5238095238

Inches	0" Rise	0" Slope	1" Rise	1" Slope	2" Rise	2" Slope	3" Rise	3" Slope	4" Rise	4" Slope	5" Rise	5" Slope
0	0	0	$\frac{21}{32}$	$1\frac{3}{16}$	$1\frac{5}{16}$	$2\frac{13}{32}$	2	$3\frac{19}{32}$	$2\frac{21}{32}$	$4\frac{25}{32}$	$3\frac{5}{16}$	6
$\frac{1}{16}$	$\frac{1}{32}$	$\frac{1}{16}$	$\frac{11}{16}$	$1\frac{9}{32}$	$1\frac{3}{8}$	$2\frac{15}{32}$	$2\frac{1}{32}$	$3\frac{21}{32}$	$2\frac{11}{32}$	$4\frac{7}{8}$	$3\frac{11}{16}$	$6\frac{1}{16}$
$\frac{1}{8}$	$\frac{3}{32}$	$\frac{5}{32}$	$\frac{3}{4}$	$1\frac{11}{32}$	$1\frac{13}{32}$	$2\frac{9}{16}$	$2\frac{1}{16}$	$3\frac{3}{4}$	$2\frac{23}{32}$	$4\frac{15}{16}$	$3\frac{3}{8}$	$6\frac{5}{32}$
$\frac{3}{16}$	$\frac{1}{8}$	$\frac{7}{32}$	$\frac{25}{32}$	$1\frac{7}{16}$	$1\frac{7}{16}$	$2\frac{5}{8}$	$2\frac{3}{32}$	$3\frac{13}{16}$	$2\frac{25}{32}$	$5\frac{1}{32}$	$3\frac{7}{16}$	$6\frac{7}{32}$
$\frac{1}{4}$	$\frac{5}{32}$	$\frac{5}{16}$	$\frac{13}{16}$	$1\frac{1}{2}$	$1\frac{1}{2}$	$2\frac{11}{16}$	$2\frac{5}{32}$	$3\frac{29}{32}$	$2\frac{13}{16}$	$5\frac{3}{32}$	$3\frac{15}{32}$	$6\frac{9}{32}$
$\frac{5}{16}$	$\frac{7}{32}$	$\frac{3}{8}$	$\frac{7}{8}$	$1\frac{9}{16}$	$1\frac{17}{32}$	$2\frac{25}{32}$	$2\frac{3}{16}$	$3\frac{31}{32}$	$2\frac{7}{32}$	$5\frac{5}{32}$	$3\frac{1}{2}$	$6\frac{3}{8}$
$\frac{3}{8}$	$\frac{1}{4}$	$\frac{7}{16}$	$\frac{29}{32}$	$1\frac{21}{32}$	$1\frac{9}{16}$	$2\frac{27}{32}$	$2\frac{7}{32}$	$4\frac{1}{32}$	$2\frac{9}{32}$	$5\frac{1}{4}$	$3\frac{9}{16}$	$6\frac{7}{16}$
$\frac{7}{16}$	$\frac{9}{32}$	$\frac{17}{32}$	$\frac{15}{16}$	$1\frac{23}{32}$	$1\frac{5}{8}$	$2\frac{15}{16}$	$2\frac{9}{32}$	$4\frac{1}{8}$	$2\frac{15}{32}$	$5\frac{5}{16}$	$3\frac{19}{32}$	$6\frac{17}{32}$
$\frac{1}{2}$	$\frac{11}{32}$	$\frac{19}{32}$	1	$1\frac{13}{16}$	$1\frac{21}{32}$	3	$2\frac{5}{16}$	$4\frac{3}{16}$	$2\frac{31}{32}$	$5\frac{13}{32}$	$3\frac{5}{8}$	$6\frac{19}{32}$
$\frac{9}{16}$	$\frac{3}{8}$	$\frac{11}{16}$	$1\frac{1}{32}$	$1\frac{7}{8}$	$1\frac{11}{16}$	$3\frac{1}{16}$	$2\frac{11}{32}$	$4\frac{9}{32}$	$3\frac{1}{32}$	$5\frac{15}{32}$	$3\frac{11}{16}$	$6\frac{21}{32}$
$\frac{5}{8}$	$\frac{13}{32}$	$\frac{3}{4}$	$1\frac{1}{16}$	$1\frac{15}{16}$	$1\frac{3}{4}$	$3\frac{5}{32}$	$2\frac{13}{32}$	$4\frac{11}{32}$	$3\frac{1}{16}$	$5\frac{17}{32}$	$3\frac{23}{32}$	$6\frac{3}{4}$
$\frac{11}{16}$	$\frac{15}{32}$	$\frac{13}{16}$	$1\frac{1}{8}$	$2\frac{1}{32}$	$1\frac{25}{32}$	$3\frac{7}{32}$	$2\frac{7}{16}$	$4\frac{13}{32}$	$3\frac{3}{32}$	$5\frac{5}{8}$	$3\frac{3}{4}$	$6\frac{13}{16}$
$\frac{3}{4}$	$\frac{1}{2}$	$\frac{29}{32}$	$1\frac{5}{32}$	$2\frac{3}{32}$	$1\frac{13}{16}$	$3\frac{5}{16}$	$2\frac{15}{32}$	$4\frac{1}{2}$	$3\frac{5}{32}$	$5\frac{11}{16}$	$3\frac{13}{16}$	$6\frac{29}{32}$
$\frac{13}{16}$	$\frac{17}{32}$	$\frac{31}{32}$	$1\frac{3}{16}$	$2\frac{3}{16}$	$1\frac{7}{8}$	$3\frac{3}{8}$	$2\frac{17}{32}$	$4\frac{9}{16}$	$3\frac{3}{16}$	$5\frac{25}{32}$	$3\frac{27}{32}$	$6\frac{31}{32}$
$\frac{7}{8}$	$\frac{19}{32}$	$1\frac{1}{16}$	$1\frac{1}{4}$	$2\frac{1}{4}$	$1\frac{29}{32}$	$3\frac{7}{16}$	$2\frac{9}{16}$	$4\frac{21}{32}$	$3\frac{7}{32}$	$5\frac{27}{32}$	$3\frac{7}{8}$	$7\frac{1}{32}$
$\frac{15}{16}$	$\frac{5}{8}$	$1\frac{1}{8}$	$1\frac{9}{32}$	$2\frac{5}{16}$	$1\frac{15}{16}$	$3\frac{17}{32}$	$2\frac{19}{32}$	$4\frac{23}{32}$	$3\frac{9}{32}$	$5\frac{29}{32}$	$3\frac{15}{16}$	$7\frac{1}{8}$

Inches	6" Rise	6" Slope	7" Rise	7" Slope	8" Rise	8" Slope	9" Rise	9" Slope	10" Rise	10" Slope	11" Rise	11" Slope
0	$3\frac{31}{32}$	$7\frac{3}{8}$	$4\frac{5}{8}$	$8\frac{13}{32}$	$5\frac{9}{32}$	$9\frac{19}{32}$	$5\frac{15}{16}$	$10\frac{25}{32}$	$6\frac{5}{8}$	1-0	$7\frac{9}{32}$	$1\text{-}1\frac{3}{16}$
$\frac{1}{16}$	4	$7\frac{9}{32}$	$4\frac{21}{32}$	$8\frac{15}{32}$	$5\frac{11}{32}$	$9\frac{21}{32}$	6	$10\frac{7}{8}$	$6\frac{21}{32}$	$1\text{-}0\frac{1}{16}$	$7\frac{5}{16}$	$1\text{-}1\frac{1}{4}$
$\frac{1}{8}$	$4\frac{1}{16}$	$7\frac{11}{32}$	$4\frac{23}{32}$	$8\frac{17}{32}$	$5\frac{3}{8}$	$9\frac{3}{4}$	$6\frac{1}{16}$	$10\frac{15}{16}$	$6\frac{11}{16}$	$1\text{-}0\frac{1}{8}$	$7\frac{11}{32}$	$1\text{-}1\frac{11}{32}$
$\frac{3}{16}$	$4\frac{3}{32}$	$7\frac{13}{32}$	$4\frac{3}{4}$	$8\frac{5}{8}$	$5\frac{13}{32}$	$9\frac{13}{16}$	$6\frac{1}{16}$	11	$6\frac{3}{4}$	$1\text{-}0\frac{7}{32}$	$7\frac{13}{32}$	$1\text{-}1\frac{13}{32}$
$\frac{1}{4}$	$4\frac{1}{8}$	$7\frac{1}{2}$	$4\frac{25}{32}$	$8\frac{11}{16}$	$5\frac{15}{32}$	$9\frac{29}{32}$	$6\frac{1}{8}$	$11\frac{3}{32}$	$6\frac{25}{32}$	$1\text{-}0\frac{9}{32}$	$7\frac{7}{16}$	$1\text{-}1\frac{1}{2}$
$\frac{5}{16}$	$4\frac{3}{16}$	$7\frac{9}{16}$	$4\frac{27}{32}$	$8\frac{25}{32}$	$5\frac{1}{2}$	$9\frac{31}{32}$	$6\frac{5}{32}$	$11\frac{5}{32}$	$6\frac{13}{16}$	$1\text{-}0\frac{3}{8}$	$7\frac{15}{32}$	$1\text{-}1\frac{9}{16}$
$\frac{3}{8}$	$4\frac{7}{32}$	$7\frac{21}{32}$	$4\frac{7}{8}$	$8\frac{27}{32}$	$5\frac{17}{32}$	$10\frac{1}{32}$	$6\frac{3}{16}$	$11\frac{1}{4}$	$6\frac{7}{8}$	$1\text{-}0\frac{7}{16}$	$7\frac{17}{32}$	$1\text{-}1\frac{5}{8}$
$\frac{7}{16}$	$4\frac{1}{4}$	$7\frac{23}{32}$	$4\frac{29}{32}$	$8\frac{29}{32}$	$5\frac{19}{32}$	$10\frac{1}{8}$	$6\frac{1}{4}$	$11\frac{5}{16}$	$6\frac{29}{32}$	$1\text{-}0\frac{1}{2}$	$7\frac{9}{16}$	$1\text{-}1\frac{23}{32}$
$\frac{1}{2}$	$4\frac{5}{16}$	$7\frac{25}{32}$	$4\frac{31}{32}$	9	$5\frac{5}{8}$	$10\frac{3}{16}$	$6\frac{9}{32}$	$11\frac{3}{8}$	$6\frac{15}{16}$	$1\text{-}0\frac{19}{32}$	$7\frac{19}{32}$	$1\text{-}1\frac{25}{32}$
$\frac{9}{16}$	$4\frac{11}{32}$	$7\frac{7}{8}$	5	$9\frac{1}{16}$	$5\frac{21}{32}$	$10\frac{9}{32}$	$6\frac{5}{16}$	$11\frac{15}{32}$	7	$1\text{-}0\frac{21}{32}$	$7\frac{21}{32}$	$1\text{-}1\frac{7}{8}$
$\frac{5}{8}$	$4\frac{3}{8}$	$7\frac{15}{16}$	$5\frac{1}{32}$	$9\frac{5}{32}$	$5\frac{23}{32}$	$10\frac{11}{32}$	$6\frac{3}{8}$	$11\frac{17}{32}$	$7\frac{1}{2}$	$1\text{-}0\frac{3}{4}$	$7\frac{11}{16}$	$1\text{-}1\frac{15}{16}$
$\frac{11}{16}$	$4\frac{7}{16}$	$8\frac{1}{32}$	$5\frac{3}{32}$	$9\frac{7}{32}$	$5\frac{3}{4}$	$10\frac{13}{32}$	$6\frac{13}{32}$	$11\frac{5}{8}$	$7\frac{1}{16}$	$1\text{-}0\frac{13}{32}$	$7\frac{23}{32}$	1-2
$\frac{3}{4}$	$4\frac{15}{32}$	$8\frac{3}{32}$	$5\frac{1}{8}$	$9\frac{9}{32}$	$5\frac{25}{32}$	$10\frac{1}{2}$	$6\frac{7}{16}$	$11\frac{11}{16}$	$7\frac{1}{8}$	$1\text{-}0\frac{7}{8}$	$7\frac{25}{32}$	$1\text{-}2\frac{3}{32}$
$\frac{13}{16}$	$4\frac{1}{2}$	$8\frac{5}{32}$	$5\frac{5}{32}$	$9\frac{3}{8}$	$5\frac{27}{32}$	$10\frac{9}{16}$	$6\frac{1}{2}$	$11\frac{3}{4}$	$7\frac{5}{32}$	$1\text{-}0\frac{31}{32}$	$7\frac{13}{16}$	$1\text{-}2\frac{5}{32}$
$\frac{7}{8}$	$4\frac{9}{16}$	$8\frac{1}{4}$	$5\frac{7}{32}$	$9\frac{7}{16}$	$5\frac{7}{8}$	$10\frac{21}{32}$	$6\frac{17}{32}$	$11\frac{27}{32}$	$7\frac{3}{16}$	$1\text{-}1\frac{1}{32}$	$7\frac{27}{32}$	$1\text{-}2\frac{1}{4}$
$\frac{15}{16}$	$4\frac{19}{32}$	$8\frac{5}{16}$	$5\frac{1}{4}$	$9\frac{17}{32}$	$5\frac{29}{32}$	$10\frac{23}{32}$	$6\frac{9}{16}$	$11\frac{29}{32}$	$7\frac{1}{4}$	$1\text{-}1\frac{1}{8}$	$7\frac{29}{32}$	$1\text{-}2\frac{5}{16}$

Feet	0' Rise	0' Slope	10' Rise	10' Slope	20' Rise	20' Slope	30' Rise	30' Slope
0	0	0	$6\text{-}7\frac{3}{8}$	$11\text{-}11\frac{7}{8}$	$13\text{-}2\frac{3}{4}$	$23\text{-}11\frac{3}{4}$	$19\text{-}10\frac{1}{4}$	$35\text{-}11\frac{5}{8}$
1	$7\frac{15}{16}$	$1\text{-}2\frac{3}{8}$	$7\text{-}3\frac{5}{8}$	$13\text{-}2\frac{1}{4}$	$13\text{-}10\frac{11}{16}$	$25\text{-}2\frac{1}{8}$	$20\text{-}6\frac{1}{4}$	$37\text{-}2\frac{3}{32}$
2	$1\text{-}3\frac{7}{8}$	$2\text{-}4\frac{25}{32}$	$7\text{-}11\frac{1}{4}$	$14\text{-}4\frac{21}{32}$	$14\text{-}6\frac{5}{8}$	$26\text{-}4\frac{17}{32}$	21-2	$38\text{-}4\frac{13}{32}$
3	$1\text{-}11\frac{13}{16}$	$3\text{-}7\frac{5}{32}$	$8\text{-}7\frac{3}{16}$	$15\text{-}7\frac{1}{32}$	$15\text{-}2\frac{9}{16}$	$27\text{-}6\frac{29}{32}$	$21\text{-}9\frac{15}{16}$	$39\text{-}6\frac{25}{32}$
4	$2\text{-}7\frac{3}{4}$	$4\text{-}9\frac{9}{16}$	$9\text{-}3\frac{1}{8}$	$16\text{-}9\frac{7}{16}$	$15\text{-}10\frac{1}{2}$	$28\text{-}9\frac{5}{16}$	$22\text{-}5\frac{7}{8}$	$40\text{-}9\frac{3}{16}$
5	$3\text{-}3\frac{11}{16}$	$5\text{-}11\frac{15}{16}$	$9\text{-}11\frac{1}{16}$	$17\text{-}11\frac{13}{16}$	$16\text{-}6\frac{7}{16}$	$29\text{-}11\frac{11}{16}$	$23\text{-}1\frac{13}{16}$	$41\text{-}11\frac{9}{16}$
6	$3\text{-}11\frac{5}{8}$	$7\text{-}2\frac{5}{16}$	10-7	$19\text{-}2\frac{3}{16}$	$17\text{-}2\frac{3}{8}$	$31\text{-}2\frac{3}{32}$	$23\text{-}9\frac{3}{4}$	$43\text{-}1\frac{31}{32}$
7	$4\text{-}7\frac{9}{16}$	$8\text{-}4\frac{23}{32}$	$11\text{-}2\frac{15}{16}$	$20\text{-}4\frac{19}{32}$	$17\text{-}10\frac{5}{16}$	$32\text{-}4\frac{15}{32}$	$24\text{-}5\frac{11}{16}$	$44\text{-}4\frac{11}{32}$
8	$5\text{-}3\frac{1}{2}$	$9\text{-}7\frac{3}{32}$	$11\text{-}10\frac{7}{8}$	$21\text{-}6\frac{31}{32}$	$18\text{-}6\frac{1}{4}$	$33\text{-}6\frac{27}{32}$	$25\text{-}1\frac{5}{8}$	$45\text{-}6\frac{23}{32}$
9	$5\text{-}11\frac{7}{16}$	$10\text{-}9\frac{1}{2}$	$12\text{-}6\frac{13}{16}$	$22\text{-}9\frac{3}{8}$	$19\text{-}2\frac{3}{16}$	$34\text{-}9\frac{1}{4}$	$25\text{-}9\frac{9}{16}$	$46\text{-}9\frac{1}{8}$

A = 33° 28′ 59″; logsin A = 9.74169; logcos A = 9.92119; logtan A = 9.82050; logcot A = 0.17950

Ins.	12″ Rise	12″ Slope	13″ Rise	13″ Slope	14″ Rise	14″ Slope	15″ Rise	15″ Slope	16″ Rise	16″ Slope
0	7 15/16	1-2 3/8	8 19/32	1-3 19/32–	9 1/4	1-4 25/32	9 15/16	1-6	10 19/32–	1-7 3/16
1/16	7 31/32	1-2 15/32–	8 5/8	1-3 21/32	9 5/16	1-4 7/8	9 31/32–	1-6 1/16	10 5/8	1-7 1/4
1/8	8 1/32–	1-2 17/32	8 11/16	1-3 3/4	9 11/32–	1-4 15/16	10	1-6 1/8	10 21/32	1-7 11/32–
3/16	8 1/16	1-2 5/8	8 23/32	1-3 13/16	9 3/8	1-5	10 1/32	1-6 7/32–	10 23/32–	1-7 13/32
1/4	8 3/32	1-2 11/16	8 3/4	1-3 7/8	9 7/16	1-5 3/32–	10 3/32–	1-6 9/32	10 3/4	1-7 15/32
5/16	8 5/32–	1-2 3/4	8 13/16	1-3 31/32–	9 15/32–	1-5 5/32	10 1/8	1-6 11/32	10 25/32	1-7 9/16
3/8	8 3/16	1-2 27/32–	8 27/32	1-4 1/32	9 1/2	1-5 1/4	10 5/32	1-6 7/16	10 27/32–	1-7 5/8
7/16	8 7/32	1-2 29/32	8 7/8	1-4 1/8	9 9/16	1-5 5/16	10 7/32–	1-6 1/2	10 7/8	1-7 23/32–
1/2	8 9/32–	1-3	8 15/16	1-4 3/16	9 19/32–	1-5 3/8	10 1/4	1-6 19/32–	10 29/32	1-7 25/32
9/16	8 5/16	1-3 1/16	8 31/32	1-4 1/4	9 5/8	1-5 15/32–	10 9/32	1-6 21/32	10 31/32–	1-7 27/32
5/8	8 11/32	1-3 1/8	9	1-4 11/32–	9 11/16	1-5 17/32	10 11/32–	1-6 23/32	11	1-7 15/16
11/16	8 13/32–	1-3 7/32–	9 1/16	1-4 13/32	9 23/32–	1-5 5/8	10 3/8	1-6 13/16	11 1/32	1-8
3/4	8 7/16	1-3 9/32	9 3/32	1-4 1/2	9 3/4	1-5 11/16	10 13/32	1-6 7/8	11 3/32–	1-8 3/32–
13/16	8 15/32	1-3 3/8	9 1/8	1-4 9/16	9 13/16	1-5 3/4	10 15/32–	1-6 31/32–	11 1/8	1-8 5/32
7/8	8 17/32–	1-3 7/16	9 3/16	1-4 5/8	9 27/32–	1-5 27/32–	10 1/2	1-7 1/32	11 5/32	1-8 7/32
15/16	8 9/16	1-3 1/2	9 7/32	1-4 23/32–	9 7/8	1-5 29/32	10 17/32	1-7 3/32	11 7/32–	1-8 5/16

Ins.	17″ Rise	17″ Slope	18″ Rise	18″ Slope	19″ Rise	19″ Slope	20″ Rise	20″ Slope	21″ Rise	21″ Slope
0	11 1/4	1-8 3/8	11 29/32	1-9 19/32–	1-0 9/16	1-10 25/32–	1-1 7/32	1-11 31/32	1-1 7/8	2-1 3/16
1/16	11 9/32	1-8 15/32–	11 15/16	1-9 21/32	1-0 19/32	1-10 27/32	1-1 9/32–	2-0 1/16	1-1 15/16	2-1 1/4
1/8	11 5/16	1-8 17/32	1-0	1-9 23/32	1-0 21/32–	1-10 15/16	1-1 5/16	2-0 1/8	1-1 31/32	2-1 11/32–
3/16	11 3/8	1-8 19/32	1-0 1/32–	1-9 13/16	1-0 11/16	1-11	1-1 11/32	2-0 7/32–	1-2	2-1 13/32–
1/4	11 13/32	1-8 11/16	1-0 1/16	1-9 7/8	1-0 23/32	1-11 3/32–	1-1 13/32–	2-0 9/32–	1-2 1/16	2-1 15/32
5/16	11 7/16	1-8 3/4	1-0 1/8	1-9 31/32–	1-0 25/32–	1-11 5/32–	1-1 7/16	2-0 11/32	1-2 3/32	2-1 9/16
3/8	11 1/2	1-8 27/32–	1-0 5/32–	1-10 1/32–	1-0 13/16	1-11 7/32	1-1 15/32	2-0 7/16	1-2 1/8	2-1 5/8
7/16	11 17/32	1-8 29/32	1-0 3/16	1-10 3/32	1-0 27/32	1-11 5/16	1-1 17/32–	2-0 1/2	1-2 3/16	2-1 11/16
1/2	11 9/16	1-8 31/32	1-0 1/4	1-10 3/16	1-0 29/32–	1-11 3/8	1-1 9/16	2-0 19/32–	1-2 7/32	2-1 25/32–
9/16	11 5/8	1-9 1/16	1-0 9/32–	1-10 1/4	1-0 15/16	1-11 15/32–	1-1 19/32	2-0 21/32–	1-2 1/4	2-1 27/32
5/8	11 21/32	1-9 1/8	1-0 5/16	1-10 11/32–	1-0 31/32	1-11 17/32–	1-1 21/32–	2-0 23/32	1-2 5/16	2-1 15/16
11/16	11 11/16	1-9 7/32–	1-0 3/8	1-10 13/32–	1-1 1/32–	1-11 19/32	1-1 11/16	2-0 13/16	1-2 11/32	2-2
3/4	11 3/4	1-9 9/32	1-0 13/32–	1-10 15/32	1-1 1/16	1-11 11/16	1-1 23/32	2-0 7/8	1-2 3/8	2-2 1/16
13/16	11 25/32	1-9 11/32	1-0 7/16	1-10 9/16	1-1 3/32	1-11 3/4	1-1 25/32–	2-0 31/32–	1-2 7/16	2-2 5/32–
7/8	11 13/16	1-9 7/16	1-0 1/2	1-10 5/8	1-1 5/32–	1-11 27/32–	1-1 13/16	2-1 1/32–	1-2 15/32	2-2 7/32
15/16	11 7/8	1-9 1/2	1-0 17/32–	1-10 23/32–	1-1 3/16	1-11 29/32–	1-1 27/32	2-1 3/32	1-2 1/2	2-2 5/16

Feet	40′ Rise	40′ Slope	50′ Rise	50′ Slope	60′ Rise	60′ Slope	70′ Rise	70′ Slope
0	26-5 1/2	47-11 1/2	33-0 7/8	59-11 3/8	39-8 1/4	71-11 1/4	46-3 5/8	83-11 1/8
1	27-1 7/16	49-1 29/32–	33-8 13/16	61-1 25/32–	40-4 3/16	73-1 21/32–	46-11 9/16	85-1 17/32–
2	27-9 3/8	50-4 9/32–	34-4 3/4	62-4 5/32	41-0 1/8	74-4 1/32	47-7 1/2	86-3 29/32
3	28-5 5/16	51-6 21/32	35-0 11/16	63-6 17/32	41-8 1/16	75-6 13/32	48-3 7/16	87-6 5/16
4	29-1 1/4	52-9 1/16	35-8 5/8	64-8 15/16	42-4	76-8 13/16	48-11 3/8	88-8 11/16
5	29-9 3/16	53-11 7/16	36-4 9/16	65-11 5/16	42-11 15/16	77-11 3/16	49-7 5/16	89-11 1/16
6	30-5 1/8	55-1 27/32–	37-0 1/2	67-1 23/32–	43-7 7/8	79-1 19/32–	50-3 1/4	91-1 15/32–
7	31-1 1/16	56-4 7/32–	37-8 7/16	68-4 3/32	44-3 13/16	80-3 31/32	50-11 3/16	92-3 27/32
8	31-9	57-6 19/32	38-4 3/8	69-6 15/32	44-11 3/4	81-6 11/32	51-7 1/8	93-6 1/4
9	32-4 15/16	58-9	39-0 5/16	70-8 7/8	45-7 11/16	82-8 3/4	52-3 1/16	94-8 5/8

natsin A=0.5516891817: natcos A=0.8340497866; nattan A=0.6614583333; natcot A=1.5118110236

Inches	0" Rise	Slope	1" Rise	Slope	2" Rise	Slope	3" Rise	Slope	4" Rise	Slope	5" Rise	Slope
0	0	0	21/32	1 3/16	1 11/32	2 13/32	2	3 19/32	2 21/32	4 13/16	3 11/32	6
1/16	1/32	1/16	23/32	1 9/32	1 3/8	2 15/32	2 1/32	3 11/16	2 23/32	4 7/8	3 3/8	6 3/32
1/8	3/32	5/32	3/4	1 11/32	1 13/32	2 9/16	2 3/32	3 3/4	2 3/4	4 31/32	3 13/32	6 5/32
3/16	1/8	7/32	25/32	1 7/16	1 15/32	2 5/8	2 1/8	3 27/32	2 25/32	5 1/32	3 15/32	6 1/4
1/4	5/32	5/16	27/32	1 1/2	1 1/2	2 23/32	2 5/32	3 29/32	2 27/32	5 3/32	3 1/2	6 5/16
5/16	7/32	3/8	7/8	1 9/16	1 17/32	2 25/32	2 7/32	3 31/32	2 7/8	5 3/16	3 17/32	6 3/8
3/8	1/4	7/16	29/32	1 21/32	1 19/32	2 27/32	2 1/4	4 1/16	2 29/32	5 1/4	3 19/32	6 15/32
7/16	9/32	17/32	31/32	1 23/32	1 5/8	2 15/16	2 9/32	4 1/8	2 31/32	5 11/32	3 5/8	6 17/32
1/2	11/32	19/32	1	1 13/16	1 21/32	3	2 11/32	4 7/32	3	5 13/32	3 21/32	6 5/8
9/16	3/8	11/16	1 1/32	1 7/8	1 23/32	3 3/32	2 3/8	4 9/32	3 1/32	5 15/32	3 23/32	6 11/16
5/8	13/32	3/4	1 3/32	1 15/16	1 3/4	3 5/32	2 13/32	4 11/32	3 3/32	5 9/16	3 3/4	6 3/4
11/16	15/32	15/16	1 1/8	2 1/32	1 25/32	3 7/32	2 15/32	4 7/16	3 1/8	5 5/8	3 25/32	6 27/32
3/4	1/2	29/32	1 5/32	2 3/32	1 27/32	3 5/16	2 1/2	4 1/2	3 5/32	5 23/32	3 27/32	6 29/32
13/16	17/32	31/32	1 7/32	2 3/16	1 7/8	3 3/8	2 17/32	4 19/32	3 7/32	5 25/32	3 7/8	7
7/8	19/32	1 1/16	1 1/4	2 1/4	1 29/32	3 15/32	2 19/32	4 21/32	3 1/4	5 27/32	3 29/32	7 1/16
15/16	5/8	1 1/8	1 9/32	2 11/32	1 31/32	3 17/32	2 5/8	4 23/32	3 9/32	5 15/16	3 31/32	7 1/8

Inches	6" Rise	Slope	7" Rise	Slope	8" Rise	Slope	9" Rise	Slope	10" Rise	Slope	11" Rise	Slope
0	4	7 7/32	4 21/32	8 13/32	5 11/32	9 5/8	6	10 13/16	6 23/32	1-0 1/32	7 11/32	1-1 7/32
1/16	4 1/32	7 9/32	4 23/32	8 1/2	5 3/8	9 11/16	6 1/32	10 29/32	6 23/32	1-0 3/32	7 3/8	1-1 9/32
1/8	4 3/32	7 3/8	4 3/4	8 9/16	5 13/32	9 3/4	6 3/32	10 31/32	6 3/4	1-0 5/32	7 13/32	1-1 3/8
3/16	4 1/8	7 7/16	4 25/32	8 5/8	5 15/32	9 27/32	6 1/8	11 1/32	6 25/32	1-0 1/4	7 15/32	1-1 7/16
1/4	4 5/32	7 1/2	4 27/32	8 23/32	5 1/2	9 29/32	6 5/32	11 1/8	6 27/32	1-0 5/16	7 1/2	1-1 17/32
5/16	4 7/32	7 19/32	4 7/8	8 25/32	5 17/32	10	6 7/32	11 3/16	6 7/8	1-0 13/32	7 17/32	1-1 19/32
3/8	4 1/4	7 21/32	4 29/32	8 7/8	5 19/32	10 1/16	6 1/4	11 9/32	6 29/32	1-0 15/32	7 19/32	1-1 21/32
7/16	4 9/32	7 3/4	4 31/32	8 15/16	5 5/8	10 1/8	6 9/32	11 11/32	6 31/32	1-0 17/32	7 5/8	1-1 3/4
1/2	4 11/32	7 13/16	5	9	5 21/32	10 7/32	6 11/32	11 13/32	7	1-0 5/8	7 21/32	1-1 13/16
9/16	4 3/8	7 7/8	5 1/32	9 3/32	5 23/32	10 9/32	6 3/8	11 1/2	7 1/32	1-0 11/16	7 23/32	1-1 29/32
5/8	4 13/32	7 31/32	5 3/32	9 5/32	5 3/4	10 3/8	6 13/32	11 9/16	7 3/32	1-0 25/32	7 3/4	1-1 31/32
11/16	4 15/32	8 1/32	5 1/8	9 1/4	5 25/32	10 7/16	6 15/32	11 21/32	7 1/8	1-0 27/32	7 25/32	1-2 1/32
3/4	4 1/2	8 1/8	5 5/32	9 5/16	5 27/32	10 17/32	6 1/2	11 23/32	7 5/32	1-0 29/32	7 27/32	1-2 1/8
13/16	4 17/32	8 3/16	5 7/32	9 3/8	5 7/8	10 19/32	6 17/32	11 25/32	7 7/32	1-1	7 7/8	1-2 3/16
7/8	4 19/32	8 1/4	5 1/4	9 15/32	5 29/32	10 21/32	6 19/32	11 7/8	7 1/4	1-1 1/16	7 29/32	1-2 9/32
15/16	4 5/8	8 11/32	5 9/32	9 17/32	5 31/32	10 3/4	6 5/8	11 15/16	7 9/32	1-1 5/32	7 31/32	1-2 11/32

Feet	0' Rise	Slope	10' Rise	Slope	20' Rise	Slope	30' Rise	Slope
0	0	0	6-8	12-0 1/32	13-4	24-0 1/16	20-0	36-0 21/32
1	8	1-2 1/16	7-4	13-2 21/32	14-0	25-2 7/8	20-8	37-3 3/32
2	1-4	2-4 27/32	8-0	14-5 1/16	14-8	26-5 9/32	21-4	38-5 1/2
3	2-0	3-7 9/32	8-8	15-7 1/2	15-4	27-7 23/32	22-0	39-7 15/16
4	2-8	4-9 11/16	9-4	16-9 29/32	16-0	28-10 1/8	22-8	40-10 11/32
5	3-4	6-0 1/8	10-0	18-0 11/32	16-8	30-0 9/16	23-4	42-0 25/32
6	4-0	7-2 17/32	10-8	19-2 3/4	17-4	31-2 31/32	24-0	43-3 3/16
7	4-8	8-4 31/32	11-4	20-5 3/16	18-0	32-5 13/32	24-8	44-5 5/8
8	5-4	9-7 3/8	12-0	21-7 19/32	18-8	33-7 13/16	25-4	45-8 1/32
9	6-0	10-9 13/16	12-8	22-10 1/32	19-4	34-10 1/4	26-0	46-10 15/32

See page 129b (located page 219) for angle and trigonometric functions.

Ins.	12″ Rise	Slope	13″ Rise	Slope	14″ Rise	Slope	15″ Rise	Slope	16″ Rise	Slope
0	8	1-2 7/16	8 21/32	1-3 5/8	9 11/32	1-4 13/16	10	1-6 1/32	10 21/32	1-7 7/32
1/16	8 1/32	1-2 1/2	8 23/32	1-3 11/16	9 3/8	1-4 29/32	10 1/32	1-6 3/32	10 23/32	1-7 5/16
1/8	8 3/32	1-2 9/16	8 3/4	1-3 25/32	9 13/32	1-4 31/32	10 3/32	1-6 3/16	10 3/4	1-7 3/8
3/16	8 1/8	1-2 21/32	8 25/32	1-3 27/32	9 15/32	1-5 1/16	10 1/8	1-6 1/4	10 25/32	1-7 15/32
1/4	8 5/32	1-2 23/32	8 27/32	1-3 15/16	9 1/2	1-5 1/8	10 5/32	1-6 11/32	10 27/32	1-7 17/32
5/16	8 7/32	1-2 13/16	8 7/8	1-4	9 17/32	1-5 3/16	10 7/32	1-6 13/32	10 7/8	1-7 19/32
3/8	8 1/4	1-2 7/8	8 29/32	1-4 1/16	9 19/32	1-5 9/32	10 1/4	1-6 15/32	10 29/32	1-7 11/16
7/16	8 9/32	1-2 15/16	8 31/32	1-4 5/32	9 5/8	1-5 11/32	10 9/32	1-6 9/16	10 31/32	1-7 3/4
1/2	8 11/32	1-3 1/32	9	1-4 7/32	9 21/32	1-5 7/16	10 11/32	1-6 5/8	11	1-7 27/32
9/16	8 3/8	1-3 3/32	9 1/16	1-4 5/16	9 23/32	1-5 1/2	10 3/8	1-6 23/32	11 1/16	1-7 29/32
5/8	8 13/32	1-3 3/16	9 3/32	1-4 3/8	9 3/4	1-5 9/16	10 13/32	1-6 25/32	11 3/32	1-7 31/32
11/16	8 15/32	1-3 1/4	9 1/8	1-4 7/16	9 25/32	1-5 21/32	10 15/32	1-6 27/32	11 1/8	1-8 1/16
3/4	8 1/2	1-3 5/16	9 5/32	1-4 17/32	9 27/32	1-5 23/32	10 1/2	1-6 15/16	11 5/32	1-8 1/8
13/16	8 17/32	1-3 13/32	9 7/32	1-4 19/32	9 7/8	1-5 13/16	10 17/32	1-7	11 7/32	1-8 7/32
7/8	8 19/32	1-3 15/32	9 1/4	1-4 11/16	9 29/32	1-5 7/8	10 19/32	1-7 3/32	11 1/4	1-8 9/32
15/16	8 5/8	1-3 9/16	9 9/32	1-4 3/4	9 31/32	1-5 15/16	10 5/8	1-7 5/32	11 9/32	1-8 11/32

Ins.	17″ Rise	Slope	18″ Rise	Slope	19″ Rise	Slope	20″ Rise	Slope	21″ Rise	Slope
0	11 11/32	1-8 7/16	1-0	1-9 5/8	1-0 21/32	1-10 27/32	1-1 11/32	2-0 1/32	1-2	2-1 1/4
1/16	11 3/8	1-8 1/2	1-0 1/32	1-9 23/32	1-0 23/32	1-10 29/32	1-1 3/8	2-0 1/8	1-2 1/32	2-1 5/16
1/8	11 13/32	1-8 19/32	1-0 3/32	1-9 25/32	1-0 3/4	1-11	1-1 13/32	2-0 3/16	1-2 3/32	2-1 3/8
3/16	11 15/32	1-8 21/32	1-0 1/8	1-9 27/32	1-0 25/32	1-11 1/16	1-1 15/32	2-0 1/4	1-2 1/8	2-1 15/32
1/4	11 1/2	1-8 23/32	1-0 5/32	1-9 15/16	1-0 27/32	1-11 1/8	1-1 1/2	2-0 11/32	1-2 5/32	2-1 17/32
5/16	11 17/32	1-8 13/16	1-0 7/32	1-10	1-0 7/8	1-11 7/32	1-1 17/32	2-0 13/32	1-2 7/32	2-1 5/8
3/8	11 19/32	1-8 7/8	1-0 1/4	1-10 3/32	1-0 29/32	1-11 9/32	1-1 19/32	2-0 1/2	1-2 1/4	2-1 11/32
7/16	11 5/8	1-8 31/32	1-0 9/32	1-10 5/32	1-0 31/32	1-11 3/8	1-1 5/8	2-0 9/16	1-2 9/32	2-1 3/4
1/2	11 21/32	1-9 1/32	1-0 11/32	1-10 7/32	1-1	1-11 7/16	1-1 21/32	2-0 5/8	1-2 11/32	2-1 27/32
9/16	11 23/32	1-9 3/32	1-0 3/8	1-10 5/16	1-1 1/32	1-11 1/2	1-1 23/32	2-0 23/32	1-2 3/8	2-1 29/32
5/8	11 3/4	1-9 3/16	1-0 13/32	1-10 3/8	1-1 3/32	1-11 19/32	1-1 3/4	2-0 25/32	1-2 13/32	2-2
11/16	11 25/32	1-9 1/4	1-0 15/32	1-10 15/32	1-1 1/8	1-11 21/32	1-1 25/32	2-0 7/8	1-2 15/32	2-2 1/16
3/4	11 27/32	1-9 11/32	1-0 1/2	1-10 17/32	1-1 5/32	1-11 3/4	1-1 27/32	2-0 15/16	1-2 1/2	2-2 1/8
13/16	11 7/8	1-9 13/32	1-0 17/32	1-10 5/8	1-1 7/32	1-11 13/16	1-1 7/8	2-1	1-2 17/32	2-2 7/32
7/8	11 29/32	1-9 15/32	1-0 19/32	1-10 11/16	1-1 1/4	1-11 7/8	1-1 29/32	2-1 3/32	1-2 19/32	2-2 9/32
15/16	11 31/32	1-9 9/16	1-0 5/8	1-10 3/4	1-1 9/32	1-11 31/32	1-1 31/32	2-1 5/32	1-2 5/8	2-2 3/8

Feet	40′ Rise	Slope	50′ Rise	Slope	60′ Rise	Slope	70′ Rise	Slope
0	26-8	48-0 7/8	33-4	60-1 1/8	40-0	72-1 11/32	46-8	84-1 9/16
1	27-4	49-3 5/16	34-0	61-3 17/32	40-8	73-3 3/4	47-4	85-3 31/32
2	28-0	50-5 23/32	34-8	62-5 31/32	41-4	74-6 3/16	48-0	86-6 13/32
3	28-8	51-8 5/32	35-4	63-8 3/8	42-0	75-8 19/32	48-8	87-8 13/16
4	29-4	52-10 9/16	36-0	64-10 13/16	42-8	76-11 1/32	49-4	88-11 1/4
5	30-0	54-1	36-8	66-1 7/32	43-4	78-1 7/16	50-0	90-1 21/32
6	30-8	55-3 13/32	37-4	67-3 21/32	44-0	79-3 7/8	50-8	91-4 3/32
7	31-4	56-5 27/32	38-0	68-6 1/16	44-8	80-6 9/32	51-4	92-6 1/2
8	32-0	57-8 9/32	38-8	69-8 1/2	45-4	81-8 23/32	52-0	93-8 15/16
9	32-8	58-10 11/16	39-4	70-10 29/32	46-0	82-11 1/8	52-8	94-11 11/32

natsin A=0.5547001962; natcos A=0.8320502944; nattan A=0.6666666666; natcot A=1.5000000000
See page 129b (located page 219) for angle and trigonometric functions.

Inches	0" Rise	0" Slope	1" Rise	1" Slope	2" Rise	2" Slope	3" Rise	3" Slope	4" Rise	4" Slope	5" Rise	5" Slope
0	0	0	11/16	1 7/32	1 11/32	2 13/32	2	3 5/8	2 11/16	4 13/16	3 3/8	6 1/32
1/16	1/32	1/16	23/32	1 9/32	1 3/8	2 1/2	2 1/16	3 11/16	2 23/32	4 29/32	3 13/32	6 3/32
1/8	3/32	5/32	3/4	1 11/32	1 7/16	2 9/16	2 3/32	3 3/4	2 25/32	4 31/32	3 7/16	6 3/16
3/16	1/8	7/32	13/16	1 7/16	1 15/32	2 5/8	2 5/32	3 27/32	2 13/16	5 1/32	3 1/2	6 1/4
1/4	5/32	5/16	27/32	1 1/2	1 1/2	2 23/32	2 3/16	3 29/32	2 27/32	5 1/8	3 17/32	6 5/16
5/16	7/32	3/8	7/8	1 19/32	1 9/16	2 25/32	2 7/32	4	2 29/32	5 3/16	3 9/16	6 13/32
3/8	1/4	7/16	15/16	1 21/32	1 19/32	2 7/8	2 9/32	4 1/16	2 15/16	5 9/32	3 5/8	6 15/32
7/16	9/32	17/32	31/32	1 23/32	1 21/32	2 15/16	2 5/16	4 5/32	2 31/32	5 11/32	3 21/32	6 9/16
1/2	11/32	19/32	1	1 13/16	1 11/16	3	2 11/32	4 7/32	3 1/32	5 13/32	3 11/16	6 5/8
9/16	3/8	11/16	1 1/16	1 7/8	1 23/32	3 3/32	2 13/32	4 9/32	3 1/16	5 1/2	3 3/4	6 11/16
5/8	13/32	3/4	1 3/32	1 31/32	1 3/4	3 5/32	2 7/16	4 3/8	3 3/32	5 9/16	3 25/32	6 25/32
11/16	15/32	27/32	1 1/8	2 1/32	1 13/16	3 1/4	2 15/32	4 7/16	3 5/32	5 21/32	3 13/16	6 27/32
3/4	1/2	29/32	1 3/16	2 3/32	1 27/32	3 5/16	2 17/32	4 17/32	3 3/16	5 23/32	3 7/8	6 15/16
13/16	17/32	31/32	1 7/32	2 3/16	1 7/8	3 3/8	2 9/16	4 19/32	3 7/32	5 13/16	3 29/32	7
7/8	19/32	1 1/16	1 1/4	2 1/4	1 15/16	3 15/32	2 19/32	4 21/32	3 9/32	5 7/8	3 15/16	7 1/16
15/16	5/8	1 1/8	1 5/16	2 11/32	1 31/32	3 17/32	2 21/32	4 3/4	3 5/16	5 15/16	4	7 5/32

Inches	6" Rise	6" Slope	7" Rise	7" Slope	8" Rise	8" Slope	9" Rise	9" Slope	10" Rise	10" Slope	11" Rise	11" Slope
0	4 1/32	7 7/32	4 11/16	8 7/16	5 3/8	9 5/8	6 1/16	10 27/32	6 23/32	1-0 1/16	7 3/8	1-1 1/4
1/16	4 1/16	7 5/16	4 3/4	8 1/2	5 13/32	9 23/32	6 3/32	10 29/32	6 3/4	1-0 1/8	7 7/16	1-1 5/16
1/8	4 1/8	7 3/8	4 25/32	8 19/32	5 15/32	9 25/32	6 1/8	11	6 13/16	1-0 3/16	7 15/32	1-1 13/32
3/16	4 5/32	7 15/32	4 27/32	8 21/32	5 1/2	9 7/8	6 3/16	11 1/16	6 27/32	1-0 9/32	7 17/32	1-1 15/32
1/4	4 3/16	7 17/32	4 7/8	8 23/32	5 17/32	9 15/16	6 7/32	11 5/32	6 7/8	1-0 11/32	7 9/16	1-1 9/16
5/16	4 1/4	7 19/32	4 29/32	8 13/16	5 19/32	10	6 1/4	11 7/32	6 15/16	1-0 7/16	7 19/32	1-1 5/8
3/8	4 9/32	7 11/16	4 31/32	8 7/8	5 5/8	10 3/32	6 5/16	11 9/32	6 31/32	1-0 1/2	7 21/32	1-1 23/32
7/16	4 5/16	7 3/4	5	8 31/32	5 21/32	10 5/32	6 11/32	11 3/8	7	1-0 9/16	7 11/16	1-1 25/32
1/2	4 3/8	7 27/32	5 1/32	9 1/32	5 23/32	10 1/4	6 3/8	11 7/16	7 1/16	1-0 21/32	7 23/32	1-1 27/32
9/16	4 13/32	7 29/32	5 3/32	9 3/32	5 3/4	10 5/16	6 7/16	11 17/32	7 3/32	1-0 23/32	7 25/32	1-1 15/16
5/8	4 7/16	7 31/32	5 1/8	9 3/16	5 25/32	10 13/32	6 15/32	11 19/32	7 1/8	1-0 13/16	7 13/16	1-2
11/16	4 1/2	8 1/16	5 5/32	9 1/4	5 27/32	10 15/32	6 1/2	11 21/32	7 3/16	1-0 7/8	7 27/32	1-2 3/32
3/4	4 17/32	8 1/8	5 7/32	9 11/32	5 7/8	10 17/32	6 9/16	11 3/4	7 7/32	1-0 15/16	7 29/32	1-2 5/32
13/16	4 9/16	8 7/32	5 1/4	9 13/32	5 29/32	10 5/8	6 19/32	11 13/16	7 1/4	1-1 1/32	7 15/16	1-2 7/32
7/8	4 5/8	8 9/32	5 9/32	9 15/32	5 31/32	10 11/16	6 5/8	11 29/32	7 5/16	1-1 3/32	7 31/32	1-2 5/16
15/16	4 21/32	8 11/32	5 11/32	9 9/16	6	10 25/32	6 11/16	11 31/32	7 11/32	1-1 3/16	8 1/32	1-2 3/8

Feet	0' Rise	0' Slope	10' Rise	10' Slope	20' Rise	20' Slope	30' Rise	30' Slope
0	0	0	6-8 5/8	12-0 9/16	13-5 1/4	24-1 1/8	20-1 7/8	36-1 23/32
1	8 1/16	1-2 15/32	7-4 11/16	13-3 1/32	14-1 5/16	25-3 19/32	20-9 15/16	37-4 5/32
2	1-4 1/8	2-4 29/32	8-0 3/4	14-5 15/32	14-9 3/8	26-6 1/16	21-6	38-6 5/8
3	2-0 3/16	3-7 3/8	8-8 13/16	15-7 15/16	15-5 7/16	27-8 1/2	22-2 1/16	39-9 3/32
4	2-8 1/4	4-9 13/16	9-4 7/8	16-10 13/32	16-1 1/2	28-10 31/32	22-10 1/8	40-11 17/32
5	3-4 5/16	6-0 9/32	10-0 15/16	18-0 27/32	16-9 9/16	30-1 7/16	23-6 3/16	42-2
6	4-0 3/8	7-2 3/4	10-9	19-3 5/16	17-5 5/8	31-3 7/8	24-2 1/4	43-4 7/16
7	4-8 7/16	8-5 3/16	11-5 1/16	20-5 25/32	18-1 11/16	32-6 11/32	24-10 5/16	44-6 29/32
8	5-4 1/2	9-7 21/32	12-1 1/8	21-8 7/32	18-9 3/4	33-8 25/32	25-6 3/8	45-9 3/8
9	6-0 9/16	10-10 1/8	12-9 3/16	22-10 11/16	19-5 13/16	34-11 1/4	26-2 7/16	46-11 13/16

A = 33° 53' 46''; logsin A = 9.74639; logcos A = 9.91910; logtan A = 9.82729; logcot A = 0.17271

In.	12″ Rise	12″ Slope	13″ Rise	13″ Slope	14″ Rise	14″ Slope	15″ Rise	15″ Slope	16″ Rise	16″ Slope
0	8 1/16	1-2 15/32	8 3/4	1-3 21/32	9 13/32	1-4 7/8	10 1/16	1-6 1/16	10 3/4	1-7 9/32
1/16	8 3/32	1-2 17/32	8 25/32	1-3 3/4	9 7/16	1-4 15/16	10 1/8	1-6 5/32	10 25/32	1-7 11/32
1/8	8 5/32	1-2 19/32	8 13/16	1-3 13/16	9 1/2	1-5 1/32	10 5/32	1-6 7/32	10 27/32	1-7 7/16
3/16	8 3/16	1-2 11/16	8 7/8	1-3 7/8	9 17/32	1-5 3/32	10 7/32	1-6 5/16	10 7/8	1-7 1/2
1/4	8 7/32	1-2 3/4	8 29/32	1-3 31/32	9 9/16	1-5 5/32	10 1/4	1-6 3/8	10 29/32	1-7 9/16
5/16	8 9/32	1-2 27/32	8 15/16	1-4 1/32	9 5/8	1-5 1/4	10 9/32	1-6 7/16	10 31/32	1-7 21/32
3/8	8 5/16	1-2 29/32	9	1-4 1/8	9 21/32	1-5 5/16	10 11/32	1-6 17/32	11	1-7 23/32
7/16	8 11/32	1-2 31/32	9 1/32	1-4 3/16	9 11/16	1-5 13/32	10 3/8	1-6 19/32	11 1/32	1-7 13/16
1/2	8 13/32	1-3 1/16	9 1/16	1-4 1/4	9 3/4	1-5 15/32	10 13/32	1-6 11/16	11 3/32	1-7 7/8
9/16	8 7/16	1-3 1/8	9 1/8	1-4 11/32	9 25/32	1-5 17/32	10 15/32	1-6 3/4	11 1/8	1-7 31/32
5/8	8 15/32	1-3 7/32	9 5/32	1-4 13/32	9 13/16	1-5 5/8	10 1/2	1-6 13/16	11 5/32	1-8 1/32
11/16	8 17/32	1-3 9/32	9 3/16	1-4 1/2	9 7/8	1-5 11/16	10 17/32	1-6 29/32	11 7/32	1-8 3/32
3/4	8 9/16	1-3 3/8	9 1/4	1-4 9/16	9 29/32	1-5 25/32	10 19/32	1-6 31/32	11 1/4	1-8 3/16
13/16	8 19/32	1-3 7/16	9 9/32	1-4 5/8	9 15/16	1-5 27/32	10 5/8	1-7 1/16	11 9/32	1-8 1/4
7/8	8 21/32	1-3 1/2	9 5/16	1-4 23/32	10	1-5 29/32	10 21/32	1-7 1/8	11 11/32	1-8 11/32
15/16	8 11/16	1-3 19/32	9 3/8	1-4 25/32	10 1/32	1-6	10 23/32	1-7 3/16	11 3/8	1-8 13/32

In.	17″ Rise	17″ Slope	18″ Rise	18″ Slope	19″ Rise	19″ Slope	20″ Rise	20″ Slope	21″ Rise	21″ Slope
0	11 7/16	1-8 15/32	1-0 3/32	1-9 11/16	1-0 3/4	1-10 7/8	1-1 7/16	2-0 3/32	1-2 1/8	2-1 5/16
1/16	11 15/32	1-8 9/16	1-0 1/8	1-9 3/4	1-0 13/16	1-10 31/32	1-1 15/32	2-0 5/32	1-2 5/32	2-1 3/8
1/8	11 1/2	1-8 5/8	1-0 3/16	1-9 27/32	1-0 27/32	1-11 1/32	1-1 17/32	2-0 1/4	1-2 3/16	2-1 7/16
3/16	11 9/16	1-8 23/32	1-0 7/32	1-9 29/32	1-0 29/32	1-11 1/8	1-1 9/16	2-0 5/16	1-2 1/4	2-1 17/32
1/4	11 19/32	1-8 25/32	1-0 1/4	1-10	1-0 15/16	1-11 3/16	1-1 19/32	2-0 13/32	1-2 9/32	2-1 19/32
5/16	11 5/8	1-8 27/32	1-0 5/16	1-10 1/16	1-0 31/32	1-11 9/32	1-1 21/32	2-0 15/32	1-2 5/16	2-1 11/16
3/8	11 11/16	1-8 15/16	1-0 11/32	1-10 1/8	1-1 1/32	1-11 11/32	1-1 11/16	2-0 17/32	1-2 3/8	2-1 3/4
7/16	11 23/32	1-9	1-0 3/8	1-10 7/32	1-1 1/16	1-11 13/32	1-1 23/32	2-0 5/8	1-2 13/32	2-1 13/16
1/2	11 3/4	1-9 3/32	1-0 7/16	1-10 9/32	1-1 3/32	1-11 1/2	1-1 25/32	2-0 11/16	1-2 7/16	2-1 29/32
9/16	11 13/16	1-9 5/32	1-0 15/32	1-10 3/8	1-1 5/32	1-11 9/16	1-1 13/16	2-0 25/32	1-2 1/2	2-1 31/32
5/8	11 27/32	1-9 7/32	1-0 1/2	1-10 7/16	1-1 3/16	1-11 21/32	1-1 27/32	2-0 27/32	1-2 17/32	2-2 1/16
11/16	11 7/8	1-9 5/16	1-0 9/16	1-10 1/2	1-1 7/32	1-11 23/32	1-1 29/32	2-0 15/16	1-2 9/16	2-2 1/8
3/4	11 15/16	1-9 3/8	1-0 19/32	1-10 19/32	1-1 9/32	1-11 25/32	1-1 15/16	2-1	1-2 5/8	2-2 3/16
13/16	11 31/32	1-9 15/32	1-0 5/8	1-10 21/32	1-1 5/16	1-11 7/8	1-1 31/32	2-1 1/16	1-2 21/32	2-2 9/32
7/8	1-0	1-9 17/32	1-0 11/16	1-10 3/4	1-1 11/32	1-11 15/16	1-2 1/32	2-1 5/32	1-2 11/16	2-2 11/32
15/16	1-0 1/16	1-9 5/8	1-0 23/32	1-10 13/16	1-1 13/32	2-0 1/32	1-2 1/16	2-1 7/32	1-2 3/4	2-2 7/16

Feet	40′ Rise	40′ Slope	50′ Rise	50′ Slope	60′ Rise	60′ Slope	70′ Rise	70′ Slope
0	26-10 1/2	48-2 9/32	33-7 1/2	60-2 27/32	40-3 3/4	72-3 13/32	47-0 3/8	84-4
1	27-6 9/16	49-4 3/4	34-3 9/16	61-5 5/16	40-11 13/16	73-5 7/8	47-8 7/16	85-6 7/16
2	28-2 5/8	50-7 3/16	34-11 5/8	62-7 3/4	41-7 7/8	74-8 11/32	48-4 1/2	86-8 29/32
3	28-10 11/16	51-9 21/32	35-7 5/16	63-10 7/32	42-3 15/16	75-10 25/32	49-0 9/16	87-11 11/32
4	29-6 3/4	53-0 3/32	36-3 3/8	65-0 11/16	43-0	77-1 1/4	49-8 5/8	89-1 13/16
5	30-2 13/16	54-2 9/16	36-11 7/16	66-3 1/8	43-8 1/16	78-3 11/16	50-4 11/16	90-4 9/32
6	30-10 7/8	55-5 1/32	37-7 1/2	67-5 9/16	44-4 1/8	79-6 5/32	51-0 3/4	91-6 23/32
7	31-6 15/16	56-7 15/32	38-3 9/16	68-8 1/16	45-0 3/16	80-8 5/8	51-8 13/16	92-9 3/16
8	32-3	57-9 15/16	38-11 5/8	69-10 1/2	45-8 1/4	81-11 1/16	52-4 7/8	93-11 21/32
9	32-11 1/16	59-0 13/32	39-7 11/16	71-0 31/32	46-4 5/16	83-1 17/32	53-0 15/16	95-2 3/32

natsin A=0.5576895748; natcos A=0.8300495997; nattan A=0.671875000; natcot A=1.4883720930

Inches	0" Rise	Slope	1" Rise	Slope	2" Rise	Slope	3" Rise	Slope	4" Rise	Slope	5" Rise	Slope
0	0	0	11/16	1 7/32	1 11/32	2 13/32	2 1/2	3 5/8	2 23/32	4 27/32	3 3/8	6 1/8
1/16	1/32	1/16	23/32	1 9/32	1 13/32	2 1/2	2 1/16	3 11/16	2 3/4	4 29/32	3 7/16	6 1/8
1/8	3/32	5/32	3/4	1 11/32	1 7/16	2 9/16	2 1/8	3 25/32	2 25/32	4 31/32	3 15/16	6 3/16
3/16	1/8	7/32	13/16	1 7/16	1 15/32	2 21/32	2 5/32	3 27/32	2 27/32	5 1/16	3 1/2	6 1/4
1/4	5/32	5/16	27/32	1 1/2	1 17/32	2 23/32	2 3/16	3 15/16	2 7/8	5 1/8	3 9/16	6 11/32
5/16	7/32	3/8	7/8	1 19/32	1 9/16	2 25/32	2 1/4	4	2 29/32	5 7/32	3 19/32	6 13/32
3/8	1/4	7/16	15/16	1 21/32	1 19/32	2 7/8	2 9/32	4 1/16	2 31/32	5 9/32	3 5/8	6 1/2
7/16	9/32	17/32	31/32	1 3/4	1 21/32	2 15/16	2 5/16	4 5/32	3	5 11/32	3 11/16	6 9/16
1/2	11/32	19/32	1	1 13/16	1 11/16	3 1/32	2 3/8	4 7/32	3 1/16	5 7/16	3 23/32	6 21/32
9/16	3/8	11/16	1 1/16	1 7/8	1 3/4	3 3/32	2 13/32	4 5/16	3 3/32	5 1/2	3 25/32	6 23/32
5/8	7/16	3/4	1 3/32	1 31/32	1 25/32	3 5/32	2 15/32	4 3/8	3 1/8	5 19/32	3 13/16	6 25/32
11/16	15/32	27/32	1 5/32	2 1/32	1 13/16	3 1/4	2 1/2	4 15/32	3 3/16	5 21/32	3 27/32	6 7/8
3/4	1/2	29/32	1 3/16	2 1/8	1 7/8	3 5/16	2 17/32	4 17/32	3 7/32	5 3/4	3 29/32	6 15/16
13/16	9/16	31/32	1 7/32	2 3/16	1 29/32	3 13/32	2 19/32	4 19/32	3 1/4	5 13/16	3 15/16	7 1/2
7/8	19/32	1 1/16	1 9/32	2 1/4	1 15/16	3 15/32	2 5/8	4 11/16	3 5/16	5 7/8	3 31/32	7 3/32
15/16	5/8	1 1/8	1 5/16	2 11/32	2	3 9/16	2 21/32	4 3/4	3 11/32	5 31/32	4 1/32	7 5/32

Inches	6" Rise	Slope	7" Rise	Slope	8" Rise	Slope	9" Rise	Slope	10" Rise	Slope	11" Rise	Slope
0	4 1/16	7 1/4	4 3/4	8 15/32	5 13/32	9 21/32	6 3/32	10 7/8	6 25/32	1-0 1/16	7 7/16	1-1 9/32
1/16	4 3/32	7 5/16	4 25/32	8 17/32	5 15/32	9 3/4	6 1/8	10 15/16	6 13/16	1-0 5/32	7 1/2	1-1 3/8
1/8	4 5/32	7 13/32	4 13/16	8 19/32	5 1/2	9 13/16	6 3/16	11 1/32	6 27/32	1-0 7/32	7 17/32	1-1 7/16
3/16	4 3/16	7 15/32	4 7/8	8 11/16	5 17/32	9 7/8	6 7/32	11 3/32	6 29/32	1-0 5/16	7 9/16	1-1 1/2
1/4	4 7/32	7 9/16	4 29/32	8 3/4	5 19/32	9 31/32	6 1/4	11 5/32	6 15/16	1-0 3/8	7 5/8	1-1 19/32
5/16	4 9/32	7 5/8	4 15/16	8 27/32	5 5/8	10 1/32	6 5/16	11 1/4	6 31/32	1-0 15/32	7 21/32	1-1 21/32
3/8	4 5/16	7 11/16	5	8 29/32	5 21/32	10 1/8	6 11/32	11 5/16	7 1/32	1-0 17/32	7 11/16	1-1 3/4
7/16	4 11/32	7 25/32	5 1/32	8 31/32	5 23/32	10 3/16	6 3/8	11 13/32	7 1/16	1-0 19/32	7 3/4	1-1 13/16
1/2	4 13/32	7 27/32	5 1/16	9 1/16	5 3/4	10 1/4	6 7/16	11 15/32	7 1/8	1-0 11/16	7 25/32	1-1 7/8
9/16	4 7/16	7 15/16	5 1/8	9 1/8	5 13/16	10 11/32	6 15/32	11 9/16	7 5/32	1-0 3/4	7 27/32	1-1 31/32
5/8	4 1/2	8	5 5/32	9 7/32	5 27/32	10 13/32	6 17/32	11 5/8	7 3/16	1-0 27/32	7 7/8	1-2 1/32
11/16	4 17/32	8 1/16	5 7/32	9 9/32	5 7/8	10 1/2	6 9/16	11 11/16	7 1/4	1-0 29/32	7 29/32	1-2 1/8
3/4	4 9/16	8 5/32	5 1/4	9 11/32	5 15/16	10 9/16	6 19/32	11 25/32	7 9/32	1-0 31/32	7 31/32	1-2 3/16
13/16	4 5/8	8 7/32	5 9/32	9 7/16	5 31/32	10 21/32	6 21/32	11 27/32	7 5/16	1-1 1/16	8	1-2 1/4
7/8	4 21/32	8 5/16	5 11/32	9 1/2	6	10 23/32	6 11/16	11 15/16	7 3/8	1-1 1/8	8 1/32	1-2 11/32
15/16	4 11/16	8 3/8	5 3/8	9 19/32	6 1/16	10 25/32	6 23/32	1-0	7 13/32	1-1 7/32	8 3/32	1-2 13/32

Feet	0' Rise	Slope	10' Rise	Slope	20' Rise	Slope	30' Rise	Slope
0	0	0	6-9 1/4	12-0 29/32	13-6 1/2	24-1 27/32	20-3 3/4	36-2 3/4
1	8 1/8	1-2 1/2	7-5 3/8	13-3 15/32	14-2 5/8	25-4 11/32	20-11 7/8	37-5 1/4
2	1-4 1/4	2-4 31/32	8-1 1/2	14-5 29/32	14-10 3/4	26-6 13/16	21-8	38-7 3/4
3	2-0 3/8	3-7 15/32	8-9 5/8	15-8 15/32	15-6 7/8	27-9 5/16	22-4 1/8	39-10 1/4
4	2-8 1/2	4-9 31/32	9-5 3/4	16-10 7/8	16-3	28-11 13/16	23-0 1/4	41-0 23/32
5	3-4 5/8	6-0 15/32	10-1 7/8	18-1 3/8	16-11 1/8	30-2 5/16	23-8 3/8	42-3 7/32
6	4-0 3/4	7-2 15/16	10-10	19-3 7/8	17-7 1/4	31-4 25/32	24-4 1/2	43-5 23/32
7	4-8 7/8	8-5 7/16	11-6 1/8	20-6 3/8	18-3 3/8	32-7 9/32	25-0 5/8	44-8 3/16
8	5-5	9-7 15/16	12-2 1/4	21-8 27/32	18-11 1/2	33-9 25/32	25-8 3/4	45-10 11/16
9	6-1 1/8	10-10 7/16	12-10 3/8	22-11 11/32	19-7 5/8	35-0 1/4	26-4 7/8	47-1 3/16

A = 34° 06' 05"; logsin A = 9.74870; logcos A = 9.91806; logtan A = 9.83064; logcot A = 0.16936

Ins.	12″ Rise	Slope	13″ Rise	Slope	14″ Rise	Slope	15″ Rise	Slope	16″ Rise	Slope
0	8 1/8	1-2 1/2	8 13/16	1-3 11/16	9 15/32	1-4 29/32	10 5/32	1-6 1/8	10 27/32	1-7 5/16
1/16	8 5/32	1-2 9/16	8 27/32	1-3 25/32	9 17/32	1-4 31/32	10 7/32	1-6 3/16	10 7/8	1-7 13/32
1/8	8 7/32	1-2 21/32	8 7/8	1-3 27/32	9 9/16	1-5 1/16	10 1/4	1-6 9/32	10 29/32	1-7 15/32
3/16	8 1/4	1-2 23/32	8 15/16	1-3 15/16	9 19/32	1-5 1/8	10 9/32	1-6 11/32	10 31/32	1-7 9/16
1/4	8 9/32	1-2 25/32	8 31/32	1-4	9 21/32	1-5 7/32	10 5/16	1-6 13/32	11	1-7 5/8
5/16	8 11/32	1-2 7/8	9	1-4 1/16	9 11/16	1-5 9/32	10 3/8	1-6 1/2	11 1/32	1-7 11/16
3/8	8 3/8	1-2 15/16	9 1/16	1-4 5/32	9 23/32	1-5 3/8	10 13/32	1-6 9/16	11 3/32	1-7 25/32
7/16	8 13/32	1-3 1/32	9 3/32	1-4 7/32	9 3/4	1-5 7/16	10 7/16	1-6 21/32	11 1/8	1-7 27/32
1/2	8 15/32	1-3 3/32	9 1/8	1-4 5/16	9 13/16	1-5 1/2	10 1/2	1-6 23/32	11 3/16	1-7 15/16
9/16	8 1/2	1-3 5/32	9 3/16	1-4 3/8	9 7/8	1-5 19/32	10 17/32	1-6 25/32	11 7/32	1-8
5/8	8 9/16	1-3 1/4	9 7/32	1-4 15/32	9 29/32	1-5 21/32	10 19/32	1-6 7/8	11 1/4	1-8 1/16
11/16	8 19/32	1-3 5/16	9 9/32	1-4 17/32	9 15/16	1-5 3/4	10 5/8	1-6 15/16	11 5/16	1-8 5/32
3/4	8 5/8	1-3 13/32	9 5/16	1-4 19/32	10	1-5 13/16	10 21/32	1-7 1/32	11 11/32	1-8 7/32
13/16	8 11/16	1-3 15/32	9 11/32	1-4 11/16	10 1/32	1-5 7/8	10 23/32	1-7 3/32	11 3/8	1-8 9/32
7/8	8 23/32	1-3 9/16	9 13/32	1-4 3/4	10 1/16	1-5 31/32	10 3/4	1-7 5/32	11 7/16	1-8 3/8
15/16	8 3/4	1-3 5/8	9 7/16	1-4 27/32	10 1/8	1-6 1/32	10 25/32	1-7 1/4	11 15/32	1-8 15/32

Ins.	17″ Rise	Slope	18″ Rise	Slope	19″ Rise	Slope	20″ Rise	Slope	21″ Rise	Slope
0	11 1/2	1-8 17/32	1-0 3/16	1-9 3/4	1-0 7/8	1-10 15/16	1-1 17/32	2-0 5/32	1-2 7/32	2-1 3/8
1/16	11 9/16	1-8 19/32	1-0 7/32	1-9 13/16	1-0 29/32	1-11 1/32	1-1 19/32	2-0 7/32	1-2 1/4	2-1 7/16
1/8	11 19/32	1-8 11/16	1-0 9/32	1-9 7/8	1-0 15/16	1-11 3/32	1-1 5/8	2-0 5/16	1-2 5/16	2-1 1/2
3/16	11 5/8	1-8 3/4	1-0 5/16	1-9 31/32	1-1	1-11 3/16	1-1 21/32	2-0 3/8	1-2 11/32	2-1 19/32
1/4	11 11/16	1-8 27/32	1-0 11/32	1-10 1/32	1-1 1/16	1-11 1/4	1-1 23/32	2-0 15/32	1-2 3/8	2-1 21/32
5/16	11 23/32	1-8 29/32	1-0 13/32	1-10 1/8	1-1 1/8	1-11 5/16	1-1 3/4	2-0 17/32	1-2 7/16	2-1 3/4
3/8	11 3/4	1-8 31/32	1-0 7/16	1-10 3/16	1-1 3/16	1-11 13/32	1-1 25/32	2-0 19/32	1-2 15/32	2-1 13/16
7/16	11 13/16	1-9 1/16	1-0 15/32	1-10 9/32	1-1 5/32	1-11 15/32	1-1 27/32	2-0 11/16	1-2 1/2	2-1 7/8
1/2	11 27/32	1-9 1/8	1-0 17/32	1-10 11/32	1-1 3/16	1-11 1/2	1-1 7/8	2-0 3/4	1-2 9/16	2-1 31/32
9/16	11 29/32	1-9 7/32	1-0 9/16	1-10 13/32	1-1 1/4	1-11 5/8	1-1 15/16	2-0 27/32	1-2 19/32	2-2 1/32
5/8	11 15/16	1-9 9/32	1-0 5/8	1-10 1/2	1-1 9/32	1-11 11/16	1-1 31/32	2-0 29/32	1-2 21/32	2-2 1/8
11/16	11 31/32	1-9 3/8	1-0 21/32	1-10 9/16	1-1 11/32	1-11 25/32	1-2	2-0 31/32	1-2 11/16	2-2 3/16
3/4	1-0 1/32	1-9 7/16	1-0 11/16	1-10 21/32	1-1 3/8	1-11 27/32	1-2 1/16	2-1 1/16	1-2 23/32	2-2 9/32
13/16	1-0 1/16	1-9 1/2	1-0 3/4	1-10 23/32	1-1 13/32	1-11 15/16	1-2 3/32	2-1 1/8	1-2 25/32	2-2 11/32
7/8	1-0 3/32	1-9 19/32	1-0 25/32	1-10 25/32	1-1 1/2	2-0	1-2 1/8	2-1 7/32	1-2 13/16	2-2 13/32
15/16	1-0 5/32	1-9 21/32	1-0 13/16	1-10 7/8	1-1 1/2	2-0 1/16	1-2 3/16	2-1 9/32	1-2 27/32	2-2 1/2

Feet	40′ Rise	Slope	50′ Rise	Slope	60′ Rise	Slope	70′ Rise	Slope
0	27-1	48-3 11/32	33-10 1/4	60-4 19/32	40-7 1/2	72-5 1/2	47-4 3/4	84-6 7/16
1	27-9 1/8	49-6 5/32	34-6 3/8	61-7 3/4	41-3 5/8	73-8	48-0 7/8	85-8 15/16
2	28-5 1/4	50-8 21/32	35-2 1/2	62-9 19/32	41-11 3/4	74-10 1/2	48-9	86-11 13/32
3	29-1 3/8	51-11 5/32	35-10 5/8	64-0 1/4	42-7 7/8	76-1	49-5 1/8	88-1 29/32
4	29-9 1/2	53-1 21/32	36-6 3/4	65-2 9/32	43-4	77-3 15/32	50-1 1/4	89-4 13/32
5	30-5 5/8	54-4 1/8	37-2 7/8	66-5 1/16	44-0 1/8	78-5 31/32	50-9 3/8	90-6 29/32
6	31-1 3/4	55-6 5/8	37-11	67-7 9/16	44-8 1/4	79-8 15/32	51-5 1/2	91-9 3/8
7	31-9 7/8	56-9 1/8	38-7 1/8	68-10 1/32	45-4 3/8	80-10 31/32	52-1 5/8	92-11 7/8
8	32-6	57-11 5/8	39-3 1/4	70-0 17/32	46-0 1/2	82-1 7/16	52-9 3/4	94-2 3/8
9	33-2 1/8	59-2 3/32	39-11 3/8	71-3 1/32	46-8 5/8	83-3 15/16	53-5 7/8	95-4 7/8

natsin A=0.5606574095; natcos A=0.8280478664; nattan A=0.6770833333; natcot A=1.4769230769

Inches	0" Rise	0" Slope	1" Rise	1" Slope	2" Rise	2" Slope	3" Rise	3" Slope	4" Rise	4" Slope	5" Rise	5" Slope
0	0	0	11/16	1 7/32	1 3/8	2 13/32	2 1/16	3 5/8	2 23/32	4 27/32	3 13/32	6 1/16
1/16	1/32	1/16	23/32	1 9/32	1 13/32	2 1/2	2 3/32	3 23/32	2 25/32	4 29/32	3 15/32	6 1/8
1/8	3/32	5/32	25/32	1 3/8	1 7/16	2 9/16	2 1/8	3 25/32	2 13/16	5	3 1/2	6 7/32
3/16	1/8	7/32	13/16	1 7/16	1 1/2	2 21/32	2 3/16	3 27/32	2 27/32	5 1/16	3 17/32	6 9/32
1/4	5/32	5/16	27/32	1 1/2	1 17/32	2 23/32	2 7/32	3 15/16	2 29/32	5 5/32	3 19/32	6 11/32
5/16	7/32	3/8	29/32	1 19/32	1 9/16	2 13/16	2 1/4	4	2 15/16	5 7/32	3 5/8	6 7/16
3/8	1/4	15/32	15/16	1 21/32	1 5/8	2 7/8	2 5/16	4 3/32	3	5 9/32	3 21/32	6 1/2
7/16	5/16	17/32	31/32	1 3/4	1 21/32	2 15/16	2 11/32	4 5/32	3 1/32	5 3/8	3 23/32	6 19/32
1/2	11/32	19/32	1 1/32	1 13/16	1 23/32	3 1/32	2 3/8	4 1/4	3 1/16	5 7/16	3 3/4	6 21/32
9/16	3/8	11/16	1 1/16	1 29/32	1 3/4	3 3/32	2 7/16	4 5/16	3 1/8	5 17/32	3 25/32	6 23/32
5/8	7/16	3/4	1 3/32	1 31/32	1 25/32	3 3/16	2 15/32	4 3/8	3 5/32	5 19/32	3 27/32	6 13/16
11/16	15/32	27/32	1 5/32	2 1/32	1 27/32	3 1/4	2 17/32	4 15/32	3 3/16	5 11/16	3 7/8	6 7/8
3/4	1/2	29/32	1 3/16	2 1/8	1 7/8	3 11/32	2 9/16	4 17/32	3 1/4	5 3/4	3 15/16	6 31/32
13/16	9/16	31/32	1 1/4	2 3/16	1 29/32	3 13/32	2 19/32	4 5/8	3 9/32	5 13/16	3 31/32	7 1/32
7/8	19/32	1 1/16	1 9/32	2 9/32	1 31/32	3 15/32	2 21/32	4 11/16	3 5/16	5 29/32	4	7 1/8
15/16	5/8	1 1/8	1 5/16	2 11/32	2	3 9/16	2 11/16	4 25/32	3 3/8	5 31/32	4 1/16	7 3/16

Inches	6" Rise	6" Slope	7" Rise	7" Slope	8" Rise	8" Slope	9" Rise	9" Slope	10" Rise	10" Slope	11" Rise	11" Slope
0	4 3/32	7 1/4	4 25/32	8 15/32	5 15/32	9 11/16	6 1/8	10 29/32	6 13/16	1-0 3/32	7 1/2	1-1 5/16
1/16	4 1/8	7 11/32	4 13/16	8 9/16	5 1/2	9 3/4	6 3/16	10 31/32	6 7/8	1-0 3/16	7 9/16	1-1 13/32
1/8	4 3/16	7 13/32	4 7/8	8 5/8	5 17/32	9 27/32	6 7/32	11 1/16	6 29/32	1-0 1/4	7 19/32	1-1 15/32
3/16	4 7/32	7 1/2	4 29/32	8 11/16	5 19/32	9 29/32	6 9/32	11 1/8	6 15/16	1-0 11/32	7 5/8	1-1 17/32
1/4	4 1/4	7 9/16	4 15/16	8 25/32	5 5/8	10	6 5/16	11 3/16	7	1-0 13/32	7 11/16	1-1 5/8
5/16	4 5/16	7 21/32	5	8 27/32	5 11/16	10 1/16	6 11/32	11 9/32	7 1/32	1-0 1/2	7 23/32	1-1 11/16
3/8	4 11/32	7 23/32	5 1/32	8 15/16	5 23/32	10 1/8	6 13/32	11 11/32	7 3/32	1-0 9/16	7 3/4	1-1 25/32
7/16	4 13/32	7 25/32	5 1/16	9	5 3/4	10 7/32	6 7/16	11 7/16	7 1/8	1-0 5/8	7 13/16	1-1 27/32
1/2	4 7/16	7 7/8	5 1/8	9 3/32	5 13/16	10 9/32	6 15/32	11 1/2	7 5/32	1-0 23/32	7 27/32	1-1 15/16
9/16	4 15/32	7 15/16	5 5/32	9 5/32	5 27/32	10 3/8	6 17/32	11 9/16	7 7/32	1-0 25/32	7 7/8	1-2
5/8	4 17/32	8 1/32	5 3/16	9 7/32	5 7/8	10 7/16	6 9/16	11 21/32	7 1/4	1-0 7/8	7 15/16	1-2 1/16
11/16	4 9/16	8 3/32	5 1/4	9 5/16	5 15/16	10 17/32	6 5/8	11 23/32	7 9/32	1-0 15/16	7 31/32	1-2 5/32
3/4	4 19/32	8 3/16	5 9/32	9 3/8	5 31/32	10 19/32	6 21/32	11 13/16	7 11/32	1-1	8 1/32	1-2 7/32
13/16	4 21/32	8 1/4	5 11/32	9 15/32	6	10 21/32	6 11/16	11 7/8	7 3/8	1-1 3/32	8 1/16	1-2 5/16
7/8	4 11/16	8 5/16	5 3/8	9 17/32	6 1/16	10 3/4	6 3/4	11 31/32	7 13/32	1-1 5/32	8 3/32	1-2 3/8
15/16	4 23/32	8 13/32	5 13/32	9 5/8	6 3/32	10 13/16	6 25/32	1-0 1/32	7 15/32	1-1 1/4	8 5/32	1-2 7/16

Feet	0' Rise	0' Slope	10' Rise	10' Slope	20' Rise	20' Slope	30' Rise	30' Slope
0	0	0	6-9 7/8	12-1 9/32	13-7 3/4	24-2 9/16	20-5 5/8	36-3 13/16
1	8 3/16	1-2 17/32	7-6 1/16	13-3 13/16	14-3 15/16	25-5 1/16	21-1 13/16	37-6 11/32
2	1-4 3/8	2-5 1/16	8-2 1/4	14-6 5/16	15-0 1/16	26-7 19/32	21-10	38-8 7/8
3	2-0 9/16	3-7 19/32	8-10 7/16	15-8 27/32	15-8 5/16	27-10 1/8	22-6 3/16	39-11 13/32
4	2-8 3/4	4-10 3/32	9-6 5/8	16-11 3/8	16-4 1/2	29-0 21/32	23-2 3/8	41-1 29/32
5	3-4 15/16	6-0 5/8	10-2 13/16	18-1 29/32	17-0 11/16	30-3 3/16	23-10 9/16	42-4 7/16
6	4-1 1/8	7-3 5/32	10-11	19-4 7/16	17-8 7/8	31-5 23/32	24-6 3/4	43-6 31/32
7	4-9 5/16	8-5 11/16	11-7 3/16	20-6 31/32	18-5 1/16	32-8 1/4	25-2 15/16	44-9 1/2
8	5-5 1/2	9-8 7/32	12-3 3/8	21-9 1/2	19-1 1/4	33-10 3/4	25-11 1/8	46-0 1/32
9	6-1 11/16	10-10 3/4	12-11 9/16	23-0	19-9 7/16	35-1 9/32	26-7 5/16	47-2 9/16

A = 34° 18′ 19″; logsin A = 9.75097; logcos A = 9.91700; logtan A = 9.83397; logcot A = 0.16603

Ins.	12″ Rise	Slope	13″ Rise	Slope	14″ Rise	Slope	15″ Rise	Slope	16″ Rise	Slope
0	8 3/16	1-2 17/32	8 7/8	1-3 3/4	9 9/16	1-4 15/16	10 1/4	1-6 5/32	10 29/32	1-7 3/8
1/16	8 7/32	1-2 19/32	8 29/32	1-3 13/16	9 19/32	1-5 1/32	10 9/32	1-6 1/4	10 31/32	1-7 7/16
1/8	8 9/32	1-2 11/16	8 31/32	1-3 7/8	9 5/8	1-5 3/32	10 5/16	1-6 5/16	11	1-7 17/32
3/16	8 5/16	1-2 3/4	9	1-3 31/32	9 11/16	1-5 3/16	10 3/8	1-6 3/8	11 1/32	1-7 19/32
1/4	8 11/32	1-2 27/32	9 1/32	1-4 1/32	9 23/32	1-5 1/4	10 13/32	1-6 15/32	11 3/32	1-7 11/16
5/16	8 13/32	1-2 29/32	9 3/32	1-4 1/8	9 3/4	1-5 5/16	10 7/16	1-6 17/32	11 1/8	1-7 3/4
3/8	8 7/16	1-2 31/32	9 1/8	1-4 3/16	9 13/16	1-5 13/32	10 1/2	1-6 5/8	11 3/16	1-7 13/16
7/16	8 1/2	1-3 1/16	9 5/32	1-4 9/32	9 27/32	1-5 15/32	10 17/32	1-6 11/16	11 7/32	1-7 29/32
1/2	8 17/32	1-3 1/8	9 7/32	1-4 11/32	9 29/32	1-5 9/16	10 9/16	1-6 3/4	11 1/4	1-7 31/32
9/16	8 9/16	1-3 7/32	9 1/4	1-4 13/32	9 15/16	1-5 5/8	10 5/8	1-6 27/32	11 5/16	1-8 1/16
5/8	8 5/8	1-3 9/32	9 9/32	1-4 1/2	9 31/32	1-5 23/32	10 21/32	1-6 29/32	11 11/32	1-8 1/8
11/16	8 21/32	1-3 11/32	9 11/32	1-4 9/16	10 1/32	1-5 25/32	10 23/32	1-7	11 3/8	1-8 3/16
3/4	8 11/16	1-3 7/16	9 3/8	1-4 21/32	10 1/16	1-5 27/32	10 3/4	1-7 1/16	11 7/16	1-8 9/32
13/16	8 3/4	1-3 1/2	9 7/16	1-4 23/32	10 3/32	1-5 15/16	10 25/32	1-7 5/32	11 15/32	1-8 11/32
7/8	8 25/32	1-3 19/32	9 15/32	1-4 13/16	10 5/32	1-6	10 27/32	1-7 11/32	11 1/2	1-8 7/16
15/16	8 13/16	1-3 21/32	9 1/2	1-4 7/8	10 3/16	1-6 3/32	10 7/8	1-7 9/32	11 9/16	1-8 1/2

Ins.	17″ Rise	Slope	18″ Rise	Slope	19″ Rise	Slope	20″ Rise	Slope	21″ Rise	Slope
0	11 19/32	1-8 19/32	1-0 9/32	1-9 25/32	1-0 31/32	1-11	1-1 21/32	2-0 7/32	1-2 5/16	2-1 7/16
1/16	11 21/32	1-8 21/32	1-0 5/16	1-9 7/8	1-1	1-11 1/16	1-1 11/16	2-0 9/32	1-2 3/8	2-1 1/2
1/8	11 11/16	1-8 23/32	1-0 3/8	1-9 15/16	1-1 1/16	1-11 5/32	1-1 23/32	2-0 3/8	1-2 13/32	2-1 9/16
3/16	11 23/32	1-8 13/16	1-0 13/32	1-10 1/32	1-1 3/32	1-11 7/32	1-1 25/32	2-0 1/2	1-2 15/32	2-1 21/32
1/4	11 25/32	1-8 7/8	1-0 7/16	1-10 3/32	1-1 1/8	1-11 15/32	1-1 13/16	2-0 1/2	1-2 1/2	2-1 23/32
5/16	11 13/16	1-8 31/32	1-0 1/2	1-10 5/32	1-1 3/16	1-11 3/8	1-1 27/32	2-0 19/32	1-2 17/32	2-1 13/16
3/8	11 27/32	1-9 1/32	1-0 17/32	1-10 1/4	1-1 7/32	1-11 15/32	1-1 29/32	2-0 21/32	1-2 19/32	2-1 7/8
7/16	11 29/32	1-9 1/8	1-0 19/32	1-10 5/16	1-1 1/4	1-11 17/32	1-1 15/16	2-0 3/4	1-2 5/8	2-1 15/16
1/2	11 15/16	1-9 3/16	1-0 5/8	1-10 13/32	1-1 5/16	1-11 19/32	1-2	2-0 13/16	1-2 21/32	2-2 1/32
9/16	11 31/32	1-9 1/4	1-0 21/32	1-10 15/32	1-1 11/32	1-11 11/16	1-2 1/16	2-0 29/32	1-2 23/32	2-2 3/32
5/8	1-0 1/32	1-9 11/32	1-0 23/32	1-10 9/16	1-1 3/8	1-11 3/4	1-2 1/16	2-0 31/32	1-2 3/4	2-2 3/16
11/16	1-0 1/16	1-9 13/32	1-0 3/4	1-10 5/8	1-1 7/16	1-11 27/32	1-2 1/8	2-1 1/8	1-2 13/16	2-2 1/4
3/4	1-0 1/8	1-9 1/2	1-0 25/32	1-10 11/16	1-1 15/32	1-11 29/32	1-2 5/32	2-1 1/8	1-2 27/32	2-2 11/32
13/16	1-0 5/32	1-9 9/16	1-0 27/32	1-10 25/32	1-1 17/32	2-0	1-2 3/16	2-1 13/32	1-2 7/8	2-2 13/32
7/8	1-0 3/16	1-9 5/8	1-0 7/8	1-10 27/32	1-1 9/16	2-0 1/16	1-2 1/4	2-1 9/32	1-2 15/16	2-2 15/32
15/16	1-0 1/4	1-9 23/32	1-0 29/32	1-10 15/16	1-1 19/32	2-0 1/8	1-2 9/32	2-1 11/32	1-2 31/32	2-2 9/16

Feet	40′ Rise	Slope	50′ Rise	Slope	60′ Rise	Slope	70′ Rise	Slope
0	27-3 1/2	48-5 3/32	34-1 3/8	60-6 11/32	40-11 1/4	72-7 5/8	47-9 1/8	84-8 29/32
1	27-11 11/16	49-7 19/32	34-9 9/16	61-8 7/8	41-7 7/16	73-10 5/32	48-5 5/16	85-11 13/32
2	28-7 7/8	50-10 1/2	35-5 3/4	62-11 13/32	42-3 5/8	75-0 11/16	49-1 1/2	87-1 15/32
3	29-4 1/4	52-0 21/32	36-1 15/32	64-1 15/32	42-11 13/16	76-3 1/32	49-9 11/16	88-4 15/32
4	30-0 1/4	53-3 3/16	36-10 1/8	65-4 15/32	43-8	77-5 23/32	50-5 7/8	89-7
5	30-8 7/16	54-5 23/32	37-6 5/16	66-7	44-4 3/16	78-8 1/4	51-2 1/16	90-9 17/32
6	31-4 5/8	55-8 1/4	38-2 1/2	67-9 1/2	45-0 3/8	79-10 25/32	51-10 1/4	92-0 1/16
7	32-0 13/16	56-10 25/32	38-10 11/16	69-0 1/32	45-8 9/16	81-1 5/16	52-6 7/16	93-2 19/32
8	32-9	58-1 5/16	39-6 7/8	70-2 9/16	46-4 3/4	82-3 27/32	53-2 5/8	94-5 1/8
9	33-5 3/16	59-3 13/16	40-3 1/16	71-5 3/32	47-0 15/16	83-6 3/8	53-10 13/16	95-7 5/8

natsin A=0.5636037938; natcos A=0.8260452551; nattan A=0.6822916666; natcot A=1.4656488549

Inches	0" Rise	0" Slope	1" Rise	1" Slope	2" Rise	2" Slope	3" Rise	3" Slope	4" Rise	4" Slope	5" Rise	5" Slope
0	0	0	11/16	1 7/32	1 3/8	2 7/16	2 1/16	3 5/8	2 3/4	4 27/32	3 7/16	6 1/16
1/16	1/32	1/16	23/32	1 9/32	1 13/32	2 1/2	2 3/32	3 23/32	2 25/32	4 15/16	3 15/32	6 5/32
1/8	3/32	5/32	25/32	1 3/8	1 15/32	2 19/32	2 5/32	3 25/32	2 27/32	5	3 17/32	6 7/32
3/16	1/8	7/32	13/16	1 7/16	1 1/2	2 21/32	2 3/16	3 7/8	2 7/8	5 3/32	3 9/16	6 9/32
1/4	3/16	5/16	7/8	1 17/32	1 9/16	2 23/32	2 1/4	3 15/16	2 15/16	5 5/32	3 5/8	6 3/8
5/16	7/32	3/8	29/32	1 19/32	1 19/32	2 13/16	2 9/32	4 1/32	2 31/32	5 7/32	3 21/32	6 7/16
3/8	1/4	15/32	15/16	1 21/32	1 5/8	2 7/8	2 5/16	4 3/32	3	5 5/16	3 11/16	6 17/32
7/16	5/16	17/32	1	1 3/4	1 11/16	2 31/32	2 3/8	4 5/32	3 1/16	5 3/8	3 3/4	6 19/32
1/2	11/32	19/32	1 1/32	1 13/16	1 23/32	3 1/16	2 13/32	4 1/4	3 3/32	5 15/32	3 25/32	6 11/16
9/16	3/8	11/16	1 1/16	1 29/32	1 3/4	3 1/8	2 7/16	4 5/16	3 1/8	5 17/32	3 13/16	6 3/4
5/8	7/16	3/4	1 1/8	1 31/32	1 13/16	3 3/16	2 1/2	4 13/32	3 3/16	5 5/8	3 7/8	6 13/16
11/16	15/32	27/32	1 5/32	2 1/16	1 27/32	3 1/4	2 17/32	4 15/32	3 7/32	5 11/16	3 29/32	6 29/32
3/4	1/2	29/32	1 3/16	2 1/8	1 7/8	3 11/32	2 9/16	4 9/16	3 1/4	5 3/4	3 15/16	6 31/32
13/16	9/16	1	1 1/4	2 3/16	1 15/16	3 13/32	2 5/8	4 5/8	3 5/16	5 27/32	4	7 1/16
7/8	19/32	1 1/16	1 9/32	2 9/32	1 31/32	3 1/2	2 21/32	4 11/16	3 11/32	5 29/32	4 1/32	7 1/8
15/16	21/32	1 1/8	1 11/32	2 11/32	2 1/32	3 9/16	2 23/32	4 25/32	3 13/32	6	4 3/32	7 7/32

Inches	6" Rise	6" Slope	7" Rise	7" Slope	8" Rise	8" Slope	9" Rise	9" Slope	10" Rise	10" Slope	11" Rise	11" Slope
0	4 1/8	7 9/32	4 13/16	8 1/2	5 1/2	9 23/32	6 3/16	10 29/32	6 7/8	1-0 1/8	7 9/16	1-1 11/32
1/16	4 5/32	7 11/32	4 27/32	8 9/16	5 17/32	9 25/32	6 7/32	11	6 29/32	1-0 7/32	7 19/32	1-1 7/16
1/8	4 7/32	7 7/16	4 29/32	8 21/32	5 19/32	9 7/8	6 9/32	11 1/16	6 31/32	1-0 9/32	7 21/32	1-1 1/2
3/16	4 1/4	7 1/2	4 15/16	8 23/32	5 5/8	9 15/16	6 5/16	11 5/32	7	1-0 3/8	7 11/16	1-1 9/16
1/4	4 5/16	7 19/32	5	8 13/16	5 11/16	10	6 3/8	11 7/32	7 1/16	1-0 7/16	7 3/4	1-1 21/32
5/16	4 11/32	7 21/32	5 1/32	8 7/8	5 23/32	10 3/32	6 13/32	11 5/16	7 3/32	1-0 1/2	7 25/32	1-1 23/32
3/8	4 3/8	7 3/4	5 1/16	8 15/16	5 3/4	10 5/32	6 7/16	11 3/8	7 1/8	1-0 19/32	7 13/16	1-1 13/16
7/16	4 7/16	7 13/16	5 1/8	9 1/32	5 13/16	10 1/4	6 1/2	11 7/16	7 3/16	1-0 21/32	7 7/8	1-1 7/8
1/2	4 15/32	7 7/8	5 5/32	9 3/32	5 27/32	10 5/16	6 17/32	11 17/32	7 7/32	1-0 3/4	7 29/32	1-1 31/32
9/16	4 1/2	7 31/32	5 3/16	9 3/16	5 7/8	10 13/32	6 9/16	11 19/32	7 1/4	1-0 13/16	7 15/16	1-2 1/32
5/8	4 9/16	8 1/32	5 1/4	9 1/4	5 15/16	10 15/32	6 5/8	11 11/16	7 5/16	1-0 29/32	8	1-2 3/32
11/16	4 19/32	8 1/8	5 9/32	9 11/32	5 31/32	10 17/32	6 21/32	11 3/4	7 11/32	1-0 31/32	8 1/32	1-2 3/16
3/4	4 5/8	8 3/16	5 5/16	9 13/32	6	10 5/8	6 11/16	11 27/32	7 3/8	1-1 1/32	8 1/16	1-2 1/4
13/16	4 11/16	8 9/32	5 3/8	9 15/32	6 1/16	10 11/16	6 3/4	11 29/32	7 7/16	1-1 1/8	8 1/8	1-2 11/32
7/8	4 23/32	8 11/32	5 13/32	9 9/16	6 3/32	10 25/32	6 25/32	11 31/32	7 15/32	1-1 3/16	8 5/32	1-2 13/32
15/16	4 25/32	8 13/32	5 15/32	9 5/8	6 5/32	10 27/32	6 27/32	1-0 1/16	7 17/32	1-1 9/32	8 7/32	1-2 1/2

Feet	0' Rise	0' Slope	10' Rise	10' Slope	20' Rise	20' Slope	30' Rise	30' Slope
0	0	0	6-10 1/2	12-1 5/8	13-9	24-3 1/4	20-7 1/2	36-4 7/8
1	8 1/4	1-2 9/16	7-6 3/4	13-4 5/16	14-5 1/4	25-5 13/16	21-3 3/4	37-7 7/16
2	1-4 1/2	2-5 1/8	8-3	14-6 3/4	15-1 1/2	26-8 3/8	22-0	38-10
3	2-0 3/4	3-7 11/16	8-11 1/4	15-9 5/16	15-9 3/4	27-10 15/16	22-8 1/4	40-0 9/16
4	2-9	4-10 1/4	9-7 1/2	16-11 7/8	16-6	29-1 1/2	23-4 1/2	41-3 1/8
5	3-5 1/4	6-0 13/16	10-3 3/4	18-2 7/16	17-2 1/4	30-4 1/16	24-0 3/4	42-5 11/16
6	4-1 1/2	7-3 3/8	11-0	19-5	17-10 1/2	31-6 5/8	24-9	43-8 1/4
7	4-9 3/4	8-5 15/16	11-8 1/4	20-7 9/16	18-6 3/4	32-9 3/16	25-5 1/4	44-10 13/16
8	5-6	9-8 1/2	12-4 1/2	21-10 1/8	19-3	33-11 3/4	26-1 1/2	46-1 3/8
9	6-2 1/4	10-11 1/16	13-0 3/4	23-0 11/16	19-11 1/4	35-2 5/16	26-9 3/4	47-3 15/16

A = 34° 30′ 31″; logsin A = 9.75322; logcos A = 9.91595; logtan A = 9.83727; logcot A = 0.16273

Ins.	12" Rise	12" Slope	13" Rise	13" Slope	14" Rise	14" Slope	15" Rise	15" Slope	16" Rise	16" Slope
0	8 1/4	1-2 9/16	8 15/16	1-3 25/32	9 5/8	1-5	10 5/16	1-6 3/16	11	1-7 13/32
1/16	8 9/32	1-2 5/8	8 31/32	1-3 27/32	9 21/32	1-5 1/16	10 11/32	1-6 9/32	11 1/32	1-7 1/2
1/8	8 11/32	1-2 23/32	9 1/32	1-3 15/16	9 23/32	1-5 5/32	10 13/32	1-6 11/32	11 3/32	1-7 9/16
3/16	8 3/8	1-2 25/32	9 1/16	1-4	9 3/4	1-5 7/32	10 7/16	1-6 7/16	11 1/8	1-7 21/32
1/4	8 7/16	1-2 7/8	9 1/8	1-4 3/32	9 13/16	1-5 9/32	10 1/2	1-6 1/2	11 3/16	1-7 23/32
5/16	8 15/32	1-2 15/16	9 5/32	1-4 5/32	9 27/32	1-5 3/8	10 17/32	1-6 19/32	11 7/32	1-7 25/32
3/8	8 1/2	1-3 1/32	9 3/16	1-4 7/32	9 7/8	1-5 7/16	10 9/16	1-6 21/32	11 1/4	1-7 7/8
7/16	8 9/16	1-3 3/32	9 1/4	1-4 5/16	9 15/16	1-5 17/32	10 5/8	1-6 23/32	11 5/16	1-7 15/16
1/2	8 19/32	1-3 5/32	9 9/32	1-4 3/8	9 31/32	1-5 19/32	10 21/32	1-6 13/16	11 11/32	1-8 1/32
9/16	8 5/8	1-3 1/4	9 5/16	1-4 15/32	10	1-5 11/16	10 11/16	1-6 7/8	11 3/8	1-8 3/32
5/8	8 11/16	1-3 5/16	9 3/8	1-4 17/32	10 1/16	1-5 3/4	10 3/4	1-6 31/32	11 7/16	1-8 3/16
11/16	8 23/32	1-3 13/32	9 13/32	1-4 5/8	10 3/32	1-5 13/16	10 25/32	1-7 1/32	11 15/32	1-8 1/4
3/4	8 3/4	1-3 15/32	9 7/16	1-4 11/16	10 1/8	1-5 29/32	10 13/16	1-7 1/8	11 1/2	1-8 5/16
13/16	8 13/16	1-3 9/16	9 1/2	1-4 3/4	10 3/16	1-5 31/32	10 7/8	1-7 3/16	11 9/16	1-8 13/32
7/8	8 27/32	1-3 5/8	9 17/32	1-4 27/32	10 7/32	1-6 1/16	10 29/32	1-7 1/4	11 19/32	1-8 15/32
15/16	8 29/32	1-3 11/16	9 19/32	1-4 29/32	10 9/32	1-6 1/8	10 31/32	1-7 11/32	11 21/32	1-8 9/16

Ins.	17" Rise	17" Slope	18" Rise	18" Slope	19" Rise	19" Slope	20" Rise	20" Slope	21" Rise	21" Slope
0	11 11/16	1-8 5/8	1-0 3/8	1-9 27/32	1-1 1/16	1-11 1/16	1-1 3/4	2-0 9/32	1-2 7/16	2-1 15/32
1/16	11 23/32	1-8 23/32	1-0 13/32	1-9 29/32	1-1 3/32	1-11 1/8	1-1 25/32	2-0 11/32	1-2 15/32	2-1 9/16
1/8	11 25/32	1-8 25/32	1-0 15/32	1-10	1-1 5/32	1-11 7/32	1-1 27/32	2-0 7/16	1-2 17/32	2-1 5/8
3/16	11 13/16	1-8 27/32	1-0 1/2	1-10 1/16	1-1 3/16	1-11 9/32	1-1 7/8	2-0 1/2	1-2 9/16	2-1 23/32
1/4	11 7/8	1-8 15/16	1-0 9/16	1-10 5/32	1-1 1/4	1-11 3/8	1-1 15/16	2-0 9/16	1-2 5/8	2-1 25/32
5/16	11 29/32	1-9	1-0 19/32	1-10 7/32	1-1 9/32	1-11 7/16	1-1 31/32	2-0 21/32	1-2 21/32	2-1 7/8
3/8	11 15/16	1-9 3/32	1-0 5/8	1-10 5/16	1-1 5/16	1-11 1/2	1-2	2-0 23/32	1-2 11/16	2-1 15/16
7/16	1-0	1-9 5/32	1-0 11/16	1-10 3/8	1-1 3/8	1-11 19/32	1-2 1/16	2-0 13/16	1-2 3/4	2-2
1/2	1-0 1/32	1-9 1/4	1-0 23/32	1-10 7/16	1-1 13/32	1-11 21/32	1-2 3/32	2-0 7/8	1-2 25/32	2-2 3/32
9/16	1-0 1/16	1-9 5/16	1-0 3/4	1-10 17/32	1-1 7/16	1-11 3/4	1-2 1/8	2-0 31/32	1-2 13/16	2-2 5/32
5/8	1-0 1/8	1-9 3/8	1-0 13/16	1-10 19/32	1-1 1/2	1-11 13/16	1-2 3/16	2-1 1/32	1-2 7/8	2-2 1/4
11/16	1-0 5/32	1-9 15/32	1-0 27/32	1-10 11/16	1-1 17/32	1-11 29/32	1-2 7/32	2-1 3/32	1-2 29/32	2-2 5/16
3/4	1-0 3/16	1-9 17/32	1-0 7/8	1-10 3/4	1-1 9/16	1-11 31/32	1-2 1/4	2-1 3/16	1-2 15/16	2-2 13/32
13/16	1-0 1/4	1-9 5/8	1-0 15/16	1-10 27/32	1-1 5/8	2-0 1/32	1-2 5/16	2-1 1/4	1-3	2-2 15/32
7/8	1-0 9/32	1-9 11/16	1-0 31/32	1-10 29/32	1-1 21/32	2-0 1/8	1-2 11/32	2-1 11/32	1-3 1/32	2-2 17/32
15/16	1-0 11/32	1-9 25/32	1-1 1/32	1-10 31/32	1-1 23/32	2-0 3/16	1-2 13/32	2-1 13/32	1-3 3/32	2-2 5/8

Feet	40' Rise	40' Slope	50' Rise	50' Slope	60' Rise	60' Slope	70' Rise	70' Slope
0	27-6	48-6 1/2	34-4 1/2	60-8 1/8	41-3	72-9 3/4	48-1 1/2	84-11 3/8
1	28-2 1/4	49-9 1/16	35-0 3/4	61-10 11/16	41-11 1/4	74-0 5/16	48-9 3/4	86-1 15/16
2	28-10 1/2	50-11 5/8	35-9	63-1 1/4	42-7 1/2	75-2 7/8	49-6	87-4 1/2
3	29-6 3/4	52-2 3/16	36-5 1/4	64-3 13/16	43-3 3/4	76-5 7/16	50-2 1/4	88-7 1/16
4	30-3	53-4 3/4	37-1 1/2	65-6 3/8	44-0	77-8	50-10 5/8	89-9 5/8
5	30-11 1/4	54-7 5/16	37-9 3/4	66-8 15/16	44-8 1/4	78-10 9/16	51-6 3/4	91-0 3/16
6	31-7 1/2	55-9 7/8	38-6	67-11 1/2	45-4 1/2	80-1 1/8	52-3	92-2 3/4
7	32-3 3/4	57-0 7/16	39-2 1/4	69-2 1/16	46-0 3/4	81-3 11/16	52-11 1/4	93-5 5/16
8	33-0	58-3	39-10 1/2	70-4 5/8	46-9	82-6 1/4	53-7 1/2	94-7 7/8
9	33-8 1/4	59-5 9/16	40-6 3/4	71-7 3/16	47-5 1/4	83-8 13/16	54-3 3/4	95-10 7/16

natsin A=0.5665288229; **natcos** A=0.8240419242; **nattan** A=0.6875000000; **natcot** A=1.4545454545

Inches	0″ Rise	0″ Slope	1″ Rise	1″ Slope	2″ Rise	2″ Slope	3″ Rise	3″ Slope	4″ Rise	4″ Slope	5″ Rise	5″ Slope
0	0	0	11/16	1 7/32	1 3/8	2 7/16	2 1/16	3 21/32	2 25/32	4 7/8	3 15/32	6 3/32
1/16	1/32	1/16	3/4	1 9/32	1 7/16	2 1/2	2 1/8	3 23/32	2 13/16	4 15/16	3 1/2	6 5/32
1/8	3/32	5/32	25/32	1 3/8	1 15/32	2 19/32	2 5/32	3 13/16	2 27/32	5 1/32	3 9/16	6 1/4
3/16	1/8	7/32	13/16	1 7/16	1 1/2	2 21/32	2 7/32	3 7/8	2 29/32	5 3/32	3 19/32	6 5/16
1/4	3/16	5/16	7/8	1 17/32	1 9/16	2 3/4	2 1/4	3 31/32	2 15/16	5 5/32	3 5/8	6 3/8
5/16	7/32	3/8	29/32	1 19/32	1 19/32	2 13/16	2 9/32	4 1/32	3	5 1/4	3 11/16	6 15/32
3/8	1/4	15/32	15/16	1 11/16	1 21/32	2 7/8	2 11/32	4 3/32	3 1/32	5 5/16	3 23/32	6 17/32
7/16	5/16	17/32	1	1 3/4	1 11/16	2 31/32	2 3/8	4 3/16	3 1/16	5 13/32	3 25/32	6 5/8
1/2	11/32	19/32	1 1/16	1 13/16	1 23/32	3 1/32	2 7/16	4 1/4	3 1/8	5 15/32	3 13/16	6 11/16
9/16	3/8	11/16	1 3/32	1 29/32	1 25/32	3 1/8	2 15/32	4 11/32	3 5/32	5 9/16	3 27/32	6 25/32
5/8	7/16	3/4	1 1/8	1 31/32	1 13/16	3 3/16	2 1/2	4 13/32	3 7/32	5 5/8	3 29/32	6 27/32
11/16	15/32	27/32	1 5/32	2 1/16	1 7/8	3 9/32	2 9/16	4 1/2	3 1/4	5 11/16	3 15/16	6 29/32
3/4	17/32	29/32	1 7/32	2 1/8	1 29/32	3 11/32	2 19/32	4 9/16	3 9/32	5 25/32	3 31/32	7
13/16	9/16	1	1 1/4	2 7/32	1 15/16	3 13/32	2 21/32	4 5/8	3 11/32	5 27/32	4 1/32	7 1/16
7/8	19/32	1 1/16	1 5/16	2 9/32	2	3 1/2	2 11/16	4 23/32	3 3/8	5 15/16	4 1/16	7 5/32
15/16	21/32	1 3/32	1 11/32	2 11/32	2 1/32	3 9/16	2 23/32	4 25/32	3 13/32	6	4 1/8	7 7/32

Inches	6″ Rise	6″ Slope	7″ Rise	7″ Slope	8″ Rise	8″ Slope	9″ Rise	9″ Slope	10″ Rise	10″ Slope	11″ Rise	11″ Slope
0	4 5/32	7 5/32	4 27/32	8 1/2	5 17/32	9 23/32	6 1/8	10 15/16	6 15/16	1-0 5/32	7 5/8	1-1 3/8
1/16	4 3/16	7 3/8	4 29/32	8 19/32	5 19/32	9 13/16	6 9/32	11 1/32	6 31/32	1-0 1/4	7 21/32	1-1 15/32
1/8	4 1/4	7 7/16	4 15/16	8 21/32	5 5/8	9 7/8	6 5/16	11 3/32	7	1-0 5/16	7 23/32	1-1 17/32
3/16	4 9/32	7 17/32	4 31/32	8 3/4	5 21/32	9 31/32	6 3/8	11 3/16	7 1/16	1-0 13/32	7 3/4	1-1 5/8
1/4	4 11/32	7 19/32	5 1/32	8 13/16	5 23/32	10 1/16	6 13/32	11 1/4	7 3/32	1-0 15/32	7 25/32	1-1 11/16
5/16	4 3/8	7 11/16	5 1/16	8 29/32	5 3/4	10 1/8	6 7/16	11 11/32	7 5/32	1-0 17/32	7 27/32	1-1 3/4
3/8	4 13/32	7 3/4	5 3/32	8 31/32	5 13/16	10 3/16	6 1/2	11 13/32	7 3/16	1-0 5/8	7 7/8	1-1 27/32
7/16	4 15/32	7 27/32	5 5/32	9 1/16	5 27/32	10 1/4	6 17/32	11 15/32	7 1/4	1-0 11/16	7 15/16	1-1 29/32
1/2	4 1/2	7 29/32	5 3/16	9 1/8	5 7/8	10 11/32	6 19/32	11 9/16	7 9/32	1-0 25/32	7 31/32	1-2
9/16	4 17/32	7 31/32	5 1/4	9 3/16	5 15/16	10 13/32	6 5/8	11 5/8	7 5/16	1-0 27/32	8	1-2 1/16
5/8	4 19/32	8 1/16	5 9/32	9 9/32	5 31/32	10 1/2	6 21/32	11 23/32	7 3/8	1-0 15/16	8 1/16	1-2 5/32
11/16	4 5/8	8 1/8	5 5/16	9 11/32	6 1/32	10 9/16	6 23/32	11 25/32	7 13/32	1-1	8 3/32	1-2 7/32
3/4	4 11/16	8 7/32	5 3/8	9 7/16	6 1/16	10 21/32	6 3/4	11 7/8	7 7/16	1-1 1/16	8 1/8	1-2 9/32
13/16	4 23/32	8 9/32	5 13/32	9 1/2	6 3/32	10 23/32	6 13/16	11 15/16	7 1/2	1-1 5/32	8 3/16	1-2 3/8
7/8	4 3/4	8 3/8	5 15/32	9 19/32	6 5/32	10 25/32	6 27/32	1-0	7 17/32	1-1 7/32	8 7/32	1-2 7/16
15/16	4 13/16	8 7/16	5 1/2	9 21/32	6 3/16	10 7/8	6 7/8	1-0 3/32	7 9/16	1-1 5/16	8 9/32	1-2 17/32

Feet	0′ Rise	0′ Slope	10′ Rise	10′ Slope	20′ Rise	20′ Slope	30′ Rise	30′ Slope
0	0	0	6-11 1/8	12-1 31/32	13-10 1/4	24-3 31/32	20-9 3/8	36-5 15/16
1	8 5/16	1-2 19/32	7-7 7/16	13-4 9/16	14-6 9/16	25-6 9/16	21-5 11/16	37-8 17/32
2	1-4 5/8	2-5 3/16	8-3 3/4	14-7 3/16	15-2 7/8	26-9 5/32	22-2	38-11 1/8
3	2-0 15/16	3-7 25/32	9-0 1/16	15-9 25/32	15-11 3/16	27-11 3/4	22-10 5/16	40-1 23/32
4	2-9 1/4	4-10 13/32	9-8 3/8	17-0 3/8	16-7 1/2	29-2 11/32	23-6 5/8	41-4 5/16
5	3-5 9/16	6-1	10-4 11/16	18-2 31/32	17-3 13/16	30-4 15/16	24-2 15/16	42-6 15/16
6	4-1 7/8	7-3 19/32	11-1	19-5 9/16	18-0 1/8	31-7 17/32	24-11 1/4	43-9 17/32
7	4-10 3/16	8-6 3/16	11-9 5/16	20-8 5/32	18-8 7/16	32-10 5/32	25-7 9/16	45-0 1/8
8	5-6 1/2	9-8 25/32	12-5 5/8	21-10 3/4	19-4 3/4	34-0 3/4	26-3 7/8	46-2 23/32
9	6-2 13/16	10-11 3/8	13-1 15/16	23-1 3/8	20-1 1/16	35-3 11/32	27-0 3/16	47-5 5/16

A = 34° 42′ 38″; logsin A = 9.75544; logcos A = 9.91489; logtan A = 9.84055; logcot A = 0.15945

In.	12″ Rise	Slope	13″ Rise	Slope	14″ Rise	Slope	15″ Rise	Slope	16″ Rise	Slope
0	8 5/16	1-2 19/32	9	1-3 13/16	9 11/16	1-5 1/32	10 3/8	1-6 1/4	11 3/32	1-7 15/32
1/16	8 11/32	1-2 11/16	9 1/16	1-3 7/8	9 3/4	1-5 3/32	10 7/16	1-6 5/16	11 1/8	1-7 17/32
1/8	8 13/32	1-2 3/4	9 3/32	1-3 31/32	9 25/32	1-5 3/16	10 15/32	1-6 13/32	11 5/32	1-7 5/8
3/16	8 7/16	1-2 13/16	9 1/8	1-4 1/32	9 13/16	1-5 1/4	10 17/32	1-6 15/32	11 7/32	1-7 11/16
1/4	8 1/2	1-2 29/32	9 3/16	1-4 1/8	9 7/8	1-5 11/32	10 9/16	1-6 9/16	11 1/4	1-7 25/32
5/16	8 17/32	1-2 31/32	9 7/32	1-4 3/16	9 29/32	1-5 13/32	10 19/32	1-6 5/8	11 5/16	1-7 27/32
3/8	8 9/16	1-3 1/16	9 1/4	1-4 9/32	9 31/32	1-5 1/2	10 21/32	1-6 23/32	11 11/32	1-7 29/32
7/16	8 5/8	1-3 1/8	9 5/16	1-4 11/32	10	1-5 9/16	10 11/16	1-6 25/32	11 3/8	1-8
1/2	8 21/32	1-3 7/32	9 11/32	1-4 7/16	10 1/32	1-5 5/8	10 3/4	1-6 27/32	11 7/16	1-8 1/32
9/16	8 11/16	1-3 9/32	9 13/32	1-4 1/2	10 3/32	1-5 23/32	10 25/32	1-6 15/16	11 15/32	1-8 5/32
5/8	8 3/4	1-3 11/32	9 7/16	1-4 9/16	10 1/8	1-5 25/32	10 13/16	1-7	11 17/32	1-8 7/32
11/16	8 25/32	1-3 7/16	9 15/32	1-4 21/32	10 3/16	1-5 7/8	10 7/8	1-7 3/32	11 9/16	1-8 5/16
3/4	8 27/32	1-3 1/2	9 17/32	1-4 23/32	10 7/32	1-5 15/16	10 29/32	1-7 5/32	11 19/32	1-8 3/8
13/16	8 7/8	1-3 19/32	9 9/16	1-4 13/16	10 1/4	1-6 1/32	10 31/32	1-7 1/4	11 21/32	1-8 7/16
7/8	8 29/32	1-3 21/32	9 5/8	1-4 7/8	10 5/16	1-6 3/32	11	1-7 5/16	11 11/16	1-8 17/32
15/16	8 31/32	1-3 3/4	9 21/32	1-4 31/32	10 11/32	1-6 3/16	11 1/32	1-7 3/8	11 23/32	1-8 19/32

In.	17″ Rise	Slope	18″ Rise	Slope	19″ Rise	Slope	20″ Rise	Slope	21″ Rise	Slope
0	11 25/32	1-8 11/16	1-0 15/32	1-9 29/32	1-1 5/32	1-11 1/8	1-1 27/32	2-0 11/32	1-2 9/16	2-1 17/32
1/16	11 13/16	1-8 3/4	1-0 1/2	1-9 31/32	1-1 7/32	1-11 3/16	1-1 29/32	2-0 13/32	1-2 19/32	2-1 5/8
1/8	11 7/8	1-8 27/32	1-0 9/16	1-10 1/16	1-1 1/4	1-11 1/4	1-1 15/16	2-0 15/32	1-2 5/8	2-1 11/16
3/16	11 29/32	1-8 29/32	1-0 19/32	1-10 1/8	1-1 9/32	1-11 11/32	1-1 31/32	2-0 9/16	1-2 11/16	2-1 25/32
1/4	11 15/16	1-9	1-0 21/32	1-10 3/16	1-1 11/32	1-11 13/32	1-2 1/32	2-0 5/8	1-2 23/32	2-1 27/32
5/16	1-0	1-9 1/16	1-0 11/16	1-10 9/32	1-1 3/8	1-11 1/2	1-2 1/16	2-0 23/32	1-2 3/4	2-1 15/16
3/8	1-0 1/16	1-9 1/8	1-0 23/32	1-10 11/32	1-1 13/32	1-11 19/32	1-2 1/8	2-0 25/32	1-2 13/16	2-2
7/16	1-0 3/32	1-9 7/32	1-0 25/32	1-10 7/16	1-1 15/32	1-11 21/32	1-2 5/32	2-0 7/8	1-2 27/32	2-2 3/32
1/2	1-0 1/8	1-9 9/32	1-0 13/16	1-10 1/2	1-1 1/2	1-11 23/32	1-2 3/16	2-0 15/16	1-2 29/32	2-2 5/32
9/16	1-0 5/32	1-9 3/8	1-0 27/32	1-10 19/32	1-1 9/16	1-11 13/16	1-2 1/4	2-1	1-2 15/16	2-2 7/32
5/8	1-0 7/32	1-9 7/16	1-0 29/32	1-10 21/32	1-1 19/32	1-11 7/8	1-2 9/32	2-1 3/32	1-2 31/32	2-2 5/16
11/16	1-0 1/4	1-9 17/32	1-0 15/16	1-10 23/32	1-1 5/8	1-11 15/16	1-2 11/32	2-1 5/32	1-3 1/32	2-2 3/8
3/4	1-0 9/32	1-9 19/32	1-1	1-10 13/16	1-1 11/16	2-0 1/32	1-2 3/8	2-1 1/4	1-3 1/16	2-2 15/32
13/16	1-0 11/32	1-9 21/32	1-1 1/32	1-10 7/8	1-1 23/32	2-0 3/32	1-2 13/32	2-1 5/16	1-3 1/8	2-2 17/32
7/8	1-0 3/8	1-9 3/4	1-1 1/16	1-10 31/32	1-1 25/32	2-0 3/16	1-2 15/32	2-1 13/32	1-3 5/32	2-2 5/8
15/16	1-0 7/16	1-9 13/16	1-1 1/8	1-11 1/32	1-1 13/16	2-0 1/4	1-2 1/2	2-1 15/32	1-3 3/16	2-2 11/16

Feet	40′ Rise	Slope	50′ Rise	Slope	60′ Rise	Slope	70′ Rise	Slope
0	27-8 1/2	48-7 29/32	34-7 5/8	60-9 29/32	41-6 3/4	72-11 7/8	48-5 7/8	85-1 27/32
1	28-4 13/16	49-10 1/2	35-3 15/16	62-0 1/2	42-3 1/16	74-2 15/32	49-2 3/16	86-4 7/16
2	29-1 1/8	51-1 1/8	36-0 1/4	63-3 3/32	42-11 3/8	75-5 1/16	49-10 1/2	87-7 1/32
3	29-9 7/16	52-3 23/32	36-8 9/16	64-5 11/32	43-7 11/16	76-7 21/32	50-6 13/16	88-9 21/32
4	30-5 3/4	53-6 5/16	37-4 7/8	65-8 9/32	44-4	77-10 1/4	51-3 1/8	90-0 1/4
5	31-2 1/16	54-8 29/32	38-1 3/8	66-10 7/8	45-0 5/16	79-0 7/8	51-11 7/16	91-2 27/32
6	31-10 3/8	55-11 1/2	38-9 1/2	68-1 15/32	45-8 5/8	80-3 15/32	52-7 3/4	92-5 7/16
7	32-6 11/16	57-2 3/32	39-5 13/16	69-4 3/32	46-4 15/16	81-6 1/16	53-4 1/16	93-8 1/32
8	33-3	58-4 11/16	40-2 1/8	70-6 11/16	47-1 1/4	82-8 21/32	54-0 3/8	94-10 5/8
9	33-11 5/16	59-7 9/32	40-10 7/16	71-9 9/32	47-9 9/16	83-11 1/4	54-8 11/16	96-1 7/32

natsin A=0.5694325932; natcos A=0.8220380293; nattan A=0.6927083333; natcot A=1.4436090225

Inches	0" Rise	0" Slope	1" Rise	1" Slope	2" Rise	2" Slope	3" Rise	3" Slope	4" Rise	4" Slope	5" Rise	5" Slope
0	0	0	11/16	17/32	1 13/32	2 7/16	2 3/32	3 21/32	2 25/32	4 7/8	3 1/2	6 3/32
1/16	1/32	1/16	3/4	1 9/32	1 7/16	2 1/2	2 1/8	3 3/4	2 27/32	4 31/32	3 17/32	6 3/16
1/8	3/32	5/32	25/32	1 3/8	1 15/32	2 19/32	2 3/16	3 13/16	2 7/8	5 1/32	3 9/16	6 1/4
3/16	1/8	1/32	27/32	1 7/16	1 17/32	2 21/32	2 7/32	3 7/8	2 15/16	5 3/32	3 5/8	6 5/16
1/4	3/16	5/16	7/8	1 17/32	1 9/16	2 3/4	2 9/32	3 31/32	2 31/32	5 3/16	3 21/32	6 13/32
5/16	7/32	3/8	29/32	1 19/32	1 5/8	2 13/16	2 5/16	4 1/32	3	5 1/4	3 23/32	6 15/32
3/8	1/4	15/32	31/32	1 11/16	1 21/32	2 29/32	2 11/32	4 1/8	3 1/16	5 11/32	3 3/4	6 9/16
7/16	5/16	17/32	1	1 3/4	1 11/16	2 31/32	2 13/32	4 3/16	3 3/32	5 13/32	3 25/32	6 5/8
1/2	11/32	5/8	1 1/16	1 27/32	1 3/4	3 1/16	2 7/16	4 9/32	3 1/8	5 1/2	3 27/32	6 23/32
9/16	13/32	11/16	1 3/32	1 29/32	1 25/32	3 1/8	2 1/2	4 11/32	3 3/16	5 9/16	3 7/8	6 25/32
5/8	7/16	3/4	1 1/8	1 31/32	1 27/32	3 3/16	2 17/32	4 13/32	3 7/32	5 5/8	3 15/16	6 7/8
11/16	15/32	27/32	1 3/16	2 1/16	1 7/8	3 9/32	2 9/16	4 1/2	3 9/32	5 23/32	3 31/32	6 15/16
3/4	17/32	29/32	1 7/32	2 1/8	1 29/32	3 11/32	2 5/8	4 9/16	3 5/16	5 25/32	4	7
13/16	9/16	1	1 1/4	2 7/32	1 31/32	3 7/16	2 21/32	4 21/32	3 11/32	5 7/8	4 1/16	7 3/32
7/8	5/8	1 1/16	1 5/16	2 9/32	2	3 1/2	2 23/32	4 23/32	3 13/32	5 15/16	4 3/32	7 5/32
15/16	21/32	1 5/32	1 11/32	2 3/8	2 1/16	3 19/32	2 3/4	4 13/16	3 7/16	6 1/32	4 5/32	7 1/4

Inches	6" Rise	6" Slope	7" Rise	7" Slope	8" Rise	8" Slope	9" Rise	9" Slope	10" Rise	10" Slope	11" Rise	11" Slope
0	4 3/16	7 5/32	4 7/8	8 17/32	5 19/32	9 3/4	6 9/32	10 31/32	6 31/32	1-0 3/16	7 11/16	1-1 13/32
1/16	4 7/32	7 13/32	4 15/16	8 5/8	5 5/8	9 27/32	6 5/16	11 1/16	7 1/32	1-0 9/32	7 23/32	1-1 1/2
1/8	4 9/32	7 15/32	4 31/32	8 11/16	5 21/32	9 29/32	6 3/8	11 1/8	7 1/16	1-0 11/32	7 3/4	1-1 9/16
3/16	4 5/16	7 17/32	5 1/32	8 3/4	5 23/32	9 31/32	6 13/32	11 3/16	7 1/8	1-0 7/16	7 13/16	1-1 21/32
1/4	4 3/8	7 5/8	5 1/16	8 27/32	5 3/4	10 1/16	6 15/32	11 9/32	7 5/32	1-0 1/2	7 27/32	1-1 23/32
5/16	4 13/32	7 11/16	5 3/32	8 29/32	5 13/16	10 1/8	6 1/2	11 11/32	7 3/16	1-0 9/16	7 29/32	1-1 25/32
3/8	4 7/16	7 25/32	5 5/32	9	5 27/32	10 7/32	6 17/32	11 7/16	7 1/4	1-0 21/32	7 15/16	1-1 7/8
7/16	4 1/2	7 27/32	5 3/16	9 1/16	5 7/8	10 9/32	6 19/32	11 1/2	7 9/32	1-0 23/32	7 31/32	1-1 15/16
1/2	4 17/32	7 15/16	5 1/4	9 5/32	5 15/16	10 3/8	6 5/8	11 19/32	7 5/16	1-0 13/16	8 1/32	1-2 1/32
9/16	4 19/32	8	5 9/32	9 7/32	5 31/32	10 7/16	6 11/16	11 21/32	7 3/8	1-0 7/8	8 1/16	1-2 3/32
5/8	4 5/8	8 3/32	5 5/16	9 5/16	6 1/32	10 17/32	6 23/32	11 3/4	7 13/32	1-0 31/32	8 1/8	1-2 3/16
11/16	4 21/32	8 5/32	5 3/8	9 3/8	6 1/16	10 19/32	6 3/4	11 13/16	7 15/32	1-1 1/32	8 5/32	1-2 1/4
3/4	4 23/32	8 7/32	5 13/32	9 7/16	6 3/32	10 21/32	6 13/16	11 7/8	7 1/2	1-1 3/32	8 3/16	1-2 11/32
13/16	4 3/4	8 5/16	5 7/16	9 17/32	6 5/32	10 3/4	6 27/32	11 31/32	7 17/32	1-1 3/16	8 1/4	1-2 13/32
7/8	4 13/16	8 3/8	5 1/2	9 19/32	6 3/16	10 13/16	6 29/32	1-0 1/32	7 19/32	1-1 1/4	8 9/32	1-2 15/32
15/16	4 27/32	8 15/32	5 17/32	9 11/16	6 1/4	10 29/32	6 15/16	1-0 1/8	7 5/8	1-1 11/32	8 11/32	1-2 9/16

Feet	0' Rise	0' Slope	10' Rise	10' Slope	20' Rise	20' Slope	30' Rise	30' Slope
0	0	0	6-11 3/4	12-2 11/32	13-11 1/2	24-4 21/32	20-11 1/4	36-7
1	8 3/8	1-2 5/8	7-8 1/8	13-4 31/32	14-7 7/8	25-7 5/16	21-7 5/8	37-9 5/8
2	1-4 3/4	2-5 9/32	8-4 1/2	14-7 19/32	15-4 1/4	26-9 15/16	22-4	39-0 9/32
3	2-1 1/8	3-7 29/32	9-0 7/8	15-10 1/4	16-0 5/8	28-0 9/16	23-0 3/8	40-2 29/32
4	2-9 1/2	4-10 17/32	9-9 1/4	17-0 7/8	16-9	29-3 7/32	23-8 3/4	41-5 17/32
5	3-5 7/8	6-1 5/32	10-5 5/8	18-3 1/2	17-5 3/8	30-5 27/32	24-5 1/8	42-8 3/16
6	4-2 1/4	7-3 13/16	11-2	19-6 1/8	18-1 3/4	31-8 15/32	25-1 1/2	43-10 13/16
7	4-10 5/8	8-6 7/16	11-10 3/8	20-8 25/32	18-10 1/8	32-11 3/32	25-9 7/8	45-1 7/16
8	5-7	9-9 1/16	12-6 3/4	21-11 13/32	19-6 1/2	34-1 3/4	26-6 1/4	46-4 1/16
9	6-3 3/8	10-11 11/16	13-3 1/8	23-2 1/32	20-2 7/8	35-4 3/8	27-2 5/8	47-6 23/32

A = 34° 54' 43''; logsin A = 9.75764; logcos A = 9.91383; logtan A = 9.84380; logcot A = 0.15620

In.	12″ Rise	12″ Slope	13″ Rise	13″ Slope	14″ Rise	14″ Slope	15″ Rise	15″ Slope	16″ Rise	16″ Slope
0	$8\frac{3}{8}$	$1\text{-}2\frac{5}{8}$	$9\frac{1}{16}$	$1\text{-}3\frac{27}{32}$	$9\frac{25}{32}$	$1\text{-}5\frac{1}{16}$	$10\frac{15}{32}$	$1\text{-}6\frac{9}{32}$	$11\frac{5}{8}$	$1\text{-}7\frac{1}{2}$
1/16	$8\frac{13}{32}$	$1\text{-}2\frac{23}{32}$	$9\frac{1}{8}$	$1\text{-}3\frac{15}{16}$	$9\frac{13}{16}$	$1\text{-}5\frac{5}{32}$	$10\frac{1}{2}$	$1\text{-}6\frac{3}{8}$	$11\frac{7}{32}$	$1\text{-}7\frac{19}{32}$
1/8	$8\frac{15}{32}$	$1\text{-}2\frac{25}{32}$	$9\frac{5}{32}$	$1\text{-}4$	$9\frac{27}{32}$	$1\text{-}5\frac{7}{32}$	$10\frac{9}{16}$	$1\text{-}6\frac{7}{16}$	$11\frac{1}{4}$	$1\text{-}7\frac{21}{32}$
3/16	$8\frac{1}{2}$	$1\text{-}2\frac{7}{8}$	$9\frac{7}{32}$	$1\text{-}4\frac{3}{32}$	$9\frac{29}{32}$	$1\text{-}5\frac{5}{16}$	$10\frac{19}{32}$	$1\text{-}6\frac{17}{32}$	$11\frac{5}{16}$	$1\text{-}7\frac{3}{4}$
1/4	$8\frac{9}{16}$	$1\text{-}2\frac{15}{16}$	$9\frac{1}{4}$	$1\text{-}4\frac{5}{32}$	$9\frac{15}{16}$	$1\text{-}5\frac{3}{8}$	$10\frac{21}{32}$	$1\text{-}6\frac{19}{32}$	$11\frac{11}{32}$	$1\text{-}7\frac{13}{16}$
5/16	$8\frac{19}{32}$	$1\text{-}3$	$9\frac{9}{32}$	$1\text{-}4\frac{7}{32}$	10	$1\text{-}5\frac{15}{32}$	$10\frac{11}{16}$	$1\text{-}6\frac{11}{16}$	$11\frac{3}{8}$	$1\text{-}7\frac{29}{32}$
3/8	$8\frac{5}{8}$	$1\text{-}3\frac{3}{32}$	$9\frac{11}{32}$	$1\text{-}4\frac{5}{16}$	$10\frac{1}{8}$	$1\text{-}5\frac{17}{32}$	$10\frac{23}{32}$	$1\text{-}6\frac{3}{4}$	$11\frac{7}{16}$	$1\text{-}7\frac{31}{32}$
7/16	$8\frac{11}{16}$	$1\text{-}3\frac{5}{32}$	$9\frac{3}{8}$	$1\text{-}4\frac{3}{8}$	$10\frac{1}{16}$	$1\text{-}5\frac{19}{32}$	$10\frac{25}{32}$	$1\text{-}6\frac{13}{16}$	$11\frac{15}{32}$	$1\text{-}8\frac{1}{2}$
1/2	$8\frac{23}{32}$	$1\text{-}3\frac{1}{4}$	$9\frac{7}{16}$	$1\text{-}4\frac{15}{32}$	$10\frac{1}{8}$	$1\text{-}5\frac{11}{16}$	$10\frac{13}{16}$	$1\text{-}6\frac{29}{32}$	$11\frac{1}{2}$	$1\text{-}8\frac{1}{8}$
9/16	$8\frac{25}{32}$	$1\text{-}3\frac{5}{16}$	$9\frac{15}{32}$	$1\text{-}4\frac{17}{32}$	$10\frac{5}{32}$	$1\text{-}5\frac{3}{4}$	$10\frac{7}{8}$	$1\text{-}6\frac{31}{32}$	$11\frac{9}{16}$	$1\text{-}8\frac{3}{16}$
5/8	$8\frac{13}{16}$	$1\text{-}3\frac{13}{32}$	$9\frac{1}{2}$	$1\text{-}4\frac{5}{8}$	$10\frac{7}{32}$	$1\text{-}5\frac{27}{32}$	$10\frac{29}{32}$	$1\text{-}7\frac{1}{16}$	$11\frac{19}{32}$	$1\text{-}8\frac{9}{32}$
11/16	$8\frac{27}{32}$	$1\text{-}3\frac{15}{32}$	$9\frac{9}{16}$	$1\text{-}4\frac{11}{16}$	$10\frac{1}{4}$	$1\text{-}5\frac{29}{32}$	$10\frac{15}{16}$	$1\text{-}7\frac{1}{8}$	$11\frac{21}{32}$	$1\text{-}8\frac{11}{32}$
3/4	$8\frac{29}{32}$	$1\text{-}3\frac{9}{16}$	$9\frac{19}{32}$	$1\text{-}4\frac{25}{32}$	$10\frac{9}{32}$	$1\text{-}6$	11	$1\text{-}7\frac{7}{32}$	$11\frac{11}{16}$	$1\text{-}8\frac{7}{16}$
13/16	$8\frac{15}{16}$	$1\text{-}3\frac{5}{8}$	$9\frac{5}{8}$	$1\text{-}4\frac{27}{32}$	$10\frac{11}{32}$	$1\text{-}6\frac{1}{16}$	$11\frac{1}{32}$	$1\text{-}7\frac{9}{32}$	$11\frac{23}{32}$	$1\text{-}8\frac{1}{2}$
7/8	9	$1\text{-}3\frac{11}{16}$	$9\frac{11}{16}$	$1\text{-}4\frac{29}{32}$	$10\frac{3}{8}$	$1\text{-}6\frac{1}{8}$	$11\frac{3}{32}$	$1\text{-}7\frac{11}{32}$	$11\frac{25}{32}$	$1\text{-}8\frac{19}{32}$
15/16	$9\frac{1}{32}$	$1\text{-}3\frac{25}{32}$	$9\frac{23}{32}$	$1\text{-}5$	$10\frac{7}{16}$	$1\text{-}6\frac{7}{32}$	$11\frac{1}{8}$	$1\text{-}7\frac{3}{4}$	$11\frac{13}{16}$	$1\text{-}8\frac{21}{32}$

In.	17″ Rise	17″ Slope	18″ Rise	18″ Slope	19″ Rise	19″ Slope	20″ Rise	20″ Slope	21″ Rise	21″ Slope
0	$11\frac{7}{8}$	$1\text{-}8\frac{23}{32}$	$1\text{-}0\frac{9}{16}$	$1\text{-}9\frac{15}{16}$	$1\text{-}1\frac{1}{4}$	$1\text{-}11\frac{5}{32}$	$1\text{-}1\frac{31}{32}$	$2\text{-}0\frac{3}{8}$	$1\text{-}2\frac{21}{32}$	$2\text{-}1\frac{19}{32}$
1/16	$11\frac{29}{32}$	$1\text{-}8\frac{13}{16}$	$1\text{-}0\frac{19}{32}$	$1\text{-}10\frac{1}{32}$	$1\text{-}1\frac{5}{16}$	$1\text{-}11\frac{1}{4}$	$1\text{-}2$	$2\text{-}0\frac{15}{32}$	$1\text{-}2\frac{11}{16}$	$2\text{-}1\frac{11}{16}$
1/8	$11\frac{15}{16}$	$1\text{-}8\frac{7}{8}$	$1\text{-}0\frac{21}{32}$	$1\text{-}10\frac{3}{32}$	$1\text{-}1\frac{11}{32}$	$1\text{-}11\frac{5}{16}$	$1\text{-}2\frac{1}{16}$	$2\text{-}0\frac{17}{32}$	$1\text{-}2\frac{3}{4}$	$2\text{-}1\frac{3}{4}$
3/16	$1\text{-}0$	$1\text{-}8\frac{31}{32}$	$1\text{-}0\frac{11}{16}$	$1\text{-}10\frac{3}{16}$	$1\text{-}1\frac{13}{32}$	$1\text{-}11\frac{13}{32}$	$1\text{-}2\frac{3}{32}$	$2\text{-}0\frac{5}{8}$	$1\text{-}2\frac{25}{32}$	$2\text{-}1\frac{27}{32}$
1/4	$1\text{-}0\frac{1}{2}$	$1\text{-}9\frac{1}{32}$	$1\text{-}0\frac{3}{4}$	$1\text{-}10\frac{1}{4}$	$1\text{-}1\frac{7}{16}$	$1\text{-}11\frac{15}{32}$	$1\text{-}2\frac{1}{8}$	$2\text{-}0\frac{11}{16}$	$1\text{-}2\frac{27}{32}$	$2\text{-}1\frac{29}{32}$
5/16	$1\text{-}0\frac{3}{32}$	$1\text{-}9\frac{1}{8}$	$1\text{-}0\frac{25}{32}$	$1\text{-}10\frac{11}{32}$	$1\text{-}1\frac{15}{32}$	$1\text{-}11\frac{9}{16}$	$1\text{-}2\frac{3}{16}$	$2\text{-}0\frac{25}{32}$	$1\text{-}2\frac{7}{8}$	$2\text{-}2$
3/8	$1\text{-}0\frac{1}{8}$	$1\text{-}9\frac{3}{32}$	$1\text{-}0\frac{13}{16}$	$1\text{-}10\frac{13}{32}$	$1\text{-}1\frac{17}{32}$	$1\text{-}11\frac{5}{8}$	$1\text{-}2\frac{7}{32}$	$2\text{-}0\frac{27}{32}$	$1\text{-}2\frac{29}{32}$	$2\text{-}2\frac{1}{16}$
7/16	$1\text{-}0\frac{5}{32}$	$1\text{-}9\frac{1}{4}$	$1\text{-}0\frac{7}{8}$	$1\text{-}10\frac{15}{32}$	$1\text{-}1\frac{9}{16}$	$1\text{-}11\frac{23}{32}$	$1\text{-}2\frac{1}{4}$	$2\text{-}0\frac{15}{16}$	$1\text{-}2\frac{31}{32}$	$2\text{-}2\frac{5}{32}$
1/2	$1\text{-}0\frac{7}{32}$	$1\text{-}9\frac{11}{32}$	$1\text{-}0\frac{29}{32}$	$1\text{-}10\frac{9}{16}$	$1\text{-}1\frac{5}{8}$	$1\text{-}11\frac{25}{32}$	$1\text{-}2\frac{5}{16}$	$2\text{-}1$	$1\text{-}3$	$2\text{-}2\frac{7}{32}$
9/16	$1\text{-}0\frac{1}{4}$	$1\text{-}9\frac{13}{32}$	$1\text{-}0\frac{31}{32}$	$1\text{-}10\frac{5}{8}$	$1\text{-}1\frac{21}{32}$	$1\text{-}11\frac{27}{32}$	$1\text{-}2\frac{11}{32}$	$2\text{-}1\frac{1}{16}$	$1\text{-}3\frac{1}{16}$	$2\text{-}2\frac{9}{32}$
5/8	$1\text{-}0\frac{5}{16}$	$1\text{-}9\frac{1}{2}$	$1\text{-}1$	$1\text{-}10\frac{23}{32}$	$1\text{-}1\frac{11}{16}$	$1\text{-}11\frac{15}{16}$	$1\text{-}2\frac{13}{32}$	$2\text{-}1\frac{5}{32}$	$1\text{-}3\frac{3}{32}$	$2\text{-}2\frac{3}{8}$
11/16	$1\text{-}0\frac{11}{32}$	$1\text{-}9\frac{9}{16}$	$1\text{-}1\frac{1}{32}$	$1\text{-}10\frac{25}{32}$	$1\text{-}1\frac{3}{4}$	$2\text{-}0$	$1\text{-}2\frac{7}{16}$	$2\text{-}1\frac{7}{32}$	$1\text{-}3\frac{1}{8}$	$2\text{-}2\frac{7}{16}$
3/4	$1\text{-}0\frac{3}{8}$	$1\text{-}9\frac{21}{32}$	$1\text{-}1\frac{3}{32}$	$1\text{-}10\frac{7}{8}$	$1\text{-}1\frac{25}{32}$	$2\text{-}0\frac{3}{32}$	$1\text{-}2\frac{15}{32}$	$2\text{-}1\frac{5}{16}$	$1\text{-}3\frac{3}{16}$	$2\text{-}2\frac{17}{32}$
13/16	$1\text{-}0\frac{7}{16}$	$1\text{-}9\frac{23}{32}$	$1\text{-}1\frac{1}{8}$	$1\text{-}10\frac{15}{16}$	$1\text{-}1\frac{13}{16}$	$2\text{-}0\frac{5}{32}$	$1\text{-}2\frac{17}{32}$	$2\text{-}1\frac{3}{8}$	$1\text{-}3\frac{7}{32}$	$2\text{-}2\frac{19}{32}$
7/8	$1\text{-}0\frac{15}{32}$	$1\text{-}9\frac{13}{16}$	$1\text{-}1\frac{3}{16}$	$1\text{-}11\frac{1}{32}$	$1\text{-}1\frac{7}{8}$	$2\text{-}0\frac{1}{4}$	$1\text{-}2\frac{9}{16}$	$2\text{-}1\frac{15}{32}$	$1\text{-}3\frac{9}{32}$	$2\text{-}2\frac{11}{16}$
15/16	$1\text{-}0\frac{17}{32}$	$1\text{-}9\frac{7}{8}$	$1\text{-}1\frac{7}{32}$	$1\text{-}11\frac{3}{32}$	$1\text{-}1\frac{29}{32}$	$2\text{-}0\frac{5}{16}$	$1\text{-}2\frac{5}{8}$	$2\text{-}1\frac{17}{32}$	$1\text{-}3\frac{5}{16}$	$2\text{-}2\frac{3}{4}$

Feet	40′ Rise	40′ Slope	50′ Rise	50′ Slope	60′ Rise	60′ Slope	70′ Rise	70′ Slope
0	27-11	$48\text{-}9\frac{11}{32}$	$34\text{-}10\frac{3}{4}$	$60\text{-}11\frac{11}{16}$	$41\text{-}10\frac{1}{2}$	73-2	$48\text{-}10\frac{1}{4}$	$85\text{-}4\frac{11}{32}$
1	$28\text{-}7\frac{3}{8}$	$49\text{-}11\frac{31}{32}$	$35\text{-}7\frac{3}{8}$	$62\text{-}2\frac{5}{16}$	$42\text{-}6\frac{7}{8}$	$74\text{-}4\frac{21}{32}$	$49\text{-}6\frac{5}{8}$	$86\text{-}6\frac{31}{32}$
2	$29\text{-}3\frac{3}{4}$	$51\text{-}2\frac{19}{32}$	$36\text{-}3\frac{1}{2}$	$63\text{-}4\frac{15}{16}$	$43\text{-}3\frac{1}{4}$	$75\text{-}7\frac{9}{32}$	50-3	$87\text{-}9\frac{5}{8}$
3	$30\text{-}0\frac{1}{8}$	$52\text{-}5\frac{1}{4}$	$36\text{-}11\frac{7}{8}$	$64\text{-}7\frac{9}{16}$	$43\text{-}11\frac{5}{8}$	$76\text{-}9\frac{29}{32}$	$50\text{-}11\frac{3}{8}$	$89\text{-}0\frac{1}{4}$
4	$30\text{-}8\frac{1}{2}$	$53\text{-}7\frac{7}{8}$	$37\text{-}8\frac{1}{4}$	$65\text{-}10\frac{7}{32}$	44-8	$78\text{-}0\frac{17}{32}$	$51\text{-}7\frac{3}{4}$	$90\text{-}2\frac{7}{8}$
5	$31\text{-}4\frac{7}{8}$	$54\text{-}10\frac{1}{2}$	$38\text{-}4\frac{5}{8}$	$67\text{-}0\frac{27}{32}$	$45\text{-}4\frac{3}{4}$	$79\text{-}3\frac{3}{16}$	$52\text{-}4\frac{1}{8}$	$91\text{-}5\frac{17}{32}$
6	$32\text{-}1\frac{1}{4}$	$56\text{-}1\frac{5}{32}$	39-1	$68\text{-}3\frac{15}{32}$	$46\text{-}0\frac{3}{4}$	$80\text{-}5\frac{13}{16}$	$53\text{-}0\frac{1}{2}$	$92\text{-}8\frac{5}{32}$
7	$32\text{-}9\frac{5}{8}$	$57\text{-}3\frac{25}{32}$	$39\text{-}9\frac{3}{8}$	$69\text{-}6\frac{1}{8}$	$46\text{-}9\frac{1}{8}$	$81\text{-}8\frac{7}{16}$	$53\text{-}8\frac{7}{8}$	$93\text{-}10\frac{25}{32}$
8	33-6	$58\text{-}6\frac{13}{32}$	$40\text{-}5\frac{3}{4}$	$70\text{-}8\frac{3}{4}$	$47\text{-}5\frac{1}{2}$	$82\text{-}11\frac{3}{32}$	$54\text{-}5\frac{1}{4}$	$95\text{-}1\frac{13}{32}$
9	$34\text{-}2\frac{3}{8}$	$59\text{-}9\frac{1}{32}$	$41\text{-}2\frac{1}{8}$	$71\text{-}11\frac{3}{8}$	$48\text{-}1\frac{7}{8}$	$84\text{-}1\frac{23}{32}$	$55\text{-}1\frac{5}{8}$	$96\text{-}4\frac{1}{16}$

natsin A=0.5723152031; natcos A=0.8200337239; nattan A=0.6979166666; natcot A=1.4328358208

Inches	0″ Rise	0″ Slope	1″ Rise	1″ Slope	2″ Rise	2″ Slope	3″ Rise	3″ Slope	4″ Rise	4″ Slope	5″ Rise	5″ Slope
0	0	0	11/16	1 7/32	1 13/32	2 7/16	2 1/8	3 21/32	2 13/16	4 7/8	3 1/2	6 1/8
1/16	1/32	1/16	3/4	1 5/16	1 7/16	2 17/32	2 5/32	3 3/4	2 27/32	4 31/32	3 9/16	6 3/16
1/8	3/32	5/32	25/32	1 3/8	1 1/2	2 19/32	2 3/16	3 13/16	2 29/32	5 1/32	3 19/32	6 1/4
3/16	1/8	7/32	27/32	1 7/16	1 17/32	2 11/16	2 1/4	3 29/32	2 15/16	5 1/8	3 21/32	6 11/32
1/4	3/16	5/16	7/8	1 17/32	1 19/32	2 3/4	2 9/32	3 31/32	3	5 3/16	3 11/16	6 13/32
5/16	7/32	3/8	15/16	1 19/32	1 5/8	2 13/16	2 11/32	4 1/16	3 1/32	5 9/32	3 3/4	6 1/2
3/8	1/4	15/32	31/32	1 11/16	1 21/32	2 29/32	2 3/8	4 1/8	3 1/16	5 11/32	3 25/32	6 9/16
7/16	5/16	17/32	1	1 3/4	1 23/32	2 31/32	2 13/32	4 3/16	3 1/8	5 7/16	3 13/16	6 21/32
1/2	11/32	5/8	1 1/16	1 27/32	1 3/4	3 1/16	2 15/32	4 9/32	3 5/32	5 1/2	3 7/8	6 23/32
9/16	13/32	11/16	1 3/32	1 29/32	1 13/16	3 1/8	2 1/2	4 11/32	3 7/32	5 9/16	3 29/32	6 13/16
5/8	7/16	3/4	1 5/32	2	1 27/32	3 7/32	2 9/16	4 7/16	3 1/4	5 21/32	3 31/32	6 7/8
11/16	15/32	27/32	1 3/16	2 1/16	1 7/8	3 9/32	2 19/32	4 1/2	3 9/32	5 23/32	4	6 15/16
3/4	17/32	29/32	1 7/32	2 1/8	1 15/16	3 3/8	2 5/8	4 19/32	3 11/32	5 13/16	4 1/16	7 1/32
13/16	9/16	1	1 9/32	2 7/32	1 31/32	3 7/16	2 11/16	4 21/32	3 3/8	5 7/8	4 3/32	7 3/32
7/8	5/8	1 1/16	1 5/16	2 9/32	2 1/32	3 1/2	2 23/32	4 3/4	3 7/16	5 31/32	4 1/8	7 3/16
15/16	21/32	1 5/32	1 3/8	2 3/8	2 1/16	3 19/32	2 25/32	4 13/16	3 15/32	6 1/32	4 3/16	7 1/4

Inches	6″ Rise	6″ Slope	7″ Rise	7″ Slope	8″ Rise	8″ Slope	9″ Rise	9″ Slope	10″ Rise	10″ Slope	11″ Rise	11″ Slope
0	4 7/32	7 11/32	4 15/16	8 9/16	5 5/8	9 25/32	6 5/16	11	7 1/32	1-0 7/32	7 3/4	1-1 7/16
1/16	4 1/4	7 13/32	4 31/32	8 5/8	5 21/32	9 27/32	6 3/8	11 3/32	7 1/16	1-0 5/32	7 25/32	1-1 17/32
1/8	4 5/16	7 1/2	5	8 23/32	5 23/32	9 15/16	6 13/32	11 5/32	7 3/32	1-0 3/8	7 13/16	1-1 19/32
3/16	4 11/32	7 9/16	5 1/16	8 25/32	5 3/4	10	6 15/32	11 7/32	7 5/32	1-0 15/32	7 7/8	1-1 11/16
1/4	4 13/32	7 5/8	5 3/32	8 7/8	5 13/16	10 3/32	6 1/2	11 5/16	7 7/32	1-0 17/32	7 29/32	1-1 3/4
5/16	4 7/16	7 23/32	5 5/32	8 15/16	5 27/32	10 5/32	6 9/16	11 3/8	7 1/4	1-0 19/32	7 31/32	1-1 27/32
3/8	4 15/32	7 25/32	5 3/16	9	5 7/8	10 1/4	6 19/32	11 15/32	7 9/32	1-0 11/16	8	1-1 29/32
7/16	4 17/32	7 7/8	5 1/4	9 3/32	5 15/16	10 5/16	6 5/8	11 17/32	7 11/32	1-0 3/4	8 1/32	1-1 31/32
1/2	4 9/16	7 15/16	5 9/32	9 5/32	5 31/32	10 13/32	6 11/16	11 5/8	7 3/8	1-0 27/32	8 3/32	1-2 1/16
9/16	4 5/8	8 1/32	5 5/16	9 1/4	6 1/32	10 15/32	6 23/32	11 11/16	7 7/16	1-0 29/32	8 1/8	1-2 1/8
5/8	4 21/32	8 3/32	5 3/8	9 5/16	6 1/16	10 17/32	6 25/32	11 25/32	7 15/32	1-1	8 3/16	1-2 7/32
11/16	4 11/16	8 3/16	5 13/32	9 13/32	6 3/32	10 5/8	6 13/16	11 27/32	7 1/2	1-1 1/16	8 7/32	1-2 9/32
3/4	4 3/4	8 1/4	5 7/16	9 15/32	6 5/32	10 11/16	6 27/32	11 29/32	7 9/16	1-1 5/32	8 1/4	1-2 3/8
13/16	4 25/32	8 5/16	5 1/2	9 9/16	6 3/16	10 25/32	6 29/32	1-0	7 19/32	1-1 7/32	8 5/16	1-2 7/16
7/8	4 27/32	8 13/32	5 17/32	9 5/8	6 1/4	10 27/32	6 15/16	1-0 1/16	7 21/32	1-1 9/32	8 11/32	1-2 17/32
15/16	4 7/8	8 15/32	5 19/32	9 23/32	6 9/32	10 15/16	7	1-0 5/32	7 11/16	1-1 3/8	8 13/32	1-2 19/32

Feet	0′ Rise	0′ Slope	10′ Rise	10′ Slope	20′ Rise	20′ Slope	30′ Rise	30′ Slope
0	0	0	7-0 3/8	12-2 11/16	14-0 3/4	24-5 3/8	21-1 1/8	36-8 3/32
1	8 7/16	1-2 21/32	7-8 13/16	13-5 3/8	14-9 3/16	25-8 1/16	21-9 9/16	37-10 3/4
2	1-4 7/8	2-5 11/32	8-5 1/4	14-8 1/32	15-5 5/8	26-10 23/32	22-6	39-1 13/32
3	2-1 5/16	3-8	9-1 11/16	15-10 11/16	16-2 1/16	28-1 13/32	23-2 7/16	40-4 3/32
4	2-9 3/4	4-10 11/16	9-10 1/8	17-1 3/8	16-10 1/2	29-4 1/16	23-10 7/8	41-6 3/4
5	3-6 3/16	6-1 11/32	10-6 9/16	18-4 1/32	17-6 15/16	30-6 3/4	24-7 5/16	42-9 7/16
6	4-2 5/8	7-4 1/32	11-3	19-6 23/32	18-3 3/8	31-9 13/32	25-3 3/4	44-0 3/32
7	4-11 1/16	8-6 11/16	11-11 7/16	20-9 3/8	18-11 13/16	33-0 1/16	26-0 3/16	45-2 25/32
8	5-7 1/2	9-9 11/32	12-7 7/8	22-0 1/16	19-8 1/4	34-2 3/4	26-8 5/8	46-5 7/16
9	6-3 15/16	11-0 1/32	13-4 5/16	23-2 23/32	20-4 11/16	35-5 13/32	27-5 1/16	47-8 3/32

A = 35° 06′ 43″; logsin A = **9.75980**; logcos A = **9.91277**; logtan A = **9.84703**; logcot A = **0.15297**

In.	12″ Rise	12″ Slope	13″ Rise	13″ Slope	14″ Rise	14″ Slope	15″ Rise	15″ Slope	16″ Rise	16″ Slope
0	8 7/16	1-2 21/32	9 1/8	1-3 29/32	9 27/32	1-5 1/8	10 9/16	1-6 11/32	11 1/4	1-7 9/16
1/16	8 15/32	1-2 3/4	9 3/16	1-3 31/32	9 7/8	1-5 3/16	10 19/32	1-6 13/32	11 9/32	1-7 5/8
1/8	8 17/32	1-2 13/16	9 7/32	1-4 1/32	9 15/16	1-5 9/32	10 5/8	1-6 1/2	11 11/32	1-7 23/32
3/16	8 9/16	1-2 29/32	9 9/32	1-4 1/8	9 31/32	1-5 11/32	10 11/16	1-6 9/16	11 3/8	1-7 25/32
1/4	8 5/8	1-2 31/32	9 5/16	1-4 3/16	10 1/2	1-5 13/32	10 23/32	1-6 21/32	11 7/16	1-7 7/8
5/16	8 21/32	1-3 1/16	9 3/8	1-4 9/32	10 1/16	1-5 1/2	10 25/32	1-6 23/32	11 15/32	1-7 15/16
3/8	8 11/16	1-3 1/8	9 13/32	1-4 11/32	10 3/32	1-5 9/16	10 13/16	1-6 25/32	11 1/2	1-8 1/32
7/16	8 3/4	1-3 7/32	9 7/16	1-4 7/16	10 5/32	1-5 21/32	10 27/32	1-6 7/8	11 9/16	1-8 3/32
1/2	8 25/32	1-3 9/32	9 1/2	1-4 1/2	10 3/16	1-5 23/32	10 29/32	1-6 15/16	11 19/32	1-8 5/32
9/16	8 27/32	1-3 11/32	9 17/32	1-4 19/32	10 1/4	1-5 13/16	10 15/16	1-7 1/32	11 21/32	1-8 1/4
5/8	8 7/8	1-3 7/16	9 19/32	1-4 21/32	10 9/32	1-5 7/8	11	1-7 3/32	11 11/16	1-8 5/16
11/16	8 29/32	1-3 1/2	9 5/8	1-4 23/32	10 5/16	1-5 31/32	11 1/32	1-7 3/16	11 23/32	1-8 13/32
3/4	8 31/32	1-3 19/32	9 21/32	1-4 13/16	10 3/8	1-6 1/32	11 1/16	1-7 1/4	11 25/32	1-8 15/32
13/16	9	1-3 21/32	9 23/32	1-4 7/8	10 13/32	1-6 3/32	11 1/8	1-7 11/32	11 13/16	1-8 9/16
7/8	9 1/16	1-3 3/4	9 3/4	1-4 31/32	10 15/32	1-6 3/16	11 5/32	1-7 13/32	11 7/8	1-8 5/8
15/16	9 3/32	1-3 13/16	9 13/16	1-5 1/32	10 1/2	1-6 1/4	11 7/32	1-7 15/32	11 29/32	1-8 23/32

In.	17″ Rise	17″ Slope	18″ Rise	18″ Slope	19″ Rise	19″ Slope	20″ Rise	20″ Slope	21″ Rise	21″ Slope
0	11 15/16	1-8 25/32	1-0 21/32	1-10	1-1 3/8	1-11 7/32	1-2 1/16	2-0 7/16	1-2 3/4	2-1 21/32
1/16	1-0	1-8 27/32	1-0 11/16	1-10 3/32	1-1 13/32	1-11 5/16	1-2 3/32	2-0 17/32	1-2 13/16	2-1 3/4
1/8	1-0 1/32	1-8 15/16	1-0 3/4	1-10 5/32	1-1 7/16	1-11 3/8	1-2 5/32	2-0 19/32	1-2 27/32	2-1 13/16
3/16	1-0 3/32	1-9	1-0 25/32	1-10 7/32	1-1 1/2	1-11 15/32	1-2 3/16	2-0 11/16	1-2 29/32	2-1 29/32
1/4	1-0 1/8	1-9 3/32	1-0 27/32	1-10 5/16	1-1 17/32	1-11 17/32	1-2 1/4	2-0 3/4	1-2 15/16	2-1 31/32
5/16	1-0 3/16	1-9 5/32	1-0 7/8	1-10 3/8	1-1 19/32	1-11 19/32	1-2 9/32	2-0 27/32	1-3	2-2 1/8
3/8	1-0 7/32	1-9 1/4	1-0 29/32	1-10 15/32	1-1 5/8	1-11 11/16	1-2 5/16	2-0 29/32	1-3 1/32	2-2 1/8
7/16	1-0 1/4	1-9 5/16	1-0 31/32	1-10 17/32	1-1 21/32	1-11 3/4	1-2 3/8	2-0 31/32	1-3 1/16	2-2 7/32
1/2	1-0 5/16	1-9 13/32	1-1	1-10 5/8	1-1 23/32	1-11 27/32	1-2 13/32	2-1 1/16	1-3 1/8	2-2 9/32
9/16	1-0 11/32	1-9 15/32	1-1 1/16	1-10 11/16	1-1 3/4	1-11 29/32	1-2 15/32	2-1 1/8	1-3 5/32	2-2 11/32
5/8	1-0 13/32	1-9 17/32	1-1 3/32	1-10 25/32	1-1 13/16	2-0	1-2 1/2	2-1 7/32	1-3 7/32	2-2 7/16
11/16	1-0 7/16	1-9 5/8	1-1 1/8	1-10 27/32	1-1 27/32	2-0 1/16	1-2 17/32	2-1 9/32	1-3 1/4	2-2 1/2
3/4	1-0 15/32	1-9 11/16	1-1 3/16	1-10 29/32	1-1 7/8	2-0 5/32	1-2 19/32	2-1 3/8	1-3 9/32	2-2 19/32
13/16	1-0 17/32	1-9 25/32	1-1 7/32	1-11	1-1 15/16	2-0 7/32	1-2 5/8	2-1 7/16	1-3 11/32	2-2 21/32
7/8	1-0 9/16	1-9 27/32	1-1 9/32	1-11 1/16	1-1 31/32	2-0 9/32	1-2 11/16	2-1 17/32	1-3 3/8	2-2 3/4
15/16	1-0 5/8	1-9 15/16	1-1 5/16	1-11 5/32	1-2 1/32	2-0 3/8	1-2 23/32	2-1 19/32	1-3 7/16	2-2 13/16

Feet	40′ Rise	40′ Slope	50′ Rise	50′ Slope	60′ Rise	60′ Slope	70′ Rise	70′ Slope
0	28-1 1/2	48-10 25/32	35-1 7/8	61-1 15/32	42-2 1/4	73-4 5/32	49-2 5/8	85-6 27/32
1	28-9 15/16	50-1 7/16	35-10 5/16	62-4 1/8	42-10 11/16	74-6 27/32	49-11 1/16	86-9 17/32
2	29-6 3/8	51-4 1/8	36-6 3/4	63-6 13/16	43-7 1/8	75-9 1/2	50-7 1/2	88-0 3/16
3	30-2 13/16	52-6 25/32	37-3 3/16	64-9 15/32	44-3 9/16	77-0 3/16	51-3 15/16	89-2 7/8
4	30-11 1/4	53-9 15/32	37-11 5/8	66-0 5/32	45-0	78-2 27/32	52-0 3/8	90-5 17/32
5	31-7 11/16	55-0 1/8	38-8 1/16	67-2 13/16	45-8 7/16	79-5 1/2	52-8 13/16	91-8 7/32
6	32-4 1/8	56-2 25/32	39-4 1/2	68-5 1/2	46-4 7/8	80-8 3/16	53-5 1/4	92-10 7/8
7	33-0 9/16	57-5 15/32	40-0 15/16	69-8 5/32	47-1 5/16	81-10 27/32	54-1 11/16	94-1 17/32
8	33-9	58-8 1/8	40-9 3/8	70-10 13/16	47-9 3/4	83-1 17/32	54-10 1/8	95-4 7/32
9	34-5 7/16	59-10 13/16	41-5 13/16	72-1 1/2	48-6 3/16	84-4 3/16	55-6 9/16	96-6 7/8

natsin A=0.5751767520; natcos A=0.8180291584; nattan A=0.7031250000; natcot A=1.4222222222

Inches	0″ Rise	0″ Slope	1″ Rise	1″ Slope	2″ Rise	2″ Slope	3″ Rise	3″ Slope	4″ Rise	4″ Slope	5″ Rise	5″ Slope
0	0	0	23/32	1 1/32	1 13/32	2 7/16	2 1/8	3 11/16	2 27/32	4 29/32	3 17/32	6 1/8
1/16	1/32	1/16	3/4	1 5/16	1 15/32	2 17/32	2 5/32	3 3/4	2 7/8	4 31/32	3 19/32	6 7/32
1/8	3/32	5/32	13/16	1 3/8	1 1/2	2 19/32	2 7/32	3 27/32	2 15/16	5 1/16	3 5/8	6 9/32
3/16	1/8	7/32	27/32	1 15/32	1 9/16	2 11/16	2 1/4	3 29/32	2 31/32	5 1/8	3 11/16	6 11/32
1/4	3/16	5/16	7/8	1 17/32	1 19/32	2 3/4	2 5/16	3 31/32	3	5 7/32	3 23/32	6 7/16
5/16	7/32	3/8	15/16	1 19/32	1 5/8	2 27/32	2 11/32	4 1/16	3 1/16	5 9/32	3 3/4	6 1/2
3/8	1/4	15/32	31/32	1 11/16	1 11/16	2 29/32	2 3/8	4 1/8	3 3/32	5 3/8	3 13/16	6 19/32
7/16	5/16	17/32	1 1/32	1 3/4	1 23/32	3	2 7/16	4 7/32	3 5/32	5 7/16	3 27/32	6 21/32
1/2	11/32	5/8	1 1/16	1 27/32	1 25/32	3 1/16	2 15/32	4 9/32	3 3/16	5 1/2	3 29/32	6 3/4
9/16	13/32	11/16	1 3/32	1 29/32	1 13/16	3 1/8	2 17/32	4 3/8	3 7/32	5 19/32	3 15/16	6 13/16
5/8	7/16	25/32	1 5/32	2	1 7/8	3 7/32	2 9/16	4 7/16	3 9/32	5 21/32	4	6 29/32
11/16	1/2	27/32	1 3/16	2 1/16	1 29/32	3 9/32	2 5/8	4 17/32	3 5/16	5 3/4	4 1/32	6 31/32
3/4	17/32	29/32	1 1/4	2 5/32	1 15/16	3 3/8	2 21/32	4 19/32	3 3/8	5 13/16	4 1/16	7 1/32
13/16	9/16	1	1 9/32	2 7/32	2	3 7/16	2 11/16	4 11/16	3 13/32	5 29/32	4 1/8	7 1/8
7/8	5/8	1 1/16	1 5/16	2 5/16	2 1/32	3 17/32	2 3/4	4 3/4	3 7/16	5 31/32	4 5/32	7 3/16
15/16	21/32	15/32	1 3/8	2 3/8	2 3/32	3 19/32	2 25/32	4 13/16	3 1/2	6 1/16	4 7/32	7 9/32

Inches	6″ Rise	6″ Slope	7″ Rise	7″ Slope	8″ Rise	8″ Slope	9″ Rise	9″ Slope	10″ Rise	10″ Slope	11″ Rise	11″ Slope
0	4 1/4	7 11/32	4 31/32	8 19/32	5 21/32	9 13/16	6 3/8	11 1/32	7 3/32	1-0 1/4	7 25/32	1-1 15/32
1/16	4 9/32	7 7/16	5	8 21/32	5 23/32	9 7/8	6 13/32	11 3/32	7 1/8	1-0 11/32	7 27/32	1-1 9/16
1/8	4 11/32	7 1/2	5 1/16	8 23/32	5 3/4	9 31/32	6 15/32	11 3/16	7 3/16	1-0 13/32	7 7/8	1-1 5/8
3/16	4 3/8	7 19/32	5 3/32	8 13/16	5 13/16	10 1/32	6 1/2	11 1/4	7 7/32	1-0 15/32	7 15/16	1-1 23/32
1/4	4 7/16	7 21/32	5 1/8	8 7/8	5 27/32	10 1/8	6 9/16	11 11/32	7 1/4	1-0 9/16	7 31/32	1-1 25/32
5/16	4 15/32	7 3/4	5 3/16	8 31/32	5 7/8	10 3/16	6 19/32	11 13/32	7 5/16	1-0 5/8	8	1-1 7/8
3/8	4 1/2	7 13/16	5 7/32	9 1/32	5 15/16	10 1/4	6 5/8	11 1/2	7 11/32	1-0 23/32	8 1/16	1-1 15/16
7/16	4 9/16	7 7/8	5 9/32	9 1/8	5 31/32	10 11/32	6 11/16	11 9/16	7 13/32	1-0 25/32	8 3/32	1-2 1/32
1/2	4 19/32	7 31/32	5 5/16	9 3/16	6 1/32	10 13/32	6 23/32	11 21/32	7 7/16	1-0 7/8	8 5/32	1-2 3/32
9/16	4 21/32	8 1/32	5 11/32	9 9/32	6 1/16	10 1/2	6 25/32	11 23/32	7 15/32	1-0 15/16	8 3/16	1-2 5/32
5/8	4 11/16	8 1/8	5 13/32	9 11/32	6 1/8	10 9/16	6 13/16	11 25/32	7 17/32	1-1 1/32	8 1/4	1-2 1/4
11/16	4 3/4	8 3/16	5 7/16	9 13/32	6 5/32	10 21/32	6 7/8	11 7/8	7 9/16	1-1 3/32	8 9/32	1-2 5/16
3/4	4 25/32	8 9/32	5 1/2	9 1/2	6 3/16	10 23/32	6 29/32	11 15/16	7 5/8	1-1 3/16	8 5/16	1-2 13/32
13/16	4 13/16	8 11/32	5 17/32	9 9/16	6 1/4	10 13/16	6 15/16	1-0 1/32	7 21/32	1-1 1/4	8 3/8	1-2 15/32
7/8	4 7/8	8 7/16	5 9/16	9 21/32	6 9/32	10 7/8	7	1-0 3/32	7 11/16	1-1 5/16	8 13/32	1-2 9/16
15/16	4 29/32	8 1/2	5 5/8	9 23/32	6 11/32	10 15/16	7 1/32	1-0 3/16	7 3/4	1-1 13/32	8 15/32	1-2 5/8

Feet	0′ Rise	0′ Slope	10′ Rise	10′ Slope	20′ Rise	20′ Slope	30′ Rise	30′ Slope
0	0	0	7-1	12-3 1/16	14-2	24-6 3/32	21-3	36-9 5/32
1	8 1/2	1-2 23/32	7-9 1/2	13-5 3/4	14-10 1/2	25-8 13/16	21-11 1/2	37-11 7/8
2	1-5	2-5 13/32	8-6	14-8 15/32	15-7	26-11 17/32	22-8	39-2 9/16
3	2-1 1/2	3-8 1/8	9-2 1/2	15-11 5/32	16-3 1/2	28-2 7/32	23-4 1/2	40-5 9/32
4	2-10	4-10 13/16	9-11	17-1 7/8	17-0	29-4 15/16	24-1	41-8
5	3-6 1/2	6-1 17/32	10-7 1/2	18-4 19/32	17-8 1/2	30-7 5/8	24-9 1/2	42-10 11/16
6	4-3	7-4 7/32	11-4	19-7 9/32	18-5	31-10 11/32	25-6	44-1 13/32
7	4-11 1/2	8-6 15/32	12-0 1/2	20-10	19-1 1/2	33-1 1/16	26-2 1/2	45-4 3/32
8	5-8	9-9 21/32	12-9	22-0 11/16	19-10	34-3 3/4	26-11	46-6 13/16
9	6-4 1/2	11-0 11/32	13-5 1/2	23-3 13/32	20-6 1/2	35-6 15/32	27-7 1/2	47-9 1/2

A = 35° 18′ 40″; logsin A = 9.76194; logcos A = 9.91170: logtan A = 9.85024; logcot A = 0.14976

Ins.	12″ Rise	12″ Slope	13″ Rise	13″ Slope	14″ Rise	14″ Slope	15″ Rise	15″ Slope	16″ Rise	16″ Slope
0	$8\frac{1}{2}$	$1\text{-}2\frac{23}{32}$	$9\frac{7}{32}$	$1\text{-}3\frac{15}{16}$	$9\frac{29}{32}$	$1\text{-}5\frac{5}{32}$	$10\frac{5}{8}$	$1\text{-}6\frac{3}{8}$	$11\frac{11}{32}$	$1\text{-}7\frac{19}{32}$
$\frac{1}{16}$	$8\frac{17}{32}$	$1\text{-}2\frac{25}{32}$	$9\frac{1}{4}$	$1\text{-}4$	$9\frac{31}{32}$	$1\text{-}5\frac{7}{32}$	$10\frac{21}{32}$	$1\text{-}6\frac{15}{32}$	$11\frac{3}{8}$	$1\text{-}7\frac{11}{16}$
$\frac{1}{8}$	$8\frac{19}{32}$	$1\text{-}2\frac{27}{32}$	$9\frac{5}{16}$	$1\text{-}4\frac{3}{32}$	10	$1\text{-}5\frac{5}{16}$	$10\frac{23}{32}$	$1\text{-}6\frac{17}{32}$	$11\frac{7}{16}$	$1\text{-}7\frac{3}{4}$
$\frac{3}{16}$	$8\frac{5}{8}$	$1\text{-}2\frac{15}{16}$	$9\frac{11}{32}$	$1\text{-}4\frac{5}{32}$	$10\frac{1}{16}$	$1\text{-}5\frac{3}{8}$	$10\frac{3}{4}$	$1\text{-}6\frac{5}{8}$	$11\frac{15}{32}$	$1\text{-}7\frac{27}{32}$
$\frac{1}{4}$	$8\frac{11}{16}$	$1\text{-}3$	$9\frac{3}{8}$	$1\text{-}4\frac{1}{4}$	$10\frac{3}{32}$	$1\text{-}5\frac{15}{32}$	$10\frac{13}{16}$	$1\text{-}6\frac{11}{16}$	$11\frac{1}{2}$	$1\text{-}7\frac{29}{32}$
$\frac{5}{16}$	$8\frac{23}{32}$	$1\text{-}3\frac{3}{32}$	$9\frac{7}{16}$	$1\text{-}4\frac{5}{16}$	$10\frac{1}{8}$	$1\text{-}5\frac{17}{32}$	$10\frac{27}{32}$	$1\text{-}6\frac{3}{4}$	$11\frac{9}{16}$	$1\text{-}8$
$\frac{3}{8}$	$8\frac{3}{4}$	$1\text{-}3\frac{5}{32}$	$9\frac{15}{32}$	$1\text{-}4\frac{3}{8}$	$10\frac{3}{16}$	$1\text{-}5\frac{5}{8}$	$10\frac{7}{8}$	$1\text{-}6\frac{27}{32}$	$11\frac{19}{32}$	$1\text{-}8\frac{1}{16}$
$\frac{7}{16}$	$8\frac{13}{16}$	$1\text{-}3\frac{1}{4}$	$9\frac{17}{32}$	$1\text{-}4\frac{15}{32}$	$10\frac{7}{32}$	$1\text{-}5\frac{11}{32}$	$10\frac{15}{16}$	$1\text{-}6\frac{29}{32}$	$11\frac{21}{32}$	$1\text{-}8\frac{5}{32}$
$\frac{1}{2}$	$8\frac{27}{32}$	$1\text{-}3\frac{5}{16}$	$9\frac{9}{16}$	$1\text{-}4\frac{17}{32}$	$10\frac{9}{32}$	$1\text{-}5\frac{25}{32}$	$10\frac{31}{32}$	$1\text{-}7$	$11\frac{11}{16}$	$1\text{-}8\frac{7}{32}$
$\frac{9}{16}$	$8\frac{29}{32}$	$1\text{-}3\frac{13}{32}$	$9\frac{19}{32}$	$1\text{-}4\frac{5}{8}$	$10\frac{5}{16}$	$1\text{-}5\frac{27}{32}$	$11\frac{1}{32}$	$1\text{-}7\frac{1}{16}$	$11\frac{23}{32}$	$1\text{-}8\frac{9}{32}$
$\frac{5}{8}$	$8\frac{15}{16}$	$1\text{-}3\frac{15}{32}$	$9\frac{21}{32}$	$1\text{-}4\frac{11}{16}$	$10\frac{3}{8}$	$1\text{-}5\frac{15}{16}$	$11\frac{1}{16}$	$1\text{-}7\frac{5}{32}$	$11\frac{25}{32}$	$1\text{-}8\frac{3}{8}$
$\frac{11}{16}$	9	$1\text{-}3\frac{9}{16}$	$9\frac{11}{16}$	$1\text{-}4\frac{25}{32}$	$10\frac{13}{32}$	$1\text{-}6$	$11\frac{1}{8}$	$1\text{-}7\frac{7}{32}$	$11\frac{13}{16}$	$1\text{-}8\frac{7}{16}$
$\frac{3}{4}$	$9\frac{1}{32}$	$1\text{-}3\frac{5}{8}$	$9\frac{3}{4}$	$1\text{-}4\frac{27}{32}$	$10\frac{7}{16}$	$1\text{-}6\frac{1}{16}$	$11\frac{5}{32}$	$1\text{-}7\frac{5}{16}$	$11\frac{7}{8}$	$1\text{-}8\frac{17}{32}$
$\frac{13}{16}$	$9\frac{1}{16}$	$1\text{-}3\frac{11}{16}$	$9\frac{25}{32}$	$1\text{-}4\frac{15}{16}$	$10\frac{1}{2}$	$1\text{-}6\frac{5}{32}$	$11\frac{3}{16}$	$1\text{-}7\frac{3}{8}$	$11\frac{29}{32}$	$1\text{-}8\frac{19}{32}$
$\frac{7}{8}$	$9\frac{1}{8}$	$1\text{-}3\frac{25}{32}$	$9\frac{13}{16}$	$1\text{-}5$	$10\frac{17}{32}$	$1\text{-}6\frac{7}{32}$	$11\frac{1}{4}$	$1\text{-}7\frac{15}{32}$	$11\frac{15}{16}$	$1\text{-}8\frac{11}{16}$
$\frac{15}{16}$	$9\frac{5}{32}$	$1\text{-}3\frac{27}{32}$	$9\frac{7}{8}$	$1\text{-}5\frac{3}{32}$	$10\frac{19}{32}$	$1\text{-}6\frac{5}{16}$	$11\frac{9}{32}$	$1\text{-}7\frac{17}{32}$	$1\text{-}0$	$1\text{-}8\frac{3}{4}$

Ins.	17″ Rise	17″ Slope	18″ Rise	18″ Slope	19″ Rise	19″ Slope	20″ Rise	20″ Slope	21″ Rise	21″ Slope
0	$1\text{-}0\frac{1}{32}$	$1\text{-}8\frac{27}{32}$	$1\text{-}0\frac{3}{4}$	$1\text{-}10\frac{1}{16}$	$1\text{-}1\frac{15}{32}$	$1\text{-}11\frac{9}{32}$	$1\text{-}2\frac{5}{32}$	$2\text{-}0\frac{1}{2}$	$1\text{-}2\frac{7}{8}$	$2\text{-}1\frac{3}{4}$
$\frac{1}{16}$	$1\text{-}0\frac{3}{32}$	$1\text{-}8\frac{29}{32}$	$1\text{-}0\frac{25}{32}$	$1\text{-}10\frac{1}{8}$	$1\text{-}1\frac{1}{2}$	$1\text{-}11\frac{3}{8}$	$1\text{-}2\frac{7}{32}$	$2\text{-}0\frac{19}{32}$	$1\text{-}2\frac{29}{32}$	$2\text{-}1\frac{13}{16}$
$\frac{1}{8}$	$1\text{-}0\frac{1}{8}$	$1\text{-}9$	$1\text{-}0\frac{27}{32}$	$1\text{-}10\frac{7}{32}$	$1\text{-}1\frac{9}{16}$	$1\text{-}11\frac{7}{16}$	$1\text{-}2\frac{1}{4}$	$2\text{-}0\frac{21}{32}$	$1\text{-}2\frac{31}{32}$	$2\text{-}1\frac{7}{8}$
$\frac{3}{16}$	$1\text{-}0\frac{3}{16}$	$1\text{-}9\frac{1}{16}$	$1\text{-}0\frac{7}{8}$	$1\text{-}10\frac{9}{32}$	$1\text{-}1\frac{19}{32}$	$1\text{-}11\frac{1}{2}$	$1\text{-}2\frac{5}{16}$	$2\text{-}0\frac{3}{4}$	$1\text{-}3$	$2\text{-}1\frac{31}{32}$
$\frac{1}{4}$	$1\text{-}0\frac{7}{32}$	$1\text{-}9\frac{1}{8}$	$1\text{-}0\frac{15}{16}$	$1\text{-}10\frac{3}{8}$	$1\text{-}1\frac{5}{8}$	$1\text{-}11\frac{19}{32}$	$1\text{-}2\frac{11}{32}$	$2\text{-}0\frac{13}{16}$	$1\text{-}3\frac{1}{16}$	$2\text{-}2\frac{1}{32}$
$\frac{5}{16}$	$1\text{-}0\frac{1}{4}$	$1\text{-}9\frac{7}{32}$	$1\text{-}0\frac{31}{32}$	$1\text{-}10\frac{7}{16}$	$1\text{-}1\frac{11}{16}$	$1\text{-}11\frac{21}{32}$	$1\text{-}2\frac{3}{8}$	$2\text{-}0\frac{29}{32}$	$1\text{-}3\frac{3}{32}$	$2\text{-}2\frac{1}{8}$
$\frac{3}{8}$	$1\text{-}0\frac{5}{16}$	$1\text{-}9\frac{9}{32}$	$1\text{-}1$	$1\text{-}10\frac{17}{32}$	$1\text{-}1\frac{23}{32}$	$1\text{-}11\frac{3}{4}$	$1\text{-}2\frac{7}{16}$	$2\text{-}0\frac{31}{32}$	$1\text{-}3\frac{1}{8}$	$2\text{-}2\frac{3}{16}$
$\frac{7}{16}$	$1\text{-}0\frac{11}{32}$	$1\text{-}9\frac{3}{8}$	$1\text{-}1\frac{1}{16}$	$1\text{-}10\frac{19}{32}$	$1\text{-}1\frac{25}{32}$	$1\text{-}11\frac{13}{16}$	$1\text{-}2\frac{15}{32}$	$2\text{-}1\frac{1}{32}$	$1\text{-}3\frac{3}{16}$	$2\text{-}2\frac{9}{32}$
$\frac{1}{2}$	$1\text{-}0\frac{13}{32}$	$1\text{-}9\frac{7}{16}$	$1\text{-}1\frac{3}{8}$	$1\text{-}10\frac{21}{32}$	$1\text{-}1\frac{13}{16}$	$1\text{-}11\frac{29}{32}$	$1\text{-}2\frac{17}{32}$	$2\text{-}1\frac{1}{8}$	$1\text{-}3\frac{7}{32}$	$2\text{-}2\frac{11}{32}$
$\frac{9}{16}$	$1\text{-}0\frac{7}{16}$	$1\text{-}9\frac{17}{32}$	$1\text{-}1\frac{5}{32}$	$1\text{-}10\frac{3}{4}$	$1\text{-}1\frac{27}{32}$	$1\text{-}11\frac{31}{32}$	$1\text{-}2\frac{9}{16}$	$2\text{-}1\frac{3}{16}$	$1\text{-}3\frac{9}{32}$	$2\text{-}2\frac{7}{16}$
$\frac{5}{8}$	$1\text{-}0\frac{1}{2}$	$1\text{-}9\frac{19}{32}$	$1\text{-}1\frac{3}{16}$	$1\text{-}10\frac{13}{16}$	$1\text{-}1\frac{29}{32}$	$2\text{-}0\frac{1}{16}$	$1\text{-}2\frac{5}{8}$	$2\text{-}1\frac{9}{32}$	$1\text{-}3\frac{5}{16}$	$2\text{-}2\frac{1}{2}$
$\frac{11}{16}$	$1\text{-}0\frac{17}{32}$	$1\text{-}9\frac{11}{16}$	$1\text{-}1\frac{1}{4}$	$1\text{-}10\frac{29}{32}$	$1\text{-}1\frac{15}{16}$	$2\text{-}0\frac{1}{8}$	$1\text{-}2\frac{21}{32}$	$2\text{-}1\frac{11}{32}$	$1\text{-}3\frac{3}{8}$	$2\text{-}2\frac{9}{16}$
$\frac{3}{4}$	$1\text{-}0\frac{9}{16}$	$1\text{-}9\frac{3}{4}$	$1\text{-}1\frac{9}{32}$	$1\text{-}10\frac{31}{32}$	$1\text{-}2$	$2\text{-}0\frac{3}{16}$	$1\text{-}2\frac{11}{16}$	$2\text{-}1\frac{7}{16}$	$1\text{-}3\frac{13}{32}$	$2\text{-}2\frac{21}{32}$
$\frac{13}{16}$	$1\text{-}0\frac{5}{8}$	$1\text{-}9\frac{27}{32}$	$1\text{-}1\frac{5}{16}$	$1\text{-}11\frac{1}{16}$	$1\text{-}2\frac{1}{32}$	$2\text{-}0\frac{9}{32}$	$1\text{-}2\frac{3}{4}$	$2\text{-}1\frac{1}{2}$	$1\text{-}3\frac{7}{16}$	$2\text{-}2\frac{23}{32}$
$\frac{7}{8}$	$1\text{-}0\frac{21}{32}$	$1\text{-}9\frac{29}{32}$	$1\text{-}1\frac{3}{8}$	$1\text{-}11\frac{1}{8}$	$1\text{-}2\frac{1}{8}$	$2\text{-}0\frac{11}{32}$	$1\text{-}2\frac{25}{32}$	$2\text{-}1\frac{19}{32}$	$1\text{-}3\frac{1}{2}$	$2\text{-}2\frac{13}{16}$
$\frac{15}{16}$	$1\text{-}0\frac{23}{32}$	$1\text{-}9\frac{31}{32}$	$1\text{-}1\frac{13}{32}$	$1\text{-}11\frac{17}{32}$	$1\text{-}2\frac{1}{8}$	$2\text{-}0\frac{7}{16}$	$1\text{-}2\frac{27}{32}$	$2\text{-}1\frac{21}{32}$	$1\text{-}3\frac{17}{32}$	$2\text{-}2\frac{7}{8}$

Feet	40′ Rise	40′ Slope	50′ Rise	50′ Slope	60′ Rise	60′ Slope	70′ Rise	70′ Slope
0	$28\text{-}4$	$49\text{-}0\frac{7}{32}$	$35\text{-}5$	$61\text{-}3\frac{9}{32}$	$42\text{-}6$	$73\text{-}6\frac{5}{16}$	$49\text{-}7$	$85\text{-}9\frac{3}{8}$
1	$29\text{-}0\frac{1}{2}$	$50\text{-}2\frac{15}{16}$	$36\text{-}1\frac{1}{2}$	$62\text{-}5\frac{31}{32}$	$43\text{-}2\frac{1}{2}$	$74\text{-}9\frac{1}{32}$	$50\text{-}3\frac{1}{2}$	$87\text{-}0\frac{3}{32}$
2	$29\text{-}9$	$51\text{-}5\frac{5}{8}$	$36\text{-}10$	$63\text{-}8\frac{11}{16}$	$43\text{-}11$	$75\text{-}11\frac{3}{4}$	$51\text{-}0$	$88\text{-}2\frac{25}{32}$
3	$30\text{-}5\frac{1}{2}$	$52\text{-}8\frac{11}{32}$	$37\text{-}6\frac{1}{2}$	$64\text{-}11\frac{3}{8}$	$44\text{-}7\frac{1}{2}$	$77\text{-}2\frac{7}{16}$	$51\text{-}8\frac{1}{2}$	$89\text{-}5\frac{1}{2}$
4	$31\text{-}2$	$53\text{-}11\frac{1}{32}$	$38\text{-}3$	$66\text{-}2\frac{3}{32}$	$45\text{-}4$	$78\text{-}5\frac{5}{32}$	$52\text{-}5$	$90\text{-}8\frac{3}{16}$
5	$31\text{-}10\frac{1}{2}$	$55\text{-}1\frac{3}{4}$	$38\text{-}11\frac{1}{2}$	$67\text{-}4\frac{13}{16}$	$46\text{-}0\frac{1}{2}$	$79\text{-}7\frac{27}{32}$	$53\text{-}1\frac{1}{2}$	$91\text{-}10\frac{29}{32}$
6	$32\text{-}7$	$56\text{-}4\frac{7}{16}$	$39\text{-}8$	$68\text{-}7\frac{1}{2}$	$46\text{-}9$	$80\text{-}10\frac{9}{16}$	$53\text{-}10$	$93\text{-}1\frac{5}{8}$
7	$33\text{-}3\frac{1}{2}$	$57\text{-}7\frac{5}{32}$	$40\text{-}4\frac{1}{2}$	$69\text{-}10\frac{7}{32}$	$47\text{-}5\frac{1}{2}$	$82\text{-}1\frac{1}{4}$	$54\text{-}6\frac{1}{2}$	$94\text{-}4\frac{5}{16}$
8	$34\text{-}0$	$58\text{-}9\frac{7}{8}$	$41\text{-}1$	$71\text{-}0\frac{29}{32}$	$48\text{-}2$	$83\text{-}3\frac{31}{32}$	$55\text{-}3$	$95\text{-}7\frac{1}{32}$
9	$34\text{-}8\frac{1}{2}$	$60\text{-}0\frac{9}{16}$	$41\text{-}9\frac{1}{2}$	$72\text{-}3\frac{5}{8}$	$48\text{-}10\frac{1}{2}$	$84\text{-}6\frac{11}{16}$	$55\text{-}11\frac{1}{2}$	$96\text{-}9\frac{23}{32}$

natsin A=0.5780173408; natcos A=0.8160244811; nattan A=0.7083333333; natcot A=1.4117647058

Inches	0" Rise	0" Slope	1" Rise	1" Slope	2" Rise	2" Slope	3" Rise	3" Slope	4" Rise	4" Slope	5" Rise	5" Slope
0	0	0	23/32	1 7/32	1 7/16	2 15/32	2 1/8	3 11/16	2 27/32	4 29/32	3 9/16	6 5/32
1/16	1/32	1/16	3/4	1 5/16	1 15/32	2 17/32	2 3/16	3 3/4	2 29/32	5	3 5/8	6 7/32
1/8	3/32	5/32	13/16	1 3/8	1 17/32	2 5/8	2 7/32	3 27/32	2 15/16	5 1/16	3 21/32	6 9/32
3/16	1/8	7/32	27/32	1 15/32	1 9/16	2 11/16	2 9/32	3 29/32	3	5 5/32	3 11/16	6 3/8
1/4	3/16	5/16	29/32	1 17/32	1 19/32	2 3/4	2 5/16	4	3 1/32	5 7/32	3 3/4	6 1/16
5/16	7/32	3/8	15/16	1 5/8	1 21/32	2 27/32	2 3/8	4 1/16	3 1/16	5 5/16	3 25/32	6 17/32
3/8	1/4	15/32	31/32	1 11/16	1 11/16	2 29/32	2 13/32	4 5/32	3 1/8	5 3/8	3 27/32	6 19/32
7/16	5/16	17/32	1 1/32	1 25/32	1 3/4	3	2 7/16	4 7/32	3 5/32	5 7/16	3 7/8	6 11/16
1/2	11/32	5/8	1 1/16	1 27/32	1 25/32	3 1/16	2 1/2	4 5/32	3 7/32	5 17/32	3 15/16	6 3/4
9/16	13/32	11/16	1 1/8	1 29/32	1 27/32	3 5/32	2 17/32	4 3/8	3 1/4	5 19/32	3 31/32	6 27/32
5/8	7/16	25/32	1 5/32	2	1 7/8	3 7/32	2 19/32	4 15/32	3 5/16	5 11/16	4	6 29/32
11/16	1/2	27/32	1 7/32	2 1/16	1 29/32	3 5/16	2 5/8	4 17/32	3 11/32	5 3/4	4 1/16	7
3/4	17/32	29/32	1 1/4	2 5/32	1 31/32	3 3/8	2 11/16	4 19/32	3 3/8	5 27/32	4 3/32	7 1/16
13/16	19/32	1	1 9/32	2 7/32	2	3 15/32	2 23/32	4 11/16	3 7/16	5 29/32	4 9/32	7 1/8
7/8	5/8	1 1/16	1 11/32	2 5/16	2 1/16	3 17/32	2 3/4	4 3/4	3 15/32	6	4 3/16	7 7/32
15/16	21/32	1 3/32	1 3/8	2 3/8	2 3/32	3 19/32	2 13/16	4 27/32	3 17/32	6 1/16	4 1/4	7 9/32

Inches	6" Rise	6" Slope	7" Rise	7" Slope	8" Rise	8" Slope	9" Rise	9" Slope	10" Rise	10" Slope	11" Rise	11" Slope
0	4 9/32	7 3/8	5	8 19/32	5 23/32	9 13/16	6 7/16	11 1/16	7 1/8	1-0 9/32	7 27/32	1-1 1/2
1/16	4 5/16	7 7/16	5 1/32	8 11/16	5 3/4	9 29/32	6 15/32	11 1/8	7 3/16	1-0 3/8	7 29/32	1-1 19/32
1/8	4 3/8	7 11/32	5 3/32	8 3/4	5 13/16	9 31/32	6 1/2	11 7/32	7 7/32	1-0 7/16	7 15/16	1-1 21/32
3/16	4 13/32	7 19/32	5 1/8	8 27/32	5 27/32	10 1/16	6 9/16	11 9/32	7 9/32	1-0 1/2	7 31/32	1-1 3/4
1/4	4 15/32	7 11/16	5 3/16	8 29/32	5 7/8	10 1/8	6 19/32	11 3/8	7 5/16	1-0 19/32	8 1/32	1-1 13/16
5/16	4 1/2	7 3/4	5 7/32	8 31/32	5 15/16	10 7/32	6 21/32	11 7/16	7 11/32	1-0 21/32	8 1/16	1-1 29/32
3/8	4 9/16	7 27/32	5 1/4	9 1/16	5 31/32	10 9/32	6 11/16	11 1/2	7 13/32	1-0 3/4	8 1/8	1-1 31/32
7/16	4 19/32	7 29/32	5 5/16	9 1/8	6 1/32	10 3/8	6 23/32	11 9/16	7 7/16	1-0 13/16	8 5/32	1-2 1/16
1/2	4 5/8	8	5 11/32	9 7/32	6 1/16	10 7/16	6 25/32	11 21/32	7 1/2	1-0 29/32	8 7/32	1-2 1/8
9/16	4 11/16	8 1/16	5 13/32	9 9/32	6 1/8	10 17/32	6 13/16	11 3/4	7 17/32	1-0 31/32	8 1/4	1-2 7/32
5/8	4 23/32	8 1/8	5 7/16	9 3/8	6 5/32	10 19/32	6 7/8	11 13/16	7 19/32	1-1 1/16	8 9/32	1-2 9/32
11/16	4 25/32	8 7/32	5 1/2	9 7/16	6 3/16	10 11/16	6 29/32	11 29/32	7 5/8	1-1 1/8	8 11/32	1-2 11/32
3/4	4 13/16	8 9/32	5 17/32	9 17/32	6 1/4	10 3/4	6 31/32	11 31/32	7 21/32	1-1 7/32	8 3/8	1-2 7/16
13/16	4 7/8	8 3/8	5 9/16	9 19/32	6 9/32	10 13/16	7	1-0 1/16	7 23/32	1-1 9/32	8 7/16	1-2 1/2
7/8	4 29/32	8 7/16	5 5/8	9 11/16	6 11/32	10 29/32	7 1/32	1-0 1/8	7 3/4	1-1 3/8	8 15/32	1-2 19/32
15/16	4 15/16	8 17/32	5 21/32	9 3/4	6 3/8	10 31/32	7 3/32	1-0 7/32	7 13/16	1-1 7/16	8 17/32	1-2 21/32

Feet	0' Rise	0' Slope	10' Rise	10' Slope	20' Rise	20' Slope	30' Rise	30' Slope
0	0	0	7-1 5/8	12-3 13/32	14-3 1/4	24-6 27/32	21-4 7/8	36-10 1/4
1	8 9/16	1-2 3/4	7-10 3/16	13-6 5/32	14-11 13/16	25-9 9/16	22-1 7/16	38-1
2	1-5 1/8	2-5 15/32	8-6 3/4	14-8 29/32	15-8 3/8	27-0 5/16	22-10	39-3 23/32
3	2-1 11/16	3-8 7/32	9-3 5/16	15-11 21/32	16-4 15/16	28-3 1/16	23-6 9/16	40-6 15/32
4	2-10 1/4	4-10 31/32	9-11 7/8	17-2 3/8	17-1 1/2	29-5 13/16	24-3 1/8	41-9 7/32
5	3-6 13/16	6-1 23/32	10-8 7/16	18-5 1/8	17-10 1/16	30-8 17/32	24-11 11/16	42-11 31/32
6	4-3 3/8	7-4 7/16	11-5	19-7 7/8	18-6 5/8	31-11 9/32	25-8 1/4	44-2 11/16
7	4-11 15/16	8-7 3/16	12-1 9/16	20-10 19/32	19-3 3/16	33-2 1/32	26-4 13/16	45-5 7/16
8	5-8 1/2	9-9 15/16	12-10 1/8	22-1 11/32	19-11 3/4	34-4 25/32	27-1 3/8	46-8 3/16
9	6-5 1/16	11-0 11/16	13-6 11/16	23-4 3/32	20-8 5/16	35-7 1/2	27-9 15/16	47-10 15/16

A = 35° 30′ 34″; logsin A = 9.76405; logcos A = 9.91063; logtan A = 9.85342; logcot A = 0.14658

	12"		13"		14"		15"		16"	
Ins.	Rise	Slope	Rise	Slope	Rise	Slope	Rise	Slope	Rise	Slope
0	$8\frac{9}{16}$	$1\text{-}2\frac{3}{4}$	$9\frac{9}{32}$	$1\text{-}3\frac{31}{32}$	10	$1\text{-}5\frac{3}{16}$	$10\frac{11}{16}$	$1\text{-}6\frac{7}{16}$	$11\frac{13}{32}$	$1\text{-}7\frac{21}{32}$
$\frac{1}{16}$	$8\frac{19}{32}$	$1\text{-}2\frac{13}{16}$	$9\frac{5}{16}$	$1\text{-}4\frac{1}{16}$	$10\frac{1}{32}$	$1\text{-}5\frac{9}{32}$	$10\frac{3}{4}$	$1\text{-}6\frac{1}{2}$	$11\frac{15}{32}$	$1\text{-}7\frac{23}{32}$
$\frac{1}{8}$	$8\frac{21}{32}$	$1\text{-}2\frac{29}{32}$	$9\frac{3}{8}$	$1\text{-}4\frac{1}{8}$	$10\frac{3}{32}$	$1\text{-}5\frac{11}{32}$	$10\frac{25}{32}$	$1\text{-}6\frac{19}{32}$	$11\frac{1}{2}$	$1\text{-}7\frac{13}{16}$
$\frac{3}{16}$	$8\frac{11}{16}$	$1\text{-}2\frac{31}{32}$	$9\frac{13}{32}$	$1\text{-}4\frac{3}{16}$	$10\frac{1}{8}$	$1\text{-}5\frac{7}{16}$	$10\frac{27}{32}$	$1\text{-}6\frac{21}{32}$	$11\frac{9}{16}$	$1\text{-}7\frac{7}{8}$
$\frac{1}{4}$	$8\frac{3}{4}$	$1\text{-}3\frac{1}{16}$	$9\frac{15}{32}$	$1\text{-}4\frac{9}{32}$	$10\frac{5}{32}$	$1\text{-}5\frac{1}{2}$	$10\frac{7}{8}$	$1\text{-}6\frac{23}{32}$	$11\frac{19}{32}$	$1\text{-}7\frac{31}{32}$
$\frac{5}{16}$	$8\frac{25}{32}$	$1\text{-}3\frac{1}{8}$	$9\frac{1}{2}$	$1\text{-}4\frac{11}{32}$	$10\frac{7}{32}$	$1\text{-}5\frac{19}{32}$	$10\frac{15}{16}$	$1\text{-}6\frac{13}{16}$	$11\frac{5}{8}$	$1\text{-}8\frac{1}{32}$
$\frac{3}{8}$	$8\frac{27}{32}$	$1\text{-}3\frac{3}{16}$	$9\frac{17}{32}$	$1\text{-}4\frac{7}{16}$	$10\frac{1}{4}$	$1\text{-}5\frac{21}{32}$	$10\frac{31}{32}$	$1\text{-}6\frac{7}{8}$	$11\frac{11}{16}$	$1\text{-}8\frac{1}{8}$
$\frac{7}{16}$	$8\frac{7}{8}$	$1\text{-}3\frac{9}{32}$	$9\frac{19}{32}$	$1\text{-}4\frac{1}{2}$	$10\frac{5}{16}$	$1\text{-}5\frac{3}{4}$	11	$1\text{-}6\frac{31}{32}$	$11\frac{23}{32}$	$1\text{-}8\frac{3}{16}$
$\frac{1}{2}$	$8\frac{29}{32}$	$1\text{-}3\frac{11}{32}$	$9\frac{5}{8}$	$1\text{-}4\frac{19}{32}$	$10\frac{11}{32}$	$1\text{-}5\frac{13}{16}$	$11\frac{1}{16}$	$1\text{-}7\frac{1}{32}$	$11\frac{25}{32}$	$1\text{-}8\frac{9}{32}$
$\frac{9}{16}$	$8\frac{31}{32}$	$1\text{-}3\frac{7}{16}$	$9\frac{11}{16}$	$1\text{-}4\frac{21}{32}$	$10\frac{13}{32}$	$1\text{-}5\frac{7}{8}$	$11\frac{3}{32}$	$1\text{-}7\frac{1}{8}$	$11\frac{13}{16}$	$1\text{-}8\frac{11}{32}$
$\frac{5}{8}$	9	$1\text{-}3\frac{1}{2}$	$9\frac{23}{32}$	$1\text{-}4\frac{3}{4}$	$10\frac{7}{16}$	$1\text{-}5\frac{31}{32}$	$11\frac{5}{32}$	$1\text{-}7\frac{3}{16}$	$11\frac{7}{8}$	$1\text{-}8\frac{7}{16}$
$\frac{11}{16}$	$9\frac{1}{16}$	$1\text{-}3\frac{19}{32}$	$9\frac{25}{32}$	$1\text{-}4\frac{13}{16}$	$10\frac{15}{32}$	$1\text{-}6\frac{1}{32}$	$11\frac{3}{16}$	$1\text{-}7\frac{9}{32}$	$11\frac{29}{32}$	$1\text{-}8\frac{1}{2}$
$\frac{3}{4}$	$9\frac{3}{32}$	$1\text{-}3\frac{21}{32}$	$9\frac{13}{16}$	$1\text{-}4\frac{29}{32}$	$10\frac{17}{32}$	$1\text{-}6\frac{1}{8}$	$11\frac{1}{4}$	$1\text{-}7\frac{11}{32}$	$11\frac{15}{16}$	$1\text{-}8\frac{9}{16}$
$\frac{13}{16}$	$9\frac{5}{32}$	$1\text{-}3\frac{3}{4}$	$9\frac{27}{32}$	$1\text{-}4\frac{31}{32}$	$10\frac{9}{16}$	$1\text{-}6\frac{3}{16}$	$11\frac{9}{32}$	$1\text{-}7\frac{7}{16}$	$1\text{-}0$	$1\text{-}8\frac{21}{32}$
$\frac{7}{8}$	$9\frac{3}{16}$	$1\text{-}3\frac{13}{16}$	$9\frac{29}{32}$	$1\text{-}5\frac{1}{32}$	$10\frac{5}{8}$	$1\text{-}6\frac{9}{32}$	$11\frac{5}{16}$	$1\text{-}7\frac{1}{2}$	$1\text{-}0\frac{1}{32}$	$1\text{-}8\frac{23}{32}$
$\frac{15}{16}$	$9\frac{7}{32}$	$1\text{-}3\frac{29}{32}$	$9\frac{15}{16}$	$1\text{-}5\frac{1}{8}$	$10\frac{21}{32}$	$1\text{-}6\frac{11}{32}$	$11\frac{3}{8}$	$1\text{-}7\frac{19}{32}$	$1\text{-}0\frac{3}{32}$	$1\text{-}8\frac{13}{16}$

	17"		18"		19"		20"		21"	
Ins.	Rise	Slope	Rise	Slope	Rise	Slope	Rise	Slope	Rise	Slope
0	$1\text{-}0\frac{1}{8}$	$1\text{-}8\frac{7}{8}$	$1\text{-}0\frac{27}{32}$	$1\text{-}10\frac{1}{8}$	$1\text{-}1\frac{9}{16}$	$1\text{-}11\frac{11}{32}$	$1\text{-}2\frac{9}{32}$	$2\text{-}0\frac{9}{16}$	$1\text{-}3$	$2\text{-}1\frac{13}{16}$
$\frac{1}{16}$	$1\text{-}0\frac{3}{32}$	$1\text{-}8\frac{31}{32}$	$1\text{-}0\frac{7}{8}$	$1\text{-}10\frac{3}{16}$	$1\text{-}1\frac{19}{32}$	$1\text{-}11\frac{13}{32}$	$1\text{-}2\frac{5}{16}$	$2\text{-}0\frac{21}{32}$	$1\text{-}3\frac{1}{32}$	$2\text{-}1\frac{7}{8}$
$\frac{1}{8}$	$1\text{-}0\frac{7}{32}$	$1\text{-}9\frac{1}{32}$	$1\text{-}0\frac{15}{16}$	$1\text{-}10\frac{9}{32}$	$1\text{-}1\frac{21}{32}$	$1\text{-}11\frac{1}{2}$	$1\text{-}2\frac{3}{8}$	$2\text{-}0\frac{23}{32}$	$1\text{-}3\frac{1}{16}$	$2\text{-}1\frac{15}{16}$
$\frac{3}{16}$	$1\text{-}0\frac{1}{4}$	$1\text{-}9\frac{1}{8}$	$1\text{-}0\frac{31}{32}$	$1\text{-}10\frac{11}{32}$	$1\text{-}1\frac{11}{16}$	$1\text{-}11\frac{9}{16}$	$1\text{-}2\frac{13}{32}$	$2\text{-}0\frac{13}{16}$	$1\text{-}3\frac{1}{8}$	$2\text{-}2\frac{1}{32}$
$\frac{1}{4}$	$1\text{-}0\frac{5}{16}$	$1\text{-}9\frac{3}{16}$	$1\text{-}1\frac{1}{32}$	$1\text{-}10\frac{13}{32}$	$1\text{-}1\frac{3}{4}$	$1\text{-}11\frac{21}{32}$	$1\text{-}2\frac{7}{16}$	$2\text{-}0\frac{7}{8}$	$1\text{-}3\frac{5}{32}$	$2\text{-}2\frac{3}{32}$
$\frac{5}{16}$	$1\text{-}0\frac{11}{32}$	$1\text{-}9\frac{9}{32}$	$1\text{-}1\frac{1}{16}$	$1\text{-}10\frac{1}{2}$	$1\text{-}1\frac{25}{32}$	$1\text{-}11\frac{23}{32}$	$1\text{-}2\frac{1}{2}$	$2\text{-}0\frac{31}{32}$	$1\text{-}3\frac{7}{32}$	$2\text{-}2\frac{3}{32}$
$\frac{3}{8}$	$1\text{-}0\frac{13}{32}$	$1\text{-}9\frac{11}{32}$	$1\text{-}1\frac{1}{8}$	$1\text{-}10\frac{9}{16}$	$1\text{-}1\frac{13}{16}$	$1\text{-}11\frac{13}{16}$	$1\text{-}2\frac{17}{32}$	$2\text{-}1\frac{1}{32}$	$1\text{-}3\frac{1}{4}$	$2\text{-}2\frac{1}{4}$
$\frac{7}{16}$	$1\text{-}0\frac{7}{16}$	$1\text{-}9\frac{13}{32}$	$1\text{-}1\frac{5}{32}$	$1\text{-}10\frac{21}{32}$	$1\text{-}1\frac{7}{8}$	$1\text{-}11\frac{7}{8}$	$1\text{-}2\frac{19}{32}$	$2\text{-}1\frac{3}{32}$	$1\text{-}3\frac{9}{32}$	$2\text{-}2\frac{11}{32}$
$\frac{1}{2}$	$1\text{-}0\frac{1}{2}$	$1\text{-}9\frac{1}{2}$	$1\text{-}1\frac{3}{16}$	$1\text{-}10\frac{23}{32}$	$1\text{-}1\frac{29}{32}$	$1\text{-}11\frac{31}{32}$	$1\text{-}2\frac{5}{8}$	$2\text{-}1\frac{3}{16}$	$1\text{-}3\frac{11}{32}$	$2\text{-}2\frac{13}{32}$
$\frac{9}{16}$	$1\text{-}0\frac{17}{32}$	$1\text{-}9\frac{9}{16}$	$1\text{-}1\frac{1}{4}$	$1\text{-}10\frac{13}{16}$	$1\text{-}1\frac{31}{32}$	$2\text{-}0\frac{1}{32}$	$1\text{-}2\frac{11}{16}$	$2\text{-}1\frac{1}{4}$	$1\text{-}3\frac{3}{8}$	$2\text{-}2\frac{1}{2}$
$\frac{5}{8}$	$1\text{-}0\frac{9}{16}$	$1\text{-}9\frac{21}{32}$	$1\text{-}1\frac{9}{32}$	$1\text{-}10\frac{7}{8}$	$1\text{-}2$	$2\text{-}0\frac{3}{32}$	$1\text{-}2\frac{23}{32}$	$2\text{-}1\frac{11}{32}$	$1\text{-}3\frac{7}{16}$	$2\text{-}2\frac{9}{16}$
$\frac{11}{16}$	$1\text{-}0\frac{5}{8}$	$1\text{-}9\frac{23}{32}$	$1\text{-}1\frac{11}{32}$	$1\text{-}10\frac{31}{32}$	$1\text{-}2\frac{1}{16}$	$2\text{-}0\frac{3}{16}$	$1\text{-}2\frac{3}{4}$	$2\text{-}1\frac{13}{32}$	$1\text{-}3\frac{15}{32}$	$2\text{-}2\frac{21}{32}$
$\frac{3}{4}$	$1\text{-}0\frac{21}{32}$	$1\text{-}9\frac{13}{16}$	$1\text{-}1\frac{3}{8}$	$1\text{-}11\frac{1}{32}$	$1\text{-}2\frac{3}{32}$	$2\text{-}0\frac{1}{4}$	$1\text{-}2\frac{13}{16}$	$2\text{-}1\frac{1}{2}$	$1\text{-}3\frac{17}{32}$	$2\text{-}2\frac{23}{32}$
$\frac{13}{16}$	$1\text{-}0\frac{23}{32}$	$1\text{-}9\frac{7}{8}$	$1\text{-}1\frac{7}{16}$	$1\text{-}11\frac{1}{8}$	$1\text{-}2\frac{1}{8}$	$2\text{-}0\frac{11}{32}$	$1\text{-}2\frac{27}{32}$	$2\text{-}1\frac{9}{16}$	$1\text{-}3\frac{9}{16}$	$2\text{-}2\frac{25}{32}$
$\frac{7}{8}$	$1\text{-}0\frac{3}{4}$	$1\text{-}9\frac{31}{32}$	$1\text{-}1\frac{15}{32}$	$1\text{-}11\frac{3}{16}$	$1\text{-}2\frac{3}{16}$	$2\text{-}0\frac{13}{32}$	$1\text{-}2\frac{29}{32}$	$2\text{-}1\frac{21}{32}$	$1\text{-}3\frac{19}{32}$	$2\text{-}2\frac{7}{8}$
$\frac{15}{16}$	$1\text{-}0\frac{13}{16}$	$1\text{-}10\frac{1}{32}$	$1\text{-}1\frac{1}{2}$	$1\text{-}11\frac{1}{4}$	$1\text{-}2\frac{7}{32}$	$2\text{-}0\frac{1}{2}$	$1\text{-}2\frac{15}{16}$	$2\text{-}1\frac{23}{32}$	$1\text{-}3\frac{21}{32}$	$2\text{-}2\frac{15}{16}$

	40'		50'		60'		70'	
Feet	Rise	Slope	Rise	Slope	Rise	Slope	Rise	Slope
0	$28\text{-}6\frac{1}{2}$	$49\text{-}1\frac{21}{32}$	$35\text{-}8\frac{1}{8}$	$61\text{-}5\frac{3}{8}$	$42\text{-}9\frac{3}{4}$	$73\text{-}8\frac{1}{2}$	$49\text{-}11\frac{3}{8}$	$85\text{-}11\frac{29}{32}$
1	$29\text{-}3\frac{1}{16}$	$50\text{-}4\frac{13}{32}$	$36\text{-}4\frac{11}{16}$	$62\text{-}7\frac{13}{16}$	$43\text{-}6\frac{5}{16}$	$74\text{-}11\frac{1}{4}$	$50\text{-}7\frac{15}{16}$	$87\text{-}2\frac{21}{32}$
2	$29\text{-}11\frac{5}{8}$	$51\text{-}7\frac{5}{32}$	$37\text{-}1\frac{1}{4}$	$63\text{-}10\frac{9}{16}$	$44\text{-}2\frac{7}{8}$	$76\text{-}1\frac{31}{32}$	$51\text{-}4\frac{1}{2}$	$88\text{-}5\frac{13}{32}$
3	$30\text{-}8\frac{3}{8}$	$52\text{-}9\frac{29}{32}$	$37\text{-}9\frac{13}{16}$	$65\text{-}1\frac{5}{16}$	$44\text{-}11\frac{7}{16}$	$77\text{-}4\frac{23}{32}$	$52\text{-}1\frac{1}{16}$	$89\text{-}8\frac{5}{32}$
4	$31\text{-}4\frac{3}{4}$	$54\text{-}0\frac{5}{8}$	$38\text{-}6\frac{3}{8}$	$66\text{-}4\frac{1}{16}$	$45\text{-}8$	$78\text{-}7\frac{15}{32}$	$52\text{-}9\frac{5}{8}$	$90\text{-}10\frac{7}{8}$
5	$32\text{-}1\frac{5}{16}$	$55\text{-}3\frac{3}{8}$	$39\text{-}2\frac{15}{16}$	$67\text{-}6\frac{25}{32}$	$46\text{-}4\frac{9}{16}$	$79\text{-}10\frac{7}{32}$	$53\text{-}6\frac{3}{16}$	$92\text{-}1\frac{5}{8}$
6	$32\text{-}9\frac{7}{8}$	$56\text{-}6\frac{1}{8}$	$39\text{-}11\frac{1}{2}$	$68\text{-}9\frac{17}{32}$	$47\text{-}1\frac{1}{8}$	$81\text{-}0\frac{15}{16}$	$54\text{-}2\frac{3}{4}$	$93\text{-}4\frac{3}{8}$
7	$33\text{-}6\frac{7}{16}$	$57\text{-}8\frac{27}{32}$	$40\text{-}8\frac{1}{16}$	$70\text{-}0\frac{9}{32}$	$47\text{-}9\frac{11}{16}$	$82\text{-}3\frac{11}{16}$	$54\text{-}11\frac{5}{16}$	$94\text{-}7\frac{3}{32}$
8	$34\text{-}3$	$58\text{-}11\frac{19}{32}$	$41\text{-}4\frac{5}{8}$	$71\text{-}3\frac{1}{32}$	$48\text{-}6\frac{1}{4}$	$83\text{-}6\frac{7}{16}$	$55\text{-}7\frac{7}{8}$	$95\text{-}9\frac{27}{32}$
9	$34\text{-}11\frac{9}{16}$	$60\text{-}2\frac{11}{32}$	$42\text{-}1\frac{3}{16}$	$72\text{-}5\frac{3}{4}$	$49\text{-}2\frac{13}{16}$	$84\text{-}9\frac{3}{16}$	$56\text{-}4\frac{7}{16}$	$97\text{-}0\frac{19}{32}$

natsin A=0.5808370716; natcos A=0.8140198377; nattan A=0.7135416666; natcot A=1.4014598540

Inches	0" Rise	0" Slope	1" Rise	1" Slope	2" Rise	2" Slope	3" Rise	3" Slope	4" Rise	4" Slope	5" Rise	5" Slope
0	0	0	23/32	1 7/32	1 7/16	2 15/32	2 5/32	3 11/16	2 7/8	4 15/16	3 19/32	6 5/32
1/16	1/32	1/16	3/4	1 5/16	1 15/32	2 17/32	2 3/16	3 25/32	2 29/32	5	3 5/8	6 1/4
1/8	2/32	5/32	13/16	1 3/8	1 17/32	2 5/8	2 1/4	3 27/32	2 31/32	5 3/32	3 11/16	6 5/16
3/16	1/8	7/32	27/32	1 15/32	1 9/16	2 11/16	2 9/32	3 15/16	3	5 5/32	3 23/32	6 3/8
1/4	3/16	5/16	29/32	1 17/32	1 5/8	2 25/32	2 11/32	4	3 1/16	5 7/32	3 25/32	6 15/32
5/16	7/32	3/8	15/16	1 5/8	1 21/32	2 27/32	2 3/8	4 3/32	3 3/32	5 9/32	3 13/16	6 17/32
3/8	9/32	15/32	1	1 11/16	1 23/32	2 15/16	2 7/16	4 5/32	3 5/32	5 3/8	3 7/8	6 5/8
7/16	5/16	17/32	1 1/2	1 25/32	1 3/4	3	2 15/32	4 7/32	3 3/16	5 15/32	3 29/32	6 11/16
1/2	3/8	5/8	1 1/16	1 27/32	1 13/16	3 3/32	2 1/2	4 5/16	3 1/4	5 17/32	3 15/16	6 25/32
9/16	13/32	11/16	1 1/8	1 15/16	1 27/32	3 5/32	2 9/16	4 3/8	3 9/32	5 5/8	4	6 27/32
5/8	7/16	25/32	1 5/32	2	1 7/8	3 7/32	2 19/32	4 15/32	3 5/16	5 11/16	4 1/32	6 15/16
11/16	1/2	27/32	1 7/32	2 3/32	1 15/16	3 5/16	2 21/32	4 17/32	3 3/8	5 25/32	4 3/32	7
3/4	17/32	15/16	1 1/4	2 5/32	1 31/32	3 3/8	2 11/16	4 5/8	3 13/32	5 27/32	4 1/8	7 3/32
13/16	19/32	1	1 5/16	2 7/32	2 1/32	3 15/32	2 3/4	4 11/16	3 15/32	5 15/16	4 3/16	7 5/32
7/8	5/8	1 1/16	1 11/32	2 5/16	2 1/16	3 17/32	2 25/32	4 25/32	3 1/2	6	4 7/32	7 1/4
15/16	11/16	1 5/32	1 13/32	2 3/8	2 1/8	3 5/8	2 27/32	4 27/32	3 9/16	6 3/32	4 9/32	7 5/32

Inches	6" Rise	6" Slope	7" Rise	7" Slope	8" Rise	8" Slope	9" Rise	9" Slope	10" Rise	10" Slope	11" Rise	11" Slope
0	4 5/16	7 3/8	5 1/32	8 5/8	5 3/4	9 27/32	6 15/32	11 3/32	7 3/16	1-0 5/16	7 29/32	1-1 17/32
1/16	4 11/32	7 15/32	5 1/16	8 11/16	5 25/32	9 15/16	6 1/2	11 5/32	7 7/32	1-0 13/32	7 15/16	1-1 5/8
1/8	4 13/32	7 17/32	5 1/8	8 25/32	5 27/32	10	6 9/16	11 1/4	7 9/32	1-0 15/32	8	1-1 11/16
3/16	4 7/16	7 5/8	5 5/32	8 27/32	5 7/8	10 3/32	6 19/32	11 5/16	7 5/16	1-0 17/32	8 1/32	1-1 25/32
1/4	4 1/2	7 11/16	5 7/32	8 15/16	5 15/16	10 5/32	6 21/32	11 13/32	7 3/8	1-0 5/8	8 3/32	1-1 27/32
5/16	4 17/32	7 25/32	5 1/4	9	5 31/32	10 1/4	6 11/16	11 15/32	7 13/32	1-0 11/16	8 1/8	1-1 15/16
3/8	4 19/32	7 27/32	5 5/16	9 3/32	6 1/32	10 5/16	6 3/4	11 17/32	7 15/32	1-0 25/32	8 5/32	1-2
7/16	4 5/8	7 15/16	5 11/32	9 5/32	6 3/32	10 13/32	6 25/32	11 5/8	7 1/2	1-0 27/32	8 7/32	1-2 3/32
1/2	4 11/16	8	5 3/8	9 1/4	6 1/8	10 15/32	6 13/16	11 11/16	7 9/16	1-0 15/16	8 1/4	1-2 5/32
9/16	4 23/32	8 3/32	5 7/16	9 5/16	6 5/32	10 17/32	6 7/8	11 25/32	7 19/32	1-1	8 5/16	1-2 1/4
5/8	4 3/4	8 5/32	5 15/32	9 3/8	6 3/16	10 5/8	6 29/32	11 27/32	7 5/8	1-1 3/32	8 11/32	1-2 5/16
11/16	4 13/16	8 1/4	5 17/32	9 15/32	6 1/4	10 11/16	6 31/32	11 15/16	7 11/16	1-1 5/32	8 13/32	1-2 13/32
3/4	4 27/32	8 5/16	5 9/16	9 17/32	6 9/32	10 25/32	7	1-0	7 23/32	1-1 1/4	8 7/16	1-2 15/32
13/16	4 29/32	8 3/8	5 5/8	9 5/8	6 11/32	10 27/32	7 1/16	1-0 3/32	7 25/32	1-1 5/16	8 1/2	1-2 9/16
7/8	4 15/16	8 15/32	5 21/32	9 11/16	6 3/8	10 15/16	7 3/32	1-0 5/32	7 13/16	1-1 13/32	8 17/32	1-2 5/8
15/16	5	8 17/32	5 23/32	9 25/32	6 7/16	11	7 5/32	1-0 1/4	7 7/8	1-1 15/32	8 19/32	1-2 11/16

Feet	0' Rise	0' Slope	10' Rise	10' Slope	20' Rise	20' Slope	30' Rise	30' Slope
0	0	0	7-2 1/4	12-3 25/32	14-4 1/2	24-7 9/16	21-6 3/4	36-11 11/32
1	-8 5/8	1-2 25/32	7-10 1/8	13-6 9/16	15-1 1/8	25-10 11/32	22-3 3/8	38-2 1/8
2	1-5 1/4	2-5 9/16	8-7 1/2	14-9 11/32	15-9 3/4	27-1 1/8	23-0	39-4 29/32
3	2-1 7/8	3-8 11/32	9-4 1/8	16-0 1/8	16-6 3/8	28-3 29/32	23-8 5/8	40-7 11/16
4	2-10 1/2	4-11 1/8	10-0 3/4	17-2 29/32	17-3	29-6 11/16	24-5 1/4	41-10 15/32
5	3-7 1/8	6-1 7/8	10-9 3/8	18-5 21/32	17-11 5/8	30-9 7/16	25-1 7/8	43-1 7/32
6	4-3 3/4	7-4 21/32	11-6	19-8 7/16	18-8 1/4	32-0 7/32	25-10 1/2	44-4
7	5-0 3/8	8-7 7/16	12-2 5/8	20-11 7/32	19-4 7/8	33-3	26-7 1/8	45-6 25/32
8	5-9	9-10 7/32	12-11 1/4	22-2	20-1 1/2	34-5 25/32	27-3 3/4	46-9 9/16
9	6-5 5/8	11-1	13-7 7/8	23-4 25/32	20-10 1/8	35-8 9/16	28-0 3/8	48-0 11/32

A = 35° 42′ 24″; logsin A = 9.76614; logcos A = 9.90956; logtan A = 9.85658; logcot A = 0.14342

Ins.	12″ Rise	12″ Slope	13″ Rise	13″ Slope	14″ Rise	14″ Slope	15″ Rise	15″ Slope	16″ Rise	16″ Slope
0	8 5/8	1-2 25/32	9 11/32	1-4	10 1/16	1-5 1/4	10 25/32	1-6 15/32	11 1/2	1-7 23/32
1/16	8 21/32	1-2 27/32	9 3/8	1-4 3/32	10 5/32	1-5 5/16	10 13/16	1-6 9/16	11 17/32	1-7 25/32
1/8	8 23/32	1-2 15/16	9 7/16	1-4 5/32	10 5/32	1-5 13/32	10 7/8	1-6 5/8	11 19/32	1-7 27/32
3/16	8 3/4	1-3	9 15/32	1-4 1/4	10 3/16	1-5 15/32	10 29/32	1-6 23/32	11 5/8	1-7 15/16
1/4	8 13/16	1-3 3/32	9 17/32	1-4 5/16	10 1/4	1-5 9/32	10 31/32	1-6 25/32	11 11/16	1-8
5/16	8 27/32	1-3 5/32	9 9/16	1-4 13/32	10 9/32	1-5 5/8	11	1-6 27/32	11 23/32	1-8 3/32
3/8	8 29/32	1-3 1/4	9 5/8	1-4 15/32	10 11/32	1-5 11/16	11 1/16	1-6 15/16	11 25/32	1-8 5/32
7/16	8 15/16	1-3 5/16	9 21/32	1-4 9/16	10 3/8	1-5 25/32	11 3/32	1-7	11 13/16	1-8 1/4
1/2	9	1-3 13/32	9 11/16	1-4 5/8	10 7/16	1-5 27/32	11 1/8	1-7 3/32	11 7/8	1-8 5/16
9/16	9 1/16	1-3 15/32	9 3/4	1-4 11/16	10 15/32	1-5 15/16	11 3/16	1-7 5/32	11 29/32	1-8 13/32
5/8	9 1/16	1-3 9/16	9 25/32	1-4 25/32	10 1/2	1-6	11 7/32	1-7 1/4	11 15/16	1-8 15/32
11/16	9 1/8	1-3 5/8	9 27/32	1-4 27/32	10 9/16	1-6 3/32	11 9/32	1-7 5/16	1-0	1-8 9/16
3/4	9 5/32	1-3 11/16	9 7/8	1-4 15/16	10 19/32	1-6 5/32	11 5/16	1-7 13/32	1-0 1/32	1-8 5/8
13/16	9 7/32	1-3 25/32	9 15/16	1-5	10 21/32	1-6 1/4	11 3/8	1-7 15/32	1-0 3/32	1-8 23/32
7/8	9 1/4	1-3 27/32	9 31/32	1-5 3/32	10 11/16	1-6 5/16	11 13/32	1-7 9/16	1-0 1/8	1-8 25/32
15/16	9 5/16	1-3 15/16	10 1/32	1-5 5/32	10 3/4	1-6 13/32	11 15/32	1-7 5/8	1-0 3/16	1-8 27/32

Ins.	17″ Rise	17″ Slope	18″ Rise	18″ Slope	19″ Rise	19″ Slope	20″ Rise	20″ Slope	21″ Rise	21″ Slope
0	1-0 7/32	1-8 15/16	1-0 15/16	1-10 5/32	1-1 21/32	1-11 13/32	1-2 3/8	2-0 5/8	1-3 3/8	2-1 1/8
1/16	1-0 1/4	1-9	1-0 31/32	1-10 1/4	1-1 11/16	1-11 15/32	1-2 13/32	2-0 23/32	1-3 1/8	2-1 15/16
1/8	1-0 5/16	1-9 3/32	1-1 1/32	1-10 5/16	1-1 3/4	1-11 9/16	1-2 15/32	2-0 25/32	1-3 3/16	2-2
3/16	1-0 11/32	1-9 5/32	1-1 1/16	1-10 13/32	1-1 25/32	1-11 5/8	1-2 1/2	2-0 7/8	1-3 7/32	2-2 3/32
1/4	1-0 13/32	1-9 1/4	1-1 1/8	1-10 15/32	1-1 27/32	1-11 23/32	1-2 9/16	2-0 15/16	1-3 9/32	2-2 5/32
5/16	1-0 7/16	1-9 5/16	1-1 5/32	1-10 9/16	1-1 7/8	1-11 25/32	1-2 19/32	2-1	1-3 5/16	2-2 1/4
3/8	1-0 1/2	1-9 13/32	1-1 7/32	1-10 5/8	1-1 15/16	1-11 7/8	1-2 21/32	2-1 3/32	1-3 3/8	2-2 5/16
7/16	1-0 17/32	1-9 15/32	1-1 1/4	1-10 23/32	1-1 31/32	1-11 15/16	1-2 11/16	2-1 5/32	1-3 13/32	2-2 13/32
1/2	1-0 9/16	1-9 9/16	1-1 5/16	1-10 25/32	1-2	2-0	1-2 3/4	2-1 1/4	1-3 7/16	2-2 15/32
9/16	1-0 5/8	1-9 5/8	1-1 11/32	1-10 7/8	1-2 1/16	2-0 3/32	1-2 25/32	2-1 5/16	1-3 1/2	2-2 9/16
5/8	1-0 21/32	1-9 23/32	1-1 3/8	1-10 15/16	1-2 3/32	2-0 5/32	1-2 13/16	2-1 13/32	1-3 17/32	2-2 5/8
11/16	1-0 23/32	1-9 25/32	1-1 7/16	1-11	1-2 5/32	2-0 1/4	1-2 7/8	2-1 15/32	1-3 19/32	2-2 23/32
3/4	1-0 3/4	1-9 27/32	1-1 15/32	1-11 3/32	1-2 3/16	2-0 5/16	1-2 29/32	2-1 9/16	1-3 5/8	2-2 25/32
13/16	1-0 13/16	1-9 15/16	1-1 17/32	1-11 5/32	1-2 1/4	2-0 13/32	1-2 31/32	2-1 5/8	1-3 11/16	2-2 7/8
7/8	1-0 27/32	1-10	1-1 9/16	1-11 1/4	1-2 9/32	2-0 15/32	1-3	2-1 23/32	1-3 23/32	2-2 15/16
15/16	1-0 29/32	1-10 3/32	1-1 5/8	1-11 15/32	1-2 11/32	2-0 9/16	1-3 1/16	2-1 25/32	1-3 25/32	2-3 1/32

Feet	40′ Rise	40′ Slope	50′ Rise	50′ Slope	60′ Rise	60′ Slope	70′ Rise	70′ Slope
0	28-9	49-3 1/8	35-11 1/4	61-6 29/32	43-1 1/2	73-10 11/16	50-3 3/4	86-2 15/32
1	29-5 5/8	50-5 29/32	36-7 7/8	62-9 11/16	43-10 1/8	75-1 15/32	51-0 3/8	87-5 1/4
2	30-2 1/4	51-8 11/16	37-4 1/2	64-0 15/32	44-6 3/4	76-4 1/4	51-9	88-8 1/32
3	30-10 7/8	52-11 15/32	38-1 1/8	65-3 1/4	45-3 3/8	77-7 1/32	52-5 5/8	89-10 13/16
4	31-7 1/2	54-2 1/4	38-9 3/4	66-6	46-0	78-9 25/32	53-2 1/4	91-1 1/16
5	32-4 1/8	55-5	39-6 3/8	67-8 25/32	46-8 5/8	80-0 9/16	53-10 7/8	92-4 11/32
6	33-0 3/4	56-7 25/32	40-3	68-11 9/16	47-5 1/4	81-3 11/32	54-7 1/2	93-7 1/8
7	33-9 3/8	57-10 9/16	40-11 5/8	70-2 11/32	48-1 7/8	82-6 1/8	55-4 1/8	94-9 29/32
8	34-6	59-1 11/32	41-8 1/4	71-5 1/8	48-10 1/2	83-8 29/32	56-0 3/4	96-0 11/16
9	35-2 5/8	60-4 1/8	42-4 7/8	72-7 29/32	49-7 1/8	84-11 11/16	56-9 3/8	97-3 15/32

natsin A=0.5836360481; natcos A=0.8120153713; nattan A=0.7187500000; natcot A=1.3913043478

Inches	0" Rise	0" Slope	1" Rise	1" Slope	2" Rise	2" Slope	3" Rise	3" Slope	4" Rise	4" Slope	5" Rise	5" Slope
0	0	0	23/32	1 1/4	1 7/16	2 15/32	2 3/16	3 23/32	2 29/32	4 15/16	3 5/8	6 3/16
1/16	1/16	1/16	25/32	1 5/16	1 1/2	2 17/32	2 7/32	3 25/32	2 15/16	5	3 21/32	6 1/4
1/8	3/32	5/32	13/16	1 3/8	1 17/32	2 5/8	2 1/4	3 27/32	3	5 3/32	3 23/32	6 5/16
3/16	1/8	7/32	7/8	1 15/32	1 19/32	2 11/32	2 5/16	3 15/16	3 1/32	5 5/32	3 3/4	6 13/32
1/4	3/16	5/16	29/32	1 17/32	1 5/8	2 25/32	2 11/32	4	3 1/16	5 1/4	3 13/16	6 15/32
5/16	7/32	3/8	15/16	1 5/8	1 11/16	2 27/32	2 13/32	4 3/32	3 1/8	5 5/16	3 27/32	6 9/16
3/8	9/32	15/32	1	1 11/16	1 23/32	2 15/16	2 7/16	4 5/32	3 5/32	5 13/16	3 29/32	6 5/8
7/16	5/16	17/32	1 1/32	1 25/32	1 3/4	3	2 1/2	4 1/4	3 7/32	5 15/32	3 15/16	6 23/32
1/2	3/8	5/8	1 3/32	1 27/32	1 13/16	3 3/32	2 17/32	4 5/16	3 1/4	5 9/16	3 31/32	6 25/32
9/16	13/32	11/16	1 3/8	1 15/16	1 27/32	3 5/32	2 19/32	4 13/32	3 5/16	5 5/8	4 1/32	6 7/8
5/8	7/16	25/32	1 3/16	2	1 29/32	3 1/4	2 5/8	4 15/32	3 11/32	5 23/32	4 1/16	6 15/16
11/16	1/2	27/32	1 7/32	2 3/32	1 15/16	3 5/16	2 21/32	4 9/16	3 13/32	5 25/32	4 1/8	7 1/32
3/4	17/32	15/16	1 9/32	2 5/32	2	3 13/32	2 23/32	4 5/8	3 7/16	5 7/8	4 5/32	7 3/32
13/16	19/32	1	1 5/16	2 1/4	2 1/4	3 15/32	2 3/4	4 23/32	3 15/32	5 15/16	4 7/32	7 3/16
7/8	5/8	1 1/32	1 11/32	2 5/16	2 3/32	3 9/16	2 13/16	4 25/32	3 17/32	6 1/32	4 1/4	7 1/4
15/16	11/16	1 5/32	1 13/32	2 13/32	2 1/8	3 5/8	2 27/32	4 7/8	3 9/16	6 3/32	4 5/16	7 11/32

Inches	6" Rise	6" Slope	7" Rise	7" Slope	8" Rise	8" Slope	9" Rise	9" Slope	10" Rise	10" Slope	11" Rise	11" Slope
0	4 11/32	7 13/32	5 1/16	8 21/32	5 25/32	9 7/8	6 1/2	11 1/8	7 1/4	1-0 11/32	7 31/32	1-1 19/32
1/16	4 3/8	7 1/2	5 1/8	8 23/32	5 27/32	9 31/32	6 9/16	11 3/16	7 9/32	1-0 7/16	8	1-1 21/32
1/8	4 7/16	7 9/16	5 5/32	8 25/32	5 7/8	10 1/32	6 19/32	11 1/4	7 11/32	1-0 1/2	8 1/16	1-1 23/32
3/16	4 15/32	7 5/8	5 7/32	8 7/8	5 15/16	10 3/32	6 21/32	11 11/32	7 3/8	1-0 9/16	8 3/32	1-1 13/16
1/4	4 17/32	7 23/32	5 1/4	8 15/16	5 31/32	10 3/16	6 11/16	11 13/32	7 13/32	1-0 21/32	8 5/32	1-1 7/8
5/16	4 9/16	7 25/32	5 9/32	9 1/32	6 1/32	10 1/4	6 3/4	11 1/2	7 15/32	1-0 23/32	8 3/16	1-1 31/32
3/8	4 5/8	7 7/8	5 11/32	9 3/32	6 1/16	10 11/32	6 25/32	11 9/16	7 1/2	1-0 13/16	8 1/4	1-2 1/32
7/16	4 21/32	7 15/16	5 3/8	9 3/16	6 3/32	10 13/32	6 27/32	11 21/32	7 9/16	1-0 7/8	8 9/32	1-2 1/8
1/2	4 23/32	8 1/32	5 7/16	9 1/4	6 5/32	10 1/2	6 7/8	11 23/32	7 19/32	1-0 31/32	8 5/16	1-2 3/16
9/16	4 3/4	8 3/32	5 15/32	9 11/32	6 3/16	10 9/16	6 15/16	11 13/16	7 21/32	1-1 1/32	8 3/8	1-2 9/32
5/8	4 25/32	8 3/16	5 17/32	9 13/32	6 1/4	10 21/32	6 31/32	11 7/8	7 11/16	1-1 1/8	8 13/32	1-2 11/32
11/16	4 27/32	8 1/4	5 9/16	9 1/2	6 9/32	10 23/32	7	11 31/32	7 3/4	1-1 3/16	8 15/32	1-2 7/16
3/4	4 7/8	8 11/32	5 5/8	9 9/16	6 11/32	10 13/16	7 1/16	1-0 1/32	7 25/32	1-1 9/32	8 1/2	1-2 1/2
13/16	4 15/16	8 13/32	5 21/32	9 21/32	6 3/8	10 7/8	7 3/32	1-0 1/8	7 13/16	1-1 11/32	8 9/16	1-2 19/32
7/8	4 31/32	8 1/2	5 11/16	9 23/32	6 7/16	10 31/32	7 5/32	1-0 3/16	7 7/8	1-1 7/16	8 19/32	1-2 21/32
15/16	5 1/32	8 9/16	5 3/4	9 13/16	6 15/32	11 1/32	7 3/16	1-0 9/32	7 29/32	1-1 1/2	8 21/32	1-2 3/4

Feet	0' Rise	0' Slope	10' Rise	10' Slope	20' Rise	20' Slope	30' Rise	30' Slope
0	0	0	7-2 7/8	12-4 5/32	14-5 3/4	24-8 5/32	21-8 5/8	37-0 1/16
1	-8 11/16	1-2 13/16	7-11 9/16	13-6 31/32	15-2 7/16	25-11 3/32	22-5 5/16	38-3 1/4
2	1-5 3/8	2-5 5/8	8-8 1/4	14-9 25/32	15-11 1/8	27-1 29/32	23-2	39-6 1/16
3	2-2 1/16	3-8 7/16	9-4 15/16	16-0 19/32	16-7 13/16	28-4 3/4	23-10 11/16	40-8 7/8
4	2-10 3/4	4-11 1/4	10-1 5/8	17-3 13/32	17-4 1/2	29-7 9/16	24-7 3/8	41-11 11/16
5	3-7 7/16	6-2 1/16	10-10 5/16	18-6 7/32	18-1 3/16	30-10 3/8	25-4 1/16	43-2 1/2
6	4-4 1/8	7-4 7/8	11-7	19-9 1/32	18-9 7/8	32-1 3/16	26-0 3/4	44-5 5/16
7	5-0 13/16	8-7 11/16	12-3 11/16	20-11 27/32	19-6 9/16	33-4	26-9 7/16	45-8 1/8
8	5-9 1/2	9-10 17/32	13-0 3/8	22-2 21/32	20-3 1/4	34-6 13/16	27-6 1/8	46-10 31/32
9	6-6 3/16	11-1 11/32	13-9 1/16	23-5 15/32	20-11 15/16	35-9 5/8	28-2 13/16	48-1 25/32

A = 35° 54' 11"; logsin A = 9.76820; logcos A = 9.90849; logtan A = 9.85971; logcot A = 0.14029

Ins.	12″ Rise	Slope	13″ Rise	Slope	14″ Rise	Slope	15″ Rise	Slope	16″ Rise	Slope
0	8 11/16	1-2 13/16	9 13/32	1-4 1/32	10 1/8	1-5 9/32	10 7/8	1-6 17/32	11 19/32	1-7 3/4
1/16	8 23/32	1-2 29/32	9 15/32	1-4 1/8	10 3/16	1-5 3/8	10 29/32	1-6 19/32	11 5/8	1-7 27/32
1/8	8 25/32	1-2 31/32	9 1/2	1-4 7/32	10 7/32	1-5 7/16	10 15/16	1-6 11/16	11 11/16	1-7 29/32
3/16	8 13/16	1-3 1/32	9 9/16	1-4 9/32	10 9/32	1-5 1/2	11	1-6 3/4	11 23/32	1-7 31/32
1/4	8 7/8	1-3 1/8	9 19/32	1-4 11/32	10 5/16	1-5 19/32	11 1/2	1-6 13/16	11 3/4	1-8 1/16
5/16	8 29/32	1-3 3/16	9 5/8	1-4 7/16	10 3/8	1-5 21/32	11 3/32	1-6 29/32	11 13/16	1-8 1/8
3/8	8 31/32	1-3 9/32	9 11/16	1-4 1/2	10 13/32	1-5 3/4	11 1/8	1-6 31/32	11 27/32	1-8 7/32
7/16	9	1-3 11/32	9 23/32	1-4 19/32	10 7/16	1-5 13/16	11 3/16	1-7 1/16	11 29/32	1-8 5/32
1/2	9 1/16	1-3 7/16	9 25/32	1-4 21/32	10 1/2	1-5 29/32	11 7/32	1-7 1/8	11 15/16	1-8 3/8
9/16	9 3/32	1-3 1/2	9 13/16	1-4 3/4	10 17/32	1-5 31/32	11 1/4	1-7 7/32	1-0	1-8 7/16
5/8	9 1/8	1-3 19/32	9 7/8	1-4 13/16	10 19/32	1-6 1/16	11 5/16	1-7 9/32	1-0 1/32	1-8 17/32
11/16	9 3/16	1-3 21/32	9 29/32	1-4 29/32	10 5/8	1-6 1/8	11 11/32	1-7 3/8	1-0 3/32	1-8 19/32
3/4	9 7/32	1-3 3/4	9 31/32	1-4 31/32	10 11/16	1-6 7/32	11 13/32	1-7 7/16	1-0 1/8	1-8 11/16
13/16	9 1/4	1-3 13/16	10	1-5 1/16	10 23/32	1-6 3/8	11 7/16	1-7 17/32	1-0 5/32	1-8 3/4
7/8	9 5/16	1-3 29/32	10 1/2	1-5 1/8	10 25/32	1-6 3/8	11 1/2	1-7 19/32	1-0 7/32	1-8 27/32
15/16	9 3/8	1-3 31/32	10 3/32	1-5 7/32	10 13/16	1-6 7/16	11 17/32	1-7 11/16	1-0 1/4	1-8 29/32

Ins.	17″ Rise	Slope	18″ Rise	Slope	19″ Rise	Slope	20″ Rise	Slope	21″ Rise	Slope
0	1-0 5/16	1-9	1-1 1/2	1-10 7/32	1-1 3/4	1-11 15/32	1-2 15/32	2-0 11/16	1-3 3/16	2-1 15/16
1/16	1-0 11/32	1-9 1/16	1-1 11/16	1-10 5/16	1-1 13/16	1-11 17/32	1-2 17/32	2-0 25/32	1-3 1/4	2-2
1/8	1-0 13/32	1-9 5/32	1-1 1/8	1-10 3/8	1-1 27/32	1-11 5/8	1-2 9/16	2-0 27/32	1-3 9/32	2-2 1/8
3/16	1-0 7/16	1-9 7/32	1-1 5/32	1-10 15/32	1-1 29/32	1-11 11/16	1-2 5/8	2-0 15/16	1-3 11/32	2-2 5/32
1/4	1-0 1/2	1-9 9/32	1-1 7/32	1-10 17/32	1-1 15/16	1-11 3/4	1-2 21/32	2-1	1-3 3/8	2-2 7/32
5/16	1-0 17/32	1-9 3/8	1-1 1/4	1-10 19/32	1-1 31/32	1-11 7/8	1-2 23/32	2-1 1/16	1-3 7/16	2-2 5/16
3/8	1-0 19/32	1-9 7/16	1-1 9/32	1-10 11/16	1-2 1/32	1-11 29/32	1-2 3/4	2-1 1/8	1-3 15/32	2-2 3/8
7/16	1-0 5/8	1-9 17/32	1-1 11/32	1-10 3/4	1-2 1/16	2-0	1-2 25/32	2-1 7/32	1-3 17/32	2-2 15/32
1/2	1-0 21/32	1-9 19/32	1-1 13/32	1-10 27/32	1-2 1/8	2-0 1/16	1-2 27/32	2-1 5/16	1-3 9/16	2-2 17/32
9/16	1-0 23/32	1-9 11/16	1-1 7/16	1-10 29/32	1-2 5/32	2-0 5/32	1-2 7/8	2-1 3/8	1-3 5/8	2-2 5/8
5/8	1-0 3/4	1-9 3/4	1-1 15/32	1-11	1-2 7/32	2-0 7/32	1-2 15/16	2-1 15/32	1-3 21/32	2-2 11/16
11/16	1-0 13/16	1-9 27/32	1-1 17/32	1-11 1/16	1-2 1/4	2-0 5/16	1-2 31/32	2-1 17/32	1-3 11/16	2-2 25/32
3/4	1-0 27/32	1-9 29/32	1-1 9/16	1-11 5/32	1-2 5/16	2-0 3/8	1-3 1/32	2-1 5/8	1-3 3/4	2-2 27/32
13/16	1-0 29/32	1-10	1-1 5/8	1-11 7/32	1-2 11/32	2-0 15/32	1-3 1/16	2-1 11/16	1-3 25/32	2-2 15/16
7/8	1-0 15/16	1-10 1/16	1-1 21/32	1-11 5/16	1-2 3/8	2-0 17/32	1-3 1/8	2-1 25/32	1-3 27/32	2-3
15/16	1-1	1-10 5/32	1-1 23/32	1-11 3/8	1-2 7/16	2-0 5/8	1-3 5/32	2-1 27/32	1-3 7/8	2-3 3/32

Feet	40′ Rise	Slope	50′ Rise	Slope	60′ Rise	Slope	70′ Rise	Slope
0	28-11 1/2	49-4 19/32	36-2 3/8	61-8 23/32	43-5 1/4	74-0 7/8	50-8 1/8	86-5 1/32
1	29-8 3/8	50-7 13/32	36-11 1/16	62-11 17/32	44-1 15/16	75-3 11/16	51-4 13/16	87-7 27/32
2	30-4 7/8	51-10 7/32	37-7 3/4	64-2 3/8	44-10 5/8	76-6 1/2	52-1 1/2	88-10 21/32
3	31-1 5/16	53-1 1/32	38-4 7/16	65-5 3/32	45-7 5/16	77-9 5/16	52-10 3/16	90-1 15/32
4	31-10 1/4	54-3 27/32	39-1 1/8	66-8	46-4	79-0 1/8	53-6 7/8	91-4 9/32
5	32-6 15/16	55-6 21/32	39-9 13/16	67-10 13/16	47-0 11/16	80-2 15/16	54-3 9/16	92-7 3/32
6	33-3 5/8	56-9 15/32	40-6 1/2	69-1 5/8	47-9 3/8	81-5 3/4	55-0 1/4	93-9 29/32
7	34-0 5/16	58-0 9/32	41-3 3/16	70-4 7/16	48-6 1/16	82-8 19/32	55-8 15/16	95-0 23/32
8	34-9	59-3 3/32	41-11 7/8	71-7 1/4	49-2 3/4	83-11 13/32	56-5 5/8	96-3 17/32
9	35-5 11/16	60-5 29/32	42-8 9/16	72-10 1/16	49-11 7/16	85-2 7/32	57-2 5/16	97-6 11/32

natsin A=0.5864143748; natcos A=0.8100112228; nattan A=0.7239583333; natcot A=1.3812949640

Bevel 8¾" to 12"

Inches	0" Rise	0" Slope	1" Rise	1" Slope	2" Rise	2" Slope	3" Rise	3" Slope	4" Rise	4" Slope	5" Rise	5" Slope
0	0	0	$^{23}/_{32}$	$1\frac{1}{4}$	$1^{15}/_{32}$	$2^{15}/_{32}$	$2^3/_{16}$	$3^{23}/_{32}$	$2^{29}/_{32}$	$4^{15}/_{16}$	$3^{21}/_{32}$	$6^3/_{16}$
$^1/_{16}$	$^1/_{32}$	$^1/_{16}$	$^{25}/_{32}$	$1^5/_{16}$	$1^1/_2$	$2^9/_{16}$	$2^7/_{32}$	$3^{25}/_{32}$	$2^{31}/_{32}$	$5^1/_{32}$	$3^{11}/_{16}$	$6^1/_4$
$^1/_8$	$^3/_{32}$	$^5/_{32}$	$^{13}/_{16}$	$1^{13}/_{32}$	$1^9/_{16}$	$2^5/_8$	$2^9/_{32}$	$3^7/_8$	3	$5^3/_{32}$	$3^3/_4$	$6^{11}/_{32}$
$^3/_{16}$	$^1/_8$	$^7/_{32}$	$^7/_8$	$1^{15}/_{32}$	$1^{19}/_{32}$	$2^{23}/_{32}$	$2^5/_{16}$	$3^{15}/_{16}$	$3^1/_{16}$	$5^3/_{16}$	$3^{25}/_{32}$	$6^{13}/_{32}$
$^1/_4$	$^3/_{16}$	$^5/_{16}$	$^{29}/_{32}$	$1^9/_{16}$	$1^5/_8$	$2^{25}/_{32}$	$2^3/_8$	$4^1/_{32}$	$3^3/_{32}$	$5^1/_4$	$3^{13}/_{16}$	$6^1/_2$
$^5/_{16}$	$^7/_{32}$	$^3/_8$	$^{31}/_{32}$	$1^5/_8$	$1^{11}/_{16}$	$2^7/_8$	$2^{13}/_{32}$	$4^3/_{32}$	$3^5/_{32}$	$5^{11}/_{32}$	$3^7/_8$	$6^9/_{16}$
$^3/_8$	$^9/_{32}$	$^{15}/_{32}$	1	$1^{11}/_{16}$	$1^{23}/_{32}$	$2^{15}/_{16}$	$2^{15}/_{32}$	$4^3/_{16}$	$3^3/_{16}$	$5^{13}/_{32}$	$3^{29}/_{32}$	$6^{21}/_{32}$
$^7/_{16}$	$^5/_{16}$	$^{17}/_{32}$	$1^1/_{16}$	$1^{25}/_{32}$	$1^{25}/_{32}$	$3^1/_{32}$	$2^1/_2$	$4^1/_4$	$3^1/_4$	$5^1/_2$	$3^{31}/_{32}$	$6^{23}/_{32}$
$^1/_2$	$^3/_8$	$^5/_8$	$1^3/_{32}$	$1^{27}/_{32}$	$1^{13}/_{16}$	$3^3/_{32}$	$2^9/_{16}$	$4^{11}/_{32}$	$3^9/_{32}$	$5^9/_{16}$	4	$6^{13}/_{16}$
$^9/_{16}$	$^{13}/_{32}$	$^{11}/_{16}$	$1^1/_8$	$1^{15}/_{16}$	$1^7/_8$	$3^5/_{32}$	$2^{19}/_{32}$	$4^{13}/_{32}$	$3^5/_{16}$	$5^{21}/_{32}$	$4^1/_{16}$	$6^7/_8$
$^5/_8$	$^{15}/_{32}$	$^{25}/_{32}$	$1^3/_{16}$	2	$1^{29}/_{32}$	$3^1/_4$	$2^{21}/_{32}$	$4^1/_2$	$3^3/_8$	$5^{23}/_{32}$	$4^3/_{32}$	$6^{31}/_{32}$
$^{11}/_{16}$	$^1/_2$	$^{27}/_{32}$	$1^7/_{32}$	$2^3/_{32}$	$1^{31}/_{32}$	$3^5/_{16}$	$2^{11}/_{16}$	$4^9/_{16}$	$3^{13}/_{32}$	$5^{13}/_{16}$	$4^5/_{32}$	$7^1/_{32}$
$^3/_4$	$^9/_{16}$	$^{15}/_{16}$	$1^9/_{32}$	$2^5/_{32}$	2	$3^{13}/_{32}$	$2^3/_4$	$4^{21}/_{32}$	$3^{15}/_{32}$	$5^7/_8$	$4^3/_{16}$	$7^1/_8$
$^{13}/_{16}$	$^{19}/_{32}$	1	$1^5/_{16}$	$2^1/_4$	$2^1/_{16}$	$3^{15}/_{32}$	$2^{25}/_{32}$	$4^{23}/_{32}$	$3^1/_2$	$5^{31}/_{32}$	$4^1/_4$	$7^3/_{16}$
$^7/_8$	$^5/_8$	$1^3/_{32}$	$1^3/_8$	$2^5/_{16}$	$2^3/_{32}$	$3^9/_{16}$	$2^{13}/_{16}$	$4^{25}/_{32}$	$3^9/_{16}$	$6^1/_{32}$	$4^9/_{32}$	$7^9/_{32}$
$^{15}/_{16}$	$^{11}/_{16}$	$1^5/_{32}$	$1^{13}/_{32}$	$2^{13}/_{32}$	$2^5/_{32}$	$3^5/_8$	$2^7/_8$	$4^7/_8$	$3^{19}/_{32}$	$6^1/_8$	$4^{11}/_{32}$	$7^{11}/_{32}$

Inches	6" Rise	6" Slope	7" Rise	7" Slope	8" Rise	8" Slope	9" Rise	9" Slope	10" Rise	10" Slope	11" Rise	11" Slope
0	$4^3/_8$	$7^7/_{16}$	$5^3/_{32}$	$8^{21}/_{32}$	$5^{27}/_{32}$	$9^{29}/_{32}$	$6^9/_{16}$	$11^1/_8$	$7^9/_{32}$	$1-0^3/_8$	$8^1/_8$	$1-1^5/_8$
$^1/_{16}$	$4^{13}/_{32}$	$7^1/_2$	$5^9/_{32}$	$8^3/_4$	$5^7/_8$	$9^{31}/_{32}$	$6^{19}/_{32}$	$11^7/_{32}$	$7^{11}/_{32}$	$1-0^{15}/_{32}$	$8^1/_{16}$	$1-1^{11}/_{16}$
$^1/_8$	$4^{15}/_{32}$	$7^{19}/_{32}$	$5^3/_{16}$	$8^{13}/_{16}$	$5^{15}/_{16}$	$10^1/_{16}$	$6^{21}/_{32}$	$11^9/_{32}$	$7^3/_8$	$1-0^{17}/_{32}$	$8^1/_8$	$1-1^{25}/_{32}$
$^3/_{16}$	$4^1/_2$	$7^{21}/_{32}$	$5^1/_4$	$8^{29}/_{32}$	$5^{31}/_{32}$	$10^1/_8$	$6^{11}/_{16}$	$11^3/_8$	$7^7/_{16}$	$1-0^{19}/_{32}$	$8^5/_{32}$	$1-1^{27}/_{32}$
$^1/_4$	$4^9/_{16}$	$7^3/_4$	$5^9/_{32}$	$8^{31}/_{32}$	6	$10^7/_{32}$	$6^3/_4$	$11^7/_{16}$	$7^{15}/_{32}$	$1-0^{11}/_{16}$	$8^3/_{16}$	$1-1^{15}/_{16}$
$^5/_{16}$	$4^{19}/_{32}$	$7^{13}/_{16}$	$5^{11}/_{32}$	$9^1/_{16}$	$6^1/_{16}$	$10^9/_{32}$	$6^{25}/_{32}$	$11^1/_2$	$7^1/_2$	$1-0^3/_4$	$8^1/_4$	$1-2$
$^3/_8$	$4^{21}/_{32}$	$7^7/_8$	$5^3/_8$	$9^1/_8$	$6^3/_{32}$	$10^3/_8$	$6^{27}/_{32}$	$11^{19}/_{32}$	$7^9/_{16}$	$1-0^{27}/_{32}$	$8^9/_{32}$	$1-2^1/_{16}$
$^7/_{16}$	$4^{11}/_{16}$	$7^{31}/_{32}$	$5^7/_{16}$	$9^7/_{32}$	$6^5/_{32}$	$10^7/_{16}$	$6^7/_8$	$11^{11}/_{16}$	$7^5/_8$	$1-0^{29}/_{32}$	$8^{11}/_{32}$	$1-2^5/_{32}$
$^1/_2$	$4^3/_4$	$8^1/_{32}$	$5^{15}/_{32}$	$9^9/_{32}$	$6^3/_{16}$	$10^{17}/_{32}$	$6^{15}/_{16}$	$11^3/_4$	$7^{21}/_{32}$	$1-1$	$8^3/_8$	$1-2^7/_{32}$
$^9/_{16}$	$4^{25}/_{32}$	$8^3/_{32}$	$5^1/_2$	$9^3/_8$	$6^1/_4$	$10^{19}/_{32}$	$6^{31}/_{32}$	$11^{27}/_{32}$	$7^{11}/_{16}$	$1-1^1/_{16}$	$8^7/_{16}$	$1-2^5/_{16}$
$^5/_8$	$4^{27}/_{32}$	$8^3/_{16}$	$5^9/_{16}$	$9^7/_{16}$	$6^9/_{32}$	$10^{11}/_{16}$	$7^1/_{32}$	$11^{29}/_{32}$	$7^3/_4$	$1-1^5/_{32}$	$8^{15}/_{32}$	$1-2^3/_8$
$^{11}/_{16}$	$4^7/_8$	$8^9/_{32}$	$5^{19}/_{32}$	$9^1/_2$	$6^{11}/_{32}$	$10^3/_4$	$7^1/_{16}$	$1-0$	$7^{25}/_{32}$	$1-1^7/_{32}$	$8^{17}/_{32}$	$1-2^{15}/_{32}$
$^3/_4$	$4^{15}/_{16}$	$8^{11}/_{32}$	$5^{21}/_{32}$	$9^{19}/_{32}$	$6^3/_8$	$10^{27}/_{32}$	$7^1/_8$	$1-0^1/_{16}$	$7^{27}/_{32}$	$1-1^5/_{16}$	$8^9/_{16}$	$1-2^{17}/_{32}$
$^{13}/_{16}$	$4^{31}/_{32}$	$8^7/_{16}$	$5^{11}/_{16}$	$9^{21}/_{32}$	$6^7/_{16}$	$10^{29}/_{32}$	$7^5/_{32}$	$1-0^5/_{32}$	$7^7/_8$	$1-1^3/_8$	$8^5/_8$	$1-2^5/_8$
$^7/_8$	5	$8^1/_2$	$5^3/_4$	$9^3/_4$	$6^{15}/_{32}$	$10^{31}/_{32}$	$7^3/_{16}$	$1-0^7/_{32}$	$7^{15}/_{16}$	$1-1^{15}/_{32}$	$8^{21}/_{32}$	$1-2^{11}/_{16}$
$^{15}/_{16}$	$5^1/_{16}$	$8^{19}/_{32}$	$5^{25}/_{32}$	$9^{13}/_{16}$	$6^{17}/_{32}$	$11^1/_{16}$	$7^1/_4$	$1-0^5/_{16}$	$7^{31}/_{32}$	$1-1^{17}/_{32}$	$8^{23}/_{32}$	$1-2^{25}/_{32}$

Feet	0' Rise	0' Slope	10' Rise	10' Slope	20' Rise	20' Slope	30' Rise	30' Slope
0	0	0	$7-3^1/_2$	$12-4^1/_2$	$14-7$	$24-9^1/_{32}$	$21-10^1/_2$	$37-1^{17}/_{32}$
1	$-8^3/_4$	$1-2^{27}/_{32}$	$8-0^1/_4$	$13-7^3/_8$	$15-3^3/_4$	$25-11^7/_8$	$22-7^1/_4$	$38-4^{13}/_{32}$
2	$1-5^1/_2$	$2-5^{11}/_{16}$	$8-9$	$14-10^7/_{32}$	$16-0^1/_2$	$27-2^{23}/_{32}$	$23-4$	$39-7^1/_4$
3	$2-2^1/_4$	$3-8^9/_{16}$	$9-5^3/_4$	$16-1^1/_{16}$	$16-9^1/_4$	$28-5^{19}/_{32}$	$24-0^3/_4$	$40-10^3/_{32}$
4	$2-11$	$4-11^{13}/_{32}$	$10-2^1/_2$	$17-3^{29}/_{32}$	$17-6$	$29-8^7/_{16}$	$24-9^1/_2$	$42-0^{15}/_{16}$
5	$3-7^3/_4$	$6-2^1/_4$	$10-11^1/_4$	$18-6^{25}/_{32}$	$18-2^3/_4$	$30-11^9/_{32}$	$25-6^1/_4$	$43-3^{13}/_{16}$
6	$4-4^1/_2$	$7-5^3/_{32}$	$11-8$	$19-9^5/_8$	$18-11^1/_2$	$32-2^1/_8$	$26-3$	$44-6^{21}/_{32}$
7	$5-1^1/_4$	$8-7^{31}/_{32}$	$12-4^3/_4$	$21-0^{15}/_{32}$	$19-8^1/_4$	$33-5$	$26-11^3/_4$	$45-9^1/_2$
8	$5-10$	$9-10^{13}/_{16}$	$13-1^1/_2$	$22-3^5/_{16}$	$20-5$	$34-7^{27}/_{32}$	$27-8^1/_2$	$47-0^{11}/_{32}$
9	$6-6^3/_4$	$11-1^{21}/_{32}$	$13-10^1/_4$	$23-6^3/_{16}$	$21-1^3/_4$	$35-10^{11}/_{16}$	$28-5^1/_4$	$48-3^3/_{16}$

A = 36° 05′ 54″; logsin A = 9.77024; logcos A = 9.90742; logtan A = 9.86283; logcot A = 0.13717

Ins.	12″ Rise	12″ Slope	13″ Rise	13″ Slope	14″ Rise	14″ Slope	15″ Rise	15″ Slope	16″ Rise	16″ Slope
0	$8\frac{3}{4}$	$1\text{-}2\frac{27}{32}$	$9\frac{15}{32}$	$1\text{-}4\frac{3}{32}$	$10\frac{7}{32}$	$1\text{-}5\frac{5}{16}$	$10\frac{15}{16}$	$1\text{-}6\frac{9}{16}$	$11\frac{21}{32}$	$1\text{-}7\frac{13}{16}$
$\frac{1}{16}$	$8\frac{25}{32}$	$1\text{-}2\frac{15}{16}$	$9\frac{17}{32}$	$1\text{-}4\frac{5}{32}$	$10\frac{1}{4}$	$1\text{-}5\frac{13}{32}$	$10\frac{31}{32}$	$1\text{-}6\frac{21}{32}$	$11\frac{23}{32}$	$1\text{-}7\frac{7}{8}$
$\frac{1}{8}$	$8\frac{27}{32}$	$1\text{-}3$	$9\frac{9}{16}$	$1\text{-}4\frac{1}{4}$	$10\frac{5}{16}$	$1\text{-}5\frac{15}{32}$	$11\frac{1}{32}$	$1\text{-}6\frac{23}{32}$	$11\frac{3}{4}$	$1\text{-}7\frac{31}{32}$
$\frac{3}{16}$	$8\frac{7}{8}$	$1\text{-}3\frac{3}{32}$	$9\frac{5}{8}$	$1\text{-}4\frac{5}{16}$	$10\frac{11}{32}$	$1\text{-}5\frac{9}{16}$	$11\frac{1}{16}$	$1\text{-}6\frac{25}{32}$	$11\frac{13}{16}$	$1\text{-}8\frac{1}{32}$
$\frac{1}{4}$	$8\frac{15}{16}$	$1\text{-}3\frac{5}{32}$	$9\frac{21}{32}$	$1\text{-}4\frac{13}{32}$	$10\frac{3}{8}$	$1\text{-}5\frac{5}{8}$	$11\frac{1}{8}$	$1\text{-}6\frac{7}{8}$	$11\frac{27}{32}$	$1\text{-}8\frac{1}{8}$
$\frac{5}{16}$	$8\frac{31}{32}$	$1\text{-}3\frac{1}{4}$	$9\frac{23}{32}$	$1\text{-}4\frac{15}{32}$	$10\frac{7}{16}$	$1\text{-}5\frac{23}{32}$	$11\frac{5}{32}$	$1\text{-}6\frac{15}{16}$	$11\frac{29}{32}$	$1\text{-}8\frac{3}{16}$
$\frac{3}{8}$	$9\frac{1}{32}$	$1\text{-}3\frac{5}{16}$	$9\frac{3}{4}$	$1\text{-}4\frac{9}{16}$	$10\frac{15}{32}$	$1\text{-}5\frac{25}{32}$	$11\frac{7}{32}$	$1\text{-}7\frac{1}{32}$	$11\frac{15}{16}$	$1\text{-}8\frac{9}{32}$
$\frac{7}{16}$	$9\frac{1}{16}$	$1\text{-}3\frac{13}{32}$	$9\frac{13}{16}$	$1\text{-}4\frac{5}{8}$	$10\frac{17}{32}$	$1\text{-}5\frac{7}{8}$	$11\frac{1}{4}$	$1\text{-}7\frac{3}{28}$	$1\text{-}0$	$1\text{-}8\frac{11}{32}$
$\frac{1}{2}$	$9\frac{1}{8}$	$1\text{-}3\frac{15}{32}$	$9\frac{27}{32}$	$1\text{-}4\frac{23}{32}$	$10\frac{9}{16}$	$1\text{-}5\frac{15}{16}$	$11\frac{5}{16}$	$1\text{-}7\frac{3}{16}$	$1\text{-}0\frac{1}{32}$	$1\text{-}8\frac{13}{32}$
$\frac{9}{16}$	$9\frac{5}{32}$	$1\text{-}3\frac{9}{16}$	$9\frac{7}{8}$	$1\text{-}4\frac{25}{32}$	$10\frac{5}{8}$	$1\text{-}6\frac{1}{8}$	$11\frac{11}{32}$	$1\text{-}7\frac{1}{4}$	$1\text{-}0\frac{1}{16}$	$1\text{-}8\frac{1}{2}$
$\frac{5}{8}$	$9\frac{7}{32}$	$1\text{-}3\frac{5}{8}$	$9\frac{15}{16}$	$1\text{-}4\frac{7}{8}$	$10\frac{21}{32}$	$1\text{-}6\frac{3}{32}$	$11\frac{13}{32}$	$1\text{-}7\frac{11}{32}$	$1\text{-}0\frac{1}{8}$	$1\text{-}8\frac{9}{32}$
$\frac{11}{16}$	$9\frac{1}{4}$	$1\text{-}3\frac{11}{16}$	$9\frac{31}{32}$	$1\text{-}4\frac{15}{16}$	$10\frac{23}{32}$	$1\text{-}6\frac{3}{16}$	$11\frac{7}{16}$	$1\text{-}7\frac{13}{32}$	$1\text{-}0\frac{5}{32}$	$1\text{-}8\frac{21}{32}$
$\frac{3}{4}$	$9\frac{5}{16}$	$1\text{-}3\frac{25}{32}$	$10\frac{1}{32}$	$1\text{-}5\frac{1}{32}$	$10\frac{3}{4}$	$1\text{-}6\frac{1}{4}$	$11\frac{1}{2}$	$1\text{-}7\frac{1}{2}$	$1\text{-}0\frac{7}{32}$	$1\text{-}8\frac{23}{32}$
$\frac{13}{16}$	$9\frac{11}{32}$	$1\text{-}3\frac{27}{32}$	$10\frac{1}{8}$	$1\text{-}5\frac{3}{32}$	$10\frac{13}{16}$	$1\text{-}6\frac{11}{32}$	$11\frac{17}{32}$	$1\text{-}7\frac{9}{16}$	$1\text{-}0\frac{1}{4}$	$1\text{-}8\frac{13}{16}$
$\frac{7}{8}$	$9\frac{3}{8}$	$1\text{-}3\frac{15}{16}$	$10\frac{1}{8}$	$1\text{-}5\frac{5}{32}$	$10\frac{27}{32}$	$1\text{-}6\frac{13}{32}$	$11\frac{9}{16}$	$1\text{-}7\frac{21}{32}$	$1\text{-}0\frac{5}{16}$	$1\text{-}8\frac{7}{8}$
$\frac{15}{16}$	$9\frac{7}{16}$	$1\text{-}4$	$10\frac{5}{32}$	$1\text{-}5\frac{1}{4}$	$10\frac{29}{32}$	$1\text{-}6\frac{1}{2}$	$11\frac{5}{8}$	$1\text{-}7\frac{23}{32}$	$1\text{-}0\frac{11}{32}$	$1\text{-}8\frac{31}{32}$

Ins.	17″ Rise	17″ Slope	18″ Rise	18″ Slope	19″ Rise	19″ Slope	20″ Rise	20″ Slope	21″ Rise	21″ Slope
0	$1\text{-}0\frac{13}{32}$	$1\text{-}9\frac{1}{2}$	$1\text{-}1\frac{1}{8}$	$1\text{-}10\frac{9}{32}$	$1\text{-}1\frac{27}{32}$	$1\text{-}11\frac{1}{2}$	$1\text{-}2\frac{19}{32}$	$2\text{-}0\frac{3}{4}$	$1\text{-}3\frac{5}{16}$	$2\text{-}2$
$\frac{1}{16}$	$1\text{-}0\frac{7}{16}$	$1\text{-}9\frac{1}{4}$	$1\text{-}1\frac{5}{32}$	$1\text{-}10\frac{11}{32}$	$1\text{-}1\frac{29}{32}$	$1\text{-}11\frac{19}{32}$	$1\text{-}2\frac{5}{8}$	$2\text{-}0\frac{27}{32}$	$1\text{-}3\frac{11}{32}$	$2\text{-}2\frac{1}{16}$
$\frac{1}{8}$	$1\text{-}0\frac{1}{2}$	$1\text{-}9\frac{3}{8}$	$1\text{-}1\frac{7}{32}$	$1\text{-}10\frac{7}{16}$	$1\text{-}1\frac{15}{16}$	$1\text{-}11\frac{21}{32}$	$1\text{-}2\frac{11}{16}$	$2\text{-}0\frac{29}{32}$	$1\text{-}3\frac{13}{32}$	$2\text{-}2\frac{5}{32}$
$\frac{3}{16}$	$1\text{-}0\frac{17}{32}$	$1\text{-}9\frac{9}{32}$	$1\text{-}1\frac{1}{4}$	$1\text{-}10\frac{1}{2}$	$1\text{-}2$	$1\text{-}11\frac{3}{4}$	$1\text{-}2\frac{23}{32}$	$2\text{-}0\frac{31}{32}$	$1\text{-}3\frac{7}{16}$	$2\text{-}2\frac{7}{32}$
$\frac{1}{4}$	$1\text{-}0\frac{9}{16}$	$1\text{-}9\frac{11}{32}$	$1\text{-}1\frac{5}{16}$	$1\text{-}10\frac{19}{32}$	$1\text{-}2\frac{1}{16}$	$1\text{-}11\frac{13}{16}$	$1\text{-}2\frac{3}{4}$	$2\text{-}1\frac{1}{16}$	$1\text{-}3\frac{1}{2}$	$2\text{-}2\frac{5}{16}$
$\frac{5}{16}$	$1\text{-}0\frac{5}{8}$	$1\text{-}9\frac{7}{16}$	$1\text{-}1\frac{11}{32}$	$1\text{-}10\frac{21}{32}$	$1\text{-}2\frac{3}{32}$	$1\text{-}11\frac{29}{32}$	$1\text{-}2\frac{13}{16}$	$2\text{-}1\frac{1}{8}$	$1\text{-}3\frac{17}{32}$	$2\text{-}2\frac{3}{8}$
$\frac{3}{8}$	$1\text{-}0\frac{21}{32}$	$1\text{-}9\frac{1}{2}$	$1\text{-}1\frac{13}{32}$	$1\text{-}10\frac{3}{4}$	$1\text{-}2\frac{1}{8}$	$1\text{-}11\frac{31}{32}$	$1\text{-}2\frac{27}{32}$	$2\text{-}1\frac{7}{32}$	$1\text{-}3\frac{19}{32}$	$2\text{-}2\frac{15}{32}$
$\frac{7}{16}$	$1\text{-}0\frac{23}{32}$	$1\text{-}9\frac{19}{32}$	$1\text{-}1\frac{7}{16}$	$1\text{-}10\frac{13}{16}$	$1\text{-}2\frac{3}{16}$	$2\text{-}0\frac{1}{16}$	$1\text{-}2\frac{29}{32}$	$2\text{-}1\frac{9}{32}$	$1\text{-}3\frac{5}{8}$	$2\text{-}2\frac{17}{32}$
$\frac{1}{2}$	$1\text{-}0\frac{3}{4}$	$1\text{-}9\frac{21}{32}$	$1\text{-}1\frac{1}{2}$	$1\text{-}10\frac{29}{32}$	$1\text{-}2\frac{1}{4}$	$2\text{-}0\frac{1}{8}$	$1\text{-}2\frac{15}{16}$	$2\text{-}1\frac{3}{8}$	$1\text{-}3\frac{11}{16}$	$2\text{-}2\frac{19}{32}$
$\frac{9}{16}$	$1\text{-}0\frac{13}{16}$	$1\text{-}9\frac{3}{4}$	$1\text{-}1\frac{17}{32}$	$1\text{-}10\frac{31}{32}$	$1\text{-}2\frac{1}{4}$	$2\text{-}0\frac{7}{32}$	$1\text{-}3$	$2\text{-}1\frac{7}{16}$	$1\text{-}3\frac{23}{32}$	$2\text{-}2\frac{11}{16}$
$\frac{5}{8}$	$1\text{-}0\frac{27}{32}$	$1\text{-}9\frac{13}{16}$	$1\text{-}1\frac{19}{32}$	$1\text{-}11\frac{1}{16}$	$1\text{-}2\frac{5}{16}$	$2\text{-}0\frac{9}{32}$	$1\text{-}3\frac{1}{32}$	$2\text{-}1\frac{17}{32}$	$1\text{-}3\frac{25}{32}$	$2\text{-}2\frac{3}{4}$
$\frac{11}{16}$	$1\text{-}0\frac{29}{32}$	$1\text{-}9\frac{7}{8}$	$1\text{-}1\frac{5}{8}$	$1\text{-}11\frac{1}{8}$	$1\text{-}2\frac{11}{32}$	$2\text{-}0\frac{3}{8}$	$1\text{-}3\frac{3}{32}$	$2\text{-}1\frac{19}{32}$	$1\text{-}3\frac{13}{16}$	$2\text{-}2\frac{27}{32}$
$\frac{3}{4}$	$1\text{-}0\frac{15}{16}$	$1\text{-}9\frac{31}{32}$	$1\text{-}1\frac{11}{16}$	$1\text{-}11\frac{3}{32}$	$1\text{-}2\frac{13}{32}$	$2\text{-}0\frac{7}{16}$	$1\text{-}3\frac{1}{8}$	$2\text{-}1\frac{11}{16}$	$1\text{-}3\frac{7}{8}$	$2\text{-}2\frac{29}{32}$
$\frac{13}{16}$	$1\text{-}1$	$1\text{-}10\frac{1}{32}$	$1\text{-}1\frac{23}{32}$	$1\text{-}11\frac{9}{32}$	$1\text{-}2\frac{7}{16}$	$2\text{-}0\frac{17}{32}$	$1\text{-}3\frac{3}{16}$	$2\text{-}1\frac{3}{4}$	$1\text{-}3\frac{29}{32}$	$2\text{-}3$
$\frac{7}{8}$	$1\text{-}1\frac{1}{32}$	$1\text{-}10\frac{1}{8}$	$1\text{-}1\frac{3}{4}$	$1\text{-}11\frac{3}{8}$	$1\text{-}2\frac{1}{2}$	$2\text{-}0\frac{19}{32}$	$1\text{-}3\frac{7}{32}$	$2\text{-}1\frac{27}{32}$	$1\text{-}3\frac{15}{16}$	$2\text{-}3\frac{1}{16}$
$\frac{15}{16}$	$1\text{-}1\frac{3}{32}$	$1\text{-}10\frac{3}{16}$	$1\text{-}1\frac{13}{16}$	$1\text{-}11\frac{7}{16}$	$1\text{-}2\frac{17}{32}$	$2\text{-}0\frac{11}{16}$	$1\text{-}3\frac{9}{32}$	$2\text{-}1\frac{29}{32}$	$1\text{-}4$	$2\text{-}3\frac{5}{32}$

Feet	40′ Rise	40′ Slope	50′ Rise	50′ Slope	60′ Rise	60′ Slope	70′ Rise	70′ Slope
0	$29\text{-}2$	$49\text{-}6\frac{1}{16}$	$36\text{-}5\frac{1}{2}$	$61\text{-}10\frac{9}{16}$	$43\text{-}9$	$74\text{-}3\frac{3}{32}$	$51\text{-}0\frac{1}{2}$	$86\text{-}7\frac{19}{32}$
1	$29\text{-}10\frac{3}{4}$	$50\text{-}8\frac{29}{32}$	$37\text{-}2\frac{1}{4}$	$63\text{-}1\frac{13}{32}$	$44\text{-}5\frac{3}{4}$	$75\text{-}5\frac{15}{16}$	$51\text{-}9\frac{1}{4}$	$87\text{-}10\frac{7}{16}$
2	$30\text{-}7\frac{1}{2}$	$51\text{-}11\frac{3}{4}$	$37\text{-}11$	$64\text{-}4\frac{9}{32}$	$45\text{-}2\frac{1}{2}$	$76\text{-}8\frac{25}{32}$	$52\text{-}6$	$89\text{-}1\frac{5}{16}$
3	$31\text{-}4\frac{1}{4}$	$53\text{-}2\frac{19}{32}$	$38\text{-}7\frac{3}{4}$	$65\text{-}7\frac{1}{8}$	$45\text{-}11\frac{1}{4}$	$77\text{-}11\frac{5}{8}$	$53\text{-}2\frac{3}{4}$	$90\text{-}4\frac{5}{32}$
4	$32\text{-}1$	$54\text{-}5\frac{15}{32}$	$39\text{-}4\frac{1}{2}$	$66\text{-}9\frac{31}{32}$	$46\text{-}8$	$79\text{-}2\frac{1}{2}$	$53\text{-}11\frac{1}{2}$	$91\text{-}7$
5	$32\text{-}9\frac{3}{4}$	$55\text{-}8\frac{5}{16}$	$40\text{-}1\frac{1}{4}$	$68\text{-}0\frac{13}{16}$	$47\text{-}4\frac{3}{4}$	$80\text{-}5\frac{11}{32}$	$54\text{-}8\frac{1}{4}$	$92\text{-}9\frac{27}{32}$
6	$33\text{-}6\frac{1}{2}$	$56\text{-}11\frac{5}{32}$	$40\text{-}10$	$69\text{-}3\frac{11}{16}$	$48\text{-}1\frac{1}{2}$	$81\text{-}8\frac{3}{16}$	$55\text{-}5$	$94\text{-}0\frac{11}{16}$
7	$34\text{-}3\frac{1}{4}$	$58\text{-}2$	$41\text{-}6\frac{3}{4}$	$70\text{-}6\frac{17}{32}$	$48\text{-}10\frac{1}{4}$	$82\text{-}11\frac{1}{32}$	$56\text{-}1\frac{3}{4}$	$95\text{-}3\frac{9}{16}$
8	$35\text{-}0$	$59\text{-}4\frac{7}{8}$	$42\text{-}3\frac{1}{2}$	$71\text{-}9\frac{3}{8}$	$49\text{-}7$	$84\text{-}1\frac{29}{32}$	$56\text{-}10\frac{1}{2}$	$96\text{-}6\frac{13}{32}$
9	$35\text{-}8\frac{3}{4}$	$60\text{-}7\frac{23}{32}$	$43\text{-}0\frac{1}{4}$	$73\text{-}0\frac{7}{32}$	$50\text{-}3\frac{3}{4}$	$85\text{-}4\frac{3}{4}$	$57\text{-}7\frac{1}{4}$	$97\text{-}9\frac{1}{4}$

natsin A=0.5891721574; natcos A=0.8080075303; nattan A=0.7291666666; natcot A=1.3714285714

Inches	0" Rise	0" Slope	1" Rise	1" Slope	2" Rise	2" Slope	3" Rise	3" Slope	4" Rise	4" Slope	5" Rise	5" Slope
0	0	0	3/4	1 1/4	1 15/32	2 15/32	2 3/16	3 23/32	2 15/16	4 31/32–	3 11/16	6 7/32–
1/16	1/32	1/16	25/32–	1 5/16	1 1/2	2 9/16	2 1/4	3 13/16	2 31/32	5 1/32	3 23/32–	6 9/32–
1/8	3/32–	5/32–	13/16	1 13/32–	1 9/16	2 5/8	2 9/32	3 7/8	3 1/32–	5 1/8	3 3/4	6 11/32
3/16	1/8	7/32	7/8	1 15/32	1 19/32	2 23/32–	2 11/32–	3 31/32–	3 1/16	5 3/16	3 13/16	6 7/16
1/4	3/16	5/16	29/32	1 9/16	1 21/32–	2 25/32	2 3/8	4 1/32	3 1/8	5 9/32–	3 27/32	6 1/2
5/16	7/32	3/8	31/32–	1 5/8	1 11/16	2 7/8	2 7/16	4 1/8	3 5/32	5 11/32	3 29/32–	6 19/32–
3/8	9/32–	15/32–	1	1 23/32–	1 3/4	2 15/16	2 15/32	4 3/16	3 7/32–	5 7/16	3 15/16	6 21/32
7/16	5/16	17/32	1 1/16	1 25/32	1 25/32	3 1/32–	2 17/32–	4 1/4	3 1/4	5 1/2	4	6 3/4
1/2	3/8	5/8	1 3/32	1 7/8	1 27/32–	3 3/32	2 9/16	4 11/32–	3 5/16	5 19/32–	4 1/32	6 13/16
9/16	13/32	11/16	1 5/32–	1 15/16	1 7/8	3 3/16	2 5/8	4 13/32	3 11/32	5 21/32	4 3/32–	6 29/32–
5/8	15/32–	25/32–	1 3/16	2 1/32–	1 15/16	3 1/4	2 21/32	4 1/2	3 13/32–	5 3/4	4 1/8	6 31/32
11/16	1/2	27/32	1 1/4	2 3/32–	1 31/32	3 11/32–	2 23/32–	4 9/16	3 7/16	5 13/16	4 3/16	7 1/16
3/4	9/16	15/16	1 9/32	2 5/32	2 1/32–	3 13/32	2 3/4	4 21/32–	3 1/2	5 29/32–	4 7/32	7 1/8
13/16	19/32	1	1 11/32–	2 1/4	2 1/16	3 1/2	2 13/16	4 23/32	3 17/32	5 31/32	4 9/32–	7 7/32–
7/8	21/32–	1 3/32–	1 3/8	2 5/16	2 1/8	3 9/16	2 27/32	4 13/16	3 19/32–	6 1/16	4 5/16	7 9/32
15/16	11/16	1 5/32	1 7/16	2 13/32–	2 5/32	3 21/32–	2 29/32–	4 7/8	3 5/8	6 1/8	4 3/8	7 3/8

Inches	6" Rise	6" Slope	7" Rise	7" Slope	8" Rise	8" Slope	9" Rise	9" Slope	10" Rise	10" Slope	11" Rise	11" Slope
0	4 13/32	7 7/16	5 1/8	8 11/16	5 7/8	9 15/16	6 5/8	11 5/32	7 11/32	1-0 13/32	8 1/16	1-1 21/32–
1/16	4 7/16	7 17/32–	5 3/16	8 3/4	5 29/32	10	6 21/32–	11 1/4	7 3/8	1-0 1/2	8 1/8	1-1 23/32
1/8	4 1/2	7 19/32	5 7/32	8 27/32–	5 31/32–	10 3/32–	6 11/16	11 5/16	7 7/16	1-0 9/16	8 5/32	1-1 13/16
3/16	4 17/32	7 11/16	5 9/32–	8 29/32	6	10 5/32	6 3/4	11 13/32–	7 15/32	1-0 5/8	8 7/32–	1-1 7/8
1/4	4 19/32–	7 3/4	5 5/16	9	6 1/16	10 1/4	6 25/32	11 15/32	7 17/32–	1-0 23/32–	8 1/4	1-1 31/32–
5/16	4 5/8	7 27/32–	5 3/8	9 1/16	6 3/32	10 5/16	6 27/32–	11 9/16	7 9/16	1-0 25/32	8 5/16	1-2 1/32
3/8	4 11/16	7 29/32	5 13/32	9 5/32–	6 5/32–	10 13/32–	6 7/8	11 5/8	7 5/8	1-0 7/8	8 11/32	1-2 1/8
7/16	4 23/32	8	5 15/32–	9 7/32	6 3/16	10 15/32–	6 15/16	11 23/32–	7 21/32	1-0 15/16	8 13/32–	1-2 3/16
1/2	4 25/32–	8 1/16	5 1/2	9 5/16	6 1/4	10 17/32	6 31/32	11 25/32	7 23/32–	1-1 1/32–	8 7/16	1-2 9/32–
9/16	4 13/16	8 5/32–	5 9/16	9 3/8	6 9/32	10 5/8	7 1/32–	11 7/8	7 3/4	1-1 3/32	8 1/2	1-2 11/32
5/8	4 7/8	8 7/32	5 19/32	9 15/32–	6 11/32–	10 11/16	7 1/16	11 15/16	7 13/16	1-1 3/16	8 17/32	1-2 7/16
11/16	4 29/32	8 5/16	5 21/32–	9 17/32	6 3/8	10 25/32–	7 1/8	1-0 1/32–	7 27/32	1-1 1/4	8 19/32–	1-2 1/2
3/4	4 31/32–	8 3/8	5 11/16	9 5/8	6 7/16	10 27/32	7 5/32	1-0 3/32	7 29/32–	1-1 11/32–	8 5/8	1-2 9/16
13/16	5	8 7/16	5 3/4	9 11/16	6 15/32	10 15/16	7 7/32–	1-0 3/16	7 15/16	1-1 13/32	8 11/16	1-2 21/32–
7/8	5 1/16	8 17/32–	5 25/32	9 25/32–	6 17/32–	11	7 1/4	1-0 1/4	8	1-1 1/2	8 23/32	1-2 23/32
15/16	5 3/32	8 19/32	5 27/32–	9 27/32	6 9/16	11 3/32–	7 5/16	1-0 11/32–	8 1/32	1-1 9/16	8 25/32–	1-2 13/16

Feet	0' Rise	0' Slope	10' Rise	10' Slope	20' Rise	20' Slope	30' Rise	30' Slope
0	0	0	7-4 1/8	12-4 7/8	14-8 1/4	24-9 3/4	22-0 3/8	37-2 21/32–
1	-8 13/16	1-2 7/8	8-0 15/16	13-7 25/32–	15-5 1/16	26-0 21/32–	22-9 3/16	38-5 17/32
2	1-5 5/8	2-5 25/32–	8-9 3/4	14-10 21/32	16-1 7/8	27-3 17/32	23-6	39-8 7/16
3	2-2 7/16	3-8 21/32	9-6 9/16	16-1 9/16	16-10 11/16	28-6 7/16	24-2 13/16	40-11 5/16
4	2-11 1/4	4-11 9/16	10-3 3/8	17-4 7/16	17-7 1/2	29-9 5/16	24-11 5/8	42-2 3/16
5	3-8 1/16	6-2 7/16	11-0 3/16	18-7 5/16	18-4 5/16	31-0 7/32–	25-8 7/16	43-5 3/32–
6	4-4 7/8	7-5 11/32–	11-9	19-10 7/32–	19-1 1/8	32-3 3/32	26-5 1/4	44-7 31/32
7	5-1 11/16	8-8 7/32–	12-5 13/16	21-1 3/32	19-9 15/16	33-5 31/32	27-2 1/16	45-10 7/8
8	5-10 1/2	9-11 3/32	13-2 5/8	22-4	20-6 3/4	34-8 7/8	27-10 7/8	47-1 3/4
9	6-7 5/16	11-2	13-11 7/16	23-6 7/8	21-3 9/16	35-11 3/4	28-7 11/16	48-4 21/32–

A = 36° 17′ 33″; logsin A = 9.77226; logcos A = 9.90634; logtan A = 9.86592; logcot A = 0.13408

Ins.	12″ Rise	12″ Slope	13″ Rise	13″ Slope	14″ Rise	14″ Slope	15″ Rise	15″ Slope	16″ Rise	16″ Slope
0	$8\frac{13}{16}$	$1\text{-}2\frac{7}{8}$	$9\frac{9}{16}$	$1\text{-}4\frac{1}{8}$	$10\frac{5}{32}$	$1\text{-}5\frac{5}{8}$	11	$1\text{-}6\frac{5}{8}$	$11\frac{3}{4}$	$1\text{-}7\frac{27}{32}$
$\frac{1}{16}$	$8\frac{27}{32}$	$1\text{-}2\frac{31}{32}$	$9\frac{19}{32}$	$1\text{-}4\frac{7}{32}$	$10\frac{5}{16}$	$1\text{-}5\frac{7}{16}$	$11\frac{1}{8}$	$1\text{-}6\frac{11}{16}$	$11\frac{25}{32}$	$1\text{-}7\frac{15}{16}$
$\frac{1}{8}$	$8\frac{29}{32}$	$1\text{-}3\frac{1}{32}$	$9\frac{5}{8}$	$1\text{-}4\frac{9}{32}$	$10\frac{3}{8}$	$1\text{-}5\frac{17}{32}$	$11\frac{3}{32}$	$1\text{-}6\frac{3}{4}$	$11\frac{27}{32}$	$1\text{-}8$
$\frac{3}{16}$	$8\frac{15}{16}$	$1\text{-}3\frac{1}{8}$	$9\frac{11}{16}$	$1\text{-}4\frac{3}{8}$	$10\frac{13}{32}$	$1\text{-}5\frac{19}{32}$	$11\frac{5}{32}$	$1\text{-}6\frac{27}{32}$	$11\frac{7}{8}$	$1\text{-}8\frac{5}{32}$
$\frac{1}{4}$	9	$1\text{-}3\frac{3}{16}$	$9\frac{23}{32}$	$1\text{-}4\frac{7}{16}$	$10\frac{15}{32}$	$1\text{-}5\frac{11}{16}$	$11\frac{3}{16}$	$1\text{-}6\frac{29}{32}$	$11\frac{15}{16}$	$1\text{-}8\frac{5}{32}$
$\frac{5}{16}$	$9\frac{1}{32}$	$1\text{-}3\frac{9}{32}$	$9\frac{25}{32}$	$1\text{-}4\frac{17}{32}$	$10\frac{1}{2}$	$1\text{-}5\frac{3}{4}$	$11\frac{1}{4}$	$1\text{-}7$	$11\frac{31}{32}$	$1\text{-}8\frac{1}{4}$
$\frac{3}{8}$	$9\frac{3}{32}$	$1\text{-}3\frac{11}{32}$	$9\frac{13}{16}$	$1\text{-}4\frac{19}{32}$	$10\frac{9}{16}$	$1\text{-}5\frac{27}{32}$	$11\frac{9}{32}$	$1\text{-}7\frac{1}{16}$	$1\text{-}0\frac{1}{2}$	$1\text{-}8\frac{5}{16}$
$\frac{7}{16}$	$9\frac{1}{8}$	$1\text{-}3\frac{7}{16}$	$9\frac{7}{8}$	$1\text{-}4\frac{21}{32}$	$10\frac{19}{32}$	$1\text{-}5\frac{29}{32}$	$11\frac{11}{32}$	$1\text{-}7\frac{5}{32}$	$1\text{-}0\frac{1}{8}$	$1\text{-}8\frac{13}{32}$
$\frac{1}{2}$	$9\frac{3}{16}$	$1\text{-}3\frac{1}{2}$	$9\frac{29}{32}$	$1\text{-}4\frac{3}{4}$	$10\frac{21}{32}$	$1\text{-}6$	$11\frac{3}{8}$	$1\text{-}7\frac{7}{32}$	$1\text{-}0\frac{1}{8}$	$1\text{-}8\frac{15}{32}$
$\frac{9}{16}$	$9\frac{7}{32}$	$1\text{-}3\frac{19}{32}$	$9\frac{31}{32}$	$1\text{-}4\frac{29}{32}$	$10\frac{11}{16}$	$1\text{-}6\frac{1}{16}$	$11\frac{7}{16}$	$1\text{-}7\frac{5}{32}$	$1\text{-}0\frac{5}{32}$	$1\text{-}8\frac{9}{32}$
$\frac{5}{8}$	$9\frac{9}{32}$	$1\text{-}3\frac{21}{32}$	10	$1\text{-}4\frac{29}{32}$	$10\frac{3}{4}$	$1\text{-}6\frac{5}{32}$	$11\frac{15}{32}$	$1\text{-}7\frac{3}{8}$	$1\text{-}0\frac{7}{32}$	$1\text{-}8\frac{5}{8}$
$\frac{11}{16}$	$9\frac{5}{16}$	$1\text{-}3\frac{3}{4}$	$10\frac{1}{16}$	$1\text{-}4\frac{31}{32}$	$10\frac{25}{32}$	$1\text{-}6\frac{7}{32}$	$11\frac{17}{32}$	$1\text{-}7\frac{15}{32}$	$1\text{-}0\frac{1}{4}$	$1\text{-}8\frac{23}{32}$
$\frac{3}{4}$	$9\frac{3}{8}$	$1\text{-}3\frac{13}{16}$	$10\frac{3}{32}$	$1\text{-}5\frac{1}{16}$	$10\frac{27}{32}$	$1\text{-}6\frac{5}{16}$	$11\frac{9}{16}$	$1\text{-}7\frac{17}{32}$	$1\text{-}0\frac{5}{16}$	$1\text{-}8\frac{25}{32}$
$\frac{13}{16}$	$9\frac{13}{32}$	$1\text{-}3\frac{29}{32}$	$10\frac{5}{32}$	$1\text{-}5\frac{1}{8}$	$10\frac{7}{8}$	$1\text{-}6\frac{3}{8}$	$11\frac{5}{8}$	$1\text{-}7\frac{5}{8}$	$1\text{-}0\frac{11}{32}$	$1\text{-}8\frac{27}{32}$
$\frac{7}{8}$	$9\frac{15}{32}$	$1\text{-}3\frac{31}{32}$	$10\frac{3}{16}$	$1\text{-}5\frac{7}{32}$	$10\frac{15}{16}$	$1\text{-}6\frac{15}{32}$	$11\frac{21}{32}$	$1\text{-}7\frac{11}{16}$	$1\text{-}0\frac{13}{32}$	$1\text{-}8\frac{15}{16}$
$\frac{15}{16}$	$9\frac{1}{2}$	$1\text{-}4\frac{1}{16}$	$10\frac{1}{4}$	$1\text{-}5\frac{9}{32}$	$10\frac{31}{32}$	$1\text{-}6\frac{17}{32}$	$11\frac{23}{32}$	$1\text{-}7\frac{25}{32}$	$1\text{-}0\frac{7}{16}$	$1\text{-}9$

Ins.	17″ Rise	17″ Slope	18″ Rise	18″ Slope	19″ Rise	19″ Slope	20″ Rise	20″ Slope	21″ Rise	21″ Slope
0	$1\text{-}0\frac{1}{2}$	$1\text{-}9\frac{3}{32}$	$1\text{-}1\frac{7}{32}$	$1\text{-}10\frac{11}{32}$	$1\text{-}1\frac{15}{32}$	$1\text{-}11\frac{9}{16}$	$1\text{-}2\frac{11}{32}$	$2\text{-}0\frac{13}{16}$	$1\text{-}3\frac{1}{16}$	$2\text{-}2\frac{1}{16}$
$\frac{1}{16}$	$1\text{-}0\frac{17}{32}$	$1\text{-}9\frac{5}{32}$	$1\text{-}1\frac{1}{4}$	$1\text{-}10\frac{13}{32}$	$1\text{-}2$	$1\text{-}11\frac{21}{32}$	$1\text{-}2\frac{23}{32}$	$2\text{-}0\frac{29}{32}$	$1\text{-}3\frac{15}{32}$	$2\text{-}2\frac{1}{8}$
$\frac{1}{8}$	$1\text{-}0\frac{9}{16}$	$1\text{-}9\frac{1}{4}$	$1\text{-}1\frac{5}{16}$	$1\text{-}10\frac{1}{2}$	$1\text{-}2\frac{1}{32}$	$1\text{-}11\frac{23}{32}$	$1\text{-}2\frac{25}{32}$	$2\text{-}0\frac{31}{32}$	$1\text{-}3\frac{1}{2}$	$2\text{-}2\frac{7}{32}$
$\frac{3}{16}$	$1\text{-}0\frac{5}{8}$	$1\text{-}9\frac{5}{8}$	$1\text{-}1\frac{11}{32}$	$1\text{-}10\frac{9}{16}$	$1\text{-}2\frac{3}{32}$	$1\text{-}11\frac{13}{16}$	$1\text{-}2\frac{13}{16}$	$2\text{-}1\frac{1}{32}$	$1\text{-}3\frac{9}{16}$	$2\text{-}2\frac{9}{32}$
$\frac{1}{4}$	$1\text{-}0\frac{21}{32}$	$1\text{-}9\frac{13}{32}$	$1\text{-}1\frac{13}{32}$	$1\text{-}10\frac{21}{32}$	$1\text{-}2\frac{1}{8}$	$1\text{-}11\frac{7}{8}$	$1\text{-}2\frac{7}{8}$	$2\text{-}1\frac{1}{8}$	$1\text{-}3\frac{19}{32}$	$2\text{-}2\frac{3}{8}$
$\frac{5}{16}$	$1\text{-}0\frac{23}{32}$	$1\text{-}9\frac{15}{32}$	$1\text{-}1\frac{7}{16}$	$1\text{-}10\frac{23}{32}$	$1\text{-}2\frac{3}{16}$	$1\text{-}11\frac{31}{32}$	$1\text{-}2\frac{29}{32}$	$2\text{-}1\frac{3}{16}$	$1\text{-}3\frac{21}{32}$	$2\text{-}2\frac{7}{16}$
$\frac{3}{8}$	$1\text{-}0\frac{3}{4}$	$1\text{-}9\frac{9}{16}$	$1\text{-}1\frac{1}{2}$	$1\text{-}10\frac{13}{16}$	$1\text{-}2\frac{7}{32}$	$2\text{-}0\frac{1}{32}$	$1\text{-}2\frac{31}{32}$	$2\text{-}1\frac{9}{32}$	$1\text{-}3\frac{11}{16}$	$2\text{-}2\frac{17}{32}$
$\frac{7}{16}$	$1\text{-}0\frac{13}{32}$	$1\text{-}9\frac{5}{8}$	$1\text{-}1\frac{17}{32}$	$1\text{-}10\frac{7}{8}$	$1\text{-}2\frac{9}{32}$	$2\text{-}0\frac{1}{8}$	$1\text{-}3$	$2\text{-}1\frac{11}{32}$	$1\text{-}3\frac{3}{4}$	$2\text{-}2\frac{19}{32}$
$\frac{1}{2}$	$1\text{-}0\frac{27}{32}$	$1\text{-}9\frac{23}{32}$	$1\text{-}1\frac{19}{32}$	$1\text{-}10\frac{15}{32}$	$1\text{-}2\frac{5}{16}$	$2\text{-}0\frac{3}{16}$	$1\text{-}3\frac{1}{16}$	$2\text{-}1\frac{7}{16}$	$1\text{-}3\frac{25}{32}$	$2\text{-}2\frac{11}{16}$
$\frac{9}{16}$	$1\text{-}0\frac{29}{32}$	$1\text{-}9\frac{25}{32}$	$1\text{-}1\frac{5}{8}$	$1\text{-}11\frac{1}{32}$	$1\text{-}2\frac{3}{8}$	$2\text{-}0\frac{9}{32}$	$1\text{-}3\frac{3}{8}$	$2\text{-}1\frac{1}{2}$	$1\text{-}3\frac{27}{32}$	$2\text{-}2\frac{3}{4}$
$\frac{5}{8}$	$1\text{-}0\frac{15}{16}$	$1\text{-}9\frac{7}{8}$	$1\text{-}1\frac{11}{16}$	$1\text{-}11\frac{3}{32}$	$1\text{-}2\frac{13}{32}$	$2\text{-}0\frac{11}{32}$	$1\text{-}3\frac{5}{32}$	$2\text{-}1\frac{19}{32}$	$1\text{-}3\frac{7}{8}$	$2\text{-}2\frac{27}{32}$
$\frac{11}{16}$	$1\text{-}1$	$1\text{-}9\frac{15}{16}$	$1\text{-}1\frac{23}{32}$	$1\text{-}11\frac{3}{16}$	$1\text{-}2\frac{15}{32}$	$2\text{-}0\frac{7}{16}$	$1\text{-}3\frac{3}{16}$	$2\text{-}1\frac{21}{32}$	$1\text{-}3\frac{15}{16}$	$2\text{-}2\frac{29}{32}$
$\frac{3}{4}$	$1\text{-}1\frac{1}{32}$	$1\text{-}10\frac{1}{32}$	$1\text{-}1\frac{25}{32}$	$1\text{-}11\frac{1}{4}$	$1\text{-}2\frac{1}{2}$	$2\text{-}0\frac{1}{2}$	$1\text{-}3\frac{1}{4}$	$2\text{-}1\frac{3}{4}$	$1\text{-}3\frac{31}{32}$	$2\text{-}3$
$\frac{13}{16}$	$1\text{-}1\frac{3}{32}$	$1\text{-}10\frac{3}{32}$	$1\text{-}1\frac{13}{16}$	$1\text{-}11\frac{11}{32}$	$1\text{-}2\frac{9}{16}$	$2\text{-}0\frac{19}{32}$	$1\text{-}3\frac{9}{32}$	$2\text{-}1\frac{13}{16}$	$1\text{-}4\frac{1}{32}$	$2\text{-}3\frac{1}{16}$
$\frac{7}{8}$	$1\text{-}1\frac{1}{8}$	$1\text{-}10\frac{1}{8}$	$1\text{-}1\frac{7}{8}$	$1\text{-}11\frac{13}{32}$	$1\text{-}2\frac{19}{32}$	$2\text{-}0\frac{21}{32}$	$1\text{-}3\frac{11}{32}$	$2\text{-}1\frac{29}{32}$	$1\text{-}4\frac{1}{16}$	$2\text{-}3\frac{1}{8}$
$\frac{15}{16}$	$1\text{-}1\frac{5}{32}$	$1\text{-}10\frac{1}{4}$	$1\text{-}1\frac{29}{32}$	$1\text{-}11\frac{1}{2}$	$1\text{-}2\frac{21}{32}$	$2\text{-}0\frac{3}{4}$	$1\text{-}3\frac{3}{8}$	$2\text{-}1\frac{31}{32}$	$1\text{-}4\frac{1}{8}$	$2\text{-}3\frac{7}{32}$

Feet	40′ Rise	40′ Slope	50′ Rise	50′ Slope	60′ Rise	60′ Slope	70′ Rise	70′ Slope
0	$29\text{-}4\frac{1}{2}$	$49\text{-}7\frac{17}{32}$	$36\text{-}8\frac{5}{8}$	$62\text{-}0\frac{13}{16}$	$44\text{-}0\frac{3}{4}$	$74\text{-}5\frac{9}{32}$	$51\text{-}4\frac{7}{8}$	$86\text{-}10\frac{3}{16}$
1	$30\text{-}1\frac{5}{16}$	$50\text{-}10\frac{13}{32}$	$37\text{-}5\frac{7}{16}$	$63\text{-}3\frac{5}{16}$	$44\text{-}9\frac{9}{16}$	$75\text{-}8\frac{3}{16}$	$52\text{-}1\frac{11}{16}$	$88\text{-}1\frac{1}{16}$
2	$30\text{-}10\frac{1}{8}$	$52\text{-}1\frac{5}{16}$	$38\text{-}2\frac{1}{4}$	$64\text{-}6\frac{3}{16}$	$45\text{-}6\frac{3}{8}$	$76\text{-}11\frac{11}{16}$	$52\text{-}10\frac{1}{2}$	$89\text{-}3\frac{31}{32}$
3	$31\text{-}6\frac{15}{16}$	$53\text{-}4\frac{3}{16}$	$38\text{-}11\frac{1}{16}$	$65\text{-}9\frac{1}{16}$	$46\text{-}3\frac{3}{32}$	$78\text{-}1\frac{27}{32}$	$53\text{-}7\frac{5}{16}$	$90\text{-}6\frac{27}{32}$
4	$32\text{-}3\frac{3}{4}$	$54\text{-}7\frac{3}{32}$	$39\text{-}7\frac{7}{8}$	$66\text{-}11\frac{31}{32}$	$47\text{-}0$	$79\text{-}4\frac{27}{32}$	$54\text{-}4\frac{1}{8}$	$91\text{-}9\frac{23}{32}$
5	$33\text{-}0\frac{9}{16}$	$55\text{-}9\frac{31}{32}$	$40\text{-}4\frac{11}{16}$	$68\text{-}2\frac{27}{32}$	$47\text{-}8\frac{13}{16}$	$80\text{-}7\frac{3}{4}$	$55\text{-}0\frac{15}{16}$	$93\text{-}0\frac{5}{8}$
6	$33\text{-}9\frac{3}{8}$	$57\text{-}0\frac{7}{8}$	$41\text{-}1\frac{1}{2}$	$69\text{-}5\frac{3}{4}$	$48\text{-}5\frac{5}{8}$	$81\text{-}10\frac{5}{8}$	$55\text{-}9\frac{3}{4}$	$94\text{-}3\frac{1}{2}$
7	$34\text{-}6\frac{3}{16}$	$58\text{-}3\frac{3}{4}$	$41\text{-}10\frac{5}{16}$	$70\text{-}8\frac{5}{8}$	$49\text{-}2\frac{7}{16}$	$83\text{-}1\frac{1}{2}$	$56\text{-}6\frac{9}{16}$	$95\text{-}6\frac{13}{32}$
8	$35\text{-}3$	$59\text{-}6\frac{5}{8}$	$42\text{-}7\frac{1}{8}$	$71\text{-}11\frac{17}{32}$	$49\text{-}11\frac{1}{4}$	$84\text{-}4\frac{13}{32}$	$57\text{-}3\frac{3}{8}$	$96\text{-}9\frac{9}{32}$
9	$35\text{-}11\frac{13}{16}$	$60\text{-}9\frac{17}{32}$	$43\text{-}3\frac{15}{16}$	$73\text{-}2\frac{13}{32}$	$50\text{-}8\frac{1}{16}$	$85\text{-}7\frac{9}{32}$	$58\text{-}0\frac{3}{16}$	$98\text{-}0\frac{3}{16}$

natsin A=0.5919095029; natcos A=0.8060044294; nattan A=0.7343750000; natcot A=1.3617021276

Inches	0″ Rise	0″ Slope	1″ Rise	1″ Slope	2″ Rise	2″ Slope	3″ Rise	3″ Slope	4″ Rise	4″ Slope	5″ Rise	5″ Slope
0	0	0	3/4	1 1/4	1 15/32	2 1/2	2 7/32	3 23/32	2 31/32	4 31/32	3 11/16	6 7/32
1/16	1/16	1/16	25/32	1 5/16	1 17/32	2 9/16	2 1/4	3 13/16	3	5 1/16	3 3/4	6 9/32
1/8	3/32	5/32	27/32	1 13/32	1 9/16	2 21/32	2 5/16	3 7/8	3 1/16	5 1/8	3 25/32	6 3/8
3/16	1/8	7/32	7/8	1 15/32	1 5/8	2 23/32	2 11/32	3 31/32	3 3/32	5 7/32	3 27/32	6 7/16
1/4	3/16	5/16	15/16	1 9/16	1 21/32	2 13/16	2 13/32	4 1/32	3 5/32	5 9/32	3 7/8	6 17/32
5/16	1/32	3/8	31/32	1 5/8	1 23/32	2 7/8	2 7/16	4 1/8	3 3/16	5 3/8	3 15/16	6 19/32
3/8	9/32	15/32	1 1/32	1 23/32	1 3/4	2 31/32	2 1/2	4 3/16	3 1/4	5 7/16	3 31/32	6 11/16
7/16	5/16	17/32	1 1/16	1 25/32	1 13/16	3 1/32	2 17/32	4 9/32	3 9/32	5 17/32	4 1/32	6 3/4
1/2	3/8	5/8	1 1/8	1 7/8	1 27/32	3 1/8	2 19/32	4 11/32	3 5/16	5 19/32	4 1/16	6 27/32
9/16	13/32	11/16	1 5/32	1 15/16	1 29/32	3 3/16	2 5/8	4 7/16	3 3/8	5 11/16	4 1/8	6 29/32
5/8	15/32	25/32	1 3/16	2 1/32	1 15/16	3 1/4	2 11/16	4 1/2	3 13/32	5 3/4	4 5/32	7
11/16	1/2	27/32	1 1/4	2 3/32	2	3 11/32	2 23/32	4 19/32	3 15/32	5 27/32	4 7/32	7 1/16
3/4	9/16	15/16	1 9/32	2 3/16	2 1/32	3 13/32	2 25/32	4 21/32	3 1/2	5 29/32	4 1/4	7 5/32
13/16	19/32	1	1 11/32	2 1/4	2 3/32	3 1/2	2 13/16	4 3/4	3 9/16	6	4 5/16	7 7/32
7/8	21/32	1 3/32	1 3/8	2 11/32	2 1/8	3 9/16	2 7/8	4 13/16	3 19/32	6 1/16	4 11/32	7 5/16
15/16	11/16	1 5/32	1 7/16	2 13/32	2 3/16	3 21/32	2 29/32	4 29/32	3 21/32	6 5/32	4 13/32	7 3/8

Inches	6″ Rise	6″ Slope	7″ Rise	7″ Slope	8″ Rise	8″ Slope	9″ Rise	9″ Slope	10″ Rise	10″ Slope	11″ Rise	11″ Slope
0	4 7/16	7 15/32	5 5/16	8 23/32	5 29/32	9 15/16	6 21/32	11 3/16	7 13/32	1-0 7/16	8 1/8	1-1 11/16
1/16	4 15/32	7 17/32	5 7/32	8 25/32	5 31/32	10 1/32	6 11/16	11 9/32	7 1/2	1-0 1/2	8 3/16	1-1 3/4
1/8	4 17/32	7 5/8	5 9/32	8 7/8	6	10 3/32	6 3/4	11 11/32	7 1/2	1-0 19/32	8 1/2	1-1 27/32
3/16	4 9/16	7 11/16	5 5/16	8 15/16	6 1/16	10 3/16	6 25/32	11 7/16	7 17/32	1-0 21/32	8 9/32	1-1 29/32
1/4	4 5/8	7 25/32	5 3/8	9 1/32	6 3/32	10 1/4	6 27/32	11 1/2	7 19/32	1-0 3/4	8 5/8	1-2
5/16	4 21/32	7 27/32	5 13/32	9 3/32	6 5/32	10 11/32	6 7/8	11 19/32	7 5/8	1-0 13/16	8 3/8	1-2 1/16
3/8	4 23/32	7 15/16	5 15/32	9 3/16	6 3/16	10 13/32	6 15/16	11 21/32	7 11/16	1-0 29/32	8 13/32	1-2 5/32
7/16	4 3/4	8	5 1/2	9 1/4	6 1/4	10 1/2	7	11 3/4	7 23/32	1-0 31/32	8 15/32	1-2 7/32
1/2	4 13/16	8 3/32	5 9/16	9 11/32	6 9/32	10 9/16	7 1/32	11 13/16	7 3/4	1-1 1/16	8 1/2	1-2 5/16
9/16	4 27/32	8 5/32	5 19/32	9 13/32	6 11/32	10 21/32	7 1/16	11 29/32	7 13/16	1-1 1/8	8 9/16	1-2 3/8
5/8	4 29/32	8 1/4	5 5/8	9 15/32	6 3/8	10 23/32	7 1/8	11 31/32	7 27/32	1-1 7/32	8 19/32	1-2 15/32
11/16	4 15/16	8 5/16	5 11/16	9 9/16	6 7/16	10 13/16	7 5/32	1-0 1/16	7 29/32	1-1 9/32	8 21/32	1-2 17/32
3/4	5	8 13/32	5 23/32	9 5/8	6 1/2	10 7/8	7 7/32	1-0 1/8	7 15/16	1-1 3/8	8 11/16	1-2 5/8
13/16	5 1/4	8 15/32	5 25/32	9 23/32	6 17/32	10 31/32	7 1/4	1-0 7/32	8	1-1 7/16	8 3/4	1-2 11/16
7/8	5 3/32	8 9/16	5 13/16	9 25/32	6 9/16	11 1/32	7 5/16	1-0 9/32	8 1/2	1-1 17/32	8 25/32	1-2 25/32
15/16	5 1/8	8 5/8	5 7/8	9 7/8	6 5/8	11 1/8	7 11/32	1-0 3/8	8 3/32	1-1 19/32	8 27/32	1-2 27/32

Feet	0′ Rise	0′ Slope	10′ Rise	10′ Slope	20′ Rise	20′ Slope	30′ Rise	30′ Slope
0	0	0	7-4 3/4	12-5 1/4	14-9 1/2	24-10 1/2	22-2 1/4	37-3 3/4
1	-8 7/8	1-2 15/16	8-1 5/8	13-8 3/16	15-6 3/8	26-1 7/16	22-11 1/8	38-6 11/16
2	1-5 3/4	2-5 27/32	8-10 1/2	14-11 3/32	16-3 1/4	27-4 11/16	23-8	39-9 5/8
3	2-2 5/8	3-8 25/32	9-7 3/8	16-2 1/32	17-0 1/8	28-7 9/32	24-4 7/8	41-0 17/32
4	2-11 1/2	4-11 11/16	10-4 1/4	17-4 31/32	17-9	29-10 7/32	25-1 3/4	42-3 15/32
5	3-8 3/8	6-2 5/8	11-1 1/8	18-7 7/8	18-5 7/8	31-1 1/8	25-10 5/8	43-6 3/8
6	4-5 1/4	7-5 9/16	11-10	19-10 13/16	19-2 3/4	32-4 1/16	26-7 1/2	44-9 5/16
7	5-2 1/8	8-8 15/32	12-6 7/8	21-1 23/32	19-11 5/8	33-6 15/16	27-4 3/8	46-0 1/4
8	5-11	9-11 13/32	13-3 3/4	22-4 21/32	20-8 1/2	34-9 29/32	28-1 1/4	47-3 5/32
9	6-7 7/8	11-2 5/16	14-0 5/8	23-7 19/32	21-5 3/8	36-0 27/32	28-10 1/8	48-6 3/32

A = 36° 29′ 10″; logsin A = 9.77424; logcos A = 9.90526; logtan A = 9.86899; logcot A = 0.13101

Ins.	12″ Rise	Slope	13″ Rise	Slope	14″ Rise	Slope	15″ Rise	Slope	16″ Rise	Slope
0	$8\frac{7}{8}$	$1\text{-}2\frac{15}{16}$	$9\frac{5}{8}$	$1\text{-}4\frac{5}{32}$	$10\frac{11}{16}$	$1\text{-}5\frac{13}{32}$	$11\frac{3}{32}$	$1\text{-}6\frac{21}{32}$	$11\frac{27}{32}$	$1\text{-}7\frac{29}{32}$
$\frac{1}{16}$	$8\frac{29}{32}$	$1\text{-}3$	$9\frac{21}{32}$	$1\text{-}4\frac{1}{4}$	$10\frac{13}{32}$	$1\text{-}5\frac{1}{2}$	$11\frac{1}{8}$	$1\text{-}6\frac{3}{4}$	$11\frac{7}{8}$	$1\text{-}7\frac{31}{32}$
$\frac{1}{8}$	$8\frac{31}{32}$	$1\text{-}3\frac{3}{32}$	$9\frac{23}{32}$	$1\text{-}4\frac{5}{16}$	$10\frac{7}{16}$	$1\text{-}5\frac{9}{16}$	$11\frac{3}{16}$	$1\text{-}6\frac{13}{32}$	$11\frac{15}{16}$	$1\text{-}8\frac{1}{16}$
$\frac{3}{16}$	9	$1\text{-}3\frac{5}{32}$	$9\frac{3}{4}$	$1\text{-}4\frac{13}{32}$	$10\frac{1}{2}$	$1\text{-}5\frac{21}{32}$	$11\frac{7}{32}$	$1\text{-}6\frac{7}{8}$	$11\frac{31}{32}$	$1\text{-}8\frac{1}{8}$
$\frac{1}{4}$	$9\frac{1}{16}$	$1\text{-}3\frac{1}{4}$	$9\frac{13}{16}$	$1\text{-}4\frac{15}{32}$	$10\frac{17}{32}$	$1\text{-}5\frac{23}{32}$	$11\frac{9}{32}$	$1\text{-}6\frac{31}{32}$	$1\text{-}0\frac{1}{32}$	$1\text{-}8\frac{7}{32}$
$\frac{5}{16}$	$9\frac{3}{32}$	$1\text{-}3\frac{5}{16}$	$9\frac{27}{32}$	$1\text{-}4\frac{9}{16}$	$10\frac{19}{32}$	$1\text{-}5\frac{13}{16}$	$11\frac{5}{16}$	$1\text{-}7\frac{1}{32}$	$1\text{-}0\frac{1}{16}$	$1\text{-}8\frac{9}{32}$
$\frac{3}{8}$	$9\frac{5}{32}$	$1\text{-}3\frac{13}{32}$	$9\frac{29}{32}$	$1\text{-}4\frac{5}{8}$	$10\frac{5}{8}$	$1\text{-}5\frac{7}{8}$	$11\frac{3}{8}$	$1\text{-}7\frac{1}{8}$	$1\text{-}0\frac{1}{8}$	$1\text{-}8\frac{3}{8}$
$\frac{7}{16}$	$9\frac{3}{16}$	$1\text{-}3\frac{15}{32}$	$9\frac{15}{16}$	$1\text{-}4\frac{23}{32}$	$10\frac{11}{16}$	$1\text{-}5\frac{31}{32}$	$11\frac{13}{32}$	$1\text{-}7\frac{3}{16}$	$1\text{-}0\frac{5}{32}$	$1\text{-}8\frac{7}{16}$
$\frac{1}{2}$	$9\frac{1}{4}$	$1\text{-}3\frac{9}{16}$	10	$1\text{-}4\frac{25}{32}$	$10\frac{23}{32}$	$1\text{-}6\frac{1}{32}$	$11\frac{15}{32}$	$1\text{-}7\frac{9}{32}$	$1\text{-}0\frac{3}{16}$	$1\text{-}8\frac{17}{32}$
$\frac{9}{16}$	$9\frac{9}{32}$	$1\text{-}3\frac{5}{8}$	$10\frac{1}{32}$	$1\text{-}4\frac{7}{8}$	$10\frac{25}{32}$	$1\text{-}6\frac{1}{8}$	$11\frac{1}{2}$	$1\text{-}7\frac{11}{32}$	$1\text{-}0\frac{1}{4}$	$1\text{-}8\frac{19}{32}$
$\frac{5}{8}$	$9\frac{11}{32}$	$1\text{-}3\frac{11}{16}$	$10\frac{1}{16}$	$1\text{-}4\frac{15}{16}$	$10\frac{13}{16}$	$1\text{-}6\frac{3}{16}$	$11\frac{9}{16}$	$1\text{-}7\frac{7}{16}$	$1\text{-}0\frac{9}{32}$	$1\text{-}8\frac{11}{16}$
$\frac{11}{16}$	$9\frac{3}{8}$	$1\text{-}3\frac{25}{32}$	$10\frac{1}{8}$	$1\text{-}5\frac{1}{32}$	$10\frac{7}{8}$	$1\text{-}6\frac{9}{32}$	$11\frac{19}{32}$	$1\text{-}7\frac{1}{2}$	$1\text{-}0\frac{11}{32}$	$1\text{-}8\frac{3}{4}$
$\frac{3}{4}$	$9\frac{7}{16}$	$1\text{-}3\frac{27}{32}$	$10\frac{5}{32}$	$1\text{-}5\frac{3}{16}$	$10\frac{29}{32}$	$1\text{-}6\frac{11}{32}$	$11\frac{21}{32}$	$1\text{-}7\frac{19}{32}$	$1\text{-}0\frac{3}{8}$	$1\text{-}8\frac{27}{32}$
$\frac{13}{16}$	$9\frac{15}{32}$	$1\text{-}3\frac{15}{16}$	$10\frac{7}{32}$	$1\text{-}5\frac{3}{8}$	$10\frac{31}{32}$	$1\text{-}6\frac{7}{16}$	$11\frac{11}{16}$	$1\text{-}7\frac{21}{32}$	$1\text{-}0\frac{7}{16}$	$1\text{-}8\frac{29}{32}$
$\frac{7}{8}$	$9\frac{17}{32}$	$1\text{-}4$	$10\frac{1}{4}$	$1\text{-}5\frac{1}{2}$	11	$1\text{-}6\frac{1}{2}$	$11\frac{3}{4}$	$1\text{-}7\frac{3}{4}$	$1\text{-}0\frac{15}{32}$	$1\text{-}9$
$\frac{15}{16}$	$9\frac{9}{16}$	$1\text{-}4\frac{3}{32}$	$10\frac{5}{16}$	$1\text{-}5\frac{11}{32}$	$11\frac{1}{16}$	$1\text{-}6\frac{19}{32}$	$11\frac{25}{32}$	$1\text{-}7\frac{13}{16}$	$1\text{-}0\frac{17}{32}$	$1\text{-}9\frac{1}{16}$

Ins.	17″ Rise	Slope	18″ Rise	Slope	19″ Rise	Slope	20″ Rise	Slope	21″ Rise	Slope
0	$1\text{-}0\frac{9}{16}$	$1\text{-}9\frac{5}{32}$	$1\text{-}1\frac{5}{16}$	$1\text{-}10\frac{3}{8}$	$1\text{-}2\frac{1}{16}$	$1\text{-}11\frac{5}{8}$	$1\text{-}2\frac{25}{32}$	$2\text{-}0\frac{7}{8}$	$1\text{-}3\frac{17}{32}$	$2\text{-}2\frac{1}{8}$
$\frac{1}{16}$	$1\text{-}0\frac{5}{8}$	$1\text{-}9\frac{7}{32}$	$1\text{-}1\frac{11}{16}$	$1\text{-}10\frac{15}{32}$	$1\text{-}2\frac{3}{32}$	$1\text{-}11\frac{23}{32}$	$1\text{-}2\frac{27}{32}$	$2\text{-}0\frac{31}{32}$	$1\text{-}3\frac{9}{16}$	$2\text{-}2\frac{3}{16}$
$\frac{1}{8}$	$1\text{-}0\frac{21}{32}$	$1\text{-}9\frac{5}{16}$	$1\text{-}1\frac{13}{32}$	$1\text{-}10\frac{17}{32}$	$1\text{-}2\frac{5}{32}$	$1\text{-}11\frac{25}{32}$	$1\text{-}2\frac{7}{8}$	$2\text{-}1\frac{1}{16}$	$1\text{-}3\frac{5}{8}$	$2\text{-}2\frac{9}{32}$
$\frac{3}{16}$	$1\text{-}0\frac{23}{32}$	$1\text{-}9\frac{3}{8}$	$1\text{-}1\frac{7}{16}$	$1\text{-}10\frac{5}{8}$	$1\text{-}2\frac{3}{16}$	$1\text{-}11\frac{7}{8}$	$1\text{-}2\frac{15}{32}$	$2\text{-}1\frac{3}{32}$	$1\text{-}3\frac{21}{32}$	$2\text{-}2\frac{11}{32}$
$\frac{1}{4}$	$1\text{-}0\frac{3}{4}$	$1\text{-}9\frac{15}{32}$	$1\text{-}1\frac{1}{2}$	$1\text{-}10\frac{11}{16}$	$1\text{-}2\frac{1}{4}$	$1\text{-}11\frac{15}{16}$	$1\text{-}2\frac{31}{32}$	$2\text{-}1\frac{3}{16}$	$1\text{-}3\frac{23}{32}$	$2\text{-}2\frac{7}{16}$
$\frac{5}{16}$	$1\text{-}0\frac{13}{16}$	$1\text{-}9\frac{17}{32}$	$1\text{-}1\frac{17}{32}$	$1\text{-}10\frac{25}{32}$	$1\text{-}2\frac{9}{32}$	$2\text{-}0\frac{1}{32}$	$1\text{-}3\frac{1}{32}$	$2\text{-}1\frac{1}{4}$	$1\text{-}3\frac{3}{4}$	$2\text{-}2\frac{1}{2}$
$\frac{3}{8}$	$1\text{-}0\frac{27}{32}$	$1\text{-}9\frac{5}{8}$	$1\text{-}1\frac{19}{32}$	$1\text{-}10\frac{27}{32}$	$1\text{-}2\frac{11}{32}$	$2\text{-}0\frac{3}{32}$	$1\text{-}3\frac{1}{16}$	$2\text{-}1\frac{11}{32}$	$1\text{-}3\frac{13}{16}$	$2\text{-}2\frac{19}{32}$
$\frac{7}{16}$	$1\text{-}0\frac{29}{32}$	$1\text{-}9\frac{11}{16}$	$1\text{-}1\frac{5}{8}$	$1\text{-}10\frac{15}{16}$	$1\text{-}2\frac{3}{8}$	$2\text{-}0\frac{3}{16}$	$1\text{-}3\frac{1}{8}$	$2\text{-}1\frac{13}{32}$	$1\text{-}3\frac{27}{32}$	$2\text{-}2\frac{21}{32}$
$\frac{1}{2}$	$1\text{-}0\frac{15}{16}$	$1\text{-}9\frac{25}{32}$	$1\text{-}1\frac{11}{16}$	$1\text{-}11$	$1\text{-}2\frac{7}{16}$	$2\text{-}0\frac{1}{4}$	$1\text{-}3\frac{5}{32}$	$2\text{-}1\frac{1}{2}$	$1\text{-}3\frac{29}{32}$	$2\text{-}2\frac{3}{4}$
$\frac{9}{16}$	$1\text{-}1$	$1\text{-}9\frac{27}{32}$	$1\text{-}1\frac{23}{32}$	$1\text{-}11\frac{3}{32}$	$1\text{-}2\frac{15}{32}$	$2\text{-}0\frac{11}{32}$	$1\text{-}3\frac{7}{32}$	$2\text{-}1\frac{9}{16}$	$1\text{-}3\frac{15}{16}$	$2\text{-}2\frac{13}{16}$
$\frac{5}{8}$	$1\text{-}1\frac{1}{16}$	$1\text{-}9\frac{29}{32}$	$1\text{-}1\frac{25}{32}$	$1\text{-}11\frac{5}{32}$	$1\text{-}2\frac{1}{2}$	$2\text{-}0\frac{13}{32}$	$1\text{-}3\frac{1}{4}$	$2\text{-}1\frac{21}{32}$	$1\text{-}4$	$2\text{-}2\frac{29}{32}$
$\frac{11}{16}$	$1\text{-}1\frac{3}{32}$	$1\text{-}10$	$1\text{-}1\frac{13}{16}$	$1\text{-}11\frac{1}{4}$	$1\text{-}2\frac{9}{16}$	$2\text{-}0\frac{1}{2}$	$1\text{-}3\frac{5}{16}$	$2\text{-}1\frac{23}{32}$	$1\text{-}4\frac{1}{32}$	$2\text{-}2\frac{31}{32}$
$\frac{3}{4}$	$1\text{-}1\frac{1}{8}$	$1\text{-}10\frac{1}{16}$	$1\text{-}1\frac{7}{8}$	$1\text{-}11\frac{3}{8}$	$1\text{-}2\frac{19}{32}$	$2\text{-}0\frac{9}{16}$	$1\text{-}3\frac{11}{32}$	$2\text{-}1\frac{13}{16}$	$1\text{-}4\frac{3}{32}$	$2\text{-}3\frac{1}{16}$
$\frac{13}{16}$	$1\text{-}1\frac{3}{16}$	$1\text{-}10\frac{5}{32}$	$1\text{-}1\frac{29}{32}$	$1\text{-}11\frac{13}{16}$	$1\text{-}2\frac{21}{32}$	$2\text{-}0\frac{21}{32}$	$1\text{-}3\frac{13}{32}$	$2\text{-}1\frac{7}{8}$	$1\text{-}4\frac{1}{8}$	$2\text{-}3\frac{1}{8}$
$\frac{7}{8}$	$1\text{-}1\frac{7}{32}$	$1\text{-}10\frac{7}{32}$	$1\text{-}1\frac{31}{32}$	$1\text{-}11\frac{15}{16}$	$1\text{-}2\frac{11}{16}$	$2\text{-}0\frac{23}{32}$	$1\text{-}3\frac{7}{16}$	$2\text{-}1\frac{31}{32}$	$1\text{-}4\frac{5}{16}$	$2\text{-}3\frac{3}{32}$
$\frac{15}{16}$	$1\text{-}1\frac{9}{32}$	$1\text{-}10\frac{5}{16}$	$1\text{-}2$	$1\text{-}11\frac{9}{16}$	$1\text{-}2\frac{3}{4}$	$2\text{-}0\frac{13}{16}$	$1\text{-}3\frac{1}{2}$	$2\text{-}2\frac{1}{4}$	$1\text{-}4\frac{7}{32}$	$2\text{-}3\frac{9}{32}$

Feet	40′ Rise	Slope	50′ Rise	Slope	60′ Rise	Slope	70′ Rise	Slope
0	$29\text{-}7$	$49\text{-}9$	$36\text{-}11\frac{3}{4}$	$62\text{-}2\frac{9}{32}$	$44\text{-}4\frac{1}{2}$	$74\text{-}7\frac{17}{32}$	$51\text{-}9\frac{1}{4}$	$87\text{-}0\frac{25}{32}$
1	$30\text{-}3\frac{7}{8}$	$50\text{-}11\frac{15}{16}$	$37\text{-}8\frac{5}{8}$	$63\text{-}5\frac{5}{16}$	$45\text{-}1\frac{3}{8}$	$75\text{-}10\frac{7}{16}$	$52\text{-}6\frac{1}{8}$	$88\text{-}3\frac{11}{16}$
2	$31\text{-}0\frac{3}{4}$	$52\text{-}2\frac{7}{8}$	$38\text{-}5\frac{1}{2}$	$64\text{-}8\frac{1}{4}$	$45\text{-}10\frac{1}{4}$	$77\text{-}1\frac{3}{8}$	$53\text{-}3$	$89\text{-}6\frac{5}{8}$
3	$31\text{-}9\frac{5}{8}$	$53\text{-}5\frac{25}{32}$	$39\text{-}2\frac{3}{8}$	$65\text{-}11\frac{1}{32}$	$46\text{-}7\frac{1}{8}$	$78\text{-}4\frac{9}{32}$	$53\text{-}11\frac{7}{8}$	$90\text{-}9\frac{9}{16}$
4	$32\text{-}6\frac{1}{2}$	$54\text{-}8\frac{23}{32}$	$39\text{-}11\frac{1}{4}$	$67\text{-}1\frac{31}{32}$	$47\text{-}4$	$79\text{-}7\frac{1}{32}$	$54\text{-}8\frac{3}{4}$	$92\text{-}0\frac{15}{32}$
5	$33\text{-}3\frac{3}{8}$	$55\text{-}11\frac{5}{8}$	$40\text{-}8\frac{1}{8}$	$68\text{-}4\frac{29}{32}$	$48\text{-}0\frac{7}{8}$	$80\text{-}10\frac{5}{32}$	$55\text{-}5\frac{5}{8}$	$93\text{-}3\frac{13}{32}$
6	$34\text{-}0\frac{1}{4}$	$57\text{-}2\frac{9}{16}$	$41\text{-}5$	$69\text{-}7\frac{13}{16}$	$48\text{-}9\frac{3}{4}$	$82\text{-}1\frac{1}{16}$	$56\text{-}2\frac{1}{2}$	$94\text{-}6\frac{5}{16}$
7	$34\text{-}9\frac{1}{8}$	$58\text{-}5\frac{1}{2}$	$42\text{-}1\frac{7}{8}$	$70\text{-}10\frac{3}{4}$	$49\text{-}6\frac{5}{8}$	$83\text{-}4$	$56\text{-}11\frac{3}{8}$	$95\text{-}9\frac{1}{4}$
8	$35\text{-}6$	$59\text{-}8\frac{13}{32}$	$42\text{-}10\frac{3}{4}$	$72\text{-}1\frac{11}{16}$	$50\text{-}3\frac{1}{2}$	$84\text{-}6\frac{15}{16}$	$57\text{-}8\frac{1}{4}$	$97\text{-}0\frac{3}{16}$
9	$36\text{-}2\frac{7}{8}$	$60\text{-}11\frac{11}{32}$	$43\text{-}7\frac{5}{8}$	$73\text{-}4\frac{19}{32}$	$51\text{-}0\frac{3}{8}$	$85\text{-}9\frac{27}{32}$	$58\text{-}5\frac{1}{8}$	$98\text{-}3\frac{3}{32}$

natsin A=0.5946265190; natcos A=0.8040020540; nattan A=0.7395833333; natcot A=1.3521126760

Inches	0" Rise	0" Slope	1" Rise	1" Slope	2" Rise	2" Slope	3" Rise	3" Slope	4" Rise	4" Slope	5" Rise	5" Slope
0	0	0	3/4	1 1/4	1 1/2	2 1/2	2 1/4	3 3/4	2 23/32	5	3 23/32	6 1/4
1/16	1/16	1/16	25/32	15/16	1 17/32	2 9/16	2 9/32	3 13/32	3 1/32	5 1/16	3 25/32	6 5/16
1/8	3/32	5/32	27/32	1 13/32	1 19/32	2 21/32	2 5/16	3 29/32	3 1/16	5 5/32	3 13/16	6 3/8
3/16	1/8	7/32	7/8	1 15/32	1 5/8	2 23/32	2 3/8	3 31/32	3 1/8	5 7/32	3 7/8	6 15/32
1/4	3/16	5/16	15/16	1 9/16	1 11/16	2 13/16	2 13/32	4 1/16	3 5/32	5 5/16	3 29/32	6 17/32
5/16	7/32	3/8	31/32	1 5/8	1 23/32	2 7/8	2 15/32	4 1/8	3 7/32	5 3/8	3 31/32	6 5/8
3/8	9/32	15/32	1 1/32	1 23/32	1 25/32	2 31/32	2 1/2	4 7/32	3 1/4	5 15/32	4	6 11/16
7/16	5/16	17/32	1 1/16	1 25/32	1 13/16	3 1/32	2 9/16	4 9/32	3 5/16	5 17/32	4 1/16	6 25/32
1/2	3/8	5/8	1 1/8	1 7/8	1 7/8	3 1/8	2 19/32	4 3/8	3 11/32	5 5/8	4 3/32	6 27/32
9/16	13/32	11/16	1 5/32	1 15/16	1 29/32	3 3/16	2 21/32	4 7/16	3 13/32	5 11/16	4 5/32	6 15/16
5/8	15/32	25/32	1 7/32	2 1/32	1 31/32	3 9/32	2 11/16	4 17/32	3 7/16	5 25/32	4 3/8	7
11/16	1/2	27/32	1 1/4	2 3/32	2	3 11/32	2 3/4	4 19/32	3 1/2	5 27/32	4 1/4	7 3/32
3/4	9/16	15/16	1 5/16	2 3/16	2 1/16	3 7/16	2 25/32	4 11/16	3 17/32	5 15/16	4 9/32	7 5/32
13/16	19/32	1	1 11/32	2 1/4	2 3/32	3 1/2	2 27/32	4 3/4	3 19/32	6	4 11/32	7 1/4
7/8	21/32	1 3/32	1 13/32	2 11/32	2 5/32	3 19/32	2 7/8	4 27/32	3 5/8	6 3/32	4 3/8	7 5/16
15/16	11/16	1 5/32	1 7/16	2 13/32	2 3/16	3 21/32	2 15/16	4 29/32	3 11/16	6 5/32	4 7/16	7 13/32

Inches	6" Rise	6" Slope	7" Rise	7" Slope	8" Rise	8" Slope	9" Rise	9" Slope	10" Rise	10" Slope	11" Rise	11" Slope
0	4 15/32	7 15/32	5 7/32	8 23/32	5 31/32	9 31/32	6 11/16	11 7/32	7 1/16	1-0 15/32	8 3/16	1-1 23/32
1/16	4 1/2	7 9/16	5 1/4	8 13/16	6	10 1/16	6 3/4	11 5/16	7 1/2	1-0 17/32	8 1/4	1-1 25/32
1/8	4 9/16	7 5/8	5 5/16	8 7/8	6 1/16	10 1/8	6 25/32	11 3/8	7 17/32	1-0 5/8	8 9/32	1-1 7/8
3/16	4 19/32	7 23/32	5 11/32	8 31/32	6 3/32	10 7/32	6 27/32	11 15/32	7 19/32	1-0 11/16	8 11/32	1-1 15/16
1/4	4 21/32	7 25/32	5 13/32	9 1/32	6 5/32	10 9/32	6 7/8	11 17/32	7 5/8	1-0 25/32	8 3/8	1-2 1/32
5/16	4 11/16	7 7/8	5 7/16	9 1/8	6 3/16	10 3/8	6 15/16	11 5/8	7 11/16	1-0 27/32	8 7/16	1-2 3/32
3/8	4 3/4	7 15/16	5 1/2	9 3/16	6 1/4	10 7/16	6 31/32	11 11/16	7 23/32	1-0 15/16	8 15/32	1-2 3/16
7/16	4 25/32	8 1/32	5 17/32	9 9/32	6 9/32	10 17/32	7 1/32	11 25/32	7 25/32	1-1	8 17/32	1-2 1/4
1/2	4 27/32	8 3/32	5 19/32	9 11/32	6 11/32	10 19/32	7 1/16	11 27/32	7 13/16	1-1 3/32	8 9/16	1-2 11/32
9/16	4 7/8	8 3/16	5 5/8	9 7/16	6 3/8	10 11/16	7 1/8	11 15/16	7 7/8	1-1 5/32	8 5/8	1-2 13/32
5/8	4 15/16	8 1/4	5 11/16	9 1/2	6 7/16	10 3/4	7 5/32	1-0	7 29/32	1-1 1/4	8 21/32	1-2 1/2
11/16	4 31/32	8 11/32	5 23/32	9 19/32	6 15/32	10 27/32	7 7/32	1-0 3/32	7 31/32	1-1 11/32	8 23/32	1-2 9/16
3/4	5 1/32	8 13/32	5 25/32	9 21/32	6 17/32	10 29/32	7 1/4	1-0 5/32	8	1-1 13/32	8 3/4	1-2 21/32
13/16	5 1/16	8 1/2	5 13/16	9 3/4	6 9/16	11	7 5/16	1-0 1/4	8 1/16	1-1 15/32	8 13/16	1-2 23/32
7/8	5 1/8	8 9/16	5 7/8	9 13/16	6 5/8	11 1/16	7 11/32	1-0 5/16	8 3/32	1-1 9/16	8 27/32	1-2 13/16
15/16	5 5/32	8 21/32	5 29/32	9 29/32	6 21/32	11 5/32	7 13/32	1-0 13/32	8 5/32	1-1 5/8	8 29/32	1-2 7/8

Feet	0' Rise	0' Slope	10' Rise	10' Slope	20' Rise	20' Slope	30' Rise	30' Slope
0	0	0	7-5 3/8	12-5 5/8	14-10 3/4	24-11 1/4	22-4 1/8	37-4 7/8
1	-8 15/16	1-2 31/32	8-2 5/16	13-8 19/32	15-7 11/16	26-2 7/32	23-1 11/16	38-7 21/32
2	1-5 7/8	2-5 15/16	8-11 3/4	14-11 9/16	16-4 5/8	27-5 3/16	23-10	39-10 13/16
3	2-2 13/16	3-8 7/8	9-8 3/16	16-2 1/2	17-1 9/16	28-8 1/8	24-6 15/16	41-1 3/4
4	2-11 3/4	4-11 27/32	10-5 1/8	17-5 15/32	17-10 1/2	29-11 3/32	25-3 7/8	42-4 23/32
5	3-8 11/16	6-2 13/16	11-2 1/16	18-8 7/16	18-7 7/16	31-2 1/16	26-0 13/16	43-7 11/16
6	4-5 5/8	7-5 25/32	11-11	19-11 13/16	19-4 3/8	32-5 1/32	26-9 3/4	44-10 21/32
7	5-2 9/16	8-8 3/4	12-7 15/16	21-2 3/8	20-1 5/16	33-8	27-6 11/16	46-1 5/8
8	5-11 1/2	9-11 11/16	13-4 7/8	22-5 5/16	20-10 1/4	34-10 15/16	28-3 5/8	47-4 9/16
9	6-8 7/16	11-2 21/32	14-1 13/16	23-8 9/32	21-7 3/16	36-1 29/32	29-0 9/16	48-7 17/32

A = 36° 40′ 42″; logsin A = 9.77621; logcos A = 9.90417; logtan A = 9.87203; logcot A = 0.12797

Ins.	12″ Rise	12″ Slope	13″ Rise	13″ Slope	14″ Rise	14″ Slope	15″ Rise	15″ Slope	16″ Rise	16″ Slope
0	$8\frac{15}{16}$	$1\text{-}2\frac{31}{32}$	$9\frac{11}{16}$	$1\text{-}4\frac{7}{32}$	$10\frac{7}{16}$	$1\text{-}5\frac{15}{32}$	$11\frac{3}{16}$	$1\text{-}6\frac{23}{32}$	$11\frac{29}{32}$	$1\text{-}7\frac{15}{16}$
1/16	$8\frac{31}{32}$	$1\text{-}3\frac{1}{32}$	$9\frac{23}{32}$	$1\text{-}4\frac{9}{32}$	$10\frac{15}{32}$	$1\text{-}5\frac{17}{32}$	$11\frac{7}{32}$	$1\text{-}6\frac{25}{32}$	$11\frac{31}{32}$	$1\text{-}8\frac{1}{32}$
1/8	$9\frac{1}{32}$	$1\text{-}3\frac{1}{8}$	$9\frac{25}{32}$	$1\text{-}4\frac{3}{8}$	$10\frac{17}{32}$	$1\text{-}5\frac{5}{8}$	$11\frac{1}{4}$	$1\text{-}6\frac{27}{32}$	$1\text{-}0$	$1\text{-}8\frac{3}{32}$
3/16	$9\frac{1}{8}$	$1\text{-}3\frac{3}{16}$	$9\frac{13}{16}$	$1\text{-}4\frac{7}{16}$	$10\frac{9}{16}$	$1\text{-}5\frac{11}{16}$	$11\frac{5}{16}$	$1\text{-}6\frac{15}{16}$	$1\text{-}0\frac{1}{16}$	$1\text{-}8\frac{3}{16}$
1/4	$9\frac{1}{8}$	$1\text{-}3\frac{9}{32}$	$9\frac{7}{8}$	$1\text{-}4\frac{17}{32}$	$10\frac{5}{8}$	$1\text{-}5\frac{25}{32}$	$11\frac{11}{16}$	$1\text{-}7$	$1\text{-}0\frac{3}{32}$	$1\text{-}8\frac{1}{4}$
5/16	$9\frac{5}{32}$	$1\text{-}3\frac{11}{32}$	$9\frac{29}{32}$	$1\text{-}4\frac{19}{32}$	$10\frac{21}{32}$	$1\text{-}5\frac{27}{32}$	$11\frac{13}{32}$	$1\text{-}7\frac{3}{32}$	$1\text{-}0\frac{5}{32}$	$1\text{-}8\frac{11}{32}$
3/8	$9\frac{7}{32}$	$1\text{-}3\frac{7}{16}$	$9\frac{31}{32}$	$1\text{-}4\frac{11}{16}$	$10\frac{23}{32}$	$1\text{-}5\frac{15}{16}$	$11\frac{7}{16}$	$1\text{-}7\frac{5}{32}$	$1\text{-}0\frac{3}{16}$	$1\text{-}8\frac{13}{32}$
7/16	$9\frac{1}{4}$	$1\text{-}3\frac{1}{2}$	10	$1\text{-}4\frac{3}{4}$	$10\frac{3}{4}$	$1\text{-}6$	$11\frac{1}{2}$	$1\text{-}7\frac{1}{4}$	$1\text{-}0\frac{1}{4}$	$1\text{-}8\frac{1}{2}$
1/2	$9\frac{5}{16}$	$1\text{-}3\frac{19}{32}$	$10\frac{1}{16}$	$1\text{-}4\frac{27}{32}$	$10\frac{13}{16}$	$1\text{-}6\frac{3}{32}$	$11\frac{17}{32}$	$1\text{-}7\frac{5}{16}$	$1\text{-}0\frac{9}{32}$	$1\text{-}8\frac{9}{16}$
9/16	$9\frac{11}{32}$	$1\text{-}3\frac{21}{32}$	$10\frac{3}{32}$	$1\text{-}4\frac{29}{32}$	$10\frac{27}{32}$	$1\text{-}6\frac{5}{32}$	$11\frac{19}{32}$	$1\text{-}7\frac{13}{32}$	$1\text{-}0\frac{11}{32}$	$1\text{-}8\frac{21}{32}$
5/8	$9\frac{13}{32}$	$1\text{-}3\frac{3}{4}$	$10\frac{5}{32}$	$1\text{-}5$	$10\frac{29}{32}$	$1\text{-}6\frac{1}{4}$	$11\frac{5}{8}$	$1\text{-}7\frac{15}{32}$	$1\text{-}0\frac{3}{8}$	$1\text{-}8\frac{23}{32}$
11/16	$9\frac{7}{16}$	$1\text{-}3\frac{13}{16}$	$10\frac{3}{16}$	$1\text{-}5\frac{1}{16}$	$10\frac{15}{16}$	$1\text{-}6\frac{5}{16}$	$11\frac{11}{16}$	$1\text{-}7\frac{9}{16}$	$1\text{-}0\frac{7}{16}$	$1\text{-}8\frac{13}{16}$
3/4	$9\frac{1}{2}$	$1\text{-}3\frac{29}{32}$	$10\frac{1}{4}$	$1\text{-}5\frac{5}{32}$	11	$1\text{-}6\frac{13}{32}$	$11\frac{23}{32}$	$1\text{-}7\frac{5}{8}$	$1\text{-}0\frac{15}{32}$	$1\text{-}8\frac{7}{8}$
13/16	$9\frac{17}{32}$	$1\text{-}3\frac{31}{32}$	$10\frac{9}{32}$	$1\text{-}5\frac{7}{32}$	$11\frac{1}{32}$	$1\text{-}6\frac{15}{32}$	$11\frac{25}{32}$	$1\text{-}7\frac{23}{32}$	$1\text{-}0\frac{17}{32}$	$1\text{-}8\frac{31}{32}$
7/8	$9\frac{19}{32}$	$1\text{-}4\frac{1}{16}$	$10\frac{11}{32}$	$1\text{-}5\frac{5}{16}$	$11\frac{3}{32}$	$1\text{-}6\frac{9}{16}$	$11\frac{13}{16}$	$1\text{-}7\frac{25}{32}$	$1\text{-}0\frac{9}{16}$	$1\text{-}9\frac{1}{32}$
15/16	$9\frac{5}{8}$	$1\text{-}4\frac{1}{8}$	$10\frac{3}{8}$	$1\text{-}5\frac{3}{8}$	$11\frac{1}{8}$	$1\text{-}6\frac{5}{8}$	$11\frac{7}{8}$	$1\text{-}7\frac{7}{8}$	$1\text{-}0\frac{5}{8}$	$1\text{-}9\frac{1}{8}$

Ins.	17″ Rise	17″ Slope	18″ Rise	18″ Slope	19″ Rise	19″ Slope	20″ Rise	20″ Slope	21″ Rise	21″ Slope
0	$1\text{-}0\frac{21}{32}$	$1\text{-}9\frac{3}{16}$	$1\text{-}1\frac{13}{32}$	$1\text{-}10\frac{7}{16}$	$1\text{-}2\frac{5}{32}$	$1\text{-}11\frac{11}{16}$	$1\text{-}2\frac{29}{32}$	$2\text{-}0\frac{15}{16}$	$1\text{-}3\frac{5}{8}$	$2\text{-}2\frac{3}{16}$
1/16	$1\text{-}0\frac{23}{32}$	$1\text{-}9\frac{9}{32}$	$1\text{-}1\frac{7}{16}$	$1\text{-}10\frac{17}{32}$	$1\text{-}2\frac{3}{16}$	$1\text{-}11\frac{25}{32}$	$1\text{-}2\frac{15}{16}$	$2\text{-}1$	$1\text{-}3\frac{11}{16}$	$2\text{-}2\frac{1}{4}$
1/8	$1\text{-}0\frac{3}{4}$	$1\text{-}9\frac{11}{32}$	$1\text{-}1\frac{1}{2}$	$1\text{-}10\frac{19}{32}$	$1\text{-}2\frac{1}{4}$	$1\text{-}11\frac{27}{32}$	$1\text{-}3$	$2\text{-}1\frac{3}{32}$	$1\text{-}3\frac{23}{32}$	$2\text{-}2\frac{11}{32}$
3/16	$1\text{-}0\frac{13}{16}$	$1\text{-}9\frac{7}{16}$	$1\text{-}1\frac{17}{32}$	$1\text{-}10\frac{11}{16}$	$1\text{-}2\frac{9}{32}$	$1\text{-}11\frac{15}{16}$	$1\text{-}3\frac{1}{32}$	$2\text{-}1\frac{5}{32}$	$1\text{-}3\frac{25}{32}$	$2\text{-}2\frac{13}{32}$
1/4	$1\text{-}0\frac{27}{32}$	$1\text{-}9\frac{1}{2}$	$1\text{-}1\frac{19}{32}$	$1\text{-}10\frac{3}{4}$	$1\text{-}2\frac{11}{32}$	$2\text{-}0$	$1\text{-}3\frac{3}{32}$	$2\text{-}1\frac{1}{4}$	$1\text{-}3\frac{13}{16}$	$2\text{-}2\frac{1}{2}$
5/16	$1\text{-}0\frac{29}{32}$	$1\text{-}9\frac{19}{32}$	$1\text{-}1\frac{5}{8}$	$1\text{-}10\frac{27}{32}$	$1\text{-}2\frac{3}{8}$	$2\text{-}0\frac{3}{32}$	$1\text{-}3\frac{1}{8}$	$2\text{-}1\frac{5}{16}$	$1\text{-}3\frac{7}{8}$	$2\text{-}2\frac{9}{16}$
3/8	$1\text{-}0\frac{15}{16}$	$1\text{-}9\frac{21}{32}$	$1\text{-}1\frac{11}{16}$	$1\text{-}10\frac{29}{32}$	$1\text{-}2\frac{7}{16}$	$2\text{-}0\frac{5}{32}$	$1\text{-}3\frac{3}{16}$	$2\text{-}1\frac{13}{32}$	$1\text{-}3\frac{29}{32}$	$2\text{-}2\frac{21}{32}$
7/16	$1\text{-}1$	$1\text{-}9\frac{3}{4}$	$1\text{-}1\frac{23}{32}$	$1\text{-}11$	$1\text{-}2\frac{15}{32}$	$2\text{-}0\frac{1}{4}$	$1\text{-}3\frac{7}{32}$	$2\text{-}1\frac{15}{32}$	$1\text{-}3\frac{31}{32}$	$2\text{-}2\frac{23}{32}$
1/2	$1\text{-}1\frac{1}{16}$	$1\text{-}9\frac{13}{16}$	$1\text{-}1\frac{25}{32}$	$1\text{-}11\frac{1}{16}$	$1\text{-}2\frac{17}{32}$	$2\text{-}0\frac{5}{16}$	$1\text{-}3\frac{9}{32}$	$2\text{-}1\frac{9}{16}$	$1\text{-}4$	$2\text{-}2\frac{13}{16}$
9/16	$1\text{-}1\frac{3}{32}$	$1\text{-}9\frac{29}{32}$	$1\text{-}1\frac{13}{16}$	$1\text{-}11\frac{5}{32}$	$1\text{-}2\frac{9}{16}$	$2\text{-}0\frac{13}{32}$	$1\text{-}3\frac{5}{16}$	$2\text{-}1\frac{5}{8}$	$1\text{-}4\frac{1}{16}$	$2\text{-}2\frac{7}{8}$
5/8	$1\text{-}1\frac{1}{8}$	$1\text{-}9\frac{31}{32}$	$1\text{-}1\frac{7}{8}$	$1\text{-}11\frac{7}{32}$	$1\text{-}2\frac{5}{8}$	$2\text{-}0\frac{15}{32}$	$1\text{-}3\frac{3}{8}$	$2\text{-}1\frac{23}{32}$	$1\text{-}4\frac{3}{32}$	$2\text{-}2\frac{31}{32}$
11/16	$1\text{-}1\frac{3}{16}$	$1\text{-}10\frac{1}{16}$	$1\text{-}1\frac{29}{32}$	$1\text{-}11\frac{5}{16}$	$1\text{-}2\frac{21}{32}$	$2\text{-}0\frac{9}{16}$	$1\text{-}3\frac{13}{32}$	$2\text{-}1\frac{25}{32}$	$1\text{-}4\frac{5}{32}$	$2\text{-}3\frac{1}{32}$
3/4	$1\text{-}1\frac{7}{32}$	$1\text{-}10\frac{1}{8}$	$1\text{-}1\frac{31}{32}$	$1\text{-}11\frac{3}{8}$	$1\text{-}2\frac{23}{32}$	$2\text{-}0\frac{5}{8}$	$1\text{-}3\frac{15}{32}$	$2\text{-}1\frac{7}{8}$	$1\text{-}4\frac{3}{16}$	$2\text{-}3\frac{1}{8}$
13/16	$1\text{-}1\frac{9}{32}$	$1\text{-}10\frac{7}{32}$	$1\text{-}2$	$1\text{-}11\frac{15}{32}$	$1\text{-}2\frac{3}{4}$	$2\text{-}0\frac{23}{32}$	$1\text{-}3\frac{1}{2}$	$2\text{-}1\frac{15}{16}$	$1\text{-}4\frac{1}{4}$	$2\text{-}3\frac{3}{16}$
7/8	$1\text{-}1\frac{5}{16}$	$1\text{-}10\frac{9}{32}$	$1\text{-}2\frac{1}{16}$	$1\text{-}11\frac{17}{32}$	$1\text{-}2\frac{13}{16}$	$2\text{-}0\frac{25}{32}$	$1\text{-}3\frac{9}{16}$	$2\text{-}2\frac{1}{32}$	$1\text{-}4\frac{9}{32}$	$2\text{-}3\frac{9}{32}$
15/16	$1\text{-}1\frac{3}{8}$	$1\text{-}10\frac{3}{8}$	$1\text{-}2\frac{3}{32}$	$1\text{-}11\frac{5}{8}$	$1\text{-}2\frac{27}{32}$	$2\text{-}0\frac{7}{8}$	$1\text{-}3\frac{19}{32}$	$2\text{-}2\frac{3}{32}$	$1\text{-}4\frac{11}{32}$	$2\text{-}3\frac{11}{32}$

Feet	40′ Rise	40′ Slope	50′ Rise	50′ Slope	60′ Rise	60′ Slope	70′ Rise	70′ Slope
0	$29\text{-}9\frac{1}{2}$	$49\text{-}10\frac{1}{2}$	$37\text{-}2\frac{7}{8}$	$62\text{-}4\frac{1}{8}$	$44\text{-}8\frac{1}{4}$	$74\text{-}9\frac{3}{4}$	$52\text{-}1\frac{5}{8}$	$87\text{-}3\frac{3}{8}$
1	$30\text{-}6\frac{7}{16}$	$51\text{-}1\frac{15}{32}$	$37\text{-}11\frac{13}{16}$	$63\text{-}7\frac{3}{32}$	$45\text{-}5\frac{3}{16}$	$76\text{-}0\frac{23}{32}$	$52\text{-}10\frac{9}{16}$	$88\text{-}6\frac{11}{32}$
2	$31\text{-}3\frac{3}{8}$	$52\text{-}4\frac{7}{16}$	$38\text{-}8\frac{3}{4}$	$64\text{-}10\frac{1}{16}$	$46\text{-}2\frac{1}{8}$	$77\text{-}3\frac{11}{16}$	$53\text{-}7\frac{1}{2}$	$89\text{-}9\frac{5}{16}$
3	$32\text{-}0\frac{5}{16}$	$53\text{-}7\frac{13}{32}$	$39\text{-}5\frac{11}{16}$	$66\text{-}1\frac{1}{32}$	$46\text{-}11\frac{1}{16}$	$78\text{-}6\frac{21}{32}$	$54\text{-}4\frac{7}{16}$	$91\text{-}0\frac{9}{32}$
4	$32\text{-}9\frac{1}{4}$	$54\text{-}10\frac{11}{32}$	$40\text{-}2\frac{5}{8}$	$67\text{-}3\frac{31}{32}$	$47\text{-}8$	$79\text{-}9\frac{19}{32}$	$55\text{-}1\frac{3}{8}$	$92\text{-}3\frac{7}{32}$
5	$33\text{-}6\frac{3}{16}$	$56\text{-}1\frac{5}{16}$	$40\text{-}11\frac{9}{16}$	$68\text{-}6\frac{15}{16}$	$48\text{-}4\frac{15}{16}$	$81\text{-}0\frac{9}{16}$	$55\text{-}10\frac{5}{16}$	$93\text{-}6\frac{3}{16}$
6	$34\text{-}3\frac{1}{8}$	$57\text{-}4\frac{9}{32}$	$41\text{-}8\frac{1}{2}$	$69\text{-}9\frac{29}{32}$	$49\text{-}1\frac{7}{8}$	$82\text{-}3\frac{17}{32}$	$56\text{-}7\frac{1}{4}$	$94\text{-}9\frac{5}{32}$
7	$35\text{-}0\frac{1}{16}$	$58\text{-}7\frac{1}{4}$	$42\text{-}5\frac{7}{16}$	$71\text{-}0\frac{7}{8}$	$49\text{-}10\frac{13}{16}$	$83\text{-}6\frac{1}{2}$	$57\text{-}4\frac{3}{16}$	$96\text{-}0\frac{1}{8}$
8	$35\text{-}9$	$59\text{-}10\frac{7}{32}$	$43\text{-}2\frac{3}{8}$	$72\text{-}3\frac{27}{32}$	$50\text{-}7\frac{3}{4}$	$84\text{-}9\frac{15}{32}$	$58\text{-}1\frac{3}{8}$	$97\text{-}3\frac{3}{32}$
9	$36\text{-}5\frac{15}{16}$	$61\text{-}1\frac{5}{32}$	$43\text{-}11\frac{5}{16}$	$73\text{-}6\frac{25}{32}$	$51\text{-}4\frac{11}{16}$	$86\text{-}0\frac{13}{32}$	$58\text{-}10\frac{1}{16}$	$98\text{-}6\frac{1}{32}$

natsin A=0.5973233148; natcos A=0.8020005347; nattan A=0.7447916666; natcot A=1.3426573426

BEVEL 9″ TO 12″

Inches	0″ Rise	0″ Slope	1″ Rise	1″ Slope	2″ Rise	2″ Slope	3″ Rise	3″ Slope	4″ Rise	4″ Slope	5″ Rise	5″ Slope
0	0	0	3/4	1 1/4	1 1/2	2 1/2	2 1/4	3 3/4	3	5	3 3/4	6 1/4
1/16	1/16	1/16	13/16	1 5/16	1 9/16	2 9/16	2 5/16	3 13/16	3 1/16	5 1/16	3 13/16	6 5/16
1/8	3/32	5/32	27/32	1 13/32	1 19/32	2 21/32	2 11/32	3 29/32	3 3/32	5 5/32	3 27/32	6 13/32
3/16	1/8	1/4	7/8	1 1/2	1 5/8	2 3/4	2 3/8	4	3 1/8	5 1/4	3 7/8	6 1/2
1/4	3/16	5/16	15/16	1 9/16	1 11/16	2 13/16	2 7/16	4 1/16	3 3/16	5 5/16	3 15/16	6 9/16
5/16	1/4	3/8	1	1 5/8	1 3/4	2 7/8	2 1/2	4 1/8	3 1/4	5 3/8	4	6 5/8
3/8	9/32	15/32	1 1/32	1 23/32	1 25/32	2 31/32	2 17/32	4 7/32	3 9/32	5 15/32	4 1/32	6 23/32
7/16	5/16	9/16	1 1/16	1 13/16	1 13/16	3 1/16	2 9/16	4 5/16	3 5/16	5 9/16	4 1/16	6 13/16
1/2	3/8	5/8	1 1/8	1 7/8	1 7/8	3 1/8	2 5/8	4 3/8	3 3/8	5 5/8	4 1/8	6 7/8
9/16	7/16	11/16	1 3/16	1 15/16	1 15/16	3 3/16	2 11/16	4 7/16	3 7/16	5 11/16	4 3/16	6 15/16
5/8	15/32	25/32	1 7/32	2 1/32	1 31/32	3 9/32	2 23/32	4 17/32	3 15/32	5 25/32	4 7/32	7 1/32
11/16	1/2	7/8	1 1/4	2 1/8	2	3 3/8	2 3/4	4 5/8	3 1/2	5 7/8	4 1/4	7 1/8
3/4	9/16	15/16	1 5/16	2 3/16	2 1/16	3 7/16	2 13/16	4 11/16	3 9/16	5 15/16	4 5/16	7 3/16
13/16	5/8	1	1 3/8	2 1/4	2 1/8	3 1/2	2 7/8	4 3/4	3 5/8	6	4 3/8	7 1/4
7/8	21/32	1 3/32	1 13/32	2 11/32	2 5/32	3 19/32	2 29/32	4 27/32	3 21/32	6 3/32	4 13/32	7 11/32
15/16	11/16	1 3/16	1 7/16	2 7/16	2 3/16	3 11/16	2 15/16	4 15/16	3 11/16	6 3/16	4 7/16	7 7/16

Inches	6″ Rise	6″ Slope	7″ Rise	7″ Slope	8″ Rise	8″ Slope	9″ Rise	9″ Slope	10″ Rise	10″ Slope	11″ Rise	11″ Slope
0	4 1/2	7 1/2	5 1/4	8 3/4	6	10	6 3/4	11 1/4	7 1/2	1-0 1/2	8 1/4	1-1 3/4
1/16	4 9/16	7 9/16	5 5/16	8 13/16	6 1/16	10 1/16	6 13/16	11 5/16	7 9/16	1-0 9/16	8 5/16	1-1 13/16
1/8	4 19/32	7 21/32	5 11/32	8 29/32	6 3/32	10 5/32	6 27/32	11 13/32	7 19/32	1-0 21/32	8 11/32	1-1 29/32
3/16	4 5/8	7 3/4	5 3/8	9	6 1/8	10 1/4	6 7/8	11 1/2	7 5/8	1-0 3/4	8 3/8	1-2
1/4	4 11/16	7 13/16	5 7/16	9 1/16	6 3/16	10 5/16	6 15/16	11 9/16	7 11/16	1-0 13/16	8 7/16	1-2 1/16
5/16	4 3/4	7 7/8	5 1/2	9 1/8	6 1/4	10 3/8	7	11 5/8	7 3/4	1-0 7/8	8 1/2	1-2 1/8
3/8	4 25/32	7 31/32	5 17/32	9 7/32	6 9/32	10 15/32	7 1/32	11 23/32	7 25/32	1-0 31/32	8 17/32	1-2 7/32
7/16	4 13/16	8 1/16	5 9/16	9 5/16	6 5/16	10 9/16	7 1/16	11 13/16	7 13/16	1-1 1/16	8 9/16	1-2 5/32
1/2	4 7/8	8 1/8	5 5/8	9 3/8	6 3/8	10 5/8	7 1/8	11 7/8	7 7/8	1-1 1/8	8 5/8	1-2 3/8
9/16	4 15/16	8 3/16	5 11/16	9 7/16	6 7/16	10 11/16	7 3/16	11 15/16	7 15/16	1-1 3/16	8 11/16	1-2 7/16
5/8	4 31/32	8 9/32	5 23/32	9 17/32	6 15/32	10 25/32	7 7/32	1-0 1/32	7 31/32	1-1 9/32	8 23/32	1-2 17/32
11/16	5	8 3/8	5 3/4	9 5/8	6 1/2	10 7/8	7 1/4	1-0 1/8	8	1-1 3/8	8 3/4	1-2 5/8
3/4	5 1/16	8 7/16	5 13/16	9 11/16	6 9/16	10 15/16	7 5/16	1-0 3/16	8 1/16	1-1 7/16	8 13/16	1-2 11/16
13/16	5 1/8	8 1/2	5 7/8	9 3/4	6 5/8	11	7 3/8	1-0 1/4	8 1/8	1-1 1/2	8 7/8	1-2 3/4
7/8	5 5/32	8 19/32	5 29/32	9 27/32	6 21/32	11 3/32	7 13/32	1-0 11/32	8 5/32	1-1 19/32	8 29/32	1-2 27/32
15/16	5 3/16	8 11/16	5 15/16	9 15/16	6 11/16	11 3/16	7 7/16	1-0 7/16	8 3/16	1-1 11/16	8 15/16	1-2 15/16

Feet	0′ Rise	0′ Slope	10′ Rise	10′ Slope	20′ Rise	20′ Slope	30′ Rise	30′ Slope
0	0	0	7-6	12-6	15-0	25-0	22-6	37-6
1	-9	1-3	8-3	13-9	15-9	26-3	23-3	38-9
2	1-6	2-6	9-0	15-0	16-6	27-6	24-0	40-0
3	2-3	3-9	9-9	16-3	17-3	28-9	24-9	41-3
4	3-0	5-0	10-6	17-6	18-0	30-0	25-6	42-6
5	3-9	6-3	11-3	18-9	18-9	31-3	26-3	43-9
6	4-6	7-6	12-0	20-0	19-6	32-6	27-0	45-0
7	5-3	8-9	12-9	21-3	20-3	33-9	27-9	46-3
8	6-0	10-0	13-6	22-6	21-0	35-0	28-6	47-6
9	6-9	11-3	14-3	23-9	21-9	36-3	29-3	48-9

A = 36° 52′ 12″; logsin A = 9.77815; logcos A = 9.90309; logtan A = 9.87506; logcot A = 0.12494

Ins.	12″ Rise	12″ Slope	13″ Rise	13″ Slope	14″ Rise	14″ Slope	15″ Rise	15″ Slope	16″ Rise	16″ Slope
0	9	1-3	9 3/4	1-4 1/4	10 1/2	1-5 1/2	11 1/4	1-6 3/4	1-0	1-8
1/16	9 1/16	1-3 1/16	9 13/16	1-4 5/16	10 9/16	1-5 9/16	11 5/16	1-6 13/16	1-0 1/16	1-8 1/16
1/8	9 3/32	1-3 5/32	9 27/32	1-4 13/32	10 19/32	1-5 21/32	11 11/32	1-6 29/32	1-0 3/32	1-8 5/32
3/16	9 1/8	1-3 1/4	9 7/8	1-4 1/2	10 5/8	1-5 3/4	11 3/8	1-7	1-0 1/8	1-8 1/4
1/4	9 3/16	1-3 5/16	9 15/16	1-4 9/16	10 11/16	1-5 13/16	11 7/16	1-7 1/16	1-0 3/16	1-8 5/16
5/16	9 1/4	1-3 3/8	10	1-4 5/8	10 3/4	1-5 7/8	11 1/2	1-7 1/8	1-0 1/4	1-8 3/8
3/8	9 9/32	1-3 15/32	10 1/32	1-4 23/32	10 25/32	1-5 31/32	11 17/32	1-7 7/32	1-0 9/32	1-8 15/32
7/16	9 5/16	1-3 9/16	10 1/16	1-4 13/16	10 13/16	1-6 1/16	11 9/16	1-7 5/16	1-0 5/16	1-8 9/16
1/2	9 3/8	1-3 5/8	10 1/8	1-4 7/8	10 7/8	1-6 1/8	11 5/8	1-7 3/8	1-0 3/8	1-8 5/8
9/16	9 7/16	1-3 11/16	10 3/16	1-4 15/16	10 15/16	1-6 3/16	11 11/16	1-7 7/16	1-0 7/16	1-8 11/16
5/8	9 15/32	1-3 25/32	10 7/32	1-5 1/32	10 31/32	1-6 9/32	11 23/32	1-7 17/32	1-0 15/32	1-8 25/32
11/16	9 1/2	1-3 7/8	10 1/4	1-5 1/8	11	1-6 3/8	11 3/4	1-7 5/8	1-0 1/2	1-8 7/8
3/4	9 9/16	1-3 15/16	10 5/16	1-5 3/16	11 1/16	1-6 7/16	11 13/16	1-7 11/16	1-0 9/16	1-8 15/16
13/16	9 5/8	1-4	10 3/8	1-5 1/4	11 1/8	1-6 1/2	11 7/8	1-7 3/4	1-0 5/8	1-9
7/8	9 21/32	1-4 3/32	10 13/32	1-5 11/32	11 5/32	1-6 19/32	11 29/32	1-7 27/32	1-0 21/32	1-9 3/32
15/16	9 11/16	1-4 3/16	10 7/16	1-5 7/16	11 3/16	1-6 11/16	11 15/16	1-7 15/16	1-0 11/16	1-9 3/16

Ins.	17″ Rise	17″ Slope	18″ Rise	18″ Slope	19″ Rise	19″ Slope	20″ Rise	20″ Slope	21″ Rise	21″ Slope
0	1-0 3/4	1-9 1/4	1-1 1/2	1-10 1/2	1-2 1/4	1-11 3/4	1-3	2-1	1-3 3/4	2-2 1/4
1/16	1-0 13/16	1-9 5/16	1-1 9/16	1-10 9/16	1-2 5/16	1-11 13/16	1-3 1/16	2-1 1/16	1-3 13/16	2-2 5/16
1/8	1-0 27/32	1-9 13/32	1-1 19/32	1-10 21/32	1-2 11/32	1-11 29/32	1-3 3/32	2-1 5/32	1-3 27/32	2-2 13/32
3/16	1-0 7/8	1-9 1/2	1-1 5/8	1-10 3/4	1-2 3/8	2-0	1-3 1/8	2-1 1/4	1-3 7/8	2-2 1/2
1/4	1-0 15/16	1-9 9/16	1-1 11/16	1-10 13/16	1-2 7/16	2-0 1/16	1-3 3/16	2-1 5/16	1-3 15/16	2-2 9/16
5/16	1-1	1-9 5/8	1-1 3/4	1-10 7/8	1-2 1/2	2-0 1/8	1-3 1/4	2-1 3/8	1-4	2-2 5/8
3/8	1-1 1/32	1-9 23/32	1-1 25/32	1-10 31/32	1-2 17/32	2-0 7/32	1-3 9/32	2-1 15/32	1-4 1/32	2-2 23/32
7/16	1-1 1/16	1-9 13/16	1-1 13/16	1-11 1/16	1-2 9/16	2-0 5/16	1-3 5/16	2-1 9/16	1-4 1/16	2-2 13/16
1/2	1-1 1/8	1-9 7/8	1-1 7/8	1-11 1/8	1-2 5/8	2-0 3/8	1-3 3/8	2-1 5/8	1-4 1/8	2-2 7/8
9/16	1-1 3/16	1-9 15/16	1-1 15/16	1-11 3/16	1-2 11/16	2-0 7/16	1-3 7/16	2-1 11/16	1-4 3/16	2-2 15/16
5/8	1-1 7/32	1-10 1/32	1-1 31/32	1-11 9/32	1-2 23/32	2-0 17/32	1-3 15/32	2-1 25/32	1-4 7/32	2-3 1/32
11/16	1-1 1/4	1-10 1/8	1-2	1-11 3/8	1-2 3/4	2-0 5/8	1-3 1/2	2-1 7/8	1-4 1/4	2-3 1/8
3/4	1-1 5/16	1-10 3/16	1-2 1/16	1-11 7/16	1-2 13/16	2-0 11/16	1-3 9/16	2-1 15/16	1-4 5/16	2-3 3/16
13/16	1-1 3/8	1-10 1/4	1-2 1/8	1-11 1/2	1-2 7/8	2-0 3/4	1-3 5/8	2-2	1-4 3/8	2-3 1/4
7/8	1-1 13/32	1-10 11/32	1-2 5/32	1-11 19/32	1-2 29/32	2-0 27/32	1-3 21/32	2-2 3/32	1-4 13/32	2-3 11/32
15/16	1-1 7/16	1-10 7/16	1-2 3/16	1-11 11/16	1-2 15/16	2-0 15/16	1-3 11/16	2-2 3/16	1-4 7/16	2-3 7/16

Feet	40′ Rise	40′ Slope	50′ Rise	50′ Slope	60′ Rise	60′ Slope	70′ Rise	70′ Slope
0	30-0	50-0	37-6	62-6	45-0	75-0	52-6	87-6
1	30-9	51-3	38-3	63-9	45-9	76-3	53-3	88-9
2	31-6	52-6	39-0	65-0	46-6	77-6	54-0	90-0
3	32-3	53-9	39-9	66-3	47-3	78-9	54-9	91-3
4	33-0	55-0	40-6	67-6	48-0	80-0	55-6	92-6
5	33-9	56-3	41-3	68-9	48-9	81-3	56-3	93-9
6	34-6	57-6	42-0	70-0	49-6	82-6	57-0	95-0
7	35-3	58-9	42-9	71-3	50-3	83-9	57-9	96-3
8	36-0	60-0	43-6	72-6	51-0	85-0	58-6	97-6
9	36-9	61-3	44-3	73-9	51-9	86-3	59-3	98-9

natsin A=0.6000000000; natcosA=0.8000000000; nattan A=0.7500000000; natcot A=1.3333333333

Inches	0" Rise	0" Slope	1" Rise	1" Slope	2" Rise	2" Slope	3" Rise	3" Slope	4" Rise	4" Slope	5" Rise	5" Slope
0	0	0	3/4	1 1/4	1 1/2	2 1/2	2 1/4	3 3/4	3 1/32	5	3 25/32	6 9/32
1/16	1/16	3/32	13/16	1 11/32	1 9/16	2 19/32	2 5/16	3 27/32	3 1/16	5 3/32	3 13/16	6 11/32
1/8	3/32	5/32	27/32	1 13/32	1 19/32	2 21/32	2 3/8	3 29/32	3 1/8	5 5/32	3 7/8	6 7/16
3/16	5/32	1/4	29/32	1 1/2	1 21/32	2 3/4	2 13/32	4	3 5/32	5 1/4	3 29/32	6 1/2
1/4	3/16	5/16	15/16	1 9/16	1 11/16	2 13/16	2 15/32	4 1/16	3 7/32	5 5/16	3 31/32	6 19/32
5/16	1/4	13/32	1	1 21/32	1 3/4	2 29/32	2 1/2	4 5/32	3 1/4	5 13/32	4	6 21/32
3/8	9/32	15/32	1 1/16	1 23/32	1 25/32	2 31/32	2 9/16	4 7/32	3 5/16	5 15/32	4 1/16	6 3/4
7/16	11/32	9/16	1 3/32	1 13/16	1 27/32	3 1/16	2 19/32	4 5/16	3 11/32	5 9/16	4 3/32	6 13/16
1/2	3/8	5/8	1 1/8	1 7/8	1 7/8	3 1/8	2 21/32	4 3/8	3 13/32	5 5/8	4 5/32	6 29/32
9/16	7/16	23/32	1 3/16	1 31/32	1 15/16	3 7/32	2 11/16	4 15/32	3 7/16	5 23/32	4 3/16	6 31/32
5/8	15/32	25/32	1 7/32	2 1/32	1 31/32	3 9/32	2 3/4	4 17/32	3 1/2	5 25/32	4 1/4	7 1/16
11/16	17/32	7/8	1 9/32	2 1/8	2 1/32	3 3/8	2 25/32	4 5/8	3 17/32	5 7/8	4 9/32	7 1/8
3/4	9/16	15/16	1 5/16	2 3/16	2 1/16	3 7/16	2 27/32	4 11/16	3 19/32	5 15/16	4 11/32	7 7/32
13/16	5/8	1 1/32	1 3/8	2 9/32	2 1/8	3 11/32	2 7/8	4 25/32	3 5/8	6 1/32	4 3/8	7 9/32
7/8	21/32	1 3/32	1 13/32	2 11/32	2 5/32	3 19/32	2 15/16	4 27/32	3 11/16	6 3/32	4 7/16	7 3/8
15/16	23/32	1 3/16	1 15/32	2 7/16	2 7/32	3 11/16	2 31/32	4 15/16	3 23/32	6 3/16	4 15/32	7 7/16

Inches	6" Rise	6" Slope	7" Rise	7" Slope	8" Rise	8" Slope	9" Rise	9" Slope	10" Rise	10" Slope	11" Rise	11" Slope
0	4 17/32	7 17/32	5 9/32	8 25/32	6 1/4	10 1/32	6 13/16	11 9/32	7 9/16	1-0 17/32	8 5/16	1-1 25/32
1/16	4 19/32	7 19/32	5 11/32	8 27/32	6 3/32	10 3/32	6 27/32	11 11/32	7 19/32	1-0 5/8	8 11/32	1-1 7/8
1/8	4 5/8	7 11/16	5 3/8	8 15/16	6 1/8	10 3/16	6 29/32	11 7/16	7 21/32	1-0 11/16	8 13/32	1-1 15/16
3/16	4 11/16	7 3/4	5 1/16	9	6 3/16	10 1/4	6 15/16	11 1/2	7 11/16	1-0 25/32	8 7/16	1-2 1/32
1/4	4 23/32	7 27/32	5 15/32	9 3/32	6 7/32	10 11/32	7	11 19/32	7 3/4	1-0 27/32	8 1/2	1-2 3/32
5/16	4 25/32	7 29/32	5 17/32	9 5/32	6 9/32	10 13/32	7 1/16	11 21/32	7 25/32	1-0 15/16	8 17/32	1-2 3/16
3/8	4 13/16	8	5 9/16	9 1/4	6 5/16	10 1/2	7 3/32	11 3/4	7 27/32	1-1	8 19/32	1-2 1/4
7/16	4 7/8	8 1/16	5 5/8	9 5/16	6 3/8	10 9/16	7 1/8	11 13/16	7 7/8	1-1 3/32	8 5/8	1-2 11/32
1/2	4 29/32	8 5/32	5 21/32	9 13/32	6 13/32	10 21/32	7 3/16	11 29/32	7 15/16	1-1 5/32	8 11/16	1-2 13/32
9/16	4 31/32	8 7/32	5 23/32	9 15/32	6 15/32	10 23/32	7 7/32	11 31/32	7 31/32	1-1 1/4	8 23/32	1-2 1/2
5/8	5	8 5/16	5 3/4	9 9/16	6 1/2	10 13/16	7 9/32	1-0 1/16	8 1/32	1-1 5/16	8 25/32	1-2 9/16
11/16	5 1/16	8 3/8	5 13/16	9 5/8	6 9/16	10 7/8	7 5/16	1-0 1/8	8 1/16	1-1 13/32	8 13/16	1-2 21/32
3/4	5 3/32	8 15/32	5 27/32	9 23/32	6 19/32	10 31/32	7 3/8	1-0 7/32	8 1/8	1-1 15/32	8 7/8	1-2 23/32
13/16	5 5/32	8 17/32	5 29/32	9 25/32	6 21/32	11 1/32	7 13/32	1-0 9/32	8 5/32	1-1 9/16	8 29/32	1-2 13/16
7/8	5 3/16	8 5/8	5 15/16	9 7/8	6 11/16	11 1/8	7 15/32	1-0 3/8	8 7/32	1-1 5/8	8 31/32	1-2 7/8
15/16	5 1/4	8 11/16	6	9 15/16	6 3/4	11 3/16	7 1/2	1-0 7/16	8 1/4	1-1 23/32	9	1-2 31/32

Feet	0' Rise	0' Slope	10' Rise	10' Slope	20' Rise	20' Slope	30' Rise	30' Slope
0	0	0	7-6 5/8	12-6 3/8	15-1 1/4	25-0 3/4	22-7 7/8	37-7 1/8
1	-9 1/16	1-3 1/32	8-3 11/16	13-9 13/32	15-10 5/16	26-3 25/32	23-4 15/16	38-10 5/32
2	1-6 1/8	2-6 1/16	9-0 3/4	15-0 7/16	16-7 3/8	27-6 13/16	24-2	40-1 3/16
3	2-3 3/16	3-9 1/8	9-9 13/16	16-3 1/2	17-4 7/16	28-9 7/8	24-11 1/16	41-4 1/4
4	3-0 1/4	5-0 5/32	10-6 7/8	17-6 17/32	18-1 1/2	30-0 29/32	25-8 1/8	42-7 9/32
5	3-9 5/16	6-3 3/16	11-3 15/16	18-9 9/16	18-10 9/16	31-3 15/16	26-5 3/16	43-10 5/16
6	4-6 3/8	7-6 7/32	12-1	20-0 19/32	19-7 5/8	32-6 31/32	27-2 1/4	45-1 11/32
7	5-3 7/16	8-9 1/4	12-10 1/16	21-3 5/8	20-4 11/16	33-10	27-11 5/16	46-4 3/8
8	6-0 1/2	10-0 5/16	13-7 1/8	22-6 11/16	21-1 3/4	35-1 1/16	28-8 3/8	47-7 7/16
9	6-9 9/16	11-3 11/32	14-4 3/16	23-9 23/32	21-10 13/16	36-4 3/32	29-5 7/16	48-10 15/32

A = 37° 03' 37"; logsin A = 9.78007; logcos A = 9.90200; logtan A = 9.87807; logcot A = 0.12193

Ins.	12″ Rise	12″ Slope	13″ Rise	13″ Slope	14″ Rise	14″ Slope	15″ Rise	15″ Slope	16″ Rise	16″ Slope
0	9 1/16	1-3 1/32	9 13/16	1-4 9/32	10 9/16	1-5 17/32	11 5/16	1-6 13/16	1-0 3/32	1-8 1/16
1/16	9 1/8	1-3 1/8	9 7/8	1-4 3/8	10 5/8	1-5 5/8	11 3/8	1-6 7/8	1-0 1/8	1-8 1/8
1/8	9 5/32	1-3 3/16	9 29/32	1-4 7/16	10 21/32	1-5 11/16	11 7/16	1-6 31/32	1-0 3/16	1-8 7/32
3/16	9 7/32	1-3 9/32	9 31/32	1-4 17/32	10 23/32	1-5 25/32	11 15/32	1-7 1/32	1-0 7/32	1-8 9/32
1/4	9 1/4	1-3 11/32	10	1-4 19/32	10 3/4	1-5 27/32	11 17/32	1-7 1/8	1-0 9/32	1-8 3/8
5/16	9 5/16	1-3 7/16	10 1/16	1-4 11/16	10 13/16	1-5 15/16	11 9/16	1-7 3/16	1-0 5/16	1-8 7/16
3/8	9 11/32	1-3 1/2	10 3/32	1-4 3/4	10 27/32	1-6	11 5/8	1-7 9/32	1-0 3/8	1-8 17/32
7/16	9 13/32	1-3 19/32	10 5/32	1-4 27/32	10 29/32	1-6 3/32	11 21/32	1-7 11/32	1-0 13/32	1-8 19/32
1/2	9 7/16	1-3 21/32	10 3/16	1-4 29/32	10 15/16	1-6 5/32	11 23/32	1-7 7/16	1-0 15/32	1-8 11/16
9/16	9 1/2	1-3 3/4	10 1/4	1-5	11	1-6 1/4	11 3/4	1-7 1/2	1-0 1/2	1-8 3/4
5/8	9 17/32	1-3 13/16	10 9/32	1-5 1/16	11 1/32	1-6 5/16	11 13/16	1-7 19/32	1-0 9/16	1-8 27/32
11/16	9 19/32	1-3 29/32	10 11/32	1-5 5/32	11 3/32	1-6 13/32	11 27/32	1-7 21/32	1-0 19/32	1-8 29/32
3/4	9 5/8	1-3 31/32	10 3/8	1-5 7/32	11 1/8	1-6 15/32	11 29/32	1-7 3/4	1-0 21/32	1-9
13/16	9 11/16	1-4 1/16	10 7/16	1-5 5/16	11 3/16	1-6 9/16	11 15/16	1-7 13/16	1-0 11/16	1-9 1/16
7/8	9 23/32	1-4 1/8	10 15/32	1-5 3/8	11 7/32	1-6 5/8	1-0	1-7 29/32	1-0 3/4	1-9 5/32
15/16	9 25/32	1-4 7/32	10 17/32	1-5 15/32	11 9/32	1-6 23/32	1-0 1/2	1-7 31/32	1-0 25/32	1-9 7/32

Ins.	17″ Rise	17″ Slope	18″ Rise	18″ Slope	19″ Rise	19″ Slope	20″ Rise	20″ Slope	21″ Rise	21″ Slope
0	1-0 27/32	1-9 5/16	1-1 19/32	1-10 9/16	1-2 11/32	1-11 13/16	1-3 3/32	2-1 1/16	1-3 7/8	2-2 5/16
1/16	1-0 7/8	1-9 3/8	1-1 21/32	1-10 5/8	1-2 13/32	1-11 7/8	1-3 5/32	2-1 5/32	1-3 29/32	2-2 13/32
1/8	1-0 15/16	1-9 15/32	1-1 11/16	1-10 23/32	1-2 7/16	1-11 31/32	1-3 3/16	2-1 7/32	1-3 31/32	2-2 15/32
3/16	1-0 31/32	1-9 17/32	1-1 3/4	1-10 25/32	1-2 1/2	2-0 1/32	1-3 1/4	2-1 5/16	1-4	2-2 9/16
1/4	1-1 1/32	1-9 5/8	1-1 25/32	1-10 7/8	1-2 17/32	2-0 1/8	1-3 9/32	2-1 3/8	1-4 1/16	2-2 5/8
5/16	1-1 1/16	1-9 11/16	1-1 27/32	1-10 15/16	1-2 19/32	2-0 3/16	1-3 11/32	2-1 15/32	1-4 3/32	2-2 23/32
3/8	1-1 1/8	1-9 25/32	1-1 7/8	1-11 1/32	1-2 5/8	2-0 9/32	1-3 3/8	2-1 17/32	1-4 5/32	2-2 25/32
7/16	1-1 5/32	1-9 27/32	1-1 15/16	1-11 3/32	1-2 11/16	2-0 11/32	1-3 7/16	2-1 5/8	1-4 3/16	2-2 7/8
1/2	1-1 7/32	1-9 15/16	1-1 31/32	1-11 3/16	1-2 23/32	2-0 7/16	1-3 15/32	2-1 11/16	1-4 1/4	2-2 15/16
9/16	1-1 1/4	1-10	1-2 1/32	1-11 1/4	1-2 25/32	2-0 1/2	1-3 17/32	2-1 25/32	1-4 9/32	2-3 1/32
5/8	1-1 5/16	1-10 3/32	1-2 1/16	1-11 11/32	1-2 13/16	2-0 19/32	1-3 9/16	2-1 27/32	1-4 11/32	2-3 3/32
11/16	1-1 11/32	1-10 5/32	1-2 1/8	1-11 13/32	1-2 7/8	2-0 21/32	1-3 5/8	2-1 15/16	1-4 3/8	2-3 3/16
3/4	1-1 13/32	1-10 1/4	1-2 5/32	1-11 1/2	1-2 29/32	2-0 3/4	1-3 21/32	2-2	1-4 7/16	2-3 1/4
13/16	1-1 7/16	1-10 5/16	1-2 7/32	1-11 9/16	1-2 31/32	2-0 13/16	1-3 23/32	2-2 3/32	1-4 15/32	2-3 11/32
7/8	1-1 1/2	1-10 13/32	1-2 1/4	1-11 21/32	1-3	2-0 29/32	1-3 3/4	2-2 5/32	1-4 17/32	2-3 13/32
15/16	1-1 17/32	1-10 15/32	1-2 5/16	1-11 23/32	1-3 1/16	2-0 31/32	1-3 13/16	2-2 1/4	1-4 9/16	2-3 1/2

Feet	40′ Rise	40′ Slope	50′ Rise	50′ Slope	60′ Rise	60′ Slope	70′ Rise	70′ Slope
0	30-2 1/2	50-1 1/2	37-9 1/8	62-7 7/8	45-3 3/4	75-2 1/4	52-10 3/8	87-8 5/8
1	30-11 9/16	51-4 17/32	38-6 3/16	63-10 29/32	46-0 13/16	76-5 9/32	53-7 7/16	88-11 21/32
2	31-8 5/8	52-7 19/32	39-3 1/4	65-1 31/32	46-9 7/8	77-8 11/32	54-4 1/2	90-2 23/32
3	32-5 11/32	53-10 5/8	40-0 5/16	66-5	47-6 15/16	78-11 3/8	55-1 9/16	91-5 3/4
4	33-2 3/4	55-1 21/32	40-9 3/8	67-8 1/16	48-4	80-2 13/32	55-10 5/8	92-8 25/32
5	33-11 13/16	56-4 11/32	41-6 7/16	68-11 1/16	49-1 1/16	81-5 7/16	56-7 11/16	93-11 13/16
6	34-8 7/8	57-7 23/32	42-3 1/2	70-2 3/32	49-10 1/8	82-8 15/32	57-4 3/4	95-2 27/32
7	35-5 15/16	58-10 25/32	43-0 9/16	71-5 5/32	50-7 3/16	83-11 17/32	58-1 13/16	96-5 29/32
8	36-3	60-1 13/16	43-9 5/8	72-8 3/16	51-4 1/4	85-2 9/16	58-10 7/8	97-8 15/16
9	37-0 1/16	61-4 27/32	44-6 11/32	73-11 7/32	52-1 5/16	86-5 19/32	59-7 15/16	98-11 31/32

natsin A=0.6026566852; **natcos** A=0.7980005763; **nattan** A=0.7552083333; **natcot** A=1.3241379310

Inches	0" Rise	0" Slope	1" Rise	1" Slope	2" Rise	2" Slope	3" Rise	3" Slope	4" Rise	4" Slope	5" Rise	5" Slope
0	0	0	$\frac{3}{4}$	$1\frac{1}{4}$	$1\frac{17}{32}$	$2\frac{1}{2}$	$2\frac{3}{32}$	$3\frac{25}{32}$	$3\frac{1}{32}$	$5\frac{1}{32}$	$3\frac{13}{16}$	$6\frac{3}{32}$
$\frac{1}{16}$	$\frac{1}{16}$	$\frac{3}{32}$	$\frac{13}{16}$	$1\frac{11}{32}$	$1\frac{9}{16}$	$2\frac{19}{32}$	$2\frac{7}{32}$	$3\frac{27}{32}$	$3\frac{3}{32}$	$5\frac{3}{32}$	$3\frac{27}{32}$	$6\frac{1}{8}$
$\frac{1}{8}$	$\frac{3}{32}$	$\frac{5}{32}$	$\frac{27}{32}$	$1\frac{13}{32}$	$1\frac{5}{8}$	$2\frac{21}{32}$	$2\frac{3}{8}$	$3\frac{15}{16}$	$3\frac{1}{8}$	$5\frac{3}{16}$	$3\frac{29}{32}$	$6\frac{1}{16}$
$\frac{3}{16}$	$\frac{5}{32}$	$\frac{1}{4}$	$\frac{29}{32}$	$1\frac{1}{2}$	$1\frac{21}{32}$	$2\frac{3}{4}$	$2\frac{7}{16}$	4	$3\frac{3}{16}$	$5\frac{1}{4}$	$3\frac{15}{16}$	$6\frac{17}{32}$
$\frac{1}{4}$	$\frac{3}{16}$	$\frac{5}{16}$	$\frac{15}{16}$	$1\frac{9}{16}$	$1\frac{23}{32}$	$2\frac{13}{16}$	$2\frac{15}{32}$	$4\frac{3}{32}$	$3\frac{7}{32}$	$5\frac{11}{32}$	4	$6\frac{19}{32}$
$\frac{5}{16}$	$\frac{1}{4}$	$\frac{13}{32}$	1	$1\frac{21}{32}$	$1\frac{3}{4}$	$2\frac{29}{32}$	$2\frac{17}{32}$	$4\frac{5}{32}$	$3\frac{9}{32}$	$5\frac{13}{32}$	$4\frac{1}{8}$	$6\frac{11}{16}$
$\frac{3}{8}$	$\frac{9}{32}$	$\frac{15}{32}$	$1\frac{1}{16}$	$1\frac{23}{32}$	$1\frac{13}{16}$	$2\frac{31}{32}$	$2\frac{9}{16}$	$4\frac{1}{4}$	$3\frac{5}{16}$	$5\frac{1}{2}$	$4\frac{3}{32}$	$6\frac{3}{4}$
$\frac{7}{16}$	$\frac{11}{32}$	$\frac{9}{16}$	$1\frac{3}{32}$	$1\frac{13}{16}$	$1\frac{27}{32}$	$3\frac{1}{16}$	$2\frac{5}{8}$	$4\frac{5}{16}$	$3\frac{3}{8}$	$5\frac{9}{16}$	$4\frac{1}{8}$	$6\frac{27}{32}$
$\frac{1}{2}$	$\frac{3}{8}$	$\frac{5}{8}$	$1\frac{1}{8}$	$1\frac{7}{8}$	$1\frac{29}{32}$	$3\frac{5}{32}$	$2\frac{21}{32}$	$4\frac{13}{32}$	$3\frac{7}{16}$	$5\frac{21}{32}$	$4\frac{3}{16}$	$6\frac{29}{32}$
$\frac{9}{16}$	$\frac{7}{16}$	$\frac{23}{32}$	$1\frac{3}{16}$	$1\frac{31}{32}$	$1\frac{15}{16}$	$3\frac{7}{32}$	$2\frac{23}{32}$	$4\frac{15}{32}$	$3\frac{15}{32}$	$5\frac{23}{32}$	$4\frac{7}{32}$	7
$\frac{5}{8}$	$\frac{15}{32}$	$\frac{25}{32}$	$1\frac{1}{4}$	$2\frac{1}{32}$	2	$3\frac{9}{16}$	$2\frac{3}{4}$	$4\frac{9}{16}$	$3\frac{17}{32}$	$5\frac{13}{16}$	$4\frac{9}{32}$	$7\frac{1}{16}$
$\frac{11}{16}$	$\frac{17}{32}$	$\frac{7}{8}$	$1\frac{9}{32}$	$2\frac{1}{8}$	$2\frac{1}{32}$	$3\frac{3}{8}$	$2\frac{13}{16}$	$4\frac{5}{8}$	$3\frac{9}{16}$	$5\frac{7}{8}$	$4\frac{5}{16}$	$7\frac{5}{32}$
$\frac{3}{4}$	$\frac{9}{16}$	$\frac{15}{16}$	$1\frac{11}{32}$	$2\frac{3}{16}$	$2\frac{3}{32}$	$3\frac{15}{32}$	$2\frac{27}{32}$	$4\frac{23}{32}$	$3\frac{5}{8}$	$5\frac{31}{32}$	$4\frac{3}{8}$	$7\frac{7}{32}$
$\frac{13}{16}$	$\frac{5}{8}$	$1\frac{1}{32}$	$1\frac{3}{8}$	$2\frac{9}{32}$	$2\frac{1}{8}$	$3\frac{17}{32}$	$2\frac{29}{32}$	$4\frac{25}{32}$	$3\frac{21}{32}$	$6\frac{1}{16}$	$4\frac{13}{32}$	$7\frac{5}{16}$
$\frac{7}{8}$	$\frac{21}{32}$	$1\frac{3}{32}$	$1\frac{7}{16}$	$2\frac{11}{32}$	$2\frac{3}{16}$	$3\frac{5}{8}$	$2\frac{15}{16}$	$4\frac{7}{8}$	$3\frac{23}{32}$	$6\frac{1}{8}$	$4\frac{15}{32}$	$7\frac{3}{8}$
$\frac{15}{16}$	$\frac{23}{32}$	$1\frac{3}{16}$	$1\frac{15}{32}$	$2\frac{7}{16}$	$2\frac{7}{32}$	$3\frac{11}{16}$	3	$4\frac{15}{16}$	$3\frac{3}{4}$	$6\frac{3}{16}$	$4\frac{1}{2}$	$7\frac{15}{32}$

Inches	6" Rise	6" Slope	7" Rise	7" Slope	8" Rise	8" Slope	9" Rise	9" Slope	10" Rise	10" Slope	11" Rise	11" Slope
0	$4\frac{9}{16}$	$7\frac{11}{32}$	$5\frac{5}{16}$	$8\frac{25}{32}$	$6\frac{3}{32}$	$10\frac{1}{16}$	$6\frac{27}{32}$	$11\frac{9}{16}$	$7\frac{19}{32}$	$1\text{-}0\frac{9}{16}$	$8\frac{3}{8}$	$1\text{-}1\frac{13}{16}$
$\frac{1}{16}$	$4\frac{5}{8}$	$7\frac{5}{8}$	$5\frac{3}{8}$	$8\frac{7}{8}$	$6\frac{1}{8}$	$10\frac{1}{8}$	$6\frac{29}{32}$	$11\frac{5}{8}$	$7\frac{21}{32}$	$1\text{-}0\frac{21}{32}$	$8\frac{13}{32}$	$1\text{-}1\frac{29}{32}$
$\frac{1}{8}$	$4\frac{21}{32}$	$7\frac{11}{16}$	$5\frac{13}{32}$	$8\frac{15}{16}$	$6\frac{3}{16}$	$10\frac{7}{32}$	$6\frac{15}{16}$	$11\frac{15}{32}$	$7\frac{11}{16}$	$1\text{-}0\frac{23}{32}$	$8\frac{15}{32}$	$1\text{-}1\frac{31}{32}$
$\frac{3}{16}$	$4\frac{23}{32}$	$7\frac{25}{32}$	$5\frac{15}{32}$	$9\frac{1}{32}$	$6\frac{17}{32}$	$10\frac{9}{32}$	7	$11\frac{17}{32}$	$7\frac{3}{4}$	$1\text{-}0\frac{13}{16}$	$8\frac{1}{2}$	$1\text{-}2\frac{1}{32}$
$\frac{1}{4}$	$4\frac{3}{4}$	$7\frac{27}{32}$	$5\frac{1}{2}$	$9\frac{3}{8}$	$6\frac{9}{32}$	$10\frac{3}{8}$	$7\frac{5}{32}$	$11\frac{5}{8}$	$7\frac{25}{32}$	$1\text{-}0\frac{7}{8}$	$8\frac{9}{16}$	$1\text{-}2\frac{1}{8}$
$\frac{5}{16}$	$4\frac{13}{16}$	$7\frac{15}{16}$	$5\frac{9}{16}$	$9\frac{3}{16}$	$6\frac{5}{16}$	$10\frac{7}{16}$	$7\frac{3}{32}$	$11\frac{11}{16}$	$7\frac{27}{32}$	$1\text{-}0\frac{31}{32}$	$8\frac{19}{32}$	$1\text{-}2\frac{1}{8}$
$\frac{3}{8}$	$4\frac{27}{32}$	8	$5\frac{19}{32}$	$9\frac{1}{4}$	$6\frac{3}{8}$	$10\frac{17}{32}$	$7\frac{1}{8}$	$11\frac{25}{32}$	$7\frac{7}{8}$	$1\text{-}1\frac{1}{32}$	$8\frac{21}{32}$	$1\text{-}2\frac{9}{32}$
$\frac{7}{16}$	$4\frac{29}{32}$	$8\frac{3}{32}$	$5\frac{21}{32}$	$9\frac{11}{32}$	$6\frac{13}{32}$	$10\frac{19}{32}$	$7\frac{3}{16}$	$11\frac{27}{32}$	$7\frac{15}{16}$	$1\text{-}1\frac{1}{8}$	$8\frac{11}{16}$	$1\text{-}2\frac{3}{8}$
$\frac{1}{2}$	$4\frac{15}{16}$	$8\frac{5}{32}$	$5\frac{11}{32}$	$9\frac{7}{16}$	$6\frac{15}{32}$	$10\frac{11}{16}$	$7\frac{7}{32}$	$11\frac{15}{16}$	8	$1\text{-}1\frac{3}{16}$	$8\frac{3}{4}$	$1\text{-}2\frac{7}{16}$
$\frac{9}{16}$	5	$8\frac{1}{4}$	$5\frac{3}{4}$	$9\frac{1}{2}$	$6\frac{1}{2}$	$10\frac{3}{4}$	$7\frac{9}{32}$	$1\text{-}0$	$8\frac{1}{32}$	$1\text{-}1\frac{9}{32}$	$8\frac{25}{32}$	$1\text{-}2\frac{17}{32}$
$\frac{5}{8}$	$5\frac{1}{8}$	$8\frac{5}{16}$	$5\frac{13}{16}$	$9\frac{19}{32}$	$6\frac{9}{16}$	$10\frac{27}{32}$	$7\frac{5}{16}$	$1\text{-}0\frac{3}{32}$	$8\frac{3}{32}$	$1\text{-}1\frac{11}{32}$	$8\frac{27}{32}$	$1\text{-}2\frac{19}{32}$
$\frac{11}{16}$	$5\frac{3}{32}$	$8\frac{13}{32}$	$5\frac{27}{32}$	$9\frac{21}{32}$	$6\frac{19}{32}$	$10\frac{29}{32}$	$7\frac{3}{8}$	$1\text{-}0\frac{5}{32}$	$8\frac{1}{8}$	$1\text{-}1\frac{7}{16}$	$8\frac{7}{8}$	$1\text{-}2\frac{11}{16}$
$\frac{3}{4}$	$5\frac{1}{8}$	$8\frac{15}{32}$	$5\frac{29}{32}$	$9\frac{3}{4}$	$6\frac{21}{32}$	11	$7\frac{13}{32}$	$1\text{-}0\frac{1}{4}$	$8\frac{3}{16}$	$1\text{-}1\frac{1}{2}$	$8\frac{15}{16}$	$1\text{-}2\frac{3}{4}$
$\frac{13}{16}$	$5\frac{3}{16}$	$8\frac{9}{16}$	$5\frac{15}{16}$	$9\frac{13}{16}$	$6\frac{11}{16}$	$11\frac{1}{16}$	$7\frac{15}{32}$	$1\text{-}0\frac{5}{16}$	$8\frac{7}{32}$	$1\text{-}1\frac{19}{32}$	$8\frac{31}{32}$	$1\text{-}2\frac{27}{32}$
$\frac{7}{8}$	$5\frac{7}{32}$	$8\frac{5}{8}$	6	$9\frac{29}{32}$	$6\frac{3}{4}$	$11\frac{5}{32}$	$7\frac{1}{2}$	$1\text{-}0\frac{13}{32}$	$8\frac{9}{32}$	$1\text{-}1\frac{21}{32}$	$9\frac{1}{32}$	$1\text{-}2\frac{29}{32}$
$\frac{15}{16}$	$5\frac{9}{32}$	$8\frac{23}{32}$	$6\frac{1}{32}$	$9\frac{31}{32}$	$6\frac{25}{32}$	$11\frac{7}{32}$	$7\frac{9}{16}$	$1\text{-}0\frac{15}{32}$	$8\frac{5}{16}$	$1\text{-}1\frac{3}{4}$	$9\frac{1}{16}$	$1\text{-}3$

Feet	0' Rise	0' Slope	10' Rise	10' Slope	20' Rise	20' Slope	30' Rise	30' Slope
0	0	0	7-7$\frac{1}{4}$	12-6$\frac{3}{4}$	15-2$\frac{1}{2}$	25-1$\frac{1}{2}$	22-9$\frac{3}{4}$	37-8$\frac{1}{4}$
1	-9$\frac{1}{8}$	1-3$\frac{1}{32}$	8-4$\frac{3}{8}$	13-9$\frac{27}{32}$	15-11$\frac{5}{8}$	26-4$\frac{19}{32}$	23-6$\frac{7}{8}$	38-11$\frac{11}{32}$
2	1-6$\frac{1}{4}$	2-6$\frac{5}{32}$	9-1$\frac{1}{2}$	15-0$\frac{29}{32}$	16-8$\frac{3}{4}$	27-7$\frac{21}{32}$	24-4	40-2$\frac{13}{32}$
3	2-3$\frac{3}{8}$	3-9$\frac{5}{32}$	9-10$\frac{5}{8}$	16-3$\frac{31}{32}$	17-5$\frac{7}{8}$	28-10$\frac{23}{32}$	25-1$\frac{1}{8}$	41-5$\frac{1}{2}$
4	3-0$\frac{1}{2}$	5-0$\frac{5}{16}$	10-7$\frac{3}{4}$	17-7$\frac{1}{16}$	18-3	30-1$\frac{13}{16}$	25-10$\frac{1}{4}$	42-8$\frac{9}{16}$
5	3-9$\frac{5}{8}$	6-3$\frac{3}{8}$	11-4$\frac{7}{8}$	18-10$\frac{1}{8}$	19-0$\frac{1}{8}$	31-4$\frac{7}{8}$	26-7$\frac{3}{8}$	43-11$\frac{5}{8}$
6	4-6$\frac{3}{4}$	7-6$\frac{7}{16}$	12-2	20-1$\frac{7}{32}$	19-9$\frac{1}{4}$	32-7$\frac{31}{32}$	27-4$\frac{1}{2}$	45-2$\frac{23}{32}$
7	5-3$\frac{7}{8}$	8-9$\frac{17}{32}$	12-11$\frac{1}{8}$	21-4$\frac{9}{32}$	20-6$\frac{3}{8}$	33-11$\frac{1}{32}$	28-1$\frac{5}{8}$	46-5$\frac{25}{32}$
8	6-1	10-0$\frac{19}{32}$	13-8$\frac{1}{4}$	22-7$\frac{11}{32}$	21-3$\frac{1}{2}$	35-2$\frac{3}{32}$	28-10$\frac{3}{4}$	47-8$\frac{7}{8}$
9	6-10$\frac{1}{8}$	11-3$\frac{11}{16}$	14-5$\frac{3}{8}$	23-10$\frac{7}{16}$	22-0$\frac{5}{8}$	36-5$\frac{5}{16}$	29-7$\frac{7}{8}$	48-11$\frac{15}{16}$

$A = 37°\ 15'\ 00''$; logsin A $= 9.78197$; logcos A $= 9.90091$; logtan A $= 9.88105$; logcot A $= 0.11895$

Ins.	12″ Rise	12″ Slope	13″ Rise	13″ Slope	14″ Rise	14″ Slope	15″ Rise	15″ Slope	16″ Rise	16″ Slope
0	9 1/8	1-3 1/16	9 7/8	1-4 11/32−	10 21/32−	1-5 19/32−	11 13/32	1-6 27/32	1-0 5/32	1-8 3/32
1/16	9 3/16	1-3 5/32−	9 15/16	1-4 13/32	10 11/16	1-5 21/32	11 15/32−	1-6 15/16	1-0 7/32−	1-8 3/16
1/8	9 7/32	1-3 7/32	9 31/32	1-4 1/2	10 3/4	1-5 3/4	11 1/2	1-7	1-0 1/4	1-8 1/4
3/16	9 9/32−	1-3 5/16	10 1/32−	1-4 9/16	10 25/32	1-5 13/16	11 9/16	1-7 3/32−	1-0 5/16	1-8 11/32−
1/4	9 5/16	1-3 3/8	10 1/16	1-4 21/32−	10 27/32−	1-5 29/32−	11 19/32	1-7 5/32	1-0 11/32	1-8 13/32
5/16	9 3/8	1-3 15/32−	10 1/8	1-4 23/32	10 7/8	1-5 31/32	11 21/32−	1-7 1/4	1-0 13/32−	1-8 1/2
3/8	9 13/32	1-3 17/32	10 5/32	1-4 13/16	10 15/16	1-6 1/16	11 11/16	1-7 5/16	1-0 7/16	1-8 9/16
7/16	9 15/32−	1-3 5/8	10 7/32−	1-4 7/8	10 31/32	1-6 1/8	11 3/4	1-7 13/32−	1-0 1/2	1-8 21/32−
1/2	9 1/2	1-3 23/32−	10 1/4	1-4 31/32−	11 1/32−	1-6 7/32−	11 25/32	1-7 15/32	1-0 9/16	1-8 23/32
9/16	9 9/16	1-3 25/32	10 5/16	1-5 1/32	11 1/16	1-6 9/32	11 27/32−	1-7 9/16	1-0 19/32	1-8 13/16
5/8	9 19/32	1-3 7/8	10 3/8	1-5 1/8	11 1/8	1-6 3/8	11 7/8	1-7 5/8	1-0 21/32−	1-8 7/8
11/16	9 21/32−	1-3 15/16	10 13/32	1-5 3/16	11 5/32	1-6 7/16	11 15/16	1-7 23/32−	1-0 11/16	1-8 31/32−
3/4	9 11/16	1-4 1/32−	10 15/32−	1-5 9/32−	11 7/32−	1-6 17/32−	11 31/32	1-7 25/32	1-0 3/4	1-9 1/32
13/16	9 3/4	1-4 3/32	10 1/2	1-5 11/32	11 1/4	1-6 19/32	1-0 1/32−	1-7 7/8	1-0 25/32	1-9 1/8
7/8	9 25/32	1-4 3/16	10 9/16	1-5 7/16	11 5/16	1-6 11/16	1-0 1/16	1-7 15/16	1-0 27/32−	1-9 3/16
15/16	9 27/32−	1-4 1/4	10 19/32	1-5 1/2	11 11/32	1-6 25/32−	1-0 1/8	1-8 1/32−	1-0 7/8	1-9 9/32−

Ins.	17″ Rise	17″ Slope	18″ Rise	18″ Slope	19″ Rise	19″ Slope	20″ Rise	20″ Slope	21″ Rise	21″ Slope
0	1-0 15/16	1-9 11/32	1-1 11/16	1-10 5/8	1-2 7/16	1-11 7/8	1-3 7/32−	2-1 1/8	1-3 31/32	2-2 3/8
1/16	1-0 31/32	1-9 7/16	1-1 3/4	1-10 11/16	1-2 1/2	1-11 15/16	1-3 1/4	2-1 7/32−	1-4 1/32−	2-2 15/32−
1/8	1-1 1/32−	1-9 1/2	1-1 25/32	1-10 25/32−	1-2 17/32	2-0 1/32−	1-3 5/16	2-1 9/32	1-4 1/16	2-2 17/32
3/16	1-1 1/16	1-9 19/32−	1-1 27/32−	1-10 27/32	1-2 19/32−	2-0 3/32	1-3 11/32	2-1 3/8	1-4 1/8	2-2 5/8
1/4	1-1 1/8	1-9 21/32	1-1 7/8	1-10 15/16	1-2 5/8	2-0 3/16	1-3 13/32−	2-1 7/16	1-4 5/32	2-2 11/16
5/16	1-1 5/32	1-9 3/4	1-1 15/16	1-11	1-2 11/16	2-0 1/4	1-3 7/16	2-1 17/32−	1-4 7/32−	2-2 25/32−
3/8	1-1 7/32−	1-9 13/16	1-1 31/32	1-11 3/32−	1-2 23/32	2-0 11/32−	1-3 1/2	2-1 19/32	1-4 1/4	2-2 27/32
7/16	1-1 1/4	1-9 29/32	1-2 1/32−	1-11 5/32	1-2 25/32−	2-0 13/32	1-3 17/32	2-1 11/16	1-4 5/16	2-2 15/16
1/2	1-1 5/16	1-10	1-2 1/16	1-11 1/4	1-2 13/16	2-0 1/2	1-3 19/32−	2-1 3/4	1-4 11/32	2-3
9/16	1-1 11/32	1-10 1/16	1-2 1/8	1-11 5/16	1-2 7/8	2-0 9/16	1-3 5/8	2-1 27/32−	1-4 13/32−	2-3 3/32−
5/8	1-1 13/32−	1-10 5/32−	1-2 5/32	1-11 13/32−	1-2 15/16	2-0 21/32−	1-3 11/16	2-1 29/32	1-4 7/16	2-3 5/32
11/16	1-1 7/16	1-10 7/32	1-2 7/32−	1-11 15/32	1-2 31/32	2-0 23/32	1-3 23/32	2-2	1-4 1/2	2-3 1/4
3/4	1-1 1/2	1-10 5/16	1-2 1/4	1-11 9/16	1-3 1/32−	2-0 13/16	1-3 25/32−	2-2 1/16	1-4 17/32	2-3 5/16
13/16	1-1 17/32	1-10 3/8	1-2 5/16	1-11 5/8	1-3 1/16	2-0 7/8	1-3 13/16	2-2 5/32−	1-4 19/32−	2-3 13/32−
7/8	1-1 19/32−	1-10 15/32−	1-2 11/32	1-11 23/32−	1-3 1/8	2-0 31/32−	1-3 7/8	2-2 7/32	1-4 5/8	2-3 15/32
15/16	1-1 5/8	1-10 17/32	1-2 13/32−	1-11 25/32	1-3 5/32	2-1 1/16	1-3 29/32	2-2 5/16	1-4 11/16	2-3 9/16

Feet	40′ Rise	40′ Slope	50′ Rise	50′ Slope	60′ Rise	60′ Slope	70′ Rise	70′ Slope
0	30-5	50-3	38-0 1/4	62-9 25/32−	45-7 1/2	75-4 17/32−	53-2 3/4	87-11 9/32−
1	31-2 1/8	51-6 3/32−	38-9 3/8	64-0 27/32−	46-4 5/8	76-7 19/32	53-11 7/8	89-2 11/32
2	31-11 1/4	52-9 5/32	39-6 1/2	65-3 29/32	47-1 3/4	77-10 21/32	54-9	90-5 7/16
3	32-8 3/8	54-0 1/4	40-3 5/8	66-7	47-10 7/8	79-1 3/4	55-6 1/8	91-8 1/2
4	33-5 1/2	55-3 5/16	41-0 3/4	67-10 1/16	48-8	80-4 13/16	56-3 1/4	92-11 9/16
5	34-2 5/8	56-6 3/8	41-9 7/8	69-1 5/32−	49-5 1/8	81-7 29/32−	57-0 3/8	94-2 21/32−
6	34-11 3/4	57-9 15/32−	42-7	70-4 7/32−	50-2 1/4	82-10 31/32	57-9 1/2	95-5 23/32
7	35-8 7/8	59-0 17/32	43-4 1/8	71-7 9/32	50-11 3/8	84-2 1/16	58-6 5/8	96-8 13/16
8	36-6	60-3 5/8	44-1 1/4	72-10 3/8	51-8 1/2	85-5 1/8	59-3 3/4	97-11 7/8
9	37-3 1/8	61-6 11/16	44-10 3/8	74-1 7/16	52-5 5/8	86-8 3/16	60-0 7/8	99-2 15/16

natsin A=0.6052934819; natcos A=0.7960023873; nattan A=0.7604166666; natcot A=1.3150684931

Inches	0" Rise	0" Slope	1" Rise	1" Slope	2" Rise	2" Slope	3" Rise	3" Slope	4" Rise	4" Slope	5" Rise	5" Slope
0	0	0	3/4	1 1/4	1 17/32	2 17/32	2 5/16	3 25/32	3 1/16	5 1/32	3 13/16	6 5/16
1/16	1/16	3/32	13/16	1 11/32	1 19/32	2 19/32	2 11/32	3 27/32	3 1/8	5 1/8	3 7/8	6 3/8
1/8	3/32	5/32	7/8	1 13/32	1 5/8	2 11/16	2 13/32	3 15/16	3 5/32	5 3/16	3 15/16	6 15/32
3/16	7/32	1/4	29/32	1 1/2	1 11/16	2 3/4	2 7/16	4	3 7/32	5 9/32	3 31/32	6 17/32
1/4	3/16	5/16	31/32	1 9/16	1 23/32	2 27/32	2 1/2	4 3/32	3 1/4	5 11/32	4 1/32	6 5/8
5/16	1/4	13/32	1	1 21/32	1 25/32	2 29/32	2 17/32	4 3/16	3 5/16	5 7/16	4 1/16	6 11/16
3/8	9/32	15/32	1 1/16	1 23/32	1 13/16	3	2 19/32	4 1/4	3 11/32	5 1/2	4 1/8	6 25/32
7/16	11/32	9/16	1 3/32	1 13/16	1 7/8	3 1/16	2 5/8	4 11/32	3 13/32	5 19/32	4 5/32	6 27/32
1/2	3/8	5/8	1 5/32	1 7/8	1 29/32	3 5/32	2 11/16	4 13/32	3 7/16	5 21/32	4 7/32	6 15/16
9/16	7/16	23/32	1 3/16	1 31/32	1 31/32	3 7/32	2 23/32	4 1/2	3 1/2	5 3/4	4 1/4	7
5/8	15/32	25/32	1 1/4	2 1/32	2	3 5/16	2 25/32	4 9/16	3 17/32	5 13/16	4 5/16	7 3/32
11/16	17/32	7/8	1 9/32	2 1/8	2 1/16	3 3/8	2 13/16	4 21/32	3 19/32	5 29/32	4 11/32	7 5/32
3/4	9/16	15/16	1 11/32	2 7/32	2 3/32	3 15/32	2 7/8	4 23/32	3 5/8	5 31/32	4 13/32	7 1/4
13/16	5/8	1 11/32	1 3/8	2 9/32	2 5/32	3 17/32	2 29/32	4 13/16	3 11/16	6 1/16	4 7/16	7 5/16
7/8	21/32	1 13/32	1 13/32	2 3/8	2 3/16	3 5/8	2 31/32	4 7/8	3 23/32	6 1/8	4 1/2	7 13/32
15/16	23/32	1 13/16	1 15/32	2 7/16	2 1/4	3 11/16	3	4 31/32	3 25/32	6 7/32	4 17/32	7 15/32

Inches	6" Rise	6" Slope	7" Rise	7" Slope	8" Rise	8" Slope	9" Rise	9" Slope	10" Rise	10" Slope	11" Rise	11" Slope
0	4 19/32	7 9/16	5 3/8	8 13/16	6 1/8	10 1/16	6 7/8	11 11/32	7 21/32	1-0 19/32	8 3/16	1-1 27/32
1/16	4 21/32	7 5/8	5 13/32	8 29/32	6 3/16	10 5/32	6 15/16	11 13/32	7 23/32	1-0 11/16	8 15/32	1-1 15/32
1/8	4 11/16	7 23/32	5 15/32	8 31/32	6 7/32	10 7/32	7	11 1/2	7 3/4	1-0 3/4	8 17/32	1-2
3/16	4 3/4	7 25/32	5 1/2	9 1/16	6 9/32	10 5/16	7 1/32	11 9/16	7 13/16	1-0 27/32	8 9/16	1-2 3/32
1/4	4 25/32	7 7/8	5 9/16	9 1/8	6 5/16	10 3/8	7 3/32	11 21/32	7 27/32	1-0 29/32	8 5/8	1-2 5/32
5/16	4 27/32	7 15/16	5 19/32	9 7/32	6 3/8	10 15/32	7 1/8	11 23/32	7 29/32	1-1	8 21/32	1-2 1/4
3/8	4 7/8	8 1/32	5 21/32	9 9/32	6 13/32	10 9/16	7 3/16	11 13/16	7 15/16	1-1 1/16	8 23/32	1-2 5/16
7/16	4 15/16	8 3/32	5 11/16	9 3/8	6 15/32	10 5/8	7 1/4	11 7/8	8	1-1 5/32	8 3/4	1-2 13/32
1/2	4 31/32	8 3/16	5 3/4	9 7/16	6 1/2	10 23/32	7 9/32	11 31/32	8 1/16	1-1 7/32	8 13/16	1-2 15/32
9/16	5 1/32	8 1/4	5 25/32	9 17/32	6 9/16	10 25/32	7 5/16	1-0 1/32	8 3/32	1-1 5/16	8 27/32	1-2 9/16
5/8	5 1/16	8 11/32	5 27/32	9 19/32	6 19/32	10 7/8	7 3/8	1-0 1/8	8 1/8	1-1 3/8	8 29/32	1-2 21/32
11/16	5 1/8	8 7/16	5 7/8	9 11/16	6 21/32	10 15/16	7 13/32	1-0 3/16	8 3/16	1-1 15/32	8 15/16	1-2 23/32
3/4	5 5/32	8 1/2	5 15/16	9 3/4	6 11/16	11 1/32	7 15/32	1-0 9/32	8 7/32	1-1 17/32	9	1-2 13/16
13/16	5 7/32	8 19/32	5 31/32	9 27/32	6 3/4	11 3/32	7 1/2	1-0 11/32	8 9/32	1-1 5/8	9 1/32	1-2 7/8
7/8	5 1/4	8 21/32	6 1/32	9 29/32	6 25/32	11 3/16	7 9/16	1-0 7/16	8 5/16	1-1 11/16	9 3/32	1-2 31/32
15/16	5 5/16	8 3/4	6 1/16	10	6 27/32	11 1/4	7 19/32	1-0 17/32	8 3/8	1-1 25/32	9 1/8	1-3 1/32

Feet	0' Rise	0' Slope	10' Rise	10' Slope	20' Rise	20' Slope	30' Rise	30' Slope
0	0	0	7-7 7/8	12-7 1/8	15-3 3/4	25-2 1/4	22-11 5/8	37-9 13/32
1	-9 3/16	1-3 1/8	8-5 1/16	13-10 1/4	16-0 15/16	26-5 3/8	23-8 13/16	39-0 1/2
2	1-6 3/8	2-6 7/8	9-2 1/4	15-1 11/32	16-10 1/8	27-8 1/2	24-6	40-3 5/8
3	2-3 9/16	3-9 11/32	9-11 7/16	16-4 15/32	17-7 5/16	28-11 19/32	25-3 3/16	41-6 3/4
4	3-0 3/4	5-0 1/16	10-8 5/8	17-7 19/32	18-4 1/2	30-2 23/32	26-0 3/8	42-9 27/32
5	3-9 15/16	6-3 9/16	11-5 13/16	18-10 11/16	19-1 11/16	31-5 27/32	26-9 9/16	44-0 31/32
6	4-7 1/8	7-6 11/16	12-3	20-1 13/16	19-10 7/8	32-8 15/16	27-6 3/4	45-4 1/16
7	5-4 5/16	8-9 25/32	13-0 3/16	21-4 15/16	20-8 1/16	34-0 1/16	28-3 15/16	46-7 3/16
8	6-1 1/2	10-0 29/32	13-9 3/8	22-8 1/32	21-5 1/4	35-3 3/32	29-1 1/8	47-10 5/16
9	6-10 11/16	11-4 1/32	14-6 9/16	23-11 5/32	22-2 7/16	36-6 9/32	29-10 5/16	49-1 13/32

A = 37° 26′ 19″; log sin A = 9.78384; log cos A = 9.89982; log tan A = 9.88402; log cot A = 0.11598

Ins.	12″ Rise	12″ Slope	13″ Rise	13″ Slope	14″ Rise	14″ Slope	15″ Rise	15″ Slope	16″ Rise	16″ Slope
0	9 3/16	1-3 1/8	9 15/16	1-4 3/8	10 23/32	1-5 5/8	11 1/2	1-6 29/32	1-0 1/4	1-8 5/32
1/16	9 1/4	1-3 3/16	10	1-4 7/16	10 25/32	1-5 23/32	11 17/32	1-6 31/32	1-0 3/8	1-8 7/32
1/8	9 9/32	1-3 9/32	10 1/16	1-4 17/32	10 13/16	1-5 25/32	11 19/32	1-7 1/16	1-0 11/32	1-8 5/16
3/16	9 11/32	1-3 11/32	10 3/32	1-4 19/32	10 7/8	1-5 7/8	11 5/8	1-7 1/8	1-0 13/32	1-8 3/8
1/4	9 3/8	1-3 7/16	10 5/32	1-4 11/16	10 29/32	1-5 15/16	11 11/16	1-7 22/32	1-0 7/16	1-8 15/32
5/16	9 7/16	1-3 1/2	10 3/16	1-4 25/32	10 31/32	1-6 1/32	11 23/32	1-7 9/32	1-0 1/2	1-8 17/32
3/8	9 15/32	1-3 19/32	10 1/4	1-4 27/32	11	1-6 3/32	11 25/32	1-7 3/8	1-0 17/32	1-8 5/8
7/16	9 17/32	1-3 21/32	10 9/32	1-4 15/16	11 1/16	1-6 3/32	11 13/16	1-7 7/16	1-0 19/32	1-8 11/16
1/2	9 9/16	1-3 3/4	10 11/32	1-5	11 1/8	1-6 1/4	11 7/8	1-7 17/32	1-0 5/8	1-8 25/32
9/16	9 5/8	1-3 13/16	10 3/8	1-5 5/32	11 5/32	1-6 11/32	11 29/32	1-7 19/32	1-0 11/16	1-8 7/8
5/8	9 21/32	1-3 29/32	10 7/16	1-5 5/32	11 3/16	1-6 13/32	11 31/32	1-7 11/16	1-0 23/32	1-8 15/16
11/16	9 23/32	1-3 31/32	10 15/32	1-5 1/4	11 1/4	1-6 1/2	1-0	1-7 3/4	1-0 25/32	1-9 1/32
3/4	9 3/4	1-4 1/16	10 17/32	1-5 5/16	11 9/32	1-6 9/32	1-0 1/16	1-7 27/32	1-0 13/16	1-9 3/32
13/16	9 13/16	1-4 1/8	10 9/16	1-5 13/32	11 11/32	1-6 21/32	1-0 3/32	1-7 29/32	1-0 7/8	1-9 3/16
7/8	9 27/32	1-4 7/32	10 5/8	1-5 15/32	11 3/8	1-6 23/32	1-0 5/32	1-8	1-0 29/32	1-9 1/4
15/16	9 29/32	1-4 9/32	10 21/32	1-5 9/16	11 7/16	1-6 13/16	1-0 3/16	1-8 1/16	1-0 31/32	1-9 11/32

Ins.	17″ Rise	17″ Slope	18″ Rise	18″ Slope	19″ Rise	19″ Slope	20″ Rise	20″ Slope	21″ Rise	21″ Slope
0	1-1	1-9 13/32	1-1 25/32	1-10 21/32	1-2 9/16	1-11 15/16	1-3 5/32	2-1 3/16	1-4 1/16	2-2 7/16
1/16	1-1 1/16	1-9 1/32	1-1 27/32	1-10 3/4	1-2 19/32	2-0	1-3 3/8	2-1 9/32	1-4 1/8	2-2 17/32
1/8	1-1 1/8	1-9 9/16	1-1 7/8	1-10 13/16	1-2 21/32	2-0 3/32	1-3 13/32	2-1 11/32	1-4 7/32	2-2 19/32
3/16	1-1 5/32	1-9 21/32	1-1 15/16	1-10 29/32	1-2 11/16	2-0 5/32	1-3 15/32	2-1 7/16	1-4 7/32	2-2 11/16
1/4	1-1 7/32	1-9 23/32	1-1 31/32	1-11	1-2 3/4	2-0 1/4	1-3 1/2	2-1 1/2	1-4 9/32	2-2 3/4
5/16	1-1 1/4	1-9 13/16	1-2 1/32	1-11 1/16	1-2 25/32	2-0 5/16	1-3 9/16	2-1 19/32	1-4 5/32	2-2 27/32
3/8	1-1 5/16	1-9 7/8	1-2 1/16	1-11 5/32	1-2 27/32	2-0 13/32	1-3 19/32	2-1 21/32	1-4 3/8	2-2 29/32
7/16	1-1 11/32	1-9 31/32	1-2 1/8	1-11 7/32	1-2 7/8	2-0 15/32	1-3 21/32	2-1 3/4	1-4 13/32	2-3
1/2	1-1 13/32	1-10 1/32	1-2 5/32	1-11 5/16	1-2 15/16	2-0 9/16	1-3 11/16	2-1 13/16	1-4 15/32	2-3 1/16
9/16	1-1 17/32	1-10 5/32	1-2 5/32	1-11 3/8	1-2 31/32	2-0 5/8	1-3 3/4	2-1 29/32	1-4 1/2	2-3 5/32
5/8	1-1 1/2	1-10 3/32	1-2 1/4	1-11 15/16	1-3 1/32	2-0 23/32	1-3 25/32	2-1 31/32	1-4 9/16	2-3 1/4
11/16	1-1 17/32	1-10 9/32	1-2 5/16	1-11 17/32	1-3 1/16	2-0 25/32	1-3 27/32	2-2 1/16	1-4 19/32	2-3 5/16
3/4	1-1 19/32	1-10 11/32	1-2 11/32	1-11 5/8	1-3 1/8	2-0 7/8	1-3 7/8	2-2 1/8	1-4 21/32	2-3 13/32
13/16	1-1 5/8	1-10 7/16	1-2 13/32	1-11 11/16	1-3 1/8	2-0 15/16	1-3 15/16	2-2 7/32	1-4 11/16	2-3 15/32
7/8	1-1 11/16	1-10 1/2	1-2 7/16	1-11 25/32	1-3 7/32	2-1 1/32	1-3 31/32	2-2 9/32	1-4 3/4	2-3 9/16
15/16	1-1 23/32	1-10 19/32	1-2 1/2	1-11 27/32	1-3 1/4	2-1 1/8	1-4 1/32	2-2 3/8	1-4 25/32	2-3 5/8

Feet	40′ Rise	40′ Slope	50′ Rise	50′ Slope	60′ Rise	60′ Slope	70′ Rise	70′ Slope
0	30-7 1/2	50-4 17/32	38-3 3/8	62-11 21/32	45-11 1/4	75-6 25/32	53-7 1/8	88-1 15/16
1	31-4 11/16	51-7 21/32	39-0 9/16	64-2 25/32	46-8 7/16	76-9 29/32	54-4 5/16	89-5 1/32
2	32-1 7/8	52-10 3/4	39-9 3/4	65-5 7/8	47-5 5/8	78-1 1/32	55-1 1/2	90-8 5/32
3	32-11 11/16	54-1 7/8	40-6 15/16	66-9	48-2 13/16	79-4 1/8	55-10 11/16	91-11 9/32
4	33-8 1/4	55-4 31/32	41-4 1/8	68-0 1/8	49-0	80-7 1/4	56-7 7/8	93-2 3/8
5	34-5 7/16	56-8 5/32	42-1 5/16	69-3 7/32	49-9 3/16	81-10 3/8	57-5 1/16	94-5 1/2
6	35-2 5/8	57-11 1/32	42-10 1/2	70-6 5/32	50-6 3/8	83-1 15/32	58-2 1/4	95-8 9/32
7	35-11 13/16	59-2 5/16	43-7 11/16	71-9 5/32	51-3 9/16	84-4 19/32	58-11 7/16	96-11 23/32
8	36-9	60-5 7/16	44-4 7/8	73-0 9/16	52-0 3/4	85-7 11/16	59-8 5/8	98-2 27/32
9	37-6 3/16	61-8 9/16	45-2 1/16	74-3 11/32	52-9 15/16	86-10 13/16	60-5 13/16	99-5 15/16

natsin A=0.6079105026;   natcos A=0.7940055545;   nattan A=0.7656250000;   natcot A=1.3061224489

Inches	0" Rise	0" Slope	1" Rise	1" Slope	2" Rise	2" Slope	3" Rise	3" Slope	4" Rise	4" Slope	5" Rise	5" Slope
0	0	0	25/32	1 1/4	1 17/32	2 17/32	2 5/16	3 25/32	3 3/32	5 1/16	3 27/32	6 5/16
1/16	1/16	3/32	13/16	1 11/32	1 19/32	2 19/32	2 3/8	3 7/8	3 1/8	5 1/8	3 29/32	6 13/32
1/8	3/32	5/32	7/8	1 13/32	1 5/8	2 11/16	2 13/32	3 15/16	3 3/16	5 7/32	3 15/16	6 15/32
3/16	5/32	1/4	29/32	1 1/2	1 11/16	2 3/4	2 15/32	4 1/32	3 7/32	5 9/32	4	6 9/16
1/4	3/16	5/16	31/32	1 19/32	1 3/4	2 27/32	2 1/2	4 3/32	3 9/32	5 3/8	4 1/16	6 5/8
5/16	1/4	13/32	1	1 21/32	1 25/32	2 29/32	2 9/16	4 3/16	3 5/16	5 7/16	4 3/32	6 23/32
3/8	9/32	15/32	1 1/16	1 3/4	1 27/32	3	2 19/32	4 1/4	3 3/8	5 17/32	4 5/32	6 25/32
7/16	11/32	9/16	1 3/32	1 13/16	1 7/8	3 1/16	2 21/32	4 11/32	3 13/32	5 19/32	4 3/16	6 7/8
1/2	3/8	5/8	1 5/32	1 29/32	1 15/16	3 5/32	2 11/16	4 13/32	3 15/32	5 11/16	4 1/4	6 15/16
9/16	7/16	23/32	1 7/32	1 31/32	1 31/32	3 1/4	2 3/4	4 1/2	3 17/32	5 3/4	4 9/32	7 1/32
5/8	15/32	25/32	1 1/4	2 1/16	2 1/32	3 5/16	2 25/32	4 9/16	3 9/16	5 27/32	4 11/32	7 3/32
11/16	17/32	7/8	1 9/32	2 1/8	2 1/16	3 13/32	2 27/32	4 21/32	3 5/8	5 29/32	4 3/8	7 3/16
3/4	9/16	15/16	1 11/32	2 7/32	2 1/8	3 15/32	2 7/8	4 3/4	3 21/32	6	4 7/16	7 1/4
13/16	5/8	1 1/32	1 13/32	2 9/32	2 5/32	3 9/16	2 15/16	4 13/16	3 23/32	6 1/16	4 15/32	7 11/32
7/8	11/16	1 3/32	1 7/16	2 3/8	2 7/32	3 5/8	3	4 29/32	3 3/4	6 5/32	4 17/32	7 13/32
15/16	23/32	1 3/16	1 1/2	2 7/16	2 1/4	3 23/32	3 1/32	4 31/32	3 13/16	6 7/32	4 9/16	7 1/2

Inches	6" Rise	6" Slope	7" Rise	7" Slope	8" Rise	8" Slope	9" Rise	9" Slope	10" Rise	10" Slope	11" Rise	11" Slope
0	4 5/8	7 9/16	5 13/32	8 27/32	6 5/32	10 3/32	6 15/16	11 3/8	7 23/32	1-0 5/8	8 15/32	1-1 1/8
1/16	4 11/16	7 21/32	5 7/16	8 29/32	6 7/32	10 3/16	7	11 7/16	7 3/4	1-0 23/32	8 17/32	1-1 31/32
1/8	4 23/32	7 23/32	5 1/2	9	6 1/4	10 1/4	7 1/32	11 17/32	7 13/16	1-0 25/32	8 9/16	1-2 1/32
3/16	4 25/32	7 13/16	5 17/32	9 1/16	6 5/16	10 11/32	7 3/32	11 19/32	7 27/32	1-0 7/8	8 5/8	1-2 1/8
1/4	4 13/16	7 29/32	5 19/32	9 5/32	6 3/8	10 13/32	7 1/8	11 11/16	7 29/32	1-0 15/16	8 11/16	1-2 7/32
5/16	4 7/8	7 31/32	5 5/8	9 7/32	6 13/32	10 1/2	7 3/16	11 3/4	7 15/16	1-1 1/32	8 23/32	1-2 9/32
3/8	4 29/32	8 1/16	5 11/16	9 5/16	6 15/32	10 9/16	7 1/4	11 27/32	8	1-1 3/32	8 25/32	1-2 3/8
7/16	4 31/32	8 1/8	5 23/32	9 13/32	6 1/2	10 21/32	7 9/32	11 29/32	8 1/16	1-1 3/16	8 13/16	1-2 7/16
1/2	5	8 7/32	5 25/32	9 15/32	6 9/16	10 23/32	7 5/16	1-0	8 3/32	1-1 1/4	8 7/8	1-2 17/32
9/16	5 1/16	8 9/32	5 27/32	9 9/16	6 19/32	10 13/16	7 3/8	1-0 1/16	8 5/32	1-1 11/32	8 29/32	1-2 19/32
5/8	5 3/32	8 3/8	5 7/8	9 5/8	6 21/32	10 7/8	7 13/32	1-0 5/32	8 3/16	1-1 13/32	8 31/32	1-2 11/16
11/16	5 5/32	8 7/16	5 15/16	9 23/32	6 11/16	10 31/32	7 15/32	1-0 7/32	8 1/4	1-1 1/2	9	1-2 3/4
3/4	5 3/16	8 17/32	5 31/32	9 25/32	6 3/4	11 1/16	7 1/2	1-0 5/16	8 9/32	1-1 9/16	9 1/16	1-2 27/32
13/16	5 1/4	8 19/32	6 1/32	9 7/8	6 25/32	11 1/8	7 9/16	1-0 3/8	8 11/32	1-1 21/32	9 3/32	1-2 29/32
7/8	5 5/16	8 11/16	6 1/16	9 15/16	6 27/32	11 7/32	7 5/8	1-0 15/32	8 3/8	1-1 23/32	9 5/32	1-3
15/16	5 11/32	8 3/4	6 1/8	10 1/32	6 7/8	11 9/32	7 21/32	1-0 9/16	8 7/16	1-1 13/16	9 3/16	1-3 1/16

Feet	0' Rise	0' Slope	10' Rise	10' Slope	20' Rise	20' Slope	30' Rise	30' Slope
0	0	0	7-8 1/2	12-7 1/2	15-5	25-3 1/2	23-1 1/2	37-10 17/32
1	-9 1/4	1-3 5/32	8-5 3/4	13-10 21/32	16-2 1/4	26-6 3/16	23-10 3/4	39-1 11/16
2	1-6 1/2	2-6 5/16	9-3	15-1 13/16	16-11 1/2	27-9 11/32	24-8	40-4 27/32
3	2-3 3/4	3-9 15/32	10-0 1/4	16-4 31/32	17-8 3/4	29-0 15/32	25-5 1/4	41-8
4	3-1	5-0 19/32	10-9 1/2	17-8 1/8	18-6	30-3 5/8	26-2 1/2	42-11 5/32
5	3-10 1/4	6-3 3/4	11-6 3/4	18-11 9/32	19-3 1/4	31-6 25/32	26-11 3/4	44-2 9/32
6	4-7 1/2	7-6 29/32	12-4	20-2 13/32	20-0 1/2	32-9 15/16	27-9	45-5 7/16
7	5-4 3/4	8-10 1/16	13-1 1/4	21-5 9/16	20-9 3/4	34-1 3/32	28-6 1/4	46-8 19/32
8	6-2	10-1 7/32	13-10 1/2	22-8 23/32	21-7	35-4 1/4	29-3 1/2	47-11 3/4
9	6-11 1/4	11-4 3/8	14-7 3/4	23-11 7/8	22-4 1/4	36-7 3/8	30-0 3/4	49-2 29/32

A = 37° 37' 34"; logsin A = 9.78569; logcos A = 9.89873; logtan A = 9.88696; logcot A = 0.11304

Ins.	12″ Rise	Slope	13″ Rise	Slope	14″ Rise	Slope	15″ Rise	Slope	16″ Rise	Slope
0	9¼	1-35/32	10½	1-413/32	10 25/32	1-511/16	11 9/16	1-615/16	1-011/32	1-83/16
1/16	95/16	1-37/32	101/16	1-41/2	10 27/32	1-53/4	115/8	1-71/32	1-03/8	1-89/32
1/8	911/32	1-35/16	101/8	1-49/32	107/8	1-527/32	11 21/32	1-73/32	1-07/16	1-83/8
3/16	913/32	1-33/8	105/32	1-421/32	10 15/16	1-529/32	11 23/32	1-73/16	1-015/16	1-87/16
1/4	97/16	1-315/32	107/32	1-423/32	11	1-6	113/4	1-71/4	1-017/32	1-817/32
5/16	9½	1-317/32	101/4	1-413/16	111/2	1-61/16	11 13/16	1-711/32	1-09/16	1-819/32
3/8	917/32	1-35/8	105/16	1-47/8	113/32	1-65/32	11 27/32	1-713/32	1-05/8	1-811/16
7/16	919/32	1-323/32	1011/32	1-431/32	111/8	1-67/32	11 29/32	1-71/2	1-021/32	1-83/4
1/2	95/8	1-325/32	1013/32	1-51/32	113/32	1-65/16	11 15/16	1-79/16	1-023/32	1-827/32
9/16	911/16	1-37/8	1015/32	1-51/8	117/32	1-63/8	1-0	1-721/32	1-025/32	1-829/32
5/8	923/32	1-315/16	101/2	1-53/16	119/32	1-615/32	1-01/32	1-723/32	1-013/16	1-9
11/16	925/32	1-41/32	109/16	1-59/32	115/16	1-617/32	1-03/32	1-713/16	1-07/8	1-91/16
3/4	913/16	1-43/32	1019/32	1-53/8	113/8	1-65/8	1-01/8	1-77/8	1-029/32	1-95/32
13/16	97/8	1-43/16	1021/32	1-57/16	11 13/32	1-611/16	1-03/16	1-731/32	1-031/32	1-97/32
7/8	915/16	1-41/4	1011/16	1-517/32	11 15/32	1-625/32	1-01/4	1-81/32	1-1	1-95/16
15/16	931/32	1-411/32	103/4	1-519/32	111/2	1-67/8	1-09/32	1-81/8	1-11/16	1-93/8

Ins.	17″ Rise	Slope	18″ Rise	Slope	19″ Rise	Slope	20″ Rise	Slope	21″ Rise	Slope
0	1-13/32	1-915/32	1-17/8	1-1023/32	1-221/32	2-0	1-313/32	2-11/4	1-43/32	2-21/2
1/16	1-15/32	1-917/32	1-115/16	1-1013/16	1-211/16	2-01/16	1-315/32	2-111/32	1-41/4	2-219/32
1/8	1-13/16	1-95/8	1-131/32	1-107/8	1-23/4	2-05/32	1-31/2	2-113/32	1-49/32	2-211/16
3/16	1-11/4	1-911/16	1-21/32	1-1031/32	1-225/32	2-07/32	1-39/16	2-11/2	1-411/32	2-23/4
1/4	1-15/16	1-925/32	1-21/16	1-111/32	1-227/32	2-05/16	1-35/8	2-19/16	1-43/8	2-227/32
5/16	1-111/32	1-927/32	1-23/32	1-111/8	1-27/8	2-03/8	1-321/32	2-121/32	1-47/16	2-229/32
3/8	1-113/32	1-915/16	1-25/32	1-113/16	1-215/16	2-015/32	1-323/32	2-123/32	1-415/32	2-3
7/16	1-17/16	1-101/32	1-27/32	1-119/32	1-231/32	2-017/32	1-33/4	2-113/16	1-417/32	2-31/16
1/2	1-11/2	1-103/32	1-21/4	1-1111/32	1-31/32	2-05/8	1-313/16	2-17/8	1-49/16	2-35/32
9/16	1-117/32	1-103/16	1-25/16	1-1111/16	1-33/32	2-011/16	1-327/32	2-131/32	1-45/8	2-37/32
5/8	1-119/32	1-101/4	1-211/32	1-1117/32	1-31/8	2-025/32	1-329/32	2-21/32	1-421/32	2-35/16
11/16	1-15/8	1-1011/32	1-213/32	1-1119/32	1-33/16	2-027/32	1-315/16	2-21/8	1-423/32	2-33/8
3/4	1-111/16	1-1013/32	1-27/16	1-1111/16	1-37/32	2-015/16	1-4	2-23/16	1-43/4	2-315/32
13/16	1-123/32	1-101/2	1-21/2	1-113/4	1-39/32	2-1	1-43/32	2-29/32	1-413/16	2-317/32
7/8	1-125/32	1-109/16	1-29/16	1-1127/32	1-311/32	2-13/32	1-43/32	2-211/32	1-47/8	2-35/8
15/16	1-113/16	1-1021/32	1-219/32	1-1129/32	1-33/8	2-13/16	1-41/8	2-27/32	1-429/32	2-311/16

Feet	40′ Rise	Slope	50′ Rise	Slope	60′ Rise	Slope	70′ Rise	Slope
0	30-10	50-61/16	38-61/2	63-19/16	46-3	75-93/32	53-111/2	88-419/32
1	31-71/4	51-97/32	39-33/4	64-423/32	47-01/4	77-07/32	54-83/4	89-73/4
2	32-41/2	53-011/32	40-1	65-77/8	47-91/2	78-33/8	55-6	90-1029/32
3	33-13/4	54-31/2	40-101/4	66-1111/32	48-63/4	79-617/32	56-31/4	92-21/32
4	33-11	55-621/32	41-71/2	68-25/32	49-4	80-911/16	57-01/2	93-53/16
5	34-81/4	56-913/16	42-43/4	69-55/16	50-11/4	82-027/32	57-93/4	94-811/32
6	35-51/2	58-03/32	43-2	70-815/32	50-101/2	83-4	58-7	95-111/2
7	36-23/4	59-41/8	43-111/4	71-115/8	51-73/4	84-71/4	59-41/4	97-221/32
8	37-0	60-71/4	44-81/2	73-225/32	52-5	85-103/8	60-11/2	98-513/16
9	37-91/4	61-1013/32	45-53/4	74-515/16	53-21/4	87-11/16	60-103/4	99-831/32

natsin A=0.6105078603; natcos A=0.7920101972; nattan A=0.7708333333; natcot A=1.2972972972

Inches	0" Rise	0" Slope	1" Rise	1" Slope	2" Rise	2" Slope	3" Rise	3" Slope	4" Rise	4" Slope	5" Rise	5" Slope
0	0	0	25/32	19/32	1 9/16	2 17/32	2 5/16	3 13/16	3 3/32	5 1/16	3 1/8	6 11/32−
1/16	1/16	3/32	13/16	1 11/32	1 19/32	2 5/8	2 3/8	3 7/8	3 5/32	5 5/32	3 15/16	6 13/32
1/8	3/32	5/32	7/8	1 7/16	1 21/32	2 11/16	2 7/16	3 31/32	3 3/16	5 7/32	3 31/32	6 1/2
3/16	5/32	1/4	29/32	1 1/2	1 11/16	2 25/32	2 15/32	4 1/32	3 1/4	5 9/16	4 1/32−	6 9/16
1/4	3/16	5/16	31/32	1 19/32	1 3/4	2 27/32	2 17/32	4 1/8	3 5/16	5 3/8	4 1/16	6 21/32
5/16	1/4	13/32	1 1/32	1 21/32	1 25/32	2 15/16	2 9/16	4 3/16	3 11/32	5 15/32−	4 1/8	6 23/32
3/8	9/32	15/32	1 1/16	1 3/4	1 27/32	3	2 5/8	4 9/32−	3 13/32	5 17/32	4 5/32	6 13/32
7/16	11/32	9/16	1 1/8	1 13/16	1 29/32	3 3/32−	2 21/32	4 11/32	3 7/16	5 5/8	4 7/32	6 7/8
1/2	3/8	5/8	1 5/32	1 29/32	2	3 5/32	2 23/32−	4 7/32	3 1/2	5 11/16	4 9/32	6 31/32−
9/16	7/16	23/32	1 7/32	1 31/32	2	3 1/4	2 3/4	4 1/2	3 17/32	5 25/32−	4 5/16	7 1/32
5/8	1/2	25/32	1 1/4	2 1/16	2 1/32	3 5/16	2 13/16	4 19/32−	3 19/32	5 27/32	4 3/8	7 1/8
11/16	17/32	7/8	1 5/16	2 1/8	2 3/32	3 13/32	2 7/8	4 21/32	3 5/8	5 15/16	4 13/32	7 3/16
3/4	19/32	15/16	1 11/32	2 7/32−	2 1/8	3 15/32	2 29/32	4 3/4	3 11/16	6	4 15/32	7 9/32
13/16	5/8	1 1/32	1 13/32	2 9/32	2 3/16	3 9/16	2 31/32−	4 13/16	3 3/4	6 3/32	4 1/2	7 11/32
7/8	11/16	1 3/32	1 15/32−	2 3/8	2 1/4	3 5/8	3	4 29/32−	3 25/32	6 5/32	4 9/16	7 7/16
15/16	23/32	1 3/16	1 1/2	2 7/16	2 9/32	3 23/32−	3 1/16	4 31/32	3 27/32	6 1/4	4 19/32	7 17/32−

Inches	6" Rise	6" Slope	7" Rise	7" Slope	8" Rise	8" Slope	9" Rise	9" Slope	10" Rise	10" Slope	11" Rise	11" Slope
0	4 21/32	7 19/32	5 7/16	8 7/8	6 7/32−	10 1/8	7	11 13/32−	7 3/4	1-0 21/32	8 17/32	1-1 15/32
1/16	4 23/32	7 11/16	5 15/32	8 15/16	6 1/4	10 7/32−	7 1/32	11 15/32	7 13/16	1-0 3/4	8 19/32	1-2
1/8	4 3/4	7 3/4	5 17/32	9 1/32	6 5/16	10 9/32−	7 3/32−	11 9/16	7 27/32	1-0 13/16	8 5/8	1-2 3/32−
3/16	4 13/16	7 27/32−	5 9/16	9 3/32	6 11/32	10 3/8	7 1/8	11 5/8	7 29/32	1-0 29/32−	8 11/16	1-2 5/32
1/4	4 27/32	7 29/32−	5 5/8	9 3/16	6 13/32	10 7/16	7 3/16	11 23/32−	7 31/32	1-0 31/32−	8 23/32	1-2 1/4
5/16	4 29/32−	8	5 11/16	9 1/4	6 7/16	10 17/32−	7 7/32	11 25/32	8	1-1 1/16	8 25/32−	1-2 5/16
3/8	4 15/16	8 1/16	5 23/32	9 11/32−	6 1/2	10 19/32−	7 9/32	11 7/8	8 1/16	1-1 1/8	8 13/16	1-2 13/32−
7/16	5	8 5/32−	5 25/32	9 13/32	6 9/16	10 11/16	7 5/16	11 15/16	8 3/32	1-1 7/32−	8 7/8	1-2 15/32
1/2	5 1/32	8 7/32	5 13/16	9 1/2	6 19/32	10 3/4	7 3/8	1-0 1/32−	8 5/32	1-1 9/32	8 15/16	1-2 9/16
9/16	5 3/32−	8 5/16	5 7/8	9 9/16	6 21/32	10 27/32−	7 13/32	1-0 3/32−	8 3/16	1-1 3/8	8 31/32	1-2 5/8
5/8	5 5/32−	8 3/8	5 29/32	9 21/32−	6 11/16	10 29/32−	7 15/32	1-0 3/16	8 1/4	1-1 7/16	9 1/32−	1-2 23/32−
11/16	5 3/16	8 15/32−	5 31/32	9 23/32	6 3/4	11	7 17/32−	1-0 1/4	8 9/32	1-1 17/32−	9 1/16	1-2 25/32
3/4	5 1/4	8 17/32	6	9 13/16	6 25/32	11 1/16	7 9/16	1-0 11/32−	8 11/32−	1-1 19/32	9 1/8	1-2 7/8
13/16	5 9/32	8 5/8	6 1/16	9 7/8	6 27/32	11 5/32−	7 5/8	1-0 13/32−	8 13/32−	1-1 11/16	9 5/32−	1-2 15/16
7/8	5 11/32−	8 11/16	6 1/8	9 31/32−	6 7/8	11 7/32−	7 21/32	1-0 1/2	8 7/16	1-1 3/4	9 7/32−	1-3 1/32−
15/16	5 3/8	8 25/32	6 5/32	10 1/16	6 15/16	11 5/16	7 23/32	1-0 9/16	8 1/2	1-1 27/32−	9 1/4	1-3 1/8

Feet	0' Rise	0' Slope	10' Rise	10' Slope	20' Rise	20' Slope	30' Rise	30' Slope
0	0	0	7-9 1/8	12-7 29/32−	15-6 1/4	25-3 25/32−	23-3 3/8	37-11 11/16
1	-9 5/16	1-3 3/16	8-6 7/16	13-1 15/32−	16-3 9/16	26-6 31/32−	24-0 11/16	39-2 7/8
2	1-6 5/8	2-6 3/8	9-3 3/4	15-2 9/32−	17-0 7/8	27-10 5/32−	24-10	40-6 1/16
3	2-3 15/16	3-9 9/16	10-1 1/16	16-5 15/32−	17-10 3/16	29-1 3/8	25-7 5/16	41-9 1/4
4	3-1 1/4	5-0 3/4	10-10 3/8	17-8 21/32−	18-7 1/2	30-4 9/16	26-4 5/8	43-0 7/16
5	3-10 9/16	6-3 15/16	11-7 11/16	18-11 27/32−	19-4 13/16	31-7 3/4	27-1 15/16	44-3 5/8
6	4-7 7/8	7-7 1/8	12-5	20-3 1/16	20-2 1/8	32-10 15/16	27-11 1/4	45-6 13/16
7	5-5 3/16	8-10 5/16	13-2 5/16	21-6 1/32−	20-11 7/16	34-2 1/8	28-8 9/16	46-10
8	6-2 1/2	10-1 17/32−	13-11 5/8	22-9 13/32−	21-8 3/4	35-5 5/16	29-5 7/8	48-1 7/32−
9	6-11 13/16	11-4 23/32−	14-8 15/16	24-0 19/32−	22-6 1/16	36-8 1/2	30-3 3/16	49-4 13/32−

A = 37° 48′ 47″; logsin A = 9.78752; logcos A = 9.89764; logtan A = 9.88989; logcct A = 0.11011

Ins.	12″ Rise	12″ Slope	13″ Rise	13″ Slope	14″ Rise	14″ Slope	15″ Rise	15″ Slope	16″ Rise	16″ Slope
0	9 5/16	1-3 3/16	10 3/32	1-4 15/32	10 7/8	1-5 23/32	11 5/8	1-7	1-0 13/32	1-8 1/4
1/16	9 3/8	1-3 9/32	10 1/8	1-4 17/32	10 29/32	1-5 13/16	11 11/16	1-7 1/16	1-0 15/32	1-8 11/32
1/8	9 13/32	1-3 11/32	10 3/16	1-4 5/8	10 31/32	1-5 7/8	11 3/4	1-7 5/32	1-0 1/2	1-8 13/32
3/16	9 15/32	1-3 7/16	10 7/32	1-4 11/16	11	1-5 31/32	11 25/32	1-7 1/4	1-0 9/16	1-8 1/2
1/4	9 1/2	1-3 1/2	10 9/32	1-4 25/32	11 1/16	1-6 1/32	11 27/32	1-7 5/16	1-0 5/8	1-8 9/16
5/16	9 9/16	1-3 19/32	10 11/32	1-4 27/32	11 3/32	1-6 1/8	11 7/8	1-7 3/8	1-0 21/32	1-8 21/32
3/8	9 19/32	1-3 21/32	10 3/8	1-4 15/16	11 5/32	1-6 3/16	11 15/16	1-7 15/32	1-0 23/32	1-8 23/32
7/16	9 21/32	1-3 3/4	10 7/16	1-5	11 7/32	1-6 9/32	11 31/32	1-7 17/32	1-0 3/4	1-8 13/16
1/2	9 11/16	1-3 13/16	10 15/32	1-5 3/32	11 1/4	1-6 11/32	1-0 1/32	1-7 5/8	1-0 13/16	1-8 7/8
9/16	9 3/4	1-3 29/32	10 17/32	1-5 5/32	11 5/16	1-6 7/16	1-0 1/16	1-7 11/16	1-0 27/32	1-8 31/32
5/8	9 13/16	1-3 31/32	10 9/16	1-5 1/4	11 11/32	1-6 1/2	1-0 1/8	1-7 25/32	1-0 29/32	1-9 1/32
11/16	9 27/32	1-4 1/16	10 5/8	1-5 5/16	11 13/32	1-6 19/32	1-0 3/16	1-7 27/32	1-0 15/16	1-9 1/8
3/4	9 29/32	1-4 1/8	10 21/32	1-5 13/32	11 7/16	1-6 21/32	1-0 7/32	1-7 15/16	1-1	1-9 3/16
13/16	9 15/16	1-4 7/32	10 23/32	1-5 15/32	11 1/2	1-6 3/4	1-0 9/32	1-8	1-1 1/16	1-9 9/32
7/8	10	1-4 5/16	10 25/32	1-5 9/16	11 17/32	1-6 27/32	1-0 3/8	1-8 3/32	1-1 3/32	1-9 3/8
15/16	10 1/32	1-4 3/8	10 13/16	1-5 21/32	11 19/32	1-6 29/32	1-0 7/16	1-8 3/16	1-1 5/32	1-9 7/16

Ins.	17″ Rise	17″ Slope	18″ Rise	18″ Slope	19″ Rise	19″ Slope	20″ Rise	20″ Slope	21″ Rise	21″ Slope
0	1-1 3/16	1-9 17/32	1-1 31/32	1-10 25/32	1-2 3/4	2-0 1/16	1-3 17/32	2-1 5/16	1-4 5/16	2-2 19/32
1/16	1-1 1/4	1-9 19/32	1-2 1/32	1-10 7/8	1-2 25/32	2-0 1/8	1-3 9/16	2-1 13/32	1-4 11/32	2-2 21/32
1/8	1-1 9/32	1-9 11/16	1-2 1/16	1-10 15/16	1-2 27/32	2-0 7/32	1-3 5/8	2-1 15/32	1-4 13/32	2-2 3/4
3/16	1-1 11/32	1-9 3/4	1-2 1/8	1-11 1/32	1-2 7/8	2-0 9/32	1-3 21/32	2-1 9/16	1-4 7/16	2-2 13/16
1/4	1-1 3/8	1-9 27/32	1-2 5/32	1-11 3/32	1-2 15/16	2-0 3/8	1-3 23/32	2-1 5/8	1-4 1/2	2-2 29/32
5/16	1-1 7/16	1-9 29/32	1-2 7/32	1-11 3/16	1-3	2-0 7/16	1-3 3/4	2-1 23/32	1-4 17/32	2-2 31/32
3/8	1-1 15/32	1-10	1-2 1/4	1-11 1/4	1-3 1/32	2-0 17/32	1-3 13/16	2-1 25/32	1-4 19/32	2-3 1/16
7/16	1-1 17/32	1-10 1/16	1-2 5/16	1-11 11/32	1-3 3/32	2-0 19/32	1-3 7/8	2-1 7/8	1-4 5/8	2-3 1/8
1/2	1-1 19/32	1-10 5/32	1-2 11/32	1-11 13/32	1-3 1/8	2-0 11/16	1-3 29/32	2-1 15/16	1-4 11/16	2-3 7/32
9/16	1-1 5/8	1-10 7/32	1-2 13/32	1-11 1/2	1-3 3/16	2-0 3/4	1-3 31/32	2-2 1/32	1-4 23/32	2-3 9/32
5/8	1-1 11/16	1-10 5/16	1-2 15/32	1-11 9/16	1-3 7/32	2-0 27/32	1-4	2-2 3/32	1-4 25/32	2-3 3/8
11/16	1-1 23/32	1-10 3/8	1-2 1/2	1-11 21/32	1-3 9/32	2-0 29/32	1-4 1/16	2-2 3/16	1-4 27/32	2-3 7/16
3/4	1-1 25/32	1-10 15/32	1-2 9/16	1-11 23/32	1-3 5/16	2-1	1-4 3/32	2-2 1/4	1-4 7/8	2-3 17/32
13/16	1-1 13/16	1-10 9/16	1-2 19/32	1-11 13/16	1-3 3/8	2-1 3/32	1-4 5/32	2-2 11/32	1-4 15/16	2-3 5/8
7/8	1-1 7/8	1-10 5/8	1-2 21/32	1-11 29/32	1-3 7/16	2-1 5/32	1-4 3/16	2-2 7/16	1-4 31/32	2-3 11/16
15/16	1-1 29/32	1-10 23/32	1-2 11/16	1-11 31/32	1-3 15/32	2-1 1/4	1-4 1/4	2-2 1/2	1-5 1/32	2-3 25/32

Feet	40′ Rise	40′ Slope	50′ Rise	50′ Slope	60′ Rise	60′ Slope	70′ Rise	70′ Slope
0	31-0 1/2	50-7 19/32	38-9 5/8	63-3 15/32	46-6 3/4	75-11 3/8	54-3 7/8	88-7 9/32
1	31-9 13/16	51-10 25/32	39-6 15/16	64-6 21/32	47-4 1/16	77-2 9/16	55-1 3/16	89-10 15/32
2	32-7 1/8	53-1 31/32	40-4 1/4	65-9 27/32	48-1 3/8	78-5 3/4	55-10 1/2	91-1 21/32
3	33-4 7/16	54-5 5/32	41-1 9/16	67-1 1/32	48-10 11/16	79-8 15/16	56-7 13/16	92-4 27/32
4	34-1 3/4	55-8 11/32	41-10 7/8	68-4 1/4	49-8	81-0 1/8	57-5 1/8	93-8 1/32
5	34-11 1/16	56-11 17/32	42-8 3/16	69-7 7/16	50-5 5/16	82-3 5/16	58-2 7/16	94-11 7/32
6	35-8 3/8	58-2 23/32	43-5 1/2	70-10 5/8	51-2 5/8	83-6 1/2	58-11 3/4	96-2 13/32
7	36-5 11/16	59-5 29/32	44-2 13/16	72-1 13/16	51-11 15/16	84-9 11/16	59-9 1/16	97-5 19/32
8	37-3	60-9 3/32	45-0 1/8	73-5	52-9 1/4	86-0 7/8	60-6 3/8	98-8 25/32
9	38-0 5/16	62-0 9/32	45-9 7/16	74-8 3/16	53-6 9/16	87-4 3/32	61-3 11/16	99-11 31/32

natsin A=0.6130856686; natcos A=0.7900164320; nattan A=0.7760416666; natcot A=1.2885906040

Inches	0" Rise	0" Slope	1" Rise	1" Slope	2" Rise	2" Slope	3" Rise	3" Slope	4" Rise	4" Slope	5" Rise	5" Slope
0	0	0	25/32	1 9/32	1 9/16	2 17/32	2 11/32	3 13/16	3 1/8	5 1/16	3 29/32	6 11/32
1/16	1/16	3/32	27/32	1 11/32	1 5/8	2 5/8	2 13/32	3 7/8	3 3/16	5 5/32	3 31/32	6 7/16
1/8	3/32	5/32	7/8	1 7/16	1 21/32	2 11/16	2 7/16	3 31/32	3 7/32	5 1/4	4	6 1/2
3/16	5/32	1/4	15/16	1 1/2	1 23/32	2 25/32	2 1/2	4 1/32	3 9/32	5 5/16	4 1/16	6 19/32
1/4	3/16	5/16	31/32	1 19/32	1 3/4	2 27/32	2 17/32	4 1/8	3 5/16	5 13/32	4 3/32	6 21/32
5/16	1/4	13/32	1 1/32	1 21/32	1 13/16	2 15/16	2 19/32	4 7/32	3 3/8	5 15/32	4 5/32	6 3/4
3/8	9/32	15/32	1 1/16	1 3/4	1 27/32	3	2 5/8	4 9/32	3 13/32	5 9/16	4 3/16	6 13/16
7/16	11/32	9/16	1 1/8	1 13/16	1 29/32	3 3/32	2 11/16	4 3/8	3 15/32	5 5/8	4 1/4	6 29/32
1/2	3/8	5/8	1 3/16	1 29/32	1 15/16	3 3/16	2 3/4	4 7/16	3 1/2	5 23/32	4 5/16	6 31/32
9/16	7/16	23/32	1 7/32	1 31/32	2	3 1/4	2 25/32	4 17/32	3 9/16	5 25/32	4 11/32	7 1/16
5/8	1/2	25/32	1 9/32	2 1/16	2 1/16	3 11/32	2 27/32	4 19/32	3 5/8	5 7/8	4 13/32	7 1/8
11/16	17/32	7/8	1 5/16	2 5/32	2 3/32	3 13/32	2 7/8	4 11/16	3 21/32	5 15/16	4 7/16	7 7/32
3/4	19/32	15/16	1 3/8	2 7/32	2 5/32	3 1/2	2 15/16	4 3/4	3 23/32	6 1/32	4 1/2	7 9/32
13/16	5/8	1 1/32	1 13/32	2 5/16	2 3/16	3 9/16	2 31/32	4 27/32	3 3/4	6 3/32	4 17/32	7 3/8
7/8	11/16	1 1/8	1 15/32	2 3/8	2 1/4	3 21/32	3 1/32	4 29/32	3 13/16	6 3/16	4 19/32	7 15/32
15/16	23/32	1 3/16	1 1/2	2 15/32	2 9/32	3 23/32	3 1/16	5	3 27/32	6 9/32	4 5/8	7 17/32

Inches	6" Rise	6" Slope	7" Rise	7" Slope	8" Rise	8" Slope	9" Rise	9" Slope	10" Rise	10" Slope	11" Rise	11" Slope
0	4 11/16	7 5/8	5 15/32	8 7/8	6 1/4	10 5/32	7 1/32	11 13/32	7 13/16	1-0 11/16	8 19/32	1-3 31/32
1/16	4 3/4	7 11/16	5 17/32	8 31/32	6 5/16	10 7/32	7 3/32	11 1/2	7 7/8	1-0 25/32	8 21/32	1-2 1/32
1/8	4 25/32	7 25/32	5 9/16	9 1/32	6 11/32	10 5/16	7 1/8	11 19/32	7 29/32	1-0 27/32	8 11/16	1-2 1/8
3/16	4 27/32	7 27/32	5 5/8	9 1/8	6 13/32	10 3/8	7 3/16	11 21/32	7 31/32	1-0 15/16	8 3/4	1-2 3/16
1/4	4 7/8	7 15/16	5 21/32	9 3/8	6 7/16	10 15/32	7 7/32	11 3/4	8	1-1	8 25/32	1-2 9/32
5/16	4 15/16	8	5 23/32	9 9/32	6 1/2	10 9/16	7 9/32	11 13/16	8 1/16	1-1 3/32	8 27/32	1-2 11/32
3/8	4 31/32	8 3/32	5 3/4	9 11/32	6 17/32	10 5/8	7 5/16	11 29/32	8 3/32	1-1 5/32	8 7/8	1-2 7/16
7/16	5 1/32	8 5/32	5 13/16	9 7/16	6 19/32	10 23/32	7 3/8	11 31/32	8 5/32	1-1 1/4	8 15/16	1-2 1/2
1/2	5 1/16	8 1/4	5 7/8	9 17/32	6 5/8	10 25/32	7 7/16	1-0 1/16	8 3/16	1-1 5/16	9	1-2 19/32
9/16	5 1/8	8 5/16	5 29/32	9 19/32	6 11/16	10 7/8	7 15/32	1-0 1/8	8 1/4	1-1 13/32	9 1/32	1-2 11/16
5/8	5 3/16	8 13/32	5 31/32	9 11/16	6 3/4	10 15/16	7 17/32	1-0 7/32	8 5/16	1-1 15/32	9 3/32	1-2 3/4
11/16	5 7/32	8 1/2	6	9 3/4	6 25/32	11 1/32	7 9/16	1-0 9/32	8 11/32	1-1 9/16	9 1/8	1-2 27/32
3/4	5 9/32	8 9/16	6 1/16	9 27/32	6 27/32	11 3/32	7 5/8	1-0 3/8	8 13/32	1-1 21/32	9 3/16	1-2 29/32
13/16	5 5/16	8 21/32	6 5/32	9 29/32	6 7/8	11 3/16	7 21/32	1-0 7/16	8 7/16	1-1 23/32	9 7/32	1-3
7/8	5 3/8	8 23/32	6 5/32	10	6 15/16	11 1/4	7 23/32	1-0 17/32	8 1/2	1-1 13/16	9 9/32	1-3 1/16
15/16	5 13/32	8 13/16	6 3/4	10 1/16	6 31/32	11 11/32	7 3/4	1-0 19/32	8 17/32	1-1 7/8	9 5/16	1-3 5/32

Feet	0' Rise	0' Slope	10' Rise	10' Slope	20' Rise	20' Slope	30' Rise	30' Slope
0	0	0	7-9 3/4	12-8 9/32	15-7 1/2	25-4 9/16	23-5 1/4	38-0 27/32
1	-9 3/8	1-3 7/32	8-7 1/8	13-11 1/2	16-4 7/8	26-7 25/32	24-2 5/8	39-4 1/16
2	1-6 3/4	2-6 15/32	9-4 1/2	15-2 3/4	17-2 1/4	27-11	25-0	40-7 9/32
3	2-4 1/8	3-9 11/16	10-1 7/8	16-5 31/32	17-11 5/8	29-2 1/4	25-9 3/8	41-10 17/32
4	3-1 1/2	5-0 29/32	10-11 1/4	17-9 3/16	18-9	30-5 15/32	26-6 3/4	43-1 3/4
5	3-10 7/8	6-4 1/8	11-8 5/8	19-0 13/32	19-6 3/8	31-8 11/16	27-4 1/8	44-4 31/32
6	4-8 1/4	7-7 3/8	12-6	20-3 21/32	20-3 3/4	32-11 15/16	28-1 1/2	45-8 7/32
7	5-5 5/8	8-10 19/32	13-3 3/8	21-6 7/8	21-1 1/8	34-3 5/32	28-10 7/8	46-11 7/16
8	6-3	10-1 13/16	14-0 3/4	22-10 3/32	21-10 1/2	35-6 3/8	29-8 1/4	48-2 21/32
9	7-0 3/8	11-5 1/16	14-10 1/8	24-1 11/32	22-7 7/8	36-9 5/8	30-5 5/8	49-5 7/8

A = 37° 59' 56''; logsin A = 9.78933; logcos A = 9.89654; logtan A = 9.89279; logcot A = 0.10721

Ins.	12″		13″		14″		15″		16″	
	Rise	Slope	Rise	Slope	Rise	Slope	Rise	Slope	Rise	Slope
0	9 3/8	1-3 7/32	10 5/32	1-4 1/2	10 15/16	1-5 25/32–	11 23/32	1-7 1/32	1-0 1/2	1-8 5/16
1/16	9 7/16	1-3 5/16	10 7/32–	1-4 9/16	11	1-5 27/32	11 25/32–	1-7 1/8	1-0 9/16	1-8 3/8
1/8	9 15/32	1-3 3/8	10 1/4	1-4 21/32–	11 1/32	1-5 15/16	11 13/16	1-7 3/16	1-0 19/32	1-8 15/32–
3/16	9 17/32–	1-3 15/32–	10 5/16	1-4 3/4	11 3/32–	1-6	11 7/8	1-7 9/32–	1-0 21/32–	1-8 17/32
1/4	9 9/16	1-3 17/32	10 11/32	1-4 13/16	11 1/8	1-6 3/32–	11 29/32	1-7 11/32	1-0 11/16	1-8 5/8
5/16	9 5/8	1-3 5/8	10 13/32–	1-4 29/32–	11 3/16	1-6 5/32	11 31/32–	1-7 7/16	1-0 3/4	1-8 11/16
3/8	9 21/32	1-3 23/32–	10 7/16	1-4 31/32	11 7/32	1-6 1/4	1-0	1-7 1/2	1-0 25/32	1-8 25/32–
7/16	9 23/32–	1-3 25/32	10 1/2	1-5 1/16	11 9/32–	1-6 5/16	1-0 1/16	1-7 19/32–	1-0 27/32–	1-8 27/32
1/2	9 3/4	1-3 7/8	10 9/16	1-5 1/8	11 5/16	1-6 13/32–	1-0 1/8	1-7 21/32	1-0 7/8	1-8 15/16
9/16	9 13/16	1-3 15/16	10 19/32	1-5 7/32–	11 3/8	1-6 15/32	1-0 5/32	1-7 3/4	1-0 15/16	1-9 1/32–
5/8	9 7/8	1-4 1/32–	10 21/32–	1-5 9/32	11 7/16	1-6 9/16	1-0 7/32–	1-7 13/16	1-1	1-9 3/32
11/16	9 29/32	1-4 3/32	10 11/16	1-5 3/8	11 15/32	1-6 5/8	1-0 1/4	1-7 29/32	1-1 1/32	1-9 3/16
3/4	9 31/32–	1-4 3/16	10 3/4	1-5 7/16	11 17/32–	1-6 23/32–	1-0 5/16	1-8	1-1 3/32–	1-9 1/4
13/16	10	1-4 1/4	10 25/32	1-5 17/32–	11 9/16	1-6 13/16	1-0 11/32	1-8 1/16	1-1 1/8	1-9 11/32–
7/8	10 1/16	1-4 11/32–	10 27/32–	1-5 19/32	11 5/8	1-6 7/8	1-0 13/32–	1-8 5/32–	1-1 3/16	1-9 13/32
15/16	10 3/32	1-4 13/32	10 7/8	1-5 11/16	11 21/32	1-6 31/32–	1-0 7/16	1-8 7/32	1-1 7/32	1-9 1/2

Ins.	17″		18″		19″		20″		21″	
	Rise	Slope	Rise	Slope	Rise	Slope	Rise	Slope	Rise	Slope
0	1-1 9/32	1-9 9/16	1-2 1/16	1-10 27/32–	1-2 27/32	2-0 1/8	1-3 5/8	2-1 3/8	1-4 13/32	2-2 21/32–
1/16	1-1 11/32–	1-9 21/32–	1-2 1/8	1-10 29/32	1-2 29/32–	2-0 3/16	1-3 11/16	2-1 15/32–	1-4 15/32–	2-2 23/32
1/8	1-1 3/8	1-9 23/32	1-2 5/32	1-11	1-2 15/16	2-0 9/32–	1-3 23/32	2-1 17/32	1-4 1/2	2-2 13/16
3/16	1-1 7/16	1-9 13/16	1-2 7/32–	1-11 3/32–	1-3	2-0 11/32	1-3 25/32–	2-1 5/8	1-4 9/16	2-2 7/8
1/4	1-1 15/32	1-9 7/8	1-2 1/4	1-11 5/32	1-3 1/32	2-0 7/16	1-3 13/16	2-1 11/16	1-4 19/32	2-2 31/32–
5/16	1-1 17/32–	1-9 31/32	1-2 5/16	1-11 1/4	1-3 3/32–	2-0 1/2	1-3 7/8	2-1 25/32–	1-4 21/32–	2-3 1/32
3/8	1-1 9/16	1-10 1/16	1-2 11/32	1-11 5/16	1-3 1/8	2-0 19/32–	1-3 29/32	2-1 27/32	1-4 11/16	2-3 1/8
7/16	1-1 5/8	1-10 1/8	1-2 13/32–	1-11 13/32–	1-3 3/16	2-0 21/32	1-3 31/32–	2-1 15/16	1-4 3/4	2-3 7/32–
1/2	1-1 11/16	1-10 7/32–	1-2 7/16	1-11 15/32	1-3 1/4	2-0 3/4	1-4	2-2	1-4 13/16	2-3 9/32
9/16	1-1 23/32	1-10 9/32	1-2 1/2	1-11 9/16	1-3 9/32	2-0 13/16	1-4 1/16	2-2 3/32–	1-4 27/32	2-3 3/8
5/8	1-1 25/32–	1-10 3/8	1-2 9/16	1-11 5/8	1-3 11/32–	2-0 29/32–	1-4 1/8	2-2 3/16	1-4 29/32–	2-3 7/16
11/16	1-1 13/16	1-10 7/16	1-2 19/32	1-11 23/32–	1-3 3/8	2-0 31/32	1-4 5/32	2-2 1/4	1-4 15/16	2-3 17/32–
3/4	1-1 7/8	1-10 17/32–	1-2 21/32–	1-11 25/32	1-3 7/16	2-1 1/16	1-4 7/32–	2-2 11/32–	1-5	2-3 19/32
13/16	1-1 29/32	1-10 19/32	1-2 11/16	1-11 7/8	1-3 15/32	2-1 5/32–	1-4 1/4	2-2 13/32	1-5 1/32	2-3 11/16
7/8	1-1 31/32–	1-10 11/16	1-2 3/4	1-11 15/16	1-3 17/32–	2-1 7/32	1-4 5/16	2-2 1/2	1-5 3/32–	2-3 3/4
15/16	1-2	1-10 3/4	1-2 25/32	2-0 1/32	1-3 9/16	2-1 5/16	1-4 11/32	2-2 9/16	1-5 1/8	2-3 27/32–

Feet	40′		50′		60′		70′	
	Rise	Slope	Rise	Slope	Rise	Slope	Rise	Slope
0	31-3	50-9 1/8	39-0 3/4	63-5 13/32–	46-10 1/2	76-1 11/16	54-8 1/4	88-9 31/32–
1	32-0 3/8	52-0 11/32	39-10 1/8	64-8 5/8	47-7 7/8	77-4 29/32–	55-5 5/8	90-1 3/16
2	32-9 3/4	53-3 9/16	40-7 1/2	65-11 27/32	48-5 1/4	78-8 1/8	56-3	91-4 13/32
3	33-7 1/8	54-6 13/16	41-4 7/8	67-3 3/32–	49-2 5/8	79-11 3/8	57-0 3/8	92-7 21/32–
4	34-4 1/2	55-10 1/32–	42-2 1/4	68-6 5/16	50-0	81-2 19/32–	57-9 3/4	93-10 7/8
5	35-1 7/8	57-1 1/4	42-11 5/8	69-9 17/32	50-9 3/8	82-5 13/16	58-7 1/8	95-2 3/32
6	35-11 1/4	58-4 1/2	43-9	71-0 3/4	51-6 3/4	83-9 1/32	59-4 1/2	96-5 5/16
7	36-8 5/8	59-7 23/32–	44-6 3/8	72-4	52-4 1/8	85-0 9/32–	60-1 7/8	97-8 9/16
8	37-6	60-10 15/16	45-3 3/4	73-7 7/32	53-1 1/2	86-3 1/2	60-11 1/4	98-11 25/32–
9	38-3 3/8	62-2 5/32	46-1 1/8	74-10 7/16	53-10 7/8	87-6 23/32	61-8 5/8	100-3

natsin A=0.6156440419; natcos A=0.7880243736; nattan A=0.7812500000; natcot A=1.2800000000

Inches	0" Rise	0" Slope	1" Rise	1" Slope	2" Rise	2" Slope	3" Rise	3" Slope	4" Rise	4" Slope	5" Rise	5" Slope
0	0	0	25/32	1 9/32	1 9/16	2 17/32	2 3/8	3 13/16	3 5/32	5 3/32	3 15/16	6 3/8
1/16	1/16	3/32	27/32	1 11/32	1 5/8	2 5/8	2 13/32	3 29/32	3 3/16	5 5/32	3 31/32	6 7/16
1/8	3/32	5/32	7/8	1 7/16	1 21/32	2 23/32	2 15/32	3 31/32	3 1/4	5 1/4	4 1/32	6 17/32
3/16	5/32	1/4	15/16	1 1/2	1 23/32	2 25/32	2 1/2	4 1/16	3 9/32	5 5/16	4 3/32	6 19/32
1/4	3/16	5/16	31/32	1 19/32	1 25/32	2 7/8	2 9/16	4 1/8	3 11/32	5 13/32	4 1/8	6 11/16
5/16	1/4	13/32	1 1/32	1 21/32	1 13/16	2 15/16	2 19/32	4 7/32	3 13/32	5 1/2	4 3/16	6 3/4
3/8	9/32	15/32	1 3/32	1 3/4	1 7/8	3 1/32	2 21/32	4 9/32	3 7/16	5 9/16	4 7/32	6 27/32
7/16	11/32	9/16	1 1/8	1 27/32	1 29/32	3 3/32	2 23/32	4 3/8	3 1/2	5 21/32	4 9/32	6 29/32
1/2	13/32	5/8	1 3/16	1 29/32	1 31/32	3 3/16	2 3/4	4 7/16	3 17/32	5 23/32	4 5/16	7
9/16	7/16	23/32	1 7/32	2	2	3 1/4	2 13/16	4 17/32	3 19/32	5 13/16	4 3/8	7 1/16
5/8	1/2	25/32	1 9/32	2 1/16	2 1/16	3 11/32	2 27/32	4 5/8	3 5/8	5 7/8	4 7/16	7 5/32
11/16	17/32	7/8	1 5/16	2 5/32	2 1/8	3 13/32	2 29/32	4 11/16	3 11/16	5 31/32	4 15/32	7 1/4
3/4	19/32	31/32	1 3/8	2 7/32	2 5/32	3 1/2	2 15/16	4 25/32	3 3/4	6 1/8	4 17/32	7 5/16
13/16	5/8	1 1/32	1 7/16	2 5/16	2 7/32	3 9/16	3	4 27/32	3 25/32	6 1/8	4 9/16	7 13/32
7/8	11/16	1 1/8	1 15/32	2 3/8	2 1/4	3 21/32	3 1/16	4 15/16	3 27/32	6 3/16	4 5/8	7 15/32
15/16	3/4	1 3/16	1 17/32	2 15/32	2 5/16	3 3/4	3 3/32	5	3 7/8	6 9/32	4 21/32	7 9/16

Inches	6" Rise	6" Slope	7" Rise	7" Slope	8" Rise	8" Slope	9" Rise	9" Slope	10" Rise	10" Slope	11" Rise	11" Slope
0	4 23/32	7 5/8	5 1/2	8 29/32	6 9/32	10 3/16	7 1/16	11 7/16	7 7/8	1-0 23/32	8 21/32	1-2
1/16	4 25/32	7 23/32	5 9/16	9	6 11/32	10 1/4	7 1/8	11 17/32	7 29/32	1-0 13/16	8 11/16	1-2 1/16
1/8	4 13/16	7 25/32	5 19/32	9 1/16	6 3/8	10 11/32	7 3/16	11 19/32	7 31/32	1-0 7/8	8 3/4	1-2 5/32
3/16	4 7/8	7 7/8	5 21/32	9 5/32	6 7/16	10 13/32	7 7/32	11 11/16	8	1-0 31/32	8 13/16	1-2 7/32
1/4	4 29/32	7 15/16	5 11/16	9 7/32	6 1/2	10 1/2	7 9/32	11 25/32	8 1/16	1-1 1/32	8 27/32	1-2 5/16
5/16	4 31/32	8 1/32	5 3/4	9 5/16	6 17/32	10 9/16	7 5/16	11 27/32	8 1/8	1-1 1/8	8 29/32	1-2 13/32
3/8	5	8 1/8	5 13/16	9 3/8	6 19/32	10 21/32	7 3/8	11 15/16	8 5/32	1-1 3/16	8 15/16	1-2 15/32
7/16	5 1/16	8 3/16	5 27/32	9 15/32	6 5/8	10 23/32	7 7/16	1-0	8 7/32	1-1 9/32	9	1-2 9/16
1/2	5 1/8	8 9/32	5 29/32	9 17/32	6 11/16	10 13/16	7 15/32	1-0 3/32	8 1/4	1-1 11/32	9 1/32	1-2 5/8
9/16	5 5/32	8 11/32	5 15/16	9 5/8	6 23/32	10 29/32	7 17/32	1-0 5/32	8 5/16	1-1 7/16	9 3/32	1-2 23/32
5/8	5 7/32	8 7/16	6	9 11/16	6 25/32	10 31/32	7 9/16	1-0 1/4	8 11/32	1-1 17/32	9 5/32	1-2 25/32
11/16	5 1/4	8 1/2	6 1/32	9 25/32	6 27/32	11 1/16	7 5/8	1-0 5/16	8 13/32	1-1 19/32	9 3/16	1-2 7/8
3/4	5 5/16	8 19/32	6 3/32	9 7/8	6 7/8	11 1/8	7 21/32	1-0 13/32	8 15/32	1-1 11/16	9 1/4	1-2 15/16
13/16	5 11/32	8 21/32	6 5/32	9 15/16	6 15/16	11 7/32	7 23/32	1-0 15/32	8 1/2	1-1 3/4	9 9/32	1-3 1/32
7/8	5 13/32	8 3/4	6 3/16	10 1/32	6 31/32	11 9/32	7 25/32	1-0 9/16	8 9/16	1-1 27/32	9 11/32	1-3 3/32
15/16	5 15/32	8 13/16	6 1/4	10 3/32	7 1/32	11 3/8	7 13/16	1-0 21/32	8 19/32	1-1 29/32	9 3/8	1-3 3/8

Feet	0' Rise	0' Slope	10' Rise	10' Slope	20' Rise	20' Slope	30' Rise	30' Slope
0	0	0	7-10 3/8	12-8 21/32	15-8 3/4	25-5 11/32	23-7 1/8	38-2
1	-9 7/16	1-3 9/32	8-7 13/16	13-11 15/16	16-6 3/16	26-8 19/32	24-4 9/16	39-5 1/4
2	1-6 7/8	2-6 11/32	9-5 1/4	15-3 3/8	17-3 5/8	27-11 7/8	25-2	40-8 17/32
3	2-4 5/16	3-9 13/16	10-2 11/16	16-6 15/32	18-1 1/16	29-3 1/8	25-11 7/16	41-11 25/32
4	3-1 3/4	5-1 1/16	11-0 1/8	17-9 23/32	18-10 1/2	30-6 13/32	26-8 7/8	43-3 1/16
5	3-11 3/16	6-4 11/32	11-9 9/16	19-1	19-7 15/16	31-9 21/32	27-6 5/16	44-6 5/16
6	4-8 5/8	7-7 19/32	12-7	20-4 1/4	20-5 3/8	33-0 15/16	28-3 3/4	45-9 19/32
7	5-6 1/16	8-10 7/8	13-4 7/16	21-7 17/32	21-2 13/16	34-4 3/16	29-1 3/16	47-0 7/8
8	6-3 1/2	10-2 1/8	14-1 7/8	22-10 13/16	22-0 1/4	35-7 15/32	29-10 5/8	48-4 1/8
9	7-0 15/16	11-5 13/32	14-11 5/16	24-2 1/16	22-9 11/16	36-10 23/32	30-8 1/16	49-7 13/32

A = 38° 11′ 01″; logsin A = 9.79112; logcos A = 9.89544; logtan A = 9.89568; logcot A = 0.10432

In.	12″ Rise	12″ Slope	13″ Rise	13″ Slope	14″ Rise	14″ Slope	15″ Rise	15″ Slope	16″ Rise	16″ Slope
0	9 7/16	1-3 9/32	10 7/32	1-4 17/32	11	1-5 13/16	11 13/16	1-7 3/8	1-0 19/32	1-8 11/32
1/16	9 1/2	1-3 11/32	10 9/32	1-4 5/8	11 1/16	1-5 7/8	11 27/32	1-7 5/32	1-0 5/8	1-8 7/16
1/8	9 17/32	1-3 7/16	10 5/16	1-4 11/16	11 3/32	1-5 31/32	11 29/32	1-7 1/4	1-0 11/16	1-8 1/2
3/16	9 19/32	1-3 1/2	10 3/8	1-4 25/32	11 5/32	1-6 1/16	11 15/16	1-7 5/16	1-0 23/32	1-8 19/32
1/4	9 5/8	1-3 19/32	10 13/32	1-4 27/32	11 7/32	1-6 1/8	1-0	1-7 13/32	1-0 25/32	1-8 11/16
5/16	9 11/16	1-3 21/32	10 15/32	1-4 15/16	11 1/4	1-6 7/32	1-0 1/32	1-7 15/32	1-0 27/32	1-8 3/4
3/8	9 23/32	1-3 3/4	10 17/32	1-5 1/32	11 5/16	1-6 9/32	1-0 3/32	1-7 9/16	1-0 7/8	1-8 27/32
7/16	9 25/32	1-3 13/16	10 9/16	1-5 3/32	11 11/32	1-6 3/8	1-0 5/32	1-7 5/8	1-0 15/16	1-8 29/32
1/2	9 27/32	1-3 29/32	10 5/8	1-5 3/16	11 13/32	1-6 7/16	1-0 3/16	1-7 23/32	1-0 31/32	1-9
9/16	9 7/8	1-3 31/32	10 21/32	1-5 1/4	11 7/16	1-6 17/32	1-0 1/4	1-7 13/16	1-1 1/32	1-9 1/16
5/8	9 15/16	1-4 1/16	10 23/32	1-5 11/32	11 1/2	1-6 19/32	1-0 9/32	1-7 7/8	1-1 1/16	1-9 5/32
11/16	9 31/32	1-4 5/32	10 3/4	1-5 13/32	11 9/16	1-6 11/16	1-0 11/32	1-7 31/32	1-1 1/8	1-9 7/32
3/4	10 1/32	1-4 7/32	10 13/32	1-5 1/2	11 19/32	1-6 3/4	1-0 3/8	1-8 1/32	1-1 3/8	1-9 5/16
13/16	10 1/16	1-4 5/16	10 7/8	1-5 9/16	11 21/32	1-6 27/32	1-0 7/16	1-8 5/8	1-1 7/32	1-9 3/8
7/8	10 1/8	1-4 3/8	10 29/32	1-5 21/32	11 11/16	1-6 15/16	1-0 1/2	1-8 13/16	1-1 9/32	1-9 15/16
15/16	10 3/16	1-4 15/32	10 31/32	1-5 23/32	11 3/4	1-7	1-0 17/32	1-8 9/32	1-1 15/16	1-9 9/16

In.	17″ Rise	17″ Slope	18″ Rise	18″ Slope	19″ Rise	19″ Slope	20″ Rise	20″ Slope	21″ Rise	21″ Slope
0	1-1 3/8	1-9 5/8	1-2 5/32	1-10 29/32	1-2 15/16	2-0 3/16	1-3 23/32	2-1 7/16	1-4 1/2	2-2 23/32
1/16	1-1 13/32	1-9 23/32	1-2 7/32	1-10 31/32	1-3	2-0 1/4	1-3 25/32	2-1 17/32	1-4 9/16	2-2 25/32
1/8	1-1 15/32	1-9 25/32	1-2 1/4	1-11 1/16	1-3 1/32	2-0 11/32	1-3 13/16	2-1 19/32	1-4 5/8	2-2 7/8
3/16	1-1 17/32	1-9 7/8	1-2 5/16	1-11 1/8	1-3 3/32	2-0 13/32	1-3 7/8	2-1 11/16	1-4 21/32	2-2 31/32
1/4	1-1 9/16	1-9 15/16	1-2 11/32	1-11 7/32	1-3 1/8	2-0 1/2	1-3 15/16	2-1 3/4	1-4 23/32	2-3 1/32
5/16	1-1 5/8	1-10 1/32	1-2 13/32	1-11 5/16	1-3 3/16	2-0 9/16	1-3 31/32	2-1 27/32	1-4 3/4	2-3 1/8
3/8	1-1 21/32	1-10 3/8	1-2 7/16	1-11 3/8	1-3 1/4	2-0 21/32	1-4 1/8	2-1 29/32	1-4 13/16	2-3 3/16
7/16	1-1 23/32	1-10 3/16	1-2 1/2	1-11 15/32	1-3 9/32	2-0 23/32	1-4 1/16	2-2	1-4 7/8	2-3 9/32
1/2	1-1 3/4	1-10 1/4	1-2 9/16	1-11 17/32	1-3 11/32	2-0 13/16	1-4 1/8	2-2 3/32	1-4 29/32	2-3 11/32
9/16	1-1 13/16	1-10 11/32	1-2 19/32	1-11 5/8	1-3 3/8	2-0 7/8	1-4 5/32	2-2 1/4	1-4 31/32	2-3 7/16
5/8	1-1 7/8	1-10 7/16	1-2 21/32	1-11 11/16	1-3 7/16	2-0 31/32	1-4 7/32	2-2 1/4	1-5	2-3 1/2
11/16	1-1 29/32	1-10 1/2	1-2 11/16	1-11 25/32	1-3 15/32	2-1 1/32	1-4 9/32	2-2 5/16	1-5 1/16	2-3 19/32
3/4	1-1 31/32	1-10 19/32	1-2 3/4	1-11 27/32	1-3 17/32	2-1 1/8	1-4 5/16	2-2 13/32	1-5 3/32	2-3 21/32
13/16	1-2	1-10 21/32	1-2 25/32	1-11 15/16	1-3 19/32	2-1 7/32	1-4 3/8	2-2 15/32	1-5 5/32	2-3 3/4
7/8	1-2 1/16	1-10 3/4	1-2 27/32	2-0	1-3 5/8	2-1 9/32	1-4 13/16	2-2 9/16	1-5 7/32	2-3 27/32
15/16	1-2 3/32	1-10 13/16	1-2 29/32	2-0 3/32	1-3 11/16	2-1 3/8	1-4 15/32	2-2 5/8	1-5 1/4	2-3 29/32

Feet	40′ Rise	40′ Slope	50′ Rise	50′ Slope	60′ Rise	60′ Slope	70′ Rise	70′ Slope
0	31-5 1/2	50-10 21/32	39-3 7/8	63-7 5/16	47-2 1/4	76-4	55-0 5/8	89-0 21/32
1	32-2 15/16	52-1 15/32	40-1 5/16	64-10 19/32	47-11 11/16	77-7 1/4	55-10 11/16	90-3 15/16
2	33-0 3/8	53-5 3/16	40-10 3/4	66-1 27/32	48-9 1/8	78-10 17/32	56-7 1/2	91-7 3/16
3	33-9 13/16	54-8 15/32	41-8 1/8	67-5 1/8	49-6 9/16	80-1 25/32	57-4 15/16	92-10 15/16
4	34-7 1/4	55-11 23/32	42-5 5/8	68-8 13/32	50-4	81-5 1/16	58-2 3/8	94-1 23/32
5	35-4 11/16	57-3	43-3 1/16	69-11 21/32	51-1 7/16	82-8 5/16	58-11 13/16	95-5
6	36-2 1/8	58-6 1/4	44-0 1/2	71-2 15/16	51-10 7/8	83-11 19/32	59-9 1/4	96-8 1/4
7	36-11 9/16	59-9 17/32	44-9 15/16	72-6 3/16	52-8 5/16	85-2 27/32	60-6 11/16	97-11 17/32
8	37-9	61-0 25/32	45-7 3/8	73-9 15/32	53-5 3/4	86-6 1/8	61-4 1/8	99-2 25/32
9	38-6 7/16	62-4 1/16	46-4 13/32	75-0 23/32	54-3 3/16	87-9 3/8	62-1 9/16	100-6 1/16

natsin A=0.6181830953; natcos A=0.7860341344; nattan A=0.7864583333; natcot A=1.2715231788

Inches	0" Rise	0" Slope	1" Rise	1" Slope	2" Rise	2" Slope	3" Rise	3" Slope	4" Rise	4" Slope	5" Rise	5" Slope
0	0	0	25/32	19/32	1 19/32	2 9/16	2 3/8	3 13/16	3 5/32	5 3/32	3 31/32	6 3/8
1/16	1/16	3/32	27/32	1 11/32	1 5/8	2 5/8	2 7/16	3 29/32	3 7/32	5 3/16	4	6 15/32
1/8	3/32	5/32	7/8	1 7/16	1 11/16	2 23/32	2 15/32	4	3 1/4	5 1/4	4 1/16	6 17/32
3/16	5/32	1/4	15/16	1 1/2	1 23/32	2 25/32	2 17/32	4 1/16	3 5/16	5 11/32	4 3/32	6 5/8
1/4	3/16	5/16	1	1 19/32	1 25/32	2 7/8	2 9/16	4 5/32	3 3/8	5 13/32	4 5/32	6 11/16
5/16	1/4	13/32	1 1/32	1 11/16	1 27/32	2 15/16	2 5/8	4 7/32	3 13/32	5 1/2	4 7/32	6 25/32
3/8	5/16	15/32	1 3/32	1 3/4	1 7/8	3 1/32	2 11/16	4 5/16	3 15/32	5 19/32	4 1/4	6 27/32
7/16	11/32	9/16	1 1/8	1 27/32	1 15/16	3 3/32	2 23/32	4 3/8	3 1/2	5 21/32	4 5/16	6 15/16
1/2	13/32	5/8	1 3/16	1 29/32	1 31/32	3 3/16	2 25/32	4 15/32	3 9/16	5 3/4	4 11/32	7
9/16	7/16	23/32	1 1/4	2	2 1/32	3 9/32	2 13/16	4 17/32	3 5/8	5 13/16	4 13/32	7 3/32
5/8	1/2	13/16	1 9/32	2 1/16	2 1/8	3 11/32	2 7/8	4 5/8	3 21/32	5 29/32	4 7/16	7 3/16
11/16	17/32	7/8	1 11/32	2 5/32	2 1/8	3 7/16	2 29/32	4 23/32	3 23/32	5 31/32	4 1/2	7 1/4
3/4	19/32	31/32	1 3/8	2 7/32	2 3/16	3 1/2	2 31/32	4 25/32	3 3/4	6 1/16	4 9/16	7 11/32
13/16	21/32	1 1/32	1 7/16	2 5/16	2 7/32	3 19/32	3 1/32	4 7/8	3 13/16	6 1/8	4 19/32	7 13/32
7/8	11/16	1 1/8	1 1/2	2 13/32	2 9/32	3 21/32	3 1/16	4 15/16	3 7/8	6 7/32	4 21/32	7 1/2
15/16	3/4	1 3/16	1 17/32	2 15/32	2 5/16	3 3/4	3 1/8	5 1/32	3 29/32	6 5/16	4 11/16	7 9/16

Inches	6" Rise	6" Slope	7" Rise	7" Slope	8" Rise	8" Slope	9" Rise	9" Slope	10" Rise	10" Slope	11" Rise	11" Slope
0	4 3/4	7 21/32	5 17/32	8 15/16	6 11/32	10 7/32	7 1/8	11 15/32	7 29/32	1-0 3/4	8 23/32	1-2 1/32
1/16	4 13/16	7 23/32	5 19/32	9	6 3/8	10 9/32	7 3/16	11 9/16	7 31/32	1-0 27/32	8 3/4	1-2 1/8
1/8	4 27/32	7 13/16	5 5/8	9 3/32	6 7/16	10 3/8	7 1/4	11 5/8	8	1-0 29/32	8 13/16	1-2 3/16
3/16	4 29/32	7 29/32	5 11/16	9 5/32	6 15/32	10 7/16	7 9/32	11 23/32	8 1/16	1-1	8 27/32	1-2 9/32
1/4	4 15/16	7 31/32	5 3/4	9 1/4	6 17/32	10 17/32	7 5/16	11 13/16	8 1/8	1-1 1/16	8 29/32	1-2 11/32
5/16	5	8 1/16	5 25/32	9 5/16	6 19/32	10 19/32	7 3/8	11 7/8	8 5/32	1-1 5/32	8 31/32	1-2 7/16
3/8	5 1/16	8 1/8	5 27/32	9 13/32	6 5/8	10 11/16	7 7/16	11 31/32	8 7/32	1-1 7/32	9	1-2 1/2
7/16	5 3/32	8 7/32	5 7/8	9 1/2	6 11/16	10 3/4	7 15/32	1-0 1/32	8 1/4	1-1 5/16	9 1/16	1-2 19/32
1/2	5 5/32	8 9/32	5 15/16	9 9/16	6 23/32	10 27/32	7 17/32	1-0 1/8	8 5/16	1-1 13/32	9 3/32	1-2 21/32
9/16	5 3/16	8 3/8	6	9 21/32	6 25/32	10 29/32	7 9/16	1-0 3/16	8 3/8	1-1 15/32	9 5/32	1-2 3/4
5/8	5 1/4	8 7/16	6 1/32	9 23/32	6 13/16	11	7 5/8	1-0 9/32	8 13/32	1-1 9/16	9 3/16	1-2 13/16
11/16	5 9/32	8 17/32	6 3/32	9 13/16	6 7/8	11 3/32	7 21/32	1-0 11/32	8 15/32	1-1 5/8	9 1/4	1-2 29/32
3/4	5 11/32	8 19/32	6 1/8	9 7/8	6 15/16	11 5/32	7 23/32	1-0 7/16	8 1/2	1-1 23/32	9 5/16	1-3
13/16	5 13/32	8 11/16	6 3/16	9 31/32	6 31/32	11 1/4	7 25/32	1-0 1/2	8 9/16	1-1 25/32	9 11/32	1-3 1/16
7/8	5 7/16	8 25/32	6 1/4	10 1/32	7 1/32	11 5/16	7 13/16	1-0 19/32	8 5/8	1-1 7/8	9 13/32	1-3 5/32
15/16	5 1/2	8 27/32	6 9/32	10 1/8	7 1/16	11 13/32	7 7/8	1-0 11/16	8 21/32	1-1 15/16	9 7/16	1-3 7/32

Feet	0' Rise	0' Slope	10' Rise	10' Slope	20' Rise	20' Slope	30' Rise	30' Slope
0	0	0	7-11	12-9 1/16	15-10	25-6 3/32	23-9	38-3 5/32
1	-9 1/2	1-3 5/16	8-8 1/2	14-0 11/32	16-7 1/2	26-9 13/32	24-6 1/2	39-6 15/32
2	1-7	2-6 5/8	9-6	15-3 21/32	17-5	28-0 23/32	25-4	40-9 25/32
3	2-4 1/2	3-9 29/32	10-3 1/2	16-6 31/32	18-2 1/2	29-4 1/32	26-1 1/2	42-1 1/16
4	3-2	5-1 7/32	11-1	17-10 9/32	19-0	30-7 5/16	26-11	43-4 3/8
5	3-11 1/2	6-4 17/32	11-10 1/2	19-1 19/32	19-9 1/2	31-10 5/8	27-8 1/2	44-7 11/16
6	4-9	7-7 27/32	12-8	20-4 7/8	20-7	33-1 15/16	28-6	45-11
7	5-6 1/2	8-11 1/8	13-5 1/2	21-8 3/32	21-4 1/2	34-5 1/4	29-3 1/2	47-2 9/32
8	6-4	10-2 7/32	14-3	22-11 1/2	22-2	35-8 17/32	30-1	48-5 19/32
9	7-1 1/2	11-5 3/4	15-0 1/2	24-2 13/16	22-11 1/2	36-11 27/32	30-10 1/2	49-8 29/32

A = 38° 22′ 03″; logsin A = 9.79288; logcos A = 9.89434; logtan A = 9.89854; logcot A = 0.10146

Ins.	12" Rise	12" Slope	13" Rise	13" Slope	14" Rise	14" Slope	15" Rise	15" Slope	16" Rise	16" Slope
0	$9\frac{1}{2}$	1-3$\frac{5}{16}$	10$\frac{9}{32}$	1-4$\frac{19}{32}$	11$\frac{3}{32}$	1-5$\frac{27}{32}$	11$\frac{7}{8}$	1-7$\frac{1}{8}$	1-0$\frac{21}{32}$	1-8$\frac{13}{16}$
$\frac{1}{16}$	9$\frac{9}{16}$	1-3$\frac{3}{8}$	10$\frac{11}{32}$	1-4$\frac{21}{32}$	11$\frac{1}{8}$	1-5$\frac{15}{16}$	11$\frac{15}{16}$	1-7$\frac{7}{32}$	1-0$\frac{23}{32}$	1-8$\frac{1}{2}$
$\frac{1}{8}$	9$\frac{19}{32}$	1-3$\frac{15}{32}$	10$\frac{3}{8}$	1-4$\frac{3}{4}$	11$\frac{3}{16}$	1-6	11$\frac{31}{32}$	1-7$\frac{9}{32}$	1-0$\frac{3}{4}$	1-8$\frac{9}{16}$
$\frac{3}{16}$	9$\frac{21}{32}$	1-3$\frac{17}{32}$	10$\frac{7}{16}$	1-4$\frac{13}{32}$	11$\frac{7}{32}$	1-6$\frac{3}{32}$	1-0$\frac{1}{2}$	1-7$\frac{3}{8}$	1-0$\frac{13}{16}$	1-8$\frac{21}{32}$
$\frac{1}{4}$	9$\frac{11}{16}$	1-3$\frac{5}{8}$	10$\frac{1}{2}$	1-4$\frac{29}{32}$	11$\frac{9}{32}$	1-6$\frac{3}{16}$	1-0$\frac{1}{16}$	1-7$\frac{7}{16}$	1-0$\frac{7}{8}$	1-8$\frac{23}{32}$
$\frac{5}{16}$	9$\frac{3}{4}$	1-3$\frac{23}{32}$	10$\frac{17}{32}$	1-4$\frac{31}{32}$	11$\frac{11}{32}$	1-6$\frac{1}{4}$	1-0$\frac{1}{8}$	1-7$\frac{17}{32}$	1-0$\frac{29}{32}$	1-8$\frac{13}{16}$
$\frac{3}{8}$	9$\frac{13}{16}$	1-3$\frac{25}{32}$	10$\frac{19}{32}$	1-5$\frac{1}{16}$	11$\frac{3}{8}$	1-6$\frac{11}{32}$	1-0$\frac{3}{16}$	1-7$\frac{5}{8}$	1-0$\frac{31}{32}$	1-8$\frac{7}{8}$
$\frac{7}{16}$	9$\frac{27}{32}$	1-3$\frac{7}{8}$	10$\frac{5}{8}$	1-5$\frac{1}{8}$	11$\frac{7}{16}$	1-6$\frac{13}{32}$	1-0$\frac{7}{32}$	1-7$\frac{11}{16}$	1-1	1-8$\frac{31}{32}$
$\frac{1}{2}$	9$\frac{29}{32}$	1-3$\frac{15}{16}$	10$\frac{11}{16}$	1-5$\frac{7}{32}$	11$\frac{15}{32}$	1-6$\frac{1}{2}$	1-0$\frac{9}{32}$	1-7$\frac{25}{32}$	1-1$\frac{1}{16}$	1-9$\frac{1}{32}$
$\frac{9}{16}$	9$\frac{15}{16}$	1-4$\frac{1}{32}$	10$\frac{3}{4}$	1-5$\frac{5}{16}$	11$\frac{17}{32}$	1-6$\frac{9}{16}$	1-0$\frac{5}{16}$	1-7$\frac{27}{32}$	1-1$\frac{1}{8}$	1-9$\frac{1}{8}$
$\frac{5}{8}$	10	1-4$\frac{3}{32}$	10$\frac{25}{32}$	1-5$\frac{3}{8}$	11$\frac{9}{16}$	1-6$\frac{21}{32}$	1-0$\frac{3}{8}$	1-7$\frac{15}{16}$	1-1$\frac{5}{32}$	1-9$\frac{7}{32}$
$\frac{11}{16}$	10$\frac{1}{32}$	1-4$\frac{3}{16}$	10$\frac{27}{32}$	1-5$\frac{15}{32}$	11$\frac{5}{8}$	1-6$\frac{23}{32}$	1-0$\frac{13}{32}$	1-8	1-1$\frac{7}{32}$	1-9$\frac{9}{32}$
$\frac{3}{4}$	10$\frac{3}{32}$	1-4$\frac{1}{4}$	10$\frac{7}{8}$	1-5$\frac{17}{32}$	11$\frac{11}{16}$	1-6$\frac{13}{16}$	1-0$\frac{15}{32}$	1-8$\frac{3}{32}$	1-1$\frac{1}{4}$	1-9$\frac{3}{8}$
$\frac{13}{16}$	10$\frac{5}{32}$	1-4$\frac{11}{32}$	10$\frac{15}{16}$	1-5$\frac{5}{8}$	11$\frac{23}{32}$	1-6$\frac{29}{32}$	1-0$\frac{17}{32}$	1-8$\frac{5}{32}$	1-1$\frac{5}{16}$	1-9$\frac{7}{16}$
$\frac{7}{8}$	10$\frac{3}{16}$	1-4$\frac{13}{32}$	11	1-5$\frac{11}{16}$	11$\frac{25}{32}$	1-6$\frac{31}{32}$	1-0$\frac{9}{16}$	1-8$\frac{1}{4}$	1-1$\frac{3}{8}$	1-9$\frac{17}{32}$
$\frac{15}{16}$	10$\frac{1}{4}$	1-4$\frac{1}{2}$	11$\frac{1}{32}$	1-5$\frac{25}{32}$	11$\frac{13}{16}$	1-7$\frac{1}{16}$	1-0$\frac{5}{8}$	1-8$\frac{5}{16}$	1-1$\frac{13}{32}$	1-9$\frac{19}{32}$

Ins.	17" Rise	17" Slope	18" Rise	18" Slope	19" Rise	19" Slope	20" Rise	20" Slope	21" Rise	21" Slope
0	1-1$\frac{15}{32}$	1-9$\frac{11}{16}$	1-2$\frac{1}{4}$	1-10$\frac{31}{32}$	1-3$\frac{1}{32}$	2-0$\frac{7}{32}$	1-3$\frac{27}{32}$	2-1$\frac{1}{2}$	1-4$\frac{5}{8}$	2-2$\frac{25}{32}$
$\frac{1}{16}$	1-1$\frac{1}{2}$	1-9$\frac{3}{4}$	1-2$\frac{5}{16}$	1-11$\frac{1}{32}$	1-3$\frac{3}{32}$	2-0$\frac{5}{16}$	1-3$\frac{7}{8}$	2-1$\frac{19}{32}$	1-4$\frac{11}{16}$	2-2$\frac{7}{8}$
$\frac{1}{8}$	1-1$\frac{9}{16}$	1-9$\frac{27}{32}$	1-2$\frac{11}{32}$	1-11$\frac{1}{8}$	1-3$\frac{1}{8}$	2-0$\frac{13}{32}$	1-3$\frac{15}{16}$	2-1$\frac{21}{32}$	1-4$\frac{23}{32}$	2-2$\frac{15}{16}$
$\frac{3}{16}$	1-1$\frac{19}{32}$	1-9$\frac{29}{32}$	1-2$\frac{13}{32}$	1-11$\frac{3}{16}$	1-3$\frac{3}{16}$	2-0$\frac{15}{32}$	1-3$\frac{31}{32}$	2-1$\frac{3}{4}$	1-4$\frac{25}{32}$	2-3$\frac{1}{16}$
$\frac{1}{4}$	1-1$\frac{21}{32}$	1-10	1-2$\frac{7}{16}$	1-11$\frac{9}{32}$	1-3$\frac{1}{4}$	2-0$\frac{9}{16}$	1-4$\frac{1}{32}$	2-1$\frac{13}{16}$	1-4$\frac{13}{16}$	2-3$\frac{3}{32}$
$\frac{5}{16}$	1-1$\frac{23}{32}$	1-10$\frac{3}{32}$	1-2$\frac{1}{2}$	1-11$\frac{11}{32}$	1-3$\frac{9}{32}$	2-0$\frac{5}{8}$	1-4$\frac{3}{32}$	2-1$\frac{29}{32}$	1-4$\frac{7}{8}$	2-3$\frac{3}{16}$
$\frac{3}{8}$	1-1$\frac{3}{4}$	1-10$\frac{5}{32}$	1-2$\frac{9}{16}$	1-11$\frac{7}{16}$	1-3$\frac{11}{32}$	2-0$\frac{23}{32}$	1-4$\frac{1}{8}$	2-2	1-4$\frac{15}{16}$	2-3$\frac{1}{4}$
$\frac{7}{16}$	1-1$\frac{13}{16}$	1-10$\frac{1}{4}$	1-2$\frac{19}{32}$	1-11$\frac{17}{32}$	1-3$\frac{3}{8}$	2-0$\frac{25}{32}$	1-4$\frac{3}{16}$	2-2$\frac{1}{16}$	1-4$\frac{31}{32}$	2-3$\frac{11}{32}$
$\frac{1}{2}$	1-1$\frac{27}{32}$	1-10$\frac{5}{16}$	1-2$\frac{21}{32}$	1-11$\frac{19}{32}$	1-3$\frac{7}{16}$	2-0$\frac{7}{8}$	1-4$\frac{7}{32}$	2-2$\frac{5}{32}$	1-5$\frac{1}{16}$	2-3$\frac{13}{32}$
$\frac{9}{16}$	1-1$\frac{29}{32}$	1-10$\frac{13}{32}$	1-2$\frac{11}{16}$	1-11$\frac{11}{16}$	1-3$\frac{1}{2}$	2-0$\frac{15}{16}$	1-4$\frac{9}{32}$	2-2$\frac{7}{32}$	1-5$\frac{1}{8}$	2-3$\frac{1}{2}$
$\frac{5}{8}$	1-1$\frac{15}{16}$	1-10$\frac{15}{32}$	1-2$\frac{3}{4}$	1-11$\frac{3}{4}$	1-3$\frac{17}{32}$	2-1$\frac{1}{32}$	1-4$\frac{5}{16}$	2-2$\frac{5}{16}$	1-5$\frac{1}{8}$	2-3$\frac{19}{32}$
$\frac{11}{16}$	1-2	1-10$\frac{9}{16}$	1-2$\frac{25}{32}$	1-11$\frac{27}{32}$	1-3$\frac{19}{32}$	2-1$\frac{1}{8}$	1-4$\frac{3}{8}$	2-2$\frac{3}{8}$	1-5$\frac{9}{32}$	2-3$\frac{21}{32}$
$\frac{3}{4}$	1-2$\frac{1}{16}$	1-10$\frac{5}{8}$	1-2$\frac{27}{32}$	1-11$\frac{29}{32}$	1-3$\frac{5}{8}$	2-1$\frac{3}{16}$	1-4$\frac{7}{16}$	2-2$\frac{15}{32}$	1-5$\frac{7}{16}$	2-3$\frac{3}{4}$
$\frac{13}{16}$	1-2$\frac{3}{32}$	1-10$\frac{23}{32}$	1-2$\frac{29}{32}$	2-0	1-3$\frac{11}{16}$	2-1$\frac{9}{32}$	1-4$\frac{15}{32}$	2-2$\frac{17}{32}$	1-5$\frac{9}{32}$	2-3$\frac{13}{16}$
$\frac{7}{8}$	1-2$\frac{5}{32}$	1-10$\frac{13}{16}$	1-2$\frac{15}{16}$	2-0$\frac{1}{16}$	1-3$\frac{3}{4}$	2-1$\frac{11}{32}$	1-4$\frac{17}{32}$	2-2$\frac{5}{8}$	1-5$\frac{5}{16}$	2-3$\frac{29}{32}$
$\frac{15}{16}$	1-2$\frac{3}{16}$	1-10$\frac{7}{8}$	1-3	2-0$\frac{5}{32}$	1-3$\frac{25}{32}$	2-1$\frac{7}{16}$	1-4$\frac{9}{16}$	2-2$\frac{23}{32}$	1-5$\frac{3}{8}$	2-3$\frac{31}{32}$

Feet	40' Rise	40' Slope	50' Rise	50' Slope	60' Rise	60' Slope	70' Rise	70' Slope
0	31-8	51-0$\frac{7}{32}$	39-7	63-9$\frac{1}{4}$	47-6	76-6$\frac{5}{16}$	55-5	89-3$\frac{3}{8}$
1	32-5$\frac{1}{2}$	52-3$\frac{1}{2}$	40-4$\frac{1}{2}$	65-0$\frac{9}{16}$	48-3$\frac{1}{2}$	77-9$\frac{5}{8}$	56-2$\frac{1}{2}$	90-6$\frac{21}{32}$
2	33-3	53-6$\frac{13}{16}$	41-2	66-3$\frac{7}{8}$	49-1	79-0$\frac{15}{16}$	57-0	91-9$\frac{31}{32}$
3	34-0$\frac{1}{2}$	54-10$\frac{1}{8}$	41-11$\frac{1}{2}$	67-7$\frac{3}{16}$	49-10$\frac{1}{2}$	80-4$\frac{7}{32}$	57-9$\frac{1}{2}$	93-1$\frac{9}{32}$
4	34-10	56-1$\frac{7}{16}$	42-9	68-10$\frac{15}{32}$	50-8	81-7$\frac{11}{32}$	58-7	94-4$\frac{19}{32}$
5	35-7$\frac{1}{2}$	57-4$\frac{3}{4}$	43-6$\frac{1}{2}$	70-1$\frac{25}{32}$	51-5$\frac{1}{2}$	82-10$\frac{27}{32}$	59-4$\frac{1}{2}$	95-7$\frac{29}{32}$
6	36-5	58-8$\frac{1}{16}$	44-4	71-5$\frac{3}{32}$	52-3	84-2$\frac{5}{32}$	60-2	96-11$\frac{3}{16}$
7	37-2$\frac{1}{2}$	59-11$\frac{11}{32}$	45-1$\frac{1}{2}$	72-8$\frac{13}{32}$	53-0$\frac{1}{2}$	85-5$\frac{7}{16}$	60-11$\frac{1}{2}$	98-2$\frac{1}{2}$
8	38-0	61-2$\frac{21}{32}$	45-11	73-11$\frac{23}{32}$	53-10	86-8$\frac{3}{4}$	61-9	99-5$\frac{13}{16}$
9	38-9$\frac{1}{2}$	62-5$\frac{31}{32}$	46-8$\frac{1}{2}$	75-3	54-7$\frac{1}{2}$	88-0$\frac{1}{16}$	62-6$\frac{1}{2}$	100-9$\frac{1}{8}$

natsin A=0.6207029443; natcos A=0.7840458244; nattan A=0.7916666666; natcot A=1.2631578947

Inches	0" Rise	0" Slope	1" Rise	1" Slope	2" Rise	2" Slope	3" Rise	3" Slope	4" Rise	4" Slope	5" Rise	5" Slope
0	0	0	13/16	19/32	1 19/32	2 3/16	2 3/8	3 27/32	3 3/16	5 1/8	4	6 13/32
1/16	1/16	3/32	27/32	1 11/32	1 21/32	2 5/8	2 7/16	3 29/32	3 1/4	5 3/16	4 1/32	6 15/32
1/8	3/32	5/32	29/32	1 7/16	1 11/16	2 23/32	2 1/2	4	3 9/32	5 9/32	4 3/32	6 9/16
3/16	5/32	1/4	15/16	1 17/32	1 3/4	2 13/16	2 17/32	4 1/16	3 11/32	5 11/32	4 1/8	6 5/8
1/4	3/16	5/16	1	1 19/32	1 25/32	2 7/8	2 19/32	4 5/32	3 3/8	5 7/16	4 3/16	6 23/32
5/16	1/4	13/32	1 1/16	1 11/16	1 27/32	2 31/32	2 5/8	4 1/4	3 7/16	5 1/2	4 7/32	6 25/32
3/8	5/16	15/32	1 3/32	1 3/4	1 29/32	3 1/32	2 11/16	4 5/16	3 1/2	5 19/32	4 9/32	6 7/8
7/16	11/32	9/16	1 5/32	1 27/32	1 15/16	3 1/8	2 3/4	4 13/32	3 17/32	5 11/16	4 11/32	6 15/16
1/2	13/32	5/8	1 3/16	1 29/32	2	3 3/16	2 25/32	4 15/32	3 19/32	5 3/4	4 3/8	7 1/32
9/16	7/16	23/32	1 1/4	2	2 1/32	3 9/32	2 27/32	4 9/16	3 5/8	5 27/32	4 7/16	7 1/8
5/8	1/2	13/16	1 9/32	2 1/16	2 3/32	3 11/32	2 7/8	4 5/8	3 11/16	5 29/32	4 15/32	7 3/16
11/16	9/16	7/8	1 11/32	2 5/32	2 5/32	3 7/16	2 15/16	4 23/32	3 3/4	6	4 17/32	7 9/32
3/4	19/32	31/32	1 13/32	2 1/4	2 3/16	3 17/32	3	4 25/32	3 25/32	6 1/16	4 19/32	7 11/32
13/16	21/32	1 1/32	1 7/16	2 5/16	2 1/4	3 19/32	3 1/32	4 7/8	3 27/32	6 5/32	4 5/8	7 7/16
7/8	11/16	1 1/8	1 1/2	2 13/32	2 9/32	3 11/16	3 3/32	4 31/32	3 7/8	6 7/32	4 11/16	7 1/2
15/16	3/4	1 3/16	1 17/32	2 15/32	2 11/32	3 3/4	3 1/8	5 1/32	3 15/16	6 5/16	4 23/32	7 19/32

Inches	6" Rise	6" Slope	7" Rise	7" Slope	8" Rise	8" Slope	9" Rise	9" Slope	10" Rise	10" Slope	11" Rise	11" Slope
0	4 25/32	7 11/16	5 9/16	8 15/16	6 3/8	10 7/32	7 3/16	11 1/2	7 31/32	1-0 25/32	8 3/4	1-2 1/16
1/16	4 27/32	7 3/4	5 5/8	9 1/32	6 7/16	10 5/16	7 7/32	11 19/32	8 1/32	1-0 7/8	8 13/16	1-2 5/32
1/8	4 7/8	7 27/32	5 11/16	9 1/8	6 15/32	10 3/8	7 9/32	11 21/32	8 1/16	1-0 15/16	8 7/8	1-2 7/32
3/16	4 15/16	7 29/32	5 23/32	9 3/16	6 17/32	10 15/32	7 5/16	11 3/4	8 1/8	1-1 1/32	8 29/32	1-2 5/16
1/4	4 31/32	8	5 25/32	9 9/32	6 9/16	10 9/16	7 3/8	11 13/16	8 5/32	1-1 3/32	8 31/32	1-2 3/8
5/16	5 1/32	8 1/16	5 13/16	9 11/32	6 5/8	10 5/8	7 13/32	11 29/32	8 7/32	1-1 3/16	9	1-2 15/32
3/8	5 3/32	8 5/32	5 7/8	9 7/16	6 11/16	10 23/32	7 15/32	1-0	8 9/32	1-1 9/32	9 1/16	1-2 17/32
7/16	5 1/8	8 7/32	5 15/16	9 1/2	6 23/32	10 25/32	7 17/32	1-0 1/16	8 5/16	1-1 11/32	9 1/8	1-2 5/8
1/2	5 3/16	8 5/16	5 31/32	9 19/32	6 25/32	10 7/8	7 9/16	1-0 5/32	8 3/8	1-1 7/16	9 5/32	1-2 23/32
9/16	5 7/32	8 13/32	6 1/32	9 21/32	6 13/16	10 15/16	7 5/8	1-0 7/32	8 13/32	1-1 1/2	9 7/32	1-2 25/32
5/8	5 9/32	8 15/32	6 1/16	9 3/4	6 7/8	11 1/32	7 21/32	1-0 5/16	8 15/32	1-1 19/32	9 1/4	1-2 7/8
11/16	5 11/32	8 9/16	6 1/8	9 27/32	6 15/16	11 3/32	7 23/32	1-0 3/8	8 17/32	1-1 21/32	9 5/16	1-2 15/16
3/4	5 3/8	8 5/8	6 3/16	9 29/32	6 31/32	11 3/16	7 25/32	1-0 15/32	8 9/16	1-1 3/4	9 3/8	1-3 1/32
13/16	5 7/16	8 23/32	6 7/32	10	7 1/32	11 9/32	7 13/16	1-0 9/16	8 5/8	1-1 13/16	9 13/32	1-3 3/32
7/8	5 15/32	8 25/32	6 9/32	10 1/16	7 1/16	11 11/32	7 7/8	1-0 5/8	8 21/32	1-1 29/32	9 15/32	1-3 3/16
15/16	5 17/32	8 7/8	6 5/16	10 5/32	7 1/8	11 7/16	7 29/32	1-0 23/32	8 23/32	1-2	9 1/2	1-3 1/4

Feet	0' Rise	0' Slope	10' Rise	10' Slope	20' Rise	20' Slope	30' Rise	30' Slope
0	0	0	7-11 5/8	12-9 7/16	15-11 1/4	25-6 7/8	23-10 7/8	38-4 5/16
1	-9 9/16	1-3 11/32	8-9 3/16	14-0 25/32	16-8 13/16	26-10 7/32	24-8 7/16	39-7 21/32
2	1-7 1/8	2-6 11/16	9-6 3/4	15-4 1/8	17-6 3/8	28-1 9/16	25-6	40-11
3	2-4 11/16	3-10 1/32	10-4 5/16	16-7 15/32	18-3 15/16	29-4 29/32	26-3 9/16	42-2 11/32
4	3-2 1/4	5-1 3/8	11-1 7/8	17-10 13/16	19-1 1/2	30-8 1/4	27-1 1/8	43-5 11/16
5	3-11 13/16	6-4 23/32	11-11 7/16	19-2 5/32	19-11 1/16	31-11 19/32	27-10 11/16	44-9 1/32
6	4-9 3/8	7-8 1/16	12-9	20-5 1/2	20-8 5/8	33-2 15/16	28-8 1/4	46-0 3/8
7	5-6 15/16	8-11 13/32	13-6 9/16	21-8 27/32	21-6 3/16	34-6 9/32	29-5 13/16	47-3 23/32
8	6-4 1/2	10-2 3/4	14-4 1/8	23-0 3/16	22-3 3/4	35-9 5/8	30-3 3/8	48-7 1/16
9	7-2 1/16	11-6 3/32	15-1 11/16	24-3 17/32	23-1 5/16	37-0 31/32	31-0 15/16	49-10 13/32

A = 38° 33' 02''; logsin A = 9.79463; logcos A = 9.89324; logtan A = 9.90139; logcot A = 0.09861

Ins.	12″ Rise	12″ Slope	13″ Rise	13″ Slope	14″ Rise	14″ Slope	15″ Rise	15″ Slope	16″ Rise	16″ Slope
0	9 9/16	1-3 11/32	10 3/8	1-4 5/8	11 5/32	1-5 29/32	11 15/16	1-7 3/16	1-0 3/4	1-8 15/32
1/16	9 5/8	1-3 7/16	10 13/32	1-4 11/16	11 7/32	1-5 31/32	1-0	1-7 1/4	1-0 13/16	1-8 17/32
1/8	9 21/32	1-3 1/2	10 15/32	1-4 25/32	11 1/4	1-6 1/16	1-0 1/16	1-7 11/32	1-0 27/32	1-8 5/8
3/16	9 23/32	1-3 19/32	10 1/2	1-4 7/8	11 5/16	1-6 5/32	1-0 3/32	1-7 13/32	1-0 29/32	1-8 11/16
1/4	9 3/4	1-3 21/32	10 9/16	1-4 15/16	11 11/32	1-6 7/32	1-0 5/32	1-7 1/2	1-0 15/16	1-8 25/32
5/16	9 13/16	1-3 3/4	10 19/32	1-5 1/32	11 13/32	1-6 5/16	1-0 3/16	1-7 19/32	1-1	1-8 27/32
3/8	9 7/8	1-3 13/16	10 21/32	1-5 3/32	11 15/32	1-6 3/8	1-0 1/4	1-7 21/32	1-1 1/16	1-8 15/16
7/16	9 29/32	1-3 29/32	10 23/32	1-5 3/16	11 1/2	1-6 15/32	1-0 5/16	1-7 3/4	1-1 3/32	1-9 1/32
1/2	9 31/32	1-3 31/32	10 3/4	1-5 1/4	11 9/16	1-6 17/32	1-0 11/32	1-7 13/16	1-1 5/32	1-9 3/32
9/16	10	1-4 1/16	10 13/16	1-5 11/32	11 19/32	1-6 5/8	1-0 13/32	1-7 29/32	1-1 3/16	1-9 3/16
5/8	10 1/16	1-4 5/32	10 27/32	1-5 7/16	11 21/32	1-6 11/16	1-0 7/16	1-7 31/32	1-1 1/4	1-9 1/4
11/16	10 1/8	1-4 7/32	10 29/32	1-5 1/2	11 23/32	1-6 25/32	1-0 1/2	1-8 1/16	1-1 5/16	1-9 11/32
3/4	10 5/32	1-4 5/16	10 31/32	1-5 19/32	11 3/4	1-6 7/8	1-0 9/16	1-8 1/8	1-1 11/32	1-9 13/32
13/16	10 7/32	1-4 3/8	11	1-5 21/32	11 13/16	1-6 15/16	1-0 19/32	1-8 7/32	1-1 13/32	1-9 1/2
7/8	10 1/4	1-4 15/32	11 1/16	1-5 3/4	11 27/32	1-7 1/32	1-0 21/32	1-8 5/16	1-1 7/16	1-9 9/16
15/16	10 5/16	1-4 17/32	11 3/32	1-5 13/16	11 29/32	1-7 3/32	1-0 11/16	1-8 3/8	1-1 1/2	1-9 21/32

Ins.	17″ Rise	17″ Slope	18″ Rise	18″ Slope	19″ Rise	19″ Slope	20″ Rise	20″ Slope	21″ Rise	21″ Slope
0	1-1 9/16	1-9 3/4	1-2 11/32	1-11 1/16	1-3 1/8	2-0 9/32	1-3 15/16	2-1 9/16	1-4 3/4	2-2 27/32
1/16	1-1 19/32	1-9 13/16	1-2 13/32	1-11 3/32	1-3 3/16	2-0 3/8	1-4	2-1 21/32	1-4 25/32	2-2 15/16
1/8	1-1 21/32	1-9 29/32	1-2 7/16	1-11 1/8	1-3 1/4	2-0 15/32	1-4 1/32	2-1 23/32	1-4 27/32	2-3
3/16	1-1 11/16	1-9 31/32	1-2 1/2	1-11 1/4	1-3 9/32	2-0 17/32	1-4 3/32	2-1 13/16	1-4 7/8	2-3 3/32
1/4	1-1 3/4	1-10 1/16	1-2 17/32	1-11 11/32	1-3 11/32	2-0 5/8	1-4 1/8	2-1 29/32	1-4 15/16	2-3 5/32
5/16	1-1 25/32	1-10 1/8	1-2 19/32	1-11 13/32	1-3 3/8	2-0 11/16	1-4 3/16	2-1 31/32	1-4 31/32	2-3 1/4
3/8	1-1 27/32	1-10 7/32	1-2 21/32	1-11 1/2	1-3 7/16	2-0 25/32	1-4 1/4	2-2 1/16	1-5 1/32	2-3 11/32
7/16	1-1 29/32	1-10 5/16	1-2 11/16	1-11 9/16	1-3 1/2	2-0 27/32	1-4 9/32	2-2 1/8	1-5 3/32	2-3 13/32
1/2	1-1 15/16	1-10 3/8	1-2 3/4	1-11 21/32	1-3 17/32	2-0 15/16	1-4 11/32	2-2 7/32	1-5 1/8	2-3 1/2
9/16	1-2	1-10 15/32	1-2 25/32	1-11 3/4	1-3 19/32	2-1	1-4 3/8	2-2 9/32	1-5 3/16	2-3 9/16
5/8	1-2 1/16	1-10 17/32	1-2 27/32	1-11 13/16	1-3 5/8	2-1 1/8	1-4 7/16	2-2 3/8	1-5 7/32	2-3 21/32
11/16	1-2 3/32	1-10 5/8	1-2 29/32	1-11 29/32	1-3 11/16	2-1 3/16	1-4 1/2	2-2 7/16	1-5 9/32	2-3 23/32
3/4	1-2 5/32	1-10 11/16	1-2 15/16	1-11 31/32	1-3 3/4	2-1 1/4	1-4 17/32	2-2 17/32	1-5 11/32	2-3 13/16
13/16	1-2 3/16	1-10 25/32	1-3	2-0 1/16	1-3 25/32	2-1 11/32	1-4 19/32	2-2 5/8	1-5 3/8	2-3 29/32
7/8	1-2 1/4	1-10 27/32	1-3 1/32	2-0 1/8	1-3 27/32	2-1 13/32	1-4 5/8	2-2 11/16	1-5 7/16	2-3 31/32
15/16	1-2 9/32	1-10 15/16	1-3 3/32	2-0 7/32	1-3 7/8	2-1 1/2	1-4 11/16	2-2 25/32	1-5 15/32	2-4 1/16

Feet	40′ Rise	40′ Slope	50′ Rise	50′ Slope	60′ Rise	60′ Slope	70′ Rise	70′ Slope
0	31-10 1/2	51-1 3/4	39-10 1/8	63-11 7/32	47-9 3/4	76-8 21/32	55-9 3/8	89-6 3/32
1	32-8 5/16	52-5 3/32	40-7 11/16	65-2 9/16	48-7 5/16	78-0	56-6 15/16	90-9 7/16
2	33-5 5/8	53-8 7/16	41-5 1/4	66-5 29/32	49-4 7/8	79-3 11/32	57-4 1/2	92-0 25/32
3	34-3 3/16	54-11 25/32	42-2 13/16	67-9 1/4	50-2 7/16	80-6 11/16	58-2 1/16	93-4 1/8
4	35-0 3/4	56-3 1/8	43-0 3/8	69-0 19/32	51-0	81-10 1/32	58-11 5/8	94-7 15/32
5	35-10 5/16	57-6 1/2	43-9 15/16	70-3 15/16	51-9 9/16	83-1 3/8	59-9 3/16	95-10 13/16
6	36-7 7/8	58-9 27/32	44-7 1/2	71-7 9/32	52-7 1/8	84-4 23/32	60-6 3/4	97-2 5/32
7	37-5 7/16	60-1 3/16	45-5 1/16	72-10 5/8	53-4 11/16	85-8 1/16	61-4 5/16	98-5 1/2
8	38-3	61-4 17/32	46-2 5/8	74-1 31/32	54-2 1/4	86-11 13/32	62-1 7/8	99-8 27/32
9	39-0 9/16	62-7 7/8	47-0 3/16	75-5 5/16	54-11 13/16	88-2 3/4	62-11 7/16	101-0 3/16

natsin A=0.6232037050; natcos A=0.7820595513; nattan A=0.7968750000; natcot A=1.2549019607

Inches	0" Rise	0" Slope	1" Rise	1" Slope	2" Rise	2" Slope	3" Rise	3" Slope	4" Rise	4" Slope	5" Rise	5" Slope
0	0	0	13/16	1 9/32	1 19/32	2 9/16	2 13/32	3 27/32	3 1/32	5 1/8	4	6 13/32
1/16	1/16	3/32	27/32	1 3/8	1 21/32	2 21/32	2 15/32	3 15/16	3 1/4	5 1/8	4 1/16	6 1/2
1/8	3/32	5/32	29/32	1 7/16	1 23/32	2 23/32	2 1/2	4	3 5/16	5 9/32	4 1/8	6 9/16
3/16	5/32	1/4	15/16	1 17/32	1 3/4	2 13/16	2 9/16	4 3/32	3 11/32	5 3/8	4 5/32	6 21/32
1/4	3/16	5/16	1	1 19/32	1 13/16	2 7/8	2 19/32	4 5/32	3 13/32	5 7/16	4 7/32	6 23/32
5/16	1/4	13/32	1 1/16	1 11/16	1 27/32	2 31/32	2 21/32	4 1/4	3 15/32	5 17/32	4 1/4	6 13/16
3/8	5/16	15/32	1 3/32	1 3/4	1 29/32	3 1/32	2 23/32	4 5/16	3 1/2	5 19/32	4 5/16	6 7/8
7/16	11/32	9/16	1 5/32	1 27/32	1 31/32	3 1/8	2 3/4	4 13/32	3 9/16	5 11/16	4 3/8	6 31/32
1/2	13/32	21/32	1 3/16	1 15/16	2	3 7/32	2 13/16	4 1/2	3 5/8	5 25/32	4 13/32	7 1/16
9/16	7/16	23/32	1 1/4	2	2 1/16	3 9/32	2 27/32	4 9/16	3 21/32	5 27/32	4 15/32	7 1/8
5/8	1/2	13/16	1 5/16	2 3/32	2 3/32	3 3/8	2 29/32	4 21/32	3 23/32	5 15/16	4 1/2	7 7/32
11/16	9/16	7/8	1 11/32	2 5/32	2 5/32	3 7/16	2 31/32	4 25/32	3 3/4	6	4 9/16	7 9/32
3/4	19/32	31/32	1 13/32	2 1/4	2 7/32	3 17/32	3	4 13/16	3 13/16	6 3/32	4 5/8	7 3/8
13/16	21/32	1 1/32	1 15/32	2 5/16	2 1/4	3 19/32	3 1/16	4 7/8	3 7/8	6 9/32	4 21/32	7 7/16
7/8	11/16	1 1/8	1 1/2	2 13/32	2 5/16	3 11/16	3 3/32	4 31/32	3 29/32	6 1/4	4 23/32	7 17/32
15/16	3/4	1 3/16	1 9/16	2 15/32	2 11/32	3 25/32	3 5/32	5 1/16	3 31/32	6 11/32	4 3/4	7 5/8

Inches	6" Rise	6" Slope	7" Rise	7" Slope	8" Rise	8" Slope	9" Rise	9" Slope	10" Rise	10" Slope	11" Rise	11" Slope
0	4 13/16	7 11/16	5 5/8	8 31/32	6 13/32	10 1/4	7 7/32	11 17/32	8 1/32	1-0 13/16	8 13/16	1-2 3/32
1/16	4 7/8	7 25/32	5 21/32	9 1/16	6 15/32	10 11/32	7 9/32	11 5/8	8 1/16	1-0 29/32	8 7/8	1-2 3/16
1/8	4 29/32	7 27/32	5 23/32	9 1/8	6 17/32	10 13/32	7 5/16	11 11/16	8 1/8	1-0 31/32	8 15/16	1-2 1/4
3/16	4 31/32	7 15/16	5 3/4	9 7/32	6 9/16	10 1/2	7 3/8	11 25/32	8 5/32	1-1 1/16	8 31/32	1-2 11/32
1/4	5	8	5 13/16	9 9/32	6 5/8	10 9/16	7 13/32	11 27/32	8 7/32	1-1 1/8	9 1/32	1-2 13/32
5/16	5 1/16	8 3/32	5 7/8	9 3/8	6 21/32	10 21/32	7 15/32	11 15/16	8 9/32	1-1 7/32	9 1/16	1-2 1/2
3/8	5 1/8	8 3/16	5 29/32	9 15/32	6 23/32	10 3/4	7 17/32	1-0 1/32	8 5/16	1-1 5/16	9 1/8	1-2 19/32
7/16	5 5/32	8 1/4	5 31/32	9 17/32	6 25/32	10 13/16	7 9/16	1-0 3/32	8 3/8	1-1 3/8	9 3/16	1-2 21/32
1/2	5 7/32	8 11/32	6	9 5/8	6 13/16	10 29/32	7 5/8	1-0 5/32	8 7/16	1-1 15/32	9 7/32	1-2 3/4
9/16	5 1/4	8 13/32	6 1/16	9 11/16	6 7/8	10 31/32	7 21/32	1-0 1/4	8 15/32	1-1 17/32	9 9/32	1-2 13/16
5/8	5 5/16	8 1/2	6 1/8	9 25/32	6 29/32	11 1/16	7 23/32	1-0 11/32	8 17/32	1-1 5/8	9 5/16	1-2 29/32
11/16	5 3/8	8 9/16	6 5/32	9 27/32	6 31/32	11 1/8	7 25/32	1-0 13/32	8 9/16	1-1 11/16	9 3/8	1-2 31/32
3/4	5 13/32	8 21/32	6 7/32	9 15/16	7 1/32	11 7/32	7 13/16	1-0 1/2	8 5/8	1-1 25/32	9 7/16	1-3 1/16
13/16	5 15/32	8 23/32	6 9/32	10	7 1/16	11 5/16	7 7/8	1-0 19/32	8 11/16	1-1 7/8	9 15/32	1-3 5/32
7/8	5 1/2	8 13/16	6 5/16	10 3/32	7 1/8	11 3/8	7 29/32	1-0 21/32	8 23/32	1-1 15/16	9 17/32	1-3 7/32
15/16	5 9/16	8 7/8	6 3/8	10 3/16	7 5/32	11 15/32	7 31/32	1-0 3/4	8 25/32	1-2 1/32	9 9/16	1-3 5/16

Feet	0' Rise	0' Slope	10' Rise	10' Slope	20' Rise	20' Slope	30' Rise	30' Slope
0	0	0	8-0 1/4	12-9 27/32	16-0 1/2	25-7 21/32	24-0 3/4	38-5 1/2
1	-9 5/8	1-3 3/8	8-9 7/8	14-1 7/32	16-10 1/8	26-11 1/2	24-10 3/8	39-8 7/8
2	1-7 1/4	2-6 25/32	9-7 1/2	15-4 19/32	17-7 3/4	28-2 7/16	25-8	41-0 1/4
3	2-4 7/8	3-10 5/32	10-5 1/8	16-7 31/32	18-5 3/8	29-5 13/16	26-5 5/8	42-3 21/32
4	3-2 1/2	5-1 17/32	11-2 3/4	17-11 3/8	19-3	30-9 3/16	27-3 1/4	43-7 1/32
5	4-0 1/8	6-4 29/32	12-0 3/8	19-2 3/4	20-0 5/8	32-0 19/32	28-0 7/8	44-10 13/32
6	4-9 3/4	7-8 5/16	12-10	20-6 1/8	20-10 1/4	33-3 31/32	28-10 1/2	46-1 25/32
7	5-7 3/8	8-11 11/16	13-7 5/8	21-9 1/2	21-7 7/8	34-7 11/32	29-8 1/8	47-5 3/16
8	6-5	10-3 1/16	14-5 1/4	23-0 29/32	22-5 1/2	35-10 23/32	30-5 3/4	48-8 9/16
9	7-2 5/8	11-6 7/16	15-2 7/8	24-4 9/32	23-3 1/8	37-2 1/8	31-3 3/8	49-11 15/16

A = 38° 43' 57": logsin A = **9.79636**; logcos A = **9.89214**; logtan A = **9.90422**; logcot A = **0.09578**

Ins.	12″ Rise	12″ Slope	13″ Rise	13″ Slope	14″ Rise	14″ Slope	15″ Rise	15″ Slope	16″ Rise	16″ Slope
0	9 5/8	1-3 3/8	10 7/16	1-4 21/32	11 7/32	1-5 15/16	1-0 1/2	1-7 1/2	1-0 27/32	1-8 1/2
1/16	9 11/16	1-3 15/32	10 15/32	1-4 3/4	11 9/32	1-6 1/8	1-0 5/8	1-7 5/16	1-0 7/8	1-8 19/32
1/8	9 23/32	1-3 17/32	10 17/32	1-4 13/16	11 11/32	1-6 9/32	1-0 1/8	1-7 3/8	1-0 15/16	1-8 21/32
3/16	9 25/32	1-3 5/8	10 9/16	1-4 29/32	11 3/8	1-6 3/16	1-0 3/16	1-7 15/32	1-0 31/32	1-8 3/4
1/4	9 13/16	1-3 23/32	10 5/8	1-5	11 7/16	1-6 9/32	1-0 7/32	1-7 9/16	1-1 1/32	1-8 27/32
5/16	9 7/8	1-3 25/32	10 11/16	1-5 1/16	11 15/32	1-6 11/32	1-0 9/32	1-7 5/8	1-1 3/32	1-8 29/32
3/8	9 15/16	1-3 7/8	10 23/32	1-5 5/32	11 17/32	1-6 7/16	1-0 11/32	1-7 23/32	1-1 1/8	1-9
7/16	9 31/32	1-3 15/16	10 25/32	1-5 7/32	11 19/32	1-6 1/2	1-0 3/8	1-7 25/32	1-1 3/16	1-9 1/16
1/2	10 1/2	1-4 1/2	10 13/16	1-5 5/16	11 5/8	1-6 19/32	1-0 7/16	1-7 7/8	1-1 1/4	1-9 5/32
9/16	10 1/16	1-4 3/32	10 7/8	1-5 3/8	11 11/16	1-6 21/32	1-0 15/32	1-7 15/16	1-1 9/32	1-9 7/32
5/8	10 1/8	1-4 3/16	10 15/16	1-5 15/32	11 23/32	1-6 3/4	1-0 17/32	1-8 1/32	1-1 11/32	1-9 5/16
11/16	10 3/16	1-4 1/4	10 31/32	1-5 17/32	11 25/32	1-6 27/32	1-0 19/32	1-8 1/8	1-1 3/8	1-9 13/32
3/4	10 7/32	1-4 11/32	11 1/32	1-5 5/8	11 27/32	1-6 29/32	1-0 5/8	1-8 3/16	1-1 7/16	1-9 15/32
13/16	10 9/32	1-4 7/16	11 3/32	1-5 23/32	11 7/8	1-7	1-0 11/16	1-8 9/32	1-1 1/2	1-9 9/16
7/8	10 5/16	1-4 1/2	11 1/8	1-5 25/32	11 15/16	1-7 1/16	1-0 23/32	1-8 11/32	1-1 17/32	1-9 5/8
15/16	10 3/8	1-4 19/32	11 3/16	1-5 7/8	11 31/32	1-7 5/32	1-0 25/32	1-8 7/16	1-1 19/32	1-9 23/32

Ins.	17″ Rise	17″ Slope	18″ Rise	18″ Slope	19″ Rise	19″ Slope	20″ Rise	20″ Slope	21″ Rise	21″ Slope
0	1-1 5/8	1-9 25/32	1-2 7/16	1-11 11/16	1-3 1/4	2-0 11/32	1-4 1/32	2-1 5/8	1-4 27/32	2-2 29/32
1/16	1-1 11/16	1-9 7/8	1-2 1/2	1-11 15/32	1-3 9/32	2-0 7/16	1-4 3/32	2-1 23/32	1-4 29/32	2-3
1/8	1-1 3/4	1-9 15/16	1-2 17/32	1-11 1/4	1-3 11/32	2-0 17/32	1-4 5/32	2-1 13/16	1-4 15/16	2-3 9/32
3/16	1-1 23/32	1-10 1/32	1-2 19/32	1-11 15/32	1-3 3/8	2-0 9/32	1-4 3/16	2-1 7/8	1-5	2-3 5/32
1/4	1-1 27/32	1-10 1/16	1-2 5/8	1-11 13/32	1-3 7/16	2-0 11/32	1-4 1/4	2-1 31/32	1-5 1/32	2-3 1/4
5/16	1-1 7/8	1-10 3/16	1-2 11/16	1-11 15/32	1-3 1/2	2-0 3/4	1-4 9/32	2-2 1/16	1-5 3/32	2-3 5/16
3/8	1-1 15/16	1-10 9/32	1-2 3/4	1-11 9/16	1-3 9/16	2-0 27/32	1-4 11/32	2-2 1/8	1-5 5/32	2-3 13/32
7/16	1-2	1-10 11/32	1-2 25/32	1-11 5/8	1-3 19/32	2-0 29/32	1-4 13/32	2-2 3/16	1-5 9/16	2-3 15/32
1/2	1-2 1/32	1-10 7/16	1-2 27/32	1-11 23/32	1-3 5/8	2-1	1-4 7/16	2-2 9/32	1-5 1/4	2-3 9/16
9/16	1-2 3/32	1-10 1/2	1-2 7/8	1-11 25/32	1-3 11/16	2-1 1/16	1-4 1/2	2-2 3/8	1-5 9/32	2-3 21/32
5/8	1-2 1/8	1-10 19/32	1-2 15/16	1-11 7/8	1-3 3/4	2-1 5/32	1-4 17/32	2-2 7/16	1-5 11/32	2-3 23/32
11/16	1-2 3/16	1-10 11/32	1-3	1-11 31/32	1-3 13/16	2-1 1/4	1-4 19/32	2-2 17/32	1-5 13/32	2-3 13/16
3/4	1-2 1/4	1-10 3/4	1-3 1/8	2-0 1/32	1-3 27/32	2-1 5/16	1-4 21/32	2-2 19/32	1-5 7/16	2-3 7/8
13/16	1-2 9/32	1-10 27/32	1-3 3/16	2-0 1/16	1-3 29/32	2-1 13/32	1-4 11/16	2-2 11/16	1-5 1/2	2-3 31/32
7/8	1-2 11/32	1-10 29/32	1-3 1/8	2-0 3/16	1-3 15/16	2-1 15/32	1-4 3/4	2-2 3/4	1-5 17/32	2-4 1/32
15/16	1-2 3/8	1-11	1-3 3/16	2-0 9/32	1-4	2-1 9/16	1-4 25/32	2-2 27/32	1-5 19/32	2-4 1/8

Feet	40′ Rise	40′ Slope	50′ Rise	50′ Slope	60′ Rise	60′ Slope	70′ Rise	70′ Slope
0	32-1	51-3 5/16	40-1 1/4	64-1 5/32	48-1 1/2	76-11	56-1 3/4	89-8 13/16
1	32-10 5/8	52-6 23/32	40-10 7/8	65-4 17/32	48-11 1/8	78-2 3/8	56-11 3/8	91-0 3/16
2	33-8 1/4	53-10 3/32	41-8 1/2	66-7 15/16	49-8 3/4	79-5 3/8	57-9	92-3 19/32
3	34-5 7/8	55-1 15/32	42-6 1/8	67-11 5/8	50-6 3/8	80-9 1/8	58-6 5/8	93-6 31/32
4	35-3 1/2	56-4 27/32	43-3 3/4	69-2 11/16	51-4	82-0 17/32	59-4 1/4	94-10 11/32
5	36-1 1/8	57-8 1/4	44-1 3/8	70-6 1/16	52-1 5/8	83-3 29/32	60-1 7/8	96-1 3/4
6	36-10 3/4	58-11 5/8	44-11	71-9 15/32	52-11 1/4	84-7 9/32	60-11 1/2	97-5 1/8
7	37-8 3/8	60-3	45-8 5/8	73-0 27/32	53-8 7/8	85-10 21/32	61-9 1/8	98-8 1/2
8	38-6	61-6 3/8	46-6 1/4	74-4 7/32	54-6 1/2	87-2 1/16	62-6 3/4	99-11 7/8
9	39-3 5/8	62-9 25/32	47-3 7/8	75-7 19/32	55-4 1/8	88-5 7/16	63-4 3/8	101-3 9/32

natsin A=0.6256854939; natcos A=0.7800754210; nattan A=0.8020833333; natcot A=1.2467532467

Inches	0" Rise	0" Slope	1" Rise	1" Slope	2" Rise	2" Slope	3" Rise	3" Slope	4" Rise	4" Slope	5" Rise	5" Slope
0	0	0	13/16	1 9/32	1 5/8	2 9/16	2 7/16	3 27/32	3 7/32	5 5/32	4 1/32	6 7/16
1/16	1/16	3/32	27/32	1 3/8	1 21/32	2 21/32	2 15/32	3 15/16	3 9/32	5 7/32	4 3/32	6 1/2
1/8	3/32	5/32	29/32	1 7/16	1 23/32	2 23/32	2 17/32	4 1/32	3 11/32	5 5/16	4 1/8	6 19/32
3/16	5/32	1/4	31/32	1 17/32	1 25/32	2 13/16	2 9/16	4 3/32	3 3/8	5 3/8	4 3/16	6 21/32
1/4	3/16	5/16	1	1 19/32	1 13/16	2 29/32	2 5/8	4 3/16	3 7/16	5 15/32	4 1/4	6 3/4
5/16	1/4	13/32	1 1/16	1 11/16	1 7/8	2 31/32	2 11/16	4 1/4	3 15/32	5 17/32	4 9/32	6 13/16
3/8	5/16	15/32	1 1/8	1 25/32	1 29/32	3 1/16	2 23/32	4 11/32	3 17/32	5 5/8	4 11/32	6 29/32
7/16	11/32	9/16	1 5/32	1 27/32	1 31/32	3 1/8	2 25/32	4 13/32	3 19/32	5 11/16	4 3/8	7
1/2	13/32	21/32	1 7/32	1 15/32	2 1/32	3 7/32	2 13/16	4 1/2	3 5/8	5 25/32	4 7/16	7 1/16
9/16	15/32	23/32	1 1/4	2	2 1/16	3 9/32	2 7/8	4 19/32	3 11/16	5 7/8	4 1/2	7 5/32
5/8	1/2	13/16	1 5/16	2 3/32	2 1/8	3 3/8	2 15/16	4 21/32	3 23/32	5 15/16	4 17/32	7 7/32
11/16	9/16	7/8	1 3/8	2 5/32	2 5/32	3 15/32	2 31/32	4 3/4	3 25/32	6 1/32	4 19/32	7 5/16
3/4	19/32	31/32	1 13/32	2 1/4	2 7/32	3 17/32	3 1/32	4 13/16	3 27/32	6 3/32	4 21/32	7 3/8
13/16	21/32	1 1/32	1 15/32	2 11/32	2 9/32	3 5/8	3 1/16	4 29/32	3 7/8	6 3/16	4 11/16	7 15/32
7/8	23/32	1 1/8	1 1/2	2 13/32	2 5/16	3 11/16	3 1/8	4 31/32	3 15/16	6 1/4	4 3/4	7 9/16
15/16	3/4	1 7/32	1 9/16	2 1/2	2 3/8	3 25/32	3 3/16	5 1/16	4	6 11/32	4 25/32	7 5/8

Inches	6" Rise	6" Slope	7" Rise	7" Slope	8" Rise	8" Slope	9" Rise	9" Slope	10" Rise	10" Slope	11" Rise	11" Slope
0	4 27/32	7 23/32	5 21/32	9	6 15/32	10 9/32	7 1/4	11 9/16	8 1/8	1-0 27/32	8 7/8	1-2 1/8
1/16	4 29/32	7 25/32	5 11/16	9 1/16	6 1/2	10 3/8	7 5/16	11 21/32	8 1/8	1-0 15/16	8 15/16	1-2 7/32
1/8	4 15/16	7 7/8	5 3/4	9 5/32	6 9/16	10 7/16	7 3/8	11 23/32	8 3/16	1-1	8 31/32	1-2 5/16
3/16	5	7 15/16	5 13/16	9 1/4	6 5/8	10 17/32	7 13/32	11 13/16	8 7/32	1-1 3/32	9 1/32	1-2 3/8
1/4	5 1/32	8 1/16	5 27/32	9 5/16	6 21/32	10 19/32	7 15/32	11 7/8	8 9/32	1-1 3/16	9 3/32	1-2 15/32
5/16	5 3/32	8 1/8	5 29/32	9 13/32	6 23/32	10 11/16	7 17/32	11 31/32	8 5/16	1-1 1/4	9 1/8	1-2 17/32
3/8	5 5/32	8 3/16	5 31/32	9 15/32	6 3/4	10 3/4	7 9/16	1-0 1/16	8 3/8	1-1 11/32	9 3/16	1-2 5/8
7/16	5 3/16	8 9/32	6	9 9/16	6 13/16	10 27/32	7 5/8	1-0 1/8	8 7/16	1-1 13/32	9 7/32	1-2 11/16
1/2	5 1/4	8 11/32	6 1/16	9 5/8	6 7/8	10 15/16	7 21/32	1-0 7/32	8 15/32	1-1 1/2	9 9/32	1-2 25/32
9/16	5 5/16	8 7/16	6 3/32	9 23/32	6 29/32	11	7 23/32	1-0 9/32	8 17/32	1-1 9/16	9 11/32	1-2 7/8
5/8	5 11/32	8 1/2	6 5/32	9 13/16	6 31/32	11 3/32	7 25/32	1-0 3/8	8 9/16	1-1 21/32	9 3/8	1-2 15/16
11/16	5 13/32	8 19/32	6 1/4	9 7/8	7	11 5/32	7 13/16	1-0 7/16	8 5/8	1-1 3/4	9 7/16	1-3 1/32
3/4	5 7/16	8 11/16	6 1/4	9 31/32	7 1/16	11 1/4	7 7/8	1-0 17/32	8 11/16	1-1 13/16	9 1/2	1-3 3/32
13/16	5 1/2	8 3/4	6 5/16	10 1/32	7 1/8	11 5/16	7 29/32	1-0 5/8	8 23/32	1-1 29/32	9 17/32	1-3 3/16
7/8	5 9/16	8 27/32	6 11/32	10 1/8	7 5/32	11 13/32	7 31/32	1-0 11/16	8 25/32	1-1 31/32	9 19/32	1-3 1/4
15/16	5 19/32	8 29/32	6 13/32	10 3/16	7 7/32	11 1/2	8 1/32	1-0 25/32	8 27/32	1-2 1/32	9 5/8	1-3 11/32

Feet	0' Rise	0' Slope	10' Rise	10' Slope	20' Rise	20' Slope	30' Rise	30' Slope
0	0	0	8-0 7/8	12-10 7/32	16-1 3/4	25-8 7/16	24-2 5/8	38-6 21/32
1	-9 11/16	1-3 7/16	8-10 9/16	14-1 21/32	16-11 7/16	26-11 7/8	25-0 5/8	39-10 3/32
2	1-7 3/8	2-6 27/32	9-8 1/4	15-5 1/16	17-9 1/8	28-3 9/32	25-10	41-1 1/2
3	2-5 1/16	3-10 9/32	10-5 15/16	16-8 1/2	18-6 13/16	29-6 23/32	26-7 11/16	42-4 15/16
4	3-2 3/4	5-1 11/16	11-3 5/8	17-11 29/32	19-4 1/2	30-10 1/8	27-5 3/8	43-8 11/32
5	4-0 7/16	6-5 1/8	12-1 5/16	19-3 11/32	20-2 3/16	32-1 9/16	28-3 1/16	44-11 25/32
6	4-10 1/8	7-8 17/32	12-11	20-6 3/4	20-11 7/8	33-4 31/32	29-0 3/4	46-3 3/16
7	5-7 13/16	8-11 31/32	13-8 11/16	21-10 3/16	21-9 9/16	34-8 13/32	29-10 7/16	47-6 5/8
8	6-5 1/2	10-3 3/8	14-6 3/8	23-1 19/32	22-7 1/4	35-11 13/16	30-8 1/8	48-10 1/16
9	7-3 3/16	11-6 13/16	15-4 1/16	24-5 1/32	23-4 15/16	37-3 1/4	31-5 13/16	50-1 15/32

A = 38° 54' 49"; logsin A = 9.79806; logcos A = 9.89103; logtan A = 9.90703; logcot A = 0.09297

Ins.	12" Rise	12" Slope	13" Rise	13" Slope	14" Rise	14" Slope	15" Rise	15" Slope	16" Rise	16" Slope
0	9 11/16	1-3 7/16	10 1/2	1-4 23/32–	11 5/16	1-6	1-0 1/8	1-7 9/32–	1-0 29/32	1-8 9/16
1/16	9 3/4	1-3 1/2	10 17/32	1-4 25/32	11 11/32	1-6 1/16	1-0 5/32	1-7 11/32	1-0 31/32–	1-8 21/32–
1/8	9 25/32	1-3 19/32–	10 19/32	1-4 7/8	11 13/32–	1-6 5/32–	1-0 7/32–	1-7 7/16	1-1 1/32–	1-8 23/32
3/16	9 27/32–	1-3 21/32	10 21/32–	1-4 15/16	11 15/32–	1-6 7/32	1-0 1/4	1-7 17/32–	1-1 1/16	1-8 13/16
1/4	9 7/8	1-3 3/4	10 11/16	1-5 1/32–	11 1/2	1-6 5/16	1-0 5/16	1-7 19/32	1-1 1/8	1-8 7/8
5/16	9 15/16	1-3 13/16	10 3/4	1-5 3/32	11 9/16	1-6 13/32–	1-0 3/8	1-7 11/16	1-1 5/32	1-8 31/32–
3/8	10	1-3 29/32–	10 13/16	1-5 3/16	11 19/32	1-6 15/32	1-0 13/32	1-7 3/4	1-1 7/32	1-9 1/32
7/16	10 1/32	1-4	10 27/32	1-5 9/32–	11 21/32–	1-6 9/16	1-0 15/32–	1-7 27/32–	1-1 9/32–	1-9 1/8
1/2	10 3/32–	1-4 1/16	10 29/32–	1-5 11/32	11 23/32–	1-6 5/8	1-0 1/2	1-7 29/32	1-1 5/16	1-9 7/32–
9/16	10 5/32–	1-4 5/32–	10 15/16	1-5 7/16	11 3/4	1-6 23/32–	1-0 9/16	1-8	1-1 3/8	1-9 9/32
5/8	10 3/16	1-4 7/32	11	1-5 1/2	11 13/16	1-6 25/32	1-0 5/8	1-8 3/32–	1-1 13/32	1-9 3/8
11/16	10 1/4	1-4 5/16	11 1/16	1-5 19/32–	11 27/32	1-6 7/8	1-0 21/32	1-8 5/32	1-1 15/32	1-9 7/16
3/4	10 9/32	1-4 3/8	11 3/32	1-5 21/32	11 29/32	1-6 31/32–	1-0 23/32–	1-8 1/4	1-1 17/32–	1-9 17/32–
13/16	10 11/32–	1-4 15/32–	11 5/32–	1-5 3/4	11 31/32–	1-7 1/32	1-0 3/4	1-8 5/16	1-1 9/16	1-9 19/32
7/8	10 13/32–	1-4 17/32	11 3/16	1-5 27/32–	1-0	1-7 1/8	1-0 13/16	1-8 13/32–	1-1 5/8	1-9 11/16
15/16	10 7/16	1-4 5/8	11 1/4	1-5 29/32	1-0 1/16	1-7 3/16	1-0 7/8	1-8 15/32	1-1 11/16	1-9 25/32–

Ins.	17" Rise	17" Slope	18" Rise	18" Slope	19" Rise	19" Slope	20" Rise	20" Slope	21" Rise	21" Slope
0	1-1 23/32	1-9 27/32	1-2 17/32	1-11 1/8	1-3 11/32–	2-0 13/32	1-4 5/32–	2-1 23/32–	1-4 15/16	2-3
1/16	1-1 25/32–	1-9 15/16	1-2 19/32–	1-11 7/32–	1-3 3/8	2-0 1/2	1-4 3/16	2-1 25/32	1-5	2-3 1/16
1/8	1-1 13/16	1-10	1-2 5/8	1-11 9/32	1-3 7/16	2-0 19/32–	1-4 1/4	2-1 7/8	1-5 1/16	2-3 5/32–
3/16	1-1 7/8	1-10 3/32–	1-2 11/16	1-11 3/8	1-3 1/2	2-0 21/32	1-4 5/16	2-1 15/16	1-5 3/32	2-3 7/32
1/4	1-1 15/16	1-10 5/32	1-2 23/32	1-11 15/32–	1-3 17/32	2-0 3/4	1-4 11/32	2-2 1/32–	1-5 5/32–	2-3 5/16
5/16	1-1 31/32	1-10 1/4	1-2 25/32	1-11 17/32	1-3 19/32–	2-0 13/16	1-4 13/32–	2-2 3/32	1-5 7/32–	2-3 13/32–
3/8	1-2 1/32–	1-10 11/32–	1-2 27/32–	1-11 5/8	1-3 21/32–	2-0 29/32–	1-4 7/16	2-2 3/16	1-5 1/4	2-3 15/32
7/16	1-2 1/16	1-10 13/32	1-2 7/8	1-11 11/16	1-3 11/16	2-0 31/32	1-4 1/2	2-2 9/32–	1-5 5/16	2-3 9/16
1/2	1-2 1/8	1-10 1/2	1-2 15/16	1-11 25/32–	1-3 3/4	2-1 1/16	1-4 9/16	2-2 11/32	1-5 11/32	2-3 5/8
9/16	1-2 3/16	1-10 9/16	1-3	1-11 27/32	1-3 25/32	2-1 5/32–	1-4 19/32	2-2 7/16	1-5 13/32	2-3 23/32–
5/8	1-2 7/32	1-10 21/32–	1-3 1/32	1-11 15/16	1-3 27/32–	2-1 7/32	1-4 21/32–	2-2 1/2	1-5 15/32–	2-3 25/32
11/16	1-2 9/32–	1-10 23/32	1-3 3/32–	2-0 1/32–	1-3 29/32–	2-1 5/16	1-4 11/16	2-2 19/32–	1-5 1/2	2-3 7/8
3/4	1-2 11/32–	1-10 13/16	1-3 1/8	2-0 3/32	1-3 15/16	2-1 3/8	1-4 3/4	2-2 21/32	1-5 9/16	2-3 15/16
13/16	1-2 3/8	1-10 29/32–	1-3 3/16	2-0 3/16	1-4	2-1 15/32–	1-4 13/16	2-2 3/4	1-5 19/32	2-4 1/32
7/8	1-2 7/16	1-10 31/32	1-3 1/4	2-0 1/4	1-4 1/32	2-1 17/32	1-4 27/32	2-2 27/32–	1-5 21/32	2-4 1/8
15/16	1-2 15/32	1-11 1/16	1-3 9/32	2-0 11/32–	1-4 3/32	2-1 5/8	1-4 29/32–	2-2 29/32	1-5 23/32–	2-4 3/16

Feet	40' Rise	40' Slope	50' Rise	50' Slope	60' Rise	60' Slope	70' Rise	70' Slope
0	32-3 1/2	51-4 29/32–	40-4 3/8	64-3 1/8	48-5 1/4	77-1 11/32–	56-6 1/8	89-11 9/16
1	33-1 3/16	52-8 5/16	41-2 1/16	65-6 17/32	49-2 15/16	78-4 3/4	57-3 13/16	91-2 31/32
2	33-10 7/8	53-11 3/4	41-11 3/4	66-9 31/32–	50-0 5/8	79-8 3/16	58-1 1/2	92-6 13/32
3	34-8 9/16	55-3 5/32	42-9 7/16	68-1 3/8	50-10 5/16	80-11 19/32	58-11 3/16	93-9 27/32–
4	35-6 1/4	56-6 19/32–	43-7 1/8	69-4 13/16	51-8	82-3 1/32–	59-8 7/8	95-1 1/4
5	36-3 15/16	57-10	44-4 13/16	70-8 7/32	52-5 11/16	83-6 7/16	60-6 9/16	96-4 11/16
6	37-1 5/8	59-1 7/16	45-2 1/2	71-11 21/32–	53-3 3/8	84-9 7/8	61-4 1/4	97-8 3/32
7	37-11 5/16	60-4 27/32	46-0 3/16	73-3 1/16	54-1 1/16	86-1 9/32	62-1 15/16	98-11 17/32–
8	38-9	61-8 9/32–	46-9 7/8	74-6 1/2	54-10 3/4	87-4 23/32–	62-11 5/8	100-2 15/16
9	39-6 11/16	62-11 11/16	47-7 9/16	75-9 29/32	55-8 7/16	88-8 1/8	63-9 5/16	101-6 3/8

natsin A=0.6281484282; natcos A=0.7780935369; nattan A=0.8072916666; natcot A=1.2387096774

BEVEL 9¾" TO 12"

Inches	0" Rise	0" Slope	1" Rise	1" Slope	2" Rise	2" Slope	3" Rise	3" Slope	4" Rise	4" Slope	5" Rise	5" Slope
0	0	0	13/16	1 9/32	1 5/8	2 9/16	2 7/16	3 7/8	3 1/4	5 5/32	4 1/16	6 7/16
1/16	1/16	3/32	7/8	1 3/8	1 11/16	2 21/32	2 1/2	3 15/16	3 5/16	5 1/4	4 1/8	6 17/32
1/8	3/32	5/32	29/32	1 7/16	1 23/32	2 3/4	2 17/32	4 1/32	3 11/32	5 5/16	4 5/32	6 19/32
3/16	5/32	1/4	31/32	1 17/32	1 25/32	2 13/16	2 19/32	4 3/32	3 13/32	5 13/32	4 7/32-	6 11/16
1/4	3/16	5/16	1	1 5/8	1 13/16	2 29/32	2 5/8	4 3/16	3 7/16	5 15/32	4 1/4	6 3/4
5/16	1/4	13/32	1 1/16	1 11/16	1 7/8	2 31/32	2 11/16	4 9/32-	3 1/2	5 9/16	4 5/16	6 27/32
3/8	9/32	15/32	1 1/8	1 25/32	1 15/16	3 1/16	2 3/4	4 11/32-	3 9/16	5 5/8	4 3/8	6 15/16
7/16	11/32	9/16	1 5/32	1 27/32	1 31/32	3 5/32-	2 25/32	4 7/16	3 19/32	5 23/32-	4 13/32	7
1/2	13/32	21/32	1 7/32	1 15/16	2 1/32	3 7/32	2 27/32	4 1/2	3 21/32	5 13/16	4 15/32	7 3/32-
9/16	15/32	23/32	1 9/32	2	2 3/32	3 5/16	2 29/32	4 19/32-	3 23/32	5 7/8	4 17/32-	7 5/32-
5/8	1/2	13/16	1 5/16	2 3/32	2 1/8	3 3/8	2 15/16	4 21/32	3 3/4	5 31/32	4 9/16	7 1/4
11/16	9/16	7/8	1 3/8	2 3/16	2 3/16	3 15/32-	3	4 3/4	3 13/16	6 1/32	4 5/8	7 11/32-
3/4	5/8	31/32	1 7/16	2 1/4	2 1/4	3 17/32	3 1/16	4 27/32	3 7/8	6 1/8	4 11/16	7 13/32-
13/16	21/32	1 1/16	1 15/32	2 11/32	2 9/32	3 5/8	3 3/32	4 29/32	3 29/32	6 3/16	4 23/32	7 1/2
7/8	23/32	1 1/8	1 17/32	2 13/32	2 11/32	3 23/32-	3 5/32	5	3 31/32	6 9/32-	4 25/32	7 9/16
15/16	3/4	1 7/32-	1 9/16	2 1/2	2 3/8	3 25/32	3 3/16	5 1/16	4	6 3/8	4 13/16	7 21/32-

Inches	6" Rise	6" Slope	7" Rise	7" Slope	8" Rise	8" Slope	9" Rise	9" Slope	10" Rise	10" Slope	11" Rise	11" Slope
0	4 7/8	7 23/32	5 11/16	9 1/32-	6 1/2	10 5/16	7 5/16	11 19/32-	8 1/8	1-0 7/8	8 15/16	1-2 3/32-
1/16	4 15/16	7 13/16	5 3/4	9 3/32-	6 9/16	10 3/8	7 3/8	11 11/16-	8 3/16	1-0 31/32-	9	1-2 1/4
1/8	4 31/32	7 29/32	5 25/32	9 3/16	6 19/32	10 15/32-	7 13/32	11 3/4	8 7/32	1-1 1/32-	9 1/32	1-2 11/32-
3/16	5 1/32	7 31/32	5 27/32	9 1/4	6 21/32	10 9/16	7 15/32	11 27/32-	8 9/32	1-1 1/8	9 3/32-	1-2 13/32-
1/4	5 1/16	8 1/16	5 7/8	9 11/32-	6 11/16	10 5/8	7 1/2	11 29/32-	8 5/16	1-1 7/32-	9 1/8	1-2 1/2
5/16	5 1/8	8 1/8	5 15/16	9 7/16	6 3/4	10 23/32-	7 9/16	1-0	8 3/8	1-1 9/32-	9 3/16	1-2 9/16
3/8	5 3/16	8 7/32-	6	9 1/2	6 13/16	10 25/32-	7 5/8	1-0 3/32-	8 7/16	1-1 3/8	9 1/4	1-2 21/32-
7/16	5 7/32	8 9/32-	6 1/32	9 19/32-	6 27/32	10 7/8	7 21/32	1-0 5/32-	8 15/32	1-1 7/16	9 9/32	1-2 3/4
1/2	5 9/32	8 3/8	6 3/32	9 21/32-	6 29/32	10 15/16	7 23/32	1-0 1/4	8 17/32	1-1 17/32-	9 11/32	1-2 13/16
9/16	5 11/32	8 15/32-	6 5/32	9 3/4	6 31/32	11 1/32-	7 25/32	1-0 5/16	8 19/32	1-1 5/8	9 13/32	1-2 29/32-
5/8	5 3/8	8 17/32-	6 3/16	9 13/16	7	11 1/8	7 13/16	1-0 13/32-	8 5/8	1-1 11/16	9 7/16	1-2 31/32-
11/16	5 7/16	8 5/8	6 1/4	9 29/32-	7 1/16	11 3/16	7 7/8	1-0 15/32-	8 11/16	1-1 25/32-	9 1/2	1-3 1/16
3/4	5 1/2	8 11/16	6 5/16	10	7 1/8	11 9/32-	7 15/16	1-0 9/16	8 3/4	1-1 27/32-	9 9/16	1-3 1/8
13/16	5 17/32	8 25/32-	6 11/32	10 1/16	7 5/32	11 11/32-	7 31/32	1-0 21/32-	8 25/32	1-1 15/16	9 19/32	1-3 7/32-
7/8	5 19/32	8 27/32-	6 13/32	10 5/32-	7 7/32	11 7/16	8 1/32	1-0 23/32-	8 27/32	1-2	9 21/32	1-3 5/16
15/16	5 5/8	8 15/16	6 7/16	10 7/32-	7 1/4	11 17/32-	8 1/16	1-0 13/16	8 7/8	1-2 3/32-	9 11/16	1-3 3/8

Feet	0' Rise	0' Slope	10' Rise	10' Slope	20' Rise	20' Slope	30' Rise	30' Slope
0	0	0	8-1 1/2	12-10 5/8	16-3	25-9 7/32-	24-4 1/2	38-7 27/32-
1	-9 3/4	1-3 15/32-	8-11 1/4	14-2 1/16	17-0 3/4	27-0 11/16	25-2 1/4	39-11 5/16
2	1-7 1/2	2-6 15/16	9-9	15-5 17/32-	17-10 1/2	28-4 5/32-	26-0	41-2 25/32-
3	2-5 1/4	3-10 3/8	10-6 3/4	16-9	18-8 1/4	29-7 5/8	26-9 3/4	42-6 7/32-
4	3-3	5-1 27/32-	11-4 1/2	18-0 15/32-	19-6	30-11 3/32-	27-7 1/2	43-9 11/16
5	4-0 3/4	6-5 5/16	12-2 1/4	19-3 15/16	20-3 3/4	32-2 17/32-	28-5 1/4	45-1 5/32-
6	4-10 1/2	7-8 25/32-	13-0	20-7 5/8	21-1 1/2	33-6	29-3	46-4 5/8
7	5-8 1/4	9-0 7/32-	13-9 3/4	21-10 27/32-	21-11 1/4	34-9 15/32-	30-0 3/4	47-8 3/32-
8	6-6	10-3 11/16	14-7 1/2	23-2 5/16	22-9	36-0 15/16	30-10 1/2	48-11 17/32-
9	7-3 3/4	11-7 5/32-	15-5 1/4	24-5 25/32-	23-6 3/4	37-4 3/8	31-8 1/4	50-3

A = 39° 05' 38"; logsin A = 9.79975; logcos A = 9.88993; logtan A = 9.90982; logcot A = 0.09018

Ins.	12″ Rise	12″ Slope	13″ Rise	13″ Slope	14″ Rise	14″ Slope	15″ Rise	15″ Slope	16″ Rise	16″ Slope
0	9 3/4	1-3 15/32	10 9/16	1-4 3/4	11 3/8	1-6 1/2	1-0 3/16	1-7 5/16	1-1	1-8 5/8
1/16	9 13/16	1-3 17/32	10 5/8	1-4 27/32	11 7/16	1-6 1/8	1-0 1/4	1-7 13/32	1-1 1/16	1-8 11/16
1/8	9 27/32	1-3 5/8	10 21/32	1-4 29/32	11 15/16	1-6 3/16	1-0 9/32	1-7 1/2	1-1 3/32	1-8 25/32
3/16	9 29/32	1-3 23/32	10 23/32	1-5	11 17/32	1-6 9/32	1-0 11/32	1-7 9/16	1-1 5/32	1-8 27/32
1/4	9 15/16	1-3 25/32	10 3/4	1-5 1/16	11 9/16	1-6 3/8	1-0 3/8	1-7 21/32	1-1 3/16	1-8 15/16
5/16	10	1-3 7/8	10 13/16	1-5 5/32	11 5/8	1-6 7/16	1-0 7/16	1-7 23/32	1-1 1/4	1-9 1/2
3/8	10 1/16	1-3 15/16	10 7/8	1-5 1/4	11 11/16	1-6 17/32	1-0 1/2	1-7 13/16	1-1 5/16	1-9 3/32
7/16	10 3/32	1-4 1/32	10 29/32	1-5 5/16	11 23/32	1-6 19/32	1-0 17/32	1-7 29/32	1-1 11/32	1-9 3/16
1/2	10 5/32	1-4 3/8	10 31/32	1-5 13/32	11 25/32	1-6 11/16	1-0 19/32	1-7 31/32	1-1 13/32	1-9 1/4
9/16	10 7/32	1-4 3/4	11 1/32	1-5 15/32	11 27/32	1-6 3/4	1-0 21/32	1-8 1/16	1-1 15/32	1-9 11/32
5/8	10 1/4	1-4 9/32	11 1/16	1-5 9/16	11 7/8	1-6 27/32	1-0 11/16	1-8 1/8	1-1 1/2	1-9 13/32
11/16	10 5/16	1-4 11/32	11 1/8	1-5 5/8	11 15/16	1-6 15/16	1-0 3/4	1-8 7/32	1-1 9/16	1-9 1/2
3/4	10 3/8	1-4 7/16	11 3/16	1-5 23/32	1-0	1-7	1-0 13/16	1-8 9/32	1-1 5/8	1-9 19/32
13/16	10 13/32	1-4 1/2	11 7/32	1-5 13/16	1-0 1/32	1-7 3/32	1-0 27/32	1-8 3/8	1-1 21/32	1-9 21/32
7/8	10 15/32	1-4 9/16	11 9/32	1-5 7/8	1-0 3/32	1-7 5/32	1-0 29/32	1-8 15/32	1-1 23/32	1-9 3/4
15/16	10 1/2	1-4 21/32	11 5/16	1-5 31/32	1-0 1/8	1-7 1/4	1-0 15/32	1-8 17/32	1-1 3/4	1-9 13/16

Ins.	17″ Rise	17″ Slope	18″ Rise	18″ Slope	19″ Rise	19″ Slope	20″ Rise	20″ Slope	21″ Rise	21″ Slope
0	1-1 13/16	1-9 29/32	1-2 5/8	1-11 3/16	1-3 7/16	2-0 15/32	1-4 1/4	2-1 25/32	1-5 1/16	2-3 1/16
1/16	1-1 7/8	1-10	1-2 11/16	1-11 9/32	1-3 1/2	2-0 9/16	1-4 5/16	2-1 27/32	1-5 1/8	2-3 1/8
1/8	1-1 29/32	1-10 1/16	1-2 23/32	1-11 11/16	1-3 17/32	2-0 21/32	1-4 11/32	2-1 15/16	1-5 5/32	2-3 1/4
3/16	1-1 31/32	1-10 5/32	1-2 25/32	1-11 11/16	1-3 19/32	2-0 23/32	1-4 13/32	2-2	1-5 7/32	2-3 3/8
1/4	1-2	1-10 7/32	1-2 13/16	1-11 1/2	1-3 5/8	2-0 13/16	1-4 7/16	2-2 3/32	1-5 1/4	2-3 3/8
5/16	1-2 1/16	1-10 5/16	1-2 7/8	1-11 19/32	1-3 11/16	2-0 7/8	1-4 1/2	2-2 3/16	1-5 5/16	2-3 15/32
3/8	1-2 1/8	1-10 3/8	1-2 15/16	1-11 11/16	1-3 3/4	2-0 31/32	1-4 9/16	2-2 1/4	1-5 3/8	2-3 17/32
7/16	1-2 5/32	1-10 15/32	1-2 31/32	1-11 3/4	1-3 25/32	2-1 1/32	1-4 19/32	2-2 11/32	1-5 13/32	2-3 5/8
1/2	1-2 7/32	1-10 9/16	1-3 1/32	1-11 27/32	1-3 27/32	2-1 1/8	1-4 21/32	2-2 13/32	1-5 15/32	2-3 11/16
9/16	1-2 9/32	1-10 5/8	1-3 3/32	1-11 29/32	1-3 29/32	2-1 7/32	1-4 23/32	2-2 1/2	1-5 17/32	2-3 25/32
5/8	1-2 5/16	1-10 23/32	1-3 1/8	2-0	1-3 15/16	2-1 9/32	1-4 3/4	2-2 9/16	1-5 9/16	2-3 7/8
11/16	1-2 3/8	1-10 25/32	1-3 3/16	2-0 3/32	1-4	2-1 3/8	1-4 13/16	2-2 21/32	1-5 5/8	2-3 15/16
3/4	1-2 7/16	1-10 7/8	1-3 1/4	2-0 5/32	1-4 1/16	2-1 7/16	1-4 7/8	2-2 3/4	1-5 11/16	2-4 1/32
13/16	1-2 15/32	1-10 15/16	1-3 9/32	2-0 1/4	1-4 3/32	2-1 17/32	1-4 29/32	2-2 13/16	1-5 23/32	2-4 3/32
7/8	1-2 17/32	1-11 1/8	1-3 11/32	2-0 5/16	1-4 5/32	2-1 19/32	1-4 15/16	2-2 29/32	1-5 25/32	2-4 3/16
15/16	1-2 9/16	1-11 3/8	1-3 3/8	2-0 15/32	1-4 3/16	2-1 11/16	1-5	2-2 31/32	1-5 13/16	2-4 9/32

Feet	40′ Rise	40′ Slope	50′ Rise	50′ Slope	60′ Rise	60′ Slope	70′ Rise	70′ Slope
0	32-6	51-6 15/32	40-7 1/2	64-5 3/32	48-9	77-3 11/16	56-10 1/2	90-2 5/16
1	33-3 3/4	52-9 15/16	41-5 1/4	65-8 17/32	49-6 3/4	78-7 5/32	57-8 1/4	91-5 25/32
2	34-1 1/2	54-1 3/8	42-3	67-0	50-4 1/2	79-10 5/8	58-6	92-9 1/4
3	34-11 1/4	55-4 27/32	43-0 3/4	68-3 15/32	51-2 1/4	81-2 5/32	59-3 3/4	94-0 11/16
4	35-9	56-8 5/16	43-10 1/2	69-6 15/16	52-0	82-5 17/32	60-1 1/2	95-4 5/32
5	36-6 3/4	57-11 25/32	44-8 1/4	70-10 3/8	52-9 3/4	83-9	60-11 1/4	96-7 5/8
6	37-4 1/2	59-3 1/4	45-6	72-1 27/32	53-7 1/2	85-0 15/32	61-9	97-11 3/32
7	38-2 1/4	60-6 11/16	46-3 3/4	73-5 5/16	54-5 1/4	86-3 15/16	62-6 3/4	99-2 17/32
8	39-0	61-10 5/32	47-1 1/2	74-8 25/32	55-3	87-7 13/32	63-4 1/2	100-6
9	39-9 3/4	63-1 5/8	47-11 1/4	76-0 1/4	56-0 3/4	88-10 27/32	64-2 1/4	101-9 15/32

natsin A=0.6305926250; natcos A=0.7761140001; nattan A=0.8125000000; natcot A=1.2307692307

Inches	0" Rise	0" Slope	1" Rise	1" Slope	2" Rise	2" Slope	3" Rise	3" Slope	4" Rise	4" Slope	5" Rise	5" Slope
0	0	0	13/16	1 9/32	1 5/8	2 19/32	2 7/16	3 7/8	3 9/32	5 5/32	4 3/32	6 15/32
1/16	1/16	3/32	7/8	1 3/8	1 11/16	2 21/32	2 1/2	3 31/32	3 5/16	5 1/4	4 1/8	6 17/32
1/8	3/32	5/32	29/32	1 15/32	1 3/4	2 3/4	2 9/16	4 1/32	3 3/8	5 11/32	4 3/16	6 5/8
3/16	5/32	1/4	31/32	1 17/32	1 25/32	2 13/16	2 19/32	4 1/8	3 7/16	5 13/32	4 1/4	6 11/16
1/4	7/32	5/16	1 1/32	1 5/8	1 27/32	2 29/32	2 21/32	4 3/16	3 15/16	5 1/2	4 9/32	6 25/32
5/16	1/4	13/32	1 1/16	1 11/16	1 29/32	3	2 23/32	4 9/32	3 17/32	5 9/16	4 11/32	6 7/8
3/8	5/16	1/2	1 1/8	1 25/32	1 15/16	3 1/16	2 3/4	4 3/8	3 9/16	5 21/32	4 13/32	6 15/16
7/16	11/32	9/16	1 3/16	1 27/32	2	3 5/32	2 13/16	4 7/16	3 5/8	5 23/32	4 7/16	7 1/32
1/2	13/32	21/32	1 7/32	1 15/16	2 1/32	3 7/32	2 7/8	4 17/32	3 11/16	5 13/16	4 1/2	7 3/32
9/16	15/32	23/32	1 9/32	2 1/32	2 3/32	3 5/16	2 29/32	4 19/32	3 23/32	5 29/32	4 9/16	7 3/16
5/8	1/2	13/16	1 11/32	2 3/32	2 5/32	3 13/32	2 31/32	4 11/16	3 25/32	5 31/32	4 19/32	7 9/32
11/16	9/16	7/8	1 3/8	2 3/16	2 3/16	3 15/32	3	4 3/4	3 27/32	6 1/16	4 21/32	7 11/32
3/4	5/8	31/32	1 7/16	2 1/4	2 1/4	3 9/16	3 1/16	4 27/32	3 7/8	6 1/8	4 11/16	7 7/16
13/16	21/32	1 1/16	1 15/32	2 11/32	2 5/16	3 5/8	3 1/8	4 15/16	3 15/16	6 7/32	4 3/4	7 1/2
7/8	23/32	1 1/8	1 17/32	2 7/16	2 11/32	3 23/32	3 5/32	5	4	6 5/16	4 13/16	7 19/32
15/16	25/32	1 3/16	1 19/32	2 1/2	2 13/32	3 25/32	3 7/32	5 3/32	4 1/16	6 3/8	4 27/32	7 21/32

Inches	6" Rise	6" Slope	7" Rise	7" Slope	8" Rise	8" Slope	9" Rise	9" Slope	10" Rise	10" Slope	11" Rise	11" Slope
0	4 29/32	7 3/4	5 23/32	9 1/32	6 17/32	10 11/32	7 3/8	11 5/8	8 3/16	1-0 29/32	9	1-2 7/32
1/16	4 31/32	7 27/32	5 25/32	9 1/8	6 19/32	10 13/32	7 13/32	11 23/32	8 7/32	1-1	9 1/32	1-2 9/32
1/8	5	7 29/32	5 13/16	9 7/32	6 21/32	10 1/2	7 15/32	11 25/32	8 9/32	1-1 3/32	9 3/32	1-2 3/8
3/16	5 1/16	8	5 7/8	9 9/32	6 11/16	10 9/16	7 1/2	11 7/8	8 11/32	1-1 5/32	9 5/32	1-2 7/16
1/4	5 1/8	8 1/16	5 15/16	9 3/8	6 3/4	10 21/32	7 9/16	11 15/16	8 3/8	1-1 1/4	9 3/16	1-2 17/32
5/16	5 5/32	8 5/32	5 31/32	9 7/16	6 13/16	10 3/4	7 5/8	1-0 1/32	8 7/16	1-1 5/16	9 1/4	1-2 5/8
3/8	5 7/32	8 1/4	6 1/32	9 17/32	6 27/32	10 13/16	7 21/32	1-0 1/8	8 15/32	1-1 13/32	9 5/16	1-2 11/16
7/16	5 1/4	8 5/16	6 3/32	9 19/32	6 29/32	10 29/32	7 23/32	1-0 3/16	8 17/32	1-1 15/32	9 11/32	1-2 25/32
1/2	5 5/16	8 13/32	6 1/8	9 11/16	6 15/16	10 31/32	7 25/32	1-0 9/32	8 19/32	1-1 9/16	9 13/32	1-2 27/32
9/16	5 3/8	8 15/32	6 3/16	9 25/32	7	11 1/16	7 13/16	1-0 11/32	8 5/8	1-1 21/32	9 15/32	1-2 15/16
5/8	5 13/32	8 9/16	6 1/4	9 27/32	7 1/16	11 5/32	7 7/8	1-0 7/16	8 11/16	1-1 23/32	9 1/2	1-3 1/32
11/16	5 15/32	8 5/8	6 9/32	9 15/16	7 3/32	11 7/32	7 29/32	1-0 1/2	8 3/4	1-1 13/16	9 9/16	1-3 3/32
3/4	5 17/32	8 23/32	6 11/32	10	7 5/32	11 5/32	7 31/32	1-0 19/32	8 25/32	1-1 7/8	9 19/32	1-3 3/32
13/16	5 9/16	8 13/16	6 3/8	10 3/32	7 7/32	11 3/8	8 1/32	1-0 11/16	8 27/32	1-1 31/32	9 21/32	1-3 1/4
7/8	5 5/8	8 7/8	6 7/16	10 3/16	7 1/4	11 15/32	8 1/16	1-0 3/4	8 29/32	1-2 1/16	9 23/32	1-3 11/32
15/16	5 11/16	8 31/32	6 1/2	10 1/4	7 5/16	11 17/32	8 1/8	1-0 27/32	8 15/16	1-2 1/8	9 3/4	1-3 13/32

Feet	0' Rise	0' Slope	10' Rise	10' Slope	20' Rise	20' Slope	30' Rise	30' Slope
0	0	0	8-2 1/2	12-11	16-4 1/4	25-10 1/32	24-6 3/8	38-9 1/32
1	-9 13/16	1-3 1/2	8-11 15/16	14-2 1/2	17-2 1/16	27-1 17/32	25-4 3/16	40-0 17/32
2	1-7 5/8	2-7	9-9 3/4	15-6	17-11 7/8	28-5 3/32	26-2	41-4 1/32
3	2-5 7/16	3-10 1/2	10-7 9/16	16-9 1/2	18-9 11/16	29-8 17/32	26-11 13/16	42-7 17/32
4	3-3 1/4	5-2	11-5 3/8	18-1 1/32	19-7 1/2	31-0 1/32	27-9 5/8	43-11 1/32
5	4-1 1/16	6-5 1/2	12-3 3/16	19-4 17/32	20-5 5/16	32-3 17/32	28-7 7/16	45-2 17/32
6	4-10 7/8	7-9	13-1	20-8 1/32	21-3 1/8	33-7 1/32	29-5 1/4	46-6 1/32
7	5-8 11/16	9-0 1/2	13-10 13/16	21-11 17/32	22-0 15/16	34-10 17/32	30-3 1/16	47-9 17/32
8	6-6 1/2	10-4	14-8 5/8	23-3 1/32	22-10 3/4	36-2 1/32	31-0 7/8	49-1 1/32
9	7-4 5/16	11-7 1/2	15-6 7/16	24-6 17/32	23-8 9/16	37-5 17/32	31-10 11/16	50-4 17/32

A=39° 16' 23''; logsin A=9.80142; logcos A=9.88882; logtan A=9.91260; logcot A=0.08740

Ins.	12" Rise	12" Slope	13" Rise	13" Slope	14" Rise	14" Slope	15" Rise	15" Slope	16" Rise	16" Slope
0	9 13/16	1-3 1/2	10 5/8	1-4 25/32	11 7/16	1-6 3/32−	1-0 1/4	1-7 3/8	1-1 3/32−	1-8 21/32
1/16	9 7/8	1-3 19/32−	10 11/16	1-4 7/8	11 1/2	1-6 5/32	1-0 5/16	1-7 15/32−	1-1 1/8	1-8 3/4
1/8	9 29/32	1-3 21/32	10 23/32	1-4 31/32−	11 9/16	1-6 1/4	1-0 3/8	1-7 17/32	1-1 3/16	1-8 27/32−
3/16	9 31/32−	1-3 3/4	10 25/32	1-5 1/32	11 19/32	1-6 5/16	1-0 13/32	1-7 5/8	1-1 1/4	1-8 29/32
1/4	10 1/32−	1-3 13/16	10 27/32−	1-5 1/8	11 21/32−	1-6 13/32	1-0 15/32	1-7 11/16	1-1 9/32	1-9
5/16	10 1/16	1-3 29/32−	10 7/8	1-5 3/16	11 23/32−	1-6 1/2	1-0 17/32−	1-7 25/32−	1-1 11/32−	1-9 1/16
3/8	10 1/8	1-4	10 15/16	1-5 9/32−	11 3/4	1-6 9/16	1-0 9/16	1-7 7/8	1-1 3/8	1-9 5/32−
7/16	10 5/32	1-4 1/16	11	1-5 11/32	11 13/16	1-6 21/32−	1-0 5/8	1-7 15/16	1-1 7/16	1-9 7/32
1/2	10 7/32	1-4 5/32−	11 1/32	1-5 7/16	11 27/32	1-6 23/32	1-0 11/16	1-8 1/32−	1-1 1/2	1-9 5/16
9/16	10 9/32−	1-4 7/32	11 3/32−	1-5 17/32−	11 29/32	1-6 13/16	1-0 23/32	1-8 3/32	1-1 17/32	1-9 13/32−
5/8	10 5/16	1-4 5/16	11 5/32−	1-5 19/32	11 31/32−	1-6 29/32−	1-0 25/32−	1-8 3/16	1-1 19/32	1-9 15/32
11/16	10 3/8	1-4 3/8	11 3/16	1-5 11/16	1-0	1-6 31/32	1-0 13/16	1-8 1/4	1-1 21/32−	1-9 9/16
3/4	10 7/16	1-4 15/32	11 1/4	1-5 3/4	1-0 1/16	1-7 1/16	1-0 7/8	1-8 11/32	1-1 11/16	1-9 5/8
13/16	10 15/32	1-4 9/16	11 9/32	1-5 27/32−	1-0 1/8	1-7 1/8	1-0 15/16	1-8 7/16	1-1 3/4	1-9 23/32−
7/8	10 17/32−	1-4 5/8	11 11/32	1-5 15/16	1-0 5/32	1-7 7/32−	1-0 31/32	1-8 1/2	1-1 13/16	1-9 13/16
15/16	10 19/32−	1-4 23/32−	11 13/32−	1-6	1-0 7/32−	1-7 9/32	1-1 1/32	1-8 19/32−	1-1 27/32	1-9 7/8

Ins.	17" Rise	17" Slope	18" Rise	18" Slope	19" Rise	19" Slope	20" Rise	20" Slope	21" Rise	21" Slope
0	1-1 29/32−	1-9 31/32−	1-2 23/32	1-11 1/4	1-3 17/32	2-0 17/32	1-4 11/32	2-1 27/32−	1-5 3/16	2-3 1/8
1/16	1-1 15/16	1-10 1/32	1-2 25/32−	1-11 11/32−	1-3 19/32−	2-0 5/8	1-4 13/32−	2-1 29/32	1-5 7/32	2-3 7/32−
1/8	1-2	1-10 1/8	1-2 13/16	1-11 13/32	1-3 5/8	2-0 23/32−	1-4 15/32−	2-2	1-5 9/32−	2-3 9/32
3/16	1-2 1/16	1-10 3/16	1-2 7/8	1-11 1/2	1-3 11/16	2-0 25/32	1-4 1/2	2-2 1/16	1-5 5/16	2-3 3/8
1/4	1-2 3/32	1-10 9/32	1-2 15/16	1-11 9/16	1-3 3/4	2-0 7/8	1-4 9/16	2-2 5/32	1-5 3/8	2-3 7/16
5/16	1-2 5/32	1-10 3/8	1-2 31/32	1-11 21/32−	1-3 25/32	2-0 15/16	1-4 5/8	2-2 1/4	1-5 7/16	2-3 17/32−
3/8	1-2 7/32−	1-10 7/16	1-3 1/32−	1-11 3/4	1-3 27/32−	2-1 1/32−	1-4 21/32	2-2 5/16	1-5 15/32	2-3 5/8
7/16	1-2 1/4	1-10 17/32−	1-3 1/16	1-11 13/16	1-3 29/32−	2-1 3/32	1-4 23/32−	2-2 13/32−	1-5 17/32−	2-3 11/16
1/2	1-2 5/16	1-10 19/32	1-3 1/8	1-11 29/32−	1-3 15/16	2-1 3/16	1-4 3/4	2-2 15/32	1-5 19/32−	2-3 25/32−
9/16	1-2 3/8	1-10 11/16	1-3 3/16	1-11 31/32	1-4	2-1 9/32−	1-4 13/16	2-2 9/16	1-5 5/8	2-3 27/32
5/8	1-2 13/32	1-10 25/32−	1-3 7/32	2-0 1/16	1-4 1/16	2-1 11/32	1-4 7/8	2-2 21/32−	1-5 11/16	2-3 15/16
11/16	1-2 15/32−	1-10 27/32	1-3 9/32−	2-0 1/8	1-4 3/32	2-1 7/16	1-4 29/32	2-2 23/32	1-5 23/32	2-4
3/4	1-2 1/2	1-10 15/16	1-3 11/32−	2-0 7/32	1-4 5/32−	2-1 1/2	1-4 31/32−	2-2 13/16	1-5 25/32	2-4 3/32
13/16	1-2 9/16	1-11	1-3 3/8	2-0 5/16	1-4 3/16	2-1 19/32−	1-5 1/32−	2-2 7/8	1-5 27/32−	2-4 3/16
7/8	1-2 5/8	1-11 3/32−	1-3 7/16	2-0 3/8	1-4 1/4	2-1 11/16	1-5 1/16	2-2 31/32−	1-5 7/8	2-4 1/4
15/16	1-2 21/32	1-11 5/32	1-3 1/2	2-0 15/32−	1-4 5/16	2-1 3/4	1-5 1/8	2-3 1/32	1-5 15/16	2-4 11/32−

Feet	40' Rise	40' Slope	50' Rise	50' Slope	60' Rise	60' Slope	70' Rise	70' Slope
0	32-8 1/2	51-8 1/32	40-10 5/8	64-7 1/16	49-0 3/4	77-6 1/16	57-2 7/8	90-5 3/32−
1	33-6 5/16	52-11 17/32	41-8 7/16	65-10 9/16	49-10 9/16	78-9 9/16	58-0 11/16	91-8 19/32−
2	34-4 1/8	54-3 1/16	42-6 1/4	67-2 1/16	50-8 3/8	80-1 1/16	58-10 1/2	93-0 3/32−
3	35-1 15/16	55-6 9/16	43-4 1/16	68-5 9/16	51-6 3/16	81-4 9/16	59-8 5/16	94-3 19/32−
4	35-11 3/4	56-10 1/16	44-1 7/8	69-9 1/16	52-4	82-8 1/16	60-6 1/8	95-7 3/32−
5	36-9 9/16	58-1 9/16	44-11 11/16	71-0 9/16	53-1 13/16	83-11 9/16	61-3 15/16	96-10 19/32−
6	37-7 3/8	59-5 1/16	45-9 1/2	72-4 1/16	53-11 5/8	85-3 1/16	62-1 3/4	98-2 3/32−
7	38-5 3/16	60-8 9/16	46-7 5/16	73-7 9/16	54-9 7/16	86-6 9/16	62-11 9/16	99-5 19/32−
8	39-3	62-0 1/16	47-5 1/8	74-11 1/16	55-7 1/4	87-10 1/16	63-9 3/8	100-9 3/32−
9	40-0 13/16	63-3 9/16	48-2 15/16	76-2 9/16	56-5 1/16	89-1 19/32−	64-7 3/16	102-0 19/32−

natsin A=0.6330182024; natcos A=0.7741369100; nattan A=0.8177083333; natcot A=1.2229299363

Inches	0" Rise	0" Slope	1" Rise	1" Slope	2" Rise	2" Slope	3" Rise	3" Slope	4" Rise	4" Slope	5" Rise	5" Slope
0	0	0	13/16	1 9/32	1 21/32	2 19/32	2 15/32	3 7/8	3 9/32	5 3/16	4 1/8	6 15/32
1/16	1/16	3/32	7/8	1 3/8	1 11/16	2 21/32	2 17/32	3 31/32	3 11/32	5 1/4	4 5/32	6 9/32
1/8	3/32	5/32	15/16	1 15/32	1 3/4	2 3/4	2 9/16	4 1/16	3 13/32	5 11/32	4 7/32	6 5/8
3/16	9/32	1/4	31/32	1 17/32	1 13/16	2 27/32	2 5/8	4 1/8	3 7/16	5 7/16	4 9/32	6 23/32
1/4	7/32	5/16	1 1/32	1 5/8	1 27/32	2 29/32	2 11/16	4 7/32	3 1/2	5 1/2	4 5/16	6 13/16
5/16	5/32	3/8	1 3/32	1 11/16	1 29/32	3	2 23/32	4 9/32	3 9/16	5 19/32	4 3/8	6 7/8
3/8	5/16	1/2	1 1/8	1 25/32	1 31/32	3 1/16	2 25/32	4 3/8	3 19/32	5 21/32	4 7/16	6 31/32
7/16	3/8	9/16	1 3/16	1 7/8	2	3 5/32	2 27/32	4 7/16	3 21/32	5 3/4	4 15/32	7 1/32
1/2	13/32	21/32	1 1/4	1 15/16	2 1/16	3 1/4	2 7/8	4 17/32	3 11/16	5 13/16	4 17/32	7 1/8
9/16	15/32	23/32	1 9/32	2 1/32	2 3/32	3 5/16	2 15/16	4 5/8	3 3/4	5 29/32	4 9/16	7 7/32
5/8	1/2	13/16	1 11/32	2 3/32	2 5/32	3 13/32	2 31/32	4 11/16	3 13/16	6	4 5/8	7 9/32
11/16	9/16	7/8	1 3/8	2 3/16	2 7/32	3 15/32	3 1/32	4 25/32	3 27/32	6 1/16	4 11/16	7 3/8
3/4	5/8	31/32	1 7/16	2 9/32	2 1/4	3 9/16	3 3/32	4 27/32	3 29/32	6 5/32	4 23/32	7 7/16
13/16	11/16	1 1/16	1 1/2	2 11/32	2 5/16	3 21/32	3 1/8	4 15/16	3 31/32	6 7/32	4 25/32	7 17/32
7/8	23/32	1 1/8	1 17/32	2 7/16	2 3/8	3 23/32	3 3/16	5 1/32	4	6 5/16	4 27/32	7 19/32
15/16	25/32	1 7/32	1 19/32	2 1/2	2 13/32	3 13/16	3 1/4	5 3/32	4 1/16	6 13/32	4 7/8	7 11/16

Inches	6" Rise	6" Slope	7" Rise	7" Slope	8" Rise	8" Slope	9" Rise	9" Slope	10" Rise	10" Slope	11" Rise	11" Slope
0	4 15/16	7 25/32	5 3/4	9 1/16	6 19/32	10 3/8	7 13/32	11 21/32	8 7/32	1-0 15/16	9 1/16	1-2 1/4
1/16	5	7 27/32	5 13/16	9 5/32	6 5/8	10 7/16	7 15/32	11 3/4	8 9/32	1-1 1/32	9 3/32	1-2 5/16
1/8	5 1/32	7 15/16	5 7/8	9 7/32	6 11/16	10 17/32	7 1/2	11 13/16	8 11/32	1-1 1/8	9 5/32	1-2 13/32
3/16	5 3/32	8	5 29/32	9 5/16	6 3/4	10 19/32	7 9/16	11 29/32	8 3/8	1-1 3/16	9 7/32	1-2 1/2
1/4	5 5/32	8 3/32	5 31/32	9 3/8	6 25/32	10 11/16	7 5/8	11 31/32	8 7/16	1-1 9/32	9 1/4	1-2 9/16
5/16	5 3/16	8 3/16	6 1/32	9 15/32	6 27/32	10 3/4	7 21/32	1-0 1/16	8 1/2	1-1 11/32	9 5/16	1-2 21/32
3/8	5 1/4	8 1/4	6 1/8	9 9/16	6 29/32	10 27/32	7 23/32	1-0 5/32	8 17/32	1-1 7/16	9 3/8	1-2 23/32
7/16	5 5/16	8 11/32	6 1/8	9 5/8	6 15/16	10 15/16	7 25/32	1-0 7/32	8 19/32	1-1 17/32	9 13/32	1-2 13/16
1/2	5 11/32	8 13/32	6 3/8	9 23/32	7	11	7 13/16	1-0 5/16	8 5/8	1-1 19/32	9 15/32	1-2 29/32
9/16	5 13/32	8 1/2	6 7/32	9 25/32	7 1/2	11 3/32	7 7/8	1-0 3/8	8 11/16	1-1 11/16	9 1/2	1-2 31/32
5/8	5 7/16	8 19/32	6 9/32	9 7/8	7 3/32	11 5/32	7 29/32	1-0 15/32	8 3/4	1-1 3/4	9 9/16	1-3 1/16
11/16	5 1/2	8 21/32	6 5/16	9 31/32	7 5/32	11 1/4	7 31/32	1-0 17/32	8 25/32	1-1 27/32	9 5/8	1-3 1/8
3/4	5 9/16	8 3/4	6 3/8	10 1/32	7 3/16	11 11/32	8 1/32	1-0 5/8	8 27/32	1-1 15/16	9 21/32	1-3 7/32
13/16	5 19/32	8 13/16	6 7/16	10 1/8	7 1/4	11 13/32	8 1/16	1-0 23/32	8 29/32	1-2	9 23/32	1-3 5/16
7/8	5 21/32	8 29/32	6 15/32	10 3/16	7 5/16	11 1/2	8 1/8	1-0 25/32	8 15/16	1-2 3/32	9 25/32	1-3 3/8
15/16	5 23/32	9	6 17/32	10 9/32	7 3/8	11 9/16	8 3/16	1-0 7/8	9	1-2 5/32	9 13/16	1-3 15/32

Feet	0' Rise	0' Slope	10' Rise	10' Slope	20' Rise	20' Slope	30' Rise	30' Slope
0	0	0	8-2 3/4	12-11 13/32	16-5 1/2	25-10 13/16	24-8 1/4	38-10 7/32
1	-9 7/8	1-3 17/32	9-0 5/8	14-2 15/16	17-3 3/8	27-2 11/32	25-6 1/8	40-1 3/4
2	1-7 3/4	2-7 3/32	9-10 1/2	15-6 1/2	18-1 1/4	28-5 29/32	26-4	41-5 5/16
3	2-5 5/8	3-10 5/8	10-8 3/8	16-10 1/2	18-11 1/8	29-9 7/16	27-1 7/8	42-8 27/32
4	3-3 1/2	5-2 5/32	11-6 1/4	18-1 9/16	19-9	31-0 31/32	27-11 3/4	44-0 3/8
5	4-1 3/8	6-5 11/16	12-4 1/8	19-5 1/8	20-6 7/8	32-4 17/32	28-9 5/8	45-3 15/16
6	4-11 1/4	7-9 1/4	13-2	20-8 21/32	21-4 3/4	33-8 1/16	29-7 1/2	46-7 15/32
7	5-9 1/8	9-0 25/32	13-11 7/8	22-0 3/16	22-2 5/8	34-11 19/32	30-5 3/8	47-11
8	6-7	10-4 5/16	14-9 3/4	23-3 23/32	23-0 1/2	36-3 5/32	31-3 1/4	49-2 9/16
9	7-4 7/8	11-7 7/8	15-7 5/8	24-7 9/32	23-10 3/8	37-6 11/16	32-1 1/8	50-6 3/32

A = 39° 27′ 06″; logsin A = 9.80306; logcos A = 9.88771; logtan A = 9.91536; logcot A = 0.08464

Ins.	12″ Rise	12″ Slope	13″ Rise	13″ Slope	14″ Rise	14″ Slope	15″ Rise	15″ Slope	16″ Rise	16″ Slope
0	9 7/8	1-3 17/32	10 11/16	1-4 27/32—	11 17/32—	1-6 1/8	1-0 11/32	1-7 7/16	1-1 5/32	1-8 23/32
1/16	9 15/16	1-3 5/8	10 3/4	1-4 29/32	11 9/16	1-6 7/32—	1-0 13/32—	1-7 1/2	1-1 7/32—	1-8 13/16
1/8	9 31/32	1-3 11/16	10 13/16	1-5	11 5/8	1-6 9/32	1-0 7/16	1-7 19/32—	1-1 9/32—	1-8 7/8
3/16	10 1/32—	1-3 25/32	10 27/32	1-5 3/32—	11 11/16	1-6 3/8	1-0 1/2	1-7 21/32	1-1 5/16	1-8 31/32—
1/4	10 3/32—	1-3 7/8	10 29/32—	1-5 5/32	11 23/32	1-6 15/32—	1-0 9/16	1-7 3/4	1-1 3/8	1-9 1/32
5/16	10 1/8	1-3 15/16	10 31/32—	1-5 1/4	11 25/32—	1-6 17/32	1-0 19/32	1-7 27/32—	1-1 7/16	1-9 1/8
3/8	10 3/16	1-4 1/32—	11	1-5 5/16	11 27/32—	1-6 5/8	1-0 21/32—	1-7 29/32	1-1 15/32	1-9 7/32—
7/16	10 1/4	1-4 3/32	11 1/16	1-5 13/32—	11 7/8	1-6 11/16	1-0 23/32—	1-8	1-1 17/32—	1-9 9/32
1/2	10 9/32	1-4 3/16	11 1/8	1-5 15/32	11 15/16	1-6 25/32—	1-0 3/4	1-8 1/16	1-1 9/16	1-9 3/8
9/16	10 11/32—	1-4 9/32—	11 5/32	1-5 9/16	11 31/32	1-6 7/8	1-0 13/16	1-8 5/32—	1-1 5/8	1-9 7/16
5/8	10 3/8	1-4 11/32	11 7/32—	1-5 21/32—	1-0 1/32	1-6 15/16	1-0 27/32	1-8 1/4	1-1 11/16	1-9 17/32—
11/16	10 7/16	1-4 7/16	11 1/4	1-5 23/32	1-0 3/32—	1-7 1/32—	1-0 29/32	1-8 5/16	1-1 23/32	1-9 5/8
3/4	10 1/2	1-4 1/2	11 5/16	1-5 13/16	1-0 1/8	1-7 3/32	1-0 31/32—	1-8 13/32—	1-1 25/32	1-9 11/16
13/16	10 17/32	1-4 19/32—	11 3/8	1-5 7/8	1-0 3/16	1-7 3/16	1-1	1-8 15/32	1-1 27/32—	1-9 25/32—
7/8	10 19/32	1-4 11/16	11 13/32	1-5 31/32	1-0 1/4	1-7 1/4	1-1 1/16	1-8 9/16	1-1 7/8	1-9 27/32
15/16	10 21/32—	1-4 3/4	11 15/32	1-6 1/16	1-0 9/32	1-7 11/32	1-1 1/8	1-8 5/8	1-1 15/16	1-9 15/16

Ins.	17″ Rise	17″ Slope	18″ Rise	18″ Slope	19″ Rise	19″ Slope	20″ Rise	20″ Slope	21″ Rise	21″ Slope
0	1-2	1-10 1/32—	1-2 13/16	1-11 5/16	1-3 5/8	2-0 19/32	1-4 15/32—	2-1 29/32—	1-5 9/32	2-3 3/16
1/16	1-2 1/32	1-10 3/32	1-2 7/8	1-11 13/32—	1-3 11/16	2-0 11/16	1-4 1/2	2-1 31/32	1-5 11/32—	2-3 9/32—
1/8	1-2 3/32—	1-10 3/16	1-2 29/32	1-11 15/32	1-3 3/4	2-0 25/32—	1-4 9/16	2-2 1/16	1-5 3/8	2-3 11/32
3/16	1-2 5/32—	1-10 1/4	1-2 31/32—	1-11 9/16	1-3 25/32	2-0 27/32	1-4 5/8	2-2 5/32—	1-5 7/16	2-3 7/16
1/4	1-2 3/16	1-10 11/32—	1-3 1/32—	1-11 5/8	1-3 27/32—	2-0 15/16	1-4 21/32	2-2 7/32	1-5 1/2	2-3 17/32—
5/16	1-2 1/4	1-10 13/32	1-3 1/16	1-11 23/32—	1-3 29/32—	2-1	1-4 23/32—	2-2 5/16	1-5 17/32	2-3 19/32
3/8	1-2 5/16	1-10 1/2	1-3 1/8	1-11 25/32	1-3 15/16	2-1 3/32—	1-4 25/32—	2-2 3/8	1-5 19/32—	2-3 11/16
7/16	1-2 11/32	1-10 19/32—	1-3 3/16	1-11 7/8	1-4	2-1 3/16	1-4 13/16	2-2 15/32—	1-5 21/32—	2-3 3/4
1/2	1-2 13/32—	1-10 21/32	1-3 7/32	1-11 31/32—	1-4 1/16	2-1 1/4	1-4 7/8	2-2 9/16	1-5 11/16	2-3 27/32
9/16	1-2 7/16	1-10 3/4	1-3 9/32—	2-0 1/32	1-4 3/32	2-1 11/32—	1-4 29/32	2-2 5/8	1-5 3/4	2-3 15/16
5/8	1-2 1/2	1-10 13/16	1-3 5/16	2-0 1/8	1-4 5/32—	2-1 13/32	1-4 31/32	2-2 23/32—	1-5 25/32	2-4
11/16	1-2 9/16	1-10 29/32	1-3 3/8	2-0 3/16	1-4 3/16	2-1 1/2	1-5 1/32—	2-2 25/32	1-5 27/32	2-4 3/32—
3/4	1-2 19/32	1-11	1-3 7/16	2-0 9/32	1-4 1/4	2-1 9/16	1-5 1/16	2-2 7/8	1-5 29/32—	2-4 5/32
13/16	1-2 21/32	1-11 1/16	1-3 15/32	2-0 3/8	1-4 5/16	2-1 21/32	1-5 1/8	2-2 31/32—	1-5 15/16	2-4 1/4
7/8	1-2 23/32—	1-11 5/32—	1-3 17/32	2-0 7/16	1-4 11/32	2-1 3/4	1-5 3/16	2-3 1/32	1-6	2-4 11/32—
15/16	1-2 3/4	1-11 7/32	1-3 19/32—	2-0 17/32—	1-4 13/32	2-1 13/16	1-5 7/32	2-3 1/8	1-6 1/16	2-4 13/32

Feet	40′ Rise	40′ Slope	50′ Rise	50′ Slope	60′ Rise	60′ Slope	70′ Rise	70′ Slope
0	32-11	51-9 5/8	41-1 3/4	64-9 1/32	49-4 1/2	77-8 7/16	57-7 1/4	90-7 27/32
1	33-8 7/8	53-1 5/32	41-11 5/8	66-0 19/32—	50-2 3/8	79-0	58-5 1/8	91-11 13/32—
2	34-6 3/4	54-4 23/32—	42-9 1/2	67-4 1/8	51-0 1/4	80-3 17/32—	59-3	93-2 15/16
3	35-4 5/8	55-8 1/4	43-7 3/8	68-7 21/32	51-10 1/8	81-7 1/16	60-0 7/8	94-6 15/32
4	36-2 1/2	56-11 25/32	44-5 1/4	69-11 3/16	52-8	82-10 5/8	60-10 3/4	95-10 1/32—
5	37-0 3/8	58-3 11/32—	45-3 1/8	71-2 3/4	53-5 7/8	84-2 5/32—	61-8 5/8	97-1 9/16
6	37-10 1/4	59-6 7/8	46-1	72-6 9/32	54-3 3/4	85-5 11/16	62-6 1/2	98-5 3/32
7	38-8 1/8	60-10 13/32	46-10 7/8	73-9 13/16	55-1 5/8	86-9 7/32	63-4 3/8	99-8 5/8
8	39-6	62-1 31/32—	47-8 3/4	75-1 3/8	55-11 1/2	88-0 25/32—	64-2 1/4	101-0 3/16
9	40-3 7/8	63-5 1/2	48-6 5/8	76-4 29/32—	56-9 3/8	89-4 5/16	65-0 1/8	102-3 23/32

natsin A=0.6354252783; natcos A=0.7721623635; nattan A=0.8229166666; natcot A=1.2151898734

Inches	0″ Rise	Slope	1″ Rise	Slope	2″ Rise	Slope	3″ Rise	Slope	4″ Rise	Slope	5″ Rise	Slope
0	0	0	13/16	15/16	1 21/32	2 19/32	2 1/2	3 29/32	3 5/16	5 3/16	4 1/8	6 1/2
1/16	1/16	3/32	7/8	1 3/8	1 23/32	2 11/16	2 17/32	3 31/32	3 3/8	5 9/32	4 3/16	6 9/16
1/8	3/32	5/32	15/16	1 15/32	1 3/4	2 3/4	2 19/32	4 1/16	3 13/32	5 11/32	4 1/4	6 21/32
3/16	5/32	1/4	31/32	1 17/32	1 13/16	2 27/32	2 5/8	4 1/8	3 15/32	5 7/16	4 9/32	6 3/4
1/4	7/32	5/16	1 1/32	1 5/8	1 7/8	2 29/32	2 11/16	4 7/32	3 17/32	5 17/32	4 11/32	6 13/16
5/16	1/4	13/32	1 3/32	1 23/32	1 29/32	3	2 3/4	4 5/16	3 9/16	5 19/32	4 13/32	6 29/32
3/8	5/16	1/2	1 1/8	1 25/32	1 31/32	3 3/32	2 25/32	4 3/8	3 5/8	5 11/16	4 7/16	6 31/32
7/16	3/8	9/16	1 3/16	1 7/8	2 1/32	3 5/32	2 27/32	4 15/32	3 11/16	5 3/4	4 1/2	7 1/16
1/2	13/32	21/32	1 1/4	1 15/16	2 1/16	3 1/4	2 29/32	4 17/32	3 23/32	5 27/32	4 9/16	7 5/32
9/16	15/32	23/32	1 9/32	2 1/32	2 1/8	3 5/16	2 15/16	4 5/8	3 25/32	5 15/16	4 19/32	7 7/32
5/8	17/32	13/16	1 11/32	2 1/8	2 3/16	3 13/32	3	4 23/32	3 27/32	6	4 21/32	7 5/16
11/16	9/16	29/32	1 13/32	2 3/16	2 7/32	3 1/2	3 1/16	4 25/32	3 7/8	6 3/32	4 23/32	7 3/8
3/4	5/8	31/32	1 7/16	2 9/32	2 9/32	3 9/16	3 3/32	4 7/8	3 15/16	6 5/32	4 3/4	7 15/32
13/16	11/16	1 1/16	1 1/2	2 11/32	2 11/32	3 21/32	3 5/32	4 15/16	4	6 1/4	4 13/16	7 17/32
7/8	23/32	1 1/8	1 9/16	2 7/16	2 3/8	3 23/32	3 7/32	5 1/32	4 1/32	6 11/32	4 7/8	7 5/8
15/16	25/32	1 17/32	1 19/32	2 1/2	2 7/16	3 13/16	3 1/4	5 1/8	4 3/32	6 13/32	4 29/32	7 23/32

Inches	6″ Rise	Slope	7″ Rise	Slope	8″ Rise	Slope	9″ Rise	Slope	10″ Rise	Slope	11″ Rise	Slope
0	4 31/32	7 25/32	5 13/16	9 3/32	6 5/8	10 3/8	7 7/16	11 11/16	8 9/32	1-0 31/32	9 1/8	1-2 9/32
1/16	5 1/32	7 7/8	5 27/32	9 5/32	6 11/16	10 15/32	7 1/2	11 25/32	8 11/32	1-1 1/16	9 5/32	1-2 3/8
1/8	5 1/16	7 15/16	5 29/32	9 1/4	6 23/32	10 9/16	7 9/16	11 27/32	8 3/8	1-1 5/32	9 7/32	1-2 7/16
3/16	5 1/8	8 1/32	5 15/16	9 11/32	6 25/32	10 5/8	7 19/32	11 15/16	8 7/16	1-1 7/32	9 1/4	1-2 17/32
1/4	5 3/16	8 1/8	6	9 13/32	6 27/32	10 23/32	7 21/32	1-0	8 1/2	1-1 5/16	9 5/16	1-2 19/32
5/16	5 7/32	8 3/16	6 1/16	9 1/2	6 7/8	10 25/32	7 23/32	1-0 3/32	8 17/32	1-1 3/8	9 3/8	1-2 11/16
3/8	5 9/32	8 9/32	6 3/32	9 9/16	6 15/16	10 7/8	7 3/4	1-0 3/16	8 19/32	1-1 15/32	9 13/32	1-2 25/32
7/16	5 11/32	8 11/32	6 5/32	9 21/32	7	10 31/32	7 13/16	1-0 1/4	8 21/32	1-1 9/16	9 15/32	1-2 27/32
1/2	5 3/8	8 7/16	6 1/4	9 3/4	7 1/32	11 1/2	7 7/8	1-0 11/32	8 11/16	1-1 5/8	9 17/32	1-2 15/16
9/16	5 7/16	8 17/32	6 1/4	9 13/16	7 3/32	11 1/8	7 29/32	1-0 13/32	8 3/4	1-1 23/32	9 9/16	1-3
5/8	5 1/2	8 19/32	6 5/16	9 29/32	7 5/32	11 13/32	7 31/32	1-0 1/2	8 13/16	1-1 25/32	9 5/8	1-3 3/32
11/16	5 17/32	8 11/16	6 3/8	9 31/32	7 3/16	11 9/32	8 1/32	1-0 9/16	8 27/32	1-1 7/8	9 11/16	1-3 3/16
3/4	5 19/32	8 3/4	6 13/32	10 1/16	7 1/4	11 3/8	8 1/16	1-0 21/32	8 29/32	1-1 31/32	9 23/32	1-3 1/4
13/16	5 21/32	8 27/32	6 15/32	10 5/32	7 5/16	11 7/16	8 1/8	1-0 3/4	8 31/32	1-2 1/2	9 25/32	1-3 11/32
7/8	5 11/16	8 15/16	6 17/32	10 7/32	7 11/32	11 17/32	8 3/16	1-0 13/16	9	1-2 1/8	9 27/32	1-3 13/32
15/16	5 3/4	9	6 9/16	10 5/16	7 13/32	11 19/32	8 7/32	1-0 29/32	9 1/16	1-2 3/16	9 7/8	1-3 1/2

Feet	0′ Rise	Slope	10′ Rise	Slope	20′ Rise	Slope	30′ Rise	Slope
0	0	0	8-3 3/8	12-11 13/16	16-6 3/4	25-11 5/8	24-10 1/8	38-11 13/16
1	-9 15/16	1-3 19/16	9-1 5/16	14-3 3/8	17-4 11/16	27-3 3/16	25-8 1/16	40-3
2	1-7 7/8	2-7 5/32	9-11 1/4	15-6 31/32	18-2 5/8	28-6 25/32	26-6	41-6 9/16
3	2-5 13/16	3-10 3/4	10-9 3/16	16-10 9/16	19-0 9/16	29-10 11/32	27-3 15/16	42-10 5/32
4	3-3 3/4	5-2 5/16	11-7 1/8	18-2 1/8	19-10 1/2	31-1 15/16	28-1 7/8	44-1 3/4
5	4-1 11/16	6-5 29/32	12-5 1/16	19-5 23/32	20-8 7/16	32-5 1/2	28-11 13/16	45-5 5/16
6	4-11 5/8	7-9 15/32	13-3	20-9 9/32	21-6 3/8	33-9 3/32	29-9 3/4	46-8 29/32
7	5-9 9/16	9-1 1/16	14-0 15/16	22-0 7/8	22-4 5/16	35-0 11/16	30-7 11/16	48-0 15/32
8	6-7 1/2	10-4 21/32	14-10 7/8	23-4 7/16	23-2 1/4	36-4 1/4	31-5 5/8	49-4 1/16
9	7-5 7/16	11-8 7/32	15-8 13/16	24-8 1/32	24-0 3/16	37-7 27/32	32-3 9/16	50-7 21/32

A = 39° 37′ 44″; logsin A = 9.80469; logcos A = 9.88660; logtan A = 9.91810; logcot A = 0.08190

Ins.	12" Rise	12" Slope	13" Rise	13" Slope	14" Rise	14" Slope	15" Rise	15" Slope	16" Rise	16" Slope
0	9 15/16	1-3 19/32–	10 3/4	1-4 7/8	11 19/32	1-6 3/16	1-0 7/16	1-7 15/32	1-1 1/4	1-8 25/32–
1/16	10	1-3 21/32	10 13/16	1-4 31/32–	11 21/32–	1-6 1/4	1-0 15/32	1-7 9/16	1-1 5/16	1-8 27/32
1/8	10 1/32	1-3 3/4	10 7/8	1-5 1/32	11 11/16	1-6 11/32–	1-0 17/32–	1-7 5/8	1-1 11/32	1-8 15/16
3/16	10 3/32–	1-3 13/16	10 29/32	1-5 1/8	11 3/4	1-6 13/32	1-0 9/16	1-7 23/32	1-1 13/32–	1-9 1/32–
1/4	10 5/32–	1-3 29/32–	10 31/32	1-5 7/32–	11 13/16	1-6 1/2	1-0 5/8	1-7 13/16	1-1 15/32–	1-9 3/32
5/16	10 3/16	1-4	11 1/32–	1-5 9/32	11 27/32	1-6 19/32–	1-0 11/16	1-7 7/8	1-1 1/2	1-9 3/16
3/8	10 1/4	1-4 1/16	11 1/16	1-5 3/8	11 29/32–	1-6 21/32	1-0 23/32	1-7 31/32–	1-1 9/16	1-9 1/4
7/16	10 5/16	1-4 5/32–	11 1/8	1-5 7/16	11 31/32–	1-6 3/4	1-0 25/32	1-8 1/32	1-1 5/8	1-9 11/32–
1/2	10 11/32	1-4 7/32	11 3/16	1-5 17/32–	1-0	1-6 13/16	1-0 27/32–	1-8 1/8	1-1 21/32	1-9 7/16
9/16	10 13/32–	1-4 5/16	11 7/32	1-5 19/32	1-0 1/16	1-6 29/32	1-0 7/8	1-8 7/32–	1-1 23/32–	1-9 1/2
5/8	10 15/32–	1-4 13/32–	11 9/32	1-5 11/16	1-0 1/8	1-7	1-0 15/16	1-8 9/32	1-1 25/32–	1-9 19/32–
11/16	10 1/2	1-4 15/32	11 11/32–	1-5 25/32–	1-0 5/32	1-7 1/16	1-1	1-8 3/8	1-1 13/16	1-9 21/32
3/4	10 9/16	1-4 9/16	11 3/8	1-5 27/32	1-0 7/32–	1-7 5/32–	1-1 1/32	1-8 7/16	1-1 7/8	1-9 3/4
13/16	10 5/8	1-4 5/8	11 7/16	1-5 15/16	1-0 9/32–	1-7 7/32	1-1 3/32	1-8 17/32–	1-1 15/16	1-9 27/32–
7/8	10 21/32	1-4 23/32–	11 1/2	1-6	1-0 5/16	1-7 5/16	1-1 5/32–	1-8 5/8	1-1 31/32	1-9 29/32
15/16	10 23/32–	1-4 13/16	11 17/32	1-6 3/32	1-0 3/8	1-7 13/32–	1-1 3/16	1-8 11/16	1-2 1/32–	1-10

Ins.	17" Rise	17" Slope	18" Rise	18" Slope	19" Rise	19" Slope	20" Rise	20" Slope	21" Rise	21" Slope
0	1-2 1/16	1-10 1/16	1-2 29/32	1-11 3/8	1-3 3/4	2-0 21/32	1-4 9/16	2-1 31/32–	1-5 3/8	2-3 9/32–
1/16	1-2 1/8	1-10 5/32–	1-2 31/32–	1-11 7/16	1-3 25/32	2-0 3/4	1-4 5/8	2-2 1/16	1-5 7/16	2-3 11/32
1/8	1-2 3/16	1-10 1/4	1-3	1-11 17/32	1-3 27/32–	2-0 27/32–	1-4 21/32	2-2 1/8	1-5 1/2	2-3 7/16
3/16	1-2 7/32	1-10 5/16	1-3 1/16	1-11 5/8	1-3 7/8	2-0 29/32	1-4 23/32–	2-2 7/32–	1-5 17/32	2-3 1/2
1/4	1-2 9/32	1-10 13/32–	1-3 1/8	1-11 11/16	1-3 15/16	2-1	1-4 25/32–	2-2 9/32	1-5 19/32	2-3 19/32–
5/16	1-2 11/32–	1-10 15/32	1-3 5/32	1-11 25/32–	1-4	2-1 1/16	1-4 13/16	2-2 3/8	1-5 21/32–	2-3 21/32
3/8	1-2 3/8	1-10 9/16	1-3 7/32–	1-11 27/32	1-4 1/32	2-1 5/32–	1-4 7/8	2-2 15/32–	1-5 11/16	2-3 3/4
7/16	1-2 7/16	1-10 5/8	1-3 9/32–	1-11 15/16	1-4 3/32	2-1 1/4	1-4 15/16	2-2 17/32	1-5 3/4	2-3 27/32–
1/2	1-2 1/2	1-10 23/32	1-3 5/16	2-0 1/32–	1-4 5/32–	2-1 5/16	1-4 31/32	2-2 5/8	1-5 13/16	2-3 29/32
9/16	1-2 17/32	1-10 13/16	1-3 3/8	2-0 3/32	1-4 3/16	2-1 13/32–	1-5 1/32–	2-2 11/16	1-5 27/32	2-4
5/8	1-2 19/32	1-10 7/8	1-3 7/16	2-0 3/16	1-4 1/4	2-1 15/32	1-5 3/32–	2-2 25/32–	1-5 29/32	2-4 1/16
11/16	1-2 21/32–	1-10 31/32–	1-3 15/32	2-0 1/4	1-4 5/16	2-1 9/16	1-5 1/8	2-2 7/8	1-5 31/32–	2-4 5/32
3/4	1-2 11/16	1-11 1/32	1-3 17/32–	2-0 11/32	1-4 11/32	2-1 21/32–	1-5 3/16	2-2 15/16	1-6	2-4 1/4
13/16	1-2 3/4	1-11 1/8	1-3 19/32–	2-0 7/16	1-4 13/32	2-1 23/32	1-5 1/4	2-3 1/32–	1-6 1/16	2-4 5/16
7/8	1-2 13/16	1-11 7/32–	1-3 5/8	2-0 1/2	1-4 15/32–	2-1 13/16	1-5 9/32	2-3 3/32	1-6 1/8	2-4 13/32–
15/16	1-2 27/32	1-11 9/32	1-3 11/16	2-0 19/32–	1-4 1/2	2-1 7/8	1-5 11/32–	2-3 3/16	1-6 5/32	2-4 15/32

Feet	40' Rise	40' Slope	50' Rise	50' Slope	60' Rise	60' Slope	70' Rise	70' Slope
0	33-1 1/2	51-11 7/32	41-4 7/8	64-11 1/32–	49-8 1/4	77-10 27/32–	57-11 5/8	90-10 5/8
1	33-11 7/16	53-2 13/16	42-2 13/16	66-2 19/32	50-6 3/16	79-2 13/32	58-9 9/16	92-2 7/32
2	34-9 3/8	54-6 3/8	43-0 3/4	67-6 3/16	51-4 1/8	80-6	59-7 1/2	93-5 13/16
3	35-7 5/16	55-9 31/32–	43-10 11/16	68-9 25/32–	52-2 1/16	81-9 9/16	60-5 7/16	94-9 3/8
4	36-5 1/4	57-1 17/32	44-8 5/8	70-1 11/32	53-0	83-1 5/32–	61-3 3/8	96-0 31/32–
5	37-3 3/16	58-5 1/8	45-6 9/16	71-4 15/16	53-9 15/16	84-4 3/4	62-1 5/16	97-4 17/32
6	38-1 1/8	59-8 23/32–	46-4 1/2	72-8 1/2	54-7 7/8	85-8 5/16	62-11 1/4	98-8 1/8
7	38-11 1/16	61-0 9/32	47-2 7/16	74-0 3/32–	55-5 13/16	86-11 29/32–	63-9 3/16	99-11 23/32–
8	39-9	62-3 7/8	48-0 3/8	75-3 11/16	56-3 3/4	88-3 15/32	64-7 1/8	101-3 9/32
9	40-6 15/16	63-7 7/16	48-10 5/16	76-7 1/4	57-1 11/16	89-7 1/16	65-5 1/16	102-6 7/8

natsin A=0.6378139712; natcos A=0.7701904558; nattan A=0.8281250000; natcot A=1.2075471698

Inches	0" Rise	Slope	1" Rise	Slope	2" Rise	Slope	3" Rise	Slope	4" Rise	Slope	5" Rise	Slope
0	0	0	27/32	15/16	1 21/32	2 19/32	2 1/2	3 29/32	3 11/32	5 7/32	4 5/32	6 1/2
1/16	1/16	3/32	7/8	1 3/8	1 23/32	2 11/16	2 9/16	4	3 3/8	5 9/32	4 7/32	6 19/32
1/8	3/32	5/32	15/16	1 15/32	1 25/32	2 25/32	2 19/32	4 1/16	3 7/16	5 3/8	4 9/32	6 21/32
3/16	5/32	1/4	1	1 17/32	1 13/16	2 27/32	2 21/32	4 5/32	3 1/2	5 7/16	4 5/16	6 3/4
1/4	7/32	5/16	1 1/32	1 5/8	1 7/8	2 15/16	2 23/32	4 7/32	3 17/32	5 17/32	4 3/8	6 27/32
5/16	1/4	13/32	1 3/32	1 23/32	1 15/16	3	2 3/4	4 5/16	3 19/32	5 5/8	4 7/16	6 29/32
3/8	9/32	1/2	1 5/32	1 25/32	1 31/32	3 3/32	2 13/16	4 13/32	3 21/32	5 11/16	4 15/32	7
7/16	3/8	9/16	1 3/16	1 7/8	2 1/32	3 3/16	2 7/8	4 15/32	3 11/16	5 25/32	4 17/32	7 1/16
1/2	13/32	21/32	1 1/4	1 15/16	2 3/32	3 1/4	2 29/32	4 9/16	3 3/4	5 27/32	4 19/32	7 5/32
9/16	15/32	23/32	1 5/16	2 1/32	2 1/8	3 11/32	2 31/32	4 5/8	3 13/16	5 15/16	4 5/8	7 1/4
5/8	17/32	13/16	1 11/32	2 1/8	2 3/16	3 13/32	3 1/32	4 23/32	3 27/32	6 1/32	4 11/32	7 5/32
11/16	9/16	29/32	1 13/32	2 3/16	2 1/4	3 1/2	3 1/16	4 13/16	3 29/32	6 3/32	4 3/4	7 13/32
3/4	5/8	31/32	1 15/32	2 9/32	2 9/32	3 19/32	3 1/8	4 7/8	3 31/32	6 3/16	4 25/32	7 1/2
13/16	11/16	1 1/16	1 1/2	2 11/32	2 11/32	3 21/32	3 3/16	4 31/32	4	6 1/4	4 27/32	7 9/16
7/8	23/32	1 1/8	1 9/16	2 7/16	2 13/32	3 3/4	3 7/32	5 1/32	4 1/16	6 11/32	4 29/32	7 21/32
15/16	25/32	1 7/32	1 5/8	2 17/32	2 7/16	3 13/16	3 9/32	5 1/8	4 1/8	6 7/16	4 15/16	7 23/32

Inches	6" Rise	Slope	7" Rise	Slope	8" Rise	Slope	9" Rise	Slope	10" Rise	Slope	11" Rise	Slope
0	5	7 13/16	5 27/32	9 1/8	6 21/32	10 13/32	7 1/2	11 23/32	8 11/32	1-1 1/32	9 5/32	1-2 5/16
1/16	5 1/16	7 29/32	5 7/8	9 3/16	6 23/32	10 1/2	7 9/16	11 25/32	8 3/8	1-1 3/32	9 7/32	1-2 13/32
1/8	5 3/32	7 31/32	5 15/16	9 9/32	6 25/32	10 9/16	7 19/32	11 7/8	8 7/16	1-1 3/16	9 9/32	1-2 15/32
3/16	5 5/32	8 1/16	6	9 11/32	6 13/16	10 21/32	7 21/32	11 31/32	8 1/2	1-1 1/4	9 5/16	1-2 9/16
1/4	5 7/32	8 1/8	6 1/32	9 7/16	6 7/8	10 3/4	7 23/32	1-0 1/32	8 17/32	1-1 11/32	9 3/8	1-2 21/32
5/16	5 1/4	8 7/32	6 3/32	9 17/32	6 15/16	10 13/16	7 3/4	1-0 1/8	8 19/32	1-1 7/16	9 7/16	1-2 23/32
3/8	5 5/16	8 5/16	6 5/32	9 19/32	6 31/32	10 29/32	7 13/16	1-0 7/32	8 21/32	1-1 1/2	9 15/32	1-2 13/16
7/16	5 3/8	8 3/8	6 3/16	9 11/16	7 1/32	10 31/32	7 7/8	1-0 9/32	8 11/16	1-1 19/32	9 17/32	1-2 7/8
1/2	5 13/32	8 15/32	6 1/4	9 3/4	7 3/32	11 1/16	7 29/32	1-0 3/8	8 3/4	1-1 21/32	9 19/32	1-2 31/32
9/16	5 15/32	8 17/32	6 5/16	9 27/32	7 1/8	11 5/32	7 31/32	1-0 7/16	8 13/16	1-1 3/4	9 5/8	1-3 1/16
5/8	5 17/32	8 5/8	6 11/32	9 15/16	7 3/16	11 7/32	8 1/32	1-0 17/32	8 27/32	1-1 27/32	9 11/16	1-3 1/8
11/16	5 9/16	8 23/32	6 13/32	10	7 1/4	11 5/16	8 1/16	1-0 5/8	8 29/32	1-1 29/32	9 3/4	1-3 7/32
3/4	5 5/8	8 25/32	6 15/32	10 3/32	7 9/32	11 3/8	8 1/8	1-0 11/16	8 31/32	1-2	9 25/32	1-3 9/32
13/16	5 11/16	8 7/8	6 1/2	10 5/32	7 11/32	11 15/32	8 3/8	1-0 25/32	9	1-2 1/16	9 27/32	1-3 3/8
7/8	5 23/32	8 15/16	6 9/16	10 1/4	7 13/32	11 9/16	8 7/32	1-0 27/32	9 1/16	1-2 5/32	9 29/32	1-3 15/32
15/16	5 25/32	9 1/32	6 5/8	10 11/32	7 7/16	11 5/8	8 9/32	1-0 15/16	9 1/8	1-2 1/4	9 15/16	1-3 17/32

Feet	0' Rise	Slope	10' Rise	Slope	20' Rise	Slope	30' Rise	Slope
0	0	0	8-4	13-0 13/32	16-8	26-0 13/32	25-0	39-0 5/8
1	-10	1-3 5/8	9-2	14-3 13/16	17-6	27-4 1/32	25-10	40-4 1/4
2	1-8	2-7 1/4	10-0	15-7 7/16	18-4	28-7 21/32	26-8	41-7 27/32
3	2-6	3-10 7/8	10-10	16-11 11/16	19-2	29-11 7/8	27-6	42-11 15/32
4	3-4	5-2 15/32	11-8	18-2 11/16	20-0	31-2 29/32	28-4	44-3 3/32
5	4-2	6-6 3/32	12-6	19-6 5/16	20-10	32-6 1/2	29-2	45-6 23/32
6	5-0	7-9 23/32	13-4	20-9 15/16	21-8	33-10 1/8	30-0	46-10 11/32
7	5-10	9-1 11/32	14-2	22-1 9/16	22-6	35-1 3/4	30-10	48-1 31/32
8	6-8	10-4 31/32	15-0	23-5 5/32	23-4	36-5 3/8	31-8	49-5 19/32
9	7-6	11-8 19/32	15-10	24-8 25/32	24-2	37-9	32-6	50-9 3/16

A = 39° 48′ 20″; logsin A = 9.80631; logcos A = 9.88549; logtan A = 9.92082; logcot A = 0.07918

ins.	12″ Rise	12″ Slope	13″ Rise	13″ Slope	14″ Rise	14″ Slope	15″ Rise	15″ Slope	16″ Rise	16″ Slope
0	10	1-3$\frac{5}{8}$	10$\frac{27}{32}$	1-4$\frac{15}{16}$	11$\frac{21}{32}$	1-6$\frac{1}{8}$	1-0$\frac{1}{2}$	1-7$\frac{17}{32}$	1-1$\frac{11}{32}$	1-8$\frac{13}{16}$
$\frac{1}{16}$	10$\frac{1}{16}$	1-3$\frac{11}{32}$	10$\frac{7}{8}$	1-5	11$\frac{23}{32}$	1-6$\frac{5}{16}$	1-0$\frac{9}{16}$	1-7$\frac{19}{32}$	1-1$\frac{3}{8}$	1-8$\frac{29}{32}$
$\frac{1}{8}$	10$\frac{3}{32}$	1-3$\frac{25}{32}$	10$\frac{15}{16}$	1-5$\frac{3}{32}$	11$\frac{25}{32}$	1-6$\frac{3}{8}$	1-0$\frac{19}{32}$	1-7$\frac{11}{16}$	1-1$\frac{7}{16}$	1-9
$\frac{3}{16}$	10$\frac{5}{32}$	1-3$\frac{7}{8}$	11	1-5$\frac{5}{32}$	11$\frac{13}{16}$	1-6$\frac{15}{32}$	1-0$\frac{21}{32}$	1-7$\frac{25}{32}$	1-1$\frac{1}{2}$	1-9$\frac{1}{4}$
$\frac{1}{4}$	10$\frac{7}{32}$	1-3$\frac{15}{16}$	11$\frac{1}{2}$	1-5$\frac{1}{4}$	11$\frac{7}{8}$	1-6$\frac{9}{16}$	1-0$\frac{23}{32}$	1-7$\frac{27}{32}$	1-1$\frac{17}{32}$	1-9$\frac{5}{8}$
$\frac{5}{16}$	10$\frac{1}{4}$	1-4$\frac{1}{32}$	11$\frac{3}{32}$	1-5$\frac{11}{32}$	11$\frac{15}{16}$	1-6$\frac{5}{8}$	1-0$\frac{3}{4}$	1-7$\frac{15}{16}$	1-1$\frac{19}{32}$	1-9$\frac{7}{32}$
$\frac{3}{8}$	10$\frac{5}{16}$	1-4$\frac{3}{32}$	11$\frac{5}{32}$	1-5$\frac{13}{32}$	11$\frac{15}{16}$	1-6$\frac{23}{32}$	1-0$\frac{13}{16}$	1-8	1-1$\frac{21}{32}$	1-9$\frac{5}{16}$
$\frac{7}{16}$	10$\frac{3}{8}$	1-4$\frac{3}{16}$	11$\frac{3}{32}$	1-5$\frac{1}{2}$	1-0$\frac{1}{32}$	1-6$\frac{25}{32}$	1-0$\frac{7}{8}$	1-8$\frac{3}{32}$	1-1$\frac{11}{16}$	1-9$\frac{13}{32}$
$\frac{1}{2}$	10$\frac{13}{32}$	1-4$\frac{9}{32}$	11$\frac{1}{4}$	1-5$\frac{9}{16}$	1-0$\frac{3}{32}$	1-6$\frac{7}{8}$	1-0$\frac{29}{32}$	1-8$\frac{3}{16}$	1-1$\frac{3}{4}$	1-9$\frac{15}{32}$
$\frac{9}{16}$	10$\frac{15}{32}$	1-4$\frac{11}{32}$	11$\frac{5}{16}$	1-5$\frac{21}{32}$	1-0$\frac{1}{8}$	1-6$\frac{31}{32}$	1-0$\frac{31}{32}$	1-8$\frac{1}{4}$	1-1$\frac{13}{16}$	1-9$\frac{9}{16}$
$\frac{5}{8}$	10$\frac{17}{32}$	1-4$\frac{7}{16}$	11$\frac{11}{32}$	1-5$\frac{3}{4}$	1-0$\frac{3}{16}$	1-7$\frac{1}{32}$	1-1$\frac{1}{32}$	1-8$\frac{11}{32}$	1-1$\frac{27}{32}$	1-9$\frac{21}{32}$
$\frac{11}{16}$	10$\frac{9}{16}$	1-4$\frac{1}{2}$	11$\frac{13}{32}$	1-5$\frac{13}{16}$	1-0$\frac{1}{4}$	1-7$\frac{1}{8}$	1-1$\frac{1}{16}$	1-8$\frac{13}{32}$	1-1$\frac{29}{32}$	1-9$\frac{23}{32}$
$\frac{3}{4}$	10$\frac{5}{8}$	1-4$\frac{19}{32}$	11$\frac{15}{32}$	1-5$\frac{29}{32}$	1-0$\frac{9}{32}$	1-7$\frac{3}{16}$	1-1$\frac{1}{8}$	1-8$\frac{1}{2}$	1-1$\frac{31}{32}$	1-9$\frac{13}{16}$
$\frac{13}{16}$	10$\frac{11}{16}$	1-4$\frac{11}{16}$	11$\frac{1}{2}$	1-5$\frac{31}{32}$	1-0$\frac{11}{32}$	1-7$\frac{9}{32}$	1-1$\frac{3}{16}$	1-8$\frac{19}{32}$	1-2	1-9$\frac{7}{8}$
$\frac{7}{8}$	10$\frac{23}{32}$	1-4$\frac{3}{4}$	11$\frac{9}{16}$	1-6$\frac{1}{16}$	1-0$\frac{13}{32}$	1-7$\frac{3}{8}$	1-1$\frac{7}{32}$	1-8$\frac{21}{32}$	1-2$\frac{1}{8}$	1-9$\frac{31}{32}$
$\frac{15}{16}$	10$\frac{25}{32}$	1-4$\frac{27}{32}$	11$\frac{5}{8}$	1-6$\frac{5}{32}$	1-0$\frac{7}{16}$	1-7$\frac{7}{16}$	1-1$\frac{9}{32}$	1-8$\frac{3}{4}$	1-2$\frac{1}{8}$	1-10$\frac{1}{16}$

ins.	17″ Rise	17″ Slope	18″ Rise	18″ Slope	19″ Rise	19″ Slope	20″ Rise	20″ Slope	21″ Rise	21″ Slope
0	1-2$\frac{5}{32}$	1-10$\frac{1}{8}$	1-3	1-11$\frac{7}{16}$	1-3$\frac{27}{32}$	2-0$\frac{23}{32}$	1-4$\frac{21}{32}$	2-1$\frac{1}{2}$	1-5$\frac{1}{2}$	2-3$\frac{11}{32}$
$\frac{1}{16}$	1-2$\frac{7}{32}$	1-10$\frac{7}{32}$	1-3$\frac{1}{16}$	1-11$\frac{1}{2}$	1-3$\frac{7}{8}$	2-0$\frac{13}{16}$	1-4$\frac{23}{32}$	2-1$\frac{5}{8}$	1-5$\frac{9}{16}$	2-3$\frac{13}{32}$
$\frac{1}{8}$	1-2$\frac{9}{32}$	1-10$\frac{9}{32}$	1-3$\frac{3}{32}$	1-11$\frac{19}{32}$	1-3$\frac{15}{16}$	2-0$\frac{29}{32}$	1-4$\frac{25}{32}$	2-2$\frac{3}{16}$	1-5$\frac{19}{32}$	2-3$\frac{1}{2}$
$\frac{3}{16}$	1-2$\frac{5}{16}$	1-10$\frac{3}{8}$	1-3$\frac{5}{32}$	1-11$\frac{11}{16}$	1-4	2-0$\frac{31}{32}$	1-4$\frac{13}{32}$	2-2$\frac{9}{32}$	1-5$\frac{21}{32}$	2-3$\frac{19}{32}$
$\frac{1}{4}$	1-2$\frac{3}{8}$	1-10$\frac{15}{32}$	1-3$\frac{7}{32}$	1-11$\frac{3}{4}$	1-4$\frac{1}{8}$	2-1$\frac{1}{16}$	1-4$\frac{7}{8}$	2-2$\frac{3}{8}$	1-5$\frac{23}{32}$	2-3$\frac{21}{32}$
$\frac{5}{16}$	1-2$\frac{7}{16}$	1-10$\frac{17}{32}$	1-3$\frac{1}{4}$	1-11$\frac{27}{32}$	1-4$\frac{3}{16}$	2-1$\frac{1}{8}$	1-4$\frac{15}{16}$	2-2$\frac{7}{16}$	1-5$\frac{3}{4}$	2-3$\frac{3}{4}$
$\frac{3}{8}$	1-2$\frac{15}{32}$	1-10$\frac{5}{8}$	1-3$\frac{5}{16}$	1-11$\frac{29}{32}$	1-4$\frac{5}{32}$	2-1$\frac{7}{32}$	1-4$\frac{31}{32}$	2-2$\frac{17}{32}$	1-5$\frac{13}{16}$	2-3$\frac{13}{16}$
$\frac{7}{16}$	1-2$\frac{17}{32}$	1-10$\frac{11}{16}$	1-3$\frac{3}{8}$	2-0	1-4$\frac{3}{16}$	2-1$\frac{9}{16}$	1-5$\frac{1}{32}$	2-2$\frac{19}{32}$	1-5$\frac{7}{8}$	2-3$\frac{29}{32}$
$\frac{1}{2}$	1-2$\frac{19}{32}$	1-10$\frac{25}{32}$	1-3$\frac{13}{32}$	2-0$\frac{3}{32}$	1-4$\frac{1}{4}$	2-1$\frac{3}{8}$	1-5$\frac{3}{32}$	2-2$\frac{11}{16}$	1-5$\frac{29}{32}$	2-4
$\frac{9}{16}$	1-2$\frac{5}{8}$	1-10$\frac{7}{8}$	1-3$\frac{15}{32}$	2-0$\frac{5}{32}$	1-4$\frac{5}{16}$	2-1$\frac{15}{32}$	1-5$\frac{1}{8}$	2-2$\frac{25}{32}$	1-5$\frac{31}{32}$	2-4$\frac{1}{16}$
$\frac{5}{8}$	1-2$\frac{11}{16}$	1-10$\frac{15}{16}$	1-3$\frac{17}{32}$	2-0$\frac{1}{4}$	1-4$\frac{11}{32}$	2-1$\frac{17}{32}$	1-5$\frac{3}{16}$	2-2$\frac{27}{32}$	1-6$\frac{1}{32}$	2-4$\frac{5}{32}$
$\frac{11}{16}$	1-2$\frac{3}{4}$	1-11$\frac{1}{32}$	1-3$\frac{19}{32}$	2-0$\frac{5}{16}$	1-4$\frac{13}{32}$	2-1$\frac{5}{8}$	1-5$\frac{1}{4}$	2-2$\frac{15}{16}$	1-6$\frac{1}{16}$	2-4$\frac{7}{32}$
$\frac{3}{4}$	1-2$\frac{25}{32}$	1-11$\frac{1}{8}$	1-3$\frac{5}{8}$	2-0$\frac{13}{32}$	1-4$\frac{15}{32}$	2-1$\frac{23}{32}$	1-5$\frac{9}{32}$	2-3	1-6$\frac{1}{8}$	2-4$\frac{5}{16}$
$\frac{13}{16}$	1-2$\frac{27}{32}$	1-11$\frac{3}{16}$	1-3$\frac{11}{16}$	2-0$\frac{1}{2}$	1-4$\frac{1}{2}$	2-1$\frac{25}{32}$	1-5$\frac{11}{32}$	2-3$\frac{3}{32}$	1-6$\frac{3}{16}$	2-4$\frac{13}{32}$
$\frac{7}{8}$	1-2$\frac{29}{32}$	1-11$\frac{19}{32}$	1-3$\frac{23}{32}$	2-0$\frac{9}{16}$	1-4$\frac{9}{16}$	2-1$\frac{7}{8}$	1-5$\frac{13}{32}$	2-3$\frac{3}{16}$	1-6$\frac{7}{32}$	2-4$\frac{15}{32}$
$\frac{15}{16}$	1-2$\frac{15}{16}$	1-11$\frac{11}{32}$	1-3$\frac{25}{32}$	2-0$\frac{21}{32}$	1-4$\frac{5}{8}$	2-1$\frac{15}{16}$	1-5$\frac{7}{16}$	2-3$\frac{1}{4}$	1-6$\frac{9}{32}$	2-4$\frac{9}{16}$

Feet	40′ Rise	40′ Slope	50′ Rise	50′ Slope	60′ Rise	60′ Slope	70′ Rise	70′ Slope
0	33-4	52-0$\frac{13}{16}$	41-8	65-1$\frac{1}{32}$	50-0	78-1$\frac{7}{32}$	58-4	91-1$\frac{7}{16}$
1	34-2	53-4$\frac{7}{16}$	42-6	66-4$\frac{21}{32}$	50-10	79-4$\frac{27}{32}$	59-2	92-5$\frac{1}{16}$
2	35-0	54-8$\frac{1}{16}$	43-4	67-8$\frac{5}{32}$	51-8	80-8$\frac{15}{32}$	60-0	93-8$\frac{11}{16}$
3	35-10	55-11$\frac{11}{16}$	44-2	68-11$\frac{7}{8}$	52-6	82-0$\frac{3}{32}$	60-10	95-0$\frac{5}{32}$
4	36-8	57-3$\frac{5}{16}$	45-0	70-3$\frac{1}{2}$	53-4	83-3$\frac{23}{32}$	61-8	96-3$\frac{29}{32}$
5	37-6	58-6$\frac{15}{16}$	45-10	71-7$\frac{1}{8}$	54-2	84-7$\frac{11}{32}$	62-6	97-7$\frac{17}{32}$
6	38-4	59-10$\frac{17}{32}$	46-8	72-10$\frac{3}{4}$	55-0	85-10$\frac{15}{16}$	63-4	98-11$\frac{5}{32}$
7	39-2	61-2$\frac{5}{32}$	47-6	74-2$\frac{3}{8}$	55-10	87-2$\frac{9}{16}$	64-2	100-2$\frac{25}{32}$
8	40-0	62-5$\frac{25}{32}$	48-4	75-6	56-8	88-6$\frac{3}{16}$	65-0	101-6$\frac{13}{32}$
9	40-10	63-9$\frac{13}{32}$	49-2	76-9$\frac{5}{8}$	57-6	89-9$\frac{13}{16}$	65-10	102-10$\frac{1}{2}$

natsin A=0.6401843996; natcos A=0.7682212796; nattan A=0.8333333333; natcot A=1.2000000000

Inches	0" Rise	0" Slope	1" Rise	1" Slope	2" Rise	2" Slope	3" Rise	3" Slope	4" Rise	4" Slope	5" Rise	5" Slope
0	0	0	27/32	1 5/16	1 11/16	2 5/8	2 1/2	3 29/32	3 11/32	5 7/32	4 3/16	6 17/32
1/16	1/16	3/32	29/32	1 3/8	1 23/32	2 11/16	2 9/16	4	3 13/32	5 5/16	4 1/4	6 19/32
1/8	3/32	5/32	15/16	1 15/32	1 25/32	2 25/32	2 5/8	4 3/32	3 15/32	5 3/8	4 5/16	6 11/16
3/16	5/32	1/4	1	1 9/16	1 27/32	2 27/32	2 11/16	4 5/32	3 1/2	5 15/32	4 11/32	6 25/32
1/4	7/32	5/16	1 1/16	1 5/8	1 7/8	2 15/16	2 23/32	4 1/4	3 9/16	5 17/32	4 13/32	6 27/32
5/16	1/4	13/32	1 3/32	1 23/32	1 15/16	3 1/32	2 25/32	4 5/16	3 5/8	5 5/8	4 15/32	6 15/16
3/8	5/16	1/2	1 5/32	1 25/32	2	3 3/32	2 27/32	4 13/32	3 21/32	5 23/32	4 1/2	7
7/16	3/8	9/16	1 7/32	1 7/8	2 1/32	3 3/16	2 7/8	4 1/2	3 23/32	5 25/32	4 9/16	7 3/32
1/2	13/32	21/32	1 1/4	1 31/32	2 3/32	3 1/4	2 15/16	4 9/16	3 25/32	5 7/8	4 5/8	7 3/16
9/16	15/32	23/32	1 5/16	2 1/32	2 5/32	3 11/32	3	4 21/32	3 13/16	5 31/32	4 21/32	7 1/4
5/8	17/32	13/16	1 3/8	2 1/8	2 3/16	3 7/16	3 1/32	4 23/32	3 7/8	6 1/32	4 23/32	7 11/32
11/16	9/16	29/32	1 13/32	2 3/16	2 1/4	3 1/2	3 3/32	4 13/16	3 15/16	6 1/8	4 25/32	7 7/16
3/4	5/8	31/32	1 15/32	2 9/32	2 5/16	3 19/32	3 5/32	4 29/32	3 31/32	6 3/16	4 13/16	7 1/2
13/16	11/16	1 1/16	1 17/32	2 3/8	2 11/32	3 21/32	3 3/16	4 31/32	4 1/32	6 9/32	4 7/8	7 19/32
7/8	23/32	1 5/32	1 9/16	2 7/16	2 13/32	3 3/4	3 1/4	5 1/16	4 3/32	6 3/8	4 15/16	7 21/32
15/16	25/32	1 7/32	1 5/8	2 17/32	2 15/32	3 27/32	3 5/16	5 1/8	4 1/8	6 15/32	4 31/32	7 3/4

Inches	6" Rise	6" Slope	7" Rise	7" Slope	8" Rise	8" Slope	9" Rise	9" Slope	10" Rise	10" Slope	11" Rise	11" Slope
0	5 7/32	7 27/32	5 7/8	9 1/8	6 23/32	10 7/16	7 9/16	11 3/4	8 3/8	1-1 1/16	9 7/32	1-2 11/32
1/16	5 9/32	7 29/32	5 15/16	9 7/32	6 3/4	10 17/32	7 19/32	11 13/16	8 7/16	1-1 1/8	9 9/32	1-2 7/16
1/8	5 1/8	8	5 31/32	9 5/16	6 13/16	10 19/32	7 21/32	11 29/32	8 1/2	1-1 7/32	9 11/32	1-2 17/32
3/16	5 3/16	8 1/16	6 1/32	9 3/8	6 7/8	10 11/16	7 23/32	1-0	8 17/32	1-1 9/32	9 3/8	1-2 19/32
1/4	5 1/4	8 5/32	6 3/32	9 15/32	6 29/32	10 25/32	7 3/4	1-0 1/16	8 19/32	1-1 3/8	9 7/16	1-2 11/16
5/16	5 9/32	8 1/4	6 1/8	9 17/32	6 31/32	10 27/32	7 13/16	1-0 5/32	8 21/32	1-1 15/32	9 1/2	1-2 3/4
3/8	5 11/32	8 5/16	6 3/16	9 5/8	7	10 15/16	7 7/8	1-0 1/4	8 11/16	1-1 17/32	9 17/32	1-2 27/32
7/16	5 13/32	8 13/32	6 1/4	9 23/32	7 1/16	11	7 29/32	1-0 5/16	8 3/4	1-1 5/8	9 19/32	1-2 15/16
1/2	5 7/16	8 15/32	6 9/32	9 25/32	7 1/8	11 3/32	7 31/32	1-0 13/32	8 13/16	1-1 11/16	9 21/32	1-3
9/16	5 1/2	8 9/16	6 11/32	9 7/8	7 3/16	11 3/16	8 1/32	1-0 15/32	8 27/32	1-1 25/32	9 11/16	1-3 3/32
5/8	5 9/16	8 21/32	6 13/32	9 15/16	7 7/32	11 1/4	8 1/16	1-0 9/16	8 29/32	1-1 7/8	9 3/4	1-3 5/32
11/16	5 19/32	8 23/32	6 7/16	10 1/32	7 9/32	11 11/32	8 1/8	1-0 21/32	8 31/32	1-1 15/16	9 13/16	1-3 1/4
3/4	5 21/32	8 13/16	6 1/2	10 1/8	7 11/32	11 13/32	8 3/16	1-0 23/32	9	1-2 1/32	9 27/32	1-3 11/32
13/16	5 23/32	8 29/32	6 9/16	10 3/16	7 3/8	11 1/2	8 7/32	1-0 13/16	9 1/16	1-2 1/8	9 29/32	1-3 13/32
7/8	5 3/4	8 31/32	6 19/32	10 9/32	7 7/16	11 19/32	8 9/32	1-0 7/8	9 1/8	1-2 3/16	9 31/32	1-3 1/2
15/16	5 13/16	9 1/16	6 21/32	10 11/32	7 1/2	11 21/32	8 11/32	1-0 31/32	9 5/32	1-2 9/32	10	1-3 19/32

Feet	0' Rise	0' Slope	10' Rise	10' Slope	20' Rise	20' Slope	30' Rise	30' Slope
0	0	0	8-4 5/8	13-0 19/32	16-9 1/4	26-1 7/32	25-1 7/8	39-1 13/16
1	-10 1/16	1-3 21/32	9-2 11/16	14-4 1/4	17-7 5/16	27-4 7/8	25-11 15/16	40-5 15/32
2	1-8 1/8	2-7 5/16	10-0 3/4	15-7 15/16	18-5 3/8	28-8 17/32	26-10	41-9 1/8
3	2-6 3/16	3-10 31/32	10-10 13/16	16-11 19/32	19-3 7/16	30-0 3/16	27-8 1/16	43-0 25/32
4	3-4 1/4	5-2 21/32	11-8 7/8	18-3 1/4	20-1 1/2	31-3 27/32	28-6 1/8	44-4 15/32
5	4-2 5/16	6-6 5/16	12-6 15/16	19-6 29/32	20-11 9/16	32-7 1/2	29-4 3/16	45-8 1/8
6	5-0 3/8	7-9 31/32	13-5	20-10 9/16	21-9 5/8	33-11 3/16	30-2 1/4	46-11 25/32
7	5-10 7/16	9-1 5/8	14-3 1/16	22-2 7/32	22-7 11/16	35-2 27/32	31-0 5/16	48-3 7/16
8	6-8 1/2	10-5 9/32	15-1 1/8	23-5 7/8	23-5 3/4	36-6 1/2	31-10 3/8	49-7 3/32
9	7-6 9/16	11-8 15/16	15-11 3/16	24-9 9/16	24-3 13/16	37-10 5/32	32-8 7/16	50-10 3/4

A = 39° 58′ 52″; logsin A = 9.80790; logcos A = 9.88437; logtan A = 9.92352; logcot A = 0.07648

Ins.	12" Rise	12" Slope	13" Rise	13" Slope	14" Rise	14" Slope	15" Rise	15" Slope	16" Rise	16" Slope
0	10 1/16	1-3 21/32	10 29/32–	1-4 31/32–	11 3/4	1-6 9/32–	1-0 9/16	1-7 9/16	1-1 13/32	1-8 7/8
1/16	10 1/8	1-3 3/4	10 31/32–	1-5 1/16	11 25/32	1-6 11/32	1-0 5/8	1-7 21/32	1-1 15/32	1-8 31/32–
1/8	10 5/32	1-3 13/16	11	1-5 1/8	11 27/32	1-6 7/16	1-0 11/16	1-7 3/4	1-1 17/32–	1-9 1/32
3/16	10 7/32	1-3 29/32–	11 1/16	1-5 7/32–	11 29/32–	1-6 1/2	1-0 3/4	1-7 13/16	1-1 9/16	1-9 1/8
1/4	10 9/32–	1-4	11 1/8	1-5 9/32	11 15/16	1-6 19/32	1-0 25/32	1-7 29/32–	1-1 5/8	1-9 7/32–
5/16	10 5/16	1-4 1/16	11 5/32	1-5 3/8	1-0	1-6 11/16	1-0 27/32–	1-7 31/32	1-1 11/16	1-9 9/32
3/8	10 3/8	1-4 5/32–	11 7/32–	1-5 15/32–	1-0 1/16	1-6 3/4	1-0 29/32–	1-8 1/16	1-1 23/32	1-9 3/8
7/16	10 7/16	1-4 7/32	11 9/32–	1-5 17/32	1-0 3/32	1-6 27/32–	1-0 15/16	1-8 5/32–	1-1 25/32	1-9 7/16
1/2	10 15/32	1-4 5/16	11 5/16	1-5 5/8	1-0 5/32	1-6 15/16	1-1	1-8 7/32	1-1 27/32–	1-9 17/32
9/16	10 17/32	1-4 13/32–	11 3/8	1-5 11/16	1-0 7/32–	1-7	1-1 1/16	1-8 5/16	1-1 7/8	1-9 5/8
5/8	10 19/32–	1-4 15/32	11 7/16	1-5 25/32	1-0 1/4	1-7 3/32–	1-1 3/32	1-8 13/32–	1-1 15/16	1-9 11/16
11/16	10 5/8	1-4 9/16	11 15/32	1-5 7/8	1-0 5/16	1-7 5/32	1-1 5/32–	1-8 15/32	1-2	1-9 25/32–
3/4	10 11/16	1-4 5/8	11 17/32–	1-5 15/16	1-0 3/8	1-7 1/4	1-1 7/32–	1-8 9/16	1-2 1/32	1-9 7/8
13/16	10 3/4	1-4 23/32	11 19/32–	1-6 1/32–	1-0 13/32	1-7 11/32–	1-1 1/4	1-8 5/8	1-2 3/32	1-9 15/16
7/8	10 25/32	1-4 13/16	11 5/8	1-6 3/32	1-0 15/32	1-7 13/32	1-1 5/16	1-8 23/32–	1-2 5/32–	1-10 1/32–
15/16	10 27/32	1-4 7/8	11 11/16	1-6 3/16	1-0 17/32–	1-7 1/2	1-1 3/8	1-8 13/16	1-2 3/16	1-10 3/32

Ins.	17" Rise	17" Slope	18" Rise	18" Slope	19" Rise	19" Slope	20" Rise	20" Slope	21" Rise	21" Slope
0	1-2 1/4	1-10 3/16	1-3 3/32	1-11 1/2	1-3 15/16	2-0 25/32	1-4 25/32–	2-2 3/32	1-5 5/8	2-3 13/32–
1/16	1-2 5/16	1-10 9/32–	1-3 5/32–	1-11 9/16	1-4	2-0 7/8	1-4 13/16	2-2 3/16	1-5 21/32	2-3 1/2
1/8	1-2 3/8	1-10 11/32	1-3 3/16	1-11 21/32–	1-4 1/32	2-0 31/32–	1-4 7/8	2-2 1/4	1-5 23/32–	2-3 9/16
3/16	1-2 13/32	1-10 7/16	1-3 1/4	1-11 3/4	1-4 3/32–	2-1 1/32	1-4 15/16	2-2 11/32	1-5 25/32–	2-3 21/32–
1/4	1-2 15/32–	1-10 1/2	1-3 5/16	1-11 13/16	1-4 5/32–	2-1 1/8	1-4 31/32	2-2 7/16	1-5 13/16	2-3 23/32
5/16	1-2 17/32–	1-10 19/32–	1-3 11/32	1-11 29/32–	1-4 3/16	2-1 7/32–	1-5 1/32	2-2 1/2	1-5 7/8	2-3 13/16
3/8	1-2 9/16	1-10 11/16	1-3 13/32	1-11 31/32	1-4 1/4	2-1 9/32	1-5 3/32–	2-2 19/32–	1-5 15/16	2-3 29/32–
7/16	1-2 5/8	1-10 3/4	1-3 15/32–	2-0 1/16	1-4 5/16	2-1 3/8	1-5 1/8	2-2 11/16	1-5 31/32	2-3 31/32
1/2	1-2 11/16	1-10 27/32–	1-3 1/2	2-0 5/32–	1-4 11/32	2-1 7/16	1-5 3/16	2-2 3/4	1-6 1/32–	2-4 1/16
9/16	1-2 23/32	1-10 29/32	1-3 9/16	2-0 7/32	1-4 13/32–	2-1 17/32–	1-5 1/4	2-2 27/32–	1-6 3/32–	2-4 1/8
5/8	1-2 25/32–	1-11	1-3 5/8	2-0 5/16	1-4 15/32–	2-1 5/8	1-5 9/32	2-2 29/32	1-6 1/8	2-4 7/32
11/16	1-2 27/32–	1-11 3/32–	1-3 21/32	2-0 3/8	1-4 1/2	2-1 11/16	1-5 11/32	2-3	1-6 3/16	2-4 5/16
3/4	1-2 7/8	1-11 5/32	1-3 23/32	2-0 15/32	1-4 9/16	2-1 25/32–	1-5 13/32–	2-3 3/32–	1-6 1/4	2-4 3/8
13/16	1-2 15/16	1-11 1/4	1-3 25/32–	2-0 9/16	1-4 5/8	2-1 27/32	1-5 7/16	2-3 5/32	1-6 9/32	2-4 15/32–
7/8	1-3	1-11 5/16	1-3 13/16	2-0 5/8	1-4 21/32	2-1 15/16	1-5 1/2	2-3 1/4	1-6 11/32–	2-4 9/16
15/16	1-3 1/32	1-11 13/32	1-3 7/8	2-0 23/32–	1-4 23/32–	2-2 1/32–	1-5 9/16	2-3 5/16	1-6 13/32–	2-4 5/8

Feet	40' Rise	40' Slope	50' Rise	50' Slope	60' Rise	60' Slope	70' Rise	70' Slope
0	33-6 1/2	52-2 7/16	41-11 1/8	65-3 1/32–	50-3 3/4	78-3 5/8	58-8 3/8	91-4 1/4
1	34-4 9/16	53-6 /32–	42-9 3/16	66-6 11/16	51-1 13/16	79-7 9/32	59-6 7/16	92-7 29/32–
2	35-2 5/8	54-9 3/4	43-7 1/4	67-10 11/32	51-11 7/8	80-10 31/32–	60-4 1/2	93-11 9/16
3	36-0 11/16	56-1 13/32–	44-5 5/16	69-2	52-9 15/16	82-2 5/8	61-2 9/16	95-3 7/32
4	36-10 3/4	57-5 1/16	45-3 3/8	70-5 21/32	53-8	83-6 9/32–	62-0 5/8	96-6 7/8
5	37-8 13/16	58-8 23/32	46-1 7/16	71-9 11/32–	54-6 1/16	84-9 15/16	62-10 11/16	97-10 17/32
6	38-6 7/8	60-0 3/8	46-11 1/2	73-1	55-4 1/8	86-1 19/32	63-8 3/4	99-2 7/32–
7	39-4 15/16	61-4 1/16	47-9 9/16	74-4 21/32–	56-2 3/16	87-5 1/4	64-6 13/16	100-5 7/8
8	40-3	62-7 23/32–	48-7 5/8	75-8 5/16	57-0 1/4	88-8 29/32	65-4 7/8	101-9 17/32–
9	41-1 1/16	63-11 3/8	49-5 11/16	76-11 31/32	57-10 5/16	90-0 19/32–	66-2 15/16	103-1 3/16

natsin A = 0.6425366825; natcos A = 0.7662549258; nattan A = 0.8385416666; natcot A = 1.1925465838

Inches	0″ Rise	0″ Slope	1″ Rise	1″ Slope	2″ Rise	2″ Slope	3″ Rise	3″ Slope	4″ Rise	4″ Slope	5″ Rise	5″ Slope
0	0	0	27/32	1 5/16	1 11/16	2 5/8	2 17/32	3 15/16	3 3/8	5 7/32	4 7/32	6 17/32
1/16		3/32	29/32	1 3/8	1 3/4	2 11/16	2 19/32	4	3 7/16	5 5/16	4 9/32	6 5/8
1/8	3/32	5/32	15/16	1 15/16	1 25/32	2 25/32	2 5/8	4 3/32	3 15/32	5 13/32	4 5/16	6 23/32
3/16	5/32	1/4	1	1 9/16	1 27/32	2 7/8	2 11/16	4 5/32	3 17/32	5 15/32	4 3/8	6 25/32
1/4	7/32	5/16	1 1/16	1 5/8	1 29/32	2 15/16	2 3/4	4 1/4	3 19/32	5 9/16	4 7/16	6 7/8
5/16	1/4	13/32	1 3/32	1 23/32	1 15/16	3 1/32	2 25/32	4 11/32	3 5/8	5 21/32	4 15/32	6 15/16
3/8	5/16	1/2	1 5/32	1 13/16	2	3 3/32	2 27/32	4 13/32	3 11/16	5 23/32	4 17/32	7 1/32
7/16	3/8	9/16	1 7/32	1 7/8	2 1/16	3 3/16	2 29/32	4 1/2	3 3/4	5 13/16	4 19/32	7 1/8
1/2	7/16	21/32	1 1/4	1 31/32	2 1/8	3 9/32	2 15/16	4 19/32	3 13/16	5 7/8	4 5/8	7 3/16
9/16	15/32	3/4	1 5/16	2 1/32	2 5/32	3 11/32	3	4 21/32	3 27/32	5 31/32	4 11/16	7 9/32
5/8	17/32	13/16	1 11/32	2 1/8	2 7/32	3 7/16	3 1/16	4 3/4	3 29/32	6 1/16	4 3/4	7 3/8
11/16	19/32	29/32	1 7/16	2 7/32	2 9/32	3 17/32	3 1/8	4 13/16	3 31/32	6 1/8	4 13/16	7 7/16
3/4	5/8	31/32	1 15/32	2 9/32	2 5/16	3 19/32	3 5/32	4 29/32	4	6 1/2	4 27/32	7 11/32
13/16	11/16	1 1/16	1 17/32	2 3/8	2 3/8	3 11/16	3 7/32	5	4 1/16	6 9/32	4 29/32	7 19/32
7/8	3/4	1 5/32	1 19/32	2 15/32	2 7/16	3 3/4	3 9/32	5 1/16	4 1/8	6 3/8	4 31/32	7 11/16
15/16	25/32	1 7/32	1 5/8	2 17/32	2 15/32	3 27/32	3 5/16	5 5/32	4 5/32	6 15/32	5	7 25/32

Inches	6″ Rise	6″ Slope	7″ Rise	7″ Slope	8″ Rise	8″ Slope	9″ Rise	9″ Slope	10″ Rise	10″ Slope	11″ Rise	11″ Slope
0	5 1/16	7 27/32	5 29/32	9 5/32	6 3/4	10 15/32	7 19/32	11 25/32	8 7/16	1-1 3/32	9 9/32	1-2 13/32
1/16	5 1/8	7 15/16	5 31/32	9 1/4	6 13/16	10 9/16	7 21/32	11 27/32	8 1/2	1-1 5/32	9 11/32	1-2 15/32
1/8	5 5/32	8	6	9 5/16	6 27/32	10 5/8	7 11/16	11 15/16	8 17/32	1-1 1/4	9 3/8	1-2 9/16
3/16	5 7/32	8 3/32	6 1/16	9 13/32	6 29/32	10 23/32	7 3/4	1-0 1/32	8 19/32	1-1 11/32	9 7/16	1-2 5/8
1/4	5 9/32	8 3/16	6 1/8	9 1/2	6 31/32	10 25/32	7 13/16	1-0 3/32	8 21/32	1-1 13/32	9 1/2	1-2 23/32
5/16	5 5/16	8 1/4	6 5/32	9 9/16	7	10 7/8	7 27/32	1-0 3/16	8 11/16	1-1 1/2	9 17/32	1-2 13/16
3/8	5 3/8	8 11/32	6 7/32	9 21/32	7 1/16	10 31/32	7 29/32	1-0 9/32	8 3/4	1-1 9/16	9 19/32	1-2 7/8
7/16	5 7/16	8 7/16	6 9/32	9 23/32	7 1/8	11 1/32	7 31/32	1-0 11/32	8 13/16	1-1 21/32	9 21/32	1-2 31/32
1/2	5 1/2	8 1/2	6 5/16	9 13/16	7 3/16	11 1/8	8	1-0 7/16	8 7/8	1-1 3/4	9 11/16	1-3 1/32
9/16	5 17/32	8 19/32	6 3/8	9 29/32	7 7/32	11 7/32	8 1/16	1-0 1/2	8 29/32	1-1 13/16	9 3/4	1-3 1/8
5/8	5 19/32	8 21/32	6 7/16	9 31/32	7 9/32	11 9/32	8 1/8	1-0 19/32	8 31/32	1-1 29/32	9 13/16	1-3 7/32
11/16	5 21/32	8 3/4	6 1/2	10 1/16	7 11/32	11 3/8	8 3/16	1-0 11/16	9 1/32	1-1 31/32	9 7/8	1-3 9/32
3/4	5 11/16	8 27/32	6 17/32	10 1/8	7 3/8	11 7/16	8 7/32	1-0 3/4	9 1/16	1-2 1/16	9 29/32	1-3 3/8
13/16	5 3/4	8 29/32	6 15/32	10 7/32	7 7/16	11 17/32	8 9/32	1-0 27/32	9 1/8	1-2 5/32	9 31/32	1-3 15/32
7/8	5 13/16	9	6 21/32	10 5/16	7 1/2	11 5/8	8 11/32	1-0 29/32	9 3/16	1-2 1/4	10 1/32	1-3 17/32
15/16	5 27/32	9 1/16	6 11/16	10 3/8	7 17/32	11 11/16	8 3/8	1-1	9 7/32	1-2 5/16	10 1/16	1-3 5/8

Feet	0′ Rise	0′ Slope	10′ Rise	10′ Slope	20′ Rise	20′ Slope	30′ Rise	30′ Slope
0	0	0	8-5 1/4	13-1	16-10 1/2	26-2 1/32	25-3 3/4	39-3 1/32
1	-10 1/8	1-3 11/16	9-3 3/8	14-4 23/32	17-8 5/8	27-5 25/32	26-1 7/8	40-6 23/32
2	1-8 1/4	2-7 13/32	10-1 1/2	15-8 15/32	18-6 3/4	28-9 13/32	27-0	41-10 1/32
3	2-6 3/8	3-11 3/32	10-11 5/8	17-0 1/8	19-4 7/8	30-1 1/8	27-10 1/8	43-2 1/8
4	3-4 1/2	5-2 13/16	11-9 3/4	18-3 13/16	20-3	31-4 13/16	28-8 1/4	44-5 13/16
5	4-2 5/8	6-6 1/2	12-7 7/8	19-7 1/2	21-1 1/8	32-8 17/32	29-6 3/8	45-9 17/32
6	5-0 3/4	7-10 7/32	13-6	20-11 7/32	21-11 1/4	34-0 7/32	30-4 1/2	47-1 7/32
7	5-10 7/8	9-1 29/32	14-4 1/8	22-2 29/32	22-9 3/8	35-3 15/16	31-2 5/8	48-4 15/16
8	6-9	10-5 19/32	15-2 1/4	23-6 5/8	23-7 1/2	36-7 5/8	32-0 3/4	49-8 5/8
9	7-7 1/8	11-9 5/16	16-0 3/8	24-10 5/16	24-5 5/8	37-11 5/16	32-10 7/8	51-0 11/32

A = 40° 09′ 22″; logsin A = 9.80947; logcos A = 9.88326; logtan A = 9.92621; logcot A = 0.07379

In.	12″ Rise	12″ Slope	13″ Rise	13″ Slope	14″ Rise	14″ Slope	15″ Rise	15″ Slope	16″ Rise	16″ Slope
0	10 1/8	1-3 11/16	10 31/32	1-5	11 13/16	1-6 5/16	1-0 21/32	1-7 5/8	1-1 1/2	1-8 15/16
1/16	10 3/16	1-3 25/32	11 1/32	1-5 3/32	11 7/8	1-6 13/32	1-0 23/32	1-7 23/32	1-1 9/16	1-9 1/32
1/8	10 7/32	1-3 7/8	11 1/16	1-5 3/16	11 29/32	1-6 15/32	1-0 3/4	1-7 25/32	1-1 19/32	1-9 3/32
3/16	10 9/32	1-3 15/16	11 1/8	1-5 1/4	11 31/32	1-6 9/16	1-0 13/16	1-7 7/8	1-1 21/32	1-9 3/16
1/4	10 11/32	1-4 1/32	11 3/16	1-5 11/32	1-0 1/32	1-6 21/32	1-0 7/8	1-7 15/16	1-1 23/32	1-9 1/4
5/16	10 3/8	1-4 1/8	11 7/32	1-5 13/32	1-0 1/16	1-6 23/32	1-0 29/32	1-8 1/32	1-1 3/4	1-9 11/32
3/8	10 7/16	1-4 3/16	11 9/32	1-5 1/2	1-0 1/8	1-6 13/16	1-0 31/32	1-8 1/8	1-1 13/16	1-9 7/16
7/16	10 1/2	1-4 9/32	11 11/32	1-5 19/32	1-0 3/16	1-6 7/8	1-1 1/32	1-8 3/16	1-1 7/8	1-9 1/2
1/2	10 9/16	1-4 11/32	11 3/8	1-5 21/32	1-0 1/4	1-6 31/32	1-1 1/16	1-8 9/32	1-1 15/16	1-9 19/32
9/16	10 19/32	1-4 7/16	11 7/16	1-5 3/4	1-0 9/32	1-7 1/16	1-1 1/8	1-8 3/8	1-1 31/32	1-9 21/32
5/8	10 21/32	1-4 17/32	11 1/2	1-5 13/16	1-0 11/32	1-7 1/4	1-1 3/16	1-8 7/16	1-2 1/32	1-9 3/4
11/16	10 23/32	1-4 19/32	11 9/16	1-5 29/32	1-0 13/32	1-7 7/32	1-1 1/4	1-8 17/32	1-2 3/32	1-9 27/32
3/4	10 3/4	1-4 11/16	11 19/32	1-6	1-0 7/16	1-7 5/16	1-1 9/32	1-8 19/32	1-2 1/8	1-9 29/32
13/16	10 13/16	1-4 3/4	11 21/32	1-6 1/16	1-0 1/2	1-7 3/8	1-1 11/32	1-8 11/16	1-2 3/16	1-10
7/8	10 7/8	1-4 27/32	11 23/32	1-6 5/32	1-0 9/16	1-7 15/32	1-1 13/32	1-8 25/32	1-2 1/4	1-10 3/32
15/16	10 29/32	1-4 15/16	11 3/4	1-6 1/4	1-0 19/32	1-7 17/32	1-1 7/16	1-8 27/32	1-2 9/32	1-10 5/32

In.	17″ Rise	17″ Slope	18″ Rise	18″ Slope	19″ Rise	19″ Slope	20″ Rise	20″ Slope	21″ Rise	21″ Slope
0	1-2 11/32	1-10 1/4	1-3 3/16	1-11 9/16	1-4 1/32	2-0 7/8	1-4 7/8	2-2 5/32	1-5 23/32	2-3 15/32
1/16	1-2 13/32	1-10 5/16	1-3 1/4	1-11 5/8	1-4 3/32	2-0 15/16	1-4 15/16	2-2 1/4	1-5 25/32	2-3 9/16
1/8	1-2 7/16	1-10 13/32	1-3 9/32	1-11 23/32	1-4 1/8	2-1 1/32	1-4 31/32	2-2 11/32	1-5 13/16	2-3 5/8
3/16	1-2 1/2	1-10 1/2	1-3 11/32	1-11 25/32	1-4 3/16	2-1 3/32	1-5 1/32	2-2 13/32	1-5 7/8	2-3 23/32
1/4	1-2 9/16	1-10 9/16	1-3 13/32	1-11 7/8	1-4 1/4	2-1 3/16	1-5 3/32	2-2 1/2	1-5 15/16	2-3 13/16
5/16	1-2 19/32	1-10 21/32	1-3 7/16	1-11 31/32	1-4 9/32	2-1 9/32	1-5 1/8	2-2 9/16	1-5 31/32	2-3 7/8
3/8	1-2 21/32	1-10 23/32	1-3 1/2	2-0 1/32	1-4 11/32	2-1 11/32	1-5 3/16	2-2 21/32	1-6 1/32	2-3 31/32
7/16	1-2 23/32	1-10 13/16	1-3 9/16	2-0 1/8	1-4 13/32	2-1 7/16	1-5 1/4	2-2 3/4	1-6 3/32	2-4 1/16
1/2	1-2 3/4	1-10 29/32	1-3 5/8	2-0 7/32	1-4 7/16	2-1 1/2	1-5 5/16	2-2 13/16	1-6 1/8	2-4 1/8
9/16	1-2 13/16	1-10 31/32	1-3 21/32	2-0 9/32	1-4 1/2	2-1 19/32	1-5 11/32	2-2 29/32	1-6 3/16	2-4 7/32
5/8	1-2 7/8	1-11 1/16	1-3 23/32	2-0 3/8	1-4 9/16	2-1 11/16	1-5 13/32	2-3	1-6 1/4	2-4 9/32
11/16	1-2 15/16	1-11 5/32	1-3 25/32	2-0 7/16	1-4 5/8	2-1 3/4	1-5 15/32	2-3 1/16	1-6 5/16	2-4 3/8
3/4	1-2 31/32	1-11 7/32	1-3 13/16	2-0 17/32	1-4 21/32	2-1 27/32	1-5 1/2	2-3 5/32	1-6 11/32	2-4 15/32
13/16	1-3 1/32	1-11 5/16	1-3 7/8	2-0 5/8	1-4 23/32	2-1 15/16	1-5 9/16	2-3 7/32	1-6 13/32	2-4 17/32
7/8	1-3 3/32	1-11 3/8	1-3 15/16	2-0 11/16	1-4 25/32	2-2	1-5 5/8	2-3 5/16	1-6 15/32	2-4 5/8
15/16	1-3 1/8	1-11 15/32	1-3 31/32	2-0 25/32	1-4 13/16	2-2 3/32	1-5 21/32	2-3 13/32	1-6 1/2	2-4 11/16

Feet	40′ Rise	40′ Slope	50′ Rise	50′ Slope	60′ Rise	60′ Slope	70′ Rise	70′ Slope
0	33-9	52-4 1/32	42-2 1/4	65-5 1/32	50-7 1/2	78-6 1/16	59-0 3/4	91-7 1/16
1	34-7 1/8	53-7 23/32	43-0 3/8	66-8 3/4	51-5 5/8	79-9 3/4	59-10 7/8	92-10 3/4
2	35-5 1/4	54-11 7/16	43-10 1/2	68-0 7/16	52-3 3/4	81-1 7/16	60-9	94-2 15/32
3	36-3 3/8	56-3 1/8	44-8 5/8	69-4 5/32	53-1 7/8	82-5 5/32	61-7 1/8	95-6 5/32
4	37-1 1/2	57-6 27/32	45-6 3/4	70-7 27/32	54-0	83-8 27/32	62-5 1/4	96-9 7/8
5	37-11 5/8	58-10 17/32	46-4 7/8	71-11 17/32	54-10 1/8	85-0 9/16	63-3 3/8	98-1 9/16
6	38-9 3/4	60-2 1/4	47-3	73-3 1/4	55-8 1/4	86-4 1/4	64-1 1/2	99-5 1/4
7	39-7 7/8	61-5 15/16	48-1 1/8	74-6 15/16	56-6 3/8	87-7 31/32	64-11 5/8	100-8 31/32
8	40-6	62-9 5/8	48-11 1/4	75-10 21/32	57-4 1/2	88-11 21/32	65-9 3/4	102-0 21/32
9	41-4 1/8	64-1 11/32	49-9 3/8	77-2 11/32	58-2 5/8	90-3 11/32	66-7 7/8	103-4 3/8

natsin A = 0.6448709392; natcos A = 0.7642914835; nattan A = 0.8437500000; natcot A = 1.1851851851

Inches	0" Rise	0" Slope	1" Rise	1" Slope	2" Rise	2" Slope	3" Rise	3" Slope	4" Rise	4" Slope	5" Rise	5" Slope
0	0	0	27/32	15/16	1 11/16	2 5/8	2 9/16	3 15/16	3 13/32	5 1/4	4 1/4	6 9/16
1/16	1/16	3/32	29/32	1 13/32	1 3/4	2 23/32	2 19/32	4 1/32	3 7/16	5 11/32	4 5/16	6 21/32
1/8	3/32	5/32	31/32	1 15/32	1 13/16	2 25/32	2 21/32	4 3/32	3 1/2	5 13/32	4 11/32	6 23/32
3/16	5/32	1/4	1	1 9/16	1 27/32	2 7/8	2 23/32	4 3/16	3 9/16	5 1/2	4 13/32	6 13/16
1/4	7/32	5/16	1 1/16	1 5/8	1 29/32	2 15/16	2 3/4	4 1/4	3 19/32	5 9/16	4 15/32	6 7/8
5/16	1/4	13/32	1 1/8	1 23/32	1 31/32	3 1/32	2 13/16	4 11/32	3 21/32	5 21/32	4 1/2	6 31/32
3/8	5/16	1/2	1 5/32	1 13/16	2 1/32	3 1/8	2 7/8	4 7/16	3 23/32	5 3/4	4 9/16	7 1/16
7/16	3/8	9/16	1 7/32	1 7/8	2 1/16	3 3/16	2 29/32	4 1/2	3 25/32	5 13/16	4 5/8	7 1/8
1/2	7/16	21/32	1 9/32	1 31/32	2 1/8	3 9/32	2 31/32	4 19/32	3 13/16	5 29/32	4 21/32	7 7/32
9/16	15/32	3/4	1 5/16	2 1/16	2 3/16	3 3/8	3 1/32	4 11/16	3 7/8	6	4 23/32	7 9/32
5/8	17/32	13/16	1 3/8	2 1/8	2 7/32	3 7/16	3 1/16	4 3/4	3 15/16	6 1/16	4 25/32	7 3/8
11/16	19/32	29/32	1 7/16	2 7/32	2 9/32	3 17/32	3 1/8	4 27/32	3 31/32	6 5/32	4 27/32	7 15/32
3/4	5/8	31/32	1 1/2	2 9/32	2 11/32	3 19/32	3 3/16	4 29/32	4 1/2	6 1/4	4 7/8	7 11/32
13/16	11/16	1 1/16	1 17/32	2 3/8	2 3/8	3 11/16	3 1/4	5	4 3/32	6 5/16	4 15/16	7 5/8
7/8	3/4	1 5/32	1 19/32	2 15/32	2 7/16	3 25/32	3 9/32	5 3/32	4 1/8	6 13/32	5	7 23/32
15/16	25/32	1 7/32	1 21/32	2 17/32	2 1/2	3 27/32	3 11/32	5 5/32	4 3/16	6 15/32	5 1/32	7 25/32

Inches	6" Rise	6" Slope	7" Rise	7" Slope	8" Rise	8" Slope	9" Rise	9" Slope	10" Rise	10" Slope	11" Rise	11" Slope
0	5 3/32	7 7/8	5 15/16	9 3/16	6 25/32	10 1/2	7 5/8	11 13/16	8 1/2	1-1 1/8	9 11/32	1-2 7/16
1/16	5 5/32	7 15/16	6	9 1/4	6 27/32	10 9/16	7 11/16	11 7/8	8 17/32	1-1 3/16	9 13/32	1-2 1/2
1/8	5 3/16	8 1/32	6 1/16	9 11/32	6 29/32	10 21/32	7 3/4	11 31/32	8 19/32	1-1 9/32	9 7/16	1-2 19/32
3/16	5 1/4	8 1/8	6 3/32	9 7/16	6 15/16	10 3/4	7 13/16	1-0 1/16	8 21/32	1-1 3/8	9 1/2	1-2 11/16
1/4	5 5/16	8 3/16	6 5/32	9 1/2	7	10 13/16	7 27/32	1-0 1/8	8 11/16	1-1 7/16	9 9/16	1-2 3/4
5/16	5 11/32	8 9/32	6 7/32	9 19/32	7 1/16	10 29/32	7 29/32	1-0 7/32	8 3/4	1-1 17/32	9 19/32	1-2 27/32
3/8	5 13/32	8 3/8	6 1/4	9 11/16	7 1/8	11	7 31/32	1-0 5/16	8 13/16	1-1 5/8	9 21/32	1-2 29/32
7/16	5 15/32	8 7/16	6 5/16	9 3/4	7 5/32	11 1/16	8	1-0 3/8	8 7/8	1-1 11/16	9 23/32	1-3
1/2	5 17/32	8 17/32	6 3/8	9 27/32	7 7/32	11 5/32	8 1/16	1-0 15/32	8 29/32	1-1 25/32	9 3/4	1-3 3/32
9/16	5 9/16	8 19/32	6 13/32	9 29/32	7 9/32	11 7/32	8 1/8	1-0 17/32	8 31/32	1-1 27/32	9 13/16	1-3 5/32
5/8	5 5/8	8 11/16	6 15/32	10	7 5/16	11 5/16	8 5/32	1-0 5/8	9 1/32	1-1 15/16	9 7/8	1-3 1/4
11/16	5 11/16	8 25/32	6 17/32	10 3/32	7 3/8	11 13/32	8 7/32	1-0 23/32	9 1/16	1-2 1/32	9 15/16	1-3 11/32
3/4	5 23/32	8 27/32	6 19/32	10 5/32	7 7/16	11 15/32	8 9/32	1-0 25/32	9 1/8	1-2 3/32	9 31/32	1-3 13/32
13/16	5 25/32	8 15/16	6 5/8	10 1/4	7 15/32	11 9/16	8 11/32	1-0 7/8	9 3/16	1-2 3/16	10 1/32	1-3 1/2
7/8	5 27/32	9 1/32	6 11/16	10 11/32	7 17/32	11 21/32	8 3/8	1-0 31/32	9 7/32	1-2 1/4	10 3/32	1-3 9/16
15/16	5 7/8	9 3/32	6 3/4	10 13/32	7 19/32	11 23/32	8 7/16	1-1 1/16	9 9/32	1-2 11/32	10 1/8	1-3 21/32

Feet	0' Rise	0' Slope	10' Rise	10' Slope	20' Rise	20' Slope	30' Rise	30' Slope
0	0	0	8-5 7/8	13-1 13/32	16-11 3/4	26-2 13/16	25-5 5/8	39-4 1/4
1	-10 3/16	1-3 3/4	9-4 1/16	14-5 5/32	17-9 15/16	27-6 9/16	26-3 13/16	40-7 31/32
2	1-8 3/8	2-7 15/32	10-2 1/4	15-8 29/32	18-8 1/8	28-10 5/16	27-2	41-11 23/32
3	2-6 9/16	3-11 7/32	11-0 7/16	17-0 5/8	19-6 5/16	30-2 1/16	28-0 3/16	43-3 15/32
4	3-4 3/4	5-2 31/32	11-10 5/8	18-4 3/8	20-4 1/2	31-5 25/32	28-10 3/8	44-7 3/16
5	4-2 15/16	6-6 23/32	12-8 13/16	19-8 1/8	21-2 11/16	32-9 17/32	29-8 9/16	45-10 15/16
6	5-1 1/8	7-10 7/16	13-7	20-11 27/32	22-0 7/8	34-1 9/32	30-6 3/4	47-2 11/16
7	5-11 5/16	9-2 3/16	14-5 3/16	22-3 19/32	22-11 1/16	35-5	31-4 15/16	48-6 7/16
8	6-9 1/2	10-5 15/16	15-3 3/8	23-7 11/32	23-9 1/4	36-8 3/4	32-3 1/8	49-10 5/32
9	7-7 11/16	11-9 21/32	16-1 9/16	24-11 3/32	24-7 7/16	38-0 1/2	33-1 5/16	51-1 29/32

A = 40° 19′ 48″; logsin A = 9.81103; logcos A = 9.88214; logtan A = 9.92889; logcot A = 0.07111

Ins.	12″ Rise	12″ Slope	13″ Rise	13″ Slope	14″ Rise	14″ Slope	15″ Rise	15″ Slope	16″ Rise	16″ Slope
0	10 3/16	1-3 3/4	11 1/32	1-5 1/16	11 7/8	1-6 3/8	1-0 3/4	1-7 11/16	1-1 19/32—	1-9
1/16	10 1/4	1-3 13/16	11 3/32—	1-5 1/8	11 15/16	1-6 7/16	1-0 25/32	1-7 3/4	1-1 5/8	1-9 1/16
1/8	10 9/32	1-3 29/32—	11 5/32—	1-5 7/32—	1-0	1-6 17/32—	1-0 27/32—	1-7 27/32—	1-1 11/16	1-9 5/32—
3/16	10 11/32	1-4	11 3/16	1-5 5/16	1-0 1/32	1-6 5/8	1-0 29/32—	1-7 15/16	1-1 3/4	1-9 7/32
1/4	10 13/32—	1-4 1/16	11 1/4	1-5 3/8	1-0 3/32	1-6 11/16	1-0 15/16	1-8	1-1 25/32	1-9 5/16
5/16	10 7/16	1-4 5/32—	11 5/16	1-5 15/32—	1-0 5/32—	1-6 25/32—	1-1	1-8 3/32—	1-1 27/32	1-9 13/32—
3/8	10 1/2	1-4 7/32	11 11/32	1-5 17/32	1-0 7/32—	1-6 27/32	1-1 1/16	1-8 5/32	1-1 29/32—	1-9 15/32
7/16	10 9/16	1-4 5/16	11 13/32	1-5 5/8	1-0 1/4	1-6 15/16	1-1 3/32	1-8 1/4	1-1 31/32—	1-9 9/16
1/2	10 5/8	1-4 13/32—	11 15/32—	1-5 23/32—	1-0 5/16	1-7 1/32—	1-1 5/32	1-8 11/32—	1-2	1-9 21/32—
9/16	10 21/32	1-4 15/32	11 1/2	1-5 25/32	1-0 3/8	1-7 3/32	1-1 7/32—	1-8 13/32	1-2 1/16	1-9 23/32
5/8	10 23/32—	1-4 9/16	11 9/16	1-5 7/8	1-0 13/32	1-7 3/16	1-1 1/4	1-8 1/2	1-2 1/8	1-9 13/16
11/16	10 25/32—	1-4 21/32—	11 5/8	1-5 31/32—	1-0 15/32	1-7 9/32—	1-1 5/16	1-8 19/32—	1-2 5/32	1-9 7/8
3/4	10 13/16	1-4 23/32	11 11/16	1-6 1/32	1-0 17/32—	1-7 11/32	1-1 3/8	1-8 21/32	1-2 7/32	1-9 31/32
13/16	10 7/8	1-4 13/16	11 23/32	1-6 1/8	1-0 9/16	1-7 7/16	1-1 7/16	1-8 3/4	1-2 9/32—	1-10 1/16
7/8	10 15/16	1-4 7/8	11 25/32—	1-6 3/16	1-0 5/8	1-7 1/2	1-1 15/32	1-8 13/16	1-2 5/16	1-10 1/8
15/16	10 31/32	1-4 31/32	11 27/32—	1-6 9/32	1-0 11/16	1-7 19/32	1-1 17/32—	1-8 29/32	1-2 3/8	1-10 7/32—

Ins.	17″ Rise	17″ Slope	18″ Rise	18″ Slope	19″ Rise	19″ Slope	20″ Rise	20″ Slope	21″ Rise	21″ Slope
0	1-2 7/16	1-10 5/16	1-3 9/32	1-11 5/8	1-4 1/8	2-0 15/16	1-4 31/32	2-2 1/4	1-5 13/16	2-3 9/16
1/16	1-2 1/2	1-10 3/8	1-3 11/32—	1-11 11/16	1-4 3/16	2-1	1-5 1/32	2-2 5/16	1-5 7/8	2-3 5/8
1/8	1-2 17/32	1-10 15/32—	1-3 3/8	1-11 25/32—	1-4 1/4	2-1 3/32—	1-5 3/32—	2-2 13/32—	1-5 15/16	2-3 23/32—
3/16	1-2 19/32—	1-10 17/32	1-3 7/16	1-11 27/32	1-4 9/32	2-1 5/32	1-5 1/8	2-2 15/32	1-6	2-3 25/32
1/4	1-2 21/32—	1-10 5/8	1-3 1/2	1-11 15/16	1-4 11/32—	2-1 1/4	1-5 3/16	2-2 9/16	1-6 1/32	2-3 7/8
5/16	1-2 11/16	1-10 23/32—	1-3 17/32	2-0 1/32—	1-4 13/32—	2-1 11/32—	1-5 1/4	2-2 21/32—	1-6 3/32—	2-3 31/32—
3/8	1-2 3/4	1-10 25/32	1-3 19/32	2-0 3/32	1-4 7/16	2-1 13/32	1-5 5/16	2-2 23/32	1-6 5/32—	2-4 1/32
7/16	1-2 13/16	1-10 7/8	1-3 21/32—	2-0 3/16	1-4 1/2	2-1 1/2	1-5 11/32	2-2 13/16	1-6 3/16	2-4 1/8
1/2	1-2 27/32	1-10 31/32—	1-3 23/32—	2-0 9/32—	1-4 9/16	2-1 19/32—	1-5 13/32—	2-2 29/32—	1-6 1/4	2-4 3/16
9/16	1-2 29/32	1-11 1/32	1-3 3/4	2-0 11/32	1-4 19/32	2-1 21/32	1-5 15/32—	2-2 31/32	1-6 5/16	2-4 9/32
5/8	1-2 31/32—	1-11 1/8	1-3 13/16	2-0 7/16	1-4 21/32	2-1 3/4	1-5 1/2	2-3 1/16	1-6 11/32	2-4 3/8
11/16	1-3 1/32—	1-11 3/16	1-3 7/8	2-0 1/2	1-4 23/32—	2-1 13/16	1-5 9/16	2-3 1/8	1-6 13/32	2-4 7/16
3/4	1-3 1/16	1-11 9/32	1-3 29/32	2-0 19/32	1-4 25/32—	2-1 29/32	1-5 5/8	2-3 7/32	1-6 15/32—	2-4 17/32—
13/16	1-3 1/8	1-11 3/8	1-3 31/32	2-0 11/16	1-4 13/16	2-2	1-5 21/32	2-3 5/16	1-6 17/32—	2-4 5/8
7/8	1-3 3/16	1-11 7/16	1-4 1/32—	2-0 3/4	1-4 7/8	2-2 1/16	1-5 23/32	2-3 3/8	1-6 9/16	2-4 11/16
15/16	1-3 7/32	1-11 17/32—	1-4 1/16	2-0 27/32—	1-4 15/16	2-2 5/32—	1-5 25/32—	2-3 15/32—	1-6 5/8	2-4 25/32—

Feet	40′ Rise	40′ Slope	50′ Rise	50′ Slope	60′ Rise	60′ Slope	70′ Rise	70′ Slope
0	33-11 1/2	52-5 21/32—	42-5 3/8	65-7 1/16	50-11 1/4	78-8 15/32	59-5 1/8	91-9 7/8
1	34-9 11/16	53-9 3/8	43-3 9/16	66-10 13/16	51-9 7/16	80-0 7/32—	60-3 5/16	93-1 5/8
2	35-7 7/8	55-1 1/8	44-1 3/4	68-2 17/32	52-7 5/8	81-3 31/32—	61-1 1/2	94-5 3/8
3	36-6 1/16	56-4 7/8	44-11 15/16	69-6 9/32	53-5 13/16	82-7 11/16	61-11 11/16	95-9 3/32
4	37-4 1/4	57-8 5/8	45-10 1/8	70-10 1/32—	54-4	83-11 7/16	62-9 7/8	97-0 27/32
5	38-2 7/16	59-0 11/32	46-8 5/16	72-1 3/4	55-2 3/16	85-3 3/16	63-8 1/16	98-4 19/32—
6	39-0 5/8	60-4 3/32	47-6 1/2	73-5 1/2	56-0 3/8	86-6 29/32	64-6 1/4	99-8 11/32—
7	39-10 13/16	61-7 27/32—	48-4 11/16	74-9 1/4	56-10 9/16	87-10 21/32	65-4 7/16	101-0 1/16
8	40-9	62-11 9/16	49-2 7/8	76-1	57-8 3/4	89-2 13/32—	66-2 5/8	102-3 13/16
9	41-7 3/16	64-3 5/16	50-1 1/16	77-4 23/32	58-6 15/16	90-6 5/32—	67-0 13/16	103-7 9/16

natsin A=0.6471872885; natcos A=0.7623310393; nattan A=0.8489583333; natcot A=1.1779141104

Inches	0" Rise	0" Slope	1" Rise	1" Slope	2" Rise	2" Slope	3" Rise	3" Slope	4" Rise	4" Slope	5" Rise	5" Slope
0	0	0	21/32	1 5/16	1 23/32	2 5/8	2 29/32	3 15/16	3 13/32	5 1/4	4 9/32	6 9/16
1/16	1/16	3/32	29/32	1 13/32	1 3/4	2 23/32	2 5/8	4 1/32	3 15/32	5 11/32	4 5/16	6 21/32
1/8	3/32	5/32	31/32	1 15/32	1 13/16	2 25/32	2 21/32	4 1/8	3 17/32	5 7/16	4 3/8	6 3/4
3/16	5/32	1/4	1	1 9/16	1 7/8	2 7/8	2 23/32	4 3/16	3 9/16	5 1/2	4 7/16	6 13/16
1/4	7/32	11/32	1 1/16	1 21/32	1 15/16	2 31/32	2 25/32	4 9/32	3 5/8	5 19/32	4 1/2	6 29/32
5/16	9/32	13/32	1 1/8	1 23/32	1 31/32	3 1/32	2 27/32	4 11/32	3 11/16	5 21/32	4 17/32	7
3/8	5/16	1/2	1 3/16	1 13/16	2 1/32	3 1/8	2 7/8	4 7/16	3 3/4	5 3/4	4 19/32	7 1/16
7/16	3/8	9/16	1 7/32	1 7/8	2 3/32	3 7/32	2 15/16	4 17/32	3 25/32	5 27/32	4 21/32	7 5/32
1/2	7/16	21/32	1 9/32	1 31/32	2 1/8	3 9/32	3	4 19/32	3 27/32	5 29/32	4 11/16	7 7/32
9/16	15/32	3/4	1 11/32	2 1/16	2 3/16	3 3/8	3 1/2	4 11/16	3 29/32	6	4 3/4	7 5/16
5/8	17/32	13/16	1 3/8	2 1/8	2 1/4	3 7/16	3 3/8	4 25/32	3 15/16	6 3/32	4 13/16	7 13/32
11/16	19/32	29/32	1 7/16	2 7/32	2 9/32	3 17/32	3 5/32	4 27/32	4	6 5/32	4 27/32	7 15/32
3/4	5/8	1	1 1/2	2 5/16	2 11/32	3 5/8	3 3/16	4 15/16	4 1/16	6 1/4	4 29/32	7 9/16
13/16	11/16	1 1/16	1 9/16	2 3/8	2 13/32	3 11/16	3 1/4	5	4 1/8	6 11/32	4 31/32	7 21/32
7/8	3/4	1 5/32	1 19/32	2 15/32	2 15/32	3 25/32	3 5/16	5 3/32	4 5/32	6 13/32	5 1/32	7 23/32
15/16	13/16	1 7/32	1 21/32	2 9/16	2 1/2	3 7/8	3 3/8	5 3/16	4 7/32	6 1/2	5 1/16	7 13/16

Inches	6" Rise	6" Slope	7" Rise	7" Slope	8" Rise	8" Slope	9" Rise	9" Slope	10" Rise	10" Slope	11" Rise	11" Slope
0	5 1/8	7 29/32	5 31/32	9 7/32	6 27/32	10 17/32	7 11/16	11 27/32	8 17/32	1-1 5/32	9 13/32	1-2 15/32
1/16	5 3/16	7 31/32	6 1/32	9 9/32	6 7/8	10 19/32	7 3/4	11 29/32	8 19/32	1-1 7/32	9 7/16	1-2 9/16
1/8	5 7/32	8 1/16	6 3/32	9 3/8	6 15/16	10 11/16	7 25/32	1-0	8 21/32	1-1 5/16	9 1/2	1-2 5/8
3/16	5 9/32	8 1/8	6 1/8	9 7/16	7	10 25/32	7 27/32	1-0 3/32	8 11/16	1-1 13/32	9 9/16	1-2 23/32
1/4	5 11/32	8 7/32	6 3/16	9 17/32	7 1/16	10 27/32	7 29/32	1-0 5/32	8 3/4	1-1 15/32	9 5/8	1-2 25/32
5/16	5 13/32	8 5/16	6 1/4	9 5/8	7 3/32	10 15/16	7 31/32	1-0 1/4	8 13/16	1-1 9/16	9 21/32	1-2 7/8
3/8	5 7/16	8 3/8	6 5/16	9 11/16	7 5/32	11	8	1-0 11/32	8 7/8	1-1 21/32	9 23/32	1-2 31/32
7/16	5 1/2	8 15/32	6 11/32	9 25/32	7 7/32	11 3/32	8 1/16	1-0 13/32	8 29/32	1-1 23/32	9 25/32	1-3 1/32
1/2	5 9/16	8 9/16	6 13/32	9 7/8	7 1/4	11 3/16	8 1/8	1-0 1/2	8 31/32	1-1 13/16	9 13/16	1-3 1/8
9/16	5 19/32	8 5/8	6 15/32	9 15/16	7 5/16	11 1/4	8 5/32	1-0 9/16	9 1/32	1-1 29/32	9 7/8	1-3 7/32
5/8	5 21/32	8 23/32	6 1/2	10 1/32	7 3/8	11 11/32	8 7/32	1-0 21/32	9 1/16	1-1 31/32	9 15/16	1-3 9/32
11/16	5 23/32	8 25/32	6 9/16	10 1/8	7 13/32	11 7/16	8 9/32	1-0 3/4	9 1/8	1-2 1/16	9 31/32	1-3 3/8
3/4	5 3/4	8 7/8	6 5/8	10 3/16	7 15/32	11 1/2	8 5/16	1-0 13/16	9 3/16	1-2 1/8	10 1/16	1-3 7/16
13/16	5 13/16	8 31/32	6 11/16	10 9/32	7 17/32	11 19/32	8 3/8	1-0 29/32	9 1/4	1-2 7/32	10 3/32	1-3 17/32
7/8	5 7/8	9 1/32	6 23/32	10 11/32	7 19/32	11 11/16	8 7/16	1-1	9 9/32	1-2 5/16	10 5/32	1-3 5/8
15/16	5 15/16	9 1/8	6 25/32	10 7/16	7 5/8	11 3/4	8 1/2	1-1 1/16	9 11/32	1-2 3/8	10 3/16	1-3 11/16

Feet	0' Rise	0' Slope	10' Rise	10' Slope	20' Rise	20' Slope	30' Rise	30' Slope
0	0	0	8-6 1/2	13-1 13/16	17-1	26-3 5/8	25-7 1/2	39-5 7/16
1	-10 1/4	1-3 25/32	9-4 3/4	14-5 19/32	17-11 1/2	27-7 13/32	26-5 3/4	40-9 7/32
2	1-8 1/2	2-7 9/16	10-3	15-9 3/8	18-9 1/2	28-11 3/16	27-4	42-1
3	2-6 3/4	3-11 11/32	11-1 1/4	17-1 5/32	19-7 3/4	30-2 31/32	28-2 1/4	43-4 25/32
4	3-5	5-3 1/8	11-11 1/2	18-4 15/16	20-6	31-6 3/4	29-0 1/2	44-8 19/32
5	4-3 1/4	6-6 29/32	12-9 3/4	19-8 23/32	21-4 1/4	32-10 17/32	29-10 3/4	46-0 3/8
6	5-1 1/2	7-10 11/16	13-8	21-0 1/2	22-2 1/2	34-2 5/16	30-9	47-4 5/32
7	5-11 3/4	9-2 15/32	14-6 1/4	22-4 9/32	23-0 3/4	35-6 3/32	31-7 1/4	48-7 15/32
8	6-10	10-6 1/4	15-4 1/2	23-8 1/16	23-11	36-9 7/8	32-5 1/2	49-11 23/32
9	7-8 1/4	11-10 1/2	16-2 3/4	24-11 27/32	24-9 1/4	38-1 21/32	33-3 3/4	51-3 1/2

A = 40° 30′ 10″; logsin A = 9.81257; logcos A = 9.88103; logtan A = 9.93154; logcot A = 0.06846

Ins.	12" Rise	12" Slope	13" Rise	13" Slope	14" Rise	14" Slope	15" Rise	15" Slope	16" Rise	16" Slope
0	10 1/4	1-3 25/32	11 3/32	1-5 3/32	11 31/32—	1-6 13/32	1-0 13/16	1-7 23/32	1-1 21/32	1-9 1/32
1/16	10 5/16	1-3 7/8	11 5/32	1-5 3/16	1-0	1-6 1/2	1-0 7/8	1-7 13/16	1-1 23/32	1-9 1/8
1/8	10 11/32	1-3 15/16	11 7/32—	1-5 1/4	1-0 1/16	1-6 9/16	1-0 29/32	1-7 29/32—	1-1 25/32—	1-9 7/32—
3/16	10 13/32	1-4 1/32—	11 1/4	1-5 11/32—	1-0 1/8	1-6 21/32	1-0 31/32	1-7 31/32	1-1 13/16	1-9 9/32
1/4	10 15/32—	1-4 1/8	11 5/16	1-5 7/16	1-0 3/16	1-6 3/4	1-1 1/32—	1-8 1/16	1-1 7/8	1-9 3/8
5/16	10 17/32—	1-4 3/16	11 3/8	1-5 1/2	1-0 7/32	1-6 13/16	1-1 3/32—	1-8 1/8	1-1 15/16	1-9 15/32—
3/8	10 9/16	1-4 9/32—	11 7/16	1-5 19/32—	1-0 9/32—	1-6 29/32—	1-1 1/8	1-8 7/32	1-2	1-9 17/32
7/16	10 5/8	1-4 11/32	11 15/32	1-5 11/16	1-0 11/32—	1-7	1-1 3/16	1-8 5/16	1-2 1/32	1-9 5/8
1/2	10 11/16	1-4 7/16	11 17/32	1-5 3/4	1-0 3/8	1-7 1/16	1-1 1/4	1-8 3/8	1-2 3/32	1-9 11/16
9/16	10 23/32	1-4 17/32—	11 19/32—	1-5 27/32—	1-0 7/16	1-7 5/32—	1-1 9/32	1-8 15/32—	1-2 5/32—	1-9 25/32
5/8	10 25/32	1-4 19/32	11 5/8	1-5 29/32	1-0 1/2	1-7 7/32	1-1 11/32	1-8 9/16	1-2 3/16	1-9 7/8
11/16	10 27/32—	1-4 11/16	11 11/16	1-6	1-0 17/32	1-7 5/16	1-1 13/32—	1-8 5/8	1-2 1/4	1-9 15/16
3/4	10 7/8	1-4 25/32—	11 3/4	1-6 3/32—	1-0 19/32	1-7 13/32—	1-1 7/16	1-8 23/32—	1-2 5/16	1-10 1/32—
13/16	10 15/16	1-4 27/32	11 13/16	1-6 5/32	1-0 21/32—	1-7 15/32	1-1 1/2	1-8 25/32	1-2 3/8	1-10 1/8
7/8	11	1-4 15/16	11 27/32	1-6 1/4	1-0 23/32—	1-7 9/16	1-1 9/16	1-8 7/8	1-2 13/32	1-10 3/16
15/16	11 1/16	1-5	11 29/32—	1-6 11/32—	1-0 3/4	1-7 21/32—	1-1 5/8	1-8 31/32—	1-2 15/32—	1-10 9/32—

Ins.	17" Rise	17" Slope	18" Rise	18" Slope	19" Rise	19" Slope	20" Rise	20" Slope	21" Rise	21" Slope
0	1-2 17/32—	1-10 11/32	1-3 3/8	1-11 11/16	1-4 7/32	2-1	1-5 3/32—	2-2 5/16	1-5 15/16	2-3 5/8
1/16	1-2 9/16	1-10 7/16	1-3 7/16	1-11 3/4	1-4 9/32	2-1 1/16	1-5 1/8	2-2 3/8	1-6	2-3 11/16
1/8	1-2 5/8	1-10 17/32—	1-3 15/32	1-11 27/32—	1-4 11/32—	2-1 5/32—	1-5 3/16	2-2 15/32—	1-6 1/32	2-3 25/32
3/16	1-2 11/16	1-10 19/32	1-3 17/32	1-11 29/32	1-4 3/8	2-1 7/32	1-5 1/4	2-2 9/16	1-6 3/32	2-3 7/8
1/4	1-2 3/4	1-10 11/16	1-3 19/32—	2-0	1-4 7/16	2-1 5/16	1-5 5/16	2-2 5/8	1-6 5/32—	2-3 15/16
5/16	1-2 25/32	1-10 25/32—	1-3 21/32—	2-0 3/32—	1-4 1/2	2-1 13/32—	1-5 11/32	2-2 23/32—	1-6 7/32—	2-4 1/32—
3/8	1-2 27/32—	1-10 27/32	1-3 11/16	2-0 5/32	1-4 9/16	2-1 15/32	1-5 13/32—	2-2 25/32	1-6 1/4	2-4 1/8
7/16	1-2 29/32—	1-10 15/16	1-3 3/4	2-0 1/4	1-4 19/32	2-1 9/16	1-5 15/32—	2-2 7/8	1-6 5/16	2-4 3/16
1/2	1-2 15/16	1-11	1-3 13/16	2-0 11/32—	1-4 21/32	2-1 21/32—	1-5 1/2	2-2 31/32—	1-6 3/8	2-4 9/32—
9/16	1-3	1-11 3/32	1-3 27/32	2-0 13/32	1-4 23/32—	2-1 23/32	1-5 9/16	2-3 1/32	1-6 13/32	2-4 11/32
5/8	1-3 1/16	1-11 3/16	1-3 29/32	2-0 1/2	1-4 3/4	2-1 13/16	1-5 5/8	2-3 1/8	1-6 15/32	2-4 7/16
11/16	1-3 3/32	1-11 1/4	1-3 31/32—	2-0 9/16	1-4 13/16	2-1 29/32—	1-5 21/32	2-3 7/32—	1-6 17/32—	2-4 17/32—
3/4	1-3 5/32	1-11 11/32	1-4	2-0 21/32	1-4 7/8	2-1 31/32	1-5 23/32	2-3 9/32	1-6 9/16	2-4 19/32
13/16	1-3 7/32—	1-11 7/16	1-4 1/16	2-0 3/4	1-4 15/16	2-2 1/16	1-5 25/32—	2-3 3/8	1-6 5/8	2-4 11/16
7/8	1-3 9/32—	1-11 1/2	1-4 1/8	2-0 13/16	1-4 31/32	2-2 1/8	1-5 27/32—	2-3 15/32—	1-6 11/16	2-4 25/32—
15/16	1-3 5/16	1-11 19/32—	1-4 3/16	2-0 29/32—	1-5 1/32—	2-2 7/32	1-5 7/8	2-3 17/32	1-6 3/4	2-4 27/32

Feet	40' Rise	40' Slope	50' Rise	50' Slope	60' Rise	60' Slope	70' Rise	70' Slope
0	34-2	52-7 9/32—	42-8 1/2	65-9 3/32—	51-3	78-10 29/32—	59-9 1/2	92-0 23/32
1	35-0 1/4	53-11 1/16	43-6 3/4	67-0 7/8	52-1 1/4	80-2 11/16	60-7 3/4	93-4 1/2
2	35-10 1/2	55-2 27/32—	44-5	68-4 21/32—	52-11 1/2	81-6 15/32—	61-6	94-8 9/32
3	36-8 3/4	56-6 5/8	45-3 1/4	69-8 7/16	53-9 3/4	82-10 1/4	62-4 1/4	96-0 1/16
4	37-7	57-10 13/32—	46-1 1/2	71-0 7/32—	54-8	84-2 1/32—	63-2 1/2	97-3 27/32
5	38-5 1/4	59-2 3/16	46-11 3/4	72-4	55-6 1/4	85-5 13/16	64-0 3/4	98-7 5/8
6	39-3 1/2	60-5 31/32—	47-10	73-7 25/32—	56-4 1/2	86-9 19/32—	64-11	99-11 13/32
7	40-1 3/4	61-9 3/4	48-8 1/4	74-11 9/16	57-2 3/4	88-1 3/8	65-9 1/4	101-3 3/16
8	41-0	63-1 17/32—	49-6 1/2	76-3 11/32—	58-1	89-5 5/32	66-7 1/2	102-6 31/32
9	41-10 1/4	64-5 5/16	50-4 3/4	77-7 1/8	58-11 1/4	90-8 15/16	67-5 3/4	103-10 3/4

natsin A=0.6494858501; natcos A=0.7603736782; nattan A=0.8541666666; natcot A=1.1707317073

Inches	0"		1"		2"		3"		4"		5"	
	Rise	Slope	Rise	Slope	Rise	Slope	Rise	Slope	Rise	Slope	Rise	Slope
0	0	0	7/8	1 5/16	1 23/32	2 5/8	2 9/16	3 31/32	3 7/16	5 9/32	4 5/16	6 19/32
1/16	1/16	3/32	29/32	1 13/32	1 25/32	2 23/32	2 5/8	4 1/32	3 1/2	5 11/32	4 11/32	6 11/16
1/8	3/32	5/32	31/32	1 15/32	1 13/16	2 13/16	2 11/16	4 1/8	3 17/32	5 7/16	4 13/32	6 3/4
3/16	5/32	1/4	1 1/32	1 9/16	1 7/8	2 7/8	2 3/4	4 3/16	3 19/32	5 17/32	4 15/32	6 27/32
1/4	7/32	11/32	1 1/16	1 21/32	1 15/16	2 31/32	2 25/32	4 9/32	3 21/32	5 19/32	4 1/2	6 15/16
5/16	9/32	13/32	1 1/8	1 23/32	2	3 1/16	2 27/32	4 3/8	3 23/32	5 11/16	4 9/16	7
3/8	5/16	1/2	1 3/16	1 13/16	2 1/16	3 1/8	2 29/32	4 7/16	3 3/4	5 25/32	4 5/8	7 3/32
7/16	3/8	9/16	1 1/4	1 29/32	2 3/32	3 7/32	2 31/32	4 17/32	3 13/16	5 27/32	4 11/32	7 5/32
1/2	7/16	21/32	1 9/32	1 31/32	2 5/32	3 9/32	3	4 5/8	3 7/8	5 15/32	4 23/32	7 1/4
9/16	15/32	3/4	1 11/32	2 1/16	2 3/16	3 3/8	3 1/16	4 11/16	3 29/32	6 1/32	4 25/32	7 11/32
5/8	17/32	13/16	1 13/32	2 5/32	2 1/4	3 15/32	3 1/8	4 25/32	3 31/32	6 3/32	4 27/32	7 13/32
11/16	19/32	29/32	1 7/16	2 7/32	2 5/16	3 17/32	3 5/32	4 7/8	4 1/32	6 3/16	4 7/8	7 1/2
3/4	21/32	1	1 1/2	2 5/16	2 3/8	3 5/8	3 7/32	4 15/16	4 3/32	6 1/4	4 15/16	7 19/32
13/16	11/16	1 1/16	1 9/16	2 3/8	2 13/32	3 23/32	3 9/32	5 1/32	4 1/8	6 11/32	5	7 21/32
7/8	3/4	1 5/32	1 5/8	2 7/16	2 15/32	3 25/32	3 11/32	5 3/32	4 3/16	6 7/16	5 1/16	7 3/4
15/16	13/16	1 1/4	1 21/32	2 9/16	2 17/32	3 7/8	3 3/8	5 3/16	4 1/4	6 1/2	5 3/32	7 27/32

Inches	6"		7"		8"		9"		10"		11"	
	Rise	Slope	Rise	Slope	Rise	Slope	Rise	Slope	Rise	Slope	Rise	Slope
0	5 5/32	7 29/32	6	9 7/32	6 7/8	10 9/16	7 3/4	11 7/8	8 19/32	1-1 3/8	9 7/16	1-2 1/2
1/16	5 7/32	8	6 1/16	9 5/16	6 15/16	10 5/8	7 25/32	11 15/16	8 21/32	1-1 9/32	9 1/2	1-2 9/32
1/8	5 1/4	8 1/16	6 1/8	9 13/32	6 31/32	10 23/32	7 27/32	1-0 1/32	8 11/16	1-1 11/32	9 9/16	1-2 21/32
3/16	5 5/16	8 5/32	6 3/16	9 15/32	7 1/16	10 25/32	7 29/32	1-0 1/8	8 3/4	1-1 7/16	9 5/8	1-2 3/4
1/4	5 3/8	8 1/4	6 7/32	9 9/16	7 3/32	10 7/8	7 15/16	1-0 3/16	8 13/16	1-1 1/2	9 21/32	1-2 27/32
5/16	5 7/16	8 5/16	6 9/32	9 21/32	7 5/32	10 31/32	8	1-0 9/32	8 7/8	1-1 19/32	9 23/32	1-2 29/32
3/8	5 15/32	8 13/32	6 11/32	9 23/32	7 1/4	11 1/32	8 1/16	1-0 3/8	8 29/32	1-1 11/16	9 25/32	1-3
7/16	5 17/32	8 1/2	6 13/32	9 13/16	7 11/32	11 1/8	8 1/8	1-0 7/16	8 31/32	1-1 3/4	9 27/32	1-3 3/32
1/2	5 19/32	8 9/16	6 7/16	9 7/8	7 5/16	11 7/32	8 5/32	1-0 17/32	9 1/32	1-1 27/32	9 7/8	1-3 5/32
9/16	5 5/8	8 21/32	6 1/2	9 31/32	7 11/32	11 9/32	8 7/32	1-0 19/32	9 1/16	1-1 15/16	9 15/16	1-3 1/4
5/8	5 11/16	8 3/4	6 9/16	10 1/16	7 13/32	11 3/8	8 9/32	1-0 11/16	9 1/8	1-2	10	1-3 5/16
11/16	5 3/4	8 13/16	6 19/32	10 1/8	7 15/32	11 15/32	8 5/16	1-0 25/32	9 3/16	1-2 3/32	10 1/32	1-3 13/16
3/4	5 13/16	8 29/32	6 21/32	10 7/32	7 17/32	11 17/32	8 3/8	1-0 27/32	9 1/4	1-2 3/16	10 3/32	1-3 1/2
13/16	5 27/32	8 31/32	6 23/32	10 5/16	7 9/16	11 5/8	8 7/16	1-0 15/32	9 9/32	1-2 1/4	10 5/32	1-3 9/16
7/8	5 29/32	9 1/16	6 25/32	10 3/8	7 5/8	11 11/16	8 1/2	1-1 1/32	9 11/32	1-2 11/32	10 7/32	1-3 21/32
15/16	5 31/32	9 5/32	6 13/16	10 15/32	7 11/16	11 25/32	8 17/32	1-1 3/32	9 13/32	1-2 13/32	10 1/4	1-3 3/4

Feet	0'		10'		20'		30'	
	Rise	Slope	Rise	Slope	Rise	Slope	Rise	Slope
0	0	0	8-7 1/8	13-2 7/32	17-2 1/4	26-4 7/16	25-9 3/8	39-6 21/32
1	-10 5/16	1-3 13/16	9-5 7/16	14-6 1/32	18-0 9/16	27-8 9/32	26-7 11/16	40-10 1/2
2	1-8 5/8	2-7 21/32	10-3 3/4	15-9 7/8	18-10 7/8	29-0 5/32	27-6	42-2 5/16
3	2-6 15/16	3-11 15/32	11-2 1/16	17-1 11/16	19-9 3/16	30-3 29/32	28-4 5/16	43-6 1/8
4	3-5 1/4	5-3 9/32	12-0 3/8	18-5 1/4	20-7 1/2	31-7 3/4	29-2 5/8	44-9 31/32
5	4-3 9/16	6-7 1/8	12-10 11/16	19-9 11/32	21-5 13/16	32-11 9/16	30-0 15/16	46-1 25/32
6	5-1 7/8	7-10 15/16	13-9	21-1 5/32	22-4 1/8	34-3 3/8	30-11 1/4	47-5 19/32
7	6-0 3/16	9-2 3/4	14-7 5/16	22-4 31/32	23-2 7/16	35-7 7/32	31-9 9/16	48-9 7/16
8	6-10 1/2	10-6 9/32	15-5 5/8	23-8 13/16	24-0 3/4	36-11 1/32	32-7 7/8	50-1 1/4
9	7-8 13/16	11-10 13/32	16-3 15/16	25-0 5/8	24-11 1/16	38-2 27/32	33-6 3/16	51-5 1/16

A = 40° 40′ 30″; logsin A = 9.81409; logcos A = 9.87991; logtan A = 9.93418; logcot A = 0.06582

In.	12″ Rise	12″ Slope	13″ Rise	13″ Slope	14″ Rise	14″ Slope	15″ Rise	15″ Slope	16″ Rise	16″ Slope
0	$10\frac{5}{16}$	$1\text{-}3\frac{13}{16}$	$11\frac{3}{16}$	$1\text{-}5\frac{5}{32}$	$1\text{-}0\frac{1}{32}$	$1\text{-}6\frac{15}{32}$	$1\text{-}0\frac{7}{8}$	$1\text{-}7\frac{25}{32}$	$1\text{-}1\frac{3}{4}$	$1\text{-}9\frac{3}{32}$
1/16	$10\frac{3}{8}$	$1\text{-}3\frac{29}{32}$	$11\frac{7}{32}$	$1\text{-}5\frac{7}{32}$	$1\text{-}0\frac{3}{32}$	$1\text{-}6\frac{17}{32}$	$1\text{-}0\frac{15}{16}$	$1\text{-}7\frac{7}{8}$	$1\text{-}1\frac{13}{16}$	$1\text{-}9\frac{3}{16}$
1/8	$10\frac{13}{32}$	$1\text{-}4$	$11\frac{9}{32}$	$1\text{-}5\frac{5}{16}$	$1\text{-}0\frac{1}{8}$	$1\text{-}6\frac{5}{8}$	$1\text{-}1$	$1\text{-}7\frac{15}{16}$	$1\text{-}1\frac{27}{32}$	$1\text{-}9\frac{1}{4}$
3/16	$10\frac{15}{32}$	$1\text{-}4\frac{1}{16}$	$11\frac{11}{32}$	$1\text{-}5\frac{3}{8}$	$1\text{-}0\frac{3}{16}$	$1\text{-}6\frac{23}{32}$	$1\text{-}1\frac{1}{16}$	$1\text{-}8\frac{1}{32}$	$1\text{-}1\frac{29}{32}$	$1\text{-}9\frac{11}{32}$
1/4	$10\frac{17}{32}$	$1\text{-}4\frac{5}{32}$	$11\frac{3}{8}$	$1\text{-}5\frac{15}{32}$	$1\text{-}0\frac{1}{4}$	$1\text{-}6\frac{25}{32}$	$1\text{-}1\frac{1}{8}$	$1\text{-}8\frac{3}{32}$	$1\text{-}1\frac{31}{32}$	$1\text{-}9\frac{7}{16}$
5/16	$10\frac{19}{32}$	$1\text{-}4\frac{1}{4}$	$11\frac{7}{16}$	$1\text{-}5\frac{9}{16}$	$1\text{-}0\frac{5}{16}$	$1\text{-}6\frac{7}{8}$	$1\text{-}1\frac{5}{32}$	$1\text{-}8\frac{3}{16}$	$1\text{-}2\frac{1}{16}$	$1\text{-}9\frac{1}{2}$
3/8	$10\frac{5}{8}$	$1\text{-}4\frac{5}{16}$	$11\frac{1}{2}$	$1\text{-}5\frac{5}{8}$	$1\text{-}0\frac{11}{32}$	$1\text{-}6\frac{31}{32}$	$1\text{-}1\frac{7}{32}$	$1\text{-}8\frac{9}{32}$	$1\text{-}2\frac{1}{8}$	$1\text{-}9\frac{19}{32}$
7/16	$10\frac{11}{16}$	$1\text{-}4\frac{13}{32}$	$11\frac{9}{16}$	$1\text{-}5\frac{23}{32}$	$1\text{-}0\frac{13}{32}$	$1\text{-}7\frac{1}{32}$	$1\text{-}1\frac{9}{32}$	$1\text{-}8\frac{11}{32}$	$1\text{-}2\frac{1}{8}$	$1\text{-}9\frac{11}{16}$
1/2	$10\frac{3}{4}$	$1\text{-}4\frac{15}{32}$	$11\frac{19}{32}$	$1\text{-}5\frac{13}{32}$	$1\text{-}0\frac{15}{32}$	$1\text{-}7\frac{1}{8}$	$1\text{-}1\frac{5}{16}$	$1\text{-}8\frac{7}{16}$	$1\text{-}2\frac{3}{16}$	$1\text{-}9\frac{3}{4}$
9/16	$10\frac{25}{32}$	$1\text{-}4\frac{9}{16}$	$11\frac{21}{32}$	$1\text{-}5\frac{7}{8}$	$1\text{-}0\frac{1}{2}$	$1\text{-}7\frac{3}{16}$	$1\text{-}1\frac{3}{8}$	$1\text{-}8\frac{17}{32}$	$1\text{-}2\frac{7}{32}$	$1\text{-}9\frac{27}{32}$
5/8	$10\frac{27}{32}$	$1\text{-}4\frac{21}{32}$	$11\frac{23}{32}$	$1\text{-}5\frac{31}{32}$	$1\text{-}0\frac{9}{16}$	$1\text{-}7\frac{9}{32}$	$1\text{-}1\frac{7}{16}$	$1\text{-}8\frac{19}{32}$	$1\text{-}2\frac{9}{32}$	$1\text{-}9\frac{29}{32}$
11/16	$10\frac{29}{32}$	$1\text{-}4\frac{23}{32}$	$11\frac{3}{4}$	$1\text{-}6\frac{1}{16}$	$1\text{-}0\frac{5}{8}$	$1\text{-}7\frac{3}{8}$	$1\text{-}1\frac{15}{32}$	$1\text{-}8\frac{11}{16}$	$1\text{-}2\frac{11}{32}$	$1\text{-}10$
3/4	$10\frac{31}{32}$	$1\text{-}4\frac{13}{16}$	$11\frac{13}{16}$	$1\text{-}6\frac{1}{8}$	$1\text{-}0\frac{11}{16}$	$1\text{-}7\frac{7}{16}$	$1\text{-}1\frac{17}{32}$	$1\text{-}8\frac{25}{32}$	$1\text{-}2\frac{13}{32}$	$1\text{-}10\frac{3}{32}$
13/16	11	$1\text{-}4\frac{29}{32}$	$11\frac{7}{8}$	$1\text{-}6\frac{7}{32}$	$1\text{-}0\frac{23}{32}$	$1\text{-}7\frac{17}{32}$	$1\text{-}1\frac{19}{32}$	$1\text{-}8\frac{27}{32}$	$1\text{-}2\frac{7}{16}$	$1\text{-}10\frac{5}{32}$
7/8	$11\frac{1}{16}$	$1\text{-}4\frac{31}{32}$	$11\frac{15}{16}$	$1\text{-}6\frac{9}{32}$	$1\text{-}0\frac{25}{32}$	$1\text{-}7\frac{5}{8}$	$1\text{-}1\frac{21}{32}$	$1\text{-}8\frac{15}{16}$	$1\text{-}2\frac{1}{2}$	$1\text{-}10\frac{1}{4}$
15/16	$11\frac{1}{8}$	$1\text{-}5\frac{1}{16}$	$11\frac{31}{32}$	$1\text{-}6\frac{3}{8}$	$1\text{-}0\frac{27}{32}$	$1\text{-}7\frac{11}{16}$	$1\text{-}1\frac{11}{16}$	$1\text{-}9$	$1\text{-}2\frac{5}{8}$	$1\text{-}10\frac{11}{32}$

In.	17″ Rise	17″ Slope	18″ Rise	18″ Slope	19″ Rise	19″ Slope	20″ Rise	20″ Slope	21″ Rise	21″ Slope
0	$1\text{-}2\frac{5}{8}$	$1\text{-}10\frac{13}{32}$	$1\text{-}3\frac{15}{32}$	$1\text{-}11\frac{23}{32}$	$1\text{-}4\frac{5}{16}$	$2\text{-}1\frac{1}{16}$	$1\text{-}5\frac{3}{16}$	$2\text{-}2\frac{3}{8}$	$1\text{-}6\frac{1}{16}$	$2\text{-}3\frac{11}{16}$
1/16	$1\text{-}2\frac{21}{32}$	$1\text{-}10\frac{1}{2}$	$1\text{-}3\frac{17}{32}$	$1\text{-}11\frac{13}{16}$	$1\text{-}4\frac{3}{8}$	$2\text{-}1\frac{1}{8}$	$1\text{-}5\frac{1}{4}$	$2\text{-}2\frac{7}{16}$	$1\text{-}6\frac{3}{32}$	$2\text{-}3\frac{25}{32}$
1/8	$1\text{-}2\frac{23}{32}$	$1\text{-}10\frac{19}{32}$	$1\text{-}3\frac{9}{16}$	$1\text{-}11\frac{29}{32}$	$1\text{-}4\frac{7}{16}$	$2\text{-}1\frac{7}{32}$	$1\text{-}5\frac{9}{32}$	$2\text{-}2\frac{17}{32}$	$1\text{-}6\frac{5}{32}$	$2\text{-}3\frac{27}{32}$
3/16	$1\text{-}2\frac{25}{32}$	$1\text{-}10\frac{21}{32}$	$1\text{-}3\frac{5}{8}$	$1\text{-}11\frac{31}{32}$	$1\text{-}4\frac{1}{2}$	$2\text{-}1\frac{5}{16}$	$1\text{-}5\frac{11}{32}$	$2\text{-}2\frac{5}{8}$	$1\text{-}6\frac{7}{32}$	$2\text{-}3\frac{15}{16}$
1/4	$1\text{-}2\frac{13}{16}$	$1\text{-}10\frac{3}{4}$	$1\text{-}3\frac{11}{16}$	$2\text{-}0\frac{1}{16}$	$1\text{-}4\frac{17}{32}$	$2\text{-}1\frac{3}{8}$	$1\text{-}5\frac{13}{32}$	$2\text{-}2\frac{11}{16}$	$1\text{-}6\frac{1}{4}$	$2\text{-}4\frac{1}{32}$
5/16	$1\text{-}2\frac{7}{8}$	$1\text{-}10\frac{13}{16}$	$1\text{-}3\frac{3}{4}$	$2\text{-}0\frac{5}{32}$	$1\text{-}4\frac{19}{32}$	$2\text{-}1\frac{15}{32}$	$1\text{-}5\frac{15}{32}$	$2\text{-}2\frac{25}{32}$	$1\text{-}6\frac{5}{16}$	$2\text{-}4\frac{3}{32}$
3/8	$1\text{-}2\frac{15}{16}$	$1\text{-}10\frac{29}{32}$	$1\text{-}3\frac{25}{32}$	$2\text{-}0\frac{7}{32}$	$1\text{-}4\frac{21}{32}$	$2\text{-}1\frac{17}{32}$	$1\text{-}5\frac{1}{2}$	$2\text{-}2\frac{7}{8}$	$1\text{-}6\frac{3}{8}$	$2\text{-}4\frac{3}{16}$
7/16	$1\text{-}3$	$1\text{-}11$	$1\text{-}3\frac{27}{32}$	$2\text{-}0\frac{9}{32}$	$1\text{-}4\frac{23}{32}$	$2\text{-}1\frac{5}{8}$	$1\text{-}5\frac{9}{16}$	$2\text{-}2\frac{15}{16}$	$1\text{-}6\frac{7}{16}$	$2\text{-}4\frac{9}{32}$
1/2	$1\text{-}3\frac{1}{32}$	$1\text{-}11\frac{1}{16}$	$1\text{-}3\frac{29}{32}$	$2\text{-}0\frac{13}{32}$	$1\text{-}4\frac{3}{4}$	$2\text{-}1\frac{23}{32}$	$1\text{-}5\frac{5}{8}$	$2\text{-}3\frac{1}{32}$	$1\text{-}6\frac{15}{32}$	$2\text{-}4\frac{11}{32}$
9/16	$1\text{-}3\frac{3}{32}$	$1\text{-}11\frac{1}{8}$	$1\text{-}3\frac{15}{16}$	$2\text{-}0\frac{15}{32}$	$1\text{-}4\frac{13}{16}$	$2\text{-}1\frac{25}{32}$	$1\text{-}5\frac{21}{32}$	$2\text{-}3\frac{1}{8}$	$1\text{-}6\frac{17}{32}$	$2\text{-}4\frac{7}{16}$
5/8	$1\text{-}3\frac{5}{32}$	$1\text{-}11\frac{1}{4}$	$1\text{-}4$	$2\text{-}0\frac{9}{16}$	$1\text{-}4\frac{7}{8}$	$2\text{-}1\frac{7}{8}$	$1\text{-}5\frac{23}{32}$	$2\text{-}3\frac{3}{16}$	$1\text{-}6\frac{19}{32}$	$2\text{-}4\frac{1}{2}$
11/16	$1\text{-}3\frac{3}{16}$	$1\text{-}11\frac{5}{16}$	$1\text{-}4\frac{1}{16}$	$2\text{-}0\frac{5}{8}$	$1\text{-}4\frac{29}{32}$	$2\text{-}1\frac{31}{32}$	$1\text{-}5\frac{25}{32}$	$2\text{-}3\frac{9}{32}$	$1\text{-}6\frac{5}{8}$	$2\text{-}4\frac{19}{32}$
3/4	$1\text{-}3\frac{1}{4}$	$1\text{-}11\frac{13}{32}$	$1\text{-}4\frac{1}{8}$	$2\text{-}0\frac{23}{32}$	$1\text{-}4\frac{31}{32}$	$2\text{-}2\frac{1}{32}$	$1\text{-}5\frac{27}{32}$	$2\text{-}3\frac{3}{8}$	$1\text{-}6\frac{11}{16}$	$2\text{-}4\frac{11}{16}$
13/16	$1\text{-}3\frac{5}{16}$	$1\text{-}11\frac{1}{2}$	$1\text{-}4\frac{5}{32}$	$2\text{-}0\frac{13}{16}$	$1\text{-}5\frac{1}{32}$	$2\text{-}2\frac{1}{8}$	$1\text{-}5\frac{7}{8}$	$2\text{-}3\frac{7}{16}$	$1\text{-}6\frac{3}{4}$	$2\text{-}4\frac{3}{4}$
7/8	$1\text{-}3\frac{3}{8}$	$1\text{-}11\frac{9}{16}$	$1\text{-}4\frac{7}{32}$	$2\text{-}0\frac{7}{8}$	$1\text{-}5\frac{3}{32}$	$2\text{-}2\frac{7}{32}$	$1\text{-}5\frac{15}{16}$	$2\text{-}3\frac{17}{32}$	$1\text{-}6\frac{13}{16}$	$2\text{-}4\frac{27}{32}$
15/16	$1\text{-}3\frac{13}{32}$	$1\text{-}11\frac{21}{32}$	$1\text{-}4\frac{9}{32}$	$2\text{-}0\frac{31}{32}$	$1\text{-}5\frac{1}{8}$	$2\text{-}2\frac{9}{32}$	$1\text{-}6$	$2\text{-}3\frac{19}{32}$	$1\text{-}6\frac{27}{32}$	$2\text{-}4\frac{15}{16}$

Feet	40′ Rise	40′ Slope	50′ Rise	50′ Slope	60′ Rise	60′ Slope	70′ Rise	70′ Slope
0	$34\text{-}4\frac{1}{2}$	$52\text{-}8\frac{29}{32}$	$42\text{-}11\frac{5}{8}$	$65\text{-}11\frac{1}{8}$	$51\text{-}6\frac{3}{4}$	$79\text{-}1\frac{11}{32}$	$60\text{-}1\frac{7}{8}$	$92\text{-}3\frac{9}{16}$
1	$35\text{-}2\frac{13}{16}$	$54\text{-}0\frac{23}{32}$	$43\text{-}9\frac{15}{16}$	$67\text{-}2\frac{15}{16}$	$52\text{-}5\frac{1}{16}$	$80\text{-}5\frac{5}{32}$	$61\text{-}0\frac{3}{16}$	$93\text{-}7\frac{3}{8}$
2	$36\text{-}1\frac{1}{8}$	$55\text{-}4\frac{17}{32}$	$44\text{-}8\frac{1}{4}$	$68\text{-}6\frac{3}{4}$	$53\text{-}3\frac{3}{8}$	$81\text{-}9$	$61\text{-}10\frac{1}{2}$	$94\text{-}11\frac{11}{32}$
3	$36\text{-}11\frac{7}{16}$	$56\text{-}8\frac{3}{8}$	$45\text{-}6\frac{9}{16}$	$69\text{-}10\frac{19}{32}$	$54\text{-}1\frac{11}{16}$	$83\text{-}0\frac{13}{16}$	$62\text{-}8\frac{13}{16}$	$96\text{-}3\frac{1}{32}$
4	$37\text{-}9\frac{3}{4}$	$58\text{-}0\frac{3}{16}$	$46\text{-}4\frac{7}{8}$	$71\text{-}2\frac{13}{32}$	$55\text{-}0$	$84\text{-}4\frac{5}{8}$	$63\text{-}7\frac{1}{8}$	$97\text{-}6\frac{27}{32}$
5	$38\text{-}8\frac{1}{16}$	$59\text{-}4$	$47\text{-}3\frac{3}{16}$	$72\text{-}6\frac{7}{32}$	$55\text{-}10\frac{5}{16}$	$85\text{-}8\frac{15}{32}$	$64\text{-}5\frac{7}{16}$	$98\text{-}10\frac{11}{16}$
6	$39\text{-}6\frac{3}{8}$	$60\text{-}7\frac{27}{32}$	$48\text{-}1\frac{1}{2}$	$73\text{-}10\frac{1}{16}$	$56\text{-}8\frac{5}{8}$	$87\text{-}0\frac{9}{32}$	$65\text{-}3\frac{3}{4}$	$100\text{-}2\frac{1}{2}$
7	$40\text{-}4\frac{11}{16}$	$61\text{-}11\frac{21}{32}$	$48\text{-}11\frac{13}{16}$	$75\text{-}1\frac{7}{8}$	$57\text{-}6\frac{15}{16}$	$88\text{-}4\frac{3}{32}$	$66\text{-}2\frac{1}{16}$	$101\text{-}6\frac{5}{16}$
8	$41\text{-}3$	$63\text{-}3\frac{15}{32}$	$49\text{-}10\frac{1}{8}$	$76\text{-}5\frac{11}{16}$	$58\text{-}5\frac{1}{4}$	$89\text{-}7\frac{29}{32}$	$67\text{-}0\frac{3}{8}$	$102\text{-}10\frac{5}{32}$
9	$42\text{-}1\frac{5}{16}$	$64\text{-}7\frac{9}{32}$	$50\text{-}8\frac{7}{16}$	$77\text{-}9\frac{17}{32}$	$59\text{-}3\frac{9}{16}$	$90\text{-}11\frac{3}{4}$	$67\text{-}10\frac{11}{16}$	$104\text{-}1\frac{31}{32}$

natsin A=0.6517667432; natcos A=0.7584194831; nattan A=0.8593750000; natcot A=1.1636363636

Inches	0" Rise	0" Slope	1" Rise	1" Slope	2" Rise	2" Slope	3" Rise	3" Slope	4" Rise	4" Slope	5" Rise	5" Slope
0	0	0	7/8	1 5/16	1 23/32	2 21/32	2 19/32	3 31/32	3 15/32	5 9/32	4 5/16	6 5/8
1/16	1/16	3/32	29/32	1 13/32	1 25/32	2 23/32	2 21/32	4 1/16	3 1/2	5 3/8	4 3/8	6 11/16
1/8	3/32	5/32	31/32	1 1/2	1 27/32	2 13/16	2 11/16	4 1/8	3 9/16	5 7/16	4 7/16	6 25/32
3/16	5/32	1/4	1 1/32	1 9/16	1 29/32	2 29/32	2 3/4	4 7/32	3 5/8	5 17/32	4 1/2	6 27/32
1/4	7/32	11/32	1 3/32	1 21/32	1 15/16	2 31/32	2 13/16	4 9/32	3 11/16	5 5/8	4 17/32	6 15/16
5/16	9/32	13/32	1 1/8	1 3/4	2	3 1/16	2 7/8	4 3/8	3 23/32	5 11/16	4 19/32	7 1/32
3/8	5/16	1/2	1 3/16	1 13/16	2 1/16	3 1/8	2 29/32	4 15/32	3 25/32	5 25/32	4 21/32	7 3/32
7/16	3/8	19/32	1 1/4	1 29/32	2 3/32	3 7/32	2 31/32	4 17/32	3 27/32	5 7/8	4 11/16	7 3/16
1/2	7/16	21/32	1 5/16	1 31/32	2 5/32	3 5/16	3 1/32	4 5/8	3 7/8	5 15/16	4 3/4	7 9/32
9/16	1/2	3/4	1 11/32	2 1/16	2 7/32	3 3/8	3 3/32	4 23/32	3 15/16	6 1/32	4 13/16	7 11/32
5/8	17/32	13/16	1 13/32	2 5/32	2 9/32	3 15/32	3 1/8	4 25/32	4	6 1/8	4 7/8	7 7/16
11/16	19/32	29/32	1 15/32	2 7/32	2 5/16	3 9/16	3 3/16	4 7/8	4 1/16	6 3/16	4 29/32	7 17/32
3/4	21/32	1	1 1/2	2 5/16	2 3/8	3 5/8	3 1/4	4 31/32	4 3/32	6 9/32	4 31/32	7 19/32
13/16	11/16	1 1/16	1 9/16	2 13/32	2 7/16	3 23/32	3 9/32	5 1/16	4 5/32	6 3/8	5 1/32	7 11/16
7/8	3/4	1 5/32	1 5/8	2 15/32	2 1/2	3 13/16	3 11/32	5 1/8	4 7/32	6 7/16	5 3/32	7 25/32
15/16	13/16	1 1/4	1 11/16	2 9/16	2 17/32	3 7/8	3 13/32	5 7/32	4 9/32	6 17/32	5 1/8	7 27/32

Inches	6" Rise	6" Slope	7" Rise	7" Slope	8" Rise	8" Slope	9" Rise	9" Slope	10" Rise	10" Slope	11" Rise	11" Slope
0	5 3/16	7 15/16	6 1/16	9 1/4	6 29/32	10 9/16	7 25/32	11 29/32	8 21/32	1-1 7/32	9 1/2	1-2 17/32
1/16	5 1/4	8	6 3/32	9 11/32	6 31/32	10 21/32	7 27/32	11 31/32	8 11/16	1-1 5/16	9 9/16	1-2 5/8
1/8	5 9/32	8 3/32	6 5/32	9 13/32	7 1/32	10 3/4	7 7/8	1-0 1/16	8 3/4	1-1 3/8	9 5/8	1-2 23/32
3/16	5 11/32	8 3/16	6 7/32	9 1/2	7 3/32	10 13/16	7 15/16	1-0 5/32	8 13/16	1-1 15/32	9 11/16	1-2 25/32
1/4	5 13/32	8 1/4	6 9/32	9 19/32	7 1/8	10 29/32	8	1-0 7/32	8 7/8	1-1 9/16	9 23/32	1-2 7/8
5/16	5 15/32	8 11/32	6 5/16	9 21/32	7 3/16	11	8 1/16	1-0 5/16	8 29/32	1-1 5/8	9 25/32	1-2 31/32
3/8	5 1/2	8 7/16	6 3/8	9 3/4	7 1/4	11 1/16	8 3/32	1-0 13/32	8 31/32	1-1 23/32	9 27/32	1-3 1/32
7/16	5 9/16	8 1/2	6 7/16	9 27/32	7 5/16	11 5/32	8 5/32	1-0 15/32	9 1/32	1-1 13/16	9 7/8	1-3 1/8
1/2	5 5/8	8 19/32	6 1/2	9 29/32	7 11/32	11 1/4	8 7/32	1-0 9/16	9 1/16	1-1 7/8	9 15/16	1-3 3/16
9/16	5 11/16	8 11/16	6 17/32	10	7 13/32	11 5/16	8 9/32	1-0 21/32	9 1/8	1-1 31/32	10	1-3 9/32
5/8	5 23/32	8 3/4	6 19/32	10 3/32	7 15/32	11 13/32	8 5/16	1-0 23/32	9 3/16	1-2 1/32	10 1/16	1-3 3/8
11/16	5 25/32	8 27/32	6 21/32	10 5/32	7 1/2	11 15/32	8 3/8	1-0 13/16	9 1/4	1-2 1/8	10 3/32	1-3 7/16
3/4	5 27/32	8 15/16	6 11/16	10 1/4	7 9/16	11 9/16	8 7/16	1-0 7/8	9 9/32	1-2 7/32	10 5/32	1-3 17/32
13/16	5 7/8	9	6 3/4	10 5/16	7 5/8	11 21/32	8 15/32	1-0 31/32	9 11/32	1-2 9/32	10 7/32	1-3 5/8
7/8	5 15/16	9 3/32	6 13/16	10 13/32	7 11/16	11 23/32	8 17/32	1-1 1/16	9 13/32	1-2 3/8	10 9/32	1-3 11/16
15/16	6	9 3/32	6 7/8	10 1/2	7 23/32	11 13/16	8 19/32	1-1 1/8	9 15/32	1-2 15/32	10 5/16	1-3 25/32

Feet	0' Rise	0' Slope	10' Rise	10' Slope	20' Rise	20' Slope	30' Rise	30' Slope
0	0	0	8-7 3/4	13-2 5/8	17-3 1/2	26-5 1/4	25-11 1/4	39-7 29/32
1	-10 3/8	1-3 7/8	9-6 1/8	14-6 1/2	18-1 7/8	27-9 1/8	26-9 5/8	40-11 3/4
2	1-8 3/4	2-7 23/32	10-4 1/2	15-10 11/32	19-0 1/4	29-1	27-8	42-3 5/8
3	2-7 1/8	3-11 19/32	11-2 7/8	17-2 7/32	19-10 5/8	30-4 27/32	28-6 3/8	43-7 1/2
4	3-5 1/2	5-3 7/16	12-1 1/4	18-6 3/32	20-9	31-8 23/32	29-4 3/4	44-11 11/32
5	4-3 7/8	6-7 5/16	12-11 5/8	19-9 15/16	21-7 3/8	33-0 19/32	30-3 1/8	46-3 7/32
6	5-2 1/4	7-11 3/16	13-10	21-1 13/16	22-5 3/4	34-4 7/16	31-1 1/2	47-7 1/16
7	6-0 5/8	9-3 1/32	14-8 3/8	22-5 11/32	23-4 1/8	35-8 5/16	31-11 7/8	48-10 15/16
8	6-11	10-6 29/32	15-6 3/4	23-9 17/32	24-2 1/2	37-0 5/32	32-10 1/4	50-2 13/16
9	7-9 3/8	11-10 25/32	16-5 1/8	25-1 13/32	25-0 7/8	38-4 1/32	33-8 5/8	51-6 21/32

A = 40° 50′ 46″; logsin A = 9.81560; logcos A = 9.87879; logtan A = 9.93681; logcot A = 0.06319

Ins.	12″ Rise	12″ Slope	13″ Rise	13″ Slope	14″ Rise	14″ Slope	15″ Rise	15″ Slope	16″ Rise	16″ Slope
0	10 3/8	1-3 7/8	11 1/4	1-5 3/16	1-0 3/32	1-6 1/2	1-0 31/32	1-7 27/32–	1-1 27/32–	1-9 5/32–
1/16	10 7/16	1-3 15/16	11 9/32	1-5 9/32–	1-0 5/32	1-6 19/32–	1-1 1/32–	1-7 29/32	1-1 7/8	1-9 7/32
1/8	10 15/32	1-4 1/32–	11 11/32	1-5 11/32	1-0 7/32–	1-6 11/16	1-1 1/16	1-8	1-1 15/16	1-9 5/16
3/16	10 17/32	1-4 1/8	11 13/32–	1-5 7/16	1-0 9/32–	1-6 3/4	1-1 1/8	1-8 1/16	1-2	1-9 13/32–
1/4	10 19/32–	1-4 3/16	11 15/32–	1-5 1/2	1-0 5/16	1-6 27/32–	1-1 3/16	1-8 5/32	1-2 1/16	1-9 15/32
5/16	10 21/32–	1-4 9/32–	11 1/2	1-5 19/32	1-0 3/8	1-6 29/32	1-1 1/4	1-8 1/4	1-2 3/32	1-9 9/16
3/8	10 11/16	1-4 11/32	11 9/16	1-5 11/16	1-0 7/16	1-7	1-1 9/32	1-8 5/16	1-2 5/32	1-9 21/32–
7/16	10 3/4	1-4 7/16	11 5/8	1-5 3/4	1-0 15/32	1-7 3/32–	1-1 11/32	1-8 13/32	1-2 7/32–	1-9 23/32
1/2	10 13/16	1-4 17/32–	11 11/16	1-5 27/32	1-0 17/32	1-7 5/32	1-1 13/32–	1-8 1/2	1-2 1/4	1-9 13/16
9/16	10 7/8	1-4 19/32	11 23/32	1-5 15/16	1-0 19/32–	1-7 1/4	1-1 15/32–	1-8 9/16	1-2 5/16	1-9 29/32–
5/8	10 29/32	1-4 11/16	11 25/32–	1-6	1-0 21/32–	1-7 11/32–	1-1 1/2	1-8 21/32–	1-2 3/8	1-9 31/32
11/16	10 31/32	1-4 25/32–	11 27/32–	1-6 3/32	1-0 11/16	1-7 13/32	1-1 9/16	1-8 3/4	1-2 7/16	1-10 1/16
3/4	11 1/32–	1-4 27/32	11 7/8	1-6 3/16	1-0 3/4	1-7 1/2	1-1 5/8	1-8 13/16	1-2 15/32	1-10 5/32–
13/16	11 1/16	1-4 15/16	11 15/16	1-6 1/4	1-0 13/16	1-7 19/32–	1-1 21/32	1-8 29/32–	1-2 17/32	1-10 7/32
7/8	11 1/8	1-5 1/32–	1-0	1-6 11/32–	1-0 7/8	1-7 21/32	1-1 23/32	1-9	1-2 19/32–	1-10 5/16
15/16	11 3/16	1-5 3/32	1-0 1/16	1-6 7/16	1-0 29/32	1-7 3/4	1-1 25/32–	1-9 1/16	1-2 21/32–	1-10 3/8

Ins.	17″ Rise	17″ Slope	18″ Rise	18″ Slope	19″ Rise	19″ Slope	20″ Rise	20″ Slope	21″ Rise	21″ Slope
0	1-2 11/16	1-10 15/32	1-3 9/16	1-11 25/32	1-4 7/16	2-1 1/8	1-5 9/32	2-2 7/16	1-6 5/32	2-3 3/4
1/16	1-2 3/4	1-10 9/16	1-3 5/8	1-11 7/8	1-4 15/32	2-1 3/16	1-5 11/32	2-2 17/32–	1-6 7/32–	2-3 27/32–
1/8	1-2 13/16	1-10 5/8	1-3 21/32	1-11 31/32–	1-4 17/32	2-1 9/32	1-5 13/32–	2-2 19/32	1-6 1/4	2-3 15/16
3/16	1-2 7/8	1-10 23/32	1-3 23/32	2-0 1/32	1-4 19/32–	2-1 3/8	1-5 15/32–	2-2 11/16	1-6 5/16	2-4
1/4	1-2 29/32	1-10 13/16	1-3 25/32–	2-0 1/8	1-4 21/32–	2-1 7/16	1-5 1/2	2-2 25/32–	1-6 3/8	2-4 3/32–
5/16	1-2 31/32–	1-10 7/8	1-3 27/32–	2-0 7/32–	1-4 11/16	2-1 17/32–	1-5 9/16	2-2 27/32	1-6 7/16	2-4 3/16
3/8	1-3 1/32–	1-10 31/32–	1-3 7/8	2-0 9/32	1-4 3/4	2-1 5/8	1-5 5/8	2-2 15/16	1-6 15/32	2-4 1/4
7/16	1-3 1/16	1-11 1/16	1-3 15/16	2-0 3/8	1-4 13/16	2-1 11/16	1-5 21/32	2-3 1/32–	1-6 17/32	2-4 11/32–
1/2	1-3 1/8	1-11 1/8	1-4	2-0 15/32–	1-4 7/8	2-1 25/32–	1-5 23/32	2-3 3/32	1-6 19/32–	2-4 13/32
9/16	1-3 3/16	1-11 7/32–	1-4 1/16	2-0 17/32	1-4 29/32	2-1 7/8	1-5 25/32–	2-3 3/16	1-6 21/32–	2-4 1/2
5/8	1-3 1/4	1-11 5/16	1-4 3/32	2-0 5/8	1-4 31/32–	2-1 15/16	1-5 27/32–	2-3 1/4	1-6 11/16	2-4 19/32–
11/16	1-3 9/32	1-11 3/8	1-4 5/32	2-0 23/32–	1-5 1/32–	2-2 1/32–	1-5 7/8	2-3 11/32	1-6 3/4	2-4 21/32
3/4	1-3 11/32	1-11 15/32–	1-4 7/32–	2-0 25/32	1-5 1/16	2-2 3/32	1-5 15/16	2-3 7/16	1-6 13/16	2-4 3/4
13/16	1-3 13/32–	1-11 9/16	1-4 1/4	2-0 7/8	1-5 1/8	2-2 3/16	1-6	2-3 1/2	1-6 27/32	2-4 27/32–
7/8	1-3 15/32–	1-11 5/8	1-4 5/16	2-0 15/16	1-5 3/16	2-2 9/32–	1-6 1/16	2-3 19/32	1-6 29/32	2-4 29/32
15/16	1-3 1/2	1-11 23/32–	1-4 3/8	2-1 1/32	1-5 1/4	2-2 11/32	1-6 3/32	2-3 11/16	1-6 31/32–	2-5

Feet	40′ Rise	40′ Slope	50′ Rise	50′ Slope	60′ Rise	60′ Slope	70′ Rise	70′ Slope
0	34-7	52-10 17/32–	43-2 3/4	66-1 5/32	51-10 1/2	79-3 25/32	60-6 1/4	92-6 7/16
1	35-5 3/8	54-2 3/8	44-1 1/8	67-5 1/32–	52-8 7/8	80-7 21/32–	61-4 5/8	93-10 9/32
2	36-3 3/4	55-6 1/4	44-11 1/2	68-8 7/8	53-7 1/4	81-11 17/32–	62-3	95-2 5/32–
3	37-2 1/8	56-10 1/8	45-9 7/8	70-0 3/4	54-5 5/8	83-3 3/8	63-1 3/8	96-6
4	38-0 1/2	58-1 31/32	46-8 1/4	71-4 5/8	55-4	84-7 1/4	63-11 3/4	97-9 7/8
5	38-10 7/8	59-5 27/32–	47-6 5/8	72-8 15/32	56-2 3/8	85-11 3/32	64-10 1/8	99-1 3/4
6	39-9 1/4	60-9 23/32–	48-5	74-0 11/32–	57-0 3/4	87-2 31/32	65-8 1/2	100-5 19/32
7	40-7 5/8	62-1 9/16	49-3 3/8	75-4 3/16	57-11 1/8	88-6 27/32–	66-6 7/8	101-9 15/32–
8	41-6	63-5 7/16	50-1 3/4	76-8 1/16	58-9 1/2	89-10 11/16	67-5 1/4	103-1 11/32–
9	42-4 3/8	64-9 9/32	51-0 1/8	77-11 15/16	59-7 7/8	91-2 9/16	68-3 5/8	104-5 3/16

natsin A=0.6540300876; natcos A=0.7564685350; nattan A=0.8645833333; natcot A=1.1566265060

Inches	0" Rise	0" Slope	1" Rise	1" Slope	2" Rise	2" Slope	3" Rise	3" Slope	4" Rise	4" Slope	5" Rise	5" Slope
0	0	0	7/8	15/16	1 3/4	2 21/32	2 5/8	3 31/32	3 15/32	5 5/16	4 11/32	6 5/8
1/16	1/16	3/32	15/16	1 13/16	1 25/32	2 23/32	2 21/32	4 1/16	3 17/32	5 3/8	4 13/32	6 23/32
1/8	3/32	5/32	31/32	1 1/2	1 27/32	2 13/16	2 23/32	4 5/32	3 19/32	5 15/32	4 15/32	6 25/32
3/16	5/32	1/4	1 1/32	1 9/16	1 29/32	2 29/32	2 25/32	4 7/32	3 21/32	5 9/16	4 1/2	6 7/8
1/4	7/32	11/32	1 3/32	1 21/32	1 31/32	2 31/32	2 13/16	4 5/16	3 11/16	5 5/8	4 9/16	6 31/32
5/16	9/32	13/32	1 5/32	1 3/4	2	3 1/16	2 7/8	4 3/8	3 3/4	5 23/32	4 5/8	7 1/32
3/8	5/16	1/2	1 3/16	1 13/16	2 1/16	3 5/32	2 15/16	4 15/32	3 13/16	5 13/16	4 11/16	7 1/8
7/16	3/8	19/32	1 1/4	1 29/32	2 1/8	3 7/32	3	4 9/16	3 7/8	5 7/8	4 23/32	7 7/32
1/2	7/16	21/32	1 5/16	2	2 3/16	3 5/16	3 1/32	4 5/8	3 29/32	5 31/32	4 25/32	7 9/32
9/16	1/2	3/4	1 11/32	2 1/16	2 7/32	3 13/32	3 3/32	4 23/32	3 31/32	6 1/16	4 27/32	7 3/8
5/8	17/32	27/32	1 13/32	2 5/32	2 9/32	3 15/32	3 5/32	4 13/16	4 1/32	6 1/8	4 29/32	7 15/32
11/16	19/32	29/32	1 15/32	2 1/4	2 11/32	3 9/16	3 7/32	4 7/8	4 1/16	6 7/32	4 15/16	7 17/32
3/4	21/32	1	1 17/32	2 5/16	2 13/32	3 21/32	3 1/4	4 31/32	4 1/8	6 9/32	5	7 5/8
13/16	23/32	1 1/16	1 9/16	2 13/32	2 7/16	3 23/32	3 5/16	5 1/16	4 3/16	6 3/8	5 1/16	7 23/32
7/8	3/4	1 15/32	1 5/8	2 1/2	2 1/2	3 13/16	3 3/8	5 1/8	4 1/4	6 15/32	5 1/8	7 25/32
15/16	13/16	1 1/4	1 11/16	2 9/16	2 9/16	3 29/32	3 7/16	5 7/32	4 9/32	6 17/32	5 5/32	7 7/8

Inches	6" Rise	6" Slope	7" Rise	7" Slope	8" Rise	8" Slope	9" Rise	9" Slope	10" Rise	10" Slope	11" Rise	11" Slope
0	5 7/32	7 15/16	6 3/32	9 9/32	6 31/32	10 19/32	7 13/16	11 15/16	8 11/16	1-1 1/4	9 9/16	1-2 19/32
1/16	5 9/32	8 1/32	6 5/32	9 3/8	7	10 11/16	7 7/8	1-0	8 3/4	1-1 11/32	9 5/8	1-2 21/32
1/8	5 5/16	8 1/8	6 3/16	9 7/16	7 1/16	10 25/32	7 15/16	1-0 3/32	8 13/16	1-1 13/32	9 11/16	1-2 3/4
3/16	5 3/8	8 3/16	6 1/4	9 17/32	7 1/8	10 27/32	8	1-0 3/16	8 7/8	1-1 1/2	9 23/32	1-2 13/16
1/4	5 7/16	8 9/32	6 5/16	9 19/32	7 3/16	10 15/16	8 1/16	1-0 1/4	8 29/32	1-1 19/32	9 25/32	1-2 29/32
5/16	5 1/2	8 3/8	6 3/8	9 11/16	7 7/32	11 1/32	8 3/32	1-0 11/32	8 31/32	1-1 21/32	9 27/32	1-3
3/8	5 17/32	8 7/16	6 13/32	9 25/32	7 9/32	11 3/32	8 5/32	1-0 7/16	9 1/32	1-1 3/4	9 29/32	1-3 1/16
7/16	5 19/32	8 17/32	6 15/32	9 27/32	7 11/32	11 3/16	8 7/32	1-0 1/2	9 3/32	1-1 27/32	9 15/16	1-3 5/32
1/2	5 21/32	8 5/8	6 17/32	9 15/16	7 13/32	11 1/4	8 1/4	1-0 9/32	9 1/8	1-1 29/32	10	1-3 1/4
9/16	5 23/32	8 11/16	6 9/16	10 1/32	7 7/16	11 11/32	8 5/16	1-0 11/16	9 3/16	1-2	10 1/16	1-3 5/16
5/8	5 3/4	8 25/32	6 5/8	10 3/32	7 1/2	11 7/16	8 3/8	1-0 3/4	9 1/4	1-2 3/32	10 1/8	1-3 13/32
11/16	5 13/16	8 7/8	6 11/16	10 3/16	7 9/16	11 1/2	8 7/16	1-0 27/32	9 9/32	1-2 5/32	10 5/32	1-3 1/2
3/4	5 7/8	8 15/16	6 3/4	10 9/32	7 5/8	11 19/32	8 15/32	1-0 15/16	9 11/32	1-2 1/4	10 7/32	1-3 9/16
13/16	5 15/16	9 1/32	6 25/32	10 11/32	7 21/32	11 11/16	8 17/32	1-1	9 13/32	1-2 11/32	10 9/32	1-3 21/32
7/8	5 31/32	9 1/8	6 27/32	10 7/16	7 23/32	11 3/4	8 19/32	1-1 3/32	9 15/32	1-2 13/32	10 11/32	1-3 3/4
15/16	6 1/32	9 3/16	6 29/32	10 17/32	7 25/32	11 27/32	8 21/32	1-1 5/32	9 1/2	1-2 1/2	10 3/8	1-3 13/16

Feet	0' Rise	0' Slope	10' Rise	10' Slope	20' Rise	20' Slope	30' Rise	30' Slope
0			8-8 3/8	13-3 1/2	17-4 3/4	26-6 3/32	26-1 1/8	39-9 1/8
1	-10 7/16	1-3 29/32	9-6 13/16	14-6 15/16	18-3 3/16	27-10	26-11 9/16	41-1 1/2
2	1-8 7/8	2-7 13/16	10-5 1/4	15-10 27/32	19-1 5/8	29-1 29/32	27-10	42-4 15/16
3	2-7 5/16	3-11 23/32	11-3 11/16	17-2 3/4	20-0 1/2	30-5 25/32	28-8 7/16	43-8 27/32
4	3-5 3/4	5-3 5/8	12-2 1/8	18-6 21/32	20-10 1/2	31-9 11/16	29-6 7/8	45-0 3/4
5	4-4 3/8	6-7 17/32	13-0 9/16	19-10 9/16	21-8 15/16	33-1 19/32	30-5 5/16	46-4 21/32
6	5-2 5/8	7-11 7/16	13-11	21-2 15/32	22-7 3/8	34-5 1/2	31-3 3/4	47-8 9/16
7	6-1 1/16	9-3 11/32	14-9 7/16	22-6 3/8	23-5 13/16	35-9 13/32	32-2 3/16	49-0 7/16
8	6-11 1/2	10-7 7/32	15-7 7/8	23-10 9/32	24-4 1/4	37-1 5/16	33-0 5/8	50-4 11/32
9	7-9 15/16	11-11 1/8	16-6 5/16	25-2 3/16	25-2 11/16	38-5 7/32	33-11 1/16	51-8 1/4

A = 41° 00′ 59″; logsin A = 9.81709; logcos A = 9.87767; logtan A = 9.93942; logcot A = 0.06058

In.	12″ Rise	12″ Slope	13″ Rise	13″ Slope	14″ Rise	14″ Slope	15″ Rise	15″ Slope	16″ Rise	16″ Slope
0	$10\frac{7}{16}$	$1\text{-}3\frac{29}{32}$	$11\frac{5}{16}$	$1\text{-}5\frac{7}{32}$	$1\text{-}0\frac{3}{16}$	$1\text{-}6\frac{9}{16}$	$1\text{-}1\frac{1}{16}$	$1\text{-}7\frac{7}{8}$	$1\text{-}1\frac{29}{32}$	$1\text{-}9\frac{7}{32}$
1/16	$10\frac{1}{2}$	$1\text{-}4$	$11\frac{3}{8}$	$1\text{-}5\frac{5}{16}$	$1\text{-}0\frac{7}{32}$	$1\text{-}6\frac{5}{8}$	$1\text{-}1\frac{3}{32}$	$1\text{-}7\frac{31}{32}$	$1\text{-}1\frac{31}{32}$	$1\text{-}9\frac{9}{32}$
1/8	$10\frac{17}{32}$	$1\text{-}4\frac{1}{16}$	$11\frac{13}{32}$	$1\text{-}5\frac{13}{32}$	$1\text{-}0\frac{9}{32}$	$1\text{-}6\frac{23}{32}$	$1\text{-}1\frac{5}{32}$	$1\text{-}8\frac{1}{32}$	$1\text{-}2\frac{1}{32}$	$1\text{-}9\frac{3}{8}$
3/16	$10\frac{19}{32}$	$1\text{-}4\frac{5}{32}$	$11\frac{15}{32}$	$1\text{-}5\frac{15}{32}$	$1\text{-}0\frac{11}{32}$	$1\text{-}6\frac{13}{16}$	$1\text{-}1\frac{7}{32}$	$1\text{-}8\frac{1}{8}$	$1\text{-}2\frac{3}{32}$	$1\text{-}9\frac{15}{32}$
1/4	$10\frac{21}{32}$	$1\text{-}4\frac{1}{4}$	$11\frac{17}{32}$	$1\text{-}5\frac{9}{16}$	$1\text{-}0\frac{13}{32}$	$1\text{-}6\frac{7}{8}$	$1\text{-}1\frac{1}{4}$	$1\text{-}8\frac{7}{32}$	$1\text{-}2\frac{1}{8}$	$1\text{-}9\frac{17}{32}$
5/16	$10\frac{23}{32}$	$1\text{-}4\frac{5}{16}$	$11\frac{19}{32}$	$1\text{-}5\frac{21}{32}$	$1\text{-}0\frac{7}{16}$	$1\text{-}6\frac{31}{32}$	$1\text{-}1\frac{5}{16}$	$1\text{-}8\frac{9}{32}$	$1\text{-}2\frac{3}{16}$	$1\text{-}9\frac{5}{8}$
3/8	$10\frac{3}{4}$	$1\text{-}4\frac{13}{32}$	$11\frac{5}{8}$	$1\text{-}5\frac{23}{32}$	$1\text{-}0\frac{1}{2}$	$1\text{-}7\frac{1}{16}$	$1\text{-}1\frac{3}{8}$	$1\text{-}8\frac{3}{8}$	$1\text{-}2\frac{1}{4}$	$1\text{-}9\frac{11}{16}$
7/16	$10\frac{13}{16}$	$1\text{-}4\frac{15}{32}$	$11\frac{11}{16}$	$1\text{-}5\frac{13}{16}$	$1\text{-}0\frac{9}{16}$	$1\text{-}7\frac{1}{8}$	$1\text{-}1\frac{7}{16}$	$1\text{-}8\frac{15}{32}$	$1\text{-}2\frac{5}{16}$	$1\text{-}9\frac{25}{32}$
1/2	$10\frac{7}{8}$	$1\text{-}4\frac{9}{16}$	$11\frac{3}{4}$	$1\text{-}5\frac{29}{32}$	$1\text{-}0\frac{5}{8}$	$1\text{-}7\frac{7}{32}$	$1\text{-}1\frac{15}{32}$	$1\text{-}8\frac{17}{32}$	$1\text{-}2\frac{11}{32}$	$1\text{-}9\frac{7}{8}$
9/16	$10\frac{15}{16}$	$1\text{-}4\frac{21}{32}$	$11\frac{25}{32}$	$1\text{-}5\frac{31}{32}$	$1\text{-}0\frac{21}{32}$	$1\text{-}7\frac{5}{16}$	$1\text{-}1\frac{17}{32}$	$1\text{-}8\frac{5}{8}$	$1\text{-}2\frac{13}{32}$	$1\text{-}9\frac{15}{16}$
5/8	$10\frac{31}{32}$	$1\text{-}4\frac{23}{32}$	$11\frac{27}{32}$	$1\text{-}6\frac{1}{16}$	$1\text{-}0\frac{23}{32}$	$1\text{-}7\frac{3}{8}$	$1\text{-}1\frac{19}{32}$	$1\text{-}8\frac{23}{32}$	$1\text{-}2\frac{15}{32}$	$1\text{-}10\frac{1}{32}$
11/16	$11\frac{1}{32}$	$1\text{-}4\frac{13}{16}$	$11\frac{29}{32}$	$1\text{-}6\frac{5}{32}$	$1\text{-}0\frac{25}{32}$	$1\text{-}7\frac{19}{32}$	$1\text{-}1\frac{21}{32}$	$1\text{-}8\frac{25}{32}$	$1\text{-}2\frac{1}{2}$	$1\text{-}10\frac{1}{8}$
3/4	$11\frac{3}{32}$	$1\text{-}4\frac{29}{32}$	$11\frac{31}{32}$	$1\text{-}6\frac{7}{32}$	$1\text{-}0\frac{27}{32}$	$1\text{-}7\frac{9}{16}$	$1\text{-}1\frac{11}{16}$	$1\text{-}8\frac{7}{8}$	$1\text{-}2\frac{9}{16}$	$1\text{-}10\frac{3}{16}$
13/16	$11\frac{5}{32}$	$1\text{-}4\frac{31}{32}$	$1\text{-}0$	$1\text{-}6\frac{5}{16}$	$1\text{-}0\frac{7}{8}$	$1\text{-}7\frac{5}{8}$	$1\text{-}1\frac{3}{4}$	$1\text{-}8\frac{31}{32}$	$1\text{-}2\frac{5}{8}$	$1\text{-}10\frac{9}{16}$
7/8	$11\frac{3}{16}$	$1\text{-}5\frac{1}{16}$	$1\text{-}0\frac{1}{16}$	$1\text{-}6\frac{3}{8}$	$1\text{-}0\frac{15}{16}$	$1\text{-}7\frac{23}{32}$	$1\text{-}1\frac{13}{16}$	$1\text{-}9\frac{1}{32}$	$1\text{-}2\frac{11}{16}$	$1\text{-}10\frac{3}{8}$
15/16	$11\frac{1}{4}$	$1\text{-}5\frac{5}{32}$	$1\text{-}0\frac{1}{8}$	$1\text{-}6\frac{15}{32}$	$1\text{-}1$	$1\text{-}7\frac{13}{16}$	$1\text{-}1\frac{7}{8}$	$1\text{-}9\frac{1}{8}$	$1\text{-}2\frac{23}{32}$	$1\text{-}10\frac{7}{16}$

In.	17″ Rise	17″ Slope	18″ Rise	18″ Slope	19″ Rise	19″ Slope	20″ Rise	20″ Slope	21″ Rise	21″ Slope
0	$1\text{-}2\frac{25}{32}$	$1\text{-}10\frac{17}{32}$	$1\text{-}3\frac{21}{32}$	$1\text{-}11\frac{27}{32}$	$1\text{-}4\frac{17}{32}$	$2\text{-}1\frac{3}{16}$	$1\text{-}5\frac{13}{32}$	$2\text{-}2\frac{1}{2}$	$1\text{-}6\frac{1}{4}$	$2\text{-}3\frac{27}{32}$
1/16	$1\text{-}2\frac{27}{32}$	$1\text{-}10\frac{5}{8}$	$1\text{-}3\frac{23}{32}$	$1\text{-}11\frac{15}{16}$	$1\text{-}4\frac{19}{32}$	$2\text{-}1\frac{1}{4}$	$1\text{-}5\frac{7}{16}$	$2\text{-}2\frac{19}{32}$	$1\text{-}6\frac{5}{16}$	$2\text{-}3\frac{29}{32}$
1/8	$1\text{-}2\frac{29}{32}$	$1\text{-}10\frac{11}{16}$	$1\text{-}3\frac{3}{4}$	$2\text{-}0\frac{1}{32}$	$1\text{-}4\frac{5}{8}$	$2\text{-}1\frac{11}{32}$	$1\text{-}5\frac{1}{2}$	$2\text{-}2\frac{11}{16}$	$1\text{-}6\frac{3}{8}$	$2\text{-}4$
3/16	$1\text{-}2\frac{15}{16}$	$1\text{-}10\frac{25}{32}$	$1\text{-}3\frac{13}{16}$	$2\text{-}0\frac{3}{32}$	$1\text{-}4\frac{11}{16}$	$2\text{-}1\frac{7}{16}$	$1\text{-}5\frac{9}{16}$	$2\text{-}2\frac{3}{4}$	$1\text{-}6\frac{7}{16}$	$2\text{-}4\frac{3}{32}$
1/4	$1\text{-}3$	$1\text{-}10\frac{7}{8}$	$1\text{-}3\frac{7}{8}$	$2\text{-}0\frac{3}{16}$	$1\text{-}4\frac{3}{4}$	$2\text{-}1\frac{1}{2}$	$1\text{-}5\frac{5}{8}$	$2\text{-}2\frac{27}{32}$	$1\text{-}6\frac{15}{32}$	$2\text{-}4\frac{5}{32}$
5/16	$1\text{-}3\frac{1}{16}$	$1\text{-}10\frac{15}{16}$	$1\text{-}3\frac{15}{16}$	$2\text{-}0\frac{9}{32}$	$1\text{-}4\frac{13}{16}$	$2\text{-}1\frac{19}{32}$	$1\text{-}5\frac{21}{32}$	$2\text{-}2\frac{29}{32}$	$1\text{-}6\frac{17}{32}$	$2\text{-}4\frac{1}{4}$
3/8	$1\text{-}3\frac{1}{8}$	$1\text{-}11\frac{1}{32}$	$1\text{-}3\frac{31}{32}$	$2\text{-}0\frac{11}{32}$	$1\text{-}4\frac{27}{32}$	$2\text{-}1\frac{11}{16}$	$1\text{-}5\frac{23}{32}$	$2\text{-}3$	$1\text{-}6\frac{19}{32}$	$2\text{-}4\frac{11}{32}$
7/16	$1\text{-}3\frac{5}{32}$	$1\text{-}11\frac{1}{8}$	$1\text{-}4\frac{1}{8}$	$2\text{-}0\frac{7}{16}$	$1\text{-}4\frac{29}{32}$	$2\text{-}1\frac{3}{4}$	$1\text{-}5\frac{25}{32}$	$2\text{-}3\frac{3}{32}$	$1\text{-}6\frac{21}{32}$	$2\text{-}4\frac{13}{32}$
1/2	$1\text{-}3\frac{7}{32}$	$1\text{-}11\frac{3}{16}$	$1\text{-}4\frac{3}{32}$	$2\text{-}0\frac{17}{32}$	$1\text{-}4\frac{31}{32}$	$2\text{-}1\frac{27}{32}$	$1\text{-}5\frac{27}{32}$	$2\text{-}3\frac{5}{32}$	$1\text{-}6\frac{11}{16}$	$2\text{-}4\frac{1}{2}$
9/16	$1\text{-}3\frac{9}{32}$	$1\text{-}11\frac{9}{32}$	$1\text{-}4\frac{5}{32}$	$2\text{-}0\frac{19}{32}$	$1\text{-}5$	$2\text{-}1\frac{15}{16}$	$1\text{-}5\frac{7}{8}$	$2\text{-}3\frac{1}{4}$	$1\text{-}6\frac{3}{4}$	$2\text{-}4\frac{9}{16}$
5/8	$1\text{-}3\frac{11}{32}$	$1\text{-}11\frac{11}{32}$	$1\text{-}4\frac{3}{16}$	$2\text{-}0\frac{11}{16}$	$1\text{-}5\frac{1}{16}$	$2\text{-}2$	$1\text{-}5\frac{15}{16}$	$2\text{-}3\frac{11}{32}$	$1\text{-}6\frac{13}{16}$	$2\text{-}4\frac{21}{32}$
11/16	$1\text{-}3\frac{3}{8}$	$1\text{-}11\frac{7}{16}$	$1\text{-}4\frac{1}{4}$	$2\text{-}0\frac{25}{32}$	$1\text{-}5\frac{1}{8}$	$2\text{-}2\frac{3}{32}$	$1\text{-}6$	$2\text{-}3\frac{13}{32}$	$1\text{-}6\frac{7}{8}$	$2\text{-}4\frac{3}{4}$
3/4	$1\text{-}3\frac{7}{16}$	$1\text{-}11\frac{17}{32}$	$1\text{-}4\frac{5}{16}$	$2\text{-}0\frac{27}{32}$	$1\text{-}5\frac{3}{16}$	$2\text{-}2\frac{3}{16}$	$1\text{-}6\frac{1}{16}$	$2\text{-}3\frac{1}{2}$	$1\text{-}6\frac{29}{32}$	$2\text{-}4\frac{13}{16}$
13/16	$1\text{-}3\frac{1}{2}$	$1\text{-}11\frac{19}{32}$	$1\text{-}4\frac{3}{8}$	$2\text{-}0\frac{15}{16}$	$1\text{-}5\frac{7}{32}$	$2\text{-}2\frac{1}{4}$	$1\text{-}6\frac{3}{32}$	$2\text{-}3\frac{19}{32}$	$1\text{-}6\frac{31}{32}$	$2\text{-}4\frac{29}{32}$
7/8	$1\text{-}3\frac{9}{16}$	$1\text{-}11\frac{11}{16}$	$1\text{-}4\frac{13}{32}$	$2\text{-}1\frac{1}{32}$	$1\text{-}5\frac{9}{32}$	$2\text{-}2\frac{11}{32}$	$1\text{-}6\frac{5}{8}$	$2\text{-}3\frac{21}{32}$	$1\text{-}7\frac{1}{32}$	$2\text{-}5$
15/16	$1\text{-}3\frac{19}{32}$	$1\text{-}11\frac{25}{32}$	$1\text{-}4\frac{15}{32}$	$2\text{-}1\frac{3}{32}$	$1\text{-}5\frac{11}{32}$	$2\text{-}2\frac{7}{16}$	$1\text{-}6\frac{7}{32}$	$2\text{-}3\frac{3}{4}$	$1\text{-}7\frac{3}{32}$	$2\text{-}5\frac{1}{16}$

Feet	40′ Rise	40′ Slope	50′ Rise	50′ Slope	60′ Rise	60′ Slope	70′ Rise	70′ Slope
0	$34\text{-}9\frac{1}{2}$	$53\text{-}0\frac{5}{32}$	$43\text{-}5\frac{7}{8}$	$66\text{-}3\frac{7}{32}$	$52\text{-}2\frac{1}{4}$	$79\text{-}6\frac{1}{4}$	$60\text{-}10\frac{5}{8}$	$92\text{-}9\frac{9}{32}$
1	$35\text{-}7\frac{15}{16}$	$54\text{-}4\frac{1}{16}$	$44\text{-}4\frac{5}{8}$	$67\text{-}7\frac{3}{8}$	$53\text{-}0\frac{11}{16}$	$80\text{-}10\frac{5}{8}$	$61\text{-}9\frac{1}{16}$	$94\text{-}1\frac{3}{16}$
2	$36\text{-}6\frac{3}{8}$	$55\text{-}7\frac{31}{32}$	$45\text{-}2\frac{3}{4}$	$68\text{-}11$	$53\text{-}11\frac{1}{16}$	$82\text{-}2\frac{1}{16}$	$62\text{-}7\frac{1}{2}$	$95\text{-}5\frac{3}{32}$
3	$37\text{-}4\frac{13}{16}$	$56\text{-}11\frac{7}{8}$	$46\text{-}1\frac{3}{16}$	$70\text{-}2\frac{29}{32}$	$54\text{-}9\frac{9}{16}$	$83\text{-}5\frac{31}{32}$	$63\text{-}5\frac{15}{16}$	$96\text{-}9$
4	$38\text{-}3\frac{1}{4}$	$58\text{-}3\frac{25}{32}$	$46\text{-}11\frac{5}{8}$	$71\text{-}6\frac{13}{16}$	$55\text{-}8$	$84\text{-}9\frac{7}{8}$	$64\text{-}4\frac{3}{8}$	$98\text{-}0\frac{29}{32}$
5	$39\text{-}1\frac{11}{16}$	$59\text{-}7\frac{11}{16}$	$47\text{-}10\frac{1}{16}$	$72\text{-}10\frac{23}{32}$	$56\text{-}6\frac{7}{16}$	$86\text{-}1\frac{25}{32}$	$65\text{-}2\frac{13}{16}$	$99\text{-}4\frac{13}{16}$
6	$40\text{-}0\frac{1}{8}$	$60\text{-}11\frac{19}{32}$	$48\text{-}8\frac{1}{2}$	$74\text{-}2\frac{5}{8}$	$57\text{-}4\frac{7}{8}$	$87\text{-}5\frac{11}{16}$	$66\text{-}1\frac{1}{4}$	$100\text{-}8\frac{23}{32}$
7	$40\text{-}10\frac{9}{16}$	$62\text{-}3\frac{1}{2}$	$49\text{-}6\frac{15}{16}$	$75\text{-}6\frac{17}{32}$	$58\text{-}3\frac{5}{16}$	$88\text{-}9\frac{9}{16}$	$66\text{-}11\frac{11}{16}$	$102\text{-}0\frac{5}{8}$
8	$41\text{-}9$	$63\text{-}7\frac{13}{32}$	$50\text{-}5\frac{3}{8}$	$76\text{-}10\frac{7}{16}$	$59\text{-}1\frac{3}{4}$	$90\text{-}1\frac{15}{32}$	$67\text{-}10\frac{1}{8}$	$103\text{-}4\frac{17}{32}$
9	$42\text{-}7\frac{15}{16}$	$64\text{-}11\frac{5}{16}$	$51\text{-}3\frac{13}{16}$	$78\text{-}2\frac{11}{32}$	$60\text{-}0\frac{3}{16}$	$91\text{-}5\frac{3}{8}$	$68\text{-}8\frac{9}{16}$	$104\text{-}8\frac{7}{16}$

natsin A=0.6562760026; natcos A=0.7545209132; nattan A=0.8697916666; natcot A=1.1497005988

Bevel 10½" to 12"

Inches	0" Rise	0" Slope	1" Rise	1" Slope	2" Rise	2" Slope	3" Rise	3" Slope	4" Rise	4" Slope	5" Rise	5" Slope
0	0	0	7/8	1 11/32–	1 3/4	2 21/32	2 5/8	4	3 1/2	5 5/16	4 3/8	6 21/32–
1/16	1/16	3/32–	15/16	1 13/32	1 13/16	2 3/4	2 11/16	4 1/16	3 9/16	5 13/32–	4 7/16	6 23/32
1/8	1/8	5/32	1	1 1/2	1 7/8	2 13/16	2 3/4	4 5/32–	3 5/8	5 15/32	4 1/2	6 13/16
3/16	5/32	1/4	1 1/32	1 9/16	1 29/32	2 29/32	2 25/32	4 1/4	3 21/32	5 9/16	4 17/32	6 29/32–
1/4	7/32	11/32–	1 3/32	1 21/32	1 31/32	3	2 27/32	4 5/16	3 23/32	5 21/32	4 19/32	6 31/32
5/16	9/32–	13/32	1 5/32–	1 3/4	2 1/32–	3 1/16	2 29/32–	4 13/32–	3 25/32–	5 23/32	4 21/32–	7 1/16
3/8	5/16	1/2	1 3/16	1 13/16	2 1/16	3 5/32–	2 15/16	4 1/2	3 13/16	5 13/16	4 11/16	7 5/32–
7/16	3/8	19/32–	1 1/4	1 29/32	2 1/8	3 1/4	3	4 9/16	3 7/8	5 29/32–	4 3/4	7 7/32
1/2	7/16	21/32	1 5/16	2	2 3/16	3 5/16	3 1/16	4 21/32	3 15/16	5 31/32	4 13/16	7 5/16
9/16	1/2	3/4	1 3/8	2 1/16	2 1/4	3 13/32–	3 1/8	4 23/32	4	6 1/16	4 7/8	7 13/32–
5/8	9/16	27/32–	1 7/16	2 5/32	2 5/16	3 1/2	3 3/16	4 13/16	4 1/16	6 5/32–	4 15/16	7 15/32
11/16	19/32	29/32	1 15/32	2 1/4	2 11/32	3 9/16	3 7/32	4 29/32–	4 3/32	6 7/32	4 31/32	7 9/16
3/4	21/32	1	1 17/32	2 5/16	2 13/32	3 21/32–	3 9/32	4 31/32	4 5/32	6 5/16	5 1/32	7 5/8
13/16	23/32–	1 3/32–	1 19/32–	2 13/32	2 15/32–	3 3/4	3 11/32–	5 1/16	4 7/32–	6 13/32–	5 3/32–	7 23/32
7/8	3/4	1 5/32	1 5/8	2 1/2	2 1/2	3 13/16	3 3/8	5 5/32–	4 1/4	6 15/32	5 1/8	7 13/16
15/16	13/16	1 1/4	1 11/16	2 9/16	2 9/16	3 29/32–	3 7/16	5 7/32	4 5/16	6 9/16	5 3/16	7 7/8

Inches	6" Rise	6" Slope	7" Rise	7" Slope	8" Rise	8" Slope	9" Rise	9" Slope	10" Rise	10" Slope	11" Rise	11" Slope
0	5 1/4	7 31/32	6 1/8	9 5/16	7	10 5/8	7 7/8	11 31/32–	8 3/4	1-1 9/32	9 5/8	1-2 5/8
1/16	5 5/16	8 1/16	6 3/16	9 3/8	7 1/16	10 23/32–	7 15/16	1-0 1/32	8 13/16	1-1 3/8	9 11/16	1-2 11/16
1/8	5 3/8	8 1/8	6 1/4	9 15/32–	7 1/8	10 25/32	8	1-0 1/8	8 7/8	1-1 15/32–	9 3/4	1-2 25/32
3/16	5 13/32	8 7/32	6 9/32	9 9/16	7 5/32	10 7/8	8 1/32	1-0 7/32–	8 29/32	1-1 17/32	9 25/32	1-2 7/8
1/4	5 15/32	8 5/16	6 11/32	9 5/8	7 7/32	10 31/32–	8 3/32	1-0 9/32	8 31/32	1-1 5/8	9 27/32	1-2 15/16
5/16	5 17/32–	8 3/8	6 13/32–	9 23/32–	7 9/32–	11 1/32	8 5/32–	1-0 3/8	9 1/32–	1-1 11/16	9 29/32–	1-3 1/32
3/8	5 9/16	8 15/32	6 7/16	9 13/16	7 5/16	11 1/8	8 3/16	1-0 15/32–	9 1/16	1-1 25/32	9 15/16	1-3 1/8
7/16	5 5/8	8 9/16	6 1/2	9 7/8	7 3/8	11 7/32–	8 1/4	1-0 17/32	9 1/8	1-1 7/8	10	1-3 3/16
1/2	5 11/16	8 5/8	6 9/16	9 31/32–	7 7/16	11 9/32	8 5/16	1-0 5/8	9 3/16	1-1 15/16	10 1/16	1-3 9/32–
9/16	5 3/4	8 23/32	6 5/8	10 1/16	7 1/2	11 3/8	8 3/8	1-0 23/32–	9 1/4	1-2 1/32	10 1/8	1-3 3/8
5/8	5 13/16	8 13/16	6 11/16	10 1/8	7 9/16	11 15/32–	8 7/16	1-0 25/32	9 5/16	1-2 1/8	10 3/16	1-3 7/16
11/16	5 27/32	8 7/8	6 23/32	10 7/32–	7 19/32	11 17/32	8 15/32	1-0 7/8	9 11/32	1-2 3/16	10 7/32	1-3 17/32–
3/4	5 29/32	8 31/32	6 25/32	10 5/16	7 21/32	11 5/8	8 17/32	1-0 31/32–	9 13/32	1-2 9/32	10 9/32	1-3 5/8
13/16	5 31/32–	9 1/16	6 27/32–	10 3/8	7 23/32–	11 23/32–	8 19/32–	1-1 1/32	9 15/32–	1-2 3/8	10 11/32–	1-3 11/16
7/8	6	9 1/8	6 7/8	10 15/32–	7 3/4	11 25/32	8 5/8	1-1 1/8	9 1/2	1-2 7/16	10 3/8	1-3 25/32–
15/16	6 1/16	9 7/32–	6 15/16	10 9/16	7 13/16	11 7/8	8 11/16	1-1 7/32–	9 9/16	1-2 17/32	10 7/16	1-3 7/8

Feet	0' Rise	0' Slope	10' Rise	10' Slope	20' Rise	20' Slope	30' Rise	30' Slope
0	0	0	8-9	13-3 7/16	17-6	26-6 29/32–	26-3	39-10 11/32
1	-10 1/2	1-3 15/16	9-7 1/2	14-7 13/32–	18-4 1/2	27-10 27/32	27-1 1/2	41-2 5/16
2	1-9	2-7 7/8	10-6	15-11 11/32–	19-3	29-2 25/32	28-0	42-6 1/4
3	2-7 1/2	3-11 27/32–	11-4 1/2	17-3 9/32	20-1 1/2	30-6 3/4	28-10 1/2	43-10 3/16
4	3-6	5-3 25/32–	12-3	18-7 7/32	21-0	31-10 11/16	29-9	45-2 1/8
5	4-4 1/2	6-7 23/32	13-1 1/2	19-11 3/16	21-10 1/2	33-2 5/8	30-7 1/2	46-6 3/32–
6	5-3	7-11 21/32	14-0	21-3 1/8	22-9	34-6 9/16	31-6	47-10 1/32–
7	6-1 1/2	9-3 5/8	14-10 1/2	22-7 1/16	23-7 1/2	35-10 17/32–	32-4 1/2	49-1 31/32
8	7-0	10-7 9/16	15-9	23-11	24-6	37-2 15/32–	33-3	50-5 29/32
9	7-10 1/2	11-11 1/2	16-7 1/2	25-2 31/32–	25-4 1/2	38-6 13/32	34-1 1/2	51-9 7/8

A = 41° 11′ 09″; logsin A = 9.81856; logcos A = 9.87655; logtan A = 9.94201; logcot A = 0.05799

Ins.	12″ Rise	12″ Slope	13″ Rise	13″ Slope	14″ Rise	14″ Slope	15″ Rise	15″ Slope	16″ Rise	16″ Slope
0	10$\frac{1}{2}$	1-3$\frac{15}{16}$	11$\frac{3}{8}$	1-5$\frac{9}{32}$	1-0$\frac{1}{4}$	1-6$\frac{19}{32}$	1-1$\frac{1}{8}$	1-7$\frac{15}{16}$	1-2	1-9$\frac{1}{4}$
$\frac{1}{16}$	10$\frac{9}{16}$	1-4$\frac{1}{32}$	11$\frac{7}{16}$	1-5$\frac{11}{32}$	1-0$\frac{5}{16}$	1-6$\frac{11}{16}$	1-1$\frac{3}{16}$	1-8	1-2$\frac{1}{16}$	1-9$\frac{11}{32}$
$\frac{1}{8}$	10$\frac{5}{8}$	1-4$\frac{1}{8}$	11$\frac{1}{2}$	1-5$\frac{7}{16}$	1-0$\frac{3}{8}$	1-6$\frac{25}{32}$	1-1$\frac{1}{4}$	1-8$\frac{3}{32}$	1-2$\frac{1}{8}$	1-9$\frac{7}{16}$
$\frac{3}{16}$	10$\frac{21}{32}$	1-4$\frac{3}{16}$	11$\frac{17}{32}$	1-5$\frac{17}{32}$	1-0$\frac{13}{32}$	1-6$\frac{27}{32}$	1-1$\frac{9}{32}$	1-8$\frac{3}{16}$	1-2$\frac{5}{32}$	1-9$\frac{1}{2}$
$\frac{1}{4}$	10$\frac{23}{32}$	1-4$\frac{9}{32}$	11$\frac{19}{32}$	1-5$\frac{19}{32}$	1-0$\frac{15}{32}$	1-6$\frac{15}{16}$	1-1$\frac{11}{32}$	1-8$\frac{1}{4}$	1-2$\frac{7}{32}$	1-9$\frac{19}{32}$
$\frac{5}{16}$	10$\frac{25}{32}$	1-4$\frac{3}{8}$	11$\frac{21}{32}$	1-5$\frac{11}{16}$	1-0$\frac{17}{32}$	1-7$\frac{1}{32}$	1-1$\frac{13}{32}$	1-8$\frac{11}{32}$	1-2$\frac{9}{32}$	1-9$\frac{11}{16}$
$\frac{3}{8}$	10$\frac{13}{16}$	1-4$\frac{7}{16}$	11$\frac{11}{16}$	1-5$\frac{25}{32}$	1-0$\frac{9}{16}$	1-7$\frac{3}{32}$	1-1$\frac{7}{16}$	1-8$\frac{7}{16}$	1-2$\frac{5}{16}$	1-9$\frac{3}{4}$
$\frac{7}{16}$	10$\frac{7}{8}$	1-4$\frac{17}{32}$	11$\frac{3}{4}$	1-5$\frac{27}{32}$	1-0$\frac{5}{8}$	1-7$\frac{3}{16}$	1-1$\frac{1}{2}$	1-8$\frac{1}{2}$	1-2$\frac{3}{8}$	1-9$\frac{27}{32}$
$\frac{1}{2}$	10$\frac{15}{16}$	1-4$\frac{5}{8}$	11$\frac{13}{16}$	1-5$\frac{15}{16}$	1-0$\frac{11}{16}$	1-7$\frac{9}{32}$	1-1$\frac{9}{16}$	1-8$\frac{19}{32}$	1-2$\frac{7}{16}$	1-9$\frac{15}{16}$
$\frac{9}{16}$	11	1-4$\frac{11}{32}$	11$\frac{7}{8}$	1-6$\frac{1}{32}$	1-0$\frac{3}{4}$	1-7$\frac{11}{32}$	1-1$\frac{5}{8}$	1-8$\frac{11}{16}$	1-2$\frac{1}{2}$	1-10
$\frac{5}{8}$	11$\frac{1}{16}$	1-4$\frac{25}{32}$	11$\frac{15}{16}$	1-6$\frac{3}{32}$	1-0$\frac{13}{16}$	1-7$\frac{7}{16}$	1-1$\frac{11}{16}$	1-8$\frac{3}{4}$	1-2$\frac{9}{16}$	1-10$\frac{3}{32}$
$\frac{11}{16}$	11$\frac{3}{32}$	1-4$\frac{27}{32}$	11$\frac{31}{32}$	1-6$\frac{3}{16}$	1-0$\frac{27}{32}$	1-7$\frac{17}{32}$	1-1$\frac{23}{32}$	1-8$\frac{27}{32}$	1-2$\frac{19}{32}$	1-10$\frac{3}{16}$
$\frac{3}{4}$	11$\frac{5}{32}$	1-4$\frac{15}{16}$	1-0$\frac{1}{32}$	1-6$\frac{9}{32}$	1-0$\frac{29}{32}$	1-7$\frac{19}{32}$	1-1$\frac{25}{32}$	1-8$\frac{15}{16}$	1-2$\frac{21}{32}$	1-10$\frac{1}{4}$
$\frac{13}{16}$	11$\frac{7}{32}$	1-5$\frac{1}{32}$	1-0$\frac{3}{32}$	1-6$\frac{11}{32}$	1-0$\frac{31}{32}$	1-7$\frac{11}{16}$	1-1$\frac{27}{32}$	1-9	1-2$\frac{23}{32}$	1-10$\frac{11}{32}$
$\frac{7}{8}$	11$\frac{1}{4}$	1-5$\frac{3}{32}$	1-0$\frac{1}{8}$	1-6$\frac{7}{16}$	1-1	1-7$\frac{3}{4}$	1-1$\frac{7}{8}$	1-9$\frac{3}{32}$	1-2$\frac{3}{4}$	1-10$\frac{7}{16}$
$\frac{15}{16}$	11$\frac{5}{16}$	1-5$\frac{3}{16}$	1-0$\frac{3}{16}$	1-6$\frac{17}{32}$	1-1$\frac{1}{16}$	1-7$\frac{27}{32}$	1-1$\frac{15}{16}$	1-9$\frac{3}{16}$	1-2$\frac{13}{16}$	1-10$\frac{1}{2}$

Ins.	17″ Rise	17″ Slope	18″ Rise	18″ Slope	19″ Rise	19″ Slope	20″ Rise	20″ Slope	21″ Rise	21″ Slope
0	1-2$\frac{7}{8}$	1-10$\frac{19}{32}$	1-3$\frac{3}{4}$	1-11$\frac{29}{32}$	1-4$\frac{5}{8}$	2-1$\frac{1}{4}$	1-5$\frac{1}{2}$	2-2$\frac{9}{16}$	1-6$\frac{3}{8}$	2-3$\frac{29}{32}$
$\frac{1}{16}$	1-2$\frac{15}{16}$	1-10$\frac{11}{16}$	1-3$\frac{13}{16}$	2-0	1-4$\frac{11}{16}$	2-1$\frac{11}{32}$	1-5$\frac{9}{16}$	2-2$\frac{21}{32}$	1-6$\frac{7}{16}$	2-4
$\frac{1}{8}$	1-3	1-10$\frac{3}{4}$	1-3$\frac{7}{8}$	2-0$\frac{3}{32}$	1-4$\frac{3}{4}$	2-1$\frac{13}{32}$	1-5$\frac{5}{8}$	2-2$\frac{3}{4}$	1-6$\frac{1}{2}$	2-4$\frac{1}{32}$
$\frac{3}{16}$	1-3$\frac{1}{16}$	1-10$\frac{27}{32}$	1-3$\frac{29}{32}$	2-0$\frac{5}{32}$	1-4$\frac{25}{32}$	2-1$\frac{1}{2}$	1-5$\frac{21}{32}$	2-2$\frac{13}{16}$	1-6$\frac{17}{32}$	2-4$\frac{5}{32}$
$\frac{1}{4}$	1-3$\frac{3}{32}$	1-10$\frac{29}{32}$	1-3$\frac{31}{32}$	2-0$\frac{1}{4}$	1-4$\frac{27}{32}$	2-1$\frac{19}{32}$	1-5$\frac{23}{32}$	2-2$\frac{29}{32}$	1-6$\frac{19}{32}$	2-4$\frac{1}{4}$
$\frac{5}{16}$	1-3$\frac{5}{32}$	1-11	1-4$\frac{1}{32}$	2-0$\frac{11}{32}$	1-4$\frac{29}{32}$	2-1$\frac{21}{32}$	1-5$\frac{25}{32}$	2-3	1-6$\frac{21}{32}$	2-4$\frac{5}{16}$
$\frac{3}{8}$	1-3$\frac{3}{16}$	1-11$\frac{3}{32}$	1-4$\frac{1}{16}$	2-0$\frac{13}{32}$	1-4$\frac{15}{16}$	2-1$\frac{3}{4}$	1-5$\frac{13}{16}$	2-3$\frac{1}{16}$	1-6$\frac{11}{16}$	2-4$\frac{13}{32}$
$\frac{7}{16}$	1-3$\frac{1}{4}$	1-11$\frac{5}{32}$	1-4$\frac{1}{8}$	2-0$\frac{1}{2}$	1-5	2-1$\frac{13}{16}$	1-5$\frac{7}{8}$	2-3$\frac{5}{32}$	1-6$\frac{3}{4}$	2-4$\frac{1}{2}$
$\frac{1}{2}$	1-3$\frac{5}{16}$	1-11$\frac{1}{4}$	1-4$\frac{3}{16}$	2-0$\frac{19}{32}$	1-5$\frac{1}{16}$	2-1$\frac{29}{32}$	1-5$\frac{15}{16}$	2-3$\frac{1}{4}$	1-6$\frac{13}{16}$	2-4$\frac{9}{16}$
$\frac{9}{16}$	1-3$\frac{3}{8}$	1-11$\frac{11}{32}$	1-4$\frac{1}{4}$	2-0$\frac{21}{32}$	1-5$\frac{1}{8}$	2-2	1-6	2-3$\frac{5}{16}$	1-6$\frac{7}{8}$	2-4$\frac{21}{32}$
$\frac{5}{8}$	1-3$\frac{7}{16}$	1-11$\frac{13}{32}$	1-4$\frac{5}{16}$	2-0$\frac{3}{4}$	1-5$\frac{3}{16}$	2-2$\frac{1}{16}$	1-6$\frac{1}{16}$	2-3$\frac{13}{32}$	1-6$\frac{15}{16}$	2-4$\frac{3}{4}$
$\frac{11}{16}$	1-3$\frac{15}{16}$	1-11$\frac{1}{2}$	1-4$\frac{11}{32}$	2-0$\frac{27}{32}$	1-5$\frac{7}{32}$	2-2$\frac{5}{32}$	1-6$\frac{3}{32}$	2-3$\frac{1}{2}$	1-6$\frac{31}{32}$	2-4$\frac{13}{16}$
$\frac{3}{4}$	1-3$\frac{17}{32}$	1-11$\frac{19}{32}$	1-4$\frac{13}{32}$	2-0$\frac{29}{32}$	1-5$\frac{9}{32}$	2-2$\frac{1}{4}$	1-6$\frac{5}{32}$	2-3$\frac{9}{16}$	1-7$\frac{1}{2}$	2-4$\frac{29}{32}$
$\frac{13}{16}$	1-3$\frac{19}{32}$	1-11$\frac{21}{32}$	1-4$\frac{15}{32}$	2-1	1-5$\frac{11}{32}$	2-2$\frac{5}{16}$	1-6$\frac{7}{32}$	2-3$\frac{21}{32}$	1-7$\frac{3}{32}$	2-4$\frac{31}{32}$
$\frac{7}{8}$	1-3$\frac{5}{8}$	1-11$\frac{3}{4}$	1-4$\frac{1}{2}$	2-1$\frac{3}{32}$	1-5$\frac{3}{8}$	2-2$\frac{13}{32}$	1-6$\frac{1}{4}$	2-3$\frac{3}{4}$	1-7$\frac{1}{8}$	2-5$\frac{1}{16}$
$\frac{15}{16}$	1-3$\frac{11}{16}$	1-11$\frac{27}{32}$	1-4$\frac{9}{16}$	2-1$\frac{5}{32}$	1-5$\frac{7}{16}$	2-2$\frac{1}{2}$	1-6$\frac{5}{16}$	2-3$\frac{13}{16}$	1-7$\frac{3}{16}$	2-5$\frac{5}{32}$

Feet	40′ Rise	40′ Slope	50′ Rise	50′ Slope	60′ Rise	60′ Slope	70′ Rise	70′ Slope
0	35-0	53-1$\frac{13}{16}$	43-9	66-5$\frac{1}{4}$	52-6	79-8$\frac{23}{32}$	61-3	93-0$\frac{5}{32}$
1	35-10$\frac{1}{2}$	54-5$\frac{3}{4}$	44-7$\frac{1}{2}$	67-9$\frac{7}{32}$	53-4$\frac{1}{2}$	81-0$\frac{21}{32}$	62-1$\frac{1}{2}$	94-4$\frac{1}{8}$
2	36-9	55-9$\frac{11}{16}$	45-6	69-1$\frac{5}{32}$	54-3	82-4$\frac{19}{32}$	63-0	95-8$\frac{1}{16}$
3	37-7$\frac{1}{2}$	57-1$\frac{21}{32}$	46-4$\frac{1}{2}$	70-5$\frac{3}{32}$	55-1$\frac{1}{2}$	83-8$\frac{9}{16}$	63-10$\frac{1}{2}$	97-0
4	38-6	58-5$\frac{19}{32}$	47-3	71-9$\frac{1}{32}$	56-0	85-0$\frac{1}{2}$	64-9	98-3$\frac{15}{16}$
5	39-4$\frac{1}{2}$	59-9$\frac{17}{32}$	48-1$\frac{1}{2}$	73-1	56-10$\frac{1}{2}$	86-4$\frac{7}{16}$	65-7$\frac{1}{2}$	99-7$\frac{29}{32}$
6	40-3	61-1$\frac{15}{32}$	49-0	74-4$\frac{15}{16}$	57-9	87-8$\frac{3}{8}$	66-6	100-11$\frac{27}{32}$
7	41-1$\frac{1}{2}$	62-5$\frac{7}{16}$	49-10$\frac{1}{2}$	75-8$\frac{7}{8}$	58-7$\frac{1}{2}$	89-0$\frac{11}{32}$	67-4$\frac{1}{2}$	102-3$\frac{25}{32}$
8	42-0	63-9$\frac{3}{8}$	50-9	77-0$\frac{13}{16}$	59-6	90-4$\frac{9}{32}$	68-3	103-7$\frac{23}{32}$
9	42-10$\frac{1}{2}$	65-1$\frac{5}{16}$	51-7$\frac{1}{2}$	78-4$\frac{25}{32}$	60-4$\frac{1}{2}$	91-8$\frac{7}{32}$	69-1$\frac{1}{2}$	104-11$\frac{11}{16}$

natsin A=0.6585046078; natcos A=0.7525766947; nattan A=0.8750000000; natcot A=1.1428571428

Inches	0″ Rise	0″ Slope	1″ Rise	1″ Slope	2″ Rise	2″ Slope	3″ Rise	3″ Slope	4″ Rise	4″ Slope	5″ Rise	5″ Slope
0	0	0	7/8	1 11/32	1 3/4	2 21/32	2 5/8	4	3 17/32	5 11/32	4 13/32	6 21/32
1/16	1/16	3/32	15/16	1 13/32	1 13/16	2 3/4	2 11/16	4 3/32	3 9/16	5 13/32	4 15/32	6 3/4
1/8	1/8	5/32	1	1 1/2	1 7/8	2 27/32	2 3/4	4 5/32	3 5/8	5 1/2	4 1/2	6 13/16
3/16	5/32	1/4	1 1/32	1 19/32	1 15/16	2 29/32	2 13/16	4 1/4	3 11/16	5 19/32	4 9/16	6 29/32
1/4	7/32	11/32	1 3/32	1 21/32	1 31/32	3	2 7/8	4 11/32	3 3/4	5 21/32	4 5/8	7
5/16	9/32	13/32	1 5/32	1 3/4	2 1/32	3 3/32	2 29/32	4 13/32	3 25/32	5 3/4	4 11/16	7 1/16
3/8	11/32	1/2	1 7/32	1 27/32	2 3/32	3 5/32	2 31/32	4 1/2	3 27/32	5 27/32	4 23/32	7 5/32
7/16	3/8	19/32	1 1/4	1 29/32	2 5/32	3 1/4	3 1/32	4 19/32	3 29/32	5 29/32	4 25/32	7 1/4
1/2	7/16	21/32	1 5/16	2	2 3/16	3 11/32	3 3/32	4 21/32	3 31/32	6	4 27/32	7 5/16
9/16	1/2	3/4	1 3/8	2 3/32	2 1/4	3 13/32	3 1/8	4 3/4	4 1/32	6 3/32	4 29/32	7 13/32
5/8	9/16	27/32	1 7/16	2 5/32	2 5/16	3 1/2	3 3/16	4 27/32	4 1/16	6 5/32	4 15/16	7 1/2
11/16	19/32	29/32	1 1/2	2 1/4	2 3/8	3 19/32	3 1/4	4 29/32	4 1/8	6 1/4	5	7 9/16
3/4	21/32	1	1 17/32	2 11/32	2 13/32	3 21/32	3 5/16	5	4 3/16	6 5/16	5 1/16	7 21/32
13/16	23/32	1 3/32	1 19/32	2 13/32	2 15/32	3 3/4	3 11/32	5 3/32	4 1/4	6 13/32	5 1/8	7 3/4
7/8	25/32	1 5/32	1 21/32	2 1/2	2 17/32	3 27/32	3 13/32	5 5/32	4 9/32	6 1/2	5 5/32	7 13/16
15/16	13/16	1 1/4	1 23/32	2 19/32	2 19/32	3 29/32	3 15/32	5 1/4	4 11/32	6 9/16	5 7/32	7 29/32

Inches	6″ Rise	6″ Slope	7″ Rise	7″ Slope	8″ Rise	8″ Slope	9″ Rise	9″ Slope	10″ Rise	10″ Slope	11″ Rise	11″ Slope
0	5 9/32	8	6 5/32	9 5/16	7 1/32	10 21/32	7 15/16	1-0	8 13/16	1-1 5/16	9 11/16	1-2 21/32
1/16	5 11/32	8 1/16	6 7/32	9 13/32	7 3/32	10 3/4	7 31/32	1-0 1/16	8 27/32	1-1 13/32	9 3/4	1-2 3/4
1/8	5 13/32	8 5/32	6 9/32	9 1/2	7 5/32	10 13/16	8 1/32	1-0 5/32	8 29/32	1-1 1/2	9 25/32	1-2 13/16
3/16	5 7/16	8 1/4	6 5/16	9 9/16	7 7/32	10 29/32	8 3/32	1-0 1/4	8 31/32	1-1 9/16	9 27/32	1-2 29/32
1/4	5 1/2	8 5/16	6 3/8	9 21/32	7 1/4	11	8 5/32	1-0 5/16	9 1/32	1-1 21/32	9 29/32	1-3
5/16	5 9/16	8 13/32	6 7/16	9 3/4	7 5/16	11 1/16	8 3/16	1-0 13/32	9 1/16	1-1 3/4	9 31/32	1-3 1/16
3/8	5 5/8	8 1/2	6 1/2	9 13/16	7 3/8	11 5/32	8 1/4	1-0 1/2	9 1/8	1-1 13/16	10	1-3 5/32
7/16	5 21/32	8 9/16	6 17/32	9 29/32	7 7/16	11 1/4	8 5/16	1-0 9/16	9 3/16	1-1 29/32	10 1/16	1-3 1/4
1/2	5 23/32	8 21/32	6 19/32	10	7 15/32	11 5/16	8 3/8	1-0 21/32	9 1/4	1-2	10 1/8	1-3 5/16
9/16	5 25/32	8 3/4	6 21/32	10 1/16	7 17/32	11 13/32	8 13/32	1-0 3/4	9 5/16	1-2 1/16	10 3/16	1-3 13/32
5/8	5 27/32	8 13/16	6 23/32	10 5/32	7 19/32	11 1/2	8 15/32	1-0 13/16	9 11/32	1-2 5/32	10 7/32	1-3 1/2
11/16	5 7/8	8 29/32	6 25/32	10 1/4	7 21/32	11 9/16	8 17/32	1-0 29/32	9 13/32	1-2 1/4	10 9/32	1-3 9/16
3/4	5 15/16	9	6 13/16	10 5/16	7 11/16	11 21/32	8 19/32	1-1	9 15/32	1-2 5/16	10 11/32	1-3 21/32
13/16	6	9 1/16	6 7/8	10 13/32	7 3/4	11 3/4	8 5/8	1-1 1/16	9 17/32	1-2 13/32	10 13/32	1-3 3/4
7/8	6 1/16	9 5/32	6 15/16	10 1/2	7 13/16	11 13/16	8 11/16	1-1 5/32	9 9/16	1-2 1/2	10 7/16	1-3 13/16
15/16	6 3/32	9 1/4	7	10 9/16	7 7/8	11 29/32	8 3/4	1-1 1/4	9 5/8	1-2 9/16	10 1/2	1-3 29/32

Feet	0′ Rise	0′ Slope	10′ Rise	10′ Slope	20′ Rise	20′ Slope	30′ Rise	30′ Slope
0	0	0	8-9 5/8	13-3 7/8	17-7 1/4	26-7 23/32	26-4 7/8	39-11 19/32
1	-10 9/16	1-4	9-8 3/16	14-7 27/32	18-5 13/16	27-11 23/32	27-3 7/16	41-3 19/32
2	1-9 1/8	2-7 31/32	10-6 3/4	15-11 27/32	19-4 3/8	29-3 11/16	28-2	42-7 9/16
3	2-7 11/16	3-11 31/32	11-5 5/16	17-3 13/16	20-2 15/16	30-7 11/16	29-0 9/16	43-11 9/16
4	3-6 1/4	5-3 15/16	12-3 7/8	18-7 13/16	21-1 1/2	31-11 11/16	29-11 1/8	45-3 17/32
5	4-4 13/16	6-7 15/16	13-2 7/16	19-11 25/32	22-0 1/16	33-3 21/32	30-9 11/16	46-7 17/32
6	5-3 3/8	7-11 29/32	14-1	21-3 25/32	22-10 5/8	34-7 21/32	31-8 1/4	47-11 1/2
7	6-1 15/16	9-3 29/32	14-11 9/16	22-7 25/32	23-9 3/16	35-11 5/8	32-6 13/16	49-3 1/2
8	7-0 1/2	10-7 29/32	15-10 1/8	23-11 3/4	24-7 3/4	37-3 5/8	33-5 3/8	50-7 1/2
9	7-11 1/16	11-11 7/8	16-8 11/16	25-3 3/4	25-6 5/16	38-7 19/32	34-3 15/16	51-11 15/16

A = 41° 21′ 16″; logsin A = 9.82001; logcos A = 9.87543; logtan A = 9.94459; logcot A = 0.05541.

Ins.	12″ Rise	Slope	13″ Rise	Slope	14″ Rise	Slope	15″ Rise	Slope	16″ Rise	Slope
0	10 9/16	1-4	11 7/16	1-5 5/16	1-0 5/16	1-6 21/32	1-1 3/32	1-7 31/32	1-2 1/32	1-9 5/16
1/16	10 5/8	1-4 1/16	11 1/2	1-5 13/32	1-0 3/8	1-6 23/32	1-1 1/4	1-8 1/16	1-2 1/8	1-9 13/32
1/8	10 11/16	1-4 5/32	11 9/16	1-5 1/2	1-0 7/16	1-6 13/16	1-1 5/16	1-8 5/32	1-2 3/16	1-9 15/32
3/16	10 23/32	1-4 1/4	11 19/32	1-5 9/16	1-0 1/2	1-6 29/32	1-1 3/8	1-8 7/32	1-2 1/4	1-9 9/16
1/4	10 25/32	1-4 5/16	11 21/32	1-5 21/32	1-0 17/32	1-6 31/32	1-1 7/16	1-8 5/16	1-2 5/16	1-9 21/32
5/16	10 27/32	1-4 13/32	11 23/32	1-5 3/4	1-0 19/32	1-7 1/16	1-1 15/32	1-8 13/32	1-2 11/32	1-9 23/32
3/8	10 29/32	1-4 1/2	11 25/32	1-5 13/16	1-0 21/32	1-7 5/32	1-1 17/32	1-8 15/32	1-2 13/32	1-9 13/16
7/16	10 15/16	1-4 9/16	11 13/16	1-5 29/32	1-0 23/32	1-7 7/32	1-1 19/32	1-8 9/16	1-2 15/32	1-9 29/32
1/2	11	1-4 21/32	11 7/8	1-6	1-0 3/4	1-7 5/16	1-1 21/32	1-8 21/32	1-2 17/32	1-9 31/32
9/16	11 1/16	1-4 3/4	11 15/16	1-6 1/16	1-0 13/16	1-7 13/32	1-1 11/16	1-8 23/32	1-2 19/32	1-10 1/16
5/8	11 1/8	1-4 13/16	1-0	1-6 5/32	1-0 7/8	1-7 15/32	1-1 3/4	1-8 13/16	1-2 5/8	1-10 5/32
11/16	11 5/32	1-4 29/32	1-0 1/16	1-6 1/4	1-0 15/16	1-7 9/16	1-1 13/16	1-8 29/32	1-2 11/16	1-10 7/32
3/4	11 7/32	1-5	1-0 3/32	1-6 5/16	1-0 31/32	1-7 21/32	1-1 7/8	1-8 31/32	1-2 3/4	1-10 5/16
13/16	11 9/32	1-5 1/16	1-0 5/32	1-6 13/32	1-1 1/32	1-7 23/32	1-1 29/32	1-9 1/16	1-2 13/16	1-10 13/32
7/8	11 11/32	1-5 5/32	1-0 7/32	1-6 15/32	1-1 3/32	1-7 13/16	1-1 31/32	1-9 5/32	1-2 27/32	1-10 15/32
15/16	11 3/8	1-5 1/4	1-0 9/32	1-6 9/16	1-1 5/32	1-7 29/32	1-2 1/32	1-9 7/32	1-2 29/32	1-10 9/16

Ins.	17″ Rise	Slope	18″ Rise	Slope	19″ Rise	Slope	20″ Rise	Slope	21″ Rise	Slope
0	1-2 31/32	1-10 21/32	1-3 27/32	1-11 31/32	1-4 23/32	2-1 5/16	1-5 19/32	2-2 21/32	1-6 1/2	2-3 31/32
1/16	1-3 1/32	1-10 23/32	1-3 29/32	2-0 1/16	1-4 25/32	2-1 13/32	1-5 21/32	2-2 23/32	1-6 17/32	2-4 1/16
1/8	1-3 1/16	1-10 13/16	1-3 31/32	2-0 5/32	1-4 27/32	2-1 15/32	1-5 23/32	2-2 13/16	1-6 19/32	2-4 5/32
3/16	1-3 1/8	1-10 29/32	1-4	2-0 7/32	1-4 7/8	2-1 9/16	1-5 25/32	2-2 29/32	1-6 21/32	2-4 7/32
1/4	1-3 3/16	1-10 31/32	1-4 1/16	2-0 5/16	1-4 15/16	2-1 21/32	1-5 13/16	2-2 31/32	1-6 23/32	2-4 5/16
5/16	1-3 1/4	1-11 1/16	1-4 1/8	2-0 13/32	1-5	2-1 23/32	1-5 7/8	2-3 1/16	1-6 3/4	2-4 13/32
3/8	1-3 9/32	1-11 5/32	1-4 3/16	2-0 15/32	1-5 1/16	2-1 13/16	1-5 15/16	2-3 5/32	1-6 13/16	2-4 15/32
7/16	1-3 11/32	1-11 7/32	1-4 7/32	2-0 9/16	1-5 3/32	2-1 29/32	1-6	2-3 7/32	1-6 7/8	2-4 9/16
1/2	1-3 13/32	1-11 5/16	1-4 9/32	2-0 21/32	1-5 5/32	2-1 31/32	1-6 1/32	2-3 5/16	1-6 15/16	2-4 21/32
9/16	1-3 15/32	1-11 13/32	1-4 11/32	2-0 23/32	1-5 7/32	2-2 1/16	1-6 3/32	2-3 13/32	1-6 31/32	2-4 23/32
5/8	1-3 1/2	1-11 15/32	1-4 13/32	2-0 13/16	1-5 9/32	2-2 5/32	1-6 5/32	2-3 15/32	1-7 1/32	2-4 13/16
11/16	1-3 9/16	1-11 9/16	1-4 7/16	2-0 29/32	1-5 11/32	2-2 7/32	1-6 7/32	2-3 9/16	1-7 3/32	2-4 29/32
3/4	1-3 5/8	1-11 21/32	1-4 1/2	2-0 31/32	1-5 3/8	2-2 5/16	1-6 1/4	2-3 21/32	1-7 5/32	2-4 31/32
13/16	1-3 11/16	1-11 23/32	1-4 9/16	2-1 1/16	1-5 7/16	2-2 13/32	1-6 5/16	2-3 23/32	1-7 3/16	2-5 1/16
7/8	1-3 23/32	1-11 13/16	1-4 5/8	2-1 5/32	1-5 1/2	2-2 15/32	1-6 3/8	2-3 13/16	1-7 1/4	2-5 5/32
15/16	1-3 25/32	1-11 29/32	1-4 21/32	2-1 7/32	1-5 9/16	2-2 9/16	1-6 7/16	2-3 29/32	1-7 5/16	2-5 7/32

Feet	40′ Rise	Slope	50′ Rise	Slope	60′ Rise	Slope	70′ Rise	Slope
0	35-2 1/2	53-3 15/32	44-0 1/8	66-7 5/16	52-9 3/4	79-11 3/16	61-7 3/8	93-3 1/16
1	36-1 1/16	54-7 7/16	44-10 11/16	67-11 5/16	53-8 5/16	81-3 3/16	62-5 15/16	94-7 1/32
2	36-11 5/8	55-11 7/16	45-9 1/4	69-3 9/32	54-6 7/8	82-7 5/32	63-4 1/2	95-11 1/32
3	37-10 3/16	57-3 13/32	46-7 13/16	70-7 9/32	55-5 7/16	83-11 5/32	64-3 1/16	97-3
4	38-8 3/4	58-7 13/32	47-6 3/8	71-11 9/32	56-4	85-3 1/8	65-1 5/8	98-7
5	39-7 5/16	59-11 3/8	48-4 15/16	73-3 1/4	57-2 9/16	86-7 1/8	66-0 3/16	99-10 31/32
6	40-5 7/8	61-3 3/8	49-3 1/2	74-7 1/4	58-1 1/8	87-11 3/32	66-10 3/4	101-2 31/32
7	41-4 7/16	62-7 3/8	50-2 1/16	75-11 7/32	58-11 11/16	89-3 3/32	67-9 5/16	102-6 31/32
8	42-3	63-11 11/32	51-0 5/8	77-3 7/32	59-10 1/4	90-7 1/16	68-7 7/8	103-10 15/16
9	43-1 9/16	65-3 11/32	51-11 3/16	78-7 3/16	60-8 13/16	91-11 1/16	69-6 7/16	105-2 15/16

natsin A=0.6607160229; natcos A=0.7506359551; nattan A=0.8802083333; natcot A=1.1360946745

Inches	0" Rise	Slope	1" Rise	Slope	2" Rise	Slope	3" Rise	Slope	4" Rise	Slope	5" Rise	Slope
0	0	0	7/8	1 11/32	1 25/32	2 21/32	2 21/32	4	3 17/32	5 11/32	4 7/16	6 11/16
1/16	1/16	3/32	15/16	1 13/32	1 13/16	2 3/4	2 23/32	4 3/32	3 19/32	5 7/16	4 15/32	6 3/4
1/8	1/8	5/32	1	1 1/2	1 7/8	2 27/32	2 25/32	4 3/16	3 21/32	5 1/2	4 17/32	6 27/32
3/16	5/32	1/4	1 1/16	1 19/32	1 15/16	2 29/32	2 13/16	4 1/4	3 23/32	5 19/32	4 19/32	6 15/16
1/4	7/32	11/32	1 3/32	1 21/32	2	3	2 7/8	4 11/32	3 3/4	5 11/16	4 21/32	7
5/16	9/32	13/32	1 5/32	1 3/4	2 1/16	3 3/32	2 15/16	4 7/16	3 13/16	5 3/4	4 23/32	7 3/32
3/8	11/32	1/2	1 7/32	1 27/32	2 3/32	3 3/16	3	4 1/2	3 7/8	5 27/32	4 3/4	7 3/16
7/16	3/8	19/32	1 9/32	1 29/32	2 5/32	3 1/4	3 1/32	4 19/32	3 15/16	5 15/16	4 13/16	7 1/4
1/2	7/16	21/32	1 5/16	2	2 7/32	3 11/32	3 3/32	4 11/16	4	6	4 7/8	7 11/32
9/16	1/2	3/4	1 3/8	2 3/32	2 9/32	3 7/16	3 5/32	4 3/4	4 1/32	6 3/32	4 15/16	7 7/16
5/8	9/16	27/32	1 7/16	2 5/32	2 5/16	3 1/2	3 7/32	4 27/32	4 3/32	6 3/16	4 31/32	7 1/2
11/16	19/32	29/32	1 1/2	2 1/4	2 3/8	3 19/32	3 1/4	4 15/16	4 5/32	6 1/4	5 1/32	7 19/32
3/4	21/32	1	1 9/16	2 11/32	2 7/16	3 11/16	3 5/16	5	4 7/32	6 11/32	5 3/32	7 11/16
13/16	23/32	1 3/32	1 19/32	2 13/32	2 1/2	3 3/4	3 3/8	5 3/32	4 1/4	6 7/16	5 5/32	7 3/4
7/8	25/32	1 5/32	1 21/32	2 1/2	2 17/32	3 27/32	3 7/16	5 3/16	4 5/16	6 1/2	5 3/16	7 27/32
15/16	27/32	1 1/4	1 23/32	2 19/32	2 19/32	3 15/16	3 1/2	5 1/4	4 3/8	6 19/32	5 1/4	7 15/16

Inches	6" Rise	Slope	7" Rise	Slope	8" Rise	Slope	9" Rise	Slope	10" Rise	Slope	11" Rise	Slope
0	5 5/16	8	6 3/16	9 11/32	7 3/32	10 11/16	7 31/32	1-0 1/32	8 27/32	1-1 11/32	9 3/4	1-2 11/16
1/16	5 3/8	8 3/32	6 1/4	9 7/16	7 1/8	10 25/32	8 1/32	1-0 3/32	8 29/32	1-1 7/16	9 25/32	1-2 25/32
1/8	5 7/16	8 3/16	6 5/16	9 17/32	7 3/16	10 27/32	8 3/32	1-0 3/16	8 31/32	1-1 17/32	9 27/32	1-2 27/32
3/16	5 15/32	8 1/4	6 3/8	9 19/32	7 1/4	10 15/16	8 1/8	1-0 9/32	9 1/32	1-1 19/32	9 29/32	1-2 15/16
1/4	5 17/32	8 11/32	6 13/32	9 11/16	7 5/16	11 1/32	8 3/16	1-0 11/32	9 1/16	1-1 11/16	9 31/32	1-3 1/32
5/16	5 19/32	8 7/16	6 15/32	9 25/32	7 3/8	11 3/32	8 1/4	1-0 7/16	9 1/8	1-1 25/32	10 1/32	1-3 1/8
3/8	5 21/32	8 1/2	6 17/32	9 27/32	7 13/32	11 3/16	8 5/16	1-0 17/32	9 3/16	1-1 27/32	10 1/16	1-3 3/16
7/16	5 11/16	8 19/32	6 19/32	9 15/16	7 15/32	11 9/32	8 11/32	1-0 15/32	9 1/4	1-1 15/16	10 1/8	1-3 9/32
1/2	5 3/4	8 11/16	6 5/8	10 1/32	7 17/32	11 11/32	8 13/32	1-0 11/16	9 5/16	1-2 1/32	10 3/16	1-3 3/8
9/16	5 13/16	8 3/4	6 11/16	10 3/32	7 19/32	11 7/16	8 15/32	1-0 25/32	9 11/32	1-2 3/32	10 1/4	1-3 7/16
5/8	5 7/8	8 27/32	6 3/4	10 3/16	7 5/8	11 17/32	8 17/32	1-0 27/32	9 13/32	1-2 3/16	10 9/32	1-3 17/32
11/16	5 29/32	8 15/16	6 13/16	10 9/32	7 11/16	11 19/32	8 9/16	1-0 15/16	9 15/32	1-2 9/32	10 11/32	1-3 5/8
3/4	5 31/32	9 1/32	6 7/8	10 11/32	7 3/4	11 11/16	8 5/8	1-1 1/32	9 17/32	1-2 11/32	10 13/32	1-3 11/16
13/16	6 1/32	9 3/32	6 29/32	10 7/16	7 13/16	11 25/32	8 11/16	1-1 3/32	9 9/16	1-2 7/16	10 15/32	1-3 25/32
7/8	6 3/32	9 3/16	6 31/32	10 17/32	7 27/32	11 27/32	8 3/4	1-1 3/16	9 5/8	1-2 17/32	10 1/2	1-3 7/8
15/16	6 5/32	9 9/32	7 1/32	10 19/32	7 29/32	11 15/16	8 13/16	1-1 9/32	9 11/16	1-2 19/32	10 9/16	1-3 15/16

Feet	0' Rise	Slope	10' Rise	Slope	20' Rise	Slope	30' Rise	Slope
0	0	0	8-10 1/4	13-4 9/32	17-8 1/2	26-8 9/16	26-6 3/4	40-0 27/32
1	-10 5/8	1-4 1/32	9-8 7/8	14-8 5/16	18-7 1/8	28-0 19/32	27-5 5/8	41-4 7/8
2	1-9 1/4	2-8 1/16	10-7 1/2	16-0 11/32	19-5 3/4	29-4 5/8	28-4	42-8 7/8
3	2-7 7/8	4-0 3/32	11-6 1/8	17-4 3/8	20-4 3/8	30-8 5/8	29-2 5/8	44-0 29/32
4	3-6 1/2	5-4 1/8	12-4 3/4	18-8 3/8	21-3	32-0 21/32	30-1 1/4	45-4 15/16
5	4-5 1/8	6-8 1/8	13-3 3/8	20-0 13/32	22-1 5/8	33-4 11/16	30-11 7/8	46-8 31/32
6	5-3 3/4	8-0 5/32	14-2	21-4 7/16	23-0 1/4	34-8 23/32	31-10 1/2	48-1
7	6-2 3/8	9-4 3/16	15-0 5/8	22-8 15/32	23-10 7/8	36-0 3/4	32-9 1/8	49-5 1/32
8	7-1	10-8 7/32	15-11 1/4	24-0 1/2	24-9 1/2	37-4 25/32	33-7 3/4	50-9 1/16
9	7-11 5/8	12-0 1/4	16-9 7/8	25-4 17/32	25-8 1/8	38-8 13/16	34-6 3/8	52-1 3/32

A = 41° 31′ 20″; logsin A = 9.82145; logcos A = 9.87431; logtan A = 9.94715; logcot A = 0.05285

Ins.	12" Rise	12" Slope	13" Rise	13" Slope	14" Rise	14" Slope	15" Rise	15" Slope	16" Rise	16" Slope
0	10 5/8	1-4 1/32–	11 1/2	1-5 3/8	1-0 13/32–	1-6 11/16	1-1 9/32	1-8 1/32	1-2 5/32	1-9 3/8
1/16	10 11/16	1-4 1/8	11 9/16	1-5 7/16	1-0 7/16	1-6 25/32	1-1 11/32–	1-8 1/8	1-2 7/32	1-9 15/32–
1/8	10 3/4	1-4 3/16	11 5/8	1-5 17/32–	1-0 1/2	1-6 7/8	1-1 13/32–	1-8 3/16	1-2 9/32–	1-9 17/32
3/16	10 25/32	1-4 9/32–	11 11/16	1-5 5/8	1-0 9/16	1-6 15/16	1-1 7/16	1-8 9/32	1-2 11/32–	1-9 5/8
1/4	10 27/32	1-4 3/8	11 23/32	1-5 11/16	1-0 5/8	1-7 1/32	1-1 1/2	1-8 3/8	1-2 3/8	1-9 23/32–
5/16	10 29/32–	1-4 7/16	11 25/32	1-5 25/32–	1-0 11/16	1-7 1/8	1-1 9/16	1-8 7/16	1-2 7/16	1-9 25/32
3/8	10 31/32–	1-4 17/32–	11 27/32–	1-5 7/8	1-0 23/32	1-7 3/16	1-1 5/8	1-8 17/32	1-2 1/2	1-9 7/8
7/16	11	1-4 5/8	11 29/32–	1-5 15/16	1-0 25/32	1-7 9/32	1-1 21/32	1-8 5/8	1-2 9/16	1-9 31/32–
1/2	11 1/16	1-4 11/16	11 15/16	1-6 1/32	1-0 27/32–	1-7 3/8	1-1 23/32	1-8 11/16	1-2 5/8	1-10 1/32
9/16	11 1/8	1-4 25/32–	1-0	1-6 1/8	1-0 29/32–	1-7 7/16	1-1 25/32–	1-8 25/32	1-2 21/32	1-10 1/8
5/8	11 3/16	1-4 7/8	1-0 1/16	1-6 3/16	1-0 15/16	1-7 17/32	1-1 27/32–	1-8 7/8	1-2 23/32	1-10 7/32–
11/16	11 7/32	1-4 15/16	1-0 1/8	1-6 9/32	1-1	1-7 5/8	1-1 7/8	1-8 15/16	1-2 25/32–	1-10 9/32
3/4	11 9/32	1-5 1/32–	1-0 3/16	1-6 3/8	1-1 1/16	1-7 11/16	1-1 15/16	1-9 1/32	1-2 27/32–	1-10 3/8
13/16	11 11/32	1-5 1/8	1-0 7/32	1-6 7/16	1-1 1/8	1-7 25/32	1-2	1-9 1/8	1-2 7/8	1-10 15/32–
7/8	11 13/32–	1-5 3/16	1-0 9/32	1-6 17/32	1-1 5/32	1-7 7/8	1-2 1/16	1-9 7/32–	1-2 15/16	1-10 17/32
15/16	11 15/32–	1-5 9/32–	1-0 11/32–	1-6 5/8	1-1 7/32	1-7 15/16	1-2 1/8	1-9 9/32	1-3	1-10 5/8

Ins.	17" Rise	17" Slope	18" Rise	18" Slope	19" Rise	19" Slope	20" Rise	20" Slope	21" Rise	21" Slope
0	1-3 1/16	1-10 23/32–	1-3 15/16	2-0 1/32	1-4 13/16	2-1 3/8	1-5 23/32–	2-2 23/32–	1-6 19/32	2-4 1/16
1/16	1-3 3/32	1-10 25/32	1-4	2-0 1/8	1-4 7/8	2-1 15/32–	1-5 3/4	2-2 25/32	1-6 21/32–	2-4 1/8
1/8	1-3 5/32	1-10 7/8	1-4 1/16	2-0 7/32–	1-4 15/16	2-1 17/32	1-5 13/16	2-2 7/8	1-6 23/32–	2-4 7/32–
3/16	1-3 7/32–	1-10 31/32–	1-4 3/32	2-0 9/32	1-5	2-1 5/8	1-5 7/8	2-2 31/32–	1-6 3/4	2-4 5/16
1/4	1-3 9/32–	1-11 1/32	1-4 5/32	2-0 3/8	1-5 1/32	2-1 23/32–	1-5 15/16	2-3 1/16	1-6 13/16	2-4 3/8
5/16	1-3 11/32–	1-11 1/8	1-4 7/32–	2-0 15/32–	1-5 3/32	2-1 25/32	1-6	2-3 1/8	1-6 7/8	2-4 15/32–
3/8	1-3 3/8	1-11 7/32–	1-4 9/32–	2-0 17/32	1-5 5/32–	2-1 7/8	1-6 1/32	2-3 7/32–	1-6 15/16	2-4 9/16
7/16	1-3 7/16	1-11 9/32	1-4 5/16	2-0 5/8	1-5 7/32–	2-1 31/32–	1-6 3/32	2-3 5/16	1-6 31/32	2-4 5/8
1/2	1-3 1/2	1-11 3/8	1-4 3/8	2-0 23/32–	1-5 1/4	2-2 1/32	1-6 5/32–	2-3 3/8	1-7 1/32	2-4 23/32–
9/16	1-3 9/16	1-11 15/32–	1-4 7/16	2-0 25/32	1-5 5/16	2-2 1/8	1-6 7/32–	2-3 15/32–	1-7 3/32–	2-4 13/16
5/8	1-3 19/32	1-11 17/32	1-4 1/2	2-0 7/8	1-5 3/8	2-2 7/32–	1-6 1/4	2-3 9/16	1-7 5/32–	2-4 7/8
11/16	1-3 21/32	1-11 5/8	1-4 17/32	2-0 31/32–	1-5 7/16	2-2 9/32	1-6 5/16	2-3 5/8	1-7 3/16	2-4 31/32–
3/4	1-3 23/32–	1-11 23/32–	1-4 19/32	2-1 1/32	1-5 1/2	2-2 3/8	1-6 3/8	2-3 23/32–	1-7 1/4	2-5 1/16
13/16	1-3 25/32–	1-11 25/32	1-4 21/32	2-1 1/8	1-5 17/32	2-2 15/32–	1-6 7/16	2-3 13/16	1-7 5/16	2-5 1/8
7/8	1-3 13/16	1-11 7/8	1-4 23/32–	2-1 7/32–	1-5 19/32	2-2 17/32	1-6 15/32	2-3 7/8	1-7 3/8	2-5 7/32–
15/16	1-3 7/8	1-11 31/32–	1-4 25/32–	2-1 9/32	1-5 21/32–	2-2 5/8	1-6 17/32	2-3 31/32–	1-7 7/16	2-5 5/16

Feet	40' Rise	40' Slope	50' Rise	50' Slope	60' Rise	60' Slope	70' Rise	70' Slope
0	35-5	53-5 1/8	44-3 1/4	66-9 3/8	53-1 1/2	80-1 21/32	61-11 3/4	93-5 15/16
1	36-3 5/8	54-9 1/8	45-1 7/8	68-1 13/32	54-0 1/8	81-5 11/16	62-10 3/8	94-9 31/32
2	37-2 1/4	56-1 5/32	46-0 1/2	69-5 7/16	54-10 3/4	82-9 23/32	63-9	96-2
3	38-0 7/8	57-5 3/16	46-11 1/8	70-9 15/32	55-9 3/8	84-1 3/4	64-7 5/8	97-6 1/32–
4	38-11 1/2	58-9 7/32	47-9 3/4	72-1 1/2	56-8	85-5 25/32–	65-6 1/4	98-10 1/16
5	39-10 1/8	60-1 1/4	48-8 3/8	73-5 17/32–	57-6 5/8	86-9 13/16	66-4 7/8	100-2 3/32–
6	40-8 3/4	61-5 9/32–	49-7	74-9 9/16	58-5 1/4	88-1 27/32–	67-3 1/2	101-6 1/8
7	41-7 3/8	62-9 5/16	50-5 5/8	76-1 19/32–	59-3 7/8	89-5 7/8	68-2 1/8	102-10 5/32–
8	42-6	64-1 11/32–	51-4 1/4	77-5 5/8	60-2 1/2	90-9 29/32–	69-0 3/4	104-2 5/32
9	43-4 5/8	65-5 3/8	52-2 7/8	78-9 21/32–	61-1 1/8	92-1 29/32	69-11 3/8	105-6 3/16

natsin A = 0.6629103673; natcos A = 0.7486987678; nattan A = 0.8854166666; natcot A = 1.1294117647

Inches	0" Rise	0" Slope	1" Rise	1" Slope	2" Rise	2" Slope	3" Rise	3" Slope	4" Rise	4" Slope	5" Rise	5" Slope
0	0	0	7/8	1 11/32	1 25/32	2 11/16	2 11/16	4 1/32	3 9/16	5 11/32	4 7/16	6 11/16
1/16	1/16	3/32	15/16	1 7/16	1 27/32	2 3/4	2 23/32	4 3/32	3 5/8	5 7/16	4 1/2	6 25/32
1/8	1/8	5/32	1	1 1/2	1 29/32	2 27/32	2 25/32	4 3/16	3 11/16	5 17/32	4 9/16	6 7/8
3/16	5/32	1/4	1 1/16	1 19/32	1 15/16	2 15/16	2 27/32	4 9/32	3 23/32	5 19/32	4 5/8	6 15/16
1/4	7/32	11/32	1 1/8	1 11/16	2	3	2 29/32	4 11/32	3 25/32	5 11/16	4 11/16	7 1/32
5/16	9/32	13/32	1 5/32	1 3/4	2 1/16	3 3/32	2 15/16	4 7/16	3 27/32	5 25/32	4 23/32	7 1/8
3/8	11/32	1/2	1 7/32	1 27/32	2 1/8	3 3/16	3	4 17/32	3 29/32	5 27/32	4 25/32	7 3/16
7/16	3/8	19/32	1 9/32	1 15/16	2 5/32	3 1/4	3 1/16	4 19/32	3 15/16	5 15/16	4 27/32	7 9/32
1/2	7/16	21/32	1 11/32	2	2 7/32	3 11/32	3 1/8	4 11/16	4	6 1/32	4 29/32	7 3/8
9/16	1/2	3/4	1 13/32	2 3/32	2 9/32	3 7/16	3 3/16	4 25/32	4 1/16	6 1/8	4 31/32	7 7/16
5/8	9/16	27/32	1 7/16	2 3/16	2 11/32	3 1/2	3 7/32	4 27/32	4 1/8	6 3/16	5	7 17/32
11/16	5/8	29/32	1 1/2	2 1/4	2 13/32	3 19/32	3 9/32	4 15/16	4 3/16	6 9/32	5 1/16	7 5/8
3/4	21/32	1	1 9/16	2 11/32	2 7/16	3 11/16	3 11/32	5 1/32	4 7/32	6 3/8	5 1/8	7 11/16
13/16	23/32	1 3/32	1 5/8	2 7/16	2 1/2	3 25/32	3 13/32	5 3/32	4 9/32	6 7/16	5 3/16	7 25/32
7/8	25/32	1 5/32	1 21/32	2 1/2	2 9/16	3 27/32	3 7/16	5 3/16	4 11/32	6 17/32	5 7/32	7 7/8
15/16	27/32	1 1/4	1 23/32	2 19/32	2 5/8	3 15/16	3 1/2	5 9/32	4 13/32	6 5/8	5 9/32	7 15/16

Inches	6" Rise	6" Slope	7" Rise	7" Slope	8" Rise	8" Slope	9" Rise	9" Slope	10" Rise	10" Slope	11" Rise	11" Slope
0	5 11/32	8 1/32	6 1/4	9 3/8	7 1/8	10 23/32	8	1-0 1/16	8 29/32	1-1 13/32	9 13/16	1-2 23/32
1/16	5 13/32	8 1/8	6 9/32	9 15/32	7 3/16	10 25/32	8 1/16	1-0 1/8	8 31/32	1-1 15/32	9 27/32	1-2 13/16
1/8	5 15/32	8 3/16	6 11/32	9 17/32	7 1/4	10 7/8	8 1/8	1-0 1/8	9 1/32	1-1 9/16	9 29/32	1-2 29/32
3/16	5 1/2	8 9/32	6 13/32	9 5/8	7 9/32	10 31/32	8 3/16	1-0 5/16	9 1/16	1-1 21/32	9 31/32	1-2 31/32
1/4	5 9/16	8 3/8	6 15/32	9 23/32	7 11/32	11 1/16	8 1/4	1-0 3/8	9 1/8	1-1 23/32	10 1/32	1-3 1/16
5/16	5 5/8	8 15/32	6 1/2	9 25/32	7 13/32	11 1/8	8 9/32	1-0 15/32	9 3/16	1-1 13/16	10 1/16	1-3 5/32
3/8	5 11/32	8 17/32	6 9/16	9 7/8	7 15/32	11 7/32	8 11/32	1-0 9/16	9 1/4	1-1 29/32	10 1/8	1-3 7/32
7/16	5 23/32	8 5/8	6 5/8	9 31/32	7 1/2	11 5/16	8 13/32	1-0 5/8	9 9/32	1-1 31/32	10 3/16	1-3 5/16
1/2	5 25/32	8 23/32	6 11/16	10 1/32	7 9/16	11 3/8	8 15/32	1-0 23/32	9 11/32	1-2 1/16	10 1/4	1-3 13/32
9/16	5 27/32	8 25/32	6 3/4	10 1/8	7 5/8	11 15/32	8 17/32	1-0 13/16	9 13/32	1-2 5/32	10 5/16	1-3 15/32
5/8	5 29/32	8 7/8	6 25/32	10 7/32	7 11/16	11 9/16	8 9/16	1-0 7/8	9 15/32	1-2 7/32	10 11/32	1-3 9/16
11/16	5 31/32	8 31/32	6 27/32	10 9/32	7 3/4	11 5/8	8 5/8	1-0 31/32	9 17/32	1-2 5/16	10 13/32	1-3 21/32
3/4	6	9 1/32	6 29/32	10 3/8	7 25/32	11 23/32	8 11/16	1-1 1/16	9 9/16	1-2 13/32	10 15/32	1-3 3/4
13/16	6 1/16	9 1/8	6 31/32	10 15/32	7 27/32	11 13/16	8 3/4	1-1 1/8	9 5/8	1-2 15/32	10 17/32	1-3 13/16
7/8	6 1/8	9 7/32	7	10 17/32	7 29/32	11 7/8	8 25/32	1-1 7/32	9 11/16	1-2 9/16	10 9/16	1-3 29/32
15/16	6 3/16	9 9/32	7 1/16	10 5/8	7 31/32	11 31/32	8 27/32	1-1 5/16	9 3/4	1-2 21/32	10 5/8	1-4

Feet	0' Rise	0' Slope	10' Rise	10' Slope	20' Rise	20' Slope	30' Rise	30' Slope
0	0	0	8-10 7/8	13-4 11/16	17-9 3/4	26-9 3/8	26-8 5/8	40-2 3/32
1	-10 11/16	1-4 1/16	9-9 9/16	14-8 3/4	18-8 7/16	28-1 15/32	27-7 5/16	41-6 5/32
2	1-9 3/8	2-8 1/8	10-8 1/4	16-0 27/32	19-7 1/8	29-5 17/32	28-6	42-10 7/32
3	2-8 1/16	4-0 7/32	11-6 15/16	17-4 29/32	20-5 13/16	30-9 19/32	29-4 11/16	44-2 9/32
4	3-6 3/4	5-4 9/32	12-5 5/8	18-8 31/32	21-4 1/2	32-1 21/32	30-3 3/8	45-6 11/32
5	4-5 7/16	6-8 11/32	13-4 5/16	20-1 1/32	22-3 3/16	33-5 23/32	31-2 1/16	46-10 7/16
6	5-4 1/8	8-0 13/32	14-3	21-5 3/32	23-1 7/8	34-9 13/16	32-0 3/4	48-2 1/2
7	6-2 13/16	9-4 1/2	15-1 11/16	22-9 3/16	24-0 9/16	36-1 7/8	32-11 7/16	49-6 9/16
8	7-1 1/2	10-8 9/16	16-0 3/8	24-1 1/4	24-11 1/4	37-5 15/16	33-10 1/8	50-10 5/8
9	8-0 3/16	12-0 5/8	16-11 1/16	25-5 5/16	25-9 15/16	38-10	34-8 13/16	52-2 11/16

A = 41° 41' 21''; logsin A = 9.82288; logcos A = 9.87318; logtan A = 9.94969; logcot A = 0.05031

Ins.	12″ Rise	12″ Slope	13″ Rise	13″ Slope	14″ Rise	14″ Slope	15″ Rise	15″ Slope	16″ Rise	16″ Slope
0	10 11/16	1-4 1/16	11 9/16	1-5 13/32	1-0 15/32	1-6 3/4	1-1 3/8	1-8 3/32–	1-2 1/4	1-9 7/16
1/16	10 3/4	1-4 5/32–	11 5/8	1-5 1/2	1-0 17/32–	1-6 27/32–	1-1 13/32	1-8 5/32	1-2 5/16	1-9 1/2
1/8	10 13/16	1-4 1/4	11 11/16	1-5 9/16	1-0 19/32–	1-6 29/32	1-1 15/32	1-8 1/4	1-2 3/8	1-9 19/32–
3/16	10 27/32	1-4 5/16	11 3/4	1-5 21/32	1-0 5/8	1-7	1-1 17/32–	1-8 11/32–	1-2 13/32	1-9 11/16
1/4	10 29/32	1-4 13/32–	11 13/16	1-5 3/4	1-0 11/16	1-7 3/32–	1-1 19/32–	1-8 13/32	1-2 15/32	1-9 3/4
5/16	10 31/32–	1-4 1/2	11 27/32	1-5 13/16	1-0 3/4	1-7 5/32	1-1 5/8	1-8 1/2	1-2 17/32–	1-9 27/32
3/8	11 1/32–	1-4 9/16	11 29/32	1-5 29/32	1-0 13/16	1-7 1/4	1-1 11/16	1-8 19/32–	1-2 19/32–	1-9 15/16
7/16	11 1/16	1-4 21/32–	11 31/32–	1-6	1-0 27/32	1-7 11/32–	1-1 3/4	1-8 11/16	1-2 5/8	1-10
1/2	11 1/8	1-4 3/4	1-0 1/32–	1-6 1/16	1-0 29/32	1-7 13/32	1-1 13/16	1-8 3/4	1-2 11/16	1-10 3/32
9/16	11 3/16	1-4 13/16	1-0 3/32–	1-6 5/32	1-0 31/32	1-7 1/2	1-1 7/8	1-8 27/32–	1-2 3/4	1-10 3/16
5/8	11 1/4	1-4 29/32	1-0 1/8	1-6 1/4	1-1 1/32–	1-7 19/32–	1-1 29/32	1-8 15/16	1-2 13/16	1-10 1/4
11/16	11 5/16	1-5	1-0 3/16	1-6 11/32–	1-1 3/32–	1-7 21/32	1-1 31/32	1-9	1-2 7/8	1-10 11/32
3/4	11 11/32	1-5 1/16	1-0 1/4	1-6 13/32	1-1 1/8	1-7 3/4	1-2 1/32–	1-9 3/32–	1-2 29/32	1-10 7/16
13/16	11 13/32	1-5 5/32	1-0 5/16	1-6 1/2	1-1 3/16	1-7 27/32–	1-2 3/32–	1-9 3/16	1-2 31/32	1-10 1/2
7/8	11 15/32–	1-5 1/4	1-0 11/32	1-6 19/32–	1-1 1/4	1-7 29/32	1-2 1/8	1-9 1/4	1-3 1/32–	1-10 19/32
15/16	11 17/32–	1-5 5/16	1-0 13/32	1-6 21/32	1-1 5/16	1-8	1-2 3/16	1-9 11/32–	1-3 3/32–	1-10 11/16

Ins.	17″ Rise	17″ Slope	18″ Rise	18″ Slope	19″ Rise	19″ Slope	20″ Rise	20″ Slope	21″ Rise	21″ Slope
0	1-3 1/8	1-10 3/4	1-4 1/32	2-0 3/32	1-4 15/16	2-1 7/16	1-5 13/16	2-2 25/32	1-6 11/16	2-4 1/8
1/16	1-3 3/16	1-10 27/32	1-4 3/32–	2-0 3/16	1-4 31/32	2-1 17/32–	1-5 7/8	2-2 7/8	1-6 3/4	2-4 7/32–
1/8	1-3 1/4	1-10 15/16	1-4 5/32–	2-0 9/32–	1-5 1/32	2-1 5/8	1-5 15/16	2-2 15/16	1-6 13/16	2-4 9/32
3/16	1-3 5/16	1-11 1/32–	1-4 3/16	2-0 11/32	1-5 3/32–	2-1 11/16	1-5 31/32	2-3 1/32	1-6 7/8	2-4 3/8
1/4	1-3 3/8	1-11 3/32	1-4 1/4	2-0 7/16	1-5 5/32–	2-1 25/32–	1-6 1/32	2-3 1/8	1-6 15/16	2-4 15/32–
5/16	1-3 13/32	1-11 3/16	1-4 5/16	2-0 17/32–	1-5 3/16	2-1 7/8	1-6 3/32–	2-3 3/16	1-6 31/32	2-4 17/32
3/8	1-3 15/32	1-11 9/32–	1-4 3/8	2-0 19/32	1-5 1/4	2-1 15/16	1-6 5/32–	2-3 9/32	1-7 1/32	2-4 5/8
7/16	1-3 17/32–	1-11 11/32	1-4 13/32	2-0 11/16	1-5 5/16	2-2 1/32–	1-6 3/16	2-3 3/8	1-7 3/32–	2-4 23/32–
1/2	1-3 19/32–	1-11 7/16	1-4 15/32	2-0 25/32–	1-5 3/8	2-2 1/8	1-6 1/4	2-3 7/16	1-7 5/32–	2-4 25/32
9/16	1-3 21/32–	1-11 17/32–	1-4 17/32	2-0 27/32	1-5 7/16	2-2 3/16	1-6 5/16	2-3 17/32	1-7 7/32–	2-4 7/8
5/8	1-3 11/16	1-11 19/32	1-4 19/32–	2-0 15/16	1-5 15/32	2-2 9/32–	1-6 3/8	2-3 5/8	1-7 1/4	2-4 31/32–
11/16	1-3 3/4	1-11 11/16	1-4 21/32–	2-1 1/32–	1-5 17/32	2-2 3/8	1-6 7/16	2-3 11/16	1-7 5/16	2-5 1/32
3/4	1-3 13/16	1-11 25/32–	1-4 11/16	2-1 3/32	1-5 19/32–	2-2 7/16	1-6 15/32	2-3 25/32	1-7 3/8	2-5 1/8
13/16	1-3 7/8	1-11 27/32	1-4 3/4	2-1 3/16	1-5 21/32–	2-2 17/32–	1-6 17/32	2-3 7/8	1-7 7/16	2-5 7/32–
7/8	1-3 29/32	1-11 15/16	1-4 13/16	2-1 9/32–	1-5 11/16	2-2 5/8	1-6 19/32–	2-3 31/32–	1-7 15/32	2-5 9/32
15/16	1-3 31/32	2-0 1/32–	1-4 7/8	2-1 3/8	1-5 3/4	2-2 11/16	1-6 21/32–	2-4 1/32	1-7 17/32	2-5 3/8

Feet	40′ Rise	40′ Slope	50′ Rise	50′ Slope	60′ Rise	60′ Slope	70′ Rise	70′ Slope
0	35-7 1/2	53-6 25/32–	44-6 3/8	66-11 15/32–	53-5 1/4	80-4 5/32	62-4 1/8	93-8 27/32
1	36-6 3/16	54-10 27/32–	45-5 1/16	68-3 17/32	54-3 15/16	81-8 7/32	63-2 13/16	95-0 29/32
2	37-4 7/8	56-2 29/32	46-3 3/4	69-7 19/32	55-2 5/8	83-0 5/16	64-1 1/2	96-5
3	38-3 9/16	57-6 31/32	47-2 7/16	70-11 11/16	56-1 5/16	84-4 3/8	65-0 3/16	97-9 1/16
4	39-2 1/4	58-11 1/16	48-1 1/8	72-3 3/4	57-0	85-8 7/16	65-10 7/8	99-1 1/8
5	40-0 15/16	60-3 1/8	48-11 13/16	73-7 13/16	57-10 11/16	87-0 1/2	66-9 9/16	100-5 3/16
6	40-11 5/8	61-7 3/16	49-10 1/2	74-11 7/8	58-9 3/8	88-4 9/16	67-8 1/4	101-9 9/32–
7	41-10 5/16	62-11 1/4	50-9 3/16	76-3 15/16	59-8 1/16	89-8 21/32–	68-6 15/16	103-1 11/32–
8	42-9	64-3 5/16	51-7 7/8	77-8 1/32–	60-6 3/4	91-0 23/32–	69-5 5/8	104-5 13/32–
9	43-7 11/16	65-7 13/32–	52-6 9/16	79-0 3/32–	61-5 7/16	92-4 25/32	70-4 5/16	105-9 15/32

natsin A=0.6650877603; natcos A=0.7467652046; nattan A=0.8906250000; natcot A=1.1228070175

Inches	0" Rise	0" Slope	1" Rise	1" Slope	2" Rise	2" Slope	3" Rise	3" Slope	4" Rise	4" Slope	5" Rise	5" Slope
0	0	0	29/32	1 11/32	1 25/32	2 11/16	2 11/16	4 1/32	3 19/32	5 3/8	4 15/32	6 23/32
1/16	1/16	3/32	15/16	1 7/16	1 27/32	2 25/32	2 3/4	4 1/8	3 5/8	5 15/32	4 17/32	6 25/32
1/8	1/8	5/32	1	1 1/2	1 29/32	2 27/32	2 13/16	4 3/16	3 11/16	5 17/32	4 19/32	6 7/8
3/16	5/32	1/4	1 1/16	1 19/32	1 31/32	2 15/16	2 27/32	4 9/32	3 3/4	5 5/8	4 21/32	6 31/32
1/4	7/32	11/32	1 1/8	1 11/16	2	3 1/32	2 29/32	4 3/8	3 13/16	5 23/32	4 11/16	7 1/16
5/16	9/32	13/32	1 3/16	1 3/4	2 1/16	3 3/32	2 31/32	4 7/16	3 7/8	5 25/32	4 3/4	7 1/8
3/8	11/32	1/2	1 7/32	1 27/32	2 1/8	3 3/16	3 1/32	4 17/32	3 29/32	5 7/8	4 13/16	7 7/32
7/16	13/32	19/32	1 9/32	1 15/16	2 3/16	3 9/32	3 3/32	4 5/8	3 31/32	5 31/32	4 7/8	7 5/16
1/2	7/16	21/32	1 11/32	2	2 1/4	3 11/32	3 1/8	4 11/16	4 1/32	6 1/2	4 15/16	7 3/8
9/16	1/2	3/4	1 13/32	2 3/32	2 9/32	3 7/16	3 3/16	4 25/32	4 3/32	6 1/8	4 31/32	7 15/32
5/8	9/16	27/32	1 15/32	2 3/16	2 11/32	3 17/32	3 1/4	4 7/8	4 5/32	6 7/32	5 1/32	7 9/16
11/16	5/8	15/16	1 1/2	2 1/4	2 13/32	3 19/32	3 5/16	4 15/16	4 3/16	6 9/32	5 3/32	7 5/8
3/4	11/16	1	1 9/16	2 11/32	2 15/32	3 11/16	3 3/8	5 1/32	4 1/4	6 3/8	5 5/32	7 23/32
13/16	23/32	1 3/32	1 5/8	2 7/16	2 17/32	3 25/32	3 13/32	5 1/8	4 5/16	6 15/32	5 7/32	7 13/16
7/8	25/32	1 3/16	1 11/16	2 17/32	2 9/16	3 7/8	3 15/32	5 3/16	4 3/8	6 17/32	5 1/4	7 7/8
15/16	27/32	1 1/4	1 3/4	2 19/32	2 5/8	3 15/16	3 17/32	5 9/32	4 7/16	6 5/8	5 5/16	7 31/32

Inches	6" Rise	6" Slope	7" Rise	7" Slope	8" Rise	8" Slope	9" Rise	9" Slope	10" Rise	10" Slope	11" Rise	11" Slope
0	5 3/8	8 1/16	6 9/32	9 13/32	7 5/32	10 3/4	8 1/16	1-0 5/32	8 31/32	1-1 7/16	9 27/32	1-2 25/32
1/16	5 7/16	8 1/8	6 5/16	9 15/32	7 7/32	10 13/16	8 1/8	1-0 5/32	9	1-1 1/2	9 29/32	1-2 27/32
1/8	5 1/2	8 7/32	6 3/8	9 9/16	7 9/32	10 29/32	8 3/16	1-0 1/4	9 1/16	1-1 19/32	9 31/32	1-2 15/16
3/16	5 17/32	8 5/16	6 7/16	9 21/32	7 11/32	11	8 7/32	1-0 11/32	9 1/8	1-1 11/16	10 1/32	1-3 1/32
1/4	5 19/32	8 13/32	6 1/2	9 23/32	7 3/8	11 1/16	8 9/32	1-0 13/32	9 3/16	1-1 3/4	10 1/16	1-3 3/32
5/16	5 21/32	8 15/32	6 9/16	9 13/16	7 7/16	11 5/32	8 11/32	1-0 1/2	9 1/4	1-1 27/32	10 1/8	1-3 3/16
3/8	5 23/32	8 9/16	6 19/32	9 29/32	7 1/2	11 1/4	8 13/32	1-0 19/32	9 9/32	1-1 15/16	10 3/16	1-3 9/32
7/16	5 25/32	8 21/32	6 21/32	10	7 9/16	11 5/16	8 15/32	1-0 21/32	9 11/32	1-2	10 1/4	1-3 11/32
1/2	5 13/16	8 23/32	6 23/32	10 1/16	7 5/8	11 13/32	8 1/2	1-0 3/4	9 13/32	1-2 3/32	10 5/16	1-3 7/16
9/16	5 7/8	8 13/16	6 25/32	10 5/32	7 21/32	11 1/2	8 9/16	1-0 27/32	9 15/32	1-2 3/16	10 11/32	1-3 17/32
5/8	5 15/16	8 29/32	6 27/32	10 1/4	7 23/32	11 19/32	8 5/8	1-0 15/16	9 17/32	1-2 1/4	10 13/32	1-3 19/32
11/16	6	8 31/32	6 7/8	10 5/16	7 25/32	11 21/32	8 11/16	1-1	9 9/16	1-2 11/32	10 15/32	1-3 11/16
3/4	6 1/16	9 1/16	6 15/16	10 13/32	7 27/32	11 3/4	8 3/4	1-1 3/32	9 5/8	1-2 7/16	10 17/32	1-3 25/32
13/16	6 3/32	9 5/32	7	10 1/2	7 29/32	11 27/32	8 25/32	1-1 3/16	9 11/16	1-2 17/32	10 19/32	1-3 27/32
7/8	6 5/32	9 7/32	7 1/16	10 9/16	7 15/16	11 29/32	8 27/32	1-1 1/4	9 3/4	1-2 19/32	10 5/8	1-3 15/16
15/16	6 7/32	9 5/16	7 1/8	10 21/32	8	1-0	8 29/32	1-1 11/32	9 13/16	1-2 11/16	10 11/16	1-4 1/32

Feet	0' Rise	0' Slope	10' Rise	10' Slope	20' Rise	20' Slope	30' Rise	30' Slope
0	0	0	8-11 1/2	13-5 1/8	17-11	26-10 5/32	26-10 1/2	40-3 11/32
1	-10 3/4	1-4 1/8	9-10 1/4	14-9 7/32	18-9 3/4	28-2 11/32	27-9 1/4	41-7 7/16
2	1-9 1/2	2-8 1/32	10-9	16-1 11/32	19-8 1/2	29-6 7/16	28-8	42-11 9/16
3	2-8 1/4	4-0 11/32	11-7 3/4	17-5 7/16	20-7 1/4	30-10 9/16	29-6 3/4	44-3 21/32
4	3-7	5-4 7/16	12-6 1/2	18-9 9/16	21-6	32-2 21/32	30-5 1/2	45-7 25/32
5	4-5 3/4	6-8 9/16	13-5 1/4	20-1 21/32	22-4 3/4	33-6 25/32	31-4 1/4	46-11 7/8
6	5-4 1/2	8-0 21/32	14-4	21-5 25/32	23-3 1/2	34-10 7/8	32-3	48-4
7	6-3 1/4	9-4 25/32	15-2 3/4	22-9 7/8	24-2 1/4	36-3	33-1 3/4	49-8 3/32
8	7-2	10-8 7/8	16-1 1/2	24-2	25-1	37-7 3/32	34-0 1/2	51-0 7/32
9	8-0 3/4	12-1	17-0 1/4	25-6 3/32	25-11 3/4	38-11 7/32	34-11 1/4	52-4 5/16

A = 41° 51′ 18″; logsin A = 9.82429; logcos A = 9.87206; logtan A = 9.95223; logcot A = 0.04777

Ins.	12″ Rise	12″ Slope	13″ Rise	13″ Slope	14″ Rise	14″ Slope	15″ Rise	15″ Slope	16″ Rise	16″ Slope
0	10 3/4	1-4 1/8	11 21/32—	1-5 15/32—	1-0 17/32	1-6 25/32	1-1 7/16	1-8 1/8	1-2 11/32—	1-9 15/32
1/16	10 13/16	1-4 3/16	11 11/16	1-5 17/32	1-0 19/32	1-6 7/8	1-1 1/2	1-8 7/32	1-2 3/8	1-9 9/16
1/8	10 7/8	1-4 9/32—	11 3/4	1-5 5/8	1-0 21/32—	1-6 31/32—	1-1 9/16	1-8 5/16	1-2 7/16	1-9 21/32—
3/16	10 29/32	1-4 3/8	11 13/16	1-5 23/32—	1-0 23/32—	1-7 1/16	1-1 19/32	1-8 3/8	1-2 1/2	1-9 23/32
1/4	10 31/32	1-4 7/16	11 7/8	1-5 25/32	1-0 3/4	1-7 1/8	1-1 21/32	1-8 15/32	1-2 9/16	1-9 13/16
5/16	11 1/32—	1-4 17/32—	11 15/16	1-5 7/8	1-0 13/16	1-7 7/32—	1-1 23/32—	1-8 9/16	1-2 5/8	1-9 29/32—
3/8	11 3/32—	1-4 5/8	11 31/32	1-5 31/32—	1-0 7/8	1-7 5/16	1-1 25/32—	1-8 21/32—	1-2 21/32	1-10
7/16	11 5/32—	1-4 11/16	1-0 1/32	1-6 1/32	1-0 15/16	1-7 3/8	1-1 27/32—	1-8 23/32	1-2 23/32	1-10 1/16
1/2	11 3/16	1-4 25/32	1-0 3/32	1-6 1/8	1-1	1-7 15/32—	1-1 7/8	1-8 13/16	1-2 25/32	1-10 5/32—
9/16	11 1/4	1-4 7/8	1-0 5/32—	1-6 7/32—	1-1 1/32	1-7 9/16	1-1 15/16	1-8 29/32—	1-2 27/32—	1-10 1/4
5/8	11 5/16	1-4 15/16	1-0 7/32—	1-6 9/32	1-1 3/32	1-7 5/8	1-2	1-8 31/32	1-2 29/32—	1-10 5/16
11/16	11 3/8	1-5 1/32	1-0 1/4	1-6 3/8	1-1 5/32	1-7 23/32	1-2 1/16	1-9 1/16	1-2 15/16	1-10 13/32—
3/4	11 7/16	1-5 1/8	1-0 5/16	1-6 15/32—	1-1 7/32—	1-7 13/16	1-2 1/8	1-9 5/32—	1-3	1-10 1/2
13/16	11 15/32	1-5 3/16	1-0 3/8	1-6 17/32—	1-1 9/32—	1-7 7/8	1-2 5/32	1-9 7/32	1-3 1/16	1-10 9/16
7/8	11 17/32	1-5 9/32	1-0 7/16	1-6 5/8	1-1 5/16	1-7 31/32	1-2 7/32	1-9 5/16	1-3 1/8	1-10 21/32—
15/16	11 19/32—	1-5 3/8	1-0 1/2	1-6 23/32—	1-1 3/8	1-8 1/16	1-2 9/32—	1-9 13/32—	1-3 3/16	1-10 3/4

Ins.	17″ Rise	17″ Slope	18″ Rise	18″ Slope	19″ Rise	19″ Slope	20″ Rise	20″ Slope	21″ Rise	21″ Slope
0	1-3 7/32	1-10 13/16	1-4 1/8	2-0 5/32	1-5 1/32—	2-1 1/2	1-5 29/32	2-2 27/32	1-6 13/16	2-4 3/16
1/16	1-3 9/32	1-10 29/32	1-4 3/16	2-0 1/4	1-5 1/16	2-1 19/32—	1-5 31/32	2-2 15/16	1-6 7/8	2-4 9/32—
1/8	1-3 11/32—	1-11	1-4 1/4	2-0 11/32—	1-5 1/8	2-1 11/16	1-6 1/32—	2-3 1/32—	1-6 15/16	2-4 3/8
3/16	1-3 13/32—	1-11 1/16	1-4 9/32	2-0 13/32	1-5 3/16	2-1 3/4	1-6 3/32—	2-3 3/32	1-6 31/32	2-4 7/16
1/4	1-3 7/16	1-11 5/32	1-4 11/32	2-0 1/2	1-5 1/4	2-1 27/32	1-6 1/8	2-3 3/16	1-7 1/32	2-4 17/32—
5/16	1-3 1/2	1-11 1/4	1-4 13/32—	2-0 19/32—	1-5 5/16	2-1 15/16	1-6 3/16	2-3 9/32—	1-7 3/32—	2-4 5/8
3/8	1-3 9/16	1-11 5/16	1-4 15/32—	2-0 21/32	1-5 11/32	2-2	1-6 1/4	2-3 11/32	1-7 5/32—	2-4 11/16
7/16	1-3 5/8	1-11 13/32	1-4 17/32—	2-0 3/4	1-5 13/32	2-2 3/32	1-6 5/16	2-3 7/16	1-7 7/32—	2-4 25/32
1/2	1-3 11/16	1-11 1/2	1-4 9/16	2-0 27/32—	1-5 15/32	2-2 3/16	1-6 3/8	2-3 17/32—	1-7 1/4	2-4 7/8
9/16	1-3 23/32	1-11 19/32—	1-4 5/8	2-0 29/32	1-5 17/32—	2-2 1/4	1-6 13/32	2-3 19/32	1-7 5/16	2-4 15/16
5/8	1-3 25/32	1-11 21/32	1-4 11/16	2-1	1-5 19/32—	2-2 11/32	1-6 15/32	2-3 11/16	1-7 3/8	2-5 1/32
11/16	1-3 27/32	1-11 3/4	1-4 3/4	2-1 3/32—	1-5 5/8	2-2 7/16	1-6 17/32	2-3 25/32—	1-7 7/16	2-5 1/8
3/4	1-3 29/32—	1-11 27/32—	1-4 13/16	2-1 3/16	1-5 11/16	2-2 17/32—	1-6 19/32—	2-3 27/32	1-7 1/2	2-5 3/16
13/16	1-3 31/32—	1-11 29/32	1-4 27/32	2-1 1/4	1-5 3/4	2-2 19/32	1-6 21/32—	2-3 15/16	1-7 17/32	2-5 9/32
7/8	1-4	2-0	1-4 29/32	2-1 11/32—	1-5 13/16	2-2 11/16	1-6 11/16	2-4 1/32—	1-7 19/32	2-5 3/8
15/16	1-4 1/16	2-0 3/32—	1-4 31/32—	2-1 7/16	1-5 7/8	2-2 25/32—	1-6 3/4	2-4 1/8	1-7 21/32—	2-5 7/16

Feet	40′ Rise	40′ Slope	50′ Rise	50′ Slope	60′ Rise	60′ Slope	70′ Rise	70′ Slope
0	35-10	53-8 7/16	44-9 1/2	67-1 9/16	53-9	80-6 21/32	62-8 1/2	93-11 25/32—
1	36-8 3/4	55-0 9/16	45-8 1/4	68-5 21/32	54-7 3/4	81-10 25/32—	63-7 1/4	95-3 7/8
2	37-7 1/2	56-4 21/32	46-7	69-9 25/32—	55-6 1/2	83-2 7/8	64-6	96-8
3	38-6 1/4	57-8 25/32—	47-5 3/4	71-1 7/8	56-5 1/4	84-7	65-4 3/4	98-0 3/32
4	39-5	59-0 7/8	48-4 1/2	72-6	57-4	85-11 3/32	66-3 1/2	99-4 7/32—
5	40-3 3/4	60-5	49-3 1/4	73-10 3/32	58-2 3/4	87-3 7/32—	67-2 1/4	100-8 5/16
6	41-2 1/2	61-9 3/32	50-2	75-2 7/32—	59-1 1/2	88-7 5/16	68-1	102-0 7/16
7	42-1 1/4	63-1 7/32—	51-0 3/4	76-6 5/16	60-0 1/4	89-11 7/16	68-11 3/4	103-4 17/32
8	43-0	64-5 5/16	51-11 1/2	77-10 7/16	60-11	91-3 17/32	69-10 1/2	104-8 21/32—
9	43-10 3/4	65-9 7/16	52-10 1/4	79-2 17/32	61-9 3/4	92-7 21/32—	70-9 1/4	106-0 3/4

natsin A=0.6672483215; natcos A=0.7448353357; nattan A=0.8958333333; natcot A=1.1162790697

Inches	0" Rise	Slope	1" Rise	Slope	2" Rise	Slope	3" Rise	Slope	4" Rise	Slope	5" Rise	Slope
0	0	0	29/32	1 11/16	1 13/16	2 11/16	2 11/16	4 1/32	3 19/32	5 3/8	4 1/2	6 23/32
1/16	1/16	3/32	31/32	1 7/16	1 27/32	2 25/32	2 3/4	4 1/8	3 21/32	5 15/32	4 9/16	6 13/16
1/8	1/8	5/32	1	1 1/2	1 29/32	2 7/8	2 13/16	4 7/32	3 23/32	5 9/16	4 5/8	6 29/32
3/16	5/32	1/4	1 1/16	1 19/32	1 31/32	2 15/16	2 7/8	4 9/32	3 25/32	5 5/8	4 11/16	6 31/32
1/4	7/32	11/32	1 1/8	1 11/16	2 1/32	3 1/32	2 15/16	4 3/8	3 27/32	5 23/32	4 23/32	7 1/16
5/16	9/32	13/32	1 3/16	1 25/32	2 3/32	3 1/8	3	4 15/32	3 7/8	5 13/16	4 25/32	7 5/32
3/8	11/32	1/2	1 1/4	1 27/32	2 1/8	3 3/16	3 1/32	4 17/32	3 15/16	5 7/8	4 27/32	7 1/4
7/16	13/32	19/32	1 9/32	1 15/16	2 3/16	3 9/32	3 3/32	4 5/8	4	5 31/32	4 29/32	7 5/16
1/2	7/16	11/16	1 11/32	2 1/32	2 1/4	3 3/8	3 5/32	4 23/32	4 1/16	6 1/16	4 31/32	7 13/32
9/16	1/2	3/4	1 13/32	2 3/32	2 5/16	3 7/16	3 7/32	4 25/32	4 1/8	6 5/32	5	7 1/2
5/8	9/16	27/32	1 15/32	2 3/16	2 3/8	3 17/32	3 9/32	4 7/8	4 5/32	6 7/32	5 1/16	7 9/16
11/16	5/8	15/16	1 17/32	2 9/32	2 13/32	3 5/8	3 5/16	4 31/32	4 7/32	6 5/16	5 1/8	7 21/32
3/4	11/16	1	1 9/16	2 11/32	2 15/32	3 11/16	3 3/8	5 1/16	4 9/32	6 13/32	5 3/16	7 3/4
13/16	23/32	1 3/32	1 5/8	2 7/16	2 17/32	3 25/32	3 7/16	5 1/8	4 11/32	6 15/32	5 1/4	7 13/16
7/8	25/32	1 3/16	1 11/16	2 17/32	2 19/32	3 7/8	3 1/2	5 7/32	4 13/32	6 9/16	5 9/32	7 29/32
15/16	27/32	1 1/4	1 3/4	2 19/32	2 21/32	3 31/32	3 9/16	5 5/16	4 7/32	6 21/32	5 11/32	

Inches	6" Rise	Slope	7" Rise	Slope	8" Rise	Slope	9" Rise	Slope	10" Rise	Slope	11" Rise	Slope
0	5 13/32	8 1/16	6 5/16	9 7/16	7 7/32	10 25/32	8 1/8	1-0 1/8	9	1-1 15/32	9 29/32	1-2 13/16
1/16	5 15/32	8 5/32	6 3/8	9 1/2	7 1/4	10 27/32	8 5/32	1-0 3/16	9 1/16	1-1 17/32	9 31/32	1-2 29/32
1/8	5 17/32	8 1/4	6 13/32	9 19/32	7 5/16	10 15/16	8 7/32	1-0 9/32	9 1/8	1-1 5/8	10 1/2	1-2 31/32
3/16	5 9/16	8 11/32	6 15/32	9 11/16	7 3/8	11 1/32	8 9/32	1-0 3/8	9 3/16	1-1 23/32	10 3/8	1-3 1/16
1/4	5 5/8	8 13/32	6 17/32	9 3/4	7 7/16	11 3/32	8 11/32	1-0 7/16	9 1/4	1-1 13/16	10 1/8	1-3 5/32
5/16	5 11/16	8 1/2	6 19/32	9 27/32	7 1/2	11 3/16	8 13/32	1-0 17/32	9 9/32	1-1 7/8	10 3/16	1-3 7/32
3/8	5 3/4	8 19/32	6 21/32	9 15/16	7 17/32	11 9/32	8 7/16	1-0 5/8	9 11/32	1-1 31/32	10 1/4	1-3 5/16
7/16	5 13/16	8 21/32	6 11/16	10	7 19/32	11 11/32	8 1/2	1-0 23/32	9 13/32	1-2 1/16	10 5/16	1-3 13/32
1/2	5 27/32	8 3/4	6 3/4	10 3/32	7 21/32	11 7/16	8 9/16	1-0 25/32	9 15/32	1-2 1/8	10 3/8	1-3 15/32
9/16	5 29/32	8 27/32	6 13/16	10 3/16	7 23/32	11 17/32	8 5/8	1-0 7/8	9 17/32	1-2 7/32	10 13/32	1-3 9/16
5/8	5 31/32	8 29/32	6 7/8	10 1/4	7 25/32	11 5/8	8 11/16	1-0 31/32	9 9/16	1-2 5/16	10 15/32	1-3 21/32
11/16	6 1/32	9	6 15/16	10 11/32	7 13/16	11 11/16	8 23/32	1-1 1/32	9 5/8	1-2 3/8	10 17/32	1-3 23/32
3/4	6 3/32	9 3/32	6 31/32	10 7/16	7 7/8	11 25/32	8 25/32	1-1 1/8	9 11/16	1-2 15/32	10 19/32	1-3 13/16
13/16	6 1/8	9 5/32	7 1/32	10 17/32	7 15/16	11 7/8	8 27/32	1-1 7/32	9 3/4	1-2 9/16	10 21/32	1-3 29/32
7/8	6 3/16	9 1/4	7 3/32	10 19/32	8	11 15/16	8 29/32	1-1 9/32	9 13/16	1-2 5/8	10 11/16	1-4
15/16	6 1/4	9 11/32	7 5/32	10 11/16	8 1/16	1-0 1/32	8 31/32	1-1 3/8	9 27/32	1-2 23/32	10 3/4	1-4 1/16

Feet	0' Rise	Slope	10' Rise	Slope	20' Rise	Slope	30' Rise	Slope
0	0	0	9-0 1/8	13-5 17/32	18-0 1/4	26-11 11/16	27-0 3/8	40-4 19/32
1	-10 13/16	1-4 5/32	9-10 15/16	14-9 11/16	18-11 1/2	28-3 1/2	27-11 3/16	41-8 23/32
2	1-9 5/8	2-8 5/16	10-9 3/4	16-1 27/32	19-9 7/8	29-7 3/8	28-10	43-0 7/8
3	2-8 7/16	4-0 15/32	11-8 9/16	17-6	20-8 11/16	30-11 1/2	29-8 13/16	44-5 1/32
4	3-7 1/4	5-4 5/8	12-7 3/8	18-10 1/8	21-7 1/2	32-3 21/32	30-7 5/8	45-9 9/16
5	4-6 1/16	6-8 3/4	13-6 3/16	20-2 9/32	22-6 5/16	33-7 13/16	31-6 7/16	47-1 11/32
6	5-4 7/8	8-0 29/32	14-5	21-6 7/16	23-5 1/8	34-11 31/32	32-5 1/4	48-5 1/2
7	6-3 11/16	9-5 1/16	15-3 13/16	22-10 19/32	24-3 15/16	36-4 1/8	33-4 1/16	49-9 21/32
8	7-2 1/2	10-9 7/32	16-2 5/8	24-2 3/4	25-2 3/4	37-8 9/32	34-2 7/8	51-1 13/16
9	8-1 5/16	12-1 3/8	17-1 7/16	25-6 29/32	26-1 9/16	39-0 7/16	35-1 11/16	52-5 31/32

A = 42° 01' 13"; logsin A = 9.82568; logcos A = 9.87094; logtan A = 9.95474; logcot A = 0.04526

Ins.	12″ Rise	12″ Slope	13″ Rise	13″ Slope	14″ Rise	14″ Slope	15″ Rise	15″ Slope	16″ Rise	16″ Slope
0	$10\frac{13}{16}$	$1\text{-}4\frac{5}{32}$	$11\frac{23}{32}$	$1\text{-}5\frac{1}{2}$	$1\text{-}0\frac{5}{8}$	$1\text{-}6\frac{27}{32}$	$1\text{-}1\frac{1}{2}$	$1\text{-}8\frac{3}{16}$	$1\text{-}2\frac{13}{32}$	$1\text{-}9\frac{17}{32}$
$\frac{1}{16}$	$10\frac{7}{8}$	$1\text{-}4\frac{1}{4}$	$11\frac{25}{32}$	$1\text{-}5\frac{19}{32}$	$1\text{-}0\frac{21}{32}$	$1\text{-}6\frac{15}{16}$	$1\text{-}1\frac{9}{16}$	$1\text{-}8\frac{9}{32}$	$1\text{-}2\frac{15}{32}$	$1\text{-}9\frac{5}{8}$
$\frac{1}{8}$	$10\frac{15}{16}$	$1\text{-}4\frac{5}{16}$	$11\frac{13}{16}$	$1\text{-}5\frac{21}{32}$	$1\text{-}0\frac{23}{32}$	$1\text{-}7$	$1\text{-}1\frac{5}{8}$	$1\text{-}8\frac{11}{32}$	$1\text{-}2\frac{17}{32}$	$1\text{-}9\frac{23}{32}$
$\frac{3}{16}$	$10\frac{31}{32}$	$1\text{-}4\frac{13}{32}$	$11\frac{7}{8}$	$1\text{-}5\frac{3}{4}$	$1\text{-}0\frac{25}{32}$	$1\text{-}7\frac{3}{32}$	$1\text{-}1\frac{11}{16}$	$1\text{-}8\frac{7}{16}$	$1\text{-}2\frac{19}{32}$	$1\text{-}9\frac{25}{32}$
$\frac{1}{4}$	$11\frac{1}{32}$	$1\text{-}4\frac{1}{2}$	$11\frac{15}{16}$	$1\text{-}5\frac{27}{32}$	$1\text{-}0\frac{27}{32}$	$1\text{-}7\frac{3}{16}$	$1\text{-}1\frac{3}{4}$	$1\text{-}8\frac{17}{32}$	$1\text{-}2\frac{21}{32}$	$1\text{-}9\frac{7}{8}$
$\frac{5}{16}$	$11\frac{3}{32}$	$1\text{-}4\frac{9}{16}$	$1\text{-}0$	$1\text{-}5\frac{29}{32}$	$1\text{-}0\frac{29}{32}$	$1\text{-}7\frac{1}{4}$	$1\text{-}1\frac{13}{16}$	$1\text{-}8\frac{5}{8}$	$1\text{-}2\frac{11}{16}$	$1\text{-}9\frac{31}{32}$
$\frac{3}{8}$	$11\frac{5}{32}$	$1\text{-}4\frac{21}{32}$	$1\text{-}0\frac{1}{16}$	$1\text{-}6$	$1\text{-}0\frac{15}{16}$	$1\text{-}7\frac{11}{16}$	$1\text{-}1\frac{27}{32}$	$1\text{-}8\frac{11}{16}$	$1\text{-}2\frac{3}{4}$	$1\text{-}10\frac{1}{32}$
$\frac{7}{16}$	$11\frac{7}{32}$	$1\text{-}4\frac{3}{4}$	$1\text{-}0\frac{3}{32}$	$1\text{-}6\frac{3}{32}$	$1\text{-}1$	$1\text{-}7\frac{7}{16}$	$1\text{-}1\frac{29}{32}$	$1\text{-}8\frac{25}{32}$	$1\text{-}2\frac{13}{16}$	$1\text{-}10\frac{1}{8}$
$\frac{1}{2}$	$11\frac{1}{4}$	$1\text{-}4\frac{13}{16}$	$1\text{-}0\frac{5}{32}$	$1\text{-}6\frac{5}{32}$	$1\text{-}1\frac{1}{16}$	$1\text{-}7\frac{17}{32}$	$1\text{-}1\frac{31}{32}$	$1\text{-}8\frac{7}{8}$	$1\text{-}2\frac{7}{8}$	$1\text{-}10\frac{7}{32}$
$\frac{9}{16}$	$11\frac{5}{16}$	$1\text{-}4\frac{29}{32}$	$1\text{-}0\frac{7}{32}$	$1\text{-}6\frac{1}{4}$	$1\text{-}1\frac{1}{8}$	$1\text{-}7\frac{19}{32}$	$1\text{-}2\frac{1}{32}$	$1\text{-}8\frac{15}{16}$	$1\text{-}2\frac{15}{16}$	$1\text{-}10\frac{9}{32}$
$\frac{5}{8}$	$11\frac{3}{8}$	$1\text{-}5$	$1\text{-}0\frac{9}{32}$	$1\text{-}6\frac{11}{32}$	$1\text{-}1\frac{3}{16}$	$1\text{-}7\frac{11}{16}$	$1\text{-}2\frac{3}{32}$	$1\text{-}9\frac{1}{32}$	$1\text{-}2\frac{31}{32}$	$1\text{-}10\frac{3}{8}$
$\frac{11}{16}$	$11\frac{7}{16}$	$1\text{-}5\frac{3}{32}$	$1\text{-}0\frac{11}{32}$	$1\text{-}6\frac{7}{16}$	$1\text{-}1\frac{7}{32}$	$1\text{-}7\frac{25}{32}$	$1\text{-}2\frac{1}{8}$	$1\text{-}9\frac{1}{8}$	$1\text{-}3\frac{1}{32}$	$1\text{-}10\frac{15}{32}$
$\frac{3}{4}$	$11\frac{1}{2}$	$1\text{-}5\frac{5}{32}$	$1\text{-}0\frac{3}{8}$	$1\text{-}6\frac{1}{2}$	$1\text{-}1\frac{9}{32}$	$1\text{-}7\frac{27}{32}$	$1\text{-}2\frac{3}{16}$	$1\text{-}9\frac{3}{16}$	$1\text{-}3\frac{3}{32}$	$1\text{-}10\frac{17}{32}$
$\frac{13}{16}$	$11\frac{17}{32}$	$1\text{-}5\frac{1}{4}$	$1\text{-}0\frac{7}{16}$	$1\text{-}6\frac{19}{32}$	$1\text{-}1\frac{11}{32}$	$1\text{-}7\frac{15}{16}$	$1\text{-}2\frac{1}{4}$	$1\text{-}9\frac{9}{32}$	$1\text{-}3\frac{5}{32}$	$1\text{-}10\frac{5}{8}$
$\frac{7}{8}$	$11\frac{19}{32}$	$1\text{-}5\frac{11}{32}$	$1\text{-}0\frac{1}{2}$	$1\text{-}6\frac{11}{16}$	$1\text{-}1\frac{13}{32}$	$1\text{-}8\frac{1}{32}$	$1\text{-}2\frac{5}{16}$	$1\text{-}9\frac{3}{8}$	$1\text{-}3\frac{7}{32}$	$1\text{-}10\frac{23}{32}$
$\frac{15}{16}$	$11\frac{21}{32}$	$1\text{-}5\frac{13}{32}$	$1\text{-}0\frac{9}{16}$	$1\text{-}6\frac{3}{4}$	$1\text{-}1\frac{15}{32}$	$1\text{-}8\frac{3}{32}$	$1\text{-}2\frac{3}{8}$	$1\text{-}9\frac{7}{16}$	$1\text{-}3\frac{1}{4}$	$1\text{-}10\frac{13}{16}$

Ins.	17″ Rise	17″ Slope	18″ Rise	18″ Slope	19″ Rise	19″ Slope	20″ Rise	20″ Slope	21″ Rise	21″ Slope
0	$1\text{-}3\frac{5}{16}$	$1\text{-}10\frac{7}{8}$	$1\text{-}4\frac{7}{32}$	$2\text{-}0\frac{7}{32}$	$1\text{-}5\frac{1}{8}$	$2\text{-}1\frac{9}{16}$	$1\text{-}6\frac{1}{32}$	$2\text{-}2\frac{29}{32}$	$1\text{-}6\frac{15}{16}$	$2\text{-}4\frac{9}{32}$
$\frac{1}{16}$	$1\text{-}3\frac{3}{8}$	$1\text{-}10\frac{31}{32}$	$1\text{-}4\frac{9}{32}$	$2\text{-}0\frac{5}{16}$	$1\text{-}5\frac{3}{16}$	$2\text{-}1\frac{21}{32}$	$1\text{-}6\frac{1}{16}$	$2\text{-}3$	$1\text{-}6\frac{31}{32}$	$2\text{-}4\frac{11}{32}$
$\frac{1}{8}$	$1\text{-}3\frac{7}{16}$	$1\text{-}11\frac{1}{16}$	$1\text{-}4\frac{11}{32}$	$2\text{-}0\frac{13}{32}$	$1\text{-}5\frac{7}{32}$	$2\text{-}1\frac{3}{4}$	$1\text{-}6\frac{1}{8}$	$2\text{-}3\frac{3}{32}$	$1\text{-}7\frac{1}{32}$	$2\text{-}4\frac{7}{16}$
$\frac{3}{16}$	$1\text{-}3\frac{1}{2}$	$1\text{-}11\frac{1}{8}$	$1\text{-}4\frac{3}{8}$	$2\text{-}0\frac{15}{32}$	$1\text{-}5\frac{9}{32}$	$2\text{-}1\frac{13}{16}$	$1\text{-}6\frac{3}{16}$	$2\text{-}3\frac{3}{16}$	$1\text{-}7\frac{3}{32}$	$2\text{-}4\frac{17}{32}$
$\frac{1}{4}$	$1\text{-}3\frac{17}{32}$	$1\text{-}11\frac{7}{32}$	$1\text{-}4\frac{7}{16}$	$2\text{-}0\frac{9}{16}$	$1\text{-}5\frac{11}{32}$	$2\text{-}1\frac{29}{32}$	$1\text{-}6\frac{1}{4}$	$2\text{-}3\frac{1}{4}$	$1\text{-}7\frac{5}{32}$	$2\text{-}4\frac{19}{32}$
$\frac{5}{16}$	$1\text{-}3\frac{19}{32}$	$1\text{-}11\frac{5}{16}$	$1\text{-}4\frac{1}{2}$	$2\text{-}0\frac{21}{32}$	$1\text{-}5\frac{13}{32}$	$2\text{-}2$	$1\text{-}6\frac{5}{16}$	$2\text{-}3\frac{11}{32}$	$1\text{-}7\frac{1}{4}$	$2\text{-}4\frac{11}{16}$
$\frac{3}{8}$	$1\text{-}3\frac{21}{32}$	$1\text{-}11\frac{3}{8}$	$1\text{-}4\frac{9}{16}$	$2\text{-}0\frac{23}{32}$	$1\text{-}5\frac{15}{32}$	$2\text{-}2\frac{3}{32}$	$1\text{-}6\frac{11}{32}$	$2\text{-}3\frac{7}{16}$	$1\text{-}7\frac{1}{4}$	$2\text{-}4\frac{25}{32}$
$\frac{7}{16}$	$1\text{-}3\frac{23}{32}$	$1\text{-}11\frac{15}{16}$	$1\text{-}4\frac{5}{8}$	$2\text{-}0\frac{13}{16}$	$1\text{-}5\frac{1}{2}$	$2\text{-}2\frac{5}{32}$	$1\text{-}6\frac{13}{32}$	$2\text{-}3\frac{1}{2}$	$1\text{-}7\frac{5}{16}$	$2\text{-}4\frac{27}{32}$
$\frac{1}{2}$	$1\text{-}3\frac{25}{32}$	$1\text{-}11\frac{9}{16}$	$1\text{-}4\frac{21}{32}$	$2\text{-}0\frac{29}{32}$	$1\text{-}5\frac{9}{16}$	$2\text{-}2\frac{1}{4}$	$1\text{-}6\frac{15}{32}$	$2\text{-}3\frac{19}{32}$	$1\text{-}7\frac{3}{8}$	$2\text{-}4\frac{15}{16}$
$\frac{9}{16}$	$1\text{-}3\frac{13}{16}$	$1\text{-}11\frac{5}{8}$	$1\text{-}4\frac{23}{32}$	$2\text{-}1$	$1\text{-}5\frac{5}{8}$	$2\text{-}2\frac{11}{32}$	$1\text{-}6\frac{17}{32}$	$2\text{-}3\frac{11}{16}$	$1\text{-}7\frac{7}{16}$	$2\text{-}5\frac{1}{32}$
$\frac{5}{8}$	$1\text{-}3\frac{7}{8}$	$1\text{-}11\frac{23}{32}$	$1\text{-}4\frac{25}{32}$	$2\text{-}1\frac{1}{16}$	$1\text{-}5\frac{11}{16}$	$2\text{-}2\frac{13}{32}$	$1\text{-}6\frac{19}{32}$	$2\text{-}3\frac{3}{4}$	$1\text{-}7\frac{1}{2}$	$2\text{-}5\frac{3}{32}$
$\frac{11}{16}$	$1\text{-}3\frac{15}{16}$	$1\text{-}11\frac{13}{16}$	$1\text{-}4\frac{27}{32}$	$2\text{-}1\frac{5}{32}$	$1\text{-}5\frac{3}{4}$	$2\text{-}2\frac{1}{2}$	$1\text{-}6\frac{5}{8}$	$2\text{-}3\frac{27}{32}$	$1\text{-}7\frac{17}{32}$	$2\text{-}5\frac{3}{16}$
$\frac{3}{4}$	$1\text{-}4$	$1\text{-}11\frac{29}{32}$	$1\text{-}4\frac{29}{32}$	$2\text{-}1\frac{1}{4}$	$1\text{-}5\frac{25}{32}$	$2\text{-}2\frac{19}{32}$	$1\text{-}6\frac{11}{16}$	$2\text{-}3\frac{15}{16}$	$1\text{-}7\frac{19}{32}$	$2\text{-}5\frac{9}{32}$
$\frac{13}{16}$	$1\text{-}4\frac{1}{16}$	$1\text{-}11\frac{31}{32}$	$1\text{-}4\frac{15}{16}$	$2\text{-}1\frac{5}{16}$	$1\text{-}5\frac{27}{32}$	$2\text{-}2\frac{21}{32}$	$1\text{-}6\frac{3}{4}$	$2\text{-}4$	$1\text{-}7\frac{21}{32}$	$2\text{-}5\frac{3}{8}$
$\frac{7}{8}$	$1\text{-}4\frac{3}{32}$	$2\text{-}0\frac{1}{16}$	$1\text{-}5$	$2\text{-}1\frac{13}{32}$	$1\text{-}5\frac{29}{32}$	$2\text{-}2\frac{3}{4}$	$1\text{-}6\frac{13}{16}$	$2\text{-}4\frac{3}{32}$	$1\text{-}7\frac{23}{32}$	$2\text{-}5\frac{7}{16}$
$\frac{15}{16}$	$1\text{-}4\frac{5}{32}$	$2\text{-}0\frac{5}{32}$	$1\text{-}5\frac{1}{16}$	$2\text{-}1\frac{1}{2}$	$1\text{-}5\frac{31}{32}$	$2\text{-}2\frac{27}{32}$	$1\text{-}6\frac{7}{8}$	$2\text{-}4\frac{3}{16}$	$1\text{-}7\frac{25}{32}$	$2\text{-}5\frac{17}{32}$

Feet	40′ Rise	40′ Slope	50′ Rise	50′ Slope	60′ Rise	60′ Slope	70′ Rise	70′ Slope
0	$36\text{-}0\frac{1}{2}$	$53\text{-}10\frac{3}{32}$	$45\text{-}0\frac{5}{8}$	$67\text{-}3\frac{5}{8}$	$54\text{-}0\frac{3}{4}$	$80\text{-}9\frac{5}{32}$	$63\text{-}0\frac{7}{8}$	$94\text{-}2\frac{11}{16}$
1	$36\text{-}11\frac{5}{16}$	$55\text{-}2\frac{1}{4}$	$45\text{-}11\frac{7}{16}$	$68\text{-}7\frac{25}{32}$	$54\text{-}11\frac{9}{16}$	$82\text{-}1\frac{5}{16}$	$63\text{-}11\frac{11}{16}$	$95\text{-}6\frac{27}{32}$
2	$37\text{-}10\frac{1}{4}$	$56\text{-}6\frac{13}{32}$	$46\text{-}10\frac{3}{4}$	$69\text{-}11\frac{15}{16}$	$55\text{-}10\frac{3}{8}$	$83\text{-}5\frac{15}{32}$	$64\text{-}10\frac{1}{2}$	$96\text{-}11$
3	$38\text{-}8\frac{15}{32}$	$57\text{-}10\frac{9}{16}$	$47\text{-}9\frac{1}{16}$	$71\text{-}4\frac{3}{32}$	$56\text{-}9\frac{3}{16}$	$84\text{-}9\frac{5}{8}$	$65\text{-}9\frac{5}{16}$	$98\text{-}3\frac{5}{32}$
4	$39\text{-}7\frac{3}{4}$	$59\text{-}2\frac{3}{32}$	$48\text{-}7\frac{7}{8}$	$72\text{-}8\frac{1}{4}$	$57\text{-}8$	$86\text{-}1\frac{25}{32}$	$66\text{-}8\frac{1}{8}$	$99\text{-}7\frac{5}{16}$
5	$40\text{-}6\frac{9}{16}$	$60\text{-}6\frac{7}{8}$	$49\text{-}6\frac{11}{32}$	$74\text{-}0\frac{13}{32}$	$58\text{-}6\frac{13}{16}$	$87\text{-}5\frac{15}{16}$	$67\text{-}6\frac{15}{16}$	$100\text{-}11\frac{15}{32}$
6	$41\text{-}5\frac{3}{8}$	$61\text{-}11\frac{1}{32}$	$50\text{-}5\frac{1}{2}$	$75\text{-}4\frac{9}{16}$	$59\text{-}5\frac{5}{8}$	$88\text{-}10\frac{3}{32}$	$68\text{-}5\frac{3}{4}$	$102\text{-}3\frac{19}{32}$
7	$42\text{-}4\frac{3}{16}$	$63\text{-}3\frac{3}{16}$	$51\text{-}4\frac{5}{16}$	$76\text{-}8\frac{23}{32}$	$60\text{-}4\frac{7}{16}$	$90\text{-}2\frac{7}{32}$	$69\text{-}4\frac{9}{16}$	$103\text{-}7\frac{3}{4}$
8	$43\text{-}3$	$64\text{-}7\frac{11}{32}$	$52\text{-}3\frac{1}{8}$	$78\text{-}0\frac{27}{32}$	$61\text{-}3\frac{1}{4}$	$91\text{-}6\frac{3}{8}$	$70\text{-}3\frac{3}{8}$	$104\text{-}11\frac{29}{32}$
9	$44\text{-}1\frac{13}{16}$	$65\text{-}11\frac{15}{32}$	$53\text{-}1\frac{15}{16}$	$79\text{-}5$	$62\text{-}2\frac{1}{16}$	$92\text{-}10\frac{17}{32}$	$71\text{-}2\frac{3}{16}$	$106\text{-}4\frac{1}{16}$

natsin A=0.6693921699; natcos A=0.7429092291; nattan A=0.9010416666; natcot A=1.1098265895

Inches	0" Rise	0" Slope	1" Rise	1" Slope	2" Rise	2" Slope	3" Rise	3" Slope	4" Rise	4" Slope	5" Rise	5" Slope
0	0	0	29/32	1 11/32	1 13/16	2 11/16	2 23/32	4 1/16	3 5/8	5 13/32	4 17/32	6 3/4
1/16	1/16	3/32	31/32	1 7/16	1 7/8	2 25/32	2 25/32	4 1/8	3 11/16	5 15/32	4 19/32	6 21/32
1/8	1/8	5/32	1 1/32	1 17/32	1 15/16	2 7/8	2 27/32	4 7/32	3 3/4	5 9/16	4 21/32	6 29/32
3/16	5/32	1/4	1 1/16	1 19/32	1 31/32	2 15/16	2 7/8	4 5/16	3 25/32	5 21/32	4 11/16	7
1/4	7/32	11/32	1 1/8	1 11/16	2 1/16	3 1/32	2 15/16	4 3/8	3 27/32	5 3/4	4 3/4	7 3/32
5/16	9/32	13/32	1 3/16	1 25/32	2 3/32	3 1/8	3	4 15/32	3 29/32	5 13/16	4 13/16	7 5/32
3/8	11/32	1/2	1 1/4	1 27/32	2 5/32	3 7/32	3 1/16	4 9/16	3 31/32	5 29/32	4 7/8	7 1/4
7/16	13/32	19/32	1 5/16	1 15/16	2 7/32	3 9/32	3 1/8	4 5/8	4 1/32	6	4 15/16	7 11/32
1/2	7/16	11/16	1 3/8	2 1/32	2 1/4	3 3/8	3 3/16	4 23/32	4 1/16	6 1/16	5	7 7/16
9/16	1/2	3/4	1 13/32	2 3/32	2 5/16	3 15/32	3 7/32	4 13/16	4 1/8	6 5/32	5 1/8	7 1/2
5/8	9/16	27/32	1 15/32	2 3/16	2 3/8	3 17/32	3 9/32	4 29/32	4 3/16	6 1/4	5 3/32	7 19/32
11/16	5/8	15/16	1 17/32	2 9/32	2 7/16	3 5/8	3 11/32	4 31/32	4 1/4	6 5/16	5 9/32	7 11/16
3/4	11/16	1	1 19/32	2 3/8	2 1/2	3 23/32	3 13/32	5 1/16	4 5/16	6 13/32	5 7/32	7 3/4
13/16	3/4	1 3/32	1 21/32	2 7/16	2 9/16	3 25/32	3 15/32	5 5/32	4 3/8	6 1/2	5 9/32	7 27/32
7/8	25/32	1 3/16	1 11/16	2 17/32	2 19/32	3 7/8	3 1/2	5 7/32	4 13/32	6 19/32	5 5/16	7 15/16
15/16	27/32	1 1/4	1 3/4	2 5/8	2 21/32	3 31/32	3 9/16	5 11/32	4 15/32	6 21/32	5 3/8	8

Inches	6" Rise	6" Slope	7" Rise	7" Slope	8" Rise	8" Slope	9" Rise	9" Slope	10" Rise	10" Slope	11" Rise	11" Slope
0	5 7/16	8 3/32	6 11/32	9 7/16	7 1/4	10 25/32	8 5/8	1-0 5/32	9 1/16	1-1 1/2	9 31/32	1-2 7/32
1/16	5 1/2	8 3/16	6 13/32	9 17/32	7 5/16	10 7/8	8 7/32	1-0 7/32	9 1/8	1-1 19/32	10 1/32	1-2 15/32
1/8	5 9/16	8 9/32	6 15/32	9 5/8	7 3/8	10 31/32	8 9/32	1-0 5/16	9 3/16	1-1 21/32	10 3/32	1-3
3/16	5 19/32	8 11/32	6 1/2	9 11/16	7 13/32	11 1/16	8 5/16	1-0 13/32	9 7/32	1-1 3/4	10 1/8	1-3 3/32
1/4	5 21/32	8 7/16	6 9/16	9 25/32	7 15/32	11 1/8	8 3/8	1-0 15/32	9 9/32	1-1 27/32	10 3/16	1-3 3/8
5/16	5 23/32	8 17/32	6 5/8	9 7/8	7 17/32	11 7/32	8 7/16	1-0 9/16	9 11/32	1-1 29/32	10 1/4	1-3 9/32
3/8	5 25/32	8 19/32	6 11/16	9 15/16	7 19/32	11 5/16	8 1/2	1-0 21/32	9 13/32	1-2	10 5/16	1-3 11/32
7/16	5 27/32	8 11/16	6 3/4	10 1/32	7 21/32	11 3/8	8 9/16	1-0 3/4	9 15/32	1-2 3/32	10 3/8	1-3 7/16
1/2	5 7/8	8 25/32	6 13/16	10 1/8	7 11/16	11 15/32	8 5/8	1-0 13/16	9 1/2	1-2 5/32	10 7/16	1-3 17/32
9/16	5 15/16	8 27/32	6 27/32	10 7/32	7 3/4	11 9/16	8 21/32	1-0 29/32	9 9/16	1-2 1/4	10 15/32	1-3 19/32
5/8	6	8 15/16	6 29/32	10 9/32	7 13/16	11 5/8	8 23/32	1-1	9 5/8	1-2 11/32	10 17/32	1-3 11/16
11/16	6 1/16	9 1/32	6 31/32	10 3/8	7 7/8	11 23/32	8 25/32	1-1 1/16	9 11/16	1-2 7/16	10 19/32	1-3 25/32
3/4	6 1/8	9 1/8	7 1/32	10 15/32	7 15/16	11 13/16	8 27/32	1-1 5/32	9 3/4	1-2 1/2	10 21/32	1-3 27/32
13/16	6 3/16	9 3/16	7 3/32	10 17/32	8	11 29/32	8 29/32	1-1 1/4	9 13/16	1-2 19/32	10 23/32	1-3 15/16
7/8	6 7/32	9 9/32	7 1/8	10 5/8	8 1/32	11 31/32	8 15/16	1-1 5/16	9 27/32	1-2 11/16	10 3/4	1-4 1/32
15/16	6 9/32	9 3/8	7 3/16	10 23/32	8 3/32	1-0 1/16	9	1-1 13/32	9 29/32	1-2 3/4	10 13/16	1-4 1/8

Feet	0' Rise	0' Slope	10' Rise	10' Slope	20' Rise	20' Slope	30' Rise	30' Slope
0	0	0	9-0 3/8	13-5 15/16	18-1 1/2	26-11 29/32	27-2 1/4	40-5 27/32
1	-10 7/8	1-4 3/16	9-11 5/8	14-10 5/32	19-0 3/8	28-4 3/32	28-1 1/8	41-10 1/32
2	1-9 3/4	2-8 3/8	10-10 1/2	16-2 11/32	19-11 1/4	29-8 9/32	29-0	43-2 7/32
3	2-8 5/8	4-0 19/32	11-9 3/8	17-6 17/32	20-10 1/8	31-0 15/32	29-10 7/8	44-6 7/16
4	3-7 1/2	5-4 25/32	12-8 1/4	18-10 23/32	21-9	32-4 21/32	30-9 3/4	45-10 5/8
5	4-6 3/8	6-8 31/32	13-7 1/8	20-2 29/32	22-7 7/8	33-8 7/8	31-8 5/8	47-2 13/16
6	5-5 1/4	8-1 5/32	14-6	21-7 1/8	23-6 3/4	35-1 1/16	32-7 1/2	48-7
7	6-4 1/8	9-5 3/8	15-4 7/8	22-11 5/16	24-5 5/8	36-5 1/4	33-6 3/8	49-11 3/16
8	7-3	10-9 9/16	16-3 3/4	24-3 1/2	25-4 1/2	37-9 7/16	34-5 1/4	51-3 13/16
9	8-1 7/8	12-1 3/4	17-2 5/8	25-7 11/16	26-3 3/8	39-1 21/32	35-4 1/8	52-7 19/32

A = 42° 11' 04''; logsin A = 9.82706; logcos A = 9.86981; logtan A = 9.95725; logcot A = 0.04275

Ins.	12″ Rise	12″ Slope	13″ Rise	13″ Slope	14″ Rise	14″ Slope	15″ Rise	15″ Slope	16″ Rise	16″ Slope
0	$10\frac{7}{8}$	$1\text{-}4\frac{3}{16}$	$11\frac{25}{32}$	$1\text{-}5\frac{17}{32}$	$1\text{-}0\frac{11}{16}$	$1\text{-}6\frac{29}{32}$	$1\text{-}1\frac{19}{32}$	$1\text{-}8\frac{1}{4}$	$1\text{-}2\frac{1}{2}$	$1\text{-}9\frac{19}{32}$
$\frac{1}{16}$	$10\frac{15}{16}$	$1\text{-}4\frac{9}{32}$	$11\frac{27}{32}$	$1\text{-}5\frac{5}{8}$	$1\text{-}0\frac{3}{4}$	$1\text{-}6\frac{31}{32}$	$1\text{-}1\frac{21}{32}$	$1\text{-}8\frac{5}{16}$	$1\text{-}2\frac{9}{16}$	$1\text{-}9\frac{11}{16}$
$\frac{1}{8}$	11	$1\text{-}4\frac{3}{8}$	$11\frac{29}{32}$	$1\text{-}5\frac{23}{32}$	$1\text{-}0\frac{13}{16}$	$1\text{-}7\frac{1}{16}$	$1\text{-}1\frac{23}{32}$	$1\text{-}8\frac{13}{32}$	$1\text{-}2\frac{5}{8}$	$1\text{-}9\frac{3}{4}$
$\frac{3}{16}$	$11\frac{1}{16}$	$1\text{-}4\frac{7}{16}$	$11\frac{15}{16}$	$1\text{-}5\frac{13}{16}$	$1\text{-}0\frac{27}{32}$	$1\text{-}7\frac{5}{32}$	$1\text{-}1\frac{3}{4}$	$1\text{-}8\frac{1}{2}$	$1\text{-}2\frac{21}{32}$	$1\text{-}9\frac{27}{32}$
$\frac{1}{4}$	$11\frac{3}{32}$	$1\text{-}4\frac{17}{32}$	$1\text{-}0$	$1\text{-}5\frac{7}{8}$	$1\text{-}0\frac{29}{32}$	$1\text{-}7\frac{7}{32}$	$1\text{-}1\frac{13}{16}$	$1\text{-}8\frac{19}{32}$	$1\text{-}2\frac{23}{32}$	$1\text{-}9\frac{15}{16}$
$\frac{5}{16}$	$11\frac{5}{32}$	$1\text{-}4\frac{5}{8}$	$1\text{-}0\frac{1}{16}$	$1\text{-}5\frac{31}{32}$	$1\text{-}0\frac{31}{32}$	$1\text{-}7\frac{9}{32}$	$1\text{-}1\frac{7}{8}$	$1\text{-}8\frac{21}{32}$	$1\text{-}2\frac{25}{32}$	$1\text{-}10$
$\frac{3}{8}$	$11\frac{7}{32}$	$1\text{-}4\frac{11}{16}$	$1\text{-}0\frac{1}{8}$	$1\text{-}6\frac{1}{16}$	$1\text{-}1\frac{1}{32}$	$1\text{-}7\frac{13}{32}$	$1\text{-}1\frac{15}{16}$	$1\text{-}8\frac{3}{4}$	$1\text{-}2\frac{27}{32}$	$1\text{-}10\frac{3}{32}$
$\frac{7}{16}$	$11\frac{9}{32}$	$1\text{-}4\frac{25}{32}$	$1\text{-}0\frac{3}{16}$	$1\text{-}6\frac{1}{8}$	$1\text{-}1\frac{3}{32}$	$1\text{-}7\frac{15}{32}$	$1\text{-}2$	$1\text{-}8\frac{27}{32}$	$1\text{-}2\frac{29}{32}$	$1\text{-}10\frac{3}{16}$
$\frac{1}{2}$	$11\frac{5}{16}$	$1\text{-}4\frac{7}{8}$	$1\text{-}0\frac{1}{4}$	$1\text{-}6\frac{7}{32}$	$1\text{-}1\frac{1}{8}$	$1\text{-}7\frac{9}{16}$	$1\text{-}2\frac{1}{16}$	$1\text{-}8\frac{29}{32}$	$1\text{-}2\frac{15}{16}$	$1\text{-}10\frac{9}{32}$
$\frac{9}{16}$	$11\frac{3}{8}$	$1\text{-}4\frac{31}{32}$	$1\text{-}0\frac{9}{32}$	$1\text{-}6\frac{5}{16}$	$1\text{-}1\frac{3}{16}$	$1\text{-}7\frac{21}{32}$	$1\text{-}2\frac{3}{32}$	$1\text{-}9$	$1\text{-}3$	$1\text{-}10\frac{11}{32}$
$\frac{5}{8}$	$11\frac{7}{16}$	$1\text{-}5\frac{1}{32}$	$1\text{-}0\frac{11}{32}$	$1\text{-}6\frac{3}{8}$	$1\text{-}1\frac{1}{4}$	$1\text{-}7\frac{3}{4}$	$1\text{-}2\frac{5}{32}$	$1\text{-}9\frac{3}{32}$	$1\text{-}3\frac{1}{16}$	$1\text{-}10\frac{7}{16}$
$\frac{11}{16}$	$11\frac{1}{2}$	$1\text{-}5\frac{1}{8}$	$1\text{-}0\frac{13}{32}$	$1\text{-}6\frac{15}{32}$	$1\text{-}1\frac{5}{16}$	$1\text{-}7\frac{13}{16}$	$1\text{-}2\frac{7}{32}$	$1\text{-}9\frac{5}{32}$	$1\text{-}3\frac{1}{8}$	$1\text{-}10\frac{17}{32}$
$\frac{3}{4}$	$11\frac{9}{16}$	$1\text{-}5\frac{7}{32}$	$1\text{-}0\frac{15}{32}$	$1\text{-}6\frac{9}{16}$	$1\text{-}1\frac{3}{8}$	$1\text{-}7\frac{29}{32}$	$1\text{-}2\frac{9}{32}$	$1\text{-}9\frac{1}{4}$	$1\text{-}3\frac{3}{32}$	$1\text{-}10\frac{19}{32}$
$\frac{13}{16}$	$11\frac{5}{8}$	$1\text{-}5\frac{9}{32}$	$1\text{-}0\frac{17}{32}$	$1\text{-}6\frac{21}{32}$	$1\text{-}1\frac{7}{16}$	$1\text{-}8$	$1\text{-}2\frac{11}{32}$	$1\text{-}9\frac{11}{32}$	$1\text{-}3\frac{1}{4}$	$1\text{-}10\frac{11}{16}$
$\frac{7}{8}$	$11\frac{21}{32}$	$1\text{-}5\frac{3}{8}$	$1\text{-}0\frac{9}{16}$	$1\text{-}6\frac{23}{32}$	$1\text{-}1\frac{15}{16}$	$1\text{-}8\frac{1}{8}$	$1\text{-}2\frac{3}{8}$	$1\text{-}9\frac{7}{16}$	$1\text{-}3\frac{9}{32}$	$1\text{-}10\frac{25}{32}$
$\frac{15}{16}$	$11\frac{23}{32}$	$1\text{-}5\frac{15}{32}$	$1\text{-}0\frac{5}{8}$	$1\text{-}6\frac{13}{16}$	$1\text{-}1\frac{17}{32}$	$1\text{-}8\frac{5}{32}$	$1\text{-}2\frac{7}{16}$	$1\text{-}9\frac{1}{2}$	$1\text{-}3\frac{11}{32}$	$1\text{-}10\frac{27}{32}$

Ins.	17″ Rise	17″ Slope	18″ Rise	18″ Slope	19″ Rise	19″ Slope	20″ Rise	20″ Slope	21″ Rise	21″ Slope
0	$1\text{-}3\frac{13}{32}$	$1\text{-}10\frac{15}{16}$	$1\text{-}4\frac{5}{16}$	$2\text{-}0\frac{9}{32}$	$1\text{-}5\frac{7}{32}$	$2\text{-}1\frac{21}{32}$	$1\text{-}6\frac{1}{8}$	$2\text{-}3$	$1\text{-}7\frac{1}{32}$	$2\text{-}4\frac{11}{32}$
$\frac{1}{16}$	$1\text{-}3\frac{15}{32}$	$1\text{-}11\frac{1}{32}$	$1\text{-}4\frac{3}{8}$	$2\text{-}0\frac{3}{8}$	$1\text{-}5\frac{9}{32}$	$2\text{-}1\frac{23}{32}$	$1\text{-}6\frac{3}{16}$	$2\text{-}3\frac{1}{16}$	$1\text{-}7\frac{3}{32}$	$2\text{-}4\frac{7}{16}$
$\frac{1}{8}$	$1\text{-}3\frac{17}{32}$	$1\text{-}11\frac{1}{8}$	$1\text{-}4\frac{7}{16}$	$2\text{-}0\frac{15}{32}$	$1\text{-}5\frac{11}{32}$	$2\text{-}1\frac{13}{16}$	$1\text{-}6\frac{1}{4}$	$2\text{-}3\frac{5}{32}$	$1\text{-}7\frac{5}{32}$	$2\text{-}4\frac{1}{2}$
$\frac{3}{16}$	$1\text{-}3\frac{9}{32}$	$1\text{-}11\frac{3}{16}$	$1\text{-}4\frac{15}{32}$	$2\text{-}0\frac{17}{32}$	$1\text{-}5\frac{3}{8}$	$2\text{-}1\frac{29}{32}$	$1\text{-}6\frac{9}{32}$	$2\text{-}3\frac{1}{4}$	$1\text{-}7\frac{3}{16}$	$2\text{-}4\frac{19}{32}$
$\frac{1}{4}$	$1\text{-}3\frac{5}{8}$	$1\text{-}11\frac{9}{32}$	$1\text{-}4\frac{17}{32}$	$2\text{-}0\frac{5}{8}$	$1\text{-}5\frac{7}{16}$	$2\text{-}1\frac{31}{32}$	$1\text{-}6\frac{11}{32}$	$2\text{-}3\frac{11}{32}$	$1\text{-}7\frac{1}{4}$	$2\text{-}4\frac{11}{16}$
$\frac{5}{16}$	$1\text{-}3\frac{11}{16}$	$1\text{-}11\frac{3}{8}$	$1\text{-}4\frac{19}{32}$	$2\text{-}0\frac{23}{32}$	$1\text{-}5\frac{1}{2}$	$2\text{-}2\frac{1}{16}$	$1\text{-}6\frac{13}{32}$	$2\text{-}3\frac{13}{32}$	$1\text{-}7\frac{5}{16}$	$2\text{-}4\frac{3}{4}$
$\frac{3}{8}$	$1\text{-}3\frac{3}{4}$	$1\text{-}11\frac{7}{16}$	$1\text{-}4\frac{21}{32}$	$2\text{-}0\frac{13}{16}$	$1\text{-}5\frac{9}{16}$	$2\text{-}2\frac{5}{32}$	$1\text{-}6\frac{15}{32}$	$2\text{-}3\frac{1}{2}$	$1\text{-}7\frac{3}{8}$	$2\text{-}4\frac{27}{32}$
$\frac{7}{16}$	$1\text{-}3\frac{13}{16}$	$1\text{-}11\frac{17}{32}$	$1\text{-}4\frac{23}{32}$	$2\text{-}0\frac{7}{8}$	$1\text{-}5\frac{5}{8}$	$2\text{-}2\frac{7}{32}$	$1\text{-}6\frac{17}{32}$	$2\text{-}3\frac{19}{32}$	$1\text{-}7\frac{7}{16}$	$2\text{-}4\frac{15}{16}$
$\frac{1}{2}$	$1\text{-}3\frac{7}{8}$	$1\text{-}11\frac{5}{8}$	$1\text{-}4\frac{3}{4}$	$2\text{-}0\frac{31}{32}$	$1\text{-}5\frac{11}{16}$	$2\text{-}2\frac{5}{16}$	$1\text{-}6\frac{9}{16}$	$2\text{-}3\frac{21}{32}$	$1\text{-}7\frac{1}{2}$	$2\text{-}5$
$\frac{9}{16}$	$1\text{-}3\frac{29}{32}$	$1\text{-}11\frac{11}{16}$	$1\text{-}4\frac{13}{16}$	$2\text{-}1\frac{1}{16}$	$1\text{-}5\frac{23}{32}$	$2\text{-}2\frac{13}{32}$	$1\text{-}6\frac{5}{8}$	$2\text{-}3\frac{3}{4}$	$1\text{-}7\frac{17}{32}$	$2\text{-}5\frac{3}{32}$
$\frac{5}{8}$	$1\text{-}3\frac{31}{32}$	$1\text{-}11\frac{25}{32}$	$1\text{-}4\frac{7}{8}$	$2\text{-}1\frac{1}{8}$	$1\text{-}5\frac{25}{32}$	$2\text{-}2\frac{1}{2}$	$1\text{-}6\frac{11}{16}$	$2\text{-}3\frac{27}{32}$	$1\text{-}7\frac{19}{32}$	$2\text{-}5\frac{3}{16}$
$\frac{11}{16}$	$1\text{-}4\frac{1}{32}$	$1\text{-}11\frac{7}{8}$	$1\text{-}4\frac{15}{16}$	$2\text{-}1\frac{7}{32}$	$1\text{-}5\frac{27}{32}$	$2\text{-}2\frac{9}{16}$	$1\text{-}6\frac{3}{4}$	$2\text{-}3\frac{29}{32}$	$1\text{-}7\frac{21}{32}$	$2\text{-}5\frac{9}{32}$
$\frac{3}{4}$	$1\text{-}4\frac{3}{32}$	$1\text{-}11\frac{31}{32}$	$1\text{-}5$	$2\text{-}1\frac{5}{16}$	$1\text{-}5\frac{29}{32}$	$2\text{-}2\frac{21}{32}$	$1\text{-}6\frac{13}{16}$	$2\text{-}4$	$1\text{-}7\frac{23}{32}$	$2\text{-}5\frac{11}{32}$
$\frac{13}{16}$	$1\text{-}4\frac{5}{32}$	$2\text{-}0\frac{1}{32}$	$1\text{-}5\frac{1}{16}$	$2\text{-}1\frac{3}{8}$	$1\text{-}5\frac{31}{32}$	$2\text{-}2\frac{3}{4}$	$1\text{-}6\frac{7}{8}$	$2\text{-}4\frac{3}{32}$	$1\text{-}7\frac{25}{32}$	$2\text{-}5\frac{7}{16}$
$\frac{7}{8}$	$1\text{-}4\frac{3}{16}$	$2\text{-}0\frac{1}{8}$	$1\text{-}5\frac{3}{32}$	$2\text{-}1\frac{15}{32}$	$1\text{-}6$	$2\text{-}2\frac{13}{16}$	$1\text{-}6\frac{29}{32}$	$2\text{-}4\frac{3}{16}$	$1\text{-}7\frac{13}{16}$	$2\text{-}5\frac{17}{32}$
$\frac{15}{16}$	$1\text{-}4\frac{1}{4}$	$2\text{-}0\frac{7}{32}$	$1\text{-}5\frac{5}{32}$	$2\text{-}1\frac{9}{16}$	$1\text{-}6\frac{1}{16}$	$2\text{-}2\frac{29}{32}$	$1\text{-}6\frac{31}{32}$	$2\text{-}4\frac{1}{4}$	$1\text{-}7\frac{7}{8}$	$2\text{-}5\frac{19}{32}$

Feet	40′ Rise	40′ Slope	50′ Rise	50′ Slope	60′ Rise	60′ Slope	70′ Rise	70′ Slope
0	$36\text{-}3$	$53\text{-}11\frac{25}{32}$	$45\text{-}3\frac{3}{4}$	$67\text{-}5\frac{23}{32}$	$54\text{-}4\frac{1}{2}$	$80\text{-}11\frac{11}{16}$	$63\text{-}5\frac{1}{4}$	$94\text{-}5\frac{5}{8}$
1	$37\text{-}1\frac{7}{8}$	$55\text{-}3\frac{31}{32}$	$46\text{-}2\frac{5}{8}$	$68\text{-}9\frac{15}{16}$	$55\text{-}3\frac{3}{8}$	$82\text{-}3\frac{7}{8}$	$64\text{-}4\frac{1}{8}$	$95\text{-}9\frac{13}{16}$
2	$38\text{-}0\frac{3}{8}$	$56\text{-}8\frac{3}{16}$	$47\text{-}1\frac{1}{2}$	$70\text{-}2\frac{1}{8}$	$56\text{-}2\frac{1}{4}$	$83\text{-}8\frac{1}{16}$	$65\text{-}3$	$97\text{-}2$
3	$38\text{-}11\frac{5}{8}$	$58\text{-}0\frac{3}{8}$	$48\text{-}0\frac{3}{8}$	$71\text{-}6\frac{5}{16}$	$57\text{-}1\frac{1}{8}$	$85\text{-}0\frac{1}{4}$	$66\text{-}1\frac{7}{8}$	$98\text{-}6\frac{7}{32}$
4	$39\text{-}10\frac{1}{2}$	$59\text{-}4\frac{9}{16}$	$48\text{-}11\frac{1}{4}$	$72\text{-}10\frac{1}{2}$	$58\text{-}0$	$86\text{-}4\frac{15}{32}$	$67\text{-}0\frac{3}{4}$	$99\text{-}10\frac{13}{32}$
5	$40\text{-}9\frac{3}{8}$	$60\text{-}8\frac{3}{4}$	$49\text{-}10\frac{1}{8}$	$74\text{-}2\frac{23}{32}$	$58\text{-}10\frac{7}{8}$	$87\text{-}8\frac{21}{32}$	$67\text{-}11\frac{5}{8}$	$101\text{-}2\frac{19}{32}$
6	$41\text{-}8\frac{1}{4}$	$62\text{-}0\frac{15}{16}$	$50\text{-}9$	$75\text{-}6\frac{29}{32}$	$59\text{-}9\frac{3}{4}$	$89\text{-}0\frac{27}{32}$	$68\text{-}10\frac{1}{2}$	$102\text{-}6\frac{25}{32}$
7	$42\text{-}7\frac{1}{8}$	$63\text{-}5\frac{5}{32}$	$51\text{-}7\frac{7}{8}$	$76\text{-}11\frac{3}{32}$	$60\text{-}8\frac{5}{8}$	$90\text{-}5\frac{1}{32}$	$69\text{-}9\frac{3}{8}$	$103\text{-}11$
8	$43\text{-}6$	$64\text{-}9\frac{11}{32}$	$52\text{-}6\frac{3}{4}$	$78\text{-}3\frac{9}{32}$	$61\text{-}7\frac{1}{2}$	$91\text{-}9\frac{7}{32}$	$70\text{-}8\frac{1}{4}$	$105\text{-}3\frac{3}{16}$
9	$44\text{-}4\frac{7}{8}$	$66\text{-}1\frac{17}{32}$	$53\text{-}5\frac{5}{8}$	$79\text{-}7\frac{15}{32}$	$62\text{-}6\frac{3}{8}$	$93\text{-}1\frac{7}{16}$	$71\text{-}7\frac{1}{8}$	$106\text{-}7\frac{3}{8}$

natsin A=0.6715194247; natcos A=0.7409869514; nattan A=0.9062500000; natcot A=1.1034482758

Inches	0" Rise	0" Slope	1" Rise	1" Slope	2" Rise	2" Slope	3" Rise	3" Slope	4" Rise	4" Slope	5" Rise	5" Slope
0	0	0	29/32	1 11/32	1 13/16	2 23/32	2 3/4	4 1/16	3 21/32	5 13/32	4 9/16	6 3/4
1/16	1/16	3/32	31/32	1 7/16	1 7/8	2 25/32	2 25/32	4 5/32	3 11/16	5 1/2	4 5/8	6 27/32
1/8	1/8	5/32	1 1/32	1 17/32	1 15/16	2 7/8	2 27/32	4 7/32	3 3/4	5 19/32	4 21/32	6 15/16
3/16	5/32	1/4	1 3/32	1 19/32	2	2 31/32	2 29/32	4 5/16	3 13/16	5 21/32	4 23/32	7 1/32
1/4	7/32	11/32	1 1/8	1 11/16	2 1/16	3 1/16	2 31/32	4 13/32	3 7/8	5 3/4	4 25/32	7 3/32
5/16	9/32	7/16	1 3/16	1 25/32	2 3/32	3 1/8	3 1/32	4 15/32	3 15/16	5 27/32	4 27/32	7 3/16
3/8	11/32	1/2	1 1/4	1 7/8	2 5/32	3 7/32	3 1/16	4 9/16	4	5 29/32	4 29/32	7 9/32
7/16	13/32	19/32	1 5/16	1 15/16	2 7/32	3 5/16	3 1/8	4 21/32	4 1/16	6	4 31/32	7 11/32
1/2	15/32	11/16	1 3/8	2 1/16	2 9/32	3 3/8	3 3/16	4 3/4	4 3/32	6 3/32	5	7 7/16
9/16	1/2	3/4	1 7/16	2 1/8	2 11/32	3 15/32	3 1/4	4 13/16	4 5/32	6 3/16	5 1/16	7 17/32
5/8	9/16	27/32	1 15/32	2 3/16	2 13/32	3 9/16	3 5/16	4 29/32	4 7/32	6 1/4	5 1/8	7 5/8
11/16	5/8	15/16	1 17/32	2 9/32	2 7/16	3 5/8	3 3/8	5	4 9/32	6 11/32	5 3/16	7 11/16
3/4	11/16	1	1 19/32	2 3/8	2 1/2	3 23/32	3 13/32	5 1/16	4 11/32	6 7/16	5 1/4	7 25/32
13/16	3/4	1 3/32	1 21/32	2 7/16	2 9/16	3 13/16	3 15/32	5 5/32	4 3/8	6 1/2	5 5/16	7 7/8
7/8	13/16	1 3/16	1 23/32	2 17/32	2 5/8	3 7/8	3 17/32	5 1/4	4 7/16	6 19/32	5 11/32	7 15/16
15/16	27/32	1 9/32	1 25/32	2 5/8	2 11/16	3 31/32	3 19/32	5 5/16	4 1/2	6 11/16	5 13/32	8 1/32

Inches	6" Rise	6" Slope	7" Rise	7" Slope	8" Rise	8" Slope	9" Rise	9" Slope	10" Rise	10" Slope	11" Rise	11" Slope
0	5 15/32	8 1/8	6 3/8	9 15/32	7 9/32	10 13/16	8 3/16	1-0 3/16	9 1/8	1-1 17/32	10 1/32	1-2 7/8
1/16	5 17/32	8 3/16	6 7/16	9 9/16	7 11/32	10 29/32	8 1/4	1-0 1/4	9 5/32	1-1 5/8	10 3/32	1-2 31/32
1/8	5 19/32	8 9/32	6 1/2	9 5/8	7 13/32	11	8 5/16	1-0 11/32	9 7/32	1-1 11/16	10 1/8	1-3 1/16
3/16	5 5/8	8 3/8	6 9/16	9 23/32	7 15/32	11 1/16	8 3/8	1-0 7/16	9 9/32	1-1 25/32	10 3/16	1-3 3/16
1/4	5 11/16	8 15/32	6 19/32	9 13/16	7 17/32	11 5/32	8 7/16	1-0 17/32	9 11/32	1-1 7/8	10 1/4	1-3 7/32
5/16	5 3/4	8 17/32	6 21/32	9 29/32	7 9/16	11 1/4	8 1/2	1-0 19/32	9 13/32	1-1 31/32	10 5/16	1-3 5/16
3/8	5 13/16	8 5/8	6 23/32	9 31/32	7 5/8	11 11/32	8 17/32	1-0 11/16	9 15/32	1-2 1/32	10 3/8	1-3 13/32
7/16	5 7/8	8 23/32	6 25/32	10 1/16	7 11/16	11 13/32	8 19/32	1-0 25/32	9 1/2	1-2 1/8	10 7/16	1-3 15/32
1/2	5 15/16	8 25/32	6 27/32	10 5/32	7 3/4	11 1/2	8 21/32	1-0 27/32	9 9/16	1-2 7/32	10 15/32	1-3 9/16
9/16	5 31/32	8 7/8	6 29/32	10 7/32	7 13/16	11 19/32	8 23/32	1-0 15/16	9 5/8	1-2 9/32	10 17/32	1-3 21/32
5/8	6 1/32	8 31/32	6 15/16	10 5/16	7 7/8	11 21/32	8 25/32	1-1 1/32	9 11/16	1-2 3/8	10 19/32	1-3 23/32
11/16	6 3/32	9 1/16	7	10 13/32	7 29/32	11 3/4	8 27/32	1-1 3/32	9 3/4	1-2 15/32	10 21/32	1-3 13/16
3/4	6 5/32	9 1/8	7 1/16	10 1/2	7 31/32	11 27/32	8 7/8	1-1 3/16	9 13/16	1-2 17/32	10 23/32	1-3 29/32
13/16	6 7/32	9 7/32	7 1/8	10 9/16	8 1/32	11 15/16	8 15/16	1-1 9/32	9 27/32	1-2 5/8	10 25/32	1-3 31/32
7/8	6 9/32	9 5/16	7 3/16	10 21/32	8 3/32	1-0	9	1-1 3/8	9 29/32	1-2 23/32	10 13/16	1-4 1/16
15/16	6 5/16	9 3/8	7 1/4	10 3/4	8 5/32	1-0 3/32	9 1/16	1-1 7/16	9 31/32	1-2 13/16	10 7/8	1-4 5/32

Feet	0' Rise	0' Slope	10' Rise	10' Slope	20' Rise	20' Slope	30' Rise	30' Slope
0	0	0	9-1 3/8	13-6 3/8	18-2 3/4	27-0 23/32	27-4 1/8	40-7 3/32
1	-10 15/16	1-4 1/4	10-0 5/16	14-10 19/32	19-1 11/16	28-4 31/32	28-3 1/16	41-11 11/32
2	1-9 7/8	2-8 15/32	10-11 1/4	16-2 27/32	20-0 5/8	29-9 7/32	29-2	43-3 9/16
3	2-8 13/16	4-0 23/32	11-10 3/16	17-7 1/16	20-11 9/16	31-1 7/16	30-0 15/16	44-7 13/16
4	3-7 3/4	5-4 15/16	12-9 1/8	18-11 5/16	21-10 1/2	32-5 11/16	30-11 7/8	46-0 1/32
5	4-6 11/16	6-9 3/16	13-8 1/16	20-3 9/16	22-9 7/16	33-9 29/32	31-10 13/16	47-4 9/32
6	5-5 5/8	8-1 13/32	14-7	21-7 25/32	23-8 3/8	35-2 5/32	32-9 3/4	48-8 17/32
7	6-4 9/16	9-5 21/32	15-5 15/16	23-0 1/32	24-7 5/16	36-6 3/8	33-8 11/16	50-0 3/4
8	7-3 1/2	10-9 29/32	16-4 7/8	24-4 1/4	25-6 1/4	37-10 5/8	34-7 5/8	51-5
9	8-2 7/16	12-2 1/8	17-3 13/16	25-8 1/2	26-5 3/16	39-2 7/8	35-6 9/16	52-9 7/32

A = 42° 20' 52''; logsin A = 9.82842; logcos A = 9.86868; logtan A = 9.95974; logcot A = 0.04026

Ins.	12″ Rise	12″ Slope	13″ Rise	13″ Slope	14″ Rise	14″ Slope	15″ Rise	15″ Slope	16″ Rise	16″ Slope
0	10¹⁵⁄₁₆	1-4¼	11²⁷⁄₃₂	1-5¹⁹⁄₃₂	1-0¾	1-6¹⁵⁄₁₆	1-1¹¹⁄₁₆	1-8⁹⁄₃₂	1-2¹⁹⁄₃₂	1-9²¹⁄₃₂
¹⁄₁₆	11	1-4⁵⁄₁₆	11²⁹⁄₃₂	1-5¹¹⁄₁₆	1-0¹³⁄₁₆	1-7¹⁄₃₂	1-1²³⁄₃₂	1-8⅜	1-2⅝	1-9²³⁄₃₂
⅛	11¹⁄₁₆	1-4¹³⁄₃₂	11³¹⁄₃₂	1-5¾	1-0⅞	1-7⅛	1-1²⁵⁄₃₂	1-8¹⁵⁄₃₂	1-2¹¹⁄₁₆	1-9¹³⁄₁₆
³⁄₁₆	11³⁄₃₂	1-4½	1-0¹⁄₃₂	1-5²⁷⁄₃₂	1-0¹⁵⁄₁₆	1-7³⁄₁₆	1-1²⁷⁄₃₂	1-8⁹⁄₁₆	1-2¾	1-9²⁹⁄₃₂
¼	11⁵⁄₃₂	1-4⁹⁄₁₆	1-0¹⁄₁₆	1-5¹⁵⁄₁₆	1-1	1-7⁹⁄₃₂	1-1²⁹⁄₃₂	1-8⅝	1-2¹³⁄₁₆	1-10
⁵⁄₁₆	11⁷⁄₃₂	1-4²¹⁄₃₂	1-0⅛	1-6	1-1¹⁄₃₂	1-7⅜	1-1³¹⁄₃₂	1-8²³⁄₃₂	1-2⅞	1-10¹⁄₁₆
⅜	11⁹⁄₃₂	1-4¾	1-0³⁄₁₆	1-6³⁄₃₂	1-1³⁄₃₂	1-7⁷⁄₁₆	1-2	1-8¹³⁄₁₆	1-2¹⁵⁄₁₆	1-10⁵⁄₃₂
⁷⁄₁₆	11¹¹⁄₃₂	1-4²⁷⁄₃₂	1-0¼	1-6³⁄₁₆	1-1⁵⁄₃₂	1-7¹⁷⁄₃₂	1-2¹⁄₁₆	1-8⅞	1-2³¹⁄₃₂	1-10¼
½	11¹³⁄₃₂	1-4²⁹⁄₃₂	1-0⁵⁄₁₆	1-6⁹⁄₃₂	1-1⁷⁄₃₂	1-7⅝	1-2⅛	1-8³¹⁄₃₂	1-3¹⁄₃₂	1-10⁵⁄₁₆
⁹⁄₁₆	11⁷⁄₁₆	1-5	1-0⅜	1-6¹¹⁄₃₂	1-1⁹⁄₃₂	1-7²³⁄₃₂	1-2³⁄₁₆	1-9¹⁄₁₆	1-3³⁄₃₂	1-10¹³⁄₃₂
⅝	11½	1-5³⁄₃₂	1-0¹³⁄₃₂	1-6⁷⁄₁₆	1-1¹¹⁄₃₂	1-7²⁵⁄₃₂	1-2¼	1-9⁵⁄₃₂	1-3⁵⁄₃₂	1-10½
¹¹⁄₁₆	11⁹⁄₁₆	1-5⁵⁄₃₂	1-0¹⁵⁄₃₂	1-6¹⁷⁄₃₂	1-1⅜	1-7⅞	1-2⁵⁄₁₆	1-9⁷⁄₃₂	1-3⁷⁄₃₂	1-10¹⁹⁄₃₂
¾	11⅝	1-5¼	1-0¹⁷⁄₃₂	1-6¹⁹⁄₃₂	1-1⁷⁄₁₆	1-7³¹⁄₃₂	1-2¹¹⁄₃₂	1-9⁵⁄₁₆	1-3⁹⁄₃₂	1-10²¹⁄₃₂
¹³⁄₁₆	11¹¹⁄₁₆	1-5¹¹⁄₃₂	1-0¹⁹⁄₃₂	1-6¹¹⁄₁₆	1-1½	1-8¹⁄₃₂	1-2¹³⁄₃₂	1-9¹³⁄₃₂	1-3⁵⁄₁₆	1-10¾
⅞	11¾	1-5¹³⁄₃₂	1-0²¹⁄₃₂	1-6²⁵⁄₃₂	1-1⁹⁄₁₆	1-8⅛	1-2¹⁵⁄₃₂	1-9¹⁵⁄₃₂	1-3⅜	1-10²⁷⁄₃₂
¹⁵⁄₁₆	11²⁵⁄₃₂	1-5½	1-0²³⁄₃₂	1-6²⁷⁄₃₂	1-1⅝	1-8⁷⁄₃₂	1-2¹⁷⁄₃₂	1-9⁹⁄₁₆	1-3⁷⁄₁₆	1-10²⁹⁄₃₂

Ins.	17″ Rise	17″ Slope	18″ Rise	18″ Slope	19″ Rise	19″ Slope	20″ Rise	20″ Slope	21″ Rise	21″ Slope
0	1-3½	1-11	1-4¹³⁄₃₂	2-0¹¹⁄₃₂	1-5⁵⁄₁₆	2-1²³⁄₃₂	1-6⁷⁄₃₂	2-3¹⁄₁₆	1-7⅛	2-4¹³⁄₃₂
¹⁄₁₆	1-3⁹⁄₁₆	1-11³⁄₃₂	1-4¹⁵⁄₃₂	2-0⁷⁄₁₆	1-5⅜	2-1²⁵⁄₃₂	1-6⁹⁄₃₂	2-3⁵⁄₃₂	1-7³⁄₁₆	2-4½
⅛	1-3¹⁹⁄₃₂	1-11⁵⁄₃₂	1-4¹⁷⁄₃₂	2-0¹⁷⁄₃₂	1-5⁷⁄₁₆	2-1⅞	1-6¹¹⁄₃₂	2-3⁷⁄₃₂	1-7¼	2-4¹⁹⁄₃₂
³⁄₁₆	1-3²¹⁄₃₂	1-11¼	1-4⁹⁄₁₆	2-0¹⁹⁄₃₂	1-5½	2-1³¹⁄₃₂	1-6¹³⁄₃₂	2-3⁵⁄₁₆	1-7⁵⁄₁₆	2-4²¹⁄₃₂
¼	1-3²³⁄₃₂	1-11¹¹⁄₃₂	1-4⅝	2-0¹¹⁄₁₆	1-5¹⁷⁄₃₂	2-2¹⁄₃₂	1-6¹⁵⁄₃₂	2-3¹³⁄₃₂	1-7⅜	2-4¾
⁵⁄₁₆	1-3²⁵⁄₃₂	1-11⁷⁄₁₆	1-4¹¹⁄₁₆	2-0²⁵⁄₃₂	1-5¹⁹⁄₃₂	2-2⅛	1-6½	2-3¹⁵⁄₃₂	1-7⁷⁄₁₆	2-4²⁷⁄₃₂
⅜	1-3²⁷⁄₃₂	1-11½	1-4¾	2-0⅞	1-5²¹⁄₃₂	2-2⁷⁄₃₂	1-6⁹⁄₁₆	2-3⁹⁄₁₆	1-7¹⁵⁄₃₂	2-4²⁹⁄₃₂
⁷⁄₁₆	1-3²⁹⁄₃₂	1-11¹⁹⁄₃₂	1-4¹³⁄₁₆	2-0¹⁵⁄₁₆	1-5²³⁄₃₂	2-2⁵⁄₁₆	1-6⅝	2-3²¹⁄₃₂	1-7¹⁷⁄₃₂	2-5
½	1-3¹⁵⁄₁₆	1-11¹¹⁄₁₆	1-4⅞	2-1¹⁄₃₂	1-5²⁵⁄₃₂	2-2⅜	1-6¹¹⁄₁₆	2-3¾	1-7¹⁹⁄₃₂	2-5³⁄₃₂
⁹⁄₁₆	1-4	1-11¾	1-4²⁹⁄₃₂	2-1⅛	1-5²⁷⁄₃₂	2-2¹⁵⁄₃₂	1-6¾	2-3¹³⁄₁₆	1-7²¹⁄₃₂	2-5³⁄₁₆
⅝	1-4¹⁄₁₆	1-11²⁷⁄₃₂	1-4³¹⁄₃₂	2-1³⁄₁₆	1-5⅞	2-2⁹⁄₁₆	1-6¹³⁄₁₆	2-3²⁹⁄₃₂	1-7²³⁄₃₂	2-5¼
¹¹⁄₁₆	1-4⅛	1-11¹⁵⁄₁₆	1-5¹⁄₃₂	2-1⁹⁄₃₂	1-5¹⁵⁄₁₆	2-2⅝	1-6²⁷⁄₃₂	2-4	1-7²⁵⁄₃₂	2-5¹¹⁄₃₂
¾	1-4³⁄₁₆	2-0¹⁄₃₂	1-5³⁄₃₂	2-1⅜	1-6	2-2²³⁄₃₂	1-6²⁹⁄₃₂	2-4¹⁄₁₆	1-7¹³⁄₁₆	2-5⁷⁄₁₆
¹³⁄₁₆	1-4¼	2-0³⁄₃₂	1-5⁵⁄₃₂	2-1¹⁵⁄₃₂	1-6¹⁄₁₆	2-2¹³⁄₁₆	1-6³¹⁄₃₂	2-4⁵⁄₃₂	1-7⅞	2-5½
⅞	1-4⁹⁄₃₂	2-0³⁄₁₆	1-5⁷⁄₃₂	2-1¹⁷⁄₃₂	1-6⅛	2-2²⁹⁄₃₂	1-7¹⁄₃₂	2-4¼	1-7¹⁵⁄₁₆	2-5¹⁹⁄₃₂
¹⁵⁄₁₆	1-4¹¹⁄₃₂	2-0⁹⁄₃₂	1-5¼	2-1⅝	1-6³⁄₁₆	2-2³¹⁄₃₂	1-7³⁄₃₂	2-4¹¹⁄₃₂	1-8	2-5¹¹⁄₁₆

Feet	40′ Rise	40′ Slope	50′ Rise	50′ Slope	60′ Rise	60′ Slope	70′ Rise	70′ Slope
0	36-5½	54-1¹⁵⁄₃₂	45-6⅞	67-7²⁷⁄₃₂	54-8¼	81-2³⁄₁₆	63-9⅝	94-8⁹⁄₁₆
1	37-4⁷⁄₁₆	55-5¹¹⁄₁₆	46-5¹³⁄₁₆	69-0¹⁄₁₆	55-7³⁄₁₆	82-6⁷⁄₁₆	64-8⁹⁄₁₆	96-0¹³⁄₁₆
2	38-3⅜	56-9¹⁵⁄₁₆	47-4¾	70-4⁵⁄₁₆	56-6⅛	83-10¹¹⁄₁₆	65-7½	97-5¹⁄₃₂
3	39-2⁵⁄₁₆	58-2³⁄₁₆	48-3¹¹⁄₁₆	71-8¹⁷⁄₃₂	57-5¹⁄₁₆	85-2²⁹⁄₃₂	66-6⁷⁄₁₆	98-9⁹⁄₃₂
4	40-1¼	59-6¹³⁄₃₂	49-2⅝	73-0²⁵⁄₃₂	58-4	86-7⁵⁄₃₂	67-5⅜	100-1½
5	41-0³⁄₁₆	60-10²¹⁄₃₂	50-1⁹⁄₁₆	74-5¹⁄₃₂	59-2¹⁵⁄₁₆	87-11⅜	68-4⁵⁄₁₆	101-5¾
6	41-11⅛	62-2⅞	51-0½	75-9¼	60-1⅞	89-3⅝	69-3¼	102-10
7	42-10¹⁄₁₆	63-7⅛	51-11⁷⁄₁₆	77-1½	61-0¹³⁄₁₆	90-7²⁷⁄₃₂	70-2³⁄₁₆	104-2⁷⁄₃₂
8	43-9	64-11¹¹⁄₃₂	52-10⅜	78-5²³⁄₃₂	61-11¾	92-0³⁄₃₂	71-1⅛	105-6¹⁵⁄₃₂
9	44-7¹⁵⁄₁₆	66-3¹⁹⁄₃₂	53-9⁵⁄₁₆	79-9³¹⁄₃₂	62-10¹¹⁄₁₆	93-4¹¹⁄₃₂	72-0¹⁄₁₆	106-10¹¹⁄₁₆

natsin A=0.6736302046; natcos A=0.7390685674; nattan A=0.9114583333; natcot A=1.0971428571

Inches	0″ Rise	0″ Slope	1″ Rise	1″ Slope	2″ Rise	2″ Slope	3″ Rise	3″ Slope	4″ Rise	4″ Slope	5″ Rise	5″ Slope
0	0	0	$\frac{29}{32}$	$1\frac{1}{32}$	$1\frac{27}{32}$	$2\frac{23}{32}$	$2\frac{3}{4}$	$4\frac{1}{16}$	$3\frac{21}{32}$	$5\frac{7}{16}$	$4\frac{19}{32}$	$6\frac{25}{32}$
$\frac{1}{16}$	$\frac{1}{16}$	$\frac{3}{32}$	$\frac{31}{32}$	$1\frac{7}{16}$	$1\frac{7}{8}$	$2\frac{13}{16}$	$2\frac{13}{16}$	$4\frac{5}{32}$	$3\frac{23}{32}$	$5\frac{1}{2}$	$4\frac{5}{8}$	$6\frac{7}{8}$
$\frac{1}{8}$	$\frac{1}{8}$	$\frac{5}{32}$	$1\frac{1}{32}$	$1\frac{17}{32}$	$1\frac{15}{16}$	$2\frac{7}{8}$	$2\frac{7}{8}$	$4\frac{1}{4}$	$3\frac{25}{32}$	$5\frac{19}{32}$	$4\frac{11}{16}$	$6\frac{15}{16}$
$\frac{3}{16}$	$\frac{3}{16}$	$\frac{1}{4}$	$1\frac{3}{32}$	$1\frac{5}{8}$	2	$2\frac{31}{32}$	$2\frac{15}{16}$	$4\frac{5}{16}$	$3\frac{27}{32}$	$5\frac{11}{16}$	$4\frac{3}{4}$	$7\frac{1}{32}$
$\frac{1}{4}$	$\frac{7}{32}$	$\frac{11}{32}$	$1\frac{5}{32}$	$1\frac{11}{16}$	$2\frac{1}{16}$	$3\frac{1}{16}$	$2\frac{31}{32}$	$4\frac{13}{32}$	$3\frac{29}{32}$	$5\frac{3}{4}$	$4\frac{13}{16}$	$7\frac{1}{8}$
$\frac{5}{16}$	$\frac{9}{32}$	$\frac{7}{16}$	$1\frac{3}{16}$	$1\frac{25}{32}$	$2\frac{1}{8}$	$3\frac{1}{8}$	$3\frac{1}{32}$	$4\frac{1}{2}$	$3\frac{15}{16}$	$5\frac{27}{32}$	$4\frac{7}{8}$	$7\frac{1}{2}$
$\frac{3}{8}$	$\frac{11}{32}$	$\frac{1}{2}$	$1\frac{1}{4}$	$1\frac{7}{8}$	$2\frac{3}{16}$	$3\frac{7}{32}$	$3\frac{3}{32}$	$4\frac{19}{32}$	4	$5\frac{15}{16}$	$4\frac{15}{16}$	$7\frac{9}{32}$
$\frac{7}{16}$	$\frac{13}{32}$	$\frac{19}{32}$	$1\frac{9}{32}$	$1\frac{15}{16}$	$2\frac{1}{4}$	$3\frac{9}{32}$	$3\frac{5}{32}$	$4\frac{21}{32}$	$4\frac{1}{16}$	$6\frac{1}{2}$	5	$7\frac{3}{8}$
$\frac{1}{2}$	$\frac{15}{32}$	$\frac{11}{16}$	$1\frac{3}{8}$	$2\frac{1}{32}$	$2\frac{9}{32}$	$3\frac{13}{32}$	$3\frac{7}{32}$	$4\frac{3}{4}$	$4\frac{1}{8}$	$6\frac{3}{32}$	$5\frac{1}{32}$	$7\frac{15}{32}$
$\frac{9}{16}$	$\frac{1}{2}$	$\frac{3}{4}$	$1\frac{7}{16}$	$2\frac{1}{8}$	$2\frac{11}{32}$	$3\frac{15}{32}$	$3\frac{1}{4}$	$4\frac{27}{32}$	$4\frac{3}{16}$	$6\frac{3}{16}$	$5\frac{3}{32}$	$7\frac{17}{32}$
$\frac{5}{8}$	$\frac{9}{16}$	$\frac{27}{32}$	$1\frac{1}{2}$	$2\frac{7}{32}$	$2\frac{13}{32}$	$3\frac{9}{16}$	$3\frac{5}{16}$	$4\frac{29}{32}$	$4\frac{1}{4}$	$6\frac{9}{32}$	$5\frac{5}{32}$	$7\frac{5}{8}$
$\frac{11}{16}$	$\frac{5}{8}$	$\frac{15}{16}$	$1\frac{9}{16}$	$2\frac{9}{32}$	$2\frac{15}{32}$	$3\frac{21}{32}$	$3\frac{3}{8}$	5	$4\frac{5}{16}$	$6\frac{11}{32}$	$5\frac{7}{32}$	$7\frac{23}{32}$
$\frac{3}{4}$	$\frac{11}{16}$	$1\frac{1}{32}$	$1\frac{19}{32}$	$2\frac{3}{8}$	$2\frac{17}{32}$	$3\frac{23}{32}$	$3\frac{7}{16}$	$5\frac{3}{32}$	$4\frac{11}{32}$	$6\frac{7}{16}$	$5\frac{9}{32}$	$7\frac{13}{16}$
$\frac{13}{16}$	$\frac{3}{4}$	$1\frac{3}{32}$	$1\frac{21}{32}$	$2\frac{15}{32}$	$2\frac{9}{16}$	$3\frac{13}{16}$	$3\frac{1}{2}$	$5\frac{3}{16}$	$4\frac{13}{32}$	$6\frac{17}{32}$	$5\frac{5}{16}$	$7\frac{7}{8}$
$\frac{7}{8}$	$\frac{13}{16}$	$1\frac{3}{16}$	$1\frac{23}{32}$	$2\frac{17}{32}$	$2\frac{5}{8}$	$3\frac{29}{32}$	$3\frac{9}{16}$	$5\frac{1}{4}$	$4\frac{15}{32}$	$6\frac{5}{8}$	$5\frac{3}{8}$	$7\frac{31}{32}$
$\frac{15}{16}$	$\frac{7}{8}$	$1\frac{9}{32}$	$1\frac{25}{32}$	$2\frac{5}{8}$	$2\frac{11}{16}$	4	$3\frac{5}{8}$	$5\frac{11}{32}$	$4\frac{17}{32}$	$6\frac{11}{16}$	$5\frac{7}{16}$	$8\frac{1}{16}$

Inches	6″ Rise	6″ Slope	7″ Rise	7″ Slope	8″ Rise	8″ Slope	9″ Rise	9″ Slope	10″ Rise	10″ Slope	11″ Rise	11″ Slope
0	$5\frac{1}{2}$	$8\frac{1}{8}$	$6\frac{13}{32}$	$9\frac{1}{2}$	$7\frac{11}{32}$	$10\frac{27}{32}$	$8\frac{1}{4}$	$1\text{-}0\frac{7}{32}$	$9\frac{5}{32}$	$1\text{-}1\frac{3}{16}$	$10\frac{1}{8}$	$1\text{-}2\frac{15}{16}$
$\frac{1}{16}$	$5\frac{9}{16}$	$8\frac{7}{32}$	$6\frac{15}{32}$	$9\frac{19}{32}$	$7\frac{3}{8}$	$10\frac{15}{16}$	$8\frac{5}{16}$	$1\text{-}0\frac{9}{32}$	$9\frac{7}{32}$	$1\text{-}1\frac{21}{32}$	$10\frac{1}{8}$	$1\text{-}3$
$\frac{1}{8}$	$5\frac{5}{8}$	$8\frac{5}{16}$	$6\frac{17}{32}$	$9\frac{21}{32}$	$7\frac{7}{16}$	$11\frac{1}{32}$	$8\frac{3}{8}$	$1\text{-}0\frac{3}{8}$	$9\frac{9}{32}$	$1\text{-}1\frac{3}{4}$	$10\frac{3}{16}$	$1\text{-}3\frac{3}{32}$
$\frac{3}{16}$	$5\frac{11}{16}$	$8\frac{13}{32}$	$6\frac{19}{32}$	$9\frac{3}{4}$	$7\frac{1}{2}$	$11\frac{3}{32}$	$8\frac{7}{16}$	$1\text{-}0\frac{15}{32}$	$9\frac{11}{32}$	$1\text{-}1\frac{13}{16}$	$10\frac{1}{4}$	$1\text{-}3\frac{3}{16}$
$\frac{1}{4}$	$5\frac{23}{32}$	$8\frac{15}{32}$	$6\frac{21}{32}$	$9\frac{27}{32}$	$7\frac{9}{16}$	$11\frac{3}{16}$	$8\frac{15}{32}$	$1\text{-}0\frac{9}{16}$	$9\frac{13}{32}$	$1\text{-}1\frac{29}{32}$	$10\frac{5}{16}$	$1\text{-}3\frac{1}{4}$
$\frac{5}{16}$	$5\frac{25}{32}$	$8\frac{9}{16}$	$6\frac{11}{16}$	$9\frac{29}{32}$	$7\frac{5}{8}$	$11\frac{9}{32}$	$8\frac{17}{32}$	$1\text{-}0\frac{5}{8}$	$9\frac{7}{16}$	$1\text{-}2$	$10\frac{3}{8}$	$1\text{-}3\frac{11}{32}$
$\frac{3}{8}$	$5\frac{27}{32}$	$8\frac{21}{32}$	$6\frac{3}{4}$	10	$7\frac{11}{16}$	$11\frac{3}{8}$	$8\frac{19}{32}$	$1\text{-}0\frac{23}{32}$	$9\frac{1}{2}$	$1\text{-}2\frac{1}{16}$	$10\frac{7}{16}$	$1\text{-}3\frac{7}{16}$
$\frac{7}{16}$	$5\frac{29}{32}$	$8\frac{23}{32}$	$6\frac{13}{16}$	$10\frac{3}{32}$	$7\frac{3}{4}$	$11\frac{7}{16}$	$8\frac{21}{32}$	$1\text{-}0\frac{13}{16}$	$9\frac{9}{16}$	$1\text{-}2\frac{5}{32}$	$10\frac{1}{2}$	$1\text{-}3\frac{17}{32}$
$\frac{1}{2}$	$5\frac{31}{32}$	$8\frac{13}{16}$	$6\frac{7}{8}$	$10\frac{3}{16}$	$7\frac{25}{32}$	$11\frac{17}{32}$	$8\frac{23}{32}$	$1\text{-}0\frac{7}{8}$	$9\frac{5}{8}$	$1\text{-}2\frac{1}{4}$	$10\frac{17}{32}$	$1\text{-}3\frac{19}{32}$
$\frac{9}{16}$	6	$8\frac{29}{32}$	$6\frac{15}{16}$	$10\frac{9}{32}$	$7\frac{27}{32}$	$11\frac{5}{8}$	$8\frac{3}{4}$	$1\text{-}0\frac{31}{32}$	$9\frac{11}{16}$	$1\text{-}2\frac{11}{32}$	$10\frac{19}{32}$	$1\text{-}3\frac{11}{16}$
$\frac{5}{8}$	$6\frac{1}{16}$	9	7	$10\frac{11}{32}$	$7\frac{29}{32}$	$11\frac{11}{16}$	$8\frac{13}{16}$	$1\text{-}1\frac{1}{16}$	$9\frac{3}{4}$	$1\text{-}2\frac{13}{32}$	$10\frac{21}{32}$	$1\text{-}3\frac{25}{32}$
$\frac{11}{16}$	$6\frac{1}{8}$	$9\frac{1}{16}$	$7\frac{1}{16}$	$10\frac{7}{16}$	$7\frac{31}{32}$	$11\frac{25}{32}$	$8\frac{7}{8}$	$1\text{-}1\frac{5}{32}$	$9\frac{13}{16}$	$1\text{-}2\frac{1}{2}$	$10\frac{23}{32}$	$1\text{-}3\frac{27}{32}$
$\frac{3}{4}$	$6\frac{3}{16}$	$9\frac{5}{32}$	$7\frac{3}{32}$	$10\frac{1}{2}$	$8\frac{1}{32}$	$11\frac{7}{8}$	$8\frac{15}{16}$	$1\text{-}1\frac{7}{32}$	$9\frac{27}{32}$	$1\text{-}2\frac{19}{32}$	$10\frac{25}{32}$	$1\text{-}3\frac{15}{16}$
$\frac{13}{16}$	$6\frac{1}{4}$	$9\frac{1}{4}$	$7\frac{5}{32}$	$10\frac{19}{32}$	$8\frac{1}{16}$	$11\frac{31}{32}$	9	$1\text{-}1\frac{5}{16}$	$9\frac{29}{32}$	$1\text{-}2\frac{21}{32}$	$10\frac{13}{16}$	$1\text{-}4\frac{1}{16}$
$\frac{7}{8}$	$6\frac{5}{16}$	$9\frac{5}{16}$	$7\frac{7}{32}$	$10\frac{11}{16}$	$8\frac{1}{8}$	$1\text{-}0\frac{1}{32}$	$9\frac{1}{16}$	$1\text{-}1\frac{13}{32}$	$9\frac{31}{32}$	$1\text{-}2\frac{3}{4}$	$10\frac{7}{8}$	$1\text{-}4\frac{5}{32}$
$\frac{15}{16}$	$6\frac{3}{8}$	$9\frac{13}{32}$	$7\frac{9}{32}$	$10\frac{25}{32}$	$8\frac{3}{16}$	$1\text{-}0\frac{1}{8}$	$9\frac{1}{8}$	$1\text{-}1\frac{15}{32}$	$10\frac{1}{32}$	$1\text{-}2\frac{27}{32}$	$10\frac{15}{16}$	$1\text{-}4\frac{3}{16}$

Feet	0′ Rise	0′ Slope	10′ Rise	10′ Slope	20′ Rise	20′ Slope	30′ Rise	30′ Slope
0	0	0	9-2	$13\text{-}6\frac{25}{32}$	18-4	$27\text{-}1\frac{9}{16}$	27-6	$40\text{-}8\frac{3}{8}$
1	-11	$1\text{-}4\frac{9}{32}$	10-1	$14\text{-}11\frac{1}{16}$	19-3	$28\text{-}5\frac{27}{32}$	28-5	$42\text{-}0\frac{21}{32}$
2	1-10	$2\text{-}8\frac{9}{16}$	11-0	$16\text{-}3\frac{11}{32}$	20-2	$29\text{-}10\frac{1}{8}$	29-4	$43\text{-}4\frac{15}{32}$
3	2-9	$4\text{-}0\frac{27}{32}$	11-11	$17\text{-}7\frac{5}{8}$	21-1	$31\text{-}2\frac{13}{32}$	30-3	$44\text{-}9\frac{3}{16}$
4	3-8	$5\text{-}5\frac{1}{8}$	12-10	$18\text{-}11\frac{29}{32}$	22-0	$32\text{-}6\frac{11}{16}$	31-2	$46\text{-}1\frac{15}{32}$
5	4-7	$6\text{-}9\frac{13}{32}$	13-9	$20\text{-}4\frac{3}{16}$	22-11	$33\text{-}10\frac{31}{32}$	32-1	$47\text{-}5\frac{3}{4}$
6	5-6	$8\text{-}1\frac{11}{16}$	14-8	$21\text{-}8\frac{15}{32}$	23-10	$35\text{-}3\frac{1}{4}$	33-0	$48\text{-}10\frac{1}{2}$
7	6-5	$9\text{-}5\frac{15}{16}$	15-7	$23\text{-}0\frac{3}{4}$	24-9	$36\text{-}7\frac{17}{32}$	33-11	$50\text{-}2\frac{5}{16}$
8	7-4	$10\text{-}10\frac{7}{32}$	16-6	$24\text{-}5\frac{1}{32}$	25-8	$37\text{-}11\frac{13}{16}$	34-10	$51\text{-}6\frac{19}{32}$
9	8-3	$12\text{-}2\frac{1}{2}$	17-5	$25\text{-}9\frac{5}{16}$	26-7	$39\text{-}4\frac{3}{32}$	35-9	$52\text{-}10\frac{7}{8}$

A = 42° 30′ 38″; logsin A = 9.82977; logcos A = 9.86756; logtan A = 9.96221; logcot A = 0.03779

Ins.	12″ Rise	12″ Slope	13″ Rise	13″ Slope	14″ Rise	14″ Slope	15″ Rise	15″ Slope	16″ Rise	16″ Slope
0	11	$1\text{-}4\frac{9}{32}$	$11\frac{29}{32}$	$1\text{-}5\frac{5}{8}$	$1\text{-}0\frac{27}{32}$	$1\text{-}7$	$1\text{-}1\frac{3}{4}$	$1\text{-}8\frac{11}{32}$	$1\text{-}2\frac{21}{32}$	$1\text{-}9\frac{23}{32}$
$\frac{1}{16}$	$11\frac{1}{16}$	$1\text{-}4\frac{3}{8}$	$11\frac{31}{32}$	$1\text{-}5\frac{23}{32}$	$1\text{-}0\frac{7}{8}$	$1\text{-}7\frac{1}{16}$	$1\text{-}1\frac{13}{16}$	$1\text{-}8\frac{7}{16}$	$1\text{-}2\frac{23}{32}$	$1\text{-}9\frac{25}{32}$
$\frac{1}{8}$	$11\frac{1}{8}$	$1\text{-}4\frac{7}{16}$	$1\text{-}0\frac{1}{32}$	$1\text{-}5\frac{13}{16}$	$1\text{-}0\frac{15}{16}$	$1\text{-}7\frac{5}{32}$	$1\text{-}1\frac{7}{8}$	$1\text{-}8\frac{17}{32}$	$1\text{-}2\frac{25}{32}$	$1\text{-}9\frac{7}{8}$
$\frac{3}{16}$	$11\frac{3}{16}$	$1\text{-}4\frac{17}{32}$	$1\text{-}0\frac{3}{32}$	$1\text{-}5\frac{7}{8}$	$1\text{-}1$	$1\text{-}7\frac{1}{4}$	$1\text{-}1\frac{15}{16}$	$1\text{-}8\frac{19}{32}$	$1\text{-}2\frac{27}{32}$	$1\text{-}9\frac{31}{32}$
$\frac{1}{4}$	$11\frac{7}{32}$	$1\text{-}4\frac{5}{8}$	$1\text{-}0\frac{5}{32}$	$1\text{-}5\frac{31}{32}$	$1\text{-}1\frac{1}{16}$	$1\text{-}7\frac{11}{32}$	$1\text{-}1\frac{31}{32}$	$1\text{-}8\frac{11}{16}$	$1\text{-}2\frac{29}{32}$	$1\text{-}10\frac{1}{2}$
$\frac{5}{16}$	$11\frac{9}{32}$	$1\text{-}4\frac{11}{32}$	$1\text{-}0\frac{3}{16}$	$1\text{-}6\frac{1}{16}$	$1\text{-}1\frac{1}{8}$	$1\text{-}7\frac{13}{32}$	$1\text{-}2\frac{1}{32}$	$1\text{-}8\frac{25}{32}$	$1\text{-}2\frac{15}{16}$	$1\text{-}10\frac{1}{8}$
$\frac{3}{8}$	$11\frac{11}{32}$	$1\text{-}4\frac{25}{32}$	$1\text{-}0\frac{1}{4}$	$1\text{-}6\frac{5}{32}$	$1\text{-}1\frac{3}{16}$	$1\text{-}7\frac{1}{2}$	$1\text{-}2\frac{3}{32}$	$1\text{-}8\frac{27}{32}$	$1\text{-}3$	$1\text{-}10\frac{7}{32}$
$\frac{7}{16}$	$11\frac{13}{32}$	$1\text{-}4\frac{7}{8}$	$1\text{-}0\frac{5}{16}$	$1\text{-}6\frac{7}{32}$	$1\text{-}1\frac{1}{4}$	$1\text{-}7\frac{19}{32}$	$1\text{-}2\frac{5}{32}$	$1\text{-}8\frac{15}{16}$	$1\text{-}3\frac{1}{16}$	$1\text{-}10\frac{5}{16}$
$\frac{1}{2}$	$11\frac{15}{32}$	$1\text{-}4\frac{31}{32}$	$1\text{-}0\frac{3}{8}$	$1\text{-}6\frac{5}{16}$	$1\text{-}1\frac{9}{32}$	$1\text{-}7\frac{21}{32}$	$1\text{-}2\frac{7}{32}$	$1\text{-}9\frac{1}{32}$	$1\text{-}3\frac{1}{8}$	$1\text{-}10\frac{3}{8}$
$\frac{9}{16}$	$11\frac{1}{2}$	$1\text{-}5\frac{1}{32}$	$1\text{-}0\frac{7}{16}$	$1\text{-}6\frac{13}{32}$	$1\text{-}1\frac{11}{32}$	$1\text{-}7\frac{3}{4}$	$1\text{-}2\frac{1}{4}$	$1\text{-}9\frac{1}{8}$	$1\text{-}3\frac{3}{32}$	$1\text{-}10\frac{15}{32}$
$\frac{5}{8}$	$11\frac{9}{16}$	$1\text{-}5\frac{1}{8}$	$1\text{-}0\frac{1}{2}$	$1\text{-}6\frac{15}{32}$	$1\text{-}1\frac{13}{32}$	$1\text{-}7\frac{27}{32}$	$1\text{-}2\frac{5}{16}$	$1\text{-}9\frac{3}{16}$	$1\text{-}3\frac{1}{4}$	$1\text{-}10\frac{9}{16}$
$\frac{11}{16}$	$11\frac{5}{8}$	$1\text{-}5\frac{7}{32}$	$1\text{-}0\frac{9}{16}$	$1\text{-}6\frac{9}{16}$	$1\text{-}1\frac{15}{16}$	$1\text{-}7\frac{15}{16}$	$1\text{-}2\frac{3}{8}$	$1\text{-}9\frac{9}{32}$	$1\text{-}3\frac{5}{16}$	$1\text{-}10\frac{5}{8}$
$\frac{3}{4}$	$11\frac{11}{16}$	$1\text{-}5\frac{9}{32}$	$1\text{-}0\frac{19}{32}$	$1\text{-}6\frac{21}{32}$	$1\text{-}1\frac{17}{32}$	$1\text{-}8$	$1\text{-}2\frac{7}{16}$	$1\text{-}9\frac{3}{8}$	$1\text{-}3\frac{11}{32}$	$1\text{-}10\frac{23}{32}$
$\frac{13}{16}$	$11\frac{3}{4}$	$1\text{-}5\frac{3}{8}$	$1\text{-}0\frac{21}{32}$	$1\text{-}6\frac{3}{4}$	$1\text{-}1\frac{9}{16}$	$1\text{-}8\frac{3}{32}$	$1\text{-}2\frac{1}{2}$	$1\text{-}9\frac{7}{16}$	$1\text{-}3\frac{13}{32}$	$1\text{-}10\frac{13}{16}$
$\frac{7}{8}$	$11\frac{13}{16}$	$1\text{-}5\frac{15}{32}$	$1\text{-}0\frac{23}{32}$	$1\text{-}6\frac{29}{32}$	$1\text{-}1\frac{5}{8}$	$1\text{-}8\frac{3}{16}$	$1\text{-}2\frac{9}{16}$	$1\text{-}9\frac{17}{32}$	$1\text{-}3\frac{15}{32}$	$1\text{-}10\frac{29}{32}$
$\frac{15}{16}$	$11\frac{7}{8}$	$1\text{-}5\frac{9}{16}$	$1\text{-}0\frac{25}{32}$	$1\text{-}6\frac{29}{32}$	$1\text{-}1\frac{11}{16}$	$1\text{-}8\frac{1}{4}$	$1\text{-}2\frac{5}{8}$	$1\text{-}9\frac{5}{8}$	$1\text{-}3\frac{17}{32}$	$1\text{-}10\frac{31}{32}$

Ins.	17″ Rise	17″ Slope	18″ Rise	18″ Slope	19″ Rise	19″ Slope	20″ Rise	20″ Slope	21″ Rise	21″ Slope
0	$1\text{-}3\frac{19}{32}$	$1\text{-}11\frac{11}{16}$	$1\text{-}4\frac{1}{2}$	$2\text{-}0\frac{13}{32}$	$1\text{-}5\frac{13}{32}$	$2\text{-}1\frac{25}{32}$	$1\text{-}6\frac{11}{32}$	$2\text{-}3\frac{1}{8}$	$1\text{-}7\frac{1}{4}$	$2\text{-}4\frac{1}{2}$
$\frac{1}{16}$	$1\text{-}3\frac{5}{8}$	$1\text{-}11\frac{15}{32}$	$1\text{-}4\frac{9}{16}$	$2\text{-}0\frac{1}{2}$	$1\text{-}5\frac{15}{32}$	$2\text{-}1\frac{7}{8}$	$1\text{-}6\frac{3}{8}$	$2\text{-}3\frac{7}{32}$	$1\text{-}7\frac{5}{16}$	$2\text{-}4\frac{9}{16}$
$\frac{1}{8}$	$1\text{-}3\frac{11}{32}$	$1\text{-}11\frac{17}{32}$	$1\text{-}4\frac{5}{8}$	$2\text{-}0\frac{19}{32}$	$1\text{-}5\frac{17}{32}$	$2\text{-}1\frac{15}{16}$	$1\text{-}6\frac{7}{16}$	$2\text{-}3\frac{5}{16}$	$1\text{-}7\frac{3}{8}$	$2\text{-}4\frac{21}{32}$
$\frac{3}{16}$	$1\text{-}3\frac{3}{4}$	$1\text{-}11\frac{15}{16}$	$1\text{-}4\frac{11}{16}$	$2\text{-}0\frac{11}{16}$	$1\text{-}5\frac{19}{32}$	$2\text{-}2\frac{1}{32}$	$1\text{-}6\frac{1}{2}$	$2\text{-}3\frac{3}{8}$	$1\text{-}7\frac{11}{16}$	$2\text{-}4\frac{3}{4}$
$\frac{1}{4}$	$1\text{-}3\frac{13}{16}$	$1\text{-}11\frac{13}{32}$	$1\text{-}4\frac{23}{32}$	$2\text{-}0\frac{3}{4}$	$1\text{-}5\frac{21}{32}$	$2\text{-}2\frac{1}{8}$	$1\text{-}6\frac{9}{16}$	$2\text{-}3\frac{15}{32}$	$1\text{-}7\frac{15}{32}$	$2\text{-}4\frac{13}{16}$
$\frac{5}{16}$	$1\text{-}3\frac{7}{8}$	$1\text{-}11\frac{1}{2}$	$1\text{-}4\frac{25}{32}$	$2\text{-}0\frac{27}{32}$	$1\text{-}5\frac{11}{16}$	$2\text{-}2\frac{3}{16}$	$1\text{-}6\frac{5}{8}$	$2\text{-}3\frac{9}{16}$	$1\text{-}7\frac{17}{32}$	$2\text{-}4\frac{29}{32}$
$\frac{3}{8}$	$1\text{-}3\frac{15}{16}$	$1\text{-}11\frac{9}{16}$	$1\text{-}4\frac{27}{32}$	$2\text{-}0\frac{15}{16}$	$1\text{-}5\frac{3}{4}$	$2\text{-}2\frac{9}{32}$	$1\text{-}6\frac{11}{16}$	$2\text{-}3\frac{5}{8}$	$1\text{-}7\frac{19}{32}$	$2\text{-}5$
$\frac{7}{16}$	$1\text{-}4$	$1\text{-}11\frac{21}{32}$	$1\text{-}4\frac{29}{32}$	$2\text{-}1$	$1\text{-}5\frac{13}{16}$	$2\text{-}2\frac{3}{8}$	$1\text{-}6\frac{3}{4}$	$2\text{-}3\frac{23}{32}$	$1\text{-}7\frac{21}{32}$	$2\text{-}5\frac{3}{32}$
$\frac{1}{2}$	$1\text{-}4\frac{1}{16}$	$1\text{-}11\frac{3}{4}$	$1\text{-}4\frac{31}{32}$	$2\text{-}1\frac{3}{32}$	$1\text{-}5\frac{7}{8}$	$2\text{-}2\frac{7}{16}$	$1\text{-}6\frac{25}{32}$	$2\text{-}3\frac{13}{16}$	$1\text{-}7\frac{23}{32}$	$2\text{-}5\frac{5}{32}$
$\frac{9}{16}$	$1\text{-}4\frac{3}{32}$	$1\text{-}11\frac{13}{16}$	$1\text{-}5$	$2\text{-}1\frac{3}{16}$	$1\text{-}5\frac{15}{16}$	$2\text{-}2\frac{17}{32}$	$1\text{-}6\frac{27}{32}$	$2\text{-}3\frac{29}{32}$	$1\text{-}7\frac{3}{4}$	$2\text{-}5\frac{1}{4}$
$\frac{5}{8}$	$1\text{-}4\frac{5}{32}$	$1\text{-}11\frac{29}{32}$	$1\text{-}5\frac{1}{16}$	$2\text{-}1\frac{9}{32}$	$1\text{-}6$	$2\text{-}2\frac{5}{8}$	$1\text{-}6\frac{29}{32}$	$2\text{-}3\frac{31}{32}$	$1\text{-}7\frac{13}{16}$	$2\text{-}5\frac{11}{32}$
$\frac{11}{16}$	$1\text{-}4\frac{7}{32}$	$2\text{-}0$	$1\text{-}5\frac{1}{8}$	$2\text{-}1\frac{11}{32}$	$1\text{-}6\frac{1}{16}$	$2\text{-}2\frac{23}{32}$	$1\text{-}6\frac{31}{32}$	$2\text{-}4\frac{1}{16}$	$1\text{-}7\frac{7}{8}$	$2\text{-}5\frac{13}{32}$
$\frac{3}{4}$	$1\text{-}4\frac{9}{32}$	$2\text{-}0\frac{3}{32}$	$1\text{-}5\frac{3}{16}$	$2\text{-}1\frac{7}{16}$	$1\text{-}6\frac{3}{32}$	$2\text{-}2\frac{25}{32}$	$1\text{-}7\frac{1}{32}$	$2\text{-}4\frac{5}{32}$	$1\text{-}7\frac{15}{16}$	$2\text{-}5\frac{1}{2}$
$\frac{13}{16}$	$1\text{-}4\frac{5}{16}$	$2\text{-}0\frac{5}{32}$	$1\text{-}5\frac{1}{4}$	$2\text{-}1\frac{17}{32}$	$1\text{-}6\frac{5}{32}$	$2\text{-}2\frac{7}{8}$	$1\text{-}7\frac{1}{16}$	$2\text{-}4\frac{7}{32}$	$1\text{-}8$	$2\text{-}5\frac{19}{32}$
$\frac{7}{8}$	$1\text{-}4\frac{3}{8}$	$2\text{-}0\frac{1}{4}$	$1\text{-}5\frac{5}{16}$	$2\text{-}1\frac{19}{32}$	$1\text{-}6\frac{7}{32}$	$2\text{-}2\frac{31}{32}$	$1\text{-}7\frac{1}{8}$	$2\text{-}4\frac{5}{16}$	$1\text{-}8\frac{1}{16}$	$2\text{-}5\frac{11}{32}$
$\frac{15}{16}$	$1\text{-}4\frac{7}{16}$	$2\text{-}0\frac{11}{32}$	$1\text{-}5\frac{3}{8}$	$2\text{-}1\frac{11}{16}$	$1\text{-}6\frac{9}{32}$	$2\text{-}3\frac{1}{32}$	$1\text{-}7\frac{3}{16}$	$2\text{-}4\frac{13}{16}$	$1\text{-}8\frac{1}{8}$	$2\text{-}5\frac{3}{4}$

Feet	40′ Rise	40′ Slope	50′ Rise	50′ Slope	60′ Rise	60′ Slope	70′ Rise	70′ Slope
0	36-8	$54\text{-}3\frac{5}{32}$	45-10	$67\text{-}9\frac{15}{16}$	55-0	$81\text{-}4\frac{23}{32}$	64-2	$94\text{-}11\frac{17}{32}$
1	37-7	$55\text{-}7\frac{7}{16}$	46-9	$69\text{-}2\frac{7}{32}$	55-11	$82\text{-}9$	65-1	$96\text{-}3\frac{25}{32}$
2	38-6	$56\text{-}11\frac{23}{32}$	47-8	$70\text{-}6\frac{1}{2}$	56-10	$84\text{-}1\frac{3}{8}$	66-0	$97\text{-}8\frac{1}{16}$
3	39-5	$58\text{-}4$	48-7	$71\text{-}10\frac{25}{32}$	57-9	$85\text{-}5\frac{9}{16}$	66-11	$99\text{-}0\frac{11}{32}$
4	40-4	$59\text{-}8\frac{9}{32}$	49-6	$73\text{-}3\frac{1}{16}$	58-8	$86\text{-}9\frac{27}{32}$	67-10	$100\text{-}4\frac{5}{8}$
5	41-3	$61\text{-}0\frac{9}{16}$	50-5	$74\text{-}7\frac{11}{32}$	59-7	$88\text{-}2\frac{1}{8}$	68-9	$101\text{-}8\frac{29}{32}$
6	42-2	$62\text{-}4\frac{13}{16}$	51-4	$75\text{-}11\frac{5}{8}$	60-6	$89\text{-}6\frac{13}{32}$	69-8	$103\text{-}1\frac{3}{16}$
7	43-1	$63\text{-}9\frac{3}{32}$	52-3	$77\text{-}3\frac{29}{32}$	61-5	$90\text{-}10\frac{11}{16}$	70-7	$104\text{-}5\frac{15}{32}$
8	44-0	$65\text{-}1\frac{3}{8}$	53-2	$78\text{-}8\frac{5}{32}$	62-4	$92\text{-}2\frac{31}{32}$	71-6	$105\text{-}9\frac{3}{4}$
9	44-11	$66\text{-}5\frac{21}{32}$	54-1	$80\text{-}0\frac{7}{16}$	63-3	$93\text{-}7\frac{1}{4}$	72-5	$107\text{-}2\frac{1}{4}$

natsin A=0.6757246284; natcos A=0.7371541402; nattan A=0.9166666666; natcot A=1.0909090909

Inches	0" Rise	0" Slope	1" Rise	1" Slope	2" Rise	2" Slope	3" Rise	3" Slope	4" Rise	4" Slope	5" Rise	5" Slope
0	0	0	15/16	1 3/8	1 27/32	2 23/32	2 3/4	4 3/32	3 11/16	5 1/16	4 5/8	6 13/16
1/16	1/16	3/32	31/32	1 7/16	1 29/32	2 13/16	2 13/16	4 5/32	3 3/4	5 17/32	4 21/32	6 1/8
1/8	1/8	5/32	1 1/32	1 17/32	1 31/32	2 7/8	2 7/8	4 1/4	3 13/16	5 5/8	4 23/32	6 31/32
3/16	3/16	1/4	1 3/32	1 5/8	2 1/32	2 31/32	2 15/16	4 11/32	3 7/8	5 11/16	4 25/32	7 1/16
1/4	7/32	11/32	1 5/32	1 11/16	2 1/16	3 1/16	3	4 13/32	3 29/32	5 25/32	4 27/32	7 1/8
5/16	9/32	7/16	1 7/32	1 25/32	2 1/8	3 5/32	3 1/16	4 1/2	3 31/32	5 7/8	4 29/32	7 1/4
3/8	11/32	1/2	1 9/32	1 7/8	2 3/16	3 7/32	3 1/8	4 19/32	4 1/32	5 15/16	4 31/32	7 5/16
7/16	13/32	19/32	1 5/16	1 31/32	2 1/4	3 5/16	3 5/32	4 11/32	4 3/32	6 1/2	5	7 13/32
1/2	15/32	11/16	1 3/8	2 1/16	2 5/16	3 13/32	3 7/32	4 3/4	4 5/32	6 1/8	5 1/16	7 15/32
9/16	17/32	3/4	1 7/16	2 1/8	2 3/8	3 1/2	3 9/32	4 27/32	4 7/32	6 1/2	5 1/8	7 9/16
5/8	9/16	27/32	1 1/2	2 7/32	2 13/32	3 9/16	3 11/32	4 15/16	4 1/4	6 9/32	5 3/16	7 21/32
11/16	5/8	15/16	1 9/16	2 9/32	2 15/32	3 21/32	3 13/32	5	4 5/16	6 3/8	5 1/4	7 3/4
3/4	11/16	1 1/32	1 5/8	2 3/8	2 17/32	3 3/4	3 15/32	5 3/32	4 3/8	6 15/32	5 5/16	7 13/16
13/16	3/4	1 3/32	1 21/32	2 15/32	2 19/32	3 13/16	3 1/2	5 3/16	4 7/16	6 17/32	5 11/32	7 29/32
7/8	13/16	1 3/16	1 23/32	2 9/16	2 21/32	3 29/32	3 9/16	5 9/32	4 1/2	6 5/8	5 13/32	8
15/16	7/8	1 9/32	1 25/32	2 5/8	2 23/32	4	3 5/8	5 11/32	4 9/16	6 23/32	5 15/32	8 1/16

Inches	6" Rise	6" Slope	7" Rise	7" Slope	8" Rise	8" Slope	9" Rise	9" Slope	10" Rise	10" Slope	11" Rise	11" Slope
0	5 17/32	8 5/32	6 7/16	9 17/32	7 3/8	10 7/8	8 5/16	1-0 1/4	9 7/32	1-1 19/32	10 1/8	1-2 31/32
1/16	5 19/32	8 1/4	6 1/2	9 19/32	7 7/16	10 31/32	8 11/32	1-0 5/32	9 9/32	1-1 11/16	10 3/16	1-3 1/32
1/8	5 21/32	8 11/32	6 9/16	9 11/16	7 1/2	11 1/16	8 13/32	1-0 13/32	9 11/32	1-1 25/32	10 1/4	1-3 1/8
3/16	5 23/32	8 13/32	6 5/8	9 25/32	7 9/16	11 1/8	8 15/32	1-0 1/2	9 13/32	1-1 27/32	10 5/16	1-3 7/32
1/4	5 3/4	8 1/2	6 11/16	9 7/8	7 19/32	11 7/32	8 17/32	1-0 19/32	9 7/16	1-1 15/16	10 3/8	1-3 5/16
5/16	5 13/16	8 19/32	6 3/4	9 15/16	7 21/32	11 5/16	8 19/32	1-0 21/32	9 1/2	1-2 1/32	10 7/16	1-3 3/8
3/8	5 7/8	8 21/32	6 13/16	10 1/32	7 23/32	11 13/32	8 21/32	1-0 3/4	9 9/16	1-2 1/8	10 1/2	1-3 15/32
7/16	5 15/16	8 3/4	6 27/32	10 1/8	7 25/32	11 15/32	8 11/16	1-0 27/32	9 5/8	1-2 3/16	10 17/32	1-3 9/16
1/2	6	8 27/32	6 29/32	10 3/16	7 27/32	11 9/16	8 3/4	1-0 29/32	9 11/16	1-2 9/32	10 19/32	1-3 21/32
9/16	6 1/16	8 15/16	6 31/32	10 9/32	7 29/32	11 21/32	8 13/16	1-1	9 3/4	1-2 3/8	10 21/32	1-3 23/32
5/8	6 3/32	9	7 1/32	10 3/8	7 15/16	11 23/32	8 7/8	1-1 3/32	9 25/32	1-2 7/16	10 23/32	1-3 13/16
11/16	6 5/32	9 3/32	7 3/32	10 15/32	8	11 13/16	8 15/16	1-1 3/16	9 27/32	1-2 17/32	10 25/32	1-3 29/32
3/4	6 7/32	9 3/16	7 5/32	10 17/32	8 1/16	11 29/32	9	1-1 1/4	9 29/32	1-2 5/8	10 27/32	1-3 31/32
13/16	6 9/32	9 9/32	7 3/16	10 5/8	8 1/8	1-0	9 1/32	1-1 11/32	9 31/32	1-2 23/32	10 7/8	1-4 1/16
7/8	6 11/32	9 11/32	7 1/4	10 23/32	8 3/16	1-0 1/16	9 3/32	1-1 7/16	10 1/16	1-2 25/32	10 15/16	1-4 5/32
15/16	6 13/32	9 7/16	7 5/16	10 25/32	8 1/4	1-0 5/32	9 5/32	1-1 17/32	10 3/32	1-2 7/8	11	1-4 1/4

Feet	0' Rise	0' Slope	10' Rise	10' Slope	20' Rise	20' Slope	30' Rise	30' Slope
0	0	0	9-2 5/8	13-7 7/32	18-5 1/4	27-2 1/16	27-7 1/8	40-9 5/8
1	-1 1 1/16	1-4 5/16	10-1 11/16	14-11 17/32	19-4 5/16	28-6 3/4	28-6 15/16	42-1 31/32
2	1-10 1/8	2-8 21/32	11-0 3/4	16-3 27/32	20-3 3/8	29-11 1/16	29-6	43-6 9/32
3	2-9 3/16	4-0 31/32	11-11 13/16	17-8 3/16	21-2 7/16	31-3 3/8	30-5 1/16	44-10 19/32
4	3-8 1/4	5-5 9/32	12-10 7/8	19-0 1/2	22-1 1/2	32-7 23/32	31-4 1/8	46-2 29/32
5	4-7 5/16	6-9 19/32	13-9 15/16	20-4 13/16	23-0 9/16	34-0 1/32	32-3 3/16	47-7 1/4
6	5-6 3/8	8-1 15/16	14-9	21-9 1/8	23-11 5/8	35-4 11/32	33-2 1/4	48-11 9/16
7	6-5 7/16	9-6 1/4	15-8 1/16	23-1 15/32	24-10 11/16	36-8 21/32	34-1 5/16	50-3 7/8
8	7-4 1/2	10-10 9/16	16-7 1/8	24-5 25/32	25-9 3/4	38-1	35-0 3/8	51-8 3/16
9	8-3 9/16	12-2 7/8	17-6 3/16	25-10 3/32	26-8 13/16	39-5 5/16	35-11 7/16	53-0 17/32

A = 42° 40′ 20″; logsin A = 9.83110; logcos A = 9.86643; logtan A = 9.96467; logcot A = 0.03533

Ins.	12″ Rise	12″ Slope	13″ Rise	13″ Slope	14″ Rise	14″ Slope	15″ Rise	15″ Slope	16″ Rise	16″ Slope
0	11 1/16	1-4 5/16	1-0	1-5 11/16	1-0 29/32	1-7 1/32	1-1 13/16	1-8 13/32	1-2 3/4	1-9 3/4
1/16	11 1/8	1-4 13/32	1-0 1/32	1-5 25/32	1-0 31/32	1-7 1/8	1-1 7/8	1-8 1/2	1-2 13/16	1-9 27/32
1/8	11 3/16	1-4 1/2	1-0 3/32	1-5 27/32	1-1 1/32	1-7 1/32	1-1 15/16	1-8 9/16	1-2 7/8	1-9 15/16
3/16	11 1/4	1-4 9/16	1-0 5/32	1-5 15/16	1-1 3/32	1-7 9/32	1-2	1-8 21/32	1-2 15/16	1-10 1/32
1/4	11 9/32	1-4 21/32	1-0 7/32	1-6 1/32	1-1 1/8	1-7 3/8	1-2 1/16	1-8 3/4	1-2 31/32	1-10 3/32
5/16	11 11/32	1-4 3/4	1-0 9/32	1-6 3/32	1-1 3/16	1-7 15/32	1-2 3/8	1-8 13/16	1-3 1/32	1-10 3/16
3/8	11 13/32	1-4 27/32	1-0 11/32	1-6 3/16	1-1 1/4	1-7 9/16	1-2 3/16	1-8 29/32	1-3 3/32	1-10 9/32
7/16	11 15/32	1-4 29/32	1-0 3/8	1-6 9/32	1-1 5/16	1-7 5/8	1-2 7/32	1-9	1-3 5/32	1-10 11/32
1/2	11 17/32	1-5	1-0 7/16	1-6 3/8	1-1 3/8	1-7 23/32	1-2 9/32	1-9 3/32	1-3 7/32	1-10 7/16
9/16	11 19/32	1-5 3/32	1-0 1/2	1-6 7/16	1-1 7/16	1-7 13/16	1-2 11/32	1-9 5/32	1-3 9/32	1-10 17/32
5/8	11 5/8	1-5 5/32	1-0 9/16	1-6 17/32	1-1 15/32	1-7 29/32	1-2 13/32	1-9 1/4	1-3 5/16	1-10 5/8
11/16	11 11/16	1-5 1/4	1-0 5/8	1-6 5/8	1-1 17/32	1-7 31/32	1-2 15/32	1-9 11/32	1-3 3/8	1-10 11/16
3/4	11 3/4	1-5 11/32	1-0 11/16	1-6 11/16	1-1 19/32	1-8 1/16	1-2 17/32	1-9 13/32	1-3 7/16	1-10 25/32
13/16	11 13/16	1-5 7/16	1-0 23/32	1-6 25/32	1-1 21/32	1-8 5/32	1-2 9/16	1-9 1/2	1-3 1/2	1-10 7/8
7/8	11 7/8	1-5 1/2	1-0 25/32	1-6 7/8	1-1 23/32	1-8 7/32	1-2 5/8	1-9 19/32	1-3 9/16	1-10 15/16
15/16	11 15/16	1-5 19/32	1-0 27/32	1-6 31/32	1-1 25/32	1-8 5/16	1-2 11/16	1-9 11/32	1-3 5/8	1-11 1/32

Ins.	17″ Rise	17″ Slope	18″ Rise	18″ Slope	19″ Rise	19″ Slope	20″ Rise	20″ Slope	21″ Rise	21″ Slope
0	1-3 11/16	1-11 1/8	1-4 19/32	2-0 15/32	1-5 1/2	2-1 27/32	1-6 7/16	2-3 3/16	1-7 3/8	2-4 9/16
1/16	1-3 23/32	1-11 7/32	1-4 21/32	2-0 9/16	1-5 9/16	2-1 15/16	1-6 1/2	2-3 9/32	1-7 13/32	2-4 21/32
1/8	1-3 25/32	1-11 9/32	1-4 23/32	2-0 21/32	1-5 5/8	2-2	1-6 9/16	2-3 3/8	1-7 15/32	2-4 23/32
3/16	1-3 27/32	1-11 3/8	1-4 25/32	2-0 3/4	1-5 11/16	2-2 3/32	1-6 5/8	2-3 15/32	1-7 17/32	2-4 13/16
1/4	1-3 29/32	1-11 15/32	1-4 13/16	2-0 13/16	1-5 3/4	2-2 3/16	1-6 21/32	2-3 17/32	1-7 19/32	2-4 29/32
5/16	1-3 31/32	1-11 17/32	1-4 7/8	2-0 29/32	1-5 13/16	2-2 9/32	1-6 23/32	2-3 5/8	1-7 21/32	2-5
3/8	1-4 1/32	1-11 5/8	1-4 15/16	2-1	1-5 7/8	2-2 11/32	1-6 25/32	2-3 23/32	1-7 23/32	2-5 3/32
7/16	1-4 1/32	1-11 23/32	1-5	2-1 1/16	1-5 29/32	2-2 7/16	1-6 27/32	2-3 13/16	1-7 3/4	2-5 5/32
1/2	1-4 1/8	1-11 13/16	1-5 1/16	2-1 5/32	1-5 31/32	2-2 17/32	1-6 29/32	2-3 7/8	1-7 13/16	2-5 1/4
9/16	1-4 3/16	1-11 7/8	1-5 1/8	2-1 1/4	1-6 1/32	2-2 19/32	1-6 31/32	2-3 31/32	1-7 7/8	2-5 5/16
5/8	1-4 1/4	1-11 31/32	1-5 5/32	2-1 11/32	1-6 3/32	2-2 11/16	1-7	2-4 1/16	1-7 15/16	2-5 13/32
11/16	1-4 5/16	2-0 1/16	1-5 7/32	2-1 13/32	1-6 5/32	2-2 25/32	1-7 1/16	2-4 1/8	1-8	2-5 1/2
3/4	1-4 3/8	2-0 5/32	1-5 9/32	2-1 1/2	1-6 7/32	2-2 7/8	1-7 1/8	2-4 7/32	1-8 1/16	2-5 19/32
13/16	1-4 13/32	2-0 7/32	1-5 11/32	2-1 19/32	1-6 1/4	2-2 15/16	1-7 3/16	2-4 5/16	1-8 3/32	2-5 21/32
7/8	1-4 15/32	2-0 5/16	1-5 13/32	2-1 21/32	1-6 5/16	2-3 1/32	1-7 1/4	2-4 13/32	1-8 5/32	2-5 3/4
15/16	1-4 17/32	2-0 13/32	1-5 15/32	2-1 3/4	1-6 3/8	2-3 1/8	1-7 5/32	2-4 15/32	1-8 7/32	2-5 27/32

Feet	40′ Rise	40′ Slope	50′ Rise	50′ Slope	60′ Rise	60′ Slope	70′ Rise	70′ Slope
0	36-10 1/2	54-4 27/32	46-1 1/8	68-0 1/16	55-3 3/4	81-7 9/32	64-6 3/8	95-2 15/32
1	37-9 9/16	55-9 5/32	47-0 3/16	69-4 3/8	56-2 15/16	82-11 19/32	65-5 7/16	96-6 13/16
2	38-8 5/8	57-1 1/2	47-11 1/4	70-8 11/16	57-1 7/8	84-3 29/32	66-4 1/2	97-11 1/8
3	39-7 11/16	58-5 13/16	48-10 5/16	72-1 1/32	58-0 15/16	85-8 7/32	67-3 9/16	99-3 7/16
4	40-6 3/4	59-10 1/8	49-9 3/8	73-5 11/32	59-0	87-0 9/16	68-2 5/8	100-7 3/4
5	41-5 13/16	61-2 7/16	50-8 7/16	74-9 21/32	59-11 1/16	88-4 7/8	69-1 11/16	102-0 3/32
6	42-4 7/8	62-6 25/32	51-7 1/2	76-1 31/32	60-10 1/8	89-9 3/16	70-0 3/4	103-4 13/32
7	43-3 15/16	63-11 3/32	52-6 9/16	77-6 5/16	61-9 3/16	91-1 1/2	70-11 13/16	104-8 23/32
8	44-3	65-3 13/32	53-5 5/8	78-10 5/8	62-8 1/4	92-5 27/32	71-10 7/8	106-1 1/16
9	45-2 1/16	66-7 3/4	54-4 11/16	80-2 15/16	63-7 5/16	93-10 5/32	72-9 15/16	107-5 3/8

natsin A=0.6778028147; natcos A=0.7352437312; nattan A=0.9218750000; natcot A=1.0847457627

Inches	0" Rise	0" Slope	1" Rise	1" Slope	2" Rise	2" Slope	3" Rise	3" Slope	4" Rise	4" Slope	5" Rise	5" Slope
0	0	0	15/16	1 3/8	1 27/32	2 23/32	2 25/32	4 3/32	3 23/32	5 15/32	4 5/8	6 13/16
1/16	1/16	3/32	1	1 7/16	1 29/32	2 13/16	2 27/32	4 3/16	3 25/32	5 17/32	4 11/16	6 29/32
1/8	1/8	5/32	1 1/16	1 17/32	1 31/32	2 29/32	2 29/32	4 1/4	3 13/16	5 5/8	4 3/4	7
3/16	3/16	1/4	1 3/32	1 5/8	2 1/32	2 31/32	2 31/32	4 11/32	3 7/8	5 23/32	4 13/16	7 1/16
1/4	7/32	11/32	1 5/32	1 23/32	2 3/32	3 1/16	3	4 7/16	3 15/32	5 25/32	4 7/8	7 5/32
5/16	9/32	1/16	1 7/32	1 25/32	2 5/32	3 5/32	3 1/16	4 17/32	4	5 7/8	4 15/16	7 1/4
3/8	11/32	1/2	1 9/32	1 7/8	2 3/16	3 1/4	3 1/8	4 19/32	4 1/16	5 31/32	4 31/32	7 11/32
7/16	13/32	19/32	1 11/32	1 31/32	2 1/4	3 5/16	3 3/16	4 11/16	4 1/8	6 1/16	5 1/32	7 13/32
1/2	15/32	11/16	1 3/8	2 1/32	2 5/16	3 13/32	3 1/4	4 25/32	4 3/16	6 1/8	5 3/32	7 1/2
9/16	17/32	25/32	1 7/16	2 1/8	2 3/8	3 1/2	3 5/16	4 27/32	4 7/32	6 7/32	5 5/32	7 19/32
5/8	19/32	27/32	1 1/2	2 7/32	2 7/16	3 19/32	3 3/8	4 15/16	4 9/32	6 5/16	5 7/32	7 21/32
11/16	5/8	15/32	1 9/16	2 5/16	2 1/2	3 21/32	3 13/32	5 1/32	4 11/32	6 13/32	5 9/32	7 3/4
3/4	11/16	11/32	1 5/8	2 3/8	2 9/16	3 3/4	3 15/32	5 1/8	4 13/32	6 15/32	5 11/32	7 27/32
13/16	3/4	13/32	1 11/16	2 15/32	2 19/32	3 27/32	3 17/32	5 3/16	4 15/32	6 9/16	5 3/8	7 15/16
7/8	13/16	13/16	1 3/4	2 9/16	2 21/32	3 29/32	3 19/32	5 9/32	4 17/32	6 21/32	5 7/16	8
15/16	7/8	19/32	1 25/32	2 21/32	2 23/32	4	3 21/32	5 3/8	4 9/16	6 23/32	5 1/2	8 3/32

Inches	6" Rise	6" Slope	7" Rise	7" Slope	8" Rise	8" Slope	9" Rise	9" Slope	10" Rise	10" Slope	11" Rise	11" Slope
0	5 9/16	8 3/16	6 1/2	9 17/32	7 13/32	10 29/32	8 11/32	1-0 9/32	9 1/4	1-1 5/8	10 3/16	1-3
1/16	5 5/8	8 9/32	6 9/16	9 5/8	7 15/32	11	8 13/32	1-0 11/32	9 11/32	1-1 23/32	10 1/4	1-3 3/32
1/8	5 11/16	8 11/32	6 19/32	9 23/32	7 17/32	11 3/32	8 15/32	1-0 7/16	9 3/8	1-1 13/16	10 5/16	1-3 5/32
3/16	5 3/4	8 7/16	6 21/32	9 13/16	7 19/32	11 5/32	8 17/32	1-0 17/32	9 7/16	1-1 29/32	10 3/8	1-3 1/4
1/4	5 25/32	8 17/32	6 23/32	9 7/8	7 21/32	11 1/4	8 9/16	1-0 5/8	9 1/2	1-1 31/32	10 7/16	1-3 11/32
5/16	5 27/32	8 19/32	6 25/32	9 31/32	7 23/32	11 11/32	8 5/8	1-0 11/16	9 9/16	1-2 1/16	10 1/2	1-3 7/16
3/8	5 29/32	8 11/16	6 27/32	10 1/16	7 3/4	11 13/32	8 11/16	1-0 25/32	9 5/8	1-2 5/32	10 17/32	1-3 1/2
7/16	5 31/32	8 25/32	6 29/32	10 5/32	7 13/16	11 1/2	8 3/4	1-0 7/8	9 11/16	1-2 7/32	10 19/32	1-3 19/32
1/2	6 1/32	8 7/8	6 15/16	10 7/32	7 7/8	11 19/32	8 13/16	1-0 31/32	9 3/4	1-2 5/16	10 21/32	1-3 11/16
9/16	6 3/32	8 15/16	7	10 5/16	7 15/16	11 11/16	8 7/8	1-1 1/32	9 25/32	1-2 13/32	10 23/32	1-3 25/32
5/8	6 5/32	9 1/32	7 1/16	10 13/32	8	11 3/4	8 15/16	1-1 1/8	9 27/32	1-2 1/2	10 25/32	1-3 27/32
11/16	6 3/16	9 1/8	7 1/8	10 15/32	8 1/16	11 27/32	8 31/32	1-1 7/32	9 29/32	1-2 9/16	10 27/32	1-3 15/16
3/4	6 1/4	9 7/32	7 3/16	10 9/16	8 1/8	11 15/16	9 1/16	1-1 9/32	9 31/32	1-2 21/32	10 29/32	1-4 1/32
13/16	6 5/16	9 9/32	7 1/4	10 21/32	8 5/32	1-0 1/32	9 3/32	1-1 3/8	10 1/32	1-2 3/4	10 15/16	1-4 3/32
7/8	6 3/8	9 3/8	7 5/16	10 3/4	8 7/32	1-0 3/32	9 5/32	1-1 15/32	10 3/32	1-2 27/32	11	1-4 3/16
15/16	6 7/16	9 15/32	7 11/32	10 13/16	8 9/32	1-0 3/16	9 7/32	1-1 9/16	10 1/8	1-2 29/32	11 1/16	1-4 9/32

Feet	0' Rise	0' Slope	10' Rise	10' Slope	20' Rise	20' Slope	30' Rise	30' Slope
0	0	0	9-3 1/4	13-7 5/8	18-6 1/2	27-3 9/32	27-9 3/4	40-10 29/32
1	-11 1/8	1-4 3/8	10-2 3/8	15-0	19-5 5/8	28-7 5/8	28-8 7/8	42-3 9/32
2	1-10 1/4	2-8 23/32	11-1 1/2	16-4 3/8	20-4 3/4	30-0	29-8	43-7 5/8
3	2-9 3/8	4-1 3/32	12-0 5/8	17-8 23/32	21-3 7/8	31-4 3/8	30-7 1/8	45-0
4	3-8 1/2	5-5 15/32	12-11 3/4	19-1 3/32	22-3	32-8 23/32	31-6 1/4	46-4 3/8
5	4-7 5/8	6-9 13/16	13-10 7/8	20-5 15/32	23-2 1/8	34-1 3/32	32-5 3/8	47-8 23/32
6	5-6 3/4	8-2 3/16	14-10	21-9 13/16	24-1 1/4	35-5 7/16	33-4 1/2	49-1 3/32
7	6-5 7/8	9-6 17/32	15-9 1/4	23-2 3/16	25-0 3/8	36-9 13/16	34-3 5/8	50-5 7/16
8	7-5	10-10 29/32	16-8 1/4	24-6 17/32	25-11 1/2	38-2 3/16	35-2 3/4	51-9 13/16
9	8-4 1/8	12-3 9/32	17-7 3/8	25-10 29/32	26-10 5/8	39-6 17/32	36-1 7/8	53-2 3/16

A = 42° 49′ 59″; logsin A = 9.83242; logcos A = 9.86530; logtan A = 9.96712; logcot A = 0.03288

In.	12″ Rise	12″ Slope	13″ Rise	13″ Slope	14″ Rise	14″ Slope	15″ Rise	15″ Slope	16″ Rise	16″ Slope
0	$11\frac{3}{8}$	$1\text{-}4\frac{3}{8}$	$1\text{-}0\frac{1}{16}$	$1\text{-}5\frac{23}{32}$	$1\text{-}0\frac{31}{32}$	$1\text{-}7\frac{3}{32}$	$1\text{-}1\frac{29}{32}$	$1\text{-}8\frac{15}{32}$	$1\text{-}2\frac{27}{32}$	$1\text{-}9\frac{13}{16}$
1/16	$11\frac{3}{16}$	$1\text{-}4\frac{7}{16}$	$1\text{-}0\frac{1}{8}$	$1\text{-}5\frac{13}{16}$	$1\text{-}1\frac{1}{32}$	$1\text{-}7\frac{3}{16}$	$1\text{-}1\frac{31}{32}$	$1\text{-}8\frac{17}{32}$	$1\text{-}2\frac{29}{32}$	$1\text{-}9\frac{29}{32}$
1/8	$11\frac{1}{4}$	$1\text{-}4\frac{17}{32}$	$1\text{-}0\frac{5}{32}$	$1\text{-}5\frac{29}{32}$	$1\text{-}1\frac{3}{32}$	$1\text{-}7\frac{1}{4}$	$1\text{-}2\frac{1}{32}$	$1\text{-}8\frac{5}{8}$	$1\text{-}2\frac{15}{16}$	$1\text{-}10$
3/16	$11\frac{5}{16}$	$1\text{-}4\frac{5}{8}$	$1\text{-}0\frac{7}{32}$	$1\text{-}5\frac{31}{32}$	$1\text{-}1\frac{5}{32}$	$1\text{-}7\frac{11}{32}$	$1\text{-}2\frac{3}{32}$	$1\text{-}8\frac{23}{32}$	$1\text{-}3$	$1\text{-}10\frac{1}{16}$
1/4	$11\frac{11}{32}$	$1\text{-}4\frac{23}{32}$	$1\text{-}0\frac{9}{32}$	$1\text{-}6\frac{1}{16}$	$1\text{-}1\frac{7}{32}$	$1\text{-}7\frac{7}{16}$	$1\text{-}2\frac{1}{8}$	$1\text{-}8\frac{25}{32}$	$1\text{-}3\frac{1}{16}$	$1\text{-}10\frac{5}{32}$
5/16	$11\frac{13}{32}$	$1\text{-}4\frac{25}{32}$	$1\text{-}0\frac{11}{32}$	$1\text{-}6\frac{5}{32}$	$1\text{-}1\frac{9}{32}$	$1\text{-}7\frac{17}{32}$	$1\text{-}2\frac{3}{16}$	$1\text{-}8\frac{7}{8}$	$1\text{-}3\frac{1}{8}$	$1\text{-}10\frac{1}{4}$
3/8	$11\frac{15}{32}$	$1\text{-}4\frac{7}{8}$	$1\text{-}0\frac{13}{32}$	$1\text{-}6\frac{1}{4}$	$1\text{-}1\frac{5}{16}$	$1\text{-}7\frac{19}{32}$	$1\text{-}2\frac{1}{4}$	$1\text{-}8\frac{31}{32}$	$1\text{-}3\frac{3}{16}$	$1\text{-}10\frac{11}{32}$
7/16	$11\frac{17}{32}$	$1\text{-}4\frac{31}{32}$	$1\text{-}0\frac{15}{32}$	$1\text{-}6\frac{5}{16}$	$1\text{-}1\frac{3}{8}$	$1\text{-}7\frac{11}{16}$	$1\text{-}2\frac{5}{16}$	$1\text{-}9\frac{1}{16}$	$1\text{-}3\frac{1}{4}$	$1\text{-}10\frac{13}{32}$
1/2	$11\frac{19}{32}$	$1\text{-}5\frac{1}{32}$	$1\text{-}0\frac{1}{2}$	$1\text{-}6\frac{13}{32}$	$1\text{-}1\frac{7}{16}$	$1\text{-}7\frac{25}{32}$	$1\text{-}2\frac{3}{8}$	$1\text{-}9\frac{1}{8}$	$1\text{-}3\frac{5}{16}$	$1\text{-}10\frac{1}{2}$
9/16	$11\frac{21}{32}$	$1\text{-}5\frac{1}{8}$	$1\text{-}0\frac{9}{16}$	$1\text{-}6\frac{1}{2}$	$1\text{-}1\frac{1}{2}$	$1\text{-}7\frac{27}{32}$	$1\text{-}2\frac{7}{16}$	$1\text{-}9\frac{7}{32}$	$1\text{-}3\frac{11}{32}$	$1\text{-}10\frac{19}{32}$
5/8	$11\frac{23}{32}$	$1\text{-}5\frac{7}{32}$	$1\text{-}0\frac{5}{8}$	$1\text{-}6\frac{19}{32}$	$1\text{-}1\frac{9}{16}$	$1\text{-}7\frac{15}{16}$	$1\text{-}2\frac{1}{2}$	$1\text{-}9\frac{5}{16}$	$1\text{-}3\frac{13}{32}$	$1\text{-}10\frac{21}{32}$
11/16	$11\frac{3}{4}$	$1\text{-}5\frac{5}{16}$	$1\text{-}0\frac{11}{32}$	$1\text{-}6\frac{21}{32}$	$1\text{-}1\frac{5}{8}$	$1\text{-}8\frac{1}{32}$	$1\text{-}2\frac{17}{32}$	$1\text{-}9\frac{13}{32}$	$1\text{-}3\frac{15}{32}$	$1\text{-}10\frac{3}{4}$
3/4	$11\frac{13}{16}$	$1\text{-}5\frac{3}{8}$	$1\text{-}0\frac{3}{4}$	$1\text{-}6\frac{3}{4}$	$1\text{-}1\frac{11}{16}$	$1\text{-}8\frac{1}{8}$	$1\text{-}2\frac{19}{32}$	$1\text{-}9\frac{15}{32}$	$1\text{-}3\frac{17}{32}$	$1\text{-}10\frac{27}{32}$
13/16	$11\frac{7}{8}$	$1\text{-}5\frac{15}{32}$	$1\text{-}0\frac{13}{16}$	$1\text{-}6\frac{27}{32}$	$1\text{-}1\frac{23}{32}$	$1\text{-}8\frac{3}{16}$	$1\text{-}2\frac{21}{32}$	$1\text{-}9\frac{9}{16}$	$1\text{-}3\frac{19}{32}$	$1\text{-}10\frac{15}{16}$
7/8	$11\frac{15}{16}$	$1\text{-}5\frac{9}{16}$	$1\text{-}0\frac{7}{8}$	$1\text{-}6\frac{29}{32}$	$1\text{-}1\frac{25}{32}$	$1\text{-}8\frac{9}{32}$	$1\text{-}2\frac{23}{32}$	$1\text{-}9\frac{21}{32}$	$1\text{-}3\frac{21}{32}$	$1\text{-}11$
15/16	$1\text{-}0$	$1\text{-}5\frac{21}{32}$	$1\text{-}0\frac{29}{32}$	$1\text{-}7$	$1\text{-}1\frac{27}{32}$	$1\text{-}8\frac{3}{8}$	$1\text{-}2\frac{25}{32}$	$1\text{-}9\frac{23}{32}$	$1\text{-}3\frac{11}{16}$	$1\text{-}11\frac{3}{32}$

In.	17″ Rise	17″ Slope	18″ Rise	18″ Slope	19″ Rise	19″ Slope	20″ Rise	20″ Slope	21″ Rise	21″ Slope
0	$1\text{-}3\frac{3}{4}$	$1\text{-}11\frac{13}{16}$	$1\text{-}4\frac{11}{16}$	$2\text{-}0\frac{7}{32}$	$1\text{-}5\frac{5}{8}$	$2\text{-}1\frac{29}{32}$	$1\text{-}6\frac{17}{32}$	$2\text{-}3\frac{9}{32}$	$1\text{-}7\frac{15}{32}$	$2\text{-}4\frac{5}{8}$
1/16	$1\text{-}3\frac{13}{16}$	$1\text{-}11\frac{13}{16}$	$1\text{-}4\frac{3}{4}$	$2\text{-}0\frac{5}{8}$	$1\text{-}5\frac{11}{16}$	$2\text{-}2$	$1\text{-}6\frac{9}{16}$	$2\text{-}3\frac{11}{32}$	$1\text{-}7\frac{17}{32}$	$2\text{-}4\frac{23}{32}$
1/8	$1\text{-}3\frac{7}{8}$	$1\text{-}11\frac{11}{32}$	$1\text{-}4\frac{13}{16}$	$2\text{-}0\frac{23}{32}$	$1\text{-}5\frac{23}{32}$	$2\text{-}2\frac{3}{8}$	$1\text{-}6\frac{21}{32}$	$2\text{-}3\frac{7}{16}$	$1\text{-}7\frac{19}{32}$	$2\text{-}4\frac{13}{16}$
3/16	$1\text{-}3\frac{15}{16}$	$1\text{-}11\frac{7}{16}$	$1\text{-}4\frac{7}{8}$	$2\text{-}0\frac{13}{32}$	$1\text{-}5\frac{25}{32}$	$2\text{-}2\frac{5}{8}$	$1\text{-}6\frac{23}{32}$	$2\text{-}3\frac{17}{32}$	$1\text{-}7\frac{21}{32}$	$2\text{-}4\frac{29}{32}$
1/4	$1\text{-}4$	$1\text{-}11\frac{17}{32}$	$1\text{-}4\frac{29}{32}$	$2\text{-}0\frac{7}{8}$	$1\text{-}5\frac{27}{32}$	$2\text{-}2\frac{1}{4}$	$1\text{-}6\frac{25}{32}$	$2\text{-}3\frac{5}{8}$	$1\text{-}7\frac{11}{16}$	$2\text{-}4\frac{31}{32}$
5/16	$1\text{-}4\frac{1}{16}$	$1\text{-}11\frac{19}{32}$	$1\text{-}4\frac{31}{32}$	$2\text{-}0\frac{31}{32}$	$1\text{-}5\frac{29}{32}$	$2\text{-}2\frac{11}{32}$	$1\text{-}6\frac{27}{32}$	$2\text{-}3\frac{11}{16}$	$1\text{-}7\frac{3}{4}$	$2\text{-}5\frac{1}{16}$
3/8	$1\text{-}4\frac{3}{32}$	$1\text{-}11\frac{11}{16}$	$1\text{-}5\frac{1}{32}$	$2\text{-}1\frac{1}{16}$	$1\text{-}5\frac{31}{32}$	$2\text{-}2\frac{13}{32}$	$1\text{-}6\frac{7}{8}$	$2\text{-}3\frac{25}{32}$	$1\text{-}7\frac{13}{16}$	$2\text{-}5\frac{5}{32}$
7/16	$1\text{-}4\frac{5}{32}$	$1\text{-}11\frac{25}{32}$	$1\text{-}5\frac{3}{32}$	$2\text{-}1\frac{5}{32}$	$1\text{-}6\frac{1}{32}$	$2\text{-}2\frac{1}{2}$	$1\text{-}6\frac{15}{16}$	$2\text{-}3\frac{7}{8}$	$1\text{-}7\frac{7}{8}$	$2\text{-}5\frac{7}{32}$
1/2	$1\text{-}4\frac{7}{32}$	$1\text{-}11\frac{7}{8}$	$1\text{-}5\frac{5}{32}$	$2\text{-}1\frac{7}{32}$	$1\text{-}6\frac{1}{16}$	$2\text{-}2\frac{19}{32}$	$1\text{-}7$	$2\text{-}3\frac{31}{32}$	$1\text{-}7\frac{15}{16}$	$2\text{-}5\frac{5}{16}$
9/16	$1\text{-}4\frac{9}{32}$	$1\text{-}11\frac{15}{16}$	$1\text{-}5\frac{7}{32}$	$2\text{-}1\frac{5}{16}$	$1\text{-}6\frac{1}{8}$	$2\text{-}2\frac{11}{16}$	$1\text{-}7\frac{1}{16}$	$2\text{-}4\frac{1}{32}$	$1\text{-}8$	$2\text{-}5\frac{13}{32}$
5/8	$1\text{-}4\frac{11}{32}$	$2\text{-}0\frac{1}{32}$	$1\text{-}5\frac{9}{32}$	$2\text{-}1\frac{13}{32}$	$1\text{-}6\frac{3}{16}$	$2\text{-}2\frac{3}{4}$	$1\text{-}7\frac{1}{8}$	$2\text{-}4\frac{1}{8}$	$1\text{-}8\frac{1}{16}$	$2\text{-}5\frac{1}{2}$
11/16	$1\text{-}4\frac{13}{32}$	$2\text{-}0\frac{1}{8}$	$1\text{-}5\frac{5}{16}$	$2\text{-}1\frac{15}{32}$	$1\text{-}6\frac{1}{4}$	$2\text{-}2\frac{27}{32}$	$1\text{-}7\frac{3}{16}$	$2\text{-}4\frac{7}{32}$	$1\text{-}8\frac{3}{32}$	$2\text{-}5\frac{9}{16}$
3/4	$1\text{-}4\frac{15}{32}$	$2\text{-}0\frac{7}{32}$	$1\text{-}5\frac{3}{8}$	$2\text{-}1\frac{9}{16}$	$1\text{-}6\frac{5}{16}$	$2\text{-}2\frac{15}{16}$	$1\text{-}7\frac{1}{4}$	$2\text{-}4\frac{9}{32}$	$1\text{-}8\frac{5}{8}$	$2\text{-}5\frac{21}{32}$
13/16	$1\text{-}4\frac{1}{2}$	$2\text{-}0\frac{9}{32}$	$1\text{-}5\frac{7}{16}$	$2\text{-}1\frac{21}{32}$	$1\text{-}6\frac{3}{8}$	$2\text{-}3\frac{1}{32}$	$1\text{-}7\frac{9}{32}$	$2\text{-}4\frac{3}{8}$	$1\text{-}8\frac{7}{32}$	$2\text{-}5\frac{3}{4}$
7/8	$1\text{-}4\frac{9}{16}$	$2\text{-}0\frac{3}{8}$	$1\text{-}5\frac{1}{2}$	$2\text{-}1\frac{3}{4}$	$1\text{-}6\frac{7}{16}$	$2\text{-}3\frac{3}{32}$	$1\text{-}7\frac{11}{32}$	$2\text{-}4\frac{15}{32}$	$1\text{-}8\frac{9}{32}$	$2\text{-}5\frac{27}{32}$
15/16	$1\text{-}4\frac{5}{8}$	$2\text{-}0\frac{15}{32}$	$1\text{-}5\frac{9}{16}$	$2\text{-}1\frac{13}{16}$	$1\text{-}6\frac{15}{32}$	$2\text{-}3\frac{3}{16}$	$1\text{-}7\frac{13}{32}$	$2\text{-}4\frac{9}{16}$	$1\text{-}8\frac{11}{32}$	$2\text{-}5\frac{29}{32}$

Feet	40′ Rise	40′ Slope	50′ Rise	50′ Slope	60′ Rise	60′ Slope	70′ Rise	70′ Slope
0	$37\text{-}1$	$54\text{-}6\frac{17}{32}$	$46\text{-}4\frac{1}{4}$	$68\text{-}2\frac{3}{16}$	$55\text{-}7\frac{1}{2}$	$81\text{-}9\frac{13}{16}$	$64\text{-}10\frac{3}{4}$	$95\text{-}5\frac{7}{16}$
1	$38\text{-}0\frac{1}{8}$	$55\text{-}10\frac{29}{32}$	$47\text{-}3\frac{3}{8}$	$69\text{-}6\frac{17}{32}$	$56\text{-}6\frac{5}{8}$	$83\text{-}2\frac{3}{16}$	$65\text{-}9\frac{7}{8}$	$96\text{-}9\frac{13}{16}$
2	$38\text{-}11\frac{1}{4}$	$57\text{-}3\frac{9}{32}$	$48\text{-}2\frac{1}{2}$	$70\text{-}10\frac{29}{32}$	$57\text{-}5\frac{3}{4}$	$84\text{-}6\frac{17}{32}$	$66\text{-}9$	$98\text{-}2\frac{3}{16}$
3	$39\text{-}10\frac{3}{8}$	$58\text{-}7\frac{5}{8}$	$49\text{-}1\frac{5}{8}$	$72\text{-}3\frac{9}{32}$	$58\text{-}4\frac{7}{8}$	$85\text{-}10\frac{29}{32}$	$67\text{-}8\frac{1}{8}$	$99\text{-}6\frac{17}{32}$
4	$40\text{-}9\frac{1}{2}$	$60\text{-}0$	$50\text{-}0\frac{3}{4}$	$73\text{-}7\frac{5}{8}$	$59\text{-}4$	$87\text{-}3\frac{9}{32}$	$68\text{-}7\frac{1}{4}$	$100\text{-}10\frac{29}{32}$
5	$41\text{-}8\frac{5}{8}$	$61\text{-}4\frac{3}{8}$	$50\text{-}11\frac{7}{8}$	$75\text{-}0$	$60\text{-}3\frac{1}{8}$	$88\text{-}7\frac{5}{8}$	$69\text{-}6\frac{3}{8}$	$102\text{-}3\frac{9}{32}$
6	$42\text{-}7\frac{3}{4}$	$62\text{-}8\frac{23}{32}$	$51\text{-}11$	$76\text{-}4\frac{11}{32}$	$61\text{-}2\frac{1}{4}$	$90\text{-}0$	$70\text{-}5\frac{1}{2}$	$103\text{-}7\frac{5}{8}$
7	$43\text{-}6\frac{7}{8}$	$64\text{-}1\frac{3}{32}$	$52\text{-}10\frac{1}{8}$	$77\text{-}8\frac{23}{32}$	$62\text{-}1\frac{3}{8}$	$91\text{-}4\frac{11}{32}$	$71\text{-}4\frac{5}{8}$	$105\text{-}0$
8	$44\text{-}6$	$65\text{-}5\frac{7}{16}$	$53\text{-}9\frac{1}{4}$	$79\text{-}1\frac{3}{32}$	$63\text{-}0\frac{1}{2}$	$92\text{-}8\frac{23}{32}$	$72\text{-}3\frac{3}{4}$	$106\text{-}4\frac{11}{32}$
9	$45\text{-}5\frac{1}{8}$	$66\text{-}9\frac{13}{16}$	$54\text{-}8\frac{3}{8}$	$80\text{-}5\frac{7}{16}$	$63\text{-}11\frac{5}{8}$	$94\text{-}1\frac{3}{32}$	$73\text{-}2\frac{7}{8}$	$107\text{-}8\frac{23}{32}$

natsin A=0.6798648815; natcos A=0.7333374003; nattan A=0.9270833333; natcot A=1.0786516853

Inches	0" Rise	0" Slope	1" Rise	1" Slope	2" Rise	2" Slope	3" Rise	3" Slope	4" Rise	4" Slope	5" Rise	5" Slope
0	0	0	$\frac{15}{16}$	$1\frac{3}{8}$	$1\frac{7}{8}$	$2\frac{23}{32}$	$2\frac{13}{16}$	$4\frac{3}{32}$	$3\frac{23}{32}$	$5\frac{15}{32}$	$4\frac{21}{32}$	$6\frac{21}{32}$
$\frac{1}{16}$	$\frac{1}{16}$	$\frac{3}{32}$	1	$1\frac{7}{16}$	$1\frac{15}{16}$	$2\frac{13}{16}$	$2\frac{27}{32}$	$4\frac{3}{16}$	$3\frac{25}{32}$	$5\frac{9}{16}$	$4\frac{23}{32}$	$6\frac{29}{32}$
$\frac{1}{8}$	$\frac{1}{8}$	$\frac{5}{32}$	$1\frac{1}{16}$	$1\frac{17}{32}$	$1\frac{31}{32}$	$2\frac{29}{32}$	$2\frac{29}{32}$	$4\frac{9}{32}$	$3\frac{27}{32}$	$5\frac{5}{8}$	$4\frac{25}{32}$	7
$\frac{3}{16}$	$\frac{3}{16}$	$\frac{1}{4}$	$1\frac{3}{32}$	$1\frac{5}{8}$	$2\frac{1}{32}$	3	$2\frac{31}{32}$	$4\frac{11}{32}$	$3\frac{29}{32}$	$5\frac{23}{32}$	$4\frac{27}{32}$	$7\frac{3}{32}$
$\frac{1}{4}$	$\frac{7}{32}$	$\frac{11}{32}$	$1\frac{5}{32}$	$1\frac{23}{32}$	$2\frac{3}{32}$	$3\frac{1}{16}$	$3\frac{1}{32}$	$4\frac{7}{16}$	$3\frac{31}{32}$	$5\frac{13}{16}$	$4\frac{29}{32}$	$7\frac{3}{16}$
$\frac{5}{16}$	$\frac{9}{32}$	$\frac{7}{16}$	$1\frac{7}{32}$	$1\frac{25}{32}$	$2\frac{5}{32}$	$3\frac{5}{32}$	$3\frac{3}{32}$	$4\frac{17}{32}$	$4\frac{1}{32}$	$5\frac{29}{32}$	$4\frac{15}{16}$	$7\frac{1}{4}$
$\frac{3}{8}$	$\frac{11}{32}$	$\frac{1}{2}$	$1\frac{9}{32}$	$1\frac{7}{8}$	$2\frac{7}{32}$	$3\frac{1}{4}$	$3\frac{5}{32}$	$4\frac{5}{8}$	$4\frac{3}{32}$	$5\frac{31}{32}$	5	$7\frac{11}{32}$
$\frac{7}{16}$	$\frac{13}{32}$	$\frac{19}{32}$	$1\frac{11}{32}$	$1\frac{31}{32}$	$2\frac{9}{32}$	$3\frac{11}{32}$	$3\frac{7}{32}$	$4\frac{11}{16}$	$4\frac{1}{8}$	$6\frac{1}{16}$	$5\frac{1}{16}$	$7\frac{7}{16}$
$\frac{1}{2}$	$\frac{15}{32}$	$\frac{11}{16}$	$1\frac{13}{32}$	$2\frac{1}{16}$	$2\frac{11}{32}$	$3\frac{13}{32}$	$3\frac{1}{4}$	$4\frac{25}{32}$	$4\frac{3}{16}$	$6\frac{5}{32}$	$5\frac{1}{8}$	$7\frac{17}{32}$
$\frac{9}{16}$	$\frac{17}{32}$	$\frac{25}{32}$	$1\frac{15}{32}$	$2\frac{1}{8}$	$2\frac{3}{8}$	$3\frac{1}{2}$	$3\frac{5}{16}$	$4\frac{7}{8}$	$4\frac{1}{4}$	$6\frac{1}{4}$	$5\frac{3}{16}$	$7\frac{19}{32}$
$\frac{5}{8}$	$\frac{19}{32}$	$\frac{27}{32}$	$1\frac{1}{2}$	$2\frac{27}{32}$	$2\frac{7}{16}$	$3\frac{19}{32}$	$3\frac{3}{8}$	$4\frac{31}{32}$	$4\frac{5}{16}$	$6\frac{5}{16}$	$5\frac{1}{4}$	$7\frac{11}{16}$
$\frac{11}{16}$	$\frac{21}{32}$	$\frac{15}{16}$	$1\frac{9}{16}$	$2\frac{5}{16}$	$2\frac{1}{2}$	$3\frac{11}{16}$	$3\frac{7}{16}$	$5\frac{1}{32}$	$4\frac{3}{8}$	$6\frac{13}{32}$	$5\frac{5}{16}$	$7\frac{25}{32}$
$\frac{3}{4}$	$\frac{11}{16}$	$1\frac{1}{32}$	$1\frac{5}{8}$	$2\frac{13}{32}$	$2\frac{9}{16}$	$3\frac{3}{4}$	$3\frac{1}{2}$	$5\frac{1}{8}$	$4\frac{7}{16}$	$6\frac{1}{2}$	$5\frac{3}{8}$	$7\frac{7}{8}$
$\frac{13}{16}$	$\frac{3}{4}$	$1\frac{1}{8}$	$1\frac{11}{16}$	$2\frac{15}{32}$	$2\frac{5}{8}$	$3\frac{27}{32}$	$3\frac{9}{16}$	$5\frac{7}{32}$	$4\frac{1}{2}$	$6\frac{19}{32}$	$5\frac{13}{32}$	$7\frac{15}{16}$
$\frac{7}{8}$	$\frac{13}{16}$	$1\frac{3}{16}$	$1\frac{3}{4}$	$2\frac{9}{16}$	$2\frac{11}{16}$	$3\frac{15}{16}$	$3\frac{5}{8}$	$5\frac{5}{16}$	$4\frac{17}{32}$	$6\frac{21}{32}$	$5\frac{15}{32}$	$8\frac{1}{32}$
$\frac{15}{16}$	$\frac{7}{8}$	$1\frac{9}{32}$	$1\frac{13}{16}$	$2\frac{21}{32}$	$2\frac{3}{4}$	$4\frac{1}{32}$	$3\frac{21}{32}$	$5\frac{3}{8}$	$4\frac{19}{32}$	$6\frac{3}{4}$	$5\frac{17}{32}$	$8\frac{1}{8}$

Inches	6" Rise	6" Slope	7" Rise	7" Slope	8" Rise	8" Slope	9" Rise	9" Slope	10" Rise	10" Slope	11" Rise	11" Slope
0	$5\frac{19}{32}$	$8\frac{3}{16}$	$6\frac{17}{32}$	$9\frac{9}{16}$	$7\frac{15}{32}$	$10\frac{15}{16}$	$8\frac{3}{8}$	$1\text{-}0\frac{5}{16}$	$9\frac{5}{16}$	$1\text{-}1\frac{21}{32}$	$10\frac{1}{4}$	$1\text{-}3\frac{1}{32}$
$\frac{1}{16}$	$5\frac{21}{32}$	$8\frac{9}{32}$	$6\frac{19}{32}$	$9\frac{21}{32}$	$7\frac{17}{32}$	$11\frac{1}{32}$	$8\frac{7}{16}$	$1\text{-}0\frac{3}{8}$	$9\frac{3}{8}$	$1\text{-}1\frac{3}{4}$	$10\frac{5}{16}$	$1\text{-}3\frac{1}{8}$
$\frac{1}{8}$	$5\frac{23}{32}$	$8\frac{3}{8}$	$6\frac{21}{32}$	$9\frac{3}{4}$	$7\frac{9}{16}$	$11\frac{3}{32}$	$8\frac{1}{2}$	$1\text{-}0\frac{15}{32}$	$9\frac{7}{16}$	$1\text{-}1\frac{27}{32}$	$10\frac{3}{8}$	$1\text{-}3\frac{7}{32}$
$\frac{3}{16}$	$5\frac{25}{32}$	$8\frac{15}{32}$	$6\frac{11}{16}$	$9\frac{13}{32}$	$7\frac{5}{8}$	$11\frac{3}{16}$	$8\frac{9}{16}$	$1\text{-}0\frac{9}{16}$	$9\frac{1}{2}$	$1\text{-}1\frac{15}{16}$	$10\frac{7}{16}$	$1\text{-}3\frac{9}{32}$
$\frac{1}{4}$	$5\frac{13}{16}$	$8\frac{17}{32}$	$6\frac{3}{4}$	$9\frac{29}{32}$	$7\frac{11}{16}$	$11\frac{9}{32}$	$8\frac{5}{8}$	$1\text{-}0\frac{21}{32}$	$9\frac{9}{16}$	$1\text{-}2$	$10\frac{1}{2}$	$1\text{-}3\frac{3}{8}$
$\frac{5}{16}$	$5\frac{7}{8}$	$8\frac{5}{8}$	$6\frac{13}{16}$	10	$7\frac{3}{4}$	$11\frac{3}{8}$	$8\frac{11}{16}$	$1\text{-}0\frac{23}{32}$	$9\frac{5}{8}$	$1\text{-}2\frac{3}{32}$	$10\frac{17}{32}$	$1\text{-}3\frac{15}{32}$
$\frac{3}{8}$	$5\frac{15}{16}$	$8\frac{23}{32}$	$6\frac{7}{8}$	$10\frac{3}{32}$	$7\frac{13}{16}$	$11\frac{7}{16}$	$8\frac{3}{4}$	$1\text{-}0\frac{13}{16}$	$9\frac{11}{16}$	$1\text{-}2\frac{3}{16}$	$10\frac{19}{32}$	$1\text{-}3\frac{9}{16}$
$\frac{7}{16}$	6	$8\frac{13}{16}$	$7\frac{11}{16}$	$10\frac{5}{32}$	$7\frac{7}{8}$	$11\frac{17}{32}$	$8\frac{13}{16}$	$1\text{-}0\frac{29}{32}$	$9\frac{23}{32}$	$1\text{-}2\frac{9}{32}$	$10\frac{21}{32}$	$1\text{-}3\frac{5}{8}$
$\frac{1}{2}$	$6\frac{1}{16}$	$8\frac{7}{8}$	7	$10\frac{1}{4}$	$7\frac{15}{32}$	$11\frac{5}{8}$	$8\frac{27}{32}$	$1\text{-}1$	$9\frac{25}{32}$	$1\text{-}2\frac{11}{32}$	$10\frac{23}{32}$	$1\text{-}3\frac{23}{32}$
$\frac{9}{16}$	$6\frac{1}{8}$	$8\frac{31}{32}$	$7\frac{1}{16}$	$10\frac{11}{32}$	$7\frac{31}{32}$	$11\frac{23}{32}$	$8\frac{29}{32}$	$1\text{-}1\frac{1}{16}$	$9\frac{27}{32}$	$1\text{-}2\frac{7}{16}$	$10\frac{25}{32}$	$1\text{-}3\frac{13}{16}$
$\frac{5}{8}$	$6\frac{3}{16}$	$9\frac{1}{16}$	$7\frac{3}{32}$	$10\frac{7}{16}$	$8\frac{1}{32}$	$11\frac{25}{32}$	$8\frac{31}{32}$	$1\text{-}1\frac{5}{32}$	$9\frac{29}{32}$	$1\text{-}2\frac{17}{32}$	$10\frac{27}{32}$	$1\text{-}3\frac{29}{32}$
$\frac{11}{16}$	$6\frac{1}{4}$	$9\frac{5}{32}$	$7\frac{5}{32}$	$10\frac{1}{2}$	$8\frac{3}{32}$	$11\frac{7}{8}$	$9\frac{1}{32}$	$1\text{-}1\frac{1}{4}$	$9\frac{31}{32}$	$1\text{-}2\frac{5}{8}$	$10\frac{29}{32}$	$1\text{-}3\frac{31}{32}$
$\frac{3}{4}$	$6\frac{9}{32}$	$9\frac{7}{32}$	$7\frac{7}{32}$	$10\frac{19}{32}$	$8\frac{5}{32}$	$11\frac{31}{32}$	$9\frac{3}{32}$	$1\text{-}1\frac{11}{32}$	$10\frac{1}{32}$	$1\text{-}2\frac{11}{32}$	$10\frac{31}{32}$	$1\text{-}4\frac{1}{16}$
$\frac{13}{16}$	$6\frac{11}{32}$	$9\frac{5}{16}$	$7\frac{9}{32}$	$10\frac{11}{16}$	$8\frac{7}{32}$	$1\text{-}0\frac{1}{16}$	$9\frac{5}{32}$	$1\text{-}1\frac{13}{32}$	$10\frac{3}{32}$	$1\text{-}2\frac{25}{32}$	11	$1\text{-}4\frac{1}{8}$
$\frac{7}{8}$	$6\frac{13}{32}$	$9\frac{13}{32}$	$7\frac{11}{32}$	$10\frac{25}{32}$	$8\frac{9}{32}$	$1\text{-}0\frac{1}{8}$	$9\frac{7}{32}$	$1\text{-}1\frac{1}{2}$	$10\frac{1}{8}$	$1\text{-}2\frac{7}{8}$	$11\frac{1}{16}$	$1\text{-}4\frac{1}{4}$
$\frac{15}{16}$	$6\frac{15}{32}$	$9\frac{1}{2}$	$7\frac{13}{32}$	$10\frac{27}{32}$	$8\frac{11}{32}$	$1\text{-}0\frac{7}{32}$	$9\frac{1}{4}$	$1\text{-}1\frac{19}{32}$	$10\frac{3}{16}$	$1\text{-}2\frac{31}{32}$	$11\frac{1}{8}$	$1\text{-}4\frac{5}{16}$

Feet	0' Rise	0' Slope	10' Rise	10' Slope	20' Rise	20' Slope	30' Rise	30' Slope
0	0	0	$9\text{-}3\frac{7}{8}$	$13\text{-}8\frac{1}{16}$	$18\text{-}7\frac{3}{4}$	$27\text{-}4\frac{1}{8}$	$27\text{-}11\frac{5}{8}$	$41\text{-}0\frac{9}{16}$
1	$-1\frac{13}{16}$	$1\text{-}4\frac{13}{32}$	$10\text{-}3\frac{1}{16}$	$15\text{-}0\frac{15}{32}$	$19\text{-}6\frac{15}{16}$	$28\text{-}8\frac{17}{32}$	$28\text{-}10\frac{13}{16}$	$42\text{-}4\frac{19}{32}$
2	$1\text{-}0\frac{3}{8}$	$2\text{-}8\frac{13}{16}$	$11\text{-}2\frac{1}{4}$	$16\text{-}4\frac{7}{8}$	$20\text{-}6\frac{1}{8}$	$30\text{-}0\frac{15}{16}$	$29\text{-}10$	$43\text{-}9$
3	$2\text{-}9\frac{9}{16}$	$4\text{-}1\frac{7}{32}$	$12\text{-}1\frac{7}{16}$	$17\text{-}9\frac{9}{32}$	$21\text{-}5\frac{5}{16}$	$31\text{-}5\frac{11}{32}$	$30\text{-}9\frac{3}{16}$	$45\text{-}1\frac{13}{32}$
4	$3\text{-}8\frac{3}{4}$	$5\text{-}5\frac{5}{8}$	$13\text{-}0\frac{5}{8}$	$19\text{-}1\frac{11}{16}$	$22\text{-}4\frac{1}{2}$	$32\text{-}9\frac{3}{4}$	$31\text{-}8\frac{3}{8}$	$46\text{-}5\frac{13}{16}$
5	$4\text{-}7\frac{15}{16}$	$6\text{-}10\frac{1}{32}$	$13\text{-}11\frac{13}{16}$	$20\text{-}6\frac{3}{32}$	$23\text{-}3\frac{11}{16}$	$34\text{-}2\frac{5}{32}$	$32\text{-}7\frac{9}{16}$	$47\text{-}10\frac{7}{32}$
6	$5\text{-}7\frac{1}{8}$	$8\text{-}2\frac{7}{16}$	$14\text{-}11$	$21\text{-}10\frac{1}{2}$	$24\text{-}2\frac{7}{8}$	$35\text{-}6\frac{9}{16}$	$33\text{-}6\frac{3}{4}$	$49\text{-}2\frac{5}{8}$
7	$6\text{-}6\frac{5}{16}$	$9\text{-}6\frac{7}{32}$	$15\text{-}10\frac{3}{16}$	$23\text{-}2\frac{29}{32}$	$25\text{-}2\frac{1}{16}$	$36\text{-}10\frac{31}{32}$	$34\text{-}5\frac{15}{16}$	$50\text{-}7\frac{1}{32}$
8	$7\text{-}5\frac{1}{2}$	$10\text{-}11\frac{1}{4}$	$16\text{-}9\frac{3}{8}$	$24\text{-}7\frac{5}{16}$	$26\text{-}1\frac{1}{4}$	$38\text{-}3\frac{3}{8}$	$35\text{-}5\frac{1}{8}$	$51\text{-}11\frac{7}{16}$
9	$8\text{-}4\frac{11}{16}$	$12\text{-}3\frac{21}{32}$	$17\text{-}8\frac{9}{16}$	$25\text{-}11\frac{23}{32}$	$27\text{-}0\frac{7}{16}$	$39\text{-}7\frac{25}{32}$	$36\text{-}4\frac{5}{16}$	$53\text{-}3\frac{27}{32}$

A = 42° 59′ 35″; logsin A = 9.83373: logcos A = 9.86418; logtan A = 9.96955; logcot A = 0.03045

In.	12″ Rise	12″ Slope	13″ Rise	13″ Slope	14″ Rise	14″ Slope	15″ Rise	15″ Slope	16″ Rise	16″ Slope
0	$11\frac{3}{16}$	$1\text{-}4\frac{13}{32}$	$1\text{-}0\frac{1}{8}$	$1\text{-}5\frac{25}{32}$	$1\text{-}1\frac{1}{16}$	$1\text{-}7\frac{1}{8}$	$1\text{-}2$	$1\text{-}8\frac{1}{2}$	$1\text{-}2\frac{29}{32}$	$1\text{-}9\frac{7}{8}$
$\frac{1}{16}$	$11\frac{1}{4}$	$1\text{-}4\frac{1}{2}$	$1\text{-}0\frac{3}{16}$	$1\text{-}5\frac{27}{32}$	$1\text{-}1\frac{1}{8}$	$1\text{-}7\frac{7}{32}$	$1\text{-}2\frac{1}{16}$	$1\text{-}8\frac{19}{32}$	$1\text{-}2\frac{31}{32}$	$1\text{-}9\frac{31}{32}$
$\frac{1}{8}$	$11\frac{5}{16}$	$1\text{-}4\frac{9}{16}$	$1\text{-}0\frac{1}{4}$	$1\text{-}5\frac{15}{16}$	$1\text{-}1\frac{5}{32}$	$1\text{-}7\frac{5}{16}$	$1\text{-}2\frac{3}{32}$	$1\text{-}8\frac{11}{16}$	$1\text{-}3\frac{1}{32}$	$1\text{-}10\frac{1}{32}$
$\frac{3}{16}$	$11\frac{3}{8}$	$1\text{-}4\frac{21}{32}$	$1\text{-}0\frac{9}{32}$	$1\text{-}6\frac{1}{32}$	$1\text{-}1\frac{7}{32}$	$1\text{-}7\frac{13}{32}$	$1\text{-}2\frac{5}{32}$	$1\text{-}8\frac{3}{4}$	$1\text{-}3\frac{3}{32}$	$1\text{-}10\frac{1}{8}$
$\frac{1}{4}$	$11\frac{13}{32}$	$1\text{-}4\frac{3}{4}$	$1\text{-}0\frac{11}{32}$	$1\text{-}6\frac{1}{8}$	$1\text{-}1\frac{9}{32}$	$1\text{-}7\frac{15}{32}$	$1\text{-}2\frac{7}{32}$	$1\text{-}8\frac{27}{32}$	$1\text{-}3\frac{5}{32}$	$1\text{-}10\frac{7}{32}$
$\frac{5}{16}$	$11\frac{15}{32}$	$1\text{-}4\frac{27}{32}$	$1\text{-}0\frac{13}{32}$	$1\text{-}6\frac{3}{16}$	$1\text{-}1\frac{11}{32}$	$1\text{-}7\frac{9}{16}$	$1\text{-}2\frac{9}{32}$	$1\text{-}8\frac{15}{16}$	$1\text{-}3\frac{7}{32}$	$1\text{-}10\frac{5}{16}$
$\frac{3}{8}$	$11\frac{17}{32}$	$1\text{-}4\frac{29}{32}$	$1\text{-}0\frac{15}{32}$	$1\text{-}6\frac{9}{32}$	$1\text{-}1\frac{13}{32}$	$1\text{-}7\frac{21}{32}$	$1\text{-}2\frac{11}{32}$	$1\text{-}9\frac{1}{32}$	$1\text{-}3\frac{9}{32}$	$1\text{-}10\frac{3}{8}$
$\frac{7}{16}$	$11\frac{19}{32}$	$1\text{-}5$	$1\text{-}0\frac{17}{32}$	$1\text{-}6\frac{3}{8}$	$1\text{-}1\frac{15}{32}$	$1\text{-}7\frac{3}{4}$	$1\text{-}2\frac{13}{32}$	$1\text{-}9\frac{3}{32}$	$1\text{-}3\frac{5}{16}$	$1\text{-}10\frac{15}{32}$
$\frac{1}{2}$	$11\frac{21}{32}$	$1\text{-}5\frac{3}{32}$	$1\text{-}0\frac{19}{32}$	$1\text{-}6\frac{15}{32}$	$1\text{-}1\frac{17}{32}$	$1\text{-}7\frac{13}{16}$	$1\text{-}2\frac{7}{16}$	$1\text{-}9\frac{3}{16}$	$1\text{-}3\frac{3}{8}$	$1\text{-}10\frac{9}{16}$
$\frac{9}{16}$	$11\frac{23}{32}$	$1\text{-}5\frac{3}{16}$	$1\text{-}0\frac{21}{32}$	$1\text{-}6\frac{17}{32}$	$1\text{-}1\frac{9}{16}$	$1\text{-}7\frac{29}{32}$	$1\text{-}2\frac{1}{2}$	$1\text{-}9\frac{9}{32}$	$1\text{-}3\frac{7}{16}$	$1\text{-}10\frac{21}{32}$
$\frac{5}{8}$	$11\frac{25}{32}$	$1\text{-}5\frac{1}{4}$	$1\text{-}0\frac{11}{16}$	$1\text{-}6\frac{5}{8}$	$1\text{-}1\frac{5}{8}$	$1\text{-}8$	$1\text{-}2\frac{9}{16}$	$1\text{-}9\frac{3}{8}$	$1\text{-}3\frac{1}{2}$	$1\text{-}10\frac{23}{32}$
$\frac{11}{16}$	$11\frac{27}{32}$	$1\text{-}5\frac{11}{32}$	$1\text{-}0\frac{3}{4}$	$1\text{-}6\frac{23}{32}$	$1\text{-}1\frac{11}{16}$	$1\text{-}8\frac{3}{32}$	$1\text{-}2\frac{5}{8}$	$1\text{-}9\frac{7}{16}$	$1\text{-}3\frac{9}{16}$	$1\text{-}10\frac{13}{16}$
$\frac{3}{4}$	$11\frac{7}{8}$	$1\text{-}5\frac{7}{16}$	$1\text{-}0\frac{13}{16}$	$1\text{-}6\frac{13}{16}$	$1\text{-}1\frac{3}{4}$	$1\text{-}8\frac{5}{32}$	$1\text{-}2\frac{11}{16}$	$1\text{-}9\frac{17}{32}$	$1\text{-}3\frac{5}{8}$	$1\text{-}10\frac{29}{32}$
$\frac{13}{16}$	$11\frac{15}{16}$	$1\text{-}5\frac{17}{32}$	$1\text{-}0\frac{7}{8}$	$1\text{-}6\frac{7}{8}$	$1\text{-}1\frac{13}{16}$	$1\text{-}8\frac{1}{4}$	$1\text{-}2\frac{3}{4}$	$1\text{-}9\frac{5}{8}$	$1\text{-}3\frac{11}{16}$	$1\text{-}11$
$\frac{7}{8}$	$1\text{-}0$	$1\text{-}5\frac{19}{32}$	$1\text{-}0\frac{15}{16}$	$1\text{-}6\frac{31}{32}$	$1\text{-}1\frac{7}{8}$	$1\text{-}8\frac{11}{32}$	$1\text{-}2\frac{13}{16}$	$1\text{-}9\frac{23}{32}$	$1\text{-}3\frac{23}{32}$	$1\text{-}11\frac{1}{16}$
$\frac{15}{16}$	$1\text{-}0\frac{1}{16}$	$1\text{-}5\frac{11}{16}$	$1\text{-}1$	$1\text{-}7\frac{1}{16}$	$1\text{-}1\frac{15}{16}$	$1\text{-}8\frac{7}{16}$	$1\text{-}2\frac{27}{32}$	$1\text{-}9\frac{25}{32}$	$1\text{-}3\frac{25}{32}$	$1\text{-}11\frac{1}{8}$

In.	17″ Rise	17″ Slope	18″ Rise	18″ Slope	19″ Rise	19″ Slope	20″ Rise	20″ Slope	21″ Rise	21″ Slope
0	$1\text{-}3\frac{27}{32}$	$1\text{-}11\frac{1}{4}$	$1\text{-}4\frac{25}{32}$	$2\text{-}0\frac{19}{32}$	$1\text{-}5\frac{23}{32}$	$2\text{-}1\frac{31}{32}$	$1\text{-}6\frac{21}{32}$	$2\text{-}3\frac{11}{32}$	$1\text{-}7\frac{9}{16}$	$2\text{-}4\frac{23}{32}$
$\frac{1}{16}$	$1\text{-}3\frac{29}{32}$	$1\text{-}11\frac{5}{16}$	$1\text{-}4\frac{27}{32}$	$2\text{-}0\frac{11}{16}$	$1\text{-}5\frac{25}{32}$	$2\text{-}2\frac{1}{32}$	$1\text{-}6\frac{23}{32}$	$2\text{-}3\frac{7}{16}$	$1\text{-}7\frac{5}{8}$	$2\text{-}4\frac{25}{32}$
$\frac{1}{8}$	$1\text{-}3\frac{31}{32}$	$1\text{-}11\frac{13}{32}$	$1\text{-}4\frac{29}{32}$	$2\text{-}0\frac{25}{32}$	$1\text{-}5\frac{27}{32}$	$2\text{-}2\frac{5}{32}$	$1\text{-}6\frac{3}{4}$	$2\text{-}3\frac{1}{2}$	$1\text{-}7\frac{11}{16}$	$2\text{-}4\frac{7}{8}$
$\frac{3}{16}$	$1\text{-}4\frac{1}{32}$	$1\text{-}11\frac{1}{2}$	$1\text{-}4\frac{31}{32}$	$2\text{-}0\frac{7}{8}$	$1\text{-}5\frac{7}{8}$	$2\text{-}2\frac{7}{32}$	$1\text{-}6\frac{13}{16}$	$2\text{-}3\frac{19}{32}$	$1\text{-}7\frac{3}{4}$	$2\text{-}4\frac{31}{32}$
$\frac{1}{4}$	$1\text{-}4\frac{3}{32}$	$1\text{-}11\frac{19}{32}$	$1\text{-}5$	$2\text{-}0\frac{15}{16}$	$1\text{-}5\frac{15}{16}$	$2\text{-}2\frac{5}{16}$	$1\text{-}6\frac{7}{8}$	$2\text{-}3\frac{11}{16}$	$1\text{-}7\frac{13}{16}$	$2\text{-}5\frac{1}{16}$
$\frac{5}{16}$	$1\text{-}4\frac{1}{8}$	$1\text{-}11\frac{21}{32}$	$1\text{-}5\frac{1}{16}$	$2\text{-}1\frac{1}{32}$	$1\text{-}6$	$2\text{-}2\frac{13}{32}$	$1\text{-}6\frac{15}{16}$	$2\text{-}3\frac{25}{32}$	$1\text{-}7\frac{7}{8}$	$2\text{-}5\frac{1}{8}$
$\frac{3}{8}$	$1\text{-}4\frac{3}{16}$	$1\text{-}11\frac{3}{4}$	$1\text{-}5\frac{1}{8}$	$2\text{-}1\frac{1}{8}$	$1\text{-}6\frac{1}{16}$	$2\text{-}2\frac{1}{2}$	$1\text{-}7$	$2\text{-}3\frac{27}{32}$	$1\text{-}7\frac{15}{16}$	$2\text{-}5\frac{7}{32}$
$\frac{7}{16}$	$1\text{-}4\frac{1}{4}$	$1\text{-}11\frac{27}{32}$	$1\text{-}5\frac{3}{16}$	$2\text{-}1\frac{7}{32}$	$1\text{-}6\frac{1}{8}$	$2\text{-}2\frac{9}{16}$	$1\text{-}7\frac{1}{16}$	$2\text{-}3\frac{15}{16}$	$1\text{-}8$	$2\text{-}5\frac{5}{16}$
$\frac{1}{2}$	$1\text{-}4\frac{5}{16}$	$1\text{-}11\frac{15}{16}$	$1\text{-}5\frac{1}{4}$	$2\text{-}1\frac{9}{32}$	$1\text{-}6\frac{3}{16}$	$2\text{-}2\frac{21}{32}$	$1\text{-}7\frac{1}{8}$	$2\text{-}4\frac{1}{32}$	$1\text{-}8\frac{1}{8}$	$2\text{-}5\frac{13}{32}$
$\frac{9}{16}$	$1\text{-}4\frac{3}{8}$	$2\text{-}0$	$1\text{-}5\frac{5}{16}$	$2\text{-}1\frac{3}{8}$	$1\text{-}6\frac{1}{4}$	$2\text{-}2\frac{3}{4}$	$1\text{-}7\frac{5}{32}$	$2\text{-}4\frac{1}{8}$	$1\text{-}8\frac{3}{32}$	$2\text{-}5\frac{15}{32}$
$\frac{5}{8}$	$1\text{-}4\frac{7}{16}$	$2\text{-}0\frac{3}{32}$	$1\text{-}5\frac{3}{8}$	$2\text{-}1\frac{15}{32}$	$1\text{-}6\frac{9}{32}$	$2\text{-}2\frac{27}{32}$	$1\text{-}7\frac{7}{32}$	$2\text{-}4\frac{3}{16}$	$1\text{-}8\frac{5}{32}$	$2\text{-}5\frac{9}{16}$
$\frac{11}{16}$	$1\text{-}4\frac{1}{2}$	$2\text{-}0\frac{3}{16}$	$1\text{-}5\frac{7}{16}$	$2\text{-}1\frac{9}{16}$	$1\text{-}6\frac{11}{32}$	$2\text{-}2\frac{29}{32}$	$1\text{-}7\frac{9}{32}$	$2\text{-}4\frac{9}{32}$	$1\text{-}8\frac{7}{32}$	$2\text{-}5\frac{21}{32}$
$\frac{3}{4}$	$1\text{-}4\frac{9}{16}$	$2\text{-}0\frac{9}{32}$	$1\text{-}5\frac{15}{32}$	$2\text{-}1\frac{5}{8}$	$1\text{-}6\frac{13}{32}$	$2\text{-}3$	$1\text{-}7\frac{11}{32}$	$2\text{-}4\frac{3}{8}$	$1\text{-}8\frac{9}{32}$	$2\text{-}5\frac{3}{4}$
$\frac{13}{16}$	$1\text{-}4\frac{19}{32}$	$2\text{-}0\frac{11}{32}$	$1\text{-}5\frac{17}{32}$	$2\text{-}1\frac{23}{32}$	$1\text{-}6\frac{15}{32}$	$2\text{-}3\frac{3}{32}$	$1\text{-}7\frac{13}{32}$	$2\text{-}4\frac{15}{32}$	$1\text{-}8\frac{11}{32}$	$2\text{-}5\frac{13}{16}$
$\frac{7}{8}$	$1\text{-}4\frac{21}{32}$	$2\text{-}0\frac{7}{16}$	$1\text{-}5\frac{19}{32}$	$2\text{-}1\frac{13}{16}$	$1\text{-}6\frac{17}{32}$	$2\text{-}3\frac{3}{16}$	$1\text{-}7\frac{15}{32}$	$2\text{-}4\frac{17}{32}$	$1\text{-}8\frac{13}{32}$	$2\text{-}5\frac{29}{32}$
$\frac{15}{16}$	$1\text{-}4\frac{23}{32}$	$2\text{-}0\frac{17}{32}$	$1\text{-}5\frac{21}{32}$	$2\text{-}1\frac{29}{32}$	$1\text{-}6\frac{19}{32}$	$2\text{-}3\frac{1}{4}$	$1\text{-}7\frac{17}{32}$	$2\text{-}4\frac{5}{8}$	$1\text{-}8\frac{7}{16}$	$2\text{-}6$

Feet	40′ Rise	40′ Slope	50′ Rise	50′ Slope	60′ Rise	60′ Slope	70′ Rise	70′ Slope
0	$37\text{-}3\frac{1}{2}$	$54\text{-}8\frac{1}{4}$	$46\text{-}7\frac{7}{8}$	$68\text{-}4\frac{5}{16}$	$55\text{-}11\frac{1}{4}$	$82\text{-}0\frac{3}{8}$	$65\text{-}3\frac{1}{8}$	$95\text{-}8\frac{7}{16}$
1	$38\text{-}2\frac{11}{16}$	$56\text{-}0\frac{21}{32}$	$47\text{-}6\frac{9}{16}$	$69\text{-}8\frac{23}{32}$	$56\text{-}10\frac{7}{16}$	$83\text{-}4\frac{25}{32}$	$66\text{-}2\frac{5}{16}$	$97\text{-}0\frac{27}{32}$
2	$39\text{-}1\frac{7}{8}$	$57\text{-}5\frac{1}{16}$	$48\text{-}5\frac{3}{4}$	$71\text{-}1\frac{1}{8}$	$57\text{-}9\frac{5}{8}$	$84\text{-}9\frac{3}{16}$	$67\text{-}1\frac{1}{2}$	$98\text{-}5\frac{1}{4}$
3	$40\text{-}1\frac{1}{16}$	$58\text{-}9\frac{15}{32}$	$49\text{-}4\frac{15}{16}$	$72\text{-}5\frac{17}{32}$	$58\text{-}8\frac{13}{16}$	$86\text{-}1\frac{19}{32}$	$68\text{-}0\frac{11}{16}$	$99\text{-}9\frac{21}{32}$
4	$41\text{-}0\frac{1}{4}$	$60\text{-}1\frac{7}{8}$	$50\text{-}4\frac{1}{8}$	$73\text{-}9\frac{15}{16}$	$59\text{-}8$	$87\text{-}6$	$68\text{-}11\frac{7}{8}$	$101\text{-}2\frac{1}{16}$
5	$41\text{-}11\frac{7}{16}$	$61\text{-}6\frac{9}{32}$	$51\text{-}3\frac{5}{16}$	$75\text{-}2\frac{11}{32}$	$60\text{-}7\frac{3}{16}$	$88\text{-}10\frac{13}{32}$	$69\text{-}11\frac{1}{16}$	$102\text{-}6\frac{15}{32}$
6	$42\text{-}10\frac{5}{8}$	$62\text{-}10\frac{11}{16}$	$52\text{-}2\frac{1}{2}$	$76\text{-}6\frac{3}{4}$	$61\text{-}6\frac{3}{8}$	$90\text{-}2\frac{13}{16}$	$70\text{-}10\frac{1}{4}$	$103\text{-}10\frac{7}{8}$
7	$43\text{-}9\frac{13}{16}$	$64\text{-}3\frac{3}{32}$	$53\text{-}1\frac{11}{16}$	$77\text{-}11\frac{5}{32}$	$62\text{-}5\frac{9}{16}$	$91\text{-}7\frac{7}{32}$	$71\text{-}9\frac{7}{16}$	$105\text{-}3\frac{9}{32}$
8	$44\text{-}9$	$65\text{-}7\frac{1}{2}$	$54\text{-}0\frac{7}{8}$	$79\text{-}3\frac{9}{16}$	$63\text{-}4\frac{3}{4}$	$92\text{-}11\frac{5}{8}$	$72\text{-}8\frac{5}{8}$	$106\text{-}7\frac{11}{16}$
9	$45\text{-}8\frac{3}{16}$	$66\text{-}11\frac{29}{32}$	$55\text{-}0\frac{1}{16}$	$80\text{-}7\frac{31}{32}$	$64\text{-}3\frac{15}{16}$	$94\text{-}4\frac{1}{32}$	$73\text{-}7\frac{13}{16}$	$108\text{-}0\frac{3}{32}$

natsin A=0.6819109469; natcos A=0.7314352057; nattan A=0.9322916666; natcot A=1.0726256983

Inches	0″ Rise	0″ Slope	1″ Rise	1″ Slope	2″ Rise	2″ Slope	3″ Rise	3″ Slope	4″ Rise	4″ Slope	5″ Rise	5″ Slope
0	0	0	15/16	1 3/8	1 7/8	2 3/4	2 13/16	4 1/8	3 3/4	5 15/32	4 11/16	6 27/32
1/16	1/16	3/32	1	1 15/32	1 15/16	2 13/16	2 7/8	4 3/16	3 13/16	5 9/16	4 3/4	6 15/16
1/8	1/8	5/32	1 1/16	1 17/32	2	2 29/32	2 15/16	4 9/32	3 7/8	5 21/32	4 13/16	7 1/32
3/16	3/16	1/4	1 1/8	1 5/8	2 1/16	3	3	4 3/8	3 15/16	5 3/4	4 7/8	7 1/8
1/4	1/4	11/32	1 3/16	1 23/32	2 1/8	3 3/32	3 1/16	4 15/32	4	5 13/16	4 15/16	7 3/16
5/16	9/32	7/16	1 7/32	1 13/16	2 5/32	3 5/32	3 3/32	4 17/32	4 1/32	5 29/32	4 31/32	7 9/32
3/8	11/32	1/2	1 9/32	1 7/8	2 7/32	3 1/4	3 5/32	4 5/8	4 3/32	6	5 1/32	7 3/8
7/16	13/32	19/32	1 11/32	1 31/32	2 9/32	3 11/32	3 7/32	4 23/32	4 5/32	6 3/32	5 3/32	7 15/32
1/2	15/32	11/16	1 13/32	2 1/16	2 11/32	3 7/16	3 9/32	4 13/16	4 7/32	6 5/32	5 5/32	7 17/32
9/16	17/32	25/32	1 15/32	2 5/32	2 13/32	3 1/2	3 11/32	4 7/8	4 9/32	6 1/4	5 7/32	7 5/8
5/8	19/32	27/32	1 17/32	2 7/32	2 15/32	3 19/32	3 13/32	4 31/32	4 11/32	6 11/32	5 9/32	7 23/32
11/16	21/32	15/16	1 19/32	2 5/16	2 17/32	3 11/16	3 15/32	5 1/16	4 13/32	6 7/16	5 11/32	7 25/32
3/4	11/16	1 1/32	1 5/8	2 13/32	2 9/16	3 25/32	3 1/2	5 1/8	4 7/16	6 1/2	5 3/8	7 7/8
13/16	3/4	1 1/8	1 11/16	2 1/2	2 5/8	3 27/32	3 9/16	5 7/32	4 1/2	6 19/32	5 7/16	7 31/32
7/8	13/16	1 3/16	1 3/4	2 9/16	2 11/16	3 15/16	3 5/8	5 5/16	4 9/16	6 11/16	5 1/2	8 1/16
15/16	7/8	1 9/32	1 13/16	2 21/32	2 3/4	4 1/32	3 11/16	5 13/32	4 5/8	6 25/32	5 9/16	8 1/8

Inches	6″ Rise	6″ Slope	7″ Rise	7″ Slope	8″ Rise	8″ Slope	9″ Rise	9″ Slope	10″ Rise	10″ Slope	11″ Rise	11″ Slope
0	5 5/8	8 7/32	6 9/16	9 19/32	7 1/2	10 31/32	8 7/16	1-0 11/32	9 3/8	1-1 23/32	10 5/16	1-3 1/16
1/16	5 11/16	8 5/16	6 5/8	9 11/16	7 9/16	11 1/16	8 1/2	1-0 7/16	9 7/16	1-1 25/32	10 3/8	1-3 5/32
1/8	5 3/4	8 13/32	6 11/16	9 25/32	7 5/8	11 1/8	8 9/16	1-0 1/2	9 1/2	1-1 7/8	10 7/16	1-3 1/4
3/16	5 13/16	8 15/32	6 3/4	9 27/32	7 11/16	11 7/32	8 5/8	1-0 19/32	9 9/16	1-1 31/32	10 1/2	1-3 11/32
1/4	5 7/8	8 9/16	6 13/16	9 15/16	7 3/4	11 5/16	8 11/16	1-0 11/16	9 5/8	1-2 1/16	10 9/16	1-3 13/32
5/16	5 29/32	8 21/32	6 27/32	10 1/32	7 25/32	11 13/32	8 23/32	1-0 3/4	9 21/32	1-2 1/8	10 19/32	1-3 1/2
3/8	5 31/32	8 3/4	6 29/32	10 3/32	7 27/32	11 15/32	8 25/32	1-0 27/32	9 23/32	1-2 7/32	10 21/32	1-3 19/32
7/16	6 1/32	8 13/16	6 31/32	10 3/16	7 29/32	11 9/16	8 27/32	1-0 15/16	9 25/32	1-2 5/16	10 23/32	1-3 11/16
1/2	6 3/32	8 29/32	7 1/16	10 9/32	7 31/32	11 21/32	8 29/32	1-1 1/32	9 27/32	1-2 13/32	10 25/32	1-3 3/4
9/16	6 5/32	9	7 3/32	10 3/8	8 1/32	11 3/4	8 31/32	1-1 3/32	9 29/32	1-2 15/32	10 27/32	1-3 27/32
5/8	6 7/32	9 3/32	7 5/32	10 7/16	8 3/32	11 27/32	9 1/32	1-1 3/16	9 31/32	1-2 9/16	10 29/32	1-3 15/16
11/16	6 9/32	9 5/32	7 7/32	10 17/32	8 5/32	11 29/32	9 3/32	1-1 9/32	10 1/32	1-2 21/32	10 31/32	1-4 1/32
3/4	6 5/16	9 1/4	7 1/4	10 5/8	8 3/16	1-0	9 1/8	1-1 3/8	10 1/16	1-2 3/4	11	1-4 3/32
13/16	6 3/8	9 11/32	7 5/16	10 23/32	8 1/4	1-0 3/32	9 3/16	1-1 15/32	10 1/8	1-2 13/16	11 1/16	1-4 3/16
7/8	6 7/16	9 7/16	7 3/8	10 25/32	8 5/16	1-0 5/32	9 1/4	1-1 9/16	10 3/16	1-2 29/32	11 1/8	1-4 9/32
15/16	6 1/2	9 1/2	7 7/16	10 7/8	8 3/8	1-0 1/4	9 5/16	1-1 5/8	10 1/4	1-3	11 3/16	1-4 3/8

Feet	0' Rise	0' Slope	10' Rise	10' Slope	20' Rise	20' Slope	30' Rise	30' Slope
0	0	0	9-4 1/2	13-8 1/2	18-9	27-4 31/32	28-1 1/2	41-1 15/32
1	-11 1/4	1-4 7/16	10-3 3/4	15-0 15/16	19-8 1/4	28-9 7/16	29-0 3/4	42-5 29/32
2	1-10 1/2	2-8 29/32	11-3	16-5 5/8	20-7 1/2	30-1 7/8	30-0	43-10 3/8
3	2-9 3/4	4-1 11/32	12-2 1/4	17-9 27/32	21-6 3/4	31-6 5/16	30-11 1/4	45-2 13/32
4	3-9	5-5 25/32	13-1 1/2	19-2 9/32	22-6	32-10 25/32	31-10 1/2	46-7 1/4
5	4-8 1/4	6-10 1/4	14-0 3/4	20-6 23/32	23-5 1/4	34-3 1/2	32-9 3/4	47-11 23/32
6	5-7 1/2	8-2 11/16	15-0	21-11 3/16	24-4 1/2	35-7 21/32	33-9	49-4 5/32
7	6-6 3/4	9-7 5/32	15-11 1/4	23-3 5/8	25-3 3/4	37-0 1/8	34-8 1/4	50-8 19/32
8	7-6	10-11 19/32	16-10 1/2	24-8 3/8	26-3	38-4 9/16	35-7 1/2	52-1 1/16
9	8-5 1/4	12-4 5/32	17-9 3/4	26-0 17/32	27-2 1/4	39-9	36-6 3/4	53-5 1/2

A = 43° 09′ 09″; logsin A = 9.83502; logcos A = 9.86305; logtan A = 9.97197; logcot A = 0.02803

Ins.	12" Rise	12" Slope	13" Rise	13" Slope	14" Rise	14" Slope	15" Rise	15" Slope	16" Rise	16" Slope
0	11 1/4	1-4 7/16	1-0 3/16	1-5 13/16	1-1 1/8	1-7 3/16	1-2 1/16	1-8 9/16	1-3	1-9 15/16
1/16	11 15/16	1-4 17/32	1-0 1/4	1-5 29/32	1-1 3/16	1-7 9/32	1-2 1/8	1-8 21/32	1-3 1/16	1-10 1/32
1/8	11 3/8	1-4 5/8	1-0 5/16	1-6	1-1 1/4	1-7 3/8	1-2 3/16	1-8 23/32	1-3 1/8	1-10 3/32
3/16	11 7/16	1-4 23/32	1-0 3/8	1-6 1/16	1-1 5/16	1-7 7/16	1-2 1/4	1-8 13/16	1-3 3/16	1-10 3/16
1/4	11 1/2	1-4 25/32	1-0 7/16	1-6 5/32	1-1 3/8	1-7 17/32	1-2 5/16	1-8 29/32	1-3 1/4	1-10 9/32
5/16	11 17/32	1-4 7/8	1-0 15/32	1-6 1/4	1-1 13/32	1-7 5/8	1-2 11/32	1-9	1-3 9/32	1-10 3/8
3/8	11 19/32	1-4 31/32	1-0 17/32	1-6 11/32	1-1 15/32	1-7 23/32	1-2 13/32	1-9 1/16	1-3 11/32	1-10 7/16
7/16	11 21/32	1-5 1/16	1-0 19/32	1-6 13/32	1-1 17/32	1-7 25/32	1-2 15/32	1-9 5/32	1-3 13/32	1-10 17/32
1/2	11 23/32	1-5 1/8	1-0 21/32	1-6 1/2	1-1 19/32	1-7 7/8	1-2 17/32	1-9 1/4	1-3 15/32	1-10 5/8
9/16	11 25/32	1-5 7/32	1-0 23/32	1-6 19/32	1-1 21/32	1-7 31/32	1-2 19/32	1-9 11/32	1-3 17/32	1-10 11/16
5/8	11 27/32	1-5 5/16	1-0 25/32	1-6 11/16	1-1 23/32	1-8 1/16	1-2 21/32	1-9 13/32	1-3 19/32	1-10 25/32
11/16	11 29/32	1-5 13/32	1-0 27/32	1-6 3/4	1-1 25/32	1-8 1/8	1-2 23/32	1-9 1/2	1-3 21/32	1-10 7/8
3/4	11 15/16	1-5 15/32	1-0 7/8	1-6 27/32	1-1 13/16	1-8 7/32	1-2 3/4	1-9 19/32	1-3 11/16	1-10 31/32
13/16	1-0	1-5 9/16	1-0 15/16	1-6 15/16	1-1 7/8	1-8 5/16	1-2 13/16	1-9 11/16	1-3 3/4	1-11 1/8
7/8	1-0 1/16	1-5 21/32	1-1	1-7 1/32	1-1 15/16	1-8 3/8	1-2 7/8	1-9 3/4	1-3 13/16	1-11 3/16
15/16	1-0 1/8	1-5 23/32	1-1 1/16	1-7 3/32	1-2	1-8 15/32	1-2 15/16	1-9 27/32	1-3 7/8	1-11 7/32

Ins.	17" Rise	17" Slope	18" Rise	18" Slope	19" Rise	19" Slope	20" Rise	20" Slope	21" Rise	21" Slope
0	1-3 15/16	1-11 5/16	1-4 7/8	2-0 11/16	1-5 13/16	2-2 1/16	1-6 3/4	2-3 13/32	1-7 11/16	2-4 25/32
1/16	1-4	1-11 3/8	1-4 15/16	2-0 3/4	1-5 7/8	2-2 1/8	1-6 13/16	2-3 1/2	1-7 7/8	2-4 7/8
1/8	1-4 1/16	1-11 15/32	1-5	2-0 27/32	1-5 15/16	2-2 9/32	1-6 7/8	2-3 19/32	1-7 13/16	2-4 31/32
3/16	1-4 1/8	1-11 19/32	1-5 1/16	2-0 15/16	1-6	2-2 5/16	1-6 15/16	2-3 21/32	1-7 7/8	2-5 1/32
1/4	1-4 3/16	1-11 21/32	1-5 1/8	2-1 1/32	1-6 1/16	2-2 3/8	1-7	2-3 3/4	1-7 15/16	2-5 1/8
5/16	1-4 7/32	1-11 23/32	1-5 5/32	2-1 3/32	1-6 3/32	2-2 15/32	1-7 1/32	2-3 27/32	1-7 31/32	2-5 1/32
3/8	1-4 9/32	1-11 13/16	1-5 7/32	2-1 3/16	1-6 5/32	2-2 9/16	1-7 3/32	2-3 15/16	1-8 1/32	2-5 5/16
7/16	1-4 11/32	1-11 29/32	1-5 9/32	2-1 9/32	1-6 7/32	2-2 21/32	1-7 5/32	2-4	1-8 3/32	2-5 3/8
1/2	1-4 13/32	2-0	1-5 11/32	2-1 11/32	1-6 9/32	2-2 23/32	1-7 7/32	2-4 3/32	1-8 5/32	2-5 15/32
9/16	1-4 15/32	2-0 1/16	1-5 13/32	2-1 7/16	1-6 11/32	2-2 13/16	1-7 9/32	2-4 3/16	1-8 7/32	2-5 9/16
5/8	1-4 17/32	2-0 5/32	1-5 15/32	2-1 17/32	1-6 13/32	2-2 29/32	1-7 11/32	2-4 9/32	1-8 9/32	2-5 21/32
11/16	1-4 19/32	2-0 1/4	1-5 17/32	2-1 5/8	1-6 15/32	2-3	1-7 13/32	2-4 11/32	1-8 11/32	2-5 23/32
3/4	1-4 5/8	2-0 11/32	1-5 9/16	2-1 11/16	1-6 1/2	2-3 1/16	1-7 7/16	2-4 7/16	1-8 3/8	2-5 13/16
13/16	1-4 11/16	2-0 13/32	1-5 5/8	2-1 25/32	1-6 9/16	2-3 5/32	1-7 1/2	2-4 17/32	1-8 7/16	2-5 29/32
7/8	1-4 3/4	2-0 1/2	1-5 11/16	2-1 7/8	1-6 5/8	2-3 1/4	1-7 9/16	2-4 5/8	1-8 1/2	2-6
15/16	1-4 13/16	2-0 19/32	1-5 3/4	2-1 31/32	1-6 11/16	2-3 11/32	1-7 5/8	2-4 11/16	1-8 9/16	2-6 1/16

Feet	40' Rise	40' Slope	50' Rise	50' Slope	60' Rise	60' Slope	70' Rise	70' Slope
0	37-6	54-9 15/16	46-10 1/2	68-6 7/16	56-3	82-2 15/16	65-7 1/2	95-11 13/32
1	38-5 1/4	56-2 13/32	47-9 3/4	69-10 7/8	57-2 1/4	83-7 3/8	66-6 3/4	97-3 7/8
2	39-4 1/2	57-6 27/32	48-9	71-3 11/32	58-1 1/2	84-11 13/16	67-6	98-8 5/16
3	40-3 3/4	58-11 15/32	49-8 1/4	72-7 25/32	59-0 3/4	86-4 9/32	68-5 1/4	100-0 3/4
4	41-3	60-3 3/4	50-7 1/2	74-0 7/32	60-0	87-8 23/32	69-4 1/2	101-5 7/32
5	42-2 1/4	61-8 3/16	51-6 3/4	75-4 11/16	60-11 1/4	89-1 5/32	70-3 3/4	102-9 21/32
6	43-1 1/2	63-0 21/32	52-6	76-9 1/8	61-10 1/2	90-5 5/8	71-3	104-2 3/32
7	44-0 3/4	64-5 3/32	53-5 1/4	78-1 19/32	62-9 3/4	91-10 1/16	72-2 1/4	105-6 9/16
8	45-0	65-9 17/32	54-4 1/2	79-6 1/32	63-9	93-2 17/32	73-1 1/2	106-11
9	45-11 1/4	67-2	55-3 3/4	80-10 15/32	64-8 1/4	94-6 31/32	74-0 3/4	108-3 15/32

natsin A=0.6839411289; natcos A=0.7295372041; nattan A=0.9375000000; natcot A=1.0666666666

Inches	0" Rise	0" Slope	1" Rise	1" Slope	2" Rise	2" Slope	3" Rise	3" Slope	4" Rise	4" Slope	5" Rise	5" Slope
0	0	0	15/16	1 3/8	1 7/8	2 3/4	2 13/16	4 1/8	3 25/32	5 1/2	4 23/32	6 1/8
1/16	1/16	3/32	1	1 15/32	1 15/16	2 27/32	2 7/8	4 7/32	3 27/32	5 19/32	4 25/32	6 31/32
1/8	1/8	5/32	1 1/16	1 17/32	2	2 29/32	2 15/16	4 9/32	3 7/8	5 21/32	4 27/32	7 1/32
3/16	3/16	1/4	1 1/8	1 5/8	2 1/16	3	3	4 3/8	3 15/16	5 3/4	4 7/8	7 1/8
1/4	1/4	11/32	1 3/16	1 23/32	2 1/8	3 3/32	3 1/16	4 15/32	4	5 27/32	4 15/16	7 7/32
5/16	9/32	7/16	1 1/4	1 13/16	2 3/16	3 3/16	3 1/8	4 9/16	4 1/16	5 15/16	5	7 5/16
3/8	11/32	1/2	1 9/32	1 7/8	2 1/4	3 1/4	3 3/16	4 5/8	4 1/8	6	5 1/16	7 3/8
7/16	13/32	19/32	1 11/32	1 31/32	2 5/16	3 11/32	3 1/4	4 23/32	4 3/16	6 3/32	5 1/8	7 15/32
1/2	15/32	11/16	1 13/32	2 1/16	2 11/32	3 7/16	3 5/16	4 13/16	4 1/4	6 3/16	5 3/16	7 9/16
9/16	17/32	25/32	1 15/32	2 5/32	2 13/32	3 17/32	3 11/32	4 29/32	4 5/16	6 9/32	5 1/4	7 21/32
5/8	19/32	27/32	1 17/32	2 7/32	2 15/32	3 19/32	3 13/32	4 31/32	4 3/8	6 11/32	5 5/16	7 23/32
11/16	21/32	15/16	1 19/32	2 5/16	2 17/32	3 11/16	3 15/32	5 1/16	4 13/32	6 7/16	5 3/8	7 13/16
3/4	23/32	1 1/32	1 21/32	2 13/32	2 19/32	3 25/32	3 17/32	5 5/32	4 15/32	6 17/32	5 13/32	7 29/32
13/16	25/32	1 1/8	1 23/32	2 1/2	2 21/32	3 7/8	3 19/32	5 1/4	4 17/32	6 5/8	5 15/32	8
7/8	13/16	1 3/16	1 25/32	2 9/16	2 23/32	3 15/16	3 21/32	5 5/16	4 19/32	6 11/16	5 17/32	8 1/16
15/16	7/8	1 9/32	1 13/16	2 21/32	2 25/32	4 1/32	3 23/32	5 13/32	4 21/32	6 25/32	5 19/32	8 5/32

Inches	6" Rise	6" Slope	7" Rise	7" Slope	8" Rise	8" Slope	9" Rise	9" Slope	10" Rise	10" Slope	11" Rise	11" Slope
0	5 21/32	8 1/4	6 19/32	9 5/8	7 17/32	11	8 1/2	1-0 3/8	9 7/16	1-1 3/4	10 3/8	1-3 1/8
1/16	5 23/32	8 11/32	6 21/32	9 23/32	7 19/32	11 3/8	8 17/32	1-0 15/32	9 1/2	1-1 27/32	10 7/16	1-3 7/32
1/8	5 25/32	8 13/32	6 23/32	9 25/32	7 21/32	11 5/32	8 19/32	1-0 17/32	9 9/16	1-1 29/32	10 1/2	1-3 9/32
3/16	5 27/32	8 1/2	6 25/32	9 7/8	7 23/32	11 1/4	8 21/32	1-0 5/8	9 19/32	1-2	10 17/32	1-3 3/8
1/4	5 29/32	8 19/32	6 27/32	9 31/32	7 25/32	1-1 11/32	8 23/32	1-0 23/32	9 21/32	1-2 3/32	10 19/32	1-3 15/32
5/16	5 15/16	8 11/16	6 29/32	10 1/16	7 27/32	1-1 7/16	8 25/32	1-0 13/16	9 23/32	1-2 3/16	10 21/32	1-3 17/32
3/8	6	8 3/4	6 15/16	10 1/8	7 29/32	1-1 1/2	8 27/32	1-0 7/8	9 25/32	1-2 1/4	10 23/32	1-3 5/8
7/16	6 1/16	8 27/32	7	10 7/32	7 31/32	1-1 19/32	8 29/32	1-0 31/32	9 27/32	1-2 11/32	10 25/32	1-3 23/32
1/2	6 1/8	8 15/16	7 1/16	10 5/16	8	1-1 11/16	8 31/32	1-1 1/16	9 29/32	1-2 7/16	10 27/32	1-3 13/16
9/16	6 3/16	9 1/32	7 1/8	10 13/32	8 1/16	1-1 25/32	9	1-1 5/32	9 31/32	1-2 17/32	10 29/32	1-3 7/8
5/8	6 1/4	9 5/32	7 3/16	10 15/32	8 1/8	1-1 27/32	9 1/16	1-1 7/32	10 1/32	1-2 19/32	10 31/32	1-3 31/32
11/16	6 5/16	9 3/16	7 1/4	10 9/16	8 3/16	1-1 15/16	9 1/8	1-1 5/16	10 1/16	1-2 11/16	11 1/32	1-4 1/16
3/4	6 3/8	9 9/32	7 5/16	10 21/32	8 1/4	1-2 1/32	9 3/16	1-1 13/32	10 1/8	1-2 25/32	11 1/16	1-4 5/32
13/16	6 7/16	9 3/8	7 3/8	10 3/4	8 5/16	1-2 1/8	9 1/4	1-1 1/2	10 3/16	1-2 7/8	11 1/8	1-4 7/32
7/8	6 15/32	9 7/16	7 7/16	10 13/16	8 3/8	1-2 3/16	9 5/16	1-1 9/16	10 1/4	1-2 15/16	11 3/16	1-4 5/16
15/16	6 17/32	9 17/32	7 15/32	10 29/32	8 7/16	1-2 9/32	9 3/8	1-1 21/32	10 5/16	1-3 1/32	11 1/4	1-4 13/32

Feet	0' Rise	0' Slope	10' Rise	10' Slope	20' Rise	20' Slope	30' Rise	30' Slope
0	0	0	9-5 1/8	13-8 29/32	18-10 1/4	27-5 27/32	28-3 3/8	41-2 3/4
1	-11 5/16	1-4 1/2	10-4 7/16	15-1 13/32	19-9 9/16	28-10 5/16	29-2 11/16	42-7 1/4
2	1-10 5/8	2-8 31/32	11-3 3/4	16-5 29/32	20-8 7/8	30-2 13/16	30-2	43-11 23/32
3	2-9 15/16	4-1 15/32	12-3 1/16	17-10 13/32	21-8 3/16	31-7 5/16	31-1 5/16	45-4 7/32
4	3-9 1/4	5-5 31/32	13-2 3/8	19-2 7/8	22-7 1/2	32-11 13/16	32-0 5/8	46-8 23/32
5	4-8 9/16	6-10 15/32	14-1 11/16	20-7 3/8	23-6 13/16	34-4 9/32	32-11 15/16	48-1 1/2
6	5-7 7/8	8-2 15/16	15-1	21-11 7/8	24-6 1/8	35-8 25/32	33-11 1/4	49-5 11/16
7	6-7 3/16	9-7 7/16	16-0 5/16	23-4 11/32	25-5 7/16	37-1 9/32	34-10 9/16	50-10 3/16
8	7-6 1/2	10-11 15/16	16-11 5/8	24-8 27/32	26-4 3/4	38-5 3/4	35-9 7/8	52-2 11/16
9	8-5 13/16	12-4 7/16	17-10 15/16	26-1 11/32	27-4 1/16	39-10 1/4	36-9 3/16	53-7 3/16

A = 43° 18′ 39″; logsin A = 9.83630; logcos A = 9.86192; logtan A = 9.97438; logcot A = 0.02562

In.	12″ Rise	12″ Slope	13″ Rise	13″ Slope	14″ Rise	14″ Slope	15″ Rise	15″ Slope	16″ Rise	16″ Slope
0	11 5/16	1-4 1/2	1-0 1/4	1-5 7/8	1-1 3/16	1-7 1/4	1-2 1/8	1-8 5/8	1-3 3/32	1-10
1/16	11 3/8	1-4 9/16	1-0 5/16	1-5 15/16	1-1 1/4	1-7 5/16	1-2 3/16	1-8 11/16	1-3 5/32	1-10 1/16
1/8	11 7/16	1-4 21/32	1-0 3/8	1-6 1/16	1-1 5/16	1-7 13/32	1-2 1/4	1-8 25/32	1-3 3/16	1-10 5/32
3/16	11 1/2	1-4 3/4	1-0 7/16	1-6 1/8	1-1 3/8	1-7 1/2	1-2 5/16	1-8 7/8	1-3 1/4	1-10 1/4
1/4	11 9/16	1-4 27/32	1-0 1/2	1-6 7/32	1-1 7/16	1-7 19/32	1-2 3/8	1-8 31/32	1-3 5/16	1-10 11/32
5/16	11 19/32	1-4 29/32	1-0 9/16	1-6 9/32	1-1 1/2	1-7 21/32	1-2 7/16	1-9 1/32	1-3 3/8	1-10 13/32
3/8	11 21/32	1-5	1-0 19/32	1-6 3/8	1-1 9/16	1-7 3/4	1-2 1/2	1-9 1/8	1-3 7/16	1-10 1/2
7/16	11 23/32	1-5 3/32	1-0 21/32	1-6 15/32	1-1 5/8	1-7 27/32	1-2 9/16	1-9 7/32	1-3 1/2	1-10 19/32
1/2	11 25/32	1-5 3/16	1-0 23/32	1-6 9/16	1-1 21/32	1-7 15/16	1-2 5/8	1-9 5/16	1-3 9/16	1-10 11/16
9/16	11 27/32	1-5 1/4	1-0 25/32	1-6 5/8	1-1 23/32	1-8	1-2 21/32	1-9 3/8	1-3 5/8	1-10 3/4
5/8	11 29/32	1-5 11/32	1-0 27/32	1-6 23/32	1-1 25/32	1-8 3/32	1-2 23/32	1-9 15/32	1-3 11/16	1-10 27/32
11/16	11 31/32	1-5 7/16	1-0 29/32	1-6 13/16	1-1 27/32	1-8 3/16	1-2 25/32	1-9 9/16	1-3 23/32	1-10 15/16
3/4	1-0 1/32	1-5 17/32	1-0 31/32	1-6 29/32	1-1 29/32	1-8 9/32	1-2 27/32	1-9 21/32	1-3 25/32	1-11 1/32
13/16	1-0 3/32	1-5 19/32	1-1 1/32	1-6 31/32	1-1 31/32	1-8 11/32	1-2 29/32	1-9 23/32	1-3 27/32	1-11 3/32
7/8	1-0 1/8	1-5 11/16	1-1 1/8	1-7 1/16	1-2 1/32	1-8 7/16	1-2 31/32	1-9 13/16	1-3 29/32	1-11 3/16
15/16	1-0 3/16	1-5 25/32	1-1 1/8	1-7 5/32	1-2 3/32	1-8 17/32	1-3 1/32	1-9 29/32	1-3 31/32	1-11 9/32

In.	17″ Rise	17″ Slope	18″ Rise	18″ Slope	19″ Rise	19″ Slope	20″ Rise	20″ Slope	21″ Rise	21″ Slope
0	1-4 1/32	1-11 3/8	1-4 31/32	2-0 3/4	1-5 29/32	2-2 1/8	1-6 27/32	2-3 1/2	1-7 13/16	2-4 7/8
1/16	1-4 3/32	1-11 7/16	1-5 1/32	2-0 13/16	1-5 31/32	2-2 3/16	1-6 29/32	2-3 9/16	1-7 27/32	2-4 15/16
1/8	1-4 5/32	1-11 17/32	1-5 3/32	2-0 29/32	1-6 1/32	2-2 9/32	1-6 31/32	2-3 21/32	1-7 29/32	2-5 1/32
3/16	1-4 3/16	1-11 5/8	1-5 1/8	2-1	1-6 3/32	2-2 3/8	1-7 1/32	2-3 3/4	1-7 31/32	2-5 1/8
1/4	1-4 1/4	1-11 23/32	1-5 7/32	2-1 3/32	1-6 5/32	2-2 15/32	1-7 3/32	2-3 27/32	1-8 1/8	2-5 7/32
5/16	1-4 5/16	1-11 25/32	1-5 1/4	2-1 5/32	1-6 7/32	2-2 17/32	1-7 5/32	2-3 29/32	1-8 3/32	2-5 9/32
3/8	1-4 3/8	1-11 7/8	1-5 5/16	2-1 1/4	1-6 1/4	2-2 5/8	1-7 7/32	2-4	1-8 5/32	2-5 3/8
7/16	1-4 7/16	1-11 31/32	1-5 3/8	2-1 11/32	1-6 9/32	2-2 23/32	1-7 9/32	2-4 3/32	1-8 7/32	2-5 15/32
1/2	1-4 1/2	2-0 1/16	1-5 7/16	2-1 7/16	1-6 3/8	2-2 13/16	1-7 5/16	2-4 3/16	1-8 9/32	2-5 9/16
9/16	1-4 9/16	2-0 1/8	1-5 1/2	2-1 1/2	1-6 7/16	2-2 7/8	1-7 3/8	2-4 1/4	1-8 5/16	2-5 5/8
5/8	1-4 5/8	2-0 7/32	1-5 9/16	2-1 9/16	1-6 1/2	2-2 31/32	1-7 7/16	2-4 11/32	1-8 3/8	2-5 23/32
11/16	1-4 11/16	2-0 5/16	1-5 5/8	2-1 11/16	1-6 9/16	2-3 1/16	1-7 1/2	2-4 7/16	1-8 7/16	2-5 13/16
3/4	1-4 23/32	2-0 13/32	1-5 11/16	2-1 25/32	1-6 5/8	2-3 5/32	1-7 9/16	2-4 17/32	1-8 1/2	2-5 29/32
13/16	1-4 25/32	2-0 15/32	1-5 3/4	2-1 27/32	1-6 11/16	2-3 7/32	1-7 5/8	2-4 19/32	1-8 9/16	2-5 31/32
7/8	1-4 27/32	2-0 9/16	1-5 25/32	2-1 15/16	1-6 3/4	2-3 5/16	1-7 11/16	2-4 11/16	1-8 5/8	2-6 1/16
15/16	1-4 29/32	2-0 21/32	1-5 27/32	2-2 1/32	1-6 25/32	2-3 13/32	1-7 3/4	2-4 25/32	1-8 11/16	2-6 5/32

Feet	40′ Rise	40′ Slope	50′ Rise	50′ Slope	60′ Rise	60′ Slope	70′ Rise	70′ Slope
0	37-8 1/2	54-11 21/32	47-1 5/8	68-8 19/32	56-6 3/4	82-5 1/2	65-11 7/8	96-2 13/32
1	38-7 13/16	56-4 5/32	48-0 15/16	70-1 1/16	57-6 1/16	83-10	66-11 3/16	97-6 29/32
2	39-7 1/8	57-8 21/32	49-0 1/4	71-5 9/16	58-5 3/8	85-2 15/32	67-10 1/2	98-11 13/32
3	40-6 7/16	59-1 1/8	49-11 9/16	72-10 1/16	59-4 11/16	86-6 31/32	68-9 13/16	100-3 7/8
4	41-5 3/4	60-5 5/8	50-10 7/8	74-2 17/32	60-4	87-11 15/32	69-9 1/8	101-8 3/8
5	42-5 1/16	61-10 1/8	51-10 3/8	75-7 1/32	61-3 5/16	89-3 31/32	70-8 7/16	103-0 7/8
6	43-4 3/8	63-2 5/8	52-9 1/2	76-11 17/32	62-2 5/8	90-8 7/16	71-7 3/4	104-5 3/8
7	44-3 11/16	64-7 3/32	53-8 13/16	78-4 1/32	63-1 15/16	92-0 15/16	72-7 1/16	105-9 27/32
8	45-3	65-11 19/32	54-8 1/8	79-8 1/2	64-1 1/4	93-5 7/16	73-6 3/8	107-2 11/32
9	46-2 5/16	67-4 3/8	55-7 7/16	81-1	65-0 9/16	94-9 29/32	74-5 11/16	108-6 27/32

natsin A=0.6859555444; natcos A=0.7276434504; nattan A=0.9427083333; natcot A=1.0607734806

Inches	0" Rise	0" Slope	1" Rise	1" Slope	2" Rise	2" Slope	3" Rise	3" Slope	4" Rise	4" Slope	5" Rise	5" Slope
0	0	0	15/16	1 3/8	1 29/32	2 3/4	2 27/32	4 1/8	3 25/32	5 1/2	4 3/4	6 7/8
1/16	1/16	3/32	1	1 15/32	1 31/32	2 27/32	2 29/32	4 7/32	3 27/32	5 19/32	4 13/16	6 31/32
1/8	1/8	3/16	1 1/16	1 9/16	2	2 15/16	2 31/32	4 5/16	3 29/32	5 11/16	4 27/32	7 1/16
3/16	3/16	1/4	1 1/8	1 5/8	2 1/16	3	3 1/32	4 13/32	3 31/32	5 25/32	4 29/32	7 5/32
1/4	1/4	11/32	1 3/16	1 23/32	2 1/8	3 3/32	3 3/32	4 15/32	4 1/32	5 27/32	4 31/32	7 7/32
5/16	9/32	7/16	1 1/4	1 13/16	2 3/16	3 3/16	3 1/8	4 9/16	4 3/32	5 15/16	5 1/32	7 5/16
3/8	11/32	17/32	1 5/16	1 29/32	2 1/4	3 9/32	3 3/16	4 21/32	4 5/32	6 1/32	5 3/32	7 13/32
7/16	13/32	19/32	1 3/8	1 31/32	2 5/16	3 11/32	3 1/4	4 3/4	4 7/32	6 1/8	5 5/32	7 1/2
1/2	15/32	11/16	1 7/16	2 1/8	2 3/8	3 7/16	3 5/16	4 13/16	4 1/4	6 3/16	5 7/32	7 19/32
9/16	17/32	25/32	1 15/32	2 5/32	2 7/16	3 17/32	3 3/8	4 29/32	4 5/16	6 9/32	5 9/32	7 21/32
5/8	19/32	7/8	1 17/32	2 1/4	2 1/2	3 5/8	3 7/16	5	4 3/8	6 3/8	5 11/32	7 3/4
11/16	21/32	15/16	1 19/32	2 5/16	2 9/16	3 11/16	3 1/2	5 3/32	4 7/16	6 15/32	5 13/32	7 27/32
3/4	23/32	1 1/32	1 21/32	2 13/32	2 19/32	3 25/32	3 9/16	5 5/32	4 1/2	6 17/32	5 7/16	7 15/16
13/16	25/32	1 1/8	1 23/32	2 1/2	2 21/32	3 7/8	3 5/8	5 1/4	4 9/16	6 5/8	5 1/2	8
7/8	27/32	1 7/32	1 25/32	2 19/32	2 23/32	3 31/32	3 11/16	5 11/32	4 5/8	6 23/32	5 9/16	8 3/32
15/16	7/8	1 9/32	1 27/32	2 21/32	2 25/32	4 1/16	3 23/32	5 7/16	4 11/16	6 13/16	5 5/8	8 3/16

Inches	6" Rise	6" Slope	7" Rise	7" Slope	8" Rise	8" Slope	9" Rise	9" Slope	10" Rise	10" Slope	11" Rise	11" Slope
0	5 11/16	8 9/32	6 5/8	9 21/32	7 19/32	11 1/32	8 17/32	1-0 13/32	9 15/32	1-1 25/32	10 7/16	1-3 5/32
1/16	5 3/4	8 11/32	6 11/16	9 23/32	7 21/32	11 3/32	8 19/32	1-0 1/2	9 17/32	1-1 7/8	10 1/2	1-3 1/4
1/8	5 13/16	8 7/16	6 3/4	9 13/16	7 11/16	11 3/16	8 21/32	1-0 9/16	9 19/32	1-1 15/16	10 17/32	1-3 11/32
3/16	5 7/8	8 17/32	6 13/16	9 29/32	7 3/4	11 9/32	8 23/32	1-0 21/32	9 21/32	1-2 1/32	10 19/32	1-3 13/32
1/4	5 15/16	8 5/8	6 7/8	10	7 13/16	11 3/8	8 25/32	1-0 3/4	9 23/32	1-2 1/8	10 21/32	1-3 1/2
5/16	5 31/32	8 11/16	6 15/16	10 1/16	7 7/8	11 15/32	8 13/16	1-0 27/32	9 25/32	1-2 7/32	10 23/32	1-3 19/32
3/8	6 1/16	8 25/32	7	10 5/32	7 15/16	11 17/32	8 7/8	1-0 29/32	9 27/32	1-2 9/32	10 25/32	1-3 11/16
7/16	6 3/32	8 7/8	7 1/16	10 1/4	8	11 5/8	8 15/16	1-1	9 29/32	1-2 3/8	10 27/32	1-3 3/4
1/2	6 5/32	8 31/32	7 1/8	10 11/32	8 1/16	11 23/32	9	1-1 3/32	9 15/16	1-2 15/32	10 29/32	1-3 27/32
9/16	6 7/32	9 1/32	7 5/32	10 13/32	8 1/8	11 13/16	9 1/16	1-1 3/16	10	1-2 9/16	10 31/32	1-3 15/16
5/8	6 9/32	9 1/8	7 7/32	10 1/2	8 3/16	11 7/8	9 1/8	1-1 1/4	10 1/16	1-2 5/8	11 1/32	1-4 1/32
11/16	6 11/32	9 7/32	7 9/32	10 19/32	8 1/4	11 31/32	9 3/16	1-1 11/32	10 1/8	1-2 23/32	11 3/32	1-4 3/32
3/4	6 13/32	9 5/16	7 11/32	10 11/16	8 9/32	1-0 1/16	9 1/4	1-1 7/16	10 3/16	1-2 13/16	11 1/8	1-4 3/16
13/16	6 15/32	9 3/8	7 13/32	10 3/4	8 11/32	1-0 5/32	9 5/16	1-1 17/32	10 1/4	1-2 29/32	11 3/16	1-4 9/32
7/8	6 17/32	9 15/32	7 15/32	10 27/32	8 13/32	1-0 7/32	9 3/8	1-1 19/32	10 5/16	1-3	11 1/4	1-4 3/8
15/16	6 9/16	9 9/16	7 17/32	10 15/16	8 15/32	1-0 5/16	9 13/32	1-1 11/16	10 3/8	1-3 1/16	11 5/16	1-4 7/16

Feet	0' Rise	0' Slope	10' Rise	10' Slope	20' Rise	20' Slope	30' Rise	30' Slope
0	0	0	9-5 3/4	13-9 11/32	18-11 1/2	27-6 11/16	28-5 1/4	41-4 1/2
1	-11 3/8	1-4 17/32	10-5 1/8	15-1 7/8	19-10 7/8	28-11 1/16	29-4 5/8	42-8 9/16
2	1-10 3/4	2-9 1/16	11-4 1/2	16-6 13/32	20-10 1/4	30-3 3/4	30-4	44-1 3/32
3	2-10 1/8	4-1 19/32	12-3 7/8	17-10 15/32	21-9 5/8	31-8 9/32	31-3 3/8	45-5 5/8
4	3-9 1/2	5-6 1/8	13-3 1/4	19-3 15/32	22-9	33-0 21/32	32-2 3/4	46-10 5/16
5	4-8 7/8	6-10 11/16	14-2 5/8	20-8 1/32	23-8 3/8	34-5 3/8	33-2 1/8	48-2 23/32
6	5-8 1/4	8-3 7/32	15-2	22-0 9/16	24-7 3/4	35-9 29/32	34-1 1/2	49-7 1/4
7	6-7 5/8	9-7 3/4	16-1 3/8	23-5 3/32	25-7 1/8	37-2 1/16	35-0 7/8	50-11 25/32
8	7-7	11-0 9/32	17-0 3/4	24-9 5/8	26-6 1/2	38-6 31/32	36-0 1/4	52-4 5/16
9	8-6 3/8	12-4 13/16	18-0 1/8	26-2 5/32	27-5 7/8	39-11 1/2	36-11 5/8	53-8 27/32

A = 43° 28′ 06″; logsin A = 9.83756; logcos A = 9.86079; logtan A = 9.97677; logcot A = 0.02323

Ins.	12″ Rise	12″ Slope	13″ Rise	13″ Slope	14″ Rise	14″ Slope	15″ Rise	15″ Slope	16″ Rise	16″ Slope
0	11 3/8	1-4 17/32	1-0 5/16	1-5 29/32	1-1 9/32	1-7 3/8	1-2 1/8	1-8 21/32	1-3 5/8	1-10 1/8
1/16	11 7/16	1-4 5/8	1-0 3/8	1-6	1-1 11/32	1-7 3/8	1-2 9/32	1-8 3/4	1-3 7/32	1-10 1/8
1/8	11 1/2	1-4 23/32	1-0 7/16	1-6 3/32	1-1 3/8	1-7 15/32	1-2 11/32	1-8 27/32	1-3 9/32	1-10 7/32
3/16	11 9/16	1-4 25/32	1-0 1/2	1-6 5/32	1-1 7/16	1-7 9/16	1-2 13/32	1-8 15/16	1-3 11/32	1-10 5/16
1/4	11 5/8	1-4 7/8	1-0 9/16	1-6 1/4	1-1 1/2	1-7 5/8	1-2 15/32	1-9	1-3 13/32	1-10 3/8
5/16	11 21/32	1-4 31/32	1-0 5/8	1-6 11/32	1-1 9/16	1-7 23/32	1-2 1/2	1-9 3/32	1-3 15/32	1-10 15/32
3/8	11 23/32	1-5 1/32	1-0 11/16	1-6 7/16	1-1 5/8	1-7 13/16	1-2 9/16	1-9 3/16	1-3 17/32	1-10 9/16
7/16	11 25/32	1-5 1/8	1-0 3/4	1-6 1/2	1-1 11/16	1-7 29/32	1-2 5/8	1-9 9/32	1-3 19/32	1-10 21/32
1/2	11 27/32	1-5 7/32	1-0 13/16	1-6 19/32	1-1 3/4	1-7 31/32	1-2 11/16	1-9 11/32	1-3 5/8	1-10 3/4
9/16	11 29/32	1-5 9/32	1-0 27/32	1-6 11/16	1-1 13/16	1-8 1/16	1-2 3/4	1-9 7/16	1-3 11/16	1-10 13/16
5/8	11 31/32	1-5 13/32	1-0 29/32	1-6 25/32	1-1 7/8	1-8 5/32	1-2 13/16	1-9 17/32	1-3 3/4	1-10 29/32
11/16	1-0 1/4	1-5 15/32	1-0 31/32	1-6 7/8	1-1 15/16	1-8 1/4	1-2 7/8	1-9 5/8	1-3 13/16	1-11
3/4	1-0 3/8	1-5 9/16	1-1 1/32	1-6 15/16	1-1 31/32	1-8 5/16	1-2 15/16	1-9 11/16	1-3 7/8	1-11 3/8
13/16	1-0 1/2	1-5 21/32	1-1 3/32	1-7 1/32	1-2 1/32	1-8 13/16	1-3	1-9 25/32	1-3 15/16	1-11 5/8
7/8	1-0 7/32	1-5 3/4	1-1 5/32	1-7 1/8	1-2 3/32	1-8 1/2	1-3 1/4	1-9 7/8	1-4	1-11 1/4
15/16	1-0 1/4	1-5 13/32	1-1 7/32	1-7 7/32	1-2 5/32	1-8 19/32	1-3 3/32	1-9 31/32	1-4 1/16	1-11 11/32

Ins.	17″ Rise	17″ Slope	18″ Rise	18″ Slope	19″ Rise	19″ Slope	20″ Rise	20″ Slope	21″ Rise	21″ Slope
0	1-4 1/8	1-11 7/16	1-5 5/16	2-0 13/16	1-6	2-2 3/16	1-6 31/32	2-3 9/16	1-7 29/32	2-4 15/32
1/16	1-4 3/16	1-11 1/2	1-5 1/8	2-0 7/8	1-6 1/16	2-2 9/32	1-7 1/32	2-3 21/32	1-7 31/32	2-5 1/32
1/8	1-4 7/32	1-11 19/32	1-5 3/32	2-0 31/32	1-6 1/8	2-2 11/32	1-7 1/16	2-3 23/32	1-8 1/32	2-5 3/32
3/16	1-4 9/32	1-11 11/16	1-5 1/4	2-1 1/16	1-6 3/32	2-2 7/16	1-7 1/8	2-3 13/16	1-8 3/32	2-5 3/16
1/4	1-4 11/32	1-11 25/32	1-5 5/32	2-1 5/32	1-6 1/4	2-2 17/32	1-7 3/8	2-3 29/32	1-8 5/32	2-5 9/32
5/16	1-4 13/32	1-11 27/32	1-5 11/32	2-1 7/32	1-6 5/32	2-2 5/8	1-7 1/4	2-4	1-8 3/16	2-5 3/8
3/8	1-4 15/32	1-11 15/16	1-5 13/32	2-1 5/16	1-6 3/8	2-2 11/16	1-7 5/32	2-4 1/16	1-8 1/4	2-5 7/16
7/16	1-4 17/32	2-0 1/32	1-5 15/32	2-1 13/32	1-6 7/16	2-2 25/32	1-7 3/8	2-4 5/32	1-8 5/32	2-5 17/32
1/2	1-4 19/32	2-0 1/8	1-5 17/32	2-1 1/2	1-6 1/2	2-2 7/8	1-7 7/16	2-4 1/4	1-8 3/8	2-5 5/8
9/16	1-4 21/32	2-0 3/16	1-5 19/32	2-1 9/16	1-6 17/32	2-2 31/32	1-7 1/2	2-4 11/32	1-8 7/16	2-5 23/32
5/8	1-4 23/32	2-0 9/32	1-5 21/32	2-1 21/32	1-6 19/32	2-3 1/32	1-7 9/16	2-4 13/32	1-8 1/2	2-5 25/32
11/16	1-4 25/32	2-0 3/8	1-5 23/32	2-1 13/16	1-6 21/32	2-3 1/8	1-7 5/8	2-4 1/2	1-8 9/16	2-5 7/8
3/4	1-4 13/32	2-0 15/32	1-5 25/32	2-1 27/32	1-6 23/32	2-3 7/32	1-7 21/32	2-4 19/32	1-8 5/8	2-5 31/32
13/16	1-4 7/8	2-0 17/32	1-5 27/32	2-1 29/32	1-6 25/32	2-3 5/8	1-7 23/32	2-4 11/32	1-8 11/16	2-6 1/16
7/8	1-4 15/32	2-0 5/8	1-5 29/32	2-2	1-6 27/32	2-3 3/8	1-7 25/32	2-4 3/4	1-8 3/4	2-6 9/32
15/16	1-5	2-0 23/32	1-5 15/16	2-2 3/32	1-6 29/32	2-3 15/32	1-7 27/32	2-4 27/32	1-8 25/32	2-6 1/32

Feet	40′ Rise	40′ Slope	50′ Rise	50′ Slope	60′ Rise	60′ Slope	70′ Rise	70′ Slope
0	37-11	55-1 3/8	47-4 3/4	68-10 23/32	56-10 1/2	82-8 1/16	66-4 1/4	96-5 13/32
1	38-10 3/8	56-5 29/32	48-4 1/8	70-3 1/4	57-9 7/8	84-0 19/32	67-3 5/8	97-9 15/16
2	39-9 3/4	57-10 7/16	49-3 1/2	71-7 25/32	58-9 1/4	85-5 5/32	68-3	99-2 1/2
3	40-9 1/8	59-3	50-2 7/8	73-0 11/32	59-8 5/8	86-9 11/16	69-2 3/8	100-7 1/32
4	41-8 1/2	60-7 17/32	51-2 1/4	74-4 7/8	60-8	88-2 7/32	70-1 3/4	101-11 9/16
5	42-7 7/8	62-0 1/16	52-1 5/8	75-9 13/32	61-7 3/8	89-6 3/4	71-1 1/8	103-4 3/32
6	43-7 1/4	63-4 19/32	53-1	77-1 15/16	62-6 3/4	90-11 1/32	72-0 1/2	104-8 5/8
7	44-6 5/8	64-9 1/8	54-0 3/8	78-6 15/32	63-6 1/8	92-3 13/16	72-11 7/8	106-1 5/32
8	45-6	66-1 21/32	54-11 3/4	79-11	64-5 1/2	93-8 11/32	73-11 1/4	107-5 11/16
9	46-5 3/8	67-6 3/16	55-11 1/8	81-3 17/32	65-4 7/8	95-0 7/8	74-10 5/8	108-10 7/32

natsin A =0.6879543109; natcos A=0.7257539983; nattan A=0.9479166666; natcot A=1.0549450549

Inches	0" Rise	0" Slope	1" Rise	1" Slope	2" Rise	2" Slope	3" Rise	3" Slope	4" Rise	4" Slope	5" Rise	5" Slope
0	0	0	15/16	1 3/8	1 29/32	2 3/4	2 7/8	4 5/32	3 13/16	5 17/32	4 3/4	6 29/32
1/16	1/16	3/32	1	1 15/32	1 31/32	2 27/32	2 29/32	4 7/32	3 7/8	5 5/8	4 13/16	7
1/8	1/8	3/16	1 1/16	1 9/16	2 1/32	2 15/16	2 31/32	4 5/16	3 15/16	5 11/16	4 7/8	7 3/32
3/16	3/16	1/4	1 1/8	1 5/8	2 3/32	3 1/32	3 1/32	4 13/32	4	5 25/32	4 15/16	7 5/32
1/4	1/4	11/32	1 3/16	1 23/32	2 5/32	3 3/32	3 3/32	4 1/2	4 1/16	5 7/8	5	7 1/4
5/16	5/16	7/16	1 1/4	1 13/16	2 7/32	3 3/16	3 5/32	4 9/16	4 1/8	5 31/32	5 1/16	7 11/32
3/8	11/32	17/32	1 5/16	1 29/32	2 1/4	3 9/32	3 7/32	4 21/32	4 5/32	6 1/32	5 1/8	7 7/16
7/16	13/32	19/32	1 3/8	2	2 5/16	3 3/8	3 9/32	4 3/4	4 7/32	6 1/8	5 3/16	7 1/2
1/2	15/32	11/16	1 7/16	2 1/16	2 3/8	3 15/32	3 11/32	4 27/32	4 9/32	6 7/32	5 1/4	7 19/32
9/16	17/32	25/32	1 1/2	2 5/32	2 7/16	3 17/32	3 13/32	4 29/32	4 11/32	6 5/16	5 5/16	7 11/16
5/8	19/32	7/8	1 9/16	2 1/4	2 1/2	3 5/8	3 15/32	5	4 13/32	6 3/8	5 3/8	7 25/32
11/16	21/32	15/16	1 19/32	2 11/16	2 9/16	3 23/32	3 1/2	5 3/32	4 15/32	6 15/32	5 13/32	7 27/32
3/4	23/32	1 1/32	1 21/32	2 13/32	2 5/8	3 13/16	3 9/16	5 3/16	4 17/32	6 9/16	5 15/32	7 15/16
13/16	25/32	1 1/8	1 23/32	2 1/2	2 11/16	3 7/8	3 5/8	5 9/32	4 19/32	6 21/32	5 17/32	8 1/32
7/8	27/32	1 7/32	1 25/32	2 19/32	2 3/4	3 31/32	3 11/16	5 11/32	4 21/32	6 3/4	5 19/32	8 1/8
15/16	29/32	1 9/32	1 27/32	2 11/16	2 13/16	4 1/16	3 3/4	5 7/16	4 23/32	6 13/16	5 21/32	8 3/16

Inches	6" Rise	6" Slope	7" Rise	7" Slope	8" Rise	8" Slope	9" Rise	9" Slope	10" Rise	10" Slope	11" Rise	11" Slope
0	5 23/32	8 9/32	6 11/16	9 21/32	7 5/8	11 1/16	8 9/16	1-0 7/16	9 17/32	1-1 13/16	10 1/2	1-3 3/16
1/16	5 25/32	8 3/8	6 23/32	9 3/4	7 11/16	11 1/8	8 5/8	1-0 17/32	9 19/32	1-1 29/32	10 17/32	1-3 9/32
1/8	5 27/32	8 15/32	6 25/32	9 27/32	7 3/4	11 7/32	8 11/16	1-0 19/32	9 21/32	1-2	10 19/32	1-3 3/8
3/16	5 29/32	8 9/16	6 27/32	9 15/16	7 13/16	11 5/16	8 3/4	1-0 11/16	9 23/32	1-2 1/16	10 21/32	1-3 15/32
1/4	5 31/32	8 5/8	6 29/32	10 1/32	7 7/8	11 13/32	8 13/16	1-0 25/32	9 25/32	1-2 5/32	10 23/32	1-3 17/32
5/16	6 1/32	8 23/32	6 31/32	10 3/32	7 15/16	11 15/32	8 7/8	1-0 7/8	9 27/32	1-2 1/4	10 25/32	1-3 5/8
3/8	6 1/16	8 13/16	7 1/32	10 3/16	7 31/32	11 9/16	8 15/16	1-0 15/16	9 7/8	1-2 11/32	10 27/32	1-3 23/32
7/16	6 1/8	8 29/32	7 3/32	10 9/32	8 1/32	11 21/32	9	1-1 1/32	9 15/16	1-2 13/32	10 29/32	1-3 13/16
1/2	6 3/16	8 31/32	7 5/32	10 3/8	8 3/32	11 3/4	9 1/16	1-1 1/8	10	1-2 1/2	10 31/32	1-3 7/8
9/16	6 1/4	9 1/16	7 7/32	10 7/16	8 5/32	11 27/32	9 1/8	1-1 7/32	10 1/16	1-2 19/32	11 1/32	1-3 31/32
5/8	6 5/16	9 5/32	7 9/32	10 17/32	8 7/32	11 29/32	9 3/16	1-1 5/16	10 1/8	1-2 11/16	11 3/32	1-4 1/16
11/16	6 3/8	9 1/4	7 5/16	10 5/8	8 9/32	1-0	9 7/32	1-1 3/8	10 3/16	1-2 3/4	11 1/8	1-4 5/32
3/4	6 7/16	9 5/16	7 3/8	10 23/32	8 11/32	1-0 3/32	9 9/32	1-1 15/32	10 1/4	1-2 27/32	11 3/16	1-4 7/32
13/16	6 1/2	9 13/32	7 7/16	10 25/32	8 13/32	1-0 3/16	9 11/32	1-1 9/16	10 5/16	1-2 15/16	11 1/4	1-4 5/16
7/8	6 9/16	9 1/2	7 1/2	10 7/8	8 15/32	1-0 1/4	9 13/32	1-1 21/32	10 3/8	1-3 1/32	11 5/16	1-4 13/32
15/16	6 5/8	9 19/32	7 9/16	10 31/32	8 17/32	1-0 11/32	9 15/32	1-1 23/32	10 7/16	1-3 1/8	11 3/8	1-4 1/2

Feet	0' Rise	0' Slope	10' Rise	10' Slope	20' Rise	20' Slope	30' Rise	30' Slope
0	0	0	9-6 3/8	13-9 25/32	19-0 3/4	27-7 9/16	28-7 1/8	41-5 5/16
1	-11 7/16	1-4 9/16	10-5 13/16	15-2 11/32	20-0 3/16	29-0 1/8	29-6 9/16	42-9 29/32
2	1-10 7/8	2-9 5/32	11-5 1/4	16-6 15/16	20-11 5/8	30-4 23/32	30-6	44-2 15/32
3	2-10 5/16	4-1 23/32	12-4 11/16	17-11 1/2	21-11 1/16	31-9 9/32	31-5 7/16	45-7 1/16
4	3-9 3/4	5-6 5/16	13-4 1/8	19-4 3/32	22-10 1/2	33-1 7/8	32-4 7/8	46-11 5/8
5	4-9 3/16	6-10 7/8	14-3 9/16	20-8 21/32	23-9 15/16	34-6 7/16	33-4 5/16	48-4 7/32
6	5-8 5/8	8-3 15/32	15-3	22-1 1/4	24-9 3/8	35-11 1/2	34-3 3/4	49-8 25/32
7	6-8 1/16	9-8 1/32	16-2 7/16	23-5 13/16	25-8 13/16	37-3 19/32	35-3 3/16	51-1 3/8
8	7-7 1/2	11-0 5/8	17-1 7/8	24-10 13/32	26-8 1/4	38-8 3/16	36-2 5/8	52-5 15/16
9	8-6 15/16	12-5 3/8	18-1 5/16	26-2 31/32	27-7 11/16	40-0 3/4	37-2 1/16	53-10 17/32

A = 43° 37′ 31″; logsin A = 9.83881; logcos A = 9.85966; logtan A = 9.97915; logcot A = 0.02085.

Ins.	12″ Rise	12″ Slope	13″ Rise	13″ Slope	14″ Rise	14″ Slope	15″ Rise	15″ Slope	16″ Rise	16″ Slope
0	11 7/16	1-4 9/16	1-0 3/8	1-5 31/32	1-1 11/32	1-7 11/32	1-2 5/16	1-8 23/32	1-3 1/4	1-10 3/32
1/16	11 1/2	1-4 21/32	1-0 7/16	1-6 1/32	1-1 13/32	1-7 7/16	1-2 11/32	1-8 13/16	1-3 5/16	1-10 3/8
1/8	11 9/16	1-4 3/4	1-0 1/2	1-6 1/8	1-1 15/32	1-7 1/2	1-2 13/32	1-8 29/32	1-3 3/8	1-10 9/32
3/16	11 5/8	1-4 27/32	1-0 9/16	1-6 7/32	1-1 17/32	1-7 19/32	1-2 15/32	1-8 31/32	1-3 7/16	1-10 3/8
1/4	11 11/16	1-4 15/16	1-0 5/8	1-6 5/16	1-1 19/32	1-7 11/16	1-2 17/32	1-9 1/16	1-3 1/2	1-10 7/16
5/16	11 3/4	1-5	1-0 11/16	1-6 13/32	1-1 21/32	1-7 25/32	1-2 19/32	1-9 5/32	1-3 9/16	1-10 17/32
3/8	11 25/32	1-5 3/32	1-0 3/4	1-6 15/32	1-1 11/16	1-7 27/32	1-2 21/32	1-9 1/4	1-3 19/32	1-10 5/8
7/16	11 27/32	1-5 3/8	1-0 13/16	1-6 9/16	1-1 3/4	1-7 15/16	1-2 23/32	1-9 3/8	1-3 21/32	1-10 23/32
1/2	11 29/32	1-5 9/32	1-0 7/8	1-6 21/32	1-1 13/16	1-8 1/2	1-2 25/32	1-9 13/32	1-3 23/32	1-10 25/32
9/16	11 31/32	1-5 11/32	1-0 15/16	1-6 3/4	1-1 7/8	1-8 1/8	1-2 27/32	1-9 1/2	1-3 25/32	1-10 7/8
5/8	1-0 1/4	1-5 7/16	1-1	1-6 13/16	1-1 15/16	1-8 7/32	1-2 29/32	1-9 19/32	1-3 27/32	1-10 31/32
11/16	1-0 3/32	1-5 17/32	1-1 1/2	1-6 29/32	1-2	1-8 9/32	1-2 15/16	1-9 21/32	1-3 29/32	1-11 1/16
3/4	1-0 5/32	1-5 5/8	1-1 3/32	1-7	1-2 1/16	1-8 3/8	1-3	1-9 3/4	1-3 31/32	1-11 1/8
13/16	1-0 7/32	1-5 11/16	1-1 5/32	1-7 3/32	1-2 1/8	1-8 15/32	1-3 1/16	1-9 27/32	1-4 1/32	1-11 7/32
7/8	1-0 9/32	1-5 25/32	1-1 7/32	1-7 3/32	1-2 3/16	1-8 9/16	1-3 1/8	1-9 15/16	1-4 3/32	1-11 5/16
15/16	1-0 11/32	1-5 7/8	1-1 9/32	1-7 1/4	1-2 1/4	1-8 5/8	1-3 3/16	1-10 1/32	1-4 5/32	1-11 13/32

Ins.	17″ Rise	17″ Slope	18″ Rise	18″ Slope	19″ Rise	19″ Slope	20″ Rise	20″ Slope	21″ Rise	21″ Slope
0	1-4 3/16	1-11 1/2	1-5 5/32	2-0 7/8	1-6 1/8	2-2 1/4	1-7 1/16	2-3 5/8	1-8	2-5
1/16	1-4 1/4	1-11 9/16	1-5 7/32	2-0 15/16	1-6 5/32	2-2 11/32	1-7 1/8	2-3 23/32	1-8 1/16	2-5 3/32
1/8	1-4 5/16	1-11 21/32	1-5 9/32	2-1 1/32	1-6 7/32	2-2 13/32	1-7 3/16	2-3 13/16	1-8 1/8	2-5 3/16
3/16	1-4 3/8	1-11 3/4	1-5 11/32	2-1 1/8	1-6 9/32	2-2 1/2	1-7 1/4	2-3 7/8	1-8 3/16	2-5 9/32
1/4	1-4 7/16	1-11 27/32	1-5 13/32	2-1 7/32	1-6 11/32	2-2 19/32	1-7 5/16	2-3 31/32	1-8 1/4	2-5 11/32
5/16	1-4 1/2	1-11 29/32	1-5 15/32	2-1 5/16	1-6 13/32	2-2 11/16	1-7 3/8	2-4 1/16	1-8 5/16	2-5 7/16
3/8	1-4 9/16	2-0	1-5 1/2	2-1 3/8	1-6 15/32	2-2 25/32	1-7 13/32	2-4 5/32	1-8 3/8	2-5 17/32
7/16	1-4 5/8	2-0 3/32	1-5 9/16	2-1 15/32	1-6 17/32	2-2 27/32	1-7 15/32	2-4 7/32	1-8 7/16	2-5 5/8
1/2	1-4 11/16	2-0 3/16	1-5 5/8	2-1 9/16	1-6 19/32	2-2 15/16	1-7 17/32	2-4 5/16	1-8 1/2	2-5 11/16
9/16	1-4 3/4	2-0 1/4	1-5 11/16	2-1 21/32	1-6 21/32	2-3 1/32	1-7 19/32	2-4 13/32	1-8 9/16	2-5 25/32
5/8	1-4 13/16	2-0 11/32	1-5 3/4	2-1 23/32	1-6 23/32	2-3 1/8	1-7 21/32	2-4 1/2	1-8 5/8	2-5 7/8
11/16	1-4 27/32	2-0 7/16	1-5 13/16	2-1 13/16	1-6 3/4	2-3 3/16	1-7 23/32	2-4 19/32	1-8 21/32	2-5 31/32
3/4	1-4 29/32	2-0 17/32	1-5 7/8	2-1 29/32	1-6 13/16	2-3 9/32	1-7 25/32	2-4 21/32	1-8 23/32	2-6 1/16
13/16	1-4 31/32	2-0 19/32	1-5 15/16	2-2	1-6 7/8	2-3 3/8	1-7 27/32	2-4 3/4	1-8 25/32	2-6 1/8
7/8	1-5 1/32	2-0 11/16	1-6	2-2 1/16	1-6 15/16	2-3 15/32	1-7 29/32	2-4 27/32	1-8 27/32	2-6 7/32
15/16	1-5 3/32	2-0 25/32	1-6 1/16	2-2 5/32	1-7	2-3 17/32	1-7 31/32	2-4 15/16	1-8 29/32	2-6 5/16

Feet	40′ Rise	40′ Slope	50′ Rise	50′ Slope	60′ Rise	60′ Slope	70′ Rise	70′ Slope
0	38-1 1/2	55-3 3/32	47-7 7/8	69-0 7/8	57-2 1/4	82-10 21/32	66-8 5/8	96-8 1/16
1	39-0 15/16	56-7 11/16	48-7 5/32	70-5 15/32	58-1 11/16	84-3 7/32	67-8 1/16	98-1
2	40-0 3/8	58-0 1/4	49-6 3/4	71-10 1/32	59-1 1/8	85-7 13/16	68-7 1/2	99-5 19/32
3	40-11 13/16	59-4 27/32	50-6 3/16	73-2 5/8	60-0 5/8	87-0 3/8	69-6 15/16	100-10 5/32
4	41-11 1/4	60-9 13/32	51-5 5/8	74-7 3/16	61-0	88-4 31/32	70-6 3/8	102-2 3/4
5	42-10 11/16	62-2	52-5 1/16	75-11 25/32	61-11 7/16	89-9 17/32	71-5 13/16	103-7 5/16
6	43-10 1/8	63-6 9/16	53-4 1/2	77-4 11/32	62-10 7/8	91-2 1/8	72-5 1/4	104-11 29/32
7	44-9 9/16	64-11 5/32	54-3 15/16	78-8 15/16	63-10 5/16	92-6 11/16	73-4 11/16	106-4 15/32
8	45-9	66-3 23/32	55-3 3/8	80-1 1/2	64-9 3/4	93-11 19/32	74-4 1/8	107-9 1/16
9	46-8 7/16	67-8 5/16	56-2 13/16	81-6 1/16	65-9 3/8	95-3 27/32	75-3 9/16	109-1 5/8

natsin A=0.6899375449; natcos A=0.7238688996; nattan A=0.9531250000; natcot A=1.0491803278

Inches	0" Rise	Slope	1" Rise	Slope	2" Rise	Slope	3" Rise	Slope	4" Rise	Slope	5" Rise	Slope
0	0	0.	31/32	1 3/8	1 29/32	2 25/32	2 7/8	4 5/32	3 27/32	5 17/32	4 25/32	6 15/16
1/16	1/16	3/32	1 1/32	1 15/32	1 31/32	2 27/32	2 15/16	4 1/4	3 29/32	5 5/8	4 27/32	7
1/8	1/8	3/16	1 1/16	1 9/16	2 1/32	2 15/16	3	4 11/32	3 15/16	5 23/32	4 29/32	7 3/32
3/16	3/16	1/4	1 1/8	1 21/32	2 3/32	3 1/32	3 1/16	4 13/32	4	5 13/16	4 31/32	7 3/16
1/4	1/4	11/32	1 3/16	1 23/32	2 5/32	3 1/8	3 1/8	4 1/2	4 1/16	5 7/8	5 1/32	7 9/32
5/16	5/16	7/16	1 1/4	1 13/16	2 7/32	3 3/16	3 3/16	4 19/32	4 1/8	5 31/32	5 3/32	7 11/32
3/8	3/8	17/32	1 5/16	1 29/32	2 9/32	3 9/32	3 1/4	4 11/16	4 3/16	6 1/16	5 5/32	7 7/16
7/16	13/32	19/32	1 3/8	2	2 11/32	3 3/8	3 9/32	4 3/4	4 1/4	6 5/32	5 7/32	7 17/32
1/2	15/32	11/16	1 7/16	2 1/16	2 13/32	3 15/32	3 11/32	4 27/32	4 5/16	6 7/32	5 9/32	7 5/8
9/16	17/32	25/32	1 1/2	2 5/32	2 15/32	3 9/16	3 13/32	4 15/16	4 3/8	6 5/16	5 11/32	7 23/32
5/8	19/32	7/8	1 9/16	2 1/4	2 1/2	3 5/8	3 15/32	5 1/32	4 7/16	6 13/32	5 3/8	7 25/32
11/16	21/32	15/16	1 5/8	2 11/32	2 9/16	3 23/32	3 17/32	5 3/32	4 1/2	6 1/2	5 7/16	7 7/8
3/4	23/32	1 1/32	1 11/16	2 7/16	2 5/8	3 13/16	3 19/32	5 3/4	4 9/16	6 19/32	5 1/2	7 31/32
13/16	25/32	1 1/8	1 3/4	2 1/2	2 11/16	3 29/32	3 21/32	5 9/32	4 5/8	6 21/32	5 9/16	8 1/16
7/8	27/32	1 7/32	1 13/16	2 19/32	2 3/4	3 31/32	3 23/32	5 3/8	4 11/16	6 3/4	5 5/8	8 1/8
15/16	29/32	1 5/16	1 27/32	2 11/16	2 13/16	4 1/16	3 25/32	5 15/32	4 23/32	6 27/32	5 11/16	8 7/32

Inches	6" Rise	Slope	7" Rise	Slope	8" Rise	Slope	9" Rise	Slope	10" Rise	Slope	11" Rise	Slope
0	5 3/4	8 5/16	6 23/32	9 11/16	7 21/32	11 3/32	8 5/8	1-0 15/32	9 19/32	1-1 27/32	10 17/32	1-3 1/4
1/16	5 13/16	8 13/32	6 25/32	9 25/32	7 23/32	11 5/32	8 11/16	1-0 9/16	9 21/32	1-1 15/16	10 19/32	1-3 5/16
1/8	5 7/8	8 15/32	6 13/16	9 7/8	7 25/32	11 1/4	8 3/4	1-0 5/8	9 11/16	1-2 1/32	10 21/32	1-3 13/32
3/16	5 15/16	8 9/16	6 7/8	9 31/32	7 27/32	11 11/32	8 13/16	1-0 23/32	9 3/4	1-2 1/8	10 23/32	1-3 1/2
1/4	6	8 21/32	6 15/16	10 1/32	7 29/32	11 7/16	8 7/8	1-0 13/16	9 13/16	1-2 3/16	10 25/32	1-3 19/32
5/16	6 1/16	8 3/4	7	10 1/8	7 31/32	11 1/2	8 15/16	1-0 29/32	9 7/8	1-2 9/32	10 27/32	1-3 21/32
3/8	6 1/8	8 27/32	7 1/16	10 7/32	8 1/32	11 19/32	9	1-1	9 15/16	1-2 3/8	10 29/32	1-3 3/4
7/16	6 5/32	8 29/32	7 1/8	10 5/16	8 3/32	11 11/16	9 1/32	1-1 1/16	10	1-2 15/32	10 31/32	1-3 27/32
1/2	6 7/32	9	7 3/16	10 3/8	8 5/32	11 25/32	9 3/32	1-1 5/32	10 1/16	1-2 17/32	11 1/16	1-3 15/16
9/16	6 9/32	9 3/32	7 1/4	10 15/32	8 7/32	11 7/8	9 5/32	1-1 1/4	10 1/8	1-2 5/8	11 3/32	1-4
5/8	6 11/32	9 3/16	7 5/16	10 9/16	8 1/4	11 15/16	9 7/32	1-1 11/32	10 3/16	1-2 23/32	11 1/8	1-4 3/32
11/16	6 13/32	9 1/4	7 3/8	10 21/32	8 5/16	1-0 1/32	9 9/32	1-1 13/32	10 1/4	1-2 13/16	11 3/16	1-4 3/16
3/4	6 15/32	9 11/32	7 7/16	10 23/32	8 3/8	1-0 1/8	9 11/32	1-1 1/2	10 5/16	1-2 7/8	11 1/4	1-4 9/32
13/16	6 17/32	9 7/16	7 1/2	10 13/16	8 7/16	1-0 3/16	9 13/32	1-1 19/32	10 3/8	1-2 31/32	11 5/16	1-4 3/8
7/8	6 19/32	9 17/32	7 9/16	10 29/32	8 1/2	1-0 9/32	9 15/32	1-1 11/16	10 7/16	1-3 1/16	11 3/8	1-4 7/16
15/16	6 21/32	9 19/32	7 19/32	11	8 9/16	1-0 3/8	9 17/32	1-1 3/4	10 15/32	1-3 5/32	11 7/16	1-4 17/32

Feet	0' Rise	Slope	10' Rise	Slope	20' Rise	Slope	30' Rise	Slope
0	0	0	9-7	13-10 7/32	19-2	27-8 13/32	28-9	41-6 5/8
1	-11 1/2	1-4 5/8	10-6 1/2	15-2 27/32	20-1 1/2	29-1 1/32	29-8 1/2	42-11 1/4
2	1-11 .	2-9 1/4	11-6	16-7 7/16	21-1	30-5 21/32	30-8	44-3 7/8
3	2-10 1/2	4-1 7/8	12-5 1/2	18-0 1/16	22-0 1/2	31-10 9/32	31-7 1/2	45-8 1/2
4	3-10	5-6 15/32	13-5	19-4 11/16	23-0	33-2 29/32	32-7	47-1 3/32
5	4-9 1/2	6-11 3/32	14-4 1/2	20-9 5/16	23-11 1/2	34-7 17/32	33-6 1/2	48-5 23/32
6	5-9	8-3 23/32	15-4	22-1 15/16	24-11	36-0 1/8	34-6	49-10 11/32
7	6-8 1/2	9-8 11/32	16-3 1/2	23-6 9/16	25-10 1/2	37-4 3/4	35-5 1/2	51-2 31/32
8	7-8	11-0 31/32	17-3	24-11 3/16	26-10	38-9 3/8	36-5	52-7 19/32
9	8-7 1/2	12-5 19/32	18-2 1/2	26-3 25/32	27-9 1/2	40-2	37-4 1/2	54-0 7/32

A = 43° 66' 52''; logsin A = 9.84005; logcos A = 9.85853; logtan A = 9.98152; logcot A = 0.01848

Ins.	12″ Rise	12″ Slope	13″ Rise	13″ Slope	14″ Rise	14″ Slope	15″ Rise	15″ Slope	16″ Rise	16″ Slope
0	11 1/2	1-4 5/8	1-0 15/32–	1-6	1-1 13/32	1-7 13/32–	1-2 3/8	1-8 25/32–	1-3 11/32–	1-10 5/32
1/16	11 9/16	1-4 23/32–	1-0 17/32–	1-6 3/32–	1-1 15/32	1-7 15/32	1-2 7/16	1-8 7/8	1-3 13/32–	1-10 1/4
1/8	11 5/8	1-4 25/32	1-0 9/16	1-6 3/16	1-1 17/32	1-7 9/16	1-2 1/2	1-8 15/16	1-3 7/16	1-10 11/32–
3/16	11 11/16	1-4 7/8	1-0 5/8	1-6 1/4	1-1 19/32	1-7 21/32–	1-2 9/16	1-9 1/32	1-3 1/2	1-10 13/32
1/4	11 3/4	1-4 31/32–	1-0 11/16	1-6 11/32	1-1 21/32	1-7 3/4	1-2 5/8	1-9 1/8	1-3 9/16	1-10 1/2
5/16	11 13/16	1-5 1/16	1-0 3/4	1-6 7/16	1-1 23/32–	1-7 13/16	1-2 11/16	1-9 7/32–	1-3 5/8	1-10 19/32
3/8	11 7/8	1-5 1/8	1-0 13/16	1-6 17/32–	1-1 25/32–	1-7 29/32	1-2 3/4	1-9 9/32	1-3 11/16	1-10 11/16
7/16	11 29/32	1-5 7/32	1-0 7/8	1-6 5/8	1-1 27/32–	1-8	1-2 25/32	1-9 3/8	1-3 3/4	1-10 25/32–
1/2	11 31/32	1-5 5/16	1-0 15/16	1-6 11/16	1-1 29/32–	1-8 3/32–	1-2 27/32	1-9 15/32–	1-3 13/16	1-10 27/32
9/16	1-0 1/32	1-5 13/32–	1-1	1-6 25/32	1-1 31/32–	1-8 5/32	1-2 29/32	1-9 9/16	1-3 7/8	1-10 15/16
5/8	1-0 3/32	1-5 1/2	1-1 1/16	1-6 7/8	1-2	1-8 1/4	1-2 31/32	1-9 21/32–	1-3 15/16	1-11 1/32–
11/16	1-0 5/32	1-5 9/16	1-1 1/8	1-6 31/32–	1-2 1/16	1-8 11/32–	1-3 1/32	1-9 23/32	1-4	1-11 1/8
3/4	1-0 7/32	1-5 21/32	1-1 3/16	1-7 1/32	1-2 1/8	1-8 7/16	1-3 3/32	1-9 13/16	1-4 1/16	1-11 3/16
13/16	1-0 9/32–	1-5 3/4	1-1 1/4	1-7 1/8	1-2 3/16	1-8 17/32–	1-3 5/32–	1-9 29/32–	1-4 1/8	1-11 9/32
7/8	1-0 11/32–	1-5 27/32–	1-1 5/16	1-7 7/32–	1-2 1/4	1-8 19/32	1-3 7/32–	1-10	1-4 3/16	1-11 3/8
15/16	1-0 13/32–	1-5 29/32	1-1 11/32	1-7 5/16	1-2 5/16	1-8 11/16	1-3 9/32–	1-10 1/16	1-4 7/32	1-11 15/32–

Ins.	17″ Rise	17″ Slope	18″ Rise	18″ Slope	19″ Rise	19″ Slope	20″ Rise	20″ Slope	21″ Rise	21″ Slope
0	1-4 9/32	1-11 17/32	1-5 1/4	2-0 15/16	1-6 7/32–	2-2 5/16	1-7 5/32	2-3 11/16	1-8 1/8	2-5 3/32–
1/16	1-4 11/32	1-11 5/8	1-5 5/16	2-1 1/32–	1-6 9/32–	2-2 13/32–	1-7 7/32	2-3 25/32	1-8 3/16	2-5 3/16
1/8	1-4 13/32	1-11 23/32	1-5 3/8	2-1 3/32	1-6 5/16	2-2 1/2	1-7 9/32	2-3 7/8	1-8 1/4	2-5 1/4
3/16	1-4 15/32	1-11 13/16	1-5 7/16	2-1 3/16	1-6 3/8	2-2 9/16	1-7 11/32	2-3 31/32–	1-8 5/16	2-5 11/32
1/4	1-4 17/32	1-11 29/32–	1-5 1/2	2-1 9/32–	1-6 7/16	2-2 21/32	1-7 13/32	2-4 1/16	1-8 3/8	2-5 7/16
5/16	1-4 19/32–	1-11 31/32	1-5 9/16	2-1 3/8	1-6 1/2	2-2 3/4	1-7 15/32–	2-4 1/8	1-8 7/16	2-5 17/32–
3/8	1-4 21/32–	2-0 1/16	1-5 5/8	2-1 7/16	1-6 9/16	2-2 27/32–	1-7 17/32–	2-4 7/32	1-8 1/2	2-5 19/32
7/16	1-4 23/32–	2-0 5/32–	1-5 21/32	2-1 17/32	1-6 5/8	2-2 15/16	1-7 19/32–	2-4 5/16	1-8 17/32	2-5 11/16
1/2	1-4 25/32–	2-0 1/4	1-5 23/32	2-1 5/8	1-6 11/16	2-3	1-7 21/32–	2-4 13/32–	1-8 19/32	2-5 25/32–
9/16	1-4 27/32–	2-0 5/16	1-5 25/32	2-1 23/32–	1-6 3/4	2-3 3/32	1-7 23/32–	2-4 15/32	1-8 21/32	2-5 7/8
5/8	1-4 7/8	2-0 13/32	1-5 27/32	2-1 25/32	1-6 13/16	2-3 3/16	1-7 3/4	2-4 9/16	1-8 23/32	2-5 15/16
11/16	1-4 15/16	2-0 1/2	1-5 29/32	2-1 7/8	1-6 7/8	2-3 9/32–	1-7 13/16	2-4 21/32–	1-8 25/32	2-6 1/32
3/4	1-5	2-0 19/32–	1-5 31/32	2-1 31/32	1-6 15/16	2-3 11/32	1-7 7/8	2-4 3/4	1-8 27/32	2-6 1/8
13/16	1-5 1/16	2-0 21/32	1-6 1/32–	2-2 1/16	1-7	2-3 7/16	1-7 15/16	2-4 13/16	1-8 29/32–	2-6 7/32–
7/8	1-5 1/8	2-0 3/4	1-6 3/32–	2-2 5/32–	1-7 1/16	2-3 17/32–	1-8	2-4 29/32	1-8 31/32–	2-6 5/16
15/16	1-5 3/16	2-0 27/32	1-6 5/32–	2-2 7/32	1-7 3/32	2-3 5/8	1-8 1/16	2-5	1-9 1/32–	2-6 3/8

Feet	40′ Rise	40′ Slope	50′ Rise	50′ Slope	60′ Rise	60′ Slope	70′ Rise	70′ Slope
0	38-4	55-4 27/32–	47-11	69-3 1/32	57-6	83-1 1/4	67-1	96-11 15/32–
1	39-3 1/2	56-9 7/16	48-10 1/2	70-7 21/32	58-5 1/2	84-5 7/8	68-0 1/2	98-4 1/16
2	40-3	58-2 1/16	49-10	72-0 9/32–	59-5	85-10 1/2	69-0	99-8 11/16
3	41-2 1/2	59-6 11/16	50-9 1/2	73-4 29/32–	60-4 1/2	87-3 3/32	69-11 1/2	101-1 5/16
4	42-2	60-11 5/16	51-9	74-9 17/32–	61-4	88-7 23/32	70-11	102-5 15/16
5	43-1 1/2	62-3 15/16	52-8 1/2	76-2 5/32–	62-3 1/2	90-0 11/32	71-10 1/2	103-10 9/16
6	44-1	63-8 9/16	53-8	77-6 3/4	63-3	91-4 31/32	72-10	105-3 3/16
7	45-0 1/2	65-1 3/16	54-7 1/2	78-11 3/8	64-2 1/2	92-9 19/32–	73-9 1/2	106-7 13/16
8	46-0	66-5 13/16	55-7	80-4	65-2	94-2 7/32–	74-9	108-0 13/32
9	46-11 1/2	67-10 13/32	56-6 1/2	81-8 5/8	66-1 1/2	95-6 27/32–	75-8 1/2	109-5 1/32

natsin A=0.6919053632; natcos A=0.7219882051; nattan A=0.9583333333; natcot A=1.0434782608

Inches	0" Rise	0" Slope	1" Rise	1" Slope	2" Rise	2" Slope	3" Rise	3" Slope	4" Rise	4" Slope	5" Rise	5" Slope
0	0	0	31/32	1 3/8	1 15/16	2 25/32	2 1/8	4 5/32	3 27/32	5 9/16	4 13/16	6 15/16
1/16	1/16	3/32	1 1/32	1 15/32	2	2 7/8	2 15/16	4 1/4	3 29/32	5 21/32	4 7/8	7 1/32
1/8	1/8	3/16	1 3/32	1 9/16	2 1/16	2 15/16	3	4 11/32	3 31/32	5 23/32	4 15/16	7 1/8
3/16	3/16	1/4	1 5/32	1 21/32	2 3/32	3 1/32	3 1/16	4 7/16	4 1/32	5 13/16	5	7 7/32
1/4	1/4	11/32	1 7/32	1 3/4	2 5/32	3 1/8	3 1/8	4 1/2	4 3/32	5 29/32	5 1/16	7 9/32
5/16	5/16	7/16	1 1/4	1 13/16	2 7/32	3 7/32	3 3/16	4 19/32	4 5/32	6	5 1/8	7 3/8
3/8	3/8	17/32	1 5/16	1 29/32	2 9/32	3 5/16	3 1/4	4 11/16	4 7/32	6 1/16	5 3/16	7 15/32
7/16	13/32	19/32	1 3/8	2	2 11/32	3 3/8	3 5/16	4 25/32	4 9/32	6 5/32	5 1/4	7 9/16
1/2	15/32	11/16	1 7/16	2 3/32	2 13/32	3 15/32	3 3/8	4 7/8	4 11/32	6 1/4	5 5/16	7 5/8
9/16	17/32	25/32	1 1/2	2 5/32	2 15/32	3 9/16	3 7/16	4 15/16	4 13/32	6 11/32	5 3/8	7 23/32
5/8	19/32	7/8	1 9/16	2 1/4	2 17/32	3 21/32	3 1/2	5 1/32	4 15/32	6 7/16	5 13/32	7 13/16
11/16	21/32	31/32	1 5/8	2 11/32	2 19/32	3 23/32	3 9/16	5 1/8	4 17/32	6 1/2	5 15/32	7 29/32
3/4	23/32	1 1/32	1 11/16	2 7/16	2 21/32	3 13/16	3 5/8	5 7/32	4 9/16	6 19/32	5 17/32	8
13/16	25/32	1 1/8	1 3/4	2 17/32	2 23/32	3 29/32	3 11/16	5 9/32	4 5/8	6 11/16	5 19/32	8 1/16
7/8	27/32	1 17/32	1 13/16	2 19/32	2 25/32	4	3 23/32	5 3/8	4 11/16	6 25/32	5 21/32	8 5/32
15/16	29/32	1 15/16	1 7/8	2 11/16	2 27/32	4 3/32	3 25/32	5 15/32	4 3/4	6 27/32	5 23/32	8 1/4

Inches	6" Rise	6" Slope	7" Rise	7" Slope	8" Rise	8" Slope	9" Rise	9" Slope	10" Rise	10" Slope	11" Rise	11" Slope
0	5 25/32	8 11/32	6 3/4	9 23/32	7 23/32	11 3/32	8 11/16	1-0 1/2	9 5/8	1-1 7/8	10 19/32	1-3 9/32
1/16	5 27/32	8 13/32	6 13/16	9 13/16	7 25/32	11 3/16	8 23/32	1-0 19/32	9 11/16	1-1 31/32	10 21/32	1-3 3/8
1/8	5 29/32	8 1/2	6 7/8	9 29/32	7 27/32	11 9/32	8 25/32	1-0 21/32	9 3/4	1-2 1/16	10 23/32	1-3 7/16
3/16	5 31/32	8 19/32	6 15/16	9 31/32	7 7/8	11 3/8	8 27/32	1-0 3/4	9 13/16	1-2 5/32	10 25/32	1-3 17/32
1/4	6 1/32	8 11/16	7	10 1/16	7 15/16	11 15/32	8 29/32	1-0 27/32	9 7/8	1-2 7/32	10 27/32	1-3 5/8
5/16	6 3/32	8 25/32	7 1/2	10 5/32	8	11 17/32	8 31/32	1-0 15/16	9 15/16	1-2 5/16	10 29/32	1-3 23/32
3/8	6 5/32	8 27/32	7 3/32	10 1/4	8 1/16	11 5/8	9 1/32	1-1 1/32	10	1-2 13/32	10 31/32	1-3 25/32
7/16	6 3/16	8 15/16	7 5/32	10 11/32	8 1/8	11 23/32	9 3/32	1-1 3/32	10 1/16	1-2 1/2	11 1/32	1-3 7/8
1/2	6 1/4	9 1/32	7 7/32	10 13/32	8 3/16	11 13/16	9 5/32	1-1 3/16	10 1/8	1-2 19/32	11 3/32	1-3 31/32
9/16	6 5/16	9 1/8	7 9/32	10 1/2	8 1/4	11 7/8	9 7/32	1-1 9/32	10 3/16	1-2 21/32	11 5/32	1-4 1/16
5/8	6 3/8	9 3/16	7 11/32	10 19/32	8 5/16	11 31/32	9 1/4	1-1 3/8	10 1/4	1-2 3/4	11 3/16	1-4 5/32
11/16	6 7/16	9 9/32	7 13/32	10 11/16	8 3/8	1-0 1/32	9 11/32	1-1 7/16	10 5/16	1-2 27/32	11 1/4	1-4 7/32
3/4	6 1/2	9 3/8	7 15/32	10 3/4	8 7/16	1-0 5/32	9 13/32	1-1 17/32	10 11/32	1-2 15/16	11 5/16	1-4 5/32
13/16	6 9/16	9 15/32	7 17/32	10 27/32	8 1/2	1-0 1/4	9 15/32	1-1 5/8	10 13/32	1-3	11 3/8	1-4 13/32
7/8	6 5/8	9 17/32	7 19/32	10 15/16	8 9/16	1-0 5/16	9 1/2	1-1 23/32	10 15/32	1-3 3/32	11 7/16	1-4 1/2
15/16	6 11/16	9 5/8	7 21/32	11 1/32	8 5/8	1-0 13/32	9 9/16	1-1 13/16	10 17/32	1-3 3/16	11 1/2	1-4 9/32

Feet	0' Rise	0' Slope	10' Rise	10' Slope	20' Rise	20' Slope	30' Rise	30' Slope
0	0	0	9-7 5/8	13-10 21/32	19-3 1/4	27-9 9/32	28-10 7/8	41-7 15/16
1	-11 9/16	1-4 21/32	10-7 3/16	15-3 5/16	20-2 13/16	29-1 15/16	29-10 7/16	43-0 19/32
2	1-11 1/8	2-9 11/32	11-6 3/4	16-7 31/32	21-2 3/8	30-6 5/8	30-10	44-5 1/4
3	2-10 11/16	4-2	12-6 5/16	18-0 5/8	22-1 15/16	31-11 9/32	31-9 9/16	45-9 29/32
4	3-10 1/4	5-6 21/32	13-5 7/8	19-5 5/16	23-1 1/2	33-3 15/16	32-9 1/8	47-2 19/32
5	4-9 13/16	6-11 5/16	14-5 7/16	20-9 31/32	24-1 1/16	34-8 19/32	33-8 11/16	48-7 1/4
6	5-9 3/8	8-4	15-5	22-2 5/8	25-0 5/8	36-1 1/4	34-8 1/4	49-11 29/32
7	6-8 15/16	9-8 21/32	16-4 9/16	23-7 9/32	26-0 3/16	37-5 15/16	35-7 13/16	51-4 9/16
8	7-8 1/2	11-1 5/16	17-4 1/8	24-11 31/32	26-11 3/4	38-10 19/32	36-7 3/8	52-9 1/4
9	8-8 1/16	12-5 31/32	18-3 11/16	26-4 5/8	27-11 5/16	40-3 1/4	37-6 15/16	54-1 29/32

A = 43° 56' 11"; logsin A = 9.84127; logcos A = 9.85740; logtan A = 9.98387; logcot A = 0.01613

Ins.	12" Rise	12" Slope	13" Rise	13" Slope	14" Rise	14" Slope	15" Rise	15" Slope	16" Rise	16" Slope
0	11 9/16	1-4 21/32	1-0 17/32	1-6 1/16	1-1 1/2	1-7 7/16	1-2 7/16	1-8 27/32	1-3 13/32	1-10 7/32
1/16	11 5/8	1-4 3/4	1-0 19/32	1-6 1/8	1-1 9/16	1-7 17/32	1-2 1/2	1-8 29/32	1-3 15/32	1-10 5/16
1/8	11 11/16	1-4 27/32	1-0 21/32	1-6 7/32	1-1 5/8	1-7 5/8	1-2 9/16	1-9	1-3 17/32	1-10 13/32
3/16	11 3/4	1-4 15/16	1-0 23/32	1-6 5/16	1-1 21/32	1-7 11/16	1-2 5/8	1-9 3/32	1-3 19/32	1-10 15/32
1/4	11 13/16	1-5	1-0 25/32	1-6 13/32	1-1 23/32	1-7 25/32	1-2 11/16	1-9 3/16	1-3 21/32	1-10 9/16
5/16	11 7/8	1-5 3/32	1-0 13/16	1-6 1/2	1-1 25/32	1-7 7/8	1-2 3/4	1-9 1/4	1-3 23/32	1-10 21/32
3/8	11 15/16	1-5 3/16	1-0 7/8	1-6 9/16	1-1 27/32	1-7 31/32	1-2 13/16	1-9 11/32	1-3 25/32	1-10 3/4
7/16	11 31/32	1-5 9/32	1-0 15/32	1-6 21/32	1-1 29/32	1-8 1/16	1-2 7/8	1-9 7/16	1-3 27/32	1-10 13/16
1/2	1-0 1/32	1-5 11/32	1-1	1-6 3/4	1-1 31/32	1-8 1/8	1-2 15/16	1-9 17/32	1-3 29/32	1-10 29/32
9/16	1-0 3/32	1-5 7/16	1-1 1/16	1-6 27/32	1-2 1/32	1-8 7/32	1-3	1-9 5/8	1-3 31/32	1-11
5/8	1-0 5/32	1-5 17/32	1-1 1/8	1-6 29/32	1-2 3/32	1-8 5/16	1-3 1/16	1-9 11/16	1-4 1/32	1-11 3/32
11/16	1-0 7/32	1-5 5/8	1-1 3/16	1-7	1-2 5/32	1-8 13/32	1-3 1/8	1-9 25/32	1-4 3/32	1-11 3/16
3/4	1-0 9/32	1-5 23/32	1-1 1/4	1-7 3/32	1-2 7/32	1-8 15/32	1-3 3/16	1-9 7/8	1-4 1/8	1-11 1/4
13/16	1-0 11/32	1-5 25/32	1-1 5/16	1-7 3/16	1-2 9/32	1-8 9/16	1-3 1/4	1-9 31/32	1-4 3/8	1-11 11/32
7/8	1-0 13/32	1-5 7/8	1-1 3/8	1-7 9/32	1-2 11/32	1-8 21/32	1-3 9/32	1-10 1/32	1-4 1/4	1-11 7/16
15/16	1-0 15/32	1-5 31/32	1-1 7/16	1-7 11/32	1-2 13/32	1-8 3/4	1-3 11/32	1-10 1/8	1-4 5/16	1-11 17/32

Ins.	17" Rise	17" Slope	18" Rise	18" Slope	19" Rise	19" Slope	20" Rise	20" Slope	21" Rise	21" Slope
0	1-4 3/8	1-11 19/32	1-5 11/32	2-1	1-6 5/16	2-2 3/8	1-7 9/32	2-3 25/32	1-8 1/4	2-5 3/32
1/16	1-4 7/16	1-11 11/16	1-5 13/32	2-1 3/32	1-6 3/8	2-2 15/32	1-7 11/32	2-3 7/8	1-8 9/32	2-5 1/4
1/8	1-4 1/2	1-11 25/32	1-5 15/32	2-1 3/16	1-6 7/16	2-2 9/16	1-7 13/32	2-3 15/16	1-8 11/32	2-5 11/32
3/16	1-4 9/16	1-11 7/8	1-5 17/32	2-1 1/4	1-6 1/2	2-2 21/32	1-7 7/16	2-4 1/32	1-8 13/32	2-5 7/16
1/4	1-4 5/8	1-11 31/32	1-5 19/32	2-1 11/32	1-6 9/16	2-2 23/32	1-7 1/2	2-4 1/8	1-8 15/32	2-5 1/2
5/16	1-4 11/16	2-0 1/32	1-5 21/32	2-1 7/16	1-6 19/32	2-2 13/16	1-7 9/16	2-4 7/32	1-8 17/32	2-5 19/32
3/8	1-4 3/4	2-0 1/8	1-5 23/32	2-1 17/32	1-6 21/32	2-2 29/32	1-7 5/8	2-4 9/32	1-8 19/32	2-5 11/16
7/16	1-4 13/16	2-0 7/32	1-5 3/4	2-1 9/16	1-6 23/32	2-3	1-7 11/16	2-4 3/8	1-8 21/32	2-5 25/32
1/2	1-4 7/8	2-0 5/16	1-5 13/16	2-1 11/16	1-6 25/32	2-3 3/32	1-7 3/4	2-4 15/32	1-8 23/32	2-5 27/32
9/16	1-4 15/16	2-0 3/8	1-5 7/8	2-1 25/32	1-6 27/32	2-3 5/32	1-7 13/16	2-4 9/16	1-8 25/32	2-5 15/16
5/8	1-4 31/32	2-0 15/32	1-5 15/16	2-1 7/8	1-6 29/32	2-3 1/4	1-7 7/8	2-4 21/32	1-8 27/32	2-6 1/2
11/16	1-5 1/32	2-0 9/16	1-6	2-1 15/16	1-6 31/32	2-3 11/32	1-7 15/16	2-4 23/32	1-8 29/32	2-6 1/8
3/4	1-5 3/32	2-0 21/32	1-6 1/16	2-2 1/32	1-7 1/32	2-3 7/16	1-8	2-4 13/16	1-8 31/32	2-6 7/32
13/16	1-5 5/32	2-0 3/4	1-6 1/8	2-2 1/8	1-7 3/32	2-3 1/2	1-8 1/16	2-4 29/32	1-9 1/32	2-6 9/32
7/8	1-5 7/32	2-0 13/16	1-6 3/16	2-2 7/32	1-7 5/32	2-3 19/32	1-8 1/8	2-5	1-9 1/16	2-6 3/8
15/16	1-5 9/32	2-0 29/32	1-6 1/4	2-2 5/16	1-7 7/32	2-3 11/16	1-8 3/16	2-5 11/32	1-9 1/8	2-6 15/32

Feet	40' Rise	40' Slope	50' Rise	50' Slope	60' Rise	60' Slope	70' Rise	70' Slope
0	38-6 1/2	55-6 9/16	48-2 1/8	69-5 7/32	57-9 3/4	83-3 27/32	67-5 3/8	97-2 1/2
1	39-6 1/16	56-11 7/32	49-1 11/16	70-9 7/8	58-9 5/16	84-8 1/2	68-4 15/16	98-7 5/32
2	40-5 5/8	58-3 29/32	50-1 1/4	72-2 17/32	59-8 7/8	86-1 3/16	69-4 1/2	99-11 13/16
3	41-5 3/16	59-8 9/16	51-0 13/16	73-7 3/16	60-8 7/16	87-5 27/32	70-4 1/16	101-4 15/32
4	42-4 3/4	61-1 7/32	52-0 3/8	74-11 7/8	61-8	88-10 1/2	71-3 5/8	102-9 5/32
5	43-4 5/16	62-5 7/8	52-11 15/16	76-4 17/32	62-7 9/16	90-3 5/32	72-3 3/16	104-1 13/16
6	44-3 7/8	63-10 9/16	53-11 1/2	77-9 3/16	63-7 1/8	91-7 27/32	73-2 3/4	105-6 15/32
7	45-3 7/16	65-3 7/32	54-11 1/16	79-1 27/32	64-6 11/16	93-0 1/2	74-2 5/16	106-11 1/8
8	46-3	66-7 7/8	55-10 5/8	80-6 17/32	65-6 1/4	94-5 5/32	75-1 7/8	108-3 13/16
9	47-2 9/16	68-0 17/32	56-10 3/16	81-11 3/16	66-5 13/16	95-9 13/16	76-1 7/16	109-8 15/32

natsin A=0.6938578815; natcos A=0.7201119636; nattan A=0.9635416666; natcot A=1.0378378378

Inches	0" Rise	0" Slope	1" Rise	1" Slope	2" Rise	2" Slope	3" Rise	3" Slope	4" Rise	4" Slope	5" Rise	5" Slope
0	0	0	31/32	1 13/32	1 15/16	2 25/32	2 29/32	4 3/16	3 7/8	5 9/16	4 27/32	6 31/32
1/16		3/32	1 1/32	1 15/32	2	2 7/8	2 31/32	4 1/4	3 15/16	5 21/32	4 29/32	7 1/16
1/8	1/8	3/16	1 3/32	1 9/16	2 1/16	2 31/32	3 1/32	4 11/32	4	5 3/4	4 31/32	7 1/8
3/16	3/16	1/4	1 5/32	1 21/32	2 1/8	3 1/32	3 3/32	4 7/16	4 1/16	5 27/32	5 1/32	7 7/32
1/4	1/4	11/32	1 7/32	1 3/4	2 3/16	3 1/8	3 5/32	4 17/32	4 1/8	5 29/32	5 3/32	7 5/16
5/16	5/16	7/16	1 9/32	1 13/16	2 1/4	3 7/32	3 7/32	4 5/8	4 3/16	6	5 5/32	7 13/32
3/8	3/8	17/32	1 11/32	1 29/32	2 5/16	3 5/16	3 9/32	4 11/16	4 1/4	6 3/32	5 7/32	7 15/32
7/16	7/16	19/32	1 13/32	2	2 3/8	3 13/32	3 11/32	4 25/32	4 5/16	6 3/16	5 9/32	7 9/16
1/2	1/2	11/16	1 7/16	2 3/32	2 7/16	3 15/32	3 3/8	4 7/8	4 3/8	6 1/4	5 5/16	7 21/32
9/16	17/32	25/32	1 1/2	2 3/16	2 15/32	3 9/16	3 7/16	4 31/32	4 13/32	6 11/32	5 3/8	7 3/4
5/8	19/32	7/8	1 9/16	2 1/4	2 17/32	3 21/32	3 1/2	5 1/16	4 15/32	6 7/16	5 7/16	7 27/32
11/16	21/32	31/32	1 5/8	2 11/32	2 19/32	3 3/4	3 9/16	5 1/8	4 17/32	6 17/32	5 1/2	7 29/32
3/4	23/32	1 1/32	1 11/16	2 7/16	2 21/32	3 27/32	3 5/8	5 7/32	4 19/32	6 5/8	5 9/16	8
13/16	25/32	1 1/8	1 3/4	2 17/32	2 23/32	3 29/32	3 11/16	5 5/16	4 21/32	6 11/16	5 5/8	8 3/32
7/8	27/32	1 7/32	1 13/16	2 5/8	2 25/32	4	3 3/4	5 13/32	4 23/32	6 25/32	5 11/16	8 3/16
15/16	29/32	1 5/16	1 7/8	2 11/16	2 27/32	4 3/32	3 13/16	5 15/32	4 25/32	6 7/8	5 3/4	8 9/32

Inches	6" Rise	6" Slope	7" Rise	7" Slope	8" Rise	8" Slope	9" Rise	9" Slope	10" Rise	10" Slope	11" Rise	11" Slope
0	5 13/16	8 11/32	6 25/32	9 3/4	7 3/4	11 1/8	8 23/32	1-0 17/32	9 11/16	1-1 15/16	10 21/32	1-3 5/32
1/16	5 7/8	8 7/16	6 27/32	9 27/32	7 13/16	11 17/32	8 25/32	1-0 5/8	9 3/4	1-2	10 23/32	1-3 13/32
1/8	5 15/16	8 17/32	6 29/32	9 29/32	7 7/8	11 5/16	8 29/32	1-0 23/32	9 13/16	1-2 3/32	10 25/32	1-3 1/2
3/16	6	8 5/8	6 31/32	10	7 15/16	11 13/32	8 29/32	1-0 25/32	9 7/8	1-2 3/16	10 27/32	1-3 9/16
1/4	6 1/16	8 11/16	7 1/32	10 3/32	8	11 1/2	8 31/32	1-0 7/8	9 15/16	1-2 9/32	10 29/32	1-3 21/32
5/16	6 1/8	8 25/32	7 3/32	10 3/16	8 1/16	11 9/16	9 1/32	1-0 31/32	10	1-2 11/32	10 31/32	1-3 3/4
3/8	6 3/16	8 7/8	7 5/32	10 9/32	8 1/8	11 21/32	9 3/32	1-1 1/16	10 1/16	1-2 7/16	11 1/32	1-3 27/32
7/16	6 1/4	8 31/32	7 7/32	10 11/32	8 3/16	11 3/4	9 5/32	1-1 1/8	10 1/8	1-2 17/32	11 3/32	1-3 15/16
1/2	6 5/16	9 1/16	7 1/4	10 7/16	8 1/4	11 27/32	9 3/16	1-1 7/32	10 3/16	1-2 5/8	11 1/8	1-4
9/16	6 11/32	9 1/8	7 5/16	10 17/32	8 9/32	11 29/32	9 1/4	1-1 15/16	10 7/32	1-2 23/32	11 3/16	1-4 3/32
5/8	6 13/32	9 7/32	7 3/8	10 5/8	8 11/32	1-0	9 5/16	1-1 13/32	10 9/32	1-2 25/32	11 1/4	1-4 3/16
11/16	6 15/32	9 5/16	7 7/16	10 23/32	8 13/32	1-0 3/32	9 3/8	1-1 1/2	10 11/32	1-2 7/8	11 5/16	1-4 9/32
3/4	6 17/32	9 13/32	7 1/2	10 25/32	8 15/32	1-0 3/16	9 7/16	1-1 9/16	10 13/32	1-2 31/32	11 3/8	1-4 3/8
13/16	6 19/32	9 1/2	7 9/16	10 7/8	8 17/32	1-0 9/32	9 1/2	1-1 21/32	10 15/32	1-3 1/16	11 7/16	1-4 7/16
7/8	6 21/32	9 9/16	7 5/8	10 31/32	8 19/32	1-0 11/32	9 9/16	1-1 3/4	10 17/32	1-3 5/32	11 1/2	1-4 17/32
15/16	6 23/32	9 21/32	7 11/16	11 1/16	8 21/32	1-0 7/16	9 5/8	1-1 27/32	10 19/32	1-3 7/32	11 9/16	1-4 5/8

Feet	0' Rise	0' Slope	10' Rise	10' Slope	20' Rise	20' Slope	30' Rise	30' Slope
0	0	0	9-8 1/4	13-11 11/16	19-4 1/2	27-10 5/32	29-0 3/4	41-9 7/32
1	-11 5/8	1-4 23/32	10-7 7/8	15-3 25/32	20-4 1/8	29-2 7/32	30-0 3/8	43-1 15/16
2	1-11 1/4	2-9 13/32	11-7 1/2	16-8 1/2	21-3 3/4	30-7 9/16	31-0	44-6 5/8
3	2-10 7/8	4-2 1/8	12-7 1/8	18-1 3/16	22-3 3/8	32-0 9/32	31-11 5/8	45-11 11/32
4	3-10 1/2	5-6 27/32	13-6 3/4	19-5 29/32	23-3	33-4 31/32	32-11 1/4	47-4 1/16
5	4-10 1/8	6-11 17/32	14-6 3/8	20-10 5/8	24-2 5/8	34-9 11/16	33-10 7/8	48-8 3/4
6	5-9 3/4	8-4 1/4	15-6	22-3 5/16	25-2 1/4	36-2 13/32	34-10 1/2	50-1 15/32
7	6-9 3/8	9-8 15/16	16-5 5/8	23-8 1/32	26-1 7/8	37-7 3/32	35-10 1/2	51-6 3/16
8	7-9	11-1 21/32	17-5 1/4	25-0 3/4	27-1 1/2	38-11 13/16	36-9 3/4	52-10 7/8
9	8-8 5/8	12-6 3/8	18-4 7/8	26-5 7/16	28-1 1/8	40-4 17/32	37-9 3/8	54-3 19/32

A = 44° 05′ 26″; logsin A = 9.84248; logcos A = 9.85627; logtan A = 9.98621; logcot A = 0.01379

Ins.	12"		13"		14"		15"		16"	
	Rise	Slope	Rise	Slope	Rise	Slope	Rise	Slope	Rise	Slope
0	11 5/8	1-4 23/32–	1-0 19/32	1-6 3/32	1-1 9/16	1-7 1/2	1-2 17/32	1-8 7/8	1-3 1/2	1-10 9/32–
1/16	11 11/16	1-4 25/32	1-0 21/32–	1-6 3/16	1-1 5/8	1-7 19/32–	1-2 19/32–	1-8 31/32	1-3 9/16	1-10 3/8
1/8	11 3/4	1-4 7/8	1-0 23/32–	1-6 9/32–	1-1 11/16	1-7 21/32	1-2 21/32–	1-9 1/16	1-3 5/8	1-10 7/16
3/16	11 13/16	1-4 31/32–	1-0 25/32–	1-6 3/8	1-1 3/4	1-7 3/4	1-2 23/32–	1-9 5/32–	1-3 11/16	1-10 17/32
1/4	11 7/8	1-5 1/16	1-0 27/32–	1-6 7/16	1-1 13/16	1-7 27/32–	1-2 25/32–	1-9 7/32	1-3 3/4	1-10 5/8
5/16	11 15/16	1-5 5/32–	1-0 29/32–	1-6 17/32	1-1 7/8	1-7 15/16	1-2 27/32–	1-9 5/16	1-3 13/16	1-10 23/32–
3/8	1-0	1-5 7/32	1-0 31/32–	1-6 5/8	1-1 15/16	1-8	1-2 29/32–	1-9 13/32	1-3 7/8	1-10 13/16
7/16	1-0 1/16	1-5 5/16	1-1 1/32–	1-6 23/32–	1-2	1-8 3/32	1-2 31/32–	1-9 1/2	1-3 15/16	1-10 7/8
1/2	1-0 1/8	1-5 13/32–	1-1 1/16	1-6 25/32	1-2 1/16	1-8 3/16	1-3	1-9 19/32–	1-4	1-10 31/32
9/16	1-0 5/32	1-5 1/2	1-1 1/8	1-6 7/8	1-2 3/32	1-8 9/32–	1-3 1/16	1-9 21/32	1-4 1/32	1-11 1/16
5/8	1-0 7/32	1-5 9/16	1-1 3/16	1-6 31/32	1-2 5/32	1-8 3/8	1-3 1/8	1-9 3/4	1-4 3/32	1-11 5/32–
11/16	1-0 9/32	1-5 21/32	1-1 1/4	1-7 1/16	1-2 7/32	1-8 7/16	1-3 3/16	1-9 27/32–	1-4 5/32	1-11 7/32
3/4	1-0 11/32	1-5 3/4	1-1 5/16	1-7 5/32–	1-2 9/32	1-8 17/32	1-3 1/4	1-9 15/16	1-4 7/32	1-11 5/16
13/16	1-0 13/32	1-5 27/32–	1-1 3/8	1-7 7/32	1-2 11/32	1-8 5/8	1-3 5/16	1-10	1-4 9/32	1-11 13/32
7/8	1-0 15/32	1-5 15/16	1-1 7/16	1-7 5/16	1-2 13/32	1-8 23/32–	1-3 3/8	1-10 3/32	1-4 11/32	1-11 1/2
15/16	1-0 17/32	1-6	1-1 1/2	1-7 13/32–	1-2 15/32	1-8 13/16	1-3 7/16	1-10 3/16	1-4 13/32	1-11 19/32–

Ins.	17"		18"		19"		20"		21"	
	Rise	Slope	Rise	Slope	Rise	Slope	Rise	Slope	Rise	Slope
0	1-4 15/32	1-11 21/32	1-5 7/16	2-1 1/16	1-6 13/32	2-2 15/32–	1-7 3/8	2-3 27/32	1-8 11/32	2-5 1/4
1/16	1-4 17/32–	1-11 3/4	1-5 1/2	2-1 5/32–	1-6 15/32–	2-2 17/32	1-7 7/16	2-3 15/16	1-8 13/32–	2-5 5/16
1/8	1-4 19/32–	1-11 27/32–	1-5 9/16	2-1 1/4	1-6 17/32–	2-2 5/8	1-7 1/2	2-4 1/32–	1-8 15/32–	2-5 13/32
3/16	1-4 21/32–	1-11 15/16	1-5 5/8	2-1 5/16	1-6 19/32–	2-2 23/32–	1-7 9/16	2-4 3/32	1-8 17/32–	2-5 1/2
1/4	1-4 23/32–	2-0 1/32–	1-5 11/16	2-1 13/32	1-6 21/32–	2-2 13/16	1-7 5/8	2-4 3/16	1-8 19/32–	2-5 19/32–
5/16	1-4 25/32–	2-0 3/32	1-5 3/4	2-1 1/2	1-6 23/32–	2-2 7/8	1-7 11/16	2-4 9/32–	1-8 21/32–	2-5 11/16
3/8	1-4 27/32–	2-0 3/16	1-5 13/16	2-1 19/32–	1-6 25/32–	2-2 31/32	1-7 3/4	2-4 3/8	1-8 23/32–	2-5 3/4
7/16	1-4 29/32–	2-0 9/32–	1-5 7/8	2-1 21/32	1-6 27/32–	2-3 1/16	1-7 13/16	2-4 15/32–	1-8 25/32–	2-5 27/32
1/2	1-4 15/16	2-0 3/8	1-5 15/16	2-1 3/4	1-6 7/8	2-3 5/32–	1-7 7/8	2-4 17/32	1-8 13/16	2-5 15/16
9/16	1-5	2-0 7/16	1-5 31/32	2-1 27/32	1-6 15/16	2-3 1/4	1-7 29/32	2-4 5/8	1-8 7/8	2-6 1/32–
5/8	1-5 1/16	2-0 17/32	1-6 1/32	2-1 15/16	1-7	2-3 5/16	1-7 31/32	2-4 23/32–	1-8 15/16	2-6 3/32
11/16	1-5 1/8	2-0 5/8	1-6 3/32	2-2 1/32–	1-7 1/16	2-3 13/32	1-8 1/32	2-4 13/16	1-9	2-6 3/16
3/4	1-5 3/16	2-0 23/32–	1-6 5/32	2-2 3/32	1-7 1/8	2-3 1/2	1-8 3/32	2-4 7/8	1-9 1/16	2-6 9/32
13/16	1-5 1/4	2-0 13/16	1-6 7/32	2-2 3/16	1-7 3/16	2-3 19/32–	1-8 5/32	2-4 31/32	1-9 1/8	2-6 3/8
7/8	1-5 5/16	2-0 7/8	1-6 9/32	2-2 9/32–	1-7 1/4	2-3 21/32	1-8 7/32	2-5 1/16	1-9 3/16	2-6 15/32–
15/16	1-5 3/8	2-0 31/32	1-6 11/32	2-2 3/8	1-7 5/16	2-3 3/4	1-8 9/32	2-5 5/32–	1-9 1/4	2-6 17/32

Feet	40'		50'		60'		70'	
	Rise	Slope	Rise	Slope	Rise	Slope	Rise	Slope
0	38-9	55-8 5/16	48-5 1/4	69-7 3/8	58-1 1/2	83-6 7/16	67-9 3/4	97-5 17/32–
1	39-8 5/8	57-1	49-4 7/8	71-0 3/32–	59-1 1/8	84-11 5/32	68-9 3/8	98-10 7/32
2	40-8 1/4	58-5 23/32–	50-4 1/2	72-4 25/32	60-0 3/4	86-3 7/8	69-9	100-2 15/16
3	41-7 7/8	59-10 7/16	51-4 1/8	73-9 1/2	61-0 3/8	87-8 9/16	70-8 5/8	101-7 21/32–
4	42-7 1/2	61-3 1/8	52-3 3/4	75-2 7/32–	62-0	89-1 9/32–	71-8 1/4	103-0 11/32
5	43-7 1/8	62-7 27/32–	53-3 3/8	76-6 29/32	62-11 5/8	90-6	72-7 7/8	104-5 1/16
6	44-6 3/4	64-0 17/32	54-3	77-11 5/8	63-11 1/4	91-10 11/16	73-7 1/2	105-9 25/32–
7	45-6 3/8	65-5 1/4	55-2 5/8	79-4 5/16	64-10 7/8	93-3 13/32–	74-7 1/8	107-2 15/32
8	46-6	66-9 31/32–	56-2 1/4	80-9 1/32	65-10 1/2	94-8 1/8	75-6 3/4	108-7 3/16
9	47-5 5/8	68-2 21/32	57-1 7/8	82-1 3/4	66-10 1/8	96-0 13/16	76-6 3/8	109-11 29/32–

natsin A=0.6957952158; natcos A=0.7182402228; nattan A=0.9687500000; natcot A=1.0322580645

Inches	0" Rise	Slope	1" Rise	Slope	2" Rise	Slope	3" Rise	Slope	4" Rise	Slope	5" Rise	Slope
0	0	0	31/32	1 13/32	1 15/16	2 25/32	2 15/16	4 3/16	3 29/32	5 19/32	4 7/8	6 31/32
1/16	1/16	3/32	1 1/32	1 15/32	2	2 7/8	2 31/32	4 9/32	3 31/32	5 21/32	4 15/16	7 1/16
1/8	1/8	3/16	1 3/32	1 9/16	2 1/16	2 31/32	3 1/32	4 3/8	4 1/32	5 3/4	5	7 5/32
3/16	3/16	1/4	1 5/32	1 21/32	2 1/8	3 1/16	3 3/32	4 7/16	4 3/32	5 27/32	5 1/16	7 1/4
1/4	1/4	11/32	1 7/32	1 3/4	2 3/16	3 5/32	3 5/32	4 17/32	4 1/8	5 15/16	5 1/8	7 11/32
5/16	5/16	7/16	1 9/32	1 27/32	2 1/4	3 7/32	3 7/32	4 5/8	4 3/16	6 1/32	5 3/16	7 13/32
3/8	3/8	17/32	1 11/32	1 29/32	2 5/16	3 5/16	3 9/32	4 23/32	4 1/4	6 3/32	5 1/4	7 1/2
7/16	7/16	5/8	1 13/32	2	2 3/8	3 13/32	3 11/32	4 13/16	4 5/16	6 3/16	5 9/32	7 19/32
1/2	1/2	11/16	1 15/32	2 3/32	2 7/16	3 1/2	3 13/32	4 7/8	4 3/8	6 9/32	5 11/32	7 11/16
9/16	9/16	25/32	1 17/32	2 3/16	2 1/2	3 9/16	3 15/32	4 31/32	4 7/16	6 3/8	5 13/32	7 3/4
5/8	19/32	7/8	1 19/32	2 9/32	2 9/16	3 21/32	3 17/32	5 1/16	4 1/2	6 15/32	5 15/32	7 27/32
11/16	21/32	31/32	1 21/32	2 11/32	2 5/8	3 3/4	3 19/32	5 5/32	4 9/16	6 17/32	5 17/32	7 15/16
3/4	23/32	1 1/16	1 23/32	2 7/16	2 11/16	3 27/32	3 21/32	5 1/4	4 5/8	6 5/8	5 19/32	8 1/2
13/16	25/32	1 1/8	1 3/4	2 17/32	2 3/4	3 15/16	3 23/32	5 5/16	4 11/16	6 23/32	5 21/32	8 1/8
7/8	27/32	1 7/32	1 13/16	2 5/8	2 13/16	4	3 25/32	5 13/32	4 3/4	6 13/16	5 23/32	8 3/16
15/16	29/32	1 5/16	1 7/8	2 23/32	2 7/8	4 3/32	3 27/32	5 1/2	4 13/16	6 29/32	5 25/32	8 9/32

Inches	6" Rise	Slope	7" Rise	Slope	8" Rise	Slope	9" Rise	Slope	10" Rise	Slope	11" Rise	Slope
0	5 27/32	8 3/8	6 13/16	9 25/32	7 25/32	11 5/32	8 3/4	1-0 9/16	9 3/4	1-1 31/32	10 23/32	1-3 11/32
1/16	5 29/32	8 15/32	6 7/8	9 27/32	7 27/32	11 1/4	8 13/16	1-0 21/32	9 13/16	1-2 1/32	10 25/32	1-3 7/16
1/8	5 31/32	8 9/16	6 15/16	9 15/16	7 29/32	11 11/32	8 7/8	1-0 3/4	9 7/8	1-2 1/8	10 27/32	1-3 17/32
3/16	6 1/32	8 5/8	7	10 1/32	7 31/32	11 7/16	8 15/16	1-0 13/16	9 15/16	1-2 7/32	10 29/32	1-3 5/8
1/4	6 3/32	8 23/32	7 1/16	10 1/8	8 1/32	11 17/32	9	1-0 29/32	9 31/32	1-2 5/16	10 31/32	1-3 23/32
5/16	6 5/32	8 13/16	7 1/8	10 7/32	8 3/32	11 19/32	9 1/16	1-1	10 1/32	1-2 13/32	11 1/32	1-3 25/32
3/8	6 7/32	8 29/32	7 3/16	10 9/32	8 5/32	11 11/16	9 1/8	1-1 3/32	10 3/32	1-2 15/32	11 3/32	1-3 7/8
7/16	6 9/32	9	7 1/4	10 3/8	8 7/32	11 25/32	9 3/16	1-1 3/16	10 5/32	1-2 9/16	11 1/8	1-3 31/32
1/2	6 11/32	9 1/8	7 5/16	10 15/32	8 9/32	11 7/8	9 1/4	1-1 1/4	10 7/32	1-2 21/32	11 3/16	1-4 1/16
9/16	6 13/32	9 5/32	7 3/8	10 9/16	8 11/32	11 15/16	9 5/16	1-1 11/32	10 9/32	1-2 3/4	11 1/4	1-4 1/8
5/8	6 7/16	9 1/4	7 7/16	10 21/32	8 13/32	1-0 1/32	9 3/8	1-1 7/16	10 11/32	1-2 27/32	11 5/16	1-4 7/32
11/16	6 1/2	9 11/32	7 1/2	10 23/32	8 15/32	1-0 1/8	9 7/16	1-1 17/32	10 13/32	1-2 29/32	11 3/8	1-4 5/16
3/4	6 9/16	9 7/16	7 9/16	10 13/16	8 17/32	1-0 7/32	9 1/2	1-1 5/8	10 15/32	1-3	11 7/16	1-4 13/32
13/16	6 5/8	9 1/2	7 19/32	10 29/32	8 19/32	1-0 5/16	9 9/16	1-1 11/16	10 17/32	1-3 3/32	11 1/2	1-4 1/2
7/8	6 11/16	9 19/32	7 21/32	11	8 21/32	1-0 3/8	9 5/8	1-1 25/32	10 19/32	1-3 3/16	11 9/16	1-4 9/16
15/16	6 3/4	9 11/16	7 23/32	11 3/32	8 23/32	1-0 15/32	9 11/16	1-1 7/8	10 21/32	1-3 9/32	11 5/8	1-4 21/32

Feet	0' Rise	Slope	10' Rise	Slope	20' Rise	Slope	30' Rise	Slope
0	0	0	9-8 7/8	13-11 1/2	19-5 3/4	27-11 1/32	29-2 5/8	41-10 17/32
1	-11 11/16	1-4 3/4	10-8 9/16	15-4 1/4	20-5 7/16	29-3 25/32	30-2 5/16	43-3 9/32
2	1-11 3/8	2-9 1/2	11-8 1/4	16-9	21-5 1/8	30-8 17/32	31-2	44-8 1/32
3	2-11 1/16	4-2 1/4	12-7 15/16	18-1 3/4	22-4 13/16	32-1 9/32	32-1 11/16	46-0 25/32
4	3-10 3/4	5-7	13-7 5/8	19-6 1/2	23-4 1/2	33-6 1/32	33-1 3/8	47-5 17/32
5	4-10 7/16	6-11 3/4	14-7 5/16	20-11 1/2	24-4 3/16	34-10 25/32	34-1 1/16	48-10 9/32
6	5-10 1/8	8-4 1/2	15-7	22-4 1/4	25-3 7/8	36-3 17/32	35-0 3/4	50-3 1/32
7	6-9 13/16	9-9 1/4	16-6 11/16	23-8 25/32	26-3 9/16	37-8 9/32	36-0 7/16	51-7 25/32
8	7-9 1/2	11-2	17-6 3/8	25-1 17/32	27-3 1/4	39-1 1/32	37-0 1/8	53-0 17/32
9	8-9 3/16	12-6 3/4	18-6 1/16	26-6 9/32	28-2 15/16	40-5 25/32	37-11 13/16	54-5 9/32

A = 44° 14' 39"; logsin A = 9.84368; logcos A = 9.85514; logtan A = 9.98854; logcot A = 0.01146

In.	12″ Rise	12″ Slope	13″ Rise	13″ Slope	14″ Rise	14″ Slope	15″ Rise	15″ Slope	16″ Rise	16″ Slope
0	11 11/16	1-4 3/4	1-0 21/32	1-6 5/32	1-1 5/8	1-7 17/32	1-2 5/8	1-8 15/16	1-3 19/32	1-10 11/32
1/16	11 3/4	1-4 27/32	1-0 23/32	1-6 7/32	1-1 11/16	1-7 5/8	1-2 21/32	1-9 1/32	1-3 21/32	1-10 7/16
1/8	11 13/16	1-4 15/16	1-0 25/32	1-6 5/16	1-1 3/4	1-7 23/32	1-2 23/32	1-9 1/8	1-3 23/32	1-10 1/2
3/16	11 7/8	1-5	1-0 27/32	1-6 13/32	1-1 13/16	1-7 13/16	1-2 25/32	1-9 3/16	1-3 25/32	1-10 19/32
1/4	11 15/16	1-5 3/32	1-0 29/32	1-6 1/2	1-1 7/8	1-7 29/32	1-2 27/32	1-9 9/32	1-3 13/16	1-10 11/16
5/16	1-0	1-5 3/16	1-0 31/32	1-6 19/32	1-1 15/16	1-7 31/32	1-2 29/32	1-9 3/8	1-3 7/8	1-10 25/32
3/8	1-0 1/16	1-5 9/32	1-1 1/32	1-6 21/32	1-2	1-8 1/16	1-2 31/32	1-9 15/32	1-3 15/16	1-10 27/32
7/16	1-0 1/8	1-5 3/8	1-1 3/32	1-6 3/4	1-2 1/16	1-8 5/32	1-3 1/32	1-9 9/16	1-4	1-10 15/16
1/2	1-0 3/16	1-5 7/16	1-1 5/32	1-6 27/32	1-2 1/8	1-8 1/4	1-3 3/32	1-9 5/8	1-4 1/16	1-11 1/32
9/16	1-0 1/4	1-5 17/32	1-1 7/32	1-6 15/16	1-2 3/16	1-8 5/16	1-3 5/32	1-9 23/32	1-4 1/8	1-11 1/8
5/8	1-0 9/32	1-5 5/8	1-1 9/32	1-7 1/32	1-2 1/4	1-8 13/32	1-3 7/32	1-9 13/16	1-4 3/16	1-11 7/32
11/16	1-0 11/32	1-5 23/32	1-1 11/32	1-7 3/32	1-2 5/16	1-8 1/2	1-3 9/32	1-9 29/32	1-4 1/4	1-11 9/32
3/4	1-0 13/32	1-5 13/16	1-1 13/32	1-7 3/16	1-2 3/8	1-8 19/32	1-3 11/32	1-10	1-4 5/16	1-11 3/8
13/16	1-0 15/32	1-5 7/8	1-1 7/16	1-7 9/32	1-2 7/16	1-8 11/16	1-3 13/32	1-10 1/32	1-4 3/8	1-11 15/32
7/8	1-0 17/32	1-5 31/32	1-1 1/2	1-7 3/8	1-2 1/2	1-8 3/4	1-3 15/32	1-10 5/32	1-4 7/16	1-11 9/16
15/16	1-0 19/32	1-6 1/16	1-1 9/16	1-7 15/32	1-2 9/16	1-8 27/32	1-3 17/32	1-10 1/4	1-4 1/2	1-11 21/32

In.	17″ Rise	17″ Slope	18″ Rise	18″ Slope	19″ Rise	19″ Slope	20″ Rise	20″ Slope	21″ Rise	21″ Slope
0	1-4 9/16	1-11 23/32	1-5 17/32	2-1 1/8	1-6 1/2	2-2 17/32	1-7 15/32	2-3 29/32	1-8 1/16	2-5 5/16
1/16	1-4 5/8	1-11 13/16	1-5 19/32	2-1 7/32	1-6 9/16	2-2 5/8	1-7 17/32	2-4	1-8 1/2	2-5 13/32
1/8	1-4 11/16	1-11 29/32	1-5 21/32	2-1 5/16	1-6 5/8	2-2 11/16	1-7 19/32	2-4 3/32	1-8 9/16	2-5 1/2
3/16	1-4 3/4	2-0	1-5 23/32	2-1 3/8	1-6 11/16	2-2 25/32	1-7 21/32	2-4 3/16	1-8 5/8	2-5 9/16
1/4	1-4 13/16	2-0 3/32	1-5 25/32	2-1 15/32	1-6 3/4	2-2 7/8	1-7 23/32	2-4 9/32	1-8 11/16	2-5 21/32
5/16	1-4 7/8	2-0 5/32	1-5 27/32	2-1 9/16	1-6 13/16	2-2 31/32	1-7 25/32	2-4 11/32	1-8 3/4	2-5 3/4
3/8	1-4 15/16	2-0 1/4	1-5 29/32	2-1 21/32	1-6 7/8	2-3 1/32	1-7 27/32	2-4 7/16	1-8 13/16	2-5 27/32
7/16	1-4 31/32	2-0 11/32	1-5 31/32	2-1 3/4	1-6 15/16	2-3 1/8	1-7 29/32	2-4 17/32	1-8 7/8	2-5 15/16
1/2	1-5 1/32	2-0 7/16	1-6 1/32	2-1 13/16	1-7	2-3 7/32	1-7 31/32	2-4 5/8	1-8 15/16	2-6
9/16	1-5 3/32	2-0 17/32	1-6 3/32	2-1 29/32	1-7 1/16	2-3 5/16	1-8 1/32	2-4 23/32	1-9	2-6 3/32
5/8	1-5 5/32	2-0 19/32	1-6 1/8	2-2	1-7 1/8	2-3 13/32	1-8 3/32	2-4 25/32	1-9 1/16	2-6 3/16
11/16	1-5 7/32	2-0 11/16	1-6 5/32	2-2 3/32	1-7 3/16	2-3 15/32	1-8 5/32	2-4 7/8	1-9 1/8	2-6 9/32
3/4	1-5 9/32	2-0 25/32	1-6 1/4	2-2 3/16	1-7 1/4	2-3 9/16	1-8 7/32	2-4 31/32	1-9 3/16	2-6 3/8
13/16	1-5 11/32	2-0 7/8	1-6 5/16	2-2 1/4	1-7 9/32	2-3 21/32	1-8 9/32	2-5 1/16	1-9 1/4	2-6 7/16
7/8	1-5 13/32	2-0 15/16	1-6 3/8	2-2 11/32	1-7 11/32	2-3 3/4	1-8 11/32	2-5 1/8	1-9 5/16	2-6 17/32
15/16	1-5 15/32	2-1 1/32	1-6 7/16	2-2 7/16	1-7 13/32	2-3 27/32	1-8 13/32	2-5 7/32	1-9 3/8	2-6 5/8

Feet	40′ Rise	40′ Slope	50′ Rise	50′ Slope	60′ Rise	60′ Slope	70′ Rise	70′ Slope
0	38-11 1/2	55-10 1/32	48-8 3/8	69-9 9/16	58-5 1/4	83-9 1/16	68-2 1/8	97-8 9/16
1	39-11 3/16	57-2 25/32	49-8 1/16	71-2 5/16	59-4 15/16	85-1 13/16	69-1 13/16	99-1 5/16
2	40-10 7/8	58-7 17/32	50-7 3/4	72-7 11/16	60-4 5/8	86-6 9/16	70-1 1/2	100-6 1/16
3	41-10 9/16	60-0 9/32	51-7 7/16	73-11 13/16	61-4 5/16	87-11 5/16	71-1 3/16	101-10 13/16
4	42-10 1/4	61-5 1/32	52-7 1/8	75-4 9/16	62-4	89-4 1/16	72-0 7/8	103-3 9/16
5	43-9 15/16	62-9 13/16	53-6 13/16	76-9 5/16	63-3 11/16	90-8 13/16	73-0 9/16	104-8 11/32
6	44-9 5/8	64-2 9/16	54-6 1/2	78-2 1/16	64-3 3/8	92-1 9/16	74-0 1/4	106-1 3/32
7	45-9 5/16	65-7 5/16	55-6 3/16	79-6 13/16	65-3 1/16	93-6 5/16	74-11 15/16	107-5 27/32
8	46-9	67-0 1/16	56-5 7/8	80-11 9/16	66-2 3/4	94-11 1/16	75-11 5/8	108-10 19/32
9	47-8 11/16	68-4 13/16	57-5 9/16	82-4 5/16	67-2 7/16	96-3 13/16	76-11 5/16	110-3 11/32

natsin A=0.6977174812; natcos A=0.7163730288; nattan A=0.9739583333; natcot A=1.0267379679

Inches	0" Rise	0" Slope	1" Rise	1" Slope	2" Rise	2" Slope	3" Rise	3" Slope	4" Rise	4" Slope	5" Rise	5" Slope
0	0	0	31/32	1 13/32	1 31/32	2 13/16	2 15/16	4 3/16	3 29/32	5 19/32	4 29/32	7
1/16	1/16	3/32	1 1/32	1 1/2	2 1/32	2 7/8	3	4 9/32	3 31/32	5 11/16	4 31/32	7 3/32
1/8	1/8	3/16	1 3/32	1 9/16	2 3/32	2 31/32	3 1/16	4 3/8	4 1/32	5 25/32	5 1/32	7 3/16
3/16	3/16	1/4	1 5/32	1 21/32	2 5/32	3 1/16	3 1/8	4 15/32	4 3/32	5 7/8	5 3/32	7 1/4
1/4	1/4	11/32	1 7/32	1 3/4	2 3/16	3 5/32	3 3/16	4 9/16	4 5/32	5 15/16	5 1/8	7 11/32
5/16	5/16	7/16	1 9/32	1 27/32	2 1/4	3 1/4	3 1/4	4 5/8	4 7/32	6 1/8	5 3/16	7 7/16
3/8	3/8	17/32	1 11/32	1 15/16	2 5/16	3 5/16	3 5/16	4 23/32	4 9/32	6 1/8	5 1/4	7 17/32
7/16	7/16	5/8	1 13/32	2	2 3/8	3 13/32	3 3/8	4 13/16	4 11/32	6 7/32	5 5/16	7 5/8
1/2	1/2	11/16	1 15/32	2 3/32	2 7/16	3 1/2	3 7/16	4 29/32	4 13/32	6 5/16	5 3/8	7 11/16
9/16	9/16	25/32	1 17/32	2 3/16	2 1/2	3 19/32	3 1/2	5	4 15/32	6 3/8	5 7/16	7 25/32
5/8	5/8	7/8	1 19/32	2 9/32	2 9/16	3 11/16	3 9/16	5 1/16	4 17/32	6 15/32	5 1/2	7 7/8
11/16	11/16	31/32	1 21/32	2 3/8	2 5/8	3 3/4	3 5/8	5 5/32	4 19/32	6 9/16	5 9/16	7 31/32
3/4	3/4	1 1/16	1 23/32	2 7/16	2 11/16	3 27/32	3 11/16	5 1/4	4 21/32	6 21/32	5 5/8	8 1/16
13/16	25/32	1 1/8	1 25/32	2 17/32	2 3/4	3 15/16	3 23/32	5 11/32	4 23/32	6 3/4	5 11/16	8 1/8
7/8	27/32	1 7/32	1 27/32	2 5/8	2 13/16	4 1/32	3 25/32	5 7/16	4 25/32	6 13/16	5 3/4	8 7/32
15/16	29/32	1 5/16	1 29/32	2 23/32	2 7/8	4 1/8	3 27/32	5 1/2	4 27/32	6 29/32	5 13/16	8 5/16

Inches	6" Rise	6" Slope	7" Rise	7" Slope	8" Rise	8" Slope	9" Rise	9" Slope	10" Rise	10" Slope	11" Rise	11" Slope
0	5 7/8	8 13/32	6 27/32	9 13/16	7 27/32	11 3/16	8 13/16	1-0 19/32	9 25/32	1-2	10 25/32	1-3 13/32
1/16	5 15/16	8 1/2	6 29/32	9 7/8	7 29/32	11 9/32	8 7/8	1-0 11/16	9 27/32	1-2 3/32	10 27/32	1-3 15/32
1/8	6	8 9/16	6 31/32	9 31/32	7 31/32	11 3/8	8 15/16	1-0 25/32	9 29/32	1-2 5/32	10 29/32	1-3 9/16
3/16	6 1/16	8 21/32	7 1/32	10 1/32	8 1/32	11 15/32	9	1-0 27/32	9 31/32	1-2 1/4	10 31/32	1-3 21/32
1/4	6 1/8	8 3/4	7 3/32	10 5/32	8 1/8	11 17/32	9 1/16	1-0 15/16	10 1/32	1-2 11/32	11	1-3 3/4
5/16	6 3/16	8 27/32	7 5/32	10 7/32	8 1/8	11 5/8	9 1/8	1-1 1/32	10 3/32	1-2 7/16	11 1/16	1-3 27/32
3/8	6 1/4	8 15/16	7 7/32	10 5/16	8 3/16	11 23/32	9 3/16	1-1 1/8	10 5/32	1-2 17/32	11 1/8	1-3 29/32
7/16	6 5/16	9	7 9/32	10 13/32	8 1/4	11 13/16	9 1/4	1-1 17/32	10 7/32	1-2 19/32	11 3/16	1-4
1/2	6 3/8	9 3/32	7 11/32	10 1/2	8 5/16	11 29/32	9 5/16	1-1 9/32	10 9/32	1-2 11/16	11 1/4	1-4 3/32
9/16	6 7/16	9 3/16	7 13/32	10 19/32	8 3/8	11 31/32	9 3/8	1-1 3/8	10 11/32	1-2 25/32	11 5/16	1-4 3/32
5/8	6 1/2	9 9/32	7 15/32	10 21/32	8 7/16	1-0 1/16	9 7/16	1-1 15/32	10 13/32	1-2 7/8	11 3/8	1-4 9/32
11/16	6 9/16	9 3/8	7 17/32	10 3/4	8 1/2	1-0 5/32	9 1/2	1-1 9/16	10 15/32	1-2 31/32	11 7/16	1-4 11/32
3/4	6 5/8	9 7/16	7 19/32	10 27/32	8 9/16	1-0 1/4	9 9/16	1-1 21/32	10 17/32	1-3 1/32	11 1/2	1-4 7/16
13/16	6 21/32	9 17/32	7 21/32	10 15/16	8 5/8	1-0 11/32	9 19/32	1-1 23/32	10 19/32	1-3 1/8	11 9/16	1-4 17/32
7/8	6 23/32	9 5/8	7 23/32	11 1/32	8 11/16	1-0 13/32	9 21/32	1-1 13/16	10 21/32	1-3 7/32	11 5/8	1-4 5/8
15/16	6 25/32	9 23/32	7 25/32	11 3/32	8 3/4	1-0 1/2	9 23/32	1-1 29/32	10 23/32	1-3 5/16	11 11/16	1-4 23/32

Feet	0' Rise	0' Slope	10' Rise	10' Slope	20' Rise	20' Slope	30' Rise	30' Slope
0	0	0	9-9 1/2	13-11 15/16	19-7	27-11 19/32	29-4 1/2	41-11 27/32
1	-11 3/4	1-4 25/32	10-9 1/4	15-4 3/4	20-6 3/4	29-4 11/16	30-4 1/4	43-4 5/8
2	1-11 1/2	2-9 19/32	11-9	16-9 17/32	21-6 1/2	30-9 15/32	31-4	44-9 7/16
3	2-11 1/4	4-2 3/8	12-8 3/4	18-2 11/32	22-6 1/4	32-2 9/32	32-3 3/4	46-2 7/32
4	3-11	5-7 3/16	13-8 1/2	19-7 1/8	23-6	33-7 1/16	33-3 1/2	47-7 1/2
5	4-10 3/4	6-11 31/32	14-8 1/4	20-11 29/32	24-5 3/4	34-11 7/8	34-3 1/4	48-11 13/16
6	5-10 1/2	8-4 25/32	15-8	22-4 23/32	25-5 1/2	36-4 21/32	35-3	50-4 5/8
7	6-10 1/4	9-9 9/16	16-7 3/4	23-9 1/2	26-5 1/4	37-9 15/32	36-2 3/4	51-9 13/32
8	7-10	11-2 11/32	17-7 1/2	25-2 5/16	27-5	39-2 1/4	37-2 1/2	53-2 3/16
9	8-9 3/4	12-7 5/32	18-7 1/4	26-7 3/32	28-4 3/4	40-7 1/16	38-2 1/4	54-7

A = 44° 23′ 49″; logsin A = 9.84487; logcos A = 9.85401; logtan A = 9.99086; logcot A = 0.00914

In.	12" Rise	12" Slope	13" Rise	13" Slope	14" Rise	14" Slope	15" Rise	15" Slope	16" Rise	16" Slope
0	$11\frac{3}{4}$	$1\text{-}4\frac{25}{32}$	$1\text{-}0\frac{23}{32}$	$1\text{-}6\frac{3}{16}$	$1\text{-}1\frac{23}{32}$	$1\text{-}7\frac{19}{32}$	$1\text{-}2\frac{11}{16}$	$1\text{-}9$	$1\text{-}3\frac{21}{32}$	$1\text{-}10\frac{13}{32}$
$\frac{1}{16}$	$11\frac{13}{16}$	$1\text{-}4\frac{7}{8}$	$1\text{-}0\frac{25}{32}$	$1\text{-}6\frac{9}{32}$	$1\text{-}1\frac{25}{32}$	$1\text{-}7\frac{11}{16}$	$1\text{-}2\frac{3}{4}$	$1\text{-}9\frac{3}{32}$	$1\text{-}3\frac{23}{32}$	$1\text{-}10\frac{15}{32}$
$\frac{1}{8}$	$11\frac{7}{8}$	$1\text{-}4\frac{31}{32}$	$1\text{-}0\frac{27}{32}$	$1\text{-}6\frac{3}{8}$	$1\text{-}1\frac{27}{32}$	$1\text{-}7\frac{25}{32}$	$1\text{-}2\frac{13}{16}$	$1\text{-}9\frac{5}{32}$	$1\text{-}3\frac{25}{32}$	$1\text{-}10\frac{9}{16}$
$\frac{3}{16}$	$11\frac{15}{16}$	$1\text{-}5\frac{1}{16}$	$1\text{-}0\frac{29}{32}$	$1\text{-}6\frac{15}{32}$	$1\text{-}1\frac{29}{32}$	$1\text{-}7\frac{27}{32}$	$1\text{-}2\frac{7}{8}$	$1\text{-}9\frac{1}{4}$	$1\text{-}3\frac{27}{32}$	$1\text{-}10\frac{21}{32}$
$\frac{1}{4}$	$1\text{-}0$	$1\text{-}5\frac{5}{32}$	$1\text{-}0\frac{31}{32}$	$1\text{-}6\frac{17}{32}$	$1\text{-}1\frac{15}{16}$	$1\text{-}7\frac{15}{16}$	$1\text{-}2\frac{15}{16}$	$1\text{-}9\frac{11}{32}$	$1\text{-}3\frac{29}{32}$	$1\text{-}10\frac{3}{4}$
$\frac{5}{16}$	$1\text{-}0\frac{1}{16}$	$1\text{-}5\frac{7}{32}$	$1\text{-}1\frac{1}{32}$	$1\text{-}6\frac{5}{8}$	$1\text{-}2$	$1\text{-}8\frac{1}{32}$	$1\text{-}3$	$1\text{-}9\frac{7}{16}$	$1\text{-}3\frac{31}{32}$	$1\text{-}10\frac{27}{32}$
$\frac{3}{8}$	$1\text{-}0\frac{1}{8}$	$1\text{-}5\frac{5}{16}$	$1\text{-}1\frac{3}{32}$	$1\text{-}6\frac{23}{32}$	$1\text{-}2\frac{1}{16}$	$1\text{-}8\frac{1}{8}$	$1\text{-}3\frac{1}{16}$	$1\text{-}9\frac{17}{32}$	$1\text{-}4\frac{1}{32}$	$1\text{-}10\frac{29}{32}$
$\frac{7}{16}$	$1\text{-}0\frac{3}{16}$	$1\text{-}5\frac{13}{32}$	$1\text{-}1\frac{5}{32}$	$1\text{-}6\frac{15}{16}$	$1\text{-}2\frac{1}{8}$	$1\text{-}8\frac{7}{32}$	$1\text{-}3\frac{1}{8}$	$1\text{-}9\frac{19}{32}$	$1\text{-}4\frac{3}{32}$	$1\text{-}11$
$\frac{1}{2}$	$1\text{-}0\frac{1}{4}$	$1\text{-}5\frac{1}{2}$	$1\text{-}1\frac{7}{32}$	$1\text{-}6\frac{29}{32}$	$1\text{-}2\frac{3}{16}$	$1\text{-}8\frac{9}{32}$	$1\text{-}3\frac{3}{16}$	$1\text{-}9\frac{11}{16}$	$1\text{-}4\frac{5}{32}$	$1\text{-}11\frac{3}{32}$
$\frac{9}{16}$	$1\text{-}0\frac{5}{16}$	$1\text{-}5\frac{19}{32}$	$1\text{-}1\frac{9}{32}$	$1\text{-}6\frac{31}{32}$	$1\text{-}2\frac{1}{4}$	$1\text{-}8\frac{3}{8}$	$1\text{-}3\frac{1}{4}$	$1\text{-}9\frac{25}{32}$	$1\text{-}4\frac{7}{32}$	$1\text{-}11\frac{3}{16}$
$\frac{5}{8}$	$1\text{-}0\frac{3}{8}$	$1\text{-}5\frac{21}{32}$	$1\text{-}1\frac{11}{32}$	$1\text{-}7\frac{1}{16}$	$1\text{-}2\frac{5}{16}$	$1\text{-}8\frac{15}{32}$	$1\text{-}3\frac{5}{16}$	$1\text{-}9\frac{7}{8}$	$1\text{-}4\frac{9}{32}$	$1\text{-}11\frac{9}{32}$
$\frac{11}{16}$	$1\text{-}0\frac{7}{16}$	$1\text{-}5\frac{3}{4}$	$1\text{-}1\frac{13}{32}$	$1\text{-}7\frac{5}{32}$	$1\text{-}2\frac{3}{8}$	$1\text{-}8\frac{9}{16}$	$1\text{-}3\frac{3}{8}$	$1\text{-}9\frac{31}{32}$	$1\text{-}4\frac{11}{32}$	$1\text{-}11\frac{11}{32}$
$\frac{3}{4}$	$1\text{-}0\frac{1}{2}$	$1\text{-}5\frac{27}{32}$	$1\text{-}1\frac{15}{32}$	$1\text{-}7\frac{1}{4}$	$1\text{-}2\frac{7}{16}$	$1\text{-}8\frac{21}{32}$	$1\text{-}3\frac{7}{16}$	$1\text{-}10\frac{1}{32}$	$1\text{-}4\frac{13}{32}$	$1\text{-}11\frac{7}{16}$
$\frac{13}{16}$	$1\text{-}0\frac{17}{32}$	$1\text{-}5\frac{15}{16}$	$1\text{-}1\frac{17}{32}$	$1\text{-}7\frac{11}{32}$	$1\text{-}2\frac{1}{2}$	$1\text{-}8\frac{23}{32}$	$1\text{-}3\frac{15}{32}$	$1\text{-}10\frac{1}{8}$	$1\text{-}4\frac{15}{32}$	$1\text{-}11\frac{17}{32}$
$\frac{7}{8}$	$1\text{-}0\frac{19}{32}$	$1\text{-}6\frac{1}{32}$	$1\text{-}1\frac{19}{32}$	$1\text{-}7\frac{13}{32}$	$1\text{-}2\frac{9}{16}$	$1\text{-}8\frac{13}{16}$	$1\text{-}3\frac{17}{32}$	$1\text{-}10\frac{7}{32}$	$1\text{-}4\frac{17}{32}$	$1\text{-}11\frac{5}{8}$
$\frac{15}{16}$	$1\text{-}0\frac{21}{32}$	$1\text{-}6\frac{3}{32}$	$1\text{-}1\frac{21}{32}$	$1\text{-}7\frac{1}{2}$	$1\text{-}2\frac{5}{8}$	$1\text{-}8\frac{29}{32}$	$1\text{-}3\frac{19}{32}$	$1\text{-}10\frac{5}{16}$	$1\text{-}4\frac{19}{32}$	$1\text{-}11\frac{23}{32}$

In.	17" Rise	17" Slope	18" Rise	18" Slope	19" Rise	19" Slope	20" Rise	20" Slope	21" Rise	21" Slope
0	$1\text{-}4\frac{21}{32}$	$1\text{-}11\frac{25}{32}$	$1\text{-}5\frac{5}{8}$	$2\text{-}1\frac{3}{16}$	$1\text{-}6\frac{19}{32}$	$2\text{-}2\frac{19}{32}$	$1\text{-}7\frac{19}{32}$	$2\text{-}4$	$1\text{-}8\frac{9}{16}$	$2\text{-}5\frac{13}{32}$
$\frac{1}{16}$	$1\text{-}4\frac{23}{32}$	$1\text{-}11\frac{7}{8}$	$1\text{-}5\frac{11}{16}$	$2\text{-}1\frac{9}{32}$	$1\text{-}6\frac{21}{32}$	$2\text{-}2\frac{11}{16}$	$1\text{-}7\frac{21}{32}$	$2\text{-}4\frac{3}{32}$	$1\text{-}8\frac{5}{8}$	$2\text{-}5\frac{15}{32}$
$\frac{1}{8}$	$1\text{-}4\frac{25}{32}$	$1\text{-}11\frac{31}{32}$	$1\text{-}5\frac{3}{4}$	$2\text{-}1\frac{3}{8}$	$1\text{-}6\frac{23}{32}$	$2\text{-}2\frac{25}{32}$	$1\text{-}7\frac{23}{32}$	$2\text{-}4\frac{5}{32}$	$1\text{-}8\frac{11}{16}$	$2\text{-}5\frac{9}{16}$
$\frac{3}{16}$	$1\text{-}4\frac{27}{32}$	$2\text{-}0\frac{1}{16}$	$1\text{-}5\frac{13}{16}$	$2\text{-}1\frac{15}{32}$	$1\text{-}6\frac{25}{32}$	$2\text{-}2\frac{27}{32}$	$1\text{-}7\frac{25}{32}$	$2\text{-}4\frac{1}{4}$	$1\text{-}8\frac{3}{4}$	$2\text{-}5\frac{21}{32}$
$\frac{1}{4}$	$1\text{-}4\frac{7}{8}$	$2\text{-}0\frac{5}{32}$	$1\text{-}5\frac{7}{8}$	$2\text{-}1\frac{17}{32}$	$1\text{-}6\frac{27}{32}$	$2\text{-}2\frac{15}{16}$	$1\text{-}7\frac{13}{16}$	$2\text{-}4\frac{11}{32}$	$1\text{-}8\frac{13}{16}$	$2\text{-}5\frac{3}{4}$
$\frac{5}{16}$	$1\text{-}4\frac{15}{16}$	$2\text{-}0\frac{7}{32}$	$1\text{-}5\frac{15}{16}$	$2\text{-}1\frac{5}{8}$	$1\text{-}6\frac{29}{32}$	$2\text{-}3\frac{1}{32}$	$1\text{-}7\frac{7}{8}$	$2\text{-}4\frac{7}{16}$	$1\text{-}8\frac{7}{8}$	$2\text{-}5\frac{13}{16}$
$\frac{3}{8}$	$1\text{-}5$	$2\text{-}0\frac{9}{16}$	$1\text{-}6$	$2\text{-}1\frac{23}{32}$	$1\text{-}6\frac{31}{32}$	$2\text{-}3\frac{1}{8}$	$1\text{-}7\frac{15}{16}$	$2\text{-}4\frac{17}{32}$	$1\text{-}8\frac{15}{16}$	$2\text{-}5\frac{29}{32}$
$\frac{7}{16}$	$1\text{-}5\frac{1}{16}$	$2\text{-}0\frac{13}{32}$	$1\text{-}6\frac{1}{16}$	$2\text{-}1\frac{13}{16}$	$1\text{-}7\frac{1}{32}$	$2\text{-}3\frac{7}{32}$	$1\text{-}8$	$2\text{-}4\frac{19}{32}$	$1\text{-}9$	$2\text{-}6$
$\frac{1}{2}$	$1\text{-}5\frac{1}{8}$	$2\text{-}0\frac{1}{2}$	$1\text{-}6\frac{1}{8}$	$2\text{-}1\frac{29}{32}$	$1\text{-}7\frac{3}{32}$	$2\text{-}3\frac{9}{32}$	$1\text{-}8\frac{1}{16}$	$2\text{-}4\frac{11}{16}$	$1\text{-}9\frac{1}{16}$	$2\text{-}6\frac{3}{32}$
$\frac{9}{16}$	$1\text{-}5\frac{3}{16}$	$2\text{-}0\frac{19}{32}$	$1\text{-}6\frac{3}{16}$	$2\text{-}1\frac{31}{32}$	$1\text{-}7\frac{5}{32}$	$2\text{-}3\frac{3}{8}$	$1\text{-}8\frac{1}{8}$	$2\text{-}4\frac{25}{32}$	$1\text{-}9\frac{1}{8}$	$2\text{-}6\frac{3}{16}$
$\frac{5}{8}$	$1\text{-}5\frac{1}{4}$	$2\text{-}0\frac{21}{32}$	$1\text{-}6\frac{1}{4}$	$2\text{-}2\frac{1}{16}$	$1\text{-}7\frac{7}{32}$	$2\text{-}3\frac{15}{32}$	$1\text{-}8\frac{3}{16}$	$2\text{-}4\frac{7}{8}$	$1\text{-}9\frac{3}{16}$	$2\text{-}6\frac{1}{4}$
$\frac{11}{16}$	$1\text{-}5\frac{5}{16}$	$2\text{-}0\frac{3}{4}$	$1\text{-}6\frac{5}{16}$	$2\text{-}2\frac{5}{32}$	$1\text{-}7\frac{9}{32}$	$2\text{-}3\frac{9}{16}$	$1\text{-}8\frac{1}{4}$	$2\text{-}4\frac{31}{32}$	$1\text{-}9\frac{1}{4}$	$2\text{-}6\frac{11}{16}$
$\frac{3}{4}$	$1\text{-}5\frac{3}{8}$	$2\text{-}0\frac{27}{32}$	$1\text{-}6\frac{3}{8}$	$2\text{-}2\frac{1}{4}$	$1\text{-}7\frac{11}{32}$	$2\text{-}3\frac{21}{32}$	$1\text{-}8\frac{5}{16}$	$2\text{-}5\frac{1}{32}$	$1\text{-}9\frac{5}{16}$	$2\text{-}6\frac{7}{32}$
$\frac{13}{16}$	$1\text{-}5\frac{15}{16}$	$2\text{-}0\frac{15}{16}$	$1\text{-}6\frac{13}{32}$	$2\text{-}2\frac{11}{32}$	$1\text{-}7\frac{13}{32}$	$2\text{-}3\frac{23}{32}$	$1\text{-}8\frac{3}{8}$	$2\text{-}5\frac{1}{8}$	$1\text{-}9\frac{11}{32}$	$2\text{-}6\frac{17}{32}$
$\frac{7}{8}$	$1\text{-}5\frac{1}{2}$	$2\text{-}1\frac{1}{32}$	$1\text{-}6\frac{15}{32}$	$2\text{-}2\frac{13}{32}$	$1\text{-}7\frac{15}{32}$	$2\text{-}3\frac{13}{16}$	$1\text{-}8\frac{7}{16}$	$2\text{-}5\frac{7}{32}$	$1\text{-}9\frac{13}{32}$	$2\text{-}6\frac{5}{8}$
$\frac{15}{16}$	$1\text{-}5\frac{9}{16}$	$2\text{-}1\frac{3}{32}$	$1\text{-}6\frac{17}{32}$	$2\text{-}2\frac{1}{2}$	$1\text{-}7\frac{17}{32}$	$2\text{-}3\frac{29}{32}$	$1\text{-}8\frac{1}{2}$	$2\text{-}5\frac{5}{16}$	$1\text{-}9\frac{15}{32}$	$2\text{-}6\frac{11}{16}$

Feet	40' Rise	40' Slope	50' Rise	50' Slope	60' Rise	60' Slope	70' Rise	70' Slope
0	$39\text{-}2$	$55\text{-}11\frac{25}{32}$	$48\text{-}11\frac{1}{2}$	$69\text{-}11\frac{3}{4}$	$58\text{-}9$	$83\text{-}11\frac{11}{32}$	$68\text{-}6\frac{1}{2}$	$97\text{-}11\frac{5}{8}$
1	$40\text{-}1\frac{3}{4}$	$57\text{-}4\frac{19}{32}$	$49\text{-}11\frac{1}{4}$	$71\text{-}4\frac{17}{32}$	$59\text{-}8\frac{3}{4}$	$85\text{-}4\frac{15}{32}$	$69\text{-}6\frac{1}{4}$	$99\text{-}4\frac{7}{16}$
2	$41\text{-}1\frac{1}{2}$	$58\text{-}9\frac{3}{8}$	$50\text{-}11$	$72\text{-}9\frac{5}{16}$	$60\text{-}8\frac{1}{2}$	$86\text{-}9\frac{9}{32}$	$70\text{-}6$	$100\text{-}9\frac{7}{32}$
3	$42\text{-}1\frac{1}{4}$	$60\text{-}2\frac{3}{16}$	$51\text{-}10\frac{3}{4}$	$74\text{-}2\frac{1}{32}$	$61\text{-}8\frac{1}{4}$	$88\text{-}2\frac{1}{32}$	$71\text{-}5\frac{3}{4}$	$102\text{-}2$
4	$43\text{-}1$	$61\text{-}6\frac{31}{32}$	$52\text{-}10\frac{1}{2}$	$75\text{-}6\frac{29}{32}$	$62\text{-}8$	$89\text{-}6\frac{7}{8}$	$72\text{-}5\frac{1}{2}$	$103\text{-}6\frac{13}{16}$
5	$44\text{-}0\frac{3}{4}$	$62\text{-}11\frac{3}{4}$	$53\text{-}10\frac{1}{4}$	$76\text{-}11\frac{23}{32}$	$63\text{-}7\frac{3}{4}$	$90\text{-}11\frac{21}{32}$	$73\text{-}5\frac{1}{4}$	$104\text{-}11\frac{19}{32}$
6	$45\text{-}0\frac{1}{2}$	$64\text{-}4\frac{9}{16}$	$54\text{-}10$	$78\text{-}4\frac{1}{2}$	$64\text{-}7\frac{1}{2}$	$92\text{-}4\frac{7}{16}$	$74\text{-}5$	$106\text{-}4\frac{13}{32}$
7	$46\text{-}0\frac{1}{4}$	$65\text{-}9\frac{11}{32}$	$55\text{-}9\frac{3}{4}$	$79\text{-}9\frac{5}{16}$	$65\text{-}7\frac{1}{4}$	$93\text{-}9\frac{1}{4}$	$75\text{-}4\frac{3}{4}$	$107\text{-}9\frac{3}{16}$
8	$47\text{-}0$	$67\text{-}2\frac{5}{32}$	$56\text{-}9\frac{1}{2}$	$81\text{-}2\frac{3}{32}$	$66\text{-}7$	$95\text{-}2\frac{1}{32}$	$76\text{-}4\frac{1}{2}$	$109\text{-}2$
9	$47\text{-}11\frac{3}{4}$	$68\text{-}6\frac{15}{32}$	$57\text{-}9\frac{1}{4}$	$82\text{-}6\frac{7}{8}$	$67\text{-}6\frac{3}{4}$	$96\text{-}6\frac{27}{32}$	$77\text{-}4\frac{1}{4}$	$110\text{-}6\frac{25}{32}$

natsin A=0.6996247926; natcos A=0.7145104265; nattan A=0.9791666666; natcot A=1.0212765957

Inches	0" Rise	0" Slope	1" Rise	1" Slope	2" Rise	2" Slope	3" Rise	3" Slope	4" Rise	4" Slope	5" Rise	5" Slope
0	0	0	1	1 13/32	1 31/32	2 13/16	2 15/16	4 7/32	3 15/16	5 5/8	4 15/16	7 1/32
1/16	1/16	3/32	1 1/32	1 1/2	2 1/32	2 29/32	3	4 5/16	4	5 11/16	4 31/32	7 3/32
1/8	1/8	3/16	1 3/32	1 19/32	2 3/32	2 31/32	3 1/16	4 3/8	4 1/16	5 25/32	5 1/32	7 3/16
3/16	3/16	1/4	1 5/32	1 21/32	2 5/32	3 1/16	3 1/8	4 15/32	4 1/8	5 7/8	5 3/32	7 9/32
1/4	1/4	11/32	1 7/32	1 3/4	2 7/32	3 5/32	3 3/16	4 9/16	4 3/16	5 31/32	5 5/32	7 3/8
5/16	5/16	7/16	1 9/32	1 27/32	2 9/32	3 1/4	3 1/4	4 21/32	4 1/4	6 1/16	5 7/32	7 15/32
3/8	3/8	17/32	1 11/32	1 15/16	2 11/32	3 11/32	3 5/16	4 3/4	4 5/16	6 1/8	5 9/32	7 17/32
7/16	7/16	5/8	1 13/32	2 1/32	2 13/32	3 13/32	3 3/8	4 13/16	4 3/8	6 7/32	5 11/32	7 5/8
1/2	1/2	11/16	1 15/32	2 3/32	2 15/32	3 1/2	3 7/16	4 29/32	4 7/16	6 5/16	5 13/32	7 23/32
9/16	9/16	25/32	1 17/32	2 3/16	2 17/32	3 19/32	3 1/2	5	4 1/2	6 13/32	5 15/32	7 13/16
5/8	5/8	7/8	1 19/32	2 9/32	2 19/32	3 11/16	3 9/16	5 3/32	4 9/16	6 1/2	5 17/32	7 29/32
11/16	11/16	31/32	1 21/32	2 3/8	2 21/32	3 25/32	3 5/8	5 3/16	4 5/8	6 9/16	5 19/32	7 31/32
3/4	3/4	1 1/16	1 23/32	2 15/32	2 23/32	3 27/32	3 11/16	5 1/4	4 11/16	6 21/32	5 21/32	8 1/16
13/16	13/16	1 1/8	1 25/32	2 17/32	2 25/32	3 15/16	3 3/4	5 11/32	4 3/4	6 3/4	5 23/32	8 5/32
7/8	7/8	1 7/32	1 27/32	2 5/8	2 27/32	4 1/32	3 13/16	5 7/16	4 13/16	6 27/32	5 25/32	8 1/4
15/16	15/16	1 5/16	1 29/32	2 23/32	2 29/32	4 1/8	3 7/8	5 17/32	4 7/8	6 15/16	5 27/32	8 11/32

Inches	6" Rise	6" Slope	7" Rise	7" Slope	8" Rise	8" Slope	9" Rise	9" Slope	10" Rise	10" Slope	11" Rise	11" Slope
0	5 29/32	8 13/32	6 7/8	9 13/16	7 7/8	11 7/32	8 7/8	1-0 5/8	9 27/32	1-2 1/32	10 13/16	1-3 7/16
1/16	5 31/32	8 1/2	6 15/16	9 29/32	7 15/16	11 5/16	8 29/32	1-0 23/32	9 29/32	1-2 1/8	10 7/8	1-3 17/32
1/8	6 1/32	8 19/32	7	10	8	11 13/32	8 31/32	1-0 13/16	9 31/32	1-2 7/32	10 15/16	1-3 5/8
3/16	6 3/32	8 11/16	7 1/16	10 3/32	8 1/16	11 1/2	9 1/32	1-0 29/32	10 1/32	1-2 9/32	11	1-3 11/16
1/4	6 5/32	8 25/32	7 1/8	10 3/16	8 1/8	11 9/16	9 3/32	1-0 31/32	10 3/32	1-2 3/8	11 1/16	1-3 25/32
5/16	6 7/32	8 27/32	7 3/16	10 1/4	8 3/16	11 21/32	9 5/32	1-1 1/16	10 5/32	1-2 15/32	11 1/8	1-3 7/8
3/8	6 9/32	8 15/16	7 1/4	10 11/32	8 1/4	11 3/4	9 7/32	1-1 5/32	10 7/32	1-2 9/16	11 3/16	1-3 31/32
7/16	6 11/32	9 1/32	7 5/16	10 7/16	8 5/16	11 27/32	9 9/32	1-1 1/4	10 9/32	1-2 21/32	11 1/4	1-4 1/16
1/2	6 13/32	9 1/8	7 3/8	10 17/32	8 3/8	11 15/16	9 11/32	1-1 11/32	10 11/32	1-2 23/32	11 5/16	1-4 1/8
9/16	6 15/32	9 7/32	7 7/16	10 5/8	8 7/16	1-0	9 13/32	1-1 13/32	10 13/32	1-2 13/16	11 3/8	1-4 7/32
5/8	6 17/32	9 9/32	7 1/2	10 11/16	8 1/2	1-0 3/32	9 15/32	1-1 1/2	10 15/32	1-2 29/32	11 7/16	1-4 5/16
11/16	6 19/32	9 3/8	7 9/16	10 25/32	8 9/16	1-0 3/16	9 17/32	1-1 19/32	10 17/32	1-3	11 1/2	1-4 13/32
3/4	6 21/32	9 15/32	7 5/8	10 7/8	8 5/8	1-0 9/32	9 19/32	1-1 11/16	10 19/32	1-3 3/32	11 9/16	1-4 1/2
13/16	6 23/32	9 9/16	7 11/16	10 31/32	8 11/16	1-0 3/8	9 21/32	1-1 25/32	10 21/32	1-3 3/16	11 5/8	1-4 9/16
7/8	6 25/32	9 21/32	7 3/4	11 1/16	8 3/4	1-0 15/32	9 23/32	1-1 27/32	10 23/32	1-3 1/4	11 11/16	1-4 21/32
15/16	6 27/32	9 3/4	7 13/16	11 1/8	8 13/16	1-0 17/32	9 25/32	1-1 15/16	10 25/32	1-3 11/32	11 3/4	1-4 3/4

Feet	0' Rise	0' Slope	10' Rise	10' Slope	20' Rise	20' Slope	30' Rise	30' Slope
0	0	0	9-10 1/8	14-0 3/8	19-8 1/4	28-0 25/32	29-6 3/8	42-1 5/32
1	-11 13/16	1-4 27/32	10-9 15/16	15-5 7/32	20-8 1/16	29-5 19/32	30-6 3/16	43-6
2	1-11 5/8	2-9 11/16	11-9 3/4	16-10 1/16	21-7 7/8	30-10 7/16	31-6	44-10 27/32
3	2-11 7/16	4-2 1/2	12-9 9/16	18-2 29/32	22-7 11/16	32-3 9/32	32-5 13/16	46-3 21/32
4	3-11 1/4	5-7 11/32	13-9 3/8	19-7 3/4	23-7 1/2	33-8 1/8	33-5 5/8	47-8 1/2
5	4-11 1/16	7-0 3/16	14-9 3/16	21-0 9/16	24-7 5/16	35-0 31/32	34-5 7/16	49-1 11/32
6	5-10 7/8	8-5 1/32	15-9	22-5 13/32	25-7 1/8	36-5 13/16	35-5 1/4	50-6 3/16
7	6-10 11/16	9-9 7/8	16-8 13/16	23-10 1/4	26-6 15/16	37-10 5/8	36-5 1/16	51-11 1/32
8	7-10 1/2	11-2 23/32	17-8 5/8	25-3 3/32	27-6 3/4	39-3 15/32	37-4 7/8	53-3 7/8
9	8-10 5/16	12-7 17/32	18-8 7/16	26-7 15/16	28-6 9/16	40-8 5/16	38-4 11/16	54-8 11/16

A = 44° 32′ 56″; logsin A = 9.84604; logcos A = 9.85288; logtan A = 9.99316; logcot A = 0.00684.

Ins.	12″ Rise	Slope	13″ Rise	Slope	14″ Rise	Slope	15″ Rise	Slope	16″ Rise	Slope
0	$11\tfrac{13}{16}$	$1\text{-}4\tfrac{27}{32}$	$1\text{-}0\tfrac{13}{16}$	$1\text{-}6\tfrac14$	$1\text{-}1\tfrac{25}{32}$	$1\text{-}7\tfrac{21}{32}$	$1\text{-}2\tfrac34$	$1\text{-}9\tfrac1{16}$	$1\text{-}3\tfrac34$	$1\text{-}10\tfrac7{16}$
1/16	$11\tfrac78$	$1\text{-}4\tfrac{15}{16}$	$1\text{-}0\tfrac{27}{32}$	$1\text{-}6\tfrac{11}{32}$	$1\text{-}1\tfrac{27}{32}$	$1\text{-}7\tfrac{23}{32}$	$1\text{-}2\tfrac{13}{16}$	$1\text{-}9\tfrac18$	$1\text{-}3\tfrac{13}{16}$	$1\text{-}10\tfrac{17}{32}$
1/8	$11\tfrac{15}{16}$	$1\text{-}5$	$1\text{-}0\tfrac{29}{32}$	$1\text{-}6\tfrac{13}{32}$	$1\text{-}1\tfrac{29}{32}$	$1\text{-}7\tfrac{13}{16}$	$1\text{-}2\tfrac78$	$1\text{-}9\tfrac7{32}$	$1\text{-}3\tfrac78$	$1\text{-}10\tfrac58$
3/16	$1\text{-}0$	$1\text{-}5\tfrac3{32}$	$1\text{-}0\tfrac{31}{32}$	$1\text{-}6\tfrac12$	$1\text{-}1\tfrac{31}{32}$	$1\text{-}7\tfrac{29}{32}$	$1\text{-}2\tfrac{15}{16}$	$1\text{-}9\tfrac5{16}$	$1\text{-}3\tfrac{15}{16}$	$1\text{-}10\tfrac{23}{32}$
1/4	$1\text{-}0\tfrac1{16}$	$1\text{-}5\tfrac3{16}$	$1\text{-}1\tfrac1{16}$	$1\text{-}6\tfrac{19}{32}$	$1\text{-}2\tfrac1{16}$	$1\text{-}8$	$1\text{-}3$	$1\text{-}9\tfrac{13}{32}$	$1\text{-}4$	$1\text{-}10\tfrac{13}{16}$
5/16	$1\text{-}0\tfrac18$	$1\text{-}5\tfrac9{32}$	$1\text{-}1\tfrac3{32}$	$1\text{-}6\tfrac{11}{16}$	$1\text{-}2\tfrac3{32}$	$1\text{-}8\tfrac3{32}$	$1\text{-}3\tfrac1{16}$	$1\text{-}9\tfrac12$	$1\text{-}4\tfrac1{16}$	$1\text{-}10\tfrac78$
3/8	$1\text{-}0\tfrac3{16}$	$1\text{-}5\tfrac38$	$1\text{-}1\tfrac5{32}$	$1\text{-}6\tfrac{25}{32}$	$1\text{-}2\tfrac5{32}$	$1\text{-}8\tfrac5{32}$	$1\text{-}3\tfrac18$	$1\text{-}9\tfrac9{16}$	$1\text{-}4\tfrac18$	$1\text{-}10\tfrac{31}{32}$
7/16	$1\text{-}0\tfrac14$	$1\text{-}5\tfrac7{32}$	$1\text{-}1\tfrac7{32}$	$1\text{-}6\tfrac{27}{32}$	$1\text{-}2\tfrac7{32}$	$1\text{-}8\tfrac14$	$1\text{-}3\tfrac3{16}$	$1\text{-}9\tfrac{21}{32}$	$1\text{-}4\tfrac3{16}$	$1\text{-}11\tfrac1{16}$
1/2	$1\text{-}0\tfrac5{16}$	$1\text{-}5\tfrac{17}{32}$	$1\text{-}1\tfrac9{32}$	$1\text{-}6\tfrac{15}{16}$	$1\text{-}2\tfrac9{32}$	$1\text{-}8\tfrac{11}{32}$	$1\text{-}3\tfrac14$	$1\text{-}9\tfrac34$	$1\text{-}4\tfrac14$	$1\text{-}11\tfrac5{32}$
9/16	$1\text{-}0\tfrac38$	$1\text{-}5\tfrac58$	$1\text{-}1\tfrac{11}{32}$	$1\text{-}7\tfrac1{32}$	$1\text{-}2\tfrac{11}{32}$	$1\text{-}8\tfrac7{16}$	$1\text{-}3\tfrac5{16}$	$1\text{-}9\tfrac{27}{32}$	$1\text{-}4\tfrac5{16}$	$1\text{-}11\tfrac14$
5/8	$1\text{-}0\tfrac7{16}$	$1\text{-}5\tfrac{23}{32}$	$1\text{-}1\tfrac{13}{32}$	$1\text{-}7\tfrac18$	$1\text{-}2\tfrac{13}{32}$	$1\text{-}8\tfrac{17}{32}$	$1\text{-}3\tfrac38$	$1\text{-}9\tfrac{15}{16}$	$1\text{-}4\tfrac38$	$1\text{-}11\tfrac{11}{32}$
11/16	$1\text{-}0\tfrac12$	$1\text{-}5\tfrac{13}{16}$	$1\text{-}1\tfrac{15}{32}$	$1\text{-}7\tfrac7{32}$	$1\text{-}2\tfrac{15}{32}$	$1\text{-}8\tfrac58$	$1\text{-}3\tfrac7{16}$	$1\text{-}10$	$1\text{-}4\tfrac7{16}$	$1\text{-}11\tfrac{13}{32}$
3/4	$1\text{-}0\tfrac9{16}$	$1\text{-}5\tfrac{29}{32}$	$1\text{-}1\tfrac{17}{32}$	$1\text{-}7\tfrac9{32}$	$1\text{-}2\tfrac{17}{32}$	$1\text{-}8\tfrac{11}{16}$	$1\text{-}3\tfrac12$	$1\text{-}10\tfrac3{32}$	$1\text{-}4\tfrac12$	$1\text{-}11\tfrac12$
13/16	$1\text{-}0\tfrac58$	$1\text{-}5\tfrac{31}{32}$	$1\text{-}1\tfrac{19}{32}$	$1\text{-}7\tfrac38$	$1\text{-}2\tfrac{19}{32}$	$1\text{-}8\tfrac{25}{32}$	$1\text{-}3\tfrac9{16}$	$1\text{-}10\tfrac3{16}$	$1\text{-}4\tfrac9{16}$	$1\text{-}11\tfrac{19}{32}$
7/8	$1\text{-}0\tfrac{11}{16}$	$1\text{-}6\tfrac1{16}$	$1\text{-}1\tfrac{21}{32}$	$1\text{-}7\tfrac{15}{32}$	$1\text{-}2\tfrac{21}{32}$	$1\text{-}8\tfrac78$	$1\text{-}3\tfrac58$	$1\text{-}10\tfrac9{32}$	$1\text{-}4\tfrac58$	$1\text{-}11\tfrac{11}{16}$
15/16	$1\text{-}0\tfrac34$	$1\text{-}6\tfrac5{32}$	$1\text{-}1\tfrac{23}{32}$	$1\text{-}7\tfrac9{16}$	$1\text{-}2\tfrac{23}{32}$	$1\text{-}8\tfrac{31}{32}$	$1\text{-}3\tfrac{11}{16}$	$1\text{-}10\tfrac38$	$1\text{-}4\tfrac{11}{16}$	$1\text{-}11\tfrac{25}{32}$

Ins.	17″ Rise	Slope	18″ Rise	Slope	19″ Rise	Slope	20″ Rise	Slope	21″ Rise	Slope
0	$1\text{-}4\tfrac34$	$1\text{-}11\tfrac{27}{32}$	$1\text{-}5\tfrac{23}{32}$	$2\text{-}1\tfrac14$	$1\text{-}6\tfrac{11}{16}$	$2\text{-}2\tfrac{23}{32}$	$1\text{-}7\tfrac{11}{16}$	$2\text{-}4\tfrac1{16}$	$1\text{-}8\tfrac{11}{16}$	$2\text{-}5\tfrac{15}{32}$
1/16	$1\text{-}4\tfrac{25}{32}$	$1\text{-}11\tfrac{15}{16}$	$1\text{-}5\tfrac{25}{32}$	$2\text{-}1\tfrac{11}{32}$	$1\text{-}6\tfrac34$	$2\text{-}2\tfrac34$	$1\text{-}7\tfrac34$	$2\text{-}4\tfrac5{32}$	$1\text{-}8\tfrac{23}{32}$	$2\text{-}5\tfrac9{16}$
1/8	$1\text{-}4\tfrac{27}{32}$	$2\text{-}0\tfrac1{32}$	$1\text{-}5\tfrac{27}{32}$	$2\text{-}1\tfrac7{16}$	$1\text{-}6\tfrac{13}{16}$	$2\text{-}2\tfrac{27}{32}$	$1\text{-}7\tfrac{13}{16}$	$2\text{-}4\tfrac14$	$1\text{-}8\tfrac{25}{32}$	$2\text{-}5\tfrac{21}{32}$
3/16	$1\text{-}4\tfrac{29}{32}$	$2\text{-}0\tfrac18$	$1\text{-}5\tfrac{29}{32}$	$2\text{-}1\tfrac{17}{32}$	$1\text{-}6\tfrac78$	$2\text{-}2\tfrac{15}{16}$	$1\text{-}7\tfrac78$	$2\text{-}4\tfrac5{16}$	$1\text{-}8\tfrac{27}{32}$	$2\text{-}5\tfrac{23}{32}$
1/4	$1\text{-}4\tfrac{31}{32}$	$2\text{-}0\tfrac7{32}$	$1\text{-}5\tfrac{31}{32}$	$2\text{-}1\tfrac{19}{32}$	$1\text{-}6\tfrac{15}{16}$	$2\text{-}3$	$1\text{-}7\tfrac{15}{16}$	$2\text{-}4\tfrac{13}{32}$	$1\text{-}8\tfrac{29}{32}$	$2\text{-}5\tfrac{13}{16}$
5/16	$1\text{-}5\tfrac1{32}$	$2\text{-}0\tfrac9{32}$	$1\text{-}6\tfrac1{32}$	$2\text{-}1\tfrac{11}{16}$	$1\text{-}7$	$2\text{-}3\tfrac3{32}$	$1\text{-}8$	$2\text{-}4\tfrac12$	$1\text{-}8\tfrac{31}{32}$	$2\text{-}5\tfrac{29}{32}$
3/8	$1\text{-}5\tfrac3{32}$	$2\text{-}0\tfrac38$	$1\text{-}6\tfrac3{32}$	$2\text{-}1\tfrac{25}{32}$	$1\text{-}7\tfrac1{16}$	$2\text{-}3\tfrac3{16}$	$1\text{-}8\tfrac1{16}$	$2\text{-}4\tfrac{19}{32}$	$1\text{-}9\tfrac1{32}$	$2\text{-}6$
7/16	$1\text{-}5\tfrac5{32}$	$2\text{-}0\tfrac{15}{32}$	$1\text{-}6\tfrac5{32}$	$2\text{-}1\tfrac78$	$1\text{-}7\tfrac18$	$2\text{-}3\tfrac9{32}$	$1\text{-}8\tfrac18$	$2\text{-}4\tfrac{11}{16}$	$1\text{-}9\tfrac3{32}$	$2\text{-}6\tfrac3{32}$
1/2	$1\text{-}5\tfrac7{32}$	$2\text{-}0\tfrac9{16}$	$1\text{-}6\tfrac7{32}$	$2\text{-}1\tfrac{31}{32}$	$1\text{-}7\tfrac3{16}$	$2\text{-}3\tfrac38$	$1\text{-}8\tfrac3{16}$	$2\text{-}4\tfrac{25}{32}$	$1\text{-}9\tfrac5{32}$	$2\text{-}6\tfrac5{32}$
9/16	$1\text{-}5\tfrac9{32}$	$2\text{-}0\tfrac{21}{32}$	$1\text{-}6\tfrac9{32}$	$2\text{-}2\tfrac1{16}$	$1\text{-}7\tfrac14$	$2\text{-}3\tfrac7{16}$	$1\text{-}8\tfrac14$	$2\text{-}4\tfrac{27}{32}$	$1\text{-}9\tfrac7{32}$	$2\text{-}6\tfrac14$
5/8	$1\text{-}5\tfrac{11}{32}$	$2\text{-}0\tfrac{23}{32}$	$1\text{-}6\tfrac{11}{32}$	$2\text{-}2\tfrac14$	$1\text{-}7\tfrac5{16}$	$2\text{-}3\tfrac{17}{32}$	$1\text{-}8\tfrac5{16}$	$2\text{-}4\tfrac{15}{16}$	$1\text{-}9\tfrac9{32}$	$2\text{-}6\tfrac{11}{32}$
11/16	$1\text{-}5\tfrac{13}{32}$	$2\text{-}0\tfrac{13}{16}$	$1\text{-}6\tfrac{13}{32}$	$2\text{-}2\tfrac7{32}$	$1\text{-}7\tfrac38$	$2\text{-}3\tfrac58$	$1\text{-}8\tfrac38$	$2\text{-}5\tfrac1{32}$	$1\text{-}9\tfrac{11}{32}$	$2\text{-}6\tfrac7{16}$
3/4	$1\text{-}5\tfrac{15}{32}$	$2\text{-}0\tfrac{29}{32}$	$1\text{-}6\tfrac{15}{32}$	$2\text{-}2\tfrac5{16}$	$1\text{-}7\tfrac7{16}$	$2\text{-}3\tfrac{23}{32}$	$1\text{-}8\tfrac7{16}$	$2\text{-}5\tfrac18$	$1\text{-}9\tfrac{13}{32}$	$2\text{-}6\tfrac{17}{32}$
13/16	$1\text{-}5\tfrac{17}{32}$	$2\text{-}1$	$1\text{-}6\tfrac{17}{32}$	$2\text{-}2\tfrac{13}{32}$	$1\text{-}7\tfrac12$	$2\text{-}3\tfrac{13}{16}$	$1\text{-}8\tfrac12$	$2\text{-}5\tfrac7{32}$	$1\text{-}9\tfrac{15}{32}$	$2\text{-}6\tfrac{19}{32}$
7/8	$1\text{-}5\tfrac{19}{32}$	$2\text{-}1\tfrac3{32}$	$1\text{-}6\tfrac{19}{32}$	$2\text{-}2\tfrac12$	$1\text{-}7\tfrac9{16}$	$2\text{-}3\tfrac78$	$1\text{-}8\tfrac9{16}$	$2\text{-}5\tfrac9{32}$	$1\text{-}9\tfrac{17}{32}$	$2\text{-}6\tfrac{11}{16}$
15/16	$1\text{-}5\tfrac{21}{32}$	$2\text{-}1\tfrac5{32}$	$1\text{-}6\tfrac{21}{32}$	$2\text{-}2\tfrac9{16}$	$1\text{-}7\tfrac58$	$2\text{-}3\tfrac{31}{32}$	$1\text{-}8\tfrac58$	$2\text{-}5\tfrac38$	$1\text{-}9\tfrac{19}{32}$	$2\text{-}6\tfrac{25}{32}$

Feet	40' Rise	Slope	50' Rise	Slope	60' Rise	Slope	70' Rise	Slope
0	$39\text{-}4\tfrac12$	$56\text{-}1\tfrac{17}{32}$	$49\text{-}2\tfrac58$	$70\text{-}1\tfrac{15}{16}$	$59\text{-}0\tfrac34$	$84\text{-}2\tfrac5{16}$	$68\text{-}10\tfrac78$	$98\text{-}2\tfrac{11}{16}$
1	$40\text{-}4\tfrac34$	$57\text{-}6\tfrac38$	$50\text{-}2\tfrac7{16}$	$71\text{-}6\tfrac34$	$60\text{-}0\tfrac9{16}$	$85\text{-}7\tfrac5{32}$	$69\text{-}10\tfrac{11}{16}$	$99\text{-}7\tfrac{17}{32}$
2	$41\text{-}4\tfrac18$	$58\text{-}11\tfrac7{32}$	$51\text{-}2\tfrac14$	$72\text{-}11\tfrac{19}{32}$	$61\text{-}0\tfrac38$	$87\text{-}0$	$70\text{-}10\tfrac12$	$101\text{-}0\tfrac38$
3	$42\text{-}3\tfrac{15}{16}$	$60\text{-}4\tfrac1{16}$	$52\text{-}2\tfrac1{16}$	$74\text{-}4\tfrac7{16}$	$62\text{-}0\tfrac3{16}$	$88\text{-}4\tfrac{13}{16}$	$71\text{-}10\tfrac5{16}$	$102\text{-}5\tfrac7{32}$
4	$43\text{-}3\tfrac34$	$61\text{-}8\tfrac{29}{32}$	$53\text{-}1\tfrac78$	$75\text{-}9\tfrac9{32}$	$63\text{-}0$	$89\text{-}9\tfrac{21}{32}$	$72\text{-}10\tfrac18$	$103\text{-}10\tfrac1{16}$
5	$44\text{-}3\tfrac9{16}$	$63\text{-}1\tfrac{23}{32}$	$54\text{-}1\tfrac{11}{16}$	$77\text{-}2\tfrac18$	$63\text{-}11\tfrac{13}{16}$	$91\text{-}2\tfrac12$	$73\text{-}9\tfrac{15}{16}$	$105\text{-}2\tfrac78$
6	$45\text{-}3\tfrac38$	$64\text{-}6\tfrac9{16}$	$55\text{-}1\tfrac12$	$78\text{-}6\tfrac{31}{32}$	$64\text{-}11\tfrac58$	$92\text{-}7\tfrac{11}{32}$	$74\text{-}9\tfrac34$	$106\text{-}7\tfrac{23}{32}$
7	$46\text{-}3\tfrac3{16}$	$65\text{-}11\tfrac{13}{32}$	$56\text{-}1\tfrac5{16}$	$79\text{-}11\tfrac{25}{32}$	$65\text{-}11\tfrac7{16}$	$94\text{-}0\tfrac3{16}$	$75\text{-}9\tfrac9{16}$	$108\text{-}0\tfrac9{16}$
8	$47\text{-}3$	$67\text{-}4\tfrac14$	$57\text{-}1\tfrac18$	$81\text{-}4\tfrac58$	$66\text{-}11\tfrac14$	$95\text{-}5\tfrac1{16}$	$76\text{-}9\tfrac38$	$109\text{-}5\tfrac{13}{32}$
9	$48\text{-}2\tfrac{13}{16}$	$68\text{-}9\tfrac3{32}$	$58\text{-}0\tfrac{15}{32}$	$82\text{-}9\tfrac{15}{32}$	$67\text{-}11\tfrac1{16}$	$96\text{-}9\tfrac{27}{32}$	$77\text{-}9\tfrac3{16}$	$110\text{-}10\tfrac14$

natsin A = 0.7015172644;   natcos A = 0.7126524591;   nattan A = 0.9843750000;   natcot A = 1.0158730158

Inches	0" Rise	0" Slope	1" Rise	1" Slope	2" Rise	2" Slope	3" Rise	3" Slope	4" Rise	4" Slope	5" Rise	5" Slope
0	0	0	1	1 13/32	1 31/32	2 13/16	2 31/32	4 7/32	3 31/32	5 5/8	4 15/16	7 1/32
1/16	1/16	3/32	1 1/16	1 1/2	2 1/32	2 29/32	3 1/32	4 5/16	4 1/32	5 23/32	5	7 1/8
1/8	1/8	3/16	1 1/8	1 19/32	2 3/32	3	3 3/32	4 13/32	4 3/32	5 13/16	5 1/16	7 7/32
3/16	3/16	1/4	1 3/16	1 21/32	2 5/32	3 1/16	3 5/32	4 1/2	4 5/32	5 29/32	5 1/8	7 5/16
1/4	1/4	11/32	1 1/4	1 3/4	2 7/32	3 5/32	3 7/32	4 9/16	4 7/32	5 31/32	5 3/16	7 3/8
5/16	5/16	7/16	1 5/16	1 27/32	2 9/32	3 1/4	3 9/32	4 21/32	4 9/32	6 1/16	5 1/4	7 15/32
3/8	3/8	17/32	1 3/8	1 15/16	2 11/32	3 11/32	3 11/32	4 3/4	4 11/32	6 5/32	5 5/16	7 9/16
7/16	7/16	5/8	1 7/16	2 1/32	2 13/32	3 7/16	3 13/32	4 27/32	4 13/32	6 1/4	5 3/8	7 21/32
1/2	1/2	23/32	1 1/2	2 1/8	2 15/32	3 17/32	3 15/32	4 15/16	4 7/16	6 11/32	5 7/16	7 3/4
9/16	9/16	25/32	1 17/32	2 3/16	2 17/32	3 19/32	3 17/32	5	4 1/2	6 13/32	5 1/2	7 13/16
5/8	5/8	7/8	1 19/32	2 9/32	2 19/32	3 11/16	3 19/32	5 3/32	4 9/16	6 1/2	5 9/16	7 29/32
11/16	11/16	31/32	1 21/32	2 3/8	2 21/32	3 25/32	3 21/32	5 3/16	4 5/8	6 19/32	5 5/8	8
3/4	3/4	11/16	1 23/32	2 15/32	2 23/32	3 7/8	3 23/32	5 9/32	4 11/16	6 11/16	5 11/16	8 3/32
13/16	13/16	15/32	1 25/32	2 9/16	2 25/32	3 31/32	3 25/32	5 3/8	4 3/4	6 25/32	5 3/4	8 3/16
7/8	7/8	17/32	1 27/32	2 5/8	2 27/32	4 1/32	3 27/32	5 7/16	4 13/16	6 27/32	5 13/16	8 1/4
15/16	15/16	15/16	1 29/32	2 23/32	2 29/32	4 1/8	3 29/32	5 17/32	4 7/8	6 15/16	5 7/8	8 11/32

Inches	6" Rise	6" Slope	7" Rise	7" Slope	8" Rise	8" Slope	9" Rise	9" Slope	10" Rise	10" Slope	11" Rise	11" Slope
0	5 15/16	8 7/16	6 15/16	9 27/32	7 29/32	11 1/4	8 29/32	1-0 21/32	9 29/32	1-2 1/16	10 7/8	1-3 15/32
1/16	6	8 17/32	7	9 15/16	7 31/32	11 11/32	8 31/32	1-0 3/4	9 31/32	1-2 5/32	10 15/16	1-3 9/16
1/8	6 1/16	8 5/8	7 1/16	10 1/32	8 1/32	11 7/16	9 1/32	1-0 27/32	10 1/32	1-2 1/4	11	1-3 21/32
3/16	6 1/8	8 23/32	7 1/8	10 1/8	8 3/32	11 17/32	9 3/32	1-0 15/16	10 3/32	1-2 11/32	11 1/16	1-3 3/4
1/4	6 3/16	8 25/32	7 3/16	10 3/16	8 5/32	11 19/32	9 5/32	1-1	10 5/32	1-2 13/32	11 1/8	1-3 13/16
5/16	6 1/4	8 27/32	7 1/4	10 9/32	8 7/32	11 11/16	9 7/32	1-1 3/32	10 7/32	1-2 1/2	11 3/16	1-3 29/32
3/8	6 5/16	8 31/32	7 5/16	10 3/8	8 9/32	11 25/32	9 9/32	1-1 3/16	10 9/32	1-2 19/32	11 1/4	1-4
7/16	6 3/8	9 1/16	7 3/8	10 15/32	8 11/32	11 7/8	9 11/32	1-1 9/32	10 11/32	1-2 11/16	11 5/16	1-4 3/32
1/2	6 7/16	9 5/32	7 7/16	10 9/16	8 13/32	11 31/32	9 13/32	1-1 3/8	10 3/8	1-2 25/32	11 3/8	1-4 3/16
9/16	6 1/2	9 7/32	7 15/32	10 5/8	8 15/32	1-0 1/32	9 15/32	1-1 15/32	10 7/16	1-2 7/8	11 7/16	1-4 9/32
5/8	6 9/16	9 5/16	7 17/32	10 23/32	8 17/32	1-0 1/8	9 17/32	1-1 17/32	10 1/2	1-2 15/16	11 1/2	1-4 11/32
11/16	6 5/8	9 13/32	7 19/32	10 13/16	8 19/32	1-0 1/4	9 19/32	1-1 5/8	10 1/2	1-3 1/32	11 9/16	1-4 7/16
3/4	6 11/16	9 1/2	7 21/32	10 29/32	8 21/32	1-0 5/16	9 21/32	1-1 23/32	10 5/8	1-3 1/8	11 5/8	1-4 17/32
13/16	6 3/4	9 19/32	7 23/32	11	8 23/32	1-0 13/32	9 23/32	1-1 13/16	10 11/16	1-3 7/32	11 11/16	1-4 5/8
7/8	6 13/16	9 11/16	7 25/32	11 3/32	8 25/32	1-0 1/2	9 25/32	1-1 29/32	10 3/4	1-3 5/16	11 3/4	1-4 23/32
15/16	6 7/8	9 3/4	7 27/32	11 5/32	8 27/32	1-0 9/16	9 27/32	1-1 31/32	10 13/16	1-3 3/8	11 13/16	1-4 25/32

Feet	0' Rise	0' Slope	10' Rise	10' Slope	20' Rise	20' Slope	30' Rise	30' Slope
0	0	0	9-10 3/4	14-0 13/16	19-9 1/2	28-1 21/32	29-8 1/4	42-2 15/32
1	-11 7/8	1-4 7/8	10-10 5/8	15-5 23/32	20-9 3/8	29-6 17/32	30-8 1/8	43-7 11/32
2	1-11 3/4	2-9 3/4	11-10 1/2	16-10 19/32	21-9 1/4	30-11 13/32	31-8	45-0 1/4
3	2-11 5/8	4-2 21/32	12-10 3/8	18-3 15/32	22-9 1/8	32-4 9/32	32-7 7/8	46-5 1/8
4	3-11 1/2	5-7 17/32	13-10 1/4	19-8 11/32	23-9	33-9 3/16	33-7 3/4	47-10
5	4-11 3/8	7-0 13/32	14-10 1/8	21-1 1/4	24-8 7/8	35-2 1/16	34-7 5/8	49-2 7/8
6	5-11 1/4	8-5 9/32	15-10	22-6 1/8	25-8 3/4	36-6 15/32	35-7 1/2	50-7 25/32
7	6-11 1/8	9-10 3/16	16-9 7/8	23-11	26-8 5/8	37-11 13/16	36-7 3/8	52-0 21/32
8	7-11	11-3 1/16	17-9 3/4	25-3 7/8	27-8 1/2	39-4 23/32	37-7 1/4	53-5 17/32
9	8-10 7/8	12-7 15/32	18-9 5/8	26-8 25/32	28-8 3/8	40-9 19/32	38-7 1/8	54-10 13/32

A = 44° 42′ 00″; logsin A = 9.84720; logcos A = 9.85175; logtan A = 9.99545; logcot A = 0.00455

Ins.	12″ Rise	12″ Slope	13″ Rise	13″ Slope	14″ Rise	14″ Slope	15″ Rise	15″ Slope	16″ Rise	16″ Slope
0	11 7/8	1-4 7/8	1-0 7/8	1-6 9/32	1-1 27/32	1-7 11/16	1-2 27/32	1-9 3/32	1-3 27/32-	1-10 1/2
1/16	11 15/16	1-4 31/32	1-0 15/16	1-6 3/8	1-1 29/32	1-7 25/32	1-2 29/32-	1-9 3/16	1-3 29/32-	1-10 19/32
1/8	1-0	1-5 1/16	1-1	1-6 15/32-	1-1 31/32	1-7 7/8	1-2 31/32-	1-9 9/32-	1-3 31/32-	1-10 11/16
3/16	1-0 1/16	1-5 5/32-	1-1 1/16	1-6 9/16	1-2 1/32	1-7 31/32-	1-3 1/32-	1-9 3/8	1-4 1/32-	1-10 25/32-
1/4	1-0 1/8	1-5 7/32	1-1 1/8	1-6 21/32-	1-2 3/32	1-8 1/16	1-3 3/32-	1-9 15/32-	1-4 3/32-	1-10 7/8
5/16	1-0 3/16	1-5 5/16	1-1 3/16	1-6 23/32	1-2 5/32	1-8 1/8	1-3 5/32-	1-9 17/32	1-4 5/32-	1-10 15/16
3/8	1-0 1/4	1-5 13/32	1-1 1/4	1-6 13/16	1-2 7/32	1-8 7/32	1-3 7/32-	1-9 5/8	1-4 7/32-	1-11 1/32
7/16	1-0 5/16	1-5 1/2	1-1 5/16	1-6 29/32-	1-2 9/32	1-8 5/16	1-3 9/32-	1-9 23/32-	1-4 9/32-	1-11 1/8
1/2	1-0 3/8	1-5 19/32-	1-1 3/8	1-7	1-2 11/32	1-8 13/32-	1-3 11/32-	1-9 13/16	1-4 5/16	1-11 7/32-
9/16	1-0 7/16	1-5 11/16	1-1 13/32	1-7 3/32-	1-2 13/32	1-8 1/2	1-3 13/32-	1-9 29/32-	1-4 3/8	1-11 5/16
5/8	1-0 1/2	1-5 3/4	1-1 15/32	1-7 5/32	1-2 15/32	1-8 9/16	1-3 15/32-	1-9 31/32	1-4 7/16	1-11 3/8
11/16	1-0 9/16	1-5 27/32	1-1 17/32	1-7 1/4	1-2 17/32	1-8 21/32	1-3 17/32-	1-10 1/16	1-4 1/2	1-11 15/32
3/4	1-0 5/8	1-5 15/16	1-1 19/32	1-7 11/32	1-2 19/32	1-8 3/4	1-3 19/32-	1-10 5/32	1-4 9/16	1-11 9/16
13/16	1-0 11/16	1-6 1/32-	1-1 21/32	1-7 7/16	1-2 21/32	1-8 27/32-	1-3 21/32-	1-10 1/4	1-4 5/8	1-11 21/32-
7/8	1-0 3/4	1-6 1/8	1-1 23/32	1-7 17/32-	1-2 23/32	1-8 15/16	1-3 23/32-	1-10 11/32-	1-4 11/16	1-11 3/4
15/16	1-0 13/16	1-6 3/16	1-1 25/32	1-7 19/32	1-2 25/32	1-9	1-3 25/32-	1-10 7/16	1-4 3/4	1-11 27/32-

Ins.	17″ Rise	17″ Slope	18″ Rise	18″ Slope	19″ Rise	19″ Slope	20″ Rise	20″ Slope	21″ Rise	21″ Slope
0	1-4 13/16	1-11 29/32	1-5 13/16	2-1 5/16	1-6 13/16	2-2 23/32	1-7 25/32	2-4 1/8	1-8 25/32	2-5 17/32
1/16	1-4 7/8	2-0	1-5 7/8	2-1 13/32	1-6 7/8	2-2 13/16	1-7 27/32	2-4 7/32	1-8 27/32-	2-5 5/8
1/8	1-4 15/16	2-0 3/32-	1-5 15/16	2-1 1/2	1-6 15/16	2-2 29/32	1-7 29/32	2-4 5/16	1-8 29/32-	2-5 23/32
3/16	1-5	2-0 3/16	1-6	2-1 19/32-	1-7	2-3	1-7 31/32	2-4 13/32-	1-8 31/32-	2-5 13/16
1/4	1-5 1/16	2-0 9/32-	1-6 1/16	2-1 11/16	1-7 1/16	2-3 3/32-	1-8 1/32	2-4 1/2	1-9 1/32-	2-5 29/32-
5/16	1-5 1/8	2-0 11/32	1-6 1/8	2-1 3/4	1-7 1/8	2-3 5/32	1-8 3/32	2-4 9/16	1-9 3/32-	2-5 31/32
3/8	1-5 3/16	2-0 7/16	1-6 3/16	2-1 27/32	1-7 3/16	2-3 1/4	1-8 5/32	2-4 21/32	1-9 5/32-	2-6 1/16
7/16	1-5 1/4	2-0 17/32	1-6 1/4	2-1 15/16	1-7 1/4	2-3 11/32	1-8 7/32	2-4 3/4	1-9 7/32-	2-6 5/32
1/2	1-5 5/16	2-0 5/8	1-6 5/16	2-2 1/32-	1-7 5/16	2-3 7/16	1-8 9/32	2-4 27/32-	1-9 9/32-	2-6 1/4
9/16	1-5 3/8	2-0 23/32-	1-6 3/8	2-2 1/8	1-7 11/32	2-3 17/32-	1-8 11/32	2-4 15/16	1-9 11/32-	2-6 11/32-
5/8	1-5 7/16	2-0 25/32	1-6 7/16	2-2 3/16	1-7 13/32	2-3 5/8	1-8 13/32	2-5 1/32-	1-9 13/32-	2-6 7/16
11/16	1-5 1/2	2-0 7/8	1-6 1/2	2-2 9/32	1-7 15/32	2-3 11/16	1-8 15/32	2-5 3/32	1-9 15/32-	2-6 1/2
3/4	1-5 9/16	2-0 31/32	1-6 9/16	2-2 3/8	1-7 17/32	2-3 25/32	1-8 17/32	2-5 3/16	1-9 17/32-	2-6 19/32
13/16	1-5 5/8	2-1 1/16	1-6 5/8	2-2 15/32-	1-7 19/32	2-3 7/8	1-8 19/32	2-5 9/32-	1-9 19/32-	2-6 11/16
7/8	1-5 11/16	2-1 5/32-	1-6 11/16	2-2 9/16	1-7 21/32	2-3 31/32-	1-8 21/32	2-5 3/8	1-9 21/32-	2-6 25/32-
15/16	1-5 3/4	2-1 1/4	1-6 3/4	2-2 21/32-	1-7 23/32	2-4 1/16	1-8 23/32	2-5 15/32-	1-9 23/32-	2-6 7/8

Feet	40′ Rise	40′ Slope	50′ Rise	50′ Slope	60′ Rise	60′ Slope	70′ Rise	70′ Slope
0	39-7	56-3 9/32	49-5 3/4	70-4 1/8	59-4 1/2	84-4 15/16	69-3 1/4	98-5 25/32-
1	40-6 7/8	57-8 3/16	50-5 5/8	71-9	60-4 3/8	85-9 13/16	70-3 1/8	99-10 21/32-
2	41-6 3/4	59-1 1/16	51-5 1/2	73-1 7/8	61-4 1/4	87-2 23/32-	71-3	101-3 17/32
3	42-6 5/8	60-5 15/16	52-5 3/8	74-6 25/32-	62-4 1/8	88-7 19/32-	72-2 7/8	102-8 13/32
4	43-6 1/2	61-10 13/16	53-5 1/4	75-11 21/32-	63-4	90-0 15/32	73-2 3/4	104-1 5/16
5	44-6 3/8	63-3 23/32-	54-5 1/8	77-4 17/32	64-3 7/8	91-5 11/32	74-2 5/8	105-6 3/16
6	45-6 1/4	64-8 19/32-	55-5	78-9 13/32	65-3 3/4	92-10 1/4	75-2 1/2	106-11 1/16
7	46-6 1/8	66-1 15/32	56-4 7/8	80-2 5/16	66-3 5/8	94-3 1/8	76-2 3/8	108-3 15/16
8	47-6	67-6 11/32	57-4 3/4	81-7 3/16	67-3 1/2	95-8	77-2 1/4	109-8 13/16
9	48-5 7/8	68-11 1/4	58-4 5/8	83-0 1/16	68-3 3/8	97-0 7/8	78-2 1/8	111-1 23/32-

natsin A=0.7033950109; natcos A=0.7107991689; nattan A=0.9895833333; natcot A=1.0105263157

Inches	0" Rise	0" Slope	1" Rise	1" Slope	2" Rise	2" Slope	3" Rise	3" Slope	4" Rise	4" Slope	5" Rise	5" Slope
0	0	0	1	1 13/32	2	2 13/16	3	4 7/32	3 31/32	5 21/32	4 31/32	7 1/16
1/16	1/16	3/32	1 1/16	1 1/2	2 1/16	2 29/32	3 1/32	4 5/16	4 1/32	5 23/32	5 1/32	7 5/32
1/8	1/8	3/16	1 1/8	1 19/32	2 1/8	3	3 3/32	4 13/32	4 3/32	5 13/16	5 3/32	7 7/32
3/16	3/16	1/4	1 3/16	1 11/16	2 3/16	3 3/32-	3 5/32	4 1/2	4 5/32	5 29/32	5 5/32	7 5/16
1/4	1/4	11/32	1 1/4	1 3/4	2 1/4	3 3/16	3 7/32	4 19/32	4 7/32	6	5 7/32	7 13/32
5/16	5/16	7/16	1 5/16	1 27/32	2 5/16	3 1/4	3 9/32	4 11/16	4 9/32	6 3/32	5 9/32	7 1/2
3/8	3/8	17/32	1 3/8	1 15/16	2 3/8	3 11/32	3 11/32	4 3/4	4 11/32	6 5/32	5 11/32	7 19/32
7/16	7/16	5/8	1 7/16	2 1/32	2 7/16	3 7/16	3 13/32	4 27/32	4 13/32	6 1/4	5 13/32	7 21/32
1/2	1/2	23/32	1 1/2	2 1/8	2 1/2	3 17/32	3 15/32	4 15/16	4 15/32	6 11/32	5 15/32	7 3/4
9/16	9/16	25/32	1 9/16	2 7/32	2 9/16	3 5/8	3 17/32	5 1/32-	4 17/32	6 7/16	5 17/32	7 27/32
5/8	5/8	7/8	1 5/8	2 9/32	2 5/8	3 11/16	3 19/32	5 1/8	4 19/32	6 17/32	5 19/32	7 15/16
11/16	11/16	31/32	1 11/16	2 3/8	2 11/16	3 25/32	3 21/32	5 3/16	4 21/32	6 5/8	5 21/32	8 1/32-
3/4	3/4	1 1/32	1 3/4	2 15/32	2 3/4	3 7/8	3 23/32	5 9/32	4 23/32	6 11/16	5 23/32	8 1/8
13/16	13/16	1 5/32	1 13/16	2 9/16	2 13/16	3 31/32	3 25/32	5 3/8	4 25/32	6 25/32	5 25/32	8 3/16
7/8	7/8	1 7/32	1 7/8	2 21/32	2 7/8	4 1/16	3 27/32	5 15/32	4 27/32	6 7/8	5 27/32	8 9/32
15/16	15/16	1 5/16	1 15/16	2 23/32	2 15/16	4 5/32-	3 29/32	5 9/16	4 29/32	6 31/32	5 29/32	8 3/8

Inches	6" Rise	6" Slope	7" Rise	7" Slope	8" Rise	8" Slope	9" Rise	9" Slope	10" Rise	10" Slope	11" Rise	11" Slope
0	5 31/32	8 15/32	6 31/32	9 7/8	7 31/32	11 9/32	8 15/16	1-0 11/16	9 15/16	1-2 3/32	10 15/16	1-3 17/32
1/16	6 1/32	8 9/16	7 1/32	9 31/32	8 1/32	11 3/8	9	1-0 25/32	10	1-2 3/16	11	1-3 19/32
1/8	6 3/32	8 5/8	7 3/32	10 1/16	8 3/32	11 15/32-	9 1/16	1-0 7/8	10 1/16	1-2 9/32	11 1/16	1-3 11/16
3/16	6 5/32	8 23/32	7 5/32	10 1/8	8 5/32	11 9/16	9 1/8	1-0 31/32	10 1/8	1-2 3/8	11 1/8	1-3 25/32
1/4	6 7/32	8 13/16	7 7/32	10 7/32	8 7/32	11 5/8	9 3/16	1-1 1/16	10 3/16	1-2 15/32	11 3/16	1-3 7/8
5/16	6 9/32	8 29/32	7 9/32	10 5/16	8 9/32	11 23/32	9 1/4	1-1 1/8	10 1/4	1-2 17/32	11 1/4	1-3 31/32
3/8	6 11/32	9	7 11/32	10 13/32	8 11/32	11 13/16	9 5/16	1-1 7/32	10 5/16	1-2 5/8	11 5/16	1-4 1/32
7/16	6 13/32	9 3/32	7 13/32	10 1/2	8 13/32	11 29/32	9 3/8	1-1 5/16	10 3/8	1-2 23/32	11 3/8	1-4 1/8
1/2	6 15/32	9 5/32	7 15/32	10 19/32	8 15/32	1-0	9 7/16	1-1 13/32	10 7/16	1-2 13/16	11 7/16	1-4 7/32
9/16	6 17/32	9 1/4	7 17/32	10 21/32	8 17/32	1-0 1/16	9 1/2	1-1 1/2	10 1/2	1-2 29/32	11 1/2	1-4 5/16
5/8	6 19/32	9 11/32	7 19/32	10 3/4	8 19/32	1-0 5/32	9 9/16	1-1 9/16	10 9/16	1-3	11 9/16	1-4 13/32
11/16	6 21/32	9 7/16	7 21/32	10 27/32	8 21/32	1-0 1/4	9 5/8	1-1 21/32	10 5/8	1-3 1/16	11 5/8	1-4 1/2
3/4	6 23/32	9 17/32	7 23/32	10 15/16	8 23/32	1-0 11/32	9 11/16	1-1 3/4	10 11/16	1-3 5/32	11 11/16	1-4 9/16
13/16	6 25/32	9 19/32	7 25/32	11 1/32	8 25/32	1-0 7/16	9 3/4	1-1 27/32	10 3/4	1-3 1/4	11 3/4	1-4 21/32
7/8	6 27/32	9 11/16	7 27/32	11 3/32	8 27/32	1-0 17/32	9 13/16	1-1 15/16	10 13/16	1-3 11/32	11 13/16	1-4 3/4
15/16	6 29/32	9 25/32	7 29/32	11 3/16	8 29/32	1-0 19/32	9 7/8	1-2 1/32	10 7/8	1-3 7/16	11 7/8	1-4 27/32

Feet	0' Rise	0' Slope	10' Rise	10' Slope	20' Rise	20' Slope	30' Rise	30' Slope
0	0	0	9-11 3/8	14-1 1/4	19-10 3/4	28-2 17/32	29-10 1/8	42-3 25/32
1	-11 15/16	1-4 15/16	10-11 5/16	15-6 3/16	20-10 11/16	29-7 15/32	30-10 1/16	43-8 23/32
2	1-11 7/8	2-9 27/32	11-11 1/4	16-11 1/8	21-10 5/8	31-0 3/8	31-10	45-1 21/32
3	2-11 13/16	4-2 25/32	12-11 3/16	18-4 1/16	22-10 1/2	32-5 5/16	32-9 15/16	46-6 9/16
4	3-11 3/4	5-7 23/32	13-11 1/8	19-8 31/32	23-10 1/2	33-10 7/32	33-9 7/8	47-11 1/2
5	4-11 11/16	7-0 5/8	14-11 1/16	21-1 29/32	24-10 7/16	35-3 5/32	34-9 13/16	49-4 7/16
6	5-11 5/8	8-5 9/16	15-11	22-6 13/16	25-10 3/8	36-8 3/32	35-9 3/4	50-9 11/32
7	6-11 9/16	9-10 1/2	16-10 15/16	23-11 3/4	26-10 5/16	38-1	36-9 11/16	52-2 9/32
8	7-11 1/2	11-3 13/32	17-10 7/8	25-4 11/16	27-10 1/4	39-5 15/16	37-9 5/8	53-7 7/32
9	8-11 7/16	12-8 11/32	18-10 13/16	26-9 19/32	28-10 3/16	40-10 7/8	38-9 9/16	55-0 1/8

A = 44° 51' 01''; logsin A = 9.84835; logcos A = 9.85062; logtan A = 9.99773; logcot A = 0.00227

Ins.	12" Rise	12" Slope	13" Rise	13" Slope	14" Rise	14" Slope	15" Rise	15" Slope	16" Rise	16" Slope
0	11 15/16	1-4 15/16	1-0 15/16	1-6 11/32—	1-1 15/16	1-7 3/4	1-2 15/16	1-9 5/32	1-3 29/32	1-10 9/16
1/16	1-0	1-5	1-1	1-6 7/16	1-2	1-7 27/32—	1-2 31/32	1-9 1/4	1-3 31/32	1-10 21/32
1/8	1-0 1/16	1-5 3/32	1-1 1/16	1-6 1/2	1-2 1/16	1-7 15/16	1-3 1/32	1-9 11/32—	1-4 1/32	1-10 3/4
3/16	1-0 1/8	1-5 3/16	1-1 1/8	1-6 19/32	1-2 1/8	1-8	1-3 3/32	1-9 7/16	1-4 3/32	1-10 27/32—
1/4	1-0 3/16	1-5 9/32—	1-1 3/16	1-6 11/16	1-2 3/16	1-8 3/32	1-3 5/32	1-9 1/2	1-4 5/32	1-10 29/32
5/16	1-0 1/4	1-5 3/8	1-1 1/4	1-6 25/32—	1-2 1/4	1-8 3/16	1-3 7/32	1-9 19/32	1-4 7/32	1-11
3/8	1-0 5/16	1-5 15/32—	1-1 5/16	1-6 7/8	1-2 5/16	1-8 9/32—	1-3 9/32	1-9 11/16	1-4 9/32	1-11 3/32
7/16	1-0 3/8	1-5 17/32	1-1 3/8	1-6 31/32—	1-2 3/8	1-8 3/8	1-3 11/32	1-9 25/32—	1-4 11/32	1-11 3/16
1/2	1-0 7/16	1-5 5/8	1-1 7/16	1-7 1/32	1-2 7/16	1-8 7/16	1-3 13/32	1-9 7/8	1-4 13/32	1-11 9/32—
9/16	1-0 1/2	1-5 23/32	1-1 1/2	1-7 1/8	1-2 1/2	1-8 17/32	1-3 15/32	1-9 15/16	1-4 15/32	1-11 3/8
5/8	1-0 9/16	1-5 13/16	1-1 9/16	1-7 7/32—	1-2 9/16	1-8 5/8	1-3 17/32	1-10 1/32	1-4 17/32	1-11 7/16
11/16	1-0 5/8	1-5 29/32—	1-1 5/8	1-7 5/16	1-2 5/8	1-8 23/32—	1-3 19/32	1-10 1/8	1-4 19/32	1-11 17/32
3/4	1-0 11/16	1-5 31/32	1-1 11/16	1-7 13/32—	1-2 11/16	1-8 13/16	1-3 21/32	1-10 7/32—	1-4 21/32	1-11 5/8
13/16	1-0 3/4	1-6 1/16	1-1 3/4	1-7 15/32	1-2 3/4	1-8 29/32—	1-3 23/32	1-10 5/16	1-4 23/32	1-11 23/32—
7/8	1-0 13/16	1-6 5/32	1-1 13/16	1-7 9/16	1-2 13/16	1-8 31/32	1-3 25/32	1-10 13/32—	1-4 25/32	1-11 13/16
15/16	1-0 7/8	1-6 1/4	1-1 7/8	1-7 21/32	1-2 7/8	1-9 1/16	1-3 27/32	1-10 15/32	1-4 27/32	1-11 29/32—

Ins.	17" Rise	17" Slope	18" Rise	18" Slope	19" Rise	19" Slope	20" Rise	20" Slope	21" Rise	21" Slope
0	1-4 29/32	1-11 31/32	1-5 29/32	2-1 3/8	1-6 29/32—	2-2 13/16	1-7 29/32—	2-4 7/32—	1-8 7/8	2-5 5/8
1/16	1-4 31/32	2-0 1/16	1-5 31/32—	2-1 15/32	1-6 31/32—	2-2 7/8	1-7 31/32—	2-4 5/16	1-8 15/16	2-5 23/32—
1/8	1-5 1/32	2-0 5/32—	1-6 1/32—	2-1 9/16	1-7 1/32—	2-2 31/32	1-8 1/32—	2-4 3/8	1-9	2-5 13/16
3/16	1-5 3/32	2-0 1/4	1-6 3/32—	2-1 21/32—	1-7 3/32—	2-3 1/16	1-8 3/32—	2-4 15/32	1-9 1/16	2-5 7/8
1/4	1-5 5/32	2-0 11/32—	1-6 5/32—	2-1 3/4	1-7 5/32—	2-3 5/32—	1-8 5/32—	2-4 9/16	1-9 1/8	2-5 31/32
5/16	1-5 7/32	2-0 13/32	1-6 7/32—	2-1 27/32—	1-7 7/32—	2-3 1/4	1-8 7/32—	2-4 21/32—	1-9 3/16	2-6 1/16
3/8	1-5 9/32	2-0 1/2	1-6 9/32—	2-1 29/32	1-7 9/32—	2-3 11/32—	1-8 9/32—	2-4 3/4	1-9 1/4	2-6 5/32—
7/16	1-5 11/32	2-0 19/32	1-6 11/32—	2-2	1-7 11/32—	2-3 13/32	1-8 11/32—	2-4 13/16	1-9 5/16	2-6 1/4
1/2	1-5 13/32	2-0 11/16	1-6 13/32—	2-2 3/32	1-7 13/32—	2-3 1/2	1-8 13/32—	2-4 29/32	1-9 3/8	2-6 5/16
9/16	1-5 15/32	2-0 25/32—	1-6 15/32—	2-2 3/16	1-7 15/32—	2-3 19/32—	1-8 15/32—	2-5	1-9 7/16	2-6 13/32
5/8	1-5 17/32	2-0 7/8	1-6 17/32—	2-2 9/32—	1-7 17/32—	2-3 11/16	1-8 17/32—	2-5 3/32—	1-9 1/2	2-6 1/2
11/16	1-5 19/32	2-0 15/16	1-6 19/32—	2-2 3/8	1-7 19/32—	2-3 25/32—	1-8 19/32—	2-5 3/16	1-9 9/16	2-6 19/32—
3/4	1-5 21/32	2-1 1/32	1-6 21/32—	2-2 7/16	1-7 21/32—	2-3 27/32	1-8 21/32—	2-5 9/32—	1-9 5/8	2-6 11/16
13/16	1-5 23/32	2-1 1/8	1-6 23/32—	2-2 17/32	1-7 23/32—	2-3 15/16	1-8 23/32—	2-5 11/32	1-9 11/16	2-6 25/32—
7/8	1-5 25/32	2-1 7/32—	1-6 25/32—	2-2 5/8	1-7 25/32—	2-4 1/32	1-8 25/32—	2-5 7/16	1-9 3/4	2-6 27/32
15/16	1-5 27/32	2-1 5/16	1-6 27/32—	2-2 23/32—	1-7 27/32—	2-4 1/8	1-8 27/32—	2-5 17/32	1-9 13/16	2-6 15/16

Feet	40' Rise	40' Slope	50' Rise	50' Slope	60' Rise	60' Slope	70' Rise	70' Slope
0	39-9 1/2	56-5 1/16	49-8 7/8	70-6 5/16	59-8 1/4	84-7 19/32—	69-7 5/8	98-8 27/32
1	40-9 7/16	57-9 31/32	50-8 13/16	71-11 1/4	60-8 3/16	86-0 1/2	70-7 9/16	100-1 25/32—
2	41-9 3/8	59-2 29/32	51-8 3/4	73-4 3/16	61-8 1/8	87-5 7/16	71-7 1/2	101-6 11/16
3	42-9 5/16	60-7 27/32—	52-8 11/16	74-9 3/32	62-8 1/16	88-10 3/8	72-7 7/16	102-11 5/8
4	43-9 1/4	62-0 3/4	53-8 5/8	76-2 1/32—	63-8	90-3 9/32	73-7 3/8	104-4 9/16
5	44-9 3/16	63-5 11/16	54-8 9/16	77-6 31/32—	64-7 15/16	91-8 7/32—	74-7 5/16	105-9 15/32
6	45-9 1/8	64-10 5/8	55-8 1/2	78-11 7/8	65-7 7/8	93-1 5/32—	75-7 1/4	107-2 13/32
7	46-9 1/16	66-3 17/32	56-8 7/16	80-4 13/16	66-7 13/16	94-6 1/16	76-7 3/16	108-7 11/32—
8	47-9	67-8 15/32—	57-8 3/8	81-9 23/32	67-7 3/4	95-11	77-7 1/8	110-0 1/4
9	48-8 15/16	69-1 13/32—	58-8 5/16	83-2 21/32	68-7 11/16	97-3 15/16	78-7 1/16	111-5 3/16

natsin A=0.7052581454; natcos A=0.7089505965; nattan A=0.9947916666; natcot A=1.0052356020

Inches	0" Rise	0" Slope	1" Rise	1" Slope	2" Rise	2" Slope	3" Rise	3" Slope	4" Rise	4" Slope	5" Rise	5" Slope
0	0	0	1	$1\frac{13}{32}$	2	$2\frac{27}{32}$	3	$4\frac14$	4	$5\frac{21}{32}$	5	$7\frac{1}{16}$
$\frac1{16}$	$\frac1{16}$	$\frac3{32}$	$1\frac1{16}$	$1\frac12$	$2\frac1{16}$	$2\frac{29}{32}$	$3\frac1{16}$	$4\frac{11}{32}$	$4\frac1{16}$	$5\frac34$	$5\frac1{16}$	$7\frac5{32}$
$\frac18$	$\frac18$	$\frac3{16}$	$1\frac18$	$1\frac{19}{32}$	$2\frac18$	3	$3\frac18$	$4\frac{13}{32}$	$4\frac18$	$5\frac{27}{32}$	$5\frac18$	$7\frac14$
$\frac3{16}$	$\frac3{16}$	$\frac14$	$1\frac3{16}$	$1\frac{11}{16}$	$2\frac3{16}$	$3\frac3{32}$	$3\frac3{16}$	$4\frac12$	$4\frac3{16}$	$5\frac{15}{16}$	$5\frac3{16}$	$7\frac{11}{32}$
$\frac14$	$\frac14$	$\frac{11}{32}$	$1\frac14$	$1\frac{25}{32}$	$2\frac14$	$3\frac3{16}$	$3\frac14$	$4\frac{19}{32}$	$4\frac14$	6	$5\frac14$	$7\frac7{16}$
$\frac5{16}$	$\frac5{16}$	$\frac7{16}$	$1\frac5{16}$	$1\frac{27}{32}$	$2\frac5{16}$	$3\frac9{32}$	$3\frac5{16}$	$4\frac{11}{16}$	$4\frac5{16}$	$6\frac3{32}$	$5\frac5{16}$	$7\frac12$
$\frac38$	$\frac38$	$\frac{17}{32}$	$1\frac38$	$1\frac{15}{16}$	$2\frac38$	$3\frac{11}{32}$	$3\frac38$	$4\frac{25}{32}$	$4\frac38$	$6\frac3{16}$	$5\frac38$	$7\frac{19}{32}$
$\frac7{16}$	$\frac7{16}$	$\frac58$	$1\frac7{16}$	$2\frac1{32}$	$2\frac7{16}$	$3\frac7{16}$	$3\frac7{16}$	$4\frac78$	$4\frac7{16}$	$6\frac9{32}$	$5\frac7{16}$	$7\frac{11}{16}$
$\frac12$	$\frac12$	$\frac{23}{32}$	$1\frac12$	$2\frac18$	$2\frac12$	$3\frac{17}{32}$	$3\frac12$	$4\frac{15}{16}$	$4\frac12$	$6\frac38$	$5\frac12$	$7\frac{25}{32}$
$\frac9{16}$	$\frac9{16}$	$\frac{25}{32}$	$1\frac9{16}$	$2\frac7{32}$	$2\frac9{16}$	$3\frac58$	$3\frac9{16}$	$5\frac1{32}$	$4\frac9{16}$	$6\frac7{16}$	$5\frac9{16}$	$7\frac78$
$\frac58$	$\frac58$	$\frac78$	$1\frac58$	$2\frac5{16}$	$2\frac58$	$3\frac{23}{32}$	$3\frac58$	$5\frac18$	$4\frac58$	$6\frac{17}{32}$	$5\frac58$	$7\frac{31}{32}$
$\frac{11}{16}$	$\frac{11}{16}$	$\frac{31}{32}$	$1\frac{11}{16}$	$2\frac38$	$2\frac{11}{16}$	$3\frac{13}{16}$	$3\frac{11}{16}$	$5\frac7{32}$	$4\frac{11}{16}$	$6\frac58$	$5\frac{11}{16}$	$8\frac1{32}$
$\frac34$	$\frac34$	$1\frac1{16}$	$1\frac34$	$2\frac{15}{32}$	$2\frac34$	$3\frac78$	$3\frac34$	$5\frac5{16}$	$4\frac34$	$6\frac{23}{32}$	$5\frac34$	$8\frac18$
$\frac{13}{16}$	$\frac{13}{16}$	$1\frac5{32}$	$1\frac{13}{16}$	$2\frac9{16}$	$2\frac{13}{16}$	$3\frac{31}{32}$	$3\frac{13}{16}$	$5\frac{13}{32}$	$4\frac{13}{16}$	$6\frac{13}{16}$	$5\frac{13}{16}$	$8\frac7{32}$
$\frac78$	$\frac78$	$1\frac14$	$1\frac78$	$2\frac{21}{32}$	$2\frac78$	$4\frac1{16}$	$3\frac78$	$5\frac{15}{32}$	$4\frac78$	$6\frac{29}{32}$	$5\frac78$	$8\frac5{16}$
$\frac{15}{16}$	$\frac{15}{16}$	$1\frac5{16}$	$1\frac{15}{16}$	$2\frac34$	$2\frac{15}{16}$	$4\frac5{32}$	$3\frac{15}{16}$	$5\frac9{16}$	$4\frac{15}{16}$	$6\frac{31}{32}$	$5\frac{15}{16}$	$8\frac{13}{32}$

Inches	6" Rise	6" Slope	7" Rise	7" Slope	8" Rise	8" Slope	9" Rise	9" Slope	10" Rise	10" Slope	11" Rise	11" Slope
0	6	$8\frac12$	7	$9\frac{29}{32}$	8	$11\frac5{16}$	9	$1\text{-}0\frac{23}{32}$	10	$1\text{-}2\frac5{32}$	11	$1\text{-}3\frac9{16}$
$\frac1{16}$	$6\frac1{16}$	$8\frac9{16}$	$7\frac1{16}$	10	$8\frac1{16}$	$11\frac{13}{32}$	$9\frac1{16}$	$1\text{-}0\frac{13}{16}$	$10\frac1{16}$	$1\text{-}2\frac7{32}$	$11\frac1{16}$	$1\text{-}3\frac{21}{32}$
$\frac18$	$6\frac18$	$8\frac{21}{32}$	$7\frac18$	$10\frac14$	$8\frac18$	$11\frac12$	$9\frac18$	$1\text{-}0\frac{29}{32}$	$10\frac18$	$1\text{-}2\frac5{16}$	$11\frac18$	$1\text{-}3\frac{23}{32}$
$\frac3{16}$	$6\frac3{16}$	$8\frac34$	$7\frac3{16}$	$10\frac5{32}$	$8\frac3{16}$	$11\frac{19}{32}$	$9\frac3{16}$	$1\text{-}1$	$10\frac3{16}$	$1\text{-}2\frac{13}{32}$	$11\frac3{16}$	$1\text{-}3\frac{13}{16}$
$\frac14$	$6\frac14$	$8\frac{27}{32}$	$7\frac14$	$10\frac14$	$8\frac14$	$11\frac{21}{32}$	$9\frac14$	$1\text{-}1\frac3{32}$	$10\frac14$	$1\text{-}2\frac12$	$11\frac14$	$1\text{-}3\frac{29}{32}$
$\frac5{16}$	$6\frac5{16}$	$8\frac{15}{16}$	$7\frac5{16}$	$10\frac{11}{32}$	$8\frac5{16}$	$11\frac34$	$9\frac5{16}$	$1\text{-}1\frac5{32}$	$10\frac5{16}$	$1\text{-}2\frac{19}{32}$	$11\frac5{16}$	$1\text{-}4$
$\frac38$	$6\frac38$	9	$7\frac38$	$10\frac7{16}$	$8\frac38$	$11\frac{27}{32}$	$9\frac38$	$1\text{-}1\frac14$	$10\frac38$	$1\text{-}2\frac{11}{16}$	$11\frac38$	$1\text{-}4\frac3{32}$
$\frac7{16}$	$6\frac7{16}$	$9\frac3{32}$	$7\frac7{16}$	$10\frac{17}{32}$	$8\frac7{16}$	$11\frac{15}{16}$	$9\frac7{16}$	$1\text{-}1\frac{11}{32}$	$10\frac7{16}$	$1\text{-}2\frac34$	$11\frac7{16}$	$1\text{-}4\frac3{16}$
$\frac12$	$6\frac12$	$9\frac3{16}$	$7\frac12$	$10\frac{19}{32}$	$8\frac12$	$1\text{-}0\frac1{32}$	$9\frac12$	$1\text{-}1\frac7{16}$	$10\frac12$	$1\text{-}2\frac{27}{32}$	$11\frac12$	$1\text{-}4\frac14$
$\frac9{16}$	$6\frac9{16}$	$9\frac9{32}$	$7\frac9{16}$	$10\frac{11}{16}$	$8\frac9{16}$	$1\text{-}0\frac3{32}$	$9\frac9{16}$	$1\text{-}1\frac{17}{32}$	$10\frac9{16}$	$1\text{-}2\frac{15}{16}$	$11\frac9{16}$	$1\text{-}4\frac{11}{32}$
$\frac58$	$6\frac58$	$9\frac38$	$7\frac58$	$10\frac{25}{32}$	$8\frac58$	$1\text{-}0\frac3{16}$	$9\frac58$	$1\text{-}1\frac58$	$10\frac58$	$1\text{-}3\frac1{32}$	$11\frac58$	$1\text{-}4\frac7{16}$
$\frac{11}{16}$	$6\frac{11}{16}$	$9\frac{15}{32}$	$7\frac{11}{16}$	$10\frac78$	$8\frac{11}{16}$	$1\text{-}0\frac9{32}$	$9\frac{11}{16}$	$1\text{-}1\frac{11}{16}$	$10\frac{11}{16}$	$1\text{-}3\frac18$	$11\frac{11}{16}$	$1\text{-}4\frac{17}{32}$
$\frac34$	$6\frac34$	$9\frac{17}{32}$	$7\frac34$	$10\frac{31}{32}$	$8\frac34$	$1\text{-}0\frac38$	$9\frac34$	$1\text{-}1\frac{25}{32}$	$10\frac34$	$1\text{-}3\frac3{16}$	$11\frac34$	$1\text{-}4\frac58$
$\frac{13}{16}$	$6\frac{13}{16}$	$9\frac58$	$7\frac{13}{16}$	$11\frac1{16}$	$8\frac{13}{16}$	$1\text{-}0\frac{15}{32}$	$9\frac{13}{16}$	$1\text{-}1\frac78$	$10\frac{13}{16}$	$1\text{-}3\frac9{32}$	$11\frac{13}{16}$	$1\text{-}4\frac{23}{32}$
$\frac78$	$6\frac78$	$9\frac{23}{32}$	$7\frac78$	$11\frac18$	$8\frac78$	$1\text{-}0\frac9{16}$	$9\frac78$	$1\text{-}1\frac{31}{32}$	$10\frac78$	$1\text{-}3\frac38$	$11\frac78$	$1\text{-}4\frac{25}{32}$
$\frac{15}{16}$	$6\frac{15}{16}$	$9\frac{13}{16}$	$7\frac{15}{16}$	$11\frac7{32}$	$8\frac{15}{16}$	$1\text{-}0\frac58$	$9\frac{15}{16}$	$1\text{-}2\frac1{16}$	$10\frac{15}{16}$	$1\text{-}3\frac{15}{32}$	$11\frac{15}{16}$	$1\text{-}4\frac78$

Feet	0' Rise	0' Slope	10' Rise	10' Slope	20' Rise	20' Slope	30' Rise	30' Slope
0	0	0	10-0	$14\text{-}1\frac{23}{32}$	20-0	$28\text{-}3\frac{13}{32}$	30-0	$42\text{-}5\frac18$
1	1-0	$1\text{-}4\frac{31}{32}$	11-0	$15\text{-}6\frac{11}{16}$	21-0	$29\text{-}8\frac38$	31-0	$43\text{-}10\frac3{32}$
2	2-0	$2\text{-}9\frac{15}{16}$	12-0	$16\text{-}11\frac{21}{32}$	22-0	$31\text{-}1\frac{11}{32}$	32-0	$45\text{-}3\frac1{16}$
3	3-0	$4\text{-}2\frac{29}{32}$	13-0	$18\text{-}4\frac58$	23-0	$32\text{-}6\frac5{16}$	33-0	$46\text{-}8\frac1{32}$
4	4-0	$5\text{-}7\frac78$	14-0	$19\text{-}9\frac{19}{32}$	24-0	$33\text{-}11\frac9{32}$	34-0	$48\text{-}1$
5	5-0	$7\text{-}0\frac{27}{32}$	15-0	$21\text{-}2\frac9{16}$	25-0	$35\text{-}4\frac14$	35-0	$49\text{-}5\frac{31}{32}$
6	6-0	$8\text{-}5\frac{13}{16}$	16-0	$22\text{-}7\frac{17}{32}$	26-0	$36\text{-}9\frac14$	36-0	$50\text{-}10\frac{15}{32}$
7	7-0	$9\text{-}10\frac{25}{32}$	17-0	$24\text{-}0\frac12$	27-0	$38\text{-}2\frac7{32}$	37-0	$52\text{-}3\frac{29}{32}$
8	8-0.	$11\text{-}3\frac34$	18-0	$25\text{-}5\frac{15}{32}$	28-0	$39\text{-}7\frac3{16}$	38-0	$53\text{-}8\frac78$
9	9-0	$12\text{-}8\frac34$	19-0	$26\text{-}10\frac7{16}$	29-0	$41\text{-}0\frac5{32}$	39-0	$55\text{-}1\frac{27}{32}$

A = 45° 00' 00"; logsin A = 9.84949; logcos A = 9.84949; logtan A = 0.00000; logcot A = 0.00000

Ins.	12″ Rise	12″ Slope	13″ Rise	13″ Slope	14″ Rise	14″ Slope	15″ Rise	15″ Slope	16″ Rise	16″ Slope
0	1-0	1-4 31/32	1-1	1-6 3/8	1-2	1-7 13/16	1-3	1-9 7/32	1-4	1-10 5/8
1/16	1-0 1/16	1-5 1/16	1-1 1/16	1-6 15/32	1-2 1/16	1-7 7/8	1-3 1/16	1-9 5/16	1-4 1/16	1-10 23/32
1/8	1-0 1/8	1-5 5/32	1-1 1/8	1-6 9/16	1-2 1/8	1-7 31/32	1-3 1/8	1-9 3/8	1-4 1/8	1-10 13/16
3/16	1-0 3/16	1-5 1/4	1-1 3/16	1-6 21/32	1-2 3/16	1-8 1/16	1-3 3/16	1-9 15/32	1-4 3/16	1-10 29/32
1/4	1-0 1/4	1-5 5/16	1-1 1/4	1-6 3/4	1-2 1/4	1-8 5/32	1-3 1/4	1-9 9/16	1-4 1/4	1-10 31/32
5/16	1-0 5/16	1-5 13/32	1-1 5/16	1-6 13/16	1-2 5/16	1-8 1/4	1-3 5/16	1-9 21/32	1-4 5/16	1-11 1/16
3/8	1-0 3/8	1-5 1/2	1-1 3/8	1-6 29/32	1-2 3/8	1-8 11/32	1-3 3/8	1-9 3/4	1-4 3/8	1-11 5/32
7/16	1-0 7/16	1-5 19/32	1-1 7/16	1-7	1-2 7/16	1-8 13/32	1-3 7/16	1-9 27/32	1-4 7/16	1-11 1/4
1/2	1-0 1/2	1-5 11/16	1-1 1/2	1-7 3/32	1-2 1/2	1-8 1/2	1-3 1/2	1-9 29/32	1-4 1/2	1-11 11/32
9/16	1-0 9/16	1-5 25/32	1-1 9/16	1-7 3/16	1-2 9/16	1-8 19/32	1-3 9/16	1-10	1-4 9/16	1-11 7/16
5/8	1-0 5/8	1-5 27/32	1-1 5/8	1-7 9/32	1-2 5/8	1-8 11/16	1-3 5/8	1-10 3/32	1-4 5/8	1-11 1/2
11/16	1-0 11/16	1-5 15/16	1-1 11/16	1-7 11/32	1-2 11/16	1-8 25/32	1-3 11/16	1-10 3/16	1-4 11/16	1-11 19/32
3/4	1-0 3/4	1-6 1/32	1-1 3/4	1-7 7/16	1-2 3/4	1-8 7/8	1-3 3/4	1-10 9/32	1-4 3/4	1-11 11/16
13/16	1-0 13/16	1-6 1/8	1-1 13/16	1-7 17/32	1-2 13/16	1-8 15/16	1-3 13/16	1-10 3/8	1-4 13/16	1-11 25/32
7/8	1-0 7/8	1-6 7/32	1-1 7/8	1-7 5/8	1-2 7/8	1-9 1/32	1-3 7/8	1-10 7/16	1-4 7/8	1-11 7/8
15/16	1-0 15/16	1-6 9/32	1-1 15/16	1-7 23/32	1-2 15/16	1-9 1/8	1-3 15/16	1-10 17/32	1-4 15/16	1-11 31/32

Ins.	17″ Rise	17″ Slope	18″ Rise	18″ Slope	19″ Rise	19″ Slope	20″ Rise	20″ Slope	21″ Rise	21″ Slope
0	1-5	2-0 1/32	1-6	2-1 15/32	1-7	2-2 7/8	1-8	2-4 9/32	1-9	2-5 11/16
1/16	1-5 1/16	2-0 1/8	1-6 1/16	2-1 17/32	1-7 1/16	2-2 31/32	1-8 1/16	2-4 3/8	1-9 1/16	2-5 25/32
1/8	1-5 1/8	2-0 7/32	1-6 1/8	2-1 5/8	1-7 1/8	2-3 1/32	1-8 1/8	2-4 15/32	1-9 1/8	2-5 7/8
3/16	1-5 3/16	2-0 5/16	1-6 3/16	2-1 23/32	1-7 3/16	2-3 1/8	1-8 3/16	2-4 9/16	1-9 3/16	2-5 31/32
1/4	1-5 1/4	2-0 13/32	1-6 1/4	2-1 13/16	1-7 1/4	2-3 7/32	1-8 1/4	2-4 5/8	1-9 1/4	2-6 1/16
5/16	1-5 5/16	2-0 15/32	1-6 5/16	2-1 29/32	1-7 5/16	2-3 5/16	1-8 5/16	2-4 23/32	1-9 5/16	2-6 1/8
3/8	1-5 3/8	2-0 9/16	1-6 3/8	2-2	1-7 3/8	2-3 13/32	1-8 3/8	2-4 13/16	1-9 3/8	2-6 7/32
7/16	1-5 7/16	2-0 21/32	1-6 7/16	2-2 1/16	1-7 7/16	2-3 1/2	1-8 7/16	2-4 29/32	1-9 7/16	2-6 5/16
1/2	1-5 1/2	2-0 3/4	1-6 1/2	2-2 5/32	1-7 1/2	2-3 9/16	1-8 1/2	2-5	1-9 1/2	2-6 13/32
9/16	1-5 9/16	2-0 27/32	1-6 9/16	2-2 1/4	1-7 9/16	2-3 21/32	1-8 9/16	2-5 3/32	1-9 9/16	2-6 1/2
5/8	1-5 5/8	2-0 15/16	1-6 5/8	2-2 11/32	1-7 5/8	2-3 3/4	1-8 5/8	2-5 5/32	1-9 5/8	2-6 19/32
11/16	1-5 11/16	2-1	1-6 11/16	2-2 7/16	1-7 11/16	2-3 27/32	1-8 11/16	2-5 1/4	1-9 11/16	2-6 21/32
3/4	1-5 3/4	2-1 3/32	1-6 3/4	2-2 17/32	1-7 3/4	2-3 15/16	1-8 3/4	2-5 11/32	1-9 3/4	2-6 3/4
13/16	1-5 13/16	2-1 3/16	1-6 13/16	2-2 19/32	1-7 13/16	2-4 1/32	1-8 13/16	2-5 7/16	1-9 13/16	2-6 27/32
7/8	1-5 7/8	2-1 9/32	1-6 7/8	2-2 11/16	1-7 7/8	2-4 3/32	1-8 7/8	2-5 17/32	1-9 7/8	2-6 15/16
15/16	1-5 15/16	2-1 3/8	1-6 15/16	2-2 25/32	1-7 15/16	2-4 3/16	1-8 15/16	2-5 5/8	1-9 15/16	2-7 1/32

Feet	40′ Rise	40′ Slope	50′ Rise	50′ Slope	60′ Rise	60′ Slope	70′ Rise	70′ Slope
0	40-0	56-6 13/16	50-0	70-8 17/32	60-0	84-10 7/32	70-0	98-11 15/16
1	41-0	57-11 25/32	51-0	72-1 1/2	61-0	86-3 7/32	71-0	100-4 29/32
2	42-0	59-4 3/4	52-0	73-6 15/32	62-0	87-8 3/16	72-0	101-9 7/8
3	43-0	60-9 23/32	53-0	74-11 7/16	63-0	89-1 5/32	73-0	103-2 21/32
4	44-0	62-2 23/32	54-0	76-4 13/32	64-0	90-6 1/8	74-0	104-7 13/16
5	45-0	63-7 11/16	55-0	77-9 3/8	65-0	91-11 3/32	75-0	106-0 25/32
6	46-0	65-0 21/32	56-0	79-2 11/32	66-0	93-4 1/16	76-0	107-5 3/4
7	47-0	66-5 5/8	57-0	80-7 5/16	67-0	94-9 1/32	77-0	108-10 23/32
8	48-0	67-10 19/32	58-0	82-0 9/32	68-0	96-2	78-0	110-3 21/32
9	49-0	69-3 9/16	59-0	83-5 1/4	69-0	97-6 31/32	79-0	111-8 11/16

natsin A=0.7071067812;   natcos A=0.7071067812;   nattan A=1.0000000000;   natcot A=1.0000000000

Inch	0″ Rise	0″ Slope	1″ Rise	1″ Slope	2″ Rise	2″ Slope	3″ Rise	3″ Slope	4″ Rise	4″ Slope	5″ Rise	5″ Slope
0	0	0	1/16	1	1/8	2	3/16	3	1/4	4	5/16	5
1/16	0	1/16	1/16	1 1/16	1/8	2 1/16	3/16	3 1/16	9/32–	4 1/16	11/32	5 1/16
1/8	0	1/8	1/16	1 1/8	1/8	2 1/8	7/32	3 1/8	9/32–	4 1/8	11/32	5 1/8
3/16	0	3/16	1/16	1 3/16	5/32	2 3/16	7/32	3 3/16	9/32–	4 3/16	11/32	5 3/16
1/4	1/32–	1/4	3/32	1 1/4	5/32	2 1/4	7/32	3 1/4	9/32–	4 1/4	11/32	5 1/4
5/16	1/32–	5/16	3/32	1 5/16	5/32	2 5/16	7/32	3 5/16	9/32–	4 5/16	11/32	5 5/16
3/8	1/32–	3/8	3/32	1 3/8	5/32	2 3/8	7/32	3 3/8	9/32–	4 3/8	3/8	5 3/8
7/16	1/32–	7/16	3/32	1 7/16	5/32	2 7/16	7/32	3 7/16	9/32–	4 7/16	3/8	5 7/16
1/2	1/32–	1/2	3/32	1 1/2	5/32	2 1/2	7/32	3 1/2	9/32–	4 1/2	3/8	5 1/2
9/16	1/32–	9/16	3/32	1 9/16	3/16	2 9/16	7/32	3 9/16	5/16	4 9/16	3/8	5 9/16
5/8	1/32–	5/8	3/32	1 5/8	3/16	2 5/8	1/4	3 5/8	5/16	4 5/8	3/8	5 5/8
11/16	1/32–	11/16	1/8	1 11/16	3/16	2 11/16	1/4	3 11/16	5/16	4 11/16	3/8	5 11/16
3/4	1/16	3/4	1/8	1 3/4	3/16	2 3/4	1/4	3 3/4	5/16	4 3/4	3/8	5 3/4
13/16	1/16	13/16	1/8	1 13/16	3/16	2 13/16	1/4	3 13/16	5/16	4 13/16	3/8	5 13/16
7/8	1/16	7/8	1/8	1 7/8	3/16	2 7/8	1/4	3 7/8	5/16	4 7/8	3/8	5 7/8
15/16	1/16	15/16	1/8	1 15/16	3/16	2 15/16	1/4	3 15/16	5/16	4 15/16	3/8	5 15/16

Inch	6″ Rise	6″ Slope	7″ Rise	7″ Slope	8″ Rise	8″ Slope	9″ Rise	9″ Slope	10″ Rise	10″ Slope	11″ Rise	11″ Slope
0	13/32	6	15/32	7	17/32	8 1/32	19/32	9 1/32	21/32	10 1/32	23/32	11 1/32
1/16	13/32	6 1/16	15/32	7 1/16	17/32	8 3/32	19/32	9 3/32	21/32	10 3/32	23/32	11 3/32
1/8	13/32	6 1/8	15/32	7 1/8	17/32	8 5/32	19/32	9 5/32	21/32	10 5/32	23/32	11 5/32
3/16	13/32	6 3/16	15/32	7 3/16	17/32	8 7/32	19/32	9 7/32	21/32	10 7/32	23/32	11 7/32
1/4	13/32	6 1/4	15/32	7 1/4	17/32	8 9/32	19/32	9 9/32	21/32	10 9/32	3/4	11 9/32
5/16	13/32	6 5/16	15/32	7 11/32	17/32	8 11/32	5/8	9 11/32	11/16	10 11/32	3/4	11 11/32
3/8	13/32	6 3/8	15/32	7 13/32	9/16	8 13/32	5/8	9 13/32	11/16	10 13/32	3/4	11 13/32
7/16	7/16	6 7/16	1/2	7 15/32	9/16	8 15/32	5/8	9 15/32	11/16	10 15/32	3/4	11 15/32
1/2	7/16	6 1/2	1/2	7 17/32	9/16	8 17/32	5/8	9 17/32	11/16	10 17/32	3/4	11 17/32
9/16	7/16	6 9/16	1/2	7 19/32	9/16	8 19/32	5/8	9 19/32	11/16	10 19/32	3/4	11 19/32
5/8	7/16	6 5/8	1/2	7 21/32	9/16	8 21/32	5/8	9 21/32	11/16	10 21/32	3/4	11 21/32
11/16	7/16	6 11/16	1/2	7 23/32	9/16	8 23/32	5/8	9 23/32	11/16	10 23/32	25/32	11 23/32
3/4	7/16	6 3/4	1/2	7 25/32	9/16	8 25/32	5/8	9 25/32	23/32	10 25/32	25/32	11 25/32
13/16	7/16	6 13/16	1/2	7 27/32	9/16	8 27/32	21/32	9 27/32	23/32	10 27/32	25/32	11 27/32
7/8	7/16	6 7/8	17/32	7 29/32	19/32	8 29/32	21/32	9 29/32	23/32	10 29/32	25/32	11 29/32
15/16	15/32	6 15/16	17/32	7 31/32	19/32	8 31/32	21/32	9 31/32	23/32	10 31/32	25/32	11 31/32

Feet	0′ Rise	0′ Slope	10′ Rise	10′ Slope	20′ Rise	20′ Slope	30′ Rise	30′ Slope
0	0	0	7 7/8	10-0 1/4	1- 3 23/32	20-0 1/2	1-11 19/32	30-0 25/32–
1	25/32	1-0 1/32–	8 21/32	11-0 9/32	1- 4 17/32–	21-0 17/32	2- 0 3/8	31-0 13/16
2	1 9/16	2-0 1/16	9 7/16	12-0 5/16	1- 5 5/16	22-0 9/16	2- 1 5/32	32-0 13/16
3	2 3/8	3-0 1/16	10 7/32	13-0 11/32–	1- 6 3/32	23-0 19/32–	2- 1 31/32–	33-0 27/32
4	3 5/32–	4-0 3/32	11	14-0 3/8	1- 6 7/8	24-0 5/8	2- 2 3/4	34-0 7/8
5	3 15/16	5-0 1/8	11 13/16	15-0 3/8	1- 7 21/32	25-0 21/32–	2- 3 17/32–	35-0 29/32–
6	4 23/32	6-0 5/32–	1- 0 19/32–	16-0 13/32–	1- 8 7/16	26-0 21/32–	2- 4 5/16	36-0 15/16
7	5 1/2	7-0 3/16	1- 1 3/8	17-0 7/16	1- 9 1/4	27-0 11/16	2- 5 3/32–	37-0 15/16
8	6 9/32	8-0 7/32–	1- 2 5/32	18-0 15/32–	1-10 1/32–	28-0 23/32	2- 5 7/8	38-0 31/32
9	7 3/32–	9-0 7/32	1- 2 15/16	19-0 1/2	1-10 13/16	29-0 3/4	2- 6 11/16	39-1

Inch	12″ Rise	12″ Slope	13″ Rise	13″ Slope	14″ Rise	14″ Slope	15″ Rise	15″ Slope	16″ Rise	16″ Slope
0	25/32	1-0 1/32	27/32	1-1 1/32	29/32	1-2 1/32	31/32	1-3 1/32	1 1/16	1-4 1/32
1/16	25/32	1-0 3/32	27/32	1-1 3/32	29/32	1-2 3/32	1	1-3 3/32	1 1/16	1-4 3/32
1/8	25/32	1-0 5/32	7/8	1-1 5/32	15/16	1-2 5/32	1	1-3 5/32	1 1/16	1-4 5/32
3/16	13/16	1-0 7/32	7/8	1-1 7/32	15/16	1-2 7/32	1	1-3 7/32	1 1/16	1-4 7/32
1/4	13/16	1-0 9/32	7/8	1-1 9/32	15/16	1-2 9/32	1	1-3 9/32	1 1/16	1-4 9/32
5/16	13/16	1-0 11/32	7/8	1-1 11/32	15/16	1-2 11/32	1	1-3 11/32	1 1/16	1-4 11/32
3/8	13/16	1-0 13/32	7/8	1-1 13/32	15/16	1-2 13/32	1	1-3 13/32	1 1/16	1-4 13/32
7/16	13/16	1-0 15/32	7/8	1-1 15/32	15/16	1-2 15/32	1	1-3 15/32	1 1/16	1-4 15/32
1/2	13/16	1-0 17/32	7/8	1-1 17/32	15/16	1-2 17/32	1 1/32	1-3 17/32	1 3/32	1-4 17/32
9/16	13/16	1-0 19/32	7/8	1-1 19/32	31/32—	1-2 19/32	1 1/32	1-3 19/32	1 3/32	1-4 19/32
5/8	13/16	1-0 21/32	29/32—	1-1 21/32	31/32—	1-2 21/32	1 1/32	1-3 21/32	1 3/32	1-4 21/32
11/16	27/32	1-0 23/32	29/32—	1-1 23/32	31/32—	1-2 23/32	1 1/32	1-3 23/32	1 3/32	1-4 23/32
3/4	27/32	1-0 25/32	29/32—	1-1 25/32	31/32—	1-2 25/32	1 1/32	1-3 25/32	1 3/32	1-4 25/32
13/16	27/32	1-0 27/32	29/32—	1-1 27/32	31/32	1-2 27/32	1 1/32	1-3 27/32	1 3/32	1-4 27/32
7/8	27/32	1-0 29/32	29/32—	1-1 29/32	31/32	1-2 29/32	1 1/32	1-3 29/32	1 3/32	1-4 29/32
15/16	27/32	1-0 31/32	29/32—	1-1 31/32	31/32	1-2 31/32	1 1/32	1-3 31/32	1 1/8	1-4 31/32

Inch	17″ Rise	17″ Slope	18″ Rise	18″ Slope	19″ Rise	19″ Slope	20″ Rise	20″ Slope	21″ Rise	21″ Slope
0	1 1/8	1-5 1/32	1 3/16	1-6 1/32	1 1/4	1-7 1/32	1 5/16	1-8 1/32	1 3/8	1- 9 1/32
1/16	1 1/8	1-5 3/32	1 3/16	1-6 3/32	1 1/4	1-7 3/32	1 5/16	1-8 3/32	1 3/8	1- 9 3/32
1/8	1 1/8	1-5 5/32	1 3/16	1-6 5/32	1 1/4	1-7 5/32	1 5/16	1-8 5/32	1 3/8	1- 9 5/32
3/16	1 1/8	1-5 7/32	1 3/16	1-6 7/32	1 1/4	1-7 7/32	1 5/16	1-8 7/32	1 3/8	1- 9 7/32
1/4	1 1/8	1-5 9/32	1 3/16	1-6 9/32	1 1/4	1-7 9/32	1 5/16	1-8 9/32	1 13/32	1- 9 9/32
5/16	1 1/8	1-5 11/32	1 3/16	1-6 11/32	1 9/32—	1-7 11/32	1 11/32—	1-8 11/32	1 13/32	1- 9 11/32
3/8	1 1/8	1-5 13/32	1 7/32—	1-6 13/32	1 9/32—	1-7 13/32	1 11/32—	1-8 13/32	1 13/32	1- 9 13/32
7/16	1 5/32—	1-5 15/32	1 7/32—	1-6 15/32	1 9/32—	1-7 15/32	1 11/32—	1-8 15/32	1 13/32	1- 9 15/32
1/2	1 5/32—	1-5 17/32	1 7/32—	1-6 17/32	1 9/32—	1-7 17/32	1 11/32—	1-8 17/32	1 13/32	1- 9 17/32
9/16	1 5/32—	1-5 19/32	1 7/32—	1-6 19/32	1 9/32—	1-7 19/32	1 11/32—	1-8 19/32	1 13/32	1- 9 19/32
5/8	1 5/32	1-5 21/32	1 7/32	1-6 21/32	1 9/32	1-7 21/32	1 11/32	1-8 21/32	1 13/32	1- 9 21/32
11/16	1 5/32	1-5 23/32	1 7/32	1-6 23/32	1 9/32	1-7 23/32	1 11/32	1-8 23/32	1 13/32	1- 9 23/32
3/4	1 5/32	1-5 25/32	1 7/32	1-6 25/32	1 9/32	1-7 25/32	1 3/8	1-8 25/32	1 7/16	1- 9 25/32
13/16	1 5/32	1-5 27/32	1 7/32	1-6 27/32	1 5/16	1-7 27/32	1 3/8	1-8 27/32	1 7/16	1- 9 27/32
7/8	1 5/32	1-5 29/32	1 1/4	1-6 29/32	1 5/16	1-7 29/32	1 3/8	1-8 29/32	1 7/16	1- 9 15/16
15/16	1 3/16	1-5 31/32	1 1/4	1-6 31/32	1 5/16	1-7 31/32	1 3/8	1-8 31/32	1 7/16	1-10

Feet	40′ Rise	40′ Slope	50′ Rise	50′ Slope	60′ Rise	60′ Slope	70′ Rise	70′ Slope
0	2- 7 15/32—	40-1 1/32—	3- 3 5/16	50-1 9/32	3-11 3/16	60-1 17/32	4- 7 1/16	70-1 13/16
1	2- 8 1/4	41-1 1/16	3- 4 1/8	51-1 5/16	3-11 31/32	61-1 9/16	4- 7 27/32—	71-1 13/16
2	2- 9 1/32	42-1 3/32—	3- 4 29/32—	52-1 11/32—	4- 0 3/4	62-1 19/32	4- 8 5/8	72-1 27/32
3	2- 9 13/16	43-1 3/32	3- 5 11/16	53-1 3/8	4- 1 9/16	63-1 5/8	4- 9 13/16	73-1 7/8
4	2-10 19/32	44-1 1/8	3- 6 15/32	54-1 3/8	4- 2 11/32—	64-1 21/32—	4-10 3/16	74-1 29/32—
5	2-11 13/32—	45-1 5/32	3- 7 1/4	55-1 13/32—	4- 3 1/8	65-1 11/16	4-11	75-1 15/16
6	3- 0 3/16	46-1 3/16	3- 8 1/32	56-1 7/16	4- 3 29/32	66-1 11/16	4-11 25/32—	76-1 31/32—
7	3- 0 31/32—	47-1 7/32	3- 8 27/32—	57-1 15/32—	4- 4 11/16	67-1 23/32	5- 0 9/16	77-1 31/32
8	3- 1 3/4	48-1 1/4	3- 9 5/8	58-1 1/2	4- 5 15/32	68-1 3/4	5- 1 11/32	78-2
9	3- 2 17/32	49-1 1/4	3-10 13/32—	59-1 17/32—	4- 6 9/32—	69-1 25/32—	5- 2 1/8	79-2 1/32

3°45′ PITCH (Bevel between $\frac{3}{4}''$ to $12''$ and $\frac{13}{16}''$ to $12''$)

Inch	22″ Rise	22″ Slope	23″ Rise	23″ Slope	24″ Rise	24″ Slope	25″ Rise	25″ Slope	26″ Rise	26″ Slope
0	$1\frac{7}{16}$	$1\text{-}10\frac{1}{16}$	$1\frac{1}{2}$	$1\text{-}11\frac{1}{16}$	$1\frac{9}{16}$	$2\text{-}0\frac{1}{16}$	$1\frac{5}{8}$	$2\text{-}1\frac{1}{16}$	$1\frac{23}{32}$	$2\text{-}2\frac{1}{16}$
$\frac{1}{16}$	$1\frac{7}{16}$	$1\text{-}10\frac{1}{8}$	$1\frac{1}{2}$	$1\text{-}11\frac{1}{8}$	$1\frac{9}{16}$	$2\text{-}0\frac{1}{8}$	$1\frac{21}{32}$	$2\text{-}1\frac{1}{8}$	$1\frac{23}{32}$	$2\text{-}2\frac{1}{8}$
$\frac{1}{8}$	$1\frac{7}{16}$	$1\text{-}10\frac{3}{16}$	$1\frac{17}{32}$	$1\text{-}11\frac{3}{16}$	$1\frac{19}{32}$	$2\text{-}0\frac{3}{16}$	$1\frac{21}{32}$	$2\text{-}1\frac{3}{16}$	$1\frac{23}{32}$	$2\text{-}2\frac{3}{16}$
$\frac{3}{16}$	$1\frac{15}{32}$	$1\text{-}10\frac{1}{4}$	$1\frac{17}{32}$	$1\text{-}11\frac{1}{4}$	$1\frac{19}{32}$	$2\text{-}0\frac{1}{4}$	$1\frac{21}{32}$	$2\text{-}1\frac{1}{4}$	$1\frac{23}{32}$	$2\text{-}2\frac{1}{4}$
$\frac{1}{4}$	$1\frac{15}{32}$	$1\text{-}10\frac{5}{16}$	$1\frac{17}{32}$	$1\text{-}11\frac{5}{16}$	$1\frac{19}{32}$	$2\text{-}0\frac{5}{16}$	$1\frac{21}{32}$	$2\text{-}1\frac{5}{16}$	$1\frac{23}{32}$	$2\text{-}2\frac{5}{16}$
$\frac{5}{16}$	$1\frac{15}{32}$	$1\text{-}10\frac{3}{8}$	$1\frac{17}{32}$	$1\text{-}11\frac{3}{8}$	$1\frac{19}{32}$	$2\text{-}0\frac{3}{8}$	$1\frac{21}{32}$	$2\text{-}1\frac{3}{8}$	$1\frac{23}{32}$	$2\text{-}2\frac{3}{8}$
$\frac{3}{8}$	$1\frac{15}{32}$	$1\text{-}10\frac{7}{16}$	$1\frac{17}{32}$	$1\text{-}11\frac{7}{16}$	$1\frac{19}{32}$	$2\text{-}0\frac{7}{16}$	$1\frac{21}{32}$	$2\text{-}1\frac{7}{16}$	$1\frac{23}{32}$	$2\text{-}2\frac{7}{16}$
$\frac{7}{16}$	$1\frac{15}{32}$	$1\text{-}10\frac{1}{2}$	$1\frac{17}{32}$	$1\text{-}11\frac{1}{2}$	$1\frac{19}{32}$	$2\text{-}0\frac{1}{2}$	$1\frac{21}{32}$	$2\text{-}1\frac{1}{2}$	$1\frac{23}{32}$	$2\text{-}2\frac{1}{2}$
$\frac{1}{2}$	$1\frac{15}{32}$	$1\text{-}10\frac{9}{16}$	$1\frac{17}{32}$	$1\text{-}11\frac{9}{16}$	$1\frac{19}{32}$	$2\text{-}0\frac{9}{16}$	$1\frac{21}{32}$	$2\text{-}1\frac{9}{16}$	$1\frac{3}{4}$	$2\text{-}2\frac{9}{16}$
$\frac{9}{16}$	$1\frac{15}{32}$	$1\text{-}10\frac{5}{8}$	$1\frac{17}{32}$	$1\text{-}11\frac{5}{8}$	$1\frac{5}{8}$	$2\text{-}0\frac{5}{8}$	$1\frac{11}{16}$	$2\text{-}1\frac{5}{8}$	$1\frac{3}{4}$	$2\text{-}2\frac{5}{8}$
$\frac{5}{8}$	$1\frac{15}{32}$	$1\text{-}10\frac{11}{16}$	$1\frac{9}{16}$	$1\text{-}11\frac{11}{16}$	$1\frac{5}{8}$	$2\text{-}0\frac{11}{16}$	$1\frac{11}{16}$	$2\text{-}1\frac{11}{16}$	$1\frac{3}{4}$	$2\text{-}2\frac{11}{16}$
$\frac{11}{16}$	$1\frac{1}{2}$	$1\text{-}10\frac{3}{4}$	$1\frac{9}{16}$	$1\text{-}11\frac{3}{4}$	$1\frac{5}{8}$	$2\text{-}0\frac{3}{4}$	$1\frac{11}{16}$	$2\text{-}1\frac{3}{4}$	$1\frac{3}{4}$	$2\text{-}2\frac{3}{4}$
$\frac{3}{4}$	$1\frac{1}{2}$	$1\text{-}10\frac{13}{16}$	$1\frac{9}{16}$	$1\text{-}11\frac{13}{16}$	$1\frac{5}{8}$	$2\text{-}0\frac{13}{16}$	$1\frac{11}{16}$	$2\text{-}1\frac{13}{16}$	$1\frac{3}{4}$	$2\text{-}2\frac{13}{16}$
$\frac{13}{16}$	$1\frac{1}{2}$	$1\text{-}10\frac{7}{8}$	$1\frac{9}{16}$	$1\text{-}11\frac{7}{8}$	$1\frac{5}{8}$	$2\text{-}0\frac{7}{8}$	$1\frac{11}{16}$	$2\text{-}1\frac{7}{8}$	$1\frac{3}{4}$	$2\text{-}2\frac{7}{8}$
$\frac{7}{8}$	$1\frac{1}{2}$	$1\text{-}10\frac{15}{16}$	$1\frac{9}{16}$	$1\text{-}11\frac{15}{16}$	$1\frac{5}{8}$	$2\text{-}0\frac{15}{16}$	$1\frac{11}{16}$	$2\text{-}1\frac{15}{16}$	$1\frac{3}{4}$	$2\text{-}2\frac{15}{16}$
$\frac{15}{16}$	$1\frac{1}{2}$	$1\text{-}11$	$1\frac{9}{16}$	$2\text{-}0$	$1\frac{5}{8}$	$2\text{-}1$	$1\frac{11}{16}$	$2\text{-}2$	$1\frac{3}{4}$	$2\text{-}3$

Inch	27″ Rise	27″ Slope	28″ Rise	28″ Slope	29″ Rise	29″ Slope	30″ Rise	30″ Slope	31″ Rise	31″ Slope
0	$1\frac{25}{32}$	$2\text{-}3\frac{1}{16}$	$1\frac{27}{32}$	$2\text{-}4\frac{1}{16}$	$1\frac{29}{32}$	$2\text{-}5\frac{1}{16}$	$1\frac{31}{32}$	$2\text{-}6\frac{1}{16}$	$2\frac{1}{32}$	$2\text{-}7\frac{1}{16}$
$\frac{1}{16}$	$1\frac{25}{32}$	$2\text{-}3\frac{1}{8}$	$1\frac{27}{32}$	$2\text{-}4\frac{1}{8}$	$1\frac{29}{32}$	$2\text{-}5\frac{1}{8}$	$1\frac{31}{32}$	$2\text{-}6\frac{1}{8}$	$2\frac{1}{32}$	$2\text{-}7\frac{1}{8}$
$\frac{1}{8}$	$1\frac{25}{32}$	$2\text{-}3\frac{3}{16}$	$1\frac{27}{32}$	$2\text{-}4\frac{3}{16}$	$1\frac{29}{32}$	$2\text{-}5\frac{3}{16}$	$1\frac{31}{32}$	$2\text{-}6\frac{3}{16}$	$2\frac{1}{32}$	$2\text{-}7\frac{3}{16}$
$\frac{3}{16}$	$1\frac{25}{32}$	$2\text{-}3\frac{1}{4}$	$1\frac{27}{32}$	$2\text{-}4\frac{1}{4}$	$1\frac{29}{32}$	$2\text{-}5\frac{1}{4}$	$1\frac{31}{32}$	$2\text{-}6\frac{1}{4}$	$2\frac{1}{32}$	$2\text{-}7\frac{1}{4}$
$\frac{1}{4}$	$1\frac{25}{32}$	$2\text{-}3\frac{5}{16}$	$1\frac{27}{32}$	$2\text{-}4\frac{5}{16}$	$1\frac{29}{32}$	$2\text{-}5\frac{5}{16}$	$1\frac{31}{32}$	$2\text{-}6\frac{5}{16}$	$2\frac{1}{16}$	$2\text{-}7\frac{5}{16}$
$\frac{5}{16}$	$1\frac{25}{32}$	$2\text{-}3\frac{3}{8}$	$1\frac{27}{32}$	$2\text{-}4\frac{3}{8}$	$1\frac{29}{32}$	$2\text{-}5\frac{3}{8}$	2	$2\text{-}6\frac{3}{8}$	$2\frac{1}{16}$	$2\text{-}7\frac{3}{8}$
$\frac{3}{8}$	$1\frac{25}{32}$	$2\text{-}3\frac{7}{16}$	$1\frac{7}{8}$	$2\text{-}4\frac{7}{16}$	$1\frac{15}{16}$	$2\text{-}5\frac{7}{16}$	2	$2\text{-}6\frac{7}{16}$	$2\frac{1}{16}$	$2\text{-}7\frac{7}{16}$
$\frac{7}{16}$	$1\frac{13}{16}$	$2\text{-}3\frac{1}{2}$	$1\frac{7}{8}$	$2\text{-}4\frac{1}{2}$	$1\frac{15}{16}$	$2\text{-}5\frac{1}{2}$	2	$2\text{-}6\frac{1}{2}$	$2\frac{1}{16}$	$2\text{-}7\frac{1}{2}$
$\frac{1}{2}$	$1\frac{13}{16}$	$2\text{-}3\frac{9}{16}$	$1\frac{7}{8}$	$2\text{-}4\frac{9}{16}$	$1\frac{15}{16}$	$2\text{-}5\frac{9}{16}$	2	$2\text{-}6\frac{9}{16}$	$2\frac{1}{16}$	$2\text{-}7\frac{9}{16}$
$\frac{9}{16}$	$1\frac{13}{16}$	$2\text{-}3\frac{5}{8}$	$1\frac{7}{8}$	$2\text{-}4\frac{5}{8}$	$1\frac{15}{16}$	$2\text{-}5\frac{5}{8}$	2	$2\text{-}6\frac{5}{8}$	$2\frac{1}{16}$	$2\text{-}7\frac{5}{8}$
$\frac{5}{8}$	$1\frac{13}{16}$	$2\text{-}3\frac{11}{16}$	$1\frac{7}{8}$	$2\text{-}4\frac{11}{16}$	$1\frac{15}{16}$	$2\text{-}5\frac{11}{16}$	2	$2\text{-}6\frac{11}{16}$	$2\frac{1}{16}$	$2\text{-}7\frac{11}{16}$
$\frac{11}{16}$	$1\frac{13}{16}$	$2\text{-}3\frac{3}{4}$	$1\frac{7}{8}$	$2\text{-}4\frac{3}{4}$	$1\frac{15}{16}$	$2\text{-}5\frac{3}{4}$	2	$2\text{-}6\frac{3}{4}$	$2\frac{1}{16}$	$2\text{-}7\frac{3}{4}$
$\frac{3}{4}$	$1\frac{13}{16}$	$2\text{-}3\frac{13}{16}$	$1\frac{7}{8}$	$2\text{-}4\frac{13}{16}$	$1\frac{15}{16}$	$2\text{-}5\frac{13}{16}$	2	$2\text{-}6\frac{13}{16}$	$2\frac{3}{32}$	$2\text{-}7\frac{13}{16}$
$\frac{13}{16}$	$1\frac{13}{16}$	$2\text{-}3\frac{7}{8}$	$1\frac{7}{8}$	$2\text{-}4\frac{7}{8}$	$1\frac{31}{32}$	$2\text{-}5\frac{7}{8}$	$2\frac{1}{32}$	$2\text{-}6\frac{7}{8}$	$2\frac{3}{32}$	$2\text{-}7\frac{7}{8}$
$\frac{7}{8}$	$1\frac{13}{16}$	$2\text{-}3\frac{15}{16}$	$1\frac{29}{32}$	$2\text{-}4\frac{15}{16}$	$1\frac{31}{32}$	$2\text{-}5\frac{15}{16}$	$2\frac{1}{32}$	$2\text{-}6\frac{15}{16}$	$2\frac{3}{32}$	$2\text{-}7\frac{15}{16}$
$\frac{15}{16}$	$1\frac{27}{32}$	$2\text{-}4$	$1\frac{29}{32}$	$2\text{-}5$	$1\frac{31}{32}$	$2\text{-}6$	$2\frac{1}{32}$	$2\text{-}7$	$2\frac{3}{32}$	$2\text{-}8$

GIVEN ANGLE, ITS NATURAL AND LOGARITHMIC FUNCTIONS

Natural Functions		Logarithmic Functions
Sin..... 0.0654031		Sin........8.8155985
Csc....15.2897883		Csc.......1.1844015
Tan.... 0.0655435	Given Angle	Tan......8.8165294
Cot....15.2570517	3°45′	Cot.......1.1834706
Cos.... 0.9978589		Cos......9.9990691
Sec..... 1.0021457		Sec.......0.0009309

Inch	0" Rise	0" Slope	1" Rise	1" Slope	2" Rise	2" Slope	3" Rise	3" Slope	4" Rise	4" Slope	5" Rise	5" Slope
0	0	0	3/32	1	3/16	2	9/32	3	13/32	4 1/32-	1/2	5 1/32-
1/16	0	1/16	3/32	1 1/16	7/32	2 1/16	5/16	3 1/16	13/32	4 3/32-	1/2	5 3/32-
1/8	0	1/8	1/8	1 1/8	7/32	2 1/8	5/16	3 1/8	13/32	4 5/32-	1/2	5 5/32-
3/16	1/32-	3/16	1/8	1 3/16	7/32	2 3/16	5/16	3 3/16	13/32	4 7/32-	1/2	5 7/32-
1/4	1/32-	1/4	1/8	1 1/4	7/32	2 1/4	5/16	3 9/32-	13/32	4 9/32-	17/32	5 9/32-
5/16	1/32-	5/16	1/8	1 5/16	7/32	2 5/16	5/16	3 11/32-	7/16	4 11/32-	17/32	5 11/32-
3/8	1/32-	3/8	1/8	1 3/8	7/32	2 3/8	11/32-	3 13/32-	7/16	4 13/32-	17/32	5 13/32-
7/16	1/32-	7/16	5/32-	1 7/16	1/4	2 7/16	11/32-	3 15/32-	7/16	4 15/32-	17/32	5 15/32-
1/2	1/16	1/2	5/32-	1 1/2	1/4	2 1/2	11/32-	3 17/32-	7/16	4 17/32-	17/32	5 17/32-
9/16	1/16	9/16	5/32-	1 9/16	1/4	2 9/16	11/32-	3 19/32-	7/16	4 19/32-	9/16	5 19/32-
5/8	1/16	5/8	5/32-	1 5/8	1/4	2 5/8	11/32-	3 21/32-	15/32-	4 21/32-	9/16	5 21/32-
11/16	1/16	11/16	5/32-	1 11/16	1/4	2 11/16	3/8	3 23/32-	15/32-	4 23/32-	9/16	5 23/32-
3/4	1/16	3/4	3/16	1 3/4	9/32-	2 3/4	3/8	3 25/32-	15/32-	4 25/32-	9/16	5 25/32-
13/16	3/32-	13/16	3/16	1 13/16	9/32-	2 13/16	3/8	3 27/32-	15/32-	4 27/32-	9/16	5 27/32-
7/8	3/32-	7/8	3/16	1 7/8	9/32-	2 7/8	3/8	3 29/32-	15/32-	4 29/32-	19/32-	5 29/32-
15/16	3/32-	15/16	3/16	1 15/16	9/32-	2 15/16	3/8	3 31/32-	1/2	4 31/32-	19/32-	5 31/32-

Inch	6" Rise	6" Slope	7" Rise	7" Slope	8" Rise	8" Slope	9" Rise	9" Slope	10" Rise	10" Slope	11" Rise	11" Slope
0	19/32-	6 1/32-	11/16	7 1/32-	25/32-	8 1/32-	7/8	9 1/32-	1	10 1/16	1 3/32-	11 1/16
1/16	19/32-	6 3/32-	11/16	7 3/32-	25/32-	8 3/32-	29/32-	9 3/32-	1	10 1/8	1 3/32-	11 1/8
1/8	19/32-	6 5/32-	11/16	7 5/32-	13/16	8 5/32-	29/32-	9 5/32-	1	10 3/16	1 3/32-	11 3/16
3/16	5/8	6 7/32-	23/32-	7 7/32-	13/16	8 7/32-	29/32-	9 7/32-	1	10 1/4	1 3/32-	11 1/4
1/4	5/8	6 9/32-	23/32-	7 9/32-	13/16	8 9/32-	29/32-	9 9/32-	1	10 5/32-	1 3/32-	11 5/32-
5/16	5/8	6 11/32-	23/32-	7 11/32-	13/16	8 11/32-	29/32-	9 11/32-	1 1/32-	10 3/8	1 1/8	11 3/8
3/8	5/8	6 13/32-	23/32-	7 13/32-	13/16	8 13/32-	15/16	9 13/32-	1 1/32-	10 7/16	1 1/8	11 7/16
7/16	5/8	6 15/32-	23/32-	7 15/32-	27/32-	8 15/32-	15/16	9 15/32-	1 1/32-	10 1/2	1 1/8	11 1/2
1/2	5/8	6 17/32-	3/4	7 17/32-	27/32-	8 17/32-	15/16	9 17/32-	1 1/32-	10 9/16	1 1/8	11 9/16
9/16	21/32-	6 19/32-	3/4	7 19/32-	27/32-	8 19/32-	15/16	9 19/32-	1 1/32-	10 5/8	1 1/8	11 5/8
5/8	21/32-	6 21/32-	3/4	7 21/32-	27/32-	8 21/32-	15/16	9 21/32-	1 1/32-	10 11/16	1 5/32-	11 11/16
11/16	21/32-	6 23/32-	3/4	7 23/32-	27/32-	8 23/32-	31/32-	9 23/32-	1 1/16	10 3/4	1 5/32-	11 3/4
3/4	21/32-	6 25/32-	3/4	7 25/32-	7/8	8 25/32-	31/32-	9 13/16	1 1/16	10 13/16	1 5/32-	11 13/16
13/16	21/32-	6 27/32-	25/32-	7 27/32-	7/8	8 27/32-	31/32-	9 7/8	1 1/16	10 7/8	1 5/32-	11 7/8
7/8	11/16	6 29/32-	25/32-	7 29/32-	7/8	8 29/32-	31/32-	9 15/16	1 1/16	10 15/16	1 5/32-	11 15/16
15/16	11/16	6 31/32-	25/32-	7 31/32-	7/8	8 31/32-	31/32-	10	1 1/16	11	1 3/16	1- 0

Feet	0' Rise	0' Slope	10' Rise	10' Slope	20' Rise	20' Slope	30' Rise	30' Slope
0	0	0	11 13/16	10-0 19/32-	1-11 5/8	20-1 5/32-	2-11 15/32-	30-1 3/4
1	1 3/16	1-0 1/16	1- 1	11-0 5/8	2- 0 13/16	21-1 7/32-	3- 0 5/8	31-1 13/16
2	2 3/8	2-0 1/8	1- 2 3/16	12-0 11/16	2- 2	22-1 9/32-	3- 1 13/16	32-1 27/32-
3	3 17/32-	3-0 3/16	1- 3 3/8	13-0 3/4	2- 3 3/16	23-1 11/32-	3- 3	33-1 29/32-
4	4 23/32-	4-0 7/32-	1- 4 17/32-	14-0 13/16	2- 4 3/8	24-1 13/32-	3- 4 3/16	34-1 31/32-
5	5 29/32-	5-0 9/32-	1- 5 23/32-	15-0 7/8	2- 5 9/16	25-1 7/16	3- 5 3/8	35-2 1/32-
6	7 3/32-	6-0 11/32-	1- 6 29/32-	16-0 15/16	2- 6 23/32-	26-1 1/2	3- 6 9/16	36-2 3/32-
7	8 9/32-	7-0 13/32-	1- 8 3/32-	17-1	2- 7 29/32-	27-1 9/16	3- 7 23/32-	37-2 5/32-
8	9 15/32-	8-0 15/32-	1- 9 9/32-	18-1 1/32-	2- 9 3/32-	28-1 5/8	3- 8 29/32-	38-2 7/32-
9	10 5/8	9-0 17/32-	1-10 15/32-	19-1 3/32-	2-10 9/32-	29-1 11/16	3-10 3/32-	39-2 1/4

Inch	12″ Rise	12″ Slope	13″ Rise	13″ Slope	14″ Rise	14″ Slope	15″ Rise	15″ Slope	16″ Rise	16″ Slope
0	$1\frac{3}{16}$	$1\text{-}0\frac{1}{16}$	$1\frac{9}{32}$	$1\text{-}1\frac{1}{16}$	$1\frac{3}{8}$	$1\text{-}2\frac{1}{16}$	$1\frac{15}{32}$	$1\text{-}3\frac{1}{16}$	$1\frac{9}{16}$	$1\text{-}4\frac{1}{16}$
$\frac{1}{16}$	$1\frac{3}{16}$	$1\text{-}0\frac{1}{8}$	$1\frac{9}{32}$	$1\text{-}1\frac{1}{8}$	$1\frac{3}{8}$	$1\text{-}2\frac{1}{8}$	$1\frac{15}{32}$	$1\text{-}3\frac{1}{8}$	$1\frac{19}{32}$	$1\text{-}4\frac{1}{8}$
$\frac{1}{8}$	$1\frac{3}{16}$	$1\text{-}0\frac{3}{16}$	$1\frac{9}{32}$	$1\text{-}1\frac{3}{16}$	$1\frac{13}{32}$	$1\text{-}2\frac{3}{16}$	$1\frac{1}{2}$	$1\text{-}3\frac{3}{16}$	$1\frac{19}{32}$	$1\text{-}4\frac{3}{16}$
$\frac{3}{16}$	$1\frac{3}{16}$	$1\text{-}0\frac{1}{4}$	$1\frac{5}{16}$	$1\text{-}1\frac{1}{4}$	$1\frac{13}{32}$	$1\text{-}2\frac{1}{4}$	$1\frac{1}{2}$	$1\text{-}3\frac{1}{4}$	$1\frac{19}{32}$	$1\text{-}4\frac{9}{32}$
$\frac{1}{4}$	$1\frac{7}{32}$	$1\text{-}0\frac{5}{16}$	$1\frac{5}{16}$	$1\text{-}1\frac{5}{16}$	$1\frac{13}{32}$	$1\text{-}2\frac{5}{16}$	$1\frac{1}{2}$	$1\text{-}3\frac{5}{16}$	$1\frac{19}{32}$	$1\text{-}4\frac{11}{32}$
$\frac{5}{16}$	$1\frac{7}{32}$	$1\text{-}0\frac{3}{8}$	$1\frac{5}{16}$	$1\text{-}1\frac{3}{8}$	$1\frac{13}{32}$	$1\text{-}2\frac{3}{8}$	$1\frac{1}{2}$	$1\text{-}3\frac{3}{8}$	$1\frac{19}{32}$	$1\text{-}4\frac{13}{32}$
$\frac{3}{8}$	$1\frac{7}{32}$	$1\text{-}0\frac{7}{16}$	$1\frac{5}{16}$	$1\text{-}1\frac{7}{16}$	$1\frac{13}{32}$	$1\text{-}2\frac{7}{16}$	$1\frac{1}{2}$	$1\text{-}3\frac{7}{16}$	$1\frac{5}{8}$	$1\text{-}4\frac{15}{32}$
$\frac{7}{16}$	$1\frac{7}{32}$	$1\text{-}0\frac{1}{2}$	$1\frac{5}{16}$	$1\text{-}1\frac{1}{2}$	$1\frac{7}{16}$	$1\text{-}2\frac{1}{2}$	$1\frac{17}{32}$	$1\text{-}3\frac{1}{2}$	$1\frac{5}{8}$	$1\text{-}4\frac{17}{32}$
$\frac{1}{2}$	$1\frac{7}{32}$	$1\text{-}0\frac{9}{16}$	$1\frac{11}{32}$	$1\text{-}1\frac{9}{16}$	$1\frac{7}{16}$	$1\text{-}2\frac{9}{16}$	$1\frac{17}{32}$	$1\text{-}3\frac{9}{16}$	$1\frac{5}{8}$	$1\text{-}4\frac{19}{32}$
$\frac{9}{16}$	$1\frac{1}{4}$	$1\text{-}0\frac{5}{8}$	$1\frac{11}{32}$	$1\text{-}1\frac{5}{8}$	$1\frac{7}{16}$	$1\text{-}2\frac{5}{8}$	$1\frac{17}{32}$	$1\text{-}3\frac{5}{8}$	$1\frac{5}{8}$	$1\text{-}4\frac{21}{32}$
$\frac{5}{8}$	$1\frac{1}{4}$	$1\text{-}0\frac{11}{16}$	$1\frac{11}{32}$	$1\text{-}1\frac{11}{16}$	$1\frac{7}{16}$	$1\text{-}2\frac{11}{16}$	$1\frac{17}{32}$	$1\text{-}3\frac{11}{16}$	$1\frac{5}{8}$	$1\text{-}4\frac{23}{32}$
$\frac{11}{16}$	$1\frac{1}{4}$	$1\text{-}0\frac{3}{4}$	$1\frac{11}{32}$	$1\text{-}1\frac{3}{4}$	$1\frac{7}{16}$	$1\text{-}2\frac{3}{4}$	$1\frac{17}{32}$	$1\text{-}3\frac{3}{4}$	$1\frac{21}{32}$	$1\text{-}4\frac{25}{32}$
$\frac{3}{4}$	$1\frac{1}{4}$	$1\text{-}0\frac{13}{16}$	$1\frac{11}{32}$	$1\text{-}1\frac{13}{16}$	$1\frac{7}{16}$	$1\text{-}2\frac{13}{16}$	$1\frac{9}{16}$	$1\text{-}3\frac{13}{16}$	$1\frac{21}{32}$	$1\text{-}4\frac{27}{32}$
$\frac{13}{16}$	$1\frac{1}{4}$	$1\text{-}0\frac{7}{8}$	$1\frac{3}{8}$	$1\text{-}1\frac{7}{8}$	$1\frac{15}{32}$	$1\text{-}2\frac{7}{8}$	$1\frac{9}{16}$	$1\text{-}3\frac{7}{8}$	$1\frac{21}{32}$	$1\text{-}4\frac{29}{32}$
$\frac{7}{8}$	$1\frac{9}{32}$	$1\text{-}0\frac{15}{16}$	$1\frac{3}{8}$	$1\text{-}1\frac{15}{16}$	$1\frac{15}{32}$	$1\text{-}2\frac{15}{16}$	$1\frac{9}{16}$	$1\text{-}3\frac{15}{16}$	$1\frac{21}{32}$	$1\text{-}4\frac{31}{32}$
$\frac{15}{16}$	$1\frac{9}{32}$	$1\text{-}1$	$1\frac{3}{8}$	$1\text{-}2$	$1\frac{15}{32}$	$1\text{-}3$	$1\frac{9}{16}$	$1\text{-}4$	$1\frac{21}{32}$	$1\text{-}5\frac{1}{32}$

Inch	17″ Rise	17″ Slope	18″ Rise	18″ Slope	19″ Rise	19″ Slope	20″ Rise	20″ Slope	21″ Rise	21″ Slope
0	$1\frac{11}{16}$	$1\text{-}5\frac{3}{32}\text{-}$	$1\frac{25}{32}$	$1\text{-}6\frac{3}{32}\text{-}$	$1\frac{7}{8}$	$1\text{-}7\frac{3}{32}\text{-}$	$1\frac{31}{32}$	$1\text{-}8\frac{3}{32}\text{-}$	$2\frac{1}{16}$	$1\text{-} 9\frac{3}{32}\text{-}$
$\frac{1}{16}$	$1\frac{11}{16}$	$1\text{-}5\frac{5}{32}\text{-}$	$1\frac{25}{32}$	$1\text{-}6\frac{5}{32}\text{-}$	$1\frac{7}{8}$	$1\text{-}7\frac{5}{32}\text{-}$	$1\frac{31}{32}$	$1\text{-}8\frac{5}{32}\text{-}$	$2\frac{1}{16}$	$1\text{-} 9\frac{5}{32}\text{-}$
$\frac{1}{8}$	$1\frac{11}{16}$	$1\text{-}5\frac{7}{32}\text{-}$	$1\frac{25}{32}$	$1\text{-}6\frac{7}{32}\text{-}$	$1\frac{7}{8}$	$1\text{-}7\frac{7}{32}\text{-}$	$1\frac{31}{32}$	$1\text{-}8\frac{7}{32}\text{-}$	$2\frac{3}{32}$	$1\text{-} 9\frac{7}{32}\text{-}$
$\frac{3}{16}$	$1\frac{11}{16}$	$1\text{-}5\frac{9}{32}\text{-}$	$1\frac{25}{32}$	$1\text{-}6\frac{9}{32}\text{-}$	$1\frac{7}{8}$	$1\text{-}7\frac{9}{32}\text{-}$	2	$1\text{-}8\frac{9}{32}\text{-}$	$2\frac{3}{32}$	$1\text{-} 9\frac{9}{32}\text{-}$
$\frac{1}{4}$	$1\frac{11}{16}$	$1\text{-}5\frac{11}{32}\text{-}$	$1\frac{13}{16}$	$1\text{-}6\frac{11}{32}\text{-}$	$1\frac{29}{32}$	$1\text{-}7\frac{11}{32}\text{-}$	2	$1\text{-}8\frac{11}{32}\text{-}$	$2\frac{3}{32}$	$1\text{-} 9\frac{11}{32}\text{-}$
$\frac{5}{16}$	$1\frac{23}{32}$	$1\text{-}5\frac{13}{32}\text{-}$	$1\frac{13}{16}$	$1\text{-}6\frac{13}{32}\text{-}$	$1\frac{29}{32}$	$1\text{-}7\frac{13}{32}\text{-}$	2	$1\text{-}8\frac{13}{32}\text{-}$	$2\frac{3}{32}$	$1\text{-} 9\frac{13}{32}\text{-}$
$\frac{3}{8}$	$1\frac{23}{32}$	$1\text{-}5\frac{15}{32}\text{-}$	$1\frac{13}{16}$	$1\text{-}6\frac{15}{32}\text{-}$	$1\frac{29}{32}$	$1\text{-}7\frac{15}{32}\text{-}$	2	$1\text{-}8\frac{15}{32}\text{-}$	$2\frac{1}{8}$	$1\text{-} 9\frac{15}{32}\text{-}$
$\frac{7}{16}$	$1\frac{23}{32}$	$1\text{-}5\frac{17}{32}\text{-}$	$1\frac{13}{16}$	$1\text{-}6\frac{17}{32}\text{-}$	$1\frac{29}{32}$	$1\text{-}7\frac{17}{32}\text{-}$	2	$1\text{-}8\frac{17}{32}\text{-}$	$2\frac{1}{8}$	$1\text{-} 9\frac{17}{32}\text{-}$
$\frac{1}{2}$	$1\frac{23}{32}$	$1\text{-}5\frac{19}{32}\text{-}$	$1\frac{13}{16}$	$1\text{-}6\frac{19}{32}\text{-}$	$1\frac{29}{32}$	$1\text{-}7\frac{19}{32}\text{-}$	$2\frac{1}{32}$	$1\text{-}8\frac{19}{32}\text{-}$	$2\frac{1}{8}$	$1\text{-} 9\frac{19}{32}\text{-}$
$\frac{9}{16}$	$1\frac{23}{32}$	$1\text{-}5\frac{21}{32}\text{-}$	$1\frac{27}{32}$	$1\text{-}6\frac{21}{32}\text{-}$	$1\frac{15}{16}$	$1\text{-}7\frac{21}{32}\text{-}$	$2\frac{1}{32}$	$1\text{-}8\frac{21}{32}\text{-}$	$2\frac{1}{8}$	$1\text{-} 9\frac{21}{32}\text{-}$
$\frac{5}{8}$	$1\frac{3}{4}$	$1\text{-}5\frac{23}{32}\text{-}$	$1\frac{27}{32}$	$1\text{-}6\frac{23}{32}\text{-}$	$1\frac{15}{16}$	$1\text{-}7\frac{23}{32}\text{-}$	$2\frac{1}{32}$	$1\text{-}8\frac{23}{32}\text{-}$	$2\frac{1}{8}$	$1\text{-} 9\frac{23}{32}\text{-}$
$\frac{11}{16}$	$1\frac{3}{4}$	$1\text{-}5\frac{25}{32}\text{-}$	$1\frac{27}{32}$	$1\text{-}6\frac{25}{32}\text{-}$	$1\frac{15}{16}$	$1\text{-}7\frac{25}{32}\text{-}$	$2\frac{1}{32}$	$1\text{-}8\frac{25}{32}\text{-}$	$2\frac{1}{8}$	$1\text{-} 9\frac{25}{32}\text{-}$
$\frac{3}{4}$	$1\frac{3}{4}$	$1\text{-}5\frac{27}{32}\text{-}$	$1\frac{27}{32}$	$1\text{-}6\frac{27}{32}\text{-}$	$1\frac{15}{16}$	$1\text{-}7\frac{27}{32}\text{-}$	$2\frac{1}{32}$	$1\text{-}8\frac{27}{32}\text{-}$	$2\frac{5}{32}$	$1\text{-} 9\frac{27}{32}\text{-}$
$\frac{13}{16}$	$1\frac{3}{4}$	$1\text{-}5\frac{29}{32}\text{-}$	$1\frac{27}{32}$	$1\text{-}6\frac{29}{32}\text{-}$	$1\frac{31}{32}$	$1\text{-}7\frac{29}{32}\text{-}$	$2\frac{1}{16}$	$1\text{-}8\frac{29}{32}\text{-}$	$2\frac{5}{32}$	$1\text{-} 9\frac{29}{32}\text{-}$
$\frac{7}{8}$	$1\frac{3}{4}$	$1\text{-}5\frac{31}{32}\text{-}$	$1\frac{27}{32}$	$1\text{-}6\frac{31}{32}\text{-}$	$1\frac{31}{32}$	$1\text{-}7\frac{31}{32}\text{-}$	$2\frac{1}{16}$	$1\text{-}8\frac{31}{32}\text{-}$	$2\frac{5}{32}$	$1\text{-} 9\frac{31}{32}\text{-}$
$\frac{15}{16}$	$1\frac{25}{32}$	$1\text{-}6\frac{1}{32}\text{-}$	$1\frac{7}{8}$	$1\text{-}7\frac{1}{32}\text{-}$	$1\frac{31}{32}$	$1\text{-}8\frac{1}{32}\text{-}$	$2\frac{1}{16}$	$1\text{-}9\frac{1}{32}\text{-}$	$2\frac{5}{32}$	$1\text{-}10\frac{1}{32}$

Feet	40′ Rise	40′ Slope	50′ Rise	50′ Slope	60′ Rise	60′ Slope	70′ Rise	70′ Slope
0	$3\text{-}11\frac{9}{32}\text{-}$	$40\text{-}2\frac{5}{16}$	$4\text{-}11\frac{3}{32}$	$50\text{-}2\frac{29}{32}\text{-}$	$5\text{-}10\frac{29}{32}\text{-}$	$60\text{-}3\frac{15}{32}$	$6\text{-}10\frac{23}{32}\text{-}$	$70\text{-}4\frac{1}{16}$
1	$4\text{-} 0\frac{15}{32}\text{-}$	$41\text{-}2\frac{3}{8}$	$5\text{-} 0\frac{9}{32}\text{-}$	$51\text{-}2\frac{31}{32}\text{-}$	$6\text{-} 0\frac{3}{32}\text{-}$	$61\text{-}3\frac{17}{32}\text{-}$	$6\text{-}11\frac{29}{32}\text{-}$	$71\text{-}4\frac{1}{8}$
2	$4\text{-} 1\frac{5}{8}$	$42\text{-}2\frac{7}{16}$	$5\text{-} 1\frac{15}{32}\text{-}$	$52\text{-}3\frac{1}{32}\text{-}$	$6\text{-} 1\frac{9}{32}\text{-}$	$62\text{-}3\frac{19}{32}\text{-}$	$7\text{-} 1\frac{3}{32}\text{-}$	$72\text{-}4\frac{3}{16}$
3	$4\text{-} 2\frac{13}{16}$	$43\text{-}2\frac{1}{2}$	$5\text{-} 2\frac{5}{8}$	$53\text{-}3\frac{1}{8}$	$6\text{-} 2\frac{15}{32}\text{-}$	$63\text{-}3\frac{21}{32}\text{-}$	$7\text{-} 2\frac{9}{32}\text{-}$	$73\text{-}4\frac{1}{4}$
4	$4\text{-} 4$	$44\text{-}2\frac{9}{16}$	$5\text{-} 3\frac{13}{16}$	$54\text{-}3\frac{1}{8}$	$6\text{-} 3\frac{21}{32}\text{-}$	$64\text{-}3\frac{23}{32}\text{-}$	$7\text{-} 3\frac{15}{32}\text{-}$	$74\text{-}4\frac{9}{32}$
5	$4\text{-} 5\frac{3}{16}$	$45\text{-}2\frac{5}{8}$	$5\text{-} 5$	$55\text{-}3\frac{3}{16}$	$6\text{-} 4\frac{13}{16}$	$65\text{-}3\frac{25}{32}\text{-}$	$7\text{-} 4\frac{21}{32}\text{-}$	$75\text{-}4\frac{11}{32}$
6	$4\text{-} 6\frac{3}{8}$	$46\text{-}2\frac{21}{32}$	$5\text{-} 6\frac{3}{16}$	$56\text{-}3\frac{1}{4}$	$6\text{-} 6$	$66\text{-}3\frac{27}{32}\text{-}$	$7\text{-} 5\frac{13}{16}$	$76\text{-}4\frac{13}{32}$
7	$4\text{-} 7\frac{9}{16}$	$47\text{-}2\frac{23}{32}$	$5\text{-} 7\frac{3}{8}$	$57\text{-}3\frac{5}{16}$	$6\text{-} 7\frac{3}{16}$	$67\text{-}3\frac{7}{8}$	$7\text{-} 7$	$77\text{-}4\frac{15}{32}$
8	$4\text{-} 8\frac{23}{32}$	$48\text{-}2\frac{25}{32}$	$5\text{-} 8\frac{9}{16}$	$58\text{-}3\frac{3}{8}$	$6\text{-} 8\frac{3}{8}$	$68\text{-}3\frac{15}{16}$	$7\text{-} 8\frac{3}{16}$	$78\text{-}4\frac{17}{32}\text{-}$
9	$4\text{-} 9\frac{29}{32}$	$49\text{-}2\frac{27}{32}$	$5\text{-} 9\frac{23}{32}$	$59\text{-}3\frac{7}{16}$	$6\text{-} 9\frac{9}{16}$	$69\text{-}4$	$7\text{-} 9\frac{3}{8}$	$79\text{-}4\frac{19}{32}\text{-}$

Inch	22" Rise	22" Slope	23" Rise	23" Slope	24" Rise	24" Slope	25" Rise	25" Slope	26" Rise	26" Slope
0	2 5/32	1-10 3/32	2 1/4	1-11 1/8	2 3/8	2-0 1/8	2 15/32-	2-1 1/8	2 9/16	2-2 1/8
1/16	2 3/16	1-10 5/32	2 9/32-	1-11 3/16	2 3/8	2-0 3/16	2 15/32-	2-1 3/16	2 9/16	2-2 3/16
1/8	2 3/16	1-10 7/32	2 9/32-	1-11 1/4	2 3/8	2-0 1/4	2 15/32	2-1 1/4	2 9/16	2-2 1/4
3/16	2 3/16	1-10 9/32	2 9/32	1-11 5/16	2 3/8	2-0 5/16	2 15/32	2-1 5/16	2 19/32-	2-2 5/16
1/4	2 3/16	1-10 11/32	2 9/32	1-11 3/8	2 3/8	2-0 3/8	2 1/2	2-1 3/8	2 19/32-	2-2 3/8
5/16	2 3/16	1-10 13/32	2 9/32	1-11 7/16	2 13/32-	2-0 7/16	2 1/2	2-1 7/16	2 19/32-	2-2 7/16
3/8	2 7/32	1-10 15/32	2 5/16	1-11 1/2	2 13/32-	2-0 1/2	2 1/2	2-1 1/2	2 19/32-	2-2 1/2
7/16	2 7/32	1-10 17/32	2 5/16	1-11 9/16	2 13/32-	2-0 9/16	2 1/2	2-1 9/16	2 19/32-	2-2 9/16
1/2	2 7/32	1-10 19/32	2 5/16	1-11 5/8	2 13/32	2-0 5/8	2 1/2	2-1 5/8	2 5/8	2-2 5/8
9/16	2 7/32	1-10 21/32	2 5/16	1-11 11/16	2 13/32	2-0 11/16	2 17/32-	2-1 11/16	2 5/8	2-2 11/16
5/8	2 7/32	1-10 3/4	2 5/16	1-11 3/4	2 7/16	2-0 3/4	2 17/32-	2-1 3/4	2 5/8	2-2 3/4
11/16	2 1/4	1-10 13/16	2 11/32-	1-11 13/16	2 7/16	2-0 13/16	2 17/32-	2-1 13/16	2 5/8	2-2 13/16
3/4	2 1/4	1-10 7/8	2 11/32-	1-11 7/8	2 7/16	2-0 7/8	2 17/32-	2-1 7/8	2 5/8	2-2 7/8
13/16	2 1/4	1-10 15/16	2 11/32-	1-11 15/16	2 7/16	2-0 15/16	2 17/32-	2-1 15/16	2 21/32-	2-2 15/16
7/8	2 1/4	1-11	2 11/32-	2- 0	2 7/16	2-1	2 9/16	2-2	2 21/32-	2-3
15/16	2 1/4	1-11 1/16	2 11/32-	2- 0 1/16	2 15/32-	2-1 1/16	2 9/16	2-2 1/16	2 21/32-	2-3 1/16

Inch	27" Rise	27" Slope	28" Rise	28" Slope	29" Rise	29" Slope	30" Rise	30" Slope	31" Rise	31" Slope
0	2 21/32	2-3 1/8	2 3/4	2-4 1/8	2 27/32	2-5 1/8	2 31/32-	2-6 5/32-	3 1/16	2-7 5/32-
1/16	2 21/32	2-3 3/16	2 3/4	2-4 3/16	2 7/8	2-5 3/16	2 31/32-	2-6 7/32-	3 1/16	2-7 7/32-
1/8	2 21/32	2-3 1/4	2 25/32-	2-4 1/4	2 7/8	2-5 9/32-	2 31/32-	2-6 9/32-	3 1/16	2-7 9/32-
3/16	2 11/16	2-3 5/16	2 25/32-	2-4 5/16	2 7/8	2-5 11/32-	2 31/32-	2-6 11/32-	3 1/16	2-7 11/32-
1/4	2 11/16	2-3 3/8	2 25/32-	2-4 3/8	2 7/8	2-5 13/32-	2 31/32-	2-6 13/32-	3 1/16	2-7 13/32-
5/16	2 11/16	2-3 7/16	2 25/32-	2-4 7/16	2 7/8	2-5 15/32-	3	2-6 15/32-	3 3/32-	2-7 15/32-
3/8	2 11/16	2-3 1/2	2 25/32-	2-4 1/2	2 29/32-	2-5 17/32-	3	2-6 17/32-	3 3/32-	2-7 17/32-
7/16	2 11/16	2-3 9/16	2 13/16	2-4 9/16	2 29/32-	2-5 19/32-	3	2-6 19/32-	3 3/32-	2-7 19/32-
1/2	2 23/32-	2-3 5/8	2 13/16	2-4 5/8	2 29/32-	2-5 21/32-	3	2-6 21/32-	3 3/32-	2-7 21/32-
9/16	2 23/32-	2-3 11/16	2 13/16	2-4 11/16	2 29/32-	2-5 23/32-	3	2-6 23/32-	3 3/32-	2-7 23/32-
5/8	2 23/32-	2-3 3/4	2 13/16	2-4 3/4	2 29/32-	2-5 25/32-	3 1/32-	2-6 25/32-	3 1/8	2-7 25/32-
11/16	2 23/32-	2-3 13/16	2 13/16	2-4 13/16	2 15/16	2-5 27/32-	3 1/32-	2-6 27/32-	3 1/8	2-7 27/32-
3/4	2 23/32-	2-3 7/8	2 27/32-	2-4 7/8	2 15/16	2-5 29/32-	3 1/32-	2-6 29/32-	3 1/8	2-7 29/32-
13/16	2 3/4	2-3 15/16	2 27/32-	2-4 15/16	2 15/16	2-5 31/32-	3 1/32-	2-6 31/32-	3 1/8	2-7 31/32-
7/8	2 3/4	2-4	2 27/32-	2-5	2 15/16	2-6 1/32-	3 1/8	2-7 1/32-	3 1/8	2-8 1/32-
15/16	2 3/4	2-4 1/16	2 27/32-	2-5 1/16	2 15/16	2-6 3/32-	3 1/16	2-7 3/32-	3 5/32-	2-8 3/32-

Given Angle, Its Natural and Logarithmic Functions

Natural Functions		Logarithmic Functions
Sin..... 0.0980171		Sin...... 8.9913020
Csc.... 10.2022972		Csc...... 1.0086980
Tan.... 0.0984914	Given Angle	Tan..... 8.9933983
Cot.... 10.1531704	5°37'30"	Cot...... 1.0066017
Cos.... 0.9951847		Cos..... 9.9979037
Sec..... 1.0048386		Sec...... 0.0020963

Inch	0″ Rise	0″ Slope	1″ Rise	1″ Slope	2″ Rise	2″ Slope	3″ Rise	3″ Slope	4″ Rise	4″ Slope	5″ Rise	5″ Slope
0	0	0	1/8	1	1/4	2 1/2	13/32	3 1/32	17/32	4 1/32	21/32	5 1/32
1/16	0	1/16	1/8	1 1/16	9/32	2 3/32	13/32	3 3/32	17/32	4 3/32	21/32	5 3/32
1/8	1/32	1/8	5/32	1 1/8	9/32	2 5/32	13/32	3 5/32	17/32	4 5/32	11/16	5 5/32
3/16	1/32	3/16	5/32	1 3/16	9/32	2 7/32	13/32	3 7/32	9/16	4 7/32	11/16	5 7/32
1/4	1/32	1/4	5/32	1 1/4	9/32	2 9/32	7/16	3 9/32	9/16	4 9/32	11/16	5 9/32
5/16	1/32	5/16	3/16	1 5/16	5/16	2 11/32	7/16	3 11/32	9/16	4 11/32	11/16	5 11/32
3/8	1/16	3/8	3/16	1 3/8	5/16	2 13/32	7/16	3 13/32	9/16	4 13/32	23/32	5 13/32
7/16	1/16	7/16	3/16	1 7/16	5/16	2 15/32	7/16	3 15/32	19/32	4 15/32	23/32	5 1/2
1/2	1/16	1/2	3/16	1 1/2	11/32	2 17/32	15/32	3 17/32	19/32	4 17/32	23/32	5 9/16
9/16	1/16	9/16	7/32	1 9/16	11/32	2 19/32	15/32	3 19/32	19/32	4 19/32	23/32	5 5/8
5/8	3/32	5/8	7/32	1 5/8	11/32	2 21/32	15/32	3 21/32	19/32	4 21/32	3/4	5 11/16
11/16	3/32	11/16	7/32	1 11/16	11/32	2 23/32	1/2	3 23/32	5/8	4 23/32	3/4	5 3/4
3/4	3/32	3/4	7/32	1 3/4	3/8	2 25/32	1/2	3 25/32	5/8	4 25/32	3/4	5 13/16
13/16	3/32	13/16	1/4	1 27/32	3/8	2 27/32	1/2	3 27/32	5/8	4 27/32	3/4	5 7/8
7/8	1/8	7/8	1/4	1 29/32	3/8	2 29/32	1/2	3 29/32	21/32	4 29/32	25/32	5 15/16
15/16	1/8	15/16	1/4	1 31/32	3/8	2 31/32	17/32	3 31/32	21/32	4 31/32	25/32	6

Inch	6″ Rise	6″ Slope	7″ Rise	7″ Slope	8″ Rise	8″ Slope	9″ Rise	9″ Slope	10″ Rise	10″ Slope	11″ Rise	11″ Slope
0	25/32	6 1/16	29/32	7 1/16	1 1/16	8 1/16	1 3/16	9 1/16	1 5/16	10 3/32	1 7/16	11 3/32
1/16	13/16	6 1/8	15/16	7 1/8	1 1/16	8 1/8	1 3/16	9 5/32	1 5/16	10 5/32	1 15/32	11 5/32
1/8	13/16	6 3/16	15/16	7 3/16	1 1/16	8 3/16	1 3/16	9 7/32	1 11/32	10 7/32	1 15/32	11 7/32
3/16	13/16	6 1/4	15/16	7 1/4	1 1/16	8 1/4	1 7/32	9 9/32	1 11/32	10 9/32	1 15/32	11 9/32
1/4	13/16	6 5/16	31/32	7 5/16	1 3/32	8 5/16	1 7/32	9 11/32	1 11/32	10 11/32	1 15/32	11 11/32
5/16	27/32	6 3/8	31/32	7 3/8	1 3/32	8 3/8	1 7/32	9 13/32	1 11/32	10 13/32	1 1/2	11 13/32
3/8	27/32	6 7/16	31/32	7 7/16	1 3/32	8 7/16	1 7/32	9 15/32	1 3/8	10 15/32	1 1/2	11 15/32
7/16	27/32	6 1/2	31/32	7 1/2	1 1/8	8 1/2	1 1/4	9 17/32	1 3/8	10 17/32	1 1/2	11 17/32
1/2	27/32	6 9/16	1	7 9/16	1 1/8	8 9/16	1 1/4	9 19/32	1 3/8	10 19/32	1 1/2	11 19/32
9/16	7/8	6 5/8	1	7 5/8	1 1/8	8 5/8	1 1/4	9 21/32	1 3/8	10 21/32	1 17/32	11 21/32
5/8	7/8	6 11/16	1	7 11/16	1 1/8	8 11/16	1 9/32	9 23/32	1 13/32	10 23/32	1 17/32	11 23/32
11/16	7/8	6 3/4	1	7 3/4	1 5/32	8 3/4	1 9/32	9 25/32	1 13/32	10 25/32	1 17/32	11 25/32
3/4	7/8	6 13/16	1 1/32	7 13/16	1 5/32	8 13/16	1 9/32	9 27/32	1 13/32	10 27/32	1 9/16	11 27/32
13/16	29/32	6 7/8	1 1/32	7 7/8	1 5/32	8 7/8	1 9/32	9 29/32	1 7/16	10 29/32	1 9/16	11 29/32
7/8	29/32	6 15/16	1 1/32	7 15/16	1 5/32	8 15/16	1 5/16	9 31/32	1 7/16	10 31/32	1 9/16	11 31/32
15/16	29/32	7	1 1/32	8	1 3/16	9	1 5/16	10 1/32	1 7/16	11 1/32	1 9/16	1-0 1/32

Feet	0′ Rise	0′ Slope	10′ Rise	10′ Slope	20′ Rise	20′ Slope	30′ Rise	30′ Slope
0	0-0	0-0	1-3 13/16	10-1 1/32	2-7 19/32	20-2 1/16	3-11 13/32	30-3 3/32
1	0-1 19/32	1-0 3/32	1-5 3/8	11-1 1/8	2-9 3/16	21-2 3/16	4-0 31/32	31-3 7/32
2	0-3 5/32	2-0 7/32	1-6 31/32	12-1 1/4	2-10 3/4	22-2 9/32	4-2 9/16	32-3 5/16
3	0-4 3/4	3-0 5/16	1-8 17/32	13-1 11/32	3-0 11/32	23-2 3/8	4-4 1/8	33-3 13/32
4	0-6 5/16	4-0 13/32	1-10 1/8	14-1 7/16	3-1 29/32	24-2 1/2	4-5 23/32	34-3 17/32
5	0-7 29/32	5-0 17/32	1-11 11/16	15-1 9/16	3-3 1/2	25-2 19/32	4-7 9/32	35-3 5/8
6	0-9 15/32	6-0 5/8	2-1 9/32	16-1 21/32	3-5 1/16	26-2 11/16	4-8 7/8	36-3 23/32
7	0-11 1/16	7-0 23/32	2-2 27/32	17-1 3/4	3-6 21/32	27-2 25/32	4-10 15/32	37-3 27/32
8	1-0 5/8	8-0 27/32	2-4 7/16	18-1 7/8	3-8 1/4	28-2 29/32	5-0 1/32	38-3 15/16
9	1-2 7/32	9-0 15/16	2-6 1/32	19-1 31/32	3-9 13/16	29-3	5-1 5/8	39-4 1/32

Inch	12″ Rise	12″ Slope	13″ Rise	13″ Slope	14″ Rise	14″ Slope	15″ Rise	15″ Slope	16″ Rise	16″ Slope
0	1 19/32	1-0 3/8	1 23/32	1-1 1/8	1 27/32	1-2 1/8	1 31/32	1-3 1/8	2 3/32	1-4 1/8
1/16	1 19/32	1-0 5/32	1 23/32	1-1 3/16	1 27/32	1-2 3/16	1 31/32	1-3 3/16	2 1/8	1-4 3/16
1/8	1 19/32	1-0 7/32	1 23/32	1-1 1/4	1 7/8	1-2 1/4	2	1-3 1/4	2 1/8	1-4 1/4
3/16	1 19/32	1-0 9/32	1 3/4	1-1 5/16	1 7/8	1-2 5/16	2	1-3 5/16	2 1/8	1-4 5/16
1/4	1 5/8	1-0 11/32	1 3/4	1-1 3/8	1 7/8	1-2 3/8	2	1-3 3/8	2 1/8	1-4 3/8
5/16	1 5/8	1-0 13/32	1 3/4	1-1 7/16	1 7/8	1-2 7/16	2 1/32	1-3 7/16	2 5/32	1-4 15/32
3/8	1 5/8	1-0 15/32	1 3/4	1-1 1/2	1 29/32	1-2 1/2	2 1/32	1-3 1/2	2 5/32	1-4 17/32
7/16	1 5/8	1-0 17/32	1 25/32	1-1 9/16	1 29/32	1-2 9/16	2 1/32	1-3 9/16	2 5/32	1-4 19/32
1/2	1 21/32	1-0 19/32	1 25/32	1-1 5/8	1 29/32	1-2 5/8	2 1/32	1-3 5/8	2 3/16	1-4 21/32
9/16	1 21/32	1-0 21/32	1 25/32	1-1 11/16	1 29/32	1-2 11/16	2 1/16	1-3 11/16	2 3/16	1-4 23/32
5/8	1 21/32	1-0 23/32	1 25/32	1-1 3/4	1 15/16	1-2 3/4	2 1/16	1-3 3/4	2 3/16	1-4 25/32
11/16	1 21/32	1-0 13/16	1 13/16	1-1 13/16	1 15/16	1-2 13/16	2 1/16	1-3 13/16	2 3/16	1-4 27/32
3/4	1 11/16	1-0 7/8	1 13/16	1-1 7/8	1 15/16	1-2 7/8	2 1/16	1-3 7/8	2 7/32	1-4 29/32
13/16	1 11/16	1-0 15/16	1 13/16	1-1 15/16	1 15/16	1-2 15/16	2 3/32	1-3 15/16	2 7/32	1-4 31/32
7/8	1 11/16	1-1	1 13/16	1-2	1 31/32	1-3	2 3/32	1-4	2 7/32	1-5 1/32
15/16	1 23/32	1-1 1/16	1 27/32	1-2 1/16	1 31/32	1-3 1/16	2 3/32	1-4 1/16	2 7/32	1-5 3/32

Inch	17″ Rise	17″ Slope	18″ Rise	18″ Slope	19″ Rise	19″ Slope	20″ Rise	20″ Slope	21″ Rise	21″ Slope
0	2 1/4	1-5 5/32	2 3/8	1-6 5/32	2 1/2	1-7 5/32	2 5/8	1-8 3/16	2 3/4	1- 9 3/16
1/16	2 1/4	1-5 7/32	2 3/8	1-6 7/32	2 1/2	1-7 7/32	2 21/32	1-8 1/4	2 25/32	1- 9 1/4
1/8	2 1/4	1-5 9/32	2 3/8	1-6 9/32	2 17/32	1-7 9/32	2 21/32	1-8 5/16	2 25/32	1- 9 5/16
3/16	2 1/4	1-5 11/32	2 13/32	1-6 11/32	2 17/32	1-7 11/32	2 21/32	1-8 3/8	2 25/32	1- 9 3/8
1/4	2 9/32	1-5 13/32	2 13/32	1-6 13/32	2 17/32	1-7 13/32	2 21/32	1-8 7/16	2 13/16	1- 9 7/16
5/16	2 9/32	1-5 15/32	2 13/32	1-6 15/32	2 17/32	1-7 15/32	2 11/16	1-8 1/2	2 13/16	1- 9 1/2
3/8	2 9/32	1-5 17/32	2 13/32	1-6 17/32	2 9/16	1-7 17/32	2 11/16	1-8 9/16	2 13/16	1- 9 9/16
7/16	2 9/32	1-5 19/32	2 7/16	1-6 19/32	2 9/16	1-7 19/32	2 11/16	1-8 5/8	2 13/16	1- 9 5/8
1/2	2 5/16	1-5 21/32	2 7/16	1-6 21/32	2 9/16	1-7 21/32	2 11/16	1-8 11/16	2 27/32	1- 9 11/16
9/16	2 5/16	1-5 23/32	2 7/16	1-6 23/32	2 9/16	1-7 23/32	2 23/32	1-8 3/4	2 27/32	1- 9 3/4
5/8	2 5/16	1-5 25/32	2 7/16	1-6 25/32	2 19/32	1-7 25/32	2 23/32	1-8 13/16	2 27/32	1- 9 13/16
11/16	2 11/32	1-5 27/32	2 15/32	1-6 27/32	2 19/32	1-7 27/32	2 23/32	1-8 7/8	2 27/32	1- 9 7/8
3/4	2 11/32	1-5 29/32	2 15/32	1-6 29/32	2 19/32	1-7 29/32	2 23/32	1-8 15/16	2 7/8	1- 9 15/16
13/16	2 11/32	1-5 31/32	2 15/32	1-6 31/32	2 19/32	1-7 31/32	2 3/4	1-9	2 7/8	1-10
7/8	2 11/32	1-6 1/32	2 1/2	1-7 1/32	2 5/8	1-8 1/32	2 3/4	1-9 1/16	2 7/8	1-10 1/16
15/16	2 3/8	1-6 3/32	2 1/2	1-7 3/32	2 5/8	1-8 1/8	2 3/4	1-9 1/8	2 7/8	1-10 1/8

Feet	40′ Rise	40′ Slope	50′ Rise	50′ Slope	60′ Rise	60′ Slope	70′ Rise	70′ Slope
0	5- 3 3/16	40-4 5/32	6- 7	50-5 3/16	7-10 25/32	60-6 7/32	9- 2 19/32	70-7 1/4
1	5- 4 25/32	41-4 1/4	6- 8 9/16	51-5 9/32	8- 0 3/8	61-6 5/16	9- 4 5/32	71-7 11/32
2	5- 6 11/32	42-4 11/32	6-10 5/32	52-5 3/8	8- 1 15/16	62-6 13/32	9- 5 3/4	72-7 15/32
3	5- 7 15/16	43-4 7/16	6-11 23/32	53-5 1/2	8- 3 17/32	63-6 17/32	9- 7 5/16	73-7 9/16
4	5- 9 1/2	44-4 9/16	7- 1 5/16	54-5 19/32	8- 5 3/32	64-6 5/8	9- 8 29/32	74-7 21/32
5	5-11 3/32	45-4 21/32	7- 2 29/32	55-5 11/16	8- 6 11/16	65-6 23/32	9-10 1/2	75-7 25/32
6	6- 0 11/32	46-4 3/4	7- 4 15/16	56-5 13/16	8- 8 9/32	66-6 27/32	10- 0 1/16	76-7 7/8
7	6- 2 1/4	47-4 7/8	7- 6 1/16	57-5 29/32	8- 9 27/32	67-6 15/16	10- 1 21/32	77-7 31/32
8	6- 3 27/32	48-4 31/32	7- 7 5/8	58-6	8-11 7/16	68-7 1/32	10- 3 7/32	78-8 1/16
9	6- 5 13/32	49-5 1/16	7- 9 7/32	59-6 3/32	9- 1	69-7 5/32	10- 4 13/16	79-8 3/16

Inch	22″ Rise	22″ Slope	23″ Rise	23″ Slope	24″ Rise	24″ Slope	25″ Rise	25″ Slope	26″ Rise	26″ Slope
0	$2\frac{29}{32}-$	$1\text{-}10\frac{3}{16}$	$3\frac{1}{32}$	$1\text{-}11\frac{3}{16}$	$3\frac{5}{32}$	$2\text{-}0\frac{7}{32}-$	$3\frac{9}{32}$	$2\text{-}1\frac{7}{32}-$	$3\frac{7}{16}$	$2\text{-}2\frac{7}{32}-$
$\frac{1}{16}$	$2\frac{29}{32}-$	$1\text{-}10\frac{1}{4}$	$3\frac{1}{32}$	$1\text{-}11\frac{1}{4}$	$3\frac{5}{32}$	$2\text{-}0\frac{9}{32}-$	$3\frac{5}{16}$	$2\text{-}1\frac{9}{32}-$	$3\frac{7}{16}$	$2\text{-}2\frac{9}{32}-$
$\frac{1}{8}$	$2\frac{29}{32}-$	$1\text{-}10\frac{5}{16}$	$3\frac{1}{32}$	$1\text{-}11\frac{5}{16}$	$3\frac{3}{16}$	$2\text{-}0\frac{11}{32}-$	$3\frac{5}{16}$	$2\text{-}1\frac{11}{32}-$	$3\frac{7}{16}$	$2\text{-}2\frac{11}{32}-$
$\frac{3}{16}$	$2\frac{29}{32}$	$1\text{-}10\frac{3}{8}$	$3\frac{1}{16}$	$1\text{-}11\frac{3}{8}$	$3\frac{3}{16}$	$2\text{-}0\frac{13}{32}-$	$3\frac{5}{16}$	$2\text{-}1\frac{13}{32}-$	$3\frac{7}{16}$	$2\text{-}2\frac{13}{32}-$
$\frac{1}{4}$	$2\frac{15}{16}$	$1\text{-}10\frac{7}{16}$	$3\frac{1}{16}$	$1\text{-}11\frac{7}{16}$	$3\frac{3}{16}$	$2\text{-}0\frac{15}{32}-$	$3\frac{5}{16}$	$2\text{-}1\frac{15}{32}-$	$3\frac{15}{32}-$	$2\text{-}2\frac{15}{32}-$
$\frac{5}{16}$	$2\frac{15}{16}$	$1\text{-}10\frac{1}{2}$	$3\frac{1}{16}$	$1\text{-}11\frac{1}{2}$	$3\frac{3}{16}$	$2\text{-}0\frac{17}{32}-$	$3\frac{5}{16}$	$2\text{-}1\frac{17}{32}-$	$3\frac{15}{32}-$	$2\text{-}2\frac{17}{32}-$
$\frac{3}{8}$	$2\frac{15}{16}$	$1\text{-}10\frac{9}{16}$	$3\frac{1}{16}$	$1\text{-}11\frac{9}{16}$	$3\frac{7}{32}$	$2\text{-}0\frac{19}{32}-$	$3\frac{11}{32}$	$2\text{-}1\frac{19}{32}-$	$3\frac{15}{32}-$	$2\text{-}2\frac{19}{32}-$
$\frac{7}{16}$	$2\frac{31}{32}-$	$1\text{-}10\frac{5}{8}$	$3\frac{3}{32}$	$1\text{-}11\frac{5}{8}$	$3\frac{7}{32}$	$2\text{-}0\frac{21}{32}-$	$3\frac{11}{32}$	$2\text{-}1\frac{21}{32}-$	$3\frac{15}{32}-$	$2\text{-}2\frac{21}{32}-$
$\frac{1}{2}$	$2\frac{31}{32}-$	$1\text{-}10\frac{11}{16}$	$3\frac{3}{32}$	$1\text{-}11\frac{11}{32}-$	$3\frac{7}{32}$	$2\text{-}0\frac{23}{32}-$	$3\frac{11}{32}$	$2\text{-}1\frac{23}{32}-$	$3\frac{1}{2}$	$2\text{-}2\frac{23}{32}-$
$\frac{9}{16}$	$2\frac{31}{32}-$	$1\text{-}10\frac{3}{4}$	$3\frac{3}{32}$	$1\text{-}11\frac{25}{32}-$	$3\frac{7}{32}$	$2\text{-}0\frac{25}{32}-$	$3\frac{3}{8}$	$2\text{-}1\frac{25}{32}-$	$3\frac{1}{2}$	$2\text{-}2\frac{25}{32}-$
$\frac{5}{8}$	$2\frac{31}{32}-$	$1\text{-}10\frac{13}{16}$	$3\frac{1}{8}$	$1\text{-}11\frac{27}{32}-$	$3\frac{1}{4}$	$2\text{-}0\frac{27}{32}-$	$3\frac{3}{8}$	$2\text{-}1\frac{27}{32}-$	$3\frac{1}{2}$	$2\text{-}2\frac{27}{32}-$
$\frac{11}{16}$	3	$1\text{-}10\frac{7}{8}$	$3\frac{1}{8}$	$1\text{-}11\frac{29}{32}-$	$3\frac{1}{4}$	$2\text{-}0\frac{29}{32}-$	$3\frac{3}{8}$	$2\text{-}1\frac{29}{32}-$	$3\frac{1}{2}$	$2\text{-}2\frac{29}{32}-$
$\frac{3}{4}$	3	$1\text{-}10\frac{15}{16}$	$3\frac{1}{8}$	$1\text{-}11\frac{31}{32}-$	$3\frac{1}{4}$	$2\text{-}0\frac{31}{32}-$	$3\frac{3}{8}$	$2\text{-}1\frac{31}{32}-$	$3\frac{17}{32}-$	$2\text{-}2\frac{31}{32}-$
$\frac{13}{16}$	3	$1\text{-}11$	$3\frac{1}{8}$	$2\text{-}0\frac{1}{32}-$	$3\frac{9}{32}$	$2\text{-}1\frac{1}{32}-$	$3\frac{13}{32}$	$2\text{-}2\frac{1}{32}-$	$3\frac{17}{32}-$	$2\text{-}3\frac{1}{32}-$
$\frac{7}{8}$	3	$1\text{-}11\frac{1}{16}$	$3\frac{5}{32}-$	$2\text{-}0\frac{3}{32}-$	$3\frac{9}{32}$	$2\text{-}1\frac{3}{32}-$	$3\frac{13}{32}$	$2\text{-}2\frac{3}{32}-$	$3\frac{17}{32}-$	$2\text{-}3\frac{3}{32}-$
$\frac{15}{16}$	$3\frac{1}{32}-$	$1\text{-}11\frac{1}{8}$	$3\frac{5}{32}-$	$2\text{-}0\frac{5}{32}-$	$3\frac{9}{32}$	$2\text{-}1\frac{5}{32}-$	$3\frac{13}{32}$	$2\text{-}2\frac{5}{32}-$	$3\frac{17}{32}-$	$2\text{-}3\frac{5}{32}-$

Inch	27″ Rise	27″ Slope	28″ Rise	28″ Slope	29″ Rise	29″ Slope	30″ Rise	30″ Slope	31″ Rise	31″ Slope
0	$3\frac{9}{16}$	$2\text{-}3\frac{7}{32}-$	$3\frac{11}{16}$	$2\text{-}4\frac{1}{4}$	$3\frac{13}{16}$	$2\text{-}5\frac{1}{4}$	$3\frac{15}{16}$	$2\text{-}6\frac{1}{4}$	$4\frac{3}{32}-$	$2\text{-}7\frac{9}{32}-$
$\frac{1}{16}$	$3\frac{9}{16}$	$2\text{-}3\frac{9}{32}-$	$3\frac{11}{16}$	$2\text{-}4\frac{5}{16}$	$3\frac{13}{16}$	$2\text{-}5\frac{5}{16}$	$3\frac{31}{32}-$	$2\text{-}6\frac{5}{16}$	$4\frac{3}{32}-$	$2\text{-}7\frac{11}{32}-$
$\frac{1}{8}$	$3\frac{9}{16}$	$2\text{-}3\frac{11}{32}-$	$3\frac{11}{16}$	$2\text{-}4\frac{3}{8}$	$3\frac{27}{32}-$	$2\text{-}5\frac{3}{8}$	$3\frac{31}{32}-$	$2\text{-}6\frac{3}{8}$	$4\frac{3}{32}-$	$2\text{-}7\frac{13}{32}-$
$\frac{3}{16}$	$3\frac{19}{32}-$	$2\text{-}3\frac{7}{16}$	$3\frac{23}{32}-$	$2\text{-}4\frac{7}{16}$	$3\frac{27}{32}-$	$2\text{-}5\frac{7}{16}$	$3\frac{31}{32}-$	$2\text{-}6\frac{7}{16}$	$4\frac{3}{32}-$	$2\text{-}7\frac{15}{32}-$
$\frac{1}{4}$	$3\frac{19}{32}-$	$2\text{-}3\frac{1}{2}$	$3\frac{23}{32}-$	$2\text{-}4\frac{1}{2}$	$3\frac{27}{32}-$	$2\text{-}5\frac{1}{2}$	$3\frac{31}{32}-$	$2\text{-}6\frac{1}{2}$	$4\frac{1}{8}$	$2\text{-}7\frac{17}{32}-$
$\frac{5}{16}$	$3\frac{19}{32}-$	$2\text{-}3\frac{9}{16}$	$3\frac{23}{32}-$	$2\text{-}4\frac{9}{16}$	$3\frac{27}{32}-$	$2\text{-}5\frac{9}{16}$	4	$2\text{-}6\frac{9}{16}$	$4\frac{1}{8}$	$2\text{-}7\frac{19}{32}-$
$\frac{3}{8}$	$3\frac{19}{32}-$	$2\text{-}3\frac{5}{8}$	$3\frac{3}{4}$	$2\text{-}4\frac{5}{8}$	$3\frac{7}{8}$	$2\text{-}5\frac{5}{8}$	4	$2\text{-}6\frac{5}{8}$	$4\frac{1}{8}$	$2\text{-}7\frac{21}{32}-$
$\frac{7}{16}$	$3\frac{5}{8}$	$2\text{-}3\frac{11}{16}$	$3\frac{3}{4}$	$2\text{-}4\frac{11}{16}$	$3\frac{7}{8}$	$2\text{-}5\frac{11}{16}$	4	$2\text{-}6\frac{11}{16}$	$4\frac{1}{8}$	$2\text{-}7\frac{23}{32}-$
$\frac{1}{2}$	$3\frac{5}{8}$	$2\text{-}3\frac{3}{4}$	$3\frac{3}{4}$	$2\text{-}4\frac{3}{4}$	$3\frac{7}{8}$	$2\text{-}5\frac{3}{4}$	4	$2\text{-}6\frac{3}{4}$	$4\frac{5}{32}-$	$2\text{-}7\frac{25}{32}-$
$\frac{9}{16}$	$3\frac{5}{8}$	$2\text{-}3\frac{13}{16}$	$3\frac{3}{4}$	$2\text{-}4\frac{13}{16}$	$3\frac{29}{32}-$	$2\text{-}5\frac{13}{16}$	$4\frac{1}{32}-$	$2\text{-}6\frac{13}{16}$	$4\frac{5}{32}-$	$2\text{-}7\frac{27}{32}-$
$\frac{5}{8}$	$3\frac{5}{8}$	$2\text{-}3\frac{7}{8}$	$3\frac{25}{32}-$	$2\text{-}4\frac{7}{8}$	$3\frac{29}{32}-$	$2\text{-}5\frac{7}{8}$	$4\frac{1}{32}-$	$2\text{-}6\frac{7}{8}$	$4\frac{5}{32}-$	$2\text{-}7\frac{29}{32}-$
$\frac{11}{16}$	$3\frac{21}{32}-$	$2\text{-}3\frac{15}{16}$	$3\frac{25}{32}-$	$2\text{-}4\frac{15}{16}$	$3\frac{29}{32}-$	$2\text{-}5\frac{15}{16}$	$4\frac{1}{32}-$	$2\text{-}6\frac{15}{16}$	$4\frac{5}{32}-$	$2\text{-}7\frac{31}{32}-$
$\frac{3}{4}$	$3\frac{21}{32}-$	$2\text{-}4$	$3\frac{25}{32}-$	$2\text{-}5$	$3\frac{29}{32}-$	$2\text{-}6$	$4\frac{1}{16}$	$2\text{-}7$	$4\frac{3}{16}$	$2\text{-}8\frac{1}{32}-$
$\frac{13}{16}$	$3\frac{21}{32}-$	$2\text{-}4\frac{1}{16}$	$3\frac{25}{32}-$	$2\text{-}5\frac{1}{16}$	$3\frac{15}{16}$	$2\text{-}6\frac{1}{16}$	$4\frac{1}{16}$	$2\text{-}7\frac{3}{32}-$	$4\frac{3}{16}$	$2\text{-}8\frac{3}{32}-$
$\frac{7}{8}$	$3\frac{21}{32}-$	$2\text{-}4\frac{1}{8}$	$3\frac{13}{16}$	$2\text{-}5\frac{1}{8}$	$3\frac{15}{16}$	$2\text{-}6\frac{1}{8}$	$4\frac{1}{16}$	$2\text{-}7\frac{5}{32}-$	$4\frac{3}{16}$	$2\text{-}8\frac{5}{32}-$
$\frac{15}{16}$	$3\frac{11}{16}$	$2\text{-}4\frac{3}{16}$	$3\frac{13}{16}$	$2\text{-}5\frac{3}{16}$	$3\frac{15}{16}$	$2\text{-}6\frac{3}{16}$	$4\frac{1}{16}$	$2\text{-}7\frac{7}{32}-$	$4\frac{7}{32}-$	$2\text{-}8\frac{7}{32}-$

GIVEN ANGLE, ITS NATURAL AND LOGARITHMIC FUNCTIONS

Natural Functions		Logarithmic Functions
Sin......0.1305262		Sin......9.1156977
Csc......7.6612976		Csc......0.8843023
Tan......0.1316525	Given Angle	Tan......9.1194291
Cot......7.5957541	7°30′	Cot......0.8805709
Cos......0.9914449		Cos......9.9962686
Sec......1.0086290		Sec......0.0037314

Inch	0″ Rise	0″ Slope	1″ Rise	1″ Slope	2″ Rise	2″ Slope	3″ Rise	3″ Slope	4″ Rise	4″ Slope	5″ Rise	5″ Slope
0	0	0	3/16	1 1/32	13/32	2 1/32	19/32	3 1/16	25/32	4 3/32−	1	5 3/32
1/16	0	1/16	7/32	1 3/32	13/32	2 3/32	19/32	3 1/8	13/16	4 5/32−	1	5 5/32
1/8	1/32	1/8	7/32	1 5/32	7/16	2 5/32	5/8	3 3/16	13/16	4 7/32−	1 1/32−	5 7/32
3/16	1/32	3/16	1/4	1 7/32	7/16	2 7/32	5/8	3 1/4	27/32	4 9/32−	1 1/32	5 9/32
1/4	1/16	1/4	1/4	1 9/32	7/16	2 9/32	21/32	3 5/16	27/32	4 11/32−	1 1/32	5 11/32
5/16	1/16	5/16	1/4	1 11/32	15/32	2 11/32	21/32	3 3/8	27/32	4 13/32−	1 1/16	5 13/32
3/8	1/16	3/8	9/32	1 13/32	15/32	2 13/32	21/32	3 7/16	7/8	4 15/32−	1 1/16	5 15/32
7/16	3/32	7/16	9/32	1 15/32	1/2	2 1/2	11/16	3 1/2	7/8	4 17/32−	1 3/32−	5 17/32
1/2	3/32	1/2	5/16	1 17/32	1/2	2 9/16	11/16	3 9/16	29/32	4 19/32−	1 3/32	5 19/32
9/16	1/8	9/16	5/16	1 19/32	1/2	2 5/8	23/32	3 5/8	29/32	4 21/32−	1 3/32	5 21/32
5/8	1/8	5/8	5/16	1 21/32	17/32	2 11/16	23/32	3 11/16	29/32	4 23/32−	1 1/8	5 3/4
11/16	1/8	11/16	11/32−	1 23/32	17/32	2 3/4	23/32	3 3/4	15/16	4 25/32−	1 1/8	5 13/16
3/4	5/32	3/4	11/32	1 25/32	9/16	2 13/16	3/4	3 13/16	15/16	4 27/32−	1 5/32−	5 7/8
13/16	5/32	27/32	3/8	1 27/32	9/16	2 7/8	3/4	3 7/8	31/32	4 29/32−	1 5/32	5 15/16
7/8	3/16	29/32	3/8	1 29/32	9/16	2 15/16	25/32−	3 15/16	31/32	4 31/32−	1 5/32	6
15/16	3/16	31/32	3/8	1 31/32	19/32	3	25/32	4	31/32	5½	1 3/16	6 1/16

Inch	6″ Rise	6″ Slope	7″ Rise	7″ Slope	8″ Rise	8″ Slope	9″ Rise	9″ Slope	10″ Rise	10″ Slope	11″ Rise	11″ Slope
0	1 3/16	6 1/8	1 13/32−	7 1/8	1 19/32−	8 5/32−	1 25/32−	9 3/16	2	10 3/16	2 3/16	11 7/32−
1/16	1 7/32	6 3/16	1 13/32	7 3/16	1 19/32	8 7/32−	1 13/16	9 1/4	2	10 1/4	2 3/16	11 9/32−
1/8	1 7/32	6 1/4	1 13/32	7 1/4	1 5/8	8 9/32−	1 13/16	9 5/16−	2	10 5/16−	2 7/32−	11 11/32−
3/16	1 7/32	6 5/16	1 7/16	7 11/32−	1 5/8	8 11/32−	1 13/16	9 3/8	2 1/32−	10 3/8	2 7/32	11 13/32−
1/4	1 1/4	6 3/8	1 7/16	7 13/32−	1 21/32−	8 13/32−	1 27/32−	9 7/16	2 1/32	10 7/16	2 1/4	11 15/32−
5/16	1 1/4	6 7/16	1 15/32−	7 15/32−	1 21/32	8 15/32−	1 27/32	9 1/2	2 1/32	10 1/2	2 1/4	11 17/32−
3/8	1 9/32	6 1/2	1 15/32	7 17/32−	1 21/32	8 17/32−	1 7/8	9 9/16	2 1/16	10 19/32−	2 1/4	11 19/32−
7/16	1 9/32	6 9/16	1 15/32	7 19/32−	1 11/16	8 19/32−	1 7/8	9 5/8	2 1/16	10 21/32−	2 9/32−	11 21/32−
1/2	1 9/32	6 5/8	1 1/2	7 21/32−	1 11/16	8 21/32−	1 7/8	9 11/16	2 3/32−	10 23/32−	2 9/32	11 23/32−
9/16	1 5/16	6 11/16	1 1/2	7 23/32−	1 23/32−	8 23/32−	1 29/32−	9 3/4	2 3/32	10 25/32−	2 5/16	11 25/32−
5/8	1 5/16	6 3/4	1 17/32−	7 25/32−	1 23/32	8 25/32−	1 29/32	9 13/16−	2 1/8	10 27/32−	2 5/16	11 27/32−
11/16	1 11/32−	6 13/16	1 17/32	7 27/32−	1 23/32	8 27/32−	1 15/16	9 7/8	2 1/8	10 29/32−	2 5/16	11 29/32−
3/4	1 11/32	6 7/8	1 17/32	7 29/32−	1 3/4	8 29/32−	1 15/16	9 15/16−	2 1/8	10 31/32−	2 11/32−	11 31/32−
13/16	1 11/32	6 15/16	1 9/16	7 31/32−	1 3/4	9	1 15/16	10	2 5/32−	11 1/32−	2 11/32	1-0 1/32
7/8	1 3/8	7	1 9/16	8 1/32−	1 3/4	9 1/16	1 31/32−	10 1/16	2 5/32	11 3/32−	2 3/8	1-0 3/32
15/16	1 3/8	7 1/16	1 19/32−	8 3/32−	1 25/32−	9 1/8	1 31/32	10 1/8	2 3/16	11 5/32−	2 3/8	1-0 5/32

Feet	0′ Rise	0′ Slope	10′ Rise	10′ Slope	20′ Rise	20′ Slope	30′ Rise	30′ Slope
0	0	0	1-11 7/8	10-2 11/32−	3-11 3/4	20-4 11/16	5-11 19/32−	30-7 1/16
1	2 3/8	1-0 1/4	2-2 1/4	11-2 19/32−	4-2 1/8	21-4 15/16	6-2	31-7 9/32−
2	4 25/32	2-0 15/32	2-4 21/32	12-2 13/16	4-4 1/2	22-5 3/16	6-4 3/8	32-7 11/32−
3	7 5/32	3-0 23/32−	2-7 1/32	13-3 1/16	4-6 29/32−	23-5 13/32−	6-6 25/32−	33-7 3/4
4	9 9/16	4-0 15/16	2-9 13/32	14-3 9/32−	4-9 9/32	24-5 21/32−	6-9 5/32	34-8
5	11 15/16	5-1 3/16	2-11 13/16	15-3 17/32−	4-11 11/16	25-5 7/8	6-11 17/32−	35-8 7/32−
6	1-2 5/16	6-1 13/32−	3-2 3/16	16-3 3/4	5-2 1/16	26-6 1/8	7-1 15/16	36-8 15/32−
7	1-4 23/32−	7-1 21/32−	3-4 9/16	17-4	5-4 7/16	27-6 11/32−	7-4 5/16	37-8 11/16
8	1-7 3/32	8-1 7/8	3-6 31/32−	18-4 7/32−	5-6 27/32−	28-6 19/32−	7-6 23/32−	38-8 15/16
9	1-9 15/32	9-2 1/8	3-9 11/32−	19-4 15/32−	5-9 7/32	29-6 13/16	7-9 3/32−	39-9 5/32−

Inch	12″ Rise	12″ Slope	13″ Rise	13″ Slope	14″ Rise	14″ Slope	15″ Rise	15″ Slope	16″ Rise	16″ Slope
0	2 3/8	1-0 1/4	2 19/32	1-1 1/4	2 25/32	1-2 9/32	2 31/32	1-3 9/32	3 3/16	1-4 5/16
1/16	2 13/32	1-0 5/16	2 19/32	1-1 5/16	2 13/16	1-2 11/32	3	1-3 11/32	3 3/16	1-4 3/8
1/8	2 13/32	1-0 3/8	2 5/8	1-1 3/8	2 13/16	1-2 13/32	3	1-3 13/32	3 7/32	1-4 7/16
3/16	2 7/16	1-0 7/16	2 5/8	1-1 7/16	2 13/16	1-2 15/32	3 1/32	1-3 1/2	3 7/32	1-4 1/2
1/4	2 7/16	1-0 1/2	2 5/8	1-1 1/2	2 27/32	1-2 17/32	3 1/32	1-3 9/16	3 7/32	1-4 9/16
5/16	2 7/16	1-0 9/16	2 21/32	1-1 9/16	2 27/32	1-2 19/32	3 1/32	1-3 5/8	3 1/4	1-4 5/8
3/8	2 15/32	1-0 5/8	2 21/32	1-1 5/8	2 27/32	1-2 21/32	3 1/16	1-3 11/16	3 1/4	1-4 11/16
7/16	2 15/32	1-0 11/16	2 11/16	1-1 11/16	2 7/8	1-2 23/32	3 1/16	1-3 3/4	3 9/32	1-4 3/4
1/2	2 1/2	1-0 3/4	2 11/16	1-1 3/4	2 7/8	1-2 25/32	3 3/32	1-3 13/16	3 9/32	1-4 13/16
9/16	2 1/2	1-0 13/16	2 11/16	1-1 27/32	2 29/32	1-2 27/32	3 3/32	1-3 7/8	3 9/32	1-4 7/8
5/8	2 1/2	1-0 7/8	2 23/32	1-1 29/32	2 29/32	1-2 29/32	3 3/32	1-3 15/16	3 5/16	1-4 15/16
11/16	2 17/32	1-0 15/16	2 23/32	1-1 31/32	2 29/32	1-2 31/32	3 1/8	1-4	3 5/16	1-5
3/4	2 17/32	1-1	2 3/4	1-2 1/32	2 15/16	1-3 1/32	3 1/8	1-4 1/16	3 11/32	1-5 3/32
13/16	2 9/16	1-1 1/16	2 3/4	1-2 3/32	2 15/16	1-3 3/32	3 5/32	1-4 1/8	3 11/32	1-5 5/32
7/8	2 9/16	1-1 1/8	2 3/4	1-2 5/32	2 31/32	1-3 5/32	3 5/32	1-4 3/16	3 11/32	1-5 7/32
15/16	2 9/16	1-1 3/16	2 25/32	1-2 7/32	2 31/32	1-3 7/32	3 5/32	1-4 1/4	3 3/8	1-5 9/32

Inch	17″ Rise	17″ Slope	18″ Rise	18″ Slope	19″ Rise	19″ Slope	20″ Rise	20″ Slope	21″ Rise	21″ Slope
0	3 3/8	1-5 11/32	3 19/32	1-6 11/32	3 25/32	1-7 3/8	3 31/32	1-8 13/32	4 3/16	1-9 13/32
1/16	3 13/32	1-5 13/32	3 19/32	1-6 13/32	3 25/32	1-7 7/16	4	1-8 15/32	4 3/16	1-9 15/32
1/8	3 13/32	1-5 15/32	3 19/32	1-6 15/32	3 13/16	1-7 1/2	4	1-8 17/32	4 3/16	1-9 17/32
3/16	3 13/32	1-5 17/32	3 5/8	1-6 17/32	3 13/16	1-7 9/16	4	1-8 19/32	4 7/32	1-9 19/32
1/4	3 7/16	1-5 19/32	3 5/8	1-6 19/32	3 27/32	1-7 5/8	4 1/32	1-8 21/32	4 7/32	1-9 21/32
5/16	3 7/16	1-5 21/32	3 21/32	1-6 21/32	3 27/32	1-7 11/16	4 1/32	1-8 23/32	4 1/4	1-9 23/32
3/8	3 15/32	1-5 23/32	3 21/32	1-6 3/4	3 27/32	1-7 3/4	4 1/16	1-8 25/32	4 1/4	1-9 25/32
7/16	3 15/32	1-5 25/32	3 21/32	1-6 13/16	3 7/8	1-7 13/16	4 1/16	1-8 27/32	4 1/4	1-9 27/32
1/2	3 15/32	1-5 27/32	3 11/16	1-6 7/8	3 7/8	1-7 7/8	4 1/16	1-8 29/32	4 9/32	1-9 29/32
9/16	3 1/2	1-5 29/32	3 11/16	1-6 15/16	3 29/32	1-7 15/16	4 3/32	1-8 31/32	4 9/32	1-10
5/8	3 1/2	1-5 31/32	3 23/32	1-7	3 29/32	1-8	4 3/32	1-9 1/32	4 5/16	1-10 1/16
11/16	3 17/32	1-6 1/32	3 23/32	1-7 1/16	3 29/32	1-8 1/16	4 1/8	1-9 3/32	4 5/16	1-10 1/8
3/4	3 17/32	1-6 3/32	3 23/32	1-7 1/8	3 15/16	1-8 1/8	4 1/8	1-9 5/32	4 5/16	1-10 3/16
13/16	3 17/32	1-6 5/32	3 3/4	1-7 3/16	3 15/16	1-8 3/16	4 1/8	1-9 7/32	4 11/32	1-10 1/4
7/8	3 9/16	1-6 7/32	3 3/4	1-7 1/4	3 31/32	1-8 1/4	4 5/32	1-9 9/32	4 11/32	1-10 5/16
15/16	3 9/16	1-6 9/32	3 25/32	1-7 5/16	3 31/32	1-8 5/16	4 5/32	1-9 11/32	4 3/8	1-10 3/8

Feet	40′ Rise	40′ Slope	50′ Rise	50′ Slope	60′ Rise	60′ Slope	70′ Rise	70′ Slope
0	7-11 15/32	40-9 13/32	9-11 11/32	50-11 3/4	11-11 7/32	61-2 3/32	13-11 3/32	71-4 15/32
1	8-1 7/8	41-9 5/8	10-1 23/32	52-0	12-1 19/32	62-2 11/32	14-1 15/32	72-4 11/16
2	8-4 1/4	42-9 7/8	10-4 1/8	53-0 7/32	12-4	63-2 9/16	14-3 7/8	73-4 15/16
3	8-6 5/8	43-10 3/32	10-6 1/2	54-0 15/32	12-6 3/8	64-2 13/16	14-6 1/4	74-5 5/32
4	8-9 1/32	44-10 11/32	10-8 29/32	55-0 11/16	12-8 3/4	65-3 1/32	14-8 5/8	75-5 13/32
5	8-11 13/32	45-10 19/32	10-11 9/32	56-0 15/16	12-11 5/32	66-3 9/32	14-11 1/2	76-5 5/8
6	9-1 13/16	46-10 13/16	11-1 21/32	57-1 5/32	13-1 17/32	67-3 17/32	15-1 13/32	77-5 7/8
7	9-4 3/16	47-11 1/16	11-4 1/16	58-1 3/32	13-3 15/16	68-3 3/4	15-3 25/32	78-6 3/32
8	9-6 9/16	48-11 9/32	11-6 7/16	59-1 5/8	13-6 5/16	69-4	15-6 3/16	79-6 11/32
9	9-8 31/32	49-11 17/32	11-8 27/32	60-1 7/8	13-8 11/16	70-4 7/32	15-8 9/16	80-6 9/16

Inch	22″ Rise	22″ Slope	23″ Rise	23″ Slope	24″ Rise	24″ Slope	25″ Rise	25″ Slope	26″ Rise	26″ Slope
0	4 3/8	1-10 7/16	4 9/16	1-11 7/16	4 25/32	2-0 15/32	4 31/32	2-1 1/2	5 5/32	2-2 1/2
1/16	4 3/8	1-10 1/2	4 19/32	1-11 1/2	4 25/32	2-0 17/32	5	2-1 9/16	5 3/16	2-2 9/16
1/8	4 13/32	1-10 9/16	4 19/32	1-11 9/16	4 13/16	2-0 19/32	5	2-1 5/8	5 3/16	2-2 5/8
3/16	4 13/32	1-10 5/8	4 5/8	1-11 21/32	4 13/16	2-0 21/32	5	2-1 11/16	5 7/32	2-2 11/16
1/4	4 7/16	1-10 11/16	4 5/8	1-11 23/32	4 13/16	2-0 23/32	5 1/32	2-1 3/4	5 7/32	2-2 3/4
5/16	4 7/16	1-10 3/4	4 5/8	1-11 25/32	4 27/32	2-0 25/32	5 1/32	2-1 13/16	5 7/32	2-2 13/16
3/8	4 7/16	1-10 13/16	4 21/32	1-11 27/32	4 27/32	2-0 27/32	5 1/16	2-1 7/8	5 1/4	2-2 29/32
7/16	4 15/32	1-10 7/8	4 21/32	1-11 29/32	4 7/8	2-0 29/32	5 1/16	2-1 15/16	5 1/4	2-2 31/32
1/2	4 15/32	1-10 15/16	4 11/16	1-11 31/32	4 7/8	2-0 31/32	5 1/16	2-2	5 9/32	2-3 1/32
9/16	4 1/2	1-11	4 11/16	2- 0 1/32	4 7/8	2-1 1/32	5 3/32	2-2 1/16	5 9/32	2-3 3/32
5/8	4 1/2	1-11 1/16	4 11/16	2- 0 3/32	4 29/32	2-1 3/32	5 3/32	2-2 1/8	5 5/16	2-3 5/32
11/16	4 1/2	1-11 1/8	4 23/32	2- 0 5/32	4 29/32	2-1 5/32	5 1/8	2-2 3/16	5 5/16	2-3 7/32
3/4	4 17/32	1-11 3/16	4 23/32	2- 0 7/32	4 15/16	2-1 1/4	5 1/8	2-2 1/4	5 5/16	2-3 9/32
13/16	4 17/32	1-11 1/4	4 3/4	2- 0 9/32	4 15/16	2-1 5/16	5 1/8	2-2 5/16	5 11/32	2-3 11/32
7/8	4 9/16	1-11 5/16	4 3/4	2- 0 11/32	4 15/16	2-1 3/8	5 5/32	2-2 3/8	5 11/32	2-3 13/32
15/16	4 9/16	1-11 3/8	4 3/4	2- 0 13/32	4 31/32	2-1 7/16	5 5/32	2-2 7/16	5 11/32	2-3 15/32

Inch	27″ Rise	27″ Slope	28″ Rise	28″ Slope	29″ Rise	29″ Slope	30″ Rise	30″ Slope	31″ Rise	31″ Slope
0	5 3/8	2-3 17/32	5 9/16	2-4 9/16	5 25/32	2-5 9/16	5 31/32	2-6 19/32	6 5/32	2-7 19/32
1/16	5 3/8	2-3 19/32	5 19/32	2-4 5/8	5 25/32	2-5 5/8	5 31/32	2-6 21/32	6 3/16	2-7 21/32
1/8	5 13/32	2-3 21/32	5 19/32	2-4 11/16	5 25/32	2-5 11/16	6	2-6 23/32	6 3/16	2-7 3/4
3/16	5 13/32	2-3 23/32	5 19/32	2-4 3/4	5 13/16	2-5 3/4	6	2-6 25/32	6 3/16	2-7 13/16
1/4	5 13/32	2-3 25/32	5 5/8	2-4 13/16	5 13/16	2-5 13/16	6 1/32	2-6 27/32	6 7/32	2-7 7/8
5/16	5 7/16	2-3 27/32	5 5/8	2-4 7/8	5 27/32	2-5 7/8	6 1/32	2-6 29/32	6 7/32	2-7 15/16
3/8	5 7/16	2-3 29/32	5 21/32	2-4 15/16	5 27/32	2-5 15/16	6 1/32	2-6 31/32	6 1/4	2-8
7/16	5 15/32	2-3 31/32	5 21/32	2-5	5 27/32	2-6	6 1/16	2-7 1/32	6 1/4	2-8 1/16
1/2	5 15/32	2-4 1/32	5 21/32	2-5 1/16	5 7/8	2-6 1/16	6 1/16	2-7 3/32	6 9/32	2-8 1/8
9/16	5 15/32	2-4 3/32	5 11/16	2-5 1/8	5 7/8	2-6 1/8	6 3/32	2-7 5/32	6 9/32	2-8 3/16
5/8	5 1/2	2-4 5/32	5 11/16	2-5 3/16	5 29/32	2-6 3/16	6 3/32	2-7 7/32	6 5/16	2-8 1/4
11/16	5 1/2	2-4 7/32	5 23/32	2-5 1/4	5 29/32	2-6 9/32	6 3/32	2-7 9/32	6 5/16	2-8 5/16
3/4	5 17/32	2-4 9/32	5 23/32	2-5 5/16	5 29/32	2-6 11/32	6 1/8	2-7 11/32	6 5/16	2-8 3/8
13/16	5 17/32	2-4 11/32	5 23/32	2-5 3/8	5 15/16	2-6 13/32	6 1/8	2-7 13/32	6 11/32	2-8 7/16
7/8	5 17/32	2-4 13/32	5 3/4	2-5 7/16	5 15/16	2-6 15/32	6 5/32	2-7 15/32	6 11/32	2-8 1/2
15/16	5 9/16	2-4 1/2	5 3/4	2-5 1/2	5 31/32	2-6 17/32	6 5/32	2-7 17/32	6 11/32	2-8 9/16

GIVEN ANGLE, ITS NATURAL AND LOGARITHMIC FUNCTIONS

Natural Functions	Given Angle	Logarithmic Functions
Sin......0.1950903		Sin......9.2902357
Csc......5.1258309		Csc......0.7097643
Tan......0.1989124	Given Angle	Tan......9.2986618
Cot......5.0273395	11°15′	Cot......0.7013382
Cos......0.9807853		Cos......9.9915739
Sec......1.0195912		Sec......0.0084261

Inch	0″ Rise	0″ Slope	1″ Rise	1″ Slope	2″ Rise	2″ Slope	3″ Rise	3″ Slope	4″ Rise	4″ Slope	5″ Rise	5″ Slope
0	0	0	9/32−	1 1/32	17/32−	2 1/8	13/16	3 3/32	1 1/16	4 5/32	1 11/32−	5 3/16
1/16	1/32−	1/16	9/32	1 3/32	9/16	2 1/8	13/16	3 5/32	1 3/32−	4 7/32−	1 11/32−	5 1/4
1/8	1/32−	1/8	5/16	1 5/32	9/16	2 3/16	27/32−	3 1/4	1 3/32	4 9/32−	1 3/8	5 5/32−
3/16	1/32−	3/16	5/16	1 7/32	19/32−	2 1/4	27/32−	3 5/16	1 1/8	4 11/32−	1 3/8	5 3/8
1/4	1/16−	1/4	11/32−	1 9/32	19/32	2 11/32−	7/8	3 3/8	1 1/8	4 13/32−	1 13/32	5 7/16
5/16	3/32−	5/16	11/32	1 11/32	5/8	2 13/32−	7/8	3 7/16	1 5/32−	4 15/32−	1 7/16	5 1/2
3/8	3/32−	3/8	3/8	1 7/16	5/8	2 15/32−	29/32−	3 1/2	1 3/16	4 17/32−	1 7/16	5 9/16
7/16	1/8−	7/16	3/8	1 1/2	21/32−	2 17/32−	29/32−	3 9/16	1 3/16	4 19/32−	1 15/32−	5 5/8
1/2	1/8	17/32	13/32−	1 9/16	21/32	2 19/32−	15/16	3 5/8	1 7/32−	4 21/32−	1 15/32	5 11/16
9/16	5/32−	19/32−	13/32	1 5/8	11/16	2 21/32−	15/16	3 11/16	1 7/32	4 23/32−	1 1/2	5 3/4
5/8	5/32−	21/32−	7/16	1 11/16	23/32−	2 23/32−	31/32−	3 3/4	1 1/4	4 25/32−	1 1/2	5 13/16
11/16	3/16−	23/32−	7/16	1 3/4	23/32	2 25/32−	1	3 13/16	1 1/4	4 27/32−	1 17/32−	5 7/8
3/4	3/16−	25/32−	15/32−	1 13/16	3/4	2 27/32−	1	3 7/8	1 9/32−	4 29/32−	1 9/16	5 15/16
13/16	7/32−	27/32−	15/32	1 7/8	3/4	2 29/32−	1 1/32−	3 15/16	1 9/32	4 31/32−	1 9/16	6 1/32−
7/8	1/4	29/32−	1/2	1 15/16	25/32−	2 31/32−	1 1/32	4	1 5/16	5 1/16	1 19/32−	6 3/32−
15/16	1/4	31/32	17/32−	2	25/32	3 1/32−	1 1/16	4 1/16	1 5/16	5 1/8	1 19/32	6 5/32−

Inch	6″ Rise	6″ Slope	7″ Rise	7″ Slope	8″ Rise	8″ Slope	9″ Rise	9″ Slope	10″ Rise	10″ Slope	11″ Rise	11″ Slope
0	1 19/32−	6 7/32−	1 7/8	7 1/4	2 5/32−	8 9/32−	2 13/32−	9 5/16	2 11/16	10 11/32−	2 15/16	11 3/8
1/16	1 5/8	6 9/32−	1 29/32−	7 5/16	2 5/32	8 11/32−	2 7/16	9 3/8	2 11/16	10 13/32−	2 31/32−	11 7/16
1/8	1 21/32−	6 11/32−	1 29/32	7 3/8	2 3/16	8 13/32−	2 7/16	9 7/16	2 23/32−	10 15/32−	2 31/32−	11 17/32−
3/16	1 21/32	6 13/32−	1 15/16	7 7/16	2 3/16	8 15/32−	2 15/32−	9 1/2	2 23/32	10 9/16	3	11 19/32−
1/4	1 11/16	6 15/32−	1 15/16	7 1/2	2 7/32−	8 17/32−	2 15/32	9 9/16	2 3/4	10 5/8	3	11 21/32−
5/16	1 11/16	6 17/32−	1 31/32−	7 9/16	2 7/32	8 19/32−	2 1/2	9 21/32−	2 3/4	10 11/16	3 1/32−	11 23/32−
3/8	1 23/32−	6 19/32−	1 31/32	7 5/8	2 1/4	8 21/32−	2 1/2	9 23/32−	2 25/32−	10 3/4	3 1/16	11 25/32−
7/16	1 23/32	6 21/32−	2	7 11/16	2 1/4	8 3/4	2 17/32−	9 25/32−	2 25/32	10 13/16	3 1/16	11 27/32−
1/2	1 3/4	6 23/32−	2	7 3/4	2 9/32−	8 13/16	2 17/32	9 27/32−	2 13/16	10 7/8	3 3/32−	11 29/32−
9/16	1 3/4	6 25/32−	2 1/32−	7 27/32−	2 9/32	8 7/8	2 9/16	9 29/32−	2 27/32−	10 15/16	3 3/32	11 31/32−
5/8	1 25/32−	6 27/32−	2 1/32	7 29/32−	2 5/16	8 15/16	2 19/32−	9 31/32−	2 27/32	11	3 1/8	1-0 1/32−
11/16	1 25/32	6 15/16	2 1/16	7 31/32−	2 5/16	9	2 19/32	10 1/32−	2 7/8	11 1/16	3 1/8	1-0 3/32−
3/4	1 13/16	7	2 1/16	8 1/32−	2 11/32−	9 1/16	2 5/8	10 3/32−	2 7/8	11 1/8	3 5/32−	1-0 5/32−
13/16	1 13/16	7 1/16	2 3/32−	8 3/32−	2 3/8	9 1/8	2 5/8	10 5/32−	2 29/32−	11 3/16	3 5/32	1-0 7/32−
7/8	1 27/32−	7 1/8	2 1/8	8 5/32−	2 3/8	9 3/16	2 21/32−	10 7/32−	2 29/32	11 1/4	3 3/16	1-0 9/32−
15/16	1 27/32	7 3/16	2 1/8	8 7/32−	2 13/32−	9 1/4	2 21/32	10 9/32−	2 15/16	11 5/16	3 3/16	1-0 11/32−

Feet	0′ Rise	0′ Slope	10′ Rise	10′ Slope	20′ Rise	20′ Slope	30′ Rise	30′ Slope
0	0	0	2-8 5/32−	10-4 7/8	5-4 5/16	20-8 15/32−	8-0 15/32−	31-0 11/16
1	3 7/32−	1-0 7/16	2-11 3/8	11-4 21/32−	5-7 17/32−	21-8 7/8	8-3 11/16	32-1 1/8
2	6 7/16	2-0 27/32−	3-2 19/32−	12-5 3/32−	5-10 3/4	22-9 5/16	8-6 29/32−	33-1 17/32−
3	9 21/32−	3-1 9/32−	3-5 13/16	13-5 1/2	6-1 31/32−	23-9 3/4	8-10 3/32	34-1 31/32−
4	1-0 7/8	4-1 11/16	3-9	14-5 15/16	6-5 5/32−	24-10 5/32−	9-1 5/16	35-2 13/32−
5	1-4 1/16	5-2 1/8	4-0 7/32	15-6 11/32−	6-8 3/8	25-10 19/32−	9-4 17/32−	36-2 13/16
6	1-7 9/32−	6-2 17/32−	4-3 7/16	16-6 25/32−	6-11 19/32−	26-11	9-7 3/4	37-3 1/4
7	1-10 1/2	7-2 31/32−	4-6 21/32−	17-7 3/16	7-2 13/16	27-11 7/16	9-10 31/32−	38-3 21/32−
8	2-1 23/32−	8-3 3/8	4-9 7/8	18-7 5/8	7-6 1/32−	28-11 27/32−	10-2 3/16	39-4 3/32−
9	2-4 15/16	9-3 13/16	5-1 3/32−	19-8 1/32	7-9 1/4	30-0 9/32−	10-5 13/32−	40-4 1/2

Inch	12″ Rise	12″ Slope	13″ Rise	13″ Slope	14″ Rise	14″ Slope	15″ Rise	15″ Slope	16″ Rise	16″ Slope
0	3 7/32	1-0 7/16	3 15/32	1-1 15/32	3 3/4	1-2 1/2	4 1/32	1-3 17/32	4 9/32	1-4 9/16
1/16	3 7/32	1-0 1/2	3 1/2	1-1 17/32	3 25/32	1-2 9/16	4 1/32	1-3 19/32	4 5/16	1-4 5/8
1/8	3 1/4	1-0 9/16	3 17/32	1-1 19/32	3 25/32	1-2 5/8	4 1/16	1-3 21/32	4 5/16	1-4 11/16
3/16	3 9/32	1-0 5/8	3 17/32	1-1 21/32	3 13/16	1-2 11/16	4 1/16	1-3 23/32	4 11/32	1-4 3/4
1/4	3 9/32	1-0 11/16	3 9/16	1-1 23/32	3 13/16	1-2 3/4	4 3/32	1-3 25/32	4 11/32	1-4 13/16
5/16	3 5/16	1-0 3/4	3 9/16	1-1 25/32	3 27/32	1-2 13/16	4 3/32	1-3 27/32	4 3/8	1-4 7/8
3/8	3 5/16	1-0 13/16	3 19/32	1-1 27/32	3 27/32	1-2 7/8	4 1/8	1-3 29/32	4 3/8	1-4 15/16
7/16	3 11/32	1-0 7/8	3 19/32	1-1 29/32	3 7/8	1-2 15/16	4 1/8	1-3 31/32	4 13/32	1-5 1/32
1/2	3 11/32	1-0 15/16	3 5/8	1-1 31/32	3 7/8	1-3	4 5/32	1-4 1/32	4 13/32	1-5 3/32
9/16	3 3/8	1-1	3 5/8	1-2 1/32	3 29/32	1-3 1/16	4 5/32	1-4 1/8	4 7/16	1-5 5/32
5/8	3 3/8	1-1 1/16	3 21/32	1-2 3/32	3 29/32	1-3 5/32	4 3/16	1-4 3/16	4 15/32	1-5 7/32
11/16	3 13/32	1-1 1/8	3 21/32	1-2 5/32	3 15/32	1-3 7/32	4 7/32	1-4 1/4	4 15/32	1-5 9/32
3/4	3 13/32	1-1 3/16	3 11/16	1-2 1/4	3 15/16	1-3 9/32	4 7/32	1-4 5/16	4 1/2	1-5 11/32
13/16	3 7/16	1-1 1/4	3 11/16	1-2 5/16	3 31/32	1-3 11/32	4 1/4	1-4 3/8	4 1/2	1-5 13/32
7/8	3 7/16	1-1 11/32	3 23/32	1-2 3/8	4	1-3 13/32	4 1/4	1-4 7/16	4 17/32	1-5 15/32
15/16	3 15/32	1-1 13/32	3 3/4	1-2 7/16	4	1-3 15/32	4 9/32	1-4 1/2	4 17/32	1-5 17/32

Inch	17″ Rise	17″ Slope	18″ Rise	18″ Slope	19″ Rise	19″ Slope	20″ Rise	20″ Slope	21″ Rise	21″ Slope
0	4 9/16	1-5 19/32	4 13/16	1-6 5/8	5 3/32	1-7 21/32	5 11/32	1-8 23/32	5 5/8	1- 9 3/4
1/16	4 9/16	1-5 21/32	4 27/32	1-6 11/16	5 3/32	1-7 3/4	5 3/8	1-8 25/32	5 21/32	1- 9 13/16
1/8	4 19/32	1-5 23/32	4 27/32	1-6 3/4	5 1/8	1-7 13/16	5 13/32	1-8 27/32	5 21/32	1- 9 7/8
3/16	4 19/32	1-5 25/32	4 7/8	1-6 27/32	5 5/32	1-7 7/8	5 13/32	1-8 29/32	5 11/16	1- 9 15/16
1/4	4 5/8	1-5 27/32	4 7/8	1-6 29/32	5 5/32	1-7 15/16	5 7/16	1-8 31/32	5 11/16	1-10
5/16	4 5/8	1-5 15/16	4 29/32	1-6 31/32	5 3/16	1-8	5 7/16	1-9 1/32	5 23/32	1-10 1/16
3/8	4 21/32	1-6	4 15/16	1-7 1/32	5 3/16	1-8 1/16	5 15/32	1-9 3/32	5 23/32	1-10 1/8
7/16	4 11/16	1-6 1/16	4 15/16	1-7 3/32	5 7/32	1-8 1/8	5 15/32	1-9 5/32	5 3/4	1-10 3/16
1/2	4 11/16	1-6 1/8	4 31/32	1-7 5/32	5 1/4	1-8 3/16	5 1/2	1-9 7/32	5 3/4	1-10 1/4
9/16	4 23/32	1-6 3/16	4 31/32	1-7 7/32	5 1/4	1-8 1/4	5 1/2	1-9 9/32	5 25/32	1-10 5/16
5/8	4 23/32	1-6 1/4	5	1-7 9/32	5 1/4	1-8 5/16	5 17/32	1-9 11/32	5 25/32	1-10 3/8
11/16	4 3/4	1-6 5/16	5	1-7 11/32	5 9/32	1-8 3/8	5 17/32	1-9 13/32	5 13/16	1-10 7/16
3/4	4 3/4	1-6 3/8	5 1/32	1-7 13/32	5 9/32	1-8 7/16	5 9/16	1-9 15/32	5 13/16	1-10 17/32
13/16	4 25/32	1-6 7/16	5 1/32	1-7 15/32	5 5/16	1-8 1/2	5 9/16	1-9 17/32	5 27/32	1-10 19/32
7/8	4 25/32	1-6 1/2	5 1/16	1-7 17/32	5 5/16	1-8 9/16	5 19/32	1-9 5/8	5 7/8	1-10 21/32
15/16	4 13/16	1-6 9/16	5 1/16	1-7 19/32	5 11/32	1-8 21/32	5 5/8	1-9 11/16	5 7/8	1-10 23/32

Feet	40′ Rise	40′ Slope	50′ Rise	50′ Slope	60′ Rise	60′ Slope	70′ Rise	70′ Slope
0	10- 8 5/8	41-4 15/16	13- 4 25/32	51- 9 5/32	16- 0 15/16	62-1 13/32	18- 9 1/16	72-5 5/8
1	10-11 27/32	42-5 11/32	13- 8	52- 9 19/32	16- 4 1/8	63-1 13/16	19- 0 9/32	73-6 1/16
2	11- 3 1/32	43-5 25/32	13-11 3/16	53-10	16- 7 11/32	64-2 1/4	19- 3 1/2	74-6 15/32
3	11- 6 1/4	44-6 3/16	14- 2 13/32	54-10 7/32	16-10 9/16	65-2 21/32	19- 6 23/32	75-6 29/32
4	11- 9 15/32	45-6 5/8	14- 5 5/8	55-10 27/32	17- 1 25/32	66-3 3/32	19- 9 15/16	76-7 3/8
5	12- 0 11/16	46-7 1/16	14- 8 27/32	56-11 9/32	17- 5	67-3 1/2	20- 1 5/32	77-7 3/4
6	12- 3 29/32	47-7 15/32	15- 0 1/16	57-11 23/32	17- 8 27/32	68-3 15/16	20- 4 3/8	78-8 3/8
7	12- 7 1/8	48-7 29/32	15- 3 9/32	59- 0 1/8	17-11 11/16	69-4 3/8	20- 7 19/32	79-8 19/32
8	12-10 11/32	49-8 5/16	15- 6 1/2	60- 0 9/16	18- 2 21/32	70-4 25/32	20-10 3/16	80-9 1/2
9	13- 1 9/16	50-8 3/4	15- 9 23/32	61- 0 31/32	18- 5 7/8	71-5 7/32	21- 2 1/32	81-9 7/16

15° PITCH (Bevel between $3\frac{3}{16}''$ to $12''$ and $3\frac{1}{4}''$ to $12''$)

Inch	22″ Rise	22″ Slope	23″ Rise	23″ Slope	24″ Rise	24″ Slope	25″ Rise	25″ Slope	26″ Rise	26″ Slope
0	$5\frac{29}{32}$	$1\text{-}10\frac{25}{32}$	$6\frac{5}{32}$	$1\text{-}11\frac{13}{16}$	$6\frac{7}{16}$	$2\text{-}0\frac{27}{32}$	$6\frac{11}{16}$	$2\text{-}1\frac{7}{8}$	$6\frac{31}{32}$	$2\text{-}2\frac{29}{32}$
$\frac{1}{16}$	$5\frac{29}{32}$	$1\text{-}10\frac{27}{32}$	$6\frac{3}{16}$	$1\text{-}11\frac{7}{8}$	$6\frac{7}{16}$	$2\text{-}0\frac{29}{32}$	$6\frac{23}{32}$	$2\text{-}1\frac{15}{16}$	$6\frac{31}{32}$	$2\text{-}2\frac{31}{32}$
$\frac{1}{8}$	$5\frac{15}{16}$	$1\text{-}10\frac{29}{32}$	$6\frac{3}{16}$	$1\text{-}11\frac{15}{16}$	$6\frac{15}{32}$	$2\text{-}0\frac{31}{32}$	$6\frac{23}{32}$	$2\text{-}2$	7	$2\text{-}3\frac{1}{32}$
$\frac{3}{16}$	$5\frac{15}{16}$	$1\text{-}10\frac{31}{32}$	$6\frac{7}{32}$	$2\text{-}0$	$6\frac{15}{32}$	$2\text{-}1\frac{1}{32}$	$6\frac{3}{4}$	$2\text{-}2\frac{1}{16}$	$7\frac{1}{2}{-}$	$2\text{-}3\frac{1}{8}$
$\frac{1}{4}$	$5\frac{31}{32}$	$1\text{-}11\frac{1}{32}$	$6\frac{7}{32}$	$2\text{-}0\frac{1}{16}$	$6\frac{1}{2}$	$2\text{-}1\frac{3}{32}$	$6\frac{25}{32}$	$2\text{-}2\frac{5}{32}$	$7\frac{1}{32}$	$2\text{-}3\frac{3}{16}$
$\frac{5}{16}$	$5\frac{31}{32}$	$1\text{-}11\frac{3}{32}$	$6\frac{1}{4}$	$2\text{-}0\frac{1}{8}$	$6\frac{1}{2}$	$2\text{-}1\frac{5}{32}$	$6\frac{25}{32}$	$2\text{-}2\frac{7}{32}$	$7\frac{1}{16}$	$2\text{-}3\frac{1}{4}$
$\frac{3}{8}$	6	$1\text{-}11\frac{5}{32}$	$6\frac{1}{4}$	$2\text{-}0\frac{3}{16}$	$6\frac{17}{32}$	$2\text{-}1\frac{1}{4}$	$6\frac{13}{16}$	$2\text{-}2\frac{9}{32}$	$7\frac{1}{16}$	$2\text{-}3\frac{5}{16}$
$\frac{7}{16}$	6	$1\text{-}11\frac{7}{32}$	$6\frac{9}{32}$	$2\text{-}0\frac{1}{4}$	$6\frac{9}{16}$	$2\text{-}1\frac{5}{16}$	$6\frac{13}{16}$	$2\text{-}2\frac{11}{32}$	$7\frac{3}{32}$	$2\text{-}3\frac{3}{8}$
$\frac{1}{2}$	$6\frac{1}{32}$	$1\text{-}11\frac{9}{32}$	$6\frac{9}{32}$	$2\text{-}0\frac{11}{32}$	$6\frac{9}{16}$	$2\text{-}1\frac{3}{8}$	$6\frac{27}{32}$	$2\text{-}2\frac{13}{32}$	$7\frac{3}{32}$	$2\text{-}3\frac{7}{16}$
$\frac{9}{16}$	$6\frac{1}{32}$	$1\text{-}11\frac{11}{32}$	$6\frac{5}{16}$	$2\text{-}0\frac{13}{32}$	$6\frac{19}{32}$	$2\text{-}1\frac{7}{16}$	$6\frac{27}{32}$	$2\text{-}2\frac{15}{32}$	$7\frac{1}{8}$	$2\text{-}3\frac{1}{2}$
$\frac{5}{8}$	$6\frac{1}{16}$	$1\text{-}11\frac{7}{16}$	$6\frac{11}{32}$	$2\text{-}0\frac{15}{32}$	$6\frac{19}{32}$	$2\text{-}1\frac{1}{2}$	$6\frac{7}{8}$	$2\text{-}2\frac{17}{32}$	$7\frac{1}{8}$	$2\text{-}3\frac{9}{16}$
$\frac{11}{16}$	$6\frac{3}{32}$	$1\text{-}11\frac{1}{2}$	$6\frac{11}{32}$	$2\text{-}0\frac{17}{32}$	$6\frac{5}{8}$	$2\text{-}1\frac{9}{16}$	$6\frac{7}{8}$	$2\text{-}2\frac{19}{32}$	$7\frac{5}{32}$	$2\text{-}3\frac{5}{8}$
$\frac{3}{4}$	$6\frac{3}{32}$	$1\text{-}11\frac{9}{16}$	$6\frac{3}{8}$	$2\text{-}0\frac{19}{32}$	$6\frac{5}{8}$	$2\text{-}1\frac{5}{8}$	$6\frac{29}{32}$	$2\text{-}2\frac{21}{32}$	$7\frac{5}{32}$	$2\text{-}3\frac{11}{16}$
$\frac{13}{16}$	$6\frac{1}{8}$	$1\text{-}11\frac{5}{8}$	$6\frac{3}{8}$	$2\text{-}0\frac{21}{32}$	$6\frac{21}{32}$	$2\text{-}1\frac{11}{16}$	$6\frac{29}{32}$	$2\text{-}2\frac{23}{32}$	$7\frac{3}{16}$	$2\text{-}3\frac{3}{4}$
$\frac{7}{8}$	$6\frac{1}{8}$	$1\text{-}11\frac{11}{16}$	$6\frac{13}{32}$	$2\text{-}0\frac{23}{32}$	$6\frac{21}{32}$	$2\text{-}1\frac{3}{4}$	$6\frac{15}{16}$	$2\text{-}2\frac{25}{32}$	$7\frac{3}{16}$	$2\text{-}3\frac{13}{16}$
$\frac{15}{16}$	$6\frac{5}{32}$	$1\text{-}11\frac{3}{4}$	$6\frac{13}{32}$	$2\text{-}0\frac{25}{32}$	$6\frac{11}{16}$	$2\text{-}1\frac{13}{16}$	$6\frac{15}{16}$	$2\text{-}2\frac{27}{32}$	$7\frac{5}{32}{-}$	$2\text{-}3\frac{7}{8}$

Inch	27″ Rise	27″ Slope	28″ Rise	28″ Slope	29″ Rise	29″ Slope	30″ Rise	30″ Slope	31″ Rise	31″ Slope
0	$7\frac{1}{4}$	$2\text{-}3\frac{15}{16}$	$7\frac{1}{2}$	$2\text{-}5$	$7\frac{25}{32}$	$2\text{-}6\frac{1}{32}$	$8\frac{1}{32}$	$2\text{-}7\frac{1}{16}$	$8\frac{5}{16}$	$2\text{-}8\frac{3}{32}$
$\frac{1}{16}$	$7\frac{1}{4}$	$2\text{-}4\frac{1}{32}$	$7\frac{17}{32}$	$2\text{-}5\frac{1}{16}$	$7\frac{25}{32}$	$2\text{-}6\frac{3}{32}$	$8\frac{1}{16}$	$2\text{-}7\frac{1}{8}$	$8\frac{5}{16}$	$2\text{-}8\frac{5}{32}$
$\frac{1}{8}$	$7\frac{9}{32}$	$2\text{-}4\frac{3}{32}$	$7\frac{17}{32}$	$2\text{-}5\frac{1}{8}$	$7\frac{13}{16}$	$2\text{-}6\frac{5}{32}$	$8\frac{1}{16}$	$2\text{-}7\frac{3}{16}$	$8\frac{11}{32}$	$2\text{-}8\frac{7}{32}$
$\frac{3}{16}$	$7\frac{9}{32}$	$2\text{-}4\frac{5}{32}$	$7\frac{9}{16}$	$2\text{-}5\frac{3}{16}$	$7\frac{13}{16}$	$2\text{-}6\frac{7}{32}$	$8\frac{3}{32}$	$2\text{-}7\frac{1}{4}$	$8\frac{11}{32}$	$2\text{-}8\frac{9}{32}$
$\frac{1}{4}$	$7\frac{5}{16}$	$2\text{-}4\frac{7}{32}$	$7\frac{9}{16}$	$2\text{-}5\frac{1}{4}$	$7\frac{27}{32}$	$2\text{-}6\frac{9}{32}$	$8\frac{3}{32}$	$2\text{-}7\frac{5}{16}$	$8\frac{3}{8}$	$2\text{-}8\frac{11}{32}$
$\frac{5}{16}$	$7\frac{5}{16}$	$2\text{-}4\frac{9}{32}$	$7\frac{19}{32}$	$2\text{-}5\frac{5}{16}$	$7\frac{27}{32}$	$2\text{-}6\frac{11}{32}$	$8\frac{1}{8}$	$2\text{-}7\frac{3}{8}$	$8\frac{3}{8}$	$2\text{-}8\frac{13}{32}$
$\frac{3}{8}$	$7\frac{11}{32}$	$2\text{-}4\frac{11}{32}$	$7\frac{19}{32}$	$2\text{-}5\frac{3}{8}$	$7\frac{7}{8}$	$2\text{-}6\frac{13}{32}$	$8\frac{1}{8}$	$2\text{-}7\frac{7}{16}$	$8\frac{13}{32}$	$2\text{-}8\frac{15}{32}$
$\frac{7}{16}$	$7\frac{11}{32}$	$2\text{-}4\frac{13}{32}$	$7\frac{5}{8}$	$2\text{-}5\frac{7}{16}$	$7\frac{7}{8}$	$2\text{-}6\frac{15}{32}$	$8\frac{5}{32}$	$2\text{-}7\frac{1}{2}$	$8\frac{7}{16}$	$2\text{-}8\frac{17}{32}$
$\frac{1}{2}$	$7\frac{3}{8}$	$2\text{-}4\frac{15}{32}$	$7\frac{5}{8}$	$2\text{-}5\frac{1}{2}$	$7\frac{29}{32}$	$2\text{-}6\frac{17}{32}$	$8\frac{3}{16}$	$2\text{-}7\frac{9}{16}$	$8\frac{7}{16}$	$2\text{-}8\frac{5}{8}$
$\frac{9}{16}$	$7\frac{3}{8}$	$2\text{-}4\frac{17}{32}$	$7\frac{21}{32}$	$2\text{-}5\frac{9}{16}$	$7\frac{29}{32}$	$2\text{-}6\frac{19}{32}$	$8\frac{3}{16}$	$2\text{-}7\frac{5}{8}$	$8\frac{15}{32}$	$2\text{-}8\frac{11}{16}$
$\frac{5}{8}$	$7\frac{13}{32}$	$2\text{-}4\frac{19}{32}$	$7\frac{21}{32}$	$2\text{-}5\frac{5}{8}$	$7\frac{15}{16}$	$2\text{-}6\frac{21}{32}$	$8\frac{7}{32}$	$2\text{-}7\frac{23}{32}$	$8\frac{15}{32}$	$2\text{-}8\frac{3}{4}$
$\frac{11}{16}$	$7\frac{13}{32}$	$2\text{-}4\frac{21}{32}$	$7\frac{11}{16}$	$2\text{-}5\frac{11}{16}$	$7\frac{15}{16}$	$2\text{-}6\frac{23}{32}$	$8\frac{7}{32}$	$2\text{-}7\frac{25}{32}$	$8\frac{1}{2}$	$2\text{-}8\frac{13}{16}$
$\frac{3}{4}$	$7\frac{7}{16}$	$2\text{-}4\frac{23}{32}$	$7\frac{23}{32}$	$2\text{-}5\frac{3}{4}$	$7\frac{31}{32}$	$2\text{-}6\frac{13}{16}$	$8\frac{1}{4}$	$2\text{-}7\frac{27}{32}$	$8\frac{1}{2}$	$2\text{-}8\frac{7}{8}$
$\frac{13}{16}$	$7\frac{7}{16}$	$2\text{-}4\frac{25}{32}$	$7\frac{23}{32}$	$2\text{-}5\frac{27}{32}$	$7\frac{31}{32}$	$2\text{-}6\frac{13}{16}$	$8\frac{1}{4}$	$2\text{-}7\frac{29}{32}$	$8\frac{17}{32}$	$2\text{-}8\frac{15}{16}$
$\frac{7}{8}$	$7\frac{15}{32}$	$2\text{-}4\frac{27}{32}$	$7\frac{3}{4}$	$2\text{-}5\frac{29}{32}$	8	$2\text{-}6\frac{7}{8}$	$8\frac{9}{32}$	$2\text{-}7\frac{31}{32}$	$8\frac{17}{32}$	$2\text{-}9$
$\frac{15}{16}$	$7\frac{1}{2}$	$2\text{-}4\frac{15}{16}$	$7\frac{3}{4}$	$2\text{-}5\frac{31}{32}$	$8\frac{1}{32}{-}$	$2\text{-}7$	$8\frac{9}{32}$	$2\text{-}8\frac{1}{32}{-}$	$8\frac{9}{16}$	$2\text{-}9\frac{1}{16}$

GIVEN ANGLE, ITS NATURAL AND LOGARITHMIC FUNCTIONS

Natural Functions		Logarithmic Functions
Sin......0.2588190		Sin......9.4129962
Csc......3.8637033		Csc......0.5870038
Tan......0.2679492		Tan......9.4280525
Cot......3.7320508	Given Angle	Cot......0.5719475
Cos......0.9659258	15°	Cos......9.9849438
Sec......1.0352762		Sec......0.0150562

Inches	0" Rise	0" Slope	1" Rise	1" Slope	2" Rise	2" Slope	3" Rise	3" Slope	4" Rise	4" Slope	5" Rise	5" Slope
0	0	0	13/32	1 1/16	13/16	2 5/32	1 3/16	3 7/32	1 19/32	4 5/16	2	5 3/8
1/16	1/32	1/16	7/16	1 5/32	13/16	2 7/32	1 7/32	3 5/16	1 5/8	4 3/8	2 1/32	5 7/16
1/8	1/16	1/8	7/16	1 7/32	27/32	2 9/32	1 1/4	3 3/8	1 21/32	4 7/16	2 1/16	5 17/32
3/16	1/16	3/16	15/32	1 9/32	7/8	2 11/32	1 9/32	3 7/16	1 11/16	4 1/2	2 1/16	5 19/32
1/4	3/32	9/32	1/2	1 11/32	29/32	2 7/16	1 5/16	3 1/2	1 11/16	4 9/16	2 3/32	5 21/32
5/16	1/8	11/32	17/32	1 13/32	15/16	2 1/2	1 5/16	3 9/16	1 23/32	4 21/32	2 1/8	5 23/32
3/8	5/32	13/32	9/16	1 15/32	15/16	2 9/16	1 11/32	3 5/8	1 3/4	4 23/32	2 5/32	5 25/32
7/16	3/16	15/32	9/16	1 9/16	31/32	2 5/8	1 3/8	3 11/16	1 25/32	4 25/32	2 3/16	5 27/32
1/2	3/16	17/32	19/32	1 5/8	1	2 11/16	1 13/32	3 25/32	1 13/16	4 27/32	2 3/16	5 15/16
9/16	7/32	19/32	5/8	1 11/16	1 1/32	2 3/4	1 7/16	3 27/32	1 13/16	4 29/32	2 7/32	6
5/8	1/4	11/16	21/32	1 3/4	1 1/16	2 13/16	1 7/16	3 29/32	1 27/32	4 31/32	2 1/4	6 1/16
11/16	9/32	3/4	11/16	1 13/16	1 1/16	2 29/32	1 15/32	3 31/32	1 7/8	5 1/16	2 9/32	6 1/8
3/4	5/16	13/16	11/16	1 7/8	1 3/32	2 31/32	1 1/2	4 1/32	1 29/32	5 1/8	2 5/16	6 3/16
13/16	5/16	7/8	23/32	1 15/16	1 1/8	3 1/32	1 17/32	4 3/32	1 15/16	5 3/16	2 5/16	6 1/4
7/8	11/32	15/16	3/4	2 1/32	1 5/32	3 3/32	1 9/16	4 3/16	1 15/16	5 1/4	2 11/32	6 5/16
15/16	3/8	1	25/32	2 3/32	1 3/16	3 5/32	1 9/16	4 1/4	1 31/32	5 5/16	2 3/8	6 13/32

Inches	6" Rise	6" Slope	7" Rise	7" Slope	8" Rise	8" Slope	9" Rise	9" Slope	10" Rise	10" Slope	11" Rise	11" Slope
0	2 13/32	6 15/32	2 13/16	7 17/32	3 3/16	8 5/8	3 19/32	9 11/16	4	10 25/32	4 13/32	11 27/32
1/16	2 7/16	6 17/32	2 13/16	7 19/32	3 7/32	8 11/16	3 5/8	9 3/4	4 1/32	10 27/32	4 7/16	11 29/32
1/8	2 7/16	6 19/32	2 27/32	7 11/16	3 1/4	8 3/4	3 21/32	9 13/16	4 1/16	10 29/32	4 7/16	11 31/32
3/16	2 15/32	6 21/32	2 7/8	7 3/4	3 9/32	8 13/16	3 11/16	9 29/32	4 1/16	10 31/32	4 15/32	1-0 1/16
1/4	2 1/2	6 23/32	2 29/32	7 13/16	3 5/16	8 7/8	3 11/16	9 31/32	4 3/32	11 1/32	4 1/2	1-0 1/8
5/16	2 17/32	6 13/16	2 15/16	7 7/8	3 5/16	8 15/16	3 23/32	10 1/32	4 1/8	11 3/32	4 17/32	1-0 3/16
3/8	2 9/16	6 7/8	2 15/16	7 15/16	3 11/32	9 1/32	3 3/4	10 3/32	4 5/32	11 3/16	4 9/16	1-0 1/4
7/16	2 9/16	6 15/16	2 31/32	8	3 3/8	9 3/32	3 25/32	10 5/32	4 3/16	11 1/4	4 9/16	1-0 5/16
1/2	2 19/32	7	3	8 1/32	3 13/32	9 5/32	3 13/16	10 7/32	4 3/16	11 5/16	4 19/32	1-0 3/8
9/16	2 5/8	7 1/16	3 1/32	8 5/32	3 7/16	9 7/32	3 13/16	10 5/16	4 7/32	11 3/8	4 5/8	1-0 15/32
5/8	2 21/32	7 1/8	3 1/16	8 7/32	3 7/16	9 9/32	3 27/32	10 3/8	4 1/4	11 7/16	4 21/32	1-0 17/32
11/16	2 11/16	7 3/16	3 1/16	8 9/32	3 15/32	9 11/32	3 7/8	10 7/16	4 9/32	11 1/2	4 11/16	1-0 19/32
3/4	2 11/16	7 9/32	3 3/32	8 11/32	3 1/2	9 7/16	3 29/32	10 1/2	4 5/16	11 9/16	4 11/16	1-0 21/32
13/16	2 23/32	7 11/32	3 1/8	8 13/32	3 17/32	9 1/2	3 15/16	10 9/16	4 5/16	11 21/32	4 23/32	1-0 23/32
7/8	2 3/4	7 13/32	3 5/32	8 15/32	3 9/16	9 9/16	3 15/16	10 5/8	4 11/32	11 23/32	4 3/4	1-0 25/32
15/16	2 25/32	7 15/32	3 3/16	8 9/16	3 9/16	9 5/8	3 31/32	10 11/16	4 3/8	11 25/32	4 25/32	1-0 27/32

Feet	0' Rise	0' Slope	10' Rise	10' Slope	20' Rise	20' Slope	30' Rise	30' Slope
0	0	0	4-0	10-9 1/4	8-0	21-6 1/2	12-0	32-3 23/32
1	4 13/16	1-0 15/16	4-4 13/16	11-10 5/32	8-4 13/16	22-7 13/32	12-4 13/16	33-4 21/32
2	9 19/32	2-1 27/32	4-9 19/32	12-11 13/32	8-9 19/32	23-8 11/32	12-9 19/32	34-5 19/32
3	1-2 13/32	3-2 25/32	5-2 13/32	14-0 1/2	9-2 13/32	24-9 1/4	13-2 13/32	35-6 1/2
4	1-7 3/16	4-3 11/16	5-7 3/16	15-0 15/16	9-7 3/16	25-10 3/16	13-7 3/16	36-7 7/16
5	2-0	5-4 5/8	6-0	16-1 7/8	10-0	26-11 1/8	14-0	37-8 11/32
6	2-4 13/16	6-5 17/32	6-4 13/16	17-2 25/32	10-4 13/16	28-0 1/32	14-4 13/16	38-9 9/32
7	2-9 19/32	7-6 15/32	6-9 19/32	18-3 23/32	10-9 19/32	29-0 31/32	14-9 19/32	39-10 3/16
8	3-2 13/32	8-7 13/32	7-2 13/32	19-4 5/8	11-2 13/32	30-1 7/8	15-2 13/32	40-11 1/8
9	3-7 3/16	9-8 5/16	7-7 3/16	20-5 9/16	11-7 3/16	31-2 13/16	15-7 3/16	42-0 1/16

Inches	12″ Rise	12″ Slope	13″ Rise	13″ Slope	14″ Rise	14″ Slope	15″ Rise	15″ Slope	16″ Rise	16″ Slope
0	4 13/16	1-0 15/16	5 3/16	1-2	5 19/32	1-3 3/32	6	1-4 5/32	6 13/32	1-5 1/4
1/16	4 13/16	1-1	5 7/32	1-2 1/16	5 5/8	1-3 5/32	6 1/32	1-4 7/32	6 7/16	1-5 5/16
1/8	4 27/32	1-1 1/16	5 1/4	1-2 1/8	5 21/32	1-3 7/32	6 1/16	1-4 9/32	6 7/16	1-5 3/8
3/16	4 7/8	1-1 1/8	5 9/32	1-2 7/32	5 11/16	1-3 9/32	6 1/16	1-4 11/32	6 15/32	1-5 7/16
1/4	4 29/32	1-1 3/16	5 5/16	1-2 9/32	5 11/16	1-3 11/32	6 3/32	1-4 7/16	6 1/2	1-5 1/2
5/16	4 15/16	1-1 1/4	5 5/16	1-2 11/32	5 23/32	1-3 13/32	6 1/8	1-4 1/2	6 17/32	1-5 9/16
3/8	4 15/16	1-1 11/32	5 11/32	1-2 13/32	5 3/4	1-3 15/32	6 5/32	1-4 9/16	6 9/16	1-5 5/8
7/16	4 31/32	1-1 13/32	5 3/8	1-2 15/32	5 25/32	1-3 9/16	6 3/16	1-4 5/8	6 9/16	1-5 23/32
1/2	5	1-1 15/32	5 13/32	1-2 17/32	5 13/16	1-3 5/8	6 3/16	1-4 11/16	6 19/32	1-5 25/32
9/16	5 1/32	1-1 17/32	5 7/16	1-2 19/32	5 13/16	1-3 11/16	6 7/32	1-4 3/4	6 5/8	1-5 27/32
5/8	5 1/16	1-1 19/32	5 7/16	1-2 11/16	5 27/32	1-3 3/4	6 1/4	1-4 27/32	6 21/32	1-5 29/32
11/16	5 1/16	1-1 21/32	5 15/32	1-2 3/4	5 7/8	1-3 13/16	6 9/32	1-4 29/32	6 11/16	1-5 31/32
3/4	5 3/32	1-1 23/32	5 1/2	1-2 13/16	5 29/32	1-3 7/8	6 5/16	1-4 31/32	6 11/16	1-6 1/32
13/16	5 1/8	1-1 13/16	5 17/32	1-2 7/8	5 15/16	1-3 31/32	6 5/16	1-5 1/32	6 23/32	1-6 3/32
7/8	5 5/32	1-1 7/8	5 9/16	1-2 15/16	5 15/16	1-4 1/32	6 11/32	1-5 3/32	6 3/4	1-6 3/16
15/16	5 3/16	1-1 15/16	5 9/16	1-3	5 31/32	1-4 3/32	6 3/8	1-5 5/32	6 25/32	1-6 1/4

Inches	17″ Rise	17″ Slope	18″ Rise	18″ Slope	19″ Rise	19″ Slope	20″ Rise	20″ Slope	21″ Rise	21″ Slope
0	6 13/16	1-6 5/16	7 3/16	1-7 3/8	7 19/32	1-8 15/32	8	1-9 17/32	8 13/32	1-10 5/8
1/16	6 13/16	1-6 3/8	7 7/32	1-7 15/32	7 5/8	1-8 17/32	8 1/32	1-9 19/32	8 7/16	1-10 11/32
1/8	6 27/32	1-6 7/16	7 1/4	1-7 17/32	7 21/32	1-8 19/32	8 1/16	1-9 11/16	8 7/16	1-10 3/4
3/16	6 7/8	1-6 1/2	7 9/32	1-7 19/32	7 11/16	1-8 21/32	8 1/16	1-9 3/4	8 15/32	1-10 13/32
1/4	6 29/32	1-6 19/32	7 5/16	1-7 21/32	7 11/16	1-8 23/32	8 3/32	1-9 13/16	8 1/2	1-10 7/8
5/16	6 15/16	1-6 21/32	7 5/16	1-7 23/32	7 23/32	1-8 13/16	8 1/8	1-9 7/8	8 17/32	1-10 31/32
3/8	6 15/16	1-6 23/32	7 11/32	1-7 25/32	7 3/4	1-8 7/8	8 5/32	1-9 15/16	8 9/16	1-11 1/32
7/16	6 31/32	1-6 25/32	7 3/8	1-7 27/32	7 25/32	1-8 15/16	8 3/16	1-10	8 9/16	1-11 3/32
1/2	7	1-6 27/32	7 13/32	1-7 15/16	7 13/16	1-9	8 3/16	1-10 3/32	8 19/32	1-11 5/32
9/16	7 1/32	1-6 29/32	7 7/16	1-8	7 13/16	1-9 1/16	8 7/32	1-10 5/32	8 5/8	1-11 7/32
5/8	7 1/16	1-6 31/32	7 7/16	1-8 1/16	7 27/32	1-9 1/8	8 1/4	1-10 7/32	8 21/32	1-11 9/32
11/16	7 1/16	1-7 1/16	7 15/32	1-8 1/8	7 7/8	1-9 7/32	8 9/32	1-10 9/32	8 11/16	1-11 11/32
3/4	7 3/32	1-7 1/8	7 1/2	1-8 3/16	7 29/32	1-9 9/32	8 5/16	1-10 11/32	8 11/16	1-11 17/32
13/16	7 1/8	1-7 3/16	7 17/32	1-8 1/4	7 15/16	1-9 11/32	8 5/16	1-10 13/32	8 23/32	1-11 1/2
7/8	7 5/32	1-7 1/4	7 9/16	1-8 11/32	7 15/16	1-9 13/32	8 11/32	1-10 15/32	8 3/4	1-11 9/16
15/16	7 3/16	1-7 5/16	7 9/16	1-8 13/32	7 31/32	1-9 15/32	8 3/8	1-10 9/16	8 25/32	1-11 5/8

Feet	40′ Rise	40′ Slope	50′ Rise	50′ Slope	60′ Rise	60′ Slope	70′ Rise	70′ Slope
0	16-0	43-0 31/32	20-0	53-10 7/32	24-0	64-7 15/32	28-0	75-4 23/32
1	16-4 13/16	44-1 29/32	20-4 13/16	54-11 5/32	24-4 13/16	65-8 3/8	28-4 13/16	76-5 5/8
2	16-9 9/32	45-2 13/16	20-9 9/32	56-0 1/16	24-9 9/32	66-9 5/16	28-9 9/32	77-6 9/16
3	17-2 13/32	46-3 3/4	21-2 13/32	57-1	25-2 13/32	67-10 1/4	29-2 13/32	78-7 15/32
4	17-7 3/16	47-4 11/16	21-7 3/16	58-1 29/32	25-7 3/16	68-11 5/32	29-7 3/16	79-8 13/32
5	18-0	48-5 19/32	22-0	59-2 27/32	26-0	70-0 3/32	30-0	80-9 11/32
6	18-4 13/16	49-6 17/32	22-4 13/16	60-3 25/32	26-4 13/16	71-1	30-4 13/16	81-10 1/4
7	18-9 9/32	50-7 7/16	22-9 9/32	61-4 11/16	26-9 9/32	72-1 15/16	30-9 9/32	82-11 3/16
8	19-2 13/32	51-8 3/8	23-2 13/32	62-5 5/8	27-2 13/32	73-2 27/32	31-2 13/32	84-0 3/32
9	19-7 3/16	52-9 9/32	23-7 3/16	63-6 17/32	27-7 3/16	74-3 25/32	31-7 3/16	85-1 1/32

Inches	22" Rise	22" Slope	23" Rise	23" Slope	24" Rise	24" Slope	25" Rise	25" Slope	26" Rise	26" Slope
0	8 13/16	1-11 11/16	9 3/16	2-0 25/32	9 19/32	2-1 27/32	10	2-2 15/16	10 13/32	2-4
1/16	8 13/16	1-11 3/4	9 7/32	2-0 27/32	9 5/8	2-1 29/32	10 1/32	2-3	10 7/16	2-4 1/16
1/8	8 27/32	1-11 27/32	9 1/4	2-0 29/32	9 21/32	2-1 31/32	10 1/16	2-3 1/16	10 7/16	2-4 1/8
3/16	8 7/8	1-11 29/32	9 9/32	2-0 31/32	9 11/16	2-2 1/16	10 1/16	2-3 1/8	10 15/32	2-4 7/32
1/4	8 29/32	1-11 31/32	9 5/16	2-1 1/32	9 11/16	2-2 1/8	10 3/32	2-3 3/16	10 1/2	2-4 9/32
5/16	8 15/16	2-0 1/32	9 5/16	2-1 3/32	9 23/32	2-2 3/16	10 1/8	2-3 1/4	10 17/32	2-4 11/32
3/8	8 15/16	2-0 3/32	9 11/32	2-1 3/16	9 3/4	2-2 1/4	10 5/32	2-3 11/32	10 9/16	2-4 13/32
7/16	8 31/32	2-0 5/32	9 3/8	2-1 1/4	9 25/32	2-2 5/16	10 3/16	2-3 13/32	10 9/16	2-4 15/32
1/2	9	2-0 7/32	9 13/32	2-1 5/16	9 13/16	2-2 3/8	10 3/16	2-3 15/32	10 19/32	2-4 17/32
9/16	9 1/32	2-0 5/16	9 7/16	2-1 3/8	9 13/16	2-2 15/32	10 7/32	2-3 17/32	10 5/8	2-4 19/32
5/8	9 1/16	2-0 3/8	9 7/16	2-1 7/16	9 27/32	2-2 17/32	10 1/4	2-3 19/32	10 21/32	2-4 11/16
11/16	9 1/16	2-0 7/16	9 15/32	2-1 1/2	9 7/8	2-2 19/32	10 9/32	2-3 21/32	10 11/16	2-4 3/4
3/4	9 3/32	2-0 1/2	9 1/2	2-1 19/32	9 29/32	2-2 21/32	10 5/16	2-3 23/32	10 11/16	2-4 13/16
13/16	9 1/8	2-0 9/16	9 17/32	2-1 21/32	9 15/16	2-2 23/32	10 5/16	2-3 13/16	10 23/32	2-4 7/8
7/8	9 5/32	2-0 5/8	9 9/16	2-1 23/32	9 15/16	2-2 25/32	10 11/32	2-3 7/8	10 3/4	2-4 15/16
15/16	9 3/16	2-0 23/32	9 9/16	2-1 25/32	9 31/32	2-2 27/32	10 3/8	2-3 15/16	10 25/32	2-5

Inches	27" Rise	27" Slope	28" Rise	28" Slope	29" Rise	29" Slope	30" Rise	30" Slope	31" Rise	31" Slope
0	10 13/16	2-5 3/32	11 3/16	2-6 5/32	11 19/32	2-7 1/32	1-0	2-8 5/16	1-0 13/32	2-9 3/8
1/16	10 13/16	2-5 5/32	11 7/32	2-6 1/4	11 5/8	2-7 5/16	1-0 1/32	2-8 3/8	1-0 7/16	2-9 15/32
1/8	10 27/32	2-5 7/32	11 1/4	2-6 9/32	11 21/32	2-7 3/8	1-0 1/16	2-8 7/16	1-0 7/16	2-9 17/32
3/16	10 7/8	2-5 9/32	11 9/32	2-6 11/32	11 11/16	2-7 7/16	1-0 1/16	2-8 1/2	1-0 15/32	2-9 19/32
1/4	10 29/32	2-5 11/32	11 5/16	2-6 7/16	11 11/16	2-7 1/2	1-0 3/32	2-8 19/32	1-0 1/2	2-9 21/32
5/16	10 15/16	2-5 13/32	11 5/16	2-6 1/2	11 23/32	2-7 9/16	1-0 1/8	2-8 21/32	1-0 17/32	2-9 23/32
3/8	10 15/16	2-5 15/32	11 11/32	2-6 9/16	11 3/4	2-7 5/8	1-0 5/32	2-8 23/32	1-0 9/16	2-9 25/32
7/16	10 31/32	2-5 9/16	11 3/8	2-6 5/8	11 25/32	2-7 23/32	1-0 3/16	2-8 25/32	1-0 9/16	2-9 27/32
1/2	11	2-5 5/8	11 13/32	2-6 11/16	11 13/16	2-7 25/32	1-0 3/16	2-8 27/32	1-0 19/32	2-9 15/16
9/16	11 1/32	2-5 11/16	11 7/16	2-6 3/4	11 13/16	2-7 27/32	1-0 7/32	2-8 29/32	1-0 5/8	2-10
5/8	11 1/16	2-5 3/4	11 7/16	2-6 27/32	11 27/32	2-7 29/32	1-0 1/4	2-8 31/32	1-0 21/32	2-10 1/16
11/16	11 1/16	2-5 13/16	11 15/32	2-6 29/32	11 7/8	2-7 31/32	1-0 9/32	2-9 1/16	1-0 11/16	2-10 1/8
3/4	11 3/32	2-5 7/8	11 1/2	2-6 31/32	11 29/32	2-8 1/32	1-0 5/16	2-9 1/8	1-0 11/16	2-10 3/16
13/16	11 1/8	2-5 31/32	11 17/32	2-7 1/32	11 15/16	2-8 3/32	1-0 5/16	2-9 3/16	1-0 23/32	2-10 1/4
7/8	11 5/32	2-6 1/32	11 9/16	2-7 3/32	11 15/16	2-8 3/16	1-0 11/32	2-9 1/4	1-0 3/4	2-10 11/32
15/16	11 3/16	2-6 3/32	11 9/16	2-7 5/32	11 31/32	2-8 1/4	1-0 3/8	2-9 5/16	1-0 25/32	2-10 13/32

CORRESPONDING ANGLE, ITS NATURAL AND LOGARITHMIC FUNCTIONS

Logarithmic Functions	Corresponding Angle	Natural Functions
Sin......9.5698310		Sin......0.3713907
Csc......0.4301690	21° 48' 5.07"	Csc......2.6925826
Tan......9.6020600		Tan......0.4000000
Cot......0.3979400		Cot......2.5000000
Cos......9.9677710		Cos......0.9284766
Sec......0.0322290		Sec......1.0770330

22°30′ Pitch (Bevel between $4\frac{15}{16}''$ to $12''$ and $5''$ to $12''$)

Inch	0″ Rise	0″ Slope	1″ Rise	1″ Slope	2″ Rise	2″ Slope	3″ Rise	3″ Slope	4″ Rise	4″ Slope	5″ Rise	5″ Slope
0	0	0	$\frac{13}{32}$	$1\frac{3}{32}$	$\frac{27}{32}$	$2\frac{5}{32}$	$1\frac{1}{4}$	$3\frac{1}{4}$	$1\frac{21}{32}$	$4\frac{11}{32}$	$2\frac{1}{16}$	$5\frac{13}{32}$
$\frac{1}{16}$	$\frac{1}{32}$	$\frac{1}{16}$	$\frac{7}{16}$	$1\frac{5}{32}$	$\frac{27}{32}$	$2\frac{7}{32}$	$1\frac{9}{32}$	$3\frac{5}{16}$	$1\frac{11}{16}$	$4\frac{13}{32}$	$2\frac{3}{32}$	$5\frac{15}{32}$
$\frac{1}{8}$	$\frac{1}{16}$	$\frac{1}{8}$	$\frac{15}{32}$	$1\frac{7}{32}$	$\frac{7}{8}$	$2\frac{5}{16}$	$1\frac{5}{16}$	$3\frac{3}{8}$	$1\frac{23}{32}$	$4\frac{15}{32}$	$2\frac{1}{8}$	$5\frac{9}{16}$
$\frac{3}{16}$	$\frac{3}{32}$	$\frac{3}{16}$	$\frac{1}{2}$	$1\frac{9}{32}$	$\frac{29}{32}$	$2\frac{3}{8}$	$1\frac{11}{32}$	$3\frac{7}{16}$	$1\frac{3}{4}$	$4\frac{17}{32}$	$2\frac{5}{32}$	$5\frac{5}{8}$
$\frac{1}{4}$	$\frac{3}{32}$	$\frac{9}{32}$	$\frac{17}{32}$	$1\frac{11}{32}$	$\frac{15}{16}$	$2\frac{7}{16}$	$1\frac{11}{32}$	$3\frac{17}{32}$	$1\frac{3}{4}$	$4\frac{19}{32}$	$2\frac{3}{16}$	$5\frac{11}{16}$
$\frac{5}{16}$	$\frac{1}{8}$	$\frac{11}{32}$	$\frac{17}{32}$	$1\frac{13}{32}$	$\frac{31}{32}$	$2\frac{1}{2}$	$1\frac{3}{8}$	$3\frac{19}{32}$	$1\frac{25}{32}$	$4\frac{21}{32}$	$2\frac{3}{16}$	$5\frac{3}{4}$
$\frac{3}{8}$	$\frac{5}{32}$	$\frac{13}{32}$	$\frac{9}{16}$	$1\frac{1}{2}$	$\frac{31}{32}$	$2\frac{9}{16}$	$1\frac{13}{32}$	$3\frac{21}{32}$	$1\frac{13}{16}$	$4\frac{3}{4}$	$2\frac{7}{32}$	$5\frac{13}{16}$
$\frac{7}{16}$	$\frac{3}{16}$	$\frac{15}{32}$	$\frac{19}{32}$	$1\frac{9}{16}$	1	$2\frac{5}{8}$	$1\frac{7}{16}$	$3\frac{23}{32}$	$1\frac{27}{32}$	$4\frac{13}{16}$	$2\frac{1}{4}$	$5\frac{7}{8}$
$\frac{1}{2}$	$\frac{7}{32}$	$\frac{17}{32}$	$\frac{5}{8}$	$1\frac{5}{8}$	$1\frac{1}{16}$	$2\frac{23}{32}$	$1\frac{15}{32}$	$3\frac{25}{32}$	$1\frac{7}{8}$	$4\frac{7}{8}$	$2\frac{9}{32}$	$5\frac{31}{32}$
$\frac{9}{16}$	$\frac{7}{32}$	$\frac{19}{32}$	$\frac{21}{32}$	$1\frac{11}{16}$	$1\frac{1}{16}$	$2\frac{25}{32}$	$1\frac{15}{32}$	$3\frac{27}{32}$	$1\frac{15}{16}$	$4\frac{15}{16}$	$2\frac{5}{16}$	$6\frac{1}{32}$
$\frac{5}{8}$	$\frac{1}{4}$	$\frac{11}{16}$	$\frac{11}{16}$	$1\frac{3}{4}$	$1\frac{3}{32}$	$2\frac{27}{32}$	$1\frac{1}{2}$	$3\frac{15}{16}$	$1\frac{29}{32}$	5	$2\frac{11}{32}$	$6\frac{3}{32}$
$\frac{11}{16}$	$\frac{9}{32}$	$\frac{3}{4}$	$\frac{11}{16}$	$1\frac{13}{16}$	$1\frac{1}{8}$	$2\frac{29}{32}$	$1\frac{17}{32}$	4	$1\frac{15}{16}$	$5\frac{1}{16}$	$2\frac{11}{32}$	$6\frac{5}{32}$
$\frac{3}{4}$	$\frac{5}{16}$	$\frac{13}{16}$	$\frac{23}{32}$	$1\frac{29}{32}$	$1\frac{1}{8}$	$3\frac{1}{32}$	$1\frac{9}{16}$	$4\frac{1}{16}$	$1\frac{31}{32}$	$5\frac{5}{32}$	$2\frac{3}{8}$	$6\frac{7}{32}$
$\frac{13}{16}$	$\frac{11}{32}$	$\frac{7}{8}$	$\frac{3}{4}$	$1\frac{31}{32}$	$1\frac{5}{32}$	$3\frac{1}{8}$	$1\frac{19}{32}$	$4\frac{1}{8}$	2	$5\frac{9}{32}$	$2\frac{13}{32}$	$6\frac{9}{32}$
$\frac{7}{8}$	$\frac{3}{8}$	$\frac{15}{16}$	$\frac{25}{32}$	$2\frac{1}{16}$	$1\frac{3}{16}$	$3\frac{1}{8}$	$1\frac{19}{32}$	$4\frac{3}{16}$	$2\frac{1}{32}$	$5\frac{9}{32}$	$2\frac{7}{16}$	$6\frac{11}{32}$
$\frac{15}{16}$	$\frac{3}{8}$	1	$\frac{13}{16}$	$2\frac{3}{32}$	$1\frac{7}{32}$	$3\frac{3}{16}$	$1\frac{5}{8}$	$4\frac{1}{4}$	$2\frac{1}{16}$	$5\frac{11}{32}$	$2\frac{15}{32}$	$6\frac{7}{16}$

Inch	6″ Rise	6″ Slope	7″ Rise	7″ Slope	8″ Rise	8″ Slope	9″ Rise	9″ Slope	10″ Rise	10″ Slope	11″ Rise	11″ Slope
0	$2\frac{1}{2}$	$6\frac{1}{2}$	$2\frac{29}{32}$	$7\frac{9}{16}$	$3\frac{5}{16}$	$8\frac{21}{32}$	$3\frac{23}{32}$	$9\frac{3}{4}$	$4\frac{5}{32}$	$10\frac{13}{16}$	$4\frac{9}{16}$	$11\frac{29}{32}$
$\frac{1}{16}$	$2\frac{1}{2}$	$6\frac{9}{16}$	$2\frac{15}{16}$	$7\frac{21}{32}$	$3\frac{11}{32}$	$8\frac{23}{32}$	$3\frac{3}{4}$	$9\frac{13}{16}$	$4\frac{5}{32}$	$10\frac{29}{32}$	$4\frac{19}{32}$	$11\frac{31}{32}$
$\frac{1}{8}$	$2\frac{17}{32}$	$6\frac{5}{8}$	$2\frac{15}{16}$	$7\frac{23}{32}$	$3\frac{3}{8}$	$8\frac{25}{32}$	$3\frac{25}{32}$	$9\frac{7}{8}$	$4\frac{3}{16}$	$10\frac{31}{32}$	$4\frac{19}{32}$	$1\text{-}0\frac{1}{32}$
$\frac{3}{16}$	$2\frac{9}{16}$	$6\frac{11}{16}$	$2\frac{31}{32}$	$7\frac{25}{32}$	$3\frac{13}{32}$	$8\frac{7}{8}$	$3\frac{13}{16}$	$9\frac{15}{16}$	$4\frac{7}{32}$	$11\frac{1}{32}$	$4\frac{5}{8}$	$1\text{-}0\frac{3}{32}$
$\frac{1}{4}$	$2\frac{19}{32}$	$6\frac{3}{4}$	3	$7\frac{27}{32}$	$3\frac{13}{32}$	$8\frac{15}{16}$	$3\frac{27}{32}$	10	$4\frac{1}{4}$	$11\frac{3}{32}$	$4\frac{21}{32}$	$1\text{-}0\frac{3}{16}$
$\frac{5}{16}$	$2\frac{5}{8}$	$6\frac{27}{32}$	$3\frac{1}{32}$	$7\frac{29}{32}$	$3\frac{7}{16}$	9	$3\frac{27}{32}$	$10\frac{3}{32}$	$4\frac{9}{32}$	$11\frac{5}{32}$	$4\frac{11}{16}$	$1\text{-}0\frac{1}{4}$
$\frac{3}{8}$	$2\frac{5}{8}$	$6\frac{29}{32}$	$3\frac{1}{32}$	$7\frac{31}{32}$	$3\frac{15}{32}$	$9\frac{1}{16}$	$3\frac{7}{8}$	$10\frac{5}{32}$	$4\frac{5}{16}$	$11\frac{7}{32}$	$4\frac{23}{32}$	$1\text{-}0\frac{5}{16}$
$\frac{7}{16}$	$2\frac{21}{32}$	$6\frac{31}{32}$	$3\frac{3}{32}$	$8\frac{1}{16}$	$3\frac{1}{2}$	$9\frac{1}{8}$	$3\frac{29}{32}$	$10\frac{7}{32}$	$4\frac{5}{16}$	$11\frac{5}{16}$	$4\frac{3}{4}$	$1\text{-}0\frac{3}{8}$
$\frac{1}{2}$	$2\frac{11}{16}$	$7\frac{1}{32}$	$3\frac{3}{32}$	$8\frac{1}{8}$	$3\frac{17}{32}$	$9\frac{3}{16}$	$3\frac{15}{16}$	$10\frac{9}{32}$	$4\frac{11}{32}$	$11\frac{3}{8}$	$4\frac{3}{4}$	$1\text{-}0\frac{7}{16}$
$\frac{9}{16}$	$2\frac{23}{32}$	$7\frac{3}{32}$	$3\frac{1}{8}$	$8\frac{3}{16}$	$3\frac{17}{32}$	$9\frac{9}{32}$	$3\frac{31}{32}$	$10\frac{11}{32}$	$4\frac{3}{8}$	$11\frac{7}{16}$	$4\frac{25}{32}$	$1\text{-}0\frac{1}{2}$
$\frac{5}{8}$	$2\frac{3}{4}$	$7\frac{5}{32}$	$3\frac{5}{32}$	$8\frac{1}{4}$	$3\frac{9}{16}$	$9\frac{11}{32}$	4	$10\frac{13}{32}$	$4\frac{13}{32}$	$11\frac{1}{2}$	$4\frac{13}{16}$	$1\text{-}0\frac{19}{32}$
$\frac{11}{16}$	$2\frac{25}{32}$	$7\frac{1}{4}$	$3\frac{3}{16}$	$8\frac{5}{16}$	$3\frac{19}{32}$	$9\frac{13}{32}$	4	$10\frac{1}{2}$	$4\frac{7}{16}$	$11\frac{9}{16}$	$4\frac{27}{32}$	$1\text{-}0\frac{21}{32}$
$\frac{3}{4}$	$2\frac{25}{32}$	$7\frac{5}{16}$	$3\frac{7}{32}$	$8\frac{3}{8}$	$3\frac{5}{8}$	$9\frac{15}{32}$	$4\frac{1}{2}$	$10\frac{9}{16}$	$4\frac{7}{16}$	$11\frac{5}{8}$	$4\frac{7}{8}$	$1\text{-}0\frac{23}{32}$
$\frac{13}{16}$	$2\frac{13}{16}$	$7\frac{3}{8}$	$3\frac{1}{4}$	$8\frac{15}{32}$	$3\frac{21}{32}$	$9\frac{17}{32}$	$4\frac{1}{16}$	$10\frac{5}{8}$	$4\frac{15}{32}$	$11\frac{23}{32}$	$4\frac{29}{32}$	$1\text{-}0\frac{25}{32}$
$\frac{7}{8}$	$2\frac{27}{32}$	$7\frac{7}{16}$	$3\frac{1}{4}$	$8\frac{17}{32}$	$3\frac{11}{16}$	$9\frac{19}{32}$	$4\frac{3}{32}$	$10\frac{11}{16}$	$4\frac{1}{2}$	$11\frac{25}{32}$	$4\frac{29}{32}$	$1\text{-}0\frac{27}{32}$
$\frac{15}{16}$	$2\frac{7}{8}$	$7\frac{1}{2}$	$3\frac{9}{32}$	$8\frac{19}{32}$	$3\frac{11}{16}$	$9\frac{11}{16}$	$4\frac{1}{8}$	$10\frac{3}{4}$	$4\frac{17}{32}$	$11\frac{27}{32}$	$4\frac{15}{32}$	$1\text{-}0\frac{29}{32}$

Feet	0′ Rise	0′ Slope	10′ Rise	10′ Slope	20′ Rise	20′ Slope	30′ Rise	30′ Slope
0	0	0	$4\text{-}1\frac{23}{32}$	$10\text{-}9\frac{7}{8}$	$8\text{-}3\frac{13}{32}$	$21\text{-}7\frac{25}{32}$	$12\text{-}5\frac{1}{8}$	$32\text{-}5\frac{21}{32}$
1	$4\frac{31}{32}$	$1\text{-}1$	$4\text{-}6\frac{11}{32}$	$11\text{-}10\frac{7}{8}$	$8\text{-}8\frac{3}{8}$	$22\text{-}8\frac{3}{4}$	$12\text{-}10\frac{3}{32}$	$33\text{-}6\frac{21}{32}$
2	$9\frac{15}{16}$	$2\text{-}1\frac{31}{32}$	$4\text{-}11\frac{21}{32}$	$12\text{-}11\frac{7}{8}$	$9\text{-}1\frac{11}{32}$	$23\text{-}9\frac{3}{4}$	$13\text{-}3\frac{3}{16}$	$34\text{-}7\frac{5}{8}$
3	$1\text{-}2\frac{29}{32}$	$3\text{-}2\frac{31}{32}$	$5\text{-}4\frac{5}{8}$	$14\text{-}0\frac{27}{32}$	$9\text{-}6\frac{5}{16}$	$24\text{-}10\frac{3}{4}$	$13\text{-}8\frac{1}{32}$	$35\text{-}8\frac{5}{8}$
4	$1\text{-}7\frac{7}{8}$	$4\text{-}3\frac{31}{32}$	$5\text{-}9\frac{19}{32}$	$15\text{-}1\frac{27}{32}$	$9\text{-}11\frac{9}{32}$	$25\text{-}11\frac{23}{32}$	$14\text{-}1$	$36\text{-}9\frac{5}{8}$
5	$2\text{-}0\frac{27}{32}$	$5\text{-}4\frac{15}{16}$	$6\text{-}2\frac{9}{16}$	$16\text{-}2\frac{27}{32}$	$10\text{-}4\frac{1}{4}$	$27\text{-}0\frac{23}{32}$	$14\text{-}5\frac{31}{32}$	$37\text{-}10\frac{19}{32}$
6	$2\text{-}5\frac{13}{32}$	$6\text{-}5\frac{15}{16}$	$6\text{-}7\frac{17}{32}$	$17\text{-}3\frac{13}{16}$	$10\text{-}9\frac{1}{4}$	$28\text{-}1\frac{23}{32}$	$14\text{-}10\frac{15}{16}$	$38\text{-}11\frac{19}{32}$
7	$2\text{-}10\frac{25}{32}$	$7\text{-}6\frac{29}{32}$	$7\text{-}0\frac{1}{2}$	$18\text{-}4\frac{13}{16}$	$11\text{-}2\frac{7}{32}$	$29\text{-}2\frac{11}{16}$	$15\text{-}3\frac{29}{32}$	$40\text{-}0\frac{19}{32}$
8	$3\text{-}3\frac{3}{4}$	$8\text{-}7\frac{29}{32}$	$7\text{-}5\frac{15}{32}$	$19\text{-}5\frac{25}{32}$	$11\text{-}7\frac{3}{16}$	$30\text{-}3\frac{11}{16}$	$15\text{-}8\frac{7}{8}$	$41\text{-}1\frac{9}{16}$
9	$3\text{-}8\frac{3}{4}$	$9\text{-}8\frac{29}{32}$	$7\text{-}10\frac{7}{16}$	$20\text{-}6\frac{25}{32}$	$12\text{-}0\frac{5}{32}$	$31\text{-}4\frac{11}{16}$	$16\text{-}1\frac{27}{32}$	$42\text{-}2\frac{9}{16}$

22°30′ PITCH (Bevel between 4 15/16″ to 12″ and 5″ to 12″)

Inch	12″ Rise	12″ Slope	13″ Rise	13″ Slope	14″ Rise	14″ Slope	15″ Rise	15″ Slope	16″ Rise	16″ Slope
0	4 31/32	1-1	5 3/8	1-2 1/16	5 13/16	1-3 5/32–	6 7/32–	1-4 1/4	6 5/8	1-5 5/16
1/16	5	1-1 1/16	5 13/32	1-2 1/8	5 13/16	1-3 7/32	6 1/4	1-4 5/16	6 21/32–	1-5 3/8
1/8	5 1/32–	1-1 1/8	7 7/16	1-2 7/32–	5 27/32	1-3 9/32	6 1/4	1-4 3/8	6 11/16	1-5 15/32–
3/16	5 1/16	1-1 3/16	5 15/32–	1-2 9/32–	5 7/8	1-3 11/32	6 9/32	1-4 7/16	6 23/32–	1-5 17/32–
1/4	5 1/16	1-1 1/4	5 1/2	1-2 11/32–	5 29/32–	1-3 7/16	6 5/16	1-4 1/2	6 23/32	1-5 19/32–
5/16	5 3/32	1-1 5/16	5 1/2	1-2 13/32	5 15/16	1-3 1/2	6 11/32–	1-4 9/16	6 3/4	1-5 21/32
3/8	5 1/8	1-1 13/32–	5 17/32	1-2 15/32	5 31/32–	1-3 9/16	6 3/8	1-4 21/32–	6 25/32	1-5 23/32
7/16	5 5/32–	1-1 15/32–	5 9/16	1-2 17/32	5 31/32	1-3 5/8	6 13/32–	1-4 23/32–	6 13/16	1-5 25/32
1/2	5 3/16	1-1 17/32–	5 19/32–	1-2 5/8	6	1-3 11/16	6 13/32	1-4 25/32–	6 27/32–	1-5 7/8
9/16	5 7/32–	1-1 19/32	5 5/8	1-2 11/16	6 1/32	1-3 3/4	6 7/16	1-4 27/32	6 7/8	1-5 15/16
5/8	5 7/32	1-1 21/32	5 21/32–	1-2 3/4	6 1/16	1-3 27/32–	6 15/32	1-4 29/32	6 7/8	1-6
11/16	5 1/4	1-1 23/32	5 21/32	1-2 13/16	6 3/32–	1-3 29/32–	6 1/2	1-4 31/32	6 29/32	1-6 1/16
3/4	5 9/32–	1-1 13/16	5 11/16	1-2 7/8	6 1/8	1-3 31/32–	6 17/32–	1-5 1/16	6 15/16	1-6 1/8
13/16	5 5/16	1-1 7/8	5 23/32	1-2 15/16	6 1/8	1-4 1/32	6 9/16	1-5 1/8	6 31/32–	1-6 3/16
7/8	5 11/32–	1-1 15/16	5 3/4	1-3 1/32–	6 5/32	1-4 3/32	6 9/16	1-5 3/16	7	1-6 1/4
15/16	5 11/32	1-2	5 25/32–	1-3 3/32–	6 3/16	1-4 5/32	6 19/32	1-5 1/4	7 1/32–	1-6 11/32–

Inch	17″ Rise	17″ Slope	18″ Rise	18″ Slope	19″ Rise	19″ Slope	20″ Rise	20″ Slope	21″ Rise	21″ Slope
0	7 1/32	1-6 13/32–	7 15/32–	1-7 15/32	7 7/8	1-8 9/16	8 9/32	1-9 21/32–	8 11/16	1-10 23/32
1/16	7 1/16	1-6 15/32–	7 15/32	1-7 9/16	7 29/32–	1-8 5/8	8 5/16	1-9 23/32–	8 23/32	1-10 13/16
1/8	7 3/32–	1-6 17/32	7 1/2	1-7 5/8	7 29/32	1-8 11/16	8 11/32–	1-9 25/32	8 3/4	1-10 7/8
3/16	7 1/8	1-6 19/32	7 17/32	1-7 11/16	7 15/16	1-8 25/32–	8 3/8	1-9 27/32	8 25/32–	1-10 15/16
1/4	7 5/32–	1-6 21/32	7 9/16	1-7 3/4	7 31/32	1-8 27/32–	8 3/8	1-9 29/32	8 13/16	1-11
5/16	7 5/32	1-6 3/4	7 19/32–	1-7 13/16	8	1-8 29/32–	8 13/32	1-10	8 13/16	1-11 1/16
3/8	7 3/16	1-6 13/16	7 5/8	1-7 7/8	8 1/32–	1-8 31/32	8 7/16	1-10 1/16	8 27/32	1-11 1/8
7/16	7 7/32	1-6 7/8	7 5/8	1-7 31/32–	8 1/16	1-9 1/32	8 15/32–	1-10 1/8	8 7/8	1-11 7/32–
1/2	7 1/4	1-6 15/16	7 21/32	1-8 1/32–	8 1/16	1-9 3/32	8 1/2	1-10 3/16	8 29/32–	1-11 9/32–
9/16	7 9/32–	1-7	7 11/16	1-8 3/32–	8 3/32	1-9 3/16	8 17/32–	1-10 1/4	8 15/16	1-11 11/32–
5/8	7 5/16	1-7 1/16	7 23/32–	1-8 5/32	8 1/8	1-9 1/4	8 17/32	1-10 5/16	8 31/32–	1-11 13/32
11/16	7 5/16	1-7 5/32–	7 3/4	1-8 7/32	8 5/32–	1-9 5/16	8 9/16	1-10 13/32–	8 31/32	1-11 15/32
3/4	7 11/32	1-7 7/32–	7 25/32–	1-8 9/32	8 3/16	1-9 3/8	8 19/32	1-10 15/32–	9	1-11 17/32
13/16	7 3/8	1-7 9/32–	7 25/32	1-8 3/8	8 7/32–	1-9 7/16	8 5/8	1-10 17/32–	9 1/32	1-11 5/8
7/8	7 13/32–	1-7 11/32	7 13/16	1-8 7/16	8 7/32	1-9 1/2	8 21/32–	1-10 19/32	9 1/16	1-11 11/16
15/16	7 7/16	1-7 13/32	7 27/32	1-8 1/2	8 1/4	1-9 19/32–	8 11/16	1-10 21/32	9 3/32–	1-11 3/4

Feet	40′ Rise	40′ Slope	50′ Rise	50′ Slope	60′ Rise	60′ Slope	70′ Rise	70′ Slope
0	16-6 13/16	43-3 9/16	20-8 17/32–	54-1 7/16	24-10 7/32	64-11 5/16	28-11 15/16	75-9 7/32–
1	16-11 25/32	44-4 17/32	21-1 1/2	55-2 7/16	25-3 7/32–	66-0 5/16	29-4 29/32	76-10 3/16
2	17-4 3/4	45-5 17/32–	21-6 15/32	56-3 13/32	25-8 3/16	67-1 5/16	29-9 7/8	77-11 3/16
3	17-9 23/32	46-6 1/2	21-11 7/16	57-4 13/32–	26-1 5/32–	68-2 9/32	30-2 27/32	79-0 3/16
4	18-2 23/32–	47-7 1/2	22-4 13/32	58-5 3/8	26-6 1/8	69-3 9/32–	30-7 13/16	80-1 5/32
5	18-7 11/16	48-8 1/2	22-9 3/8	59-6 3/8	26-11 3/32–	70-4 9/32–	31-0 25/32	81-2 5/32–
6	19-0 21/32–	49-9 15/32	23-2 11/32	60-7 3/8	27-4 1/16	71-5 1/4	31-5 3/4	82-3 5/32–
7	19-5 5/8	50-10 15/32	23-7 5/16	61-8 11/32	27-9 1/32–	72-6 1/4	31-10 23/32	83-4 1/8
8	19-10 19/32–	51-11 15/32–	24-0 9/32	62-9 11/32	28-2	73-7 7/32	32-3 23/32–	84-5 1/8
9	20-3 9/16	53-0 7/16	24-5 1/4	63-10 11/32–	28-6 31/32	74-8 7/32	32-8 11/16	85-6 3/32

22°30' PITCH (Bevel between 4 15/16" to 12" and 5" to 12")

Inch	22" Rise	22" Slope	23" Rise	23" Slope	24" Rise	24" Slope	25" Rise	25" Slope	26" Rise	26" Slope
0	9 1/8	1-11 13/16	9 17/32	2-0 29/32	9 15/16	2-1 31/32	10 11/32	2-3 1/16	10 25/32	2-4 5/32
1/16	9 1/8	1-11 7/8	9 9/16	2-0 31/32	9 31/32	2-2 1/32	10 3/8	2-3 1/8	10 25/32	2-4 7/32
1/8	9 5/32	1-11 15/16	9 19/32	2-1 1/32	10	2-2 1/8	10 13/32	2-3 3/16	10 13/16	2-4 9/32
3/16	9 3/16	2-0	9 19/32	2-1 3/32	10 1/32	2-2 3/32	10 7/16	2-3 1/4	10 27/32	2-4 11/32
1/4	9 7/32	2-0 3/32	9 5/8	2-1 5/32	10 1/8	2-2 1/4	10 15/32	2-3 11/32	10 7/8	2-4 13/32
5/16	9 1/4	2-0 5/32	9 21/32	2-1 7/32	10 1/16	2-2 5/16	10 1/2	2-3 13/32	10 29/32	2-4 15/32
3/8	9 9/32	2-0 7/32	9 11/16	2-1 5/16	10 3/32	2-2 3/8	10 1/2	2-3 15/32	10 15/16	2-4 9/16
7/16	9 9/32	2-0 9/32	9 23/32	2-1 3/8	10 1/8	2-2 7/16	10 17/32	2-3 17/32	10 15/16	2-4 5/8
1/2	9 5/16	2-0 11/32	9 23/32	2-1 7/16	10 5/32	2-2 17/32	10 9/16	2-3 19/32	10 31/32	2-4 11/16
9/16	9 11/32	2-0 13/32	9 3/4	2-1 1/2	10 3/16	2-2 19/32	10 19/32	2-3 21/32	11	2-4 3/4
5/8	9 3/8	2-0 1/2	9 25/32	2-1 9/16	10 3/32	2-2 21/32	10 5/8	2-3 3/4	11 1/32	2-4 13/16
11/16	9 13/32	2-0 9/16	9 13/16	2-1 5/8	10 7/32	2-2 23/32	10 5/8	2-3 13/16	11 1/16	2-4 7/8
3/4	9 7/16	2-0 5/8	9 27/32	2-1 23/32	10 1/4	2-2 25/32	10 21/32	2-3 7/8	11 3/32	2-4 31/32
13/16	9 7/16	2-0 11/16	9 7/8	2-1 25/32	10 9/32	2-2 27/32	10 11/16	2-3 15/16	11 3/32	2-5 1/32
7/8	9 15/32	2-0 3/4	9 7/8	2-1 27/32	10 5/16	2-2 15/16	10 23/32	2-4	11 1/8	2-5 1/8
15/16	9 1/2	2-0 13/16	9 29/32	2-1 29/32	10 11/32	2-3	10 3/4	2-4 1/16	11 5/32	2-5 5/32

Inch	27" Rise	27" Slope	28" Rise	28" Slope	29" Rise	29" Slope	30" Rise	30" Slope	31" Rise	31" Slope
0	11 3/16	2-5 7/32	11 19/32	2-6 5/16	1-0	2-7 3/8	1-0 7/16	2-8 15/32	1-0 27/32	2-9 9/16
1/16	11 7/32	2-5 9/32	11 5/8	2-6 3/8	1-0 1/32	2-7 15/32	1-0 7/16	2-8 17/32	1-0 7/8	2-9 5/8
1/8	11 1/4	2-5 3/8	11 21/32	2-6 7/16	1-0 1/16	2-7 17/32	1-0 15/32	2-8 19/32	1-0 29/32	2-9 11/16
3/16	11 1/4	2-5 7/16	11 11/16	2-6 1/2	1-0 3/32	2-7 19/32	1-0 1/2	2-8 11/16	1-0 29/32	2-9 3/4
1/4	11 9/32	2-5 1/2	11 11/16	2-6 9/16	1-0 1/8	2-7 21/32	1-0 17/32	2-8 3/4	1-0 15/16	2-9 13/16
5/16	11 5/16	2-5 9/16	11 23/32	2-6 21/32	1-0 5/32	2-7 23/32	1-0 9/16	2-8 13/16	1-0 31/32	2-9 29/32
3/8	11 11/32	2-5 5/8	11 3/4	2-6 23/32	1-0 5/32	2-7 25/32	1-0 19/32	2-8 7/8	1-1	2-9 31/32
7/16	11 3/8	2-5 11/16	11 25/32	2-6 25/32	1-0 3/16	2-7 7/8	1-0 5/8	2-8 15/16	1-1 1/32	2-10 1/32
1/2	11 13/32	2-5 25/32	11 13/16	2-6 27/32	1-0 7/32	2-7 15/16	1-0 5/8	2-9	1-1 1/16	2-10 1/32
9/16	11 13/32	2-5 27/32	11 27/32	2-6 29/32	1-0 1/4	2-8	1-0 21/32	2-9 3/32	1-1 1/16	2-10 3/32
5/8	11 7/16	2-5 29/32	11 7/8	2-6 31/32	1-0 9/32	2-8 1/16	1-0 11/16	2-9 5/32	1-1 3/32	2-10 5/32
11/16	11 15/32	2-5 31/32	11 7/8	2-7 1/16	1-0 5/16	2-8 1/8	1-0 23/32	2-9 7/32	1-1 1/8	2-10 7/32
3/4	11 1/2	2-6 1/32	11 29/32	2-7 1/8	1-0 5/16	2-8 3/16	1-0 3/4	2-9 9/32	1-1 5/32	2-10 5/16
13/16	11 17/32	2-6 3/32	11 15/16	2-7 3/16	1-0 11/32	2-8 9/32	1-0 3/4	2-9 11/32	1-1 3/16	2-10 7/16
7/8	11 17/32	2-6 5/32	11 31/32	2-7 1/4	1-0 3/8	2-8 11/32	1-0 25/32	2-9 13/32	1-1 3/16	2-10 1/2
15/16	11 9/16	2-6 1/4	1-0	2-7 5/16	1-0 13/32	2-8 13/32	1-0 13/16	2-9 1/2	1-1 7/32	2-10 9/16

GIVEN ANGLE, ITS NATURAL AND LOGARITHMIC FUNCTIONS

Natural Functions		Logarithmic Functions
Sin......0.3826834		Sin.........9.5828397
Csc......2.6131259		Csc.........0.4171603
Tan......0.4142136	Given Angle	Tan.........9.6172243
Cot......2.4142136	22°30'	Cot.........0.3827757
Cos......0.9238795		Cos.........9.9656154
Sec......1.0823922		Sec.........0.0343847

Inches	22" Rise	22" Slope	23" Rise	23" Slope	24" Rise	24" Slope	25" Rise	25" Slope	26" Rise	26" Slope
0	11	2-0 19/32	11½	2-1 23/32	1-0	2-2 27/32	1-0½	2-3 15/16	1-1	2-5 1/16
1/16	11 1/32	2-0 21/32	11 17/32	2-1 25/32	1-0 1/32	2-2 29/32	1-0 17/32	2-4 1/32	1-1 1/32	2-5 1/8
1/8	11 1/16	2-0 3/4	11 9/16	2-1 27/32	1-0 1/16	2-2 31/32	1-0 9/16	2-4 3/32	1-1 1/16	2-5 5/32
3/16	11 3/32	2-0 13/16	11 19/32	2-1 15/16	1-0 3/32	2-3 1/32	1-0 19/32	2-4 5/32	1-1 3/32	2-5 9/32
1/4	11 1/8	2-0 7/8	11 5/8	2-2	1-0 1/8	2-3 1/8	1-0 5/8	2-4 7/32	1-1 1/8	2-5 11/32
5/16	11 5/32	2-0 15/16	11 21/32	2-2 1/16	1-0 5/32	2-3 3/16	1-0 21/32	2-4 5/16	1-1 5/32	2-5 13/32
3/8	11 3/16	2-1 1/32	11 11/16	2-2 1/8	1-0 3/16	2-3 1/4	1-0 11/16	2-4 3/8	1-1 3/16	2-5 1/2
7/16	11 7/32	2-1 3/32	11 23/32	2-2 7/32	1-0 7/32	2-3 5/16	1-0 23/32	2-4 7/16	1-1 7/32	2-5 9/16
1/2	11 1/4	2-1 5/32	11 3/4	2-2 9/32	1-0 1/4	2-3 13/32	1-0 3/4	2-4 1/2	1-1 1/4	2-5 5/8
9/16	11 9/32	2-1 7/32	11 25/32	2-2 11/32	1-0 9/32	2-3 15/32	1-0 25/32	2-4 19/32	1-1 9/32	2-5 11/16
5/8	11 5/16	2-1 9/32	11 13/16	2-2 13/32	1-0 5/16	2-3 17/32	1-0 13/16	2-4 21/32	1-1 5/16	2-5 25/32
11/16	11 11/32	2-1 3/8	11 27/32	2-2 15/32	1-0 11/32	2-3 19/32	1-0 27/32	2-4 23/32	1-1 11/32	2-5 27/32
3/4	11 3/8	2-1 7/16	11 7/8	2-2 9/16	1-0 3/8	2-3 21/32	1-0 7/8	2-4 25/32	1-1 3/8	2-5 29/32
13/16	11 13/32	2-1 1/2	11 29/32	2-2 5/8	1-0 13/16	2-3 3/4	1-0 29/32	2-4 27/32	1-1 13/32	2-5 31/32
7/8	11 7/16	2-1 9/16	11 15/16	2-2 11/16	1-0 7/16	2-3 13/16	1-0 15/16	2-4 15/16	1-1 7/16	2-6 1/16
15/16	11 15/32	2-1 21/32	11 31/32	2-2 3/4	1-0 15/32	2-3 7/8	1-0 31/32	2-5	1-1 15/32	2-6 1/8

Inches	27" Rise	27" Slope	28" Rise	28" Slope	29" Rise	29" Slope	30" Rise	30" Slope	31" Rise	31" Slope
0	1-1½	2-6 3/16	1-2	2-7 5/16	1-2½	2-8 7/16	1-3	2-9 17/32	1-3½	2-10 21/32
1/16	1-1 17/32	2-6 1/4	1-2 1/32	2-7 3/8	1-2 17/32	2-8 1/2	1-3 1/32	2-9 5/8	1-3 17/32	2-10 23/32
1/8	1-1 9/16	2-6 5/16	1-2 1/16	2-7 7/16	1-2 9/16	2-8 9/16	1-3 1/16	2-9 11/16	1-3 9/16	2-10 13/16
3/16	1-1 19/32	2-6 13/32	1-2 3/32	2-7 1/2	1-2 19/32	2-8 5/8	1-3 3/32	2-9 3/4	1-3 19/32	2-10 7/8
1/4	1-1 5/8	2-6 15/32	1-2 1/8	2-7 19/32	1-2 5/8	2-8 11/16	1-3 1/8	2-9 13/16	1-3 5/8	2-10 15/16
5/16	1-1 21/32	2-6 17/32	1-2 5/32	2-7 21/32	1-2 21/32	2-8 25/32	1-3 5/32	2-9 7/8	1-3 21/32	2-11
3/8	1-1 11/16	2-6 19/32	1-2 3/16	2-7 23/32	1-2 11/16	2-8 27/32	1-3 3/16	2-9 31/32	1-3 11/16	2-11 3/32
7/16	1-1 23/32	2-6 11/16	1-2 7/32	2-7 25/32	1-2 23/32	2-8 29/32	1-3 7/32	2-10 1/32	1-3 23/32	2-11 5/32
1/2	1-1 3/4	2-6 3/4	1-2 1/4	2-7 7/8	1-2 3/4	2-8 31/32	1-3 1/4	2-10 3/32	1-3 3/4	2-11 7/32
9/16	1-1 25/32	2-6 13/16	1-2 9/32	2-7 15/16	1-2 25/32	2-9 1/16	1-3 9/32	2-10 5/32	1-3 25/32	2-11 9/32
5/8	1-1 13/16	2-6 7/8	1-2 5/16	2-8	1-2 13/16	2-9 1/8	1-3 5/16	2-10 1/4	1-3 13/16	2-11 11/32
11/16	1-1 27/32	2-6 31/32	1-2 11/16	2-8 1/16	1-2 27/32	2-9 3/16	1-3 11/32	2-10 5/16	1-3 27/32	2-11 7/16
3/4	1-1 7/8	2-7 1/32	1-2 3/8	2-8 5/32	1-2 7/8	2-9 1/4	1-3 3/8	2-10 3/8	1-3 7/8	2-11 1/2
13/16	1-1 29/32	2-7 3/32	1-2 13/32	2-8 7/32	1-2 15/16	2-9 11/32	1-3 13/32	2-10 7/16	1-3 29/32	2-11 9/16
7/8	1-1 15/16	2-7 5/32	1-2 7/16	2-8 9/32	1-2 15/16	2-9 13/32	1-3 7/16	2-10 17/32	1-3 15/16	2-11 5/8
15/16	1-1 31/32	2-7 1/4	1-2 15/32	2-8 11/16	1-2 31/32	2-9 15/32	1-3 15/32	2-10 19/32	1-3 31/32	2-11 23/32

CORRESPONDING ANGLE, ITS NATURAL AND LOGARITHMIC FUNCTIONS

Natural Functions	Corresponding Angle	Logarithmic Functions
Sin......0.4472135		Sin......9.6505149
Csc......2.2360686	Corresponding	Csc......0.3494851
Tan......0.5000000	Angle	Tan......9.6989700
Cot......2.0000000	26° 33′ 54.19″	Cot......0.3010300
Cos......0.8944269		Cos......9.9515449
Sec......1.1180343		Sec......0.0484551

Inches	0″ Rise	Slope	1″ Rise	Slope	2″ Rise	Slope	3″ Rise	Slope	4″ Rise	Slope	5″ Rise	Slope
0	0	0	9/16	15/32	15/32	25/32	1 23/32	3 15/32	2 5/16	4 5/8	2 7/8	5 25/32
1/16	1/32	1/16	5/8	17/32	13/16	2 3/8	1 25/32	3 17/32	2 11/32	4 11/16	2 15/16	5 27/32
1/8	1/16	5/32	21/32	15/16	17/32	2 15/32	1 13/16	3 19/32	2 3/8	4 3/4	2 31/32	5 29/32
3/16	3/32	7/32	11/16	1 3/8	1 1/4	2 17/32	1 27/32	3 11/16	2 13/32	4 27/32	3	6
1/4	5/32	9/32	23/32	1 7/16	1 5/16	2 19/32	1 7/8	3 3/4	2 15/32	4 29/32	3 1/32	6 1/16
5/16	3/16	3/8	3/4	1 1/2	1 11/32	2 21/32	1 29/32	3 13/16	2 1/2	4 31/32	3 1/16	6 1/8
3/8	7/32	7/16	25/32	1 19/32	1 3/8	2 3/4	1 15/16	3 29/32	2 17/32	5 1/16	3 3/32	6 7/32
7/16	1/4	1/2	27/32	1 21/32	1 13/32	2 13/16	2	3 31/32	2 9/16	5 1/8	3 1/8	6 9/32
1/2	9/32	9/16	7/8	1 23/32	1 7/16	2 7/8	2 1/32	4 1/32	2 19/32	5 3/16	3 3/16	6 11/32
9/16	5/16	21/32	29/32	1 13/16	1 15/32	2 31/32	2 1/16	4 1/8	2 5/8	5 9/32	3 7/32	6 7/16
5/8	3/8	23/32	15/16	1 7/8	1 1/2	3 1/32	2 3/32	4 3/16	2 21/32	5 11/32	3 1/4	6 1/2
11/16	13/32	25/32	31/32	1 15/16	1 19/32	3 3/32	2 1/8	4 1/4	2 23/32	5 13/32	3 9/32	6 9/16
3/4	7/16	7/8	1	2 1/32	1 19/32	3 3/16	2 5/32	4 11/32	2 3/4	5 1/2	3 5/16	6 5/8
13/16	15/32	15/16	1 1/32	2 3/32	1 5/8	3 1/4	2 3/16	4 13/32	2 25/32	5 9/16	3 11/32	6 23/32
7/8	1/2	1	1 3/32	2 5/32	1 21/32	3 5/16	2 1/4	4 15/32	2 13/16	5 5/8	3 13/32	6 25/32
15/16	17/32	1 3/32	1 1/8	2 1/4	1 11/16	3 13/32	2 9/32	4 17/32	2 27/32	5 11/16	3 7/16	6 27/32

Inches	6″ Rise	Slope	7″ Rise	Slope	8″ Rise	Slope	9″ Rise	Slope	10″ Rise	Slope	11″ Rise	Slope
0	3 15/32	6 15/16	4 1/32	8 3/32	4 5/8	9 1/4	5 3/16	10 13/32	5 25/32	11 9/16	6 11/32	1-0 11/16
1/16	3 1/2	7	4 1/16	8 5/32	4 21/32	9 5/16	5 7/32	10 15/32	5 13/16	11 5/8	6 3/8	1-0 25/32
1/8	3 17/32	7 1/16	4 1/8	8 7/32	4 11/16	9 3/8	5 9/32	10 17/32	5 27/32	11 11/16	6 7/16	1-0 27/32
3/16	3 9/16	7 5/32	4 5/32	8 5/16	4 23/32	9 15/32	5 5/16	10 19/32	5 7/8	11 3/4	6 15/32	1-0 31/32
1/4	3 19/32	7 7/32	4 3/16	8 3/8	4 3/4	9 17/32	5 11/32	10 11/16	5 29/32	11 27/32	6 1/2	1-1
5/16	3 21/32	7 9/32	4 7/32	8 7/16	4 13/16	9 19/32	5 3/8	10 3/4	5 31/32	11 29/32	6 17/32	1-1 1/16
3/8	3 11/16	7 3/8	4 1/4	8 17/32	4 27/32	9 21/32	5 13/32	10 13/16	6	11 31/32	6 9/16	1-1 1/8
7/16	3 23/32	7 7/16	4 9/32	8 19/32	4 7/8	9 3/4	5 7/16	10 29/32	6 1/2	1-0 1/16	6 19/32	1-1 7/32
1/2	3 3/4	7 1/2	4 11/32	8 21/32	4 29/32	9 13/16	5 1/2	10 31/32	6 1/16	1-0 1/8	6 5/8	1-1 9/32
9/16	3 25/32	7 9/16	4 3/8	8 23/32	4 15/16	9 7/8	5 17/32	11 1/32	6 3/32	1-0 3/16	6 11/16	1-1 11/32
5/8	3 13/16	7 21/32	4 13/32	8 13/16	4 31/32	9 31/32	5 9/16	11 1/8	6 1/8	1-0 9/32	6 23/32	1-1 7/16
11/16	3 7/8	7 23/32	4 7/16	8 7/8	5 1/32	10 1/32	5 19/32	11 3/16	6 5/32	1-0 11/32	6 3/4	1-1 1/2
3/4	3 29/32	7 25/32	4 15/32	8 15/16	5 1/16	10 3/8	5 5/8	11 1/4	6 7/32	1-0 13/32	6 25/32	1-1 9/16
13/16	3 15/16	7 7/8	4 1/2	9 1/32	5 3/32	10 3/16	5 21/32	11 11/32	6 1/4	1-0 1/2	6 13/16	1-1 5/8
7/8	3 31/32	7 15/16	4 17/32	9 3/32	5 1/8	10 1/4	5 11/16	11 13/32	6 9/32	1-0 9/16	6 27/32	1-1 23/32
15/16	4	8	4 19/32	9 5/32	5 5/32	10 5/16	5 3/4	11 15/32	6 5/16	1-0 5/8	6 29/32	1-1 25/32

Feet	0′ Rise	Slope	10′ Rise	Slope	20′ Rise	Slope	30′ Rise	Slope
0	0	0	5-9 9/32	11-6 9/16	11-6 9/16	23-1 1/8	17-3 27/32	34-7 11/16
1	6 15/16	1-1 27/32	6-4 7/32	12-8 13/32	12-1 1/2	24-3	17-10 25/32	35-9 9/16
2	1-1 27/32	2-3 23/32	6-11 1/8	13-10 9/32	12-8 13/32	25-4 27/32	18-5 11/16	36-11 13/32
3	1-8 25/32	3-5 9/16	7-6 1/16	15-0 1/8	13-3 11/32	26-6 11/16	19-0 5/8	38-1 1/4
4	2-3 23/32	4-7 7/16	8-1	16-2	13-10 9/32	27-8 9/16	19-7 9/16	39-3 1/8
5	2-10 21/32	5-9 9/32	8-7 15/16	17-3 27/32	14-5 7/32	28-10 13/32	20-2 1/2	40-4 31/32
6	3-5 9/16	6-11 1/8	9-2 27/32	18-5 11/32	15-0 1/8	30-0 9/32	20-9 13/32	41-6 27/32
7	4-0 1/2	8-1	9-9 25/32	19-7 9/16	15-7 1/16	31-2 1/8	21-4 11/32	42-8 11/16
8	4-7 7/16	9-2 27/32	10-4 23/32	20-9 13/32	16-2	32-3 31/32	21-11 9/32	43-10 17/32
9	5-2 11/32	10-4 23/32	10-11 5/8	21-11 9/32	16-8 29/32	33-5 27/32	22-6 3/16	45-0 13/32

Inches	12″ Rise	12″ Slope	13″ Rise	13″ Slope	14″ Rise	14″ Slope	15″ Rise	15″ Slope	16″ Rise	16″ Slope
0	$6\frac{15}{16}$	$1\text{-}1\frac{27}{32}$	$7\frac12$	$1\text{-}3$	$8\frac{3}{32}$	$1\text{-}4\frac{5}{32}$	$8\frac{21}{32}$	$1\text{-}5\frac{5}{16}$	$9\frac14$	$1\text{-}6\frac{15}{32}$
1/16	$6\frac{31}{32}$	$1\text{-}1\frac{15}{16}$	$7\frac{17}{32}$	$1\text{-}3\frac{3}{32}$	$8\frac18$	$1\text{-}4\frac14$	$8\frac{11}{16}$	$1\text{-}5\frac{13}{32}$	$9\frac{9}{32}$	$1\text{-}6\frac{9}{16}$
1/8	7	$1\text{-}2$	$7\frac{9}{16}$	$1\text{-}3\frac{5}{32}$	$8\frac{5}{32}$	$1\text{-}4\frac{5}{16}$	$8\frac{23}{32}$	$1\text{-}5\frac{15}{32}$	$9\frac{5}{16}$	$1\text{-}6\frac58$
3/16	$7\frac{1}{32}$	$1\text{-}2\frac{1}{16}$	$7\frac58$	$1\text{-}3\frac{7}{32}$	$8\frac{3}{16}$	$1\text{-}4\frac38$	$8\frac{25}{32}$	$1\text{-}5\frac{17}{32}$	$9\frac{11}{32}$	$1\text{-}6\frac{11}{16}$
1/4	$7\frac{1}{16}$	$1\text{-}2\frac{5}{32}$	$7\frac{21}{32}$	$1\text{-}3\frac{5}{16}$	$8\frac{7}{32}$	$1\text{-}4\frac{15}{32}$	$8\frac{13}{16}$	$1\text{-}5\frac{19}{32}$	$9\frac38$	$1\text{-}6\frac34$
5/16	$7\frac{3}{32}$	$1\text{-}2\frac{7}{32}$	$7\frac{11}{16}$	$1\text{-}3\frac38$	$8\frac14$	$1\text{-}4\frac{17}{32}$	$8\frac{27}{32}$	$1\text{-}5\frac{11}{16}$	$9\frac{13}{32}$	$1\text{-}6\frac{27}{32}$
3/8	$7\frac{5}{32}$	$1\text{-}2\frac{9}{32}$	$7\frac{23}{32}$	$1\text{-}3\frac{7}{16}$	$8\frac{9}{32}$	$1\text{-}4\frac{19}{32}$	$8\frac78$	$1\text{-}5\frac34$	$9\frac{15}{32}$	$1\text{-}6\frac{29}{32}$
7/16	$7\frac{3}{16}$	$1\text{-}2\frac38$	$7\frac34$	$1\text{-}3\frac{17}{32}$	$8\frac{11}{32}$	$1\text{-}4\frac{21}{32}$	$8\frac{29}{32}$	$1\text{-}5\frac{13}{16}$	$9\frac12$	$1\text{-}6\frac{31}{32}$
1/2	$7\frac{7}{32}$	$1\text{-}2\frac{7}{16}$	$7\frac{25}{32}$	$1\text{-}3\frac{19}{32}$	$8\frac38$	$1\text{-}4\frac34$	$8\frac{15}{16}$	$1\text{-}5\frac{29}{32}$	$9\frac{17}{32}$	$1\text{-}7\frac{1}{32}$
9/16	$7\frac14$	$1\text{-}2\frac12$	$7\frac{27}{32}$	$1\text{-}3\frac{21}{32}$	$8\frac{13}{32}$	$1\text{-}4\frac{13}{16}$	9	$1\text{-}5\frac{31}{32}$	$9\frac{9}{16}$	$1\text{-}7\frac18$
5/8	$7\frac{9}{32}$	$1\text{-}2\frac{9}{16}$	$7\frac78$	$1\text{-}3\frac{23}{32}$	$8\frac{7}{16}$	$1\text{-}4\frac78$	$9\frac{1}{32}$	$1\text{-}6\frac12$	$9\frac{19}{32}$	$1\text{-}7\frac{3}{16}$
11/16	$7\frac{5}{16}$	$1\text{-}2\frac{21}{32}$	$7\frac{29}{32}$	$1\text{-}3\frac{13}{16}$	$8\frac{15}{32}$	$1\text{-}4\frac{31}{32}$	$9\frac{1}{16}$	$1\text{-}6\frac18$	$9\frac58$	$1\text{-}7\frac{9}{32}$
3/4	$7\frac38$	$1\text{-}2\frac{23}{32}$	$7\frac{15}{16}$	$1\text{-}3\frac78$	$8\frac{17}{32}$	$1\text{-}5\frac{1}{32}$	$9\frac{3}{32}$	$1\text{-}6\frac{3}{16}$	$9\frac{21}{32}$	$1\text{-}7\frac{11}{32}$
13/16	$7\frac{13}{32}$	$1\text{-}2\frac{25}{32}$	$7\frac{31}{32}$	$1\text{-}3\frac{15}{16}$	$8\frac{9}{16}$	$1\text{-}5\frac{5}{32}$	$9\frac18$	$1\text{-}6\frac14$	$9\frac{23}{32}$	$1\text{-}7\frac{13}{32}$
7/8	$7\frac{7}{16}$	$1\text{-}2\frac78$	8	$1\text{-}4\frac{1}{32}$	$8\frac{19}{32}$	$1\text{-}5\frac{3}{16}$	$9\frac{5}{32}$	$1\text{-}6\frac{11}{32}$	$9\frac34$	$1\text{-}7\frac12$
15/16	$7\frac{15}{32}$	$1\text{-}2\frac{15}{16}$	$8\frac18$	$1\text{-}4\frac{3}{32}$	$8\frac58$	$1\text{-}5\frac14$	$9\frac{3}{16}$	$1\text{-}6\frac{13}{32}$	$9\frac{25}{32}$	$1\text{-}7\frac{9}{16}$

Inches	17″ Rise	17″ Slope	18″ Rise	18″ Slope	19″ Rise	19″ Slope	20″ Rise	20″ Slope	21″ Rise	21″ Slope
0	$9\frac{13}{16}$	$1\text{-}7\frac58$	$10\frac{13}{32}$	$1\text{-}8\frac{25}{32}$	$10\frac{31}{32}$	$1\text{-}9\frac{15}{16}$	$11\frac{9}{16}$	$1\text{-}11\frac{3}{32}$	$1\text{-}0\frac18$	$2\text{-}0\frac14$
1/16	$9\frac{27}{32}$	$1\text{-}7\frac{11}{16}$	$10\frac{7}{16}$	$1\text{-}8\frac{27}{32}$	11	$1\text{-}10$	$11\frac{19}{32}$	$1\text{-}11\frac{5}{32}$	$1\text{-}0\frac{5}{32}$	$2\text{-}0\frac{5}{16}$
1/8	$9\frac78$	$1\text{-}7\frac{25}{32}$	$10\frac{15}{32}$	$1\text{-}8\frac{15}{16}$	$11\frac{1}{32}$	$1\text{-}10\frac{3}{32}$	$11\frac58$	$1\text{-}11\frac14$	$1\text{-}0\frac{3}{16}$	$2\text{-}0\frac{13}{32}$
3/16	$9\frac{15}{16}$	$1\text{-}7\frac{27}{32}$	$10\frac12$	$1\text{-}9$	$11\frac{1}{16}$	$1\text{-}10\frac{5}{32}$	$11\frac{21}{32}$	$1\text{-}11\frac{5}{16}$	$1\text{-}0\frac{7}{32}$	$2\text{-}0\frac{15}{32}$
1/4	$9\frac{31}{32}$	$1\text{-}7\frac{29}{32}$	$10\frac{17}{32}$	$1\text{-}9\frac{1}{16}$	$11\frac18$	$1\text{-}10\frac{7}{32}$	$11\frac{11}{16}$	$1\text{-}11\frac38$	$1\text{-}0\frac{9}{32}$	$2\text{-}0\frac{17}{32}$
5/16	10	$1\text{-}8$	$10\frac{9}{16}$	$1\text{-}9\frac{5}{32}$	$11\frac{5}{32}$	$1\text{-}10\frac{5}{16}$	$11\frac{23}{32}$	$1\text{-}11\frac{15}{32}$	$1\text{-}0\frac{5}{16}$	$2\text{-}0\frac58$
3/8	$10\frac{1}{32}$	$1\text{-}8\frac{1}{16}$	$10\frac{19}{32}$	$1\text{-}9\frac{7}{32}$	$11\frac{3}{16}$	$1\text{-}10\frac38$	$11\frac34$	$1\text{-}11\frac{17}{32}$	$1\text{-}0\frac{11}{32}$	$2\text{-}0\frac{11}{32}$
7/16	$10\frac{1}{16}$	$1\text{-}8\frac18$	$10\frac{21}{32}$	$1\text{-}9\frac{9}{32}$	$11\frac{7}{32}$	$1\text{-}10\frac{7}{16}$	$11\frac{13}{16}$	$1\text{-}11\frac{19}{32}$	$1\text{-}0\frac38$	$2\text{-}0\frac34$
1/2	$10\frac{3}{32}$	$1\text{-}8\frac{7}{32}$	$10\frac{11}{16}$	$1\text{-}9\frac38$	$11\frac14$	$1\text{-}10\frac{17}{32}$	$11\frac{27}{32}$	$1\text{-}11\frac{21}{32}$	$1\text{-}0\frac{13}{32}$	$2\text{-}0\frac{13}{32}$
9/16	$10\frac18$	$1\text{-}8\frac{9}{32}$	$10\frac{23}{32}$	$1\text{-}9\frac{7}{16}$	$11\frac{9}{32}$	$1\text{-}10\frac{19}{32}$	$11\frac78$	$1\text{-}11\frac34$	$1\text{-}0\frac{7}{16}$	$2\text{-}0\frac{29}{32}$
5/8	$10\frac{5}{32}$	$1\text{-}8\frac{11}{32}$	$10\frac34$	$1\text{-}9\frac12$	$11\frac{11}{32}$	$1\text{-}10\frac{21}{32}$	$11\frac{29}{32}$	$1\text{-}11\frac{13}{16}$	$1\text{-}0\frac12$	$2\text{-}0\frac{31}{32}$
11/16	$10\frac{7}{32}$	$1\text{-}8\frac{7}{16}$	$10\frac{25}{32}$	$1\text{-}9\frac{19}{32}$	$11\frac38$	$1\text{-}10\frac{23}{32}$	$11\frac{15}{16}$	$1\text{-}11\frac78$	$1\text{-}0\frac{17}{32}$	$2\text{-}1\frac{1}{32}$
3/4	$10\frac14$	$1\text{-}8\frac12$	$10\frac{13}{16}$	$1\text{-}9\frac{21}{32}$	$11\frac{13}{32}$	$1\text{-}10\frac{13}{16}$	$11\frac{31}{32}$	$1\text{-}11\frac{31}{32}$	$1\text{-}0\frac{9}{16}$	$2\text{-}1\frac18$
13/16	$10\frac{9}{32}$	$1\text{-}8\frac{9}{16}$	$10\frac78$	$1\text{-}9\frac{23}{32}$	$11\frac{7}{16}$	$1\text{-}10\frac78$	$1\text{-}0\frac{7}{32}$	$2\text{-}0\frac{1}{32}$	$1\text{-}0\frac{19}{32}$	$2\text{-}1\frac{3}{16}$
7/8	$10\frac{5}{16}$	$1\text{-}8\frac58$	$10\frac{29}{32}$	$1\text{-}9\frac{25}{32}$	$11\frac{15}{32}$	$1\text{-}10\frac{15}{16}$	$1\text{-}0\frac18$	$2\text{-}0\frac{3}{32}$	$1\text{-}0\frac58$	$2\text{-}1\frac14$
15/16	$10\frac{11}{32}$	$1\text{-}8\frac{23}{32}$	$10\frac{15}{16}$	$1\text{-}9\frac78$	$11\frac12$	$1\text{-}11\frac{1}{32}$	$1\text{-}0\frac{3}{32}$	$2\text{-}0\frac{3}{16}$	$1\text{-}0\frac{21}{32}$	$2\text{-}1\frac{11}{32}$

Feet	40′ Rise	40′ Slope	50′ Rise	50′ Slope	60′ Rise	60′ Slope	70′ Rise	70′ Slope
0	$23\text{-}1\frac18$	$46\text{-}2\frac14$	$28\text{-}10\frac{13}{32}$	$57\text{-}8\frac{13}{16}$	$34\text{-}7\frac{11}{16}$	$69\text{-}3\frac38$	$40\text{-}4\frac{31}{32}$	$80\text{-}9\frac{15}{16}$
1	$23\text{-}8\frac18$	$47\text{-}4\frac38$	$29\text{-}5\frac{11}{32}$	$58\text{-}10\frac{11}{16}$	$35\text{-}2\frac58$	$70\text{-}5\frac14$	$40\text{-}11\frac{29}{32}$	$81\text{-}11\frac{13}{16}$
2	$24\text{-}3$	$48\text{-}5\frac{31}{32}$	$30\text{-}0\frac{9}{32}$	$60\text{-}0\frac{17}{32}$	$35\text{-}9\frac{9}{16}$	$71\text{-}7\frac{3}{32}$	$41\text{-}6\frac{27}{32}$	$83\text{-}1\frac{21}{32}$
3	$24\text{-}9\frac{29}{32}$	$49\text{-}7\frac{13}{16}$	$30\text{-}7\frac{3}{16}$	$61\text{-}2\frac38$	$36\text{-}4\frac{15}{32}$	$72\text{-}8\frac{31}{32}$	$42\text{-}1\frac34$	$84\text{-}3\frac{17}{32}$
4	$25\text{-}4\frac{27}{32}$	$50\text{-}9\frac{11}{16}$	$31\text{-}2\frac18$	$62\text{-}4\frac14$	$36\text{-}11\frac{13}{32}$	$73\text{-}10\frac{13}{16}$	$42\text{-}8\frac{11}{16}$	$85\text{-}5\frac38$
5	$25\text{-}11\frac{25}{32}$	$51\text{-}11\frac{17}{32}$	$31\text{-}9\frac{1}{16}$	$63\text{-}6\frac{3}{32}$	$37\text{-}6\frac{11}{16}$	$75\text{-}0\frac{21}{32}$	$43\text{-}3\frac58$	$86\text{-}7\frac{7}{32}$
6	$26\text{-}6\frac{11}{16}$	$53\text{-}1\frac{13}{32}$	$32\text{-}3\frac{31}{32}$	$64\text{-}7\frac{31}{32}$	$38\text{-}1\frac14$	$76\text{-}2\frac{17}{32}$	$43\text{-}10\frac{17}{32}$	$87\text{-}9\frac{9}{32}$
7	$27\text{-}1\frac58$	$54\text{-}3\frac14$	$32\text{-}10\frac{29}{32}$	$65\text{-}9\frac{13}{16}$	$38\text{-}8\frac{3}{32}$	$77\text{-}4\frac38$	$44\text{-}5\frac{15}{32}$	$88\text{-}10\frac{15}{16}$
8	$27\text{-}8\frac{9}{16}$	$55\text{-}5\frac{3}{32}$	$33\text{-}5\frac{27}{32}$	$66\text{-}11\frac{21}{32}$	$39\text{-}3\frac{1}{32}$	$78\text{-}6\frac14$	$45\text{-}0\frac{13}{32}$	$90\text{-}0\frac{13}{16}$
9	$28\text{-}3\frac{15}{32}$	$56\text{-}6\frac{31}{32}$	$34\text{-}0\frac34$	$68\text{-}1\frac{17}{32}$	$39\text{-}10\frac12$	$79\text{-}8\frac{3}{32}$	$45\text{-}7\frac{5}{16}$	$91\text{-}2\frac{21}{32}$

Inches	22" Rise	22" Slope	23" Rise	23" Slope	24" Rise	24" Slope	25" Rise	25" Slope	26" Rise	26" Slope
0	1-0 11/16	2-1 13/32	1-1 9/32	2-2 9/16	1-1 27/32	2-3 23/32	1-2 7/16	2-4 7/8	1-3	2-6 1/32
1/16	1-0 3/4	2-1 15/32	1-1 5/16	2-2 5/8	1-1 29/32	2-3 25/32	1-2 15/32	2-4 15/16	1-3 1/16	2-6 3/32
1/8	1-0 25/32	2-1 9/16	1-1 11/32	2-2 11/16	1-1 15/16	2-3 27/32	1-2 1/2	2-5	1-3 3/32	2-6 5/32
3/16	1-0 13/16	2-1 5/8	1-1 3/8	2-2 25/32	1-1 31/32	2-3 15/16	1-2 17/32	2-5 3/32	1-3 1/8	2-6 1/4
1/4	1-0 27/32	2-1 11/16	1-1 7/16	2-2 27/32	1-2	2-4	1-2 9/16	2-5 5/32	1-3 5/32	2-6 5/16
5/16	1-0 7/8	2-1 3/4	1-1 15/32	2-2 29/32	1-2 1/32	2-4 1/16	1-2 5/8	2-5 7/32	1-3 3/16	2-6 3/8
3/8	1-0 29/32	2-1 27/32	1-1 1/2	2-3	1-2 1/16	2-4 1/8	1-2 21/32	2-5 5/16	1-3 7/32	2-6 15/32
7/16	1-0 31/32	2-1 29/32	1-1 17/32	2-3 1/16	1-2 3/32	2-4 7/32	1-2 11/16	2-5 3/8	1-3 1/4	2-6 17/32
1/2	1-1	2-1 31/32	1-1 9/16	2-3 1/8	1-2 5/32	2-4 9/32	1-2 23/32	2-5 7/16	1-3 5/16	2-6 19/32
9/16	1-1 1/32	2-2 1/16	1-1 19/32	2-3 7/32	1-2 3/16	2-4 3/8	1-2 3/4	2-5 17/32	1-3 11/32	2-6 21/32
5/8	1-1 1/16	2-2 1/8	1-1 5/8	2-3 9/32	1-2 7/32	2-4 7/16	1-2 25/32	2-5 19/32	1-3 3/8	2-6 3/4
11/16	1-1 3/32	2-2 3/16	1-1 11/16	2-3 11/32	1-2 1/4	2-4 1/2	1-2 27/32	2-5 21/32	1-3 13/32	2-6 13/16
3/4	1-1 1/8	2-2 9/32	1-1 23/32	2-3 7/16	1-2 9/32	2-4 19/32	1-2 7/8	2-5 23/32	1-3 7/16	2-6 7/8
13/16	1-1 5/32	2-2 11/32	1-1 3/4	2-3 1/2	1-2 5/16	2-4 21/32	1-2 29/32	2-5 13/16	1-3 15/32	2-6 31/32
7/8	1-1 7/32	2-2 13/32	1-1 25/32	2-3 9/16	1-2 3/8	2-4 23/32	1-2 15/16	2-5 7/8	1-3 17/32	2-7 1/32
15/16	1-1 1/4	2-2 1/2	1-1 13/16	2-3 21/32	1-2 13/32	2-4 25/32	1-2 31/32	2-5 15/16	1-3 9/16	2-7 3/32

Inches	27" Rise	27" Slope	28" Rise	28" Slope	29" Rise	29" Slope	30" Rise	30" Slope	31" Rise	31" Slope
0	1-3 19/32	2-7 3/16	1-4 5/32	2-8 11/32	1-4 3/4	2-9 1/2	1-5 5/16	2-10 21/32	1-5 29/32	2-11 25/32
1/16	1-3 5/8	2-7 1/4	1-4 3/16	2-8 13/32	1-4 25/32	2-9 9/16	1-5 11/32	2-10 23/32	1-5 15/16	2-11 7/8
1/8	1-3 21/32	2-7 5/16	1-4 1/4	2-8 15/32	1-4 13/16	2-9 5/8	1-5 13/32	2-10 25/32	1-5 31/32	2-11 15/16
3/16	1-3 11/16	2-7 13/32	1-4 9/32	2-8 9/16	1-4 27/32	2-9 11/16	1-5 7/16	2-10 27/32	1-6	3-0
1/4	1-3 23/32	2-7 15/32	1-4 5/16	2-8 5/8	1-4 7/8	2-9 25/32	1-5 15/32	2-10 15/16	1-6 1/32	3-0 3/32
5/16	1-3 25/32	2-7 17/32	1-4 11/32	2-8 11/16	1-4 15/16	2-9 27/32	1-5 1/2	2-11	1-6 3/32	3-0 5/32
3/8	1-3 13/16	2-7 5/8	1-4 3/8	2-8 3/4	1-4 31/32	2-9 29/32	1-5 17/32	2-11 1/16	1-6 1/8	3-0 7/32
7/16	1-3 27/32	2-7 11/16	1-4 13/32	2-8 27/32	1-5	2-10	1-5 9/16	2-11 5/32	1-6 5/32	3-0 5/16
1/2	1-3 7/8	2-7 3/4	1-4 15/32	2-8 29/32	1-5 1/32	2-10 1/16	1-5 19/32	2-11 7/32	1-6 3/16	3-0 3/8
9/16	1-3 29/32	2-7 13/16	1-4 1/2	2-8 31/32	1-5 1/16	2-10 1/8	1-5 21/32	2-11 9/32	1-6 7/32	3-0 7/16
5/8	1-3 15/16	2-7 29/32	1-4 17/32	2-9 1/16	1-5 3/32	2-10 7/32	1-5 11/16	2-11 3/8	1-6 1/4	3-0 17/32
11/16	1-4	2-7 31/32	1-4 9/16	2-9 1/8	1-5 1/8	2-10 9/32	1-5 23/32	2-11 7/16	1-6 9/32	3-0 19/32
3/4	1-4 1/32	2-8 1/32	1-4 19/32	2-9 3/16	1-5 3/16	2-10 11/32	1-5 3/4	2-11 1/2	1-6 11/32	3-0 21/32
13/16	1-4 1/16	2-8 1/8	1-4 5/8	2-9 9/32	1-5 7/32	2-10 7/16	1-5 25/32	2-11 19/32	1-6 3/8	3-0 23/32
7/8	1-4 3/32	2-8 3/16	1-4 21/32	2-9 11/32	1-5 1/4	2-10 1/2	1-5 13/16	2-11 21/32	1-6 13/32	3-0 13/16
15/16	1-4 1/8	2-8 1/4	1-4 23/32	2-9 13/32	1-5 9/32	2-10 9/16	1-5 7/8	2-11 23/32	1-6 7/16	3-0 7/8

GIVEN ANGLE, ITS NATURAL AND LOGARITHMIC FUNCTIONS

Natural Functions	Given Angle	Logarithmic Functions
Sin......0.5000000		Sin......9.6989700
Csc......2.0000000	Given	Csc......0.3010300
Tan......0.5773503	Angle	Tan......9.7614394
Cot......1.7320508	30°	Cot......0.2385606
Cos......0.8660254		Cos......9.9375306
Sec......1.1547005		Sec......0.0624694

Inches	22" Rise	Slope	23" Rise	Slope	24" Rise	Slope	25" Rise	Slope	26" Rise	Slope
0	$1\text{-}2\frac{21}{32}$	$2\text{-}2\frac{17}{32}$	$1\text{-}3\frac{11}{32}$	$2\text{-}3\frac{21}{32}$	$1\text{-}4$	$2\text{-}4\frac{27}{32}$	$1\text{-}4\frac{21}{32}$	$2\text{-}6\frac{1}{32}$	$1\text{-}5\frac{11}{32}$	$2\text{-}7\frac14$
$\frac{1}{16}$	$1\text{-}2\frac{23}{32}$	$2\text{-}2\frac{17}{32}$	$1\text{-}3\frac38$	$2\text{-}3\frac{23}{32}$	$1\text{-}4\frac1{32}$	$2\text{-}4\frac{29}{32}$	$1\text{-}4\frac{23}{32}$	$2\text{-}6\frac18$	$1\text{-}5\frac38$	$2\text{-}7\frac{5}{16}$
$\frac18$	$1\text{-}2\frac34$	$2\text{-}2\frac{19}{32}$	$1\text{-}3\frac{13}{32}$	$2\text{-}3\frac{25}{32}$	$1\text{-}4\frac3{32}$	$2\text{-}5$	$1\text{-}4\frac34$	$2\text{-}6\frac3{16}$	$1\text{-}5\frac{13}{32}$	$2\text{-}7\frac{13}{32}$
$\frac3{16}$	$1\text{-}2\frac{25}{32}$	$2\text{-}2\frac{21}{32}$	$1\text{-}3\frac{15}{32}$	$2\text{-}3\frac78$	$1\text{-}4\frac18$	$2\text{-}5\frac1{16}$	$1\text{-}4\frac{25}{32}$	$2\text{-}6\frac9{32}$	$1\text{-}5\frac{15}{32}$	$2\text{-}7\frac{15}{32}$
$\frac14$	$1\text{-}2\frac{27}{32}$	$2\text{-}2\frac34$	$1\text{-}3\frac12$	$2\text{-}3\frac{15}{16}$	$1\text{-}4\frac5{32}$	$2\text{-}5\frac5{32}$	$1\text{-}4\frac{27}{32}$	$2\text{-}6\frac{11}{32}$	$1\text{-}5\frac12$	$2\text{-}7\frac9{16}$
$\frac5{16}$	$1\text{-}2\frac78$	$2\text{-}2\frac{13}{16}$	$1\text{-}3\frac{17}{32}$	$2\text{-}4\frac1{32}$	$1\text{-}4\frac7{32}$	$2\text{-}5\frac14$	$1\text{-}4\frac78$	$2\text{-}6\frac{13}{32}$	$1\text{-}5\frac{17}{32}$	$2\text{-}7\frac58$
$\frac38$	$1\text{-}2\frac{29}{32}$	$2\text{-}2\frac{29}{32}$	$1\text{-}3\frac{19}{32}$	$2\text{-}4\frac3{32}$	$1\text{-}4\frac14$	$2\text{-}5\frac9{32}$	$1\text{-}4\frac{29}{32}$	$2\text{-}6\frac12$	$1\text{-}5\frac{19}{32}$	$2\text{-}7\frac{11}{16}$
$\frac7{16}$	$1\text{-}2\frac{31}{32}$	$2\text{-}2\frac{31}{32}$	$1\text{-}3\frac58$	$2\text{-}4\frac5{32}$	$1\text{-}4\frac9{32}$	$2\text{-}5\frac38$	$1\text{-}4\frac{31}{32}$	$2\text{-}6\frac9{16}$	$1\text{-}5\frac58$	$2\text{-}7\frac{25}{32}$
$\frac12$	$1\text{-}3$	$2\text{-}3\frac1{32}$	$1\text{-}3\frac{21}{32}$	$2\text{-}4\frac14$	$1\text{-}4\frac{11}{32}$	$2\text{-}5\frac7{16}$	$1\text{-}5$	$2\text{-}6\frac{21}{32}$	$1\text{-}5\frac{21}{32}$	$2\text{-}7\frac{27}{32}$
$\frac9{16}$	$1\text{-}3\frac1{32}$	$2\text{-}3\frac18$	$1\text{-}3\frac{23}{32}$	$2\text{-}4\frac5{16}$	$1\text{-}4\frac38$	$2\text{-}5\frac{17}{32}$	$1\text{-}5\frac1{32}$	$2\text{-}6\frac{23}{32}$	$1\text{-}5\frac{23}{32}$	$2\text{-}7\frac{15}{16}$
$\frac58$	$1\text{-}3\frac3{32}$	$2\text{-}3\frac3{16}$	$1\text{-}3\frac34$	$2\text{-}4\frac{13}{32}$	$1\text{-}4\frac{13}{32}$	$2\text{-}5\frac{19}{32}$	$1\text{-}5\frac3{32}$	$2\text{-}6\frac{13}{16}$	$1\text{-}5\frac34$	$2\text{-}8$
$\frac{11}{16}$	$1\text{-}3\frac18$	$2\text{-}3\frac9{32}$	$1\text{-}3\frac{25}{32}$	$2\text{-}4\frac{15}{32}$	$1\text{-}4\frac{15}{32}$	$2\text{-}5\frac{21}{32}$	$1\text{-}5\frac18$	$2\text{-}6\frac78$	$1\text{-}5\frac{25}{32}$	$2\text{-}8\frac1{16}$
$\frac34$	$1\text{-}3\frac5{32}$	$2\text{-}3\frac{11}{32}$	$1\text{-}3\frac{27}{32}$	$2\text{-}4\frac{17}{32}$	$1\text{-}4\frac12$	$2\text{-}5\frac34$	$1\text{-}5\frac5{32}$	$2\text{-}6\frac{15}{16}$	$1\text{-}5\frac{27}{32}$	$2\text{-}8\frac5{32}$
$\frac{13}{16}$	$1\text{-}3\frac7{32}$	$2\text{-}3\frac{13}{32}$	$1\text{-}3\frac78$	$2\text{-}4\frac58$	$1\text{-}4\frac{17}{32}$	$2\text{-}5\frac{13}{16}$	$1\text{-}5\frac7{32}$	$2\text{-}7\frac1{32}$	$1\text{-}5\frac78$	$2\text{-}8\frac7{32}$
$\frac78$	$1\text{-}3\frac14$	$2\text{-}3\frac12$	$1\text{-}3\frac{29}{32}$	$2\text{-}4\frac{11}{16}$	$1\text{-}4\frac{19}{32}$	$2\text{-}5\frac{29}{32}$	$1\text{-}5\frac14$	$2\text{-}7\frac3{32}$	$1\text{-}5\frac{29}{32}$	$2\text{-}8\frac5{16}$
$\frac{15}{16}$	$1\text{-}3\frac9{32}$	$2\text{-}3\frac9{16}$	$1\text{-}3\frac{31}{32}$	$2\text{-}4\frac{25}{32}$	$1\text{-}4\frac58$	$2\text{-}5\frac{31}{32}$	$1\text{-}5\frac9{32}$	$2\text{-}7\frac3{16}$	$1\text{-}5\frac{31}{32}$	$2\text{-}8\frac38$

Inches	27" Rise	Slope	28" Rise	Slope	29" Rise	Slope	30" Rise	Slope	31" Rise	Slope
0	$1\text{-}6$	$2\text{-}8\frac78$	$1\text{-}6\frac{21}{32}$	$2\text{-}9\frac{21}{32}$	$1\text{-}7\frac{11}{32}$	$2\text{-}10\frac{27}{32}$	$1\text{-}8$	$3\text{-}0\frac1{16}$	$1\text{-}8\frac{21}{32}$	$3\text{-}1\frac14$
$\frac1{16}$	$1\text{-}6\frac1{32}$	$2\text{-}8\frac{17}{32}$	$1\text{-}6\frac{23}{32}$	$2\text{-}9\frac{23}{32}$	$1\text{-}7\frac38$	$2\text{-}10\frac{15}{16}$	$1\text{-}8\frac1{32}$	$3\text{-}0\frac18$	$1\text{-}8\frac{23}{32}$	$3\text{-}1\frac{11}{32}$
$\frac18$	$1\text{-}6\frac3{32}$	$2\text{-}8\frac{19}{32}$	$1\text{-}6\frac34$	$2\text{-}9\frac{13}{16}$	$1\text{-}7\frac{13}{32}$	$2\text{-}11$	$1\text{-}8\frac3{32}$	$3\text{-}0\frac7{32}$	$1\text{-}8\frac34$	$3\text{-}1\frac{13}{32}$
$\frac3{16}$	$1\text{-}6\frac18$	$2\text{-}8\frac{11}{16}$	$1\text{-}6\frac{25}{32}$	$2\text{-}9\frac78$	$1\text{-}7\frac{15}{32}$	$2\text{-}11\frac3{32}$	$1\text{-}8\frac18$	$3\text{-}0\frac9{32}$	$1\text{-}8\frac{25}{32}$	$3\text{-}1\frac{15}{32}$
$\frac14$	$1\text{-}6\frac5{32}$	$2\text{-}8\frac34$	$1\text{-}6\frac{27}{32}$	$2\text{-}9\frac{15}{16}$	$1\text{-}7\frac12$	$2\text{-}11\frac5{32}$	$1\text{-}8\frac5{32}$	$3\text{-}0\frac{11}{32}$	$1\text{-}8\frac{27}{32}$	$3\text{-}1\frac9{16}$
$\frac5{16}$	$1\text{-}6\frac7{32}$	$2\text{-}8\frac{13}{16}$	$1\text{-}6\frac78$	$2\text{-}10\frac12$	$1\text{-}7\frac{17}{32}$	$2\text{-}11\frac7{32}$	$1\text{-}8\frac7{32}$	$3\text{-}0\frac7{16}$	$1\text{-}8\frac78$	$3\text{-}1\frac58$
$\frac38$	$1\text{-}6\frac14$	$2\text{-}8\frac{29}{32}$	$1\text{-}6\frac{29}{32}$	$2\text{-}10\frac3{32}$	$1\text{-}7\frac{19}{32}$	$2\text{-}11\frac5{16}$	$1\text{-}8\frac14$	$3\text{-}0\frac12$	$1\text{-}8\frac{29}{32}$	$3\text{-}1\frac{23}{32}$
$\frac7{16}$	$1\text{-}6\frac9{32}$	$2\text{-}8\frac{31}{32}$	$1\text{-}6\frac{31}{32}$	$2\text{-}10\frac3{16}$	$1\text{-}7\frac58$	$2\text{-}11\frac38$	$1\text{-}8\frac9{32}$	$3\text{-}0\frac{19}{32}$	$1\text{-}8\frac{31}{32}$	$3\text{-}1\frac{25}{32}$
$\frac12$	$1\text{-}6\frac{11}{32}$	$2\text{-}9\frac1{16}$	$1\text{-}7$	$2\text{-}10\frac14$	$1\text{-}7\frac{21}{32}$	$2\text{-}11\frac{15}{32}$	$1\text{-}8\frac{11}{32}$	$3\text{-}0\frac{21}{32}$	$1\text{-}9$	$3\text{-}1\frac{27}{32}$
$\frac9{16}$	$1\text{-}6\frac38$	$2\text{-}9\frac18$	$1\text{-}7\frac1{32}$	$2\text{-}10\frac5{16}$	$1\text{-}7\frac{23}{32}$	$2\text{-}11\frac{17}{32}$	$1\text{-}8\frac38$	$3\text{-}0\frac{23}{32}$	$1\text{-}9\frac1{32}$	$3\text{-}1\frac{15}{16}$
$\frac58$	$1\text{-}6\frac{13}{32}$	$2\text{-}9\frac3{16}$	$1\text{-}7\frac3{32}$	$2\text{-}10\frac{13}{32}$	$1\text{-}7\frac34$	$2\text{-}11\frac{19}{32}$	$1\text{-}8\frac{13}{32}$	$3\text{-}0\frac{13}{16}$	$1\text{-}9\frac3{32}$	$3\text{-}2$
$\frac{11}{16}$	$1\text{-}6\frac{15}{32}$	$2\text{-}9\frac9{32}$	$1\text{-}7\frac18$	$2\text{-}10\frac{15}{32}$	$1\text{-}7\frac{25}{32}$	$2\text{-}11\frac{11}{16}$	$1\text{-}8\frac{15}{32}$	$3\text{-}0\frac78$	$1\text{-}9\frac18$	$3\text{-}2\frac1{32}$
$\frac34$	$1\text{-}6\frac12$	$2\text{-}9\frac{11}{32}$	$1\text{-}7\frac5{32}$	$2\text{-}10\frac9{16}$	$1\text{-}7\frac{27}{32}$	$2\text{-}11\frac34$	$1\text{-}8\frac12$	$3\text{-}0\frac{31}{32}$	$1\text{-}9\frac5{32}$	$3\text{-}2\frac5{32}$
$\frac{13}{16}$	$1\text{-}6\frac{17}{32}$	$2\text{-}9\frac7{16}$	$1\text{-}7\frac7{32}$	$2\text{-}10\frac58$	$1\text{-}7\frac78$	$2\text{-}11\frac{27}{32}$	$1\text{-}8\frac{17}{32}$	$3\text{-}1\frac1{32}$	$1\text{-}9\frac7{32}$	$3\text{-}2\frac7{32}$
$\frac78$	$1\text{-}6\frac{19}{32}$	$2\text{-}9\frac12$	$1\text{-}7\frac14$	$2\text{-}10\frac{23}{32}$	$1\text{-}7\frac{29}{32}$	$2\text{-}11\frac{29}{32}$	$1\text{-}8\frac{19}{32}$	$3\text{-}1\frac3{32}$	$1\text{-}9\frac14$	$3\text{-}2\frac5{16}$
$\frac{15}{16}$	$1\text{-}6\frac58$	$2\text{-}9\frac9{16}$	$1\text{-}7\frac9{32}$	$2\text{-}10\frac{25}{32}$	$1\text{-}7\frac{31}{32}$	$2\text{-}11\frac{31}{32}$	$1\text{-}8\frac58$	$3\text{-}1\frac3{16}$	$1\text{-}9\frac9{32}$	$3\text{-}2\frac38$

CORRESPONDING ANGLE, ITS NATURAL AND LOGARITHMIC FUNCTIONS

Natural Functions	Corresponding Angle	Logarithmic Functions
Sin......0.5547003		Sin......9.7440584
Csc......1.8027754	**33° 41′ 24.26″**	Csc......0.2559416
Tan.....0.6666667		Tan.....9.8239088
Cot......1.5000000		Cot......0.1760912
Cos......0.8320504		Cos......9.9201496
Sec......1.2018504		Sec......0.0798504

CONTENTS

PART 2

PARALLEL TABLES OF

LOGARITHMS AND SQUARES

by intervals of 1/64th of an inch
from 0 to 44 inches.

Since in dealing with small dimensions greater than ordinary accuracy is sometimes required, the following table giving logarithms and squares by intervals of 1/64 inch is provided. Not only can results correct to 1/64 inch be derived by means of this table, but its special arrangement giving the 64ths in Roman and the 32ds in bold-face type enables the user to determine at a glance the nearest thirty-second of an inch.

It might be well to mention here that the charts containing Graphic Solutions of Right Triangles, given elsewhere in this book, provide another means of solving many of the problems dealing with small dimensions. These charts were drawn with great precision and are absolutely dependable. Inasmuch as by their means results can be obtained almost at a glance, they have proved to be great timer savers and are strongly recommended for use where reliable and rapid results are desired.

64ths / 32ds, etc.	0″ Log.	Square	1″ Log.	Square	2″ Log.	Square	3″ Log.	Square
0	———	.00000	8.92082	.00694	9.22185	.02778	9.39794	.06250
1	7.11464	.00000	8.92755	.00716	9.22523	.02821	9.40020	.06315
1/32	7.41567	.00001	8.93418	.00739	9.22858	.02865	9.40244	.06381
3	7.59176	.00002	8.94071	.00761	9.23191	.02910	9.40467	.06447
1/16	7.71670	.00003	8.94715	.00784	9.23521	.02954	9.40689	.06513
5	7.81361	.00004	8.95349	.00807	9.23849	.02999	9.40911	.06580
3/32	7.89279	.00006	8.95974	.00831	9.24174	.03044	9.41130	.06647
7	7.95974	.00008	8.96590	.00855	9.24497	.03090	9.41349	.06714
1/8	8.01773	.00011	8.97197	.00879	9.24818	.03136	9.41567	.06782
9	8.06888	.00014	8.97796	.00903	9.25136	.03182	9.41783	.06850
5/32	8.11464	.00017	8.98387	.00928	9.25452	.03229	9.41999	.06918
11	8.15603	.00021	8.98970	.00954	9.25765	.03276	9.42213	.06987
3/16	8.19382	.00024	8.99545	.00979	9.26077	.03323	9.42427	.07056
13	8.22858	.00029	9.00113	.01005	9.26386	.03371	9.42639	.07125
7/32	8.26077	.00033	9.00673	.01031	9.26693	.03419	9.42851	.07195
15	8.29073	.00038	9.01227	.01058	9.26997	.03467	9.43061	.07265
1/4	8.31876	.00043	9.01773	.01085	9.27300	.03516	9.43270	.07335
17	8.34509	.00049	9.02312	.01112	9.27601	.03565	9.43479	.07406
9/32	8.36991	.00055	9.02845	.01140	9.27899	.03614	9.43686	.07477
19	8.39339	.00061	9.03372	.01168	9.28196	.03664	9.43892	.07548
5/16	8.41567	.00068	9.03892	.01196	9.28490	.03714	9.44097	.07620
21	8.43686	.00075	9.04406	.01225	9.28783	.03764	9.44302	.07692
11/32	8.45706	.00082	9.04914	.01254	9.29073	.03815	9.44505	.07764
23	8.47637	.00090	9.05416	.01283	9.29362	.03866	9.44708	.07837
3/8	8.49485	.00098	9.05912	.01313	9.29648	.03917	9.44909	.07910
25	8.51258	.00106	9.06403	.01343	9.29933	.03969	9.45110	.07984
13/32	8.52961	.00115	9.06888	.01373	9.30216	.04021	9.45310	.08057
27	8.54600	.00124	9.07368	.01404	9.30497	.04073	9.45508	.08131
7/16	8.56180	.00133	9.07843	.01435	9.30776	.04126	9.45706	.08206
29	8.57704	.00143	9.08312	.01466	9.31054	.04179	9.45903	.08281
15/32	8.59176	.00153	9.08777	.01498	9.31330	.04232	9.46099	.08356
31	8.60600	.00163	9.09236	.01530	9.31604	.04286	9.46294	.08431
1/2	8.61979	.00174	9.09691	.01563	9.31876	.04340	9.46489	.08507
33	8.63315	.00185	9.10141	.01595	9.32146	.04395	9.46682	.08583
17/32	8.64612	.00196	9.10586	.01628	9.32415	.04449	9.46875	.08660
35	8.65871	.00208	9.11027	.01662	9.32683	.04505	9.47066	.08736
9/16	8.67094	.00220	9.11464	.01695	9.32948	.04560	9.47257	.08813
37	8.68284	.00232	9.11896	.01729	9.33212	.04616	9.47447	.08891
19/32	8.69442	.00245	9.12324	.01764	9.33475	.04672	9.47637	.08969
39	8.70570	.00258	9.12748	.01799	9.33736	.04728	9.47825	.09047
5/8	8.71670	.00271	9.13167	.01834	9.33995	.04785	9.48013	.09125
41	8.72742	.00285	9.13583	.01869	9.34253	.04842	9.48199	.09204
21/32	8.73789	.00299	9.13994	.01905	9.34509	.04900	9.48385	.09283
43	8.74811	.00313	9.14402	.01941	9.34763	.04958	9.48571	.09363
11/16	8.75809	.00328	9.14806	.01978	9.35017	.05016	9.48755	.09443
45	8.76785	.00343	9.15207	.02014	9.35268	.05074	9.48939	.09523
23/32	8.77740	.00359	9.15603	.02051	9.35519	.05133	9.49122	.09604
47	8.78674	.00375	9.15996	.02089	9.35768	.05192	9.49304	.09684
3/4	8.79588	.00391	9.16386	.02127	9.36015	.05252	9.49485	.09766
49	8.80483	.00407	9.16772	.02165	9.36261	.05312	9.49666	.09847
25/32	8.81361	.00424	9.17154	.02203	9.36506	.05372	9.49845	.09929
51	8.82221	.00441	9.17534	.02242	9.36749	.05432	9.50025	.10011
13/16	8.83064	.00458	9.17910	.02281	9.36991	.05493	9.50203	.10094
53	8.83891	.00476	9.18282	.02321	9.37232	.05554	9.50380	.10177
27/32	8.84703	.00494	9.18652	.02361	9.37471	.05616	9.50557	.10260
55	8.85500	.00513	9.19019	.02401	9.37709	.05678	9.50734	.10344
7/8	8.86283	.00532	9.19382	.02441	9.37946	.05740	9.50909	.10428
57	8.87051	.00551	9.19742	.02482	9.38181	.05803	9.51084	.10512
29/32	8.87807	.00570	9.20100	.02523	9.38415	.05865	9.51258	.10596
59	8.88549	.00590	9.20454	.02565	9.38648	.05929	9.51431	.10681
15/16	8.89279	.00610	9.20806	.02607	9.38880	.05992	9.51604	.10767
61	8.89997	.00631	9.21155	.02649	9.39110	.06056	9.51776	.10852
31/32	8.90703	.00652	9.21501	.02692	9.39339	.06120	9.51947	.10938
63	8.91398	.00673	9.21844	.02735	9.39567	.06185	9.52118	.11024

64ths.	32ds.	4″ Log.	Square.	5″ Log.	Square.	6″ Log.	Square.	7″ Log.	Square.
0		9.52288	.11111	9.61979	.17361	9.69897	.25000	9.76592	.34028
1		9.52457	.11198	9.62114	.17470	9.70010	.25130	9.76689	.34180
	1⁄32	9.52626	.11285	9.62249	.17579	9.70123	.25261	9.76785	.34332
3		9.52794	.11373	9.62384	.17688	9.70235	.25392	9.76882	.34485
1⁄16		9.52961	.11461	9.62518	.17798	9.70347	.25524	9.76978	.34638
5		9.53128	.11549	9.62652	.17908	9.70459	.25655	9.77074	.34792
	3⁄32	9.53294	.11638	9.62786	.18018	9.70570	.25787	9.77169	.34945
7		9.53459	.11727	9.62919	.18129	9.70682	.25920	9.77265	.35099
1⁄8		9.53624	.11816	9.63051	.18240	9.70792	.26053	9.77360	.35254
9		9.53788	.11906	9.63183	.18351	9.70903	.26186	9.77456	.35409
	5⁄32	9.53952	.11996	9.63315	.18463	9.71014	.26319	9.77550	.35564
11		9.54115	.12086	9.63447	.18575	9.71124	.26453	9.77645	.35719
3⁄16		9.54277	.12177	9.63578	.18688	9.71233	.26587	9.77740	.35875
13		9.54439	.12268	9.63708	.18800	9.71343	.26721	9.77834	.36031
	7⁄32	9.54600	.12360	9.63839	.18913	9.71452	.26856	9.77928	.36188
15		9.54761	.12451	9.63968	.19027	9.71561	.26991	9.78022	.36345
1⁄4		9.54921	.12543	9.64098	.19141	9.71670	.27127	9.78116	.36502
17		9.55080	.12636	9.64227	.19255	9.71778	.27263	9.78209	.36659
	9⁄32	9.55239	.12729	9.64356	.19369	9.71886	.27399	9.78302	.36817
19		9.55397	.12822	9.64484	.19484	9.71994	.27535	9.78396	.36975
5⁄16		9.55555	.12915	9.64612	.19599	9.72102	.27672	9.78488	.37134
21		9.55712	.13009	9.64739	.19715	9.72209	.27809	9.78581	.37293
	11⁄32	9.55868	.13103	9.64866	.19830	9.72316	.27947	9.78674	.37452
23		9.56024	.13197	9.64993	.19946	9.72423	.28084	9.78766	.37611
3⁄8		9.56180	.13292	9.65120	.20063	9.72530	.28223	9.78858	.37771
25		9.56335	.13387	9.65246	.20180	9.72636	.28361	9.78950	.37931
	13⁄32	9.56489	.13483	9.65371	.20297	9.72742	.28500	9.79042	.38092
27		9.56643	.13578	9.65497	.20414	9.72848	.28639	9.79133	.38253
7⁄16		9.56796	.13675	9.65622	.20532	9.72954	.28779	9.79225	.38414
29		9.56948	.13771	9.65746	.20650	9.73059	.28919	9.79316	.38576
	15⁄32	9.57100	.13868	9.65871	.20769	9.73164	.29059	9.79407	.38738
31		9.57252	.13965	9.65995	.20888	9.73269	.29199	9.79497	.38900
1⁄2		9.57403	.14062	9.66118	.21007	9.73373	.29340	9.79588	.39062
33		9.57554	.14160	9.66241	.21126	9.73477	.29482	9.79678	.39225
	17⁄32	9.57704	.14258	9.66364	.21246	9.73582	.29623	9.79769	.39389
35		9.57853	.14357	9.66487	.21367	9.73685	.29765	9.79859	.39552
9⁄16		9.58002	.14456	9.66609	.21487	9.73789	.29907	9.79948	.39716
37		9.58151	.14555	9.66731	.21608	9.73892	.30050	9.80038	.39881
	19⁄32	9.58299	.14655	9.66852	.21729	9.73995	.30193	9.80128	.40045
39		9.58446	.14754	9.66973	.21851	9.74098	.30336	9.80217	.40210
5⁄8		9.58593	.14855	9.67094	.21973	9.74200	.30480	9.80306	.40375
41		9.58740	.14955	9.67215	.22095	9.74303	.30624	9.80395	.40541
	21⁄32	9.58886	.15056	9.67335	.22217	9.74405	.30768	9.80483	.40707
43		9.59031	.15157	9.67455	.22340	9.74507	.30912	9.80572	.40873
11⁄16		9.59176	.15259	9.67574	.22464	9.74608	.31057	9.80660	.41040
45		9.59321	.15360	9.67693	.22587	9.74710	.31203	9.80749	.41207
	23⁄32	9.59465	.15463	9.67812	.22711	9.74811	.31348	9.80837	.41374
47		9.59608	.15565	9.67930	.22835	9.74912	.31494	9.80924	.41542
3⁄4		9.59751	.15668	9.68049	.22960	9.75012	.31641	9.81012	.41710
49		9.59894	.15772	9.68167	.23085	9.75113	.31787	9.81100	.41878
	25⁄32	9.60036	.15875	9.68284	.23210	9.75213	.31934	9.81187	.42047
51		9.60178	.15979	9.68401	.23336	9.75313	.32082	9.81274	.42216
13⁄16		9.60319	.16083	9.68518	.23462	9.75413	.32229	9.81361	.42386
53		9.60460	.16188	9.68635	.23588	9.75512	.32377	9.81448	.42555
	27⁄32	9.60600	.16293	9.68751	.23715	9.75611	.32526	9.81534	.42725
55		9.60740	.16398	9.68867	.23842	9.75710	.32674	9.81621	.42896
7⁄8		9.60879	.16504	9.68983	.23969	9.75809	.32823	9.81707	.43066
57		9.61018	.16610	9.69098	.24097	9.75908	.32973	9.81793	.43237
	29⁄32	9.61157	.16716	9.69213	.24225	9.76006	.33122	9.81879	.43409
59		9.61295	.16823	9.69328	.24353	9.76104	.33272	9.81965	.43581
15⁄16		9.61433	.16930	9.69442	.24482	9.76202	.33423	9.82050	.43753
61		9.61570	.17037	9.69556	.24611	9.76300	.33574	9.82136	.43925
	31⁄32	9.61707	.17145	9.69670	.24740	9.76397	.33725	9.82221	.44098
63		9.61843	.17253	9.69784	.24870	9.76495	.33876	9.82306	.44271

64ths.	32ds. etc.	8″ Log.	Square.	9″ Log.	Square.	10″ Log.	Square.	11″ Log.	Square.
0		9.82391	.44444	9.87506	.56250	9.92082	.69444	9.96221	.84028
1		9.82476	.44618	9.87581	.56445	9.92150	.69662	9.96283	.84267
	1/32	9.82560	.44792	9.87657	.56641	9.92217	.69879	9.96344	.84506
3		9.82645	.44967	9.87732	.56837	9.92285	.70097	9.96406	.84745
	1/16	9.82729	.45142	9.87807	.57034	9.92352	.70315	9.96467	.84985
5		9.82813	.45317	9.87881	.57231	9.92420	.70534	9.96529	.85226
	3/32	9.82897	.45492	9.87956	.57428	9.92487	.70753	9.96590	.85466
7		9.82981	.45668	9.88031	.57625	9.92554	.70972	9.96651	.85707
	1/8	9.83064	.45844	9.88105	.57823	9.92621	.71191	9.96712	.85948
9		9.83148	.46021	9.88179	.58022	9.92688	.71411	9.96773	.86190
	5/32	9.83231	.46198	9.88254	.58220	9.92755	.71632	9.96834	.86432
11		9.83314	.46375	9.88328	.58419	9.92822	.71853	9.96894	.86674
	3/16	9.83397	.46552	9.88402	.58618	9.92889	.72073	9.96955	.86917
13		9.83480	.46730	9.88475	.58818	9.92955	.72294	9.97016	.87160
	7/32	9.83562	.46908	9.88549	.59018	9.93022	.72516	9.97076	.87403
15		9.83645	.47087	9.88623	.59218	9.93088	.72738	9.97137	.87647
	1/4	9.83727	.47266	9.88696	.59418	9.93154	.72960	9.97197	.87891
17		9.83809	.47445	9.88769	.59619	9.93220	.73183	9.97257	.88135
	9/32	9.83891	.47624	9.88843	.59821	9.93286	.73406	9.97318	.88380
19		9.83973	.47804	9.88916	.60022	9.93352	.73629	9.97378	.88625
	5/16	9.84055	.47984	9.88989	.60224	9.93418	.73853	9.97438	.88870
21		9.84137	.48165	9.89061	.60426	9.93484	.74077	9.97498	.89116
	11/32	9.84218	.48346	9.89134	.60629	9.93550	.74301	9.97558	.89362
23		9.84299	.48527	9.89207	.60832	9.93615	.74525	9.97617	.89608
	5/8	9.84380	.48709	9.89279	.61035	9.93681	.74750	9.97677	.89855
25		9.84461	.48891	9.89351	.61239	9.93746	.74976	9.97737	.90102
	13/32	9.84542	.49073	9.89424	.61443	9.93811	.75201	9.97796	.90349
27		9.84623	.49256	9.89496	.61647	9.93876	.75427	9.97856	.90597
	7/16	9.84703	.49438	9.89568	.61852	9.93942	.75654	9.97915	.90845
29		9.84784	.49622	9.89639	.62057	9.94006	.75880	9.97974	.91093
	15/32	9.84864	.49805	9.89711	.62262	9.94071	.76107	9.98033	.91342
31		9.84944	.49989	9.89783	.62468	9.94136	.76335	9.98093	.91591
	1/2	9.85024	.50174	9.89854	.62674	9.94201	.76563	9.98152	.91840
33		9.85104	.50358	9.89926	.62880	9.94265	.76791	9.98211	.92090
	17/32	9.85183	.50543	9.89997	.63087	9.94330	.77019	9.98270	.92340
35		9.85263	.50729	9.90068	.63294	9.94394	.77248	9.98328	.92591
	9/16	9.85342	.50914	9.90139	.63501	9.94459	.77477	9.98387	.92841
37		9.85421	.51100	9.90210	.63709	9.94523	.77706	9.98446	.93092
	19/32	9.85500	.51286	9.90281	.63917	9.94587	.77936	9.98504	.93343
39		9.85579	.51473	9.90351	.64125	9.94651	.78166	9.98563	.93596
	5/8	9.85658	.51660	9.90422	.64334	9.94715	.78396	9.98621	.93848
41		9.85736	.51848	9.90492	.64543	9.94779	.78627	9.98680	.94100
	21/32	9.85815	.52035	9.90563	.64752	9.94842	.78858	9.98738	.94353
43		9.85893	.52223	9.90633	.64962	9.94906	.79090	9.98796	.94606
	11/16	9.85971	.52412	9.90703	.65172	9.94969	.79321	9.98854	.94859
45		9.86049	.52600	9.90773	.65382	9.95033	.79553	9.98912	.95113
	23/32	9.86127	.52789	9.90843	.65593	9.95096	.79786	9.98970	.95367
47		9.86205	.52979	9.90913	.65804	9.95160	.80019	9.99028	.95622
	3/4	9.86283	.53168	9.90982	.66016	9.95223	.80252	9.99086	.95877
49		9.86360	.53358	9.91052	.66227	9.95286	.80485	9.99143	.96132
	25/32	9.86438	.53549	9.91121	.66439	9.95349	.80719	9.99201	.96387
51		9.86515	.53740	9.91191	.66652	9.95412	.80953	9.99259	.96643
	13/16	9.86592	.53931	9.91260	.66865	9.95474	.81188	9.99316	.96899
53		9.86669	.54122	9.91329	.67078	9.95537	.81422	9.99373	.97156
	27/32	9.86746	.54314	9.91398	.67291	9.95600	.81658	9.99431	.97413
55		9.86822	.54506	9.91467	.67505	9.95662	.81893	9.99488	.97670
	7/8	9.86899	.54698	9.91536	.67719	9.95725	.82129	9.99545	.97928
57		9.86975	.54891	9.91604	.67934	9.95787	.82365	9.99602	.98185
	29/32	9.87051	.55084	9.91673	.68148	9.95849	.82602	9.99659	.98444
59		9.87127	.55278	9.91741	.68364	9.95912	.82838	9.99716	.98702
	15/16	9.87203	.55471	9.91810	.68579	9.95974	.83076	9.99773	.98961
61		9.87279	.55666	9.91878	.68795	9.96036	.83313	9.99830	.99220
	31/32	9.87355	.55860	9.91946	.69011	9.96098	.83551	9.99887	.99480
63		9.87431	.56055	9.92014	.69228	9.96159	.83789	9.99943	.99740

64ths. / 32ds, etc.	12″ Log.	12″ Square.	13″ Log.	13″ Square.	14″ Log.	14″ Square.	15″ Log.	15″ Square.
0	.00000	1.0000	.03476	1.1736	.06695	1.3611	.09691	1.5625
1	.00057	1.0026	.03528	1.1764	.06743	1.3642	.09736	1.5658
1/32	.00113	1.0052	.03580	1.1793	.06792	1.3672	.09781	1.5690
3	.00169	1.0078	.03633	1.1821	.06840	1.3702	.09827	1.5723
1/16	.00226	1.0104	.03685	1.1849	.06888	1.3733	.09872	1.5755
5	.00282	1.0131	.03736	1.1878	.06936	1.3763	.09917	1.5788
3/32	.00338	1.0157	.03788	1.1906	.06985	1.3794	.09962	1.5821
7	.00394	1.0183	.03840	1.1934	.07033	1.3825	.10007	1.5854
1/8	.00450	1.0209	.03892	1.1963	.07081	1.3855	.10051	1.5887
9	.00506	1.0236	.03943	1.1991	.07129	1.3886	.10096	1.5919
5/32	.00562	1.0262	.03995	1.2020	.07177	1.3917	.10141	1.5952
11	.00618	1.0289	.04047	1.2048	.07225	1.3947	.10186	1.5985
3/16	.00673	1.0315	.04098	1.2077	.07272	1.3978	.10231	1.6018
13	.00729	1.0341	.04150	1.2106	.07320	1.4009	.10275	1.6051
7/32	.00785	1.0368	.04201	1.2134	.07368	1.4040	.10320	1.6084
15	.00840	1.0394	.04252	1.2163	.07416	1.4071	.10364	1.6117
1/4	.00895	1.0421	.04303	1.2192	.07463	1.4102	.10409	1.6150
17	.00951	1.0448	.04355	1.2221	.07511	1.4133	.10453	1.6183
9/32	.01006	1.0474	.04406	1.2249	.07559	1.4163	.10498	1.6216
19	.01061	1.0501	.04457	1.2278	.07606	1.4194	.10542	1.6250
5/16	.01116	1.0528	.04508	1.2307	.07653	1.4226	.10586	1.6283
21	.01172	1.0554	.04559	1.2336	.07701	1.4257	.10631	1.6316
11/32	.01227	1.0581	.04610	1.2365	.07748	1.4288	.10675	1.6349
23	.01282	1.0608	.04660	1.2394	.07795	1.4319	.10719	1.6383
3/8	.01336	1.0635	.04711	1.2423	.07843	1.4350	.10763	1.6416
25	.01391	1.0662	.04762	1.2452	.07890	1.4381	.10808	1.6449
13/32	.01446	1.0689	.04813	1.2481	.07937	1.4413	.10852	1.6483
27	.01501	1.0715	.04863	1.2510	.07984	1.4444	.10896	1.6516
7/16	.01555	1.0742	.04914	1.2539	.08031	1.4475	.10940	1.6550
29	.01610	1.0769	.04964	1.2569	.08078	1.4506	.10984	1.6583
15/32	.01664	1.0797	.05015	1.2598	.08125	1.4538	.11027	1.6617
31	.01719	1.0824	.05065	1.2627	.08172	1.4569	.11071	1.6650
1/2	.01773	1.0851	.05115	1.2656	.08219	1.4601	.11115	1.6684
33	.01827	1.0878	.05165	1.2686	.08265	1.4632	.11159	1.6718
17/32	.01881	1.0905	.05216	1.2715	.08312	1.4664	.11203	1.6751
35	.01935	1.0932	.05266	1.2744	.08359	1.4695	.11246	1.6785
9/16	.01989	1.0959	.05316	1.2774	.08405	1.4727	.11290	1.6819
37	.02043	1.0987	.05366	1.2803	.08452	1.4758	.11333	1.6853
19/32	.02097	1.1014	.05416	1.2833	.08499	1.4790	.11377	1.6886
39	.02151	1.1041	.05466	1.2862	.08545	1.4822	.11420	1.6920
5/8	.02205	1.1069	.05516	1.2892	.08591	1.4854	.11464	1.6954
41	.02259	1.1096	.05565	1.2921	.08638	1.4885	.11507	1.6988
21/32	.02312	1.1124	.05615	1.2951	.08684	1.4917	.11551	1.7022
43	.02366	1.1151	.05665	1.2981	.08730	1.4949	.11594	1.7056
11/16	.02419	1.1179	.05714	1.3010	.08777	1.4981	.11637	1.7090
45	.02473	1.1206	.05764	1.3040	.08823	1.5013	.11680	1.7124
23/32	.02526	1.1234	.05813	1.3070	.08869	1.5045	.11724	1.7158
47	.02580	1.1261	.05863	1.3100	.08915	1.5077	.11767	1.7192
3/4	.02633	1.1289	.05912	1.3129	.08961	1.5109	.11810	1.7227
49	.02686	1.1317	.05961	1.3159	.09007	1.5141	.11853	1.7261
25/32	.02739	1.1344	.06011	1.3189	.09053	1.5173	.11896	1.7295
51	.02792	1.1372	.06060	1.3219	.09099	1.5205	.11939	1.7329
13/16	.02845	1.1400	.06109	1.3249	.09145	1.5237	.11982	1.7364
53	.02898	1.1428	.06158	1.3279	.09191	1.5269	.12025	1.7398
27/32	.02951	1.1456	.06207	1.3309	.09236	1.5301	.12068	1.7432
55	.03004	1.1484	.06256	1.3339	.09282	1.5333	.12110	1.7467
7/8	.03057	1.1512	.06305	1.3369	.09328	1.5366	.12153	1.7501
57	.03109	1.1539	.06354	1.3399	.09373	1.5398	.12196	1.7536
29/32	.03162	1.1567	.06403	1.3429	.09419	1.5430	.12239	1.7570
59	.03214	1.1595	.06452	1.3460	.09464	1.5463	.12281	1.7605
15/16	.03267	1.1624	.06500	1.3490	.09510	1.5495	.12324	1.7639
61	.03319	1.1652	.06549	1.3520	.09555	1.5527	.12366	1.7674
31/32	.03372	1.1680	.06598	1.3550	.09600	1.5560	.12409	1.7708
63	.03424	1.1708	.06646	1.3581	.09646	1.5592	.12451	1.7743

64ths / 32ds	16″ Log.	16″ Square	17″ Log.	17″ Square	18″ Log.	18″ Square	19″ Log.	19″ Square
0	.12494	1.7778	.15127	2.0069	.17609	2.2500	.19957	2.5069
1	.12536	1.7813	.15167	2.0106	.17647	2.2539	.19993	2.5111
1/32	.12579	1.7847	.15207	2.0143	.17684	2.2578	.20029	2.5152
3	.12621	1.7882	.15246	2.0180	.17722	2.2617	.20064	2.5193
1/16	.12663	1.7917	.15286	2.0217	.17760	2.2657	.20100	2.5235
5	.12705	1.7952	.15326	2.0254	.17797	2.2696	.20135	2.5276
3/32	.12748	1.7987	.15366	2.0291	.17835	2.2735	.20171	2.5317
7	.12790	1.8022	.15405	2.0329	.17872	2.2774	.20207	2.5359
1/8	.12832	1.8057	.15445	2.0366	.17910	2.2814	.20242	2.5400
9	.12874	1.8092	.15485	2.0403	.17947	2.2853	.20277	2.5442
5/32	.12916	1.8127	.15524	2.0440	.17984	2.2892	.20313	2.5483
11	.12958	1.8162	.15564	2.0477	.18022	2.2932	.20348	2.5525
3/16	.13000	1.8197	.15603	2.0515	.18059	2.2971	.20384	2.5567
13	.13042	1.8232	.15643	2.0552	.18096	2.3011	.20419	2.5608
7/32	.13084	1.8267	.15682	2.0589	.18134	2.3050	.20454	2.5650
15	.13125	1.8302	.15721	2.0627	.18171	2.3090	.20490	2.5692
1/4	.13167	1.8338	.15761	2.0664	.18208	2.3129	.20525	2.5734
17	.13209	1.8373	.15800	2.0702	.18245	2.3169	.20560	2.5775
9/32	.13251	1.8408	.15839	2.0739	.18282	2.3209	.20595	2.5817
19	.13292	1.8444	.15879	2.0777	.18320	2.3248	.20631	2.5859
5/16	.13334	1.8479	.15918	2.0814	.18357	2.3288	.20666	2.5901
21	.13376	1.8514	.15957	2.0852	.18394	2.3328	.20701	2.5943
11/32	.13417	1.8550	.15996	2.0889	.18431	2.3368	.20736	2.5985
23	.13459	1.8585	.16035	2.0927	.18468	2.3407	.20771	2.6027
3/8	.13500	1.8621	.16074	2.0965	.18505	2.3447	.20806	2.6069
25	.13541	1.8656	.16113	2.1002	.18542	2.3487	.20841	2.6111
13/32	.13583	1.8692	.16152	2.1040	.18578	2.3527	.20876	2.6153
27	.13624	1.8728	.16191	2.1078	.18615	2.3567	.20911	2.6195
7/16	.13665	1.8763	.16230	2.1116	.18652	2.3607	.20946	2.6237
29	.13707	1.8799	.16269	2.1154	.18689	2.3647	.20981	2.6279
15/32	.13748	1.8835	.16308	2.1191	.18726	2.3687	.21016	2.6322
31	.13789	1.8870	.16347	2.1229	.18762	2.3727	.21051	2.6364
1/2	.13830	1.8906	.16386	2.1267	.18799	2.3767	.21085	2.6406
33	.13871	1.8942	.16424	2.1305	.18836	2.3808	.21120	2.6449
17/32	.13912	1.8978	.16463	2.1343	.18872	2.3848	.21155	2.6491
35	.13953	1.9014	.16502	2.1381	.18909	2.3888	.21190	2.6533
9/16	.13994	1.9050	.16541	2.1420	.18946	2.3928	.21224	2.6576
37	.14035	1.9086	.16579	2.1458	.18982	2.3969	.21259	2.6618
19/32	.14076	1.9122	.16618	2.1496	.19019	2.4009	.21294	2.6661
39	.14117	1.9158	.16656	2.1534	.19055	2.4049	.21328	2.6703
5/8	.14158	1.9194	.16695	2.1572	.19092	2.4090	.21363	2.6746
41	.14199	1.9230	.16733	2.1611	.19128	2.4130	.21397	2.6788
21/32	.14240	1.9266	.16772	2.1649	.19164	2.4171	.21432	2.6831
43	.14280	1.9302	.16810	2.1687	.19201	2.4211	.21466	2.6874
11/16	.14321	1.9338	.16849	2.1726	.19237	2.4252	.21501	2.6917
45	.14362	1.9375	.16887	2.1764	.19273	2.4292	.21535	2.6959
23/32	.14402	1.9411	.16925	2.1802	.19310	2.4333	.21570	2.7002
47	.14443	1.9447	.16963	2.1841	.19346	2.4373	.21604	2.7045
3/4	.14483	1.9484	.17002	2.1879	.19382	2.4414	.21639	2.7088
49	.14524	1.9520	.17040	2.1918	.19418	2.4455	.21673	2.7131
25/32	.14564	1.9556	.17078	2.1956	.19454	2.4496	.21707	2.7173
51	.14605	1.9593	.17116	2.1995	.19490	2.4536	.21742	2.7216
13/16	.14645	1.9629	.17154	2.2034	.19527	2.4577	.21776	2.7259
53	.14685	1.9666	.17192	2.2072	.19563	2.4618	.21810	2.7302
27/32	.14726	1.9702	.17230	2.2111	.19599	2.4659	.21844	2.7345
55	.14766	1.9739	.17269	2.2150	.19635	2.4700	.21878	2.7389
7/8	.14806	1.9775	.17306	2.2189	.19671	2.4741	.21913	2.7432
57	.14846	1.9812	.17344	2.2227	.19707	2.4782	.21947	2.7475
29/32	.14887	1.9849	.17382	2.2266	.19742	2.4823	.21981	2.7518
59	.14927	1.9885	.17420	2.2305	.19778	2.4864	.22015	2.7561
15/16	.14967	1.9922	.17458	2.2344	.19814	2.4905	.22049	2.7604
61	.15007	1.9959	.17496	2.2383	.19850	2.4946	.22083	2.7648
31/32	.15047	1.9996	.17534	2.2422	.19886	2.4987	.22117	2.7691
63	.15087	2.0033	.17571	2.2461	.19922	2.5028	.22151	2.7734

		20″		21″		22″		23″	
64ths.	32ds.	Log.	Square	Log.	Square	Log.	Square	Log.	Square
0		**.22185**	**2.7778**	**.24304**	**3.0625**	**.26324**	**3.3611**	**.28255**	**3.6736**
1		.22219	2.7821	.24336	3.0671	.26355	3.3659	.28284	3.6786
	½₂	.22253	2.7865	.24368	3.0716	.26386	3.3707	.28314	3.6836
3		.22287	2.7908	.24401	3.0762	.26417	3.3754	.28343	3.6886
1⁄16		**.22320**	**2.7952**	**.24433**	**3.0808**	**.26447**	**3.3802**	**.28373**	**3.6936**
5		.22354	2.7995	.24465	3.0853	.26478	3.3850	.28402	3.6986
	³⁄₃₂	.22388	2.8039	.24497	3.0899	.26509	3.3898	.28431	3.7036
7		.22422	2.8082	.24529	3.0945	.26540	3.3946	.28461	3.7086
1⁄8		**.22455**	**2.8126**	**.24562**	**3.0991**	**.26570**	**3.3994**	**.28490**	**3.7137**
9		.22489	2.8170	.24594	3.1037	.26601	3.4042	.28519	3.7187
	⁵⁄₃₂	.22523	2.8214	.24626	3.1082	.26632	3.4090	.28549	3.7237
11		.22557	2.8257	.24658	3.1128	.26662	3.4138	.28578	3.7287
³⁄16		**.22590**	**2.8301**	**.24690**	**3.1174**	**.26693**	**3.4186**	**.28607**	**3.7338**
13		.22624	2.8345	.24722	3.1220	.26723	3.4235	.28637	3.7388
	⁷⁄₃₂	.22657	2.8389	.24754	3.1266	.26754	3.4283	.28666	3.7438
15		.22691	2.8433	.24786	3.1312	.26784	3.4331	.28695	3.7489
1⁄4		**.22724**	**2.8477**	**.24818**	**3.1359**	**.26815**	**3.4379**	**.28724**	**3.7539**
17		.22758	2.8521	.24850	3.1405	.26845	3.4428	.28753	3.7590
	⁹⁄₃₂	.22791	2.8565	.24882	3.1451	.26876	3.4476	.28783	3.7640
19		.22825	2.8609	.24913	3.1497	.26906	3.4524	.28812	3.7691
⁵⁄16		**.22858**	**2.8653**	**.24945**	**3.1543**	**.26937**	**3.4573**	**.28841**	**3.7741**
21		.22892	2.8697	.24977	3.1590	.26967	3.4621	.28870	3.7792
	¹¹⁄₃₂	.22925	2.8741	.25009	3.1636	.26997	3.4670	.28899	3.7842
23		.22958	2.8785	.25041	3.1682	.27028	3.4718	.28928	3.7893
³⁄8		**.22992**	**2.8829**	**.25072**	**3.1729**	**.27058**	**3.4767**	**.28957**	**3.7944**
25		.23025	2.8873	.25104	3.1775	.27088	3.4815	.28986	3.7995
	¹³⁄₃₂	.23058	2.8918	.25136	3.1821	.27119	3.4864	.29015	3.8045
27		.23091	2.8962	.25168	3.1868	.27149	3.4913	.29044	3.8096
⁷⁄16		**.23125**	**2.9006**	**.25199**	**3.1914**	**.27179**	**3.4961**	**.29073**	**3.8147**
29		.23158	2.9051	.25231	3.1961	.27210	3.5010	.29102	3.8198
	¹⁵⁄₃₂	.23191	2.9095	.25263	3.2007	.27240	3.5059	.29131	3.8249
31		.23224	2.9140	.25294	3.2054	.27270	3.5107	.29160	3.8300
1⁄2		**.23257**	**2.9184**	**.25326**	**3.2101**	**.27300**	**3.5156**	**.29189**	**3.8351†**
33		.23290	2.9229	.25357	3.2147	.27330	3.5205	.29218	3.8402
	¹⁷⁄₃₂	.23323	2.9273	.25389	3.2194	.27360	3.5254	.29246	3.8453
35		.23356	2.9318	.25420	3.2241	.27391	3.5303	.29275	3.8504
⁹⁄16		**.23389**	**2.9362**	**.25452**	**3.2288**	**.27421**	**3.5352**	**.29304**	**3.8555**
37		.23422	2.9407	.25483	3.2334	.27451	3.5401	.29333	3.8606
	¹⁹⁄₃₂	.23455	2.9452	.25515	3.2381	.27481	3.5450	.29362	3.8657
39		.23488	2.9496	.25546	3.2428	.27511	3.5499	.29390	3.8709
⁵⁄8		**.23521**	**2.9541**	**.25577**	**3.2475**	**.27541**	**3.5548**	**.29419**	**3.8760**
41		.23554	2.9586	.25609	3.2522	.27571	3.5597	.29448	3.8811
	²¹⁄₃₂	.23587	2.9631	.25640	3.2569	.27601	3.5646	.29476	3.8862
43		.23620	2.9675	.25672	3.2616	.27631	3.5695	.29505	3.8914
¹¹⁄16		**.23653**	**2.9720**	**.25703**	**3.2663**	**.27661**	**3.5745**	**.29534**	**3.8965**
45		.23685	2.9765	.25734	3.2710	.27690	3.5794	.29562	3.9017
	²³⁄₃₂	.23718	2.9810	.25765	3.2757	.27720	3.5843	.29591	3.9068
47		.23751	2.9855	.25797	3.2804	.27750	3.5892	.29620	3.9119
³⁄4		**.23784**	**2.9900**	**.25828**	**3.2852**	**.27780**	**3.5942**	**.29648**	**3.9171**
49		.23816	2.9945	.25859	3.2899	.27810	3.5991	.29677	3.9223
	²⁵⁄₃₂	.23849	2.9990	.25890	3.2946	.27840	3.6041	.29705	3.9274
51		.23882	3.0035	.25921	3.2993	.27869	3.6090	.29734	3.9326
¹³⁄16		**.23914**	**3.0081**	**.25952**	**3.3041**	**.27899**	**3.6140**	**.29762**	**3.9377**
53		.23947	3.0126	.25984	3.3088	.27929	3.6189	.29791	3.9429
	²⁷⁄₃₂	.23979	3.0171	.26015	3.3135	.27959	3.6239	.29819	3.9481
55		.24012	3.0216	.26046	3.3183	.27988	3.6288	.29848	3.9533
⁷⁄8		**.24045**	**3.0262**	**.26077**	**3.3230**	**.28018**	**3.6338**	**.29876**	**3.9584**
57		.24077	3.0307	.26108	3.3278	.28048	3.6388	.29905	3.9636
	²⁹⁄₃₂	.24109	3.0352	.26139	3.3325	.28077	3.6437	.29933	3.9688
59		.24142	3.0398	.26170	3.3373	.28107	3.6487	.29961	3.9740
¹⁵⁄16		**.24174**	**3.0443**	**.26201**	**3.3420**	**.28136**	**3.6537**	**.29990**	**3.9792**
61		.24207	3.0488	.26232	3.3468	.28166	3.6587	.30018	3.9844
	³¹⁄₃₂	.24239	3.0534	.26262	3.3516	.28196	3.6636	.30046	3.9896
63		.24271	3.0579	.26293	3.3563	.28225	3.6686	.30075	3.9948

64ths / 32ds	24″ Log.	24″ Square	25″ Log.	25″ Square	26″ Log.	26″ Square	27″ Log.	27″ Square
0	.30103	4.0000	.31876	4.3403	.33579	4.6944	.35218	5.0625
1	.30131	4.0052	.31903	4.3457	.33605	4.7001	.35243	5.0684
1/32	.30160	4.0104	.31930	4.3511	.33631	4.7057	.35268	5.0742
3	.30188	4.0156	.31957	4.3566	.33657	4.7114	.35294	5.0801
1/16	.30216	4.0209	.31984	4.3620	.33683	4.7170	.35319	5.0860
5	.30244	4.0261	.32011	4.3674	.33710	4.7227	.35344	5.0918
3/32	.30272	4.0313	.32038	4.3729	.33736	4.7284	.35369	5.0977
7	.30300	4.0365	.32065	4.3783	.33762	4.7340	.35394	5.1036
1/8	.30329	4.0418	.32092	4.3838	.33788	4.7397	.35419	5.1095
9	.30357	4.0470	.32119	4.3892	.33813	4.7454	.35444	5.1154
5/32	.30385	4.0523	.32146	4.3947	.33839	4.7510	.35469	5.1213
11	.30413	4.0575	.32173	4.4002	.33865	4.7567	.35494	5.1272
3/16	.30441	4.0627	.32200	4.4056	.33891	4.7624	.35519	5.1331
13	.30469	4.0680	.32227	4.4111	.33917	4.7681	.35544	5.1390
7/32	.30497	4.0732	.32254	4.4166	.33943	4.7738	.35569	5.1449
15	.30525	4.0785	.32281	4.4220	.33969	4.7795	.35594	5.1508
1/4	.30553	4.0838	.32308	4.4275	.33995	4.7852	.35619	5.1567
17	.30581	4.0890	.32335	4.4330	.34021	4.7909	.35643	5.1626
9/32	.30609	4.0943	.32362	4.4385	.34046	4.7966	.35668	5.1685
19	.30637	4.0996	.32389	4.4440	.34072	4.8023	.35693	5.1744
5/16	.30665	4.1048	.32415	4.4495	.34098	4.8080	.35718	5.1804
21	.30693	4.1101	.32442	4.4550	.34124	4.8137	.35743	5.1863
11/32	.30721	4.1154	.32469	4.4605	.34150	4.8194	.35768	5.1922
23	.30748	4.1207	.32496	4.4660	.34175	4.8251	.35792	5.1982
3/8	.30776	4.1260	.32522	4.4715	.34201	4.8308	.35817	5.2041
25	.30804	4.1313	.32549	4.4770	.34227	4.8366	.35842	5.2100
13/32	.30832	4.1366	.32576	4.4825	.34253	4.8423	.35867	5.2160
27	.30860	4.1419	.32603	4.4880	.34278	4.8480	.35892	5.2219
7/16	.30888	4.1472	.32629	4.4935	.34304	4.8538	.35916	5.2279
29	.30915	4.1525	.32656	4.4990	.34330	4.8595	.35941	5.2338
15/32	.30943	4.1578	.32683	4.5046	.34355	4.8652	.35966	5.2398
31	.30971	4.1631	.32709	4.5101	.34381	4.8710	.35990	5.2458
1/2	.30998	4.1684	.32736	4.5156	.34406	4.8767	.36015	5.2517
33	.31026	4.1737	.32762	4.5212	.34432	4.8825	.36040	5.2577
17/32	.31054	4.1790	.32789	4.5267	.34458	4.8882	.36064	5.2637
35	.31081	4.1844	.32816	4.5322	.34483	4.8940	.36089	5.2697
9/16	.31109	4.1897	.32842	4.5378	.34509	4.8998	.36114	5.2756
37	.31137	4.1950	.32869	4.5433	.34534	4.9055	.36138	5.2816
19/32	.31164	4.2004	.32895	4.5489	.34560	4.9113	.36163	5.2876
39	.31192	4.2057	.32922	4.5544	.34585	4.9171	.36188	5.2936
5/8	.31219	4.2110	.32948	4.5600	.34611	4.9229	.36212	5.2996
41	.31247	4.2164	.32975	4.5656	.34636	4.9286	.36237	5.3056
21/32	.31275	4.2217	.33001	4.5711	.34662	4.9344	.36261	5.3116
43	.31302	4.2271	.33028	4.5767	.34687	4.9402	.36286	5.3176
11/16	.31330	4.2324	.33054	4.5823	.34713	4.9460	.36310	5.3236
45	.31357	4.2378	.33080	4.5879	.34738	4.9518	.36335	5.3296
23/32	.31385	4.2432	.33107	4.5934	.34763	4.9576	.36359	5.3356
47	.31412	4.2485	.33133	4.5990	.34789	4.9634	.36384	5.3416
3/4	.31439	4.2539	.33160	4.6046	.34814	4.9692	.36408	5.3477
49	.31467	4.2593	.33186	4.6102	.34840	4.9750	.36433	5.3537
25/32	.31494	4.2647	.33212	4.6158	.34865	4.9808	.36457	5.3597
51	.31522	4.2700	.33239	4.6214	.34890	4.9866	.36481	5.3657
13/16	.31549	4.2754	.33265	4.6270	.34916	4.9924	.36506	5.3718
53	.31576	4.2808	.33291	4.6326	.34941	4.9983	.36530	5.3778
27/32	.31604	4.2862	.33317	4.6382	.34966	5.0041	.36555	5.3839
55	.31631	4.2916	.33344	4.6438	.34991	5.0099	.36579	5.3899
7/8	.31658	4.2970	.33370	4.6494	.35017	5.0157	.36603	5.3959
57	.31685	4.3024	.33396	4.6550	.35042	5.0216	.36628	5.4020
29/32	.31713	4.3078	.33422	4.6607	.35067	5.0274	.36652	5.4080
59	.31740	4.3132	.33449	4.6663	.35092	5.0332	.36676	5.4141
15/16	.31767	4.3186	.33475	4.6719	.35118	5.0391	.36701	5.4202
61	.31794	4.3240	.33501	4.6775	.35143	5.0449	.36725	5.4262
31/32	.31822	4.3294	.33527	4.6832	.35168	5.0508	.36749	5.4323
63	.31849	4.3349	.33553	4.6888	.35193	5.0566	.36773	5.4384

64ths / 32ds	28″ Log.	28″ Square	29″ Log.	29″ Square	30″ Log.	30″ Square	31″ Log.	31″ Square
0	.36798	5.4444	.38322	5.8403	.39794	6.2500	.41218	6.6736
1	.36822	5.4505	.38345	5.8466	.39817	6.2565	.41240	6.6803
1/32	.36846	5.4566	.38368	5.8529	.39839	6.2630	.41262	6.6871
3	.36870	5.4627	.38392	5.8592	.39862	6.2695	.41284	6.6938
1/16	.36895	5.4688	.38415	5.8655	.39884	6.2761	.41306	6.7005
5	.36919	5.4749	.38439	5.8718	.39907	6.2826	.41327	6.7073
3/32	.36943	5.4810	.38462	5.8781	.39930	6.2891	.41349	6.7140
7	.36967	5.4871	.38485	5.8844	.39952	6.2957	.41371	6.7208
1/8	.36991	5.4932	.38508	5.8907	.39975	6.3022	.41393	6.7275
9	.37015	5.4993	.38532	5.8971	.39997	6.3087	.41415	6.7343
5/32	.37039	5.5054	.38555	5.9034	.40020	6.3153	.41436	6.7411
11	.37063	5.5115	.38578	5.9097	.40042	6.3218	.41458	6.7478
3/16	.37088	5.5176	.38602	5.9160	.40065	6.3284	.41480	6.7546
13	.37112	5.5237	.38625	5.9224	.40087	6.3349	.41502	6.7614
7/32	.37136	5.5298	.38648	5.9287	.40110	6.3415	.41523	6.7681
15	.37160	5.5360	.38671	5.9351	.40132	6.3480	.41545	6.7749
1/4	.37184	5.5421	.38694	5.9414	.40154	6.3546	.41567	6.7817
17	.37208	5.5482	.38718	5.9478	.40177	6.3612	.41589	6.7885
9/32	.37232	5.5544	.38741	5.9541	.40199	6.3677	.41610	6.7953
19	.37256	5.5605	.38764	5.9605	.40222	6.3743	.41632	6.8020
5/16	.37280	5.5667	.38787	5.9668	.40244	6.3809	.41654	6.8088
21	.37304	5.5728	.38810	5.9732	.40266	6.3875	.41675	6.8156
11/32	.37328	5.5789	.38833	5.9796	.40289	6.3940	.41697	6.8224
23	.37352	5.5851	.38857	5.9859	.40311	6.4006	.41719	6.8292
3/8	.37375	5.5913	.38880	5.9923	.40334	6.4072	.41740	6.8360
25	.37399	5.5974	.38903	5.9987	.40356	6.4138	.41762	6.8429
13/32	.37423	5.6036	.38926	6.0051	.40378	6.4204	.41783	6.8497
27	.37447	5.6097	.38949	6.0114	.40400	6.4270	.41805	6.8565
7/16	.37471	5.6159	.38972	6.0178	.40423	6.4336	.41827	6.8633
29	.37495	5.6221	.38995	6.0242	.40445	6.4402	.41848	6.8701
15/32	.37519	5.6283	.39018	6.0306	.40467	6.4468	.41870	6.8770
31	.37543	5.6344	.39041	6.0370	.40490	6.4535	.41891	6.8838
1/2	.37566	5.6406	.39064	6.0434	.40512	6.4601	.41913	6.8906
33	.37590	5.6468	.39087	6.0498	.40534	6.4667	.41934	6.8975
17/32	.37614	5.6530	.39110	6.0562	.40556	6.4733	.41956	6.9043
35	.37638	5.6592	.39133	6.0626	.40579	6.4799	.41978	6.9111
9/16	.37661	5.6654	.39156	6.0690	.40601	6.4866	.41999	6.9180
37	.37685	5.6716	.39179	6.0755	.40623	6.4932	.42021	6.9248
19/32	.37709	5.6778	.39202	6.0819	.40645	6.4998	.42042	6.9317
39	.37733	5.6840	.39225	6.0883	.40667	6.5065	.42063	6.9386
5/8	.37756	5.6902	.39248	6.0947	.40689	6.5131	.42085	6.9454
41	.37780	5.6964	.39271	6.1012	.40712	6.5198	.42106	6.9523
21/32	.37804	5.7026	.39293	6.1076	.40734	6.5264	.42128	6.9592
43	.37827	5.7089	.39316	6.1140	.40756	6.5331	.42149	6.9660
11/16	.37851	5.7151	.39339	6.1205	.40778	6.5397	.42171	6.9729
45	.37875	5.7213	.39362	6.1269	.40800	6.5464	.42192	6.9798
23/32	.37898	5.7275	.39385	6.1334	.40822	6.5531	.42213	6.9867
47	.37922	5.7338	.39408	6.1398	.40844	6.5597	.42235	6.9935
3/4	.37946	5.7400	.39431	6.1463	.40866	6.5664	.42256	7.0004
49	.37969	5.7463	.39453	6.1527	.40888	6.5731	.42278	7.0073
25/32	.37993	5.7525	.39476	6.1592	.40911	6.5798	.42299	7.0142
51	.38016	5.7588	.39499	6.1657	.40933	6.5864	.42320	7.0211
13/16	.38040	5.7650	.39522	6.1721	.40955	6.5931	.42342	7.0280
53	.38064	5.7713	.39544	6.1786	.40977	6.5998	.42363	7.0349
27/32	.38087	5.7775	.39567	6.1851	.40999	6.6065	.42384	7.0418
55	.38111	5.7838	.39590	6.1915	.41021	6.6132	.42406	7.0487
7/8	.38134	5.7900	.39613	6.1980	.41043	6.6199	.42427	7.0557
57	.38158	5.7963	.39635	6.2045	.41065	6.6266	.42448	7.0626
29/32	.38181	5.8026	.39658	6.2110	.41087	6.6333	.42469	7.0695
59	.38205	5.8089	.39681	6.2175	.41108	6.6400	.42491	7.0764
15/16	.38228	5.8151	.39703	6.2240	.41130	6.6467	.42512	7.0834
61	.38251	5.8214	.39726	6.2305	.41152	6.6534	.42533	7.0903
31/32	.38275	5.8277	.39749	6.2370	.41174	6.6602	.42554	7.0972
63	.38298	5.8340	.39771	6.2435	.41196	6.6669	.42576	7.1042

64ths	32ds	32″ Log.	32″ Square	33″ Log.	33″ Square	34″ Log.	34″ Square	35″ Log.	35″ Square
0		.42597	7.1111	.43933	7.5625	.45230	8.0278	.46489	8.5069
1		.42618	7.1181	.43954	7.5697	.45250	8.0352	.46508	8.5145
	1/32	.42639	7.1250	.43974	7.5768	.45270	8.0425	.46527	8.5221
3		.42660	7.1320	.43995	7.5840	.45290	8.0499	.46547	8.5297
	1/16	.42682	7.1389	.44015	7.5912	.45310	8.0573	.46566	8.5374
5		.42703	7.1459	.44036	7.5983	.45329	8.0647	.46586	8.5450
	3/32	.42724	7.1528	.44056	7.6055	.45349	8.0721	.46605	8.5526
7		.42745	7.1598	.44077	7.6127	.45369	8.0795	.46624	8.5602
	1/8	.42766	7.1668	.44097	7.6199	.45389	8.0869	.46644	8.5678
9		.42787	7.1737	.44118	7.6271	.45409	8.0943	.46663	8.5754
	5/32	.42808	7.1807	.44138	7.6343	.45429	8.1017	.46682	8.5831
11		.42830	7.1877	.44159	7.6415	.45449	8.1091	.46701	8.5907
	3/16	.42851	7.1947	.44179	7.6487	.45469	8.1166	.46721	8.5983
13		.42872	7.2017	.44200	7.6559	.45488	8.1240	.46740	8.6060
	7/32	.42893	7.2087	.44220	7.6631	.45508	8.1314	.46759	8.6136
15		.42914	7.2157	.44241	7.6703	.45528	8.1388	.46779	8.6213
	1/4	.42935	7.2227	.44261	7.6775	.45548	8.1463	.46798	8.6289
17		.42956	7.2297	.44281	7.6847	.45568	8.1537	.46817	8.6366
	9/32	.42977	7.2367	.44302	7.6920	.45588	8.1611	.46836	8.6442
19		.42998	7.2437	.44322	7.6992	.45607	8.1686	.46856	8.6519
	5/16	.43019	7.2507	.44343	7.7064	.45627	8.1760	.46875	8.6595
21		.43040	7.2577	.44363	7.7136	.45647	8.1835	.46894	8.6672
	11/32	.43061	7.2647	.44383	7.7209	.45667	8.1909	.46913	8.6749
23		.43082	7.2717	.44404	7.7281	.45686	8.1984	.46932	8.6825
	3/8	.43103	7.2788	.44424	7.7354	.45706	8.2058	.46952	8.6902
25		.43124	7.2858	.44444	7.7426	.45726	8.2133	.46971	8.6979
	13/32	.43145	7.2928	.44465	7.7498	.45746	8.2208	.46990	8.7056
27		.43166	7.2998	.44485	7.7571	.45765	8.2282	.47009	8.7133
	7/16	.43187	7.3069	.44505	7.7644	.45785	8.2357	.47028	8 7209
29		.43208	7.3139	.44526	7.7716	.45805	8.2432	.47047	8.7286
	15/32	.43228	7.3210	.44546	7.7789	.45824	8.2507	.47066	8.7363
31		.43249	7.3280	.44566	7.7861	.45844	8.2581	.47086	8.7440
	1/2	.43270	7.3351	.44586	7.7934	.45864	8.2656	.47105	8.7517
33		.43291	7.3421	.44607	7.8007	.45883	8.2731	.47124	8.7594
	17/32	.43312	7.3492	.44627	7.8079	.45903	8.2806	.47143	8.7672
35		.43333	7.3562	.44647	7.8152	.45923	8.2881	.47162	8.7749
	9/16	.43354	7.3633	.44667	7.8225	.45942	8.2956	.47181	8.7826
37		.43374	7.3704	.44688	7.8298	.45962	8.3031	.47200	8.7903
	19/32	.43395	7.3774	.44708	7.8371	.45982	8.3106	.47219	8.7980
39		.43416	7.3845	.44728	7.8444	.46001	8.3181	.47238	8.8057
	5/8	.43437	7.3916	.44748	7.8517	.46021	8.3256	.47257	8.8135
41		.43458	7.3987	.44768	7.8590	.46040	8.3331	.47276	8.8212
	21/32	.43479	7.4058	.44788	7.8663	.46060	8.3407	.47295	8.8289
43		.43499	7.4129	.44809	7.8736	.46080	8.3482	.47314	8.8367
	11/16	.43520	7.4199	.44829	7.8809	.46099	8.3557	.47333	8.8444
45		.43541	7.4270	.44849	7.8882	.46119	8.3632	.47352	8.8522
	23/32	.43562	7.4341	.44869	7.8955	.46138	8.3708	.47372	8.8599
47		.43582	7.4412	.44889	7.9028	.46158	8.3783	.47390	8.8677
	3/4	.43603	7.4484	.44909	7.9102	.46177	8.3859	.47409	8.8754
49		.43624	7.4555	.44929	7.9175	.46197	8.3934	.47428	8.8832
	25/32	.43644	7.4626	.44949	7.9248	.46216	8.4009	.47447	8.8910
51		.43665	7.4697	.44970	7.9321	.46236	8.4085	.47466	8.8987
	13/16	.43686	7.4768	.44990	7.9395	.46255	8.4160	.47485	8.9065
53		.43706	7.4839	.45010	7.9468	.46275	8.4236	.47504	8.9143
	27/32	.43727	7.4911	.45030	7.9542	.46294	8.4312	.47523	8.9220
55		.43748	7.4982	.45050	7.9615	.46314	8.4387	.47542	8.9298
	7/8	.43768	7.5053	.45070	7.9689	.46333	8.4463	.47561	8.9376
57		.43789	7.5125	.45090	7.9762	.46353	8.4539	.47580	8.9454
	29/32	.43810	7.5196	.45110	7.9836	.46372	8.4614	.47599	8.9532
59		.43830	7.5267	.45130	7.9909	.46392	8.4690	.47618	8.9610
	15/16	.43851	7.5339	.45150	7.9983	.46411	8.4766	.47637	8.9688
61		.43872	7.5410	.45170	8.0057	.46430	8.4842	.47656	8.9766
	31/32	.43892	7.5482	.45190	8.0130	.46450	8.4918	.47674	8.9844
63		.43913	7.5553	.45210	8.0204	.46469	8.4994	.47693	8.9922

64ths. 32ds.	36″ Log.	36″ Square	37″ Log.	37″ Square	38″ Log.	38″ Square	39″ Log.	39″ Square
0	.47712	9.0000	.48902	9.5069	.50060	10.0278	.51188	10.5625
1	.47731	9.0078	.48920	9.5150	.50078	10.0360	.51206	10.5710
1/32	.47750	9.0156	.48939	9.5230	.50096	10.0443	.51223	10.5794
3	.47769	9.0235	.48957	9.5310	.50114	10.0525	.51241	10.5879
1/16	.47787	9.0313	.48975	9.5391	.50132	10.0608	.51258	10.5964
5	.47806	9.0391	.48994	9.5471	.50149	10.0691	.51275	10.6049
3/32	.47825	9.0469	.49012	9.5552	.50167	10.0773	.51293	10.6133
7	.47844	9.0548	.49030	9.5632	.50185	10.0856	.51310	10.6218
1/8	.47863	9.0626	.49049	9.5713	.50203	10.0939	.51327	10.6303
9	.47881	9.0704	.49067	9.5793	.50221	10.1021	.51345	10.6388
5/32	.47900	9.0783	.49085	9.5874	.50238	10.1104	.51362	10.6473
11	.47919	9.0861	.49103	9.5955	.50256	10.1187	.51379	10.6558
3/16	.47938	9.0940	.49122	9.6035	.50274	10.1270	.51397	10.6643
13	.47956	9.1018	.49140	9.6116	.50292	10.1353	.51414	10.6728
7/32	.47975	9.1097	.49158	9.6197	.50310	10.1436	.51431	10.6813
15	.47994	9.1176	.49176	9.6278	.50327	10.1519	.51449	10.6898
1/4	.48013	9.1254	.49195	9.6359	.50345	10.1602	.51466	10.6984
17	.48031	9.1333	.49213	9.6439	.50363	10.1685	.51483	10.7069
9/32	.48050	9.1412	.49231	9.6520	.50380	10.1768	.51500	10.7154
19	.48069	9.1490	.49249	9.6601	.50398	10.1851	.51518	10.7239
5/16	.48087	9.1569	.49267	9.6682	.50416	10.1934	.51535	10.7324
21	.48106	9.1648	.49285	9.6763	.50434	10.2017	.51552	10.7410
11/32	.48125	9.1727	.49304	9.6844	.50451	10.2100	.51569	10.7495
23	.48144	9.1806	.49322	9.6925	.50469	10.2183	.51587	10.7581
3/8	.48162	9.1885	.49340	9.7006	.50487	10.2267	.51604	10.7666
25	.48181	9.1964	.49358	9.7087	.50504	10.2350	.51621	10.7751
13/32	.48199	9.2043	.49376	9.7169	.50522	10.2433	.51638	10.7837
27	.48218	9.2122	.49394	9.7250	.50540	10.2517	.51656	10.7923
7/16	.48237	9.2201	.49413	9.7331	.50557	10.2600	.51673	10.8008
29	.48255	9.2280	.49431	9.7412	.50575	10.2684	.51690	10.8094
15/32	.48274	9.2359	.49449	9.7494	.50593	10.2767	.51707	10.8179
31	.48293	9.2438	.49467	9.7575	.50610	10.2850	.51724	10.8265
1/2	.48311	9.2517	.49485	9.7656	.50628	10.2934	.51742	10.8351
33	.48330	9.2597	.49503	9.7738	.50646	10.3018	.51759	10.8436
17/32	.48348	9.2676	.49521	9.7819	.50663	10.3101	.51776	10.8522
35	.48367	9.2755	.49539	9.7901	.50681	10.3185	.51793	10.8608
9/16	.48385	9.2834	.49557	9.7982	.50698	10.3269	.51810	10.8694
37	.48404	9.2914	.49575	9.8064	.50716	10.3352	.51827	10.8780
19/32	.48423	9.2993	.49593	9.8145	.50734	10.3436	.51845	10.8866
39	.48441	9.3073	.49611	9.8227	.50751	10.3520	.51862	10.8952
5/8	.48460	9.3152	.49630	9.8308	.50769	10.3604	.51879	10.9038
41	.48478	9.3232	.49648	9.8390	.50786	10.3687	.51896	10.9124
21/32	.48497	9.3311	.49666	9.8472	.50804	10.3771	.51913	10.9210
43	.48515	9.3391	.49684	9.8553	.50821	10.3855	.51930	10.9296
11/16	.48534	9.3470	.49702	9.8635	.50839	10.3939	.51947	10.9582
45	.48552	9.3550	.49720	9.8717	.50856	10.4023	.51964	10.9468
23/32	.48571	9.3630	.49738	9.8799	.50874	10.4107	.51981	10.9554
47	.48589	9.3709	.49756	9.8881	.50892	10.4191	.51999	10.9640
3/4	.48608	9.3789	.49774	9.8963	.50909	10.4275	.52016	10.9727
49	.48626	9.3869	.49792	9.9045	.50927	10.4359	.52033	10.9813
25/32	.48645	9.3949	.49810	9.9127	.50944	10.4443	.52050	10.9899
51	.48663	9.4028	.49827	9.9209	.50962	10.4528	.52067	10.9986
13/16	.48681	9.4108	.49845	9.9291	.50979	10.4612	.52084	11.0072
53	.48700	9.4188	.49863	9.9373	.50997	10.4696	.52101	11.0158
27/32	.48718	9.4268	.49881	9.9455	.51014	10.4780	.52118	11.0245
55	.48737	9.4348	.49899	9.9537	.51031	10.4865	.52135	11.0331
7/8	.48755	9.4428	.49917	9.9619	.51049	10.4949	.52152	11.0418
57	.48773	9.4508	.49935	9.9701	.51066	10.5033	.52169	11.0504
29/32	.48792	9.4588	.49953	9.9784	.51084	10.5118	.52186	11.0591
59	.48810	9.4668	.49971	9.9866	.51101	10.5202	.52203	11.0678
15/16	.48829	9.4749	.49989	9.9948	.51119	10.5287	.52220	11.0764
61	.48847	9.4829	.50007	10.0031	.51136	10.5371	.52237	11.0851
31/32	.48865	9.4909	.50025	10.0113	.51154	10.5456	.52254	11.0938
63	.48884	9.4989	.50042	10.0195	.51171	10.5540	.52271	11.1024

64ths. / 32ds.	40″ Log.	40″ Square	41″ Log.	41″ Square	42″ Log.	42″ Square	43″ Log.	43″ Square
0	.52288	11.1111	.53360	11.6736	.54407	12.2500	.55429	12.8403
1	.52305	11.1198	.53377	11.6825	.54423	12.2591	.55444	12.8496
1/32	.52322	11.1285	.53393	11.6914	.54439	12.2682	.55460	12.8589
3	.52339	11.1372	.53410	11.7003	.54455	12.2774	.55476	12.8683
1/16	.52356	11.1459	.53426	11.7092	.54471	12.2865	.55492	12.8776
5	.52373	11.1546	.53443	11.7181	.54488	12.2956	.55508	12.8870
3/32	.52390	11.1633	.53459	11.7271	.54504	12.3047	.55523	12.8963
7	.52406	11.1720	.53476	11.7360	.54520	12.3139	.55539	12.9057
1/8	.52423	11.1807	.53492	11.7449	.54536	12.3230	.55555	12.9150
9	.52440	11.1894	.53509	11.7538	.54552	12.3322	.55571	12.9244
5/32	.52457	11.1981	.53525	11.7628	.54568	12.3413	.55586	12.9338
11	.52474	11.2068	.53542	11.7717	.54584	12.3505	.55602	12.9431
3/16	.52491	11.2155	.53558	11.7806	.54600	12.3596	.55618	12.9525
13	.52508	11.2242	.53575	11.7896	.54616	12.3688	.55633	12.9619
7/32	.52525	11.2330	.53591	11.7985	.54632	12.3779	.55649	12.9713
15	.52542	11.2417	.53608	11.8075	.54648	12.3871	.55665	12.9806
1/4	.52558	11.2504	.53624	11.8164	.54665	12.3963	.55680	12.9900
17	.52575	11.2592	.53641	11.8254	.54681	12.4054	.55696	12.9994
9/32	.52592	11.2679	.53657	11.8343	.54697	12.4146	.55712	13.0088
19	.52609	11.2767	.53674	11.8433	.54713	12.4238	.55728	13.0182
5/16	.52626	11.2854	.53690	11.8522	.54729	12.4330	.55743	13.0276
21	.52643	11.2942	.53706	11.8612	.54745	12.4422	.55759	13.0370
11/32	.52660	11.3029	.53723	11.8702	.54761	12.4513	.55775	13.0464
23	.52676	11.3117	.53739	11.8792	.54777	12.4605	.55790	13.0558
3/8	.52693	11.3204	.53756	11.8881	.54793	12.4697	.55806	13.0652
25	.52710	11.3292	.53772	11.8971	.54809	12.4789	.55821	13.0746
13/32	.52727	11.3380	.53788	11.9061	.54825	12.4881	.55837	13.0840
27	.52744	11.3467	.53805	11.9151	.54841	12.4973	.55853	13.0935
7/16	.52760	11.3555	.53821	11.9241	.54857	12.5065	.55868	13.1029
29	.52777	11.3643	.53838	11.9331	.54873	12.5157	.55884	13.1123
15/32	.52794	11.3731	.53854	11.9421	.54889	12.5250	.55900	13.1218
31	.52811	11.3818	.53870	11.9511	.54905	12.5342	.55915	13.1312
1/2	.52827	11.3906	.53887	11.9601	.54921	12.5434	.55931	13.1406
33	.52844	11.3994	.53903	11.9691	.54937	12.5526	.55946	13.1501
17/32	.52861	11.4082	.53919	11.9781	.54953	12.5619	.55962	13.1595
35	.52878	11.4170	.53936	11.9871	.54969	12.5711	.55978	13.1690
9/16	.52894	11.4258	.53952	11.9961	.54985	12.5803	.55993	13.1784
37	.52911	11.4346	.53968	12.0051	.55001	12.5896	.56009	13.1879
19/32	.52928	11.4434	.53985	12.0142	.55016	12.5988	.56024	13.1973
39	.52945	11.4522	.54001	12.0232	.55032	12.6080	.56040	13.2068
5/8	.52961	11.4610	.54017	12.0322	.55048	12.6173	.56055	13.2163
41	.52978	11.4699	.54034	12.0413	.55064	12.6265	.56071	13.2257
21/32	.52995	11.4787	.54050	12.0503	.55080	12.6358	.56087	13.2352
43	.53011	11.4875	.54066	12.0593	.55096	12.6451	.56102	13.2447
11/16	.53028	11.4963	.54082	12.0684	.55112	12.6543	.56118	13.2542
45	.53045	11.5052	.54099	12.0774	.55128	12.6636	.56133	13.2636
23/32	.53061	11.5140	.54115	12.0865	.55144	12.6729	.56149	13.2731
47	.53078	11.5228	.54131	12.0955	.55160	12.6821	.56164	13.2826
3/4	.53095	11.5317	.54148	12.1046	.55175	12.6914	.56180	13.2921
49	.53111	11.5405	.54164	12.1137	.55191	12.7007	.56195	13.3016
25/32	.53128	11.5494	.54180	12.1227	.55207	12.7100	.56211	13.3111
51	.53145	11.5582	.54196	12.1318	.55223	12.7193	.56226	13.3206
13/16	.53161	11.5671	.54212	12.1409	.55239	12.7285	.56242	13.3301
53	.53178	11.5759	.54229	12.1499	.55255	12.7378	.56257	13.3396
27/32	.53194	11.5848	.54245	12.1590	.55271	12.7471	.56273	13.3491
55	.53211	11.5937	.54261	12.1681	.55286	12.7564	.56288	13.3586
7/8	.53228	11.6025	.54277	12.1772	.55302	12.7657	.56304	13.3682
57	.53244	11.6114	.54294	12.1863	.55318	12.7750	.56319	13.3777
29/32	.53261	11.6203	.54310	12.1954	.55334	12.7843	.56335	13.3872
59	.53277	11.6292	.54326	12.2045	.55350	12.7937	.56350	13.3967
15/16	.53294	11.6380	.54342	12.2136	.55366	12.8030	.56365	13.4063
61	.53311	11.6469	.54358	12.2227	.55381	12.8123	.56381	13.4158
31/32	.53327	11.6558	.54374	12.2318	.55397	12.8216	.56396	13.4254
63	.53344	11.6647	.54391	12.2409	.55413	12.8309	.56412	13.4349

PARALLEL TABLES OF

LOGARITHMS AND SQUARES

varying by one thirty second of an inch
from zero to ten feet.

0′

Fractions of an Inch.	0″		1″		2″	
	Log.	Square.	Log.	Square.	Log.	Square.
0	——	0.000000	8.92082	0.006944	9.22185	0.027778
1/32	7.41567	0.000007	8.93418	0.007385	9.22858	0.028653
1/16	7.71670	0.000027	8.94715	0.007840	9.23521	0.029541
3/32	7.89279	0.000061	8.95974	0.008308	9.24174	0.030443
1/8	8.01773	0.000109	8.97197	0.008789	9.24818	0.031359
5/32	8.11464	0.000170	8.98387	0.009284	9.25452	0.032288
3/16	8.19382	0.000244	8.99545	0.009793	9.26077	0.033230
7/32	8.26077	0.000332	9.00673	0.010315	9.26693	0.034186
1/4	8.31876	0.000434	9.01773	0.010851	9.27300	0.035156
9/32	8.36991	0.000549	9.02845	0.011400	9.27899	0.036140
5/16	8.41567	0.000678	9.03892	0.011963	9.28490	0.037137
11/32	8.45706	0.000821	9.04914	0.012539	9.29073	0.038147
3/8	8.49485	0.000977	9.05912	0.013129	9.29648	0.039171
13/32	8.52961	0.001146	9.06888	0.013733	9.30216	0.040209
7/16	8.56180	0.001329	9.07843	0.014350	9.30776	0.041260
15/32	8.59176	0.001526	9.08777	0.014981	9.31330	0.042324
1/2	8.61979	0.001736	9.09691	0.015625	9.31876	0.043403
17/32	8.64612	0.001960	9.10586	0.016283	9.32415	0.044495
9/16	8.67094	0.002197	9.11464	0.016954	9.32948	0.045600
19/32	8.69442	0.002448	9.12324	0.017639	9.33475	0.046719
5/8	8.71670	0.002713	9.13167	0.018338	9.33995	0.047852
21/32	8.73789	0.002991	9.13994	0.019050	9.34509	0.048998
11/16	8.75809	0.003282	9.14806	0.019775	9.35017	0.050157
23/32	8.77740	0.003588	9.15603	0.020515	9.35519	0.051331
3/4	8.79588	0.003906	9.16386	0.021267	9.36015	0.052517
25/32	8.81361	0.004239	9.17154	0.022034	9.36506	0.053718
13/16	8.83064	0.004584	9.17910	0.022814	9.36991	0.054932
27/32	8.84703	0.004944	9.18652	0.023607	9.37471	0.056159
7/8	8.86283	0.005317	9.19382	0.024414	9.37946	0.057400
29/32	8.87807	0.005703	9.20100	0.025235	9.38415	0.058655
15/16	8.89279	0.006104	9.20806	0.026069	9.38880	0.059923
31/32	8.90703	0.006517	9.21501	0.026917	9.39339	0.061205
1	8.92082	0.006944	9.22185	0.027778	9.39794	0.062500

O´

Fractions of an inch	3"		4"		5"	
	Log.	Square.	Log.	Square.	Log.	Square.
0	9.39794	0.062500	9.52288	0.111111	9.61979	0.173611
1/32	9.40244	0.063809	9.52626	0.112854	9.62249	0.175788
1/16	9.40689	0.065131	9.52961	0.114610	9.62518	0.177979
3/32	9.41130	0.066467	9.53294	0.116380	9.62786	0.180183
1/8	9.41567	0.067817	9.53624	0.118164	9.63051	0.182400
5/32	9.41999	0.069180	9.53952	0.119961	9.63315	0.184631
3/16	9.42427	0.070557	9.54277	0.121772	9.63578	0.186876
7/32	9.42851	0.071947	9.54600	0.123596	9.63839	0.189134
1/4	9.43270	0.073351	9.54921	0.125434	9.64098	0.191406
9/32	9.43686	0.074768	9.55239	0.127285	9.64356	0.193692
5/16	9.44097	0.076199	9.55555	0.129150	9.64612	0.195991
11/32	9.44505	0.077644	9.55868	0.131029	9.64866	0.198303
3/8	9.44909	0.079102	9.56180	0.132921	9.65120	0.200629
13/32	9.45310	0.080573	9.56489	0.134827	9.65371	0.202969
7/16	9.45706	0.082058	9.56796	0.136746	9.65622	0.205322
15/32	9.46099	0.083557	9.57100	0.138679	9.65871	0.207689
1/2	9.46489	0.085069	9.57403	0.140625	9.66118	0.210069
17/32	9.46875	0.086595	9.57704	0.142585	9.66364	0.212463
9/16	9.47257	0.088135	9.58002	0.144558	9.66609	0.214871
19/32	9.47637	0.089688	9.58299	0 146545	9.66852	0.217292
5/8	9.48013	0.091254	9.58593	0.148546	9.67094	0.219727
21/32	9.48385	0.092834	9.58886	0.150560	9.67335	0.222175
11/16	9.48755	0.094428	9.59176	0.152588	9.67574	0.224637
23/32	9.49122	0.096035	9.59465	0.154629	9.67812	0.227112
3/4	9.49485	0.097656	9.59751	0.156684	9.68049	0.229601
25/32	9.49845	0.099291	9.60036	0.158752	9.68284	0.232103
13/16	9.50203	0.100939	9.60319	0.160834	9.68518	0.234619
27/32	9.50557	0:102600	9.60600	0.162930	9.68751	0.237149
7/8	9.50909	0.104275	9.60879	0.165039	9.68983	0.239692
29/32	9.51258	0.105964	9.61157	0.167162	9.69213	0.242249
15/16	9.51604	0.107666	9.61433	0.169298	9.69442	0.244819
31/32	9.51947	0.109382	9.61707	0.171448	9.69670	0.247403
1	9.52288	0.111111	9.61979	0.173611	9.69897	0.250000

0′

Fractions of an Inch.	6″		7″		8″	
	Log.	Square.	Log.	Square.	Log.	Square.
0	9.69897	0.250000	9.76592	0.340278	9.82391	0.444444
1/32	9.70123	0.252611	9.76785	0.343323	9.82560	0.447923
1/16	9.70347	0.255235	9.76978	0.346381	9.82729	0.451416
3/32	9.70570	0.257874	9.77169	0.349453	9 82897	0.454922
1/8	9.70792	0.260525	9.77360	0.352539	9.83064	0.458442
5/32	9.71014	0.263190	9.77550	0.355638	9.83231	0.461975
3/16	9.71233	0.265869	9.77740	0.358751	9.83397	0.465522
7/32	9.71452	0.268561	9.77928	0.361877	9.83562	0.469082
1/4	9.71670	0.271267	9.78116	0.365017	9.83727	0.472656
9/32	9.71886	0.273987	9.78302	0.368171	9.83891	0.476244
5/16	9.72102	0.276720	9.78488	0.371338	9.84055	0.479845
11/32	9.72316	0.279466	9.78674	0.374519	9.84218	0.483459
3/8	9.72530	0.282227	9.78858	0.377713	9 84380	0.487088
13/32	9.72742	0.285000	9.79042	0.380920	9.84542	0.490729
7/16	9.72954	0.287788	9.79225	0.384142	9.84703	0.494385
15/32	9.73164	0.290588	9.79407	0.387377	9.84864	0.498054
1/2	9.73373	0.293403	9.79588	0.390625	9.85024	0.501736
17/32	9.73582	0.296231	9.79769	0.393887	9.85183	0.505432
9/16	9.73789	0.299072	9.79948	0.397163	9.85342	0.509142
19/32	9.73995	0.301927	9.80128	0.400452	9.85500	0.512865
5/8	9.74200	0.304796	9.80306	0.403754	9.85658	0.516602
21/32	9.74405	0.307678	9.80483	0.407071	9.85815	0.520352
11/16	9.74608	0.310574	9.80660	0.410400	9.85971	0.524116
23/32	9.74811	0.313483	9.80837	0.413744	9.86127	0.527893
3/4	9.75012	0.316406	9.81012	0.417101	9.86283	0.531684
25/32	9.75213	0.319343	9.81187	0.420471	9.86438	0.535489
13/16	9.75413	0.322293	9.81361	0.423855	9.86592	0.539307
27/32	9.75611	0.325256	9.81534	0.427253	9:86746	0.543138
7/8	9.75809	0.328234	9.81707	0.430664	9.86899	0.546984
29/32	9.76006	0.331224	9.81879	0.434089	9.87051	0.550842
15/16	9.76202	0.334229	9.82050	0.437527	9.87203	0.554715
31/32	9.76397	0.337246	9.82221	0.440979	9.87355	0.558601
1°	9.76592	0.340278	9.82391	0.444444	9.87506	0.562500

Fractions of an Inch.	9″		10″		11″	
	Log.	Square.	Log.	Square.	Log.	Square.
0	9.87506	0.562500	9.92082	0.694444	9.96221	0.840278
1/32	9.87657	0.566413	9.92217	0.698792	9.96344	0.845059
1/16	9.87807	0.570340	9.92352	0.703152	9.96467	0.849854
3/32	9.87956	0.574280	9.92487	0.707526	9.96590	0.854662
1/8	9.88105	0.578234	9.92621	0.711914	9.96712	0.859484
5/32	9.88254	0.582201	9.92755	0.716315	9.96834	0.864319
3/16	9.88402	0.586182	9.92889	0.720730	9.96955	0.869168
7/32	9.88549	0.590176	9.93022	0.725159	9.97076	0.874030
1/4	9.88696	0.594184	9.93154	0.729601	9.97197	0.878906
9/32	9.88843	0.598206	9.93286	0.734056	9.97318	0.883796
5/16	9.88989	0.602241	9.93418	0.738525	9.97438	0.888699
11/32	9.89134	0.606289	9.93550	0.743008	9.97558	0.893616
3/8	9.89279	0.610352	9.93681	0.747504	9.97677	0.898546
13/32	9.89424	0.614427	9.93811	0.752014	9.97796	0.903490
7/16	9.89568	0.618517	9.93942	0.756538	9.97915	0.908447
15/32	9.89711	0.622620	9.94071	0.761074	9.98033	0.913418
1/2	9.89854	0.626736	9.94201	0.765625	9.98152	0.918403
17/32	9.89997	0.630866	9.94330	0.770189	9.98270	0.923401
9/16	9.90139	0.635010	9.94459	0.774767	9.98387	0.928413
19/32	9.90281	0.639167	9.94587	0.779358	9.98504	0.933438
5/8	9.90422	0.643338	9.94715	0.783963	9.98621	0.938477
21/32	9.90563	0.647522	9.94842	0.788581	9.98738	0.943529
11/16	9.90703	0.651720	9.94969	0.793213	9.98854	0.948595
23/32	9.90843	0.655931	9.95096	0.797858	9.98970	0.953674
3/4	9.90982	0.660156	9.95223	0.802517	9.99086	0.958767
25/32	9.91121	0.664395	9.95349	0.807190	9.99201	0.963874
13/16	9.91260	0.668647	9.95474	0.811876	9.99316	0.968994
27/32	9.91398	0.672913	9.95600	0.816576	9.99431	0.974128
7/8	9.91536	0.677192	9.95725	0.821289	9.99545	0.979275
29/32	9.91673	0.681485	9.95849	0.826016	9.99659	0.984436
15/16	9.91810	0.685791	9.95974	0.830756	9.99773	0.989610
31/32	9.91946	0.690111	9.96098	0.835510	9.99887	0.994798
1	9.92082	0.694444	9.96221	0.840278	0.00000	1.000000

Fractions of an Inch.	0″		1″		2″	
	Log.	Square.	Log.	Square.	Log.	Square.
0	0.00000	1.0000	0.03476	1.1736	0.06695	1.3611
1/32	0.00113	1.0052	0.03580	1.1793	0.06792	1.3672
1/16	0.00226	1.0104	0.03685	1.1849	0.06888	1.3733
3/32	0.00338	1.0157	0.03788	1.1906	0.06985	1.3794
1/8	0.00450	1.0209	0.03892	1.1963	0.07081	1.3855
5/32	0.00562	1.0262	0.03995	1.2020	0.07177	1.3917
3/16	0.00673	1.0315	0.04098	1.2077	0.07272	1.3978
7/32	0.00785	1.0368	0.04201	1.2134	0.07368	1.4040
1/4	0.00895	1.0421	0.04303	1.2192	0.07463	1.4102
9/32	0.01006	1.0474	0.04406	1.2249	0.07558	1.4163
5/16	0.01116	1.0528	0.04508	1.2307	0.07653	1.4226
11/32	0.01227	1.0581	0.04610	1.2365	0.07748	1.4288
3/8	0.01336	1.0635	0.04711	1.2423	0.07843	1.4350
13/32	0.01446	1.0689	0.04813	1.2481	0.07937	1.4413
7/16	0.01555	1.0742	0.04914	1.2539	0.08031	1.4475
15/32	0.01664	1.0797	0.05015	1.2598	0.08125	1.4538
1/2	0.01773	1.0851	0.05115	1.2656	0.08219	1.4601
17/32	0.01881	1.0905	0.05216	1.2715	0.08312	1.4664
9/16	0.01989	1.0959	0.05316	1.2774	0.08405	1.4727
19/32	0.02097	1.1014	0.05416	1.2833	0.08499	1.4790
5/8	0.02205	1.1069	0.05516	1.2892	0.08591	1.4854
21/32	0.02312	1.1124	0.05615	1.2951	0.08684	1.4917
11/16	0.02419	1.1179	0.05714	1.3010	0.08777	1.4981
23/32	0.02526	1.1234	0.05813	1.3070	0.08839	1.5045
3/4	0.02633	1.1289	0.05912	1.3129	0.08961	1.5109
25/32	0.02739	1.1344	0.06011	1.3189	0.09053	1.5173
13/16	0.02845	1.1400	0.06109	1.3249	0.09145	1.5237
27/32	0.02951	1.1456	0.06207	1.3309	0.09236	1.5301
7/8	0.03057	1.1511	0.06305	1.3369	0.09328	1.5366
29/32	0.03162	1.1567	0.06403	1.3429	0.09419	1.5430
15/16	0.03267	1.1624	0.06500	1.3490	0.09510	1.5495
31/32	0.03372	1.1680	0.06598	1.3550	0.09600	1.5560
1	0.03476	1.1736	0.06695	1.3611	0.09691	1.5625

Fractions of an inch.	3″		4″		5″	
	Log.	Square.	Log.	Square.	Log.	Square.
0	0.09691	1.5625	0.12494	1.7778	0.15127	2.0069
1/32	0.09781	1.5690	0.12579	1.7847	0.15207	2.0143
1/16	0.09872	1.5755	0.12663	1.7917	0.15286	2.0217
3/32	0.09962	1.5821	0.12748	1.7987	0.15366	2.0291
1/8	0.10051	1.5887	0.12832	1.8057	0.15445	2.0366
5/32	0.10141	1.5952	0.12916	1.8127	0.15524	2.0440
3/16	0.10231	1.6018	0.13000	1.8197	0.15603	2.0515
7/32	0.10320	1.6084	0.13084	1.8267	0.15682	2.0589
1/4	0.10409	1.6150	0.13167	1.8338	0.15761	2.0664
9/32	0.10498	1.6216	0.13251	1.8408	0.15839	2.0739
5/16	0.10586	1.6283	0.13334	1.8479	0.15918	2.0814
11/32	0.10675	1.6349	0.13417	1.8550	0.15996	2.0889
3/8	0.10763	1.6416	0.13500	1.8621	0.16074	2.0965
13/32	0.10852	1.6483	0.13583	1.8692	0.16152	2.1040
7/16	0.10940	1.6550	0.13665	1.8763	0.16230	2.1116
15/32	0.11027	1.6617	0.13748	1.8835	0.16308	2.1191
1/2	0.11115	1.6684	0.13830	1.8906	0.16386	2.1267
17/32	0.11203	1.6751	0.13912	1.8978	0.16463	2.1343
9/16	0.11290	1.6819	0.13994	1.9050	0.16541	2.1420
19/32	0.11377	1.6886	0.14076	1.9122	0.16618	2.1496
5/8	0.11464	1.6954	0.14158	1.9194	0.16695	2.1572
21/32	0.11551	1.7022	0.14240	1.9266	0.16772	2.1649
11/16	0.11637	1.7090	0.14321	1.9338	0.16849	2.1726
23/32	0.11724	1.7158	0.14402	1.9411	0.16925	2.1802
3/4	0.11810	1.7227	0.14483	1.9484	0.17002	2.1879
25/32	0.11896	1.7295	0.14564	1.9556	0.17078	2.1956
13/16	0.11982	1.7364	0.14645	1.9629	0.17154	2.2034
27/32	0.12068	1.7432	0.14726	1.9702	0.17230	2.2111
7/8	0.12153	1.7501	0.14806	1.9775	0.17306	2.2189
29/32	0.12239	1.7570	0.14887	1.9849	0.17382	2.2266
15/16	0.12324	1.7639	0.14967	1.9922	0.17458	2.2344
31/32	0.12409	1.7708	0.15047	1.9996	0.17534	2.2422
1	0.12494	1.7778	0.15127	2.0069	0.17609	2.2500

Fractions of an inch.	6″		7″		8″	
	Log.	Square.	Log.	Square.	Log.	Square.
0	0.17609	2.2500	0.19957	2.5069	0.22185	2.7778
1/32	0.17684	2.2578	0.20029	2.5152	0.22253	2.7865
1/16	0.17760	2.2657	0.20100	2.5235	0.22320	2.7952
3/32	0.17835	2.2735	0.20171	2.5317	0.22388	2.8039
1/8	0.17910	2.2814	0.20242	2.5400	0.22455	2.8126
5/32	0.17984	2.2892	0.20313	2.5483	0.22523	2.8214
3/16	0.18059	2.2971	0.20384	2.5567	0.22590	2.8301
7/32	0.18134	2.3050	0.20454	2.5650	0.22657	2.8389
1/4	0.18208	2.3129	0.20525	2.5734	0.22724	2.8477
9/32	0.18282	2.3209	0.20595	2.5817	0.22791	2.8565
5/16	0.18357	2.3288	0.20666	2.5901	0.22858	2.8653
11/32	0.18431	2.3368	0.20736	2.5985	0.22925	2.8741
3/8	0.18505	2.3447	0.20806	2.6069	0.22992	2.8829
13/32	0.18578	2.3527	0.20876	2.6153	0.23058	2.8918
7/16	0.18652	2.3607	0.20946	2.6237	0.23125	2.9006
15/32	0.18726	2.3687	0.21016	2.6322	0.23191	2.9095
1/2	0.18799	2.3767	0.21085	2.6406	0.23257	2.9184
17/32	0.18872	2.3848	0.21155	2.6491	0.23323	2.9273
9/16	0.18946	2.3928	0.21224	2.6576	0.23389	2.9362
19/32	0.19019	2.4009	0.21294	2.6661	0.23455	2.9452
5/8	0.19092	2.4090	0.21363	2.6746	0.23521	2.9541
21/32	0.19164	2.4171	0.21432	2.6831	0.23587	2.9631
11/16	0.19237	2.4252	0.21501	2.6917	0.23653	2.9720
23/32	0.19310	2.4333	0.21570	2.7002	0.23718	2.9810
3/4	0.19382	2.4414	0.21639	2.7088	0.23784	2.9900
25/32	0.19454	2.4496	0.21707	2.7173	0.23849	2.9990
13/16	0.19527	2.4577	0.21776	2.7259	0.23914	3.0081
27/32	0.19599	2.4659	0.21844	2.7345	0.23979	3.0171
7/8	0.19671	2.4741	0.21913	2.7432	0.24045	3.0262
29/32	0.19742	2.4823	0.21981	2.7518	0.24109	3.0352
15/16	0.19814	2.4905	0.22049	2.7604	0.24174	3.0443
31/32	0.19886	2.4987	0.22117	2.7691	0.24239	3.0534
1	0.19957	2.5069	0.22185	2.7778	0.24304	3.0625

Fractions of an Inch.	9″		10″		11″	
	Log.	Square.	Log.	Square.	Log.	Square.
0	0.24304	3.0625	0.26324	3.3611	0.28255	3.6736
1/32	0.24368	3.0716	0.26386	3.3707	0.28314	3.6836
1/16	0.24433	3.0808	0.26447	3.3802	0.28373	3.6936
3/32	0.24497	3.0899	0.26509	3.3898	0.28431	3.7036
1/8	0.24562	3.0991	0.26570	3.3994	0.28490	3.7137
5/32	0.24626	3.1082	0.26632	3.4090	0.28549	3.7237
3/16	0.24690	3.1174	0.26693	3.4186	0.28607	3.7338
7/32	0.24754	3.1266	0.26754	3.4283	0.28666	3.7438
1/4	0.24818	3.1359	0.26815	3.4379	0.28724	3.7539
9/32	0.24882	3.1451	0.26876	3.4476	0.28783	3.7640
5/16	0.24945	3.1543	0.26937	3.4573	0.28841	3.7741
11/32	0.25009	3.1636	0.26997	3.4670	0.28899	3.7842
3/8	0.25072	3.1729	0.27058	3.4767	0.28957	3.7944
13/32	0.25136	3.1821	0.27119	3.4864	0.29015	3.8045
7/16	0.25199	3.1914	0.27179	3.4961	0.29073	3.8147
15/32	0.25263	3.2007	0.27240	3.5059	0.29131	3.8249
1/2	0.25326	3.2101	0.27300	3.5156	0.29189	3.8351
17/32	0.25389	3.2194	0.27360	3.5254	0.29246	3.8453
9/16	0.25452	3.2288	0.27421	3.5352	0.29304	3.8555
19/32	0.25515	3.2381	0.27481	3.5450	0.29362	3.8657
5/8	0.25577	3.2475	0.27541	3.5548	0.29419	3.8760
21/32	0.25640	3.2569	0.27601	3.5646	0.29476	3.8862
11/16	0.25703	3.2663	0.27661	3.5745	0.29534	3.8965
23/32	0.25765	3.2757	0.27720	3.5843	0.29591	3.9068
3/4	0.25828	3.2852	0.27780	3.5942	0.29648	3.9171
25/32	0.25890	3.2946	0.27840	3.6041	0.29705	3.9274
13/16	0.25952	3.3041	0.27899	3.6140	0.29762	3.9377
27/32	0.26015	3.3135	0.27959	3.6239	0.29819	3.9481
7/8	0.26077	3.3230	0.28018	3.6338	0.29876	3.9584
29/32	0.26139	3.3325	0.28077	3.6437	0.29933	3.9688
15/16	0.26201	3.3420	0.28136	3.6537	0.29990	3.9792
31/32	0.26262	3.3516	0.28196	3.6636	0.30046	3.9896
1	0.26324	3.3611	0.28255	3.6736	0.30103	4.0000

2′

Fractions of an Inch.	0″ Log.	0″ Square.	1″ Log.	1″ Square.	2″ Log.	2″ Square.
0	0.30103	4.0000	0.31876	4.3403	0.33579	4.6944
1/32	0.30160	4.0104	0.31930	4.3511	0.33631	4.7057
1/16	0.30216	4.0209	0.31984	4.3620	0.33683	4.7170
3/32	0.30272	4.0313	0.32038	4.3729	0.33736	4.7284
1/8	0.30329	4.0418	0.32092	4.3838	0.33788	4.7397
5/32	0.30385	4.0523	0.32146	4.3947	0.33839	4.7510
3/16	0.30441	4.0627	0.32200	4.4056	0.33891	4.7624
7/32	0.30497	4.0732	0.32254	4.4166	0.33943	4.7738
1/4	0.30553	4.0838	0.32308	4.4275	0.33995	4.7852
9/32	0.30609	4.0943	0.32362	4.4385	0.34046	4.7966
5/16	0.30665	4.1048	0.32415	4.4495	0.34098	4.8080
11/32	0.30721	4.1154	0.32469	4.4605	0.34150	4.8194
3/8	0.30776	4.1260	0.32522	4.4715	0.34201	4.8308
13/32	0.30832	4.1366	0.32576	4.4825	0.34253	4.8423
7/16	0.30888	4.1472	0.32629	4.4935	0.34304	4.8538
15/32	0.30943	4.1578	0.32683	4.5046	0.34355	4.8652
1/2	0.30998	4.1684	0.32736	4.5156	0.34406	4.8767
17/32	0.31054	4.1790	0.32789	4.5267	0.34458	4.8882
9/16	0.31109	4.1897	0.32842	4.5378	0.34509	4.8998
19/32	0.31164	4.2004	0.32895	4.5489	0.34560	4.9113
5/8	0.31219	4.2110	0.32948	4.5600	0.34611	4.9229
21/32	0.31275	4.2217	0.33001	4.5711	0.34662	4.9344
11/16	0.31330	4.2324	0.33054	4.5823	0.34713	4.9460
23/32	0.31385	4.2432	0.33107	4.5934	0.34763	4.9576
3/4	0.31439	4.2539	0.33160	4.6046	0.34814	4.9692
25/32	0.31494	4.2647	0.33212	4.6158	0.34865	4.9808
13/16	0.31549	4.2754	0.33265	4.6270	0.34916	4.9924
27/32	0.31604	4.2862	0.33317	4.6382	0.34966	5.0041
7/8	0.31658	4.2970	0.33370	4.6494	0.35017	5.0157
29/32	0.31713	4.3078	0.33422	4.6607	0.35067	5.0274
15/16	0.31767	4.3186	0.33475	4.6719	0.35118	5.0391
31/32	0.31822	4.3294	0.33527	4.6832	0.35168	5.0508
1	0.31876	4.3403	0.33579	.4.6944	0.35218	5.0625

Fractions of an Inch.	3″		4″		5″	
	Log.	Square.	Log.	Square.	Log.	Square.
0	0.35218	5.0625	0.36798	5.4444	0.38322	5.8403
1/32	0.35268	5.0742	0.36846	5.4566	0.38368	5.8529
1/16	0.35319	5.0860	0.36895	5.4688	0.38415	5.8655
3/32	0.35369	5.0977	0.36943	5.4810	0.38462	5.8781
1/8	0.35419	5.1095	0.36991	5.4932	0.38508	5.8907
5/32	0.35469	5.1213	0.37039	5.5054	0.38555	5.9034
3/16	0.35519	5.1331	0.37088	5.5176	0.38602	5.9160
7/32	0.35569	5.1449	0.37136	5.5298	0.38648	5.9287
1/4	0.35619	5.1567	0.37184	5.5421	0.38694	5.9414
9/32	0.35668	5.1685	0.37232	5.5544	0.38741	5.9541
5/16	0.35718	5.1804	0.37280	5.5667	0.38787	5.9668
11/32	0.35768	5.1922	0.37328	5.5789	0.38833	5.9796
3/8	0.35817	5.2041	0.37375	5.5913	0.38880	5.9923
13/32	0.35867	5.2160	0.37423	5.6036	0.38926	6.0051
7/16	0.35916	5.2279	0.37471	5.6159	0.38972	6.0178
15/32	0.35966	5.2398	0.37519	5.6283	0.39018	6.0306
1/2	0.36015	5.2517	0.37566	5.6406	0.39064	6.0434
17/32	0.36064	5.2637	0.37614	5.6530	0.39110	6.0562
9/16	0.36114	5.2756	0.37661	5.6654	0.39156	6.0690
19/32	0.36163	5.2876	0.37709	5.6778	0.39202	6.0819
5/8	0.36212	5.2996	0.37756	5.6902	0.39248	6.0947
21/32	0.36261	5.3116	0.37804	5.7026	0.39293	6.1076
11/16	0.36310	5.3236	0.37851	5.7151	0.39339	6.1205
23/32	0.36359	5.3356	0.37898	5.7275	0.39385	6.1334
3/4	0.36408	5.3477	0.37946	5.7400	0.39431	6.1463
25/32	0.36457	5.3597	0.37993	5.7525	0.39476	6.1592
13/16	0.36506	5.3718	0.38040	5.7650	0.39522	6.1721
27/32	0.36555	5.3839	0.38087	5.7775	0.39567	6.1851
7/8	0.36603	5.3959	0.38134	5.7900	0.39613	6.1980
29/32	0.36652	5.4080	0.38181	5.8026	0.39658	6.2110
15/16	0.36701	5.4202	0.38228	5.8151	0.39703	6.2240
31/32	0.36749	5.4323	0.38275	5.8277	0.39749	6.2370
1	0.36798	5.4444	0.38322	5.8403	0.39794	6.2500

Fractions of an Inch.	6″		7″		8″	
	Log.	Square.	Log.	Square.	Log.	Square.
0	0.39794	6.2500	0.41218	6.6736	0.42597	7.1111
1/32	0.39839	6.2630	0.41262	6.6871	0.42639	7.1250
1/16	0.39884	6.2761	0.41306	6.7005	0.42682	7.1389
3/32	0.39930	6.2891	0.41349	6.7140	0.42724	7.1528
1/8	0.39975	6.3022	0.41393	6.7275	0.42766	7.1668
5/32	0.40020	6.3153	0.41436	6.7411	0.42808	7.1807
3/16	0.40065	6.3284	0.41480	6.7546	0.42851	7.1947
7/32	0.40110	6.3415	0.41523	6.7681	0.42893	7.2087
1/4	0.40154	6.3546	0.41567	6.7817	0.42935	7.2227
9/32	0.40199	6.3677	0.41610	6.7953	0.42977	7.2367
5/16	0.40244	6.3809	0.41654	6.8088	0.43019	7.2507
11/32	0.40289	6.3940	0.41697	6.8224	0.43061	7.2647
3/8	0.40334	6.4072	0.41740	6.8360	0.43103	7.2788
13/32	0.40378	6.4204	0.41783	6.8497	0.43145	7.2928
7/16	0.40423	6.4336	0.41827	6.8633	0.43187	7.3069
15/32	0.40467	6.4468	0.41870	6.8770	0.43228	7.3210
1/2	0.40512	6.4601	0.41913	6.8906	0.43270	7.3351
17/32	0.40556	6.4733	0.41956	6.9043	0.43312	7.3492
9/16	0.40601	6.4866	0.41999	6.9180	0.43354	7.3633
19/32	0.40645	6.4998	0.42042	6.9317	0.43395	7.3774
5/8	0.40689	6.5131	0.42085	6.9454	0.43437	7.3916
21/32	0.40734	6.5264	0.42128	6.9592	0.43479	7.4058
11/16	0.40778	6.5397	0.42171	6.9729	0.43520	7.4199
23/32	0.40822	6.5531	0.42213	6.9867	0.43562	7.4341
3/4	0.40866	6.5664	0.42256	7.0004	0.43603	7.4484
25/32	0.40911	6.5798	0.42299	7.0142	0.43644	7.4626
13/16	0.40955	6.5931	0.42342	7.0280	0.43686	7.4768
27/32	0.40999	6.6065	0.42384	7.0418	0.43727	7.4911
7/8	0.41043	6.6199	0.42427	7.0557	0.43768	7.5053
29/32	0.41087	6.6333	0.42469	7.0695	0.43810	7.5196
15/16	0.41130	6.6467	0.42512	7.0834	0.43851	7.5339
31/32	0.41174	6.6602	0.42554	7.0972	0.43892	7.5482
1	0.41218	6.6736	0.42597	7.1111	0.43933	7.5625

2´

Fractions of an Inch.	9″ Log.	9″ Square.	10″ Log.	10″ Square.	11″ Log.	11″ Square.
0	0.43933	7.5625	0.45230	8.0278	0.46489	8.5069
1/32	0.43974	7.5768	0.45270	8.0425	0.46527	8.5221
1/16	0.44015	7.5912	0.45310	8.0573	0.46566	8.5374
3/32	0.44056	7.6055	0.45349	8.0721	0.46605	8.5526
1/8	0.44097	7.6199	0.45389	8.0869	0.46644	8.5678
5/32	0.44138	7.6343	0.45429	8.1017	0.46682	8.5831
3/16	0.44179	7.6487	0.45469	8.1166	0.46721	8.5983
7/32	0.44220	7.6631	0.45508	8.1314	0.46759	8.6136
1/4	0.44261	7.6775	0.45548	8.1463	0.46798	8.6289
9/32	0.44302	7.6920	0.45588	8.1611	0.46836	8.6442
5/16	0.44343	7.7064	0.45627	8.1760	0.46875	8.6595
11/32	0.44383	7.7209	0.45667	8.1909	0.46913	8.6749
3/8	0.44424	7.7354	0.45706	8.2058	0.46952	8.6902
13/32	0.44465	7.7498	0.45746	8.2208	0.46990	8.7056
7/16	0.44505	7.7643	0.45785	8.2357	0.47028	8.7209
15/32	0.44546	7.7789	0.45824	8.2507	0.47066	8.7363
1/2	0.44586	7.7934	0.45864	8.2656	0.47105	8.7517
17/32	0.44627	7.8079	0.45903	8.2806	0.47143	8.7672
9/16	0.44667	7.8225	0.45942	8.2956	0.47181	8.7826
19/32	0.44708	7.8371	0.45982	8.3106	0.47219	8.7980
5/8	0.44748	7.8517	0.46021	8.3256	0.47257	8.8135
21/32	0.44788	7.8663	0.46060	8.3407	0.47295	8.8289
11/16	0.44829	7.8809	0.46099	8.3557	0.47333	8.8444
23/32	0.44869	7.8955	0.46138	8.3708	0.47372	8.8599
3/4	0.44909	7.9102	0.46177	8.3859	0.47409	8.8754
25/32	0.44949	7.9248	0.46216	8.4009	0.47447	8.8910
13/16	0.44990	7.9395	0.46255	8.4160	0.47485	8.9065
27/32	0.45030	7.9542	0.46294	8.4312	0.47523	8.9220
7/8	0.45070	7.9689	0.46333	8.4463	0.47561	8.9376
29/32	0.45110	7.9836	0.46372	8.4614	0.47599	8.9532
15/16	0.45150	7.9983	0.46411	8.4766	0.47637	8.9688
31/32	0.45190	8.0130	0.46450	8.4918	0.47674	8.9844
1	0.45230	8.0278	0.46489	8.5069	0.47712	9.0000

Fractions of an Inch.	0"		1"		2"	
	Log.	Square.	Log.	Square.	Log.	Square.
0	0.47712	9.0000	0.48902	9.5069	0.50060	10.0278
1/32	0.47750	9.0156	0.48939	9.5230	0.50096	10.0443
1/16	0.47787	9.0313	0.48975	9.5391	0.50132	10.0608
3/32	0.47825	9.0469	0.49012	9.5552	0.50167	10.0773
1/8	0.47863	9.0626	0.49049	9.5713	0.50203	10.0939
5/32	0.47900	9.0783	0.49085	9.5874	0.50238	10.1104
3/16	0.47938	9.0940	0.49122	9.6035	0.50274	10.1270
7/32	0.47975	9.1097	0.49158	9.6197	0.50310	10.1436
1/4	0.48013	9.1254	0.49195	9.6359	0.50345	10.1602
9/32	0.48050	9.1412	0.49231	9.6520	0.50380	10.1768
5/16	0.48087	9.1569	0.49267	9.6682	0.50416	10.1934
11/32	0.48125	9.1727	0.49304	9.6844	0.50451	10.2100
3/8	0.48162	9.1885	0.49340	9.7006	0.50487	10.2267
13/32	0.48199	9.2043	0.49376	9.7169	0.50522	10.2433
7/16	0.48237	9.2201	0.49413	9.7331	0.50557	10.2600
15/32	0.48274	9.2359	0.49449	9.7494	0.50593	10.2767
1/2	0.48311	9.2517	0.49485	9.7656	0.50628	10.2934
17/32	0.48348	9.2676	0.49521	9.7819	0.50663	10.3101
9/16	0.48385	9.2834	0.49557	9.7982	0.50698	10.3269
19/32	0.48423	9.2993	0.49593	9.8145	0.50734	10.3436
5/8	0.48460	9.3152	0.49630	9.8308	0.50769	10.3604
21/32	0.48497	9.3311	0.49666	9.8472	0.50804	10.3771
11/16	0.48534	9.3470	0.49702	9.8635	0.50839	10.3939
23/32	0.48571	9.3630	0.49738	9.8799	0.50874	10.4107
3/4	0.48608	9.3789	0.49774	9.8963	0.50909	10.4275
25/32	0.48645	9.3949	0.49810	9.9127	0.50944	10.4443
13/16	0.48681	9.4108	0.49845	9.9291	0.50979	10.4612
27/32	0.48718	9.4268	0.49881	9.9455	0.51014	10.4780
7/8	0.48755	9.4428	0.49917	9.9619	0.51049	10.4949
29/32	0.48792	9.4588	0.49953	9.9784	0.51084	10.5118
15/16	0.48829	9.4749	0.49989	9.9948	0.51119	10.5287
31/32	0.48865	9.4909	0.50025	10.0113	0.51154	10.5456
1	0.48902	9.5069	0.50060	10.0278	0.51188	10.5625

3′

Fractions of an Inch	3″		4″		5″	
	Log.	Square.	Log.	Square.	Log.	Square.
0	0.51188	10.5625	0.52288	11.1111	0.53360	11.6736
1/32	0.51223	10.5794	0.52322	11.1285	0.53393	11.6914
1/16	0.51258	10.5964	0.52356	11.1459	0.53426	11.7092
3/32	0.51293	10.6133	0.52390	11.1633	0.53459	11.7271
1/8	0.51327	10.6303	0.52423	11.1807	0.53492	11.7449
5/32	0.51362	10.6473	0.52457	11.1981	0.53525	11.7628
3/16	0.51397	10.6643	0.52491	11.2155	0.53558	11.7806
7/32	0.51431	10.6813	0.52525	11.2330	0.53591	11.7985
1/4	0.51466	10.6984	0.52558	11.2504	0.53624	11.8164
9/32	0.51500	10.7154	0.52592	11.2679	0.53657	11.8343
5/16	0.51535	10.7324	0.52626	11.2854	0.53690	11.8522
11/32	0.51569	10.7495	0.52660	11.3029	0.53723	11.8702
3/8	0.51604	10.7666	0.52693	11.3204	0.53756	11.8881
13/32	0.51638	10.7837	0.52727	11.3380	0.53788	11.9061
7/16	0.51673	10.8008	0.52760	11.3555	0.53821	11.9241
15/32	0.51707	10.8179	0.52794	11.3731	0.53854	11.9421
1/2	0.51742	10.8351	0.52827	11.3906	0.53887	11.9601
17/32	0.51776	10.8522	0.52861	11.4082	0.53919	11.9781
9/16	0.51810	10.8694	0.52894	11.4258	0.53952	11.9961
19/32	0.51845	10.8866	0.52928	11.4434	0.53985	12.0142
5/8	0.51879	10.9038	0.52961	11.4610	0.54017	12.0322
21/32	0.51913	10.9210	0.52995	11.4787	0.54050	12.0503
11/16	0.51947	10.9382	0.53028	11.4963	0.54082	12.0684
23/32	0.51981	10.9554	0.53061	11.5140	0.54115	12.0865
3/4	0.52016	10.9727	0.53095	11.5317	0.54148	12.1046
25/32	0.52050	10.9899	0.53128	11.5494	0.54180	12.1227
13/16	0.52084	11.0072	0.53161	11.5671	0.54212	12.1409
27/32	0.52118	11.0245	0.53194	11.5848	0.54245	12.1590
7/8	0.52152	11.0418	0.53228	11.6025	0.54277	12.1772
29/32	0.52186	11.0591	0.53261	11.6203	0.54310	12.1954
15/16	0.52220	11.0764	0.53294	11.6380	0.54342	12.2136
31/32	0.52254	11.0938	0.53327	11.6558	0.54374	12.2318
1	0.52288	11.1111	0.53360	11.6736	0.54407	12.2500

Fractions of an Inch.	6″		7″		8″	
	Log.	Square.	Log.	Square.	Log.	Square.
0	0.54407	12.2500	0.55429	12.8403	0.56427	13.4444
1/32	0.54439	12.2682	0.55460	12.8589	0.56458	13.4635
1/16	0.54471	12.2865	0.55492	12.8776	0.56489	13.4827
3/32	0.54504	12.3047	0.55523	12.8963	0.56520	13.5018
1/8	0.54536	12.3230	0.55555	12.9150	0.56550	13.5209
5/32	0.54568	12.3413	0.55586	12.9338	0.56581	13.5401
3/16	0.54600	12.3596	0.55618	12.9525	0.56612	13.5593
7/32	0.54632	12.3779	0.55649	12.9713	0.56643	13.5785
1/4	0.54665	12.3963	0.55680	12.9900	0.56673	13.5977
9/32	0.54697	12.4146	0.55712	13.0088	0.56704	13.6169
5/16	0.54729	12.4330	0.55743	13.0276	0.56735	13.6361
11/32	0.54761	12.4513	0.55775	13.0464	0.56765	13.6553
3/8	0.54793	12.4697	0.55806	13.0652	0.56796	13.6746
13/32	0.54825	12.4881	0.55837	13.0840	0.56826	13.6939
7/16	0.54857	12.5065	0.55868	13.1029	0.56857	13.7131
15/32	0.54889	12.5250	0.55900	13.1218	0.56887	13.7324
1/2	0.54921	12.5434	0.55931	13.1406	0.56918	13.7517
17/32	0.54953	12.5619	0.55962	13.1595	0.56948	13.7711
9/16	0.54985	12.5803	0.55993	13.1784	0.56979	13.7904
19/32	0.55016	12.5988	0.56024	13.1973	0.57009	13.8097
5/8	0.55048	12.6173	0.56055	13.2163	0.57040	13.8291
21/32	0.55080	12.6358	0.56087	13.2352	0.57070	13.8485
11/16	0.55112	12.6543	0.56118	13.2542	0.57100	13.8679
23/32	0.55144	12.6729	0.56149	13.2731	0.57131	13.8873
3/4	0.55175	12.6914	0.56180	13.2921	0.57161	13.9067
25/32	0.55207	12.7100	0.56211	13.3111	0.57191	13.9261
13/16	0.55239	12.7285	0.56242	13.3301	0.57222	13.9456
27/32	0.55271	12.7471	0.56273	13.3491	0.57252	13.9650
7/8	0.55302	12.7657	0.56304	13.3682	0.57282	13.9845
29/32	0.55334	12.7843	0.56335	13.3872	0.57313	14.0040
15/16	0.55366	12.8030	0.56365	13.4063	0.57343	14.0235
31/32	0.55397	12.8216	0.56396	13.4254	0.57373	14.0430
1	0.55429	12.8403	0.56427	13.4444	0.57403	14.0625

3´

Fractions of an Inch.	9″		10″		11″	
	Log.	Square.	Log.	Square.	Log.	Square.
0	0.57403	14.0625	0.58358	14.6944	0.59292	15.3403
1/32	0.57433	14.0820	0.58387	14.7144	0.59321	15.3607
1/16	0.57463	14.1016	0.58417	14.7344	0.59349	15.3811
3/32	0.57494	14.1212	0.58446	14.7544	0.59378	15.4015
1/8	0.57524	14.1407	0.58476	14.7744	0.59407	15.4220
5/32	0.57554	14.1603	0.58505	14.7944	0.59436	15.4424
3/16	0.57584	14.1799	0.58534	14.8145	0.59465	15.4629
7/32	0.57614	14.1996	0.58564	14.8345	0.59493	15.4834
1/4	0.57644	14.2192	0.58593	14.8546	0.59522	15.5039
9/32	0.57674	14.2388	0.58622	14.8747	0.59551	15.5244
5/16	0.57704	14.2585	0.58652	14.8948	0.59579	15.5449
11/32	0.57734	14.2782	0.58681	14.9149	0.59608	15.5655
3/8	0.57764	14.2979	0.58710	14.9350	0.59637	15.5860
13/32	0.57793	14.3176	0.58740	14.9551	0.59665	15.6066
7/16	0.57823	14.3373	0.58769	14.9753	0.59694	15.6272
15/32	0.57853	14.3570	0.58798	14.9954	0.59723	15.6478
1/2	0.57883	14.3767	0.58827	15.0156	0.59751	15.6684
17/32	0.57913	14.3965	0.58856	15.0358	0.59780	15.6890
9/16	0.57943	14.4163	0.58886	15.0560	0.59808	15.7097
19/32	0.57972	14.4360	0.58915	15.0762	0.59837	15.7303
5/8	0.58002	14.4558	0.58944	15.0965	0.59865	15.7510
21/32	0.58032	14.4756	0.58973	15.1167	0.59894	15.7717
11/16	0.58062	14.4955	0.59002	15.1370	0.59922	15.7923
23/32	0.58091	14.5153	0.59031	15.1572	0.59951	15.8130
3/4	0.58121	14.5352	0.59060	15.1775	0.59979	15.8338
25/32	0.58151	14.5550	0.59089	15.1978	0.60008	15.8545
13/16	0.58180	14.5749	0.59118	15.2181	0.60036	15.8752
27/32	0.58210	14.5948	0.59147	15.2385	0.60064	15.8960
7/8	0.58239	14.6147	0.59176	15.2588	0.60093	15.9168
29/32	0.58269	14.6346	0.59205	15.2791	0.60121	15.9376
15/16	0.58299	14.6545	0.59234	15.2995	0.60149	15.9584
31/32	0.58328	14.6745	0.59263	15.3199	0.60178	15.9792
1	0.58358	14.6944	0.59292	15.3403	0.60206	16.0000

Fractions of an Inch.	0"		1"		2"	
	Log.	Square.	Log.	Square.	Log.	Square.
0	0.60206	16.0000	0.61101	16.6736	0.61979	17.3611
1/32	0.60234	16.0208	0.61129	16.6949	0.62006	17.3828
1/16	0.60263	16.0417	0.61157	16.7162	0.62033	17.4045
3/32	0.60291	16.0626	0.61184	16.7375	0.62060	17.4263
1/8	0.60319	16.0834	0.61212	16.7588	0.62087	17.4480
5/32	0.60347	16.1043	0.61240	16.7801	0.62114	17.4698
3/16	0.60375	16.1252	0.61267	16.8015	0.62141	17.4916
7/32	0.60403	16.1462	0.61295	16.8228	0.62168	17.5134
1/4	0.60432	16.1671	0.61322	16.8442	0.62195	17.5352
9/32	0.60460	16.1880	0.61350	16.8656	0.62222	17.5570
5/16	0.60488	16.2090	0.61378	16.8870	0.62249	17.5788
11/32	0.60516	16.2300	0.61405	16.9084	0.62276	17.6006
3/8	0.60544	16.2510	0.61433	16.9298	0.62303	17.6225
13/32	0.60572	16.2720	0.61460	16.9512	0.62330	17.6444
7/16	0.60600	16.2930	0.61488	16.9727	0.62357	17.6663
15/32	0.60628	16.3140	0.61515	16.9941	0.62384	17.6882
1/2	0.60656	16.3351	0.61542	17.0156	0.62411	17.7101
17/32	0.60684	16.3561	0.61570	17.0371	0.62438	17.7320
9/16	0.60712	16.3772	0.61597	17.0586	0.62465	17.7539
19/32	0.60740	16.3983	0.61625	17.0801	0.62492	17.7759
5/8	0.60768	16.4194	0.61652	17.1017	0.62518	17.7979
21/32	0.60796	16.4405	0.61679	17.1232	0.62545	17.8198
11/16	0.60824	16.4616	0.61707	17.1448	0.62572	17.8418
23/32	0.60851	16.4828	0.61734	17.1663	0.62599	17.8638
3/4	0.60879	16.5039	0.61761	17.1879	0.62625	17.8859
25/32	0.60907	16.5251	0.61788	17.2095	0.62652	17.9079
13/16	0.60935	16.5463	0.61816	17.2311	0.62679	17.9299
27/32	0.60963	16.5674	0.61843	17.2528	0.62706	17.9520
7/8	0.60991	16.5886	0.61870	17.2744	0.62732	17.9741
29/32	0.61018	16.6099	0.61897	17.2961	0.62759	17.9962
15/16	0.61046	16.6311	0.61925	17.3177	0.62786	18.0183
31/32	0.61074	16.6524	0.61952	17.3394	0.62812	18.0404
1	0.61101	16.6736	0.61979	17.3611	0.62839	18.0625

Fractions of an Inch.	3″		4″		5″	
	Log.	Square.	Log.	Square.	Log.	Square.
0	0.62839	18.0625	0.63682	18.7778	0.64509	19.5069
1/32	0.62865	18.0846	0.63708	18.8004	0.64535	19.5300
1/16	0.62892	18.1068	0.63734	18.8229	0.64561	19.5530
3/32	0.62919	18.1290	0.63760	18.8455	0.64586	19.5760
1/8	0.62945	18.1512	0.63786	18.8682	0.64612	19.5991
5/32	0.62972	18.1733	0.63813	18.8908	0.64637	19.6221
3/16	0.62998	18.1956	0.63839	18.9134	0.64663	19.6452
7/32	0.63025	18.2178	0.63865	18.9361	0.64688	19.6683
1/4	0.63051	18.2400	0.63891	18.9588	0.64714	19.6914
9/32	0.63078	18.2623	0.63916	18.9815	0.64739	19.7145
5/16	0.63104	18.2845	0.63942	19.0042	0.64765	19.7377
11/32	0.63131	18.3068	0.63968	19.0269	0.64790	19.7608
3/8	0.63157	18.3291	0.63994	19.0496	0.64816	19.7840
13/32	0.63183	18.3514	0.64020	19.0723	0.64841	19.8071
7/16	0.63210	18.3737	0.64046	19.0951	0.64866	19.8303
15/32	0.63236	18.3961	0.64072	19.1178	0.64892	19.8535
1/2	0.63263	18.4184	0.64098	19.1406	0.64917	19.8767
17/32	0.63289	18.4408	0.64124	19.1634	0.64943	19.9000
9/16	0.63315	18.4631	0.64149	19.1862	0.64968	19.9232
19/32	0.63342	18.4855	0.64175	19.2090	0.64993	19.9465
5/8	0.63368	18.5079	0.64201	19.2319	0.65019	19.9697
21/32	0.63394	18.5303	0.64227	19.2547	0.65044	19.9930
11/16	0.63420	18.5528	0.64253	19.2776	0.65069	20.0163
23/32	0.63447	18.5752	0.64278	19.3005	0.65094	20.0396
3/4	0.63473	18.5977	0.64304	19.3234	0.65120	20.0629
25/32	0.63499	18.6201	0.64330	19.3463	0.65145	20.0863
13/16	0.63525	18.6426	0.64356	19.3692	0.65170	20.1096
27/32	0.63552	18.6651	0.64381	19.3921	0.65195	20.1330
7/8	0.63578	18.6876	0.64407	19.4150	0.65221	20.1564
29/32	0.63604	18.7101	0.64433	19.4380	0.65246	20.1797
15/16	0.63630	18.7327	0.64458	19.4610	0.65271	20.2032
31/32	0.63656	18.7552	0.64484	19.4839	0.65296	20.2266
1	0.63682	18.7778	0.64509	19.5069	0.65321	20.2500

Fractions of an Inch.	6″		7″		8″	
	Log.	Square.	Log.	Square.	Log.	Square.
0	0.65321	20.2500	0.66118	21.0069	0.66901	21.7778
1/32	0.65346	20.2734	0.66143	21.0308	0.66925	21.8021
1/16	0.65371	20.2969	0.66167	21.0547	0.66949	21.8264
3/32	0.65397	20.3204	0.66192	21.0786	0.66973	21.8508
1/8	0.65422	20.3439	0.66217	21.1025	0.66998	21.8751
5/32	0.65447	20.3674	0.66241	21.1265	0.67022	21.8995
3/16	0.65472	20.3909	0.66266	21.1504	0.67046	21.9239
7/32	0.65497	20.4144	0.66291	21.1744	0.67070	21.9482
1/4	0.65522	20.4379	0.66315	21.1984	0.67094	21.9727
9/32	0.65547	20.4615	0.66340	21.2223	0.67118	21.9971
5/16	0.65572	20.4851	0.66364	21.2463	0.67142	22.0215
11/32	0.65597	20.5086	0.66389	21.2704	0.67166	22.0460
3/8	0.65622	20.5322	0.66413	21.2944	0.67191	22.0704
13/32	0.65647	20.5558	0.66438	21.3184	0.67215	22.0949
7/16	0.65672	20.5795	0.66462	21.3425	0.67239	22.1194
15/32	0.65697	20.6031	0.66487	21.3665	0.67263	22.1439
1/2	0.65722	20.6267	0.66511	21.3906	0.67287	22.1684
17/32	0.65746	20.6504	0.66536	21.4147	0.67311	22.1929
9/16	0.65771	20.6741	0.66560	21.4388	0.67335	22.2175
19/32	0.65796	20.6978	0.66584	21.4630	0.67359	22.2420
5/8	0.65821	20.7215	0.66609	21.4871	0.67383	22.2666
21/32	0.65846	20.7452	0.66633	21.5112	0.67407	22.2912
11/16	0.65871	20.7689	0.66658	21.5354	0.67431	22.3158
23/32	0.65895	20.7927	0.66682	21.5596	0.67455	22.3404
3/4	0.65920	20.8164	0.66706	21.5838	0.67478	22.3650
25/32	0.65945	20.8402	0.66731	21.6080	0.67502	22.3897
13/16	0.65970	20.8640	0.66755	21.6322	0.67526	22.4143
27/32	0.65995	20.8878	0.66779	21.6564	0.67550	22.4390
7/8	0.66019	20.9116	0.66804	21.6807	0.67574	22.4637
29/32	0.66044	20.9354	0.66828	21.7049	0.67598	22.4883
15/16	0.66069	20.9592	0.66852	21.7292	0.67622	22.5130
31/32	0.66093	20.9831	0.66876	21.7535	0.67646	22.5378
1	0.66118	21.0069	0.66901	21.7778	0.67669	22.5625

Fractions of an Inch.	9″		10″		11″	
	Log.	Square.	Log.	Square.	Log.	Square.
0	0.67669	22.5625	0.68425	23.3611	0.69167	24.1736
1/32	0.67693	22.5872	0.68448	23.3863	0.69190	24.1992
1/16	0.67717	22.6120	0.68471	23.4115	0.69213	24.2249
3/32	0.67741	22.6368	0.68495	23.4367	0.69236	24.2505
1/8	0.67764	22.6616	0.68518	23.4619	0.69259	24.2762
5/32	0.67788	22.6864	0.68542	23.4871	0.69282	24.3018
3/16	0.67812	22.7112	0.68565	23.5124	0.69305	24.3275
7/32	0.67836	22.7360	0.68588	23.5377	0.69328	24.3532
1/4	0.67859	22.7609	0.68611	23.5629	0.69351	24.3789
9/32	0.67883	22.7857	0.68635	23.5882	0.69374	24.4046
5/16	0.67907	22.8106	0.68658	23.6135	0.69396	24.4304
11/32	0.67930	22.8355	0.68681	23.6388	0.69419	24.4561
3/8	0.67954	22.8604	0.68705	23.6642	0.69442	24.4819
13/32	0.67978	22.8853	0.68728	23.6895	0.69465	24.5077
7/16	0.68001	22.9102	0.68751	23.7149	0.69488	24.5334
15/32	0.68025	22.9351	0.68774	23.7402	0.69511	24.5593
1/2	0.68049	22.9601	0.68797	23.7656	0.69534	24.5851
17/32	0.68072	22.9850	0.68821	23.7910	0.69556	24.6109
9/16	0.68096	23.0100	0.68844	23.8164	0.69579	24.6367
19/32	0.68119	23.0350	0.68867	23.8419	0.69602	24.6626
5/8	0.68143	23.0600	0.68890	23.8673	0.69625	24.6885
21/32	0.68167	23.0850	0.68913	23.8927	0.69647	24.7144
11/16	0.68190	23.1101	0.68936	23.9182	0.69670	24.7403
23/32	0.68214	23.1351	0.68960	23.9437	0.69693	24.7662
3/4	0.68237	23.1602	0.68983	23.9692	0.69716	24.7921
25/32	0.68261	23.1852	0.69006	23.9947	0.69738	24.8180
13/16	0.68284	23.2103	0.69029	24.0202	0.69761	24.8440
27/32	0.68308	23.2354	0.69052	24.0457	0.69784	24.8700
7/8	0.68331	23.2605	0.69075	24.0713	0.69803	24.8959
29/32	0.68354	23.2857	0.69098	24.0968	0.69829	24.9219
15/16	0.68378	23.3108	0.69121	24.1224	0.69852	24.9479
31/32	0.68401	23.3359	0.69144	24.1480	0.69874	24.9740
1	0.68425	23.3611	0.69167	24.1736	0.69897	25.0000

Fractions of an Inch.	0″		1″		2″	
	Log.	Square.	Log.	Square.	Log.	Square.
0	0.69897	25.0000	0.70615	25.8403	0.71321	26.6944
1/32	0.69920	25.0260	0.70637	25.8668	0.71343	26.7214
1/16	0.69942	25.0521	0.70659	25.8933	0.71365	26.7483
3/32	0.69965	25.0782	0.70682	25.9198	0.71387	26.7752
1/8	0.69987	25.1043	0.70704	25.9463	0.71409	26.8022
5/32	0.70010	25.1304	0.70726	25.9728	0.71430	26.8292
3/16	0.70033	25.1565	0.70748	25.9994	0.71452	26.8561
7/32	0.70055	25.1826	0.70770	26.0259	0.71474	26.8831
1/4	0.70078	25.2088	0.70792	26.0525	0.71496	26.9102
9/32	0.70100	25.2349	0.70815	26.0791	0.71518	26.9372
5/16	0.70123	25.2611	0.70837	26.1057	0.71539	26.9642
11/32	0.70145	25.2873	0.70859	26.1323	0.71561	26.9913
3/8	0.70168	25.3135	0.70881	26.1590	0.71583	27.0183
13/32	0.70190	25.3397	0.70903	26.1856	0.71605	27.0454
7/16	0.70213	25.3659	0.70925	26.2123	0.71626	27.0725
15/32	0.70235	25.3922	0.70947	26.2389	0.71648	27.0996
1/2	0.70257	25.4184	0.70969	26.2656	0.71670	27.1267
17/32	0.70280	25.4447	0.70991	26.2923	0.71692	27.1539
9/16	0.70302	25.4709	0.71014	26.3190	0.71713	27.1810
19/32	0.70325	25.4972	0.71036	26.3458	0.71735	27.2082
5/8	0.70347	25.5235	0.71058	26.3725	0.71757	27.2354
21/32	0.70369	25.5499	0.71080	26.3993	0.71778	27.2625
11/16	0.70392	25.5762	0.71102	26.4260	0.71800	27.2897
23/32	0.70414	25.6025	0.71124	26.4528	0.71822	27.3170
3/4	0.70437	25.6289	0.71146	26.4796	0.71843	27.3442
25/32	0.70459	25.6553	0.71168	26.5064	0.71865	27.3714
13/16	0.70481	25.6817	0.71190	26.5332	0.71886	27.3987
27/32	0.70503	25.7081	0.71211	26.5601	0.71908	27.4260
7/8	0.70526	25.7345	0.71233	26.5869	0.71930	27.4532
29/32	0.70548	25.7609	0.71255	26.6138	0.71951	27.4805
15/16	0.70570	25.7874	0.71277	26.6407	0.71973	27.5078
31/32	0.70593	25.8138	0.71299	26.6675	0.71994	27.5352
1	0.70615	25.8403	0.71321	26.6944	0.72016	27.5625

5′

Fractions of an inch.	3″		4″		5″	
	Log.	Square.	Log.	Square.	Log.	Square.
0	0.72016	27.5625	0.72700	28.4444	0.73373	29.3403
1/32	0.72037	27.5899	0.72721	28.4722	0.73394	29.3685
1/16	0.72059	27.6172	0.72742	28.5000	0.73415	29.3967
3/32	0.72081	27.6446	0.72763	28.5278	0.73436	29.4250
1/8	0.72102	27.6720	0.72785	28.5557	0.73457	29.4532
5/32	0.72124	27.6994	0.72806	28.5835	0.73477	29.4815
3/16	0.72145	27.7268	0.72827	28.6114	0.73498	29.5098
7/32	0.72166	27.7542	0.72848	28.6392	0.73519	29.5381
1/4	0.72188	27.7817	0.72869	28.6671	0.73540	29.5664
9/32	0.72209	27.8091	0.72890	28.6950	0.73561	29.5947
5/16	0.72231	27.8366	0.72911	28.7229	0.73582	29.6231
11/32	0.72252	27.8641	0.72933	28.7508	0.73602	29.6514
3/8	0.72274	27.8916	0.72954	28.7788	0.73623	29.6798
13/32	0.72295	27.9191	0.72975	28.8067	0.73644	29.7082
7/16	0.72316	27.9466	0.72996	28.8347	0.73665	29.7366
15/32	0.72338	27.9742	0.73017	28.8626	0.73685	29.7650
1/2	0.72359	28.0017	0.73038	28.8906	0.73706	29.7934
17/32	0.72381	28.0293	0.73059	28.9186	0.73727	29.8218
9/16	0.72402	28.0569	0.73080	28.9466	0.73747	29.8503
19/32	0.72423	28.0845	0.73101	28.9747	0.73768	29.8788
5/8	0.72445	28.1121	0.73122	29.0027	0.73789	29.9072
21/32	0.72466	28.1397	0.73143	29.0308	0.73809	29.9357
11/16	0.72487	28.1673	0.73164	29.0588	0.73830	29.9642
23/32	0.72509	28.1950	0.73185	29.0869	0.73851	29.9927
3/4	0.72530	28.2227	0.73206	29.1150	0.73871	30.0213
25/32	0.72551	28.2503	0.73227	29.1431	0.73892	30.0498
13/16	0.72572	28.2780	0.73248	29.1713	0.73913	30.0784
27/32	0.72594	28.3057	0.73269	29.1994	0.73933	30.1069
7/8	0.72615	28.3334	0.73290	29.2275	0.73954	30.1355
29/32	0.72636	28.3612	0.73311	29.2557	0.73975	30.1641
15/16	0.72657	28.3889	0.73331	29.2839	0.73995	30.1927
31/32	0.72679	28.4167	0.73352	29.3121	0.74016	30.2214
1	0.72700	28.4444	0.73373	29.3403	0.74036	30.2500

5'

Fractions of an inch.	6"		7"		8"	
	Log.	Square.	Log.	Square.	Log.	Square.
0	0.74036	30.2500	0.74689	31.1736	0.75333	32.1111
1/32	0.74057	30.2787	0.74710	31.2027	0.75353	32.1406
1/16	0.74077	30.3073	0.74730	31.2318	0.75373	32.1702
3/32	0.74098	30.3360	0.74750	31.2609	0.75393	32.1997
1/8	0.74118	30.3647	0.74770	31.2900	0.75413	32.2293
5/32	0.74139	30.3934	0.74791	31.3192	0.75432	32.2589
3/16	0.74159	30.4221	0.74811	31.3483	0.75452	32.2884
7/32	0.74180	30.4509	0.74831	31.3775	0.75472	32.3180
1/4	0.74200	30.4796	0.74851	31.4067	0.75492	32.3477
9/32	0.74221	30.5084	0.74871	31.4359	0.75512	32.3773
5/16	0.74241	30.5371	0.74891	31.4651	0.75532	32.4069
11/32	0.74262	30.5659	0.74912	31.4943	0.75552	32.4366
3/8	0.74282	30.5947	0.74932	31.5235	0.75572	32.4663
13/32	0.74303	30.6235	0.74952	31.5528	0.75591	32.4959
7/16	0.74323	30.6524	0.74972	31.5821	0.75611	32.5256
15/32	0.74344	30.6812	0.74992	31.6113	0.75631	32.5553
1/2	0.74364	30.7101	0.75012	31.6406	0.75651	32.5851
17/32	0.74384	30.7389	0.75032	31.6699	0.75671	32.6148
9/16	0.74405	30.7678	0.75052	31.6992	0.75691	32.6446
19/32	0.74425	30.7967	0.75073	31.7286	0.75710	32.6743
5/8	0.74446	30.8256	0.75093	31.7579	0.75730	32.7041
21/32	0.74466	30.8546	0.75113	31.7873	0.75750	32.7339
11/16	0.74486	30.8835	0.75133	31.8167	0.75770	32.7637
23/32	0.74507	30.9124	0.75153	31.8460	0.75789	32.7935
3/4	0.74527	30.9414	0.75173	31.8754	0.75809	32.8234
25/32	0.74547	30.9704	0.75193	31.9048	0.75829	32.8532
13/16	0.74568	30.9994	0.75213	31.9343	0.75849	32.8831
27/32	0.74588	31.0284	0.75233	31.9637	0.75868	32.9129
7/8	0.74608	31.0574	0.75253	31.9932	0.75888	32.9428
29/32	0.74629	31.0864	0.75273	32.0226	0.75908	32.9727
15/16	0.74649	31.1155	0.75293	32.0521	0.75927	33.0026
31/32	0.74669	31.1445	0.75313	32.0816	0.75947	33.0326
1	0.74689	31.1736	0.75333	32.1111	0.75967	33.0625

Fractions of an Inch.	9″		10″		11″	
	Log.	Square.	Log.	Square.	Log.	Square.
0	0.75967	33.0625	0.76592	34.0278	0.77208	35.0069
1/32	0.75986	33.0925	0.76611	34.0582	0.77227	35.0378
1/16	0.76006	33.1224	0.76630	34.0886	0.77246	35.0686
3/32	0.76026	33.1524	0.76650	34.1190	0.77265	35.0995
1/8	0.76045	33.1824	0.76669	34.1494	0.77284	35.1303
5/32	0.76065	33.2124	0.76689	34.1799	0.77303	35.1612
3/16	0.76085	33.2424	0.76708	34.2103	0.77322	35.1921
7/32	0.76104	33.2725	0.76727	34.2408	0.77341	35.2230
1/4	0.76124	33.3025	0.76747	34.2713	0.77360	35.2539
9/32	0.76143	33.3326	0.76766	34.3018	0.77379	35.2848
5/16	0.76163	33.3627	0.76785	34.3323	0.77398	35.3158
11/32	0.76183	33.3927	0.76804	34.3628	0.77417	35.3467
3/8	0.76202	33.4229	0.76824	34.3933	0.77436	35.3777
13/32	0.76222	33.4530	0.76843	34.4239	0.77455	35.4087
7/16	0.76241	33.4831	0.76862	34.4545	0.77475	35.4397
15/32	0.76261	33.5132	0.76882	34.4850	0.77493	35.4707
1/2	0.76280	33.5434	0.76901	34.5156	0.77512	35.5017
17/32	0.76300	33.5736	0.76920	34.5462	0.77531	35.5328
9/16	0.76319	33.6038	0.76939	34.5769	0.77550	35.5638
19/32	0.76339	33.6340	0.76959	34.6075	0.77569	35.5949
5/8	0.76358	33.6642	0.76978	34.6381	0.77588	35.6260
21/32	0.76378	33.6944	0.76997	34.6688	0.77607	35.6571
11/16	0.76397	33.7246	0.77016	34.6995	0.77626	35.6882
23/32	0.76417	33.7549	0.77035	34.7302	0.77645	35.7193
3/4	0.76436	33.7852	0.77055	34.7609	0.77664	35.7504
25/32	0.76456	33.8154	0.77074	34.7916	0.77683	35.7816
13/16	0.76475	33.8457	0.77093	34.8223	0.77702	35.8127
27/32	0.76495	33.8760	0.77112	34.8530	0.77721	35.8439
7/8	0.76514	33.9064	0.77131	34.8838	0.77740	35.8751
29/32	0.76533	33.9367	0.77150	34.9146	0.77759	35.9063
15/16	0.76553	33.9670	0.77169	34.9453	0.77777	35.9375
31/32	0.76572	33.9974	0.77189	34.9761	0.77796	35.9688
1	0.76592	34.0278	0.77208	35.0069	0.77815	36.0000

Fractions of an inch.	0″		1″		2″	
	Log.	Square.	Log.	Square.	Log.	Square.
0	0.77815	36.0000	0.78414	37.0069	0.79005	38.0278
1/32	0.77834	36.0313	0.78433	37.0386	0.79023	38.0599
1/16	0.77853	36.0625	0.78451	37.0703	0.79042	38.0920
3/32	0.77872	36.0938	0.78470	37.1021	0.79060	38.1242
1/8	0.77890	36.1251	0.78488	37.1338	0.79078	38.1564
5/32	0.77909	36.1564	0.78507	37.1655	0.79097	38.1885
3/16	0.77928	36.1877	0.78526	37.1973	0.79115	38.2207
7/32	0.77947	36.2191	0.78544	37.2291	0.79133	38.2529
1/4	0.77966	36.2504	0.78563	37.2609	0.79152	38.2852
9/32	0.77984	36.2818	0.78581	37.2926	0.79170	38.3174
5/16	0.78003	36.3132	0.78600	37.3245	0.79188	38.3496
11/32	0.78022	36.3446	0.78618	37.3563	0.79206	38.3819
3/8	0.78041	36.3760	0.78637	37.3881	0.79225	38.4142
13/32	0.78059	36.4074	0.78655	37.4200	0.79243	38.4465
7/16	0.78078	36.4388	0.78674	37.4518	0.79261	38.4788
15/32	0.78097	36.4703	0.78692	37.4837	0.79279	38.5111
1/2	0.78116	36.5017	0.78711	37.5156	0.79298	38.5434
17/32	0.78134	36.5332	0.78729	37.5475	0.79316	38.5757
9/16	0.78153	36.5647	0.78748	37.5795	0.79334	38.6081
19/32	0.78172	36.5962	0.78766	37.6114	0.79352	38.6405
5/8	0.78190	36.6277	0.78784	37.6433	0.79370	38.6729
21/32	0.78209	36.6592	0.78803	37.6753	0.79388	38.7052
11/16	0.78228	36.6908	0.78821	37.7073	0.79407	38.7377
23/32	0.78247	36.7223	0.78840	37.7393	0.79425	38.7701
3/4	0.78265	36.7539	0.78858	37.7713	0.79443	38.8025
25/32	0.78284	36.7855	0.78876	37.8033	0.79461	38.8350
13/16	0.78302	36.8171	0.78895	37.8353	0.79479	38.8674
27/32	0.78321	36.8487	0.78913	37.8674	0.79497	38.8999
7/8	0.78340	36.8803	0.78932	37.8994	0.79516	38.9324
29/32	0.78358	36.9120	0.78950	37.9315	0.79534	38.9649
15/16	0.78377	36.9436	0.78968	37.9636	0.79552	38.9974
31/32	0.78396	36.9753	0.78987	37.9957	0.79570	39.0300
1	0.78414	37.0069	0.79005	38.0278	0.79588	39.0625

Fractions of an Inch.	3″		4″		5″	
	Log.	Square.	Log.	Square.	Log.	Square.
0	0.79588	39.0625	0.80163	40.1111	0.80731	41.1736
1/32	0.79606	39.0951	0.80181	40.1441	0.80749	41.2070
1/16	0.79624	39.1276	0.80199	40.1771	0.80766	41.2405
3/32	0.79642	39.1602	0.80217	40.2101	0.80784	41.2739
1/8	0.79660	39.1928	0.80235	40.2432	0.80801	41.3074
5/32	0.79678	39.2254	0.80252	40.2762	0.80819	41.3409
3/16	0.79696	39.2581	0.80270	40.3093	0.80837	41.3744
7/32	0.79714	39.2907	0.80288	40.3423	0.80854	41.4079
1/4	0.79733	39.3234	0.80306	40.3754	0.80872	41.4414
9/32	0.79751	39.3560	0.80324	40.4085	0.80889	41.4749
5/16	0.79769	39.3887	0.80341	40.4417	0.80907	41.5085
11/32	0.79787	39.4214	0.80359	40.4748	0.80924	41.5421
3/8	0.79805	39.4541	0.80377	40.5079	0.80942	41.5756
13/32	0.79823	39.4868	0.80395	40.5411	0.80959	41.6092
7/16	0.79841	39.5196	0.80413	40.5742	0.80977	41.6428
15/32	0.79859	39.5523	0.80430	40.6074	0.80995	41.6764
1/2	0.79877	39.5851	0.80448	40.6406	0.81012	41.7101
17/32	0.79895	39.6178	0.80466	40.6738	0.81030	41.7437
9/16	0.79913	39.6506	0.80483	40.7071	0.81047	41.7774
19/32	0.79930	39.6834	0.80501	40.7403	0.81065	41.8110
5/8	0.79948	39.7163	0.80519	40.7735	0.81082	41.8447
21/32	0.79966	39.7491	0.80537	40.8068	0.81100	41.8784
11/16	0.79984	39.7819	0.80554	40.8401	0.81117	41.9121
23/32	0.80002	39.8148	0.80572	40.8734	0.81134	41.9459
3/4	0.80020	39.8477	0.80590	40.9067	0.81152	41.9796
25/32	0.80038	39.8805	0.80607	40.9400	0.81169	42.0134
13/16	0.80056	39.9134	0.80625	40.9733	0.81187	42.0471
27/32	0.80074	39.9464	0.80643	41.0067	0.81204	42.0809
7/8	0.80092	39.9793	0.80660	41.0400	0.81222	42.1147
29/32	0.80110	40.0122	0.80678	41.0734	0.81239	42.1485
15/16	0.80128	40.0452	0.80696	41.1068	0.81257	42.1823
31/32	0.80145	40.0781	0.80713	41.1402	0.81274	42.2162
1	0.80163	40.1111	0.80731	41.1736	0.81291	42.2500

6′

Fractions of an Inch.	6″		7″		8″	
	Log.	Square.	Log.	Square.	Log.	Square.
0	0.81291	42.2500	0.81845	43.3403	0.82391	44.4444
1⁄32	0.81309	42.2839	0.81862	43.3746	0.82408	44.4792
1⁄16	0.81326	42.3177	0.81879	43.4089	0.82425	44.5139
3⁄32	0.81344	42.3516	0.81896	43.4432	0.82442	44.5487
1⁄8	0.81361	42.3855	0.81913	43.4775	0.82459	44.5834
5⁄32	0.81378	42.4194	0.81930	43.5119	0.82476	44.6182
3⁄16	0.81396	42.4534	0.81948	43.5463	0.82493	44.6530
7⁄32	0.81413	42.4873	0.81965	43.5806	0.82509	44.6878
1⁄4	0.81430	42.5213	0.81982	43.6150	0.82526	44.7227
9⁄32	0.81448	42.5552	0.81999	43.6494	0.82543	44.7575
5⁄16	0.81465	42.5892	0.82016	43.6838	0.82560	44.7923
11⁄32	0.81482	42.6232	0.82033	43.7183	0.82577	44.8272
3⁄8	0.81500	42.6572	0.82050	43.7527	0.82594	44.8621
13⁄32	0.81517	42.6913	0.82067	43.7872	0.82611	44.8970
7⁄16	0.81534	42.7253	0.82084	43.8216	0.82628	44.9319
15⁄32	0.81552	42.7593	0.82102	43.8561	0.82645	44.9668
1⁄2	0.81569	42.7934	0.82119	43.8906	0.82661	45.0017
17⁄32	0.81586	42.8275	0.82136	43.9251	0.82678	45.0367
9⁄16	0.81603	42.8616	0.82153	43.9597	0.82695	45.0716
19⁄32	0.81621	42.8957	0.82170	43.9942	0.82712	45.1066
5⁄8	0.81638	42.9298	0.82187	44.0288	0.82729	45.1416
21⁄32	0.81655	42.9639	0.82204	44.0633	0.82746	45.1766
11⁄16	0.81672	42.9981	0.82221	44.0979	0.82763	45.2116
23⁄32	0.81690	43.0322	0.82238	44.1325	0.82779	45.2466
3⁄4	0.81707	43.0664	0.82255	44.1671	0.82796	45.2817
25⁄32	0.81724	43.1006	0.82272	44.2017	0.82813	45.3167
13⁄16	0.81741	43.1348	0.82289	44.2364	0.82830	45.3518
27⁄32	0.81759	43.1690	0.82306	44.2710	0.82847	45.3869
7⁄8	0.81776	43.2032	0.82323	44.3057	0.82863	45.4220
29⁄32	0.81793	43.2375	0.82340	44.3403	0.82880	45.4571
15⁄16	0.81810	43.2717	0.82357	44.3750	0.82897	45.4922
31⁄32	0.81827	43.3060	0.82374	44.4097	0.82914	45.5274
1	0.81845	43.3403	0.82391	44.4444	0.82930	45.5625

6′

Fractions of an Inch.	9″		10″		11″	
	Log.	Square.	Log.	Square.	Log.	Square.
0	0.82930	45.5625	0.83463	46.6944	0.83990	47.8403
1/32	0.82947	45.5977	0.83480	46.7300	0.84006	47.8763
1/16	0.82964	45.6328	0.83496	46.7657	0.84022	47.9124
3/32	0.82981	45.6680	0.83513	46.8013	0.84039	47.9484
1/8	0.82997	45.7032	0.83529	46.8369	0.84055	47.9845
5/32	0.83014	45.7385	0.83546	46.8726	0.84071	48.0206
3/16	0.83031	45.7737	0.83562	46.9082	0.84088	48.0567
7/32	0.83048	45.8089	0.83579	46.9439	0.84104	48.0928
1/4	0.83064	45.8442	0.83595	46.9796	0.84120	48.1289
9/32	0.83081	45.8795	0.83612	47.0153	0.84137	48.1650
5/16	0.83098	45.9147	0.83628	47.0510	0.84153	48.2012
11/32	0.83114	45.9500	0.83645	47.0868	0.84169	48.2374
3/8	0.83131	45.9854	0.83661	47.1225	0.84185	48.2735
13/32	0.83148	46.0207	0.83678	47.1583	0.84202	48.3097
7/16	0.83164	46.0560	0.83694	47.1940	0.84218	48.3459
15/32	0.83181	46.0914	0.83711	47.2298	0.84234	48.3822
1/2	0.83198	46.1267	0.83727	47.2656	0.84251	48.4184
17/32	0.83214	46.1621	0.83744	47.3014	0.84267	48.4547
9/16	0.83231	46.1975	0.83760	47.3373	0.84283	48.4909
19/32	0.83248	46.2329	0.83777	47.3731	0.84299	48.5272
5/8	0.83264	46.2683	0.83793	47.4090	0.84315	48.5635
21/32	0.83281	46.3038	0.83809	47.4448	0.84332	48.5998
11/16	0.83297	46.3392	0.83826	47.4807	0.84348	48.6361
23/32	0.83314	46.3747	0.83842	47.5166	0.84364	48.6724
3/4	0.83331	46.4102	0.83859	47.5525	0.84380	48.7088
25/32	0.83347	46.4456	0.83875	47.5884	0.84397	48.7451
13/16	0.83364	46.4811	0.83891	47.6244	0.84413	48.7815
27/32	0.83380	46.5167	0.83908	47.6603	0.84429	48.8179
7/8	0.83397	46.5522	0.83924	47.6963	0.84445	48.8543
29/32	0.83414	46.5877	0.83941	47.7323	0.84461	48.8907
15/16	0.83430	46.6233	0.83957	47.7683	0.84477	48.9271
31/32	0.83447	46.6589	0.83973	47.8043	0.84494	48.9635
1	0.83463	46.6944	0.83990	47.8403	0.84510	49.0000

Fractions of an Inch.	0″		1″		2″	
	Log.	Square.	Log.	Square.	Log.	Square.
0	0.84510	49.0000	0.85024	50.1736	0.85532	51.3611
1/32	0.84526	49.0365	0.85040	50.2105	0.85547	51.3984
1/16	0.84542	49.0729	0.85056	50.2474	0.85563	51.4358
3/32	0.84558	49.1094	0.85072	50.2843	0.85579	51.4732
1/8	0.84574	49.1459	0.85088	50.3213	0.85595	51.5105
5/32	0.84591	49.1825	0.85104	50.3582	0.85611	51.5479
3/16	0 84607	49.2190	0.85119	50.3952	0.85626	51.5853
7/32	0.84623	49.2555	0.85135	50.4322	0.85642	51.6227
1/4	0.84639	49.2921	0.85151	50.4692	0.85658	51.6602
9/32	0.84655	49.3287	0.85167	50.5062	0.85674	51.6976
5/16	0.84671	49.3653	0.85183	50.5432	0.85689	51.7351
11/32	0.84687	49.4019	0.85199	50.5802	0.85705	51.7725
3/8	0.84703	49.4385	0.85215	50.6173	0.85721	51.8100
13/32	0.84719	49.4751	0.85231	50.6544	0.85736	51.8475
7/16	0.84735	49.5117	0.85247	50.6914	0.85752	51.8850
15/32	0.84751	49.5484	0.85263	50.7285	0.85768	51.9225
1/2	0.84768	49.5851	0.85278	50.7656	0.85783	51.9601
17/32	0.84784	49.6218	0.85294	50.8027	0.85799	51.9976
9/16	0.84800	49.6584	0.85310	50.8399	0.85815	52.0352
19/32	0.84816	49.6952	0.85326	50.8770	0.85831	52.0728
5/8	0.84832	49.7319	0.85342	50.9142	0.85846	52.1104
21/32	0.84848	49.7686	0.85358	50.9513	0.85862	52.1480
11/16	0.84864	49.8054	0.85374	50.9885	0.85878	52.1856
23/32	0.84880	49.8421	0.85389	51.0257	0.85893	52.2232
3/4	0.84896	49.8789	0.85405	51.0629	0.85909	52.2609
25/32	0.84912	49.9157	0.85421	51.1002	0.85924	52.2985
13/16	0.84928	49.9525	0.85437	51.1374	0.85940	52.3362
27/32	0.84944	49.9893	0.85453	51.1746	0.85956	52.3739
7/8	0.84960	50.0261	0.85469	51.2119	0.85971	52.4116
29/32	0.84976	50.0630	0.85484	51.2492	0.85987	52.4493
15/16	0.84992	50.0999	0.85500	51.2865	0.86003	52.4870
31/32	0.85008	50.1367	0.85516	51.3238	0.86018	52.5247
1	0.85024	50.1736	0.85532	51.3611	0.86034	52.5625

Fractions of an Inch.	3″		4″		5″	
	Log.	Square.	Log.	Square.	Log.	Square.
0	0.86034	52.5625	0.86530	53.7778	0.87021	55.0069
1/32	0.86049	52.6003	0.86546	53.8160	0.87036	55.0456
1/16	0.86065	52.6380	0.86561	53.8542	0.87051	55.0842
3/32	0.86081	52.6758	0.86576	53.8924	0.87067	55.1229
1/8	0.86096	52.7137	0.86592	53.9307	0.87082	55.1616
5/32	0.86112	52.7515	0.86607	53.9689	0.87097	55.2003
3/16	0.86127	52.7893	0.86623	54.0072	0.87112	55.2390
7/32	0.86143	52.8272	0.86638	54.0455	0.87127	55.2777
1/4	0.86158	52.8650	0.86653	54.0838	0.87143	55.3164
9/32	0.86174	52.9029	0.86669	54.1221	0.87158	55.3552
5/16	0.86190	52.9408	0.86684	54.1604	0.87173	55.3939
11/32	0.86205	52.9787	0.86699	54.1987	0.87188	55.4327
3/8	0.86221	53.0166	0.86715	54.2371	0.87203	55.4715
13/32	0.86236	53.0545	0.86730	54.2755	0.87219	55.5103
7/16	0.86252	53.0925	0.86746	54.3138	0.87234	55.5491
15/32	0.86267	53.1304	0.86761	54.3522	0.87249	55.5879
1/2	0.86283	53.1684	0.86776	54.3906	0.87264	55.6267
17/32	0.86298	53.2064	0.86792	54.4290	0.87279	55.6656
9/16	0.86314	53.2444	0.86807	54.4675	0.87294	55.7045
19/32	0.86329	53.2824	0.86822	54.5059	0.87310	55.7433
5/8	0.86345	53.3204	0.86838	54.5444	0.87325	55.7822
21/32	0.86360	53.3585	0.86853	54.5829	0.87340	55.8211
11/16	0.86376	53.3965	0.86868	54.6213	0.87355	55.8601
23/32	0.86391	53.4346	0.86883	54.6598	0.87370	55.8990
3/4	0.86407	53.4727	0.86899	54.6984	0.87385	55.9379
25/32	0.86422	53.5107	0.86914	54.7369	0.87400	55.9769
13/16	0.86438	53.5489	0.86929	54.7754	0.87416	56.0159
27/32	0.86453	53.5870	0.86945	54.8140	0.87431	56.0549
7/8	0.86468	53.6251	0.86960	54.8525	0.87446	56.0939
29/32	0.86484	53.6633	0.86975	54.8911	0.87461	56.1329
15/16	0.86499	53.7014	0.86990	54.9297	0.87476	56.1719
31/32	0.86515	53.7396	0.87006	54.9683	0.87491	56.2109
1	0.86530	53.7778	0.87021	55.0069	0.87506	56.2500

7′

Fractions of an inch.	6″		7″		8″	
	Log.	Square.	Log.	Square.	Log.	Square.
0	0.87506	56.2500	0.87986	57.5069	0.88461	58.7778
1/32	0.87521	56.2891	0.88001	57.5464	0.88475	58.8177
1/16	0.87536	56.3282	0.88016	57.5860	0.88490	58.8577
3/32	0.87551	56.3672	0.88031	57.6255	0.88505	58.8976
1/8	0.87566	56.4064	0.88046	57.6650	0.88520	58.9376
5/32	0.87581	56.4455	0.88061	57.7046	0.88534	58.9776
3/16	0.87597	56.4846	0.88075	57.7442	0.88549	59.0176
7/32	0.87612	56.5238	0.88090	57.7838	0.88564	59.0576
1/4	0.87627	56.5629	0.88105	57.8234	0.88579	59.0977
9/32	0.87642	56.6021	0.88120	57.8630	0.88593	59.1377
5/16	0.87657	56.6413	0.88135	57.9026	0.88608	59.1778
11/32	0.87672	56.6805	0.88150	57.9422	0.88623	59.2178
3/8	0.87687	56.7197	0.88165	57.9819	0.88637	59.2579
13/32	0.87702	56.7590	0.88179	58.0215	0.88652	59.2980
7/16	0.87717	56.7982	0.88194	58.0612	0.88667	59.3381
15/32	0.87732	56.8375	0.88209	58.1009	0.88681	59.3783
1/2	0.87747	56.8767	0.88224	58.1406	0.88696	59.4184
17/32	0.87762	56.9160	0.88239	58.1803	0.88711	59.4586
9/16	0.87777	56.9553	0.88254	58.2201	0.88725	59.4987
19/32	0.87792	56.9946	0.88268	58.2598	0.88740	59.5389
5/8	0.87807	57.0340	0.88283	58.2996	0.88755	59.5791
21/32	0.87822	57.0733	0.88298	58.3394	0.88769	59.6193
11/16	0.87837	57.1127	0.88313	58.3792	0.88784	59.6595
23/32	0.87852	57.1520	0.88328	58.4190	0.88799	59.6998
3/4	0.87867	57.1914	0.88342	58.4588	0.88813	59.7400
25/32	0.87881	57.2308	0.88357	58.4986	0.88828	59.7803
13/16	0.87896	57.2702	0.88372	58.5384	0.88843	59.8206
27/32	0.87911	57.3096	0.88387	58.5783	0.88857	59.8608
7/8	0.87926	57.3491	0.88402	58.6182	0.88872	59.9011
29/32	0.87941	57.3885	0.88416	58.6580	0.88886	59.9415
15/16	0.87956	57.4280	0.88431	58.6979	0.88901	59.9818
31/32	0.87971	57.4675	0.88446	58.7379	0.88916	60.0221
1	0.87986	57.5069	0.88461	58.7778	0.88930	60.0625

Fractions of an Inch.	9"		10"		11"	
	Log.	Square.	Log.	Square.	Log.	Square.
0	0.88930	60.0625	0.89395	61.3611	0.89854	62.6736
1/32	0.88945	60.1029	0.89409	61.4019	0.89869	62.7149
1/16	0.88959	60.1433	0.89424	61.4427	0.89883	62.7561
3/32	0.88974	60.1837	0.89438	61.4836	0.89897	62.7974
1/8	0.88989	60.2241	0.89452	61.5244	0.89911	62.8387
5/32	0.89003	60.2645	0.89467	61.5653	0.89926	62.8799
3/16	0.89018	60.3049	0.89481	61.6061	0.89940	62.9213
7/32	0.89032	60.3454	0.89496	61.6470	0.89954	62.9626
1/4	0.89047	60.3859	0.89510	61.6879	0.89968	63.0039
9/32	0.89061	60.4263	0.89524	61.7288	0.89983	63.0453
5/16	0.89076	60.4668	0.89539	61.7698	0.89997	63.0866
11/32	0.89090	60.5073	0.89553	61.8107	0.90011	63.1280
3/8	0.89105	60.5479	0.89568	61.8517	0.90025	63.1694
13/32	0.89119	60.5884	0.89582	61.8926	0.90040	63.2108
7/16	0.89134	60.6289	0.89596	61.9336	0.90054	63.2522
15/32	0.89149	60.6695	0.89611	61.9746	0.90068	63.2936
1/2	0.89163	60.7101	0.89625	62.0156	0.90082	63.3351
17/32	0.89178	60.7507	0.89639	62.0566	0.90096	63.3765
9/16	0.89192	60.7913	0.89654	62.0977	0.90111	63.4180
19/32	0.89207	60.8319	0.89668	62.1387	0.90125	63.4595
5/8	0.89221	60.8725	0.89682	62.1798	0.90139	63.5010
21/32	0.89236	60.9131	0.89697	62.2209	0.90153	63.5425
11/16	0.89250	60.9538	0.89711	62.2620	0.90167	63.5840
23/32	0.89265	60.9945	0.89725	62.3031	0.90182	63.6255
3/4	0.89279	61.0352	0.89740	62.3442	0.90196	63.6671
25/32	0.89293	61.0759	0.89754	62.3853	0.90210	63.7087
13/16	0.89308	61.1166	0.89768	62.4265	0.90224	63.7502
27/32	0.89322	61.1573	0.89783	62.4676	0.90238	63.7918
7/8	0.89337	61.1980	0.89797	62.5088	0.90252	63.8334
29/32	0.89351	61.2388	0.89811	62.5500	0.90267	63.8751
15/16	0.89366	61.2795	0.89826	62.5912	0.90281	63.9167
31/32	0.89380	61.3203	0.89840	62.6324	0.90295	63.9583
1	0.89395	61.3611	0.89854	62.6736	0.90309	64.0000

Fractions of an Inch.	0″		1″		2″	
	Log.	Square.	Log.	Square.	Log.	Square.
0	0.90309	64.0000	0.90759	65.3403	0.91204	66.6944
1/32	0.90323	64.0417	0.90773	65.3824	0.91218	66.7370
1/16	0.90337	64.0834	0.90787	65.4245	0.91232	66.7795
3/32	0.90351	64.1251	0.90801	65.4666	0.91246	66.8221
1/8	0.90366	64.1668	0.90815	65.5088	0.91260	66.8647
5/32	0.90380	64.2085	0.90829	65.5510	0.91274	66.9073
3/16	0 90394	64.2502	0.90843	65.5931	0.91287	66.9499
7/32	0.90408	64.2920	0.90857	65.6353	0.91301	66.9925
1/4	0.90422	64.3338	0.90871	65.6775	0.91315	67.0352
9/32	0.90436	64.3755	0.90885	65.7197	0.91329	67.0778
5/16	0.90450	64.4173	0.90899	65.7620	0.91343	67.1205
11/32	0.90464	64.4592	0.90913	65.8042	0.91357	67.1631
3/8	0.90478	64.5010	0.90927	65.8465	0.91370	67.2058
13/32	0.90492	64.5428	0.90941	65.8887	0.91384	67.2485
7/16	0.90506	64.5847	0.90954	65.9310	0.91398	67.2913
15/32	0.90521	64.6265	0.90968	65.9733	0.91412	67.3340
1/2	0.90535	64.6684	0.90982	66.0156	0.91425	67.3767
17/32	0.90549	64.7103	0.90996	66.0579	0.91439	67.4195
9/16	0.90563	64.7522	0.91010	66.1003	0.91453	67.4623
19/32	0.90577	64.7941	0.91024	66.1426	0.91467	67.5051
5/8	0.90591	64.8360	0.91038	66.1850	0.91481	67.5479
21/32	0.90605	64.8780	0.91052	66.2274	0.91494	67.5907
11/16	0.90619	64.9199	0.91066	66.2698	0.91508	67.6335
23/32	0.90633	64.9619	0.91080	66.3122	0.91522	67.6763
3/4	0.90647	65.0039	0.91094	66.3546	0.91536	67.7192
25/32	0.90661	65.0459	0.91107	66.3970	0.91549	67.7621
13/16	0.90675	65.0879	0.91121	66.4395	0.91563	67.8049
27/32	0.90689	65.1299	0.91135	66.4819	0.91577	67.8478
7/8	0.90703	65.1720	0.91149	66.5244	0.91591	67.8907
29/32	0.90717	65.2140	0.91163	66.5669	0.91604	67.9337
15/16	0.90731	65.2561	0.91177	66.6094	0.91618	67.9766
31/32	0.90745	65.2982	0.91191	66.6519	0.91632	68.0195
1	0.90759	65.3403	0.91204	66 6944	0.91645	68.0625

Fractions of an Inch.	3"		4"		5"	
	Log.	Square.	Log.	Square.	Log.	Square.
0	0.91645	68.0625	0.92082	69.4444	0.92514	70.8403
1/32	0.91659	68.1055	0.92095	69.4879	0.92527	70.8841
1/16	0.91673	68.1485	0.92109	69.5313	0.92541	70.9280
3/32	0.91687	68.1915	0.92123	69.5747	0.92554	70.9718
1/8	0.91700	68.2345	0.92136	69.6182	0.92568	71.0157
5/32	0.91714	68.2775	0.92150	69.6616	0.92581	71.0596
3/16	0.91728	68.3206	0.92163	69.7051	0.92595	71.1035
7/32	0.91741	68.3636	0.92177	69.7486	0.92608	71.1475
1/4	0.91755	68.4067	0.92190	69.7921	0.92621	71.1914
9/32	0.91769	68.4498	0.92204	69.8356	0.92635	71.2354
5/16	0.91782	68.4929	0.92217	69.8792	0.92648	71.2793
11/32	0.91796	68.5360	0.92231	69.9227	0.92662	71.3233
3/8	0.91810	68.5791	0.92244	69.9663	0.92675	71.3673
13/32	0.91823	68.6222	0.92258	70.0098	0.92688	71.4113
7/16	0.91837	68.6654	0.92271	70.0534	0.92702	71.4553
15/32	0.91851	68.7086	0.92285	70.0970	0.92715	71.4994
1/2	0.91864	68.7517	0.92298	70.1406	0.92728	71.5434
17/32	0.91878	68.7949	0.92312	70.1843	0.92742	71.5875
9/16	0.91891	68.8381	0.92325	70.2279	0.92755	71.6315
19/32	0.91905	68.8814	0.92339	70.2715	0.92769	71.6756
5/8	0.91919	68.9246	0.92352	70.3152	0.92782	71.7197
21/32	0.91932	68.9678	0.92366	70.3589	0.92795	71.7638
11/16	0.91946	69.0111	0.92379	70.4026	0.92809	71.8080
23/32	0.91960	69.0544	0.92393	70.4463	0.92822	71.8521
3/4	0.91973	69.0977	0.92406	70.4900	0.92835	71.8963
25/32	0.91987	69.1410	0.92420	70.5338	0.92849	71.9404
13/16	0.92000	69.1843	0.92433	70.5775	0.92862	71.9846
27/32	0.92014	69.2276	0.92447	70.6213	0.92875	72.0288
7/8	0.92028	69.2709	0.92460	70.6650	0.92889	72.0730
29/32	0.92041	69.3143	0.92474	70.7088	0.92902	72.1172
15/16	0.92055	69.3577	0.92487	70.7526	0.92915	72.1615
31/32	0.92068	69.4010	0.92501	70.7964	0.92929	72.2057
1	0.92082	69.4444	0.92514	70.8403	0.92942	72.2500

Fractions of an Inch.	6"		7"		8"	
	Log.	Square.	Log.	Square.	Log.	Square.
0	0.92942	72.2500	0.93366	73.6736	0.93785	75.1111
1/32	0.92955	72.2943	0.93379	73.7183	0.93798	75.1563
1/16	0.92968	72.3386	0.93392	73.7630	0.93811	75.2014
3/32	0.92982	72.3829	0.93405	73.8078	0.93824	75.2466
1/8	0.92995	72.4272	0.93418	73.8525	0.93837	75.2918
5/32	0.93008	72.4715	0.93431	73.8973	0.93850	75.3370
3/16	0.93022	72.5159	0.93445	73.9421	0.93863	75.3822
7/32	0.93035	72.5602	0.93458	73.9869	0.93876	75.4274
1/4	0.93048	72.6046	0.93471	74.0317	0.93889	75.4727
9/32	0.93061	72.6490	0.93484	74.0765	0.93903	75.5179
5/16	0.93075	72.6934	0.93497	74.1213	0.93916	75.5632
11/32	0.93088	72.7378	0.93510	74.1662	0.93929	75.6085
3/8	0.93101	72.7822	0.93523	74.2110	0.93942	75.6538
13/32	0.93115	72.8267	0.93537	74.2559	0.93955	75.6991
7/16	0.93128	72.8711	0.93550	74.3008	0.93968	75.7444
15/32	0.93141	72.9156	0.93563	74.3457	0.93981	75.7897
1/2	0.93154	72.9601	0.93576	74.3906	0.93994	75.8351
17/32	0.93168	73.0046	0.93589	74.4356	0.94006	75.8804
9/16	0.93181	73.0491	0.93602	74.4805	0.94019	75.9258
19/32	0.93194	73.0936	0.93615	74.5255	0.94032	75.9712
5/8	0.93207	73.1381	0.93628	74.5704	0.94045	76.0166
21/32	0.93220	73.1827	0.93641	74.6154	0.94058	76.0620
11/16	0.93234	73.2272	0.93655	74.6604	0.94071	76.1074
23/32	0.93247	73.2718	0.93668	74.7054	0.94084	76.1529
3/4	0.93260	73.3164	0.93681	74.7504	0.94097	76.1984
25/32	0.93273	73.3610	0.93694	74.7955	0.94110	76.2438
13/16	0.93286	73.4056	0.93707	74.8405	0.94123	76.2893
27/32	0.93300	73.4503	0.93720	74.8856	0.94136	76.3348
7/8	0.93313	73.4949	0.93733	74.9307	0.94149	76.3803
29/32	0.93326	73.5396	0.93746	74.9758	0.94162	76.4258
15/16	0.93339	73.5842	0.93759	75.0209	0.94175	76.4714
31/32	0.93352	73.6289	0.93772	75.0660	0.94188	76.5169
1	0.93366	73.6736	0.93785	75.1111	0.94201	76.5625

Fractions of an Inch.	9″		10″		11″	
	Log.	Square.	Log.	Square.	Log.	Square.
0	0.94201	76.5625	0.94612	78.0278	0.95020	79.5069
1/32	0.94214	76.6081	0.94625	78.0738	0.95033	79.5534
1/16	0.94227	76.6537	0.94638	78.1198	0.95046	79.5999
3/32	0.94240	76.6993	0.94651	78.1659	0.95058	79.6463
1/8	0.94252	76.7449	0.94664	78.2119	0.95071	79.6928
5/32	0.94265	76.7905	0.94676	78.2580	0.95084	79.7393
3/16	0.94278	76.8362	0.94689	78.3041	0.95096	79.7858
7/32	0.94291	76.8818	0.94702	78.3502	0.95109	79.8324
1/4	0.94304	76.9275	0.94715	78.3963	0.95122	79.8789
9/32	0.94317	76.9732	0.94728	78.4424	0.95134	79.9255
5/16	0.94330	77.0189	0.94740	78.4885	0.95147	79.9720
11/32	0.94343	77.0646	0.94753	78.5347	0.95160	80.0186
3/8	0.94356	77.1104	0.94766	78.5808	0.95172	80.0652
13/32	0.94369	77.1561	0.94779	78.6270	0.95185	80.1118
7/16	0.94381	77.2018	0.94791	78.6732	0.95197	80.1584
15/32	0.94394	77.2476	0.94804	78.7194	0.95210	80.2051
1/2	0.94407	77.2934	0.94817	78.7656	0.95223	80.2517
17/32	0.94420	77.3392	0.94830	78.8119	0.95235	80.2984
9/16	0.94433	77.3850	0.94842	78.8581	0.95248	80.3451
19/32	0.94446	77.4308	0.94855	78.9044	0.95261	80.3918
5/8	0.94459	77.4767	0.94868	78.9506	0.95273	80.4385
21/32	0.94471	77.5225	0.94881	78.9969	0.95286	80.4852
11/16	0.94484	77.5684	0.94893	79.0432	0.95298	80.5319
23/32	0.94497	77.6143	0.94906	79.0895	0.95311	80.5787
3/4	0.94510	77.6602	0.94919	79.1359	0.95324	80.6254
25/32	0.94523	77.7061	0.94931	79.1822	0.95336	80.6722
13/16	0.94536	77.7520	0.94944	79.2285	0.95349	80.7190
27/32	0.94548	77.7979	0.94957	79.2749	0.95361	80.7658
7/8	0.94561	77.8439	0.94969	79.3213	0.95374	80.8126
29/32	0.94574	77.8898	0.94982	79.3677	0.95387	80.8594
15/16	0.94587	77.9358	0.94995	79.4141	0.95399	80.9063
31/32	0.94600	77.9818	0.95008	79.4605	0.95412	80.9531
1	0.94612	78.0278	0.95020	79.5069	0.95424	81.0000

9′

Fractions of an Inch.	0″		1″		2″	
	Log.	Square.	Log.	Square.	Log.	Square.
0	0.95424	81.0000	0.95825	82.5069	0.96221	84.0278
1/32	0.95437	81.0469	0.95837	82.5543	0.96233	84.0755
1/16	0.95449	81.0938	0.95849	82.6016	0.96246	84.1233
3/32	0.95462	81.1407	0.95862	82.6489	0.96258	84.1711
1/8	0.95474	81.1876	0.95874	82.6963	0.96270	84.2189
5/32	0.95487	81.2345	0.95887	82.7437	0.96283	84.2667
3/16	0.95500	81.2815	0.95899	82.7910	0.96295	84.3145
7/32	0.95512	81.3285	0.95912	82.8384	0.96307	84.3623
1/4	0.95525	81.3754	0.95924	82.8859	0.96320	84.4102
9/32	0.95537	81.4224	0.95936	82.9333	0.96332	84.4580
5/16	0.95550	81.4694	0.95949	82.9807	0.96344	84.5059
11/32	0.95562	81.5164	0.95961	83.0282	0.96357	84.5538
3/8	0.95575	81.5635	0.95974	83.0756	0.96369	84.6017
13/32	0.95587	81.6105	0.95986	83.1231	0.96381	84.6496
7/16	0.95600	81.6576	0.95998	83.1706	0.96394	84.6975
15/32	0.95612	81.7047	0.96011	83.2181	0.96406	84.7454
1/2	0.95625	81.7517	0.96023	83.2656	0.96418	84.7934
17/32	0.95637	81.7988	0.96036	83.3132	0.96430	84.8414
9/16	0.95650	81.8459	0.96048	83.3607	0.96443	84.8894
19/32	0.95662	81.8931	0.96060	83.4083	0.96455	84.9373
5/8	0.95675	81.9402	0.96073	83.4558	0.96467	84.9854
21/32	0.95687	81.9874	0.96085	83.5034	0.96479	85.0334
11/16	0.95700	82.0345	0.96098	83.5510	0.96492	85.0814
23/32	0.95712	82.0817	0.96110	83.5986	0.96504	85.1295
3/4	0.95725	82.1289	0.96122	83.6463	0.96516	85.1775
25/32	0.95737	82.1761	0.96135	83.6939	0.96529	85.2256
13/16	0.95750	82.2233	0.96147	83.7416	0.96541	85.2737
27/32	0.95762	82.2706	0.96159	83.7892	0.96553	85.3218
7/8	0.95775	82.3178	0.96172	83.8369	0.96565	85.3699
29/32	0.95787	82.3651	0.96184	83.8846	0.96577	85.4180
15/16	0.95800	82.4124	0.96196	83.9323	0.96590	85.4662
31/32	0.95812	82.4596	0.96209	83.9800	0.96602	85.5143
1	0.95825	82.5069	0.96221	84.0278	0.96614	85.5625

Fractions of an inch.	3″		4″		5″	
	Log.	Square.	Log.	Square.	Log.	Square.
0	0.96614	85.5625	0.97004	87.1111	0.97390	88.6736
1/32	0.96626	85.6107	0.97016	87.1597	0.97402	88.7227
1/16	0.96639	85.6589	0.97028	87.2084	0.97414	88.7717
3/32	0.96651	85.7071	0.97040	87.2570	0.97426	88.8208
1/8	0.96663	85.7553	0.97052	87.3057	0.97438	88.8699
5/32	0.96675	85.8036	0.97064	87.3543	0.97450	88.9190
3/16	0.96687	85.8518	0.97076	87.4030	0.97462	88.9681
7/32	0.96700	85.9001	0.97088	87.4517	0.97474	89.0173
1/4	0.96712	85.9484	0.97101	87.5004	0.97486	89.0664
9/32	0.96724	85.9966	0.97113	87.5492	0.97498	89.1156
5/16	0.96736	86.0449	0.97125	87.5979	0.97510	89.1647
11/32	0.96748	86.0933	0.97137	87.6467	0.97522	89.2139
3/8	0.96761	86.1416	0.97149	87.6954	0.97534	89.2631
13/32	0.96773	86.1899	0.97161	87.7442	0.97546	89.3123
7/16	0.96785	86.2383	0.97173	87.7930	0.97558	89.3616
15/32	0.96797	86.2867	0.97185	87.8418	0.97570	89.4108
1/2	0.96809	86.3351	0.97197	87.8906	0.97581	89.4601
17/32	0.96822	86.3835	0.97209	87.9395	0.97593	89.5093
9/16	0.96834	86.4319	0.97221	87.9883	0.97605	89.5586
19/32	0.96846	86.4803	0.97233	88.0372	0.97617	89.6079
5/8	0.96858	86.5288	0.97245	88.0860	0.97629	89.6572
21/32	0.96870	86.5772	0.97257	88.1349	0.97641	89.7065
11/16	0.96882	86.6257	0.97269	88.1838	0.97653	89.7559
23/32	0.96894	86.6742	0.97281	88.2328	0.97665	89.8052
3/4	0.96907	86.7227	0.97294	88.2817	0.97677	89.8546
25/32	0.96919	86.7712	0.97306	88.3306	0.97689	89.9040
13/16	0.96931	86.8197	0.97318	88.3796	0.97701	89.9534
27/32	0.96943	86.8682	0.97330	88.4286	0.97713	90.0028
7/8	0.96955	86.9168	0.97342	88.4775	0.97725	90.0522
29/32	0.96967	86.9653	0.97354	88.5265	0.97737	90.1010
15/16	0.96979	87.0139	0.97366	88.5755	0.97749	90.1511
31/32	0.96992	87.0625	0.97378	88.6246	0.97760	90.2005
1	0.97004	87.1111	0.97390	88.6736	0.97772	90.2500

Fractions of an Inch.	6″		7″		8″	
	Log.	Square.	Log.	Square.	Log.	Square.
0	0.97772	90.2500	0.98152	91.8403	0.98528	93.4444
1⁄32	0.97784	90.2995	0.98163	91.8902	0.98539	93.4948
1⁄16	0.97796	90.3490	0.98175	91.9401	0.98551	93.5452
3⁄32	0.97808	90.3985	0.98187	91.9901	0.98563	93.5955
1⁄8	0.97820	90.4480	0.98199	92.0400	0.98574	93.6459
5⁄32	0.97832	90.4976	0.98211	92.0900	0.98586	93.6963
3⁄16	0.97844	90.5471	0.98222	92.1400	0.98598	93.7468
7⁄32	0.97856	90.5967	0.98234	92.1900	0.98609	93.7972
1⁄4	0.97867	90.6463	0.98246	92.2400	0.98621	93.8477
9⁄32	0.97879	90.6959	0.98258	92.2900	0.98633	93.8981
5⁄16	0.97891	90.7455	0.98270	92.3401	0.98645	93.9486
11⁄32	0.97903	90.7951	0.98281	92.3901	0.98656	93.9991
3⁄8	0 97915	90.8447	0.98293	92.4402	0.98668	94.0496
13⁄32	0.97927	90.8944	0.98305	92.4903	0.98680	94.1001
7⁄16	0.97939	90.9440	0.98317	92.5404	0.98691	94.1506
15⁄32	0.97951	90.9937	0.98328	92.5905	0.98703	94.2012
1⁄2	0.97962	91.0434	0.98340	92.6406	0.98714	94.2517
17⁄32	0.97974	91.0931	0.98352	92.6908	0.98726	94.3023
9⁄16	0.97986	91.1428	0.98364	92.7409	0.98738	94.3529
19⁄32	0.97998	91.1926	0.98375	92.7911	0.98749	94.4035
5⁄8	0.98010	91.2423	0.98387	92.8413	0.98761	94.4541
21⁄32	0.98022	91.2921	0.98399	92.8914	0.98773	94.5047
11⁄16	0.98033	91.3418	0.98411	92.9417	0.98784	94.5554
23⁄32	0.98045	91.3916	0.98422	92.9919	0.98796	94.6060
3⁄4	0.98057	91.4414	0.98434	93.0421	0.98808	94.6567
25⁄32	0.98069	91.4912	0.98446	93.0923	0.98819	94.7074
13⁄16	0.98081	91.5410	0.98457	93.1426	0.98831	94.7581
27⁄32	0.98093	91.5909	0.98469	93.1929	0.98842	94.8088
7⁄8	0.98104	91.6407	0.98481	93.2432	0.98854	94.8595
29⁄32	0.98116	91.6906	0.98493	93.2935	0.98866	94.9102
15⁄16	0.98128	91.7405	0.98504	93.3438	0.98877	94.9610
31⁄32	0.98140	91.7904	0.98516	93.3941	0.98889	95.0117
1	0.98152	91.8403	0.98528	93.4444	0.98900	95.0625

Fractions of an Inch.	9″		10″		11″	
	Log.	Square.	Log.	Square.	Log.	Square.
0	0.98900	95.0625	0.99270	96.6944	0.99637	98.3403
1⁄32	0.98912	95.1133	0.99282	96.7457	0.99648	98.3919
1⁄16	0.98924	95.1641	0.99293	96.7969	0.99659	98.4436
3⁄32	0.98935	95.2149	0.99305	96.8482	0.99671	98.4953
1⁄8	0.98947	95.2657	0.99316	96.8994	0.99682	98.5470
5⁄32	0.98958	95.3166	0.99328	96.9507	0.99694	98.5987
3⁄16	0.98970	95.3674	0.99339	97.0020	0.99705	98.6504
7⁄32	0.98982	95.4183	0.99351	97.0533	0.99716	98.7022
1⁄4	0.98993	95.4692	0.99362	97.1046	0.99728	98.7539
9⁄32	0.99005	95.5201	0.99373	97.1559	0.99739	98.8057
5⁄16	0.99016	95.5710	0.99385	97.2073	0.99750	98.8574
11⁄32	0.99028	95.6219	0.99396	97.2586	0.99762	98.9092
3⁄8	0.99039	95.6729	0.99408	97.3100	0.99773	98.9610
13⁄32	0.99051	95.7238	0.99419	97.3614	0.99785	99.0129
7⁄16	0.99063	95.7748	0.99431	97.4128	0.99796	99.0647
15⁄32	0.99074	95.8257	0.99442	97.4642	0.99807	99.1165
1⁄2	0.99086	95.8767	0.99454	97.5156	0.99819	99.1684
17⁄32	0.99097	95.9277	0.99465	97.5671	0.99830	99.2203
9⁄16	0.99109	95.9788	0.99477	97.6185	0.99841	99.2722
19⁄32	0.99120	96.0298	0.99488	97.6700	0.99853	99.3241
5⁄8	0.99132	96.0808	0.99499	97.7215	0.99864	99.3760
21⁄32	0.99143	96.1319	0.99511	97.7730	0.99875	99.4279
11⁄16	0.99155	96.1830	0.99522	97.8245	0.99887	99.4798
23⁄32	0.99166	96.2341	0.99534	97.8760	0.99898	99.5318
3⁄4	0.99178	96.2852	0.99545	97.9275	0.99909	99.5838
25⁄32	0.99189	96.3363	0.99557	97.9791	0.99921	99.6357
13⁄16	0.99201	96.3874	0.99568	98.0306	0.99932	99.6877
27⁄32	0.99213	96.4385	0.99580	98.0822	0.99943	99.7398
7⁄8	0.99224	96.4897	0.99591	98.1338	0.99955	99.7918
29⁄32	0.99236	96.5409	0.99602	98.1854	0.99966	99.8438
15⁄16	0.99247	96.5920	0.99614	98.2370	0.99977	99.8959
31⁄32	0.99259	96.6432	0.99625	98.2886	0.99989	99.9479
1	0.99270	96.6944	0.99637	98.3403	1.00000	100.0000

TABLES OF

ANGLES AND TRIGONOMETRIC FUNCTIONS

natural and logarithmic, corresponding
to bevels given to 12" by
one thirty seconds of an inch.

0"

Fraction of an Inch	NATURAL FUNCTIONS						Angle		
	Sine.	Cosec.	Tang.	Cotang.	Cosine.	Sec.	Deg.	Min.	Sec.
0	0.00000	$+\infty$	0.00000	$+\infty$	1.00000	1.00000	0	0	0
1⁄32	0.00260	384.0012	0.00260	384.0000	1.00000	1.00000	0	08	57
1⁄16	0.00521	192.0026	0.00521	192.0000	0.99999	1.00001	0	17	54
3⁄32	0.00781	128.0040	0.00781	128.0000	0.99997	1.00003	0	26	51
1⁄8	0.01042	96.0052	0.01042	96.0000	0.99995	1.00005	0	35	49
5⁄32	0.01302	76.8065	0.01302	76.8000	0.99992	1.00008	0	44	46
3⁄16	0.01562	64.0078	0.01563	64.0000	0.99988	1.00012	0	53	43
7⁄32	0.01823	54.8663	0.01823	54.8571	0.99983	1.00017	1	02	40
1⁄4	0.02083	48.0104	0.02083	48.0000	0.99978	1.00022	1	11	37
9⁄32	0.02343	42.6783	0.02344	42.6667	0.99973	1.00027	1	20	33
5⁄16	0.02603	38.4130	0.02604	38.4000	0.99966	1.00034	1	29	30
11⁄32	0.02863	34.9234	0.02865	34.9091	0.99959	1.00041	1	38	27
3⁄8	0.03123	32.0156	0.03125	32.0000	0.99951	1.00049	1	47	24
13⁄32	0.03383	29.5554	0.03385	29.5385	0.99943	1.00057	1	56	20
7⁄16	0.03643	27.4468	0.03646	27.4286	0.99934	1.00066	2	05	17
15⁄32	0.03903	25.6195	0.03906	25.6000	0.99924	1.00076	2	14	13
1⁄2	0.04163	24.0208	0.04167	24.0000	0.99913	1.00087	2	23	09
17⁄32	0.04423	22.6103	0.04427	22.5882	0.99902	1.00098	2	32	06
9⁄16	0.04682	21.3568	0.04688	21.3333	0.99890	1.00110	2	41	02
19⁄32	0.04942	20.2352	0.04948	20.2105	0.99878	1.00122	2	49	57
5⁄8	0.05201	19.2260	0.05208	19.2000	0.99865	1.00136	2	58	53
21⁄32	0.05461	18.3130	0.05469	18.2857	0.99851	1.00149	3	07	49
11⁄16	0.05720	17.4430	0.05729	17.4545	0.99836	1.00164	3	16	44
23⁄32	0.05979	16.7256	0.05990	16.6957	0.99821	1.00179	3	25	40
3⁄4	0.06238	16.0312	0.06250	16.0000	0.99805	1.00195	3	34	35
25⁄32	0.06497	15.3925	0.06510	15.3600	0.99789	1.00212	3	43	30
13⁄16	0.06755	14.8031	0.06771	14.7692	0.99772	1.00229	3	52	25
27⁄32	0.07014	14.2573	0.07031	14.2222	0.99754	1.00247	4	01	19
7⁄8	0.07272	13.7507	0.07292	13.7143	0.99735	1.00266	4	10	14
29⁄32	0.07531	13.2791	0.07552	13.2414	0.99716	1.00285	4	19	08
15⁄16	0.07789	12.8390	0.07813	12.8000	0.99696	1.00305	4	28	02
31⁄32	0.08047	12.4274	0.08073	12.3871	0.99676	1.00325	4	36	56
1	0.08305	12.0416	0.08333	12.0000	0.99655	1.00347	4	45	49

Fraction of an inch	LOGARITHMIC FUNCTIONS						Angle		
	Sine.	Cosec.	Tang.	Cotang.	Cosine.	Sec.	Deg.	Min.	Sec.
0	$-\infty$	$+\infty$	$-\infty$	$+\infty$	0.00000	0.00000	**0**	**0**	**0**
¹⁄₃₂	7.41567	2.58433	7.41567	2.58433	0.00000	0.00000	0	08	57
¹⁄₁₆	7.71669	2.28331	7.71670	2.28330	9.99999	0.00001	0	17	54
³⁄₃₂	7.89278	2.10722	7.89279	2.10721	9.99999	0.00001	0	26	51
⅛	8.01771	1.98229	8.01773	1.98227	9.99998	0.00002	0	35	49
⁵⁄₃₂	8.11460	1.88540	8.11464	1.88536	9.99996	0.00004	0	44	46
³⁄₁₆	8.19377	1.80623	8.19382	1.80618	9.99995	0.00005	0	53	43
⁷⁄₃₂	8.26069	1.73931	8.26077	1.73923	9.99993	0.00007	1	02	40
¼	8.31866	1.68134	8.31876	1.68124	9.99991	0.00009	1	11	37
⁹⁄₃₂	8.36979	1.63021	8.36991	1.63009	9.99988	0.00012	1	20	33
⁵⁄₁₆	8.41552	1.58448	8.41567	1.58433	9.99985	0.00015	1	29	30
¹¹⁄₃₂	8.45688	1.54312	8.45706	1.54294	9.99982	0.00018	1	38	27
⅜	8.49464	1.50536	8.49485	1.50515	9.99979	0.00021	1	47	24
¹³⁄₃₂	8.52936	1.47064	8.52961	1.47039	9.99975	0.00025	1	56	20
⁷⁄₁₆	8.56151	1.43849	8.56180	1.43820	9.99971	0.00029	2	05	17
¹⁵⁄₃₂	8.59143	1.40857	8.59176	1.40824	9.99967	0.00033	2	14	13
½	8.61941	1.38059	8.61979	1.38021	9.99962	0.00038	2	23	09
¹⁷⁄₃₂	8.64569	1.35431	8.64612	1.35388	9.99957	0.00043	2	32	06
⁹⁄₁₆	8.67046	1.32954	8.67094	1.32906	9.99952	0.00048	2	41	02
¹⁹⁄₃₂	8.69389	1.30611	8.69442	1.30558	9.99947	0.00053	2	49	57
⅝	8.71611	1.28389	8.71670	1.28330	9.99941	0.00059	2	58	53
²¹⁄₃₂	8.73724	1.26276	8.73789	1.26211	9.99935	0.00065	3	07	49
¹¹⁄₁₆	8.75738	1.24262	8.75809	1.24191	9.99929	0.00071	3	16	44
²³⁄₃₂	8.77662	1.22338	8.77740	1.22260	9.99922	0.00078	3	25	40
¾	8.79503	1.20497	8.79588	1.20412	9.99915	0.00085	3	34	35
²⁵⁄₃₂	8.81269	1.18731	8.81361	1.18639	9.99908	0.00092	3	43	30
¹³⁄₁₆	8.82965	1.17035	8.83064	1.16936	9.99901	0.00099	3	52	25
²⁷⁄₃₂	8.84596	1.15404	8.84703	1.15297	9.99893	0.00107	4	01	19
⅞	8.86168	1.13832	8.86283	1.13717	9.99885	0.00115	4	10	14
²⁹⁄₃₂	8.87683	1.12317	8.87807	1.12193	9.99876	0.00124	4	19	08
¹⁵⁄₁₆	8.89147	1.10853	8.89279	1.10721	9.99868	0.00132	4	28	02
³¹⁄₃₂	8.90562	1.09438	8.90703	1.09297	9.99859	0.00141	4	36	56
1	8.91932	1.08068	8.92082	1.07918	9.99850	0.00150	4	45	49

1"

Fraction of an Inch	NATURAL FUNCTIONS						Angle		
	Sine.	Cosec.	Tang.	Cotang.	Cosine.	Sec.	Deg.	Min.	Sec.
0	0.08305	12.0416	0.08333	12.0000	0.99655	**1.00347**	4	45	49
1/32	0.08562	11.6793	0.08594	11.6364	0.99633	1.00369	4	54	42
1/16	0.08820	11.3383	0.08854	11.2941	0.99610	1.00391	5	03	36
3/32	0.09077	11.0169	0.09115	10.9714	0.99587	1.00415	5	12	28
1/8	0.09334	10.7134	0.09375	10.6667	0.99563	1.00438	5	21	21
5/32	0.09591	10.4264	0.09635	10.3784	0.99539	1.00463	5	30	13
3/16	0.09848	10.1546	0.09896	10.1053	0.99514	1.00488	5	39	05
7/32	0.10104	9.89680	0.10156	9.84615	0.99488	1.00514	5	47	57
1/4	0.10361	9.65194	0.10417	9.60000	0.99462	1.00541	5	56	49
9/32	0.10617	9.41908	0.10677	9.36585	0.99435	1.00568	6	05	40
5/16	0.10873	9.19738	0.10938	9.14286	0.99407	1.00596	6	14	31
11/32	0.11128	8.89605	0.11198	8.93023	0.99379	1.00625	6	23	22
3/8	0.11384	8.78437	0.11458	8.72727	0.99350	1.00654	6	32	12
13/32	0.11639	8.59172	0.11719	8.53333	0.99320	1.00684	6	41	02
7/16	0.11894	8.40751	0.11979	8.34783	0.99290	1.00715	6	49	52
15/32	0.12149	8.23119	0.12240	8.17021	0.99259	1.00746	6	58	41
1/2	0.12403	8.06226	0.12500	8.00000	0.99228	1.00778	7	07	30
17/32	0.12658	7.90028	0.12760	7.83673	0.99196	1.00811	7	16	19
9/16	0.12912	7.74483	0.13021	7.68000	0.99163	1.00844	7	25	07
19/32	0.13166	7.59552	0.13281	7.52941	0.99130	1.00878	7	33	55
5/8	0.13419	7.45202	0.13542	7.38462	0.99096	1.00913	7	42	43
21/32	0.13672	7.31396	0.13802	7.24528	0.99061	1.00948	7	51	30
11/16	0.13925	7.18108	0.14063	7.11111	0.99026	1.00984	8	00	17
23/32	0.14178	7.05307	0.14323	6.98182	0.98990	1.01021	8	09	04
3/4	0.14431	6.92967	0.14583	6.85714	0.98953	1.01058	8	17	50
25/32	0.14683	6.81065	0.14844	6.73684	0.98916	1.01096	8	26	35
13/16	0.14935	6.69579	0.15104	6.62069	0.98878	1.01134	8	35	21
27/32	0.15186	6.58485	0.15365	6.50847	0.98840	1.01173	8	44	06
7/8	0.15438	6.47766	0.15625	6.40000	0.98801	1.01213	8	52	50
29/32	0.15689	6.37401	0.15885	6.29508	0.98762	1.01254	9	01	35
15/16	0.15939	6.27376	0.16146	6.19355	0.98722	1.01295	9	10	18
31/32	0.16190	6.17673	0.16406	6.09524	0.98681	1.01337	9	19	02
1	0.16440	6.08276	0.16667	6.00000	0.98639	1.01379	9	27	44

Fraction of an Inch	LOGARITHMIC FUNCTIONS						Angle		
	Sine.	Cosec.	Tang.	Cotang.	Cosine.	Sec.	Deg.	Min.	Sec.
0	8.91932	1.08068	8.92082	1.07918	9.99850	0.00150	4	45	49
1/32	8.93258	1.06742	8.93418	1.06582	9.99840	0.00160	4	54	42
1/16	8.94545	1.05455	8.94715	1.05285	9.99830	0.00170	5	03	36
3/32	8.95794	1.04206	8.95974	1.04026	9.99820	0.00180	5	12	28
1/8	8.97007	1.02993	8.97197	1.02803	9.99810	0.00190	5	21	21
5/32	8.98186	1.01814	8.98387	1.01613	9.99799	0.00201	5	30	13
3/16	8.99334	1.00666	8.99545	1.00455	9.99788	0.00212	5	39	05
7/32	9.00450	0.99550	9.00673	0.99327	9.99777	0.00223	5	47	57
1/4	9.01539	0.98461	9.01773	0.98227	9.99766	0.00234	5	56	49
9/32	9.02599	0.97401	9.02845	0.97155	9.99754	0.00246	6	05	40
5/16	9.03634	0.96366	9.03892	0.96108	9.99742	0.00258	6	14	31
11/32	9.04643	0.95357	9.04914	0.95086	9.99729	0.00271	6	23	22
3/8	9.05629	0.94371	9.05912	0.94088	9.99717	0.00283	6	32	12
13/32	9.06592	0.93408	9.06888	0.93112	9.99704	0.00296	6	41	02
7/16	9.07533	0.92467	9.07843	0.92157	9.99691	0.00309	6	49	52
15/32	9.08454	0.91546	9.08777	0.91223	9.99677	0.00323	6	58	41
1/2	9.09354	0.90646	9.09691	0.90309	9.99663	0.00337	7	07	30
17/32	9.10236	0.89764	9.10586	0.89414	9.99649	0.00351	7	16	19
9/16	9.11099	0.88901	9.11464	0.88536	9.99635	0.00365	7	25	07
19/32	9.11944	0.88056	9.12324	0.87676	9.99620	0.00380	7	33	55
5/8	9.12773	0.87227	9.13167	0.86833	9.99605	0.00395	7	42	43
21/32	9.13585	0.86415	9.13994	0.86006	9.99590	0.00410	7	51	30
11/16	9.14381	0.85619	9.14806	0.85194	9.99575	0.00425	8	00	17
23/32	9.15162	0.84838	9.15603	0.84397	9.99559	0.00441	8	09	04
3/4	9.15929	0.84071	9.16386	0.83614	9.99543	0.00457	8	17	50
25/32	9.16681	0.83319	9.17154	0.82846	9.99527	0.00473	8	26	35
13/16	9.17420	0.82580	9.17910	0.82090	9.99510	0.00490	8	35	21
27/32	9.18145	0.81855	9.18652	0.81348	9.99493	0.00507	8	44	06
7/8	9.18858	0.81142	9.19382	0.80618	9.99476	0.00524	8	52	50
29/32	9.19559	0.80441	9.20100	0.79900	9.99459	0.00541	9	01	35
15/16	9.20247	0.79753	9.20806	0.79194	9.99441	0.00559	9	10	18
31/32	9.20924	0.79076	9.21501	0.78499	9.99423	0.00577	9	19	02
1	9.21590	0.78410	9.22185	0.77815	9.99405	0.00595	9	27	44

2"

Fraction of an Inch	NATURAL FUNCTIONS						Angle		
	Sine.	Cosec.	Tang.	Cotang.	Cosine.	Sec.	Deg.	Min.	Sec.
0	0.16440	6.08276	0.16667	6.00000	0.98639	1.01379	9	27	44
1/32	0.16690	5.99173	0.16927	5.90769	0.98597	1.01423	9	36	27
1/16	0.16939	5.90350	0.17188	5.81818	0.98555	1.01466	9	45	09
3/32	0.17188	5.81793	0.17448	5.73134	0.98512	1.01511	9	53	50
1/8	0.17437	5.73492	0.17708	5.64706	0.98468	1.01556	10	02	31
5/32	0.17686	5.65435	0.17969	5.56522	0.98424	1.01602	10	11	12
3/16	0.17934	5.57611	0.18229	5.48571	0.98379	1.01648	10	19	52
7/32	0.18181	5.50012	0.18490	5.40845	0.98333	1.01695	10	28	32
1/4	0.18429	5.42627	0.18750	5.33333	0.98287	1.01743	10	37	11
9/32	0.18676	5.35448	0.19010	5.26027	0.98241	1.01791	10	45	49
5/16	0.18923	5.28467	0.19271	5.18919	0.98193	1.01840	10	54	28
11/32	0.19169	5.21674	0.19531	5.12000	0.98146	1.01890	11	03	05
3/8	0.19415	5.15064	0.19792	5.05263	0.98097	1.01940	11	11	42
13/32	0.19661	5.08628	0.20052	4.98701	0.98048	1.01991	11	20	19
7/16	0.19906	5.02361	0.20313	4.92308	0.97999	1.02042	11	28	55
15/32	0.20151	4.96256	0.20573	4.86076	0.97949	1.02094	11	37	31
1/2	0.20395	4.90306	0.20833	4.80000	0.97898	1.02147	11	46	06
17/32	0.20640	4.84506	0.21094	4.74074	0.97847	1.02201	11	54	40
9/16	0.20883	4.78850	0.21354	4.68293	0.97795	1.02255	12	03	14
19/32	0.21127	4.73334	0.21615	4.62651	0.97743	1.02309	12	11	48
5/8	0.21370	4.67953	0.21875	4.57143	0.97690	1.02364	12	20	21
21/32	0.21612	4.62700	0.22135	4.51765	0.97637	1.02421	12	28	53
11/16	0.21854	4.57573	0.22396	4.46512	0.97583	1.02477	12	37	25
23/32	0.22096	4.52565	0.22656	4.41379	0.97528	1.02534	12	45	56
3/4	0.22338	4.47675	0.22917	4.36364	0.97473	1.02592	12	54	27
25/32	0.22579	4.42897	0.23177	4.31461	0.97418	1.02651	13	02	57
13/16	0.22819	4.38229	0.23438	4.26667	0.97362	1.02710	13	11	26
27/32	0.23059	4.33665	0.23698	4.21978	0.97305	1.02770	13	19	55
7/8	0.23299	4.29203	0.23958	4.17391	0.97248	1.02830	13	28	23
29/32	0.23538	4.24840	0.24219	4.12903	0.97190	1.02891	13	36	51
15/16	0.23777	4.20572	0.24479	4.08511	0.97132	1.02953	13	45	18
31/32	0.24016	4.16397	0.24740	4.04211	0.97073	1.03015	13	53	45
1	0.24254	4.12311	0.25000	4.00000	0.97014	1.03078	14	02	10

Fraction of an inch	LOGARITHMIC FUNCTIONS						Angle		
	Sine.	Cosec.	Tang.	Cotang.	Cosine.	Sec.	Deg.	Min.	Sec.
0	9.21590	0.78410	9.22185	0.77815	9.99405	0.00595	9	27	44
1/32	9.22245	0.77755	9.22858	0.77142	9.99387	0.00613	9	36	27
1/16	9.22889	0.77111	9.23521	0.76479	9.99368	0.00632	9	45	09
3/32	9.23523	0.76477	9.24174	0.75826	9·99349	0.00651	9	53	50
1/8	9.24147	0.75853	9.24818	0.75182	9.99330	0.00670	10	02	31
5/32	9.24762	0.75238	9.25452	0.74548	9.99310	0.00690	10	11	12
3/16	9.25367	0.74633	9.26077	0.73923	9.99290	0.00710	10	19	52
7/32	9.25963	0.74037	9.26693	0.73307	9.99270	0.00730	10	28	32
1/4	9.26550	0.73450	9.27300	0.72700	9.99250	0.00750	10	37	11
9/32	9.27128	0.72872	9.27899	0.72101	9.99229	0.00771	10	45	49
5/16	9.27698	0.72302	9.28490	0.71510	9.99208	0.00792	10	54	28
11/32	9.28260	0.71740	9.29073	0.70927	9.99187	0.00813	11	03	05
3/8	9.28814	0.71186	9.29648	0.70352	9.99166	0.00834	11	11	42
13/32	9.29360	0.70640	9.30216	0.69784	9.99144	0.00856	11	20	19
7/16	9.29898	0.70102	9.30776	0.69224	9.99122	0.00878	11	28	55
15/32	9.30429	0.69571	9.31330	0.68670	9.99100	0.00900	11	37	31
1/2	9.30953	0.69047	9.31876	0.68124	9.99077	0.00923	11	46	06
17/32	9.31470	0.68530	9.32415	0.67585	9.99055	0.00945	11	54	40
9/16	9.31980	0.68020	9.32948	0.67052	9.99032	0.00968	12	03	14
19/32	9.32483	0.67517	9.33475	0.66525	9.99008	0.00992	12	11	48
5/8	9.32980	0.67020	9.33995	0.66005	9.98985	0.01015	12	20	21
21/32	9.33470	0.66530	9.34509	0.65491	9.98961	0.01039	12	28	53
11/16	9.33954	0.66046	9.35017	0.64983	9.98937	0.01063	12	37	25
23/32	9.34432	0.65568	9.35519	0.64481	9.98913	0.01087	12	45	56
3/4	9.34904	0.65096	9.36015	0.63985	9.98889	0.01111	12	54	27
25/32	9.35370	0.64630	9.36506	0.63494	9.98864	0.01136	13	02	57
13/16	9.35830	0.64170	9.36991	0.63009	9.98839	0.01161	13	11	26
27/32	9.36285	0.63715	9.37471	0.62529	9.98814	0.01186	13	19	55
7/8	9.36734	0.63266	9.37946	0.62054	9.98788	0.01212	13	28	23
29/32	9.37177	0.62823	9.38415	0.61585	9.98762	0.01238	13	36	51
15/16	9.37616	0.62384	9.38880	0.61120	9.98736	0.01264	13	45	18
31/32	9.38049	0.61951	9.39339	0.60661	9.98710	0.01290	13	53	45
1	9.38478	0.61522	9.39794	0.60206	9.98684	0.01316	14	02	10

3"

Fraction of an Inch	NATURAL FUNCTIONS						Angle		
	Sine.	Cosec.	Tang.	Cotang.	Cosine.	Sec.	Deg.	Min.	Sec.
0	0.24254	4.12311	0.25000	4.00000	0.97014	1.03078	14	02	10
1/32	0.24491	4.08311	0.25260	3.95876	0.96955	1.03141	14	10	36
1/16	0.24728	4.04396	0.25521	3.91837	0.96894	1.03205	14	19	00
3/32	0.24965	4.00562	0.25781	3.87879	0.96834	1.03270	14	27	24
1/8	0.25201	3.96807	0.26042	3.84000	0.96772	1.03335	14	35	48
5/32	0.25437	3.93129	0.26302	3.80198	0.96711	1.03401	14	44	10
3/16	0.25672	3.89525	0.26563	3.76471	0.96649	1.03468	14	52	32
7/32	0.25907	3.85994	0.26823	3.72816	0.96586	1.03535	15	00	54
1/4	0.26142	3.82533	0.27083	3.69231	0.96523	1.03603	15	09	15
9/32	0.26375	3.79140	0.27344	3.65714	0.96459	1.03671	15	17	35
5/16	0.26609	3.75813	0.27604	3.62264	0.96395	1.03740	15	25	54
11/32	0.26842	3.72550	0.27865	3.58879	0.96330	1.03810	15	34	13
3/8	0.27075	3.69350	0.28125	3.55556	0.96265	1.03880	15	42	31
13/32	0.27307	3.66211	0.28385	3.52294	0.96200	1.03951	15	50	49
7/16	0.27538	3.63131	0.28646	3.49091	0.96133	1.04022	15	59	05
15/32	0.27769	3.60109	0.28906	3.45946	0.96067	1.04094	16	07	21
1/2	0.28000	3.57143	0.29167	3.42857	0.96000	1.04167	16	15	37
17/32	0.28230	3.54231	0.29427	3.39823	0.95933	1.04240	16	23	51
9/16	0.28460	3.51372	0.29688	3.36842	0.95865	1.04314	16	32	05
19/32	0.28689	3.48566	0.29948	3.33913	0.95796	1.04388	16	40	19
5/8	0.28918	3.45809	0.30208	3.31034	0.95728	1.04463	16	48	31
21/32	0.29146	3.43101	0.30469	3.28205	0.95658	1.04539	16	56	43
11/16	0.29374	3.40442	0.30729	3.25424	0.95589	1.04615	17	04	54
23/32	0.29601	3.37829	0.30990	3.22689	0.95519	1.04692	17	13	05
3/4	0.29827	3.35261	0.31250	3.20000	0.95448	1.04769	17	21	14
25/32	0.30054	3.32738	0.31510	3.17355	0.95377	1.04847	17	29	23
13/16	0.30279	3.30258	0.31771	3.14754	0.95306	1.04926	17	37	32
27/32	0.30505	3.27820	0.32031	3.12195	0.95234	1.05005	17	45	39
7/8	0.30729	3.25423	0.32292	3.09677	0.95161	1.05085	17	53	46
29/32	0.30953	3.23066	0.32552	3.07200	0.95089	1.05165	18	01	52
15/16	0.31177	3.20749	0.32813	3.04762	0.95016	1.05246	18	09	57
31/32	0.31400	3.18470	0.33073	3.02362	0.94942	1.05327	18	18	02
1	0.31623	3.16228	0.33333	3.00000	0.94868	1.05409	18	26	06

Fraction of an inch	LOGARITHMIC FUNCTIONS						Angle		
	Sine.	Cosec.	Tang.	Cotang.	Cosine.	Sec.	Deg.	Min.	See.
0	9.38478	0.61522	9.39794	0.60206	9.98684	0.01316	14	02	10
1/32	9.38901	0.61099	9.40244	0.59756	9.98657	0.01343	14	10	36
1/16	9.39319	0.60681	9.40689	0.59311	9.98630	0.01370	14	19	00
3/32	9.39733	0.60267	9.41130	0.58870	9.98603	0.01397	14	27	24
1/8	9.40142	0.59858	9.41567	0.58433	9 98575	0.01425	14	35	48
5/32	9.40546	0.59454	9.41999	0.58001	9.98547	0.01453	14	44	10
3/16	9.40946	0.59054	9.42427	0.57573	9.98520	0.01480	14	52	32
7/32	9.41342	0.58658	9.42851	0.57149	9.98491	0.01509	15	00	54
1/4	9.41733	0.58267	9.43270	0.56730	9.98463	0.01537	15	09	15
9/32	9.42120	0.57880	9.43686	0.56314	9.98434	0.01566	15	17	35
5/16	9.42503	0.57497	9.44097	0.55903	9.98405	0.01595	15	25	54
11/32	9.42881	0.57119	9.44505	0.55495	9.98376	0.01624	15	34	13
3/8	9.43256	0.56744	9.44909	0.55091	9.98347	0.01653	15	42	31
13/32	9.43627	0.56373	9.45310	0.54690	9.98317	0.01683	15	50	49
7/16	9.43994	0.56006	9.45706	0.54294	9.98287	0.01713	15	59	05
15/32	9.44357	0.55643	9.46099	0.53901	9.98257	0.01743	16	07	21
1/2	9.44716	0.55284	9.46489	0.53511	9.98227	0.01773	16	15	37
17/32	9.45071	0.54929	9.46875	0.53125	9.98197	0.01803	16	23	51
9/16	9.45423	0.54577	9.47257	0.52743	9.98166	0.01834	16	32	05
19/32	9.45772	0.54228	9.47637	0.52363	9.98135	0.01865	16	40	19
5/8	9.46116	0.53884	9.48013	0.51987	9.98104	0.01896	16	48	31
21/32	9.46458	0.53542	9.48385	0.51615	9.98072	0.01928	16	56	43
11/16	9.46796	0.53204	9.48755	0.51245	9.98041	0.01959	17	04	54
23/32	9.47130	0.52870	9.49122	0.50878	9.98009	0.01991	17	13	05
3/4	9.47462	0.52538	9.49485	0.50515	9.97977	0.02023	17	21	14
25/32	9.47790	0.52210	9.49845	0.50155	9.97944	0.02056	17	29	23
13/16	9.48115	0.51885	9.50203	0.49797	9.97912	0.02088	17	37	32
27/32	9.48436	0.51564	9.50557	0.49443	9.97879	0.02121	17	45	39
7/8	9.48755	0.51245	9.50909	0.49091	9.97846	0.02154	17	53	46
29/32	9.49071	0.50929	9.51258	0.48742	9.97813	0.02187	18	01	52
15/16	9.49383	0.50617	9.51604	0.48396	9.97780	0.02220	18	09	57
31/32	9.49693	0.5C307	9.51947	0.48053	9.97746	0.02254	18	18	02
1	9.50000	0.50000	9.52288	0.47712	9.97712	0.02288	18	26	06

4"

Fraction of an Inch	NATURAL FUNCTIONS						Angle		
	Sine.	Cosec.	Tang.	Cotang.	Cosine.	Sec.	Deg.	Min.	Sec.
0	0.31623	3.16228	0.33333	3.00000	0.94868	1.05409	18	26	06
1/32	0.31845	3.14022	0.33594	2.97674	0.94794	1.05492	18	34	09
1/16	0.32066	3.11853	0.33854	2.95385	0.94719	1.05575	18	42	11
3/32	0.32287	3.09718	0.34115	2.93130	0.94644	1.05659	18	50	13
1/8	0.32508	3.07617	0.34375	2.90909	0.94569	1.05743	18	58	13
5/32	0.32728	3.05549	0.34635	2.88722	0.94493	1.05828	19	06	13
3/16	0.32947	3.03514	0.34896	2.86567	0.94416	1.05914	19	14	12
7/32	0.33166	3.01511	0.35156	2.84444	0.94340	1.06000	19	22	11
1/4	0.33385	2.99538	0.35417	2.82353	0.94263	1.06086	19	30	09
9/32	0.33603	2.97596	0.35677	2.80292	0.94185	1.06174	19	38	06
5/16	0.33820	2.95684	0.35938	2.78261	0.94107	1.06262	19	46	02
11/32	0.34037	2.93801	0.36198	2.76259	0.94029	1.06350	19	53	57
3/8	0.34253	2.91946	0.36458	2.74286	0.93951	1.06439	20	01	52
13/32	0.34469	2.90119	0.36719	2.72340	0.93872	1.06528	20	09	45
7/16	0.34684	2.88320	0.36979	2.70423	0.93793	1.06618	20	17	38
15/32	0.34898	2.86547	0.37240	2.68531	0.93713	1.06709	20	25	30
1/2	0.35112	2.84800	0.37500	2.66667	0.93633	1.06800	20	33	22
17/32	0.35326	2.83079	0.37760	2.64828	0.93553	1.06892	20	41	12
9/16	0.35539	2.81383	0.38021	2.63014	0.93472	1.06984	20	49	02
19/32	0.35751	2.79711	0.38281	2.61224	0.93391	1.07077	20	56	51
5/8	0.35963	2.78063	0.38542	2.59459	0.93310	1.07170	21	04	39
21/32	0.36174	2.76439	0.38802	2.57718	0.93228	1.07264	21	12	26
11/16	0.36385	2.74838	0.39063	2.56000	0.93146	1.07359	21	20	13
23/32	0.36595	2.73260	0.39323	2.54305	0.93063	1.07454	21	27	58
3/4	0.36805	2.71703	0.39583	2.52632	0.92981	1.07549	21	35	43
25/32	0.37014	2.70169	0.39844	2.50980	0.92898	1.07645	21	43	27
13/16	0.37222	2.68656	0.40104	2.49351	0.92814	1.07742	21	51	10
27/32	0.37430	2.67163	0.40365	2.47742	0.92731	1.07839	21	58	52
7/8	0.37638	2.65691	0.40625	2.46154	0.92647	1.07937	22	06	34
29/32	0.37844	2.64239	0.40885	2.44586	0.92562	1.08035	22	14	15
15/16	0.38051	2.62807	0.41146	2.43038	0.92478	1.08134	22	21	54
31/32	0.38256	2.61394	0.41406	2.41509	0.92393	1.08233	22	29	33
1	0.38462	2.60000	0.41667	2.40000	0.92308	1.08333	22	37	12

Fraction of an Inch	LOGARITHMIC FUNCTIONS						Angle		
	Sine.	Cosec.	Tang.	Cotang.	Cosine.	Sec.	Deg.	Min.	Sec.
0	9.50000	0.50000	9.52288	0.47712	9.97712	0.02288	18	26	06
1/32	9.50304	0.49696	9.52626	0.47374	9.97678	0.02322	18	34	09
1/16	9.50605	0.49395	9.52961	0.47039	9.97644	0.02356	18	42	11
3/32	9.50903	0.49097	9.53294	0.46706	9.97609	0.02391	18	50	13
1/8	9.51199	0.48801	9.53624	0.46376	9.97575	0.02425	18	58	13
5/32	9.51492	0.48508	9.53952	0.46048	9.97540	0.02460	19	06	13
3/16	9.51782	0.48218	9.54277	0.45723	9.97505	0.02495	19	14	12
7/32	9.52070	0.47930	9.54600	0.45400	9.97469	0.02531	19	22	11
1/4	9.52355	0.47645	9.54921	0.45079	9.97434	0.02566	19	30	09
9/32	9.52637	0.47363	9.55239	0.44761	9.97398	0.02602	19	38	06
5/16	9.52917	0.47083	9.55555	0.44445	9.97362	0.02638	19	46	02
11/32	9.53195	0.46805	9.55868	0.44132	9.97326	0.02674	19	53	57
3/8	9.53470	0.46530	9.56180	0.43820	9.97290	0.02710	20	01	52
13/32	9.53742	0.46258	9.56489	0.43511	9.97254	0.02746	20	09	45
7/16	9.54013	0.45987	9.56796	0.43204	9.97217	0.02783	20	17	38
15/32	9.54280	0.45720	9.57100	0.42900	9.97180	0.02820	20	25	30
1/2	9.54546	0.45454	9.57403	0.42597	9.97143	0.02857	20	33	22
17/32	9.54809	0.45191	9.57704	0.42296	9.97106	0.02894	20	41	12
9/16	9.55070	0.44930	9.58002	0.41998	9.97068	0.02932	20	49	02
19/32	9.55329	0.44671	9.58299	0.41701	9.97030	0.02970	20	56	51
5/8	9.55586	0.44414	9.58593	0.41407	9.96993	0.03007	21	04	39
21/32	9.55840	0.44160	9.58886	0.41114	9.96955	0.03045	21	12	26
11/16	9.56092	0.43908	9.59176	0.40824	9.96916	0.03084	21	20	13
23/32	9.56342	0.43658	9.59465	0.40535	9.96878	0.03122	21	27	58
3/4	9.56591	0.43409	9.59751	0.40249	9.96839	0.03161	21	35	43
25/32	9.56836	0.43164	9.60036	0.39964	9.96800	0.03200	21	43	27
13/16	9.57080	0.42920	9.60319	0.39681	9.96761	0.03239	21	51	10
27/32	9.57322	0.42678	9.60600	0.39400	9.96722	0.03278	21	58	52
7/8	9.57562	0.42438	9.60879	0.39121	9.96683	0.03317	22	06	34
29/32	9.57800	0.42200	9.61157	0.38843	9.96643	0.03357	22	14	15
15/16	9.58036	0.41964	9.61433	0.38567	9.96604	0.03396	22	21	54
31/32	9.58270	0.41730	9.61707	0.38293	9.96564	0.03436	22	29	33
1	9.58503	0.41497	9.61979	0.38021	9.96524	0.03476	22	37	12

5"

Fraction of an Inch	NATURAL FUNCTIONS						Angle		
	Sine.	Cosec.	Tang.	Cotang.	Cosine.	Sec.	Deg.	Min.	Sec.
0	0.38462	2.60000	0.41667	2.40000	0.92308	1.08333	22	37	12
1/32	0.38666	2.58625	0.41927	2.38509	0.92222	1.08434	22	44	49
1/16	0.38870	2.57268	0.42188	2.37037	0.92136	1.08535	22	52	25
3/32	0.39073	2.55928	0.42448	2.35583	0.92050	1.08636	23	00	01
1/8	0.39276	2.54607	0.42708	2.34146	0.91964	1.08738	23	07	35
5/32	0.39479	2.53302	0.42969	2.32727	0.91877	1.08841	23	15	09
3/16	0.39680	2.52015	0.43229	2.31325	0.91790	1.08944	23	22	42
7/32	0.39881	2.50744	0.43490	2.29940	0.91703	1.09047	23	30	14
1/4	0.40082	2.49489	0.43750	2.28571	0.91616	1.09152	23	37	46
9/32	0.40282	2.48251	0.44010	2.27219	0.91528	1.09256	23	45	16
5/16	0.40481	2.47028	0.44271	2.25882	0.91440	1.09361	23	52	46
11/32	0.40680	2.45821	0.44531	2.24561	0.91352	1.09467	24	00	14
3/8	0.40878	2.44629	0.44792	2.23256	0.91263	1.09573	24	07	42
13/32	0.41076	2.43451	0.45052	2.21965	0.91174	1.09680	24	15	09
7/16	0.41273	2.42289	0.45313	2.20690	0.91085	1.09787	24	22	35
15/32	0.41470	2.41141	0.45573	2.19429	0.90996	1.09895	24	30	00
1/2	0.41666	2.40007	0.45833	2.18182	0.90907	1.10003	24	37	25
17/32	0.41861	2.38887	0.46094	2.16949	0.90817	1.10112	24	44	48
9/16	0.42056	2.37781	0.46354	2.15730	0.90727	1.10221	24	52	11
19/32	0.42250	2.36688	0.46615	2.14525	0.90636	1.10331	24	59	33
5/8	0.42443	2.35608	0.46875	2.13333	0.90546	1.10441	25	06	53
21/32	0.42636	2.34541	0.47135	2.12155	0.90455	1.10552	25	14	13
11/16	0.42829	2.33487	0.47396	2.10989	0.90364	1.10663	25	21	32
23/32	0.43021	2.32446	0.47656	2.09836	0.90273	1.10775	25	28	51
3/4	0.43212	2.31417	0.47917	2.08696	0.90182	1.10887	25	36	08
25/32	0.43403	2.30400	0.48177	2.07568	0.90090	1.11000	25	43	24
13/16	0.43593	2.29395	0.48438	2.06452	0.89998	1.11113	25	50	40
27/32	0.43782	2.28402	0.48698	2.05348	0.89906	1.11227	25	57	54
7/8	0.43971	2.27421	0.48958	2.04255	0.89814	1.11341	26	05	08
29/32	0.44160	2.26451	0.49219	2.03175	0.89721	1.11456	26	12	21
15/16	0.44348	2.25492	0.49479	2.02105	0.89629	1.11571	26	19	33
31/32	0.44535	2.24544	0.49740	2.01047	0.89536	1.11687	26	26	44
1	0.44721	2.23607	0.50000	2.00000	0.89443	1.11803	26	33	54

Fraction of an inch	\multicolumn{6}{c|}{LOGARITHMIC FUNCTIONS}	\multicolumn{3}{c}{Angle}
	Sine.	Cosec.	Tang.	Cotang.	Cosine.	Sec.	Deg.	Min.	Sec.
0	9.58503	0.41497	9.61979	0.38021	9.96524	0.03476	22	37	12
1/32	9.58733	0.41267	9.62249	0.37751	9.96484	0.03516	22	44	49
1/16	9.58962	0.41038	9.62518	0.37482	9.96443	0.03557	22	52	25
3/32	9.59188	0.40812	9.62786	0.37214	9.96403	0.03597	23	00	01
1/8	9.59413	0.40587	9.63051	0.36949	9.96362	0.03638	23	07	35
5/32	9.59636	0.40364	9.63315	0.36685	9.96321	0.03679	23	15	09
3/16	9.59857	0.40143	9.63578	0.36422	9.96280	0.03720	23	22	42
7/32	9.60077	0.39923	9.63839	0.36161	9.96238	0.03762	23	30	14
1/4	9.60295	0.39705	9.64098	0.35902	9.96197	0.03803	23	37	46
9/32	9.60511	0.39489	9.64356	0.35644	9.96155	0.03845	23	45	16
5/16	9.60725	0.39275	9.64612	0.35388	9.96114	0.03886	23	52	46
11/32	9.60938	0.39062	9.64866	0.35134	9.96072	0.03928	24	00	14
3/8	9.61149	0.38851	9.65120	0.34880	9.96030	0.03970	24	07	42
13/32	9.61359	0.38641	9.65371	0.34629	9.95987	0.04013	24	15	09
7/16	9.61567	0.38433	9.65622	0.34378	9.95945	0.04055	24	22	35
15/32	9.61773	0.38227	9.65871	0.34129	9.95902	0.04098	24	30	00
1/2	9.61978	0.38022	9.66118	0.33882	9.95859	0.04141	24	37	25
17/32	9.62181	0.37819	9.66364	0.33636	9.95817	0.04183	24	44	48
9/16	9.62382	0.37618	9.66609	0.33391	9.95773	0.04227	24	52	11
19/32	9.62582	0.37418	9.66852	0.33148	9.95730	0.04270	24	59	33
5/8	9.62781	0.37219	9.67094	0.32906	9.95687	0.04313	25	06	53
21/32	9.62978	0.37022	9.67335	0.32665	9.95643	0.04357	25	14	13
11/16	9.63174	0.36826	9.67574	0.32426	9.95600	0.04400	25	21	32
23/32	9.63368	0.36632	9.67812	0.32188	9.95556	0.04444	25	28	51
3/4	9.63560	0.36440	9.68049	0.31951	9.95512	0.04488	25	36	08
25/32	9.63752	0.36248	9.68284	0.31716	9.95468	0.04532	25	43	24
13/16	9.63942	0.36058	9.68518	0.31482	9.95423	0.04577	25	50	40
27/32	9.64130	0.35870	9.68751	0.31249	9.95379	0.04621	25	57	54
7/8	9.64317	0.35683	9.68983	0.31017	9.95334	0.04666	26	05	08
29/32	9.64503	0.35497	9.69213	0.30787	9.95290	0.04710	26	12	21
15/16	9.64687	0.35313	9.69442	0.30558	9.95245	0.04755	26	19	33
31/32	9.64870	0.35130	9.69670	0.30330	9.95200	0.04800	26	26	44
1	9.65051	0.34949	9.69897	0.30103	9.95154	0.04846	26	33	54

6"

Fraction of an inch	NATURAL FUNCTIONS						Angle		
	Sine.	Cosec.	Tang.	Cotang.	Cosine.	Sec.	Deg.	Min.	Sec.
0	0.44721	2.23607	0.50000	2.00000	0.89443	1.11803	26	33	54
1/32	0.44907	2.22680	0.50260	1.98964	0.89349	1.11920	26	41	03
1/16	0.45093	2.21765	0.50521	1.97938	0.89256	1.12037	26	48	12
3/32	0.45278	2.20859	0.50781	1.96923	0.89162	1.12155	26	55	19
1/8	0.45462	2.19964	0.51042	1.95918	0.89069	1.12273	27	02	26
5/32	0.45646	2.19078	0.51302	1.94924	0.88975	1.12392	27	09	32
3/16	0.45829	2.18203	0.51563	1.93939	0.88880	1.12511	27	16	36
7/32	0.46011	2.17337	0.51823	1.92965	0.88786	1.12630	27	23	40
1/4	0.46193	2.16481	0.52083	1.92000	0.88691	1.12751	27	30	43
9/32	0.46375	2.15634	0.52344	1.91045	0.88597	1.12871	27	37	45
5/16	0.46556	2.14797	0.52604	1.90099	0.88502	1.12992	27	44	46
11/32	0.46736	2.13968	0.52865	1.89163	0.88407	1.13114	27	51	47
3/8	0.46916	2.13149	0.53125	1.88235	0.88312	1.13235	27	58	46
13/32	0.47095	2.12339	0.53385	1.87317	0.88216	1.13358	28	05	45
7/16	0.47273	2.11537	0.53646	1.86408	0.88121	1.13481	28	12	42
15/32	0.47451	2.10744	0.53906	1.85507	0.88025	1.13604	28	19	39
1/2	0.47628	2.09959	0.54167	1.84615	0.87929	1.13728	28	26	35
17/32	0.47805	2.09183	0.54427	1.83732	0.87833	1.13852	28	33	29
9/16	0.47981	2.08415	0.54688	1.82857	0.87737	1.13977	28	40	23
19/32	0.48157	2.07655	0.54948	1.81991	0.87641	1.14102	28	47	16
5/8	0.48332	2.06903	0.55208	1.81132	0.87545	1.14228	28	54	09
21/32	0.48506	2.06159	0.55469	1.80282	0.87448	1.14354	29	01	00
11/16	0.48680	2.05423	0.55729	1.79439	0.87351	1.14480	29	07	50
23/32	0.48853	2.04694	0.55990	1.78605	0.87254	1.14607	29	14	39
3/4	0.49026	2.03973	0.56250	1.77778	0.87158	1.14735	29	21	28
25/32	0.49198	2.03259	0.56510	1.76959	0.87061	1.14863	29	28	16
13/16	0.49370	2.02553	0.56771	1.76147	0.86963	1.14991	29	35	02
27/32	0.49541	2.01854	0.57031	1.75342	0.86866	1.15120	29	41	48
7/8	0.49711	2.01162	0.57292	1.74545	0.86769	1.15249	29	48	33
29/32	0.49881	2.00477	0.57552	1.73756	0.86671	1.15379	29	55	17
15/16	0.50050	1.99799	0.57813	1.72973	0.86573	1.15509	30	02	00
31/32	0.50219	1.99128	0.58073	1.72197	0.86476	1.15639	30	08	42
1	0.50387	1.98463	0.58333	1.71429	0.86378	1.15770	30	15	23

Fraction of an inch	LOGARITHMIC FUNCTIONS						Angle		
	Sine.	Cosec.	Tang.	Cotang.	Cosine.	Sec.	Deg.	Min.	Sec.
0	9.65051	0.34949	9.69897	0.30103	9.95154	0.04846	26	33	54
1/32	9.65232	0.34768	9.70123	0.29877	9.95109	0.04891	26	41	03
1/16	9.65411	0.34589	9.70347	0.29653	9.95064	0.04936	26	48	12
3/32	9.65588	0.34412	9.70570	0.29430	9.95018	0.04982	26	55	19
1/8	9.65765	0.34235	9.70792	0.29208	9.94972	0.05028	27	02	26
5/32	9.65940	0.34060	9.71014	0.28986	9.94927	0.05073	27	09	32
3/16	9.66114	0.33886	9.71233	0.28767	9.94881	0.05119	27	16	36
7/32	9.66287	0.33713	9.71452	0.28548	9.94834	0.05166	27	23	40
1/4	9.66458	0.33542	9.71670	0.28330	9.94789	0.05212	27	30	43
9/32	9.66628	0.33372	9.71886	0.28114	9.94742	0.05258	27	37	45
5/16	9.66797	0.33203	9.72102	0.27898	9.94695	0.05305	27	44	46
11/32	9.66965	0.33035	9.72316	0.27684	9.94649	0.05351	27	51	47
3/8	9.67132	0.32868	9.72530	0.27470	9.94602	0.05398	27	58	46
13/32	9.67297	0.32703	9.72742	0.27258	9.94555	0.05445	28	05	45
7/16	9.67461	0.32539	9.72954	0.27046	9.94508	0.05492	28	12	42
15/32	9.67625	0.32375	9.73164	0.26836	9.94461	0.05539	28	19	39
1/2	9.67787	0.32213	9.73373	0.26627	9.94413	0.05587	28	26	35
17/32	9.67947	0.32053	9.73582	0.26418	9.94366	0.05634	28	33	29
9/16	9.68107	0.31893	9.73789	0.26211	9.94318	0.05682	28	40	23
19/32	9.68266	0.31734	9.73995	0.26005	9.94271	0.05729	28	47	16
5/8	9.68423	0.31577	9.74200	0.25800	9.94223	0.05777	28	54	09
21/32	9.68580	0.31420	9.74405	0.25595	9.94175	0.05825	29	01	00
11/16	9.68735	0.31265	9.74608	0.25392	9.94127	0.05873	29	07	50
23/32	9.68889	0.31110	9.74811	0.25189	9.94079	0.05921	29	14	39
3/4	9.69043	0.30957	9.75012	0.24988	9.94031	0.05969	29	21	28
25/32	9.69195	0.30805	9.75213	0.24787	9.93982	0.06018	29	28	16
13/16	9.69346	0.30654	9.75413	0.24587	9.93934	0.06066	29	35	02
27/32	9.69496	0.30504	9.75611	0.24389	9.93885	0.06115	29	41	48
7/8	9.69645	0.30355	9.75809	0.24191	9.93836	0.06164	29	48	33
29/32	9.69794	0.30206	9.76006	0.23994	9.93787	0.06213	29	55	17
15/16	9.69941	0.30059	9.76202	0.23798	9.93738	0.06262	30	02	00
31/32	9.70087	0.29913	9.76397	0.23603	9.93689	0.06311	30	08	42
1	9.70232	0.29768	9.76592	0.23408	9.93640	0.06360	30	15	23

7″

Fraction of an Inch	NATURAL FUNCTIONS						Angle		
	Sine.	Cosec.	Tang.	Cotang.	Cosine.	Sec.	Deg.	Min.	Sec.
0	0.50387	1.98463	0.58333	1.71429	0.86378	1.15770	30	15	23
1/32	0.50555	1.97806	0.58594	1.70667	0.86280	1.15902	30	22	04
1/16	0.50722	1.97155	0.58854	1.69910	0.86182	1.16034	30	28	43
3/32	0.50888	1.96510	0.59115	1.69163	0.86084	1.16166	30	35	21
1/8	0.51054	1.95871	0.59375	1.68421	0.85986	1.16299	30	41	59
5/32	0.51219	1.95239	0.59635	1.67686	0.85887	1.16432	30	48	36
3/16	0.51384	1.94614	0.59896	1.66957	0.85789	1.16566	30	55	11
7/32	0.51548	1.93994	0.60156	1.66234	0.85690	1.16700	31	01	46
1/4	0.51712	1.93380	0.60417	1.65517	0.85592	1.16834	31	08	20
9/32	0.51875	1.92773	0.60677	1.64807	0.85493	1.16969	31	14	53
5/16	0.52037	1.92171	0.60938	1.64103	0.85394	1.17104	31	21	26
11/32	0.52199	1.91575	0.61198	1.63404	0.85295	1.17240	31	27	57
3/8	0.52360	1.90985	0.61458	1.62712	0.85196	1.17376	31	34	27
13/32	0.52521	1.90400	0.61719	1.62025	0.85097	1.17513	31	40	57
7/16	0.52681	1.89821	0.61979	1.61345	0.84998	1.17650	31	47	25
15/32	0.52841	1.89248	0.62240	1.60669	0.84899	1.17787	31	53	53
1/2	0.53000	1.88680	0.62500	1.60000	0.84800	1.17925	32	00	19
17/32	0.53158	1.88117	0.62760	1.59336	0.84701	1.18063	32	06	45
9/16	0.53316	1.87560	0.63021	1.58678	0.84601	1.18202	32	13	10
19/32	0.53474	1.87008	0.63281	1.58025	0.84502	1.18341	32	19	34
5/8	0.53631	1.86461	0.63542	1.57377	0.84402	1.18480	32	25	57
21/32	0.53787	1.85919	0.63802	1.56735	0.84303	1.18620	32	32	19
11/16	0.53943	1.85382	0.64063	1.56098	0.84203	1.18760	32	38	41
23/32	0.54098	1.84850	0.64323	1.55466	0.84104	1.18901	32	45	01
3/4	0.54253	1.84323	0.64583	1.54839	0.84004	1.19042	32	51	21
25/32	0.54407	1.83801	0.64844	1.54217	0.83904	1.19184	32	57	39
13/16	0.54560	1.83284	0.65104	1.53600	0.83804	1.19325	33	03	57
27/32	0.54713	1.82771	0.65365	1.52988	0.83705	1.19468	33	10	14
7/8	0.54866	1.82263	0.65625	1.52381	0.83605	1.19610	33	16	30
29/32	0.55018	1.81760	0.65885	1.51779	0.83505	1.19753	33	22	45
15/16	0.55169	1.81261	0.66146	1.51181	0.83405	1.19897	33	28	59
31/32	0.55320	1.80767	0.66406	1.50588	0.83305	1.20041	33	35	12
1	0.55470	1.80278	0.66667	1.50000	0.83205	1.20185	33	41	24

Fraction of an Inch	LOGARITHMIC FUNCTIONS						Angle		
	Sine.	Cosec.	Tang.	Cotang.	Cosine.	Sec.	Deg.	Min.	Sec.
0	9.70232	0.29768	9.76592	0.23408	9.93640	0.06360	30	15	23
1/32	9.70376	0.29624	9.76785	0.23215	9.93591	0.06409	30	22	04
1/16	9.70519	0.29481	9.76978	0.23022	9.93542	0.06458	30	28	43
3/32	9.70662	0.29338	9.77169	0.22831	9.93492	0.06508	30	35	21
1/8	9.70803	0.29197	9.77360	0.22640	9.93443	0.06557	30	41	59
5/32	9.70943	0.29057	9.77550	0.22450	9.93393	0.06607	30	48	36
3/16	9.71083	0.28917	9.77740	0.22260	9.93343	0.06657	30	55	11
7/32	9.71221	0.28779	9.77928	0.22072	9.93293	0.06707	31	01	46
1/4	9.71359	0.28641	9.78116	0.21884	9.93243	0.06757	31	08	20
9/32	9.71495	0.28505	9.78302	0.21698	9.93193	0.06807	31	14	53
5/16	9.71631	0.28369	9.78488	0.21512	9.93143	0.06857	31	21	26
11/32	9.71766	0.28234	9.78674	0.21326	9.93092	0.06908	31	27	57
3/8	9.71900	0.28100	9.78858	0.21142	9.93042	0.06958	31	34	27
13/32	9.72033	0.27967	9.79042	0.20958	9.92992	0.07008	31	40	57
7/16	9.72166	0.27834	9.79225	0.20775	9.92941	0.07059	31	47	25
15/32	9.72297	0.27703	9.79407	0.20593	9.92890	0.07110	31	53	53
1/2	9.72427	0.27573	9.79588	0.20412	9.92839	0.07161	32	00	19
17/32	9.72557	0.27443	9.79769	0.20231	9.92789	0.07211	32	06	45
9/16	9.72686	0.27314	9.79948	0.20052	9.92738	0.07262	32	13	10
19/32	9.72814	0.27186	9.80128	0.19872	9.92687	0.07313	32	19	34
5/8	9.72941	0.27059	9.80306	0.19694	9.92635	0.07365	32	25	57
21/32	9.73068	0.26932	9.80483	0.19517	9.92584	0.07416	32	32	19
11/16	9.73193	0.26807	9.80660	0.19340	9.92533	0.07467	32	38	41
23/32	9.73318	0.26682	9.80837	0.19163	9.92481	0.07519	32	45	01
3/4	9.73442	0.26558	9.81012	0.18988	9.92430	0.07570	32	51	21
25/32	9.73565	0.26435	9.81187	0.18813	9.92378	0.07622	32	57	39
13/16	9.73688	0.26312	9.81361	0.18639	9.92327	0.07673	33	03	57
27/32	9.73809	0.26191	9.81534	0.18466	9.92275	0.07725	33	10	14
7/8	9.73930	0.26070	9.81707	0.18293	9.92223	0.07777	33	16	30
29/32	9.74050	0.25950	9.81879	0.18121	9.92171	0.07829	33	22	45
15/16	9.74169	0.25831	9.82050	0.17950	9.92119	0.07881	33	28	59
31/32	9.74288	0.25712	9.82221	0.17779	9.92067	0.07933	33	35	12
1	9.74406	0.25594	9.82391	0.17609	9.92015	0.07985	33	41	24

13

8"

Fraction of an Inch	NATURAL FUNCTIONS						Angle		
	Sine.	Cosec.	Tang.	Cotang.	Cosine.	Sec.	Deg.	Min.	Sec.
0	0.55470	1.80278	0.66667	1.50000	0.83205	1.20185	33	41	24
1/32	0.55620	1.79792	0.66927	1.49416	0.83105	1.20330	33	47	36
1/16	0.55769	1.79311	0.67188	1.48837	0.83005	1.20475	33	53	46
3/32	0.55918	1.78835	0.67448	1.48263	0.82905	1.20620	33	59	56
1/8	0.56066	1.78362	0.67708	1.47692	0.82805	1.20766	34	06	05
5/32	0.56213	1.77894	0.67969	1.47126	0.82705	1.20912	34	12	12
3/16	0.56360	1.77430	0.68229	1.46565	0.82605	1.21059	34	18	19
7/32	0.56507	1.76970	0.68490	1.46008	0.82504	1.21206	34	24	25
1/4	0.56653	1.76514	0.68750	1.45455	0.82404	1.21353	34	30	31
9/32	0.56798	1.76061	0.69010	1.44906	0.82304	1.21501	34	36	35
5/16	0.56943	1.75613	0.69271	1.44361	0.82204	1.21649	34	42	38
11/32	0.57088	1.75169	0.69531	1.43820	0.82104	1.21797	34	48	41
3/8	0.57231	1.74729	0.69792	1.43284	0.82003	1.21946	34	54	43
13/32	0.57375	1.74292	0.70052	1.42751	0.81903	1.22095	35	00	43
7/16	0.57518	1.73860	0.70313	1.42222	0.81803	1.22245	35	06	43
15/32	0.57660	1.73431	0.70573	1.41697	0.81703	1.22395	35	12	42
1/2	0.57802	1.73005	0.70833	1.41176	0.81602	1.22545	35	18	40
17/32	0.57943	1.72583	0.71094	1.40659	0.81502	1.22696	35	24	38
9/16	0.58084	1.72165	0.71354	1.40146	0.81402	1.22847	35	30	34
19/32	0.58224	1.71751	0.71615	1.39636	0.81302	1.22999	35	36	30
5/8	0.58364	1.71340	0.71875	1.39130	0.81202	1.23150	35	42	24
21/32	0.58503	1.70932	0.72135	1.38628	0.81101	1.23303	35	48	18
11/16	0.58641	1.70528	0.72396	1.38130	0.81001	1.23455	35	54	11
23/32	0.58780	1.70127	0.72656	1.37634	0.80901	1.23608	36	00	03
3/4	0.58917	1.69730	0.72917	1.37143	0.80801	1.23761	36	05	54
25/32	0.59054	1.69336	0.73177	1.36655	0.80701	1.23915	36	11	44
13/16	0.59191	1.68945	0.73438	1.36170	0.80600	1.24069	36	17	33
27/32	0.59327	1.68557	0.73698	1.35689	0.80500	1.24223	36	23	22
7/8	0.59463	1.68173	0.73958	1.35211	0.80400	1.24378	36	29	10
29/32	0.59598	1.67791	0.74219	1.34737	0.80300	1.24533	36	34	56
15/16	0.59732	1.67414	0.74479	1.34266	0.80200	1.24688	36	40	42
31/32	0.59866	1.67039	0.74740	1.33798	0.80100	1.24844	36	46	27
1	0.60000	1.66667	0.75000	1.33333	0.80000	1.25000	36	52	12

Fraction of an inch	LOGARITHMIC FUNCTIONS						Angle		
	Sine.	Cosec.	Tang.	Cotang.	Cosine.	Sec.	Deg.	Min.	Sec.
0	9.74406	0.25594	9.82391	0.17609	9.92015	0.07985	33	41	24
¹⁄₃₂	9.74523	0.25477	9.82560	0.17440	9.91963	0.08037	33	47	36
¹⁄₁₆	9.74639	0.25361	9.82729	0.17271	9.91910	0.08090	33	53	46
³⁄₃₂	9.74755	0.25245	9.82897	0.17103	9.91858	0.08142	33	59	56
⅛	9.74870	0.25130	9.83064	0.16936	9.91806	0.08194	34	06	05
⁵⁄₃₂	9.74984	0.25016	9.83231	0.16769	9.91753	0.08247	34	12	12
³⁄₁₆	9.75097	0.24903	9.83397	0.16603	9.91700	0.08300	34	18	19
⁷⁄₃₂	9.75210	0.24790	9.83562	0.16438	9.91648	0.08352	34	24	25
¼	9.75322	0.24678	9.83727	0.16273	9.91595	0.08405	34	30	31
⁹⁄₃₂	9.75434	0.24566	9.83891	0.16109	9.91542	0.08458	34	36	35
⁵⁄₁₆	9.75544	0.24456	9.84055	0.15945	9.91489	0.08511	34	42	38
¹¹⁄₃₂	9.75654	0.24346	9.84218	0.15782	9.91436	0.08564	34	48	41
⅜	9.75764	0.24236	9.84380	0.15620	9.91383	0.08617	34	54	43
¹³⁄₃₂	9.75872	0.24128	9.84542	0.15458	9.91330	0.08670	35	00	43
⁷⁄₁₆	9.75980	0.24020	9.84703	0.15297	9.91277	0.08723	35	06	43
¹⁵⁄₃₂	9.76087	0.23913	9.84864	0.15136	9.91224	0.08776	35	12	42
½	9.76194	0.23806	9.85024	0.14976	9.91170	0.08830	35	18	40
¹⁷⁄₃₂	9.76300	0.23700	9.85183	0.14817	9.91117	0.08883	35	24	38
⁹⁄₁₆	9.76405	0.23595	9.85342	0.14658	9.91063	0.08937	35	30	34
¹⁹⁄₃₂	9.76510	0.23490	9.85500	0.14500	9.91010	0.08990	35	36	30
⅝	9.76614	0.23386	9.85658	0.14342	9.90956	0.09044	35	42	24
²¹⁄₃₂	9.76718	0.23282	9.85815	0.14185	9.90903	0.09097	35	48	18
¹¹⁄₁₆	9.76820	0.23180	9.85971	0.14029	9·90849	0.09151	35	54	11
²³⁄₃₂	9.76923	0.23077	9.86127	0.13873	9.90795	0.09205	36	00	03
¾	9.77024	0.22976	9.86283	0.13717	9.90742	0.09258	36	05	54
²⁵⁄₃₂	9.77125	0.22875	9.86438	0.13562	9.90688	0.09312	36	11	44
¹³⁄₁₆	9.77226	0.22774	9.86592	0.13408	9.90634	0.09366	36	17	33
²⁷⁄₃₂	9.77325	0.22675	9.86746	0.13254	9.90580	0.09420	36	23	22
⅞	9.77424	0.22576	9.86899	0.13101	9.90526	0.09474	36	29	10
²⁹⁄₃₂	9.77523	0.22477	9.87051	0.12949	9.90472	0.09528	36	34	56
¹⁵⁄₁₆	9.77621	0.22379	9.87203	0.12797	9.90417	0.09583	36	40	42
³¹⁄₃₂	9.77718	0.22282	9.87355	0.12645	9.90363	0.09637	36	46	27
1	9.77815	0.22185	9.87506	0.12494	9.90309	0.09691	36	52	12

9"

Fraction of an Inch	NATURAL FUNCTIONS						Angle		
	Sine.	Cosec.	Tang.	Cotang.	Cosine.	Sec.	Deg.	Min.	Sec.
0	0.60000	1.66667	0.75000	1.33333	0.80000	1.25000	36	52	12
1/32	0.60133	1.66298	0.75260	1.32872	0.79900	1.25156	36	57	55
1/16	0.60266	1.65932	0.75521	1.32414	0.79800	1.25313	37	03	37
3/32	0.60398	1.65569	0.75781	1.31959	0.79700	1.25470	37	09	19
1/8	0.60529	1.65209	0.76042	1.31507	0.79600	1.25628	37	15	00
5/32	0.60660	1.64852	0.76302	1.31058	0.79500	1.25786	37	20	40
3/16	0.60791	1.64498	0.76563	1.30612	0.79401	1.25944	37	26	19
7/32	0.60921	1.64147	0.76823	1.30170	0.79301	1.26102	37	31	57
1/4	0.61051	1.63798	0.77083	1.29730	0.79201	1.26261	37	37	34
9/32	0.61180	1.63452	0.77344	1.29293	0.79101	1.26420	37	43	11
5/16	0.61309	1.63109	0.77604	1.28859	0.79002	1.26580	37	48	47
11/32	0.61437	1.62769	0.77865	1.28428	0.78902	1.26740	37	54	21
3/8	0.61564	1.62431	0.78125	1.28000	0.78802	1.26900	37	59	56
13/32	0.61692	1.62097	0.78385	1.27575	0.78703	1.27060	38	05	29
7/16	0.61818	1.61764	0.78646	1.27152	0.78603	1.27221	38	11	01
15/32	0.61945	1.61435	0.78906	1.26733	0.78504	1.27382	38	16	32
1/2	0.62070	1.61108	0.79167	1.26316	0.78405	1.27544	38	22	03
17/32	0.62196	1.60783	0.79427	1.25902	0.78305	1.27705	38	27	33
9/16	0.62320	1.60461	0.79688	1.25490	0.78206	1.27868	38	33	02
19/32	0.62445	1.60142	0.79948	1.25081	0.78107	1.28030	38	38	30
5/8	0.62569	1.59825	0.80208	1.24675	0.78008	1.28193	38	43	57
21/32	0.62692	1.59510	0.80469	1.24272	0.77908	1.28356	38	49	24
11/16	0.62815	1.59198	0.80729	1.23871	0.77809	1.28519	38	54	49
23/32	0.62937	1.58888	0.80990	1.23473	0.77710	1.28683	39	00	14
3/4	0.63059	1.58581	0.81250	1.23077	0.77611	1.28847	39	05	38
25/32	0.63181	1.58276	0.81510	1.22684	0.77512	1.29011	39	11	01
13/16	0.63302	1.57973	0.81771	1.22293	0.77414	1.29176	39	16	23
27/32	0.63422	1.57673	0.82031	1.21905	0.77315	1.29341	39	21	45
7/8	0.63542	1.57375	0.82292	1.21519	0.77216	1.29506	39	27	06
29/32	0.63662	1.57079	0.82552	1.21136	0.77118	1.29672	39	32	25
15/16	0.63781	1.56785	0.82813	1.20755	0.77019	1.29838	39	37	44
31/32	0.63900	1.56494	0.83073	1.20376	0.76921	1.30004	39	43	03
1	0.64018	1.56205	0.83333	1.20000	0.76822	1.30171	39	48	20

| Fraction of an inch | LOGARITHMIC FUNCTIONS | | | | | | Angle | | |
	Sine.	Cosec.	Tang.	Cotang.	Cosine.	Sec	Deg.	Min.	Sec.
0	9.77815	0.22185	9.87506	0.12494	9.90309	0.09691	36	52	12
1/32	9.77911	0.22089	9.87657	0.12343	9.90255	0.09745	36	57	55
1/16	9.78007	0.21993	9.87807	0.12193	9.90200	0.09800	37	03	37
3/32	9.78102	0.21898	9.87956	0.12044	9.90146	0.09854	37	09	19
1/8	9.78197	0.21803	9.88105	0.11895	9.90091	0.09909	37	15	00
5/32	9.78291	0.21709	9.88254	0.11746	9.90037	0.09963	37	20	40
3/16	9.78384	0.21616	9.88402	0.11598	9.89982	0.10018	37	26	19
7/32	9.78477	0.21523	9.88549	0.11451	9.89928	0.10072	37	31	57
1/4	9.78569	0.21431	9.88696	0.11304	9.89873	0.10127	37	37	34
9/32	9.78661	0.21339	9.88843	0.11157	9.89818	0.10182	37	43	11
5/16	9.78752	0.21248	9.88989	0.11011	9.89764	0.10236	37	48	47
11/32	9.78843	0.21157	9.89134	0.10866	9.89709	0.10291	37	54	21
3/8	9.78933	0.21067	9.89279	0.10721	9.89654	0.10346	37	59	56
13/32	9.79023	0.20977	9.89424	0.10576	9.89599	0.10401	38	05	29
7/16	9.79112	0.20888	9.89568	0.10432	9.89544	0.10456	38	11	01
15/32	9.79200	0.20800	9.89711	0.10289	9.89489	0.10511	38	16	32
1/2	9.79288	0.20712	9.89854	0.10146	9.89434	0.10566	38	22	03
17/32	9.79376	0.20624	9.89997	0.10003	9.89379	0.10621	38	27	33
9/16	9.79463	0.20537	9.90139	0.09861	9.89324	0.10676	38	33	02
19/32	9.79550	0.20450	9.90281	0.09719	9.89269	0.10731	38	38	30
5/8	9.79636	0.20364	9.90422	0.09578	9.89214	0.10786	38	43	57
21/32	9.79721	0.20279	9.90563	0.09437	9.89158	0.10842	38	49	24
11/16	9.79806	0.20194	9.90703	0.09297	9.89103	0.10897	38	54	49
23/32	9.79891	0.20109	9.90843	0.09157	9.89048	0.10952	39	00	14
3/4	9.79975	0.20025	9.90982	0.09018	9.88993	0.11007	39	05	38
25/32	9.80058	0.19942	9.91121	0.08879	9.88937	0.11063	39	11	01
13/16	9.80142	0.19858	9.91260	0.08740	9.88882	0.11118	39	16	23
27/32	9.80224	0.19776	9.91398	0.08602	9.88826	0.11174	39	21	45
7/8	9.80306	0.19694	9.91536	0.08464	9.88771	0.11229	39	27	06
29/32	9.80388	0.19612	9.91673	0.08327	9.88715	0.11285	39	32	25
15/16	9.80469	0.19531	9.91810	0.08190	9.88660	0.11340	39	37	44
31/32	9.80550	0.19450	9.91946	0.08054	9.88604	0.11396	39	43	03
1	9.80631	0.19369	9.92082	0.07918	9.88549	0.11451	39	48	20

10"

Fraction of an Inch	NATURAL FUNCTIONS						Angle		
	Sine.	Cosec.	Tang.	Cotang.	Cosine.	Sec.	Deg.	Min.	Sec.
0	0.64018	1.56205	0.83333	1.20000	0.76822	1.30171	39	48	20
1/32	0.64136	1.55918	0.83594	1.19626	0.76724	1.30338	39	53	37
1/16	0.64254	1.55633	0.83854	1.19255	0.76626	1.30505	39	58	52
3/32	0.64371	1.55350	0.84115	1.18885	0.76527	1.30672	40	04	07
1/8	0.64487	1.55070	0.84375	1.18519	0.76429	1.30840	40	09	22
5/32	0.64603	1.54791	0.84635	1.18154	0.76331	1.31008	40	14	35
3/16	0.64719	1.54515	0.84896	1.17791	0.76233	1.31177	40	19	48
7/32	0.64834	1.54240	0.85156	1.17431	0.76135	1.31345	40	24	59
1/4	0.64949	1.53968	0.85417	1.17073	0.76037	1.31514	40	30	10
9/32	0.65063	1.53698	0.85677	1.16717	0.75940	1.31684	40	35	20
5/16	0.65177	1.53429	0.85938	1.16364	0.75842	1.31853	40	40	30
11/32	0.65290	1.53163	0.86198	1.16012	0.75744	1.32023	40	45	38
3/8	0.65403	1.52898	0.86458	1.15663	0.75647	1.32193	40	50	46
13/32	0.65516	1.52636	0.86719	1.15315	0.75549	1.32364	40	55	53
7/16	0.65628	1.52375	0.86979	1.14970	0.75452	1.32534	41	00	59
15/32	0.65739	1.52116	0.87240	1.14627	0.75355	1.32706	41	06	05
1/2	0.65851	1.51859	0.87500	1.14286	0.75258	1.32877	41	11	09
17/32	0.65961	1.51604	0.87760	1.13947	0.75161	1.33048	41	16	13
9/16	0.66072	1.51351	0.88021	1.13609	0.75064	1.33220	41	21	16
19/32	0.66182	1.51100	0.88281	1.13274	0.74967	1.33393	41	26	18
5/8	0.66291	1.50850	0.88542	1.12941	0.74870	1.33565	41	31	20
21/32	0.66400	1.50602	0.88802	1.12610	0.74773	1.33738	41	36	21
11/16	0.66509	1.50356	0.89063	1.12281	0.74677	1.33911	41	41	21
23/32	0.66617	1.50112	0.89323	1.11953	0.74580	1.34084	41	46	20
3/4	0.66725	1.49869	0.89583	1.11628	0.74484	1.34258	41	51	18
25/32	0.66832	1.49628	0.89844	1.11304	0.74387	1.34432	41	56	16
13/16	0.66939	1.49389	0.90104	1.10983	0.74291	1.34606	42	01	13
27/32	0.67046	1.49152	0.90365	1.10663	0.74195	1.34780	42	06	09
7/8	0.67152	1.48916	0.90625	1.10345	0.74099	1.34955	42	11	04
29/32	0.67258	1.48682	0.90885	1.10029	0.74003	1.35130	42	15	59
15/16	0.67363	1.48449	0.91146	1.09714	0.73907	1.35305	42	20	52
31/32	0.67468	1.48219	0.91406	1.09402	0.73811	1.35481	42	25	45
1	0.67572	1.47989	0.91667	1.09091	0.73715	1.35657	42	30	38

Fraction of an Inch	LOGARITHMIC FUNCTIONS						Angle		
	Sine.	Cosec.	Tang.	Cotang.	Cosine.	Sec.	Deg.	Min.	Sec.
0	9.80631	0.19369	9.92082	0.07918	9.88549	0.11451	39	48	20
1/32	9.80710	0.19290	9.92217	0.07783	9.88493	0.11507	39	53	37
1/16	9.80790	0.19210	9.92352	0.07648	9.88437	0.11563	39	58	52
3/32	9.80869	0.19131	9.92487	0.07513	9.88382	0.11618	40	04	07
1/8	9.80947	0.19053	9.92621	0.07379	9.88326	0.11674	40	09	22
5/32	9.81025	0.18975	9.92755	0.07245	9.88270	0.11730	40	14	35
3/16	9.81103	0.18897	9.92889	0.07111	9.88214	0.11786	40	19	48
7/32	9.81180	0.18820	9.93022	0.06978	9.88159	0.11841	40	24	59
1/4	9.81257	0.18743	9.93154	0.06846	9.88103	0.11897	40	30	10
9/32	9.81333	0.18667	9.93286	0.06714	9.88047	0.11953	40	35	20
5/16	9.81409	0.18591	9.93418	0.06582	9.87991	0.12009	40	40	30
11/32	9.81485	0.18515	9.93550	0.06450	9.87935	0.12065	40	45	38
3/8	9.81560	0.18440	9.93681	0.06319	9.87879	0.12121	40	50	46
13/32	9.81634	0.18366	9.93811	0.06189	9.87823	0.12177	40	55	53
7/16	9.81709	0.18291	9.93942	0.06058	9.87767	0.12233	41	00	59
15/32	9.81782	0.18218	9.94071	0.05929	9.87711	0.12289	41	06	05
1/2	9.81856	0.18144	9.94201	0.05799	9.87655	0.12345	41	11	09
17/32	9.81929	0.18071	9.94330	0.05670	9.87599	0.12401	41	16	13
9/16	9.82001	0.17999	9.94459	0.05541	9.87543	0.12457	41	21	16
19/32	9.82074	0.17926	9.94587	0.05413	9.87487	0.12513	41	26	18
5/8	9.82145	0.17855	9.94715	0.05285	9.87431	0.12569	41	31	20
21/32	9.82217	0.17783	9.94842	0.05158	9.87375	0.12625	41	36	21
11/16	9.82288	0.17712	9.94969	0.05031	9.87318	0.12682	41	41	21
23/32	9.82359	0.17641	9.95096	0.04904	9.87262	0.12738	41	46	20
3/4	9.82429	0.17571	9.95223	0.04777	9.87206	0.12794	41	51	18
25/32	9.82499	0.17501	9.95349	0.04651	9.87150	0.12850	41	56	16
13/16	9.82568	0.17432	9.95474	0.04526	9.87094	0.12906	42	01	13
27/32	9.82637	0.17363	9.95600	0.04400	9.87037	0.12963	42	06	09
7/8	9.82706	0.17294	9.95725	0.04275	9.86981	0.13019	42	11	04
29/32	9.82774	0.17226	9.95849	0.04151	9.86925	0.13075	42	15	59
15/16	9.82842	0.17158	9.95974	0.04026	9.86868	0.13132	42	20	52
31/32	9.82910	0.17090	9.96098	0.03902	9.86812	0.13188	42	25	45
1	9.82977	0.17023	9.96221	0.03779	9.86756	0.13244	42	30	38

11"

Fraction of an Inch	Sine.	Cosec.	Tang.	Cotang.	Cosine.	Sec.	Deg.	Min.	Sec.
			NATURAL FUNCTIONS					Angle	
0	0.67572	1.47989	0.91667	1.09091	0.73715	1.35657	42	30	38
1/32	0.67677	1.47762	0.91927	1.08782	0.73620	1.35833	42	35	29
1/16	0.67780	1.47536	0.92188	1.08475	0.73524	1.36009	42	40	20
3/32	0.67884	1.47311	0.92448	1.08169	0.73429	1.36186	42	45	10
1/8	0.67987	1.47088	0.92708	1.07865	0.73334	1.36363	42	49	59
5/32	0.68089	1.46867	0.92969	1.07563	0.73239	1.36540	42	54	48
3/16	0.68191	1.46647	0.93229	1.07263	0.73144	1.36718	42	59	35
7/32	0.68293	1.46428	0.93490	1.06964	0.73049	1.36895	43	04	22
1/4	0.68394	1.46211	0.93750	1.06667	0.72954	1.37073	43	09	09
9/32	0.68495	1.45996	0.94010	1.06371	0.72859	1.37251	43	13	54
5/16	0.68596	1.45782	0.94271	1.06077	0.72764	1.37430	43	18	39
11/32	0.68696	1.45570	0.94531	1.05785	0.72670	1.37609	43	23	23
3/8	0.68795	1.45358·	0.94792	1.05495	0.72575	1.37788	43	28	06
13/32	0.68895	1.45149	0.95052	1.05205	0.72481	1.37967	43	32	49
7/16	0.68994	1.44941	0.95313	1.04918	0.72387	1.38147	43	37	31
15/32	0.69092	1.44734	0.95573	1.04632	0.72293	1.38326	43	42	12
1/2	0.69191	1.44528	0.95833	1.04348	0.72199	1.38506	43	46	52
17/32	0.69288	1.44324	0.96094	1.04065	0.72105	1.38687	43	51	32
9/16	0.69386	1.44122	0.96354	1.03784	0.72011	1.38867	43	56	11
19/32	0.69483	1.43920	0.96615	1.03504	0.71918	1.39048	44	00	49
5/8	0.69580	1.43720	0.96875	1.03226	0.71824	1.39229	44	05	26
21/32	0.69676	1.43522	0.97135	1.02949	0.71731	1.39411	44	10	03
11/16	0.69772	1.43325	0.97396	1.02674	0.71637	1 39592	44	14	39
23/32	0.69867	1.43128	0.97656	1.02400	0.71544	1.39774	44	19	14
3/4	0.69963	1.42934	0.97917	1.02128	0.71451	1.39956	44	23	49
25/32	0.70057	1.42740	0.98177	1.01857	0.71358	1.40138	44	28	23
13/16	0.70152	1.42548	0.98438	1.01587	0.71265	1.40321	44	32	56
27/32	0.70246	1.42357	0.98698	1.01319	0.71172	1.40504	44	37	28
7/8	0.70340	1.42168	0.98958	1.01053	0.71080	1.40687	44	42	00
29/32	0.70433	1.41979	0.99219	1.00787	0.70987	1.40870	44	46	31
15/16	0.70526	1.41792	0.99479	1.00524	0.70895	1.41054	44	51	01
31/32	0.70618	1.41606	0.99740	1.00261	0.70803	1.41237	44	55	31
1	0.70711	1.41421	1.00000	1.00000	0.70711	1.41421	45	00	00

Fraction of an Inch	LOGARITHMIC FUNCTIONS						Angle		
	Sine.	Cosec.	Tang.	Cotang.	Cosine.	Sec	Deg.	Min.	Sec.
0	9.82977	0.17023	9.96221	0.03779	9.86756	0.13244	42	30	38
1/32	9.83044	0.16956	9.96344	0.03656	9.86699	0.13301	42	35	29
1/16	9.83110	0.16890	9.96467	0.03533	9.86643	0.13357	42	40	20
3/32	9.83177	0.16823	9.96590	0.03410	9.86587	0.13413	42	45	10
1/8	9.83242	0.16758	9.96712	0.03288	9.86530	0.13470	42	49	59
5/32	9.83308	0.16692	9.96834	0.03166	9.86474	0.13526	42	54	48
3/16	9.83373	0.16627	9.96955	0.03045	9.86418	0.13582	42	59	35
7/32	9.83437	0.16563	9.97076	0.02924	9.86361	0.13639	43	04	22
1/4	9.83502	0.16498	9.97197	0.02803	9.86305	0.13695	43	09	09
9/32	9.83566	0.16434	9.97318	0.02682	9.86248	0.13752	43	13	54
5/16	9.83630	0.16370	9.97438	0.02562	9.86192	0.13808	43	18	39
11/32	9.83693	0.16307	9.97558	0.02442	9.86135	0.13865	43	23	23
3/8	9.83756	0.16244	9.97677	0.02323	9.86079	0.13921	43	28	06
13/32	9.83819	0.16181	9.97796	0.02204	9.86022	0.13978	43	32	49
7/16	9.83881	0.16119	9.97915	0.02085	9.85966	0.14034	43	37	31
15/32	9.83943	0.16057	9.98033	0.01967	9.85909	0.14091	43	42	12
1/2	9.84005	0.15995	9.98152	0.01848	9.85853	0.14147	43	46	52
17/32	9.84066	0.15934	9.98270	0.01730	9.85797	0.14203	43	51	32
9/16	9.84127	0.15873	9.98387	0.01613	9.85740	0.14260	43	56	11
19/32	9.84188	0.15812	9.98504	0.01496	9.85683	0.14317	44	00	49
5/8	9.84248	0.15752	9.98621	0.01379	9.85627	0.14373	44	05	26
21/32	9.84308	0.15692	9.98738	0.01262	9.85570	0.14430	44	10	03
11/16	9.84368	0.15632	9.98854	0.01146	9.85514	0.14486	44	14	39
23/32	9.84427	0.15573	9.98970	0.01030	9.85457	0.14543	44	19	14
3/4	9.84487	0.15513	9.99086	0.00914	9.85401	0.14599	44	23	49
25/32	9.84545	0.15455	9.99201	0.00799	9.85344	0.14656	44	28	23
13/16	9.84604	0.15396	9.99316	0.00684	9.85288	0.14712	44	32	56
27/32	9.84662	0.15338	9.99431	0.00569	9.85231	0.14769	44	37	28
7/8	9.84720	0.15280	9.99545	0.00455	9.85175	0.14825	44	42	00
29/32	9.84778	0.15222	9.99659	0.00341	9.85118	0.14882	44	46	31
15/16	9.84835	0.15165	9.99773	0.00227	9.85062	0.14938	44	51	01
31/32	9.84892	0.15108	9.99887	0.00113	9.85005	0.14995	44	55	31
1	9.84949	0.15051	0.00000	0.00000	9.84949	0.15051	45	00	00

MULTIPLICATION TABLE FOR RIVET SPACING.

In.	1	2	3	4	5	6	7	8	9	10
1⅛	-1⅛	- 2¼	- 3⅜	- 4½	- 5⅝	- 6¾	- 7⅞	- 9	-10⅛	-11¼
1¼	-1¼	- 2½	- 3¾	- 5	- 6¼	- 7½	- 8¾	-10	-11¼	1- 0½
1⅜	-1⅜	- 2¾	- 4⅛	- 5½	- 6⅞	- 8¼	- 9⅝	-11	1- 0⅜	1- 1¾
1½	-1½	- 3	- 4½	- 6	- 7½	- 9	-10½	1- 0	1- 1½	1- 3
1⅝	-1⅝	- 3¼	- 4⅞	- 6½	- 8⅛	- 9¾	-11⅜	1- 1	1- 2⅝	1- 4¼
1¾	-1¾	- 3½	- 5¼	- 7	- 8¾	-10½	1- 0¼	1- 2	1- 3¾	1- 5½
1⅞	-1⅞	- 3¾	- 5⅝	- 7½	- 9⅜	-11¼	1- 1⅛	1- 3	1- 4⅞	1- 6¾
2	-2	- 4	- 6	- 8	- 10	1- 0	1- 2	1- 4	1- 6	1- 8
2⅛	-2⅛	- 4¼	- 6⅜	- 8½	-10⅝	1- 0¾	1 -2⅞	1- 5	1- 7⅛	1- 9¼
2¼	-2¼	- 4½	- 6¾	- 9	-11¼	1- 1½	1- 3¾	1- 6	1- 8¼	1-10½
2⅜	-2⅜	- 4¾	- 7⅛	- 9½	-11⅞	1- 2¼	1- 4⅝	1- 7	1- 9⅜	1-11¾
2½	-2½	- 5	- 7½	-10	1- 0½	1- 3	1- 5½	1- 8	1-10½	2- 1
2⅝	-2⅝	- 5¼	- 7⅞	-10½	1- 1⅛	1- 3¾	1- 6⅜	1- 9	1-11⅝	2- 2¼
2¾	-2¾	- 5½	- 8¼	-11	1- 1¾	1- 4½	1- 7¼	1-10	2- 0¾	2- 3½
2⅞	-2⅞	- 5¾	- 8⅝	-11½	1 -2⅜	1- 5¼	1- 8⅛	1-11	2- 1⅞	2- 4¾
3	-3	- 6	- 9	1- 0	1 -3	1- 6	1- 9	2- 0	2- 3	2- 6
3⅛	-3⅛	- 6¼	- 9⅜	1- 0½	1- 3⅝	1- 6¾	1- 9⅞	2- 1	2- 4⅛	2- 7¼
3¼	-3¼	- 6½	- 9¾	1- 1	1- 4¼	1- 7½	1-10¾	2- 2	2- 5¼	2- 8½
3⅜	-3⅜	- 6¾	-10⅛	1- 1½	1- 4⅞	1- 8¼	1-11⅝	2- 3	2- 6⅜	2- 9¾
3½	-3½	- 7	-10½	1- 2	1- 5½	1- 9	2- 0½	2- 4	2- 7½	2-11
3⅝	-3⅝	- 7¼	-10⅞	1- 2½	1- 6⅛	1- 9¾	2- 1⅜	2- 5	2- 8⅝	3- 0¼
3¾	-3¾	- 7½	-11¼	1- 3	1- 6¾	1-10½	2- 2¼	2- 6	2- 9¾	3- 1½
3⅞	-3⅞	- 7¾	-11⅝	1- 3½	1- 7⅜	1-11¼	2- 3⅛	2- 7	2-10⅞	3- 2¾
4	-4	- 8	1- 0	1- 4	1- 8	2- 0	2- 4	2- 8	3- 0	3- 4
4⅛	-4⅛	- 8¼	1- 0⅜	1- 4½	1- 8⅝	2- 0¾	2- 4⅞	2- 9	3- 1⅛	3- 5¼
4¼	-4¼	- 8½	1- 0¾	1- 5	1- 9¼	2- 1½	2- 5¾	2-10	3- 2¼	3- 6½
4⅜	-4⅜	- 8¾	1- 1⅛	1- 5½	1- 9⅞	2- 2¼	2- 6⅝	2-11	3- 3⅜	3- 7¾
4½	-4½	- 9	1- 1½	1- 6	1-10½	2- 3	2- 7½	3- 0	3- 4½	3- 9
4⅝	-4⅝	- 9¼	1- 1⅞	1- 6½	1-11⅛	2- 3¾	2- 8⅜	3- 1	3- 5⅝	3-10¼
4¾	-4¾	- 9½	1- 2¼	1- 7	1-11¾	2- 4½	2- 9¼	3- 2	3- 6¾	3-11½
4⅞	-4⅞	- 9¾	1- 2⅝	1- 7½	2- 0⅜	2- 5¼	2-10⅛	3- 3	3- 7⅞	4- 0¾
5	-5	-10	1- 3	1- 8	2- 1	2- 6	2-11	3- 4	3- 9	4- 2
5⅛	-5⅛	-10¼	1- 3⅜	1- 8½	2- 1⅝	2- 6¾	2-11⅞	3- 5	3-10⅛	4 3¼
5¼	-5¼	-10½	1- 3¾	1- 9	2- 2¼	2- 7½	3- 0¾	3- 6	3-11¼	4- 4½
5⅜	-5⅜	-10¾	1- 4⅛	1- 9½	2- 2⅞	2- 8¼	3- 1⅝	3- 7	4- 0⅜	4- 5¾
5½	-5½	-11	1- 4½	1-10	2- 3½	2- 9	3- 2½	3- 8	4- 1½	4- 7
5⅝	-5⅝	-11¼	1- 4⅞	1-10½	2- 4⅛	2- 9¾	3- 3⅜	3- 9	4- 2⅝	4- 8¼
5¾	-5¾	-11½	1- 5¼	1-11	2- 4¾	2-10½	3- 4¼	3-10	4- 3¾	4- 9½
5⅞	-5⅞	-11¾	1- 5⅝	1-11½	2- 5⅜	2-11¼	3- 5⅛	3-11	4- 4⅞	4-10¾
6	-6	1- 0	1- 6	2- 0	2- 6	3- 0	3- 6	4- 0	4- 6	5- 0

In.	11	12	13	14	15	16	17	18	19	20
1⅛	1- 0⅜	1- 1½	1- 2⅝	1- 3¾	1- 4⅞	1- 6	1- 7⅛	1- 8¼	1- 9⅜	1-10½
1¼	1- 1¾	1- 3	1- 4¼	1- 5½	1- 6¾	1- 8	1- 9¼	1-10½	1-11¾	2- 1
1⅜	1- 3⅛	1- 4½	1- 5⅞	1- 7¼	1- 8⅝	1-10	1-11⅜	2- 0¾	2- 2⅛	2- 3½
1½	1- 4½	1- 6	1- 7½	1- 9	1-10½	2- 0	2- 1½	2- 3	2- 4½	2- 6
1⅝	1- 5⅞	1- 7½	1- 9⅛	1-10¾	2- 0⅜	2- 2	2- 3⅝	2- 5¼	2- 6⅞	2- 8½
1¾	1- 7¼	1- 9	1-10¾	2- 0½	2- 2¼	2- 4	2- 5¾	2- 7½	2- 9¼	2-11
1⅞	1- 8⅝	1-10½	2- 0⅜	2- 2¼	2- 4⅛	2- 6	2- 7⅞	2- 9¾	2-11⅝	3- 1½
2	1-10	2- 0	2- 2	2- 4	2- 6	2- 8	2-10	3- 0	3- 2	3- 4
2⅛	1-11⅜	2- 1½	2- 3⅝	2- 5¾	2- 7⅞	2-10	3- 0⅛	3- 2¼	3- 4⅜	3- 6½
2¼	2- 0¾	2- 3	2- 5¼	2- 7½	2- 9¾	3- 0	3- 2¼	3- 4½	3- 6¾	3- 9
2⅜	2- 2⅛	2- 4½	2- 6⅞	2- 9¼	2-11⅝	3- 2	3- 4⅜	3- 6¾	3- 9⅛	3-11½
2½	2- 3½	2- 6	2- 8½	2-11	3- 1½	3- 4	3- 6½	3- 9	3-11½	4- 2
2⅝	2- 4⅞	2- 7½	2-10⅛	3- 0¾	3- 3⅜	3- 6	3- 8⅝	3-11¼	4- 1⅞	4- 4½
2¾	2- 6¼	2- 9	2-11¾	3- 2½	3- 5¼	3- 8	3-10¾	4- 1½	4- 4¼	4- 7
2⅞	2- 7⅝	2-10½	3- 1⅜	3- 4¼	3- 7⅛	3-10	4- 0⅞	4- 3¾	4- 6⅝	4- 9½
3	2- 9	3- 0	3- 3	3- 6	3- 9	4- 0	4- 3	4- 6	4- 9	5- 0
3⅛	2-10⅜	3- 1½	3- 4⅝	3- 7¾	3-10⅞	4- 2	4- 5⅛	4- 8¼	4-11⅜	5- 2½
3¼	2-11¾	3- 3	3- 6¼	3- 9½	4- 0¾	4- 4	4- 7¼	4-10½	5- 1¾	5- 5
3⅜	3- 1⅛	3- 4½	3- 7⅞	3-11¼	4- 2⅝	4- 6	4- 9⅜	5- 0¾	5- 4⅛	5- 7½
3½	3- 2½	3- 6	3- 9½	4- 1	4- 4½	4- 8	4-11½	5- 3	5- 6½	5-10
3⅝	3- 3⅞	3- 7½	3-11⅛	4- 2¾	4- 6⅜	4-10	5- 1⅝	5- 5¼	5- 8⅞	6- 0½
3¾	3- 5¼	3- 9	4- 0¾	4- 4½	4- 8¼	5- 0	5- 3¾	5- 7½	5-11¼	6- 3
3⅞	3- 6⅝	3-10½	4- 2⅜	4- 6¼	4-10⅛	5- 2	5- 5⅞	5- 9¾	6- 1⅝	6- 5½
4	3- 8	4- 0	4- 4	4- 8	5- 0	5- 4	5- 8	6- 0	6- 4	6- 8
4⅛	3- 9⅜	4- 1½	4- 5⅝	4- 9¾	5- 1⅞	5- 6	5-10⅛	6- 2¼	6- 6⅜	6-10½
4¼	3-10¾	4- 3	4- 7¼	4-11½	5- 3¾	5- 8	6- 0¼	6- 4½	6- 8¾	7- 1
4⅜	4- 0⅛	4- 4½	4- 8⅞	5- 1¼	5- 5⅝	5-10	6- 2⅜	6- 6¾	6-11⅛	7- 3½
4½	4- 1½	4- 6	4-10½	5- 3	5- 7½	6- 0	6- 4½	6- 9	7- 1½	7- 6
4⅝	4- 2⅞	4- 7½	5- 0⅛	5- 4¾	5- 9⅜	6- 2	6- 6⅝	6-11¼	7- 3⅞	7- 8½
4¾	4- 4¼	4- 9	5- 1¾	5- 6½	5-11¼	6- 4	6- 8¾	7- 1½	7- 6¼	7-11
4⅞	4- 5⅝	4-10½	5- 3⅜	5- 8¼	6- 1⅛	6- 6	6-10⅞	7- 3¾	7- 8⅝	8- 1½
5	4- 7	5- 0	5- 5	5-10	6- 3	6- 8	7- 1	7- 6	7-11	8- 4
5⅛	4- 8⅜	5- 1½	5- 6⅝	5-11¾	6- 4⅞	6-10	7- 3⅛	7- 8¼	8- 1⅜	8- 6½
5¼	4- 9¾	5- 3	5- 8¼	6- 1½	6- 6¾	7- 0	7- 5¼	7-10½	8- 3¾	8- 9
5⅜	4-11⅛	5- 4½	5- 9⅞	6- 3¼	6- 8⅝	7- 2	7- 7⅜	8- 0¾	8- 6⅛	8-11½
5½	5- 0½	5- 6	5-11½	6- 5	6-10½	7- 4	7- 9½	8- 3	8- 8½	9- 2
5⅝	5- 1⅞	5- 7½	6- 1⅛	6- 6¾	7- 0⅜	7- 6	7-11⅝	8- 5¼	8-10⅞	9- 4½
5¾	5- 3¼	5- 9	6- 2¾	6- 8½	7- 2¼	7- 8	8- 1¾	8- 7½	9- 1¼	9- 7
5⅞	5- 4⅝	5-10½	6- 4⅜	6-10¼	7- 4⅛	7 10	8- 3⅞	8- 9¾	9- 3⅝	9- 9½
6	5- 6	6- 0	6- 6	7- 0	7- 6	8- 0	8- 6	9- 0	9- 6	10- 0

MULTIPLICATION TABLE FOR RIVET SPACING.

In.	21	22	23	24	25	26	27	28	29	30
1⅛	1-11⅝	2- 0¾	2- 1⅞	2- 3	2- 4⅛	2- 5¼	2- 6⅜	2- 7½	2- 8⅝	2- 9¾
1¼	2- 2¼	2- 3½	2- 4¾	2- 6	2- 7¼	2- 8½	2- 9¾	2-11	3- 0¼	3- 1½
1⅜	2- 4⅞	2- 6¼	2- 7⅝	2- 9	2-10⅜	2-11¾	3- 1⅛	3- 2½	3- 3⅞	3- 5¼
1½	2- 7½	2- 9	2-10½	3- 0	3- 1½	3- 3	3- 4½	3- 6	3- 7½	3- 9
1⅝	2-10⅛	2-11¾	3- 1⅜	3- 3	3- 4⅝	3- 6¼	3- 7⅞	3- 9½	3-11⅛	4- 0¾
1¾	3- 0¾	3- 2½	3- 4¼	3- 6	3- 7¾	3- 9½	3-11¼	4- 1	4- 2¾	4- 4½
1⅞	3- 3⅜	3- 5¼	3- 7⅛	3- 9	3-10⅞	4- 0¾	4- 2⅝	4- 4½	4- 6⅜	4- 8¼
2	3- 6	3- 8	3-10	4- 0	4- 2	4- 4	4- 6	4- 8	4-10	5- 0
2⅛	3- 8⅝	3-10¾	4- 0⅞	4- 3	4- 5⅛	4- 7¼	4- 9⅜	4-11½	5- 1⅝	5- 3¾
2¼	3-11¼	4- 1½	4- 3¾	4- 6	4- 8¼	4-10½	5- 0¾	5- 3	5- 5¼	5- 7½
2⅜	4- 1⅞	4- 4¼	4- 6⅝	4- 9	4-11⅜	5- 1¾	5- 4⅛	5- 6½	5- 8⅞	5-11¼
2½	4- 4½	4- 7	4- 9½	5- 0	5- 2½	5- 5	5- 7½	5-10	6- 0½	6- 3
2⅝	4- 7⅛	4- 9¾	5- 0⅜	5- 3	5- 5⅝	5- 8¼	5-10⅞	6- 1½	6- 4⅛	6- 6¾
2¾	4- 9¾	5- 0½	5- 3¼	5- 6	5- 8¾	5-11½	6- 2¼	6- 5	6- 7¾	6-10½
2⅞	5- 0⅜	5- 3¼	5- 6⅛	5- 9	5-11⅞	6- 2¾	6- 5⅝	6- 8½	6-11⅜	7-2¼
3	5- 3	5- 6	5- 9	6- 0	6- 3	6- 6	6- 9	7- 0	7- 3	7- 6
3⅛	5- 5⅝	5- 8¾	5-11⅞	6- 3	6- 6⅛	6- 9¼	7- 0⅜	7- 3½	7- 6⅝	7- 9¾
3¼	5- 8¼	5-11½	6- 2¾	6- 6	6- 9¼	7- 0½	7- 3¾	7- 7	7-10¼	8- 1½
3⅜	5-10⅞	6- 2¼	6- 5⅝	6- 9	7- 0⅜	7- 3¾	7- 7⅛	7-10½	8- 1⅞	8- 5¼
3½	6- 1½	6- 5	6- 8½	7- 0	7- 3½	7- 7	7-10½	8- 2	8- 5½	8- 9
3⅝	6- 4⅛	6- 7¾	6-11⅜	7- 3	7- 6⅝	7-10¼	8- 1⅞	8- 5½	8- 9⅛	9- 0¾
3¾	6- 6¾	6-10½	7- 2¼	7- 6	7- 9¾	8- 1½	8- 5¼	8- 9	9- 0¾	9- 4½
3⅞	6- 9⅜	7- 1¼	7- 5⅛	7- 9	8- 0⅞	8- 4¾	8- 8⅝	9- 0½	9- 4⅜	9- 8¼
4	7- 0	7- 4	7- 8	8- 0	8- 4	8- 8	9- 0	9- 4	9- 8	10- 0
4⅛	7- 2⅝	7- 6¾	7-10⅞	8- 3	8- 7⅛	8-11¼	9- 3⅜	9 7½	9-11⅝	10- 3¾
4¼	7- 5¼	7- 9½	8- 1¾	8- 6	8-10¼	9- 2½	9- 6¾	9-11	10- 3¼	10- 7½
4⅜	7- 7⅞	8- 0¼	8- 4⅝	8- 9	9- 1⅜	9- 5¾	9-10⅛	10- 2½	10- 6⅞	10-11¼
4½	7-10½	8- 3	8- 7½	9- 0	9- 4½	9- 9	10- 1½	10- 6	10-10½	11- 3
4⅝	8- 1⅛	8- 5¾	8-10⅜	9- 3	9- 7⅝	10- 0¼	10- 4⅞	10- 9½	11- 2⅛	11- 6¾
4¾	8- 3¾	8- 8½	9-.1¼	9- 6	9-10¾	10- 3½	10- 8¼	11- 1	11- 5¾	11-10½
4⅞	8- 6⅜	8-11¼	9- 4⅛	9- 9	10- 1⅞	10- 6¾	10-11⅝	11- 4½	11- 9⅜	12- 2¼
5	8- 9	9- 2	9- 7	10- 0	10- 5	10-10	11- 3	11- 8	12- 1	12- 6
5⅛	8-11⅝	9- 4¾	9- 9⅞	10- 3	10- 8⅛	11- 1¼	11- 6⅜	11-11½	12- 4⅝	12- 9¾
5¼	9- 2¼	9- 7½	10- 0¾	10- 6	10-11¼	11- 4½	11- 9¾	12- 3	12- 8¼	13- 1½
5⅜	9- 4⅞	9-10¼	10- 3⅝	10- 9	11- 2⅜	11- 7¾	12- 1⅛	12- 6½	12-11⅞	13- 5¼
5½	9- 7½	10- 1	10- 6½	11- 0	11- 5½	11-11	12- 4½	12-10	13- 3½	13- 9
5⅝	9-10⅛	10- 3¾	10- 9⅜	11- 3	11- 8⅝	12- 2¼	12- 7⅞	13- 1½	13- 7⅛	14- 0¾
5¾	10- 0¾	10- 6½	11- 0¼	11- 6	11-11¾	12- 5½	12-11¼	13- 5	13-10¾	14- 4½
5⅞	10- 3⅜	10- 9¼	11- 3⅛	11- 9	12- 2⅞	12- 8¾	13- 2⅝	13- 8½	14- 2⅜	14- 8¼
6	10- 6	11- 0	11- 6	12- 0	12- 6	13- 0	13- 6	14- 0	14- 6	15- 0

MULTIPLICATION TABLE FOR SPACING OF LATTICE BARS

No. Spaces	6"	6⅛"	6¼"	6⅜"	6½"	6⅝"	6¾"	6⅞"
2	1–0	1– 0¼	1– 0½	1– 0¾	1– 1	1– 1¼	1– 1½	1– 1¾
3	1–6	1– 6⅜	1– 6¾	1– 7⅛	1– 7½	1– 7⅞	1– 8¼	1– 8⅝
4	2–0	2– 0½	2– 1	2– 1½	2– 2	2– 2½	2– 3	2– 3½
5	2–6	2– 6⅝	2– 7¼	2– 7⅞	2– 8½	2– 9⅛	2– 9¾	2–10⅜
6	3–0	3– 0¾	3– 1½	3– 2¼	3– 3	3– 3¾	3– 4½	3– 5¼
7	3–6	3– 6⅞	3– 7¾	3– 8⅝	3– 9½	3–10⅜	3–11¼	4– 0⅛
8	4–0	4– 1	4– 2	4– 3	4– 4	4– 5	4– 6	4– 7
9	4–6	4– 7⅛	4– 8¼	4– 9⅜	4–10½	4–11⅝	5– 0¾	5– 1⅞
10	5–0	5– 1¼	5– 2½	5– 3¾	5– 5	5– 6¼	5– 7½	5– 8¾
11	5–6	5– 7⅜	5– 8¾	5–10⅛	5–11½	6– 0⅞	6– 2¼	6– 3⅝
12	6–0	6– 1½	6– 3	6– 4½	6– 6	6– 7½	6– 9	6–10½
13	6–6	6– 7⅝	6– 9¼	6–10⅞	7– 0½	7– 2⅛	7– 3¾	7– 5⅜
14	7–0	7– 1¾	7– 3½	7– 5¼	7– 7	7– 8¾	7–10½	8– 0¼
15	7–6	7– 7⅞	7– 9¾	7–11⅝	8– 1½	8– 3⅜	8– 5¼	8– 7⅛
16	8–0	8– 2	8– 4	8– 6	8– 8	8–10	9– 0	9– 2
17	8–6	8– 8⅛	8–10¼	9– 0⅜	9– 2½	9– 4⅝	9– 6¾	9– 8⅞
18	9–0	9– 2¼	9– 4½	9– 6¾	9– 9	9–11¼	10– 1½	10– 3¾
19	9–6	9– 8⅜	9–10¾	10– 1⅛	10– 3½	10– 5⅞	10– 8¼	10–10⅝
20	10–0	10– 2½	10– 5	10– 7½	10–10	11– 0½	11– 3	11– 5½

No. Spaces	7"	7⅛"	7¼"	7⅜"	7½"	7⅝"	7¾"	7⅞"
2	1– 2	1– 2¼	1– 2½	1– 2¾	1– 3	1– 3¼	1– 3½	1– 3¾
3	1– 9	1– 9⅜	1– 9¾	1–10⅛	1–10½	1–10⅞	1–11¼	1–11⅝
4	2– 4	2– 4½	2– 5	2– 5½	2– 6	2– 6½	2– 7	2– 7½
5	2–11	2–11⅝	3– 0¼	3– 0⅞	3– 1½	3– 2⅛	3– 2¾	3– 3⅜
6	3– 6	3– 6¾	3– 7½	3– 8¼	3– 9	3– 9¾	3–10½	3–11¼
7	4– 1	4– 1⅞	4– 2¾	4– 3⅝	4– 4½	4– 5⅜	4– 6¼	4– 7⅛
8	4– 8	4– 9	4–10	4–11	5– 0	5– 1	5– 2	5– 3
9	5– 3	5– 4⅛	5– 5¼	5– 6⅜	5– 7½	5– 8⅝	5– 9¾	5–10⅞
10	5–10	5–11¼	6– 0½	6– 1¾	6– 3	6– 4¼	6– 5½	6– 6¾
11	6– 5	6– 6⅜	6– 7¾	6– 9⅛	6–10½	6–11⅞	7– 1¼	7– 2⅝
12	7– 0	7– 1½	7– 3	7– 4½	7– 6	7– 7½	7– 9	7–10½
13	7– 7	7– 8⅝	7–10¼	7–11⅞	8– 1½	8– 3⅛	8– 4¾	8– 6⅜
14	8– 2	8– 3¾	8– 5½	8– 7¼	8– 9	8–10¾	9– 0½	9– 2¼
15	8– 9	8–10⅞	9– 0¾	9– 2⅝	9– 4½	9– 6⅜	9– 8¼	9–10⅛
16	9– 4	9– 6	9– 8	9–10	10– 0	10– 2	10– 4	10– 6
17	9–11	10– 1⅛	10– 3¼	10– 5⅜	10– 7½	10– 9⅝	10–11¾	11– 1⅞
18	10– 6	10– 8¼	10–10½	11– 0¾	11– 3	11– 5¼	11– 7½	11– 9¾
19	11– 1	11– 3⅜	11– 5¾	11– 8⅛	11–10½	12– 0⅞	12– 3¼	12– 5⅝
20	11– 8	11–10½	12– 1	12– 3½	12– 6	12– 8½	12–11	13– 1½

MULTIPLICATION TABLE FOR SPACING OF LATTICE BARS

No. Spaces	8"	8⅛"	8¼"	8⅜"	8½"	8⅝"	8¾"	8⅞"
2	1–4	1– 4¼	1– 4½	1– 4¾	1– 5	1– 5¼	1– 5½	1– 5¾
3	2–0	2– 0⅜	2– 0¾	2– 1⅛	2– 1½	2– 1⅞	2– 2¼	2– 2⅝
4	2–8	2– 8½	2– 9	2– 9½	2–10	2–10½	2–11	2–11½
5	3–4	3– 4⅝	3– 5¼	3– 5⅞	3– 6½	3– 7⅛	3– 7¾	3– 8⅜
6	4–0	4– 0¾	4– 1½	4– 2¼	4– 3	4– 3¾	4– 4½	4– 5¼
7	4–8	4– 8⅞	4– 9¾	4–10⅝	4–11½	5– 0⅜	5– 1¼	5– 2⅛
8	5–4	5– 5	5– 6	5– 7	5– 8	5– 9	5–10	5–11
9	6–0	6– 1⅛	6– 2¼	6– 3⅜	6– 4½	6– 5⅝	6– 6¾	6– 7⅞
10	6–8	6– 9¼	6–10½	6–11¾	7– 1	7– 2¼	7– 3½	7– 4¾
11	7–4	7– 5⅜	7– 6¾	7– 8⅛	7– 9½	7–10⅞	8– 0¼	8– 1⅝
12	8–0	8– 1½	8– 3	8– 4½	8– 6	8– 7½	8– 9	8–10½
13	8–8	8– 9⅝	8–11¼	9– 0⅞	9– 2½	9– 4⅛	9– 5¾	9– 7⅜
14	9–4	9– 5¾	9– 7½	9– 9¼	9–11	10– 0¾	10– 2½	10– 4¼
15	10–0	10– 1⅞	10– 3¾	10– 5⅝	10– 7½	10– 9⅜	10–11¼	11– 1⅛
16	10–8	10–10	11– 0	11–2	11– 4	11– 6	11– 8	11–10
17	11–4	11– 6⅛	11– 8¼	11–10⅜	12– 0½	12– 2⅝	12–4¾	12– 6⅞
18	12–0	12– 2¼	12– 4½	12– 6¾	12– 9	12–11¼	13– 1½	13– 3¾
19	12–8	12–10⅜	13– 0¾	13– 3⅛	13– 5½	13– 7⅞	13–10¼	14– 0⅝
20	13–4	13– 6½	13– 9	13–11½	14– 2	14– 4½	14– 7	14– 9½

No. Spaces	9"	9⅛"	9¼"	9⅜"	9½"	9⅝"	9¾"	9⅞"
2	1–6	1– 6¼	1– 6½	1– 6¾	1– 7	1– 7¼	1– 7½	1– 7¾
3	2–3	2– 3⅜	2– 3¾	2– 4⅛	2– 4½	2– 4⅞	2– 5¼	2– 5⅝
4	3–0	3– 0½	3– 1	3– 1½	3– 2	3– 2½	3– 3	3– 3½
5	3–9	3– 9⅝	3–10¼	3–10⅞	3–11½	4– 0⅛	4– 0¾	4– 1⅜
6	4–6	4– 6¾	4– 7½	4– 8¼	4– 9	4– 9¾	4–10½	4–11¼
7	5–3	5– 3⅞	5– 4¾	5– 5⅝	5– 6½	5– 7⅜	5– 8¼	5– 9⅛
8	6–0	6– 1	6– 2	6– 3	6– 4	6– 5	6– 6	6– 7
9	6–9	6–10⅛	6–11¼	7– 0⅜	7– 1½	7– 2⅝	7– 3¾	7– 4⅞
10	7–6	7– 7¼	7– 8½	7– 9¾	7–11	8– 0¼	8– 1½	8– 2¾
11	8–3	8– 4⅜	8– 5¾	8– 7⅛	8– 8½	8– 9⅞	8–11¼	9– 0⅝
12	9–0	9– 1½	9– 3	9– 4½	9– 6	9– 7½	9– 9	9–10½
13	9–9	9–10⅝	10– 0¼	10– 1⅞	10– 3½	10– 5⅛	10– 6¾	10– 8⅜
14	10–6	10– 7¾	10– 9½	10–11¼	11– 1	11– 2¾	11– 4½	11– 6¼
15	11–3	11– 4⅞	11– 6¾	11– 8⅝	11–10½	12– 0⅜	12– 2¼	12– 4⅛
16	12–0	12– 2	12– 4	12– 6	12– 8	12–10	13– 0	13– 2
17	12–9	12–11⅛	13– 1¼	13– 3⅜	13– 5½	13– 7⅝	13– 9¾	13–11⅞
18	13–6	13– 8¼	13–10½	14– 0¾	14– 3	14– 5¼	14– 7½	14– 9¾
19	14–3	14– 5⅜	14– 7¾	14–10⅛	15– 0½	15– 2⅞	15– 5¼	15– 7⅝
20	15–0	15– 2½	15– 5	15– 7½	15–10	16– 0½	16– 3	16– 5½

MULTIPLICATION TABLE FOR SPACING OF LATTICE BARS

No. Spaces	10"	10⅛"	10¼"	10⅜"	10½"	10⅝"	10¾"	10⅞"
2	1- 8	1- 8¼	1- 8½	1- 8¾	1- 9	1- 9¼	1- 9½	1- 9¾
3	2- 6	2- 6⅜	2- 6¾	2- 7⅛	2- 7½	2- 7⅞	2- 8¼	2- 8⅝
4	3- 4	3- 4½	3- 5	3- 5½	3- 6	3- 6½	3- 7	3- 7½
5	4- 2	4- 2⅝	4- 3¼	4- 3⅞	4- 4½	4- 5⅛	4- 5¾	4- 6⅜
6	5- 0	5- 0¾	5- 1½	5- 2¼	5- 3	5- 3¾	5- 4½	5- 5¼
7	5-10	5-10⅞	5-11¾	6- 0⅝	6- 1½	6- 2⅜	6- 3¼	6- 4⅛
8	6- 8	6- 9	6-10	6-11	7- 0	7- 1	7- 2	7- 3
9	7- 6	7- 7⅛	7- 8¼	7- 9⅜	7-10½	7-11⅝	8- 0¾	8- 1⅞
10	8- 4	8- 5¼	8- 6½	8- 7¾	8- 9	8-10¼	8-11½	9- 0¾
11	9- 2	9- 3⅜	9- 4¾	9- 6⅛	9- 7½	9- 8⅞	9-10¼	9-11⅝
12	10- 0	10- 1½	10- 3	10- 4½	10- 6	10- 7½	10- 9	10-10½
13	10-10	10-11⅝	11- 1¼	11- 2⅞	11- 4½	11- 6⅛	11- 7¾	11- 9⅜
14	11- 8	11- 9¾	11-11½	12- 1¼	12- 3	12- 4¾	12- 6½	12- 8¼
15	12- 6	12- 7⅞	12- 9¾	12-11⅝	13- 1½	13- 3⅜	13- 5¼	13- 7⅛
16	13- 4	13- 6	13- 8	13-10	14- 0	14- 2	14- 4	14- 6
17	14- 2	14- 4⅛	14- 6¼	14- 8⅜	14-10½	15- 0⅝	15- 2¾	15- 4⅞
18	15- 0	15- 2¼	15- 4½	15- 6¾	15- 9	15-11¼	16- 1½	16- 3¾
19	15-10	16- 0⅜	16- 2¾	16- 5⅛	16- 7½	16- 9⅞	17- 0¼	17- 2⅝
20	16- 8	16-10½	17- 1	17- 3½	17- 6	17- 8½	17-11	18- 1½

No. Spaces	11"	11⅛"	11¼"	11⅜"	11½"	11⅝"	11¾"	11⅞"
2	1-10	1-10¼	1-10½	1-10¾	1-11	1-11¼	1-11½	1-11¾
3	2- 9	2- 9⅜	2- 9¾	2-10⅛	2-10½	2-10⅞	2-11¼	2-11⅝
4	3- 8	3- 8½	3- 9	3- 9½	3-10	3-10½	3-11	3-11½
5	4- 7	4- 7⅝	4- 8¼	4- 8⅞	4- 9½	4-10⅛	4-10¾	4-11⅜
6	5- 6	5- 6¾	5- 7½	5- 8¼	5- 9	5- 9¾	5-10½	5-11¼
7	6- 5	6- 5⅞	6- 6¾	6- 7⅝	6- 8½	6- 9⅜	6-10¼	6-11⅛
8	7- 4	7- 5	7- 6	7- 7	7- 8	7- 9	7-10	7-11
9	8- 3	8- 4⅛	8- 5¼	8- 6⅜	8- 7½	8- 8⅝	8- 9¾	8-10⅞
10	9- 2	9- 3¼	9- 4½	9- 5¾	9- 7	9- 8¼	9- 9½	9-10¾
11	10- 1	10- 2⅜	10- 3¾	10- 5⅛	10- 6½	10- 7⅞	10- 9¼	10-10⅝
12	11- 0	11- 1½	11- 3	11- 4½	11- 6	11- 7½	11- 9	11-10½
13	11-11	12- 0⅝	12- 2¼	12- 3⅞	12- 5½	12- 7⅛	12- 8¾	12-10⅜
14	12-10	12-11¾	13- 1½	13- 3¼	13- 5	13- 6¾	13- 8½	13-10¼
15	13- 9	13-10⅞	14- 0¾	14- 2⅝	14- 4½	14- 6⅜	14- 8¼	14-10⅛
16	14- 8	14-10	15- 0	15- 2	15- 4	15- 6	15- 8	15-10
17	15- 7	15- 9⅛	15-11¼	16- 1⅜	16- 3½	16- 5⅝	16- 7¾	16- 9⅞
18	16- 6	16- 8¼	16-10½	17- 0¾	17- 3	17- 5¼	17- 7½	17- 9¾
19	17- 5	17- 7⅜	17- 9¾	18- 0⅛	18- 2½	18- 4⅞	18- 7¼	18- 9⅝
20	18- 4	18- 6½	18- 9	18-11½	19- 2	19- 4½	19- 7	19- 9½

No. Spaces	1' 0"	1' $0\frac{1}{8}$"	1' $0\frac{1}{4}$"	1' $0\frac{3}{8}$"	1' $0\frac{1}{2}$"	1' $0\frac{5}{8}$"	1' $0\frac{3}{4}$"	1' $0\frac{7}{8}$"
2	2–0	2–$0\frac{1}{4}$	2–$0\frac{1}{2}$	2–$0\frac{3}{4}$	2– 1	2– $1\frac{1}{4}$	2– $1\frac{1}{2}$	2– $1\frac{3}{4}$
3	3–0	3–$0\frac{3}{8}$	3–$0\frac{3}{4}$	3–$1\frac{1}{8}$	3– $1\frac{1}{2}$	3– $1\frac{7}{8}$	3– $2\frac{1}{4}$	3– $2\frac{5}{8}$
4	4–0	4–$0\frac{1}{2}$	4–1	4–$1\frac{1}{2}$	4– 2	4– $2\frac{1}{2}$	4– 3	4– $3\frac{1}{2}$
5	5–0	5–$0\frac{5}{8}$	5–$1\frac{1}{4}$	5–$1\frac{7}{8}$	5– $2\frac{1}{2}$	5– $3\frac{1}{8}$	5– $3\frac{3}{4}$	5– $4\frac{3}{8}$
6	6–0	6–$0\frac{3}{4}$	6–$1\frac{1}{2}$	6–$2\frac{1}{4}$	6– 3	6– $3\frac{3}{4}$	6– $4\frac{1}{2}$	6– $5\frac{1}{4}$
7	7–0	7–$0\frac{7}{8}$	7–$1\frac{3}{4}$	7–$2\frac{5}{8}$	7– $3\frac{1}{2}$	7– $4\frac{3}{8}$	7– $5\frac{1}{4}$	7– $6\frac{1}{8}$
8	8–0	8–1	8–2	8–3	8– 4	8– 5	8– 6	8– 7
9	9–0	9–$1\frac{1}{8}$	9–$2\frac{1}{4}$	9–$3\frac{3}{8}$	9– $4\frac{1}{2}$	9– $5\frac{5}{8}$	9– $6\frac{3}{4}$	9– $7\frac{7}{8}$
10	10–0	10–$1\frac{1}{4}$	10–$2\frac{1}{2}$	10–$3\frac{3}{4}$	10– 5	10– $6\frac{1}{4}$	10– $7\frac{1}{2}$	10– $8\frac{3}{4}$
11	11–0	11–$1\frac{3}{8}$	11–$2\frac{3}{4}$	11–$4\frac{1}{8}$	11– $5\frac{1}{2}$	11– $6\frac{7}{8}$	11– $8\frac{1}{4}$	11– $9\frac{5}{8}$
12	12–0	12–$1\frac{1}{2}$	12–3	12–$4\frac{1}{2}$	12– 6	12– $7\frac{1}{2}$	12– 9	12–$10\frac{1}{2}$
13	13–0	13–$1\frac{5}{8}$	13–$3\frac{1}{4}$	13–$4\frac{7}{8}$	13– $6\frac{1}{2}$	13– $8\frac{1}{8}$	13– $9\frac{3}{4}$	13–$11\frac{3}{8}$
14	14–0	14–$1\frac{3}{4}$	14–$3\frac{1}{2}$	14–$5\frac{1}{4}$	14– 7	14– $8\frac{3}{4}$	14–$10\frac{1}{2}$	15– $0\frac{1}{4}$
15	15–0	15–$1\frac{7}{8}$	15–$3\frac{3}{4}$	15–$5\frac{5}{8}$	15– $7\frac{1}{2}$	15– $9\frac{3}{8}$	15–$11\frac{1}{4}$	16– $1\frac{1}{8}$
16	16–0	16–2	16–4	16–6	16– 8	16–10	17– 0	17– 2
17	17–0	17–$2\frac{1}{8}$	17–$4\frac{1}{4}$	17–$6\frac{3}{8}$	17– $8\frac{1}{2}$	17–$10\frac{5}{8}$	18– $0\frac{3}{4}$	18– $2\frac{7}{8}$
18	18–0	18–$2\frac{1}{4}$	18–$4\frac{1}{2}$	18–$6\frac{3}{4}$	18– 9	18–$11\frac{1}{4}$	19– $1\frac{1}{2}$	19– $3\frac{3}{4}$
19	19–0	19–$2\frac{3}{8}$	19–$4\frac{3}{4}$	19–$7\frac{1}{8}$	19– $9\frac{1}{2}$	19–$11\frac{7}{8}$	20– $2\frac{1}{4}$	20– $4\frac{5}{8}$
20	20–0	20–$2\frac{1}{2}$	20–5	20–$7\frac{1}{2}$	20–10	21– $0\frac{1}{2}$	21– 3	21– $5\frac{1}{2}$

No. Spaces	1' 1"	1' $1\frac{1}{8}$"	1' $1\frac{1}{4}$"	1' $1\frac{3}{8}$"	1' $1\frac{1}{2}$"	1' $1\frac{5}{8}$"	1' $1\frac{3}{4}$"	1' $1\frac{7}{8}$"
2	2– 2	2– $2\frac{1}{4}$	2– $2\frac{1}{2}$	2– $2\frac{3}{4}$	2– 3	2– $3\frac{1}{4}$	2– $3\frac{1}{2}$	2– $3\frac{3}{4}$
3	3– 3	3– $3\frac{3}{8}$	3– $3\frac{3}{4}$	3– $4\frac{1}{8}$	3– $4\frac{1}{2}$	3– $4\frac{7}{8}$	3– $5\frac{1}{4}$	3– $5\frac{5}{8}$
4	4– 4	4– $4\frac{1}{2}$	4– 5	4– $5\frac{1}{2}$	4– 6	4– $6\frac{1}{2}$	4– 7	4– $7\frac{1}{2}$
5	5– 5	5– $5\frac{5}{8}$	5– $6\frac{1}{4}$	5– $6\frac{7}{8}$	5– $7\frac{1}{2}$	5– $8\frac{1}{8}$	5– $8\frac{3}{4}$	5– $9\frac{3}{8}$
6	6– 6	6– $6\frac{3}{4}$	6– $7\frac{1}{2}$	6– $8\frac{1}{4}$	6– 9	6– $9\frac{3}{4}$	6–$10\frac{1}{2}$	6–$11\frac{1}{4}$
7	7– 7	7– $7\frac{7}{8}$	7– $8\frac{3}{4}$	7– $9\frac{5}{8}$	7–$10\frac{1}{2}$	7–$11\frac{3}{8}$	8– $0\frac{1}{4}$	8– $1\frac{1}{8}$
8	8– 8	8– 9	8–10	8–11	9– 0	9– 1	9– 2	9– 3
9	9– 9	9–$10\frac{1}{8}$	9–$11\frac{1}{4}$	10– $0\frac{3}{8}$	10– $1\frac{1}{2}$	10– $2\frac{5}{8}$	10– $3\frac{3}{4}$	10– $4\frac{7}{8}$
10	10–10	10–$11\frac{1}{4}$	11– $0\frac{1}{2}$	11– $1\frac{3}{4}$	11– 3	11– $4\frac{1}{4}$	11– $5\frac{1}{2}$	11– $6\frac{3}{4}$
11	11–11	12– $0\frac{3}{8}$	12– $1\frac{3}{4}$	12– $3\frac{1}{8}$	12– $4\frac{1}{2}$	12– $5\frac{7}{8}$	12– $7\frac{1}{4}$	12– $8\frac{5}{8}$
12	13– 0	13– $1\frac{1}{2}$	13– 3	13– $4\frac{1}{2}$	13– 6	13– $7\frac{1}{2}$	13– 9	13–$10\frac{1}{2}$
13	14– 1	14– $2\frac{5}{8}$	14– $4\frac{1}{4}$	14– $5\frac{7}{8}$	14– $7\frac{1}{2}$	14– $9\frac{1}{8}$	14–$10\frac{3}{4}$	15– $0\frac{3}{8}$
14	15– 2	15– $3\frac{3}{4}$	15– $5\frac{1}{2}$	15– $7\frac{1}{4}$	15– 9	15–$10\frac{3}{4}$	16– $0\frac{1}{2}$	16– $2\frac{1}{4}$
15	16– 3	16– $4\frac{7}{8}$	16– $6\frac{3}{4}$	16– $8\frac{5}{8}$	16–$10\frac{1}{2}$	17– $0\frac{3}{8}$	17– $2\frac{1}{4}$	17– $4\frac{1}{8}$
16	17– 4	17– 6	17– 8	17–10	18– 0	18– 2	18– 4	18– 6
17	18– 5	18– $7\frac{1}{8}$	18– $9\frac{1}{4}$	18–$11\frac{3}{8}$	19– $1\frac{1}{2}$	19– $3\frac{5}{8}$	19– $5\frac{3}{4}$	19– $7\frac{7}{8}$
18	19– 6	19– $8\frac{1}{4}$	19–$10\frac{1}{2}$	20– $0\frac{3}{4}$	20– 3	20– $5\frac{1}{4}$	20– $7\frac{1}{2}$	20– $9\frac{3}{4}$
19	20– 7	20– $9\frac{3}{8}$	20–$11\frac{3}{4}$	21– $2\frac{1}{8}$	21– $4\frac{1}{2}$	21– $6\frac{7}{8}$	21– $9\frac{1}{4}$	21–$11\frac{5}{8}$
20	21– 8	21–$10\frac{1}{2}$	22– 1	22– $3\frac{1}{2}$	22– 6	22– $8\frac{1}{2}$	22–11	23–$1\frac{1}{2}$

MULTIPLICATION TABLE FOR SPACING OF LATTICE BARS

No. Spaces	1' 2"	1' 2⅛"	1' 2¼"	1' 2⅜"	1' 2½"	1' 2⅝"	1' 2¾"	1' 2⅞"
2	2– 4	2– 4¼	2– 4½	2– 4¾	2– 5	2– 5¼	2– 5½	2– 5¾
3	3– 6	3– 6⅜	3– 6¾	3– 7⅛	3– 7½	3– 7⅞	3– 8¼	3– 8⅝
4	4– 8	4– 8½	4– 9	4– 9½	4–10	4–10½	4–11	4–11½
5	5–10	5–10⅝	5–11¼	5–11⅞	6– 0½	6– 1⅛	6– 1¾	6– 2⅜
6	7– 0	7– 0¾	7– 1½	7– 2¼	7– 3	7– 3¾	7– 4½	7– 5¼
7	8– 2	8– 2⅞	8– 3¾	8– 4⅝	8– 5½	8– 6⅜	8– 7¼	8– 8⅛
8	9– 4	9– 5	9– 6	9– 7	9– 8	9– 9	9–10	9–11
9	10– 6	10– 7⅛	10– 8¼	10– 9⅜	10–10½	10–11⅝	11– 0¾	11– 1⅞
10	11– 8	11– 9¼	11–10½	11–11¾	12– 1	12– 2¼	12– 3½	12– 4¾
11	12–10	12–11⅜	13– 0¾	13– 2⅛	13– 3½	13– 4⅞	13– 6¼	13– 7⅝
12	14– 0	14– 1½	14– 3	14– 4½	14– 6	14– 7½	14– 9	14–10½
13	15– 2	15– 3⅝	15– 5¼	15– 6⅞	15– 8½	15–10⅛	15–11¾	16– 1⅜
14	16– 4	16– 5¾	16– 7½	16– 9¼	16–11	17– 0¾	17– 2½	17– 4¼
15	17– 6	17– 7⅞	17– 9¾	17–11⅝	18– 1½	18– 3⅜	18– 5¼	18– 7⅛
16	18– 8	18–10	19– 0	19– 2	19– 4	19– 6	19– 8	19–10
17	19–10	20– 0⅛	20– 2¼	20– 4⅜	20– 6½	20– 8⅝	20–10¾	21– 0⅞
18	21– 0	21– 2¼	21– 4½	21– 6¾	21– 9	21–11¼	22– 1½	22– 3¾
19	22– 2	22– 4⅜	22– 6¾	22– 9⅛	22–11½	23– 1⅞	23– 4¼	23– 6⅝
20	23– 4	23– 6½	23– 9	23–11½	24– 2	24– 4½	24– 7	24– 9½

No. Spaces	1' 3"	1' 3⅛"	1' 3¼"	1' 3⅜"	1' 3½"	1' 3⅝"	1' 3¾"	1' 3⅞"
2	2– 6	2– 6¼	2– 6½	2– 6¾	2– 7	2– 7¼	2– 7½	2– 7¾
3	3– 9	3– 9⅜	3– 9¾	3–10⅛	3–10½	3–10⅞	3–11¼	3–11⅝
4	5– 0	5– 0½	5– 1	5– 1½	5– 2	5– 2½	5– 3	5– 3½
5	6– 3	6– 3⅝	6– 4¼	6– 4⅞	6– 5½	6– 6⅛	6– 6¾	6– 7⅜
6	7– 6	7– 6¾	7– 7½	7– 8¼	7– 9	7– 9¾	7–10½	7–11¼
7	8– 9	8– 9⅞	8–10¾	8–11⅝	9– 0½	9– 1⅜	9– 2¼	9– 3⅛
8	10– 0	10– 1	10– 2	10– 3	10– 4	10– 5	10– 6	10– 7
9	11– 3	11– 4⅛	11– 5¼	11– 6⅜	11– 7½	11– 8⅝	11– 9¾	11–10⅞
10	12– 6	12– 7¼	12– 8½	12– 9¾	12–11	13– 0¼	13– 1½	13– 2¾
11	13– 9	13–10⅜	13–11¾	14– 1⅛	14– 2½	14– 3⅞	14– 5¼	14– 6⅝
12	15– 0	15– 1½	15– 3	15– 4½	15– 6	15– 7½	15– 9	15–10½
13	16– 3	16– 4⅝	16– 6¼	16– 7⅞	16– 9½	16–11⅛	17– 0¾	17– 2⅜
14	17– 6	17– 7¾	17– 9½	17–11¼	18– 1	18– 2¾	18– 4½	18– 6¼
15	18– 9	18–10⅞	19– 0¾	19– 2⅝	19– 4½	19– 6⅜	19– 8¼	19–10⅛
16	20– 0	20– 2	20– 4	20– 6	20– 8	20–10	21– 0	21– 2
17	21– 3	21– 5⅛	21– 7¼	21– 9⅜	21–11½	22– 1⅝	22– 3¾	22– 5⅞
18	22– 6	22– 8¼	22–10½	23– 0¾	23– 3	23– 5¼	23– 7½	23– 9¾
19	23– 9	23–11⅜	24– 1¾	24– 4⅛	24– 6½	24– 8⅞	24–11¼	25– 1⅝
20	25– 0	25– 2½	25– 5	25– 7½	25–10	26– 0½	26– 3	26– 5½

MULTIPLICATION TABLE FOR SPACING OF LATTICE BARS

No. Spaces	1' 4"	1' 4⅛"	1' 4¼"	1' 4⅜"	1' 4½"	1' 4⅝"	1' 4¾"	1' 4⅞"
2	2–8	2– 8¼	2– 8½	2– 8¾	2– 9	2– 9¼	2– 9½	2– 9¾
3	4–0	4– 0⅜	4– 0¾	4– 1⅛	4– 1½	4– 1⅞	4– 2¼	4– 2⅝
4	5–4	5– 4½	5– 5	5– 5½	5– 6	5– 6½	5– 7	5– 7½
5	6–8	6– 8⅝	6– 9¼	6– 9⅞	6–10½	6–11⅛	6–11¾	7– 0⅜
6	8–0	8– 0¾	8– 1½	8– 2¼	8– 3	8– 3¾	8– 4½	8– 5¼
7	9–4	9– 4⅞	9– 5¾	9– 6⅝	9– 7½	9– 8⅜	9– 9¼	9–10⅛
8	10–8	10– 9	10–10	10–11	11– 0	11– 1	11– 2	11– 3
9	12–0	12– 1⅛	12– 2¼	12– 3⅜	12 – 4½	12– 5⅝	12– 6¾	12– 7⅞
10	13–4	13– 5¼	13– 6½	13– 7¾	13– 9	13–10¼	13–11½	14– 0¾
11	14–8	14– 9⅜	14–10¾	15– 0⅛	15– 1½	15– 2⅞	15– 4¼	15– 5⅝
12	16–0	16– 1½	16– 3	16– 4½	16– 6	16– 7½	16– 9	16–10½
13	17–4	17– 5⅝	17– 7¼	17– 8⅞	17–10½	18– 0⅛	18– 1¾	18– 3⅜
14	18–8	18– 9¾	18–11½	19– 1¼	19– 3	19– 4¾	19– 6½	19– 8¼
15	20–0	20– 1⅞	20– 3¾	20– 5⅝	20– 7½	20– 9⅜	20–11¼	21– 1⅛
16	21–4	21– 6	21– 8	21–10	22– 0	22– 2	22– 4	22– 6
17	22–8	22–10⅛	23– 0¼	23– 2⅜	23– 4½	23– 6⅝	23– 8¾	23–10⅞
18	24–0	24– 2¼	24– 4½	24– 6¾	24– 9	24–11¼	25– 1½	25– 3¾
19	25–4	25– 6⅜	25– 8¾	25–11⅛	26– 1½	26– 3⅞	26– 6¼	26– 8⅝
20	26–8	26–10½	27– 1	27– 3½	27– 6	27– 8½	27–11	28– 1½

No. Spaces	1' 5"	1' 5⅛"	1' 5¼"	1' 5⅜"	1' 5½"	1' 5⅝"	1' 5¾"	1' 5⅞"
2	2–10	2–10¼	2–10½	2–10¾	2–11	2–11¼	2–11½	2–11¾
3	4– 3	4– 3⅜	4– 3¾	4– 4⅛	4– 4½	4– 4⅞	4– 5¼	4– 5⅝
4	5– 8	5– 8½	5– 9	5– 9½	5–10	5–10½	5–11	5–11½
5	7– 1	7– 1⅝	7– 2¼	7– 2⅞	7– 3½	7– 4⅛	7– 4¾	7– 5⅜
6	8– 6	8– 6¾	8– 7½	8– 8¼	8– 9	8– 9¾	8–10½	8–11¼
7	9–11	9–11⅞	10– 0¾	10– 1⅝	10– 2½	10– 3⅜	10– 4¼	10– 5⅛
8	11– 4	11– 5	11– 6	11– 7	11– 8	11– 9	11–10	11–11
9	12– 9	12–10⅛	12–11¼	13– 0⅜	13– 1½	13– 2⅝	13– 3¾	13– 4⅞
10	14– 2	14– 3¼	14– 4½	14– 5¾	14– 7	14– 8¼	14– 9½	14–10¾
11	15– 7	15– 8⅜	15– 9¾	15–11⅛	16– 0½	16– 1⅞	16– 3¼	16– 4⅝
12	17– 0	17– 1½	17– 3	17– 4½	17– 6	17– 7½	17– 9	17–10½
13	18– 5	18– 6⅝	18– 8¼	18– 9⅞	18–11½	19– 1⅛	19– 2¾	19– 4⅜
14	19–10	19–11¾	20– 1½	20– 3¼	20– 5	20– 6¾	20– 8½	20–10¼
15	21– 3	21– 4⅞	21– 6¾	21– 8⅝	21–10½	22– 0⅜	22– 2¼	22– 4⅛
16	22– 8	22–10	23– 0	23– 2	23– 4	23– 6	23– 8	23–10
17	24– 1	24– 3⅛	24– 5¼	24– 7⅜	24– 9½	24–11⅝	25– 1¾	25– 3⅞
18	25– 6	25– 8¼	25–10½	26– 0¾	26– 3	26– 5¼	26– 7½	26– 9¾
19	26–11	27– 1⅜	27– 3¾	27– 6⅛	27– 8½	27–10⅞	28– 1¼	28– 3⅝
20	28– 4	28– 6½	28– 9	28–11½	29– 2	29– 4½	29– 7	29– 9½

No. Spaces	1' 6"	1' 6⅛"	1' 6¼"	1' 6⅜"	1' 6½"	1' 6⅝"	1' 6¾"	1' 6⅞"
2	3-0	3-0¼	3-0½	3-0¾	3-1	3-1¼	3-1½	3-1¾
3	4-6	4-6⅜	4-6¾	4-7⅛	4-7½	4-7⅞	4-8¼	4-8⅝
4	6-0	6-0½	6-1	6-1½	6-2	6-2½	6-3	6-3½
5	7-6	7-6⅝	7-7¼	7-7⅞	7-8½	7-9⅛	7-9¾	7-10⅜
6	9-0	9-0¾	9-1½	9-2¼	9-3	9-3¾	9-4½	9-5¼
7	10-6	10-6⅞	10-7¾	10-8⅝	10-9½	10-10⅜	10-11¼	11-0⅛
8	12-0	12-1	12-2	12-3	12-4	12-5	12-6	12-7
9	13-6	13-7⅛	13-8¼	13-9⅜	13-10½	13-11⅝	14-0¾	14-1⅞
10	15-0	15-1¼	15-2½	15-3¾	15-5	15-6¼	15-7½	15-8¾
11	16-6	16-7⅜	16-8¾	16-10⅛	16-11½	17-0⅞	17-2¼	17-3⅝
12	18-0	18-1½	18-3	18-4½	18-6	18-7½	18-9	18-10½
13	19-6	19-7⅝	19-9¼	19-10⅞	20-0½	20-2⅛	20-3¾	20-5⅜
14	21-0	21-1¾	21-3½	21-5¼	21-7	21-8¾	21-10½	22-0¼
15	22-6	22-7⅞	22-9¾	22-11⅝	23-1½	23-3⅜	23-5¼	23-7⅛
16	24-0	24-2	24-4	24-6	24-8	24-10	25-0	25-2
17	25-6	25-8⅛	25-10¼	26-0⅜	26-2½	26-4⅝	26-6¾	26-8⅞
18	27-0	27-2¼	27-4½	27-6¾	27-9	27-11¼	28-1½	28-3¾
19	28-6	28-8⅜	28-10¾	29-1⅛	29-3½	29-5⅞	29-8¼	29-10⅝
20	30-0	30-2½	30-5	30-7½	30-10	31-0½	31-3	31-5½

No. Spaces	1' 7"	1' 7⅛"	1' 7¼"	1' 7⅜"	1' 7½"	1' 7⅝"	1' 7¾"	1' 7⅞"
2	3-2	3-2¼	3-2½	3-2¾	3-3	3-3¼	3-3½	3-3¾
3	4-9	4-9⅜	4-9¾	4-10⅛	4-10½	4-10⅞	4-11¼	4-11⅝
4	6-4	6-4½	6-5	6-5½	6-6	6-6½	6-7	6-7½
5	7-11	7-11⅝	8-0¼	8-0⅞	8-1½	8-2⅛	8-2¾	8-3⅜
6	9-6	9-6¾	9-7½	9-8¼	9-9	9-9¾	9-10½	9-11¼
7	11-1	11-1⅞	11-2¾	11-3⅝	11-4½	11-5⅜	11-6¼	11-7⅛
8	12-8	12-9	12-10	12-11	13-0	13-1	13-2	13-3
9	14-3	14-4⅛	14-5¼	14-6⅜	14-7½	14-8⅝	14-9¾	14-10⅞
10	15-10	15-11¼	16-0½	16-1¾	16-3	16-4¼	16-5½	16-6¾
11	17-5	17-6⅜	17-7¾	17-9⅛	17-10½	17-11⅞	18-1¼	18-2⅝
12	19-0	19-1½	19-3	19-4½	19-6	19-7½	19-9	19-10½
13	20-7	20-8⅝	20-10¼	20-11⅞	21-1½	21-3⅛	21-4¾	21-6⅜
14	22-2	22-3¾	22-5½	22-7¼	22-9	22-10¾	23-0½	23-2¼
15	23-9	23-10⅞	24-0¾	24-2⅝	24-4½	24-6⅜	24-8¼	24-10⅛
16	25-4	25-6	25-8	25-10	26-0	26-2	26-4	26-6
17	26-11	27-1⅛	27-3¼	27-5⅜	27-7½	27-9⅝	27-11¾	28-1⅞
18	28-6	28-8¼	28-10½	29-0¾	29-3	29-5¼	29-7½	29-9¾
19	30-1	30-3⅜	30-5¾	30-8⅛	30-10½	31-0⅞	31-3¼	31-5⅝
20	31-8	31-10½	32-1	32-3½	32-6	32-8½	32-11	33-1½

455

MULTIPLICATION TABLE FOR SPACING OF LATTICE BARS

No. Spaces	1' 8"	1' 8⅛"	1' 8¼"	1' 8⅜"	1' 8½"	1' 8⅝"	1' 8¾"	1' 8⅞"
2	3–4	3– 4¼	3– 4½	3– 4¾	3– 5	3– 5¼	3– 5½	3– 5¾
3	5–0	5– 0⅜	5– 0¾	5– 1⅛	5– 1½	5– 1⅞	5– 2¼	5– 2⅝
4	6–8	6– 8½	6– 9	6– 9½	6–10	6–10½	6–11	6–11½
5	8–4	8– 4⅝	8– 5¼	8– 5⅞	8– 6½	8– 7⅛	8– 7¾	8– 8⅜
6	10–0	10– 0¾	10– 1½	10– 2¼	10– 3	10– 3¾	10– 4½	10– 5¼
7	11–8	11– 8⅞	11– 9¾	11–10⅝	11–11½	12– 0⅜	12– 1¼	12– 2⅛
8	13–4	13– 5	13– 6	13– 7	13– 8	13– 9	13–10	13–11
9	15–0	15– 1⅛	15– 2¼	15– 3⅜	15– 4½	15– 5⅝	15– 6¾	15– 7⅞
10	16–8	16– 9¼	16–10½	16–11¾	17– 1	17– 2¼	17– 3½	17– 4¾
11	18–4	18– 5⅜	18– 6¾	18– 8⅛	18– 9½	18–10⅞	19– 0¼	19– 1⅝
12	20–0	20– 1½	20– 3	20– 4½	20– 6	20– 7½	20– 9	20–10½
13	21–8	21– 9⅝	21–11¼	22– 0⅞	22– 2½	22– 4⅛	22– 5¾	22– 7⅜
14	23–4	23– 5¾	23– 7½	23– 9¼	23–11	24– 0¾	24– 2½	24– 4¼
15	25–0	25– 1⅞	25– 3¾	25– 5⅝	25– 7½	25– 9⅜	25–11¼	26– 1⅛
16	26–8	26–10	27– 0	27– 2	27– 4	27– 6	27– 8	27–10
17	28–4	28– 6⅛	28– 8¼	28–10⅜	29– 0½	29– 2⅝	29– 4¾	29– 6⅞
18	30–0	30– 2¼	30– 4½	30– 6¾	30– 9	30–11¼	31– 1½	31– 3¾
19	31–8	31–10⅜	32– 0¾	32– 3⅛	32– 5½	32– 7⅞	32–10¼	33– 0⅝
20	33–4	33– 6½	33– 9	33–11½	34– 2	34– 4½	34– 7	34– 9½

No. Spaces	1' 9"	1' 9⅛"	1' 9¼"	1' 9⅜"	1' 9½"	1' 9⅝"	1' 9¾"	1' 9⅞"
2	3–6	3– 6¼	3– 6½	3– 6¾	3– 7	3– 7¼	3– 7½	3– 7¾
3	5–3	5– 3⅜	5– 3¾	5– 4⅛	5– 4½	5– 4⅞	5– 5¼	5– 5⅝
4	7–0	7– 0½	7– 1	7– 1½	7– 2	7– 2½	7– 3	7– 3½
5	8–9	8– 9⅝	8–10¼	8–10⅞	8–11½	9– 0⅛	9– 0¾	9– 1⅜
6	10–6	10– 6¾	10– 7½	10– 8¼	10– 9	10– 9¾	10–10½	10–11¼
7	12–3	12– 3⅞	12– 4¾	12– 5⅝	12– 6½	12– 7⅜	12– 8¼	12– 9⅛
8	14–0	14– 1	14– 2	14– 3	14– 4	14– 5	14– 6	14– 7
9	15–9	15–10⅛	15–11¼	16– 0⅜	16– 1½	16– 2⅝	16– 3¾	16– 4⅞
10	17–6	17– 7¼	17– 8½	17– 9¾	17–11	18– 0¼	18– 1½	18– 2¾
11	19–3	19– 4⅜	19– 5¾	19– 7⅛	19– 8½	19– 9⅞	19–11¼	20– 0⅝
12	21–0	21– 1½	21– 3	21– 4½	21– 6	21– 7½	21– 9	21–10½
13	22–9	22–10⅝	23– 0¼	23– 1⅞	23– 3½	23– 5⅛	23– 6¾	23– 8⅜
14	24–6	24– 7¾	24– 9½	24–11¼	25– 1	25– 2¾	25– 4½	25– 6¼
15	26–3	26– 4⅞	26– 6¾	26– 8⅝	26–10½	27– 0⅜	27– 2¼	27– 4⅛
16	28–0	28– 2	28– 4	28– 6	28– 8	28–10	29– 0	29– 2
17	29–9	29–11⅛	30– 1¼	30– 3⅜	30– 5½	30– 7⅝	30– 9¾	30–11⅞
18	31–6	31– 8¼	31–10½	32– 0¾	32– 3	32– 5¼	32– 7½	32– 9¾
19	33–3	33– 5⅜	33– 7¾	33–10⅛	34– 0½	34– 2⅞	34– 5¼	34– 7⅝
20	35–0	35– 2½	35– 5	35– 7½	35–10	36– 0½	36– 3	36– 5½

MULTIPLICATION TABLE FOR SPACING OF LATTICE BARS

No. Spaces	1' 10"	1' 10⅛"	1' 10¼"	1' 10⅜"	1' 10½"	1' 10⅝"	1' 10¾"	1' 10⅞"
2	3– 8	3– 8¼	3– 8½	3– 8¾	3– 9	3– 9¼	3– 9½	3– 9¾
3	5– 6	5– 6⅜	5– 6¾	5– 7⅛	5– 7½	5– 7⅞	5– 8¼	5– 8⅝
4	7– 4	7– 4½	7– 5	7– 5½	7– 6	7– 6½	7– 7	7– 7½
5	9– 2	9– 2⅝	9– 3¼	9– 3⅞	9– 4½	9– 5⅛	9– 5¾	9– 6⅜
6	11– 0	11– 0¾	11– 1½	11– 2¼	11– 3	11– 3¾	11– 4½	11– 5¼
7	12–10	12–10⅞	12–11¾	13– 0⅝	13– 1½	13– 2⅜	13– 3¼	13– 4⅛
8	14– 8	14– 9	14–10	14–11	15– 0	15– 1	15– 2	15– 3
9	16– 6	16– 7⅛	16– 8¼	16– 9⅜	16–10½	16–11⅝	17– 0¾	17– 1⅞
10	18– 4	18– 5¼	18– 6½	18– 7¾	18– 9	18–10¼	18–11½	19– 0¾
11	20– 2	20– 3⅜	20– 4¾	20– 6⅛	20– 7½	20– 8⅞	20–10¼	20–11⅝
12	22– 0	22– 1½	22– 3	22– 4½	22– 6	22– 7½	22– 9	22–10½
13	23–10	23–11⅝	24– 1¼	24– 2⅞	24– 4½	24– 6⅛	24– 7¾	24– 9⅜
14	25– 8	25– 9¾	25–11½	26– 1¼	26– 3	26– 4¾	26– 6½	26– 8¼
15	27– 6	27– 7⅞	27– 9¾	27–11⅝	28– 1½	28– 3⅜	28– 5¼	28– 7⅛
16	29– 4	29– 6	29– 8	29–10	30– 0	30– 2	30– 4	30– 6
17	31– 2	31– 4⅛	31– 6¼	31– 8⅜	31–10½	32– 0⅝	32– 2¾	32– 4⅞
18	33– 0	33– 2¼	33– 4½	33– 6¾	33– 9	33–11¼	34– 1½	34– 3¾
19	34–10	35– 0⅜	35– 2¾	35– 5⅛	35– 7½	35– 9⅞	36– 0¼	36– 2⅝
20	36– 8	36–10½	37– 1	37– 3½	37– 6	37– 8½	37–11	38– 1½

No. Spaces	1' 11"	1' 11⅛"	1' 11¼"	1' 11⅜"	1' 11½"	1' 11⅝"	1' 11¾"	1' 11⅞"
2	3–10	3–10¼	3–10½	3–10¾	3–11	3–11¼	3–11½	3–11¾
3	5– 9	5– 9⅜	5– 9¾	5–10⅛	5–10½	5–10⅞	5–11¼	5–11⅝
4	7– 8	7– 8½	7– 9	7– 9½	7–10	7–10½	7–11	7–11½
5	9– 7	9– 7⅝	9– 8¼	9– 8⅞	9– 9½	9–10⅛	9–10¾	9–11⅜
6	11– 6	11– 6¾	11– 7½	11– 8¼	11– 9	11– 9¾	11–10½	11–11¼
7	13– 5	13– 5⅞	13– 6¾	13– 7⅝	13– 8½	13– 9⅜	13–10¼	13–11⅛
8	15– 4	15– 5	15– 6	15– 7	15– 8	15– 9	15–10	15–11
9	17– 3	17– 4⅛	17– 5¼	17– 6⅜	17– 7½	17– 8⅝	17– 9¾	17–10⅞
10	19– 2	19– 3¼	19– 4½	19– 5¾	19– 7	19– 8¼	19– 9½	19–10¾
11	21– 1	21– 2⅜	21– 3¾	21– 5⅛	21– 6½	21– 7⅞	21– 9¼	21–10⅝
12	23– 0	23– 1½	23– 3	23– 4½	23– 6	23– 7½	23– 9	23–10½
13	24–11	25– 0⅝	25– 2¼	25– 3⅞	25– 5½	25– 7⅛	25– 8¾	25–10⅜
14	26–10	26–11¾	27– 1½	27– 3¼	27– 5	27– 6¾	27– 8½	27–10¼
15	28– 9	28–10⅞	29– 0¾	29– 2⅝	29– 4½	29– 6⅜	29– 8¼	29–10⅛
16	30– 8	30–10	31– 0	31– 2	31– 4	31– 6	31– 8	31–10
17	32– 7	32– 9⅛	32–11¼	33– 1⅜	33– 3½	33– 5⅝	33– 7¾	33– 9⅞
18	34– 6	34– 8¼	34–10½	35– 0¾	35– 3	35– 5¼	35– 7½	35– 9¾
19	36– 5	36– 7⅜	36– 9¾	37– 0⅛	37– 2½	37– 4⅞	37– 7¼	37– 9⅝
20	38– 4	38– 6½	38– 9	38–11½	39– 2	39– 4½	39– 7	39– 9½

No. Spaces	2'0"	2'0⅛"	2'0¼"	2'0⅜"	2'0½"	2'0⅝"	2'0¾"	2'0⅞"
2	4-0	4-0¼	4-0½	4-0¾	4- 1	4- 1¼	4- 1½	4- 1¾
3	6-0	6-0⅜	6-0¾	6-1⅛	6- 1½	6- 1⅞	6- 2¼	6- 2⅝
4	8-0	8-0½	8-1	8-1½	8- 2	8- 2½	8- 3	8- 3½
5	10-0	10-0⅝	10-1¼	10-1⅞	10- 2½	10- 3⅛	10- 3¾	10- 4⅜
6	12-0	12-0¾	12-1½	12-2¼	12- 3	12- 3¾	12- 4½	12- 5¼
7	14-0	14-0⅞	14-1¾	14-2⅝	14- 3½	14- 4⅜	14- 5¼	14- 6⅛
8	16-0	16-1	16-2	16-3	16- 4	16- 5	16- 6	16- 7
9	18-0	18-1⅛	18-2¼	18-3⅜	18- 4½	18- 5⅝	18- 6¾	18- 7⅞
10	20-0	20-1¼	20-2½	20-3¾	20- 5	20- 6¼	20- 7½	20- 8¾
11	22-0	22-1⅜	22-2¾	22-4⅛	22- 5½	22- 6⅞	22- 8¼	22- 9⅝
12	24-0	24-1½	24-3	24-4½	24- 6	24- 7½	24- 9	24-10½
13	26-0	26-1⅝	26-3¼	26-4⅞	26- 6½	26- 8⅛	26- 9¾	26-11⅜
14	28-0	28-1¾	28-3½	28-5¼	28- 7	28- 8¾	28-10½	26-11¾
15	30-0	30-1⅞	30-3¾	30-5⅝	30- 7½	30- 9⅜	30-11¼	31- 1⅛
16	32-0	32-2	32-4	32-6	32- 8	32-10	33- 0	33- 2
17	34-0	34-2⅛	34-4¼	34-6⅜	34- 8½	34-10⅝	35- 0¾	35- 2⅞
18	36-0	36-2¼	36-4½	36-6¾	36- 9	36-11¼	37- 1½	37- 3¾
19	38-0	38-2⅜	38-4¾	38-7⅛	38- 9½	38-11⅞	39- 2¼	39- 4⅝
20	40-0	40-2½	40-5	40-7½	40-10	41- 0½	41- 3	41- 5½

No. Spaces	2'1"	2'1⅛"	2'1¼"	2'1⅜"	2'1½"	2'1⅝"	2'1¾"	2'1⅞"
2	4- 2	4- 2¼	4- 2½	4- 2¾	4- 3	4- 3¼	4- 3½	4- 3¾
3	6- 3	6- 3⅜	6- 3¾	6- 4⅛	6- 4½	6- 4⅞	6- 5¼	6- 5⅝
4	8- 4	8- 4½	8- 5	8- 5½	8- 6	8- 6½	8- 7	8- 7½
5	10- 5	10- 5⅝	10- 6¼	10- 6⅞	10- 7½	10- 8⅛	10- 8¾	10- 9⅜
6	12- 6	12- 6¾	12- 7½	12- 8¼	12- 9	12- 9¾	12-10½	12-11¼
7	14- 7	14- 7⅞	14- 8¾	14- 9⅝	14-10½	14-11⅜	15- 0¼	15- 1⅛
8	16- 8	16- 9	16-10	16-11	17- 0	17- 1	17- 2	17- 3
9	18- 9	18-10⅛	18-11¼	19- 0⅜	19- 1½	19- 2⅝	19- 3¾	19- 4⅞
10	20-10	20-11¼	21- 0½	21- 1¾	21- 3	21- 4¼	21- 5½	21- 6¾
11	22-11	23- 0⅜	23- 1¾	23- 3⅛	23- 4½	23- 5⅞	23- 7¼	23- 8⅝
12	25- 0	25- 1½	25- 3	25- 4½	25- 6	25- 7½	25- 9	25-10½
13	27- 1	27- 2⅝	27- 4¼	27- 5⅞	27- 7½	27- 9⅛	27-10¾	28- 0⅜
14	29- 2	29- 3¾	29- 5½	29- 7¼	29- 9	29-10¾	30- 0½	30- 2¼
15	31- 3	31- 4⅞	31- 6¾	31- 8⅝	31-10½	32- 0⅜	32- 2¼	32- 4⅛
16	33- 4	33- 6	33- 8	33-10	34- 0	34- 2	34- 4	34- 6
17	35- 5	35- 7⅛	35- 9¼	35-11⅜	36- 1½	36- 3⅝	36- 5¾	36- 7⅞
18	37- 6	37- 8¼	37-10½	38- 0¾	38- 3	38- 5¼	38- 7½	38- 9¾
19	39- 7	39- 9⅜	39-11¾	40- 2⅛	40- 4½	40- 6⅞	40- 9¼	40-11⅝
20	41- 8	41-10½	42- 1	42- 3½	42- 6	42- 8½	42-11	43- 1½

No. Spaces	2'2"	2'2⅛"	2'2¼"	2'2⅜"	2'2½"	2'2⅝"	2'2¾"	2'2⅞"
2	4-4	4-4¼	4-4½	4-4¾	4-5	4-5¼	4-5½	4-5¾
3	6-6	6-6⅜	6-6¾	6-7⅛	6-7½	6-7⅞	6-8¼	6-8⅝
4	8-8	8-8½	8-9	8-9½	8-10	8-10½	8-11	8-11½
5	10-10	10-10⅝	10-11¼	10-11⅞	11-0½	11-1⅛	11-1¾	11-2⅜
6	13-0	13-0¾	13-1½	13-2¼	13-3	13-3¾	13-4½	13-5¼
7	15-2	15-2⅞	15-3¾	15-4⅝	15-5½	15-6⅜	15-7¼	15-8⅛
8	17-4	17-5	17-6	17-7	17-8	17-9	17-10	17-11
9	19-6	19-7⅛	19-8¼	19-9⅜	19-10½	19-11⅝	20-0¾	20-1⅞
10	21-8	21-9¼	21-10½	21-11¾	22-1	22-2¼	22-3½	22-4¾
11	23-10	23-11⅜	24-0¾	24-2⅛	24-3½	24-4⅞	24-6¼	24-7⅝
12	26-0	26-1½	26-3	26-4½	26-6	26-7½	26-9	26-10½
13	28-2	28-3⅝	28-5¼	28-6⅞	28-8½	28-10⅛	28-11¾	29-1⅜
14	30-4	30-5¾	30-7½	30-9¼	30-11	31-0¾	31-2½	31-4¼
15	32-6	32-7⅞	32-9¾	32-11⅝	33-1½	33-3⅜	33-5¼	33-7⅛
16	34-8	34-10	35-0	35-2	35-4	35-6	35-8	35-10
17	36-10	37-0⅛	37-2¼	37-4⅜	37-6½	37-8⅝	37-10¾	38-0⅞
18	39-0	39-2¼	39-4½	39-6¾	39-9	39-11¼	40-1½	40-3¾
19	41-2	41-4⅜	41-6¾	41-9⅛	41-11½	42-1⅞	42-4¼	42-6⅝
20	43-4	43-6½	43-9	43-11½	44-2	44-4½	44-7	44-9½

No. Spaces	2'3"	2'3⅛"	2'3¼"	2'3⅜"	2'3½"	2'3⅝"	2'3¾"	2'3⅞"
2	4-6	4-6¼	4-6½	4-6¾	4-7	4-7¼	4-7½	4-7¾
3	6-9	6-9⅜	6-9¾	6-10⅛	6-10½	6-10⅞	6-11¼	6-11⅝
4	9-0	9-0½	9-1	9-1½	9-2	9-2½	9-3	9-3½
5	11-3	11-3⅝	11-4¼	11-4⅞	11-5½	11-6⅛	11-6¾	11-7⅜
6	13-6	13-6¾	13-7½	13-8¼	13-9	13-9¾	13-10½	13-11¼
7	15-9	15-9⅞	15-10¾	15-11⅝	16-0½	16-1⅜	16-2¼	16-3⅛
8	18-0	18-1	18-2	18-3	18-4	18-5	18-6	18-7
9	20-3	20-4⅛	20-5¼	20-6⅜	20-7½	20-8⅝	20-9¾	20-10⅞
10	22-6	22-7¼	22-8½	22-9¾	22-11	23-0¼	23-1½	23-2¾
11	24-9	24-10⅜	24-11¾	25-1⅛	25-2½	25-3⅞	25-5¼	25-6⅝
12	27-0	27-1½	27-3	27-4½	27-6	27-7½	27-9	27-10½
13	29-3	29-4⅝	29-6¼	29-7⅞	29-9½	29-11⅛	30-0¾	30-2⅜
14	31-6	31-7¾	31-9½	31-11¼	32-1	32-2¾	32-4½	32-6¼
15	33-9	33-10⅞	34-0¾	34-2⅝	34-4½	34-6⅜	34-8¼	34-10⅛
16	36-0	36-2	36-4	36-6	36-8	36-10	37-0	37-2
17	38-3	38-5⅛	38-7¼	38-9⅜	38-11½	39-1⅝	39-3¾	39-5⅞
18	40-6	40-8¼	40-10½	41-0¾	41-3	41-5¼	41-7½	41-9¾
19	42-9	42-11⅜	43-1¾	43-4⅛	43-6½	43-8⅞	43-11¼	44-1⅝
20	45-0	45-2½	45-5	45-7½	45-10	46-0½	46-3	46-5½

No. Spaces	2′4″	2′4⅛″	2′4¼″	2′4⅜″	2′4½″	2′4⅝″	2′4¾″	2′4⅞″
2	4–8	4–8¼	4–8½	4–8¾	4–9	4–9¼	4–9½	4–9¾
3	7–0	7–0⅜	7–0¾	7–1⅛	7–1½	7–1⅞	7–2¼	7–2⅝
4	9–4	9–4½	9–5	9–5½	9–6	9–6½	9–7	9–7½
5	11–8	11–8⅝	11–9¼	11–9⅞	11–10½	11–11⅛	11–11¾	12–0⅜
6	14–0	14–0¾	14–1½	14–2¼	14–3	14–3¾	14–4½	14–5¼
7	16–4	16–4⅞	16–5¾	16–6⅝	16–7½	16–8⅜	16–9¼	16–10⅛
8	18–8	18–9	18–10	18–11	19–0	19–1	19–2	19–3
9	21–0	21–1⅛	21–2¼	21–3⅜	21–4½	21–5⅝	21–6¾	21–7⅞
10	23–4	23–5¼	23–6½	23–7¾	23–9	23–10¼	23–11½	24–0¾
11	25–8	25–9⅜	25–10¾	26–0⅛	26–1½	26–2⅞	26–4¼	26–5⅝
12	28–0	28–1½	28–3	28–4½	28–6	28–7½	28–9	28–10½
13	30–4	30–5⅝	30–7¼	30–8⅞	30–10½	31–0⅛	31–1¾	31–3⅜
14	32–8	32–9¾	32–11½	33–1¼	33–3	33–4¾	33–6½	33–8¼
15	35–0	35–1⅞	35–3¾	35–5⅝	35–7½	35–9⅜	35–11¼	36–1⅛
16	37–4	37–6	37–8	37–10	38–0	38–2	38–4	38–6
17	39–8	39–10⅛	40–0¼	40–2⅜	40–4½	40–6⅝	40–8¾	40–10⅞
18	42–0	42–2¼	42–4½	42–6¾	42–9	42–11¼	43–1½	43–3¾
19	44–4	44–6⅜	44–8¾	44–11⅛	45–1½	45–3⅞	45–6¼	45–8⅝
20	46–8	46–10½	47–1	47–3½	47–6	47–8½	47–11	48–1½

No. Spaces	2′5″	2′5⅛″	2′5¼″	2′5⅜″	2′5½″	2′5⅝″	2′5¾″	2′5⅞″
2	4–10	4–10¼	4–10½	4–10¾	4–11	4–11¼	4–11½	4–11¾
3	7–3	7–3⅜	7–3¾	7–4⅛	7–4½	7–4⅞	7–5¼	7–5⅝
4	9–8	9–8½	9–9	9–9½	9–10	9–10½	9–11	9–11½
5	12–1	12–1⅝	12–2¼	12–2⅞	12–3½	12–4⅛	12–4¾	12–5⅜
6	14–6	14–6¾	14–7½	14–8¼	14–9	14–9¾	14–10½	14–11¼
7	16–11	16–11⅞	17–0¾	17–1⅝	17–2½	17–3⅜	17–4¼	17–5⅛
8	19–4	19–5	19–6	19–7	19–8	19–9	19–10	19–11
9	21–9	21–10⅛	21–11¼	22–0⅜	22–1½	22–2⅝	22–3¾	22–4⅞
10	24–2	24–3¼	24–4½	24–5¾	24–7	24–8¼	24–9½	24–10¾
11	26–7	26–8⅜	26–9¾	26–11⅛	27–0½	27–1⅞	27–3¼	27–4⅝
12	29–0	29–1½	29–3	29–4½	29–6	29–7½	29–9	29–10½
13	31–5	31–6⅝	31–8¼	31–9⅞	31–11½	32–1⅛	32–2¾	32–4⅜
14	33–10	33–11¾	34–1½	34–3¼	34–5	34–6¾	34–8½	34–10¼
15	36–3	36–4⅞	36–6¾	36–8⅝	36–10½	37–0⅜	37–2¼	37–4⅛
16	38–8	38–10	39–0	39–2	39–4	39–6	39–8	39–10
17	41–1	41–3⅛	41–5¼	41–7⅜	41–9½	41–11⅝	42–1¾	42–3⅞
18	43–6	43–8¼	43–10½	44–0¾	44–3	44–5¼	44–7½	44–9¾
19	45–11	46–1⅜	46–3¾	46–6⅛	46–8½	46–10⅞	47–1¼	47–3⅝
20	48–4	48–6½	48–9	48–11½	49–2	49–4½	49–7	49–9½

No. Spaces	2′6″	2′6⅛″	2′6¼″	2′6⅜″	2′6½″	2′6⅝″	2′6¾″	2′6⅞″
2	5– 0	5– 0¼	5– 0½	5– 0¾	5– 1	5– 1¼	5– 1½	5– 1¾
3	7– 6	7– 6⅜	7– 6¾	7– 7⅛	7– 7½	7– 7⅞	7– 8¼	7– 8⅝
4	10– 0	10– 0½	10– 1	10– 1½	10– 2	10– 2½	10– 3	10– 3½
5	12– 6	12– 6⅝	12– 7¼	12– 7⅞	12– 8½	12– 9⅛	12– 9¾	12–10⅜
6	15– 0	15– 0¾	15– 1½	15– 2¼	15– 3	15– 3¾	15– 4½	15– 5¼
7	17– 6	17– 6⅞	17– 7¾	17– 8⅝	17– 9½	17–10⅜	17–11¼	18– 0⅛
8	20– 0	20– 1	20– 2	20– 3	20– 4	20– 5	20– 6	20– 7
9	22– 6	22– 7⅛	22– 8¼	22– 9⅜	22–10½	22–11⅝	23– 0¾	23– 1⅞
10	25– 0	25– 1¼	25– 2½	25– 3¾	25– 5	25– 6¼	25– 7½	25– 8¾
11	27– 6	27– 7⅜	27– 8¾	27–10⅛	27–11½	28– 0⅞	28– 2¼	28– 3⅝
12	30– 0	30– 1½	30– 3	30– 4½	30– 6	30– 7½	30– 9	30–10½
13	32– 6	32– 7⅝	32– 9¼	32–10⅞	33– 0½	33– 2⅛	33– 3¾	33– 5⅜
14	35– 0	35– 1¾	35– 3½	35– 5¼	35– 7	35– 8¾	35–10½	36– 0¼
15	37– 6	37– 7⅞	37– 9¾	37–11⅝	38– 1½	38– 3⅜	38– 5¼	38– 7⅛
16	40– 0	40– 2	40– 4	40– 6	40– 8	40–10	41– 0	41– 2
17	42– 6	42– 8⅛	42–10¼	43– 0⅜	43– 2½	43– 4⅝	43– 6¾	43– 8⅞
18	45– 0	45– 2¼	45– 4½	45– 6¾	45– 9	45–11¼	46– 1½	46– 3¾
19	47– 6	47– 8⅜	47–10¾	48– 1⅛	48– 3½	48– 5⅞	48– 8¼	48–10⅝
20	50– 0	50– 2½	50– 5	50– 7½	50–10	51– 0½	51– 3	51– 5½

No. Spaces	2′7″	2′7⅛″	2′7¼″	2′7⅜″	2′7½″	2′7⅝″	2′7¾″	2′7⅞″
2	5– 2	5– 2¼	5– 2½	5– 2¾	5– 3	5– 3¼	5– 3½	5– 3¾
3	7– 9	7– 9⅜	7– 9¾	7–10⅛	7–10½	7–10⅞	7–11¼	7–11⅝
4	10– 4	10– 4½	10– 5	10– 5½	10– 6	10– 6½	10– 7	10– 7½
5	12–11	12–11⅝	13– 0¼	13– 0⅞	13– 1½	13– 2⅛	13– 2¾	13– 3⅜
6	15– 6	15– 6¾	15– 7½	15– 8¼	15– 9	15– 9¾	15–10½	15–11¼
7	18– 1	18– 1⅞	18– 2¾	18– 3⅝	18– 4½	18– 5⅜	18– 6¼	18– 7⅛
8	20– 8	20– 9	20–10	20–11	21– 0	21– 1	21– 2	21– 3
9	23– 3	23– 4⅛	23– 5¼	23– 6⅜	23– 7½	23– 8⅝	23– 9¾	23–10⅞
10	25–10	25–11¼	26– 0½	26– 1¾	26– 3	26– 4¼	26– 5½	26– 6¾
11	28– 5	28– 6⅜	28– 7¾	28– 9⅛	28–10½	28–11⅞	29– 1¼	29– 2⅝
12	31– 0	31– 1½	31– 3	31– 4½	31– 6	31– 7½	31– 9	31–10½
13	33– 7	33– 8⅝	33–10¼	33–11⅞	34– 1½	34– 3⅛	34– 4¾	34– 6⅜
14	36– 2	36– 3¾	36– 5½	36– 7¼	36– 9	36–10¾	37– 0½	37– 2¼
15	38– 9	38–10⅞	39– 0¾	39– 2⅝	39– 4½	39– 6⅜	39– 8¼	39–10⅛
16	41– 4	41– 6	41– 8	41–10	42– 0	42– 2	42– 4	42– 6
17	43–11	44– 1⅛	44– 3¼	44– 5⅜	44– 7½	44– 9⅝	44–11¾	45– 1⅞
18	46– 6	46– 8¼	46–10½	47– 0¾	47– 3	47– 5¼	47– 7½	47– 9¾
19	49– 1	49– 3⅜	49– 5¾	49– 8⅛	49–10½	50– 0⅞	50– 3¼	50– 5⅝
20	51– 8	51–10½	52– 1	52– 3½	52– 6	52– 8½	52–11	53– 1½

No. Spaces	2'8"	2'8⅛"	2'8¼"	2'8⅜"	2'8½"	2'8⅝"	2'8¾"	2'8⅞"
2	5- 4	5- 4¼	5- 4½	5- 4¾	5- 5	5- 5¼	5- 5½	5- 5¾
3	8- 0	8- 0⅜	8- 0¾	8- 1⅛	8- 1½	8- 1⅞	8- 2¼	8- 2⅝
4	10- 8	10- 8½	10- 9	10- 9½	10-10	10-10½	10-11	10-11½
5	13- 4	13- 4⅝	13- 5¼	13- 5⅞	13- 6½	13- 7⅛	13- 7¾	13- 8⅜
6	16- 0	16- 0¾	16- 1½	16- 2¼	16- 3	16- 3¾	16- 4½	16- 5¼
7	18- 8	18- 8⅞	18- 9¾	18-10⅝	18-11½	19- 0⅜	19- 1¼	19- 2⅛
8	21- 4	21- 5	21- 6	21- 7	21- 8	21- 9	21-10	21-11
9	24- 0	24- 1⅛	24- 2¼	24- 3⅜	24- 4½	24- 5⅝	24- 6¾	24- 7⅞
10	26- 8	26- 9¼	26-10½	26-11¾	27- 1	27- 2¼	27- 3½	27- 4¾
11	29- 4	29- 5⅜	29- 6¾	29- 8⅛	29- 9½	29-10⅞	30- 0¼	30- 1⅝
12	32- 0	32- 1½	32- 3	32- 4½	32- 6	32- 7½	32- 9	32-10½
13	34- 8	34- 9⅝	34-11¼	35- 0⅞	35- 2½	35- 4⅛	35- 5¾	35- 7⅜
14	37- 4	37- 5¾	37- 7½	37- 9¼	37-11	38- 0¾	38- 2½	38- 4¼
15	40- 0	40- 1⅞	40- 3¾	40- 5⅝	40- 7½	40- 9⅜	40-11¼	41- 1⅛
16	42- 8	42-10	43- 0	43- 2	43- 4	43- 6	43- 8	43-10
17	45- 4	45- 6⅛	45- 8¼	45-10⅜	46- 0½	46- 2⅝	46- 4¾	46- 6⅞
18	48- 0	48- 2¼	48- 4½	48- 6¾	48- 9	48-11¼	49- 1½	49- 3¾
19	50- 8	50-10⅜	51- 0¾	51- 3⅛	51- 5½	51- 7⅞	51-10¼	52- 0⅝
20	53- 4	53- 6½	53- 9	53-11½	54- 2	54- 4½	54- 7	54- 9½

No. Spaces	2'9"	2'9⅛"	2'9¼"	2'9⅜"	2'9½"	2'9⅝"	2'9¾"	2'9⅞"
2	5- 6	5- 6¼	5- 6½	5- 6¾	5- 7	5- 7¼	5- 7½	5- 7¾
3	8- 3	8- 3⅜	8- 3¾	8- 4⅛	8- 4½	8- 4⅞	8- 5¼	8- 5⅝
4	11- 0	11- 0½	11- 1	11- 1½	11- 2	11- 2½	11- 3	11- 3½
5	13- 9	13- 9⅝	13-10¼	13-10⅞	13-11½	14- 0⅛	14- 0¾	14- 1⅜
6	16- 6	16- 6¾	16- 7½	16- 8¼	16- 9	16- 9¾	16-10½	16-11¼
7	19- 3	19- 3⅞	19- 4¾	19- 5⅝	19- 6½	19- 7⅜	19- 8¼	19- 9⅛
8	22- 0	22- 1	22- 2	22- 3	22- 4	22- 5	22- 6	22- 7
9	24- 9	24-10⅛	24-11¼	25- 0⅜	25- 1½	25- 2⅝	25- 3¾	25- 4⅞
10	27- 6	27- 7¼	27- 8½	27- 9¾	27-11	28- 0¼	28- 1½	28- 2¾
11	30- 3	30- 4⅜	30- 5¾	30- 7⅛	30- 8½	30- 9⅞	30-11¼	31- 0⅝
12	33- 0	33- 1½	33- 3	33- 4½	33- 6	33- 7½	33- 9	33-10½
13	35- 9	35-10⅝	36- 0¼	36- 1⅞	36- 3½	36- 5⅛	36- 6¾	36- 8⅜
14	38- 6	38- 7¾	38- 9½	38-11¼	39- 1	39- 2¾	39- 4½	39- 6¼
15	41- 3	41- 4⅞	41- 6¾	41- 8⅝	41-10½	42- 0⅜	42- 2¼	42- 4⅛
16	44- 0	44- 2	44- 4	44- 6	44- 8	44-10	45- 0	45- 2
17	46- 9	46-11⅛	47- 1¼	47- 3⅜	47- 5½	47- 7⅝	47- 9¾	47-11⅞
18	49- 6	49- 8¼	49-10½	50- 0¾	50- 3	50- 5¼	50- 7½	50- 9¾
19	52- 3	52- 5⅜	52- 7¾	52-10⅛	53- 0½	53- 2⅞	53- 5¼	53- 7⅝
20	55- 0	55- 2½	55- 5	55- 7½	55-10	56- 0½	56- 3	56- 5½

No. Spaces	2′10″	2′10⅛″	2′10¼″	2′10⅜″	2′10½″	2′10⅝″	2′10¾″	2′10⅞″
2	5- 8	5- 8¼	5- 8½	5- 8¾	5- 9	5- 9¼	5- 9½	5- 9¾
3	8- 6	8- 6⅜	8- 6¾	8- 7⅛	8- 7½	8- 7⅞	8- 8¼	8- 8⅝
4	11- 4	11- 4½	11- 5	11- 5½	11- 6	11- 6½	11- 7	11- 7½
5	14- 2	14- 2⅝	14- 3¼	14- 3⅞	14- 4½	14- 5⅛	14- 5¾	14- 6⅜
6	17- 0	17- 0¾	17- 1½	17- 2¼	17- 3	17- 3¾	17- 4½	17- 5¼
7	19-10	19-10⅞	19-11¾	20- 0⅝	20-1½	20- 2⅜	20- 3¼	20- 4⅛
8	22- 8	22- 9	22-10	22-11	23- 0	23- 1	23- 2	23- 3
9	25- 6	25- 7⅛	25- 8¼	25- 9⅜	25-10½	25-11⅝	26- 0¾	26- 1⅞
10	28- 4	28- 5¼	28- 6½	28- 7¾	28- 9	28-10¼	28-11½	29- 0¾
11	31- 2	31- 3⅜	31- 4¾	31- 6⅛	31- 7½	31- 8⅞	31-10¼	31-11⅝
12	34- 0	34- 1½	34- 3	34- 4½	34- 6	34- 7½	34- 9	34-10½
13	36-10	36-11⅝	37- 1¼	37- 2⅞	37- 4½	37- 6⅛	37- 7¾	37- 9⅜
14	39- 8	39- 9¾	39-11½	40- 1¼	40- 3	40- 4¾	40- 6½	40- 8¼
15	42- 6	42- 7⅞	42- 9¾	42-11⅝	43- 1½	43- 3⅜	43- 5¼	43- 7⅛
16	45- 4	45- 6	45- 8	45-10	46- 0	46- 2	46- 4	46- 6
17	48- 2	48- 4⅛	48- 6¼	48- 8⅜	48-10½	49- 0⅝	49- 2¾	49- 4⅞
18	51- 0	51- 2¼	51- 4½	51- 6¾	51- 9	51-11¼	52- 1½	52- 3¾
19	53-10	54- 0⅜	54- 2¾	54- 5⅛	54- 7½	54- 9⅞	55- 0¼	55- 2⅝
20	56- 8	56-10½	57- 1	57- 3½	57- 6	57- 8½	57-11	58- 1½

No. Spaces	2′11″	2′11⅛″	2′11¼″	2′11⅜″	2′11½″	2′11⅝″	2′11¾″	2′11⅞″
2	5-10	5-10¼	5-10½	5-10¾	5-11	5-11¼	5-11½	5-11¾
3	8- 9	8- 9⅜	8- 9¾	8-10⅛	8-10½	8-10⅞	8-11¼	8-11⅝
4	11- 8	11- 8½	11- 9	11- 9½	11-10	11-10½	11-11	11-11½
5	14- 7	14- 7⅝	14- 8¼	14- 8⅞	14- 9½	14-10⅛	14-10¾	14-11⅜
6	17- 6	17- 6¾	17- 7½	17- 8¼	17- 9	17- 9¾	17-10½	17-11¼
7	20- 5	20- 5⅞	20- 6¾	20- 7⅝	20- 8½	20- 9⅜	20-10¼	20-11⅛
8	23- 4	23- 5	23- 6	23- 7	23- 8	23- 9	23-10	23-11
9	26- 3	26- 4⅛	26- 5¼	26- 6⅜	26- 7½	26- 8⅝	26- 9¾	26-10⅞
10	29- 2	29- 3¼	29- 4½	29- 5¾	29- 7	29- 8¼	29- 9½	29-10¾
11	32- 1	32- 2⅜	32- 3¾	32- 5⅛	32- 6½	32- 7⅞	32- 9¼	32-10⅝
12	35- 0	35- 1½	35- 3	35- 4½	35- 6	35- 7½	35- 9	35-10½
13	37-11	38- 0⅝	38- 2¼	38- 3⅞	38- 5½	38- 7⅛	38- 8¾	38-10⅜
14	40-10	40-11¾	41- 1½	41- 3¼	41- 5	41- 6¾	41- 8½	41-10¼
15	43- 9	43-10⅞	44- 0¾	44- 2⅝	44- 4½	44- 6⅜	44- 8¼	44-10⅛
16	46- 8	46-10	47- 0	47- 2	47- 4	47- 6	47- 8	47-10
17	49- 7	49- 9⅛	49-11¼	50- 1	50- 3½	50- 5⅝	50- 7¾	50- 9⅞
18	52- 6	52- 8¼	52-10½	53- 0¾	53- 3	53- 5¼	53- 7½	53- 9¾
19	55- 5	55- 7⅜	55- 9¾	56- 0⅛	56- 2½	56- 4⅞	56- 7¼	56- 9⅝
20	58- 4	58- 6½	58- 9	58-11½	59- 2	59- 4½	59- 7	59- 9½

DECIMAL EQUIVALENTS

64ths	32nds	DECIMALS of a FOOT 0'	1'	2'	3'	4'	5'	6'	32nds	64ths
0		.0000	.0833	.1667	.2500	.3333	.4167	.5000	0	
		.0013	.0846	.1680	.2513	.3346	.4180	.5013		1
	1/32	.0026	.0859	.1693	.2526	.3359	.4193	.5026	1/32	
3		.0039	.0872	.1706	.2539	.3372	.4206	.5039		3
	1/16	.0052	.0885	.1719	.2552	.3385	.4219	.5052	1/16	
5		.0065	.0898	.1732	.2565	.3398	.4232	.5065		5
	3/32	.0078	.0911	.1745	.2578	.3411	.4245	.5078	3/32	
7		.0091	.0924	.1758	.2591	.3424	.4258	.5091		7
	1/8	.0104	.0937	.1771	.2604	.3437	.4271	.5104	1/8	
9		.0117	.0951	.1784	.2617	.3451	.4284	.5117		9
	5/32	.0130	.0964	.1797	.2630	.3464	.4297	.5130	5/32	
11		.0143	.0977	.1810	.2643	.3477	.4310	.5143		11
	3/16	.0156	.0990	.1823	.2656	.3490	.4323	.5156	3/16	
13		.0169	.1003	.1836	.2669	.3503	.4336	.5169		13
	7/32	.0182	.1016	.1849	.2682	.3516	.4349	.5182	7/32	
15		.0195	.1029	.1862	.2695	.3529	.4362	.5195		15
	1/4	.0208	.1042	.1875	.2708	.3542	.4375	.5208	1/4	
17		.0221	.1055	.1888	.2721	.3555	.4388	.5221		17
	9/32	.0234	.1068	.1901	.2734	.3568	.4401	.5234	9/32	
19		.0247	.1081	.1914	.2747	.3581	.4414	.5247		19
	5/16	.0260	.1094	.1927	.2760	.3594	.4427	.5260	5/16	
21		.0273	.1107	.1940	.2773	.3607	.4440	.5273		21
	11/32	.0286	.1120	.1953	.2786	.3620	.4453	.5286	11/32	
23		.0299	.1133	.1966	.2799	.3633	.4466	.5299		23
	3/8	.0312	.1146	.1979	.2812	.3646	.4479	.5312	3/8	
25		.0326	.1159	.1992	.2826	.3659	.4492	.5326		25
	13/32	.0339	.1172	.2005	.2839	.3672	.4505	.5339	13/32	
27		.0352	.1185	.2018	.2852	.3685	.4518	.5352		27
	7/16	.0365	.1198	.2031	.2865	.3698	.4531	.5365	7/16	
29		.0378	.1211	.2044	.2878	.3711	.4544	.5378		29
	15/32	.0391	.1224	.2057	.2891	.3724	.4557	.5391	15/32	
31		.0404	.1237	.2070	.2904	.3737	.4570	.5404		31
	1/2	.0417	.1250	.2083	.2917	.3750	.4583	.5417	1/2	
33		.0430	.1263	.2096	.2930	.3763	.4596	.5430		33
	17/32	.0443	.1276	.2109	.2943	.3776	.4609	.5443	17/32	
35		.0456	.1289	.2122	.2956	.3789	.4622	.5456		35
	9/16	.0469	.1302	.2135	.2969	.3802	.4635	.5469	9/16	
37		.0482	.1315	.2148	.2982	.3815	.4648	.5482		37
	19/32	.0495	.1328	.2161	.2995	.3828	.4661	.5495	19/32	
39		.0508	.1341	.2174	.3008	.3841	.4674	.5508		39
	5/8	.0521	.1354	.2188	.3021	.3854	.4688	.5521	5/8	
41		.0534	.1367	.2201	.3034	.3867	.4701	.5534		41
	21/32	.0547	.1380	.2214	.3047	.3880	.4714	.5547	21/32	
43		.0560	.1393	.2227	.3060	.3893	.4727	.5560		43
	11/16	.0573	.1406	.2240	.3073	.3906	.4740	.5573	11/16	
45		.0586	.1419	.2253	.3086	.3919	.4753	.5586		45
	23/32	.0599	.1432	.2266	.3099	.3932	.4766	.5599	23/32	
47		.0612	.1445	.2279	.3112	.3945	.4779	.5612		47
	3/4	.0625	.1458	.2292	.3125	.3958	.4792	.5625	3/4	
49		.0638	.1471	.2305	.3138	.3971	.4805	.5638		49
	25/32	.0651	.1484	.2318	.3151	.3984	.4818	.5651	25/32	
51		.0664	.1497	.2331	.3164	.3997	.4831	.5664		51
	13/16	.0677	.1510	.2344	.3177	.4010	.4844	.5677	13/16	
53		.0690	.1523	.2357	.3190	.4023	.4857	.5690		53
	27/32	.0703	.1536	.2370	.3203	.4036	.4870	.5703	27/32	
55		.0716	.1549	.2383	.3216	.4049	.4883	.5716		55
	7/8	.0729	.1562	.2396	.3229	.4062	.4896	.5729	7/8	
57		.0742	.1576	.2409	.3242	.4076	.4909	.5742		57
	29/32	.0755	.1589	.2422	.3255	.4089	.4922	.5755	29/32	
59		.0768	.1602	.2435	.3268	.4102	.4935	.5768		59
	15/16	.0781	.1615	.2448	.3281	.4115	.4948	.5781	15/16	
61		.0794	.1628	.2461	.3294	.4128	.4961	.5794		61
	31/32	.0807	.1641	.2474	.3307	.4141	.4974	.5807	31/32	
63		.0820	.1654	.2487	.3320	.4154	.4987	.5820		63

DECIMAL EQUIVALENTS

64ths	32nds	DECIMALS of a FOOT 7'	8'	9'	10'	11'	64ths	32nds	Decimals of an Inch
	0	.5833	.6667	.7500	.8333	.9167		0	
1		.5846	.6680	.7513	.8346	.9180	1		.015625
	1/32	.5859	.6693	.7526	.8359	.9193		1/32	.031250
3		.5872	.6706	.7539	.8372	.9206	3		.046875
	1/16	.5885	.6719	.7552	.8385	.9219		1/16	.062500
5		.5898	.6732	.7565	.8398	.9232	5		.078125
	3/32	.5911	.6745	.7578	.8411	.9245		3/32	.093750
7		.5924	.6758	.7591	.8424	.9258	7		.109375
	1/8	.5937	.6771	.7604	.8437	.9271		1/8	.125000
9		.5951	.6784	.7617	.8451	.9284	9		.140625
	5/32	.5964	.6797	.7630	.8464	.9297		5/32	.156250
11		.5977	.6810	.7643	.8477	.9310	11		.171875
	3/16	.5990	.6823	.7656	.8490	.9323		3/16	.187500
13		.6003	.6836	.7669	.8503	.9336	13		.203125
	7/32	.6016	.6849	.7682	.8516	.9349		7/32	.218750
15		.6029	.6862	.7695	.8529	.9362	15		.234375
	1/4	.6042	.6875	.7708	.8542	.9375		1/4	.250000
17		.6055	.6888	.7721	.8555	.9388	17		.265625
	9/32	.6068	.6901	.7734	.8568	.9401		9/32	.281250
19		.6081	.6914	.7747	.8581	.9414	19		.296875
	5/16	.6094	.6927	.7760	.8594	.9427		5/16	.312500
21		.6107	.6940	.7773	.8607	.9440	21		.328125
	11/32	.6120	.6953	.7786	.8620	.9453		11/32	.343750
23		.6133	.6966	.7799	.8633	.9466	23		.359375
	3/8	.6146	.6979	.7812	.8646	.9479		3/8	.375000
25		.6159	.6992	.7826	.8659	.9492	25		.390625
	13/32	.6172	.7005	.7839	.8672	.9505		13/32	.406250
27		.6185	.7018	.7852	.8685	.9518	27		.421875
	7/16	.6198	.7031	.7865	.8698	.9531		7/16	.437500
29		.6211	.7044	.7878	.8711	.9544	29		.453125
	15/32	.6224	.7057	.7891	.8724	.9557		15/32	.468750
31		.6237	.7070	.7904	.8737	.9570	31		.484375
	1/2	.6250	.7083	.7917	.8750	.9583		1/2	.500000
33		.6263	.7096	.7930	.8763	.9596	33		.515625
	17/32	.6276	.7109	.7943	.8776	.9609		17/32	.531250
35		.6289	.7122	.7956	.8789	.9622	35		.546875
	9/16	.6302	.7135	.7969	.8802	.9635		9/16	.562500
37		.6315	.7148	.7982	.8815	.9648	37		.578125
	19/32	.6328	.7161	.7995	.8828	.9661		19/32	.593750
39		.6341	.7174	.8008	.8841	.9674	39		.609375
	5/8	.6354	.7188	.8021	.8854	.9688		5/8	.625000
41		.6367	.7201	.8034	.8867	.9701	41		.640625
	21/32	.6380	.7214	.8047	.8880	.9714		21/32	.656250
43		.6393	.7227	.8060	.8893	.9727	43		.671875
	11/16	.6406	.7240	.8073	.8906	.9740		11/16	.687500
45		.6419	.7253	.8086	.8919	.9753	45		.703125
	23/32	.6432	.7266	.8099	.8932	.9766		23/32	.718750
47		.6445	.7279	.8112	.8945	.9779	47		.734375
	3/4	.6458	.7292	.8125	.8958	.9792		3/4	.750000
49		.6471	.7305	.8138	.8971	.9805	49		.765625
	25/32	.6484	.7318	.8151	.8984	.9818		25/32	.781250
51		.6497	.7331	.8164	.8997	.9831	51		.796875
	13/16	.6510	.7344	.8177	.9010	.9844		13/16	.812500
53		.6523	.7357	.8190	.9023	.9857	53		.828125
	27/32	.6536	.7370	.8203	.9036	.9870		27/32	.843750
55		.6549	.7383	.8216	.9049	.9883	55		.859375
	7/8	.6562	.7396	.8229	.9062	.9896		7/8	.875000
57		.6576	.7409	.8242	.9076	.9909	57		.890625
	29/32	.6589	.7422	.8255	.9089	.9922		29/32	.906250
59		.6602	.7435	.8268	.9102	.9935	59		.921875
	15/16	.6615	.7448	.8281	.9115	.9948		15/16	.937500
61		.6628	.7461	.8294	.9128	.9961	61		.953125
	31/32	.6641	.7474	.8307	.9141	.9974		31/32	.968750
63		.6654	.7487	.8320	.9154	.9987	63		.984375

32nds		0″	1″	2″	3″	4″	5″
0		0.00	25.40	50.80	76.20	101.60	127.00
1		0.79	26.19	51.59	76.99	102.39	127.79
	1/16	1.59	26.99	52.39	77.79	103.19	128.59
3		2.38	27.78	53.18	78.58	103.98	129.38
	1/8	3.18	28.58	53.98	79.38	104.78	130.18
5		3.97	29.37	54.77	80.17	105.57	130.97
	3/16	4.76	30.16	55.56	80.96	106.36	131.76
7		5.56	30.96	56.36	81.76	107.16	132.56
	1/4	6.35	31.75	57.15	82.55	107.95	133.35
9		7.14	32.54	57.94	83.34	108.74	134.14
	5/16	7.94	33.34	58.74	84.14	109.54	134.94
11		8.73	34.13	59.53	84.93	110.33	135.73
	3/8	9.53	34.93	60.33	85.73	111.13	136.53
13		10.32	35.72	61.12	86.52	111.92	137.32
	7/16	11.11	36.51	61.91	87.31	112.71	138.11
15		11.91	37.31	62.71	88.11	113.51	138.91
	1/2	12.70	38.10	63.50	88.90	114.30	139.70
17		13.49	38.89	64.29	89.69	115.09	140.49
	9/16	14.29	39.69	65.09	90.49	115.89	141.29
19		15.08	40.48	65.88	91.28	116.68	142.08
	5/8	15.88	41.28	66.68	92.08	117.48	142.88
21		16.67	42.07	67.47	92.87	118.27	143.67
	11/16	17.46	42.86	68.26	93.66	119.06	144.46
23		18.26	43.66	69.06	94.46	119.86	145.26
	3/4	19.05	44.45	69.85	95.25	120.65	146.05
25		19.84	45.24	70.64	96.04	121.44	146.84
	13/16	20.64	46.04	71.44	96.84	122.24	147.64
27		21.43	46.83	72.23	97.63	123.03	148.43
	7/8	22.23	47.63	73.03	98.43	123.83	149.23
29		23.02	48.42	73.82	99.22	124.62	150.02
	15/16	23.81	49.21	74.61	100.01	125.41	150.81
31		24.61	50.01	75.41	100.81	126.21	151.61

Feet	0′	10′	20′	30′	40′
0	0.0	3 048.0	6 096.0	9 144.0	12 192.0
1	304.8	3 352.8	6 400.8	9 448.8	12 496.8
2	609.6	3 657.6	6 705.6	9 753.6	12 801.6
3	914.4	3 962.4	7 010.4	10 058.4	13 106.4
4	1 219.2	4 267.2	7 315.2	10 363.2	13 411.2
5	1 524.0	4 572.0	7 620.0	10 668.0	13 716.0
6	1 828.8	4 876.8	7 924.8	10 972.8	14 020.8
7	2 133.6	5 181.6	8 229.6	11 277.6	14 325.6
8	2 438.4	5 486.4	8 534.4	11 582.4	14 630.4
9	2 743.2	5 791.2	8 839.2	11 887.2	14 935.2

100′	30 480.0	300′	91 440.0	500′	152 400.0
200′	60 960.0	400′	121 920.0	600′	182 880.0

32nds		6″	7″	8″	9″	10″	11″
	0	**152.40**	**177.80**	**203.20**	**228.60**	**254.00**	**279.40**
1		153.19	178.59	203.99	229.39	254.79	280.19
	¹⁄₁₆	153.99	179.39	204.79	230.19	255.59	280.99
3		154.78	180.18	205.58	230.98	256.38	281.78
	⅛	**155.58**	**180.98**	**206.38**	**231.78**	**257.18**	**282.58**
5		156.37	181.77	207.17	232.57	257.97 .	283.37
	³⁄₁₆	157.16	182.56	207.96	233.36	258.76	284.16
7		157.96	183.36	208.76	234.16	259.56	284.96
	¼	**158.75**	**184.15**	**209.55**	**234.95**	**260.35**	**285.75**
9		159.54	184.94	210.34	235.74	261.14	286.54
	⁵⁄₁₆	160.34	185.74	211.14	236.54	261.94	287.34
11		161.13	186.53	211.93	237.33	262.73	288.13
	⅜	**161.93**	**187.33**	**212.73**	**238.13**	**263.53**	**288.93**
13		162.72	188.12	213.52	238.92	264.32	289.72
	⁷⁄₁₆	163.51	188.91	214.31	239.71	265.11	290.51
15		164.31	189.71	215.11	240.51	265.91	291.31
	½	**165.10**	**190.50**	**215.90**	**241.30**	**266.70**	**292.10**
17		165.89	191.29	216.69	242.09	267.49	292.89
	⁹⁄₁₆	166.69	192.09	217.49	242.89	268.29	293.69
19		167.48	192.88	218.28	243.68	269.08	294.48
	⅝	**168.28**	**193.68**	**219.08**	**244.48**	**269.88**	**295.28**
21		169.07	194.47	219.87	245.27	270.67	296.07
	¹¹⁄₁₆	169.86	195.26	220.66	246.06	271.46	296.86
23		170.66	196.06	221.46	246.86	272.26	297.66
	¾	**171.45**	**196.85**	**222.25**	**247.65**	**273.05**	**298.45**
25		172.24	197.64	223.04	248.44	273.84	299.24
	¹³⁄₁₆	173.04	198.44	223.84	249.24	274.64	300.04
27		173.83	199.23	224.63	250.03	275.43	300.83
	⅞	**174.63**	**200.03**	**225.43**	**250.83**	**276.23**	**301.63**
29		175.42	200.82	226.22	251.62	277.02	302.42
	¹⁵⁄₁₆	176.21	201.61	227.01	252.41	277.81	303.21
31		177.01	202.41	227.81	253.21	278.61	304.01

Feet	50′	60′	70′	80′	90′
0	15 240.0	18 288.0	21 336.0	24 384.0	27 432.0
1	15 544.8	18 592.8	21 640.8	24 688.8	27 736.8
2	15 849.6	18 897.6	21 945.6	24 993.6	28 041.6
3	16 154.4	19 202.4	22 250.4	25 298.4	28.346.4
4	16 459.2	19 507.2	22 555.2	25 603.2	28 651.2
5	16 764.0	19 812.0	22 860.0	25 908.0	28 956.0
6	17 068.8	20 116.8	23 164.8	26 212.8	29 260.8
7	17 373.6	20 421.6	23 469.6	26 517.6	29.565.6
8	17 678.4	20 726.4	23 774.4	26 822.4	29 870.4
9	17 983.2	21 031.2	24 079.2	27 127.2	30 175.2

700′	213 360.0	900′	274 320.0	1/128″	0.198
800′	243 840.0	1000′	304 800.0	1/64″	0.397